EQUESTRIAN
SURFACES LTD

GALLOP
WITH CONFIDENCE

SUPPLY | MANUFACTURE | INSTALL

WINDSOR CLIVE
INTERNATIONAL

THE ESTATE AGENCY FOR THE RACING WORLD

+44 (0)1672 521155

info@windsorclive.co.uk   windsorclive.co.uk

HORSES
IN TRAINING 2018

128th YEAR OF PUBLICATION

Raceform

INDEX TO GENERAL CONTENTS

Editor	Richard Lowther; Raceform Ltd., 27 Kingfisher Court, Hambridge Road, Newbury, RG14 5SJ E-mail: richard.lowther@racingpost.com
Production Editor	Adrian Gowling; Bloodstock Services, Weatherbys
Typesetting	Maggie Elvie; Printing Services, Weatherbys, Sanders Road, Wellingborough, NN8 4BX.
Orders	Raceform Ltd., Sanders Road, Wellingborough, Northants NN8 4BX. Tel: 01933 304858 www.racingpost.com/shop E-mail: Shop@racingpost.com
Advertisements	Gary Stone, Archant Dialogue, Prospect House, Rouen Road, Norwich, NR1 1RE Tel: 01603 772463 E-mail: gary.stone@archantdialogue.co.uk
ISBN	978-1-910497-58-6

INDEX TO ADVERTISERS

2018

RACING FIXTURES

AND SALE DATES

(SUBJECT TO ALTERATION)

Flat fixtures are in **Black Type**; Jump in Light Type; Irish in *Italic*;
asterisk (☆) indicates an evening or Twilight meeting;
† indicates an All Weather meeting. Sale dates are at foot of fixtures

MARCH

Sun	Mon	Tues	Wed	Thur	Fri	Sat
				1	**2**	**3**
				Clonmel **Kempton Park**☆ Ludlow **Newcastle**† Taunton	**Chelmsford City**†☆ Doncaster *Dundalk*†☆ **Lingfield Park**† Newbury	**Chelmsford City**☆ Doncaster Kelso **Lingfield Park**† *Navan* Newbury
4	**5**	**6**	**7**	**8**	**9**	**10**
Huntingdon *Leopardstown* Sedgefield	*Leopardstown* Lingfield Park Southwell **Wolverhampton**†☆	Exeter Newcastle **Southwell**†	Catterick Bridge Fontwell Park **Kempton Park**†☆ **Lingfield Park**†	Carlisle **Newcastle**†☆ **Southwell**† *Thurles* Wincanton	Ayr *Dundalk*†☆ Leicester **Newcastle**†☆ Sandown Park	Ayr **Chelmsford City**†☆ *Gowran Park* Hereford Sandown Park **Wolverhampton**†
11	**12**	**13**	**14**	**15**	**16**	**17**
Market Rasen *Naas* Warwick	**Chelmsford City**†☆ Plumpton Stratford-On-Avon Taunton	Cheltenham **Newcastle**†☆ Sedgefield **Southwell**†	Cheltenham Huntingdon **Southwell**† **Wolverhampton**†☆	**Chelmsford City**†☆ Cheltenham Hexham Towcester	Cheltenham *Dundalk*†☆ Fakenham **Lingfield Park**† **Wolverhampton**†☆	*Down Royal* Fontwell Park Kempton Park Newcastle Uttoxeter *Wexford* **Wolverhampton**†☆
				Cheltenham Sale		
18	**19**	**20**	**21**	**22**	**23**	**24**
Carlisle *Ffos Las* *Limerick* *Navan*	Kelso *Limerick* **Lingfield Park**† Southwell	Exeter **Newcastle**†☆ Wetherby	Chepstow Haydock Park **Kempton Park**†☆ **Southwell**†	**Chelmsford City**†☆ Chepstow *Cork* Ludlow **Wolverhampton**†	*Dundalk*†☆ **Kempton Park**†☆ **Lingfield Park**† Newbury Sedgefield	Bangor-On-Dee **Doncaster** **Lingfield Park**† Newbury *Thurles* **Wolverhampton**†☆
25	**26**	**27**	**28**	**29**	**30**	**31**
Ascot **Doncaster** *Downpatrick* *Naas*	Huntingdon Market Rasen Taunton	Hereford **Newcastle**†☆ **Southwell**†	*Dundalk*†☆ **Newcastle**†☆ Warwick Wincanton **Wolverhampton**†	**Chelmsford City**† *Clonmel* Towcester Wetherby **Wolverhampton**†☆	Bath **Lingfield Park**† **Newcastle**†	Carlisle **Chelmsford City**†☆ *Cork* Haydock Park **Kempton Park**† **Musselburgh** Newton Abbot
			Ascot Sale *Fasig-Tipton Sale*			

APRIL

Sun	Mon	Tues	Wed	Thur	Fri	Sat
1 *Cork* *Fairyhouse* *Ffos Las* *Plumpton* **Southwell**†	**2** Chepstow *Cork* *Fairyhouse* Fakenham Huntingdon Market Rasen Plumpton **Redcar** **Wolverhampton**†	**3** *Fairyhouse* **Lingfield Park**† **Pontefract** Wincanton	**4** **Catterick Bridge** **Kempton Park**☆ *Leopardstown* **Lingfield Park**† **Southwell**†	**5** **Chelmsford City**†☆ **Musselburgh** Warwick **Wolverhampton**† Ascot Sale	**6** **Chelmsford City**†☆ *Dundalk*†☆ Fontwell Park **Lingfield Park**† Wetherby *Wexford*☆	**7** Kelso **Kempton Park**† *Limerick* *Navan* Stratford-On-Avon Uttoxeter **Wolverhampton**†☆
8 Carlisle Exeter *Naas* Goffs (UK) Sale	**9** Kempton Park Ludlow **Wolverhampton**†☆ Goffs (UK) Sale	**10** Hexham Southwell *Tipperary*☆ **Wolverhampton**†☆	**11** *Dundalk*†☆ **Kempton Park**†☆ **Lingfield Park**† Market Rasen **Nottingham**	**12** Aintree **Chelmsford City**†☆ *Limerick* **Southwell**† Taunton Goffs (UK) Sale at Aintree	**13** Aintree *Ballinrobe*☆ **Kempton Park**†☆ **Leicester** Sedgefield	**14** Aintree Chepstow *Leopardstown* **Lingfield Park**† Newcastle **Wolverhampton**†☆
15 *Cork* *Ffos Las* *Plumpton* *Tramore* Tattersalls Sale	**16** Kelso **Redcar** *Tramore*☆ **Windsor** Tattersalls Sale	**17** Carlisle Exeter *Fairyhouse*☆ **Newmarket** Tattersalls Sale	**18** **Beverley** Cheltenham *Dundalk*†☆ **Kempton Park**†☆ **Newmarket** Cheltenham Sale	**19** Cheltenham **Newcastle**†☆ **Newmarket** **Ripon** *Tipperary*☆	**20** Ayr **Bath**☆ Fontwell Park *Kilbeggan*☆ **Newbury** Southwell☆	**21** Ayr Bangor-On-Dee *Limerick* **Newbury** **Nottingham**☆ **Thirsk** **Wolverhampton**†☆
22 *Navan* Stratford-On-Avon Wincanton	**23** Hexham *Navan*☆ Newton Abbot **Pontefract** Sedgefield☆ **Windsor**☆	**24** **Brighton**☆ Exeter Huntingdon☆ Ludlow *Punchestown*☆ **Yarmouth**	**25** **Catterick Bridge** **Epsom Downs** **Lingfield Park**†☆ Perth *Punchestown*☆ Taunton☆ Osarus Sale	**26** **Beverley** **Chelmsford City**†☆ Kempton Park☆ Perth *Punchestown*☆ Warwick Goffs Sale	**27** Chepstow☆ **Doncaster** Perth *Punchestown*☆ **Sandown Park** Towcester☆	**28** **Doncaster**☆ **Haydock Park** **Leicester** *Punchestown* **Ripon** Sandown Park **Wolverhampton**†☆
29 *Gowran Park* **Salisbury** **Wetherby**	**30** **Ayr** **Salisbury** **Southwell**†☆ **Thirsk** **Windsor**☆					

MAY

Sun	Mon	Tues	Wed	Thur	Fri	Sat
	1 Ayr☆ *Ballinrobe☆* **Brighton** **Kempton Park**☆ **Nottingham** **Yarmouth**	**2** **Ascot** **Bath**☆ **Brighton**☆ *Dundalk*†☆ **Pontefract** **Wolverhampton**†	**3** **Chelmsford City**†☆ *Clonmel*☆ **Lingfield Park**† **Musselburgh** **Redcar** **Southwell**† Tattersalls Sale	**4** Cheltenham☆ **Chepstow** *Cork*☆ *Downpatrick*☆ **Lingfield Park**† **Musselburgh** **Newcastle**†☆ Tattersalls Sale	**5** *Cork* **Doncaster**☆ **Goodwood** Hexham☆ **Newmarket** Uttoxeter **Wetherby** *Wexford*
6 *Dundalk*† **Hamilton Park** **Newmarket** *Sligo*	**7** **Bath** **Beverley** *Down Royal* Kempton Park *Naas* Warwick **Windsor**	**8** **Brighton** Exeter☆ Fakenham Ludlow☆ *Roscommon*☆ **Thirsk**	**9** **Chester** Fontwell Park☆ Gowran Park☆ Kelso Newton Abbot **Wolverhampton**†☆	**10** **Chelmsford City**†☆ **Chester** Huntingdon *Tipperary*☆ Wincanton☆ Worcester	**11** **Ascot**☆ **Chester** *Curragh* Kilbeggan☆ **Lingfield Park** Market Rasen **Nottingham**☆ **Ripon**☆ Arqana Sale	**12** **Ascot** *Curragh* **Haydock (Mixed)** Hexham **Lingfield Park** **Nottingham** **Thirsk**☆ Warwick☆ Arqana Sale
13 *Killarney* Leopardstown Ludlow Plumpton	**14** **Catterick Bridge** Kempton Park *Killarney*☆ Towcester☆ **Windsor**☆ **Wolverhampton**†	**15** **Beverley** **Chepstow**☆ *Killarney*☆ Sedgefield Southwell☆ Wincanton Tattersalls (IRE) Sale	**16** **Bath**☆ Newton Abbot Perth☆ *Punchestown*☆ **Yarmouth** **York** Tattersalls (IRE) Sale	**17** *Clonmel*☆ Fontwell Park☆ **Newmarket**☆ Perth **Salisbury** **York**	**18** Aintree☆ *Cork*☆ *Downpatrick*☆ **Hamilton Park**☆ **Newbury** **Newmarket** **York**	**19** Bangor-On-Dee **Doncaster**☆ *Navan* **Newbury** **Newmarket** **Thirsk** Uttoxeter☆
20 *Limerick* Market Rasen *Naas* **Ripon** Stratford-On-Avon	**21** **Carlisle** **Leicester**☆ **Redcar** Towcester **Windsor**☆ Fasig-Tipton Sale	**22** **Ayr** **Chepstow** Hexham☆ Huntingdon☆ **Nottingham** *Sligo*☆ Goffs (UK) Sale Fasig-Tipton Sale	**23** **Ayr** **Kempton Park**†☆ Southwell☆ Warwick *Wexford*☆ **Yarmouth** Goffs (UK) Sale	**24** **Catterick Bridge** **Chelmsford City**†☆ **Goodwood** **Lingfield Park** **Sandown Park**☆ *Tipperary*☆ Goffs (UK) Sale Goresbridge Sale	**25** **Bath** *Down Royal*☆ **Goodwood** **Haydock Park** Leopardstown☆ **Pontefract**☆ Worcester☆ Goresbridge Sale	**26** Cartmel **Chester** *Curragh* Ffos Las☆ **Goodwood** **Haydock Park** **Salisbury**☆ **York**
27 *Curragh* Fontwell Park Kelso Uttoxeter	**28** *Ballinrobe*☆ Cartmel **Chelmsford City**† Huntingdon **Leicester** **Redcar** **Windsor**	**29** *Ballinrobe*☆ **Brighton**☆ **Leicester** **Lingfield Park**† **Redcar** **Wolverhampton**†☆	**30** **Beverley** Cartmel Gowran Park☆ **Nottingham** **Ripon**☆ Warwick☆	**31** **Chelmsford City**†☆ *Fairyhouse*☆ Ffos Las **Hamilton Park** **Lingfield Park** **Wolverhampton**† Cheltenham Sale		

JUNE

Sun	Mon	Tues	Wed	Thur	Fri	Sat
					1	**2**
					Bath☆ **Catterick Bridge** **Doncaster**☆ **Epsom Downs** **Goodwood**☆ Market Rasen *Tramore*☆	**Chepstow**☆ **Doncaster** **Epsom Downs** Hexham **Lingfield Park**☆ **Musselburgh** *Navan* *Tramore*☆ Worcester
					Baden-Baden Sale	
3	**4**	**5**	**6**	**7**	**8**	**9**
Fakenham *Kilbeggan* *Listowel* Perth	**Ayr**☆ *Gowran Park* **Leicester** *Listowel* Newton Abbot **Windsor**☆	Bangor-On-Dee Fontwell Park **Newcastle**†☆ Southwell	**Hamilton Park** **Kempton Park**†☆ Uttoxeter **Wetherby**☆ *Wexford*☆ **Wolverhampton**†	**Carlisle**☆ **Haydock Park** *Leopardstown*☆ **Ripon** **Sandown Park**☆ Yarmouth	**Brighton** **Carlisle** *Clonmel*☆ *Curragh*☆ **Goodwood**☆ **Haydock Park**☆ Stratford-On-Avon☆ **Wolverhampton**†	**Beverley** **Catterick Bridge** *Curragh* **Haydock Park** **Lingfield Park**☆ **Musselburgh** **Newmarket** Stratford-On-Avon☆
		Ascot Sale				
10	**11**	**12**	**13**	**14**	**15**	**16**
Goodwood Nottingham	**Brighton** **Pontefract**☆ *Roscommon*☆ **Windsor**☆ Worcester	**Lingfield Park**☆ *Roscommon*☆ **Salisbury** Southwell☆ **Thirsk**	**Chelmsford City**† **Hamilton Park**☆ **Haydock Park** **Kempton Park**†☆ *Punchestown*☆ Yarmouth	**Haydock Park**☆ *Leopardstown*☆ **Newbury** **Nottingham** Uttoxeter☆ Yarmouth	Aintree☆ **Chepstow**☆ *Fairyhouse*☆ **Goodwood**☆ Newton Abbot **Sandown Park** **York**	**Bath** **Chester** *Downpatrick* Fontwell Park☆ Hexham **Leicester**☆ *Limerick* **Sandown Park** **York**
		Goffs Sale	*Goffs Sale*			
17	**18**	**19**	**20**	**21**	**22**	**23**
Cork **Doncaster** *Downpatrick* **Salisbury**	**Ayr** **Carlisle** **Nottingham**☆ **Windsor**☆	**Ascot** **Beverley**☆ **Brighton**☆ *Sligo*☆ Stratford-On-Avon **Thirsk**	**Ascot** **Chelmsford City**†☆ **Hamilton Park** **Ripon**☆ Uttoxeter *Wexford*☆	**Ascot** **Chelmsford City**† *Ffos Las* *Leopardstown*☆ **Lingfield Park**†☆ **Ripon**	**Ascot** **Ayr**☆ *Down Royal*☆ *Limerick*☆ Market Rasen **Newmarket**☆ **Redcar** **Wetherby**☆	**Ascot** **Ayr** *Down Royal* *Gowran Park* **Haydock Park**☆ **Lingfield Park**☆ **Newmarket** Perth **Redcar**
	Goffs (London) Sale					
24	**25**	**26**	**27**	**28**	**29**	**30**
Gowran Park Hexham **Pontefract** Worcester	**Chepstow** *Kilbeggan*☆ Southwell **Windsor**☆ **Wolverhampton**†☆	*Ballinrobe*☆ **Beverley** **Brighton** **Newbury**☆ Newton Abbot☆	**Bath**☆ **Carlisle** **Kempton Park**†☆ *Naas*☆ **Salisbury** Worcester	**Hamilton Park**☆ **Leicester**☆ **Newcastle**† **Newmarket** **Nottingham** *Tipperary*☆	Cartmel **Chester**☆ *Curragh*☆ **Doncaster** **Newcastle**†☆ **Newmarket**☆ Yarmouth	**Chester** *Curragh* **Doncaster**☆ **Lingfield Park**☆ **Newcastle**† **Newmarket** Windsor **York**
				Tattersalls (IRE) Sale	*Tattersalls (IRE) Sale*	

JULY

Sun	Mon	Tues	Wed	Thur	Fri	Sat
1	**2**	**3**	**4**	**5**	**6**	**7**
Cartmel *Curragh* Uttoxeter **Windsor**	**Hamilton Park**☆ Pontefract **Windsor**† **Wolverhampton**† Arqana Sale	Brighton **Chepstow**☆ Hamilton Park Stratford-On-Avon☆ Arqana Sale	**Bath**☆ *Bellewstown*☆ **Kempton Park**†☆ Musselburgh Thirsk Worcester Arqana Sale	*Bellewstown*☆ **Epsom Downs**☆ Haydock Park **Newbury**☆ *Perth* *Tipperary*☆ **Yarmouth**	*Bellewstown*☆ **Beverley**☆ **Chelmsford City**†☆ Doncaster **Haydock Park**☆ Newton Abbot **Sandown Park** *Wexford*☆	*Bellewstown*☆ Beverley **Carlisle**☆ **Chelmsford City**† Haydock Park Leicester *Naas* **Nottingham**☆ **Sandown Park**
8	**9**	**10**	**11**	**12**	**13**	**14**
Ayr *Fairyhouse* *Limerick* Market Rasen	**Ayr** **Ripon** *Roscommon*☆ **Windsor**☆ Fasig-Tipton Sale	**Brighton**☆ Pontefract *Roscommon*☆ Uttoxeter☆ **Wolverhampton**† Tattersalls Sale Fasig-Tipton Sale	**Bath**☆ Catterick Bridge **Kempton Park**†☆ **Lingfield Park** Yarmouth Tattersalls Sale	Carlisle Doncaster *Dundalk*† **Epsom Downs**☆ *Leopardstown*☆ **Newbury**☆ **Newmarket** Tattersalls Sale	**Ascot**☆ **Chepstow**☆ **Chester**☆ *Cork*☆ *Downpatrick* Ffos Las☆ **Newmarket** York Tattersalls Sale	**Ascot** Chester **Hamilton Park**☆ *Limerick* *Navan* **Newmarket** Newton Abbot **Salisbury**☆ York
15	**16**	**17**	**18**	**19**	**20**	**21**
Killarney Perth *Sligo* Southwell Stratford-On-Avon	**Ayr** *Killarney*☆ **Ripon** **Windsor**☆ **Wolverhampton**†☆	**Bath** Beverley *Killarney*☆ **Thirsk**☆ Worcester☆ Ascot Sale	Catterick Bridge *Fairyhouse*☆ *Killarney*☆ **Lingfield Park** Uttoxeter **Wolverhampton**†☆ **Yarmouth**☆	Chepstow **Doncaster**☆ **Epsom Downs**☆ Hamilton Park *Killarney* Leicester *Leopardstown*☆	**Hamilton Park**☆ **Haydock Park** *Kilbeggan*☆ **Newbury** **Newmarket**☆ Nottingham Pontefract☆ Gorsebridge Sale	Cartmel *Curragh* **Haydock Park**☆ **Lingfield Park**☆ Market Rasen **Newbury** **Newmarket** Ripon
22	**23**	**24**	**25**	**26**	**27**	**28**
Curragh Newton Abbot **Redcar** Stratford-On-Avon *Tipperary*	**Ayr** *Ballinrobe*☆ **Beverley**☆ Cartmel **Windsor**☆	*Ballinrobe*☆ **Chelmsford City**†☆ Ffos Las Musselburgh Nottingham☆	**Bath** Catterick Bridge **Leicester**☆ **Lingfield Park** *Naas*☆ **Sandown Park**☆	**Doncaster**☆ *Leopardstown*☆ *Limerick*☆ **Newbury**☆ **Sandown Park** Worcester **Yarmouth**	**Ascot** **Chepstow**☆ *Down Royal*☆ **Newmarket**☆ **Thirsk** Uttoxeter *Wexford*☆ **York**☆	**Ascot** Chester *Gowran Park* **Lingfield Park**☆ **Newcastle**† **Newmarket** **Salisbury**☆ York
29	**30**	**31**				
Pontefract Uttoxeter	**Ayr** *Galway*☆ Newton Abbot **Windsor**☆ **Wolverhampton**†☆	Beverley *Galway*☆ **Goodwood** Perth☆ Worcester☆ **Yarmouth**				

AUGUST

Sun	Mon	Tues	Wed	Thur	Fri	Sat
			1 *Galway*☆ **Goodwood** **Leicester**☆ Perth **Redcar** **Sandown Park**☆	**2** **Epsom Downs**☆ *Ffos Las*☆ *Galway* **Goodwood** **Nottingham** Stratford-On-Avon	**3** Bangor-On-Dee **Bath**☆ *Galway*☆ **Goodwood** **Musselburgh**☆ **Newmarket**☆ **Thirsk**	**4** **Chelmsford City**† **Doncaster** *Galway* **Goodwood** **Hamilton Park**☆ **Lingfield Park**☆ **Newmarket** **Thirsk**
5 **Chester** *Galway* Market Rasen	**6** **Carlisle**☆ *Cork* *Curragh* Newton Abbot **Ripon** **Windsor**☆ Fasig-Tipton Sale	**7** **Ayr**☆ **Catterick Bridge** **Newbury** **Nottingham**☆ *Roscommon*☆ Goffs (UK) Sale Fasig-Tipton Sale	**8** **Bath** **Brighton** **Kempton Park**†☆ **Pontefract** *Sligo*☆ **Yarmouth**☆ Goffs (UK) Sale	**9** **Brighton** **Haydock Park** *Leopardstown*☆ **Newcastle**☆ **Sandown Park**☆ *Sligo*☆ **Yarmouth**	**10** **Brighton** **Chelmsford City**†☆ **Haydock Park**☆ **Musselburgh** **Newmarket**☆ *Tipperary*☆ **Wolverhampton**†	**11** **Ascot**☆ **Ayr**☆ **Chelmsford City**† *Cork* **Haydock Park** *Kilbeggan*☆ **Lingfield Park**☆ **Newmarket** **Redcar** Fasig-Tipton Sale
12 *Curragh* *Downpatrick* **Leicester** **Windsor** Fasig-Tipton Sale	**13** **Ayr** *Ballinrobe*☆ **Ripon** **Windsor**☆ **Wolverhampton**†☆ Tattersalls (IRE) Sale	**14** **Chelmsford City**† **Ffos Las** **Nottingham**☆ **Thirsk**☆ Tattersalls (IRE) Sale	**15** **Beverley** *Gowran Park*☆ **Kempton Park**†☆ Newton Abbot **Salisbury** **Worcester**☆	**16** **Beverley** **Chepstow**☆ *Leopardstown*☆ **Salisbury** *Tramore*☆ **Wolverhampton**†☆ **Yarmouth**☆	**17** **Catterick Bridge**☆ **Chelmsford City**†☆ *Dundalk*†☆ **Newmarket**☆ **Nottingham** *Tramore*☆ **Wolverhampton**†	**18** **Bath**☆ **Doncaster** Market Rasen☆ **Newbury** **Newmarket** Perth **Ripon**☆ *Tramore*☆ Arqana Sale
19 **Pontefract** Southwell *Tramore* Arqana Sale	**20** Bangor-On-Dee☆ **Leicester** *Roscommon*☆ **Thirsk** **Windsor**☆ Arqana Sale	**21** **Brighton** **Hamilton Park** **Kempton Park**† Newton Abbot☆ *Sligo*☆ **Yarmouth**☆ Ascot Sale Arqana Sale	**22** **Bath** **Carlisle** **Kempton Park**†☆ *Killarney* **Worcester**☆ **York**	**23** **Chepstow** Fontwell Park☆ *Killarney*☆ Stratford-On-Avon **Wolverhampton**†☆ **York**	**24** **Chelmsford City**†☆ **Ffos Las** **Goodwood**☆ *Kilbeggan*☆ *Killarney*☆ **Newmarket** **Salisbury**☆ **York**	**25** Cartmel **Chelmsford City**† *Curragh* **Goodwood** *Killarney* **Newmarket** **Redcar**☆ **Windsor**☆ **York**
26 **Beverley** *Curragh* **Goodwood** **Yarmouth**	**27** Cartmel **Chepstow** *Downpatrick* **Epsom Downs** **Ripon** **Southwell**†	**28** *Ballinrobe*☆ **Bath**☆ **Epsom Downs** **Ripon** Stratford-On-Avon☆ Goffs (UK) Sale	**29** *Bellewstown*☆ **Catterick Bridge** **Kempton Park**†☆ **Lingfield Park** **Musselburgh** **Worcester**☆ Goffs (UK) Sale	**30** *Bellewstown*☆ **Chelmsford City**† Fontwell Park☆ **Musselburgh** Sedgefield☆ *Tipperary*☆ Goffs (UK) Sale	**31** Bangor-On-Dee *Down Royal*☆ **Hamilton Park**☆ **Newcastle**†☆ **Sandown Park** **Thirsk** **Wolverhampton**†☆ Baden-Baden Sale	

SEPTEMBER

Sun	Mon	Tues	Wed	Thur	Fri	Sat
30						**1**
Epsom Downs Musselburgh *Naas*						Beverley **Chelmsford City†☆** **Chester** *Curragh* **Lingfield Park†☆** Newton Abbot **Sandown Park** **Wolverhampton†**
2	**3**	**4**	**5**	**6**	**7**	**8**
Brighton *Curragh* Worcester	**Brighton** **Chepstow** **Newcastle†☆** *Roscommon☆* **Windsor☆**	**Goodwood** **Kempton Park☆** **Leicester☆** Stratford-On-Avon	**Bath** **Ffos Las☆** *Gowran Park☆* **Lingfield Park†** Southwell **Wolverhampton†☆**	**Carlisle☆** **Chelmsford City☆** **Haydock Park** *Laytown* **Salisbury** Sedgefield	**Ascot** *Down Royal☆* **Haydock Park** **Kempton Park☆** *Kilbeggan☆* **Musselburgh☆** **Newcastle†**	**Ascot** **Haydock Park** **Kempton Park†** *Navan* Stratford-On-Avon **Thirsk** *Wexford* **Wolverhampton†☆**
		Osarus Sale	*Osarus Sale*			
9	**10**	**11**	**12**	**13**	**14**	**15**
Fontwell Park *Listowel* **York**	**Brighton** **Chelmsford City†☆** *Listowel* Newton Abbot Perth	**Catterick Bridge** **Leicester** *Listowel* **Salisbury☆** Worcester	**Carlisle** **Doncaster** **Kempton Park†☆** *Listowel* Uttoxeter	**Chepstow** **Doncaster** **Epsom Downs** **Hamilton Park☆** *Listowel*	**Chester** **Doncaster** *Listowel* **Salisbury☆** **Sandown Park**	**Bath** **Chelmsford City†** **Chester** **Doncaster** *Leopardstown* **Lingfield Park** *Listowel* **Musselburgh☆** *Goffs Sale*
Keeneland Sale	*Keeneland Sale*	*Ascot Sale* *Keeneland Sale*	*Keeneland Sale*	*Keeneland Sale*	*Keeneland Sale*	*Keeneland Sale*
16	**17**	**18**	**19**	**20**	**21**	**22**
Bath *Curragh* **Ffos Las**	**Brighton** *Galway☆* Hexham **Kempton Park†☆** Worcester	**Chepstow** *Galway☆* **Kempton Park†☆** **Redcar** **Yarmouth**	**Beverley** *Kelso☆* *Naas☆* **Sandown Park** **Yarmouth**	**Ayr** **Chelmsford City†☆** *Clonmel☆* **Pontefract** **Yarmouth**	**Ayr** *Ballinrobe☆* *Dundalk†☆* **Newbury** **Newcastle†☆** Newton Abbot	**Ayr** **Catterick Bridge** **Chelmsford City†** *Gowran Park* **Newbury** **Newmarket** **Wolverhampton†☆**
Keeneland Sale	*Keeneland Sale*	*Goffs (UK) Sale* *Keeneland Sale*	*Goffs (UK) Sale* *Keeneland Sale*	*Keeneland Sale*	*Keeneland Sale* *SGA Sale*	*Keeneland Sale* *SGA Sale*
23	**24**	**25**	**26**	**27**	**28**	**29**
Hamilton Park *Navan* Plumpton Uttoxeter	*Fairyhouse☆* **Hamilton Park** **Kempton Park†** **Leicester** **Newcastle†☆**	**Beverley** **Chelmsford City†☆** **Lingfield Park†** Warwick	**Goodwood** Perth **Redcar** **Wolverhampton†☆**	**Kempton Park☆** **Newmarket** Perth **Pontefract** *Sligo*	*Downpatrick* *Dundalk†☆* **Haydock Park** **Newcastle†☆** **Newmarket** Worcester	**Chelmsford City†☆** **Chester** **Haydock Park** Market Rasen **Newmarket** *Navan* **Ripon**
		Tattersalls (IRE) Sale	*Tattersalls (IRE) Sale*	*Tattersalls (IRE) Sale*		

OCTOBER

Sun	Mon	Tues	Wed	Thur	Fri	Sat
	1 Bath, **Catterick Bridge**, **Kempton Park†☆**, Newton Abbot, *Roscommon* — Fasig-Tipton Sale	**2** **Ayr**, **Kempton Park†☆**, Sedgefield, Southwell — Goffs Sale, Fasig-Tipton Sale	**3** Bangor-On-Dee, *Cork*, **Newcastle†☆**, **Nottingham**, **Salisbury** — Goffs Sale	**4** **Chelmsford City†☆**, *Clonmel*, Huntingdon, **Lingfield Park†**, Warwick — Goffs Sale	**5** *Ascot*, *Dundalk†☆*, Fontwell Park, *Gowran Park*, Hexham, **Wolverhampton†☆**	**6** *Ascot*, Fontwell Park, *Gowran Park*, **Newmarket**, Redcar, **Wolverhampton†☆** — Arqana Sale
7 Kelso, *Tipperary*, Uttoxeter	**8** **Kempton Park†☆**, **Pontefract**, Stratford-On-Avon, **Windsor**, *Tipperary*	**9** **Brighton**, **Catterick Bridge**, *Galway*, **Leicester**, **Newcastle†☆** — Tattersalls Sale	**10** *Cork*, **Kempton Park†☆**, Ludlow, **Nottingham**, Towcester — Tattersalls Sale	**11** **Ayr**, **Chelmsford City†☆**, Exeter, *Thurles*, Worcester — Tattersalls Sale	**12** *Downpatrick*, *Dundalk†☆*, **Newmarket**, Newton Abbot, **Wolverhampton†☆**, **York**	**13** **Chelmsford City†☆**, Chepstow, *Fairyhouse*, Hexham, *Limerick*, **Newmarket**, **York**
14 Chepstow, **Goodwood**, *Limerick*, *Navan*	**15** *Gowran Park*, **Kempton Park†☆**, **Musselburgh**, **Windsor**, **Yarmouth** — Tattersalls Sale, Fasig-Tipton Sale	**16** Hereford, Huntingdon, **Kempton Park†☆**, **Leicester**, *Punchestown* — Tattersalls Sale	**17** **Bath**, **Newcastle†☆**, **Nottingham**, *Punchestown*, Wetherby — Tattersalls Sale	**18** **Brighton**, Carlisle, **Chelmsford City†☆**, *Tramore*, Uttoxeter — Tattersalls Sale	**19** *Dundalk†☆*, Fakenham, **Haydock Park**, **Newcastle†☆**, **Redcar**, Wincanton — Tattersalls Sale, Baden-Baden Sale	**20** **Ascot**, **Catterick Bridge**, *Ffos Las*, *Leopardstown*, Market Rasen, Stratford-On-Avon, **Wolverhampton†☆** — Tattersalls Sale, Baden-Baden Sale
21 *Cork*, Kempton Park, *Naas*, Sedgefield	**22** Plumpton, **Kempton Park†☆**, **Pontefract**, **Windsor** — Fasig-Tipton Sale	**23** Exeter, **Kempton Park†☆**, **Newcastle†**, **Yarmouth** — Arqana Sale, Fasig-Tipton Sale	**24** Fontwell Park, *Navan*, **Newcastle†☆**, **Newmarket**, Worcester — Goffs (UK) Sale, Arqana Sale, Fasig-Tipton Sale	**25** Carlisle, **Chelmsford City†☆**, Ludlow, Southwell, *Thurles* — Goffs (UK) Sale, Arqana Sale, Fasig-Tipton Sale	**26** Cheltenham, **Doncaster**, *Dundalk†☆*, **Kempton Park†☆**, **Newbury** — Goffs (UK) Sale, Gorsebridge Sale, Arqana Sale	**27** Cheltenham, **Doncaster**, *Galway*, Kelso, **Kempton Park†☆**, *Leopardstown*, **Newbury**
28 Aintree, *Galway*, *Wexford*, Wincanton	**29** Ayr, **Chelmsford City†☆**, *Galway*, **Leicester**, **Redcar**, *Wexford* — Tattersalls Sale	**30** Bangor-On-Dee, **Catterick Bridge**, Chepstow, **Wolverhampton†☆** — Tattersalls Sale	**31** *Dundalk†☆*, Fakenham, **Kempton Park†☆**, **Nottingham**, Taunton — Tattersalls Sale			

NOVEMBER

Sun	Mon	Tues	Wed	Thur	Fri	Sat
			1	**2**	**3**	
			Clonmel *Lingfield Park†* Sedgefield Stratford-On-Avon **Wolverhampton†☆**	Down Royal *Dundalk†☆* **Kempton Park†☆** **Newmarket** Uttoxeter Wetherby	Ascot Ayr *Down Royal* **Newcastle†** **Newmarket** Wetherby	
				Tattersalls Sale	Tattersalls Sale	
4	**5**	**6**	**7**	**8**	**9**	**10**
Carlisle *Cork* Huntingdon *Naas*	Hereford **Kempton Park†☆** Plumpton	Exeter *Fairyhouse* **Kempton Park†☆** **Redcar** **Wolverhampton†**	Chepstow *Dundalk†☆* Musselburgh **Newcastle†☆** **Nottingham**	**Chelmsford City†☆** Market Rasen Newbury Sedgefield *Thurles*	*Dundalk†☆* Fontwell Park Hexham **Newcastle†☆** Warwick	Aintree **Chelmsford City†☆** **Doncaster** Kelso *Naas* Wincanton
Fasig-Tipton Sale	Goffs Sale Keeneland Sale	Goffs Sale Keeneland Sale	Goffs Sale Tattersalls (IRE) Sale Keeneland Sale	Tattersalls (IRE) Sale Ascot Sale Keeneland Sale	Tattersalls (IRE) Sale Keeneland Sale	Tattersalls (IRE) Sale Keeneland Sale SGA Sale
11	**12**	**13**	**14**	**15**	**16**	**17**
Ffos Las *Navan* Sandown Park	Carlisle Kempton Park **Southwell†**	**Chelmsford City†☆** Hereford Huntingdon Lingfield Park	Ayr Bangor-On-Dee Exeter *Fairyhouse* **Kempton Park†☆**	**Chelmsford City†☆** *Clonmel* Ludlow **Southwell†** Taunton	Cheltenham *Dundalk†☆* **Lingfield Park†** Newcastle **Wolverhampton†☆**	Cheltenham **Lingfield Park†** *Punchestown* Uttoxeter Wetherby **Wolverhampton†☆**
Tattersalls (IRE) Sale Keeneland Sale	Tattersalls (IRE) Sale Keeneland Sale	Tattersalls (IRE) Sale Keeneland Sale	Tattersalls (IRE) Sale Keeneland Sale	Tattersalls (IRE) Sale Keeneland Sale	Tattersalls (IRE) Sale Cheltenham Sale Keeneland Sale	Tattersalls (IRE) Sale Keeneland Sale
18	**19**	**20**	**21**	**22**	**23**	**24**
Cheltenham *Cork* Fontwell Park *Punchestown*	**Kempton Park†☆** Leicester Plumpton	Fakenham **Lingfield Park†** Southwell	Chepstow *Dundalk†☆* Hexham **Kempton Park†☆** Warwick	Market Rasen **Newcastle†** *Thurles* Wincanton **Wolverhampton†☆**	Ascot Catterick Bridge *Dundalk†☆* Ffos Las **Kempton Park†☆**	Ascot *Gowran Park* Haydock Park Huntingdon **Lingfield Park†** **Wolverhampton†☆**
Goffs Sale	Goffs Sale Arqana Sale	Goffs Sale Arqana Sale	Goffs Sale Arqana Sale	Goffs Sale	Goffs Sale	Goffs Sale
25	**26**	**27**	**28**	**29**	**30**	
Exeter *Navan* Uttoxeter	Kempton Park Ludlow Musselburgh	Lingfield Park Sedgefield **Southwell†**	Hereford **Newcastle†☆** *Punchestown* Wetherby **Wolverhampton†**	Ayr **Chelmsford City†☆** Taunton *Thurles* Towcester	Doncaster *Dundalk†☆* *Limerick* Newbury **Newcastle†☆** **Southwell†**	
Goffs Sale	Tattersalls Sale		Tattersalls Sale	Tattersalls Sale	Tattersalls Sale	

DECEMBER

Sun	Mon	Tues	Wed	Thur	Fri	Sat
30 Haydock Park, **Lingfield Park**†, Taunton	**31** **Lingfield Park**†, *Punchestown*, Uttoxeter, Warwick					**1** Bangor-On-Dee, Doncaster, *Fairyhouse*, Newbury, Newcastle, **Wolverhampton**†☆ Tattersalls Sale
2 Carlisle, *Fairyhouse*, Leicester Tattersalls Sale	**3** Musselburgh, Plumpton, **Wolverhampton**†☆ Tattersalls Sale	**4** Fakenham, **Lingfield Park**†, Southwell Tattersalls Sale / Fasig-Tipton Sale	**5** Haydock Park, **Kempton Park**†☆, **Lingfield Park**†, Ludlow Tattersalls Sale	**6** **Chelmsford City**†, *Clonmel*, Leicester, Market Rasen, Wincanton Tattersalls Sale	**7** *Dundalk*†☆, Exeter, **Kempton Park**†☆, Sandown Park, Sedgefield	**8** Aintree, Chepstow, *Navan*, Sandown Park, Wetherby, **Wolverhampton**†☆ Arqana Sale
9 *Cork*, Huntingdon, Kelso, *Punchestown* Arqana Sale	**10** Lingfield Park, Musselburgh, **Wolverhampton**†☆ Ascot Sale / Arqana Sale	**11** Fontwell Park, **Southwell**†, Uttoxeter Arqana Sale	**12** Hexham, **Kempton Park**†☆, Leicester, **Lingfield Park**† Goffs Sale	**13** **Chelmsford City**†☆, Newcastle, Taunton, *Tramore*, Warwick Goffs Sale	**14** Bangor-On-Dee, Cheltenham, Doncaster, *Dundalk*†☆, **Kempton Park**†☆ Cheltenham Sale	**15** Cheltenham, Doncaster, *Fairyhouse*, Hereford, **Newcastle**†, **Wolverhampton**†☆
16 Carlisle, *Navan*, Southwell	**17** Ffos Las, Plumpton, **Wolverhampton**†☆	**18** Catterick Bridge, Fakenham, *Naas*, **Southwell**†	**19** *Dundalk*†☆, **Lingfield Park**†, Ludlow, Newbury, **Newcastle**†☆	**20** **Chelmsford City**†☆, Exeter, **Southwell**†, Towcester	**21** Ascot, *Dundalk*†☆, **Southwell**†, Uttoxeter, **Wolverhampton**†☆	**22** Ascot, Haydock Park, **Lingfield Park**†, Newcastle, *Thurles*
23	**24**	**25**	**26** *Down Royal*, Fontwell Park, Huntingdon, Kempton Park, *Leopardstown*, *Limerick*, Market Rasen, Sedgefield, Wetherby, Wincanton	**27** Chepstow, Kempton Park, *Leopardstown*, *Limerick*, Wetherby, **Wolverhampton**† **Wolverhampton**†	**28** Catterick Bridge, Leicester, *Leopardstown*, *Limerick*, **Lingfield Park**†	**29** Doncaster, Kelso, *Leopardstown*, *Limerick*, Newbury, **Southwell**†

DATES OF PRINCIPAL RACES

(SUBJECT TO ALTERATION)

JANUARY

Ballymore Novices' Hurdle (Cheltenham)	1st
Betbright Dipper Novices' Steeplechase (Cheltenham)	1st
Betbright Best For Festival Betting Handicap SteepleChase (Cheltenham)	1st
Dornan Engineering Relkeel Hurdle (Cheltenham)	1st
EBF Stallions & Cheltenham Pony Club Standard Open National Hunt Flat Race (Cheltenham)	1st
Totepool Hogmaneigh Handicap Hurdle (Musselburgh)	1st
Totequadpot 'Auld Reekie' Handicap Steeple Chase (Musselburgh)	1st
Wilf Dooly Steeple Chase (Tramore)	1st
Sunbets.co.uk Handicap Stakes (Newcastle)	2nd
Betway Conditions Stakes (Newcastle)	2nd
32Red Handicap Stakes (Kempton Park)	6th
At The Races Sussex National Handicap Steeple Chase (Plumpton)	7th
32Red.Com Mares' Hurdle Race (Sandown Park)	7th
32Red Tolworth Novices' Hurdle (Sandown Park)	7th
Slaney Novices' Hurdle (Naas)	7th
Sky Bet Yorkshire Silver Vase Mares' Steeple Chase (Doncaster)	9th
Watt Fences North Yorkshire Grand National H'cap Steeple Chase (Catterick Bridge)	11th
Smarkets Chatteris Fen Juvenile Hurdle (Huntingdon)	12th
32Red Lanzarote Handicap Hurdle (Kempton Park)	13th
32Red Casino Steeple Chase (Kempton Park)	13th
Betfred Classic Handicap Steeple Chase (Warwick)	13th
Ballymore Leamington Novices' Hurdle (Warwick)	13th
Betfred Home of Goals Galore Hampton Novices' Steeple Chase (Warwick)	13th
Moscow Flyer Novices' Hurdle (Punchestown)	13th
Killiney Novices' Steeple Chase (Punchestown)	13th
Children's Immunology Trust Handicap Steeple Chase (Kelso)	14th
Dan Moore Memorial Handicap Steeple Chase (Fairyhouse)	14th
Smarter Bets With Matchbook Conditions Stakes (Kempton Park)	16th
Weatherbys Racing Bank Graduation Steeple Chase (Market Rasen)	17th
Higos Insurance Services Somerset National Handicap Steeple Chase (Wincanton)	18th
Navan Handicap Hurdle (Navan)	20th
Altcar Novices' Steeple Chase (Haydock Park)	20th
Sky Bet Supreme Trial Rossington Main Novices' Hurdle (Haydock Park)	20th
Unibet Champion Hurdle Trial (Haydock Park)	20th
Peter Marsh Handicap Steeple Chase (Haydock Park)	20th
OLBG.com Warfield Mares' Hurdle (Ascot)	20th
Ascot Spring Garden Show Holloway's Handicap Hurdle (Ascot)	20th
Royal Salute Whisky Clarence House Steeple Chase (Ascot)	20th
Bet365 Handicap Steeple Chase (Ascot)	20th
Coolmore EBF Mares Novices' Steeple Chase (Thurles)	21st
Kinloch Brae Steeple Chase (Thurles)	21st
Charnwood Forest Mares' Steeple Chase (Leicester)	23rd
Goffs Thyestes Handicap Steeple Chase (Gowran Park)	25th
Galmoy Hurdle (Gowran Park)	25th
Napoleons Casino & Restaurant Owlerton Sheffield Novices' Steeple Chase (Doncaster)	27th
Sky Bet Handicap Steeple Chase (Doncaster)	27th
Albert Bartlett River Don Novices' Hurdle (Doncaster)	27th
OLBG.com Yorkshire Rose Mares' Hurdle (Doncaster)	27th
Festival Trials Handicap Steeple Chase (Cheltenham)	27th
Galliardhomes.com Cleeve Hurdle (Cheltenham)	27th
JCB Triumph Trial Finesse Juvenile Hurdle (Cheltenham)	27th
Betbright Trial Cotswold Steeple Chase (Cheltenham)	27th
Ballymore Classic Novices' Hurdle (Cheltenham)	27th
Timeform Novices' Handicap Steeple Chase (Cheltenham)	27th
Steel Plate And Sections Handicap Hurdle (Cheltenham)	27th
32Red Handicap Stakes (Kempton Park)	27th
Solerina Mares' Novices' Hurdle (Fairyhouse)	27th
Woodlands Novices' Steeple Chase (Naas)	28th
Limestone Lad Hurdle (Naas)	28th
Darren Linn Memorial Handicap Steeple Chase (Hereford)	29th
32Red.com EBF Fillies' Handicap Stakes (Wolverhampton)	29th

FEBRUARY

Dick Hunt Handicap Steeple Chase (Wincanton)	1st
Betway Winter Derby Trial Stakes (Lingfield Park)	3rd
Betway Cleves Stakes (Lingfield Park)	3rd

Bet365 Scottish County Hurdle (Musselburgh) 3rd
Bet365 Edinburgh National Handicap Steeple Chase (Musselburgh) 3rd
Betfred Heroes Handicap Hurdle (Sandown Park) 3rd
Betfred Mobile Masters Handicap Steeple Chase (Sandown Park) 3rd
Betfred TV Scilly Isles Novices' Steeple Chase (Sandown Park) 3rd
Totepool Towton Novices' Steeple Chase (Wetherby) 3rd
Frank Ward Solicitors Arkle Novices' Steeple Chase (Leopardstown) 3rd
BHP Insurances Irish Champion Hurdle (Leopardstown) 3rd
Nathaniel Lacy Golden Cygnet Novices' Hurdle (Leopardstown) 3rd
Coral Dublin Steeple Chase (Leopardstown) 3rd
Goffs (Colts & Geldings) Irish National Hunt Flat Race (Leopardstown) 3rd
Coral.ie Leopardstown Handicap Hurdle (Leopardstown) 3rd
Leopardstown Handicap Chase (Leopardstown) 3rd
Bet365 Scottish Triumph Hurdle Trial Juvenile Hurdle (Musselburgh) 4th
Tattersalls Ireland Spring 4yo Hurdle (Leopardstown) 4th
Unibet Irish Gold Cup (Leopardstown) 4th
Flogas Novices' Steeple Chase (Leopardstown) 4th
Deloitte Novices' Hurdle (Leopardstown) 4th
Mares Irish National Hunt Flat Race (Leopardstown) 4th
Chanelle Group Leopardstown Steeple Chase (Leopardstown) 4th
Leopardstown Handicap Hurdle (Leopardstown) 4th
EBF Mares Handicap Hurdle (Leopardstown) 4th
Sidney Banks Memorial Novices' Hurdle (Huntingdon)..8th
Kingmaker Novices' Steeple Chase (Warwick) 10th
OLBG.com Warwick Mares' Hurdle (Warwick) 10th
Betfair Hurdle (Handicap) (Newbury) 10th
Betfair Denman Steeple Chase (Newbury) 10th
Betfair Exchange Game Spirit Steeple Chase (Newbury) 10th
Betfair Bumper (A Standard Open National Hunt Flat Race) (Newbury) 10th
Opera Hat Mares' Steeple Chase (Naas) 10th
Grand National Trial Handicap Steeple Chase (Punchestown) 11th
EBF Novices' Hurdle (Punchestown) 11th
Timeform Morebattle Hurdle (Kelso) 15th
Ivan Straker Memorial Steeple Chase (Kelso) 15th
Powerstown Novice Hurdle (Clonmel) 15th
Royal Artillery Gold Cup Steeple Chase (Sandown Park) 16th
Weatherbys GSB Goes Online Jane Seymour Mares' Novices' Hurdle (Sandown Park) 16th
Albert Bartlett Prestige Novices' Hurdle (Haydock Park) 17th
Betfred Rendlesham Hurdle (Haydock Park) 17th
Betfred Grand National Trial Handicap Steeple Chase (Haydock Park) 17th
Sodexo Reynoldstown Novices' Steeple Chase (Ascot) 17th
Betfair Ascot Steeple Chase (Ascot) 17th
Keltbray Swinley Chase (Limited Handicap) (Ascot) 17th
Ascot Handicap Hurdle (Ascot) 17th
Betway Kingwell Hurdle (Wincanton) 17th
Red Mills Trial Hurdle (Gowran Park)...17th
Red Mills Steeple Chase (Gowran Park) 17th
Boyne Hurdle (Navan) 18th
Ten Up Novices' Steeple Chase (Navan) 18th
Genius By Betbright Veterans Handicap Steeple Chase (Doncaster) 21st
32Red Conditions Stakes (Kempton Park) 21st
Quevega Mares' Hurdle (Punchestown) 21st
Lady Protectress Mares' Steeple Chase (Huntingdon)...22nd
Michael Purcell Novices' Hurdle (Thurles) 22nd
Budbrooke Handicap Steeple Chase (Warwick) 23rd
Higos Insurance Services Devon National Handicap Steeple Chase (Exeter) 23rd
Betway Winter Derby Stakes (Lingfield Park) 24th
Betway Hever Sprint Stakes (Lingfield Park) 24th
Betfred Eider Handicap Steeple Chase (Newcastle) 24th
Betbright Handicap Steeple Chase (Kempton Park) 24th
Betbright Genius Adonis Juvenile Hurdle (Kempton Park) 24th
Betbright Best For Festival Betting Pendil Novices' Steeple Chase (Kempton Park) 24th
Sky Bet Dovecote Novices' Hurdle (Kempton Park) 24th
Winning Fair Juvenile Hurdle (Fairyhouse) 24th
At The Races Bobbyjo Steeple Chase (Fairyhouse)..24th
Totepool National Spirit Hurdle (Fontwell Park) 25th
Paddy Power Johnstown Novices' Hurdle (Naas) 25th
Paddy Power Newlands Steeple Chase (Naas) 25th
Nas na Riogh Novices' Handicap Steeple Chase (Naas) 25th
British Stallion Studs/32Red EBF Fillies' Conditions Stakes (Lingfield Park) 27th

MARCH

'Road To The Kentucky Derby' Conditions Stakes (Kempton Park) 1st
Patton Stakes (Dundalk) 2nd

32Red 3 Year Old All-Weather Championships Conditions Stakes (Lingfield Park) 30th
Sunbets All-Weather Championships Apprentice Handicap Stakes (Lingfield Park) 30th
Challenger Two Mile Handicap Hurdle Final (Haydock Park) 31st
Challenger Stayers Handicap Hurdle Final (Haydock Park) 31st
Challenger Mares' Handicap Hurdle Final (Haydock Park) 31st
Challenger Staying Handicap Chase Final (Haydock Park) 31st
Challenger Middle Distance Handicap Chase Final (Haydock Park) 31st
Challenger Series Mares' Handicap Chase Final (Haydock Park) 31st
Betfred Mobile Magnolia Stakes (Kempton Park) 31st
Betfred 'Home Of Goals Galore' Rosebery Handicap Stakes (Kempton Park) 31st
Totescoop6 Borderlescott Sprint Trophy Conditions Stakes (Musselburgh) 31st
Totepoolliveinfo.com Royal Mile Handicap Stakes (Musselburgh) 31st
Totepool Queen's Cup Handicap Stakes (Musselburgh) 31st

APRIL

Persimmon Homes West Wales Handicap Stepplechase (Ffos Las) 1st
Totepool Sussex Champion Hurdle (Plumpton) 1st
Ryanair Gold Cup (Fairyhouse) 1st
EBF Mares' Novices' Hurdle Final (Fairyhouse) 1st
John Fowler Memorial Mares' Steeple Chase (Fairyhouse) 1st
INHSO Final Novices' Handicap Hurdle (Fairyhouse) 1st
Imperial Call Steeple Chase (Cork) 1st
Easter Handicap Hurdle (Cork) 1st
Percy Maynard 4yo Hurdle (Fairyhouse) 2nd
Keelings Hurdle (Fairyhouse) 2nd
Boylesports Irish Grand National Steeple Chase (Fairyhouse) 2nd
Greenogue Novices' Handicap Steeple Chase (Fairyhouse) 2nd
Rathbarry Novices' Hurdle (Fairyhouse) 3rd
Normans Grove Steeple Chase (Fairyhouse) 3rd
Coolmore NH Sires Festival Novices' Hurdle (Fairyhouse) 3rd
Total Enjoyment Mares' Bumper (Fairyhouse) 3rd
Glasscam Handicap Hurdle (Fairyhouse) 3rd
Heritage Stakes (Leopardstown) 4th
188Bet.co.uk Handicap Steeplechase (Warwick) 5th
Snowdrop Stakes (Kempton Park) 7th
Liz Adam Memorial Steeplechase (Kelso) 7th
Kevin McManus Bumper (Limerick) 7th
Hugh McMahon Memorial Novices' Steeple Chase (Limerick) 7th
Cork Sprint Stakes (Navan) 7th
Gladness Stakes (Naas) 8th
Alleged Stakes (Naas) 8th
Further Flight Stakes (Nottingham) 11th
Randox Health Fox Hunters Handicap Steeple Chase (Aintree) 12th
Aintree Hurdle (Aintree) 12th
Betway Bowl Steeple Chase (Aintree) 12th
Manifesto Novices' Steeple Chase (Aintree) 12th
Anniversary Juvenile Hurdle (Aintree) 12th
Red Rum Handicap Steeple Chase (Aintree) 12th
Nickel Coin Open National Hunt Flat Race (Aintree) 12th
Randox Health Topham Handicap Steeple Chase (Aintree) 13th
Melling Steeple Chase (Aintree) 13th
Mildmay Novices' Steeple Chase (Aintree) 13th
Sefton Novices' Hurdle (Aintree) 13th
Top Novices' Hurdle (Aintree) 13th
Alder Hey Handicap Hurdle (Aintree) 13th
Weatherbys Champion Open National Hunt Flat Race (Aintree) 13th
Randox Health Grand National Handicap Steeple Chase (Aintree) 14th
Liverpool Stayers' Hurdle (Aintree) 14th
Maghull Novices' Steeple Chase (Aintree) 14th
Mersey Novices' Hurdle (Aintree) 14th
Gaskells Handicap Hurdle (Aintree) 14th
Betway Handicap Steeple Chase (Aintree) 14th
Aintree Handicap Hurdle (Aintree) 14th
Leopardstown 2000 Guineas Trial Stakes (Leopardstown) 14th
Leopardstown 1000 Guineas Trial Stakes (Leopardstown) 14th
Ballysax Stakes (Leopardstown) 14th
Noblesse Stakes (Cork) 15th
Feilden Stakes (Newmarket) 17th
Earl of Sefton Stakes (Newmarket) 18th
Nell Gwyn Stakes (Newmarket) 18th
European Free Handicap (Newmarket) 18th
Silver Trophy Handicap Steeple Chase (Cheltenham) 18th
Bet365 Craven Stakes (Newmarket) 19th
Abernant Stakes (Newmarket) 19th

EBF Thoroughbred Breeders' Association Mares' Novices' Handicap Chase (Cheltenham) 19th
Catesby Handicap Hurdle (Cheltenham) 19th
Thoroughbred Breeders' Association Mares' Novices' Hurdle (Cheltenham) 19th
Mysilv Juvenile Handicap Hurdle (Cheltenham) 19th
EBF Lansdown Stakes (Bath) 20th
John Porter Stakes (Newbury) 21st
Greenham Stakes (Newbury) 21st
Dubai Duty Free Stakes (Newbury) 21st
Scottish Grand National Handicap Chase (Ayr) 21st
Scottish Champion Hurdle (A Limited Handicap) (Ayr) 21st
Weatherbys Hamilton Novices' Chase (Ayr) 21st
Jordan Electrics Ltd Future Champion Novices' Chase (Ayr) 21st
Scotty Brand Handicap Chase (Ayr) 21st
Committed Stakes (Navan) 22nd
Vintage Crop Stakes (Navan) 22nd
Salsabil Stakes (Navan) 22nd
Woodlands Sprint Stakes (Navan) 23rd
Growise Novices' Steeple Chase (Punchestown) 24th
Evening Herald Champion Novices' Hurdle (Punchestown) 24th
Boylesports Champion Steeple Chase (Punchestown) 24th
Kilashee Handicap Hurdle (Punchestown) 24th
Investec Corporate Banking Great Metropolitan Handicap (Epsom) 25th
Investec Blue Riband Trial Stakes (Epsom) 25th
Investec City and Suburban Handicap (Epsom) 25th
Derby Trial Stakes (Epsom) 25th
 EBF 'National Hunt' Novices' Hurdle (Perth) 25th
Irish Daily Mirror War of Attrition Novices' Hurdle (Punchestown) 25th
Bibby Financial Punchestown Gold Cup (Punchestown) 25th
Attheraces Champion Bumper (Punchestown) 25th
Guinness Handicap Steeple Chase (Punchestown) 25th
Liss A Paoraigh Mares' Bumper (Punchestown) 25th
Ryanair Novices' Steeple Chase (Punchestown) 26th
Ladbrokes World Series Hurdle (Punchestown) 26th
Three.ie Handicap Steeple Chase (Punchestown) 26th
Ballymore Eustace Handicap Hurdle (Punchestown) 26th
Mares' Novices' Hurdle (Punchestown) 26th
Bet365 Mile Stakes (Sandown Park) 27th
Gordon Richards Stakes (Sandown Park) 27th
Classic Trial Stakes (Sandown Park) 27th
TBA Fair Maid Of Perth Steeplechase (Perth) 27th
Highland National Handicap Steeplechase (Perth) 27th
Tattersalls Ireland Champion Novices' Hurdle (Punchestown) 27th
Punchestown Novices' Handicap Steeple Chase (Punchestown) 27th
Punchestown Champion Hurdle (Punchestown) 27th
Glencarraig Lady Mares' Handicap Steeple Chase (Punchestown) 27th
EBF Richard III Stakes (Leicester) 28th
Bet365 Gold Cup Steeple Chase (Sandown Park) 28th
Celebration Chase (Sandown Park) 28th
Bet365 Oaksey Chase (Sandown Park) 28th
Bet365 Select Hurdle (Sandown Park) 28th
Bet365 Hurdle (Sandown Park) 28th
Bet365 Championship Novices' Hurdle (Sandown Park) 28th
Bet365 Josh Gifford Novices' Handicap Steeplechase (Sandown Park) 28th
AES Champion 4yo Hurdle (Punchestown) 28th
EBF Mares' Champion Hurdle (Punchestown) 28th
Ballymore Handicap Hurdle (Punchestown) 28th
Palmerstown House Pat Taaffe Handicap Steeple Chase (Punchestown) 28th
Victor McCalmont Stakes (Gowran Park) 29th
Prix Ganay (Longchamp) 29th

MAY

Merriebelle Stable Pavilion Stakes (Ascot) 2nd
Longines Sagaro Stakes (Ascot) 2nd
Rundle's Paradise Stakes (Ascot) 2nd
QIPCO 2000 Guineas Stakes (Newmarket) 5th
Jockey Club Stakes (Newmarket) 5th
Palace House Stakes (Newmarket) 5th
Newmarket Stakes (Newmarket) 5th
Daisy Warwick Stakes (Goodwood) 5th
EBF Conqueror Stakes (Goodwood) 5th
Totepool Thirsk Hunt Cup (Wetherby) 5th
Bet365 Staffordshire Plate Handicap Steeplechase (Uttoxeter) 5th
QIPCO 1000 Guineas Stakes (Newmarket) 6th
Dahlia Stakes (Newmarket) 6th

Pretty Polly Stakes (Newmarket) 6th
Longholes Handicap Stakes (Newmarket) 6th
Qatar Racing Handicap Stakes (Newmarket) 6th
Tetrach Stakes (Naas) 7th
Mooresbridge Stakes (Naas) 7th
Athasi Stakes (Naas) 7th
Snellings Norfolk National Handicap Steeplechase (Fakenham) 8th
Arkle Finance Cheshire Oaks Stakes (Chester) 9th
Boodles Diamond Handicap Stakes (Chester) 9th
Chester Vase Stakes (Chester) 9th
Fillies' Listed Stakes (Gowran Park) 9th
Boodles Diamond Handicap Stakes (Chester) 10th
Boodles Ormonde Stakes (Chester) 10th
Homeserve Dee Stakes (Chester) 10th
Sportingbet Huxley Stakes (Chester) 11th
188Bet Chester Cup Stakes (Chester) 11th
188Bet Chester Plate Stakes (Chester) 11th
Crabbie's Earl Grosvenor Handicap Stakes (Chester) 11th
Derby Trial Stakes (Lingfield Park) 12th
Oaks Trial Stakes (Lingfield Park) 12th
Chartwell Stakes (Lingfield Park) 12th
Swinton Handicap Hurdle (Haydock Park) 12th
Long Distance Handicap Hurdle (Haydock Park) 12th
Pertemps Network Intermediate Handicap Steeplechase (Haydock Park) 12th
Spring Trophy Stakes (Haydock Park) 12th
Totescoop6 Victoria Cup Stakes (Ascot) 12th
Club Godolphin EBF Breeders' Handicap Stakes (Ascot) 12th
Carey Group Buckhounds Stakes (Ascot) 12th
EBF Kilvington Stakes (Nottingham) 12th
Blue Wind Stakes (Curragh) 12th
Sole Power Stakes (Curragh) 12th
Derrinstown Derby Trial Stakes (Leopardstown) 13th
Derrinstown 1000 Guineas Trial Stakes (Leopardstown) 13th
Amethyst Stakes (Leopardstown) 13th
Killarney Handicap Hurdle (Killarney) 13th
Tourist Attraction Mares Hurdle (Killarney) 13th
Poule d'Essai des Pouliches (Longchamp) 13th
Poule d'Essai des Poulains (Longchamp) 13th
Royal Windsor Stakes (Windsor) 14th
An Riocht Steeple Chase (Killarney) 14th
Duke of York Stakes (York) 16th
Musidora Stakes (York) 16th
Betfred Dante Stakes (York) 17th
Middleton Stakes (York) 17th
EBF Westow Stakes (York) 17th
Yorkshire Cup Stakes (York) 18th
Michael Seely Stakes (York) 18th
EBF Marygate Stakes (York) 18th
Aintree Handicap Steeplechase (Aintree) 18th
Fairway Stakes (Newmarket) 19th
Al Shaqab Lockinge Stakes (Newbury) 19th
Aston Park Stakes (Newbury) 19th
Fillies' Trial Stakes (Newbury) 19th
Carnarvon Stakes (Newbury) 19th
London Gold Cup Handicap Stakes (Newbury) 19th
Toronado Handicap Stakes (Newbury) 19th
Olympic Glory Stakes (Newbury) 19th
King Charles II Stakes (Newmarket) 19th
Sprint Trophy Handicap Stakes (Newmarket) 19th
Yeats Stakes (Navan) 19th
Lacken Stakes (Naas) 20th
Whitehead Memorial Stakes (Naas) 20th
Rochestown Stakes (Naas) 20th
Coolmore Stud Juvenile Fillies Stakes (Naas) 20th
Weatherby's Private Bank Leisure Stakes (Windsor) 21st
Rothesay EBF Stakes (Ayr) 23rd
Carnival Handicap Steeplechase (Warwick) 23rd
Coronation Handicap Hurdle (Warwick) 23rd
Height of Fashion Stakes (Goodwood) 24th
Henry II Stakes (Sandown Park) 24th
Brigadier Gerard Stakes (Sandown Park) 24th
Heron Stakes (Sandown Park) 24th
National Stakes (Sandown Park) 24th
EBF Cocked Hat Stakes (Goodwood) 25th
Seamus & Rosemary McGrath Memorial Savel Beg Stakes (Leopardstown) 25th

JUNE

Duke of Cambridge Stakes (Ascot) 20th
Queen Mary Stakes (Ascot) 20th
Jersey Stakes (Ascot) 20th
Queen's Vase Stakes (Ascot) 20th
Royal Hunt Cup (Ascot) 20th
Gold Cup Stakes (Ascot) 21st
Ribblesdale Stakes (Ascot) 21st
Norfolk Stakes (Ascot) 21st
Hampton Court Stakes (Ascot) 21st
Britannia Handicap Stakes (Ascot) 21st
King George V Handicap Stakes (Ascot) 21st
New Listed Stakes (Chelmsford City) 21st
Coronation Stakes (Ascot) 22nd
Commonwealth Cup Stakes (Ascot) 22nd
King Edward VII Stakes (Ascot) 22nd
Albany Stakes (Ascot) 22nd
Duke of Edinburgh Handicap Stakes (Ascot) 22nd
Sandringham Handicap Stakes (Ascot) 22nd
Windsor Castle Stakes (Ascot) 23rd
Diamond Jubilee Stakes (Ascot) 23rd
Hardwicke Stakes (Ascot) 23rd
Chesham Stakes (Ascot) 23rd
Wokingham Handicap Stakes (Ascot) 23rd
Queen Alexandra Stakes (Ascot) 23rd
Land O'Burns Stakes (Ayr) 23rd
Pontefract Castle Stakes (Pontefract) 24th
EBF Eternal Stakes (Carlisle) 27th
Cumberland Plate Handicap Stakes (Carlisle) 27th
Carlisle Bell Handicap Stakes (Carlisle) 27th
Whitsbury Manor Stud Bibury Cup Stakes (Salisbury) 27th
Naas Oaks Trial Stakes (Naas) 27th
Betfred Seaton Delaval Stakes (Newcastle) 28th
EBF Hoppings Stakes (Newcastle) 29th
Betfred Gosforth Park Cup Handicap Stakes (Newcastle) 29th
Chipchase Stakes (Newcastle) 30th
Stobart Rail Northumberland Plate Handicap Stakes (Newcastle) 30th
Criterion Stakes (Newmarket) 30th
Fred Archer Stakes (Newmarket) 30th
Empress Stakes (Newmarket) 30th
Midsummer Stakes (Windsor) 30th
Dubai Duty Free Irish Derby Stakes (Curragh) 30th
Gain Railway Stakes (Curragh) 30th
Dubai Duty Free Celebration Stakes (Curragh) 30th
Dubai Duty Free Belgrave Stakes (Curragh) 30th

JULY

Summer Cup Handicap Chase (Uttoxeter) 1st
Pretty Polly Stakes (Curragh) 1st
International Stakes (Curragh) 1st
Grangecon Stud Ballanchine Stakes (Curragh) 1st
Comer International Curragh Cup Stakes (Curragh) 1st
Grand Prix de Saint-Cloud (Saint-Cloud) 1st
Tipperary Stakes (Tipperary) 5th
Grimes Hurdle (Tipperary) 5th
Ambant Gala Stakes (Sandown Park) 6th
Dragon Stakes (Sandown Park) 6th
Lancashire Oaks Stakes (Haydock Park) 7th
Coral Eclipse Stakes (Sandown Park) 7th
Coral Sprint Stakes (Sandown Park) 7th
Coral Esher Stakes (Sandown Park) 7th
Coral Distaff Stakes (Sandown Park) 7th
Brownstown Stakes (Fairyhouse) 8th
Prix Jean Prat (Deauville) 8th
Lenebane Stakes (Roscommon) 9th
Pipalong Stakes (Pontefract) 10th
Princess of Wales Stakes (Newmarket) 12th
Bahrain Trophy Stakes (Newmarket) 12th
July Stakes (Newmarket) 12th
Sir Henry Cecil Stakes (Newmarket) 12th
Stanerra Stakes (Leopardstown) 12th
Falmouth Stakes (Newmarket) 13th
Duchess of Cambridge Stakes (Newmarket) 13th
Summer Stakes (York) 13th
Summer Mile Stakes (Ascot) 14th

Totescoop6 Handicap Stakes (Ascot) 14th
City Plate Stakes (Chester) 14th
Darley July Cup Stakes (Newmarket) 14th
Superlative Stakes (Newmarket) 14th
Bunbury Cup Handicap Stakes (Newmarket) 14th
Silver Cup Stakes (York) 14th
City Walls Stakes (York) 14th
Juddmonte Grand Prix de Paris (Longchamp) 14th
John Smith's Cup Handicap Stakes (York) 14th
Cairn Rouge Stakes (Killarney) 15th
Bourn Vincent Memorial Handicap Steeple Chase (Killarney) 18th
ICON Meld Stakes (Leopardstown) 19th
EBF Glasgow Stakes (Hamilton Park) 20th
Rose Bowl Stakes (Newbury) 20th
Summer Plate Handicap Steeple Chase (Market Rasen) 21st
Summer Handicap Hurdle (Market Rasen) 21st
Hackwood Stakes (Newbury) 21st
Weatherbys Super Sprint Stakes (Newbury) 21st
Steventon Stakes (Newbury) 21st
Aphrodite Stakes (Newmarket) 21st
Darley Irish Oaks Stakes (Curragh) 21st
Sapphire Stakes (Curragh) 21st
Jebel Ali Anglesey Stakes (Curragh) 22nd
Kilboy Estate Stakes (Curragh) 22nd
Minstrel Stakes (Curragh) 22nd
Sweet Mimosa Stakes (Naas) 25th
EBF Star Stakes (Sandown Park) 26th
Tyros Stakes (Leopardstown) 26th
Silver Flash Stakes (Leopardstown) 26th
Listed Stakes (Leopardstown) 26th
EBF Valiant Stakes (Ascot) 27th
EBF Lyric Stakes (York) 27th
Her Majesty's Plate Stakes (Down Royal) 27th
King George VI & Queen Elizabeth Stakes (Ascot) 28th
Princess Margaret Stakes (Ascot) 28th
Wooldridge Group Pat Eddery Stakes (Ascot) 28th
Winkfield Stakes (Ascot) 28th
Gigaset International Stakes (Ascot) 28th
Sky Bet York Stakes (York) 28th
Sky Bet Pomfret Stakes (Pontefract) 29th
Prix Rothschild (Deauville) 29th
Goodwood Cup Stakes (Goodwood) 31st
Lennox Stakes (Goodwood) 31st
Vintage Stakes (Goodwood) 31st
Galway Novices' Hurdle (Galway) 31st

AUGUST

Sussex Stakes (Goodwood) 1st
Molecomb Stakes (Goodwood) 1st
thetote.com Galway Plate (Handicap Steeple Chase) (Galway) 1st
Nassau Stakes (Goodwood) 2nd
Guinness Galway Hurdle (Galway) 2nd
Ballybrit Novices' Steeple Chase (Galway) 2nd
Corrib EBF Fillies Stakes (Galway) 2nd
Richmond Stakes (Goodwood) 2nd
Lillie Langtry Stakes (Goodwood) 2nd
King George Stakes (Goodwood) 3rd
Glorious Stakes (Goodwood) 3rd
Thoroughbred Stakes (Goodwood) 3rd
Oak Tree Stakes (Goodwood) 3rd
Betfred Mile Handicap (Goodwood) 3rd
Gordon Stakes (Goodwood) 4th
EBF Chalice Stakes (Newmarket) 4th
Qatar Stewards' Cup Handicap Stakes (Goodwood) 4th
Mervue Handicap Hurdle (Galway) 4th
Queensferry Stakes (Chester) 5th
LARC Prix Maurice de Gheest (Deauville) 5th
Ballyroan Stakes (Leopardstown) 9th
El Gran Senor Stakes (Tipperary) 10th
Rose of Lancashire Stakes (Haydock Park) 11th
EBF Dick Hern Stakes (Haydock Park) 11th
Sweet Solera Stakes (Newmarket) 11th
Give Thanks Stakes (Cork) 11th
Platinum Stakes (Cork) 11th

Keeneland Phoenix Stakes (Curragh) 12th
QREC Phoenix Sprint Stakes (Curragh) 12th
Prix du Haras de Fresnay-Le-Buffard Jacques Le Marois (Deauville) 12th
EBF Upavon Stakes (Salisbury) 15th
Hurry Harriet Stakes (Gowran Park) 15th
Sovereign Stakes (Salisbury) 16th
Invesco Desmond Stakes (Leopardstown) 16th
St Hugh's Stakes (Newbury) 17th
Hungerford Stakes (Newbury) 18th
Geoffrey Freer Stakes (Newbury) 18th
Denford Stud Stakes (Newbury) 18th
Flying Fillies' Stakes (Pontefract) 19th
Darley Prix Morny (Deauville) 19th
Darley Prix Jean Romanet (Deauville) 19th
International Stakes (York) 22nd
Great Voltigeur Stakes (York) 22nd
Acomb Stakes (York) 22nd
Ruby Stakes (Killarney) 22nd
Yorkshire Oaks Stakes (York) 23rd
Lowther Stakes (York) 23rd
EBF Galtres Stakes (York) 23rd
Goffs UK Premier Yearling Stakes (York) 23rd
EBF Stonehenge Stakes (Salisbury) 24th
Nunthorpe Stakes (York) 24th
Lonsdale Cup Stakes (York) 24th
Gimcrack Stakes (York) 24th
Celebration Stakes (Goodwood) 25th
March Stakes (Goodwood) 25th
Prestige Stakes (Goodwood) 25th
Hopeful Stakes (Newmarket) 25th
Winter Hill Stakes (Windsor) 25th
August Stakes (Windsor) 25th
Strensall Stakes (York) 25th
Roses Stakes (York) 25th
Betfred Melrose Handicap Stakes (York) 25th
Betfred Ebor Handicap Stakes (York) 25th
City of York Stakes (York) 25th
Curragh Stakes (Curragh) 25th
Ballycullen Stakes (Curragh) 25th
Mount Brandon Handicap Hurdle (Killarney) 25th
Lough Leane Handicap Steeple Chase (Killarney) 25th
Supreme Stakes (Goodwood) 26th
Galileo EBF Futurity Stakes (Curragh) 26th
Debutante Stakes (Curragh) 26th
Royal Whip Stakes (Curragh) 26th
Champion 2 Year Old Trophy Stakes (Ripon) 27th
Fairy Bridge Stakes (Tipperary) 30th
Abergwaun Stakes (Tipperary) 30th

SEPTEMBER

Beverley Bullet Stakes (Beverley) 1st
Chester Handicap Stakes (Chester) 1st
Atalanta Stakes (Sandown Park) 1st
Solario Stakes (Sandown Park) 1st
Round Tower Stakes (Curragh) 1st
Snow Fairy Stakes (Curragh) 1st
Flame of Tara Stakes (Curragh) 1st
Dick Poole Stakes (Salisbury) 6th
Sprint Cup Stakes (Haydock Park) 8th
Superior Mile Stakes (Haydock Park) 8th
32Red Ascendant Stakes (Haydock Park) 8th
Sirenia Stakes (Kempton Park) 8th
September Stakes (Kempton Park) 8th
Appletiser Handicap Stakes (Ascot) 8th
Qatar Prix Vermeille (Longchamp) 9th
Qatar Prix du Moulin de Longchamp (Longchamp) 9th
Garrowby Stakes (York) 9th
Listowel Stakes (Listowel) 10th
Latrigue 4yo Handicap Hurdle (Listowel) 11th
Scarbrough Stakes (Doncaster) 12th
Guinness Kerry National (Handicap Steeple Chase) (Listowel) 12th
Park Hill Stakes (Doncaster) 13th
May Hill Stakes (Doncaster) 13th
Weatherbys Racing Bank £300,000 2yo Stakes (Doncaster) 13th

Ladbrokes Handicap Hurdle (Listowel) 13th
Doncaster Cup Stakes (Doncaster) 14th
Flying Childers Stakes (Doncaster) 14th
JRA Sceptre Stakes (Doncaster) 14th
Flying Scotsman Stakes (Doncaster) 14th
St Leger Stakes (Doncaster) 15th
Park Stakes (Doncaster) 15th
Champagne Stakes (Doncaster) 15th
Stand Cup Stakes (Chester) 15th
QIPCO Irish Champion Stakes (Leopardstown) 15th
Coolmore Matron Stakes (Leopardstown) 15th
Clipper Logistics Solonaway Stakes (Leopardstown) 15th
Willis Towers Watson Golden Fleece Stakes (Leopardstown) 15th
KPMG Kilternan Stakes (Leopardstown) 15th
Goffs Vincent O'Brien National Stakes (Curragh) 16th
Moyglare Stud Stakes (Curragh) 16th
Palmerstown House St Leger Stakes (Curragh) 16th
Moyglare Stud Blandford Stakes (Curragh) 16th
Derrinstown Stud Flying Five Stakes (Curragh) 16th
Oyster Stakes (Galway) 18th
Fortune Stakes (Sandown Park) 19th
EBF John Musker Stakes (Sandown Park) 19th
Doonside Cup Stakes (Ayr) 20th
Arran Fillies' Stakes (Ayr) 21st
Harry Rosebery Stakes (Ayr) 21st
Ayr Bronze Cup Handicap Stakes (Ayr) 21st
Duty Free Cup Stakes (Newbury) 21st
Cordell Lavarack Stakes (Gowran Park) 22nd
Firth of Clyde Stakes (Ayr) 22nd
Ayr Gold Cup Handicap Stakes (Ayr) 22nd
Ayr Silver Cup Handicap Stakes (Ayr) 22nd
Mill Reef Stakes (Newbury) 22nd
Dubai Arc Trial Stakes (Newbury) 22nd
Dubai Duty Free Legacy Cup (Newbury) 22nd
World Trophy Stakes (Newbury) 22nd
Dubai Duty Free Handicap Stakes (Newbury) 22nd
Blenheim Stakes (Fairyhouse) 24th
EBF Foundation Stakes (Goodwood) 26th
Somerville Stakes (Newmarket) 27th
Rose Bowl Stakes (Newmarket) 27th
Rockfel Stakes (Newmarket) 28th
Shadwell Joel Stakes (Newmarket) 28th
Princess Royal Stakes (Newmarket) 28th
Godolphin Stakes (Newmarket) 28th
Rosemary Stakes (Newmarket) 28th
Diamond Stakes (Dundalk) 28th
Middle Park Stakes (Newmarket) 29th
Cheveley Park Stakes (Newmarket) 29th
Royal Lodge Stakes (Newmarket) 29th
Betfred Cambridgeshire Handicap Stakes (Newmarket) 29th
Prelude Handicap Steeple Chase (Market Rasen) 29th
Prelude Handicap Hurdle (Market Rasen) 29th
Juddmonte Beresford Stakes (Naas) 30th
Renaissance Stakes (Naas) 30th
CL & MF Weld Park Stakes (Naas) 30th
Loughbrown Stakes (Naas) 30th

OCTOBER

Noel Murless Stakes (Ascot) 5th
Star Appeal Stakes (Dundalk) 5th
Pat Walsh Memorial Mares Hurdle (Gowran Park) 5th
Mucklemeg Mares Bumper (Gowran Park) 5th
Bengough Stakes (Ascot) 6th
Cumberland Lodge Stakes (Ascot) 6th
EBF October Stakes (Ascot) 6th
Rous Stakes (Ascot) 6th
Totescoop6 Challenge Cup Handicap Stakes (Ascot) 6th
Sun Chariot Stakes (Newmarket) 6th
£150,000 Tattersalls October Stakes (Newmarket) 6th
EBF Fillies' Handicap Stakes (Ascot) 6th
2-Year-Old Trophy Stakes (Redcar) 6th
EBF Guisborough Stakes (Redcar) 6th
Gowran Champion Steeple Chase (Gowran Park) 6th
Kilkenny Racing Festival Handicap Hurdle (Gowran Park) 6th

Qatar Prix du Cadran (Longchamp) 6th
Concorde Stakes (Tipperary) 7th
Tipperary Hurdle (Tipperary) 7th
Joe Mac Novices' Hurdle (Tipperary) 7th
Like-A-Butterfly Novices' Steeple Chase (Tipperary) 7th
Prix de L'Opera Longines (Longchamp) 7th
Qatar Prix de L'Abbaye de Longchamp (Longchamp) 7th
Total Prix Marcel Boussac - Criterium des Pouliches (Longchamp) 7th
Qatar Prix Jean-Luc Lagardere (Grand Criterium) (Longchamp) 7th
Qatar Prix de la Foret (Longchamp) 7th
Qatar Prix de L'Arc de Triomphe (Longchamp) 7th
Legacy Stakes (Cork) 10th
Carlingford Stakes (Dundalk) 12th
Fillies' Mile Stakes (Newmarket) 12th
Challenge Stakes (Newmarket) 12th
Oh So Sharp Stakes (Newmarket) 12th
Cornwallis Stakes (Newmarket) 12th
Pride Stakes (Newmarket) 12th
bet365 Old Rowley Cup Handicap Stakes (Newmarket) 12th
Martin Molony Stakes (Limerick) 13th
Dewhurst Stakes (Newmarket) 13th
Darley Club Stakes (Newmarket) 13th
Autumn Stakes (Newmarket) 13th
EBF Boadicea Stakes (Newmarket) 13th
Zetland Stakes (Newmarket) 13th
Betfred Cesarewitch Handicap Stakes (Newmarket) 13th
Rockingham Stakes (York) 13th
Silver Trophy Hurdle (Chepstow) 13th
Totequadpot Handicap Chase (Chepstow) 13th
Waterford Testimonial Stakes (Navan) 14th
Lanwades & Staffordstown Studs Silken Glider Stakes (Navan) 14th
Navigation Stakes (Navan) 14th
Ladbrokes Munster National Handicap Steeple Chase (Limerick) 14th
Greenmount Park Novices' Hurdle (Limerick) 14th
Persian War Novices' Hurdle (Chepstow) 14th
EBF Beckford Stakes (Bath) 17th
Carvills Hill Steeple Chase (Punchestown) 17th
Buck House Novices' Steeple Chase (Punchestown) 17th
Mercury Stakes (Dundalk) 19th
QIPCO Champion Stakes (Ascot) 20th
Q.E. II Stakes (Ascot) 20th
QIPCO Champions Fillies & Mares Stakes (Ascot) 20th
QIPCO Champions Sprint Stakes (Ascot) 20th
QIPCO Long Distance Cup Stakes (Ascot) 20th
Balmoral Handicap Stakes (Ascot) 20th
Killavullan Stakes (Leopardstown) 20th
Trigo Stakes (Leopardstown) 20th
Garnet Stakes (Naas) 21st
Bluebell Stakes (Naas) 21st
Kinsale Handicap Steeple Chase (Cork) 21st
Better Odds Hurdle (Kempton Park) 21st
Matchbook Novices' Hurdle (Kempton Park) 21st
Silver Tankard Stakes (Pontefract) 22nd
Knockaire Stakes (Leopardstown) 27th
Eyrefield Stakes (Leopardstown) 27th
Criterium de Saint-Cloud (Saint-Cloud) 27th
Racing Post Trophy Stakes (Doncaster) 27th
St Simon Stakes (Newbury) 27th
Horris Hill Stakes (Newbury) 27th
Radley Stakes (Newbury) 27th
Bettyville Steeplechase (Wexford) 28th
Old Roan Handicap Steeple Chase (Aintree) 28th
Criterium International (Longchamp) 28th
Prix Royal-Oak (Longchamp) 28th

NOVEMBER

Fleur de Lys Stakes (Lingfield Park) 1st
EBF River Eden Stakes (Lingfield Park) 1st
Bosra Sham EBF Stakes (Newmarket) 2nd
Bet365 Handicap Steeple Chase (Wetherby) 2nd
Wensleydale Juvenile Hurdle (Wetherby) 2nd
WKD Hurdle (Down Royal) 2nd
Hamptons EBF Mares Novices' Hurdle (Down Royal) 2nd
Cooley Stakes (Dundalk) 2nd

James Seymour Stakes (Newmarket) 3rd
Ben Marshall Stakes (Newmarket) 3rd
EBF Montrose Stakes (Newmarket) 3rd
Sodexo Gold Cup Handicap Steeple Chase (Ascot) 3rd
Byrne Group Handicap Steeple Chase (Ascot) 3rd
William Hill Handicap Hurdle (Ascot) 3rd
Charlie Hall Steeple Chase (Wetherby) 3rd
West Yorkshire Hurdle (Wetherby) 3rd
OLBG.com Mares' Hurdle (Wetherby) 3rd
Jnwine Champion Steeple Chase (Down Royal) 3rd
Skymas Steeple Chase (Down Royal) 3rd
Mac's Joy Handicap Hurdle (Down Royal) 3rd
Paddy Power Cork Grand National Handicap Steeple Chase (Cork) 4th
Paddy Power EBF Novices' Steeple Chase (Cork) 4th
Paddy Power EBF Novices' Hurdle (Cork) 4th
Finale Stakes (Naas) 4th
Colin Parker Steeple Chase (Carlisle) 4th
Floodlit Stakes (Kempton Park) 5th
Haldon Gold Cup Steeple Chase (Exeter) 6th
Bud Booth Steeple Chase (Market Rasen) 8th
EBF Gillies Stakes (Doncaster) 10th
Wentworth Stakes (Doncaster) 10th
Badger Ales Handicap Steeple Chase (Wincanton) 10th
Elite Handicap Hurdle (Wincanton) 10th
Rising Stars Novices' Steeple Chase (Wincanton) 10th
Brown Lad Handicap Hurdle (Naas) 10th
Popular Square Steeple Chase (Naas) 10th
Fishery Lane 4yo Hurdle (Naas) 10th
Future Stars Steeple Chase (Sandown Park) 11th
Lismullen Hurdle (Navan) 11th
Fortria Steeple Chase (Navan) 11th
For Auction Novices' Hurdle (Navan) 11th
Yorton Novices' Steeple Chase (Bangor-on-Dee) 14th
Clonmel Oil Steeple Chase (Clonmel) 15th
EBF TA Morris Memorial Mares Steeple Chase (Clonmel) 15th
Hyde Novices' Hurdle (Cheltenham) 16th
BetVictor Handicap Steeple Chase (Cheltenham) 17th
Churchill Stakes (Lingfield Park) 17th
Golden Rose Stakes (Lingfield Park) 17th
Gold Cup Steeple Chase (Cheltenham) 17th
Solutions Handicap Hurdle (Cheltenham) 17th
Prestbury Juvenile Hurdle (Cheltenham) 17th
Experience Mares' Open National Hunt Flat Race (Cheltenham) 17th
Grabel Mares Hurdle (Punchestown) 17th
Greatwood Handicap Hurdle (Cheltenham) 18th
Cheltenham Steeple Chase (Cheltenham) 18th
November Novices' Steeple Chase (Cheltenham) 18th
Sharp Novices' Hurdle (Cheltenham) 18th
High Sheriff National Hunt Flat Race (Cheltenham) 18th
Morgiana Hurdle (Punchestown) 18th
Florida Pearl Novices' Steeple Chase (Punchestown) 18th
Craddockstown Novices' Steeple Chase (Punchestown) 18th
Hyde EBF Stakes (Kempton Park) 21st
Thurles Steeple Chase (Thurles) 22nd
Coral Ascot Hurdle (Ascot) 24th
1965 Steeple Chase (Ascot) 24th
Lancashire Chase (Haydock Park) 24th
Betfair Handicap Hurdle (Haydock Park) 24th
Betfair Novices' Hurdle (Haydock Park) 24th
Monksfield Novices' Hurdle (Navan) 25th
Proudstown Handicap Hurdle (Navan) 25th
Ladbrokes Troytown Handicap Steeple Chase (Navan) 25th
ITBA Mares Bumper (Navan) 25th
OLBG Mares' Hurdle (Kempton Park) 26th
Long Distance Hurdle (Newbury) 30th
Berkshire Novices' Steeple Chase (Newbury) 30th

DECEMBER

Trophy Handicap Steeplechase (Newbury) 1st
Ballyhack Handicap Steeple Chase (Fairyhouse) 1st
Gerry Feilden Hurdle (Newbury) 1st
John Francome Novices' Chase (Newbury) 1st
Ladbrokes Novices' Hurdle (Newbury) 1st
Fighting Fifth Hurdle (Newcastle) 1st

Rehearsal Handicap Steeple Chase (Newcastle) 1st
Houghton Mares' Steeple Chase (Carlisle) 2nd
Bar One Royal Bond Novices' Hurdle (Fairyhouse) 2nd
Bar One Hattons Grace Hurdle (Fairyhouse) 2nd
Bar One Drinmore Novices' Steeple Chase (Fairyhouse) 2nd
New Stand Handicap Hurdle (Fairyhouse) 2nd
Porterstown Handicap Steeple Chase (Fairyhouse) 2nd
Winter Festival Juvenile Hurdle (Fairyhouse) 2nd
Wild Flower Stakes (Kempton Park) 5th
Newton Novices' Hurdle (Haydock Park) 5th
Winter Novices' Hurdle (Sandown Park) 7th
Becher Handicap Steeple Chase (Aintree) 8th
Many Clouds Steeple Chase (Aintree) 8th
Download Juvenile Hurdle (Aintree) 8th
Tingle Creek Steeple Chase (Sandown Park) 8th
December Handicap Hurdle (Sandown Park) 8th
Henry VIII Novices' Steeple Chase (Sandown Park) 8th
Klairon Davis EBF Novices' Steeple Chase (Navan) 8th
John Durkan Memorial Steeple Chase (Punchestown) 9th
Kerry Group Hilly Way Steeple Chase (Cork) 9th
Kerry Group Cork Stayers Novices' Hurdle (Cork) 9th
Lombardstown EBF Mares Novices' Steeple Chase (Cork) 9th
Peterborough Steeple Chase (Huntingdon) 9th
Henrietta Knight Open National Hunt Flat Race (Huntingdon) 9th
Lady Godiva Novices' Steeple Chase (Warwick) 13th
Unicoin Handicap Steeple Chase (Cheltenham) 14th
Gold Cup Handicap Steeple Chase (Cheltenham) 15th
International Hurdle (Cheltenham) 15th
Bristol Novices' Hurdle (Cheltenham) 15th
Summit Juvenile Hurdle (Doncaster) 15th
December Novices' Chase (Doncaster) 15th
Navan Novices' Hurdle (Navan) 16th
Tara Handicap Hurdle (Navan) 16th
Foxrock Handicap Steeple Chase (Navan) 16th
Future Champions Bumper (Navan) 16th
TBA Mares' Novices' Steeple Chase (Newbury) 19th
Noel Novices' Steeple Chase (Ascot) 21st
Kennel Gate Novices' Hurdle (Ascot) 21st
Championship Open National Hunt Flat Race (Ascot) 21st
Wessex Youth Trust Handicap Hurdle (Ascot) 22nd
Long Walk Hurdle (Ascot) 22nd
Silver Cup Handicap Steeple Chase (Ascot) 22nd
Abram Mares' Novices' Hurdle (Haydock Park) 22nd
Quebec Stakes (Lingfield Park) 22nd
Boreen Belle EBF Mares Novices' Hurdle (Thurles) 22nd
King George VI Steeple Chase (Kempton Park) 26th
Christmas Hurdle (Kempton Park) 26th
Kauto Star Novices' Steeple Chase (Kempton Park) 26th
Rowland Meyrick Steeple Chase (Wetherby) 26th
Racing Post Novices' Steeple Chase (Leopardstown) 26th
Knight Frank Juvenile Hurdle (Leopardstown) 26th
Greenmount Park Novices' Steeple Chase (Limerick) 26th
Welsh National Handicap Steeple Chase (Chepstow) 27th
Future Champions Finale Juvenile Hurdle (Chepstow) 27th
Desert Orchid Steeple Chase (Kempton Park) 27th
Wayward Lad Novices' Steeple Chase (Kempton Park) 27th
Paddy Power Future Champions Novices' Hurdle (Leopardstown) 27th
Paddy Power Dial A Bet Steeple Chase (Leopardstown) 27th
Paddy Power Handicap Steeple Chase (Leopardstown) 27th
Tim Duggan Memorial Handicap Steeple Chase (Limerick) 27th
Lexus Steeple Chase (Leopardstown) 28th
Squared Financials Christmas Hurdle (Leopardstown) 28th
Sporting Limerick 4yo Hurdle (Limerick) 28th
Sunbets Steeple Chase (Doncaster) 29th
Ryanair December Hurdle (Leopardstown) 29th
Fort Leney Novices' Steeple Chase (Leopardstown) 29th
Willis Towers Watson EBF Mares Hurdle (Leopardstown) 29th
Dorans Pride Novices' Hurdle (Limerick) 29th
Challow Novices' Hurdle (Newbury) 29th
Totepool Novices' Hurdle (Taunton) 30th

The list of Principal Races has been supplied by the BHA and Horse Racing Ireland and is provisional. In all cases, the dates, venues, and names of sponsors are correct at time of going to press, but also subject to possible alteration.

INDEX TO TRAINERS

†denotes Permit to train under N.H. Rules only

Name	Team No.	Name	Team No.
DENNIS, MR DAVID	140	ENGLAND, MRS SAM	179
DICKIN, MR ROBIN	141	EUSTACE, MR JAMES	180
†DIXON, MR JOHN	142	EVANS, MR DAVID	181
DIXON, MR SCOTT	143	EVANS, MR JAMES	182
†DIXON, MR STEVEN	144	†EVANS, MRS MARY	183
DOBBIN, MRS ROSE	145	EVANS, MRS NIKKI	184
DODS, MR MICHAEL	146	EWART, MR JAMES	185
DORE, MR CONOR	147	EYRE, MR LES	186
DOW, MR SIMON	148		
DOWN, MR CHRIS	149		
DREW, MR CLIVE	150		

F

Name	Team No.	Name	Team No.
DRINKWATER, MR DAVID W.	151	FAHEY, MR RICHARD	187
DRINKWATER, MR SAMUEL	152	FAIRHURST, MR CHRIS	188
DU PLESSIS, MISS JACKIE	153	FANSHAWE, MR JAMES R.	189
DUFFIELD, MRS ANN	154	FARRELLY, MR JOHNNY	190
DUKE, MR BRENDAN W.	155	†FAULKNER, MS DEBORAH	191
DUNCAN, MR IAN	156	FEILDEN, MISS JULIA	192
†DUNGER, MR NIGEL	157	FELL, MR ROGER	193
DUNLOP, MR ED	158	FELLOWES, MR CHARLIE	194
DUNLOP, MR HARRY	159	FFRENCH DAVIS, MR DOMINIC	195
DUNN, MRS ALEXANDRA	160	FIERRO, MR GUISEPPE	196
DUNNETT, MRS CHRISTINE	161	FIFE, MRS MARJORIE	197
DURACK, MR SEAMUS	162	FITZGERALD, MR TIM	198
DWYER, MR CHRIS	163	FLINT, MR JOHN	199
DYSON, MISS CLAIRE	164	FLOOD, MR DAVID	200
		FLOOK, MR STEVE	201

E

Name	Team No.	Name	Team No.
EARLE, MR SIMON	165	FORBES, MR TONY	202
EASTERBY, MR MICHAEL	166	FORD, MRS PAM	203
EASTERBY, MR TIM	167	FORD, MRS RICHENDA	204
†ECKLEY, MR BRIAN	168	FORSEY, MR BRIAN	205
EDDERY, MR ROBERT	169	FORSTER, MISS SANDY	206
EDMUNDS, MR STUART	170	FOSTER, MISS JOANNE	207
†EDWARDS, MR GORDON	171	FOX, MR JIMMY	208
EGERTON, MISS LUCINDA	172	FRANCE, MISS SUZZANNE	209
ELLAM, MISS CLARE	173	†FRANKLAND, MR DEREK	210
ELLIOTT, MR GORDON	174	FROST, MR JAMES	211
ELLIS, MISS JOEY	175	FROST, MR KEVIN	212
ELLISON, MR BRIAN	176	FROUD, MR HUGO	213
ELSWORTH, MR DAVID	177	FRY, MR HARRY	214
†ENDER, MISS SARA	178	FRYER, MISS CAROLINE	215
		FURTADO, MR IVAN	216

Name	Team No.
G	
GALLAGHER, MR JOHN	217
GANSERA-LÉVÊQUE, MRS ILKA	218
GARDNER, MRS SUSAN	219
†GASSON, MRS ROSEMARY	220
GEAKE, MR JONATHAN	221
GEORGE, MISS KAREN	222
GEORGE, MR TOM	223
GIFFORD, MR NICK	224
GILLARD, MR MARK	225
GIVEN, MR JAMES	226
GOLDIE, MR JIM	227
†GOLDIE, MR ROBERT	228
GOLLINGS, MR STEVE	229
GORDON, MR CHRIS	230
GORMAN, MR J. T.	231
GOSDEN, MR JOHN	232
GRAHAM, MRS HARRIET	233
GRANT, MR CHRIS	234
GRASSICK, MR M. C.	235
GRAY, MR CARROLL	236
GREATREX, MR WARREN	237
GREENALL, MR OLIVER	238
GRETTON, MR TOM	239
GRIFFITHS, MR DAVID C.	240
†GRIFFITHS, MR SIRRELL	241
GRISSELL, MRS DIANA	242
GROUCOTT, MR JOHN	243
GUEST, MR RAE	244
GUEST, MR RICHARD	245
GUNDRY, MS POLLY	246
H	
HAGGAS, MR WILLIAM	247
HALES, MR ALEX	248
HALFORD, MR MICHAEL	249
HAMER, MRS DEBRA	250
HAMILTON, MRS ALISON	251
†HAMILTON, MR ANDREW	252
†HAMILTON, MRS ANN	253
HAMMOND, MR MICKY	254
HAMMOND, MR MIKE	255
HAMMOND, (SATELLITE), MR MIKE	256
HANMER, MR GARY	257
HANNON, MR RICHARD	258
HARKER, MR GEOFFREY	259
†HARPER, MR RICHARD	260
HARRINGTON, MRS JESSICA	261
HARRIS, MISS GRACE	262
HARRIS, MR RONALD	263
HARRIS, MR SHAUN	264
HARRISON, MISS LISA	265
HASLAM, MR BEN	266
HAWKE, MR NIGEL	267
†HAWKER, MR MICHAEL	268
HAWKER, MR RICHARD	269
†HAYNES, MR JONATHAN	270
HAYNES, MISS SALLY	271
HAYWOOD, MISS GAIL	272
HEDGER, MR PETER	273
HENDERSON, MR NICKY	274
HENDERSON, MR PAUL	275
HERRINGTON, MR MICHAEL	276
HIATT, MR PETER	277
HIDE, MR PHILIP	278
HILL, MRS LAWNEY	279
HILL, MR MARTIN	280
HILLS, MR CHARLES	281
HOAD, MR MARK	282
HOBBS, MR PHILIP	283
HOBSON, MISS CLARE	284
HOBSON, MR RICHARD	285
†HODGE, MR JOHN	286
HODGES, MR RON	287
†HOGARTH, MR HENRY	288
HOLLINSHEAD, MISS SARAH	289
HOLLINSHEAD, MRS STEPH	290
HOLMES, MR PATRICK	291
HOLT, MR JOHN	292
HONEYBALL, MR ANTHONY	293
HUGHES, MRS JO	294
HUGHES, MR RICHARD	295

Name	Team No.	Name	Team No.
†MAUNDRELL, MR G. C.	366	MURPHY, MR MIKE	408
MCBRIDE, MR PHILIP	367	MURPHY, MR OLLY	409
MCCAIN, MR DONALD	368	MURPHY, MR PAT	410
MCCARTHY, MR TIM	369	MURTAGH, MR BARRY	411
MCENTEE, MR PHIL	370		
MCGRATH, MR MURTY	371	**N**	
MCGREGOR, MRS JEAN	372	NAYLOR, DR JEREMY	412
MCJANNET, MR LUKE	373	†NEEDHAM, MR JOHN	413
MCLINTOCK, MS KAREN	374	NELMES, MRS HELEN	414
MCPHERSON, MR GRAEME	375	NEWCOMBE, MR TONY	415
MEADE, MR MARTYN	376	NEWLAND, DR RICHARD	416
MEADE, MR NOEL	377	NEWTON-SMITH, MISS ANNA	417
†MECHIE, MR NEIL	378	NICHOLLS, MR ADRIAN	418
MEEHAN, MR BRIAN	379	NICHOLLS, MR PAUL	419
MENUISIER, MR DAVID	380	NIVEN, MR PETER	420
MENZIES, MISS REBECCA	381	NORMILE, MRS LUCY	421
MIDDLETON, MR PHIL	382	NORTON, MR JOHN	422
MIDGLEY, MR PAUL	383	NOSEDA, MR JEREMY	423
MILLMAN, MR ROD	384		
MITCHELL, MR NICK	385	**O**	
MITCHELL, MR RICHARD	386	O'BRIEN, MR A. P.	424
†MITFORD-SLADE, MR RICHARD	387	O'BRIEN, MR DANIEL	425
MOFFATT, MR JAMES	388	O'BRIEN, MR FERGAL	426
MOHAMMED, MR ISMAIL	389	O'KEEFFE, MR JEDD	427
MONGAN, MRS LAURA	390	O'MEARA, MR DAVID	428
MOORE, MR ARTHUR	391	†O'NEILL, MISS DANIELLE	429
MOORE, MR GARY	392	O'NEILL, MR JOHN	430
MOORE, MR J. S.	393	O'NEILL, MR JONJO	431
MORGAN, MISS LAURA	394	O'SHEA, MR JOHN	432
MORRIS, MR M. F.	395	OLIVER, MR HENRY	433
MORRIS, MR PATRICK	396	OSBORNE, MR JAMIE	434
MORRISON, MR HUGHIE	397	OWEN, MISS EMMA	435
MOUBARAK, MR MOHAMED	398		
MUIR, MR WILLIAM	399	**P**	
MULHALL, MR CLIVE	400	PALMER, MR HUGO	436
MULHOLLAND, MR NEIL	401	PATTINSON, MR MARK	437
MULLANEY, MR LAWRENCE	402	PAULING, MR BEN	438
MULLINEAUX, MR MICHAEL	403	PEACOCK, MR RAY	439
MULLINS, MR SEAMUS	404	PEARCE, MRS LYDIA	440
MULLINS, MR WILLIAM P.	405	PEARS, MR OLLIE	441
MURPHY, MISS AMY	406		

Name	Team No.
PECKHAM, MR GEORGE	442
PERRATT, MISS LINDA	443
PERRETT, MRS AMANDA	444
PHELAN, MR PAT	445
PHILLIPS, MR ALAN	446
PHILLIPS, MR RICHARD	447
PICKARD, MISS IMOGEN	448
PINFIELD, MR TIM	449
PIPE, MR DAVID	450
PITMAN, MR MARK	451
POGSON, MR CHARLES	452
†POLLOCK, MR KEITH	453
PORTMAN, MR JONATHAN	454
POWELL, MR BRENDAN	455
PRESCOTT BT, SIR MARK	456
PRICE, MISS KATY	457
PRICE, MR RICHARD	458
PRITCHARD, MR PETER	459

Q

Name	Team No.
QUINN, MR DENIS	460
QUINN, MR JOHN	461
QUINN, MR MICK	462

R

Name	Team No.
RALPH, MR ALASTAIR	463
REED, MR TIM	464
†REED, MR WILLIAM	465
REES, MR DAVID	466
†REES, MRS HELEN	467
REGAN, MR SEAN	468
RICHARDS, MRS LYDIA	470
RICHARDS, MR NICKY	471
RICHES, MR JOHN DAVID	472
RIMELL, MR MARK	473
ROBERTS, MR DAVE	474
ROBERTS, MR MIKE	475
ROBINSON, MISS SARAH	476
ROBSON, MISS PAULINE	477
ROPER, MR W. M.	478

Name	Team No.
†ROSS, MR RUSSELL	479
ROTHWELL, MR BRIAN	480
ROUGET, MR J.-C.	481
ROWE, MR RICHARD	482
ROWLAND, MISS MANDY	483
RUSSELL, MS LUCINDA	484
RYAN, MR JOHN	485
RYAN, MR KEVIN	486

S

Name	Team No.
SADIK, MR AYTACH	487
SALAMAN, MR MATTHEW	488
SANDERSON, MR GARY	489
†SANDERSON, MRS KATHLEEN	490
SANTOS, MR JOSE	491
SAUNDERS, MR MALCOLM	492
SAYER, MRS DIANNE	493
SCARGILL, DR JON	494
†SCOTT, MR DERRICK	495
SCOTT, MR GEORGE	496
SCOTT, MR JEREMY	497
SCOTT, MISS KATIE	498
SCUDAMORE, MR MICHAEL	499
SHAW, MR DEREK	500
SHAW, MRS FIONA	501
†SHEARS, MR MARK	502
SHEPPARD, MR MATT	503
SHERWOOD, MR OLIVER	504
†SHIELS, MR RAYMOND	505
SIDDALL, MISS LYNN	506
SIMCOCK, MR DAVID	507
SKELTON, MR DAN	508
SLACK, MR KENNETH	509
SLY, MRS PAM	510
SMAGA, MR DAVID	511
SMART, MR BRYAN	512
SMITH, MR CHARLES	513
SMITH, MR JULIAN	514
SMITH, MR MARTIN	515
SMITH, MR R. MIKE	516
SMITH, MR RALPH J.	517

Name	Team No.	Name	Team No.
SMITH, MRS SUE	518	TUITE, MR JOSEPH	557
SMITH, MISS SUZY	519	TURNER, MR BILL	558
SMYLY, MR GILES	520	TUTTY, MRS KAREN	559
SNOWDEN, MR JAMIE	521	TWISTON-DAVIES, MR NIGEL	560
SOWERSBY, MR MIKE	522		
SPEARING, MR JOHN	523		
SPENCER, MR RICHARD	524	**U**	
SPENCER, MR SEB	525	UNETT, MR JAMES	561
SPILLER, MR HENRY	526	USHER, MR MARK	562
STACK, MR FOZZY	527		
STANFORD, MR EUGENE	528		
STEELE, MR DANIEL	529	**V**	
STEPHEN, MRS JACKIE	530	VARIAN, MR ROGER	563
STEPHENS, MRS KATIE	531	VAUGHAN, MR ED	564
STEPHENS, MR ROBERT	532	VAUGHAN, MR TIM	565
STONE, MR WILLIAM	533	VON DER RECKE, MR CHRISTIAN	566
STOREY, MR WILF	534		
STOUTE, SIR MICHAEL	535		
STRONGE, MRS ALI	536	**W**	
STUBBS, MISS KRISTIN	537	WADHAM, MRS LUCY	567
SUMMERS, MR ROB	538	WAGGOTT, MISS TRACY	568
†SWINSWOOD, MR ALEX	539	WAINWRIGHT, MR JOHN	569
SYMONDS, MR TOM	540	†WALEY-COHEN, MR ROBERT	570
		WALFORD, MR MARK	571
		WALFORD, MR ROBERT	572
		WALKER, MR ED	573
T		WALL, MR CHRIS	574
TATE, MR JAMES	541	WALL, MR TREVOR	575
TATE, MR TOM	542	WALLIS, MR CHARLIE	576
TEAGUE, MR COLIN	543	WALTON, MRS JANE	577
TEAL, MR ROGER	544	†WALTON, MR JASON	578
TETT, MR HENRY	545	WALTON, MRS SHEENA	579
THOMAS, MR SAM	546	WARD, MR JASON	580
THOMPSON, MR DAVID	547	†WATKINS, MISS TRACEY	581
THOMPSON, MR RONALD	548	WATSON, MR ARCHIE	582
†THOMPSON, MR VICTOR	549	WATSON, MR FREDERICK	583
THOMSON, MR SANDY	550	WATT, MRS SHARON	584
TINKLER, MR NIGEL	551	WAUGH, MR SIMON	585
TIZZARD, MR COLIN	552	WEBBER, MR PAUL	586
TODHUNTER, MR MARTIN	553	WELD, MR D. K.	587
TOMPKINS, MR MARK	554	WEST, MR ADAM	588
TREGONING, MR MARCUS	555	WEST, MISS SHEENA	589
TUER, MR GRANT	556	WEST, MR SIMON	590

Name	Team No.
†WESTON, MR DAVID	591
WESTON, MR TOM	592
†WESTWOOD, MISS JESSICA	593
WEYMES, MR JOHN	594
WHILLANS, MR ALISTAIR	595
WHILLANS, MR DONALD	596
WHITAKER, MR RICHARD	597
†WHITEHEAD, MR ARTHUR	598
†WHITING, MR ARTHUR	599
†WHITTAKER, MR CHARLES	600
WHITTINGTON, MR HARRY	601
WIGHAM, MR MICHAEL	602
WILESMITH, MR MARTIN	603
WILLIAMS, MR CHRISTIAN	604
WILLIAMS, MR DAI	605
WILLIAMS, MR EVAN	606
WILLIAMS, MR IAN	607
WILLIAMS, MR NICK	608
WILLIAMS, MR NOEL	609
WILLIAMS, MR OLLY	610

Name	Team No.
WILLIAMS, MR STUART	611
WILLIAMS, MISS VENETIA	612
WILLIAMSON, MRS LISA	613
†WILSON, MR ANDREW	614
WILSON, MR CHRISTOPHER	615
†WILSON, MR JIM	616
†WILSON, MISS MAIRI	617
WILSON, MR NOEL	618
WINGROVE, MR KEN	619
WINKS, MR PETER	620
†WINTLE, MR ADRIAN	621
†WOODMAN, MISS REBECCA	622
WOODMAN, MR STEVE	623
WOOLLACOTT, MRS KAYLEY	624

Y

Name	Team No.
†YORK, MR PHILLIP	625
YOUNG, MRS LAURA	626
†YOUNG, MR WILLIAM	627

PROPERTY OF HER MAJESTY

The Queen

Colours: Purple, gold braid, scarlet sleeves, black velvet cap with gold fringe

Trained by **Sir Michael Stoute**, Newmarket

1 FRONTISPIECE, 4, b c Shamardal (USA)—Free Verse

THREE-YEAR-OLDS

2 DESERT BREEZE, b f Dubawi (IRE)—Galatee (FR)
3 ELECTOR, b c Dansili—Enticement
4 REFRAIN (IRE), b c Dubawi (IRE)—Folk Opera (IRE)
5 SEXTANT, b c Sea The Stars (IRE)—Hypoteneuse (IRE)
6 SHARP PRACTICE, b f Redoute's Choice (AUS)—Momentary

TWO-YEAR-OLDS

7 CALCULATION, br c 4/2 Dubawi (IRE)—Estimate (IRE)(Monsun (GER))
8 INVICTUS SPIRIT, b c 8/2 Frankel—Daring Aim (Daylami (IRE))
9 SOVEREIGN GRANT, b c 16/1 Kingman—Momentary (Nayef (USA))
10 WEMYSS WARE (IRE), b c 11/2 Dubawi (IRE)—White Moonstone (USA) (Dynaformer (USA))

Trained by **William Haggas**, Newmarket

11 CALL TO MIND, 4, b c Galileo (IRE)—Memory (IRE)
12 SENIORITY, 4, ch g Dubawi (IRE)—Anna Palariva (IRE)

THREE-YEAR-OLDS

13 HUMBOLT CURRENT, b c Fastnet Rock (AUS)—Humdrum
14 ROUND THE BUOY, b c Henrythenavigator (USA)—Key Point (IRE)
15 STRATEGIST (IRE), b g Shamardal (USA)—Snow Powder (IRE)
16 WITCHING TIME, b f Dubawi (IRE)—Caraboss

TWO-YEAR-OLDS

17 BREAK OF DAY, b f 31/1 Shamardal (USA)—Dawn Glory (Oasis Dream)
18 DESERT CARAVAN, b c 12/3 Oasis Dream—Sequence (IRE) (Selkirk (USA))
19 FLAREPATH, b f 3/2 Exceed And Excel (AUS)—Fiery Sunset (Galileo (IRE))
20 MAGNETIC CHARM, b f 27/4 Exceed And Excel (AUS)—Monday Show (USA) (Maria's Mon (USA))
21 RAFFLE, b c 1/4 Iffraaj—Raymi Coya (CAN) (Van Nistelrooy (USA))
22 SPACE WALK, b c 29/3 Galileo (IRE)—Memory (IRE) (Danehill Dancer (IRE))

Trained by **Richard Hannon**, Marlborough

TWO-YEAR-OLDS

23 EQUAL SUM, br f 6/3 Paco Boy (IRE)—Hypoteneuse (IRE) (Sadler's Wells (USA))
24 TOPICAL, b c 4/4 Toronado (IRE)—Star Value (IRE) (Danehill Dancer (IRE))

Trained by **Roger Charlton**, Beckhampton

THREE-YEAR-OLDS

25 CRAFTINESS, b f Al Kazeem—Artful (IRE)
26 FLEETING VIEW, b f Sixties Icon—Flash of Gold

PROPERTY OF HER MAJESTY

The Queen

TWO-YEAR-OLDS

    27 WEST NEWTON, b c 6/2 Kitten's Joy (USA)—Queen's Prize (Dansili)

Trained by **Michael Bell**, Newmarket

    28 FABRICATE, 6, b g Makfi—Flight of Fancy
    29 MERLIN, 4, b g Oasis Dream—Momentary

THREE-YEAR-OLDS

    30 ANY LITTLE RHYME, b f Shamardal (USA)—Free Verse
    31 SAILING HOME b f Shamardal (USA)—Tidespring (IRE)

TWO-YEAR-OLDS

    32 EIGHTSOME REEL, b c 1/3 Iffraaj—Set To Music (IRE) (Danehill Dancer (IRE))
    33 METAPHOR, b g 30/3 Motivator—Flash of Gold (Darshaan)
    34 REGULAR, ch c 18/3 Exceed And Excel (AUS)—Humdrum (Dr Fong (USA))
    35 YOUTHFUL, b c 26/2 Shamardal (USA)—Good Hope (Cape Cross (IRE))

Trained by **Andrew Balding**, Kingsclere

THREE-YEAR-OLDS

    36 NATURAL HISTORY, b c Nathaniel (IRE)—Film Script

TWO-YEAR-OLDS

    37 COMPASS, b g 9/2 Henrythenavigator (USA)—Medley (Danehill Dancer (IRE))

Trained by **John Gosden**, Newmarket

TWO-YEAR-OLDS

    38 GOLD STICK (IRE), b c 6/2 Dubawi (IRE)—Gamilati (Bernardini (USA))
    39 PIANISSIMO, b c 19/4 Teofilo (IRE)—Perfect Note (Shamardal (USA))

Trained by **Richard Hughes**, Upper Lambourn

TWO-YEAR-OLDS

    40 PUZZLE, b g 10/3 Paco Boy (IRE)—Appleton Drove (USA) (Street Cry (IRE))

Trained by **Nicky Henderson**, Lambourn

    41 COMELY, 6, b m Midnight Legend—Belle Magello (FR)
    42 FLY AGAIN, 4, ch f Malinas (GER)—Spring Flight
    43 KEEN ON, 4, b g Kayf Tara—Romantic Dream
    44 SUNSHADE, 5, b m Sulamani (IRE)— Spring Flight
    45 TAKE TO HEART, 6, b g Sakhee (USA)—Romantic Dream

Trained by **Charlie Longsdon**, Chipping Norton

    46 FORTH BRIDGE, 5, b g Bernardini (USA)—Sally Forth
    47 HEATHER SONG, 4, b f Kayf Tara—Bella Macrae

SOME TRAINERS' STRINGS ARE TAKEN FROM THE BHA RACING ADMINISTRATION WEBSITE AND INCLUDE HORSES LISTED ON THERE AS IN 'PRE-TRAINING', 'AT GRASS' OR 'RESTING'

---

1 | MR N. W. ALEXANDER, Kinneston
Postal: **Kinneston, Leslie, Glenrothes, Fife, KY6 3JJ**
Contacts: **PHONE** (01592) 840774 **MOBILE** (07831) 488210
E-MAIL nicholasalexander@kinneston.com **WEBSITE** www.kinneston.com

1 **ALLTHEKINGSHORSES (IRE)**, 12, b g King's Theatre (IRE)—Penny Brae (IRE) **J. F. Alexander**
2 **ANDHAAR**, 12, b g Bahri (USA)—Deraasaat **Bissett Racing**
3 **ANOTHER MATTIE (IRE)**, 11, b g Zagreb (USA)—Silver Tassie (FR) **Quandt & Cochrane**
4 **BENNY'S SECRET (IRE)**, 8, br g Beneficial—Greenhall Rambler (IRE) **Mr B. C. Castle**
5 **BERTALUS (IRE)**, 9, b g City Honours (USA)—Deep Dalus (IRE) **Late Lord Cochrane & Partners**
6 **BUFFALO BALLET (IRE)**, 12, b g Kayf Tara—Minora (IRE) **Mr HW Turcan & Sir Simon Dunning**
7 **CALIVIGNY (IRE)**, 9, b g Gold Well—Summer Holiday (IRE) **Hugh Hodge Ltd & Alexander Family**
8 **CHRISTMAS IN USA (FR)**, 6, b g Shaanmer (IRE)—Diamond of Diana (FR) **Bowen & Nicol**
9 **CLAN LEGEND**, 8, ch g Midnight Legend—Harrietfield **Clan Gathering**
10 **CRAIGANBOY (IRE)**, 9, b g Zagreb (USA)—Barnish River (IRE) **Quandt, Cochrane, Lysaght**
11 **DANCE OF FIRE**, 6, b g Norse Dancer (IRE)—Strictly Dancing (IRE) **Turcan D-Miller Stewart Burnham Dunning**
12 **DUTCH CANYON (IRE)**, 8, b g Craigsteel—Chitabe (IRE) **Bissett Racing**
13 **ELVIS MAIL (FR)**, 4, gr g Great Pretender (IRE)—Queenly Mail (FR) **The Ladies Who**
14 **ETOILE D'ECOSSE (FR)**, 4, gr f Martaline—Etoile de Mogador (FR) **Douglas Miller, Coltman, Dunning, Turcan**
15 **FIG'S PRIDE (IRE)**, 5, br m Stowaway—Roseboreen (IRE) **Mrs F. C. C. Harper Gow**
16 **FIGHT AWAY BOYS (IRE)**, 10, ch g Vertical Speed—Say Ya Love Me (IRE) **Mr Mr R.H.T Barber & Partner**
17 **FINAL REMINDER (IRE)**, 6, b m Gold Well—Olde Kilcormac (IRE) **Mr B. C. Castle**
18 **FLY RORY FLY (IRE)**, 6, b g Milan—Thousand Wings (GER)
19 **GOLD OPERA (IRE)**, 9, b g Gold Well—Flute Opera (IRE) **MacDonalds, Cardwell & Castle**
20 **JET MASTER (IRE)**, 12, b g Brian Boru—Whats The Reason (IRE) **Mr HW Turcan & Sir Simon Dunning**
21 **JOLIE CRICKETTE (IRE)**, 6, b m Laverock (IRE)—Crickette River (FR) **Mrs J. A. Morris**
22 **JUST BROOKE**, 8, ch m Black Sam Bellamy (IRE)—Sports Express **Bissett Racing**
23 **KILLER CROW (IRE)**, 9, ch g Presenting—Rivervail (IRE) **Alexander Family**
24 **LAKE VIEW LAD (IRE)**, 8, gr g Oscar (IRE)—Missy O'brien (IRE) **Mr A. Cochrane**
25 **LANDECKER (IRE)**, 10, br g Craigsteel—Winsome Breeze (IRE) **N Hodge & I Hodge**
26 **LEFT BACK (IRE)**, 6, b g Oscar (IRE)—Baldrica (FR) **Mr N. W. Alexander**
27 **MASSINI'S LADY**, 7, b m Dr Massini (IRE)—Lady du Bost (FR) **Mr M. R. D. Fleming**
28 **MCGINTY'S DREAM (IRE)**, 7, b g Flemensfirth (USA)—Laboc **Mr B. C. Castle**
29 5, B m Ask—Minora (IRE) **Mr N. W. Alexander**
30 **MOORES NOVELTY (IRE)**, 6, b g Sholokhov (IRE)—Moricana (GER) **Mrs S. M. Irwin**
31 **OFF THE HOOK (IRE)**, 6, b m Getaway (GER)—Call Her Again (IRE) **Mrs I. Hodge**
32 **PEAK OF BEAUTY (IRE)**, 5, b m Mountain High (IRE)—Minoras Return (IRE) **Mr D. Walker**
33 **PRESENTING ROSE (IRE)**, 8, b m Presenting—Berkeley House (IRE) **Mr A. Cochrane**
34 **ROAD TO GOLD (IRE)**, 9, b br g Gold Well—Haut de Gamme (IRE) **Mrs J. Douglas Miller**
35 **ROYAL CHATELIER (FR)**, 13, b g Video Rock (FR)—Attualita (FR) **J. F. Alexander**
36 **SILK OR SCARLET (IRE)**, 6, ch g Mahler—Spirit of Clanagh (IRE) **Ken McGarrity & Dudgeon, Cundall, Liddle**
37 **SUENO TOMS**, 5, b m Oscar (IRE)—Smooth Technology (IRE) **Mr T. Carruthers**
38 **THE BISHOP (IRE)**, 10, b g Winged Love (IRE)—Charlie's Mary (IRE) **Kinneston Racing**
39 **THE ORANGE ROGUE (IRE)**, 11, br g Alderbrook—Classic Enough **Mrs S. M. Irwin**
40 **THOMOND (IRE)**, 10, b g Definite Article—Hushaby (IRE) **Alexander Family**
41 **TITIAN BOY (IRE)**, 9, ch g Spadoun (FR)—Leodotcom (IRE) **Tim Hardie & Louise Robb**
42 **TOP CAT HENRY (IRE)**, 10, b g Dr Massini (IRE)—Bells Chance (IRE) **Mr N. W. Alexander**
43 **UP HELLY AA KING**, 7, ch g And Beyond (IRE)—Gretton **Mr I. A. Gauld**

Other Owners: Mr Jamie Alexander, Mrs Nicholas Alexander, Mr Nicholas Alexander, Alexander Family, Mr R. H. T. Barber, Mr A. A. Bissett, Mrs J. Bissett, Mr A. J. Bowen, Lady Burnham, Mr Neil Cardwell, Mr Brian Castle, The Hon Thomas Cochrane, Exors of the Late Lord Cochrane of Cults, Mrs David Coltman, Mrs J. Douglas Miller, Dudgeon, Cundall, Liddle, Mr Andrew Duncan, Sir Simon Dunning, Mr Timothy Hardie, Mrs N. Hodge, Mrs I. Hodge, Hugh Hodge Ltd, Mr Cornelius Lysaght, Mr Dan Macdonald, Mrs Michelle Macdonald, Mr Ken McGarrity, Mr A. G. Nicol, Miss S. Quandt, Mrs L. Robb, Mr A. D. Stewart, Mr H. W. Turcan.

Assistant Trainer: Catriona Bissett

Jockey (NH): Lucy Alexander. **Conditional:** Grant Cockburn. **Apprentice:** Lucy Alexander. **Amateur:** Mr Kit Alexander, Mr Crawford Robertson.

2 MISS LOUISE ALLAN, Newmarket
Postal: **2 London Road, Newmarket, Suffolk, CB8 0TW**
Contacts: **MOBILE (07703) 355878**
E-MAIL **louiseallan1@hotmail.co.uk**

1 HARD TOFFEE (IRE), 7, b g Teofilo (IRE)—Speciale (USA) **Miss V. L. Allan**
2 NOISY NEIGHBOUR, 4, b f Malinas (GER)—Mooreheigh **A. M. Smith**
3 NORWEGIAN REWARD (IRE), 10, ch g Hernando (FR)—Stay Behind **A. M. Smith**
4 THEREDBALLOON, 12, ch g Sulamani (IRE)—Sovana (FR) **Miss V. L. Allan**

3 MR CONRAD ALLEN, Newmarket
Postal: Trainer did not wish details of his string to appear

4 MR ERIC ALSTON, Preston
Postal: **Edges Farm Stables, Chapel Lane, Longton, Preston, Lancashire, PR4 5NA**
Contacts: **PHONE (01772) 612120 FAX (01772) 619600 MOBILE (07879) 641660**
E-MAIL **eric1943@supanet.com**

1 ACCLAIM THE NATION (IRE), 5, b g Acclamation—Dani Ridge (IRE) **Mr C. F. Harrington**
2 BUSH BEAUTY (IRE), 7, b m Bushranger (IRE)—Scottendale **Whitehills Racing Syndicate**
3 CASTERBRIDGE, 6, b g Pastoral Pursuits—Damalis (IRE) **Liam & Tony Ferguson**
4 INVINCIBLE RIDGE (IRE), 4, b g Invincible Spirit (IRE)—Dani Ridge (IRE) **Paul Buist & John Thompson**
5 JABBAROCKIE, 5, b g Showcasing—Canina **M Balmer, K Sheedy, P Copple, C Dingwall**
6 LYDIATE LADY, 6, b m Piccolo—Hiraeth **The Scotch Piper Racing**
7 MAGHFOOR, 4, b g Cape Cross (IRE)—Thaahira (USA) **Jo-co Partnership**
8 NIQNAAQPAADIWAAQ, 6, b g Aqlaam—Aswaaq (IRE) **Paul Buist & John Thompson**
9 REDROSEZORRO, 4, b g Foxwedge (AUS)—Garter Star **Red Rose Partnership**

THREE-YEAR-OLDS

10 BIGDABOG, b g Sayif (IRE)—Alice's Girl **Mr P. S. McGuire**
11 B c Acclamation—Dani Ridge (IRE) **Mr C. F. Harrington**
12 REDTEDD, ch g Mazameer (IRE)—Mermaid Melody **Sleeve It Ltd**
13 SIR WALTER (IRE), b g Camacho—Damalis (IRE) **Liam & Tony Ferguson**

Other Owners: Miss M. C. Balmer, Mr P. G. Buist, Mr E. Cooney, Mrs D. L. Cooney, Mr P. J. Copple, M. L. Ferguson, Mr C. A. Ferguson, Mr J. A. Green, Mr M. S. Kelly, Mr A. J. Raven, M. M. Taylor, Mr J. Thompson.

Assistant Trainer: Mrs Sue Alston

5 MISS GEMMA ANDERSON, Carlisle
Postal: **Shawstown, Penton, Carlisle, Cumbria, CA6 5RT**
Contacts: **PHONE (07872) 429287 (01228) 577726 MOBILE (07950) 724367**
E-MAIL **gemmaanderson1@googlemail.com**

1 BINGO D'OLIVATE (FR), 7, b g Laverock (IRE)—Ombrelle de L'orme (FR) **Miss G. E. J. Anderson**
2 CARTA BLANCA (IRE), 5, gr m Authorized (IRE)—Alicante **Ben Greenslade & David McCrone**
3 DANGEROUS GROUND (IRE), 4, b f High Chaparral (IRE)—Laurentina **Ben Greenslade & David McCrone**
4 DEVIOUS SPIRIT (IRE), 6, br g Intikhab (USA)—Unintentional **Mr B. Greenslade**
5 FJORD (IRE), 4, b g Elzaam (AUS)—Ladood **Ben Greenslade & David McCrone**
6 ISLAND SONG (IRE), 4, b f Equiano (FR)—Fortuna Limit **Ben Greenslade & David McCrone**
7 KENNEDYS FIELD, 5, b g Multiplex—Supreme Lady (IRE) **Mr K. Barker**
8 KNOCKREA (IRE), 11, b g Pierre—Glynn Cross (IRE) **JSGG Partnership**
9 LOSTOCK HALL (IRE), 6, b g Lord Shanakill (USA)—Cannikin (IRE) **Ben Greenslade & David McCrone**
10 MY MO (FR), 6, b g Silver Frost (IRE)—Anna Ivanovna (FR) **Ben Greenslade & David McCrone**
11 RUBENESQUE (IRE), 6, b m Getaway (GER)—Shouette (IRE) **Ben Greenslade & David McCrone**

THREE-YEAR-OLDS

12 MY ROCK (IRE), b g Rock of Gibraltar (IRE)—Laureldean Lady (IRE) **Ben Greenslade & David McCrone**

MISS GEMMA ANDERSON - Continued

Other Owners: Mr S. J. Baird, Mr D. L. McCrone.
Conditional: Steven Fox. **Amateur:** Mr R. Nichol.

6	**MR CHARLIE APPLEBY, Newmarket**

Postal: **Godolphin Management Co Ltd, Moulton Paddocks, Newmarket, Suffolk, CB8 7PJ**
WEBSITE www.godolphin.com

1 **ALQAMAR**, 4, b g Dubawi (IRE)—Moonsail
2 **BACCARAT (IRE)**, 9, ch g Dutch Art—Zut Alors (IRE)
3 **BANKSEA**, 5, b g Lawman (FR)—Stars In Your Eyes
4 **BAY OF POETS (IRE)**, 4, b g Lope de Vega (IRE)—Bristol Bay (IRE)
5 **BLAIR HOUSE (IRE)**, 5, ch g Pivotal—Patroness
6 **BLUE POINT (IRE)**, 4, b c Shamardal (USA)—Scarlett Rose
7 **BOYNTON (USA)**, 4, ch g More Than Ready (USA)—Baffled (USA)
8 **BRAVO ZOLO (IRE)**, 6, b g Rip Van Winkle (IRE)—Set Fire (IRE)
9 **CAPEZZANO (USA)**, 4, b g Bernardini (USA)—Cableknit (USA)
10 **CELESTIAL SPHERES (IRE)**, 4, b g Redoute's Choice (AUS)—Copernica (IRE)
11 **COMICAS (USA)**, 5, ch g Distorted Humor (USA)—Abby's Angel (USA)
12 **CULTURATI**, 5, b g Dubawi (IRE)—Whazzis
13 **D'BAI (IRE)**, 4, b g Dubawi (IRE)—Savannah Belle
14 **EMOTIONLESS (IRE)**, 5, b g Shamardal (USA)—Unbridled Elaine (USA)
15 **ENDLESS GOLD**, 4, b g Dubawi (IRE)—Love Charm
16 **EYNHALLOW**, 4, b g Nathaniel (IRE)—Ronaldsay
17 **FESTIVAL OF AGES (USA)**, 4, b g Medaglia d'oro (USA)—November (USA)
18 **FIRST NATION**, 4, b g Dubawi (IRE)—Moyesii (USA)
19 **FLY AT DAWN (USA)**, 4, ch g Discreet Cat (USA)—Emirates Girl (USA)
20 **FOLKSWOOD**, 5, b g Exceed And Excel (AUS)—Magic Nymph (IRE)
21 **FRANCIS OF ASSISI (IRE)**, 8, b g Danehill Dancer (IRE)—Queen Cleopatra (IRE)
22 **FRONTIERSMAN**, 5, br h Dubawi (IRE)—Ouija Board
23 **G K CHESTERTON (IRE)**, 5, ch g Poet's Voice—Neptune's Bride (USA)
24 **HAMADA**, 4, b c Cape Cross (IRE)—Sahraah (USA)
25 **HAWKBILL (USA)**, 5, ch h Kitten's Joy (USA)—Trensa (USA)
26 **JUNGLE CAT (IRE)**, 6, b h Iffraaj—Mike's Wildcat (USA)
27 **KEY BID**, 4, ch g Dubawi (IRE)—Silca Chiave
28 **KIDMENEVER (IRE)**, 5, b h Baltic King—Pepys Tillergirl (IRE)
29 **MYSTIQUE MOON**, 4, ch g Shamardal (USA)—Celestial Girl
30 **OASIS CHARM**, 4, b g Oasis Dream—Albaraka
31 **OTTONIAN**, 4, ch g Dubawi (IRE)—Evil Empire (GER)
32 **POLARISATION**, 6, b g Echo of Light—Concordia
33 **RARE RHYTHM**, 6, b g Dubawi (IRE)—Demisemiquaver
34 **SALSABEEL (IRE)**, 4, b g Exceed And Excel (AUS)—Tokyo Rose (UAE)
35 **SCOTTISH (IRE)**, 6, b g Teofilo (IRE)—Zeiting (IRE)
36 **TOORMORE (IRE)**, 7, b g Arakan (USA)—Danetime Out (IRE)
37 **VAN DER DECKEN**, 4, b g Dutch Art—Celeste
38 **VIREN'S ARMY (IRE)**, 5, b g Twirling Candy (USA)—Blue Angel (IRE)
39 **WALTON STREET**, 4, b g Cape Cross (IRE)—Brom Felinity (AUS)
40 **WHITE DESERT (IRE)**, 4, ch g Teofilo (IRE)—Artisia (IRE)
41 **WILD TEMPEST**, 4, ch g Raven's Pass (USA)—Sayyedati Storm (USA)
42 **WOLF COUNTRY**, 4, b g Dubawi (IRE)—Goathemala (GER)
43 **WUHEIDA**, 4, ch f Dubawi (IRE)—Hibaayeb

THREE-YEAR-OLDS

44 **AFRICAN JAZZ (IRE)**, b c Cape Cross (IRE)—Monday Show (USA)
45 **AL HAJAR (IRE)**, b c Dark Angel (IRE)—Warshah (IRE)
46 **ANTISANA**, ch f Dubawi (IRE)—Lava Flow (IRE)
47 **AQABAH (USA)**, gr ro c Exchange Rate (USA)—Fast Tip (USA)
48 **ARABIAN GIFT (IRE)**, br f Dubawi (IRE)—Gift Range (IRE)
49 **AURUM (IRE)**, b c Exceed And Excel (AUS)—Rachelle (IRE)
50 **AUXERRE (IRE)**, b g Iffraaj—Roscoff (IRE)
51 **BEING THERE (FR)**, b c Dubawi (IRE)—Beauty Parlour
52 **BOW STREET**, ch c New Approach (IRE)—Favourable Terms
53 **BRODERIE**, br gr f Pivotal—Woven Lace

MR CHARLIE APPLEBY - Continued

54 **BRUNDTLAND (IRE),** b br c Dubawi (IRE)—Future Generation (IRE)
55 **CALLIANDRA (IRE),** ch f Dubawi (IRE)—Calipatria
56 **CALYPSO BLUE (IRE),** b f Dubawi (IRE)—Dark Orchid (USA)
57 **CARRIWITCHET (IRE),** b f Dubawi (IRE)—Claba di San Jore (IRE)
58 **CHARLES KINGSLEY,** b c New Approach (IRE)—Kailani
59 **COSMIC GLOW,** b g Exceed And Excel (AUS)—Ruby Rocket (IRE)
60 **CROSS COUNTER,** b c Teofilo (IRE)—Waitress (USA)
61 **CROWN WALK,** ch f Dubawi (IRE)—Dunnes River (USA)
62 **DATHANNA (IRE),** b f Dubawi (IRE)—Colour (AUS)
63 **DAYS OF OLD,** b f New Approach (IRE)—Historian (IRE)
64 **DREAM WARRIOR,** b c Dubawi (IRE)—I'm A Dreamer (IRE)
65 **DUBHE,** b c Dubawi (IRE)—Great Heavens
66 **DUCHESS OF BERRY,** b f New Approach (IRE)—Princesse Dansante (IRE)
67 **EAST ASIA (IRE),** b c Iffraaj—Chan Tong (BRZ)
68 **ESPADRILLE,** b f Dubawi (IRE)—High Heeled (IRE)
69 **EXPECTING TO FLY (USA),** b f Iffraaj—Lady Wingshot (IRE)
70 **EXPRESSIY (FR),** b f Siyouni (FR)—Express American (FR)
71 **FIRST CONTACT (IRE),** gr g Dark Angel (IRE)—Vanishing Grey (IRE)
72 **FLAG FESTIVAL,** gr g New Approach (IRE)—Blue Bunting (USA)
73 **FLORA SANDES (USA),** b f War Front (USA)—Aloof (IRE)
74 **FOLK TALE (IRE),** ch g Dubawi (IRE)—Causeway Lass (AUS)
75 **FOUNTAIN OF TIME (IRE),** b f Iffraaj—Key To Peace (IRE)
76 **GHAIYYATH (IRE),** b c Dubawi (IRE)—Nightime (IRE)
77 **GHOSTWATCH (IRE),** b c Dubawi (IRE)—Nature Spirits (FR)
78 **GLORIOUS JOURNEY,** b c Dubawi (IRE)—Fallen For You
79 **GOLD TOWN,** b g Street Cry (IRE)—Pimpernel (IRE)
80 **HADITH (IRE),** b br f New Approach (IRE)—Discourse (USA)
81 **IMPERIAL PAST,** b c Dubawi (IRE)—Divorces (AUS)
82 **ISPOLINI,** b c Dubawi (IRE)—Giants Play (USA)
83 **JAZIRAT (IRE),** b g Dark Angel (IRE)—Layla Jamil (IRE)
84 **KARAGINSKY,** ch c Dubawi (IRE)—Belenkaya (USA)
85 **KEY VICTORY (IRE),** b c Teofilo (IRE)—Patroness
86 **KIND ACT (USA),** b g Distorted Humor (USA)—Kind Words (USA)
87 **LAST VOYAGE (USA),** b c Eskendereya (USA)—Shipboard Romance (USA)
88 **LOXLEY (IRE),** b c New Approach (IRE)—Lady Marian (GER)
89 **LUNAR MARIA,** b f Dubawi (IRE)—Ama (USA)
90 **MAGIC LILY,** ch f New Approach (IRE)—Dancing Rain (IRE)
91 **MASAR (IRE),** ch c New Approach (IRE)—Khawlah (IRE)
92 **MENUETTO,** b f Dubawi (IRE)—Measured Tempo
93 **MORLOCK (IRE),** b c Epaulette (AUS)—Mon Bijou (IRE)
94 **MYTHICAL MAGIC (IRE),** b c Iffraaj—Mythie (FR)
95 **NATIVE APPEAL (IRE),** b c Exceed And Excel (AUS)—Picture Hat (USA)
96 **NATIVE ARROW (USA),** ch c Kitten's Joy (USA)—Dixie Shoes (USA)
97 **NIGHT CASTLE (IRE),** b g Dubawi (IRE)—Rock Opera (SAF)
98 **NIGHT STORY,** b c Shamardal (USA)—Love Everlasting
99 **NORDIC LIGHTS,** ch c Intello (GER)—Marika
100 **OLD PERSIAN,** b c Dubawi (IRE)—Indian Petal
101 **ON THE WARPATH,** ch c Declaration of War (USA)—Elusive Pearl (USA)
102 **PEACE TRAIL,** b f Kyllachy—Path of Peace
103 **POETIC CHARM,** b f Dubawi (IRE)—Speirbhean (IRE)
104 **RASTRELLI (FR),** b g Siyouni (FR)—Ponte di Legno (FR)
105 **ROMANTIC TALK,** gr f New Approach (IRE)—Galician
106 **ROUSSEL (IRE),** b c Kodiac—Sodashy (IRE)
107 **SAYF SHAMAL (USA),** ch f Elusive Quality (USA)—Alizes (NZ)
108 **SETTING SAIL,** b c Dansili—West Wind
109 **SILVERBOOK,** b c New Approach (IRE)—Sahraah (USA)
110 **SOLILOQUY,** b f Dubawi (IRE)—Dysphonia (AUS)
111 **SOUND AND SILENCE,** b c Exceed And Excel (AUS)—Veil of Silence (IRE)
112 **SPORTSWRITER,** b c Iffraaj—Sunday Times
113 **SPRING COSMOS (IRE),** b f Acclamation—Sister Red (IRE)
114 **STAGE MAGIC (IRE),** b c Dark Angel (IRE)—Witnessed
115 **STATEHOOD (IRE),** b c Kodiac—Analysis
116 **SUHAYL MOON (IRE),** b f Invincible Spirit (IRE)—Sander Camillo (USA)
117 **SWISS KNIGHT,** b c Oasis Dream—Swiss Diva
118 **SWORD OF TRUTH (IRE),** b br c Cape Cross (IRE)—Silversword (FR)

MR CHARLIE APPLEBY - Continued

119 **SYMBOLIZATION (IRE),** b br c Cape Cross (IRE)—Yorkshire Lass (IRE)
120 **TRIBAL QUEST (USA),** b g War Front (USA)—Haka (USA)
121 **WARBURTON (IRE),** ch g Dawn Approach (IRE)—Isobel Archer
122 **WILD ILLUSION,** b f Dubawi (IRE)—Rumh (GER)
123 **WINDS OF FIRE (USA),** b g Kitten's Joy (USA)—Laureldean Gale (USA)
124 **ZAMAN,** b c Dutch Art—Wake Up Call

TWO-YEAR-OLDS

125 B c 19/1 Dubawi (IRE)—Abhisheka (IRE) (Sadler's Wells (USA))
126 Ch c 19/2 Dawn Approach (IRE)—Al Baidaa (Exceed And Excel (AUS)) (180000)
127 B c 11/2 Cape Cross (IRE)—Botanique (IRE) (Pivotal)
128 B f 19/5 Slade Power (IRE)—Chaquiras (USA) (Seeking The Gold (USA))
129 Br f 25/3 Iffraaj—Constant Dream (Kheleyf (USA)) (525000)
130 Ch c 24/2 New Approach (IRE)—Dancing Rain (IRE) (Danehill Dancer (IRE))
131 B f 18/2 Teofilo (IRE)—Ethereal Sky (IRE) (Invincible Spirit (IRE))
132 B f 10/4 Cape Cross (IRE)—First Blush (IRE) (Pivotal)
133 B f 5/1 Shamardal (USA)—Flame of Gibraltar (IRE) (Rock of Gibraltar (IRE))
134 B c 3/3 Poet's Voice—Harlequin Girl (Where Or When) (80000)
135 B f 19/2 Animal Kingdom (USA)—Ihtifal (Dansili)
136 B c 10/2 Exceed And Excel (AUS)—Inspiriter (Invincible Spirit (IRE))
137 B c 1/4 Sea The Stars (IRE)—Intimhir (IRE) (Muhtathir) (162800)
138 B f 10/1 Sea The Stars (IRE)—Islington (Sadler's Wells (USA)) (550000)
139 B c 24/3 Exceleration (IRE)—It's True (IRE) (Kheleyf (USA)) (90476)
140 Ch c 17/2 Galileo (IRE)—Jacqueline Quest (IRE) (Rock of Gibraltar (IRE)) (400000)
141 B c 18/2 Sea The Stars (IRE)—Lady Rosamunde (Maria's Mon (USA)) (100000)
142 B c 14/4 Shamardal (USA)—Lura (USA) (Street Cry (IRE))
143 Ch f 25/2 Dawn Approach (IRE)—Magical Crown (USA) (Distorted Humor (USA)) (60000)
144 B c 5/4 New Approach (IRE)—Mazuna (IRE) (Cape Cross (IRE)) (150000)
145 Ch c 4/3 Teofilo (IRE)—Midget (Invincible Spirit (IRE)) (190476)
146 B f 22/3 Slade Power (IRE)—Nashama (IRE) (Pivotal)
147 B f 23/3 Exchange Rate (USA)—New Girlfriend (IRE) (Diesis) (250000)
148 B f 31/1 Australia—No Explaining (IRE) (Azamour (IRE)) (370000)
149 B f 6/3 Invincible Spirit (IRE)—Patroness (Dubawi (IRE))
150 B br c 25/1 Speightstown (USA)—Peace Preserver (USA) (War Front (USA)) (271002)
151 B f 6/2 Dubawi (IRE)—Perfect Light (IRE) (Galileo (IRE))
152 B f 17/2 Invincible Spirit (IRE)—Policoro (IRE) (Pivotal)
153 B c 20/3 Scat Daddy (USA)—Practice (USA) (Smart Strike (CAN)) (619434)
154 Ch f 13/3 Kitten's Joy (USA)—Rosby Waves (USA) (Distorted Humor (USA))
155 B f 28/3 Oasis Dream—Rumh (GER) (Monsun (GER))
156 Ch c 27/3 Iffraaj—Strictly Silca (Danehill Dancer (IRE)) (85000)
157 Gr c 28/1 Dark Angel (IRE)—Sur Choix (Galileo (IRE)) (260000)
158 B f 5/4 Galileo (IRE)—Temida (Oratorio (IRE)) (390000)
159 B f 30/3 Pivotal—Veil of Silence (IRE) (Elusive Quality (USA))
160 B c 19/4 Dubawi (IRE)—Vow (Motivator) (240000)

7	**MR MICHAEL APPLEBY, Oakham**

Postal: **The Homestead, Langham, Oakham, Leicestershire, LE15 7EJ**
Contacts: **PHONE** (01572) 722772 **MOBILE** (07884) 366421
E-MAIL mickappleby@icloud.com **WEBSITE** www.mickappleby.com

1 **ADMIRAL ANSON,** 4, br c Bahri (USA)—Bromeigan **I. R. Hatton**
2 **AFONSO DE SOUSA (USA),** 8, br g Henrythenavigator (USA)—Mien (USA) **Mick Appleby Racing**
3 **ALYS ROCK (IRE),** 9, gr m Medaaly—Rock Slide (USA) **M. Appleby**
4 **APPLEBERRY (IRE),** 6, b m Approve (IRE)—Passage To India (IRE) **M J Golding, T Pryke, M Appleby**
5 **AZAM,** 4, b g Dansili—Giants Play (USA) **The Horse Watchers**
6 **BAILE GHILIBERT (IRE),** 6, br g Majestic Missile (IRE)—Reddening **M. Appleby**
7 **BANCNUANAHEIREANN (IRE),** 11, b g Chevalier (IRE)—Alamanta (IRE) **Mr W. Sewell & Mr Michael Appleby**
8 **BERTIE MOON,** 8, b g Bertolini (USA)—Fleeting Moon **SC Oliver Racing Limited**
9 **BEYEH (IRE),** 10, b m King's Best (USA)—Cradle Rock (IRE) **T. R. Pryke**
10 **BRIGADOON,** 11, b g Compton Place—Briggsmaid **Mr N. C. Hoare**
11 **CALL OUT LOUD,** 6, b g Aqlaam—Winner's Call **Kings Head Duffield Racing Partnership**
12 **CAPE COVA (IRE),** 5, b g Cape Cross (IRE)—Sina Cova (IRE) **Mr C. Buckingham**
13 **CASE KEY,** 5, gr g Showcasing—Fluttering Rose **T. R. Pryke**

MR MICHAEL APPLEBY - Continued

14 **CHARLIE'S DREAMER**, 4, ch f Equiano (FR)—Enford Princess **Mr C. A. Blyth**
15 **CHILLILILLI**, 4, ch f Monsieur Bond (IRE)—Stunning Icon **Mr S. Tolley**
16 **CLASSIC PURSUIT**, 7, b g Pastoral Pursuits—Snake's Head **From The Front Racing**
17 **CLOUDED GOLD**, 6, ch g Resplendent Glory (IRE)—Segretezza (IRE) **Mrs B. A. Matthews**
18 **COCKNEY BOY**, 5, ch g Cockney Rebel (IRE)—Menha **M. Appleby**
19 **COPPER PRINCE (IRE)**, 5, ch g Pelder (IRE)—Kora (IRE) **M. Appleby**
20 **DANZENO**, 7, b g Denounce—Danzanora **Mr A. M. Wragg**
21 **DI'S GIFT**, 9, b g Generous (IRE)—Di's Dilemma **Mr & Mrs T. W. Readett-Bayley**
22 **DREAM SERENADE**, 5, b m Dream Eater (IRE)—Lady Santana (IRE) **Tykes & Terriers Racing Club**
23 **EBTKAAR (IRE)**, 4, b g Cape Cross (IRE)—Clare Glen (IRE) **Mr C. Buckingham**
24 **EPITAPH (IRE)**, 4, b g Henrythenavigator (USA)—Chartres (IRE) **Looksarnteverything Partnership**
25 **FANTASY GLADIATOR**, 12, b g Ishiguru (USA)—Fancier Bit **The Fantasy Fellowship**
26 **FAVORITE GIRL (GER)**, 10, b m Shirocco (GER)—Favorite (GER) **T. R. Pryke**
27 **GREATEST JOURNEY**, 6, ch g Raven's Pass (USA)—Sensationally **Midest 2**
28 **HAKAM (USA)**, 6, b br g War Front—Lauren Byrd (USA) **The Horse Watchers**
29 **HARVEST RANGER**, 4, b g Bushranger (IRE)—Time of Gold (USA) **Kaizen Racing**
30 **HISAR (IRE)**, 4, ch g Dragon Pulse (IRE)—Delphie Queen (IRE) **The Horse Watchers**
31 **INDIGO PRINCESS**, 5, b m Native Ruler—Red To Violet **Mr P. A. Jarvis**
32 **IT MUST BE FAITH**, 8, b g Mount Nelson—Purple Rain (IRE) **M. Appleby**
33 **JACK NEVISON**, 5, b g Dick Turpin (IRE)—Creative Mind (IRE) **New Kids On The Trot**
34 **KAFOO**, 5, b g Dansili—Nidhaal (IRE) **Midest 2**
35 **KATIE GALE**, 8, b m Shirocco (GER)—Karla June **Ferrybank Properties Limited**
36 **KICKBOXER (IRE)**, 7, gr g Clodovil (IRE)—Ajig Dancer **Mr M. C. Elvin**
37 **KINGFISHER GIRL**, 5, gr m Hellvelyn—Caribbean Star **Dorans & Sutton**
38 **MAGGIE PINK**, 9, b m Beat All (USA)—Top Notch **Mr A. W. Bult**
39 **MOI AUSSIE**, 5, gr m Aussie Rules (USA)—Oceana Blue **Mick Appleby Racing**
40 **MR STORYTELLER**, 6, b g Rocamadour—Flying Iris (IRE) **A. Ownership Change Pending**
41 **NAVAJO STAR (IRE)**, 4, b f Mastercraftsman (IRE)—Champagne Aerial (IRE) **Ferrybank Properties Limited**
42 **NAVAJO STORM (IRE)**, 5, gr m Dark Angel (IRE)—Strike Lightly **Ferrybank Properties Limited**
43 **NAVAJO THUNDER (IRE)**, 4, b f High Chaparral (IRE)—Evening Dress **Ferrybank Properties Limited**
44 **OMINOTAGO**, 6, ch m Aqlaam—Sharp Dresser (USA) **I. R. Hatton**
45 **OUR GRETA (IRE)**, 4, gr f Exchange Rate (USA)—Academicienne (CAN) **Mr A. Gray**
46 **OYSTER CARD**, 5, b g Rail Link—Perle d'or (IRE) **The Perle d'Or Partnership**
47 **PEARL NATION (USA)**, 9, b g Speightstown (USA)—Happy Nation (USA) **The Horse Watchers**
48 **PERCYS PRINCESS**, 7, b m Sir Percy—Enford Princess **Mr C. A. Blyth**
49 **POET'S QUEST**, 4, b f Poet's Voice—Quest For Freedom **Mr L. J. M. J. Vaessen**
50 **QUEENS ROYALE**, 4, b f Stimulation (IRE)—Sofia Royale **Mr Wayne Brackstone, Mr Steve Whitear**
51 **RAAKID (IRE)**, 6, ch g Raven's Pass (USA)—Perfect Hedge **Mick Appleby Racing**
52 **RED FLUTE**, 6, ch g Piccolo—Fee Faw Fum (IRE) **M. Appleby**
53 **RED TOUCH (USA)**, 6, b br g Bluegrass Cat (USA)—Touchnow (CAN) **Mick Appleby Racing**
54 **SAAHEQ**, 4, b g Invincible Spirit (IRE)—Brevity (USA) **The Horse Watchers**
55 **SEAN O'CASEY (IRE)**, 5, b g Galileo (IRE)—Lahinch (IRE) **Mr C. Bacon**
56 **SECRET LIGHTNING (FR)**, 6, ch m Sakhee's Secret—Dimelight **Mick Appleby Racing**
57 **SHAMROKH (IRE)**, 4, b g Invincible Spirit (IRE)—Alshakr **Mr C. Buckingham**
58 **SIR HARRY COLLINS (IRE)**, 4, gr g Zebedee—Unreal **Mick Appleby Racing**
59 **SOMETHING LUCKY (IRE)**, 6, gr g Clodovil (IRE)—Lucky Leigh **Dream Racing Club**
60 **SPUTNIK PLANUM (USA)**, 4, b g Quality Road (USA)—Shiva (JPN) **The Horse Watchers**
61 **STAPLEFORD**, 4, b f Equiano (FR)—World Spirit **Stapleford Racing Ltd**
62 **STRAGAR**, 4, br g Delegator—Roccabella (FR) **Houghton Bloodstock**
63 **SUBJECTIVITY (USA)**, 4, ch g Girolamo—Always Loyal (USA) **T. R. Pryke**
64 **TAN ARABIQ**, 5, b g Arabian Gleam—Tanning **Sarnian Racing**
65 **THA'IR (IRE)**, 8, b g New Approach (IRE)—Flashing Green **Mr R. Oliver**
66 **THE GREAT WALL (USA)**, 4, b g Bernardini (USA)—New Moon (USA) **The Horse Watchers**
67 **THE LAWLEY**, 7, b m Alflora (IRE)—La Bella Villa **K. D. Pugh**
68 **THE LOCK MASTER (IRE)**, 11, b g Key of Luck (USA)—Pitrizza (IRE) **Kenneth George Kitchen**
69 **TOPAMICHI**, 8, b g Beat Hollow—Topatori (IRE) **The Horse Watchers**
70 **TOY THEATRE**, 4, b f Lonhro (AUS)—Puppet Queen (USA) **Mr L. J. M. J. Vaessen**
71 **VODKA ISLAND (IRE)**, 9, b m Turtle Island (IRE)—Fromrussiawithlove **D J and W Skelton & D Russell**
72 **WHITMEL**, 5, b g Sulamani (IRE)—My Valentina **Mr C. T. Dennett**
73 **WILD ACCLAIM (IRE)**, 4, b g Acclamation—Anam Allta (IRE) **Rod In Pickle Partnership**
74 **WIN LOSE DRAW (IRE)**, 6, b g Dark Angel (IRE)—Caherassdotcom **Midest 1**

THREE-YEAR-OLDS

75 **ALESANDRA**, ch f Haafhd—Segretezza (IRE) **Mrs B. A. Matthews**
76 **APACHE BLAZE**, b f Champs Elysees—Polar Circle (USA) **Ferrybank Properties Limited**

MR MICHAEL APPLEBY - Continued

77 ATALANTA QUEEN, b f Canford Cliffs (IRE)—Champagne Aerial (IRE) **Ferrybank Properties Limited**
78 BLUELLA, b f Equiano (FR)—Mata Hari Blue **Mr M. J. Golding**
79 BY ROYAL APPROVAL (IRE), b g Approve (IRE)—Spring Bouquet (IRE) **Mr C. Buckingham**
80 CONSTITUENT, b c High Chaparral (IRE)—Arum Lily (USA) **K. Abdullah**
81 DENHAM, b f Denounce—Fareham **B. D. Cantle**
82 JACKPOT ROYALE, b g Sixties Icon—Sofia Royale **Mr Wayne Brackstone, Mr Steve Whitear**
83 KHAAN, ch c Kheleyf (USA)—Sharp Dresser (USA) **I. R. Hatton**
84 MISCHIEVOUS ROCK, b f Society Rock (IRE)—Twilight Pearl **Stephen Almond & Ben Spier**
85 MOPS TANGO, b f Piccolo—Tanning **Sarnian Racing, Mr M Appleby**
86 PERSIAN PRIZE (IRE), ch f Approve (IRE)—Vote Early **M. Appleby**
87 RAVEN'S RAFT (IRE), gr f Raven's Pass (USA)—Sea Drift (FR) **Mr C L Bacon & The Horse Watchers**
88 SHOW PRINCESS, b f Showcasing—Irina Princess **Mr C. Buckingham**
89 THE BAY QUEEN (IRE), b f Iffraaj—Valley of Queens (IRE) **Mr C. Buckingham**
90 TRAUMATISED, b f Kheleyf (USA)—Reveal The Light **Mrs E. Cash**
91 WATCHING SPIRITS, br g Harbour Watch (IRE)—Naayla (IRE) **Mr C. Buckingham**

Trainer did not supply details of his two-year-olds

Other Owners: Mr Stephen Almond, Mr Michael Appleby, Mr C. L. Bacon, Mr A. M. Blewitt, Mr Wayne Brackstone, Mr M. Bryson, Mr V. H. Coleman, Mr Peter Coll, Mr A. D'Arcy, Mr Christopher Dixon, Mr Peter Dorans, Mr S. Franks, Mr D. R. Gardner, Mr Andrew Gargan, Mr M. J. Golding, Mr Mick Harris, Mr N. Hassan, Mr Richard Hoiles, The Horse Watchers, Mr Phil Kirton, Mr A. W. Le Page, Mr C. Le Page, Mr Stephen J. S. Lee, Mr D. Parkinson, Mr Terry Pryke, Mrs T. W. Readett-Bayley, Mr T. W. Readett-Bayley, Mr D. Russell, Sarnian Racing, Mr W. Sewell, Mr R. Sharp, Mr P. Shaw, Mr W. N. Skelton, Mr David Skelton, Mrs Jennifer C. Skelton, Mr C. P. Smith, Mr Ben Spier, Mr Peter Sumner, Mr Stephen Sutton, Mr Matthew Taylor, Mr B. Totty, Mr J. R. Wherritt, Mr S. J. Whitear, Mr Denis Woodward.

Assistant Trainers: Terry Hind, Jonathan Clayton

Jockey (flat): Sylvestre De Sousa, Luke Morris, Andrew Mullen. **Jockey (NH):** Richard Johnson, Jack Quinlan.
Conditional: Keelan Baker, Kevin Lundie. **Apprentice:** Alistair Rawlinson. **Amateur:** Miss Serena Brotherton.

---

8   ## MR DAVID ARBUTHNOT, Beare Green
Postal: Henfold House Cottage, Henfold Lane, Beare Green, Dorking, Surrey, RH5 4RW
Contacts: **PHONE (01306) 631529 FAX (01306) 631529 MOBILE (07836) 276464**
E-MAIL dwparbuthnot@hotmail.com **WEBSITE** www.henfoldracing.co.uk

1 4, Gr g Jukebox Jury (IRE)—Alkeste (GER) **A. T. A. Wates**
2 4, B br g Jeremy (USA)—Ben Roseler (IRE) **A. T. A. Wates**
3 DANGLYDONTASK, 7, b g Lucky Story (USA)—Strat's Quest **P. Banfield**
4 DARING DEPLOY (IRE), 12, b g Deploy—Daring Perk (IRE) **The Daring Partnership**
5 EYE OF AN EAGLE (FR), 5, b g Linda's Lad—Vie des Aigles (FR) **A. T. A. Wates**
6 4, Ch g Muhtathir—High Destiny (FR) **A. T. A. Wates**
7 MAX MILAN (IRE), 9, b g Milan—Sunset Leader (IRE) **Mr P. M. Claydon**
8 QUEENS PRESENT (IRE), 7, ch m Presenting—Fairy Dawn (IRE) **A. T. A. Wates**
9 SNOWBALL (IRE), 11, gr g Alderbrook—Rosafi (IRE) **The Daring Partnership**
10 WELLUPTOSCRATCH (FR), 7, b br g Irish Wells (FR)—Aulne River (FR) **Mr A T A Wates & Mrs S Wates**
11 WINDSPIEL (IRE), 5, b g Sholokhov (IRE)—Wildfire (FR) **A. T. A. Wates**

THREE-YEAR-OLDS

12 ARIA ROSE, b g Cityscape—Leelu **P. Banfield**
13 KAP AUTEUIL (FR), b g Kapgarde (FR)—Turboka (FR) **A. T. A. Wates**
14 MY FRIENDLY COUSIN, ro g Carlotamix (FR)—The Strawberry One **The Kykie Allsopp Partnership**
15 NICKOBOY (FR), b g Full of Gold (FR)—Dikanika (FR) **A. T. A. Wates**

Other Owners: Mr W. P. Harriman, Mrs J. E. B. Leigh-Pemberton, Mrs S. M. Wates, Mr K. Wiggert.

Jockey (NH): Tom Cannon, Daryl Jacob.

9 **MR PETER ATKINSON, Northallerton**
Postal: Yafforth Hill Farm, Yafforth, Northallerton, North Yorkshire, DL7 0LT
Contacts: **PHONE (01609) 772598 MOBILE (07751) 131215**

1 **IRISH ROE (IRE)**, 7, b m Vinnie Roe (IRE)—Betty's The Best (IRE) **Mr P. G. Atkinson**
2 **MINI DREAMS**, 6, b m Josr Algarhoud (IRE)—Mini Minster **Mr P. G. Atkinson**
3 **REVERANT CUST (IRE)**, 7, gr g Daylami (IRE)—Flame Supreme (IRE) **Mr P. G. Atkinson**

10 **MR MICHAEL ATTWATER, Epsom**
Postal: Tattenham Corner Stables, Tattenham Corner Road, Epsom Downs, Surrey, KT18 5PP
Contacts: **PHONE (01737) 360066 MOBILE (07725) 423633**
E-MAIL Attwaterracing@hotmail.co.uk **WEBSITE** www.attwaterracing.com

1 **ASK THE GURU**, 8, b g Ishiguru (USA)—Tharwa (IRE) **Canisbay Bloodstock**
2 **BEAT ROUTE**, 11, ch g Beat Hollow—Steppin Out **Canisbay Bloodstock**
3 **BONGO BEAT**, 7, ch g Beat Hollow—Steppin Out **Canisbay Bloodstock**
4 **EMBANKMENT**, 9, b g Zamindar (USA)—Esplanade **Canisbay Bloodstock**
5 **FANOULPIFER**, 7, b g High Chaparral (IRE)—Furbeseta **The Attwater Partnership**
6 **FLEETWOOD POPPY**, 6, br m Kheleyf (USA)—Steppin Out **Canisbay Bloodstock**
7 **JUST THAT LORD**, 5, ch g Avonbridge—Lady Filly **Mrs M. S. Teversham**
8 **LORD OF THE STORM**, 10, b g Avonbridge—Just Run (IRE) **Mrs M. S. Teversham**
9 **MONUMENTAL MAN**, 9, b g Vital Equine (IRE)—Spark Up **Richard and Nicola Hunt**
10 **MUSIC MAJOR**, 5, br g Bertolini (USA)—Music Maid (IRE) **The Attwater Partnership**
11 **NOBLE DEED**, 8, ch g Kyllachy—Noble One **Canisbay Bloodstock**
12 **PALACE MOON**, 13, b g Fantastic Light (USA)—Palace Street (USA) **Canisbay Bloodstock**
13 **PROFESSOR**, 8, ch g Byron—Jubilee **Canisbay Bloodstock**
14 **SQUIRE**, 7, b g Teofilo (IRE)—Most Charming (FR) **The Attwater Partnership**
15 **STATION CLOSED (IRE)**, 10, b m Kutub (IRE)—Laser Supreme (IRE) **Mr A. C. D. Main**
16 **TOP BEAK (IRE)**, 5, b g Lawman (FR)—Tree Tops **Mr A. C. D. Main**
17 **TRACTIVE EFFORT**, 5, b g Rail Link—Anastasia Venture **Canisbay Bloodstock**
18 **WARRANTED**, 5, b h Authorized (USA)—Steppin Out **Canisbay Bloodstock**

THREE-YEAR-OLDS

19 **BUTTERFLY SPIRIT**, gr gr f Lethal Force (IRE)—Zubova **Mr J. M. Duggan & Mr S. Brown**
20 **FREE TALKIN**, b f Equiano (FR)—Where's Broughton **Canisbay Bloodstock**
21 **HORNBY**, b g Equiano (FR)—Kindia (IRE) **Canisbay Bloodstock**
22 **JEOPARDY JOHN**, b g Delegator—Daysiwaay (IRE) **J J's Syndicate**
23 **LAWN RANGER**, b g Cityscape—Baylini **Canisbay Bloodstock**
24 **NAMBITI HILLS (IRE)**, gr c Mastercraftsman (IRE)—Lila **Mr A. C. D. Main**
25 **PACO STYLE**, b g Paco Boy (IRE)—Al Aqabah (IRE) **B. Gubby**
26 **PASSING CLOUDS**, b g Kheleyf (USA)—Steppin Out **Canisbay Bloodstock**
27 **SUKHOVEY (USA)**, b f Lookin At Lucky (USA)—Allencat (USA) **The Attwater Partnership**

TWO-YEAR-OLDS

28 B c 31/3 Intello (GER)—Dolphina (USA) (Kingmambo (USA)) (10000) **The Attwater Partnership**
29 C c 1/5 Epaulette (AUS)—Kindia (IRE) (Cape Cross (IRE)) **Canisbay Bloodstock**
30 B f 6/3 Mayson—Royal Ivy (Mujtahid (USA)) **Canisbay Bloodstock**
31 **SCENIC LADY**, b f 26/2 Frozen Power (IRE)—
Dazzling View (USA) (Distant View (USA)) (3809) **The Attwater Partnership**
32 B c 25/2 Foxwedge (AUS)—Shared Moment (IRE) (Tagula (IRE)) (2380) **The Attwater Partnership**
33 B f 18/3 Mukhadram—Songseeker (IRE) (Oasis Dream) (11000) **The Attwater Partnership**
34 Ch c 3/3 Leroidesanimaux (BRZ)—Steppin Out (First Trump) **Canisbay Bloodstock**
35 **THE MAN OF MODE (IRE)**, b c 8/5 Society Rock (IRE)—
Prime Time Girl (Primo Dominie) (12000) **Mr A. C. D. Main**

Other Owners: Mr B. M. Attwater, Mr M. J. Attwater, Mr S. Brown, Mr J. M. Duggan, Mr R. A. Hunt, Mrs N. Hunt, R. F. Kilby, M. G. Mackenzie, Miss M. E. Stopher.

Assistant Trainer: S. Sawyer

11 **MR JEAN-RENE AUVRAY, Calne**
Postal: **West Nolands Farm, Yatesbury, Wiltshire, SN11 8YD**
Contacts: **MOBILE (07798) 645796**
E-MAIL **jr@jrauvrayracing.co.uk** WEBSITE **www.jrauvrayracing.co.uk**

1 ANIF (IRE), 4, b g Cape Cross (IRE)—Cadenza (FR) **N. R. Kelly**
2 MONTMORE (FR), 5, b g Montmartre (FR)—One For Me **Sara Spratt, Nigel Kelly & Alison Auvray**
3 NAFAAYES (IRE), 4, ch f Sea The Stars (IRE)—Shamtari (IRE) **Mr S. K. McPhee**
4 NEBUKA (IRE), 4, b f So You Think (NZ)—Nicea (GER) **Mr S. K. McPhee**
5 PORTHLEDDEN FLIGHT, 4, b f Kayf Tara—Molly Flight (FR)

Other Owners: Mrs A. L. Auvray, Mr N. R. Kelly, Mr Stuart McPhee, Mrs S. Spratt, Mrs Helen Tayton-Martin.

12 **MR ALAN BAILEY, Newmarket**
Postal: **Cavendish Stables, Hamilton Road, Newmarket, Suffolk, CB8 7JQ**
Contacts: **PHONE (01638) 664546 FAX (01638) 664546 MOBILE (07808) 734223**
E-MAIL **baileya12@sky.com**

1 ESSPEEGEE, 5, b g Paco Boy (IRE)—Goldrenched (IRE) **The Skills People Group Ltd**
2 FRANGARRY (IRE), 6, b g Lawman (FR)—Divert (IRE) **Dr S. P. Hargreaves**
3 GAMEKEEPER BILL, 4, b g Beat All (USA)—Granny McPhee **A J McNamee & L C McNamee**
4 GNAAD (IRE), 4, b g Invincible Spirit (IRE)—Areyaam (USA) **K.Sohi & Ab Racing Ltd**
5 GO FAR, 8, b g Dutch Art—Carranita (IRE) **Mr R. West**
6 STRICTLY ART (IRE), 5, b g Excellent Art—Sadinga (IRE) **AB Racing Limited**
7 STRICTLY CARTER, 5, b g Multiplex—Compolina **A. Bailey**
8 VIMY RIDGE, 6, ch g American Post—Fairy Shoes **Dr S. P. Hargreaves**
9 WIDNES, 4, b g Showcasing—Largo (IRE) **Dr S. P. Hargreaves**

THREE-YEAR-OLDS

10 FLEETING FREEDOM, b f Equiano (FR)—Fleeting Image **P. T. Tellwright**
11 GRASMERE (IRE), b f Society Rock (IRE)—Silk Point (IRE) **MPR XLIV, Mr C Martin, Mrs A Shone**
12 PABLOW, b g Delegator—Limonia (GER) **P.Barker, Tregarth Racing & K.Sohi**
13 RED RIVAL (FR), b g Redback—Amalea (IRE) **A. Bailey**

TWO-YEAR-OLDS

14 INTERROGATOR (IRE), b g 7/3 Tamayuz—Arbeel (Royal Applause) (17142) **Mr Trevor Milner**
15 MARYELLEN, b f 28/4 Mayson—Granny McPhee (Bahri (USA)) **A J McNamee & L C McNamee**
16 B f 15/4 Equiano (FR)—Megaleka (Misu Bond (IRE)) **North Cheshire Trading**

Other Owners: AB Racing Limited, Mr P. J. Barker, Mr H. Hall, Mr C. M. Martin, Mr Allan McNamee, Mr Louis C. McNamee, Middleham Park Racing XLIV & D Shapiro, Mr T. S. Palin, Mr M. Prince, Mrs A. Shone, Mr K. Sohi, Mr R. L. Williams.

Assistant Trainer: Joseph Edwin Parr

Amateur: Miss Jessica Cooley.

13 **MRS CAROLINE BAILEY, Holdenby**
Postal: **37 Eastfield Road, Brixworth, Northampton, Northamptonshire, NN6 9ED**
Contacts: **PHONE (01604) 883729 (Home) (01604) 770234 (Yard) FAX (01604) 770423**
MOBILE (07831) 373340
E-MAIL **caroline.bailey66@yahoo.com** WEBSITE **www.carolinebaileyracing.co.uk**

1 CARLI KING (IRE), 12, b g Witness Box (USA)—Abinitio Lady (IRE) **Varley, Lloyd & Bailey**
2 CROSSPARK, 8, b g Midnight Legend—Blue Shannon (IRE) **C. W. Booth**
3 DEALING RIVER, 11, b g Avonbridge—Greensand **G. T. H. Bailey**
4 DIG DEEPER, 9, b g Overbury (IRE)—Tickle The Tiller (IRE) **C. C. Shand Kydd**
5 DYLIEV (FR), 5, ch m Dylan Thomas (IRE)—Coreliev (IRE) **Herron, Nicholson, Proctor & Richards**
6 EARLY RETIREMENT (IRE), 6, b g Daylami (IRE)—Deep Lilly **Mr J. M. B. Strowbridge**
7 EDWARD ELGAR, 7, ch g Avonbridge—Scooby Dooby Do **Mrs J. M. Dixon Smith**
8 ELKSTONE, 7, b g Midnight Legend—Samandara (FR) **Tredwell, Robinson, Proctor & Nicholson**
9 GLOBAL BONUS (IRE), 9, b g Heron Island (IRE)—That's The Bonus (IRE) **Mrs S. Carsberg**
10 GLOBAL DOMINATION, 10, b g Alflora (IRE)—Lucia Forte **Mrs S. Carsberg**

MRS CAROLINE BAILEY - Continued

11 **GOLD INGOT,** 11, ch g Best of The Bests (IRE)—Realms of Gold (USA) **Mr J Cowan & Mr B Jessup**
12 **GORRAN HAVEN (IRE),** 8, ch g Stowaway—Diminished (IRE) **Lady D. C. Samworth**
13 **LADY MASTER,** 5, b m Native Ruler—Elmside Katie **Mr P. Dixon Smith**
14 **MALAPIE (IRE),** 10, b g Westerner—Victorian Lady **Varley, Lloyd & Bailey**
15 **MCCABE CREEK (IRE),** 8, b g Robin des Pres (FR)—Kick And Run (IRE) **Ian Payne & Kim Franklin**
16 **MIDNIGHT CHEERS,** 7, b m Midnight Legend—Marrasit (IRE) **Mr P. Dixon Smith**
17 **MISTER MCCOY,** 5, b g Sea Freedom—Another Tino
18 **RECKLESS BEHAVIOR (IRE),** 6, b g Gold Well—Wee Wallis **Bailey, Jessup, Lloyd & Varley**
19 **ROBIN OF LOCKSLEY (IRE),** 8, b g Robin des Pres (FR)—Duggary Dancer (IRE) **Mr S. A. Caunce**
20 **TROUFION (FR),** 9, gr g Smadoun (FR)—La Troussardiere (FR) **K. F. J. Loads**

Other Owners: Mr James E. Cowan, Miss K. M. Franklin, Mr M. S. Herron, Mr B. P. Jessup, Mr R. B. Lloyd, Mr K. M. Nicholson, Mr I. T. Payne, Mr P. S. C. Proctor, Mr S. A. Richards, Mrs B. D. Robinson, J. Tredwell, Mr M. Varley.

Jockey (NH): Sean Bowen, Harry Skelton. **Amateur:** Mr Thomas McClorey.

---

14 MR KIM BAILEY, Cheltenham
Postal: **Thorndale Farm, Withington Road, Andoversford, Cheltenham, Gloucestershire, GL54 4LL**
Contacts: **PHONE (01242) 890241 FAX (01242) 890193 MOBILE (07831) 416859**
E-MAIL info@kimbaileyracing.com WEBSITE www.kimbaileyracing.com

1 **A PERFECT GIFT (IRE),** 4, b f Presenting—Keyras Choice (IRE) **Mr M. J. D. Lambert**
2 **ABBREVIATE (GER),** 7, b g Authorized (IRE)—Azalee (GER) **Mr & Mrs K. R. Ellis**
3 **AGENT MEMPHIS (IRE),** 6, b m Scorpion (IRE)—Forces of Destiny (IRE) **Mr K. C. Bailey**
4 **ALFIE'S CHOICE (IRE),** 6, b g Shantou (USA)—Bally Bolshoi (IRE) **Mr & Mrs Paul & Clare Rooney**
5 **ALIANDY (IRE),** 7, b g Presenting—Water Rock **A & S Enterprises Ltd**
6 **ANOTHER VENTURE (IRE),** 7, ch g Stowaway—Hard Luck (IRE) **Racing For Maggie's Partnership**
7 **BANDON ROC,** 7, b g Shirocco (GER)—Azur (IRE) **The WOW Partnership**
8 **BEN ARTHUR (IRE),** 8, b g Marienbard (IRE)—Oscartrainer (IRE) **Mr & Mrs Mark Laws**
9 **BISCUIT,** 7, ch m Black Sam Bellamy (IRE)—Falcon's Gunner **Racing For Maggie's Partnership**
10 **BLAZON,** 5, b g Dansili—Zante **The Blazing Optimists**
11 **BRAW ANGUS,** 8, b g Afflora (IRE)—Suilven **I. F. W. Buchan**
12 **BY THE BOARDWALK (IRE),** 10, br g Presenting—Peripheral Vision (IRE) **Mr J. F. Perriss**
13 **CARQALIN (FR),** 6, gr g Martaline—Mica Doree (FR) **Mr M. J. D. Lambert**
14 **CASCAYE (FR),** 6, br m Merlino Mago—Castyana (IRE) **Mr M. J. D. Lambert**
15 **CHAMPAGNE TO GO (IRE),** 8, b m Beneficial—Terre d'orient (IRE) **Mr J. F. Perriss**
16 **CHARBEL (IRE),** 7, b g Iffraaj—Eoz (IRE) **Mrs Julie Martin & David R. Martin**
17 **CHATEAU ROBIN (IRE),** 7, br g Robin des Pres (FR)—Bella With A Zee (IRE) **Robins Outlaws**
18 **COMMODORE BARRY (IRE),** 5, br g Presenting—Specifiedrisk (IRE) **The Commodores**
19 **CRESSWELL LEGEND,** 7, b g Midnight Legend—Cresswell Willow (IRE) **Mrs V. W. H. Johnson**
20 **DANDY DAN (IRE),** 5, b g Midnight Legend—Playing Around **Mr P. J. Andrews**
21 **DESARAY (IRE),** 7, b g Milan—Shuil Mo Ghra (IRE) **Dare I Say Partnership**
22 **DIAMOND GAIT,** 5, b m Passing Glance—Milliegait **Mr N. Carter**
23 **DIVA RECONCE (FR),** 5, b m Kap Rock (FR)—Kruscyna (FR) **Mrs IC Sellars & Major & Mrs P Arkwright**
24 **DOCTOR HAZE,** 7, b g Dr Massini (IRE)—Gypsy Haze **Mr G. J. Singh & Mr Dil Singh Rathore**
25 **DUELING BANJOS,** 8, gr g Proclamation—Kayf Lady **Mr J. F. Perriss**
26 **DUSTY PEARL,** 5, b g Frozen Fire (GER)—Kahooting **The Oyster Catchers**
27 **EARLY LEARNER,** 6, b m Sulamani (IRE)—Slow Starter (IRE) **This Horse Is For Sale Partnership**
28 **EL PRESENTE,** 5, b g Presenting—Raitera (FR) **Davies Pilkington Yarborough Brooke**
29 **FIRST FLOW (IRE),** 6, b g Primary (USA)—Clonroche Wells (IRE) **A. N. Solomons**
30 **GALLERY EXHIBITION (IRE),** 11, b g Portrait Gallery (IRE)—Good Hearted (IRE) **Somerset Racing Gd**
31 **GALLOWS POINT,** 5, b g Black Sam Bellamy (IRE)—Jolika (FR) **Mr Dan Hall & Mrs Julie & David R Martin**
32 **GLENFORDE (IRE),** 7, ch g Flemensfirth (USA)—Feel The Pride (IRE) **Share My Dream**
33 **HARRY TOPPER,** 11, b g Sir Harry Lewis (USA)—Indeed To Goodness (IRE) **A. N. Solomons**
34 **IMPERIAL AURA (IRE),** 5, b g Kalanisi (IRE)—Missindependence (IRE) **Imperial Racing Partnership 2016**
35 **INVOLVE,** 4, b g Dansili—Popular **Got Involved**
36 **JOHNNY OCEAN (IRE),** 6, b g Whitmore's Conn (USA)—Soda Bread (IRE) **Mrs Julie Martin & David R. Martin**
37 **KAYF STORM,** 5, gr m Kayf Tara—Royal Keel **Kim Bailey Racing Partnership**
38 **KILFILUM CROSS (IRE),** 7, gr g Beneficial—Singh Street (IRE) **Mr G. Tardi**
39 4, B g Stowaway—Kilmac Princess (IRE) **Mr K. C. Bailey**
40 **KNOCKANRAWLEY (IRE),** 10, gr g Portrait Gallery (IRE)—Hot Lips **Kim Bailey Racing Partnership VIII**
41 **LADY OF THE NIGHT,** 5, b m Midnight Legend—Even Flo **Mr J. F. Perriss**
42 **LAKE FIELD (IRE),** 9, b g Golan (IRE)—Rumson Way (IRE) **Mr M. Kiely**
43 **LAVAL NOIR (FR),** 7, b g Laveron—Vale of Honor (FR) **The Mindy Partnership**

MR KIM BAILEY - Continued

44 MASTEEN (FR), 6, b g Astarabad (USA)—Manson Teene (FR) Mr K. C. Bailey
45 MILORD (GER), 9, br g Monsun (GER)—Montserrat (GER) Kim Bailey Racing Partnership VII
46 4, Br g Arakan (USA)—Miss Garbo (IRE) Mr K. C. Bailey
47 MON PALOIS (FR), 6, b g Muhaymin (USA)—Gastinaise (FR) Mrs E. A. Kellar
48 MR BRINKLEY (IRE), 7, b g Scorpion (IRE)—Mandysway (IRE) Mr K. C. Bailey
49 MR GREY SKY (IRE), 4, gr g Fame And Glory—Lakil Princess (IRE) Mr P. J. Andrews
50 MR MACHO (IRE), 6, b g Flemensfirth (USA)—
                    Accordian Rules (IRE) Mrs IC Sellars & Major & Mrs P Arkwright
51 OUR BELLE AMIE, 6, b m Black Sam Bellamy (IRE)—Very Special One (IRE) Chasing Hopefuls
52 POND ROAD (FR), 4, ch g No Risk At All (FR)—Califea (FR) No Risk Syndicate
53 PRINCE LLYWELYN, 4, ch g Schiaparelli (GER)—La Marette Mr P. Bennett-Jones
54 RED RIVER (IRE), 5, ch g Beneficial—Socker Toppen (IRE) The Red River Syndicate
55 RHAEGAR (IRE), 7, b g Milan—Green Star (FR) Mrs D. L. Whateley
56 ROBIN THE RAVEN (IRE), 6, b g Robin des Pres (FR)—Omyn Supreme (IRE) S W Racing
57 ROCKY'S TREASURE (IRE), 7, b g Westerner—Fiddlers Bar (IRE) Mr J. F. Perriss
58 ROSE TO FAME, 4, b f Fame And Glory—Cinderella Rose Jones Broughtons Wilson Weaver
59 ROSMUC RELAY (IRE), 6, br g Presenting—Aughrim Vic (IRE) Mr J. F. Perriss
60 ROYAL SUPREMO (IRE), 7, b g Beneficial—Slaney Athlete (IRE) Mr K. C. Bailey
61 SAINTE LADYLIME (IRE), 7, b m Saint des Saints (FR)—Lady Pauline (FR) Mr & Mrs Paul & Clare Rooney
62 SEA STORY, 5, b m Black Sam Bellamy (IRE)—Charlottes Webb (IRE) John & Susie Kottler, Emma Buchanan
63 SILVER KAYF, 6, gr g Kayf Tara—Silver Spinner The Lucky Spinners
64 STATION MASTER (IRE), 7, b g Scorpion (IRE)—Gastounette (IRE) Mrs P. A. Perriss
65 SUNBLAZER (IRE), 8, gr g Dark Angel (IRE)—Damask Rose (IRE) Mr N. Carter
66 THE LAST SAMURI (IRE), 10, ch g Flemensfirth (USA)—Howaboutthis (IRE) Mr & Mrs Paul & Clare Rooney
67 THEDRINKYMEISTER (IRE), 9, b g Heron Island (IRE)—Keel Row Mr J. F. Perriss
68 THIBAULT, 5, b g Kayf Tara—Seemarye Mr T. D. J. Syder
69 THOSE TIGER FEET (IRE), 4, b g Shantou (USA)—Luca Lite (IRE) Mr P. J. Andrews
70 THUMB STONE BLUES (IRE), 8, b g High Chaparral (IRE)—Jade River (FR) Mr & Mrs Paul & Clare Rooney
71 TIME FOR ANOTHER (IRE), 5, ch g Shantou (USA)—Borleagh Blonde (IRE) Mr & Mrs Paul & Clare Rooney
72 TROJAN STAR (IRE), 8, b g Tikkanen (USA)—Mystical Queen (IRE) Mr M. Lambert & Mr K. C. Bailey
73 TWO FOR GOLD (IRE), 5, b g Gold Well—Two of Each (IRE) May We Never Be Found Out Partnership 2
74 VINNDICATION (IRE), 5, b g Vinnie Roe (IRE)—Pawnee Trail (IRE) Moremoneythan
75 WANDRIN STAR (IRE), 7, b g Flemensfirth (USA)—Keralba (USA) Mrs P. A. Perriss
76 YOUNEVERCALL (IRE), 7, b g Yeats (IRE)—Afarka (IRE) Youneverknow Partnership

Other Owners: Mrs Sandra G. E. Arkwright, Major P. W. F. Arkwright, Mr P. J. Bailey, Mrs C. Bailey, Mr O. S. W. Bell, Mr A. N. C. Bengough, Sir F. Brooke, Sir M. F. Broughton, Mr S. W. Broughton, Mrs E. S. Buchanan, Mr S. R. Cannon, Mr K. T. Clancy, Mr D. M. Clancy, M. E. T. Davies, K. R. Ellis, Mrs E. Ellis, Mrs L. H. Field, D. A. Hall, Lady M. P. Hatch, Mrs N. Jones, Mr M. Kay, Mr P. S. Kerr, Mr H. Kimbell, Mr J. Kottler, Mrs S. E. Kottler, Mr M. J. Laws, Mrs J. M. Laws, D. R. Martin, Mrs J. M. T. Martin, Mr C. W. Mather, Mr R. A. Pilkington, Mr I. Robinson, Mr P. A. Rooney, Mrs C. Rooney, Mrs N. P. Sellars, Mr R. Sheppard, Mr G. J. Singh, Mr D. Singh Rathore, Mr J. A. Stanley, Miss M. L. Taylor, Mrs R. B. Weaver, Mr J. Webber, Mr R. C. Wilkin, T. C. Wilson, The Earl Of Yarborough.

Assistant Trainer: Mathew Nicholls

Jockey (NH): David Bass, Tom Bellamy. Conditional: Richard Condon, Mikey Hamill.

15	**MRS TRACEY L. BAILEY, Hungerford** Postal: **Soley Farm Stud, Chilton Foliat, Hungerford, Berkshire, RG17 0TW** Contacts: **PHONE (01488) 683321 MOBILE (07831) 300999** **E-MAIL t413@btinternet.com**

1 BROADWAY SYMPHONY (IRE), 11, ch g Broadway Flyer (USA)—Flying Hooves (IRE) N. R. A. Sutton
2 SUCH A LEGEND, 10, ch g Midnight Legend—Mrs Fizziwig N. R. A. Sutton
3 THE GUNNER BRADY (IRE), 9, b g Heron Island (IRE)—Cooling Off (IRE) N. R. A. Sutton

---

16	**MR GEORGE BAKER, Chiddingfold** Postal: **Robins Farm, Fisher Lane, Chiddingfold, Godalming, Surrey, GU8 4TB** Contacts: **PHONE (01428) 682059 MOBILE (07889) 514881** **E-MAIL gbakerracing@gmail.com WEBSITE www.georgebakerracing.com**

1 BARWICK, 10, b g Beat Hollow—Tenpence M. H. Watt
2 BELGIAN BILL, 10, b h Exceed And Excel (AUS)—Gay Romance PJL, Byrne & Baker

MR GEORGE BAKER - Continued

3 **BRISE DE MER (FR)**, 4, b g Miesque's Son (USA)—Lisselan Firefly (IRE) **Allez France**
4 **CRAZY HORSE**, 5, b g Sleeping Indian—Mainstay **George Baker**
5 **DAZIBAO (FR)**, 5, ch g Muhaymin (USA)—Adjinne (FR) **George Baker and Partners**
6 **FIFTYSHADESOFGREY (FR)**, 7, gr g Dark Angel (IRE)—Wohaida (IRE) **Team Fifty 2**
7 **GEORGE BAKER (IRE)**, 11, b g Camacho—Petite Maxine **George Baker & Partners**
8 **GUARD OF HONOUR (IRE)**, 7, b g Galileo (IRE)—Queen of France (USA) **Mrs L. M. Sherwood**
9 **HARRY HURRICANE**, 6, b g Kodiac—Eolith **PJL Racing**
10 **HIGHWAY ONE (USA)**, 4, b f Quality Road (USA)—Kinda Wonderful (USA) **On The Game Partnership**
11 **INFANTA ISABELLA**, 4, b f Lope de Vega (IRE)—Shemissa (IRE) **The Chriselliam Partnership**
12 **MAMILLIUS**, 5, b g Exceed And Excel (AUS)—Laika Lane (USA) **The Mamillius Partnership**
13 **MANTON GRANGE**, 5, b g Siyouni (FR)—Emulate **Goltz, Finegold & McGeever**
14 **MAVROS**, 5, br g Authorized (IRE)—Barley Bree (IRE) **PJL Racing**
15 **SPITFIRE LIMITED**, 4, b f Excelebration (IRE)—First Bloom (USA) **Lady N. F. Cobham**
16 **WALTER SICKERT (IRE)**, 4, b c Galileo (IRE)—Alta Anna (FR) **Mrs L. M. Sherwood**

THREE-YEAR-OLDS

17 **ATOMIC JACK**, b g Nathaniel (IRE)—Indigo River (IRE) **PJL Racing**
18 **BARRITUS**, b g Exceed And Excel (AUS)—Flambeau **Barton Partnership**
19 **CHESS MOVE (IRE)**, b g Kodiac—Azia (IRE) **PJL, Pittam & Baker**
20 **CRAGWOOD ROYALE (IRE)**, b f Invincible Spirit (IRE)—Lady Glinka (IRE) **The Bailye Baker Partnership**
21 **FRENCH CRICKET (FR)**, b g Sunday Break (JPN)—Hambye **The Eton Ramblers**
22 **FROZEN BERE (FR)**, b g Peer Gynt (JPN)—Fitness Queen (USA) **Free French**
23 **GOODBYE LULU (IRE)**, b f Exceed And Excel (AUS)—Guarantia **PJL Racing**
24 **HEPTATHLETE (IRE)**, gr f Mount Nelson—Jessica Ennis (USA) **Hot To Trot Syndicate - Heptathlete**
25 **HURRICANE LIL (IRE)**, b f Big Bad Bob (IRE)—Ladylishandra (IRE) **Black Velvets**
26 **JUST PERFECT**, ch g Mastercraftsman (IRE)—Downhill Dancer (IRE) **Thurloe Thoroughbreds XLIII**
27 **KAVORA**, b f Havana Gold (IRE)—Anadiya (FR) **Seaton Partnership**
28 **LA MAQUINA**, b c Dutch Art—Miss Meltemi (IRE) **PJL, Pittam & Baker**
29 **LUCKY LOVER BOY (IRE)**, b g Teofilo (IRE)—Mayonga (USA) **PJL Racing**
30 **PURPLE JAZZ (IRE)**, b g Red Jazz (USA)—Breakmeheart (IRE) **The Barmy Men 3**
31 **THE LAMPLIGHTER (FR)**, b g Elusive City (USA)—Plume Rouge **The Lamplighter Syndicate**
32 **WATCH TAN**, gr gr f Harbour Watch (IRE)—High Tan **Seaton Partnership**

TWO-YEAR-OLDS

33 B g 21/4 Penny's Picnic (IRE)—Barbieri (IRE) (Encosta de Lago (AUS)) **Peter Deal and Sam Hoskins**
34 Gr c 4/1 Exchange Rate (USA)—Callmenancy (USA) (Political Force (USA)) (65000) **George Baker**
35 **GOLD BERE (FR)**, b br c 2/2 Hurricane Cat (USA)—Sanisa (FR) (Panis (USA)) (8954) **Mr P. Bowden**
36 Ch f 14/3 Kendargent (FR)—I Stand Corrected (Exceed And Excel (AUS)) (13024) **Mr P. Bowden**
37 Ch f 27/3 Olympic Glory (FR)—Mambo Mistress (USA) (Kingmambo (USA)) (52096) **Free French 2**
38 B f 22/2 Dawn Approach (IRE)—Marmoom Flower (IRE) (Cape Cross (IRE)) (32560) **Crane & Evans Partnership**
39 B c 24/4 Sunday Break (JPN)—Miss Alabama (FR) (Anabaa (USA)) (40700) **Matt Firth**
40 Ro f 28/4 Evasive—Nakiya (FR) (Kendor (FR)) (13024) **Mr P. Bowden**
41 **PRINCESSE BASSETT (FR)**, b f 15/5 Wootton Bassett—Mariposa (IRE) (Oasis Dream) (48840) **Free French**
42 **RENEGADE MASTER**, b g 21/4 Paco Boy—Candle (Dansili) **Gwyn & Sam Powell**
43 B f 30/1 Lawman (FR)—Rosia Bay (Rock of Gibraltar (IRE)) (16280) **The Pantechnicons**
44 B f 27/2 Bated Breath—Self Centred (Medicean) (52000) **Julian Pittam**
45 B c 25/2 Dream Ahead (USA)—Talon Bleu (FR) (Anabaa Blue) (65120) **Highclere Thoroughbred Racing Ltd**

Other Owners: Miss E. Asprey, Mr George Baker, Mrs C. E. S. Baker, Mr Justin Byrne, Mrs E. Carson, Mr W. H. Carson, Mr A. N. Cheyne, Mr Nick Clark, Peter Crane, Mrs Jolene De'Lemos, Mr Steve De'Lemos-Pratt, Mrs R. S. Evans, R. S. Evans, Mr A Flintoff, Wayne Hennessey, Mr R. S. Hoskins, The Hot To Trot Syndicate, Ms L Hurley, Mr Luke Lillington, Col Sandy Malcolm, Mr Mike McGeever, Mr O. J. W. Pawle, Mrs S. M. Ragg, Mr A. Rennison, Mrs Sandra Robinson, Mr J. A. B. Stafford, Mr Christopher Wright.

Assistant Trainers: Patrick Murphy, Valerie Murphy.

Jockey (flat): Pat Cosgrave, Liam Keniry. **Jockey (NH):** Andrew Tinkler, Trevor Whelan. **Apprentice:** Hector Crouch.

17 MR ANDREW BALDING, Kingsclere
Postal: **Park House Stables, Kingsclere, Newbury, Berkshire, RG20 5PZ**
Contacts: **PHONE** (01635) 298210 **FAX** (01635) 298305
E-MAIL admin@kingsclere.com **WEBSITE** www.kingsclere.com

1 **ABSOLUTELY SO (IRE)**, 8, b g Acclamation—Week End **The George Smith Family Partnership**
2 **ANCIENT FOE**, 4, b g Shamardal (USA)—Pearl Dance (USA) **G. Strawbridge**
3 **BEAT THE BANK**, 4, b g Paco Boy (IRE)—Tiana **King Power Racing Co Ltd**
4 **BELLE MEADE (IRE)**, 4, ch f Roderic O'connor (IRE)—Hazardous **Dr Bridget Drew & Mr R. A. Farmiloe**
5 **BERKSHIRE BOY (IRE)**, 4, b g Elzaam (AUS)—Circuit City (IRE) **Berkshire Parts & Panels Ltd**
6 **BROROCCO**, 5, b g Shirocco (GER)—Lady Brora **Kingsclere Racing Club**
7 **CLEONTE (IRE)**, 5, ch g Sir Percy—Key Figure **King Power Racing Co Ltd**
8 **CONTANGO (IRE)**, 4, ch g Casamento (IRE)—Call Later (USA) **Kennet Valley Thoroughbreds XII**
9 **COUNT OCTAVE**, 4, b c Frankel—Honorine (IRE) **Qatar Racing Limited**
10 **DANCING STAR**, 5, b m Aqlaam—Strictly Dancing (IRE) **J. C. Smith**
11 **DONJUAN TRIUMPHANT (IRE)**, 5, b h Dream Ahead (USA)—Mathuna (IRE) **King Power Racing Co Ltd**
12 **DURETTO**, 6, ch g Manduro (GER)—Landinium (ITY) **Lord J. Blyth**
13 **FAIR CAP**, 4, b f Exceed And Excel (AUS)—Speed Cop **J. C. Smith**
14 **GENETICS (FR)**, 4, b g Manduro (GER)—Garmerita (FR) **DJT Racing Partnership**
15 **HAINES**, 7, ch g Shirocco (GER)—Spring Dream (IRE) **Bow River Racing**
16 **HERE COMES WHEN (IRE)**, 8, br g Danehill Dancer (IRE)—Quad's Melody (IRE) **Mrs F. H. Hay**
17 **HIDDEN STEPS**, 4, b f Footstepsinthesand—Hidden Valley **Kingsclere Racing Club**
18 **HIGHLAND PASS**, 4, b br f Passing Glance—Lady Brora **Kingsclere Racing Club**
19 **HORSEPLAY**, 4, b f Cape Cross (IRE)—Mischief Making (USA) **Cliveden Stud Ltd**
20 **INTIMATE ART (IRE)**, 4, ch g Dutch Art—Intimacy (IRE) **Thurloe Thoroughbreds XXXIX**
21 **INTRANSIGENT**, 9, b g Trans Island—Mara River **Kingsclere Racing Club**
22 **ISOMER (USA)**, 4, ch g Cape Blanco (IRE)—Nimue (USA) **Mrs F. H. Hay**
23 **LEONTES**, 4, ch g Paco Boy (IRE)—Robema **Mr D. E. Brownlow**
24 **LORELINA**, 5, b m Passing Glance—Diktalina **Mr Tim Wixted & Mr Tony Anderson**
25 **MAKE MUSIC**, 5, b m Acclamation—Come What May **Mrs E. A. M. Balding**
26 **MAX ZORIN (IRE)**, 4, b g Cape Cross (IRE)—My **Chelsea Thoroughbreds - Pegasus**
27 **MONTALY**, 7, b g Yeats (IRE)—Le Badie (IRE) **Farleigh Racing**
28 **MORANDO (FR)**, 5, gr g Kendargent (FR)—Moranda (FR) **King Power Racing Co Ltd**
29 **MUNSTEAD STAR**, 4, ch f Sir Percy—Royal Patron **Lady G. A. Brunton**
30 **NIGHT OF GLORY**, 4, b g Sea The Stars (IRE)—Kesara **King Power Racing Co Ltd**
31 **PERFECT ANGEL (IRE)**, 4, br f Dark Angel (IRE)—The Hermitage (IRE) **Mildmay Racing & D. H. Caslon**
32 **PIVOINE (IRE)**, 4, b g Redoute's Choice (AUS)—Fleur de Cactus (IRE) **King Power Racing Co Ltd**
33 **POET'S VANITY**, 4, b f Poet's Voice—Vanity (IRE) **Mrs C. J. Wates**
34 **SCORCHING HEAT**, 4, b g Acclamation—Pink Flames (IRE) **Qatar Racing Limited**
35 **SIR PASS I AM**, 5, b g Passing Glance—Orbital Orchid **Mrs J. S. Newton**
36 **SOUTH SEAS (IRE)**, 4, ch g Lope de Vega (IRE)—Let It Be Me (USA) **Qatar Racing Limited**
37 **ST MARY'S**, 5, b m Siyouni (FR)—Once Over **Kingsclere Racing Club**
38 **STRAIGHT RIGHT (FR)**, 4, b c Siyouni (FR)—Sailor Moon (IRE) **King Power Racing Co Ltd**
39 **TWIN STAR (IRE)**, 4, ch g Tagula (IRE)—Chronicle **King Power Racing Co Ltd**
40 **ZWAYYAN**, 5, ch g Pivotal—Mail The Desert (IRE) **King Power Racing Co Ltd**

THREE-YEAR-OLDS

41 **AIYA (IRE)**, ch c Declaration of War (USA)—Flamingo Sea (USA) **King Power Racing Co Ltd**
42 **ANGEL ISLINGTON (IRE)**, gr f Dark Angel (IRE)—Doregan (IRE) **Mr A. Gemmell**
43 **ANNIE MAE**, b f Yeats (IRE)—Spring Dream (IRE) **Rainbow Racing**
44 **BACACARAT (IRE)**, b c Raven's Pass (USA)—Mathuna (IRE) **King Power Racing Co Ltd**
45 **BALLYQUIN (IRE)**, b c Acclamation—Something Mon (USA) **Mr J. Palmer-Brown**
46 **BERKSHIRE BLUE (IRE)**, b c Champs Elysees—Lemon Rock **Berkshire Parts & Panels Ltd**
47 **BERKSHIRE ROYAL**, b g Sir Percy—Forest Express (AUS) **Berkshire Parts & Panels Ltd**
48 **BERKSHIRE SPIRIT**, gr c Mastercraftsman (IRE)—Rebecca Rolfe **Berkshire Parts & Panels Ltd**
49 **CAROUSE (IRE)**, b g Excelebration (IRE)—Terre du Vent (FR) **Mick and Janice Mariscotti**
50 **CHAI CHAI (IRE)**, b g Zoffany (IRE)—Flamenco Red **King Power Racing Co Ltd**
51 **CHANGE MAKER**, ch c Havana Gold (IRE)—Belle Allemande (CAN) **Mrs Barbara M Keller & Qatar Racing Ltd**
52 **CONSULTANT**, b g Kodiac—Mary Goodnight **Highclere Thoroughbred Racing-Ennis Hill**
53 **CROSSING THE LINE**, b f Cape Cross (IRE)—Terentia **Sheikh J. D. Al Maktoum**
54 **DANZAN (IRE)**, b c Lawman (FR)—Charanga **Mr B. Greenwood/Mr R. Homburg & Partner**
55 **DAWN DANCER**, b c Dawn Approach (IRE)—Ballet Ballon (USA) **Castle Down Racing**
56 **DELIVERANCE**, b c Havana Gold (IRE)—Tentpole (USA) **Qatar Racing Limited**
57 **DIOCLETIAN (IRE)**, b c Camelot—Saturday Girl **Mr R. J. C. Wilmot-Smith**
58 **DIXIELAND DIVA (USA)**, b f Cape Blanco (IRE)—Winnie Dixie (USA) **Mrs F. H. Hay**

MR ANDREW BALDING - Continued

59 **DREAM CATCHING (IRE)**, b g Dream Ahead (USA)—Selfara **Mr M Payton & Mr A M Balding**
60 **DURATION (IRE)**, b g Champs Elysees—Fringe **Mr A. M. Balding**
61 **ENSIGN EWART**, ch g Lope de Vega (IRE)—Caerlonore (IRE) **Mrs F. H. Hay**
62 **ESSENDON (FR)**, b g Aussie Rules (USA)—Inhibition **Kingsclere Racing Club**
63 **FACE LIKE THUNDER**, b g Passing Glance—Violet's Walk **Mrs C. J. Wates**
64 **FLINTROCK (GER)**, b c Sinndar (IRE)—Four Roses (IRE) **Mr G. C. B. Brook**
65 **FORTUNE'S PEARL (IRE)**, ch c Harbour Watch (IRE)—Princess Mood (GER) **Qatar Racing Limited**
66 **FOX MAFIA (IRE)**, b c Dawn Approach (IRE)—Zibiline **King Power Racing Co Ltd**
67 **FOXTROT LADY**, ch f Foxwedge (AUS)—Strictly Dancing (IRE) **J. C. Smith**
68 **GOLDEN SALUTE (IRE)**, b f Acclamation—Golden Shadow (IRE) **The Hot To Trot Syndicate-Golden Salute**
69 **GREAT SHOT SAM (USA)**, ch f Shackleford (USA)—Universal Peace (JPN) **Mr L. L. Register**
70 **ICONIC GIRL**, b f Cape Cross (IRE)—Snoqualmie Star **J. C. Smith**
71 **KABRIT (IRE)**, ch c Mastercraftsman (IRE)—Twinkling Ice (USA) **Mrs F. H. Hay**
72 **KING AND EMPIRE (IRE)**, b c Intello (GER)—Fraloga (IRE) **Qatar Racing Limited**
73 **KING LUD**, b c Cape Cross (IRE)—Natural Flair (USA) **Mick and Janice Mariscotti**
74 **LOPITO**, b c Lope de Vega (IRE)—Stellar Brilliant (USA) **Thurloe Thoroughbreds XLII**
75 **LORD VETINARI**, br g Lethal Force (IRE)—Princess Luna (GER) **Mick and Janice Mariscotti**
76 **LUNA ECLIPSE (IRE)**, b c Bahamian Bounty—Luna Forest (IRE) **Sheikh J. D. Al Maktoum**
77 **MACAQUE (IRE)**, b g Rock of Gibraltar (IRE)—Spiliada (FR) **Pink Hat Racing Partnership & Partner**
78 **MAID UP**, gr f Mastercraftsman (IRE)—Complexion **Brightwalton Bloodstock Limited**
79 **MASTER OF WINE (GER)**, b g Maxios—Magma (GER) **Another Bottle Racing 2**
80 **MERCURY RISING**, b c Henrythenavigator (USA)—Millistar **Qatar Racing Limited**
81 **MINUTE MILE (IRE)**, ch f Tamayuz—Moonlight Wish (IRE)
82 **MUST BE MAGIC (IRE)**, b f Camelot—Saturn Girl (IRE) **M. Tabor**
83 **NATURAL HISTORY**, b c Nathaniel (IRE)—Film Script **Her Majesty The Queen**
84 **OCALA**, ch f Nathaniel (IRE)—Night Carnation **G. Strawbridge**
85 **OENOPHILE (GER)**, b f Mamool (IRE)—Ormita (GER) **Another Bottle Racing 2**
86 **PAK CHOI**, ch c Paco Boy (IRE)—Spring Green **Highclere T'bred Racing-Edward Bevan**
87 **PAPA STOUR (USA)**, b c Scat Daddy (USA)—Illaunglass (IRE) **Chasemore Farm LLP**
88 **PERFECT ILLUSION**, b c Nathaniel (IRE)—Chicita Banana **Mr & Mrs R Gorell/N Botica & Partner**
89 **PILGRIM SOUL**, b f Yeats (IRE)—Sabah **R. J. Buckley & Mr T. Shields**
90 **PRIVATE CASHIER**, b f Leroidesanimaux (BRZ)—Vicksburg **Mr R. J. C. Wilmot-Smith**
91 **REBEL STREAK**, b g Dark Angel (IRE)—Siren's Gift **J. C. Smith**
92 **RECULVER (IRE)**, b g Tagula (IRE)—Lady Kildare (IRE) **Martin & Valerie Slade & Partner**
93 **RUX RUXX (IRE)**, b f Dark Angel (IRE)—Lady Duxyana **King Power Racing Ltd**
94 **SEASEARCH**, b g Passing Glance—Seaflower Reef (IRE) **Kingsclere Racing Club**
95 **SHAILENE (IRE)**, ch f Rip Van Winkle (IRE)—Snow Key (USA) **G. Strawbridge**
96 **SILVER SWIFT**, b f Dutch Art—Silver Kestrel (USA) **Susanne & Jeffrey Nedas**
97 **SOLDIER TO FOLLOW**, b c Soldier Hollow—Nota Bene (GER) **James/Michaelson/Greenwood 1**
98 **SOVRANO**, ch c Leroidesanimaux (BRZ)—Alchemilla **Mick and Janice Mariscotti**
99 **SWEET LADY ROSE (IRE)**, ch f Shamardal (USA)—Sweet Rose **Sheikh J. D. Al Maktoum**
100 **UNBRIDLED SPIRIT**, b g Passing Glance—Sweet Mandolin **J. C. & S. R. Hitchins**
101 **UNTIL AGAIN**, b f Iffraaj—Sara Lucille **G. Strawbridge**
102 **URBAN ASPECT**, b c Cityscape—Casual Glance **Kingsclere Racing Club**
103 **WHITE TURF (IRE)**, gr g Clodovil (IRE)—Holda (USA) **Kennet Valley Thoroughbreds IV**
104 **YOUNG BERNIE**, b g Sixties Icon—Hot Pursuits **Mr B McGuire & Partner**
105 **ZATORIUS (GER)**, b g Pastorius (GER)—Zarah Top (GER) **Mr G Rafferty & Partner**

TWO-YEAR-OLDS

106 **AGENT BASTERFIELD (IRE)**, b c 14/2 Raven's Pass (USA)—Maridiyna (IRE) (Sinndar (IRE)) (35000) **Mr P Fox**
107 **ALDENTE**, gr f 24/2 Archipenko (USA)—Albacocca (With Approval (CAN)) **Ms K Rausing**
108 **ANGRY SILENCE (FR)**, ch c 11/2 Le Havre (IRE)—
                                         Altamira (Peintre Celebre (USA)) (325000) **King Power Racing Ltd**
109 B c 12/2 Charm Spirit (IRE)—Averami (Averti (IRE)) **Kingsclere Racing Club**
110 **BANGKOK (IRE)**, b c 27/4 Australia—Tanaghum (Darshaan) (500000) **King Power Racing Ltd**
111 **BAROSSA RED (IRE)**, ch c 2/3 Tamayuz—
                       I Hearyou Knocking (IRE) (Danehill Dancer (IRE)) (34285) **Kingsclere Training Stables**
112 **BLOOD EAGLE (IRE)**, b c 6/4 Sea The Stars (IRE)—
                          Directa Princess (GER) (Dubai Destination (USA)) (100000) **Mrs F Hay**
113 B c 17/3 Paco Boy (IRE)—Caerlonore (IRE) (Traditionally (USA)) (7326) **Park House Partnership**
114 B f 28/4 Nayef (USA)—Casual Glance (Sinndar (IRE)) **Kingsclere Racing Club**
115 **CHIL CHIL**, b f 5/2 Exceed And Excel (AUS)—Tiana (Diktat) (500000) **King Power Racing Ltd**
116 **COMPASS**, b f 9/2 Henrythenavigator (USA)—Medley (Danehill Dancer (IRE)) **Her Majesty The Queen**
117 B c 24/2 Alhebayeb (IRE)—Crown Light (Zamindar (USA)) (120000) **Mr R Gorell**
118 B f 27/1 Havana Gold (IRE)—Dark Reckoning (Equiano (FR)) **Qatar Racing Ltd**

MR ANDREW BALDING - Continued

119 **DASHING WILLOUGHBY,** b c 28/4 Nathaniel (IRE)—
Miss Dashwood (Dylan Thomas (IRE)) (70000) **Mick & Janice Mariscotti**
120 **DISCO DORIS,** b f 2/4 Poet's Voice—Discophilia (Teofilo (IRE)) (26000) **Mrs P. Veenbaas**
121 **DOUNE CASTLE,** b c 15/2 Camelot—Ape Attack (Nayef (USA)) (82000) **Mick & Janice Mariscotti**
122 **DUDLEY'S BOY,** b c 22/2 Passing Glance—Lizzie Tudor (Tamayuz) **Ms K Gough**
123 **DUTCH TREAT,** ch f 26/1 Dutch Art—Syann (IRE) (Daylami (IRE)) (40000) **Mildmay Racing & D. H. Caslon**
124 B br c 3/3 Sea The Stars (IRE)—Evensong (GER) (Waky Nao) (105820) **Mrs F Hay**
125 **FORSETI,** b c 23/1 Charm Spirit (IRE)—Ravensburg (Raven's Pass (USA)) (60000) **Mick & Janice Mariscotti**
126 **FOX CHAIRMAN (IRE),** b c 17/2 Kingman—Starfish (IRE) (Galileo (IRE)) (450000) **King Power Racing Ltd**
127 **FOX LEICESTER (IRE),** gr c 24/4 Dark Angel (IRE)—
Pop Art (IRE) (Excellent Art) (252340) **King Power Racing Ltd**
128 **FOX PREMIER (IRE),** b c 17/3 Frankel—Fann (USA) (Diesis) (700000) **King Power Racing Ltd**
129 **FOX SHINJI,** b c 3/2 Iffraaj—Keene Dancer (Danehill Dancer (IRE)) (210000) **King Power Racing Ltd**
130 **FOX TAL,** b c 21/3 Sea The Stars (IRE)—
Maskunah (IRE) (Sadler's Wells (USA)) (475000) **King Power Racing Ltd**
131 **FOX WIN WIN (IRE),** ch c 3/3 Lope de Vega (IRE)—
What A Picture (FR) (Peintre Celebre (USA)) (320000) **King Power Racing Ltd**
132 **GOOD BIRTHDAY (IRE),** b c 4/4 Dabirsim (FR)—
Chica Loca (FR) (American Post) (407000) **King Power Racing Ltd**
133 **HAPPY POWER (IRE),** gr c 19/1 Dark Angel (IRE)—
Tamarisk (GER) (Selkirk (USA)) (625000) **King Power Racing Ltd**
134 **HAT YAI (IRE),** b c 17/2 Garswood—Takizada (IRE) (Sendawar (IRE)) (40700) **King Power Racing Ltd**
135 **HAVANA ROCKET (IRE),** b c 5/4 Havana Gold (IRE)—Mawaakeb (USA) (Diesis) (32560) **Rocket Racing**
136 **HERO HERO (IRE),** br c 29/2 No Nay Never (USA)—Fancy (IRE) (Galileo (IRE)) (264550) **King Power Racing Ltd**
137 Ch f 7/3 Mastercraftsman (IRE)—Impressionist Art (USA) (Giant's Causeway (USA)) **Mrs F Hay**
138 B f 22/4 Sinndar (IRE)—Inhibition (Nayef (USA)) **Kingsclere Racing Club**
139 **JOHNNY KIDD,** ch c 17/4 Australia—Sabreon (Caerleon (USA)) (75000) **Chelsea Thoroughbreds**
140 **KING POWER,** ch c f 20/3 Frankel—Prowess (IRE) (Peintre Celebre (USA)) (2500000) **King Power Racing Ltd**
141 Ch f 10/4 Intello (GER)—Lady Brora (Dashing Blade) **Kingsclere Racing Club**
142 **LANDA BEACH,** b c 8/3 Teofilo (IRE)—Jameela's Dream (Nayef (USA)) (26048) **Mr P Fox**
143 **LARIAT,** ch c 14/4 Poet's Voice—Lasso (Indian Ridge) (24420) **Mick & Janice Mariscotti**
144 **LAURAS LEGACY,** b f 12/3 Passing Glance—Rebecca Romero (Exceed And Excel (AUS)) **Kingsclere Racing Club**
145 **LE DON DE VIE,** b c 5/4 Leroidesanimaux (BRZ)—Leaderene (Selkirk (USA)) (50000) **Mick & Janice Mariscotti**
146 B c 24/4 Kingman—Liberally (IRE) (Statue of Liberty (USA)) (195360) **Mrs F Hay**
147 B c 11/3 Mastercraftsman (IRE)—Madonna Dell'orto (Montjeu (IRE)) (81400) **Mr D Brownlow**
148 B f 23/1 Phoenix Reach (IRE)—Marajuana (Robellino (USA)) **Kingsclere Racing Club**
149 Ch f 4/5 Casamento (IRE)—Money Spider (IRE) (Danehill Dancer (IRE)) (4761) **Park House Partnership**
150 B c 15/2 Invincible Spirit (IRE)—Mousse Au Chocolat (USA) (Hennessy (USA)) **Mr J C Smith**
151 **MUCHO TALENTO,** b c 10/5 Intello (GER)—Moiava (FR) (Bering) (65120) **Transatlantic Racing**
152 **MUNSTEAD MOONSHINE,** ch f 13/5 Sir Percy—Royal Patron (Royal Academy (USA)) **Lady Gillian Brunton**
153 **NEVER DO NOTHING (IRE),** b c 29/4 Casamento (IRE)—
Purple Tigress (Dubai Destination (USA)) (7326) **Mr A Brooke Rankin**
154 Br f 28/2 Passing Glance—Oasis Spirit (Oasis Dream) (857) **Kingsclere Racing Club**
155 **OLOROSO (IRE),** ch c 30/4 Fast Company (IRE)—
Convidada (IRE) (Trans Island) (27000) **Mr J C Smith**
156 Ch f 2/2 Dubawi (IRE)—Opera Gal (IRE) (Galileo (IRE)) **Mr J C Smith**
157 B f 5/4 Teofilo (IRE)—Opinionated (IRE) (Dubai Destination (USA)) (48840) **Mr N Watts & Mr D Powell**
158 **PARADISE BOY,** b c 18/3 Mamool (IRE)—Palace Secret (GER) (Big Shuffle (USA)) (7733) **Gerry & April Rafferty**
159 **PATTAYA,** b f 30/1 Poet's Voice—Talampaya (USA) (Elusive Quality (USA)) (375000) **King Power Racing Ltd**
160 Ch f 10/3 Lope de Vega (IRE)—Penelope Star (GER) (Acatenango (GER)) (48840) **Thurloe Thoroughbreds XLV**
161 B c 17/3 Dansili—Pink Damsel (IRE) (Galileo (IRE)) **Mrs F. Hay**
162 B f 27/3 Iffraaj—Pink Flames (IRE) (Redback) (65120) **Qatar Racing Ltd**
163 Ch c 2/2 Fast Company (IRE)—Portico (Pivotal) (29304) **Kennet Valley Thoroughbreds**
164 Ch c 18/3 Compton Place—Private Equity (IRE) (Haafhd) (19047) **Park House Partnership**
165 **QUEEN'S SOLDIER (GER),** b c 2/3 Soldier Hollow—
Queen Mum (GER) (Manduro (GER)) (15466) **Martin & Valerie Slade**
166 **RUX POWER,** b f 5/2 Kingman—Cut Short (USA) (Diesis) (550000) **King Power Racing Ltd**
167 B c 15/2 Camelot—Saphira's Fire (IRE) (Cape Cross (IRE)) (100000) **Sheikh Juma Dalmook Al Maktoum**
168 **SAWASDEE (IRE),** br c 20/3 Shamardal (USA)—Beneventa (Most Welcome) (264550) **King Power Racing Ltd**
169 B c 22/3 Archipenko (USA)—Seaflower Reef (IRE) (Robellino (USA)) **Kingsclere Racing Club**
170 **SEEUSOON (IRE),** b c 27/4 Sea The Moon (GER)—Village Fete (Singspiel (IRE)) (48840) **Mr P H Betts**
171 Ch f 12/4 Mastercraftsman (IRE)—Snoqualmie Star (Galileo (IRE)) **Mr J C Smith**
172 Ch f 10/2 Norse Dancer (IRE)—Strictly Dancing (IRE) (Danehill Dancer (IRE)) **Mr J C Smith**
173 B f 13/4 Dunaden (FR)—Sweet Mandolin (Soviet Star (USA)) **J. C. & S. R. Hitchins**

MR ANDREW BALDING - Continued

174 **TIPPY TIPPY (FR)**, b f 1/5 Sea The Stars (IRE)—
    Peinture Rose (USA) (Storm Cat (USA)) (725000) **King Power Racing Ltd**
175 **TOP FOX**, b c 8/3 Frankel—Lady Linda (USA) (Torrential (USA)) (550000) **King Power Racing Ltd**
176 **TUK POWER**, b f 30/1 Dubawi (IRE)—Soon (IRE) (Galileo (IRE)) (1300000) **King Power Racing Ltd**
177 Ch f 31/1 Iffraaj—Vakiyla (FR) (Galileo (IRE)) **Mrs M. E. Wates**
178 B f 15/1 Charm Spirit (IRE)—Valonia (Three Valleys (USA)) **Qatar Racing Ltd**
179 Br f 28/1 Kodiac—Ventura Mist (Pastoral Pursuits) (120000) **Sheikh Juma Dalmook Al Maktoum**
180 B c 5/4 Dunaden (FR)—Victoria Montoya (High Chaparral (IRE)) **Kingsclere Racing Club**
181 B c 14/4 Lope de Vega (IRE)—Victrix Ludorum (IRE) (Invincible Spirit (IRE)) **Qatar Racing Ltd**
182 Ch f 13/2 Dunaden (FR)—Volkovkha (Holy Roman Emperor (IRE)) **Pearl Bloodstock**
183 Gr c 12/3 Reliable Man—Why Worry (FR) (Cadeaux Genereux) (21164)
184 **YELLOW LABEL (USA)**, br c 25/4 Hat Trick (JPN)—Kazam (USA) (Dynaformer (USA)) **Mr L L Register**
185 B c 27/2 War Command (USA)—Zeyran (IRE) (Galileo (IRE)) (30476) **Mr D. Brownlow**

Other Owners: Mr Tony Anderson, Mrs I. A. Balding, Mr A. M. Balding, Mr I. A. Balding, Mr A. Black, Mrs J. E. Black, Mr N. Botica, Mr Peter Box, Mr John Bridgman, Sir Roger Buckley, His Honour Judge J. R. Carey, Mr D. H. Caslon, Chelsea Thoroughbreds Ltd, Mr Carl Conroy, Mrs G. Cullen, Mr Peter Done, Dr Bridget Drew & Partners, Miss Pippa Drew, Dr Bridget Drew, Mr N. R. R. Drew, Mrs H. S. Ellingsen, Mr R. A. Farmiloe, Mr P. E. Felton, Sir Alex Ferguson, Mr S. G. Friend, Mr R. Gorell, Mrs W. Gorell, Mr B. Greenwood, Dr E. Harris, Mr N. G. R. Harris, Mr D. A. Hazell, Mr R. R. Hetherington, Highclere Nominated Partner Limited, Highclere Thoroughbred Racing Ltd, Mr S. Hill, Mr S. R. Hitchins, Mr J. C. Hitchins, Lady Hobhouse, Sir C. J. S. Hobhouse, Mr Roy Homburg, Mr R. S. Hoskins, Mr O. J. R. Ireland, Ms Kate James, Mrs Barbara M. Keller, Mr Luke Lillingston, Mrs Julia Lukas, Mr J. Maldonado, Mrs Janice Mariscotti, Mr Mick Mariscotti, Mr Ged Mason, Mr B. P. McGuire, Mr R. P. B. Michaelson, Mildmay Racing, Mrs Terry Miller, Mrs Susanne Nedas, Mr Jeffrey Nedas, Mr O. J. W. Pawle, Mr Michael Payton, Mr David F. Powell, Qatar Racing Limited, Mr Gerry Rafferty, Mr N. J. F. Robinson, Mr Thomas Shields, Mr D. M. Slade, Mrs V. J. M. Slade, Mr M. Smith (Leicester), Mr J. A. B. Stafford, The Hot To Trot Syndicate, Ms Linda Thompson, Mr M. Weinfeld, Mr Tim Wixted.

Assistant Trainer: Nigel Walker

Jockey (flat): Liam Keniry, David Probert, Rob Hornby, Oisin Murphy. **Apprentice:** Josh Bryan, William Carver, William Cox, Kayleigh Stephens, Jason Watson. **Amateur:** Mr Callum McBride, Mr Jamie Neild.

---

18   MR JOHN BALDING, Doncaster
Postal: **Mayflower Stables, Saracens Lane, Scrooby, Doncaster, South Yorkshire, DN10 6AS**
Contacts: **HOME (01302) 710096 FAX (01302) 710096 MOBILE (07816) 612631**
E-MAIL j.balding@btconnect.com

1 **FORTINBRASS (IRE)**, 8, b g Baltic King—Greta d'argent (IRE) **Mr W. Herring**
2 **GETTIN' LUCKY**, 5, ch g Bertolini (USA)—Loose Caboose (IRE) **Timms, Timms, Baker & McCabe**
3 **GLORIUX**, 4, b g Exceed And Excel (AUS)—Najraan **Bichan Brown Firth Shepherd**
4 **MY GIRL JO (FR)**, 6, b m Whipper (USA)—Prairie Moon **Mr J. Balding**
5 **ORIENTAL RELATION (IRE)**, 7, gr g Tagula (IRE)—Rofan **Neil Grantham & David Bichan**
6 **POINT NORTH (IRE)**, 11, b g Danehill Dancer (IRE)—Briolette (IRE) **Mr W. Herring**
7 **RAZIN' HELL**, 7, b g Byron—Loose Caboose (IRE) **Timms, Timms & McCabe**
8 **SHOWBOATING (IRE)**, 10, b g Shamardal (USA)—Sadinga (IRE) **Mr M & Mrs L Cooke & Mr A McCabe**
9 **YOU'RE COOL**, 6, b g Exceed And Excel (AUS)—Ja One (IRE) **Mr D Bichan & Mr F Connor**

THREE-YEAR-OLDS
10 **BISCUIT BILLY**, b g Doncaster Rover (USA)—Enjoyment **Mr A.Timms, M. Timms & A. McCabe**
11 **UNDERCOVER BROTHER**, ch g Captain Gerrard (IRE)—Socceroo **Mr P. Southern**

Other Owners: Mr A. D. Baker, Mr D. Bichan, Mr F. S. Connor, Mr M. Cooke, Mr M. V. Firth, Mr A. J. McCabe, Mr Matthew Timms, Mr A. C. Timms.

Assistant Trainers: Claire Edmunds, Jason Edmunds

Apprentice: Lewis Edmunds.

19 MR JACK BARBER, Crewkerne
Postal: **Higher Peckmoor, Henley, Crewkerne, Somerset, TA18 8FF**
Contacts: PHONE **(01460) 76555** MOBILE **(07904) 185720**
E-MAIL **info@jackbarberracing.co.uk** WEBSITE **www.jackbarberracing.co.uk**

1 AHHA (IRE), 6, b g Milan—Elviria (IRE) **P. K. Barber**
2 AMZAC MAGIC, 6, b g Milan—Queen's Banquet **A. A. Hayward**
3 4, Ch f Doyen (IRE)—Annie May (IRE) **R. Barber**
4 ASK THE WEATHERMAN, 9, b g Tamure (IRE)—Whatagale **Mr David Martin & Mr Paul Barber**
5 ATHREEOTHREE (IRE), 7, b g Presenting—Lucina (GER) **J. M. Dare, T. Hamlin, J. W. Snook**
6 BALLYKNOCK CLOUD (IRE), 7, gr g Cloudings (IRE)—Ballyknock Present (IRE) **Ballyknock Cloud Syndicate**
7 BEYOND SUPREMACY (IRE), 6, ch g Beneficial—Slaney Athlete (IRE) **R. Barber**
8 DARCY WARD (FR), 5, b g Doctor Dino (FR)—Alzasca (FR) **Phil Fry & Charlie Walker**
9 DOCTOR TIGER, 7, b g Dr Massini (IRE)—Run Tiger (IRE) **R. Barrow, S. Maltby & R. Barber**
10 DUNN'S EARTH (FR), 7, gr g Mastercraftsman (IRE)—Prairie Moon **R. Barber**
11 EARTH SPIRIT, 5, b g Black Sam Bellamy (IRE)—Samandara (FR) **Mrs C. E. Penny**
12 EARTH STORM (IRE), 6, b g Getaway (GER)—Aguida (FR) **R. M. Penny**
13 GULSHANIGANS, 6, b g Sakhee (USA)—Gulshan **Barber, French, Newton & Wright**
14 JIMAL MAGIC (FR), 4, b g Irish Wells (FR)—Night Cire (FR) **Fry,Gale,Hayward, O'Gorman & Walker**
15 KING CALVIN (FR), 6, b g King's Theatre (IRE)—Lerichi (IRE) **P. L. Hart**
16 L'CHAMISE, 5, b m Apple Tree (FR)—Colline de Fleurs **DASH Racing**
17 MOVIE THEATRE, 6, b g Multiplex—Tintera (IRE) **Mr J. Barber**
18 POSH TOTTY, 11, ch m Midnight Legend—Well Bred **Barber, Hall, James & Slocombe**
19 REDMOND (IRE), 8, b g Tikkanen (USA)—Medal Quest (FR) **Walters, Bennett, Martin & Higgs**
20 ROXY BELLE, 8, b m Black Sam Bellamy (IRE)—Royal Roxy (IRE) **Mr J. Barber**
21 SHINTORI (FR), 6, b g Enrique—La Masai (FR) **Mrs R. E. Vicary**
22 SHORELINE (FR), 5, b m Coastal Path—Bahamas (FR) **Paul Nicholls & Jack Barber**
23 SMART BOY (IRE), 7, b g Mahler—Supreme Style (IRE) **P. Barfoot, A. Cooper, Webber & Greenway**
24 VARDS, 8, b g Tamure (IRE)—Bank On Lady **R. Barber**

Other Owners: Mr J. J. Barber, Mr P. C. Barfoot, Mr R. K. W. Barrow, Mr D. Bear, Mr D. Bennett, Mr S. M. Couling, Mr J. M. Dare, R. P. Fry, T. Hamlin, Mrs S. J. Higgs, Mrs S. J. Maltby, Mrs G. R. Martin, Mr D. J. Martin, P. F. Nicholls, J. W. Snook, C. C. Walker, Mr P. E. Walters.

20 MRS TRACEY BARFOOT-SAUNT, Wotton-under-Edge
Postal: **Cosy Farm, Huntingford, Charfield, Wotton-under-Edge, Gloucestershire, GL12 8EY**
Contacts: PHONE **(01453) 520312** FAX **(01453) 520312** MOBILE **(07976) 360626**

1 DODDINGTON DI, 6, b g Sulamani (IRE)—Maxilla (IRE) **A Good Days Racing**
2 12, B g Old Leighlin VII—Executive Blue (IRE)
3 HERE COMES MOLLY (IRE), 7, ch m Stowaway—Grange Melody (IRE) **Mrs T. M. Barfoot-Saunt**
4 HOLEINTHEWALL BAR (IRE), 10, b g Westerner—Cockpit Lady (IRE) **BS Racing**
5 LAUGHING MUSKETEER (IRE), 7, b g Azamour (IRE)—Sweet Clover **A Good Days Racing**
6 LET'S SWAY, 4, b f Authorized (IRE)—Let's Dance (IRE) **P. J. Ponting**
7 R BREN (IRE), 5, b m Curtain Time (IRE)—Bramblehill Dream **P. J. Ponting**

Other Owners: Mr G. C. Barfoot-Saunt.

21 MR MAURICE BARNES, Brampton
Postal: **Tarnside, Farlam, Brampton, Cumbria, CA8 1LA**
Contacts: PHONE/FAX **(01697) 746675** MOBILE **(07760) 433191**
E-MAIL **anne.barnes1@btinternet.com**

1 APACHE PILOT, 10, br g Indian Danehill (IRE)—Anniejo **Mr M. A. Barnes**
2 BAFANA BLUE, 7, b g Blueprint (IRE)—Anniejo **Mr M. A. Barnes**
3 BARNEY'S CAULKER, 7, b g Captain Gerrard (IRE)—Little Cascade **Mr M. A. Barnes**
4 CARRIGDHOUN (IRE), 13, gr g Goldmark (USA)—Pet Tomjammar (IRE) **Mr M. A. Barnes**
5 DESERT ISLAND DUSK, 7, b g Superior Premium—Desert Island Disc **Miss A. P. Lee**
6 FARLAM KING, 5, b g Crosspeace (IRE)—Second Bite **Mr M. A. Barnes**
7 FAROCCO (GER), 5, b g Shirocco (GER)—Fantasmatic (GER) **Miss A. P. Lee**
8 FLYING JACK, 8, b g Rob Roy (USA)—Milladella (FR) **The 3 Whisperers**
9 HOPE FOR GLORY, 9, b g Proclamation (IRE)—Aissa **Mr M. A. Barnes**
10 INDIAN VOYAGE (IRE), 10, b g Indian Haven—Voyage of Dreams (USA) **Mr D Carr & Mr M Carlyle**

MR MAURICE BARNES - Continued

11 **JOVIAL JOEY (IRE)**, 7, b g St Jovite (USA)—Like A Bird (IRE) **The Edinburgh Woollen Mill Ltd**
12 **KNOCKOURA (IRE)**, 6, b g Westerner—Lisselton Thatch (IRE) **The Edinburgh Woollen Mill Ltd**
13 **LADY SAMBACK**, 6, ch m Black Sam Bellamy (IRE)—Bob Back's Lady (IRE) **J. R. Wills**
14 **LOULOUMILLS**, 8, b m Rob Roy (USA)—Etching (USA) **Mr G. R. S. Nixon & Mr M. Barnes**
15 **MY IDEA**, 12, b g Golan (IRE)—Ghana (GER) **Mr M Barnes, Mr Scott Lowther**
16 **NO SUCH NUMBER**, 10, b g King's Best (USA)—Return (USA) **Miss H. M. Crichton**
17 **OISHIN**, 6, b g Paco Boy (IRE)—Roshina (IRE) **Ring Of Fire & Partner**
18 **PLACEDELA CONCORDE**, 5, b g Champs Elysees—Kasakiya (IRE) **Mr M. A. Barnes**
19 **PRINCE FLORBURY**, 5, b g Prince Flori (GER)—Lady Sambury **J. R. Wills**
20 **QUICK BREW**, 10, b g Denounce—Darjeeling (IRE) **The Wizards**
21 **REGARDE MOI**, 10, b g King's Best (USA)—Life At Night (IRE) **Mr M. A. Barnes**
22 **RUSSIAN RASCAL**, 5, b g Kyllachy—Russian Ruby (FR) **Castle Racing & Partner**
23 **SIR TOMMY**, 9, ch g Sir Harry Lewis (USA)—Rose of Overbury **J. R. Wills**
24 **SMART PACO**, 4, ch g Paco Boy (IRE)—La Gifted **Mr M. A. Barnes**
25 **SPINNING SCOOTER**, 8, b g Sleeping Indian—Spinning Coin **Mr M. A. Barnes**
26 **TOP CAT DJ (IRE)**, 10, ch g St Jovite (USA)—Lady Coldunell **Miss A. P. Lee**

Other Owners: Mr J. M. Carlyle, Mr David Carr, Castle Racing, Mr J. G. Graham, Mr Keith Greenwell, Mr Stevan Houliston, Mr S. G. Johnston, Mr Richard Lane, Mr Scott Lowther, Mr Steven Nightingale, Mr G. R. S. Nixon, Mr Nigel North, Ring Of Fire, Mr R. Towler, The Whisperers.

Conditional: Dale Irving.

---

22 MR BRIAN BARR, Sherborne
Postal: **Tall Trees Stud, Longburton, Sherborne, Dorset, DT9 5PH**
Contacts: **PHONE (01963) 210173 MOBILE (07826) 867881**
E-MAIL brianbarrracing@hotmail.com WEBSITE www.brianbarrracing.co.uk
Twitter: @brianbarrracing

1 **ANOMALY**, 9, ch g Pivotal—Anna Palariva (IRE) **Mr J. Barnard**
2 **BLACK ANTHEM (IRE)**, 6, b g Royal Anthem (USA)—
Rockababy (IRE) **The Highly Recommended Partnership 3**
3 **BLAINE**, 8, ch g Avonbridge—Lauren Louise **Mr G. Hitchins**
4 **BOHEMIAN RHAPSODY (IRE)**, 9, b g Galileo (IRE)—Quiet Mouse (USA) **Mr D J Todd**
5 **BYRON BLUE (IRE)**, 9, br g Dylan Thomas (IRE)—High Society (IRE) **Mr G. J. Singh & Mr Dil Singh Rathore**
6 **CHESTNUT STORM (IRE)**, 5, ch m Rip Van Winkle (IRE)—Always Attractive (IRE) **Miss D. Hitchins**
7 **CIVITESSES (FR)**, 6, b m Prince Kirk (FR)—Glenn Rose (FR) **Mr G. J. Singh & Mr Dil Singh Rathore**
8 **CLEARLY CAPABLE (IRE)**, 9, b g Bienamado (USA)—Spout Road (IRE) **Mr G. Hitchins**
9 **GREENVIEW PARADISE (IRE)**, 4, gr f Exchange Rate (USA)—Senza Rete (IRE) **Mr J. Barnard**
10 **HEAD SPACE (IRE)**, 10, b g Invincible Spirit (IRE)—Danzelline **Miss D. Hitchins**
11 **IDYLLIC (IRE)**, 5, b m Rip Van Winkle (IRE)—Cilium (IRE) **Inspire Racing Club Ltd**
12 **IOWEU**, 5, b m Cockney Rebel (IRE)—Doliouchka (IRE) **Mr G. Hitchins**
13 **MACHIATO (IRE)**, 7, b g Milan—Wychnor Dawn (IRE) **Inspire Racing Club Ltd**
14 **MIGHTY MISSILE (IRE)**, 7, ch g Majestic Missile (IRE)—Magdalene (FR) **Daisy Hitchins & Neil Budden**
15 **MOWHOOB**, 8, b g Medicean—Pappas Ruby (USA) **Miss D. Hitchins & Dayna Walsh**
16 **NANNY MAKFI**, 5, b m Makfi—Pan Galactic (USA) **Mr Chris Clark**
17 **ROBIN DE BROOME (IRE)**, 6, b g Robin des Pres (FR)—Croghan Lass (IRE) **Inspire Racing Club Ltd**
18 **ROCKET RONNIE (IRE)**, 8, b g Antonius Pius (USA)—Ctesiphon (USA) **Brian Barr Racing Club**
19 **SHANGHAI SHANE (IRE)**, 4, b g Lord Shanakill (USA)—Lamassu (IRE) **Market Avenue Racing Club Ltd**
20 **SPIKE'S PRINCESS (IRE)**, 4, b f Bushranger (IRE)—Deportment **Inspire Racing Club Ltd**
21 5, B g Fair Mix (IRE)—Tara Gale **Mr Ian Allison**
22 **TARA RIVER (FR)**, 9, b g Stormy River (FR)—Tarabela (FR) **Mr G J & Dil Singh**
23 **THEATRE ROYALE**, 6, ch m Sulamani (IRE)—Theatre Belle **Miss D. Hitchins**
24 **TOOLATETODELEGATE**, 4, b f Delegator—Little Caroline (IRE) **Inspire Racing & Partner**
25 **VEAUCE DE SIVOLA (FR)**, 9, b g Assessor (IRE)—
Eva de Chalamont (FR) **Mr G. J. Singh & Mr Dil Singh Rathore**

THREE-YEAR-OLDS

26 **BAYARDS COVE**, b f Harbour Watch (IRE)—Acicula (IRE) **Mr R. Tucker**
27 B f Dragon Pulse (IRE)—Common Rumpus (IRE) **Inspire Racing Club**
28 **CRAZIE MAISIE**, ch f Intikhab (USA)—Maisie's Moon (USA) **Mr R. Tucker**
29 Ch c Pastoral Pursuits—Crossbow **Miss D. Hitchins**
30 **PAS DE BLANC**, b f Major Cadeaux—Mancunian Way **Market Avenue Racing Club Ltd**

MR BRIAN BARR - Continued

TWO-YEAR-OLDS

31 Ch f 21/1 Haatef (USA)—Lahqa (IRE) (Tamayuz) **Inspire Racing Club**
32 B c 28/3 Equiano (FR)—Midnight Flower (IRE) (Haafhd) (14000) **Mr R. Tucker**

Other Owners: Mr Neil Budden, Miss Daisy Hitchins, Mrs Katrina Hitchins, Recommended Freight Ltd, Mr G. J. Singh, Mr Dil Singh Rathore.

Assistant Trainer: Daisy Hitchins (07975) 754622

Jockey (flat): Hollie Doyle. **Jockey (NH):** Dave Crosse, Tom Garner. **Conditional:** Jonjo O'Neil.
Apprentice: Josh Bryan. **Amateur:** Miss Harriet Godfrey, Mr Charlie Todd.

---

23 **MR RON BARR, Middlesbrough**
Postal: **Carr House Farm, Seamer, Stokesley, Middlesbrough, Cleveland, TS9 5LL**
Contacts: **PHONE (01642) 710687 MOBILE (07711) 895309**
E-MAIL christinebarr1@aol.com

1 A J COOK (IRE), 8, b g Mujadil (USA)—Undertone (IRE) **Mrs V. G. Davies**
2 GRACEFUL ACT, 10, b m Royal Applause—Minnina (IRE) **Mr D. Thomson & Mrs R. E. Barr**
3 MIDNIGHT WARRIOR, 8, b g Teofilo (IRE)—Mauri Moon **Mr K. Trimble**
4 MIGHTASWELLSMILE, 4, b f Elnadim (USA)—Intishaar (IRE) **Mr K. Trimble**
5 MITCHUM, 9, b g Elnadim (USA)—Maid To Matter **R. E. Barr**
6 PRIVATE DANCER, 7, b g Halling (USA)—Anamilina (IRE) **Mrs A. J. Mccubbin**

THREE-YEAR-OLDS

7 GO BANANAS, b f Bahamian Bounty—Ribbon Royale

Other Owners: Mrs R. E. Barr, M. Bell, P. Cartmell, B. Cunningham, J. Earl, Mr D. Thomson.

Assistant Trainer: Mrs C. Barr

Amateur: Miss V. Barr.

---

24 **MR DAVID BARRON, Thirsk**
Postal: **Maunby House, Maunby, Thirsk, North Yorkshire, YO7 4HD**
Contacts: **PHONE (01845) 587435 FAX (01845) 587331**
E-MAIL david.barron@maunbyhouse.com

1 ABOVE THE REST (IRE), 7, b g Excellent Art—Aspasias Tizzy (USA) **L. G. O'Kane**
2 BATTEN THE HATCHES, 4, b g Harbour Watch (IRE)—
Our Little Secret (IRE) **Harrowgate Bloodstock Ltd & Partner**
3 BERTIEWHITTLE, 10, ch g Bahamian Bounty—Minette **JKB Racing & Partners 2**
4 BLACK SALT, 4, b g Equiano (FR)—Marine Girl **All About York II & Partner**
5 BOB MAXWELL (IRE), 4, b g Big Bad Bob (IRE)—
Catching Stars (IRE) **Mr Peter Jones/Harrowgate Bloodstock Ltd**
6 CLON COULIS (IRE), 4, b f Vale of York (IRE)—Cloneden (IRE) **Ms Colette Twomey**
7 DANIELSFLYER (IRE), 4, b g Dandy Man (IRE)—Warm Welcome **Elliott Brothers And Peacock**
8 DIRCHILL (IRE), 4, b g Power—Bawaakeer (USA) **Elliott Brothers & Peacock & Partner**
9 ESPRIT DE CORPS, 4, b g Sepoy (AUS)—Corps de Ballet (IRE) **L. G. O'Kane**
10 FAIRY LOCK (IRE), 4, b f Sir Prancealot (IRE)—Too Close (IRE) **Mr J. Berry & Harrowgate Bloodstock Ltd**
11 FAST TRACK, 7, b g Rail Link—Silca Boo **Mrs S. C. Barron**
12 GLORIOUS POLITICS, 4, b g Delegator—Pelican Key (IRE) **Kangyu International Racing (HK) Limited**
13 GLORIOUS ROCKET, 4, b g Bated Breath—Up And About **Mr J Knotts & Partner**
14 GRANNY ROZ, 4, b f Bahamian Bounty—Hulcote Rose (IRE) **Mr M. J. Rozenbroek**
15 GUNMETAL (IRE), 5, gr g Clodovil (IRE)—March Star (IRE) **L. G. O'Kane**
16 HANDSOME DUDE, 6, b g Showcasing—Dee Dee Girl (IRE) **Mr W D & Mrs D A Glover**
17 KYNREN (IRE), 4, b g Clodovil (IRE)—Art of Gold **Elliott Brothers & Peacock & Partner**
18 LIQUID (IRE), 4, ch g Zoffany (IRE)—Playful Promises (IRE) **Mr R. Hull**
19 MAMA AFRICA (IRE), 4, br f Big Bad Bob (IRE)—
Colourpoint (USA) **Mrm.Rozenbroek/Harrowgatebloodstockltd**
20 MELONADE, 4, b f Mayson—Cambridge Duchess **Theakston Stud Syndicate & Partner**
21 MR COCO BEAN (USA), 4, b g Gio Ponti (USA)—Ing Ing (FR) **Mr S. G. Raines**
22 POET'S REWARD, 4, b g Hellvelyn—Oceanico Dot Com (IRE) **Mrlaurenceo'Kane/Harrowgatebloodstockltd**

MR DAVID BARRON - Continued

23 **QUEEN IN WAITING (IRE)**, 4, gr f Exceed And Excel (AUS)—
                                      Princess Taise (USA) **Mr Laurence O'Kane & Miss N. J. Barron**
24 **ROBBEN RAINBOW**, 4, b g Delegator—Sally Can Wait **Harrowgate Bloodstock Ltd**
25 **ROBOT BOY (IRE)**, 8, ch g Shamardal (USA)—Pivotal's Princess (IRE) **Mr Laurence O'Kane & Paul Murphy**
26 **SCUZEME**, 4, ch g Kheleyf (USA)—Barbieri (IRE) **Mr Laurence O'Kane & Miss N. J. Barron**
27 **SEMANA SANTA**, 5, b m Arabian Gleam—La Zamora **J. G. Brown**
28 **SWIFT EMPEROR (IRE)**, 6, b g Holy Roman Emperor (IRE)—Big Swifty (IRE) **DC Racing Partnership**
29 **THE COMMENDATORE**, 5, b g Starspangledbanner (AUS)—Donna Giovanna **Mr R. Hull**
30 **TWIN APPEAL (IRE)**, 7, b g Oratorio (IRE)—Velvet Appeal (IRE) **Twinacre Nurseries Ltd Partnership**
31 **VENTUROUS (IRE)**, 5, ch g Raven's Pass (USA)—Bold Desire **Mrlaurenceo'Kane/Harrowgatebloodstockltd**
32 **WILLYTHECONQUEROR (IRE)**, 5, b g Kodiac—Jazzie (FR) **L. G. O'Kane**

THREE-YEAR-OLDS

33 **CARPET TIME (IRE)**, b g Intense Focus (USA)—Beal Ban (IRE) **Harrowgate Bloodstock Ltd**
34 **FAKE NEWS**, b g Paco Boy (IRE)—Day Creek **Dr N. J. Barron**
35 **GLORIOUS ECLIPSE**, b g Pastoral Pursuits—First Eclipse (IRE) **Kangyu International Racing (HK) Limited**
36 **HERMANA SANTA (IRE)**, b f Arabian Gleam—La Zamora **J. G. Brown**
37 **HOP MADDOCKS (IRE)**, b c Roderic O'connor (IRE)—Yurituni **Dr N. J. Barron**
38 **JONBOY**, b c Delegator—Cavallo da Corsa **Mr R. Hull**
39 **KODI BEACH**, b g Kodiac—Annie Beach (IRE) **Mrs S. C. Barron**
40 **KRIPKE (IRE)**, b g Fast Company (IRE)—Tranquil Sky **Mrs S. C. Barron**
41 **LADY SANDY (IRE)**, ch f Dandy Man (IRE)—Surf's Up (IRE) **The All About York Partnership**
42 **POET'S PRIDE**, b g Arcano (IRE)—Amber Heights **Mrlaurenceo'Kane/Harrowgatebloodstockltd**
43 **ROYAL RATTLE**, b g Delegator—Rattleyurjewellery **Harrowgate Bloodstock Ltd**
44 **SHANGHAI ELASTIC**, b f Swiss Spirit—Reveille **Harrowgate Bloodstock Ltd & Associate**
45 **TEMBER**, b g Sayif (IRE)—Tranquil Flight **Mrh.D.Atkinson/Harrowgatebloodstockltd**

TWO-YEAR-OLDS

46 Ch g 7/3 Harbour Watch (IRE)—Annie Beach (IRE) (Redback) **Mrs S. C. Barron**
47 B g 9/4 Harbour Watch (IRE)—Curly Come Home (Notnowcato) (7619) **Harrowgate Bloodstock Ltd**
48 **FROSTED LASS**, gr f 17/3 Zebedee—Jofranka (Paris House) **Mrs Anne Atkinson & Partner**
49 Gr c 3/2 Aussie Rules (USA)—Grace Hull (Piccolo) **Mr R. Hull**
50 B f 7/4 Holy Roman Emperor (IRE)—Khobaraa (Invincible Spirit (IRE)) **Mr M. J. Rozenbroek**
51 **OLYMPIC SPIRIT**, ch c 9/2 Olympic Glory (IRE)—Magic Florence (IRE) (Zebedee) (61904) **Mr H. D. Atkinson**
52 B f 1/4 Requinto (IRE)—Personal Design (IRE) (Traditionally (USA)) (4069) **D G Pryde & D Van Der Hoeven**
53 B f 1/2 Gregorian (IRE)—Resist (Rock of Gibraltar (IRE)) (761) **Harrowgate Bloodstock Ltd**
54 Ch f 27/1 Excelebration (IRE)—Rozene (IRE) (Sleeping Indian) **Mr M. J. Rozenbroek**
55 B f 12/4 Holy Roman Emperor (IRE)—Shamrock Lady (IRE) (Orpen (USA)) **Mr M. J. Rozenbroek**
56 B f 13/2 Mayson—Shannon Spree (Royal Applause) (15000) **Harrowgate Bloodstock Ltd**
57 Ch c 26/3 Cityscape—Sorcellerie (Sir Percy) (9523) **Harrowgate Bloodstock Ltd**
58 B g 1/2 Zebedee—Zakyah (Exceed And Excel (AUS)) (10476) **Harrowgate Bloodstock Ltd**

Other Owners: All About York II, Mrs A. Atkinson, J. Berry, Mr C. Blaymire, R. J. Cornelius, J. M. Elliott, C. R. Elliott, Mr D. B. Ellis, Mr W. D. Glover, Mrs D. A. Glover, Mrs C. S. Greensit, C. J. Harper, Mrs J. Ingham, Mr G. M. C. Johnson, Peter Jones, Mr J. Knotts, Mr A. McIntyre, Mr P. A. Murphy, D. G. Pryde, Twinacre Nurseries Ltd, Mr J. Wells, Mr D. P. van der Hoeven.

Assistant Trainer: Nicola-Jo Barron

25
MR P. BARY, Chantilly
Postal: **5 Chemin des Aigles, 60500 Chantilly, France**
Contacts: **PHONE (0033) 3445 71403 FAX (0033) 3446 72015 MOBILE (0033) 6075 80241**
E-MAIL **p-bary@orange.fr**

1 **GOLD VIBE (IRE)**, 5, ch h Dream Ahead (USA)—Whisper Dance (USA) **Sutong Pan**
2 **ICE BREEZE**, 4, b c Nayef (USA)—Winter Silence **K. Abdullah**
3 **RATIOCINATION (IRE)**, 4, b c Excelebration (IRE)—Denebola (USA) **Flaxman Stables Ireland Ltd**
4 **SEGRA (USA)**, 4, b f Shamardal (USA)—Sarah Lynx (IRE) **R. G. Ehrnrooth**
5 **STRIX**, 8, ch h Muhtathir—Serandine (IRE) **Flaxman Stables Ireland Ltd**

THREE-YEAR-OLDS

6 **BELARGUS (FR)**, b c Authorized (IRE)—Belga Wood (USA) **G. Sandor**
7 **BEREA (FR)**, b f Manduro (GER)—Brailovskaya (ITY) **Razza Dormello Olgiata**

MR P. BARY - Continued

8 **BUGLE MAJOR (USA)**, gr ro c Mizzen Mast (USA)—Conference Call **K. Abdullah**
9 **CAPTAIN'S GIRL (FR)**, b f Captain Marvelous (USA)—New Style (GER) **M. Ohana**
10 **COMPATIBLE (USA)**, b f Pleasantly Perfect (USA)—Gateway (USA) **K. Abdullah**
11 **COUPERIN (FR)**, bl c Wootton Bassett—Canzonetta (FR) **G. Sandor**
12 **DIVINE INSPIRATION (USA)**, b f Medaglia d'oro (USA)—Divine Presence (USA) **Flaxman Stables Ireland Ltd**
13 **E SE POI FOSSI (IRE)**, ch f Mastercraftsman (IRE)—Lady Montjeu (IRE) **Esageruma Nein SAS**
14 **FALCONY (FR)**, b c Siyouni (FR)—Azalee (IRE) **Ecurie J. L. Bouchard**
15 **FELLBECK**, b f Cacique (IRE)—Orford Ness **K. Abdullah**
16 **FIRST LINK (USA)**, b br f First Defence (USA)—Unknown **K. Abdullah**
17 **FRANKELIO (FR)**, b c Frankel—Restiadargent (FR) **Hspirit**
18 **GREEN CLOUD (IRE)**, b c Invincible Spirit (IRE)—Extreme Green **Ecurie J. L. Bouchard**
19 **HAUDRICOURT (FR)**, b c Reliable Man—Happy Way (FR) **Franklin Finance SA**
20 **HOURTIN (FR)**, b c Lawman (FR)—Alnamara (FR) **Laghi France**
21 **LENNOX (GER)**, b c Maxios—La Reine Noir (GER) **Flaxman Stables Ireland Ltd**
22 **MAGNET (FR)**, ch c Exceed And Excel (AUS)—Molly Malone (FR) **Hspirit**
23 **MASTER OF REALITY (IRE)**, b c Frankel—L'ancresse (IRE) **Ecurie J. L. Bouchard**
24 **MOUNT POPA (IRE)**, b c Maxios—Mimalia (USA) **Course Investment Corporation**
25 **NATURALLY HIGH (FR)**, b c Camelot—Just Little (FR) **Ecurie J. L. Bouchard**
26 **ORPENA (IRE)**, b f Orpen (USA)—Resquilleuse (USA) **Guy Pariente Holding SPRL**
27 **PALMETTO BAY**, b f Champs Elysees—Palmette **K. Abdullah**
28 **SANSKRIT (IRE)**, ch c Mastercraftsman (IRE)—Satopanth **Course Investment Corporation**
29 **SEIZIEME**, b c Champs Elysees—Affluent **K. Abdullah**
30 **SHAPE THE SKY (FR)**, b f Le Havre—Little Jaw **Ecurie J. L. Bouchard**
31 **SNAKELESS (USA)**, ch f Animal Kingdom (USA)—Gypsy's Warning (SAF) **Flaxman Stables Ireland Ltd**
32 **STUDY OF MAN (IRE)**, b c Deep Impact (JPN)—Second Happiness (USA) **Flaxman Stables Ireland Ltd**
33 **SUBLIMINAL**, b c Arcano (IRE)—Rare Virtue (USA) **K. Abdullah**
34 **SWEETY DREAM**, ch f Dream Ahead (USA)—Excellent Girl **Guy Pariente Holding SPRL**
35 **TESTON (FR)**, ch g Rio de La Plata (USA)—Tianshan (FR) **G. Sandor**
36 **WHAT SHE WANTS (FR)**, b f Siyouni (FR)—Kanala (FR) **Laurence Bary**
37 **YAD (FR)**, b f Makfi—You Don't Love Me (IRE) **Cofinvest**

TWO-YEAR-OLDS

38 **AERONAUTICAL (USA)**, b f 23/4 Medaglia d'oro (USA)—
Witching Hour (FR) (Fairy King (USA)) **Flaxman Stables Ireland Ltd**
39 **AMHARA (USA)**, ch f 9/4 Union Rags (USA)—
Sea of Laughter (USA) (Distorted Humor (USA)) **Flaxman Stables Ireland Ltd**
40 **BERNADINE (FR)**, gr f 18/3 Slickly (FR)—Belga Wood (USA) (Woodman (USA)) **G. Sandor**
41 **BOARDMAN**, b c 28/3 Kingman—Nimble Thimble (USA) (Mizzen Mast (USA)) **K. Abdullah**
42 B c 9/1 Frankel—Body And Soul (IRE) (Captain Rio) **Sutong Pan**
43 Gr f 15/3 Dark Angel (IRE)—Ellasha (Shamardal (USA)) (280000) **Sutong Pan**
44 B c 27/3 Maxios—Game of Legs (FR) (Hernando (FR)) **Course Investment Corporation**
45 **GAZELLE (FR)**, b f 25/1 Siyouni (FR)—Grande Rousse (FR) (Act One) (40700) **Haras du Mezeray**
46 **GLACIATE**, b f 10/3 Kingman—Winter Silence (Dansili) **K. Abdullah**
47 Ch f 21/2 Dragon Pulse (IRE)—Hesperian (IRE) (Iffraaj) (21978)
48 **KENBAIO (FR)**, gr c 26/1 Kendargent (FR)—Baia Chope (FR) (Deportivo) **Guy Pariente Holding SPRL**
49 **KENMORE (FR)**, b c 3/5 Kendargent (FR)—Moranda (FR) (Indian Rocket) (48840) **Laghi France**
50 **KENWINA (FR)**, ch f 5/3 Kendargent (FR)—Ponte Bawi (IRE) (Dubawi (IRE)) (73260) **Guy Pariente Holding SPRL**
51 **LE MONT (FR)**, b c 12/5 Le Havre (IRE)—Miss Bio (FR) (River Mist (USA)) (89540) **Franklin Finance SA**
52 **LUCKY DOE (IRE)**, ch f 6/5 Dawn Approach (IRE)—
Blessed Luck (IRE) (Rock of Gibraltar (IRE)) (17908) **Mr Alaric de Murga SAS**
53 **MAKI**, b f 18/1 Le Havre (IRE)—Scallop (Oasis Dream) **K. Abdullah**
54 **MANDAAR (FR)**, b c 3/3 Canyon Creek (FR)—Madeleine's Blush (Rahy (USA)) **G. Sandor**
55 **MEXAL (FR)**, b f 3/5 Olympic Glory (IRE)—Texaloula (FR) (Kendor (FR)) (34188) **Laghi France**
56 **MONCEAU**, b c 24/3 Dansili—Palmette (Oasis Dream) **K. Abdullah**
57 **MONTABOT (FR)**, b c 18/4 Le Havre (IRE)—Salamon (Montjeu (IRE)) **Franklin Finance SA**
58 **OLENDON (FR)**, b c 16/4 Le Havre (IRE)—Talema (FR) (Sunday Break (JPN)) (52910) **Franklin Finance SA**
59 B f 16/4 Kingman—Our Little Secret (IRE) (Rossini (USA)) (400000) **Sutong Pan**
60 **PRICE RANGE (USA)**, b c 6/2 First Defence (USA)—Price Tag (Dansili) **K. Abdullah**
61 **QUITE RIVER (FR)**, b c 10/2 Dragon Pulse (IRE)—
Late Rosebud (IRE) (Jeremy (USA)) (73260) **Ecurie J. L. Bouchard**
62 **RETHOVILLE (FR)**, b f 9/4 Anodin (FR)—Absolute Lady (FR) (Galileo (IRE)) **Franklin Finance SA**
63 B c 10/5 Galileo (IRE)—Second Happiness (USA) (Storm Cat (USA)) **Flaxman Stables Ireland Ltd**
64 **SILVERY PRINCE (FR)**, b c 17/3 Kendargent (FR)—
Princess Liu (IRE) (Desert Style (IRE)) (30932) **Mr Alaric de Murga SAS**

MR P. BARY - Continued

65 **SOUND OF VICTORY (IRE)**, b c 14/2 Sea The Stars (IRE)—
    Sakarya (IRE) (Duke of Marmalade (IRE)) (97680) **Ecurie J. L. Bouchard**
66 **STORMYZA (FR)**, gr f 23/1 Nathaniel (IRE)—Stormyra (FR) (Stormy River (FR)) **Guy Pariente Holding SPRL**
67 B f 30/4 Olympic Glory (IRE)—Teepee (JPN) (Deep Impact (JPN)) **Course Investment Corporation**
68 **THEMATIC (USA)**, b c 2/3 Noble Mission—Gateway (USA) (A P Indy (USA)) **K. Abdullah**
69 **VADROUILLEUR (FR)**, b c 1/1 Dream Ahead (USA)—Vita (FR) (Elusive City (USA)) (52910) **Laghi France**
70 B f 20/2 Dark Angel (IRE)—Yoga (IRE) (Monsun (GER)) **Course Investment Corporation**

Assistant Trainer: Baratti Mario

Jockey (flat): Vincent Cheminaud, Stephane Pasquier.

---

26 MISS REBECCA BASTIMAN, Wetherby
Postal: **Goosemoor Farm, Warfield Lane, Wetherby, West Yorkshire, LS22 5EU**
Contacts: PHONE (01423) 359783 (01423) 359397 MOBILE (07818) 181313
E-MAIL rebeccabastiman@hotmail.co.uk

1 **BE BOLD**, 6, ch g Assertive—Marysienka **Mr N Barber & Partner**
2 **BERLIOS (IRE)**, 5, b g Excellent Art—Endless Peace (IRE) **Lets Be Lucky Racing 6**
3 **CLERGYMAN**, 6, b g Pastoral Pursuits—Doctor's Note **Mr Colin Dorman & Mr Thomas Dorman**
4 **DONNELLY'S RAINBOW (IRE)**, 5, b g Lilbourne Lad (IRE)—
    Donnelly's Hollow (IRE) **Bastiman, Dorman & Dorman**
5 **EDGAR ALLAN POE (IRE)**, 4, b g Zoffany—Swingsky (IRE) **I B Barker / P Bastiman**
6 **ELERFAAN (IRE)**, 4, b g Shamardal (USA)—Gorband (USA) **Ms M. Austerfield**
7 **FOXY BOY**, 4, ch g Foxwedge (AUS)—Suzy Wong **Grange Park Racing and Partner**
8 **GONE WITH THE WIND (GER)**, 7, b g Dutch Art—Gallivant **Mrs P. Bastiman**
9 **HARBOUR PATROL (IRE)**, 6, b g Acclamation—Tiaou Mad (IRE) **Mrs P. Bastiman**
10 **HAYADH**, 5, gr g Oasis Dream—Warling (IRE) **Miss R. Bastiman**
11 **HITMAN**, 5, b g Canford Cliffs (IRE)—Ballymore Celebre (IRE) **Ms M. Austerfield**
12 **INDIAN CHIEF (IRE)**, 8, b g Montjeu (IRE)—Buck Aspen (USA) **Castle Construction (North East) Ltd**
13 **JACOB'S PILLOW**, 7, b g Oasis Dream—Enticing (IRE) **Miss R. Bastiman**
14 **JAYWALKER (IRE)**, 7, b g Footstepsinthesand—Nipping (IRE) **Ms M. Austerfield**
15 **JOHN CAESAR (IRE)**, 7, b g Bushranger (IRE)—Polish Belle **Mrs K. Hall & Mrs P. Bastiman**
16 **LOGI (IRE)**, 4, b g Kodiac—Feet of Flame (USA) **Let's Be Lucky Racing 11**
17 **MAJESTE (IRE)**, 4, b g Acclamation—Winged Valkyrie (IRE) **Let's Be Lucky Racing & Miss R. Bastiman**
18 **NATAJACK**, 4, ch g Showcasing—Douro **Lets Be Lucky Racing 6**
19 **ROARING FORTIES (IRE)**, 5, b g Invincible Spirit (IRE)—Growling (IRE) **Mrs K Hall & Partner**
20 **ROYAL BRAVE (IRE)**, 7, b g Acclamation—Daqtora **James Edgar & William Donaldson**
21 **SEE VERMONT**, 10, b g Kyllachy—Orange Lily **Mr John Smith & Mrs P. Bastiman**
22 **SINGEUR (IRE)**, 11, b g Chineur (FR)—Singitta **Ms M. Austerfield**
23 **ZESHOV (IRE)**, 7, b g Acclamation—Fathoming (USA) **Mrs P. Bastiman**

THREE-YEAR-OLDS

24 **JIRO BOY**, b g Compton Place—Foolish Lady (IRE) **Miss R. Bastiman**
25 **LEESHAAN (IRE)**, b g Bated Breath—La Grande Elisa (IRE) **Let's Be Lucky Racing & Mrs P. Bastiman**
26 **MILTON ROAD**, b g Mazameer (IRE)—Blakeshall Girl **Mr W. L. Donaldson**
27 **WENSLEY**, b g Poet's Voice—Keladora (USA) **Mr John Smith & Mrs P. Bastiman**
28 **ZUMURUD (IRE)**, gr g Zebedee—Thaisy (USA) **Ms M. Austerfield**

TWO-YEAR-OLDS

29 **SINGMAN (IRE)**, b c 21/4 Dandy Man (IRE)—Singitta (Singspiel (IRE)) **Ms M. Austerfield**
30 Ch f 21/2 Monsieur Bond (IRE)—Smiddy Hill (Factual (USA)) **Mr I. B. Barker**

Other Owners: Mr E. N. Barber, Mr I. B. Barker, Mrs P. Bastiman, Miss Rebecca Bastiman, Mr Alan D. Crombie, Mr William Donaldson, Mr Tommy Dorman, Mr C. Dorman, Mr James Edgar, Mr R. A. Gorrie, Mr S. T. Gorrie, Grange Park Racing, Mrs K. Hall, Mr John Smith, Mr E. Surr.

Assistant Trainer: Harvey Bastiman

Jockey (flat): Danny Tudhope. **Apprentice:** Phil Dennis, Rowan Scott.

27 MR BRIAN BAUGH, Audley

Postal: **Meadow Cottage, 47 Scot Hay Road, Alsagers Bank, Stoke-On-Trent, Staffordshire, ST7 8BW**
Contacts: **PHONE (01782) 706222 MOBILE (07547) 495236**
E-MAIL bpjbaugh@aol.com

1 CAREYANNE, 4, ch f Mount Nelson—Mayaar (USA) **Holmes, Ratcliffe, Meakins, Mr&Mrs Kemp**
2 DAVID'S BEAUTY (IRE), 5, b m Kodiac—Thaisy (USA) **Mr G. B. Hignett**
3 WHISPERING SOUL (IRE), 5, b m Majestic Missile (IRE)—Belle of the Blues (IRE) **Mr G. B. Hignett**

THREE-YEAR-OLDS

4 PADDYWAK, b g Captain Gerrard (IRE)—Shustraya **Mr G. B. Hignett**

Other Owners: Mr S. Holmes, Mr S. D. Kemp, Mrs F. A. Kemp, Mrs B. A. Meakins, Mr G. Ratcliffe.

Assistant Trainer: S Potts

28 MR RALPH BECKETT, Kimpton

Postal: **Kimpton Down Stables, Kimpton, Andover, Hampshire, SP11 8QQ**
Contacts: **PHONE (01264) 772278 MOBILE (07802) 219022**
E-MAIL trainer@rbeckett.com

1 AIR PILOT, 9, b g Zamindar (USA)—Countess Sybil (IRE) **Lady Cobham**
2 ANOTHER BOY, 5, ch g Paco Boy (IRE)—Kurtanella **Mrs Philip Snow & Partners**
3 BATTERED, 4, b g Foxwedge (AUS)—Swan Wings **King Power Racing Co Ltd**
4 BRIYOUNI (FR), 5, b g Siyouni (FR)—Brianza (USA) **Mrs Ralph Beckett**
5 CHEMICAL CHARGE (IRE), 6, ch h Sea The Stars (IRE)—Jakonda (USA) **Qatar Racing Limited**
6 CONSIDERED OPINION, 4, b f Redoute's Choice (AUS)—Forest Crown **The Eclipse Partnership**
7 HERE AND NOW, 4, b g Dansili—Look Here **The Hon R. J. Arculli**
8 ISABEL DE URBINA (IRE), 4, b f Lope de Vega (IRE)—Roscoff (IRE) **Merriebelle Irish Farm Limited**
9 MELODIC MOTION (IRE), 4, b f Nathaniel (IRE)—Quad's Melody (IRE) **Qatar Racing Limited**
10 MISTRESS QUICKLY (IRE), 4, b f Mastercraftsman (IRE)—In My Life (IRE) **Mrs M. E. Slade**
11 MITCHUM SWAGGER, 6, b g Paco Boy (IRE)—Dont Dili Dali **The Anagram Partnership**
12 MOONRISE LANDING (IRE), 7, gr m Dalakhani (IRE)—Celtic Slipper (IRE) **Mr P. D. Savill**
13 MOUNT MORIAH, 4, b g Mount Nelson—Rule Britannia **Mr Norman Brunskill**
14 MOUNTAIN BELL, 5, b m Mount Nelson—Shenir **Qatar Racing Limited**
15 PACIFY, 6, b g Paco Boy (IRE)—Supervea (IRE) **Mr P. D. Savill**
16 STEAMING (IRE), 4, ch g Rail Link—Dazzling Day **GC Hartigan, ADG Oldrey & GHC Wakefield**
17 TAUREAN STAR (IRE), 5, b g Elnadim (USA)—Marhaba **Mr R. A. Pegum**
18 WESTERN DUKE (IRE), 4, b g High Chaparral (IRE)—Witch of Fife (USA) **London City Bloodstock**

THREE-YEAR-OLDS

19 AIRMAX (GER), br c Maxios—Artica (GER) **Mr Norman Brunskill**
20 AKVAVERA, ch f Leroidesanimaux (BRZ)—Akdarena **Miss K. Rausing**
21 ARCADIAN CAT (USA), b f Kitten's Joy (USA)—Calissa (USA) **H.H. Sheikh Mohammed bin Khalifa Al Thani**
22 AUTHENTIC ART, ch g Dutch Art—Tahirah **Thurloe Thoroughbreds XLI**
23 AZPEITIA, ch f Showcasing—Leaves You Baby (IRE) **James Ortega Bloodstock Ltd**
24 BLAZING SADDLES, b c High Chaparral (IRE)—Desert Sage **Mr J. H. Richmond-Watson**
25 BREATH CAUGHT, b c Bated Breath—Double Crossed **Mr K. Abdullah**
26 CECCHINI (IRE), br f Rip Van Winkle (IRE)—Urban Daydream (IRE) **Mr P. D. Savill**
27 CEILIDHS DREAM, b f Oasis Dream—Ceilidh House **Mr J. H. Richmond-Watson**
28 CONSTRUCT, b c Maxios—Airfield **Mr K. Abdullah**
29 CROSS MY MIND (IRE), b f Cape Cross (IRE)—Zaaqya **Kennet Valley Thoroughbreds V**
30 CULDROSE, br f Mastercraftsman (IRE)—At A Clip **Lady Cobham**
31 DAZZLING ROCK (IRE), ch c Rock of Gibraltar (IRE)—
Dazzling Light (UAE) **Carolyn Roberts & Pickford Hill Partnership**
32 DI FEDE (IRE), b f Shamardal (USA)—Dibiya (IRE) **Mr Robert Ng**
33 DIOCLES OF ROME (IRE), b c Holy Roman Emperor (IRE)—Serisia (FR) **Mrs Philip Snow & Partners**
34 EDGE OF THE WORLD (IRE), b f Fastnet Rock (AUS)—Lady Links **Qatar Racing Ltd & Barbara Keller**
35 FONT VERT (FR), b g Sinndar (IRE)—Fontaine Margot (FR) **The Calvera Partnership No. 2**
36 FORCE MAJEURE (IRE), b f Smart Strike (USA)—Forces of Darkness (IRE) **Miss K. Rausing**
37 FRESH TERMS, b f New Approach (IRE)—Best Terms **Mr R. Barnett**
38 GATTAIA (USA), ch f Kitten's Joy (USA)—Shaaraat (USA) **Professor Albert Agro**
39 GILDED HOUR (IRE), b f Bated Breath—Mimisel **Qatar Racing Limited**

MR RALPH BECKETT - Continued

40 **GLORIES (USA)**, b f Galileo (IRE)—Untouched Talent (USA) **Qatar Racing Limited**
41 **GRIPPER**, b g Thewayyouare (USA)—Hold On Tight (IRE) **Kimpton Down Racing Club**
42 **IMPERATRICE (IRE)**, ch f Kitten's Joy (USA)—
        Empress of France (USA) **H.H. Sheikh Mohammed bin Khalifa Al Thani**
43 **ISHALLAK**, b g Cityscape—Shallika (IRE) **D & J Newell**
44 **KINAESTHESIA**, b f Sea The Stars (IRE)—Kinetica **Miss K. Rausing**
45 B g Pour Moi (IRE)—Lupa Montana (USA) **Mr J. L. Rowsell**
46 **MCCOOL (IRE)**, b f Giant's Causeway (USA)—Nobilis **China Horse Club International Limited**
47 **MESQUITE**, b f High Chaparral (IRE)—Puff (IRE) **Mr & Mrs David Aykroyd**
48 **MIGHTY MAC (IRE)**, b g Dragon Pulse (IRE)—Invincible Fire (IRE) **Paul & Clare Rooney**
49 **NEYLAND**, b f Oasis Dream—Milford Sound **Mr K. Abdullah**
50 **NINE BELOW ZERO**, b g Showcasing—Finesse **Mr P. K. Gardner**
51 **OCCUPY (USA)**, b c Declaration of War (USA)—
        Circumstances (USA) **Highclere Thoroughbred Racing-David Weir**
52 **PARISIAN (IRE)**, ch g Champs Elysees—La Persiana **Gillian, Lady Howard de Walden**
53 **PODEMOS (GER)**, b c Shamardal (USA)—Pearls Or Passion (FR) **H.H. Sheikh Mohammed bin Khalifa Al Thani**
54 **POYLE CHARLOTTE**, b f Farhh—Poyle Caitlin (IRE) **Cecil and Miss Alison Wiggins**
55 **PREVENT**, br g Poet's Voice—Emergency **Mr K. Abdullah**
56 **RESPECTABLE**, b f Champs Elysees—Dalandra **Mr W. P. Wyatt**
57 **RICHENZA (FR)**, b f Holy Roman Emperor (IRE)—Nantha (IRE) **Mrs Lynn Turner & Mr Guy Brook**
58 **ROCK EAGLE**, ch g Teofilo (IRE)—Highland Shot **Mr J. C. Smith**
59 **ROSE TINTED SPIRIT**, b c Swiss Spirit—Woolfall Rose **Paul & Clare Rooney**
60 **SECRET GAZE**, b f Galileo (IRE)—Shastye (IRE) **Qatar Racing Ltd & Newsells Park Stud**
61 **SILVER CRESCENT**, b g Champs Elysees—Winter Solstice **Mr K. Abdullah**
62 B c Mastercraftsman (IRE)—Singing Bird (IRE) **Mr Chris McHale**
63 **SMART DART**, b f Mastercraftsman (IRE)—Dark Missile **Mr J. C. Smith**
64 **THIMBLEWEED**, b f Teofilo (IRE)—Prairie Flower (IRE) **Mr J. H. Richmond-Watson**
65 **TIME CHANGE**, ch f Dutch Art—Time Honoured **Mr R. Barnett**
66 **VICTORY CHIME (IRE)**, b g Campanologist (USA)—Patuca **Mr A. Nevin**
67 **WIND STORM**, b f Holy Roman Emperor (IRE)—Imperialistic (IRE) **Clipper Logistics**
68 **ZILARA (IRE)**, b f Big Bad Bob (IRE)—Celtic Slipper (IRE) **Mr P. D. Savill**

TWO-YEAR-OLDS

69 **AL SULTANA**, b f 30/3 Charm Spirit (IRE)—Centime (Royal Applause) (25000) **Mr Ahmad Abdulla Al Shaikh**
70 **ALOE VERA**, b f 2/2 Invincible Spirit (IRE)—Almiranta (Galileo (IRE)) **Miss K. Rausing**
71 **AMAZING FOX (IRE)**, b c 27/2 Aglaam (IRE)—
        Gold Again (USA) (Touch Gold (USA)) (180000) **King Power Racing Co Ltd**
72 **ANTONIA DE VEGA (IRE)**, b f 9/3 Lope de Vega (IRE)—
        Witches Brew (Duke of Marmalade (IRE)) (105820) **Jasros Racing**
73 **ARCADIENNE**, b c 27/1 Leroidesanimaux (BRZ)—Archduchess (Archipenko (USA)) **Miss K. Rausing**
74 **BRASCA**, ch c 19/4 Nathaniel (IRE)—
        Regalline (IRE) (Green Desert (USA)) (60000) **Frank Brady & Brian Scanlon**
75 **BURIRAM (IRE)**, b c 10/2 Reliable Man—
        Wild Step (GER) (Footstepsinthesand) (52910) **King Power Racing Co Ltd**
76 **CABARITA**, ch f 26/3 Leroidesanimaux (BRZ)—Catadupa (Selkirk (USA)) **Miss K. Rausing**
77 Br c 28/2 Mastercraftsman (IRE)—City Girl (IRE) (Elusive City (USA)) **Mr J. C. Smith**
78 B f 15/3 Kodiac—Cruck Realta (Sixties Icon) **Wansdyke Farms Ltd**
79 **DANCING VEGA (IRE)**, ch f 2/4 Lope de Vega (IRE)—
        We Can Say It Now (AUS) (Starcraft (NZ)) (122100) **Jasros Racing**
80 B br f 1/4 Speightstown (USA)—Dansette (Dansili) (240000) **Mr Sutong Pan**
81 **DAVE DEXTER**, b c 29/2 Stimulation (IRE)—
        Blue Crest (FR) (Verglas (IRE)) (32000) **Mrs Philip Snow & Partners I**
82 B c 3/4 Holy Roman Emperor (IRE)—
        Empress of France (USA) (Storm Cat (USA)) **H.H. Sheikh Mohammed bin Khalifa Al Thani**
83 **FELICIANA DE VEGA**, b f 15/2 Lope de Vega (IRE)—
        Along Came Casey (IRE) (Oratorio (IRE)) (69190) **Pearl Bloodstock Ltd**
84 B f 12/4 Dunaden (FR)—Forever Loved (Deploy) **Jasros Racing**
85 **FOX FEARLESS**, b c 3/2 Camelot—
        Silent Music (IRE) (Peintre Celebre (USA)) (160000) **King Power Racing Co Ltd**
86 **FRAGRANT BELLE**, ch f 27/2 Sir Percy—Palace Princess (FR) (Dubawi (IRE)) **Mr Robert Ng**
87 **FUME (IRE)**, b c 30/3 Frankel—Puff (IRE) (Camacho) **Mr & Mrs David Aykroyd**
88 **FUTURE INVESTMENT**, b c 7/5 Mount Nelson—Shenir (Mark of Esteem (IRE)) (45000) **R.N.J. Partnership**
89 **GLANCE**, b f 11/4 Dansili—Look So (Efisio) **Mr J. H. Richmond-Watson**
90 **HEREBY (IRE)**, b f 20/3 Pivotal—Look Here (Hernando (FR)) **Mr J. H. Richmond-Watson**
91 B f 23/4 Camelot—Highland Shot (Selkirk (USA)) **Mr J. C. Smith**

MR RALPH BECKETT - Continued

92 B f 28/3 Delegator—Hobby (Robellino (USA)) **Larksborough Stud**
93 B c 14/2 Sea The Stars (IRE)—Honor Bound (Authorized (IRE)) **H.H. Sheikh Mohammed bin Khalifa Al Thani**
94 Ch c 11/4 Intikhab (USA)—Indolente (IRE) (Diesis) (57000) **Qatar Racing Limited**
95 LOPE ATHENA, b f 3/2 Lope de Vega (IRE)—Elas Diamond (Danehill Dancer (IRE)) (280000) **Jasros Racing**
96 LOPE SCHOLAR (IRE), b f 24/3 Lope de Vega (IRE)—Varsity (Lomitas) (97680) **Jasros Racing**
97 Ch c 2/4 Sea The Stars (IRE)—
Mambo Light (USA) (Kingmambo (USA)) (340000) **Qatar Racing Ltd & Mr Kin Hung Kei**
98 MANUELA DE VEGA, b f 21/3 Lope de Vega (IRE)—Roscoff (IRE) (Daylami (IRE)) (81400) **Jasros Racing**
99 Br c 7/2 Sea The Moon (GER)—Maraba (IRE) (Danehill Dancer (IRE)) (48840) **What Asham Partnership**
100 B f 18/4 Charm Spirit (IRE)—Millisecond (Royal Applause) **Qatar Racing Ltd**
101 MISTY, b f 3/5 Oasis Dream—Ceilidh House (Selkirk (USA)) **Mr J. H. Richmond-Watson**
102 MRS IVY, ch f 6/4 Champs Elysees—Just Wood (FR) (Highest Honor (FR)) (30000) **Make A Circle Racing**
103 MY DEAR FRIEND, b c 24/3 Kodiac—
Time Honoured (Sadler's Wells (USA)) (100000) **King Power Racing Co Ltd**
104 B f 20/4 Mastercraftsman (IRE)—
Nina Celebre (IRE) (Peintre Celebre (USA)) (191290) **H.H. Sheikh Mohammed bin Khalifa Al Thani**
105 B c 10/5 Archipenko (USA)—Nocturne (GER) (Rock of Gibraltar (IRE)) (49654) **Quantum Leap Racing II**
106 B f 18/2 Nathaniel (IRE)—Opera Dancer (Norse Dancer (IRE)) **Mr J. C. Smith**
107 Gr f 1/3 Dark Angel (IRE)—
Parle Moi (USA) (Giant's Causeway (USA)) (95000) **Wansdyke Farms Ltd, Oghill House Stud**
108 PHILONIKIA, b f 11/2 Kingman—Colima (IRE) (Authorized (IRE)) **Mr & Mrs David Aykroyd**
109 B f 29/2 Siyouni (FR)—Photo Flash (IRE) (Bahamian Bounty) (150000) **Highclere Thoroughbred Racing**
110 PRINCESS SALAMAH (IRE), ch f 23/4 Australia—
Dubai Media (CAN) (Songandaprayer (USA)) **Mr Ahmad Abdulla Al Shaikh**
111 QUEEN POWER (IRE), ch f 12/3 Shamardal—
Princess Serena (USA) (Unbridled's Song (USA)) (500000) **King Power Racing Co Ltd**
112 RASKOLNIKOV, b c 22/2 Excelebration (IRE)—Affaire de Coeur (Dalakhani (IRE)) **Melody Racing**
113 ROVING MISSION (USA), ch f 1/3 Noble Mission—Preferential (Dansili) **Mr K. Abdullah**
114 SABAI SABAI (IRE), b f 10/4 Shamardal (USA)—
Semayyel (IRE) (Green Desert (USA)) (260000) **King Power Racing Co Ltd**
115 SAM COOKE (IRE), b c 17/2 Pour Moi (IRE)—
Saturday Girl (Peintre Celebre (USA)) (29304) **Chelsea Thoroughbreds - Wonderful World**
116 B c 24/3 Maxios—Set Dreams (FR) (Galileo (IRE)) (39886) **Mr Norman Brunskill**
117 SNOW IN SPRING, b c 26/4 Oasis Dream—Khione (Dalakhani (IRE)) (16000) **The Outlaws**
118 B f 29/3 Dark Angel (IRE)—Soxy Doxy (IRE) (Hawk Wing (USA)) (400000) **Mr Sutong Pan**
119 TEODORA DE VEGA (IRE), b f 22/3 Lope de Vega (IRE)—
Applauded (IRE) (Royal Applause) (250000) **Jasros Racing**
120 TIGERSKIN, ch c 29/2 Nathaniel (IRE)—
Jamboretta (IRE) (Danehill (USA)) **Mr A. D. G. Oldrey & Mr G. C. Hartigan**
121 TOP TOP (IRE), b c 7/2 Frankel—Jira (Medicean) (260000) **King Power Racing Co Ltd**
122 Ch f 28/3 Sea The Stars (IRE)—
Topaze Blanche (IRE) (Zamindar (USA)) **H.H. Sheikh Mohammed bin Khalifa Al Thani**
123 Gr ro f 12/4 Mastercraftsman (IRE)—What Style (IRE) (Teofilo (IRE)) (45584) **Kennet Valley Thoroughbreds**
124 B f 11/3 Sea The Stars (IRE)—Whos Mindin Who (IRE) (Danehill Dancer (IRE)) (40000) **Pearl Bloodstock Ltd**
125 WILD ABANDON, b f 20/4 Kingman—Sant Elena (Efisio) **The Eclipse Partnership**
126 B f 7/4 Kingman—Wittgenstein (IRE) (Shamardal) (97680) **Newsells Park Stud**

Assistant Trainers: Adam Kite, James Fathers

Jockey (flat): Pat Dobbs, Richard Kingscote, Oisin Murphy. **Apprentice:** Emma Wilkinson.

---

29 **MR MICHAEL BELL, Newmarket**
Postal: Fitzroy House, Newmarket, Suffolk, CB8 0JT
Contacts: **PHONE (01638) 666567 FAX (01638) 668000 MOBILE (07802) 264514**
E-MAIL office@fitzroyhouse.co.uk WEBSITE www.michaelbellracing.co.uk

1 BIG ORANGE, 7, b g Duke of Marmalade (IRE)—Miss Brown To You (IRE) **W. J. and T. C. O. Gredley**
2 FABRICATE, 6, b g Makfi—Flight of Fancy **Her Majesty The Queen**
3 FIRE BRIGADE, 4, b g Firebreak—Island Rhapsody **The Fitzrovians**
4 GRACELAND (FR), 6, gr m Mastercraftsman (IRE)—Jeunesse Lulu (IRE) **The Chriselliam Partnership**
5 MAORI BOB (IRE), 4, b g Big Bad Bob (IRE)—Tekhania (IRE) **Mr T Redman, Mr P Philipps, Mr C Philipps**
6 MERLIN, 4, b g Oasis Dream—Momentary **Her Majesty The Queen**
7 NAMIRAH, 4, b f Sepoy (AUS)—Fairy Efisio **Highclere Thoroughbred Racing**
8 NURSE NIGHTINGALE, 4, b f Nathaniel (IRE)—Whazzat **W. J. and T. C. O. Gredley**

MR MICHAEL BELL - Continued

9 **SACRED ACT**, 7, b g Oasis Dream—Stage Presence (IRE) **Mr Kulbir Sohi, Mr B.Roberts & Mr R.Cope**
10 **TOWERLANDS PARK (IRE)**, 5, b g Danehill Dancer (IRE)—Strategy **W. J. and T. C. O. Gredley**
11 **WINSTON C (IRE)**, 4, b g Rip Van Winkle (IRE)—Pitrizza (IRE) **W. J. and T. C. O. Gredley**

THREE-YEAR-OLDS

12 **ANY LITTLE RHYME**, b f Shamardal (USA)—Free Verse **Her Majesty The Queen**
13 **ARABIAN JAZZ (IRE)**, b f Red Jazz (USA)—Queen of Rap (IRE) **Ontoawinner, K Stewart & Partner**
14 **ARTARMON (IRE)**, b c So You Think (NZ)—Aljumar (IRE) **OTI Racing 1**
15 **BATTLEDORE (USA)**, b g Lonhro (AUS)—Badminton **Sheikh Marwan Al Maktoum**
16 **BEST BLUE**, b c Oasis Dream—Filia Regina **W. J. & T. C. O. Gredley & Lord Derby**
17 **CHICKPEA**, b f Rip Van Winkle (IRE)—Tahlia Ree (IRE) **Mr Paddy Barrett & Partner**
18 **CHOICE ENCOUNTER**, ch g Choisir (AUS)—Gimme Some Lovin (IRE) **Miss E. Asprey & Mr C. Wright**
19 **CHRISTOPHER WOOD (IRE)**, b c Fast Company (IRE)—Surf The Web (IRE) **Mr R. A. Green**
20 **DEMURRER (USA)**, br g First Defence (USA)—Seeking Ema (USA) **Middleham Park Racing XXXII & Partner**
21 **ESME KATE (IRE)**, b f Arch (USA)—Francisca (USA) **Mrs B. Sangster, Mr D. Hanafin, Mr N. Warnock**
22 **FLYING SPARKLE (IRE)**, b f Fast Company (IRE)—Titian Saga (IRE) **Amo Racing Ltd**
23 **FREEBE ROCKS (IRE)**, ch g Camacho—Shamardyh (IRE) **Karmaa Racing Ltd**
24 **GEETANJALI (IRE)**, b f Roderic O'connor (IRE)—Scylla Cadeaux (IRE) **Mr Hugo Merry**
25 **GIRLS TALK (IRE)**, b f Shamardal (USA)—Tasha's Dream (USA) **Mr Colin Bryce**
26 **GUARDIOLA (USA)**, b g Lonhro (AUS)—Badalona **Sheikh Marwan Al Maktoum**
27 **HIGHLIGHT REEL (IRE)**, b g Big Bad Bob (IRE)—Dance Hall Girl (IRE) **The Deflators**
28 **HOT OFF THE PRESS (IRE)**, b f Camelot—
      Jewel In The Sand (IRE) **Mrs Paul Shanahan, Mr M. V. Magnier, Mr C. P. E. Brooks & Mr C. Conroy**
29 **HOUSE EDGE**, gr c Nathaniel (IRE)—Bezique **Mr Edward J. Ware**
30 **IMMORTAL ROMANCE (IRE)**, br g Society Rock (IRE)—Sundown **32Red Syndicate**
31 **IMPERIAL CHOICE (IRE)**, ch f New Approach (IRE)—Eva's Request (IRE) **Lady Bamford**
32 **INDIA**, b f Poet's Voice—Miss Brown To You (IRE) **W. J. and T. C. O. Gredley**
33 **JOE'S SPIRIT (IRE)**, b g Swiss Spirit—Dimensional **Middleham Park Racing XCI & Partner**
34 **MAIN DESIRE (IRE)**, b f High Chaparral (IRE)—Purple Glow (IRE) **Clipper Logistics**
35 **NEVERBEEN TO PARIS (IRE)**, b g Champs Elysees—Island Paradise (IRE) **Sarah & Wayne Dale 2**
36 **QUEEN OF CONNAUGHT**, gr f Declaration of War (USA)—Warling (USA) **Mrs P Shanahan & Mrs M V Magnier**
37 **REVIVED**, b f Dark Angel (IRE)—Tan Tan **Clipper Logistics**
38 **ROULETTE**, ch f Poet's Voice—Unex Mona Lisa **W. J. and T. C. O. Gredley**
39 **RUPERT'S LASS**, b f Myboycharlie (IRE)—Elusive Flash (IRE) **Mrs G Rowland-Clark & Mr Neil Warnock**
40 **SACRED WARRIOR**, b c Declaration of War (USA)—Behkara (IRE) **Lady Bamford**
41 **SAILING HOME**, b f Shamardal (USA)—Tidespring (IRE) **Her Majesty The Queen**
42 **SHERIFF**, br g Lawman (FR)—Chatline (USA) **W. J. and T. C. O. Gredley**
43 **SPACE BANDIT**, ch c Shamardal (USA)—Hometime **Qatar Racing Limited**
44 **TAUREAN DANCER (IRE)**, b g Intello (GER)—Traou Mad (IRE) **Mr Brian Goodyear**
45 **TRINITY SQUARE**, b f Champs Elysees—Friendlier **W. J. and T. C. O. Gredley**

TWO-YEAR-OLDS

46 B c 9/3 War Command (USA)—Andrea Bellevica (IRE) (Aussie Rules) (USA)) **Mr Alan D. Gray**
47 **ANTHONY E (IRE)**, b c 23/4 No Nay Never (USA)—
      Lace (IRE) (Sadler's Wells (USA)) (100000) **W. J. and T. C. O. Gredley**
48 **ANTIGUAN DUCHESS**, ch f 25/2 Dutch Art—
      Totally Millie (Pivotal) (37142) **Mr & Mrs A Smith-Maxwell & Mr W E A Fox**
49 **ARTAIR (IRE)**, b c 1/3 Kodiac—Bonnie Lesley (IRE) (Iffraaj) (52380) **Secular Stagnation & Partner**
50 B f 2/5 Zoffany (IRE)—Bahja (USA) (Seeking The Gold (USA)) (48840) **Thurloe Thoroughbreds XLVI & Partners**
51 Ch f 22/3 Farhh—Bianca Nera (Salse (USA)) **Mr R. L. W. Frisby**
52 Gr f 25/2 Oasis Dream—Boastful (Clodovil) (IRE)) **Clipper Logistics**
53 B f 23/2 Declaration of War (USA)—Bohemian Dance (IRE) (Dansili) (42328) **Mr C. Wright & Miss E. Asprey**
54 B f 7/2 Australia—Cherrington (IRE) (Lope de Vega (IRE)) (75000) **Saif Ali**
55 Ch f 25/1 Sepoy (AUS)—Crimson Year (USA) (Dubai Millennium) **Sheikh Marwan Al Maktoum**
56 B f 17/2 Le Havre (FR)—Daliana (Verglas (IRE)) (110000) **The Hon Mrs J. M. Corbett & Mr Christopher Wright**
57 B c 19/2 Poet's Voice—Diamond Run (Hurricane Run (IRE)) (30000) **Mascalls Stud**
58 **DINAH WASHINGTON (IRE)**, ch f 23/3 Australia—
      Gainful (USA) (Gone West) (56980) **Chelsea Thoroughbreds - Mad About The Boy**
59 Ch f 29/4 Exceed And Excel (AUS)—Dresden Doll (USA) (Elusive Quality (USA)) **Sheikh Marwan Al Maktoum**
60 B c 25/3 Swiss Spirit—Easy To Love (USA) (Diesis) (21000) **Wayne & Sarah Dale & Lordship Stud**
61 **EIGHTSOME REEL**, b c 1/3 Iffraaj—Set To Music (IRE) (Danehill Dancer (IRE)) **Her Majesty The Queen**
62 **FAST ENDEAVOUR**, b f 15/2 Pastoral Pursuits—
      Scented Garden (Zamindar (USA)) (6190) **Middleham Park Racing CII & Partner 2**
63 B c 12/3 Lope de Vega (IRE)—Free Rein (Dansili) (70000) **Sheikh Abdulla Almalek Alsabah**
64 **HEATHERDOWN (IRE)**, b c 19/4 Morpheus—Hapipi (Bertolini) (IRE) (30000) **The Heatherdonians**

MR MICHAEL BELL - Continued

65 Gr c 22/3 Intikhab (USA)—
　　　　　Jessica Ennis (USA) (English Channel (USA)) (10476) **Highclere Thoroughbred Racing**
66 B c 14/3 Iffraaj—Just Like A Woman (Observatory (USA)) (30000)
67 B f 6/3 Intello (GER)—Keriyka (IRE) (Indian Ridge) (16280) **Mr A. Smith-Maxwell**
68 **L'UN DEUX TROIS (IRE)**, gr c 24/4 Mastercraftsman (IRE)—
　　　　　Moment Juste (Pivotal) (40700) **Mrs G. Rowland-Clark & Mr Timmy Hyde**
69 **LADY AIRA**, b f 14/3 Kodiac—Dot Hill (Refuse To Bend (IRE)) (125000) **Amo Racing Limited**
70 B f 18/4 Dark Angel (IRE)—Little Audio (IRE) (Shamardal (USA)) (85714) **Clipper Logistics**
71 **LOGIE BAIRD (IRE)**, b c 26/3 Mastercraftsman (IRE)—
　　　　　Strategy (Machiavellian (USA)) (75000) **Mr J. Barnett & Mrs P. Shanahan**
72 **LORCAN**, gr c 31/3 Dark Angel (IRE)—
　　　　　Vallado (IRE) (Clodovil (IRE)) (68571) **Mr A Cohen Mr D Hanafin & Mr S Kaznowski**
73 **LYSANDER BELLE (IRE)**, b f 3/4 Exceed And Excel (AUS)—
　　　　　Switcher (IRE) (Whipper (USA)) (155000) **W. J. and T. C. O. Gredley**
74 **MASTER BREWER (FR)**, b c 29/2 Reliable Man—
　　　　　Quenching (IRE) (Street Cry (IRE)) (69190) **The Fitzrovians 2 & Fair Salinia Ltd**
75 **METAPHOR**, b g 30/3 Motivator—Flash of Gold (Darshaan) **Her Majesty The Queen**
76 B br c 28/4 Sea The Stars (IRE)—Missunited (IRE) (Golan (IRE)) **Clipper Logistics**
77 **NUREMBERG (IRE)**, b c 23/2 War Command (USA)—
　　　　　Mackenzie's Friend (Selkirk (USA)) (28571) **The Fitzrovians 2**
78 **PRETTY POLLYANNA**, b f 25/2 Oasis Dream—
　　　　　Unex Mona Lisa (Shamardal (USA)) (50000) **W. J. and T. C. O. Gredley**
79 **RAPTURE (IRE)**, ch f 8/5 Pivotal—Rosa Bonheur (USA) (Mr Greeley (USA)) **Clipper Logistics**
80 **REGULAR**, ch c 18/3 Exceed And Excel (AUS)—Humdrum (Dr Fong (USA)) **Her Majesty The Queen**
81 **ROBERT FITZROY (IRE)**, b c 28/2 Big Bad Bob (IRE)—
　　　　　Semiquaver (IRE) (Mark of Esteem (IRE)) (27675) **The Fitzrovians 2**
82 **STARLIGHT**, b f 23/3 Iffraaj—Ighraa (IRE) (Tamayuz) (160000) **Mr Edward J. Ware**
83 Ch c 1/3 Australia—Susan Stroman (Monsun (GER)) (68000) **The Royal Ascot Racing Club**
84 **TAMOCK (IRE)**, b f 25/1 Australia—Anklet (IRE) (Acclamation) (400000) **Amo Racing Limited**
85 **TAUREAN PRINCE (IRE)**, b c 14/4 Kodiac—Dream Wedding (Medicean) (50000) **Mr Brian Goodyear**
86 **THOMAS CUBITT (FR)**, b c 7/4 Youmzain (IRE)—Helsinka (FR) (Pennekamp (USA)) (48840) **Men Fae the Clyde**
87 **WELD ALDAR**, ch c 20/2 Universal (IRE)—
　　　　　Crystal Wish (Exceed And Excel (AUS)) (3500) **Ahmad Abdulla Al Shaikh & Co**
88 **YOUTHFUL**, b c 26/2 Shamardal (USA)—Good Hope (Cape Cross (IRE)) **Her Majesty The Queen**

Other Owners: Miss Emily Charlotte Asprey, Mrs E. Carson, W. F. H. Carson, Mr C. N. Wright.

Assistant Trainer: Nick Bell

Jockey (flat): Jamie Spencer. **Apprentice:** Cameron Noble.

30 **MR JAMES BENNETT, Wantage**
Postal: **2 Filley Alley, Letcombe Bassett, Wantage, Oxfordshire, OX12 9LT**
Contacts: **PHONE (01235) 762163 MOBILE (07771) 523076**
E-MAIL jbennett345@btinternet.com

1 **BASSINO (USA)**, 5, b g Street Cry (IRE)—Show Me The Roses (USA) **Miss J. C. Blackwell**
2 **IDOL DEPUTY (FR)**, 12, gr g Silver Deputy (CAN)—Runaway Venus (USA) **Miss J. C. Blackwell**
3 **THE LAST MELON**, 6, ch g Sir Percy—Step Fast (USA) **Miss J. C. Blackwell**

Assistant Trainer: Miss J. Blackwell

Jockey (flat): Racheal Kneller.

31 **MR ALAN BERRY, Cockerham**
Postal: **Moss Side Racing Stables, Crimbles Lane, Cockerham, Lancashire, LA2 0ES**
Contacts: **PHONE (01524) 791179 MOBILE (07880) 553515**
E-MAIL berryracing@hotmail.com

1 **BELLANASALLY (IRE)**, 5, b g Frozen Fire (GER)—My Touch (IRE)
2 **BULGE BRACKET**, 5, b g Great Journey (JPN)—Baldovina **A Parr & A Berry**
3 **ECONOMIC CRISIS (IRE)**, 9, ch m Excellent Art—Try The Air (IRE) **W. Burns & A. Berry**
4 **EYE ON YOU (IRE)**, 5, b m Tagula (IRE)—Hollow Haze (USA) **J. Quinn & A. Berry**
5 **I'LL BE GOOD**, 9, b g Red Clubs (IRE)—Willisa **Graham Brown & Alan Berry**

MR ALAN BERRY - Continued

  6 **KING OF CASTILLA**, 4, br g Sayif (IRE)—Thicket **W. Burns & Alan Berry**
  7 **LITTLE NOSEGAY (IRE)**, 4, gr f Clodovil (IRE)—Bank On Black (IRE) **Kirkby Lonsdale Racing**
  8 **LUCATA (IRE)**, 4, b g Sir Prancealot (IRE)—Toy Show (IRE) **A Parr & Alan Berry**
  9 **PLASTIKI**, 9, b g Oasis Dream—Dayrose **Alan Berry**
10 **ROMAN TIMES (IRE)**, 5, b m Holy Roman Emperor (IRE)—Timeless Dream **W. Burns & Alan Berry**
11 **TIHANA**, 5, b m Lawman (FR)—La Bocca (USA) **J Quinn & A. Berry**
12 4, B c Kodiac—Unfortunate **Alan Berry**

THREE-YEAR-OLDS

13 B f Lilbourne Lad (IRE)—Kasalla (IRE) **A. Berry**
14 B f Distant Peak (IRE)—Martha's Way **A. Berry**

TWO-YEAR-OLDS

15 Ch f 30/4 Equiano (FR)—Millsini (Rossini (USA)) (5000) **Jack Berry & W. Burns**

Other Owners: W. Burns, A. B. Parr.

Assistant Trainer: John A. Quinn

---

32   MR J. A. BERRY, Blackwater
Postal: **Ballyroe, Blackwater, Enniscorthy, Co. Wexford, Ireland**
Contacts: **PHONE (00353) 53 91 27205 MOBILE (00353) 86 2557537**
E-MAIL johnaberry@eircom.net

1 **ABBEY MAGIC (IRE)**, 7, b m Beneficial—Magical Theatre (IRE) **G. Halley**
2 **ARTIC QUEST (IRE)**, 6, ch g Trans Island—Back The Queen (IRE) **J. A. Berry**
3 **CATCH MY DRIFT (IRE)**, 9, ch g Subtle Power (IRE)—Deliga Lady (IRE) **J. Berry**
4 **CHIP SHOT (IRE)**, 5, b g Yeats (IRE)—Nerissa (IRE) **J. P. McManus**
5 **COURT GLORY (IRE)**, 5, b m Court Cave (IRE)—Ad Gloria (IRE) **Emma Berry**
6 **DAY DAY (IRE)**, 8, b m Hurricane Run (IRE)—Mem O'rees **J. P. McManus**
7 **STORMY WATAR (IRE)**, 5, b g Watar (IRE)—Calm Luso (IRE) **J. Berry**
8 **TAKE FIVE (IRE)**, 5, b g Arakan (USA)—World of Ballet (IRE) **J. Berry**

Assistant Trainer: Mr J. P. Berry

Amateur: Mr J. P. Berry.

---

33   MR JOHN BERRY, Newmarket
Postal: **Beverley House Stables, Exeter Road, Newmarket, Suffolk, CB8 8LR**
Contacts: **PHONE (01638) 660663**
E-MAIL john@beverleyhousestables.com WEBSITE www.beverleyhousestables.com

  1 4, B c Joe Bear (IRE)—Artistic Belle (IRE) **Mrs G. A. Olive**
  2 **DELATITE**, 6, b g Schiaparelli (GER)—Desiree (IRE) **The Beverley House Stables Partnership**
  3 **DERVISH**, 4, b g Cacique (IRE)—Doggerbank **Mr John Berry**
  4 **FREEDIVER**, 4, ch f Bated Breath—Grand Coral **Emma Berry & John Berry**
  5 **HEAVENLYGINGERLILY**, 6, ch m Joe Bear (IRE)—Artistic Belle (IRE) **Mrs G. A. Olive**
  6 **HOPE IS HIGH**, 5, b m Sir Percy—Altitude **Emma Berry & John Berry**
  7 **IRENE WILDE (FR)**, 4, gr f Silver Frost (IRE)—Danse Revee (IRE) **C. V. Wentworth**
  8 **KRYPTOS**, 4, b g Cacique (IRE)—Posteritas (USA) **Mr Tony Fordham**
  9 **ROY ROCKET (IRE)**, 8, gr g Layman (USA)—Minnie's Mystery (FR) **McCarthy & Berry**
10 **SACRED ROCK (IRE)**, 5, b g Rock of Gibraltar (IRE)—Snowpalm **L. C. Wadey**
11 **SOLITARY SISTER (IRE)**, 4, br f Cockney Rebel (IRE)—Sweet Afton (IRE)
12 **SUSSEX GIRL**, 4, ch f Compton Place—Palinisa (FR) **Mr D. Tunmore & Mr John Berry**
13 **WASTED SUNSETS (FR)**, 4, b f Myboycharlie (IRE)—Freezing (USA) **Mrs Z. Wentworth**
14 **WHITE VALIANT**, 5, gr g Youmzain (FR)—Minnie's Mystery (FR) **Bruce Atkinson & John Berry**

THREE-YEAR-OLDS

15 **ALSAMARA**, b f New Approach (IRE)—Altitude **Mr John Berry**
16 **DAS KAPITAL**, b g Cityscape—Narla **The Geezers**
17 **FREE BIRD**, b f Phoenix Reach (IRE)—Love Supreme (IRE) **Mrs Emma Berry**
18 **SWEET CHARISMA (FR)**, b f Motivator—Soft Pleasure (USA) **Beverley House Partnership**

MR JOHN BERRY - Continued

TWO-YEAR-OLDS

19 DEREHAM, b g 27/1 Sir Percy—Desiree (IRE) (Desert Story (IRE)) **Mrs Emma Berry**
20 Ch g 18/3 Anodin (IRE)—Ethics Girl (IRE) (Hernando (FR)) **Mrs Emma Berry**

Other Owners: Mr Bruce Atkinson, Emma Berry, Mr John Berry, Mr & Mrs D. Collings, Mr R. Conquest, Mr H. Fraser, Mr B. Granahan, Mrs J. P Haycock, Mr P.J. Haycock, Mr N. Hilsden, Mr R. Huggins, Mr R. W. Huggins, Mr A. Mayne, Miss L. I. McCarthy, Mr Stephen F. McCormick, Mr L. Norris, Mr D. O'Rourke, Mr T. O'Rourke, Mr C. Plant, Mr D. Punshon, Mr R. Sherlock, Lesley Sinden, Mr S. Sweeting, Mr J. Targett, Mr I. Walton, Mr J. Wilson.

Jockey (flat): John Egan, Josephine Gordon. **Jockey (NH):** Will Kennedy, Jack Quinlan. **Apprentice:** Nicola Currie. **Amateur:** Mr R. Birkett.

---

34 **MR JOHN BEST, Sittingbourne**
Postal: **Eyehorn Farm, Munsgore Lane, Borden, Sittingbourne, Kent, ME9 8JU**
Contacts: **MOBILE (07889) 362154**
E-MAIL john.best@johnbestracing.com WEBSITE www.johnbestracing.com

1 BANTA BAY, 4, b g Kheleyf (USA)—Atnab (USA) **Jones, Fuller & Paine**
2 BERRAHRI (IRE), 7, b g Bahri (USA)—Band of Colour (IRE) **White Turf Racing UK**
3 CHANCE TO DREAM (IRE), 4, b g Dream Ahead (USA)—
Kerry Gal (IRE) **Mr & Mrs H Jarvis and Mr & Mrs S Malcolm**
4 EDDYSTONE ROCK (IRE), 6, ch g Rock of Gibraltar (IRE)—Bayberry (UAE) **Curtis, Malt & Williams**
5 FEARLESS LAD (IRE), 8, b g Excellent Art—Souffle **Mrs J. O. Jones**
6 GLENYS THE MENACE (FR), 4, b f American Post—Elle S'voyait Deja (USA) **Curtis, Malt & Jenkins**
7 HIORNE TOWER (FR), 7, b g Poliglote—Hierarchie (FR) **Mrs J. O. Jones**
8 LUXFORD, 4, b f Mullionmileanhour (IRE)—Dolly Parton (IRE) **Stuart Mair, Wendy Bush & Steve Summers**
9 MALT TEASER (FR), 4, ch g Muhtathir—Abondante (USA) **Ms C Hart & Curtis & Williams Bloodstock**
10 MOSSGO (IRE), 8, b g Moss Vale (IRE)—Perovskia (USA) **Hucking Horses V**
11 MULLARKEY, 4, b g Mullionmileanhour (IRE)—Hannah's Dream (IRE) **Thomson, Tobin & Sheridan**
12 MULLIONHEIR (IRE), 6, b g Mullionmileanhour (IRE)—Peyto Princess **Mr S. D. Malcolm**
13 OURMULLION (IRE), 4, b g Mullionmileanhour (IRE)—Queen Ranavola (USA) **David & Elaine Long**
14 PENDO, 7, b g Denounce—Abundant **Mr B. K. Hopson**
15 TARTARIA, 12, b m Oasis Dream—Habariya (IRE) **Mr N. Dyshaev**
16 TOO MANY SHOTS, 4, b g Mullionmileanhour (IRE)—Neissa (USA) **TMS & Beckett**

THREE-YEAR-OLDS

17 CASA COMIGO (IRE), b c Cape Cross (IRE)—Belanoiva (IRE) **Mr S. D. Malcolm**
18 CHAPEL DOWN, b g Hellvelyn—United Passion **Last Orders Racing**
19 DOLLY MIXTURE (FR), b f Mullionmileanhour (IRE)—Dolly Parton (IRE) **Eyehorn Racing**
20 KING ATHELSTAN (IRE), b g Mayson—Ashtaroute (USA) **Caplin & Sheridan**
21 MOSSKETEER, b g Moss Vale (IRE)—Gracilia (IRE) **Lingfield Park Owners Group 2016 (LPOG 2016)**
22 MULLTITUDE, b f Mullionmileanhour (IRE)—Triplicity **Cottee, Best & Williams**
23 PLANTADREAM, b g Planteur (IRE)—Phantom Ridge (IRE) **H. J. Jarvis**
24 RETAINED (FR), b f Kentucky Dynamite (USA)—Retainage (USA) **Curtis & Williams Bloodstock**
25 SEAQUINN, b f Equiano (FR)—Marine Girl **Harris & Beckett**
26 SHAMROCK EMMA (IRE), ch f Mizzen Mast (USA)—Lisselan Diva (IRE) **Caplin & Sheridan**

TWO-YEAR-OLDS

27 B f 16/3 Foxwedge (AUS)—Elounta (Dubawi (IRE)) **Laura Malcolm & Partners**
28 ESTUPENDO, b c 27/4 Moohaajim (IRE)—Gracilia (FR) (Anabaa (USA)) (13000)
29 IGNATIUS (IRE), b c 16/2 Casamento (IRE)—
Free Lance (IRE) (Grand Lodge (USA)) (14761) **Keaveney & Butcher**
30 PENTIMENTO, b c 15/2 Garswood—M'selle (IRE) (Elnadim (USA)) **Walter & Geraldine Paine**
31 B c 10/3 Muhtathir—Retainage (USA) (Polish Numbers (USA)) **Mr J. A. Coleman**
32 SPURRED ON, b g 9/4 Epaulette (AUS)—Triplicity (Three Valleys (USA)) **Sheridan Cottee & Caplin**

Other Owners: Mr P. I. Beckett, Mr J. R. Best, Mr P Butcher, Mr D. Caplin, Caplin & Sheridan, Mr M. B. Curtis, Fuller & Paine, Mrs P Jarvis, Mr G. R. Jones, Mr M. Keaveney, Mr A. Keaveney, Mr D. J. Long, Mrs E. Long, Mrs L. C. G. Malcolm, Mr R. C. Malt, Mr W. G. Paine, Ms C. Rice, Mr A. M. Sheridan, Sheridan, Cottee & Caplin, Miss H. J. Williams.

35 MRS SUZI BEST, Lewes

Postal: **Grandstand Stables, Old Lewes Racecourse, Lewes, East Sussex, BN7 1UR**
Contacts: **MOBILE (07804) 487296**
E-MAIL **sbestracing@yahoo.com**

1 **ALBERTA (IRE)**, 9, ch g Choisir (AUS)—Akita (IRE) **Allen B Pope,F O'Sullivan,Jamie Donnelly**
2 **AUSTIN FRIARS**, 6, b g New Approach (IRE)—My Luigia (IRE) **D. Edmonston, P. Arrow, S. Boyack**
3 **BLACK WIDOW**, 7, b m Bertolini (USA)—Malvadilla (IRE) **Jack Callaghan & Christopher Dillon**
4 **BORU'S BROOK (IRE)**, 10, b g Brian Boru—Collybrook Lady (IRE) **Cheltenham Dreamers**
5 **ECHO BRAVA**, 8, gr g Proclamation—Snake Skin **William Angel&the Fat Jockey Partnership**
6 **ERTIDAAD (IRE)**, 6, b g Kodiac—Little Scotland **Mr A. Cullen & Ms F.A. O'Sullivan**
7 **JAMHOORI**, 10, b h Tiger Hill (IRE)—Tanasie **Mrs A. M. Cooperwhite**
8 **MARIA'S CHOICE (IRE)**, 9, b g Oratorio (IRE)—Amathusia **Mr P. J. Arrow**
9 **NEW STREET (IRE)**, 7, gr g Acclamation—New Deal **Mr J. J. Callaghan**
10 **OFFICER DRIVEL (IRE)**, 7, b g Captain Rio—Spiritville (IRE) **Mr R. D. Sarin**
11 **OUTRATH (IRE)**, 8, b g Captain Rio—Silver Grouse (IRE) **Mr A. R. Coupland**
12 **PLANETOID (IRE)**, 10, b g Galileo (IRE)—Palmeraie (USA) **Planetoid Partnership**
13 **SIX GUN SERENADE (IRE)**, 7, b g Kalanisi (IRE)—Zenaide (IRE) **Mr J. J. Callaghan**
14 **SLOWFOOT (GER)**, 10, b h Hernando (FR)—Simply Red (GER) **Mr B Phillpott,Mr C Dillon & Mr A Gillan**
15 **THATS MY RABBIT (IRE)**, 9, b g Heron Island (IRE)—Minnie Turbo (IRE) **Mr D. Edmonston**

THREE-YEAR-OLDS

16 **ASHAREDMOMENT**, b f Swiss Spirit—Shared Moment (IRE) **Mr J. J. Callaghan**

Other Owners: Mr W. Angel, Mr S. Boyack, Mr A. Cullen, Mr C. J. Dillon, Mr J. Donnelly, Mr A. C. Gillian, Miss F. O'Sullivan, Mr B Phillpott, A. B. Pope, Mr I. R. Steadman.

Assistant Trainer: Mr Tom Best

36 MISS HARRIET BETHELL, Arnold

Postal: **Arnold Manor, Black Tup Lane, Arnold, Hull, North Humberside, HU11 5JA**
E-MAIL **harrietbethell@hotmail.co.uk**

1 **FROZON**, 5, b g Kheleyf (USA)—Crozon **W. A. Bethell**
2 **MIAMI PRESENT (IRE)**, 8, b br g Presenting—Miami Nights (GER) **W. A. Bethell**
3 **MY PAINTER (IRE)**, 7, b m Jeremy (USA)—Last Cry (FR) **W. A. Bethell**
4 **NEWBERRY NEW (IRE)**, 6, b g Kodiac—Sunblush (UAE) **W. A. Bethell**
5 **STEEL HELMET (IRE)**, 4, ch g Helmet (AUS)—Marine City (JPN) **W. A. Bethell**
6 **UNDERSTATEMENT**, 5, b g Authorized (IRE)—Usem **W. A. Bethell**
7 **VALENTINO BOY (IRE)**, 4, b g Bated Breath—Capistrano Day (USA) **W. A. Bethell**
8 **VIEWPOINT (IRE)**, 9, b g Exceed And Excel (AUS)—Lady's View (USA) **W. A. Bethell**

Jockey (NH): Danny Cook.

37 MR JAMES BETHELL, Middleham

Postal: **Thorngill, Coverham, Middleham, North Yorkshire, DL8 4TJ**
Contacts: **PHONE (01969) 640360 FAX (01969) 640360 MOBILE (07831) 683528**
E-MAIL **james@jamesbethell.co.uk WEBSITE www.jamesbethell.com**

1 **AIRTON**, 5, b g Champs Elysees—Fly In Style **Clarendon Thoroughbred Racing**
2 **BRIARDALE (IRE)**, 6, b g Arcano (IRE)—Marine City (JPN) **J. Carrick&Clarendon Thoroughbred Racing**
3 **CRAY (IRE)**, 4, b g Rip Van Winkle (IRE)—Amaya (USA) **J. Carrick&Clarendon Thoroughbred Racing**
4 **CUCKOO'S CALLING**, 4, b f So You Think (NZ)—Sinndarina (FR) **Mr C. N. Wright**
5 **FAST AND FURIOUS (IRE)**, 5, b g Rock of Gibraltar (IRE)—Ocean Talent (USA) **Mr A. Buckingham**
6 **FRUIT SALAD**, 5, ch m Monsieur Bond (IRE)—Miss Apricot **Clarendon Thoroughbred Racing**
7 **JESSINAMILLION**, 4, b g Mine (IRE)—Miss Apricot **Culture Club**
8 **MISTER BOB (GER)**, 9, ch g Black Sam Bellamy (IRE)—Mosquera (GER) **Robert Gibbons (Mister Bob)**
9 **MON AMI BOB**, 5, ch g Schiaparelli (GER)—Maid of Perth **Mr J. A. Tabet**
10 **MUDAWWAN (IRE)**, 4, b g Invincible Spirit (IRE)—Louve Sacree (USA)
11 **NEW SOCIETY (IRE)**, 4, b g Rock of Gibraltar (IRE)—Ajiaal **Mr J. E. Dance**
12 **ON FIRE**, 5, b g Olden Times—La Notte **Mrs C. M. Holliday**
13 **PENISTONE**, 4, ch g Pivotal—Dorelia (IRE) **Clarendon Thoroughbred Racing**
14 **PORTLEDGE (IRE)**, 4, b g Acclamation—Off Chance **Mr A. Buckingham**

MR JAMES BETHELL - Continued

15 **QUIET WEEKEND**, 4, b g Mawatheeq (USA)—Maid of Perth **R. F. Gibbons**
16 **RICH AGAIN (IRE)**, 9, b g Amadeus Wolf—Fully Fashioned (IRE) **Mr Richard T. Vickers Partnership**
17 **THANKYOU VERY MUCH**, 8, b m Lucky Story (USA)—Maid of Perth **R. F. Gibbons**
18 **TRUTH OR DARE**, 7, b g Invincible Spirit (IRE)—Unreachable Star **Mr J. A. Tabet**

THREE-YEAR-OLDS

19 **ADJOURNED**, gr g Rip Van Winkle (IRE)—Bite of The Cherry **Mr J. E. Dance**
20 **FIRBY (IRE)**, b g Rock of Gibraltar (IRE)—Huffoof (IRE) **Clarendon Thoroughbred Racing**
21 **HARROGATE (IRE)**, br g Society Rock (IRE)—Invincible Me (IRE) **Clarendon Thoroughbred Racing & Partner**
22 **HOWBAAR (USA)**, b g Lonhro (AUS)—Going Day (USA) **Mr J. A. Tabet**
23 **STRAWBERRYANDCREAM**, ch f Cityscape—Miss Apricot **Mrs James Bethell & Partner**
24 **TOWTON (IRE)**, b g Zebedee—Amber Tide (IRE) **The Vickers & Clark Racing Partnership**
25 **ULSHAW BRIDGE (IRE)**, b c High Chaparral (IRE)—Sharaarah (IRE) **Geoffrey van Cutsem & Partners**
26 **URBAN SOUL (IRE)**, b g Worthadd—Capsaicin (IRE) **Mr J. E. Dance**

TWO-YEAR-OLDS

27 **CONAGLEN**, b c 29/1 Toronado (IRE)—Infamous Angel (Exceed And Excel (AUS)) (30000)
28 **HESSLEWOOD (IRE)**, b c 29/4 Slade Power (IRE)—
Rochitta (USA) (Arch (USA)) (35000) **Clarendon Thoroughbred Racing**
29 B c 3/2 Dawn Approach (IRE)—Kiss Me Goodbye (Raven's Pass (USA)) (42000)
30 B f 17/3 Camelot—Malikayah (IRE) (Fasliyev (USA)) (16280) **Clarendon Thoroughbred Racing**
31 **MOSS GILL (IRE)**, b c 29/2 No Nay Never (USA)—Sharaarah (IRE) (Oasis Dream) (28571)
32 **SOPHIA MARIA**, b f 16/2 Swiss Spirit—Malelane (IRE) (Prince Sabo) (13000) **Clarendon Thoroughbred Racing**
33 **TUCSON**, b c 9/4 Lawman (FR)—Bruxcalina (FR) (Linamix (FR)) (25000) **Mr D R Kilburn & Mr A N Horncastle**
34 **WINTON**, b c 16/4 Harbour Watch (IRE)—
Arctic Song (Charnwood Forest (IRE)) (20000) **J. Carrick & Clarendon Thoroughbred Racing**

Other Owners: Mr J. D. Bethell, Mrs S. Bethell, Mr J. Carrick, Mr M. Clark, Exors of the Late P. Dixon, Mr A. N. Horncastle, D. Kilburn, Mr M. J. Rozenbroek, Mr P. P. Thorman, R. T. Vickers, Mr D. Y. Vickers, Mr G. N. van Cutsem.

Assistant Trainer: Edward Bethell

---

38   **MR GEORGE BEWLEY, Appleby-In-Westmorland**
Postal: **Jerusalem Farm, Colby, Appleby-In-Westmorland, Cumbria, CA16 6BB**
Contacts: PHONE **(01768) 353003** MOBILE **(07704) 924783**
E-MAIL **southdean.farm@btconnect.com** WEBSITE **www.georgebewleyracing.co.uk**

1 **CASUAL CAVALIER (IRE)**, 10, br g Presenting—Asklynn (IRE) **J. Wade**
2 5, B g Brian Boru—Cindy's Fancy (IRE) **martingrayracing**
3 **CLASSICAL MILANO (IRE)**, 7, b g Milan—Miss Baden (IRE) **Victoria Bewley, John Gibson & E G Tunstall**
4 4, B g Kalanisi (IRE)—Dew On The Grass (IRE) **martingrayracing**
5 **DIPPIN AND DIVING (IRE)**, 5, b g Kalanisi (IRE)—Supreme Dipper (IRE) **J. Wade**
6 **FORTY CROWN (IRE)**, 12, b g Court Cave (IRE)—Forty Quid (IRE) **Miss M. D. Myco**
7 **GRAYS CHOICE (IRE)**, 7, b g Well Chosen—Pennyworth (IRE) **martingrayracing**
8 **INNIS SHANNON (IRE)**, 8, br m Stowaway—Put On Hold (IRE) **Mrs Lesley Bewley & Mr John Gibson**
9 5, B g Winged Love (IRE)—Jenna Marie (IRE) **G. T. Bewley**
10 **LAWTOP LEGEND (IRE)**, 6, b g Milan—Nolagh Supreme (IRE) **martingrayracing**
11 4, Gr g Arcadio (GER)—Nanja Monja (IRE) **J. Wade**
12 **NEWTOWN BELLE**, 5, b m And Beyond—Coldwells (IRE) **The Newtown Partnership**
13 **ONDERUN (IRE)**, 9, b g Flemensfirth (USA)—Warts And All (IRE) **Southdean Racing Club**
14 **OUR JOEY (IRE)**, 10, b g Wareed (IRE)—Put On Hold (IRE) **John Gibson,Kevin Twentyman & Bewley**
15 **OUR MORRIS (IRE)**, 7, b g Milan—Broken Gale (IRE) **Mr R Fisher & Bewley**
16 **OUTBACK BLUE**, 5, gr g Aussie Rules (USA)—Beautiful Lady (IRE) **Mrs C. J. Todd**
17 **ROYAL SALUTE**, 8, br g Flemensfirth (USA)—Loxhill Lady **E G Tunstall, L Davidson & W Richardson**
18 **SAMBA TIME**, 6, gr m Black Sam Bellamy (IRE)—Tikk Tokk (IRE) **martingrayracing**
19 **SEVENBALLS OF FIRE (IRE)**, 9, b g Milan—Leadamurraydance (IRE)
20 **SUNNY DESTINATION (USA)**, 6, b g Dubai Destination (USA)—Railway House (IRE) **Mr Alan Udale & Bewley**
21 4, B g Scorpion (IRE)—True Britannia **martingrayracing**

Other Owners: Mr D. W. Bell, Mr P. Bell, Miss V. F. Bewley, Mrs L. Bewley, Mr L. J. Davidson, Mr R. A. Fisher, Mr J. H. Gibson, Mr I. M. Gray, Mrs G. Gray, Mr W. Richardson, Mr E. G. Tunstall, Mr K. Twentyman, Mr A. Udale.

Jockey (NH): Jonathon Bewley, Henry Brooke, Brian Hughes. **Conditional:** Grant Cockburn. **Amateur:** Mr William Easterby.

40 **MRS PIPPA BICKERTON, Almington**
Postal: Almington House, Pinfold Lane, Almington, Market Drayton, TF9 2QR
Contacts: **MOBILE (07966) 441001**

1 **TROPICAL SUNSHINE (IRE)**, 10, b g Bachelor Duke (USA)—Tropical Coral (IRE) **Mrs P. F. Bickerton**

---

41 **MR SAEED BIN SUROOR, Newmarket**
Postal: Godolphin Office, Snailwell Road, Newmarket, Suffolk, CB8 7YE
Contacts: **PHONE (01638) 569956**
WEBSITE www.godolphin.com

1 **ARABIAN HOPE (USA)**, 4, b f Distorted Humor (USA)—Achieving (USA)
2 **ARCHER'S ARROW (USA)**, 4, b c Lonhro (AUS)—Midnight Music (IRE)
3 **BATTLE STARE (IRE)**, 4, b g Dark Angel (IRE)—Wagtail
4 **BENBATL**, 4, b c Dubawi (IRE)—Nahrain
5 **BEST SOLUTION (IRE)**, 4, b c Kodiac—Al Andalyya (USA)
6 **BIG CHALLENGE (IRE)**, 4, ch c Sea The Stars (IRE)—Something Mon (USA)
7 **BIG TOUR (IRE)**, 4, b c Dubawi (IRE)—Alsindi (IRE)
8 **BRAVE HERO**, 5, ch g Poet's Voice—Classical Dancer
9 **CARRY ON DERYCK**, 6, b g Halling (USA)—Mullein
10 **COMMANDER COLE**, 4, b c Kyllachy—Welsh Angel
11 **CONFRONTATION (USA)**, 8, b br g War Pass (USA)—Successfully Sweet (USA)
12 **DAYKING**, 4, b c Dubawi (IRE)—Birjand
13 **DECEMBER SECOND (IRE)**, 4, b br c Teofilo (IRE)—Bulbul (IRE)
14 **DESERT FROST (IRE)**, 4, b c Dark Angel (IRE)—Layla Jamil (IRE)
15 **DON'T GIVE UP**, 4, b c Dubawi (IRE)—Avongrove
16 **DOWAYLA (IRE)**, 4, b f Sepoy (AUS)—Baheeja
17 **DREAM CASTLE**, 4, b c Frankel—Sand Vixen
18 **DUBAI ELEGANCE**, 4, ch f Sepoy (AUS)—Some Sunny Day
19 **DUBAI HERO (FR)**, 4, b c Dark Angel (IRE)—Bugie d'amore
20 **DUBAI HORIZON (IRE)**, 4, b g Poet's Voice—Chibola (ARG)
21 **DUBAI ONE (IRE)**, 4, ch f Exceed And Excel (AUS)—Dresden Doll (USA)
22 **DUBAI THUNDER**, 4, b c Dubawi (IRE)—Gonbarda (GER)
23 **EMIRATES FLYER**, 7, b g Acclamation—Galapagar (USA)
24 **ENNJAAZ (IRE)**, 4, b c Poet's Voice—Hall Hee (IRE)
25 **EXTRA MILE**, 4, b f Frankel—Marie de Medici (USA)
26 **FALCON'S VIEW**, 4, b c Dubawi (IRE)—New Morning (IRE)
27 **FAST LANDING**, 4, b g Raven's Pass (USA)—Miss Lucifer (FR)
28 **FINISHING TOUCH**, 4, b f Invincible Spirit (IRE)—Dubai Smile (USA)
29 **GAME STARTER (IRE)**, 4, b c Dubawi (IRE)—Opera Cloak (IRE)
30 **GLASSY WATERS (USA)**, 4, ch c Distorted Humor (USA)—Captivating Lass (USA)
31 **GOLD STAR**, 4, b c Nathaniel (IRE)—Tanzania (USA)
32 **GOLD WING (IRE)**, 4, ch c New Approach (IRE)—Ragsah (IRE)
33 **GOLDEN GOAL (IRE)**, 4, gr ro c Dark Angel (IRE)—Golden Rosie (IRE)
34 **GOOD RUN (FR)**, 5, ch g Iffraaj—Tadawul (USA)
35 **GREAT ORDER (USA)**, 5, b br h Distorted Humor (USA)—Michita (USA)
36 **HIGH END**, 4, b br g Dubawi (IRE)—Crystal Music (USA)
37 **HIGH MARK (IRE)**, 4, ch c Pivotal—Arlette (IRE)
38 **HOLD TIGHT**, 6, ch g Exceed And Excel (AUS)—Kangra Valley
39 **HUGE FUTURE**, 5, b g Shamardal (USA)—Time Honoured
40 **KANANEE (USA)**, 4, b c Exceed And Excel (AUS)—Zoowraa
41 **LEADER'S LEGACY (USA)**, 4, b br c War Front (USA)—Bauble Queen (USA)
42 **LESHLAA (USA)**, 4, ch c Street Cry (IRE)—Vine Street (IRE)
43 **MAKE IT UP**, 6, b g Halling (USA)—American Spirit (IRE)
44 **MEMORIAL DAY (IRE)**, 7, b g Cape Cross (IRE)—Reunite (IRE)
45 **MILITARY PARADE**, 4, b g Dutch Art—Bahia Emerald (IRE)
46 **MOBBHIJ**, 4, b g New Approach (IRE)—Anaamil (IRE)
47 **MOUNTAIN HUNTER (USA)**, 4, b g Lonhro (AUS)—Tamarillo
48 **MOVE UP**, 5, b h Dubawi (IRE)—Rosinka (IRE)
49 **MUTARABBY (IRE)**, 4, ch c Tamayuz—Shaarfa (USA)
50 **NAAEEBB (USA)**, 4, b br c Lonhro (AUS)—My Dubai (IRE)
51 **NATURAL SCENERY**, 5, b m Dubawi (IRE)—Argentina (IRE)
52 **NEXT CHALLENGE (GER)**, 4, ch g Shamardal (USA)—Next Holy (IRE)
53 **OCEAN OF LOVE**, 4, ch f Distorted Humor (USA)—Michita (USA)

MR SAEED BIN SUROOR - Continued

54 PERFECT SENSE, 4, b g Sepoy (AUS)—Miss Chicane
55 PRIZE MONEY, 5, b g Authorized (IRE)—Dresden Doll (USA)
56 PROMISING RUN (USA), 5, b m Hard Spun (USA)—Aviacion (BRZ)
57 RACE DAY (IRE), 5, ch g Dubawi (IRE)—Nadia
58 RACING HISTORY (IRE), 6, b h Pivotal (USA)—Gonbarda (GER)
59 REACH HIGH, 4, ch c Distorted Humor (USA)—Silent Moment (USA)
60 RED GALILEO, 7, b g Dubawi (IRE)—Ivory Gala (FR)
61 RIGHT DIRECTION (IRE), 4, b f Cape Cross (IRE)—Waitress (USA)
62 SECRET NUMBER, 8, b g Raven's Pass (USA)—Mysterial (USA)
63 SILENT ATTACK, 5, b g Dream Ahead (USA)—Chanterelle (FR)
64 SILVER LINE (IRE), 4, gr g Dark Angel (IRE)—Admire The View (IRE)
65 SILVER RIVER, 4, gr g Tamayuz—Tashelka (FR)
66 STEADY PACE, 5, b g Dark Angel (IRE)—Cool Kitten (IRE)
67 TAMLEEK (USA), 4, b br c Hard Spun (USA)—Tafaneen (USA)
68 TEAM TALK, 5, b g Teofilo (IRE)—Native Blue
69 THUNDER SNOW (IRE), 4, b c Helmet (AUS)—Eastern Joy
70 TOP MISSION, 4, b g Dubawi (IRE)—Ever Love (BRZ)
71 TOP SCORE, 4, br g Hard Spun (USA)—Windsor County (USA)
72 VERY TALENTED (IRE), 5, b h Invincible Spirit (IRE)—Crystal House (CHI)
73 VICTORY WAVE (USA), 4, ch f Distorted Humor (USA)—Angel Craft (USA)
74 YATTWEE (USA), 5, b br g Hard Spun (USA)—Alzerra (UAE)

THREE-YEAR-OLDS

75 AL MUSTASHAR (IRE), b g Shamardal (USA)—Dresden Doll (USA)
76 BEAUTIFUL MEMORY (IRE), b f Invincible Spirit (IRE)—Express Way (ARG)
77 BEAUVAIS (IRE), ch c New Approach (IRE)—Marie de Medici (IRE)
78 BEDOUIN'S STORY, b c Farhh—Time Crystal (IRE)
79 CARING TOUCH (USA), b f Elusive Quality (USA)—Blue Petrel (USA)
80 CILEOPATRA (IRE), b f Kodiac—Beatrix Potter (IRE)
81 DESERT MOUNTAIN (IRE), b g Epaulette (AUS)—Al Andalyya (USA)
82 DEYAARNA (USA), b c Kitten's Joy (USA)—Tanaami (USA)
83 DISCOVER DUBAI (IRE), b c Dubawi (IRE)—Flame of Gibraltar (IRE)
84 DRESS COAT, b c Dubawi (IRE)—Peacoat
85 FUTURE SCORE (IRE), b br g Cape Cross (IRE)—Theola (IRE)
86 HAYMAKER (IRE), b c Teofilo (IRE)—Victorian Beauty (USA)
87 JUMEIRAH JOY (IRE), br f Dawn Approach (IRE)—Bulbul (IRE)
88 KASER (IRE), b c Invincible Spirit (IRE)—Lethal Quality (USA)
89 LAIETH, b c Dubawi (IRE)—First City
90 MOKAAFI, b f Nayef (USA)—Ghasabah
91 MOQARRAB (USA), b c Speightstown (USA)—Grosse Pointe Anne (USA)
92 MOSEEB (IRE), b g Invincible Spirit (IRE)—Boastful (IRE)
93 MUTARADAH (USA), b br f Medaglia d'oro (USA)—Jaleela (USA)
94 MUZAAWEL, ch c New Approach (IRE)—Jilnaar (IRE)
95 PIECE OF HISTORY (IRE), b c Iffraaj—Moonlife (IRE)
96 PRIZERING (IRE), ch c Teofilo (IRE)—Beta
97 RACING COUNTRY (IRE), b c Dubawi (IRE)—Movin' Out (AUS)
98 RECORDMAN, ch c Dubawi (IRE)—Reunite (IRE)
99 RETURNING GLORY, b c Exceed And Excel (AUS)—Tanzania (USA)
100 SPRING WATERFALL (IRE), b f Exceed And Excel (AUS)—Forest Pearl (USA)
101 TASNEEM, ch c Teofilo (IRE)—Almass (IRE)
102 ULSTER (IRE), gr ro c Intello (GER)—Ronaldsay
103 VOLCANIC SKY, b c Street Cry (IRE)—Short Skirt
104 WAJAAHA (IRE), b c New Approach (IRE)—Thaahira (USA)
105 WELSH LORD, gr c Dark Angel (IRE)—Welsh Angel
106 WINGS OF GOLD (IRE), ch c Raven's Pass (USA)—Rosa Clara (IRE)
107 WINTER LIGHTNING (IRE), b f Shamardal (USA)—Eastern Joy
108 ZAHEE (IRE), b c Iffraaj—Havin' A Good Time (IRE)

TWO-YEAR-OLDS

109 B c 14/3 Discreet Cat (USA)—Afsana (USA) (Tiznow (USA))
110 B f 1/3 Intello (GER)—Al Tamooh (IRE) (Dalakhani (IRE))
111 B c 16/4 Invincible Spirit (IRE)—Angel's Tears (Seeking The Gold (USA))
112 B c 1/4 Dubawi (IRE)—Anjaz (USA) (Street Cry (IRE))
113 B c 21/2 New Approach (IRE)—Arabian Beauty (IRE) (Shamardal (USA))
114 B f 19/3 Iffraaj—Araqella (IRE) (Oasis Dream) (230000)

MR SAEED BIN SUROOR - Continued

115 Br gr f 19/5 Exceed And Excel (AUS)—Asi Siempre (USA) (El Prado (IRE))
116 B f 27/1 Shamardal (USA)—Beautiful Forest (Nayef (USA))
117 Ch f 16/2 Iffraaj—Belonging (Raven's Pass (USA))
118 B c 8/5 Dansili—Blue Bunting (USA) (Dynaformer (USA))
119 Ch c 22/2 City Zip (USA)—Brattothecore (CAN) (Katahaula County (CAN))
120 B f 21/1 Iffraaj—Brynica (FR) (Desert Style (IRE)) (95000)
121 B c 25/1 Bated Breath—Burn The Breeze (IRE) (Beat Hollow) (89540)
122 Ch f 6/4 More Than Ready (USA)—Cableknit (USA) (Unbridled's Song (USA))
123 Ch f 22/4 Teofilo (IRE)—Calipatria (Shamardal (USA))
124 B br f 15/2 Hard Spun (USA)—Caramel Snap (USA) (Smart Strike (CAN))
125 B c 22/3 Teofilo (IRE)—Chan Tong (BRZ) (Hampstead (URU))
126 B c 25/3 Shamardal (USA)—Colour (AUS) (More Than Ready (USA))
127 B f 24/3 Iffraaj—Dancealot (Lawman (FR)) (105000)
128 B f 13/3 Shamardal (USA)—Dark Orchid (USA) (Dansili)
129 Ch f 12/4 Shamardal (USA)—Devotee (USA) (Elusive Quality (USA))
130 B c 30/4 Dansili—Dysphonia (AUS) (Lonhro (AUS))
131 B f 1/3 Invincible Spirit (IRE)—Emily Bronte (Machiavellian (USA))
132 B br c 19/4 Arch (USA)—Enrichment (USA) (Ghostzapper (USA))
133 B c 30/3 Kingman—Epic Similie (Lomitas)
134 Ch f 11/2 Pivotal—Fading Light (King's Best (USA))
135 B c 6/2 New Approach (IRE)—Fawaayed (IRE) (Singspiel (IRE))
136 Gr f 23/3 New Approach (IRE)—Fire Blaze (IRE) (Dubawi (IRE))
137 B c 29/3 Invincible Spirit (IRE)—Floristry (Fasliyev (USA))
138 B f 29/2 Pivotal—Ghasabah (Dansili)
139 B f 21/2 Pivotal—Gonbarda (GER) (Lando (GER))
140 B c 9/2 Cape Cross (IRE)—Gower Song (Singspiel (IRE))
141 Ch c 13/3 Dubawi (IRE)—Hanky Panky (IRE) (Galileo (IRE))
142 B f 2/5 Exceed And Excel (AUS)—Heart's Content (IRE) (Daylami (IRE))
143 B f 18/2 Invincible Spirit (IRE)—Heartily (IRE) (Dubawi (IRE))
144 B c 21/4 Lope de Vega (IRE)—High Heel Sneakers (Dansili) (120000)
145 B br c 19/2 Iffraaj—Homily (Singspiel (IRE))
146 B c 26/4 Raven's Pass (USA)—Inner Secret (USA) (Singspiel (IRE))
147 B c 8/3 Delegator—Irrational (Kyllachy) (66666)
148 B f 8/4 Teofilo (IRE)—Isobel Archer (Oasis Dream)
149 Gr c 10/4 Alhebayeb (IRE)—Jawaaneb (USA) (Kingmambo (USA)) (52380)
150 JUMEIRAH ONE, b c 3/4 Dawn Approach (IRE)—Bulbul (IRE) (Shamardal (USA))
151 B br c 9/3 Dawn Approach (IRE)—Kalaatah (USA) (Dynaformer (USA))
152 Ch c 16/1 Shamardal (USA)—La Collina (IRE) (Strategic Prince)
153 B f 10/3 Invincible Spirit (IRE)—Lady Marian (GER) (Nayef (USA))
154 B c 14/2 Sea The Stars (IRE)—Lamazonia (IRE) (Elusive City (USA)) (260000)
155 Ch c 8/3 Dubawi (IRE)—Lava Flow (IRE) (Dalakhani (IRE))
156 B c 9/3 Teofilo (IRE)—Loreto (IRE) (Holy Roman Emperor (IRE)) (200000)
157 B c 20/2 Iffraaj—Lunar Spirit (Invincible Spirit (IRE)) (140000)
158 Ch f 20/3 Toronado (IRE)—Maid To Dream (Oasis Dream) (85000)
159 B c 16/1 Slade Power—Many Colours (Green Desert (USA))
160 Br c 14/3 Sea The Stars (IRE)—Martine's Spirit (IRE) (Invincible Spirit (IRE))
161 B f 25/2 Frankel—Minidress (Street Cry (IRE))
162 B f 12/3 Teofilo (IRE)—Moonlife (IRE) (Invincible Spirit (IRE))
163 B f 10/4 Invincible Spirit (IRE)—Movin' Out (AUS) (Encosta de Lago (AUS))
164 B f 6/3 Raven's Pass (USA)—Mujarah (IRE) (Marju (IRE))
165 B c 13/4 Shamardal (USA)—Petrushka (IRE) (Unfuwain (USA))
166 Ch c 5/3 Pivotal—Portrayal (USA) (Saint Ballado (CAN))
167 B c 11/4 Cape Cross (IRE)—Potent Embrace (USA) (Street Cry (IRE))
168 B c 25/3 Raven's Pass (USA)—Prussian (Dubai Destination (USA))
169 Ch f 12/2 Shamardal (USA)—Raphinae (Dubawi (IRE))
170 B c 1/3 Toronado (IRE)—Raskutani (Dansili) (325000)
171 Ch c 30/3 Dubawi (IRE)—Rehn's Nest (IRE) (Authorized (IRE)) (320000)
172 B c 24/3 Oasis Dream—Reunite (IRE) (Kingmambo (USA))
173 B c 16/4 Invincible Spirit (IRE)—Rock Opera (SAF) (Lecture (USA))
174 B c 28/4 Kodiac—Romie's Kastett (GER) (Halling (USA)) (300000)
175 Ch c 13/3 Dubawi (IRE)—Rosewater (IRE) (Pivotal)
176 B f 12/4 Exceed And Excel (AUS)—Sander Camillo (USA) (Dixie Union (USA))
177 B c 21/3 Dubawi (IRE)—Scatina (IRE) (Samum (GER))
178 Ch c 9/3 Dubawi (IRE)—Scatter Dice (IRE) (Manduro (GER))
179 Ch c 11/2 Pivotal—Secret Keeper (New Approach (IRE))

MR SAEED BIN SUROOR - Continued

180 B f 28/2 Pivotal—Shallow Lake (USA) (Bernardini (USA))
181 B f 26/4 Invincible Spirit (IRE)—Siyaadah (Shamardal (USA))
182 B c 7/5 Farhh—Siyasa (USA) (Rahy (USA)) (82000)
183 B f 22/2 Slade Power (IRE)—Sleeping Beauty (IRE) (Oasis Dream) (260000)
184 B c 15/2 Slade Power (IRE)—Snowdrops (Gulch (USA)) (72000)
185 B c 12/3 Sea The Stars (IRE)—Something Mon (USA) (Maria's Mon (USA))
186 B f 22/2 More Than Ready (USA)—Speckled (USA) (Street Cry (IRE))
187 B f 15/3 Dawn Approach (IRE)—Spring Oak (Mark of Esteem (IRE))
188 B c 28/3 Teofilo (IRE)—Star Blossom (USA) (Good Reward (USA))
189 B c 12/3 Dubawi (IRE)—Suez (Green Desert (USA))
190 B f 23/2 Dansili—Summer School (IRE) (Street Cry (IRE))
191 B c 6/3 Dubawi (IRE)—Surprise Moment (IRE) (Authorized (IRE))
192 B f 14/2 Invincible Spirit (IRE)—Tulips (IRE) (Pivotal)
193 Ch f 20/3 New Approach (IRE)—Violante (USA) (Kingmambo (USA))
194 Ch c 3/4 New Approach (IRE)—Wahgah (USA) (Distorted Humor (USA))
195 B c 5/4 Medaglia d'oro (USA)—Wavering (IRE) (Refuse To Bend (IRE))
196 Ch f 30/1 Dubawi (IRE)—White Rose (GER) (Platini (GER))
197 B br f 16/4 Teofilo (IRE)—Willow Beck (Shamardal (USA))
198 B f 7/5 Cape Cross (IRE)—Wizara (IRE) (Teofilo (IRE))
199 B c 7/3 Zebedee—Worthington (IRE) (Kodiac) (66666)
200 B c 17/3 Dutch Art—Yellow Rosebud (IRE) (Jeremy (USA))

---

42 | **MRS EMMA BISHOP, Cheltenham**
Postal: **Brockhill, Naunton, Cheltenham, Gloucestershire, GL54 3BA**
Contacts: **FAX (01451) 850199 MOBILE (07887) 845970**
E-MAIL emmajbakerracing@hotmail.co.uk WEBSITE www.emmabakerracing.com

1 **ARQUEBUSIER (FR)**, 8, br g Discover d'auteuil (FR)—Djurjura (FR) **Mr R. Foulquies**
2 **BACK BY MIDNIGHT**, 9, ch g Midnight Legend—Roberta Back (IRE) **Select Racing Club & Mrs M J Arnold**
3 **BAJARDO (IRE)**, 10, b g Jammaal—Bit of Peace **Mrs J. Arnold**
4 **BOURDELLO**, 9, b m Milan—Haudello (FR) **Mrs J. Arnold**
5 **BRINESTINE (USA)**, 9, b g Bernstein (USA)—Miss Zafonic (FR) **Brians Buddies**
6 **CHURCH HALL (IRE)**, 10, b g Craigsteel—Island Religion (IRE) **Mrs J. Arnold**
7 **GLANCE BACK**, 7, b g Passing Glance—Roberta Back (IRE) **Select Racing Club & Mrs M J Arnold**
8 **GREY MESSENGER (IRE)**, 9, gr g Heron Island (IRE)—Turlututu (FR) **Mrs E. J. Bishop**
9 **SHEEZA LEGEND**, 4, b f Midnight Legend—Roberta Back (IRE) **Mrs J. Arnold**
10 **SNOWELL (IRE)**, 11, b g Well Chosen—Snow Water (IRE) **Mrs E. J. Bishop**
11 **SUBTLE APPROACH (IRE)**, 13, b g Subtle Power (IRE)—Rotoruasprings (IRE) **Mrs J. Arnold**

Other Owners: Mr Michael J. Arnold, The Select Racing Club Limited.

---

43 | **MR KEVIN BISHOP, Bridgwater**
Postal: **Barford Park Stables, Spaxton, Bridgwater, Somerset, TA5 1AF**
Contacts: **PHONE/FAX (01278) 671437 MOBILE (07816) 837610**
E-MAIL hevbishop@hotmail.com

1 **BARATINEUR (FR)**, 7, ch g Vendangeur (IRE)—Olmantina (FR) **Mr O. J. Barratt**
2 **CALCULATED RISK**, 9, ch g Motivator—Glen Rosie (IRE) **Mr B. M. Jones**
3 **INNOX PARK**, 8, b g Helissio (FR)—Redgrave Bay **W. Davies**
4 **JUST SPOT**, 11, ch m Baryshnikov (AUS)—Just Jasmine **K. Bishop**
5 **LETS GO DUTCHESS**, 8, b m Helissio (FR)—Lets Go Dutch **K. Bishop**
6 **LIVE FOR TODAY (IRE)**, 7, b g Alflora (IRE)—Uppermost **Mr D. Bond**
7 **REFUSED A NAME**, 11, b g Montjeu (IRE)—Dixielake (IRE) **Mr J. Young**
8 **SOMERSET JEM**, 9, b g Sir Harry Lewis (USA)—Monger Lane **Slabs & Lucan**
9 **THE GREAT RAYMONDO**, 6, b g Passing Glance—Fantasy Parkes **Slabs & Lucan**
10 **THE KID**, 7, b g High Chaparral (IRE)—Shine Like A Star **Cavalier Racing**
11 **THE MAD WELL (IRE)**, 9, b g Milan—Silverfortprincess (IRE) **CAU Partnership**

Other Owners: Mr J. Barratt, Mr P. Clough, Miss S. Macey, C. J. Macey.

Assistant Trainer: Heather Bishop

Conditional: Conor Smith.

44 MISS LINDA BLACKFORD, Tiverton
Postal: **Shortlane Stables, Rackenford, Tiverton, Devon, EX16 8EH**
Contacts: **PHONE** (01884) 881589 **MOBILE** (07887) 947832
E-MAIL overthelast@outlook.com **WEBSITE** www.overthelast.com

1 **CELTIC STYLE (IRE)**, 5, b m Craigsteel—Kissangel (IRE) **Over The Last Racing**
2 **KAYF CHARMER**, 8, b m Kayf Tara—Silver Charmer **Mrs V. W. Jones & Mr B. P. Jones**
3 **LADY WETHERED (IRE)**, 6, br m Westerner—Vics Miller (IRE) **Mr M. P. Beer**
4 **LOUIS PHILLIPE (IRE)**, 11, ch g Croco Rouge (IRE)—Presenting's Wager (IRE) **Easylife Partnership**
5 **LURE DES PRES (IRE)**, 6, b g Robin des Pres (FR)—Pinkeen Lady (IRE) **Over The Last Racing**
6 **MOUNTAIN OF MOURNE (IRE)**, 9, ch g Mountain High (IRE)—Katies Native (IRE) **Over The Last Racing**
7 **ROWLEY PARK (IRE)**, 5, b g Golan (IRE)—Atomic Winner (IRE) **The Rowley Partnership**
8 **STEEL EXPRESS (IRE)**, 6, b g Craigsteel—Assidua (IRE) **Mrs Susan Quick**
9 **THATS YER MAN (IRE)**, 10, ch g Marignan (USA)—Glengarra Princess **Over The Last Racing**

Other Owners: Miss L. A. Blackford, Mr H. Bray, B. P. Jones, Mrs V. W. Jones, Mr M. J. Vanstone, Mr B. Woolfenden.

Assistant Trainer: M. J. Vanstone

Jockey (NH): James Best, Micheal Nolan, Nick Scholfield, Conor Smith. **Conditional:** Sean Houlihan.
Amateur: Mr J. O'Conor.

45 MR ALAN BLACKMORE, Hertford
Postal: **'Chasers', Stockings Lane, Little Berkhamsted, Hertford**
Contacts: **PHONE** (01707) 875060 **MOBILE** (07803) 711453

1 **COCKER**, 6, b g Shirocco (GER)—Treble Heights (IRE) **A. G. Blackmore**
2 **OCCASIONALLY YOURS (IRE)**, 14, b g Moscow Society (USA)—Kristina's Lady (IRE) **A. G. Blackmore**

Assistant Trainer: Mrs P. M. Blackmore

Jockey (NH): Marc Goldstein. **Amateur:** Miss Tabitha Worsley.

46 MR MICHAEL BLAKE, Trowbridge
Postal: **Staverton Farm, Trowbridge, Wiltshire, BA14 6PE**
Contacts: **PHONE** (01225) 782327 **MOBILE** (07971) 675180
E-MAIL mblakestavertonfarm@btinternet.com **WEBSITE** www.michaelblakeracing.co.uk

1 **BARNEY FROM TYANEE (IRE)**, 7, b g Milan—Miss Opera **Staverton Owners Group**
2 **BOUNTY PURSUIT**, 6, b g Pastoral Pursuits—Poyle Dee Dee **Racing For A Cause**
3 **BROADWAY DREAMS**, 4, b g Oasis Dream—Rosa Eglanteria **The Moonlighters**
4 **CAPTAIN GEORGE (IRE)**, 7, b g Bushranger (IRE)—High Society Girl (IRE) **Staverton Owners Group**
5 **COOLE CODY (IRE)**, 7, b g Dubai Destination (USA)—Run For Cover (IRE) **H. M. W. Clifford**
6 **DOUBLY CLEVER (IRE)**, 6, ch g Iffraaj—Smartest (IRE) **The Moonlighters**
7 **INIESTA (IRE)**, 7, b g Galileo (IRE)—Red Evie (IRE) **The Milk Sheiks**
8 **IPFLIBBYDIBBY (IRE)**, 6, b g Morozov (USA)—Sahara Storm (IRE) **The Milk Sheiks**
9 **KAABER (USA)**, 7, b g Daaher (CAN)—Taseel (USA) **Mr J. Holt**
10 **PICK A LITTLE**, 10, b g Piccolo—Little Caroline (IRE) **Mrs J. M. Haines**
11 **WAITINONASUNNYDAY (IRE)**, 5, gr g Tikkanen (USA)—Coppenagh Lady (IRE) **West Wilts Hockey Lads**

Other Owners: M. J. Blake, Mrs S. E. Blake, Mr R. C. Butcher, Mrs V. A. Butcher, Mrs J. L. Godwin, Mr K. D. Linsley, Mr G. A. Windle, Mr A. J. Windle.

Assistant Trainer: Sharon Blake (07812) 599904

47 MR MICHAEL BLANSHARD, Upper Lambourn
Postal: **Lethornes Stables, Upper Lambourn, Hungerford, Berkshire, RG17 8QP**
Contacts: **PHONE** (01488) 71091 **FAX** (01488) 73497 **MOBILE** (07785) 370093
E-MAIL blanshard.racing@btconnect.com **WEBSITE** www.michaelblanshard.com

1 **ACCOMPLICE**, 4, b f Sakhee's Secret—Witness **The Reignmakers**
2 **DELAHAY**, 4, b f Delegator—Harryana To **The Dreamers**
3 **EXSPECTATION (IRE)**, 4, b g Exceleration—Emeralds Spirit (IRE) **Mr J. K. Gale**

MR MICHAEL BLANSHARD - Continued

4 **FAMOUS DYNASTY (IRE)**, 4, b g Famous Name—Daffodil Walk (IRE) **Famous Dynasty Partnership**
5 **FEEL THE VIBES**, 4, b g Medicean—Apple Dumpling **The Reignmakers**
6 **GARCON DE SOLEIL**, 5, b g Danehill Dancer (USA)—Darinza (FR) **Lady E. Mays-Smith**
7 **IVANHOE**, 8, b g Haafhd—Marysienka **The Ivanhoe Partnership**
8 **PENNEYS HUN (IRE)**, 5, b g Arakan (USA)—De Street (IRE) **Lady E. Mays-Smith**

THREE-YEAR-OLDS

9 **BLACKWOOD**, b g Firebreak—Witness
10 **MAY SPIRIT**, b f Mayson—World Spirit **The Reignmakers**
11 **MRS BENSON (IRE)**, ch f Rip Van Winkle (IRE)—Ebble **R. P. B. Michaelson**
12 **POWERFUL ROSE**, b f Power—Fenella Rose **Lady E MaysSmith J Gale P Roberts V Ward**

TWO-YEAR-OLDS

13 Ch c 21/2 Compton Place—Artistic License (IRE) (Chevalier (IRE)) (7000)
14 B gr c 1/3 Aussie Rules (USA)—Island Rhapsody (Bahamian Bounty)
15 **MILISTORM**, b f 18/3 Sepoy (AUS)—Oasis Breeze (Oasis Dream) (18000) **V. Ward**
16 B f 5/3 Archipenko (USA)—Moonavvara (IRE) (Sadler's Wells (USA))
17 B f 6/3 Penny's Picnic (IRE)—Rue Pomereu (IRE) (Dubawi (IRE)) (3000)
18 **THE COMMANCHERO**, ch c 14/2 Equiano (FR)—Lily In Pink (Sakhee (USA)) (2000) **N. Price & Partners**

Other Owners: Mrs Jane Abraham, Mr S. Beccle, Mr M. Blanshard, Mr D. Cannings, Mrs Emma Clarke, Mr J. A. Cover, Mr John K. Gale, Dr Andrew Gay, Lady Eliza Mays-Smith, B. Mitchell, Mr M. J. Prescott, Mr Nick Price, Mr Peter Roberts, Mr Vincent Ward.

---

48 **MISS GILLIAN BOANAS**, Saltburn
Postal: **Groundhill Farm, Lingdale, Saltburn, Cleveland, TS12 3HD**
Contacts: **MOBILE (07976) 280154**
E-MAIL gillianboanas@aol.com

1 **BRAVE SPARTACUS (IRE)**, 12, b g Spartacus (IRE)—Peaches Polly **Miss Gillian Boanas Mr Douglas Renton**
2 **CLOGHOUGE BOY (IRE)**, 8, b g Westerner—Back To Cloghoge (IRE) **Miss G. L. Boanas**
3 **CRIXUS'S ESCAPE (IRE)**, 5, ch g Beneficial—Tierneys Choice (IRE) **Mr R. Collins**
4 **MADINAT**, 4, B g Sulamani (IRE)—Fairlie **Miss G. L. Boanas**
5 **FLORAMOSS**, 7, b m Alflora (IRE)—Brackenmoss (IRE) **The Lingdale Optimists & Mrs M B Thwaites**
6 **FRENCH SEVENTYFIVE**, 11, b g Pursuit of Love—Miss Tun **Miss G. L. Boanas**
7 **GREAT COLACI**, 5, b g Sulamani (IRE)—Fairlie **Rug, Grub & Pub Partnership**
8 **MADINAT**, 4, ch g Haafhd—Let It Be **Mr A. Frame**
9 **NOBEL ROSE**, 4, ch f Sholokhov (IRE)—Florarossa **Miss G. L. Boanas**
10 4, B f Schiaparelli (GER)—Nobratinetta (FR) **Mrs M B Thwaites & Mr M E Foxton**
11 **PENNY BLAK**, 5, ch g Black Sam Bellamy (IRE)—Pennys Pride (IRE) **Sir Ian Good & Mr C anderson**
12 **ROCK N'STONES (IRE)**, 7, b g Stowaway—Rock Abbey (IRE) **Miss G. L. Boanas**
13 **ST ANDREWS (IRE)**, 5, ch g Rip Van Winkle (IRE)—Stellavera (FR) **Mr John Coates Mr Richard Smith**
14 **SULTANS PRIDE**, 6, b g Sulamani (IRE)—Pennys Pride (IRE) **Reveley Racing 1 & Partner**
15 **SWEET VINETTA**, 4, b f Fair Mix (IRE)—Vinetta **The Supreme Partnership**
16 **TEESCOMPONENTS BOY (IRE)**, 4, b g Midnight Legend—Northern Native (IRE) **Tees Components Ltd**
17 **TEESCOMPONENTS LAD**, 5, b g Midnight Legend—Northern Native (IRE) **Tees Components Ltd**
18 **TEESCOMPONENTS MAX**, 9, b g Grape Tree Road—Our Tees Component (IRE) **Tees Components Ltd**
19 **TETRAITES STYLE (IRE)**, 6, b g Court Cave (IRE)—Kilmessan (IRE) **Mr R. Collins**
20 5, Br g Presenting—Tonaphuca Girl (IRE)
21 **WALTZ DARLING (IRE)**, 10, b g Iffraaj—Aljafliyah **Mrs M B Thwaites & Mr M E Foxton**

THREE-YEAR-OLDS

22 **BROCTUNE RED**, ch g Haafhd—Fairlie **Mrs M. B. Thwaites**

Other Owners: Mr T. Alderson, C. Anderson, Mrs M. A. Bauckham, Mrs C. M. Baxter, J. W. Coates, Mr A. Collins, Mr M. Cressey, B. D. Drinkall, M. E. Foxton, Sir Ian Good, Mr B. W. Goodall, D. A. Green, Mr K. S. Matthews, Mr A. J. Rae, D. C. Renton, Reveley Farms, Reveley Racing 1, R. V. Smith, D. Wild.

49 MR J. S. BOLGER, Carlow

Postal: Glebe House, Coolcullen, Carlow, Ireland
Contacts: PHONE (00353) 56 4443150 (00353) 56 4443158 FAX (00353) 56 4443256
E-MAIL racing@jsb.ie

1 CLONGOWES (IRE), 4, b c New Approach (IRE)—Punctilious **Godolphin**
2 GOLDRUSH (IRE), 4, b f Frankel—Alexander Goldrun (IRE) **China Horse Club**
3 PANSTARR, 4, b f Pivotal—Halle Bop **Godolphin**
4 RINGSIDE SUPPORT (IRE), 4, b g Teofilo (IRE)—Halla Siamsa (IRE) **Godolphin**
5 TRIBAL BEAT (IRE), 5, b h Street Cry (IRE)—Tashelka (FR) **Godolphin**
6 TWILIGHT PAYMENT (IRE), 5, b g Teofilo (IRE)—Dream On Buddy (IRE) **Godolphin**
7 ZORION, 4, b c Smart Strike (CAN)—Zofzig (USA) **Godolphin**

THREE-YEAR-OLDS

8 ACTIVE APPROACH, ch f New Approach (IRE)—Saoirse Abu (USA) **Godolphin**
9 BACK AT DAWN (IRE), br f Dawn Approach (IRE)—Yes Oh Yes (USA) **Mrs J. S. Bolger**
10 CHANGE OF VELOCITY (IRE), b c Teofilo (IRE)—Tiffilia (IRE) **Godolphin**
11 CIMEARA (IRE), b f Vocalised (USA)—Gold Mirage (IRE) **Mrs J. S. Bolger**
12 CLAIOMH GEAL, ch f Leroidesanimaux (BRZ)—Claiomh Solais (IRE) **Ms Kirsten Rausing**
13 COME AT DAWN (IRE), ch f Dawn Approach (IRE)—Luminaria (IRE) **Mrs J. S. Bolger**
14 DAWN ARRIVAL (IRE), ch c Dawn Approach (IRE)—Maoineach (USA) **Godolphin**
15 DAWN DELIVERS, ch f Dawn Approach (IRE)—Siyasa (USA) **Godolphin**
16 DAWN HOOFER (IRE), b f Dawn Approach (IRE)—Super Hoofer (IRE) **Mrs J. S. Bolger**
17 DREAM OF WORDS (IRE), ch f Dream Ahead (USA)—Cleofila (IRE) **Mrs J. S. Bolger**
18 DUBAI IS GREAT, b c Cape Cross (IRE)—Scatina (IRE) **Godolphin**
19 EPANEEMA (IRE), b f Epaulette (AUS)—Taqqara (USA) **Mrs J. S. Bolger**
20 FIANNAIOCHT (IRE), b f Vocalised (USA)—Fionnuar (IRE) **Mrs J. S. Bolger**
21 FLAMMA CLARUS (IRE), ch f Teofilo (IRE)—Tiz The Whiz (USA) **Mrs J. S. Bolger**
22 LUCEITA (IRE), ch f Dawn Approach (IRE)—Lura (USA) **Godolphin**
23 MEAGHER'S FLAG (IRE), b c Teofilo (IRE)—Gearanai (USA) **Mrs J. S. Bolger**
24 MEDIA CITY (IRE), b c Teofilo (IRE)—Khazina (USA) **Godolphin**
25 MIRACULUM (IRE), b f Teofilo (IRE)—Manayer (IRE) **Mrs J. S. Bolger**
26 NATIONAL SECURITY (IRE), ch c Teofilo (IRE)—Halla Siamsa (IRE) **Godolphin**
27 NEW TO TOWN (IRE), b f New Approach (IRE)—Tiffed (USA) **Mrs J. S. Bolger**
28 NEW TO WEXFORD (IRE), b f New Approach (IRE)—Danemarque (AUS) **Mrs J. S. Bolger**
29 NEW VOCATION (IRE), b f Vocalised (USA)—Neophilia (USA) **Mrs J. S. Bolger**
30 PARK BLOOM (IRE), b f Galileo (IRE)—Alluring Park (IRE) **Mrs Patricia Burns**
31 PLEISIUR (IRE), b f Vocalised (USA)—Toirneach (USA) **Mrs J. S. Bolger**
32 REALTIN GEAL (USA), ch f Street Boss—Bella Trella (USA) **Mrs J. S. Bolger**
33 RINCE DEIREANACH (IRE), b f Teofilo (IRE)—National Swagger (USA) **Mrs J. S. Bolger**
34 SCOIL NAISIUNTA (IRE), b f Intense Focus (USA)—Ciste Naisiunta (IRE) **Mrs J. S. Bolger**
35 SCRIOBH NUA (IRE), b f New Approach (IRE)—Scribonia (IRE) **Mrs J. S. Bolger**
36 SMART LIVING (IRE), b c Teofilo (IRE)—Ard Fheis (IRE) **Godolphin**
37 SOLAR WAVE (IRE), b f Vocalised (USA)—Solar Outburst (USA) **Mrs J. S. Bolger**
38 SOMETIMESADIAMOND (IRE), b f Vocalised (USA)—Something Graceful **Mrs June Judd**
39 SOUTH EAST (IRE), b c Vocalised (USA)—Elida (IRE) **Mrs J. S. Bolger**
40 STRIKE FOR FREEDOM (IRE), b g Dream Ahead (USA)—Saor Sinn (IRE) **Mrs J. S. Bolger**
41 STYLER LABEL (IRE), b f Vocalised (USA)—Style Queen (IRE) **Mrs J. S. Bolger**
42 SWING TILL DAWN (IRE), b f Dawn Approach (IRE)—Snas (USA) **Mrs J. S. Bolger**
43 TEOLOGIA (IRE), b f Teofilo (IRE)—Maria Lee (IRE) **Mrs J. S. Bolger**
44 THEOBALD (IRE), ch c Teofilo (IRE)—Sanaara (USA) **Mrs J. S. Bolger**
45 THEOTONIUS (IRE), b c Teofilo (IRE)—My Fere Lady **Godolphin**
46 VENETIAN ROCK (IRE), b c Fastnet Rock (AUS)—Marina of Venice (IRE) **Mrs J. S. Bolger**
47 VERBAL DEXTERITY (IRE), b c Vocalised (USA)—Lonrach (IRE) **Mrs J. S. Bolger**
48 VERBITUDE (IRE), b c Vocalised (USA)—Bring Back Matron (IRE) **Mrs J. S. Bolger**
49 VOCAL CHORD (IRE), b c Vocalised (USA)—Symmetrical (USA) **Mrs J. S. Bolger**
50 VOCAL MUSIC (IRE), b c Vocalised (USA)—Christmas Letter (IRE) **Mrs J. S. Bolger**

TWO-YEAR-OLDS

51 ABSOLUTE FOCUS (IRE), b c 21/3 Intense Focus (USA)—Absolutus (USA) (Perfect Soul (IRE)) **Mrs J. S. Bolger**
52 AEQUALIS (IRE), b c 27/3 Vocalised (USA)—Symmetrical (USA) (Unbridled's Song (USA)) **Mrs J. S. Bolger**
53 AISLING GHEAR (IRE), b f 10/5 Dream Ahead (USA)—
                      Prudent Approach (IRE) (New Approach (IRE)) **Mrs J. S. Bolger**
54 ALL AMERICAN (IRE), b c 29/4 Vocalised (USA)—Tiffed (USA) (Seattle Slew (USA)) **Mrs J. S. Bolger**

MR J. S. BOLGER - Continued

55 **ALMOST DAWN (IRE)**, ch c 8/2 New Approach (IRE)—
Hymn of The Dawn (USA) (Phone Trick (USA)) **Mrs J. S. Bolger**
56 **AMBITIOUS APPROACH (IRE)**, b c 29/2 Dawn Approach (IRE)—Estiqbaal (Oasis Dream) **Mrs J. S. Bolger**
57 **APPLY HEAT (IRE)**, b f 28/1 Pour Moi (IRE)—Teocht (IRE) (Teofilo (IRE)) **Mrs J. S. Bolger**
58 **BANDIUC EILE (IRE)**, b f 6/3 New Approach (IRE)—Dream On Buddy (IRE) (Oasis Dream) **Mrs J. S. Bolger**
59 **BOLD APPROACH (IRE)**, b c 30/1 Dawn Approach (IRE)—
Excuse Me (USA) (Distorted Humor (USA)) **Mrs J. S. Bolger**
60 **CEISTIU (IRE)**, b f 6/4 Vocalised (USA)—Ceist Eile (Noverre (USA)) **Mrs J. S. Bolger**
61 **CLOSER NOW (IRE)**, b f 11/2 New Approach (IRE)—Tiffilia (IRE) (Macho Uno (USA)) (4069) **Mrs J. S. Bolger**
62 **COPIA VERBORUM (IRE)**, b c 3/4 Vocalised (USA)—Gold Focus (IRE) (Intense Focus (USA)) **Mrs J. S. Bolger**
63 **CRANNOG (IRE)**, b f 11/5 Dawn Approach (IRE)—City Square (IRE) (Lawman (FR)) (4070) **James Dowling**
64 **CRUCIATUS (IRE)**, b c 26/3 Teofilo (IRE)—Becalm (USA) (Dixie Union (USA)) **Mrs J. S. Bolger**
65 **CUBAN HEART (IRE)**, b f 20/2 Teofilo (IRE)—Croi Na Feile (USA) (Perfect Soul (IRE)) **Mrs J. S. Bolger**
66 **CUBAN SURFER (IRE)**, b f 26/1 Teofilo (IRE)—My Girl Sophie (USA) (Danzig (USA)) **Mrs J. S. Bolger**
67 **CUILEANN (IRE)**, b f 3/3 Vocalised (USA)—Rachida (IRE) (Hurricane Run (IRE)) **Mrs J. S. Bolger**
68 **DATHULACHT (IRE)**, b f 2/3 Teofilo (IRE)—Napping (USA) (Danzig (USA)) **Mrs J. S. Bolger**
69 **DAWN OF DAY (IRE)**, b f 27/4 Dawn Approach (IRE)—Ard Fheis (IRE) (Lil's Boy (USA)) **Mrs J. S. Bolger**
70 **EARLY VOICE (IRE)**, b c 8/4 Vocalised (USA)—Maidin Moch (IRE) (High Chaparral (IRE)) **Mrs J. S. Bolger**
71 **ELEGANTER (IRE)**, b f 27/2 Vocalised (USA)—Something Graceful (Galileo (IRE)) **Mrs J. S. Bolger**
72 **EXCESS FEES (IRE)**, b c 8/5 Lawman (FR)—Solas Na Greine (IRE) (Galileo (USA)) **Mrs J. S. Bolger**
73 Ch c 31/3 New Approach (IRE)—Falls of Lora (IRE) (Street Cry (IRE)) **Godolphin**
74 **FAMOUS VOICE (IRE)**, b c 16/4 Vocalised (USA)—Cailiuil (IRE) (New Approach (IRE)) **Mrs J. S. Bolger**
75 **FERRUM (IRE)**, b c 5/4 Sea The Moon (GER)—Claiomh Solais (IRE) (Galileo (IRE)) (81400) **Mrs J. S. Bolger**
76 **FLOW OF WORDS (IRE)**, b f 21/2 Vocalised (USA)—
Danemarque (AUS) (Danehill (USA)) (29304) **Mrs J. S. Bolger**
77 **FREEDOM COME (IRE)**, b f 7/4 Dream Ahead (USA)—Saor Sinn (IRE) (Galileo (IRE)) **Mrs J. S. Bolger**
78 **FULVIO (USA)**, b c 25/4 Bernardini (USA)—Lacadena (USA) (Fasliyev (USA)) (116144) **China Horse Club**
79 **GEOLAI (IRE)**, ch f 10/3 New Approach (IRE)—
Maria Lee (IRE) (Rock of Gibraltar (IRE)) (162800) **Mrs J. S. Bolger**
80 **GIROLAMO (IRE)**, ch c 12/5 Dawn Approach (USA)—Dublin Six (USA) (Kingmambo (USA)) **Mrs J. S. Bolger**
81 **GUARANTEED (IRE)**, b c 26/2 Teofilo (IRE)—Gearanai (USA) (Toccet (USA)) **Mrs J. S. Bolger**
82 **IT'S NOT TOO LATE (IRE)**, b c 15/5 Vocalised (USA)—
Bring Back Matron (IRE) (Rock of Gibraltar (IRE)) **Mrs J. S. Bolger**
83 **LAETHANTA SAOIRE (IRE)**, ch f 2/2 New Approach (IRE)—Saoire (Pivotal) **Mrs J. S. Bolger**
84 B c 14/4 Shamardal (USA)—Lailani (Unfuwain (USA)) **Godolphin**
85 Ch c 3/4 Teofilo (IRE)—Laughing Owl (IRE) (Dubai Destination (USA)) **Godolphin**
86 **LEINSTER DAWN (IRE)**, b f 2/4 Dawn Approach (IRE)—Manayer (IRE) (Sadler's Wells (USA)) **Mrs J. S. Bolger**
87 **LINGUISTIC STYLE (IRE)**, b c 3/3 Vocalised (USA)—Legal Farce (IRE) (Lawman (FR)) **Mrs J. S. Bolger**
88 **LISTENING MODE (IRE)**, b c 15/5 Vocalised (USA)—Teoirim (IRE) (Teofilo (IRE)) **Mrs J. S. Bolger**
89 **MAKE ME SWAY (IRE)**, b f 18/3 Teofilo (IRE)—Sway Me Now (USA) (Speightstown (USA)) **Mrs J. S. Bolger**
90 Ch f 1/5 Dawn Approach (IRE)—Morning Bell (Monsun (GER)) **Godolphin**
91 **MOTHER VINCENT (IRE)**, b f 1/3 Vocalised (USA)—Teolane (IRE) (Teofilo (IRE)) **Mrs J. S. Bolger**
92 **NATIONAL IDENTITY (IRE)**, b f 28/2 New Approach (IRE)—
Irish Question (IRE) (Giant's Causeway (USA)) **Mrs J. S. Bolger**
93 **NEWS ANCHOR (IRE)**, ch c 20/1 New Approach (IRE)—Halla Na Saoire (IRE) (Teofilo (IRE)) **Mrs J. S. Bolger**
94 **NOVUS ADITUS (IRE)**, b c 17/2 Teofilo (IRE)—Novel Approach (IRE) (New Approach (IRE)) **Mrs J. S. Bolger**
95 **OICHE RE GEALAI (IRE)**, ch f 11/4 Dawn Approach (IRE)—Oiche Ghealai (IRE) (Galileo (IRE)) **Mrs J. S. Bolger**
96 **PAISEAN (IRE)**, b f 30/4 Dawn Approach (IRE)—Neophilia (IRE) (Teofilo (IRE)) **Mrs J. S. Bolger**
97 **PAISTIUL (IRE)**, ch f 25/4 Dawn Approach (IRE)—Pastilla (USA) (Pulpit (USA)) **Mrs J. S. Bolger**
98 **PLOUGHLAND (IRE)**, b f 3/2 Vocalised (USA)—Starland (USA) (Galileo (USA)) **Mrs J. S. Bolger**
99 **POISED FOR CHANGE (IRE)**, b f 25/2 Pour Moi (IRE)—Teo's Sister (IRE) (Galileo (IRE)) **Mrs J. S. Bolger**
100 **PRIMA LUX (IRE)**, b c 28/2 Dawn Approach (IRE)—Imeall Na Speire (USA) (Galileo (USA)) **Mrs J. S. Bolger**
101 **REPETITIO (IRE)**, b c 14/1 Pour Moi (IRE)—Fionnuar (IRE) (Teofilo (IRE)) (12210) **Mrs J. S. Bolger**
102 Ch f 8/3 Dubawi (IRE)—Saoirse Abu (USA) (Mr Greeley (USA)) **Godolphin**
103 **SLANEY SAND (IRE)**, ch c 14/2 Dawn Approach (IRE)—Scribonia (IRE) (Danehill (USA)) **Mrs J. S. Bolger**
104 **SMART FLIES (IRE)**, ch f 14/2 Dawn Approach (IRE)—Take Flight (IRE) (Pivotal) **Mrs J. S. Bolger**
105 **SOLAR WIND (IRE)**, b c 2/3 Dawn Approach (USA)—Solar Outburst (IRE) (Galileo (USA)) **Mrs J. S. Bolger**
106 **SON OF BEAUTY (IRE)**, b c 30/1 Vocalised (USA)—Sunset Beauty (IRE) (Whipper (USA)) **Patrick Bolger**
107 **THE HALL (IRE)**, ch c 27/5 Teofilo (IRE)—Halla Siamsa (IRE) (Montjeu (IRE)) **Mrs J. S. Bolger**
108 **TIDAL ACTION (IRE)**, b f 11/2 Cape Cross (IRE)—Attasliyah (IRE) (Marju (IRE)) **Mrs J. S. Bolger**
109 B f 1/5 New Approach (IRE)—Tidespring (IRE) (Monsun (GER)) **Godolphin**
110 **TRACKER SAGA (IRE)**, b c 8/5 Vocalised (USA)—Gold Mirage (IRE) (Galileo (IRE)) **Mrs J. S. Bolger**
111 **VERBAL POWDER (IRE)**, b f 4/2 Vocalised (USA)—Global Reach (IRE) (Galileo (IRE)) **Mrs J. S. Bolger**
112 **VERBALISE (IRE)**, b f 6/2 Vocalised (USA)—Lonrach (IRE) (Holy Roman Emperor (IRE)) **Mrs June Judd**
113 **VIATICUS (IRE)**, b c 12/3 Teofilo (IRE)—Toirneach (USA) (Thunder Gulch (USA)) **Mrs J. S. Bolger**

MR J. S. BOLGER - Continued

114 B f 20/1 Dansili—Villarrica (USA) (Selkirk (USA)) **Godolphin**
115 B br c 16/5 Teofilo (IRE)—Vincennes (King's Best (USA)) **Godolphin**
116 **VOCAL IMPACT (IRE),** b f 21/3 Vocalised (USA)—Arminta (USA) (Afleet Alex (USA)) **Mrs J. S. Bolger**
117 **VOCATUS (IRE),** b c 19/1 Vocalised (USA)—Beyond Intensity (IRE) (Intense Focus (USA)) **Mrs J. S. Bolger**
118 **WESTERN DAWN (IRE),** b c 13/3 Dawn Approach (IRE)—Yes Oh Yes (USA) (Gone West (USA)) **Mrs J. S. Bolger**
119 **WEXFORD DAWN (IRE),** ch c 21/4 Dawn Approach (IRE)—
Beyond Compare (IRE) (Galileo (IRE)) Mrs J. S. Bolger

Other Owners: Mr John Corcoran, Ennistown Stud.

Jockey (flat): R. P. Cleary, Kevin Manning, R. P. Whelan. **Apprentice:** Gavin Ryan, William Byrne, David Hannigan, Daire Davis, Luke McAteer.

---

50 MRS MYRIAM BOLLACK-BADEL, Lamorlaye
Postal: 20 Rue Blanche, 60260 Lamorlaye, France
Contacts: FAX (0033) 3442 13367 MOBILE (0033) 6108 09347
E-MAIL myriam.bollack@gmail.com WEBSITE www.myriam-bollack.com

1 **AVEC LAURA,** 5, ch h Manduro (GER)—Sign of Life **Mme M. Bollack-Badel**
2 **BENEFACTION (IRE),** 4, b f Nathaniel (IRE)—Shamdara (IRE) **Mr Anthony Smurfit**
3 **DORSET DREAM (FR),** 5, b m Canford Cliffs (IRE)—Fontcia (FR) **J. C. Smith**
4 **DYREMIS (IRE),** 5, b m Dylan Thomas (IRE)—Coremis (FR) **Jean Smolen**
5 **FARADIBA (FR),** 4, gr f Motivator—Figurelibre (IRE) **M. Motschmann**
6 **IRON SPIRIT (FR),** 8, b h Turtle Bowl (IRE)—Irish Vintage (FR) **M. Motschmann**
7 **NOUS TROIS (FR),** 4, b f Motivator—Numerologie (FR) **Nous Trois Partnership**
8 **ROYAL PRIZE,** 8, ch g Nayef (USA)—Spot Prize (USA) **J. C. Smith**
9 **SECRET LADY,** 4, b f Arcano (IRE)—Lady McBeth (IRE) **J. C. Smith**

THREE-YEAR-OLDS

10 **ARDEATINA,** ch f Harbour Watch (IRE)—May West **F. de Chatelperron**
11 **GLORIA,** gr f Showcasing—Go East (GER) **Secret Association**
12 **HOT MONEY (FR),** ch f Kendargent (FR)—Cinders' Prize **J. C. Smith**
13 **HYBRIS SHADE (FR),** b f Motivator—Hesione (IRE) **M. Motschmann**
14 **OLYMPIC FLAME (FR),** b c Motivator—Elusive Flame **J. C. Smith**
15 **SPEED LIMIT (FR),** ch f Authorized (IRE)—Speed of Sound **J. C. Smith**
16 **WING LADY (FR),** b f Delegator—Angel Wing **J. C. Smith**

TWO-YEAR-OLDS

17 Ch c 18/4 Norse Dancer (IRE)—Angel Wing (Barathea (IRE)) **J. C. Smith**
18 Ch c 4/5 Motivator—Cinders' Prize (Sinndar (IRE)) **J. C. Smith**
19 B f 16/2 Authorized (IRE)—Elusive Flame (Elusive City (USA)) **J. C. Smith**
20 Ch f 22/2 Siyouni (FR)—Green Speed (FR) (Green Tune (USA)) **J. C. Smith**
21 B f 25/2 Norse Dancer (IRE)—Ice Missile (One Cool Cat (USA)) **J. C. Smith**
22 B f 8/1 Norse Dancer (IRE)—Light Catcher (Sakhee (USA)) **J. C. Smith**
23 **NI CHAUD NI FROID (FR),** ch f 25/2 Norse Dancer (IRE)—Numerologie (FR) (Numerous (USA)) **Alain Badel**
24 **PRINCE KERALI (FR),** b c 10/3 Sinndar (FR)—Perpetual Glory (Dansili) **Ecurie Noel Forgeard**
25 B c 6/5 Motivator—Sambala (IRE) (Danehill Dancer (IRE)) **Ecurie Noel Forgeard**
26 **SINGSTREET (FR),** b c 13/4 Evasive—Sinnderelle (FR) (Sinndar (IRE)) **Ecurie Noel Forgeard**
27 **ZEITUNG (FR),** ch c 25/1 Literato (FR)—Zython (FR) (Kabool (FR)) **Mme M. Bollack-Badel**

Assistant Trainer: Alain Badel

---

51 MR MARTIN BOSLEY, Chalfont St Giles
Postal: Bowstridge Farm, Bowstridge Lane, Chalfont St. Giles, Buckinghamshire, HP8 4RF
Contacts: PHONE (01494) 875533 MOBILE (07778) 938040
E-MAIL martin@martinbosley.com WEBSITE www.martinbosleyracing.com

1 **ABSOLUTELY FRANKIE,** 8, ch g Zaha (CAN)—La Piazza (IRE) **Mrs V. Keen**
2 **BURNT CREAM,** 11, b m Exceed And Excel (AUS)—Basbousate Nadia **Mrs P. M. Brown**
3 **CATHEADANS FURY,** 4, ch f Firebreak—Dualagi **Bayard Racing**

MR MARTIN BOSLEY - Continued

4 **CHAMPION CHASE (FR)**, 6, b g Voix du Nord (FR)—Darling Frisco (FR) **Mr M. R. Bosley**
5 **COUNTERFEITER**, 8, b g Singspiel (IRE)—Grain of Truth **J. Carey**
6 **EXCEEDING POWER**, 7, b g Exceed And Excel (AUS)—Extreme Beauty (USA) **The Chalfonts**
7 **FRONT FIVE (IRE)**, 6, b g Teofilo (IRE)—Samdaniya **Mr A. Randle**
8 **GOLLY MISS MOLLY**, 7, b m Exceed And Excel (AUS)—Amicable Terms **J. Carey**
9 **LADY NAHEMA (IRE)**, 5, b m Zoffany (IRE)—Jamary (IRE) **The Chalfonts**
10 **MIDNIGHT JITTERBUG**, 6, b g Midnight Legend—Heebie Jeebie **Mrs E. A. Prowting**
11 **NORSE CASTLE**, 5, b g Norse Dancer (IRE)—Hursley Hope (IRE) **M.A.S.A.**
12 **OLYMPIC LEGEND (IRE)**, 4, ch g Choisir (AUS)—Margaret's Dream (IRE) **M.A.S.A.**

THREE-YEAR-OLDS

13 Ch f Major Cadeaux—Dualagi **Bayard Racing**

Other Owners: Mr M. R. Bosley, Mr G. H. Carson, Mr J. R. Hazeldine, Mrs K. Whitaker.

52	**MR MARCO BOTTI, Newmarket**

Postal: **Prestige Place, Snailwell Road, Newmarket, Suffolk, CB8 7DP**
Contacts: **PHONE (01638) 662416 FAX (01638) 662417 MOBILE (07775) 803007**
E-MAIL office@marcobotti.co.uk WEBSITE www.marcobotti.co.uk

1 **AL HAMDANY (IRE)**, 4, b g Kodiac—Easy Times **AlMohamediya Racing**
2 **AL REEH (IRE)**, 4, br c Invincible Spirit (IRE)—Dffra (IRE) **Mr R. El Youssef**
3 **ALJAZZI**, 5, b m Shamardal (USA)—Nouriya **Saleh Al Homaizi & Imad Al Sagar**
4 **BREX DRAGO (ITY)**, 6, b g Mujahid (USA)—Shibuni's Thea (IRE) **Ontoawinner, Pb Racing & Capla**
5 **BURCAN (FR)**, 6, ch g Astronomer Royal (USA)—Sentimental Union (USA) **Mr R. El Youssef**
6 **CASINA DI NOTTE (IRE)**, 4, ch g Casamento (IRE)—Nightswimmer (IRE) **Les Boyer Partnership**
7 **CROWNED EAGLE**, 4, b g Oasis Dream—Gull Wing (IRE) **Excel Racing & Les Boyer**
8 **DOMITILLA**, 4, b f Cape Cross (IRE)—Dan Loose Daughter **Scuderia Blueberry SRL**
9 **DYLAN MOUTH (IRE)**, 7, b h Dylan Thomas (IRE)—Cottonmouth (IRE) **E. I. Mack**
10 **HAIL CLOUD (IRE)**, 4, b c Hail (IRE)—Wasmi (IRE) **Mr M. Al Naemi**
11 **KYLLACHY GALA**, 5, b g Kyllachy—Tenuta di Gala (IRE) **Excel Racing XII**
12 **MING DYNASTY (FR)**, 6, b g King's Best (USA)—Memoire (FR) **Mr A. Staple**
13 **QATAR GLORY (IRE)**, 4, gr c Cape Cross (IRE)—Perspective **Mr M. Al Naemi**
14 **RAVEN'S LADY**, 4, ch f Raven's Pass (USA)—Pivotal Lady **Heart of the South Racing 105 & Partner**
15 **RED LABEL (IRE)**, 4, b c Dubawi (IRE)—Born Something **Les Boyer Partnership**
16 **SEPRANI**, 4, b f Sepoy (AUS)—King's Guest (IRE) **Book 3 Partnership**
17 **TAP DANCING (IRE)**, 7, ch m Galileo (IRE)—Glass Slipper (IRE) **Worsall Grange Stud**
18 **UNABATED (IRE)**, 4, b g Bated Breath—Elhareer (IRE) **Mr M. Al Naemi**
19 **VELVET REVOLUTION**, 5, ch g Pivotal—Gino's Spirits **Heart of the South Racing 104 & Partner**
20 **WILD HACKED (USA)**, 5, b h Lemon Drop Kid (USA)—Dance Pass (IRE) **Sheikh K. A. I. S. Al Khalifa**
21 **ZEFFERINO**, 4, ch g Frankel—Turama **Les Boyer Partnership**

THREE-YEAR-OLDS

22 **AL ASEF**, br c Kyllachy—Hot Reply **Mr R. El Youssef**
23 **AMERICAN ENDEAVOUR (USA)**, ch f Distorted Humor (USA)—
Crazy Party (USA) **A J Suited & Gute Freunde Partnership**
24 **ARTIESHOW (USA)**, b c Artie Schiller (USA)—Garden Music (USA) **Mr G Manfredini & Mr J Allison**
25 **BLAME ME FOREVER (USA)**, b f Blame (USA)—Empress Josephine (USA) **Mr R Bruni & Partner**
26 **CAPLA JAIPUR**, ch c Sepoy (AUS)—Parthenos **Capla Developments & Partner**
27 **CAPLA TEMPTRESS (IRE)**, b f Lope de Vega (IRE)—Mrs Beeton (IRE) **Team Valor LLC**
28 **CLOUD EIGHT (IRE)**, b c Dream Ahead (USA)—Night Cam (IRE) **Equity Racing & Sohi**
29 Ch c Helmet (AUS)—Countermarch **Mr R. El Youssef**
30 B f Intello (GER)—Crystal Swan (IRE) **Saleh Al Homaizi & Imad Al Sagar**
31 **CYCLADES (IRE)**, b f Bated Breath—Parakopi **Les Boyer Partnership**
32 **DARK ACCLAIM (IRE)**, gr c Dark Angel (IRE)—Sistine **Middleham Park Racing CXXI & Partners**
33 **DOMESTIC WAY (QA)**, b c Domestic Fund (USA)—My Sweet Natalie (USA) **Mr M. Al Naemi**
34 **DREAM MOUNT (IRE)**, b c Dream Ahead (USA)—Mistify (IRE) **Mr G Manfredini & Mr J Allison**
35 **EARLY DAWN**, ch f Dawn Approach (IRE)—Born Something (USA) **Scuderia Vittadini SRL**
36 **EESHA BEAUTY (IRE)**, b f Born To Sea (IRE)—Eastern Glow **K Sohi & Partner**
37 **ELUSIF (IRE)**, b c Elusive Quality (USA)—Appealing (IRE) **Miss Y. M. G. Jacques**
38 B f Aussie Rules (USA)—Eurolink Artemis
39 **FALLING WOOD (IRE)**, gr ro c Zebedee—Wood Nymph (IRE) **Mr M. Al Naemi**
40 **FERAGUST**, b g Poet's Voice—Faciascura **Mr Manfredini & Partner**

MR MARCO BOTTI - Continued

41 **FICANAS,** b f Sepoy (AUS)—Windermere Island **Les Boyer Partnership**
42 **FLORA TRISTAN,** ch f Zoffany (IRE)—Red Roxanne **El Catorce & Partner**
43 **GALACTIC SPIRIT,** ch c Dutch Art—Gino's Spirits **Newsells Park Stud & Partner**
44 **HEEYAAM,** b f Invincible Spirit (IRE)—Shalwa **Sheikh M. B. K. Al Maktoum**
45 **HOLY SHAMBLES (IRE),** b c Holy Roman Emperor (IRE)—Shim Sham (IRE) **Mr M. Al Naemi**
46 **HOULTON,** ch g Declaration of War (USA)—Greek Goddess (IRE) **Excel Racing XI**
47 **HOURGLASS (IRE),** b f Galileo (IRE)—Helsinki **Mr M Tabor, Mr D Smith & Mrs J Magnier**
48 **JELLMOOD,** b g Acclamation—Emotif (ARG) **Sheikh M. B. K. Al Maktoum**
49 **LADY FARHH,** b f Farhh—Monjouet (IRE) **Immobiliare Casa Paola SRL**
50 B c Hail (IRE)—Lollina Paulina **Mr M. Al Naemi**
51 **LOSINGMYRELIGION (FR),** b g Planteur (IRE)—Marie Dar (FR) **Mr Jonny Allison & Mrs L Botti**
52 B c Planteur (IRE)—Mary Frith **Mr M. Al Naemi**
53 **MEERBUSCH (USA),** b c Smart Strike (CAN)—Compelling (IRE) **Sheikh M. B. K. Al Maktoum**
54 B f Dansili—Missy O' Gwaun (IRE) **Saleh Al Homaizi & Imad Al Sagar**
55 B f Invincible Spirit (IRE)—Rappel **Saleh Al Homaizi & Imad Al Sagar**
56 **SCAPUSC,** b g Bated Breath—Fularmada **Mr Manfredini & Partner**
57 **SEEFAAT,** b f Invincible Spirit (IRE)—Safaa (USA) **Sheikh M. B. K. Al Maktoum**
58 **SPEAK IN COLOURS,** gr c Excelebration (IRE)—Maglietta Fina (IRE) **Scuderia Archi Romani**
59 B f Orpen (USA)—Splendeur (FR) **Mr M. Al Naemi**
60 **SPRING PRAISE (IRE),** b g Oasis Dream—Applauded (IRE) **Heart Of The South Racing & Partner**
61 **SUPREMATISM (USA),** b c More Than Ready (USA)—Exotic Behavior (USA) **Mr Manfredini & Partner**
62 **SWEET SYMPHONY,** ch f Helmet (AUS)—Solfilia **Mr C. J. Murfitt & Partner**
63 **SWORDCRAFT (IRE),** gr c Mastercraftsman (IRE)—Al Thumama **Mr M. Al Naemi**
64 **UNINVITED (IRE),** ch g Excelebration (IRE)—Spirit of Cuba (IRE) **K Sohi & Partner**
65 **VERSTAPPEN (IRE),** ro g Dark Angel (IRE)—Hugs 'n Kisses (IRE) **M M Stables**
67 B f Nayef (USA)—Veronica Franco (ITY) **Scuderia Blueberry SRL**
67 **WORLD BREAKER (ITY),** b c Helmet (AUS)—Serata di Gala (FR) **The Barkers & Capla Developments**
68 B f Nayef (USA)—Youda (IRE) **Mr M. Al Naemi**
69 **YUSRA,** b f Invincible Spirit (IRE)—Munyatee (ARG) **Sheikh M. B. K. Al Maktoum**

TWO-YEAR-OLDS

70 B c 8/3 Rock of Gibraltar (IRE)—African Queen (GER) (Nicaron (GER)) (16280)
71 B f 10/4 Kodiac—Awwal Malika (USA) (Kingmambo (USA)) (25714) **Heart of the South Racing 107 & Partner**
72 B br f 11/4 English Channel (USA)—Bella Bandita (USA) (Dynaformer (USA)) (44134)
73 **BRANDON (FR),** b c 24/1 Showcasing—
　　　　　　Be Released (Three Valleys (USA)) (61904) **Mr Manfredini, Mr J Allison & Mr D Fass**
74 Br c 18/2 Foxwedge (AUS)—Coachhouse Lady (USA) (Rahy (USA)) (24000)
75 Gr c 26/1 Dark Angel (IRE)—Daghashah (Authorized (IRE)) (150000) **Mr M. Al Naemi**
76 **DI MATTEO,** b f 23/3 Bated Breath—Pantile (Pivotal) **Mr C. J. Murfitt & Partner**
77 **DON JUPP (USA),** b c 8/2 More Than Ready (USA)—
　　　　　　Dame Ellen (USA) (Elusive Quality (USA)) (38714) **Gute Freunde Partnership**
78 **ECLITTICA (IRE),** b f 4/3 Pour Moi (IRE)—Ekta (Danehill Dancer (IRE)) **La Tesa SPA**
79 B f 23/4 Rip Van Winkle (IRE)—Electric Feel (Firebreak) (26000)
80 **IMPRESSIONABLE,** b f 29/4 Exceed And Excel (AUS)—Appealing (IRE) (Bertolini (USA)) **Miss Y. M. G. Jacques**
81 B f 6/2 Dark Angel (IRE)—Jellwa (IRE) (Iffraaj) **Sheikh M. B. K. Al Maktoum**
82 **LASTAGNANO (IRE),** b c 4/2 War Command (USA)—
　　　　　　Laka (IRE) (Oasis Dream) (21978) **Ambrosiana Racing & Partner**
83 Ch c 22/3 Sepoy (AUS)—Luv U (Royal Applause) **Promenade Bloodstock Limited**
84 B c 22/3 Mount Nelson—Magika (Dubawi (IRE))
85 B c 5/2 Medaglia d'oro (USA)—Queen of Denmark (USA) (Kingmambo (USA)) (38714) **Rabbah Racing**
86 **RAMBALDI (IRE),** b c 21/3 Rip Van Winkle (IRE)—
　　　　　　Shorana (IRE) (Holy Roman Emperor (IRE)) (17142) **Mr Abbas Alalawi & Partner**
87 B c 17/4 Street Sense (USA)—Royal Crystal (USA) (Tapit (USA)) (23000)
88 B f 17/4 Society Rock (IRE)—Rublevka Star (USA) (Elusive Quality (USA)) (40000)
89 B f 29/3 Born To Sea (IRE)—See Emily Play (IRE) (Galileo (IRE)) (5000)
90 **SENSAZIONE BOY,** b c 21/4 Paco Boy (IRE)—
　　　　　　Exceed Sensazione (Exceed And Excel (AUS)) **Scuderia Blueberry SRL**
91 Ch f 25/3 Lope de Vega (IRE)—Shalwa (Galileo (IRE)) **Sheikh M. B. K. Al Maktoum**
92 Ch c 6/4 Farhh—She Wolf (Medicean) (40000)
93 **SIENNA,** ch f 21/2 Toronado (IRE)—Wakeup Little Suzy (IRE) (Peintre Celebre (USA)) (20000) **Book 3 Partnership**
94 B f 22/4 Excelebration (IRE)—Snow Dust (First Defence (USA)) (10000) **Ventura Racing 5 & Partner**
95 B c 14/4 Dark Angel (IRE)—Top Trail (USA) (Exchange Rate (USA)) (23809) **Nick Bradley Racing 25 & Partner**
96 Br c 26/1 Bated Breath—Welcome Spring (IRE) (Lawman (FR)) (56980) **Excel Racing & Partner**
97 B c 17/4 Epaulette (AUS)—Where I Be (Dubawi (IRE)) (39071)

MR MARCO BOTTI - Continued

Other Owners: A J Suited Partnership, Mr P.C. Aberg, Mrs E. Adamski, Mrs E. Agostini, Mr P. Agostini, Sheikh N. M. H. Al Khalifa, Sheikh N. Al Khalifa, I. J. Al-Sagar, Mr A. Alalawi, S. Ali, Mr J. Allison, Jonny Allison & David Fass, Mr M. Almutairi, Mr M. Almutairi, Ambrosiana Racing, Mr C. Austin, Mr A. Baragiola, Miss E. M. Baragiola, Mr P. J. Barker, Mrs Z. Barker, Mr L. Biffi, Mr L. A. Bolingbroke, Mrs L. Botti, Mr N. Bradley, Mr S. Bridge, Mr S. J. Brown, Mr R. Bruni, Mr T. Denham, Equity Racing, Excel Racing, Mr D. V. Fass, Mr P. Fisher, Mr P. M. Grant, Mr P. Harper, Heart Of The South Racing, Heart of the South Racing 104, Heart of the South Racing 105, Heart of the South Racing 107, Miss S. Holden, Saleh Al Homaizi, Miss L. V. Horner, Mrs S. M. Langridge, Mrs S. Magnier, Mr G. Manfredini, Middleham Park Racing CXXI, Mr T. Muller, Mr C. J. Murfitt, Newsells Park Stud Limited, Mr J. M. Nicholson, Nick Bradley Racing 25, Mr N. J. O'Brien, Ontoawinner, T. S. Palin, Mr R. B. Patel, Mr J. R. Penny, Mr C. Pizarro, Mrs K. Pizarro, M. Prince, Dr A. Ridha, D. Smith, Mr K. Sohi, Mr P. Stubbins, M. Tabor, Ventura Racing 5.

Assistant Trainers: Lucie Botti, Karen Parris

Apprentice: Gabriele Malune, Jacob Mitchell, Marc Monaghan.

53	**MR PETER BOWEN, Haverfordwest**

Postal: **Yet-Y-Rhug, Letterston, Haverfordwest, Pembrokeshire, SA62 5TB**
Contacts: **PHONE** (01348) 840486 **FAX** (01348) 840486 **MOBILE** (07811) 111234
E-MAIL info@peterbowenracing.com **WEBSITE** www.peterbowenracing.com

1 **ALF 'N' DOR (IRE)**, 7, ch g Flemensfirth (USA)—Greenflag Princess (IRE) **Mrs K. Bowen**
2 **ATOMIC RUMBLE (IRE)**, 8, b g Oscar (IRE)—Atomic Betty (IRE) **Mr C. B. Compton & Mrs Karen Bowen**
3 **AWAYWITHTHEGREYS (IRE)**, 11, gr g Whipper (USA)—
                      Silver Sash (GER) **Karen Bowen, Saith O Ni & The Hedonists**
4 **BEGGAR'S WISHES (IRE)**, 7, b g Oscar (IRE)—Strong Wishes (IRE) **Roddy Owen & Paul Fullagar**
5 **BUACHAILL ALAINN (IRE)**, 11, b g Oscar (IRE)—Bottle A Knock (IRE) **Roddy Owen & Paul Fullagar**
6 **COUGAR'S GOLD (IRE)**, 7, b g Oscar (IRE)—Top Her Up (IRE) **Mr W. E. V. Harries**
7 **CRUISING BYE**, 12, b g Alflora (IRE)—Althrey Flame (IRE) **F. Lloyd**
8 **CURIOUS CARLOS**, 9, b g Overbury (IRE)—Classi Maureen **Mr C. W. Pyne**
9 **DIAMOND REGGIE (IRE)**, 5, ch g Stowaway—Monilea Lady (IRE) **Paul Duffy, David Semmens, Viv Williams**
10 **DR ROBIN (IRE)**, 8, b g Robin des Pres (FR)—Inter Alia (IRE) **David Robbins & Karen Bowen**
11 **DR WELLS**, 6, b g Dr Massini (IRE)—Aristi (IRE) **Mr T. E. Gibbon**
12 **DRIFT ROCK**, 4, ch c Malinas (GER)—Araucaria (IRE) **Amanda Bancroft & Patrick Bancroft**
13 **EARTHMOVES (FR)**, 8, b g Antarctique (IRE)—Red Rym (FR) **Mr H. Jones & Mrs E. Evans**
14 **EQUUS FLIGHT (IRE)**, 5, b g Vinnie Roe (IRE)—Maiden Flight (IRE) **Roddy Owen & Paul Fullagar**
15 **FAIR TO MIDDLING**, 8, gr g Fair Mix (IRE)—Mtilly **Mrs S. McDonald**
16 **FLYING EAGLE (IRE)**, 10, b g Oscar (IRE)—Fille d'argent (IRE) **Mrs K. Bowen**
17 **FORTUNES HIDING (IRE)**, 5, b g Beat Hollow—Sambre (FR) **Roddy Owen & Paul Fullagar**
18 **FRANCKY DU BERLAIS (FR)**, 5, b g Saint des Saints (FR)—Legende du Luy (FR) **Roddy Owen & Paul Fullagar**
19 **HENLLAN HARRI (IRE)**, 10, br g King's Theatre (IRE)—Told You So (IRE) **Mr W. E. V. Harries**
20 **HENRI PARRY MORGAN**, 10, b g Brian Boru—Queen of Thedaises **Ednyfed & Elizabeth Morgan**
21 **HILLARY VIEW (IRE)**, 6, b g Court Cave (IRE)—Tearaway Lady (IRE) **Mr J. A. Martin**
22 **I'MWAITINGFORYOU**, 9, ch m Needwood Blade—Elegant Lady **Mr M. B. Bowen**
23 **JEANNOT DE NONANT (FR)**, 6, ch g Full of Gold (FR)—Jolie Puce (FR) **D & H Ashley & A & L Swinburne**
24 **JERSEY JEWEL (IRE)**, 6, b m Naaqoos—Nikolenka (IRE) **C. E. R. Greenway**
25 **JUMBO'S BOY**, 4, b g Multiplex—Silver Gyre (IRE) **Mr R. Quinn**
26 **KINARI (IRE)**, 8, b g Captain Rio—Baraza (IRE) **Mr H Jones & Partner**
27 **LADY ROBYN (IRE)**, 8, b m Robin des Champs (FR)—Iseefaith (IRE) **Roddy Owen & Paul Fullagar**
28 **LIME STREET (IRE)**, 7, b g Presenting—Specifiedrisk (IRE) **Ednyfed & Elizabeth Morgan**
29 **LORD BRYAN (IRE)**, 7, b g Brian Boru—Run Cat (IRE) **Miss Jayne Brace & Mr Gwyn Brace**
30 **LORD NAPIER (IRE)**, 5, b g Galileo (IRE)—Jacqueline (IND) **F. Lloyd**
31 **MINELLA DADDY (IRE)**, 8, b g Flemensfirth (USA)—Old Moon (IRE) **Roddy Owen & Paul Fullagar**
32 **MONT CHOISY (FR)**, 8, b g Vic Toto (FR)—Rhapsodie St Eloi (FR) **Mrs N. Unsworth**
33 **PEARL SWAN (FR)**, 10, b g Gentlewave (IRE)—Swanson (USA) **Roddy Owen & Paul Fullagar**
34 **PLAY THE ACE (IRE)**, 9, b br g Scorpion (IRE)—Henris Blaze (IRE) **Roddy Owen & Paul Fullagar**
35 **POTTERS STORY**, 6, b g Kayf Tara—Lily Potter **James & Jean Potter**
36 **POTTERS TALE**, 5, b g Kayf Tara—Lily Potter **James & Jean Potter**
37 **PRINCESS ROANIA (IRE)**, 7, b m Dubai Destination (USA)—Lady Roania (IRE) **Mrs T. S. P. Stepney**
38 **ROLLING MAUL (IRE)**, 7, b g Oscar (IRE)—Water Sports (IRE) **Roddy Owen & Paul Fullagar**
39 **RONS DREAM**, 8, b m Kayf Tara—Empress of Light **Mrs T. S. P. Stepney**
40 **SAM NOIR**, 6, ch g Black Sam Bellamy (IRE)—United (GER) **Roy & Louise Swinburne**
41 **SOURIYAN (FR)**, 7, b g Alhaarth (IRE)—Serasana **G. J. Morris**
42 **STRUMBLE HEAD (IRE)**, 13, b g Anshan—Milan Moss **Mr J. A. Martin**

MR PETER BOWEN - Continued

43 WADSWICK COURT (IRE), 10, b g Court Cave (IRE)—Tarasandy (IRE) **Roddy Owen & Paul Fullagar**
44 WHAT A DIVA, 7, b m Kayf Tara—Land of Glory **Mrs T. S. P. Stepney**

Other Owners: Mrs H. Ashley, Mr D. I. Ashley, P. A. Bancroft, Mrs A. Bancroft, Mr B. G. Bowen, D. G. Brace, Miss M. J. Brace, Mr C. B. Compton, Mr D. P. Duffy, Mrs E. G. Evans, P. G. Fullagar, The Hedonists, Mr H. Jones, Mrs E. Morgan, Mr E. O. Morgan, R. R. Owen, B. S. Port, Mrs M. J. Potter, J. E. Potter, S. D. Reeve, D. J. Robbins, Mr D. M. Semmens, Mrs L. T. Swinburne, R. D. J. Swinburne, Mr P. R. Williams.

Assistant Trainers: Karen Bowen, Michael Bowen

Jockey (NH): Sean Bowen. **Conditional:** James Bowen.

---

54   **MR ROY BOWRING, Edwinstowe**
Postal: **Fir Tree Farm, Edwinstowe, Mansfield, Nottinghamshire, NG21 9JG**
Contacts: **PHONE (01623) 822451 MOBILE (07973) 712942**
E-MAIL bowrings@btconnect.com

1 ACE MASTER, 10, ch g Ballet Master (USA)—Ace Maite **S. R. Bowring**
2 CLUBLAND (IRE), 9, b g Red Clubs (IRE)—Racjilanemm **S. R. Bowring**
3 DECISION MAKER (IRE), 4, b g Iffraaj—Consensus (IRE) **K. Nicholls**
4 DUSTY BIN, 4, b g Sepoy (AUS)—Short Affair **S. R. Bowring**
5 EXCEL MATE, 4, ch f Captain Gerrard (IRE)—Exceedingly Good (IRE) **S. R. Bowring**
6 FIRST EXCEL, 6, ch g First Trump—Exceedingly Good (IRE) **S. R. Bowring**
7 FOOLAAD, 7, ch g Exceed And Excel (AUS)—Zayn Zen **K. Nicholls**
8 LITTLE CHOOSEY, 8, ch m Cadeaux Genereux—Little Nymph **Mr K. Nicholls & Mr S. R. Bowring**
9 MASTER OF SONG, 11, ch g Ballet Master (USA)—Ocean Song **S. R. Bowring**
10 MEN UNITED (FR), 5, b g Acclamation—Moore's Melody (IRE) **S. R. Bowring**
11 ZEBELINI (IRE), 6, gr m Zebedee—Ma Nikitia (IRE) **K. Nicholls**

THREE-YEAR-OLDS

12 JEAN EXCELS, b f Captain Gerrard (IRE)—Exceedingly Good (IRE) **S. R. Bowring**

---

55   **MR JIM BOYLE, Epsom**
Postal: **South Hatch Stables, Burgh Heath Road, Epsom, Surrey, KT17 4LX**
Contacts: **PHONE (01372) 748800 FAX (01372) 739410 MOBILE (07719) 554147**
E-MAIL info@jamesboyle.co.uk & jimboylesec@hotmail.co.uk (Secretary)
WEBSITE www.jamesboyle.co.uk

1 BABY GAL, 4, b f Royal Applause—Our Gal **Inside Track Racing Club**
2 BLACK BESS, 5, br m Dick Turpin (IRE)—Spring Clean (FR) **The Clean Sweep Partnership**
3 BROUGHTONS KNIGHT, 4, b g Foxwedge (AUS)—Disco Ball **Mr M. B. Spence**
4 DUKE OF NORTH (IRE), 6, b g Danehill Dancer (IRE)—Althea Rose (IRE) **The Paddock Space Partnership**
5 EL TORITO (IRE), 4, ch g Tagula (IRE)—April Green (FR) **The "In Recovery" Partnership**
6 FIRST QUEST (USA), 4, b g First Defence (USA)—Dixie Quest (USA) **The Waterboys**
7 MAN OF HARLECH, 7, b g Dansili—Ffestiniog (IRE) **Elite Racing Club**
8 MASTER OF HEAVEN, 5, b g Makfi—Maid In Heaven (IRE) **Maid In Heaven Partnership**
9 MUTHRAAB ALDAAR (IRE), 5, b g Baltic King—Vertigo On Course (IRE) **Epsom Equine Spa Partnership**
10 PERFECT PASTIME, 10, ch g Pastoral Pursuits—Puritanical (IRE) **The Paddock Space Partnership 2**
11 RATTLE ON, 5, ch g Pivotal—Sabreon **Inside Track Racing Club**
12 SHOWTIME BLUES, 6, b g Showcasing—Night Symphonie **Mr M. B. Spence**
13 SILVER PENNY, 4, gr f Hellvelyn—Pennyspider (IRE) **Inside Track Racing Club**
14 SPIRIT OF EPSOM, 4, b c Captain Gerrard (IRE)—Bettina Blue (IRE) **Taylor Anderson Racing**
15 THAMES KNIGHT, 6, b g Sir Percy—Bermondsey Girl **The King John Partnership**

THREE-YEAR-OLDS

16 AMARETTO, b c Kyllachy—Dan Loose Daughter **A. B. Pope**
17 BECKY SHARP, b f Foxwedge (AUS)—Perfect Practice **Harrier Racing 1**
18 FOLLOWING BREEZE (IRE), b f Kodiac—Xaloc (IRE) **Dr P. Wilson**
19 HATEYA (IRE), b f Footstepsinthesand—Selfsame (USA) **Inside Track Racing Club**
20 QUICK RECOVERY, gr f Lethal Force (IRE)—Lisiere (IRE) **The "In Recovery" Partnership**
21 THE NAUGHTY STEP (IRE), b g Camacho—Echad (IRE) **Partnership Terminated**

MR JIM BOYLE - Continued

TWO-YEAR-OLDS

22 B c 3/4 Nathaniel (IRE)—L'ile Aux Loups (IRE) (Rock of Gibraltar (IRE)) (13000) **Inside Track Racing Club**

Other Owners: Mr D. I. Anderson, Mr K. Booth, Mrs P. Boyle, Mr J. R. Boyle, A. J. Chambers, M. C. Cook, Mr A. C. Elliott, Ms J. E. Harrison, Mr A. J. Hill, Mr J. Hillier, Ms T. Keane, Mr P. O. Mooney, Mr A. J. R. Moseley, Miss M. Noden, Mr R. O'Dwyer, Mr E. Sames, Mr R. Stanbridge, Mr P. A. Taylor, Mrs T. Taylor.

---

56 **MR DAVID BRACE, Bridgend**
Postal: **Llanmihangel Farm, Pyle, Bridgend, Mid-Glamorgan, CF33 6RL**
Contacts: **PHONE (01656) 742313**

1 **BAJAN BLU,** 10, b g Generous (IRE)—Bajan Girl (FR)
2 **BOB THE BUTCHER,** 9, b g Needle Gun (IRE)—Brydferth Ddu (IRE) **D. Brace**
3 **BRACHO,** 6, b g Dr Massini (IRE)—Branston Lily **D. Brace**
4 **CHAMPAYNE GINGER,** 7, ch g Stowaway—Katies Dancer (IRE) **D. Brace**
5 **COLORADO DOC,** 7, b g Dr Massini (IRE)—First Royal (GER) **D. Brace**
6 **COMMANCHE CHEIF,** 5, b g Dr Massini (IRE)—Commanche Token (IRE) **D. Brace**
7 **DBOBE,** 9, b g Needle Gun (IRE)—Braceys Girl **D. Brace**
8 **DELKANTRA (IRE),** 8, b g Putra Pekan—Delheim (IRE) **D. Brace**
9 **DOC CODY,** 7, b g Dr Massini (IRE)—Brydferth Ddu (IRE) **D. Brace**
10 **DOCTOR BRAVEHEART (IRE),** 9, b g Dr Massini (IRE)—Letimavit (IRE) **D. Brace**
11 **DONT TELL PA (IRE),** 11, b g Oscar (IRE)—Glacial Snowboard (IRE)
12 **DUNRAVEN BLUE,** 5, b m Dr Massini (IRE)—Bajan Girl (FR) **D. Brace**
13 **IT'S PICALILLY,** 8, b m Needle Gun (IRE)—Branston Lily **D. Brace**
14 **LADY VERONICA,** 5, ch m Martaline—Vineuil (FR) **D. Brace**
15 **LENNIE DA LION,** 10, b g Tamure (IRE)—Lynoso
16 **MAGGIE'S DAWN,** 6, b m Bach (IRE)—Maggie's Opera **D. Brace**
17 **PAINT THE DREAM,** 4, b g Brian Boru—Vineuil (FR) **D. Brace**
18 **PINK EYED PEDRO,** 7, b g Dr Massini (IRE)—Poacher's Paddy (IRE) **D. Brace**
19 **ROBIN DES PEOPLE (IRE),** 8, br g Robin des Pres (FR)—Zelea (IRE) **D. Brace**
20 **SILVER TOKEN,** 13, gr g Silver Patriarch (IRE)—Commanche Token (IRE) **D. Brace**
21 **WILCOX AND CO,** 4, b g Dr Massini (IRE)—Betty The Bog **D. Brace**
22 **WILLIAM MONEY (IRE),** 11, b g Cloudings (IRE)—All of A Kind (IRE) **D. Brace**

Assistant Trainer: Robbie Llewellyn

---

57 **MR MILTON BRADLEY, Chepstow**
Postal: **Meads Farm, Sedbury Park, Chepstow, Gwent, NP16 7HN**
Contacts: **PHONE (01291) 622486 FAX (01291) 626939**

1 **ALQALSAR (IRE),** 4, ch g Bahamian Bounty—With Colour **E. A. Hayward**
2 **BURAUQ,** 6, b g Kyllachy—Riccoche (IRE) **D. Smith**
3 **COMPTON PRINCE,** 9, ch g Compton Place—Malelane (IRE) **E. A. Hayward**
4 **ENGLISHMAN,** 8, b g Royal Applause—Tesary **E. A. Hayward**
5 **INDIAN AFFAIR,** 8, b h Sleeping Indian—Rare Fling (USA) **J. M. Bradley**
6 **JAZRI,** 7, b g Myboycharlie (IRE)—Read Federica **J. M. Bradley**
7 **KYLLUKEY,** 5, b g Kyllachy—Money Note **E. A. Hayward**
8 **MOSTASHREQAH,** 5, ch m Equiano (FR)—China Cherub **J. M. Bradley**
9 **MURAAQEB,** 4, b g Nathaniel (IRE)—Tesary **E. A. Hayward**
10 **RAPID RISE (IRE),** 4, b g Fast Company (IRE)—French Doll (IRE) **Mr M. G. Ridley**
11 **RISING SUNSHINE (IRE),** 5, b g Dark Angel (IRE)—Little Audio (IRE) **Mr P. Banfield & Mr J. M. Bradley**
12 **SPIRIT OF GONDREE (IRE),** 10, b g Invincible Spirit (IRE)—
Kristal's Paradise (IRE) **Paul & Ann de Weck & Partner**
13 **TEMPLE ROAD (IRE),** 10, b g Street Cry (IRE)—Sugarhoneybaby (IRE) **J. M. Bradley**
14 **THE BIG SHORT,** 4, ch g Bahamian Bounty—Royal Punch **E. A. Hayward**
15 **TISA RIVER (IRE),** 4, b f Equiano (FR)—Senta's Dream **E. A. Hayward**
16 **TRIPLE DREAM,** 13, ch g Vision of Night—Triple Joy **J. M. Bradley**
17 **UNSUSPECTED GIRL (IRE),** 5, b m Rip Van Winkle (IRE)—Sweet Sioux **J. M. Bradley**

MR MILTON BRADLEY - Continued

THREE-YEAR-OLDS
18 **ALASKA (IRE)**, b g Kodiac—Sunny Hollow **E. A. Hayward**
19 **PRANCEABOOTTHETOON (IRE)**, ch c Sir Prancealot (IRE)—Cabopino (IRE) **E. A. Hayward**

TWO-YEAR-OLDS
20 B g 15/5 War Command (USA)—Divine Grace (IRE) (Definite Article) (10000) **J. M. Bradley**
21 B f 19/4 Swiss Spirit—Tintern (Diktat) (6000) **J. M. Bradley**
22 **WYE BOTHER (IRE)**, b f 18/3 Born To Sea (IRE)—Enchantment (Compton Place) (8000) **E. A. Hayward**
23 **YFENNI (IRE)**, ch f 7/3 Dutch Art—Paisley (Pivotal) (7000) **E. A. Hayward**

Other Owners: Mr Philip Banfield, Mr J. M. Bradley, Mrs Ann E. de Weck, Mr Paul de Weck.

Jockey (flat): Tom Marquand, Luke Morris, Franny Norton. **Apprentice:** Kerrie Raybould.

---

58   MR MARK BRADSTOCK, Wantage
Postal: **The Old Manor Stables, Letcombe Bassett, Wantage, Oxfordshire, OX12 9LP**
Contacts: **PHONE (01235) 760780 MOBILE (07887) 686697**
E-MAIL mark.bradstock@btconnect.com WEBSITE www.markbradstockracing.co.uk

1 **ANGEL OF HARLEM**, 5, b m Presenting—Whoops A Daisy **Patrick & Scott Bryceland**
2 **ASK NELLIE (IRE)**, 6, b m Ask—Lady Shackleton (IRE) **Colin Elgram & Jack Rowlands**
3 **BLOODY NOSE (IRE)**, 6, b g Kalanisi (IRE)—Renvyle Society (IRE) **Mr E. P. K. Weatherall**
4 **COJACK (IRE)**, 6, b g Presenting—In The Waves (IRE) **Colin Elgram & Jack Rowlands**
5 **CONEYGREE**, 11, b g Karinga Bay—Plaid Maid (IRE) **The Max Partnership**
6 **DOWN TO THE SEA (FR)**, 4, ch g No Risk At All (FR)—Majoritaire (FR)
7 **FLINTHAM**, 9, b g Kayf Tara—Plaid Maid (IRE) **The Rasher Partnership**
8 **GLENPARK (IRE)**, 4, b g Scorpion (IRE)—Don't Waste It (IRE) **Patrick & Scott Bryceland**
9 **HAYLEY BELLE (IRE)**, 7, b m Flemensfirth (USA)—Tart of Tipp (IRE) **Mr P. B. T. Armitage**
10 **JAISALMER (IRE)**, 6, b g Jeremy (USA)—Shara (IRE) **The Jeremy Partnership**
11 **JAKAMANI**, 4, b g Sulamani—Kentford Grebe **Miss C Fordham & Mr C Vernon**
12 4, Gr g Multiplex—Linen Line
13 **MIN TIKY (IRE)**, 6, b m King's Theatre (IRE)—Kon Tiky (FR) **Kiki Partnership**
14 **ROBERT'S STAR (IRE)**, 8, b g Oscar (IRE)—Halona **North Star Partnership**
15 **STEP BACK (IRE)**, 8, ch g Indian River (FR)—Stepitoutmary (IRE) **Cracker and Smodge Partnership**
16 **TALKSALOT (IRE)**, 7, b g Thousand Words—Lady Piste (IRE) **Mr J. E. Bond-Smith**
17 4, b g Jeremy (USA)—The Only Girl (IRE)

Other Owners: M. F. Bradstock, Mr S. Bryceland, Mr P. Bryceland, Mrs L. Burgess, Mrs S. Crean, Lady Dundas, C. Elgram, Miss C. Fordham, Mr D. King, Mr J. B. G. Macleod, Dr P. M. Milligan, Mr J. Reilly, Mrs S. Robinson, Mr J. R. Rowlands, M. S. Tamburro, Mr R. W. Tyrrell, C. A. Vernon, A. M. Waller.

Assistant Trainer: Sara Bradstock

Jockey (NH): Nico de Boinville.

---

59   MR BARRY BRENNAN, Marlborough
Postal: **Downs House, Baydon, Marlborough, Wiltshire, SN8 2JS**
Contacts: **MOBILE (07907) 529780**
E-MAIL barrybrennan2@hotmail.com WEBSITE www.barrybrennanracing.co.uk

1 **CEYHAN**, 6, ch g Rock of Gibraltar (IRE)—Alla Prima (IRE) **D. R. T. Gibbons**
2 **CHANGING THE GUARD**, 12, b g King's Best (USA)—Our Queen of Kings **F. J. Brennan**
3 **HOPE'S WISHES**, 8, b m Kayf Tara—Otarie (FR) **M. J. Hills**
4 **IRONDALE EXPRESS**, 7, b m Myboycharlie (IRE)—Olindera (GER) **D. R. T. Gibbons**
5 **LIGHTENTERTAINMENT (IRE)**, 10, b g King's Theatre (IRE)—Dochas Supreme (IRE) **D. R. T. Gibbons**
6 **ROSE OF DUBAI**, 5, b m Dubai Destination (USA)—Daraz Rose (IRE) **F. J. Brennan**
7 **SKY OF STARS (IRE)**, 5, b g Frozen Power (IRE)—So So Lucky (IRE) **F. J. Brennan**
8 **ULYSSES (GER)**, 4, b g Sinndar (IRE)—Ungarin (GER) **D. R. T. Gibbons**

60 **MISS RHONA BREWIS, Belford**
Postal: **Chester Hill, Belford, Northumberland, NE70 7EF**
Contacts: **PHONE (01668) 213239/213281**

1 **CLOVELLY**, 8, b m Midnight Legend—Chantilly Rose **Miss R. G. Brewis**

---

61 **MR JOHN BRIDGER, Liphook**
Postal: **Upper Hatch Farm, Liphook, Hampshire, GU30 7EL**
Contacts: **PHONE (01428) 722528 MOBILE (07785) 716614**
E-MAIL jbridger@btconnect.com

1 **AEGEAN BOUNTY (IRE)**, 4, b f Bahamian Bounty—Royal Consort (IRE) **Theobalds Stud**
2 **ARCTIC FLOWER (IRE)**, 5, gr m Roderic O'connor (IRE)—Just In Love (FR) **Mr & Mrs K. Finch**
3 **BETSALOTTIE**, 5, gr g Aqlaam—Si Belle (IRE) **Mr J. J. Bridger**
4 **BOOKMAKER**, 8, b g Byron—Cankara (IRE) **T Wallace & J J Bridger**
5 **BYRD IN HAND (IRE)**, 11, b g Fasliyev (USA)—Military Tune (IRE) **Marshall Bridger**
6 **CRYSTAL SECRET**, 4, b f Sayif (IRE)—Laser Crystal (IRE) **Mr & Mrs K. Finch**
7 **DEER SONG**, 5, b g Piccolo—Turkish Delight **The Deer's Hut**
8 **DELICATE KISS**, 4, b f Delegator—Desert Kiss **DBD Partnership**
9 **FAIRY MIST (IRE)**, 11, b g Oratorio (IRE)—Prealpina (IRE) **Mr J. J. Bridger**
10 **FLOWING CLARETS**, 5, ch m Pastoral Pursuits—Flying Clarets (IRE) **Wood Marshall Bridger**
11 **FLYING SAKHEE**, 5, b m Sakhee's Secret—Sister Moonshine **D Higgs J J Bridger**
12 **LIVE DANGEROUSLY**, 8, b g Zamindar (USA)—Desert Lynx (IRE) **W. A. Wood**
13 **MEGALALA (IRE)**, 17, b g Petardia—Avionne **Mr T. Wallace**
14 **MOOREA**, 4, ch g Medicean—Priena (IRE) **Mr & Mrs K. Finch**
15 **PETTOCHSIDE**, 9, b g Refuse To Bend (IRE)—Clear Impression (IRE) **Mr P. Cook**
16 **PHAROH JAKE**, 10, ch g Piccolo—Rose Amber **J J Bridger Mrs J Stamp**
17 **PORTO FERRO (IRE)**, 4, b f Arcano (IRE)—Sassari (IRE) **Mr J. J. Bridger**
18 **SHIFTING STAR (IRE)**, 13, ch g Night Shift (USA)—Ahshado **Night Shadow Syndicate**
19 **STARFINCH**, 13, br m Fraam—Mockingbird
20 **STARWATCH**, 11, b g Observatory (USA)—Trinity Reef **Mr J. J. Bridger**
21 **TAUREAN GOLD**, 4, b g Piccolo—Elsie's Orphan **Mr & Mrs K. Finch**
22 **WELSH INLET (IRE)**, 10, br m Kheleyf (USA)—Ervedya (IRE) **Mr J. J. Bridger**

THREE-YEAR-OLDS

23 **AEGEAN LEGEND**, b g Mayson—Aegean Mystery **Theobalds Stud**
24 **FIRENZE ROSA (IRE)**, b f Zebedee—Our Nana Rose (IRE) **Mr & Mrs K. Finch**
25 **TAGUS (IRE)**, b f Henrythenavigator (USA)—Archina (IRE)

TWO-YEAR-OLDS

26 **DARK IMPULSE (IRE)**, b g 2/5 Dark Angel (IRE)—Invincible Me (IRE) (Invincible Spirit (IRE)) **Mr & Mrs K. Finch**
27 B f 2/2 Finjaan—Oyster (IRE) (Diamond Green (FR)) (761) **Miss Katie Cook**
28 **SHADOW FORCE**, gr f 23/3 Lethal Force (IRE)—
Night Premiere (IRE) (Night Shift (USA)) (6190) **Mr & Mrs K. Finch**

Other Owners: Mrs D. Ellison, Mrs D. A. Ellison, K. Finch, Mr D. G. Higgs, C. Marshall, Mr F. R. Northcott, Mr B. Olkowicz, K. Panos, Exors of the Late Mr G. K. Panos, Mrs J. M. Stamp, Mrs D. Stewart.

Assistant Trainer: Rachel Cook

---

62 **MR DAVID BRIDGWATER, Stow-on-the-Wold**
Postal: **Wyck Hill Farm, Wyck Hill, Stow-on-the-Wold, Cheltenham, Gloucestershire, GL54 1HT**
Contacts: **PHONE (01451) 830349 FAX (01451) 830349 MOBILE (07831) 635817**
E-MAIL sales@bridgwaterracing.co.uk WEBSITE www.bridgwaterracing.co.uk

1 **ACCORD (IRE)**, 8, b g Arcadio (GER)—Detente **Mr J. H. Furlong**
2 4, Ch g Alkaased (USA)—Aster (IRE) **P. J. Cave**
3 **BELMONT PARK (FR)**, 7, br g Al Namix (FR)—Goldoulyssa (FR) **Terry & Sarah Amos**
4 **BUBLE (IRE)**, 9, b g Milan—Glorious Moments (IRE) **Mrs Mary Bridgwater & Mr & Mrs Chenery**
5 **CAMAPLU (FR)**, 6, gr m Turgeon (USA)—Line Tzigane (FR) **Terry & Sarah Amos**
6 **CHARMOND**, 5, ch m Grape Tree Road—Just Missie **Miss M. E. Steele**
7 **COHESION**, 5, b g Champs Elysees—Winter Bloom (USA) **Mr A. J. Duffield**

MR DAVID BRIDGWATER - Continued

8 **CYBALKO (FR)**, 5, b g Balko (FR)—Cybertina (FR) **Terry & Sarah Amos**
9 **DAME DU SOIR (FR)**, 5, bl m Axxos (GER)—Kassing (FR)
10 **DI'S PRIDE**, 5, b m Paco Boy (IRE)—Bramalea **P. J. Cave**
11 **DIPLOMATICO (USA)**, 5, b g Ambassador (GER)—Dulcet Tone (USA) **Mr S. Hunt**
12 **DOWNLOADTHEAPP (IRE)**, 5, b g Definite Article—Chase A Dream (IRE) **Mr G. J. Burrow**
13 **DR CUDDLES (IRE)**, 10, b g Dr Massini (IRE)—Native Emigrant (IRE) **MMG Racing**
14 **EDGAR (GER)**, 8, b g Big Shuffle (USA)—Estella (GER) **K J McCourt & Partners**
15 **ENRICHISSANT (FR)**, 4, b br g Speedmaster (GER)—Quibble (FR) **Simon & Liz Hunt**
16 **FAIR FRANK**, 7, gr g Fair Mix (IRE)—Firstflor **Farmers & Cricketers Partnership**
17 **FORT GABRIEL (FR)**, 7, ch g Ange Gabriel (FR)—Forge Neuve (FR) **CWB Plus 2 Partnership**
18 **HANGMAN JURY**, 5, gr g Indian Haven—Non Disclosure (IRE) **D. G. Bridgwater**
19 **JOT'EM DOWN (IRE)**, 7, b g Kalanisi (IRE)—Shuil A Hocht (IRE) **Mr S. Hunt**
20 **LAST WATCH**, 5, br m Sagamix—Watcha (USA) **P. J. Cave**
21 **MUILEAN NA MADOG (IRE)**, 7, b g Papal Bull—
                                        Truly Precious (IRE) **Sir A Ferguson G Clarkson M Wilkinson D Baldwin**
22 **NO APPROVAL (IRE)**, 5, b g Approve (IRE)—Night Cam (IRE) **The Happy Horse Partnership**
23 **NO BUTS**, 10, b g Kayf Tara—Wontcostalotbut **Wontcostalot Partnership**
24 **OPECHEE (IRE)**, 7, b g Robin des Champs (FR)—Falcons Gift (IRE) **AM Bostock DG Bostock**
25 **ORCHESTRATED (IRE)**, 7, b g Mahler—Rose Island **Feasibility Limited**
26 **PHARAWAY VIEW**, 4, br f Beat All (USA)—High Park Lady (IRE) **Mr T. J. Payton**
27 **REASON TO BELIEVE (FR)**, 4, b f Rip Van Winkle (IRE)—Showcall (USA) **Mr A. J. Duffield**
28 **RUBY DU BERLAIS**, 4, b f Beat All (USA)—Marina du Berlais (FR) **Building Bridgies**
29 **SAFFRON PRINCE**, 10, b g Kayf Tara—Jan's Dream (IRE) **Mrs J. A. Chenery & Mr R. J. Chenery**
30 **SUNDAY IN THE PARK**, 5, gr m Fair Mix (IRE)—Just Smokie **Mr F. W. K. Griffin**
31 **THE TIN MINER (IRE)**, 7, br g Presenting—Sidalcea (IRE) **Simon & Liz Hunt**
32 **THE YANK**, 9, b g Trade Fair—Silver Gyre (IRE) **R&S MacNaughton, P&S Roworth**
33 **THEATRE FLAME (IRE)**, 8, b g King's Theatre (IRE)—Bob's Flame (IRE) **CWB LLP**
34 **WAHWONAISA**, 6, b g Kalanisi (IRE)—Clandestine **AM Bostock DG Bostock**
35 **WENCESLAUS (GER)**, 6, b g Tiger Hill (GER)—Warrior Czarina (USA) **Deauville Daze Partnership**
36 **ZEPHYROS (GER)**, 7, br g Areion (GER)—Zandra (GER) **MMG Racing**

THREE-YEAR-OLDS

37 B g Arakan (USA)—Brioney (IRE) **D. G. Bridgwater**
38 **COMOTION (FR)**, b br g Kapgarde (FR)—Second Emotion (FR) **Terry & Sarah Amos**
39 **QUOIQUECESOIT (FR)**, b br f Turgeon (USA)—Line Tzigane (FR) **Terry & Sarah Amos**

TWO-YEAR-OLDS

40 B g 1/3 Makfi—Cinta (Monsun (GER)) (8500) **D. G. Bridgwater**
41 **IN A TIZZ (FR)**, b br f 22/3 Nicaron (GER)—Line Tzigane (FR) (Bonnet Rouge (FR)) **Terry & Sarah Amos**

Other Owners: T. P. Amos, Mrs S. P. Amos, Mr D. Baldwin, Mrs C. H. Borghoff, D. G. Bostock, Mrs A. M. Bostock, R. J. Brennan, Mrs M. A. Bridgwater, Mrs J. A. Chenery, Mr R. J. Chenery, A. J. Clarkson, A. A. Clifford, Sir A. Ferguson, A. Field, Mr A. Gunn, Miss L. M. Haywood, Mr M. V. Hill, Mrs E. A. Hunt, Mr R. C. MacNaughton, Mrs S. A. MacNaughton, Mr K. J. McCourt, Mr D. J. Pearson, Mr A. R. Pigott, Mr T. Powell, Mrs S. M. Roworth, Mr P. J. Roworth, Mr D. W. Tompkins, Mr M. Wilkinson.

Assistant Trainer: Mrs Lucy K. Bridgwater

Jockey (NH): Tom Scudamore. **Conditional:** Callum McKinnes. **Apprentice:** Poppy Bridgwater.

---

63 | **MR MARK BRISBOURNE, Nesscliffe**
Postal: Ness Strange Stables, Great Ness, Shrewsbury, Shropshire, SY4 2LE
Contacts: **PHONE (01743) 741599 MOBILE (07803) 019651**

1 **BELABOUR**, 5, b g Bernardini (USA)—Criticism **Zen Racing**
2 **EMILENE**, 4, b f Clodovil (IRE)—Spark Up **Mr G. D. Kendrick**
3 **FOSSA**, 8, b g Dubai Destination (USA)—Gayanula (USA) **Mr D. F. Slingsby**
4 **ICE CANYON**, 4, b g Raven's Pass (USA)—Picture Hat (USA) **Mr Derek & Mrs Marie Dean**
5 **LIFE OF LUXURY**, 5, b g Shamardal (USA)—Champagnelifestyle **Mr Derek & Mrs Marie Dean**
6 **STEADY MAJOR (IRE)**, 6, b g Invincible Spirit (IRE)—Combust (USA) **W. M. Brisbourne**
7 **STORM LIGHTNING**, 9, b g Exceed And Excel (AUS)—All For Laura **Law Abiding Citizens**
8 **SUTOOR (IRE)**, 4, b g Cape Cross (IRE)—Yanabeeaa (USA) **Mr R. A. Sankey**
9 **TINK**, 4, ch f Captain Gerrard (IRE)—Ensign's Trick **W. M. Brisbourne**

Other Owners: A. J. Banton, D. Dean, Mrs M. Dean, Mr C. J. Edwards, Mr A. Pitt, Mr R. A.Sankey.

MR MARK BRISBOURNE - Continued

Jockey (flat): John Egan, Shane Kelly. **Jockey (NH):** Robert Dunne. **Apprentice:** Charlie Bennett. **Amateur:** Miss Becky Brisbourne.

---

64 **MR ROBYN BRISLAND, Newmarket**
Postal: **1 Badlingham Farm, Badlingham, Chippenham, Ely, Cambridgeshire, CB7 5QQ**
Contacts: **MOBILE (07771) 656081**
E-MAIL robbris@me.com

1 **KATIE GALE**, 8, b m Shirocco (GER)—Karla June **Ferrybank Properties Ltd**
2 **MAGNUS MAXIMUS**, 7, b g Holy Roman Emperor (IRE)—Chanrossa (IRE) **L T D Racing**
3 **NATURE BOY (IRE)**, 4, ch c Intikhab (USA)—Miss Latina (IRE) **Melinda Quirk Partnership**
4 **NAVAJO GREY (IRE)**, 4, gr f Dark Angel (IRE)—Spring View **Ferrybank Properties Ltd**
5 **NAVAJO STAR (IRE)**, 4, b f Mastercraftsman (IRE)—Champagne Aerial (IRE) **Ferrybank Properties Ltd**
6 **RED SNIPER (IRE)**, 4, ch f Casamento (IRE)—Lady Caprice

THREE-YEAR-OLDS

7 B f Arcano (IRE)—Alexander Duchess (IRE) **Mrs Jo Brisland**
8 **APACHE BLAZE**, b f Champs Elysees—Polar Circle (USA) **Ferrybank Properties Ltd**
9 **GIOVANNI (IRE)**, b c So You Think (NZ)—Golden Wave (IRE) **Paul Hancock**
10 **M C MULDOON (IRE)**, gr c Mastercraftsman (IRE)—Alizaya (IRE) **Mr P. Hancock**
11 Ch f Dandy Man (IRE)—Masakira (IRE) **Mrs Jo Brisland**
12 B f Excelebration (IRE)—Thinking Positive **Mrs Jo Brisland**
13 B f Helmet (AUS)—Tidal
14 **ZYZZYVA (FR)**, b c Siyouni (FR)—Zanatiya (FR) **Paul Hancock**

TWO-YEAR-OLDS

15 B c 26/2 Charm Spirit (IRE)—Astromagick (Rainbow Quest (USA)) (2500)
16 B g 23/3 Bungle Inthejungle—Cuiseach (IRE) (Bachelor Duke (USA)) (952) **Mrs Jo Brisland**
17 B f 7/4 Poet's Voice—Elope (GER) (Tiger Hill (IRE))
18 B f 4/3 Epaulette (AUS)—Lady Benedicte (IRE) (Shamardal (USA))
19 Ch c 29/2 Sepoy (AUS)—Polka Dot (IRE) (Galileo (IRE)) (70000) **Mr P. Hancock**
20 B f 20/3 Casamento (IRE)—Spirit of Alsace (IRE) (Invincible Spirit (IRE)) **Mrs Jo Brisland**

Jockey (flat): Martin Harley, Luke Morris.

---

65 **MR ANTONY BRITTAIN, Warthlll**
Postal: **Northgate Lodge, Warthill, York, North Yorkshire, YO19 5XR**
Contacts: **PHONE (01759) 371472 FAX (01759) 372915**
E-MAIL email@antonybrittain.co.uk WEBSITE www.antonybrittain.co.uk

1 **BEATBYBEATBYBEAT**, 5, ch m Poet's Voice—Beat As One **Mr Antony Brittain**
2 **BONDI BEACH BOY**, 9, b g Misu Bond (IRE)—Nice One **Mr G. R. Turner & Mr H. Turner**
3 **COOL MUSIC (IRE)**, 8, b m One Cool Cat (USA)—Musicology (USA) **Mr Antony Brittain**
4 **DESKTOP**, 6, b g Desideratum—First Harmony **Mr Antony Brittain**
5 **DIGITAL REVOLUTION**, 4, ch f Monsieur Bond (IRE)—Lujiana **Northgate Grey**
6 **FRENCH**, 5, ch m Monsieur Bond (IRE)—Guadaloup **Mr Antony Brittain**
7 **GREY DESTINY**, 8, gr g Desideratum—Mother Corrigan (IRE) **Mr Antony Brittain**
8 **HUSSAR BALLAD (USA)**, 9, b g Hard Spun (USA)—Country Melody (USA) **Mr Antony Brittain**
9 **INTERNATIONAL LAW**, 4, gr g Exceed And Excel (AUS)—Cruel Sea (USA) **John Jarvis & Partner**
10 **LEWINSKY (IRE)**, 4, b f Famous Name—Happy Flight (IRE) **Northgate Racing**
11 **LUCKY LODGE**, 8, b g Lucky Story (USA)—Melandre **Mr Antony Brittain**
12 **MONSIEUR MEL**, 4, b g Monsieur Bond (IRE)—Melandre **Northgate White**
13 **PERCEIVED**, 6, ch m Sir Percy—New Light **Mr Antony Brittain**
14 **SOOQAAN**, 7, bl g Naaqoos—Dream Day (FR) **Mr Antony Brittain**
15 **TRAVELLER (FR)**, 4, b g Henrythenavigator (USA)—Nantes (GER) **John Jarvis & Partner**

THREE-YEAR-OLDS

16 **MUTABAAHY (IRE)**, b g Oasis Dream—Habaayib **Mr Antony Brittain**
17 **PUCHITA (IRE)**, b f Acclamation—Violet Ballerina (IRE) **Mr Antony Brittain**

MR ANTONY BRITTAIN - Continued

TWO-YEAR-OLDS

18 B f 14/4 Monsieur Bond (IRE)—Caranbola (Lucky Story (USA))
19 Ch c 26/2 Monsieur Bond (IRE)—First Harmony (First Trump)
20 Ch f 12/4 Monsieur Bond (IRE)—Guadaloup (Loup Sauvage (USA))
21 B f 5/5 Monsieur Bond (IRE)—Lujiana (Lujain (USA))
22 B c 29/4 Monsieur Bond (IRE)—Melandre (Lujain (USA))
23 Ch c 20/4 Monsieur Bond (IRE)—Mozayada (USA) (Street Cry (IRE))
24 B c 1/4 Monsieur Bond (IRE)—Sea Crest (Xaar)

Other Owners: Mr Antony Brittain, Mr Paul Chambers, Mr J. Jarvis, Mr A. Jarvis, Mr H. Turner, Mr G. R. Turner, Mr Donald B. White.

Jockey (flat): Cam Hardie.

66

MRS JULIA BROOKE, Middleham
Postal: **Brough Farm, Middleham, Leyburn, North Yorkshire, DL8 4SG**
Contacts: **MOBILE (07776) 186581**
E-MAIL jb@juliabrookeracing.com

1 **BARELY BLACK (IRE)**, 6, b m Urban Poet (USA)—Downtown Rosie (IRE) **Mr John Sagar & Mr Danny Brooke**
2 **COPT HILL**, 10, b g Avonbridge—Lalique (IRE) **John & Billy Platts**
3 **CROSSMANN**, 4, b g Crosspeace (IRE)—Perecapa (IRE) **Dr P. Stutchbury**
4 4, B g Schiaparelli (GER)—Eliza Doalott (IRE) **The Golden Oldies Racing Club**
5 **EMMA BEAG (IRE)**, 7, b m Westerner—Emma Jane (IRE) **Mrs J. A. Brooke**
6 **GLOBETROTTER (IRE)**, 4, ch g Helmet (AUS)—Shimna **Sowray Brothers**
7 **HAZY MANOR (IRE)**, 4, b f Tagula (IRE)—Hazarama (IRE) **Mr J. Douglas**
8 **MARCH TO MILAN (IRE)**, 7, b m Milan—Kay For Karbia **Mrs J. A. Brooke**
9 **MORE MADNESS (IRE)**, 11, b g Dr Massini (IRE)—Angelic Angel (IRE) **Brough Farm Racing Partnership**
10 **ONE IN A ROW (IRE)**, 11, ch g Saffron Walden (FR)—Rostarr (IRE) **Billy & Philip Platts & Liz Garner**
11 **RUARAIDH HUGH (IRE)**, 9, b g Craigsteel—Decent Shower **Harbour Rose Partnership**
12 **SHORT FLIGHT (IRE)**, 6, b g Trans Island—Surricate (FR) **Mr K S Ward & Mrs J A Brooke**
13 **STAGS LEAP (IRE)**, 11, b g Refuse To Bend (IRE)—Swingsky (IRE) **John & Billy Platts**
14 **TRICK OF THE LYTE (IRE)**, 4, b c Kodiac—Alpine River (IRE) **The Lyteproducts Partnership**
15 **VASCO D'YCY (FR)**, 9, b g Equerry (USA)—Ingrid des Mottes (FR) **Mr K. S. Ward**
16 **WEAPON OF CHOICE (IRE)**, 10, b g Iffraaj—Tullawadgeen (IRE) **Mrs J. A. Brooke**

Other Owners: Mr D. J. Brooke, Mr B. H. Dolan, Mrs E. Garner, Mr N. A. D. Hassall, Nobaj Ltd, Mr W. N. Platts, Mr J. Platts, Mr P. Platts, Mr J. Sagar, Mr S. A. Sowray, Mrs M. K. Stirk, Mr P. N. Wilcock, Miss C. Wright.

67

LADY SUSAN BROOKE, Llandrindod Wells
Postal: **Tyn-y-Berth Farm, Dolau, Llandrindod Wells, Powys, LD1 5TW**
Contacts: **PHONE (01597) 851190 MOBILE (07977) 114834**
E-MAIL suebrooke@live.co.uk

1 **ASTIGOS (FR)**, 11, b br g Trempolino (USA)—Astonishing (BRZ) **Lady Brooke**
2 **BOXER BEAT (IRE)**, 11, b g Xaar—Pantoufle **Lady Brooke**
3 **FREE WORLD (FR)**, 14, b g Lost World (IRE)—Fautine (FR) **Lady Brooke**
4 **OVER TO MIDNIGHT**, 8, b m Midnight Legend—Makeover **Lady Brooke**
5 **RADUIS BLEU (FR)**, 13, gr g Dadarissime (FR)—Regence Bleue (FR) **Lady Brooke**
6 **RIVER PURPLE**, 11, b g Bollin Eric—Cerise Bleue (FR) **Lady Brooke**
7 **SPOCK (FR)**, 13, b g Lost World (IRE)—Quark Top (FR) **Lady Brooke**

Assistant Trainer: Lorna Brooke (07786) 962911

Amateur: Miss Lorna Brooke.

68 **MR ROY BROTHERTON, Pershore**
Postal: **Mill End Racing Stables, Netherton Road, Elmley Castle, Pershore, Worcestershire, WR10 3JF**
Contacts: **PHONE/FAX (01386) 710772 MOBILE (07973) 877280**

1 **DEISE VU (IRE)**, 10, b g Brian Boru—Deise Dreamer (IRE) **Elmley Queen**
2 **FILAMENT OF GOLD (USA)**, 7, b g Street Cry (IRE)—Raw Silk (USA) **Mr M. A. Geobey**
3 **MAMNOON (IRE)**, 5, b g Cape Cross (IRE)—Masaafat **Mr M. A. Geobey**
4 **RENEWING**, 7, b g Halling (USA)—Electric Society (IRE) **Mrs C. A. Newman**
5 **RITAS LEGACY**, 4, b g Passing Glance—Rita's Rock Ape **Jan Carpenter & Bill Young**

THREE-YEAR-OLDS

6 **RHOSMAEN STREET**, b g Stimulation (IRE)—Laser Crystal (IRE) **I. M. McGready**

Other Owners: R. Brotherton, Mrs J. A. Carpenter, Mr N. A. Lavender Jones, Mr M. A. Savage, Mr B. K. C. Young.

Assistant Trainer: Justin Brotherton

Jockey (NH): Jamie Moore.

69 **MR ALAN BROWN, Malton**
Postal: **Lilac Farm, Yedingham, Malton, North Yorkshire, YO17 8SS**
Contacts: **PHONE (01944) 728090 MOBILE (07970) 672845**
E-MAIL ad.brown@hotmail.co.uk WEBSITE www.alanbrownracing.co.uk

1 **ATRAFAN (IRE)**, 4, b g Atraf—Up Front (IRE) **Mr S. Pedersen & Mr Frank Reay**
2 **IMPERIAL LEGEND (IRE)**, 9, b g Mujadil (USA)—Titian Saga (IRE) **Gaga Syndicate**
3 **LAZARUS BELL**, 8, ch g Bahamian Bounty—Snake's Head **Mr Frank Reay & Mr A. D. Brown**
4 **MEANDMYSHADOW**, 10, ch m Tobougg (IRE)—Queen Jean **Ian Stewart & Alan Brown**
5 **NIGHT SHADOW**, 4, ch g Haafhd—Totally Trusted **Ian Stewart & Alan Brown**
6 **PLAN TO BE**, 6, b m Kayf Tara—Poor Celt
7 **POPPY IN THE WIND**, 6, b m Piccolo—Vintage Steps (IRE) **Mrs M Doherty & Mrs W A D Dyason**

Other Owners: A. D. Brown, Mrs M. A. Doherty, Mrs W. A. D. Dyason, S. E. Pedersen, Mr F. E. Reay, Mr I. Stewart, Mrs S. Thomson.

70 **MR ANDI BROWN, Newmarket**
Postal: **Southfields Stables, Hamilton Road, Newmarket, Suffolk, CB8 7JQ**
Contacts: **PHONE (01638) 669652 FAX (01638) 669652 MOBILE (07980) 393263**
E-MAIL southfieldsstables@btinternet.com WEBSITE www.southfieldsstables.co.uk

1 **CAMINO**, 5, b m Equiano (FR)—Juncea **In For A Penny In For A Pound**
2 **KWIKSTEP**, 4, b f Nathaniel (IRE)—Enchufla **Ms Z. Kurdi**
3 **LA TROG (IRE)**, 4, b f Vale of York (IRE)—Nasheej (USA) **Miss L. J. Knocker**
4 **VICTORIOUSLY**, 6, b g Azamour (IRE)—Ambria (GER) **Miss L. J. Knocker**

THREE-YEAR-OLDS

5 **WAJDY (IRE)**, b g Great Rumpuscat (USA)—Steel Band (USA) **Miss L. J. Knocker**

Other Owners: A. S. Brown.

Assistant Trainer: Miss Linsey Knocker

71 **MR DAVID BROWN, Averham**
Postal: **The Old Stables, Averham Park, Newark, Nottinghamshire, NG23 5RU**
Contacts: **PHONE (01636) 613793 MOBILE (07889) 132931**
E-MAIL david@davidbrownracing.com

1 **CLOCK CHIMES**, 4, b g Foxwedge (AUS)—Passing Hour (USA) **J. C. Fretwell**
2 **MIDNIGHT MACCHIATO (IRE)**, 5, b g Dark Angel (IRE)—Lathaat **D. A. West**
3 **MUNFALLET (IRE)**, 7, b g Royal Applause—Princess Mood (GER) **J. C. Fretwell**
4 **SEAVIEW**, 4, b f Harbour Watch (IRE)—Welanga **Mrs S. Brown**

MR DAVID BROWN - Continued

  5 **SIMPLY CLEVER**, 5, ch m Stimulation (IRE)—Well of Echoes **J R Atherton & Emma Byrne**
  6 **SKY GYPSY**, 4, gr f Dandy Man (IRE)—Gypsy Style **A Birkle, P Boden & S Brown**
  7 **TRADING PUNCHES (IRE)**, 4, b g Elzaam (AUS)—Kiralik **J. C. Fretwell**

THREE-YEAR-OLDS

  8 **ARCTIC ROLL**, b f Champs Elysees—Paqueretzza (FR) **Mrs S. Brown**
  9 **BIB AND TUCKER**, br g Dandy Man (IRE)—Dhuyoof (IRE) **J. C. Fretwell**
10 **CAVENDISH PLACE**, b g Doncaster Rover (USA)—Beauty Pageant (IRE) **David Brown & J C Fretwell**
11 **CREEL**, b c Aussie Rules (USA)—Spate Rise **Mr P. Onslow**
12 **DONNY BELLE**, b f Doncaster Rover (USA)—Speedy Senorita (IRE) **Mr Browns Boy's**
13 **FORTUNATE VISION**, b g Libranno—How Fortunate **New Vision Bloodstock**
14 **HARBOUR VISION**, gr c Harbour Watch (IRE)—Holy Nola (USA) **New Vision Bloodstock**
15 **HARD GRAFT**, gr ro g Lethal Force (IRE)—Molly Brown **J. C. Fretwell**
16 **HEADWEAR (IRE)**, ch f Helmet (AUS)—Indian Dumaani **J. C. Fretwell**
17 **HIC BIBI**, b f Cityscape—Real Me **Mrs Sandra Brown & Mrs Ann Harrison**
18 **MAKE GOOD (IRE)**, b g Fast Company (IRE)—Rectify (IRE) **J. C. Fretwell**
19 **MEDICI ORO**, ch g Medicean—Anapola (GER) **Ian Guise, D A West & D H Brown**
20 **MUCH BETTER**, b f Exceed And Excel (AUS)—Mawaakeb (USA) **J. C. Fretwell**
21 **ONE MORE CHANCE (IRE)**, b f Epaulette (AUS)—Hi Katriona (IRE) **J. C. Fretwell**
22 **SNAFFLED (IRE)**, b c Camacho—Little Oz (IRE) **J. C. Fretwell**
23 **SUNSTORM**, ch c Medicean—Crimson Cloud **Exors of the Late Mrs S. M. Oakes**

Other Owners: Mr J. R. Atherton, A. C. Birkle, Mr N. J. Blencowe, Mr P. S. Boden, Mr S. P. Bolland, Mr D. H. Brown, Mrs E. K. Byrne, Mr G. S. Felston, Mr I. Guise, Mrs C. A. Harrison, Mr M. Lenton.

Assistant Trainer: Dushyant Dooyea

Jockey (flat): Tom Eaves, Philip Makin.

72
MISS MICHELLE BRYANT, Lewes
Postal: **Bevern Bridge Farm Cottage, South Chailey, Lewes, East Sussex, BN8 4QH**
Contacts: **PHONE/FAX (01273) 400638 MOBILE (07976) 217542**
E-MAIL bear_2009@live.co.uk

  1 **RON WAVERLY (IRE)**, 8, ch g Haatef (USA)—Mermaid Beach **Miss M P Bryant, David & Eileen Bryant**

Other Owners: Miss M. Bryant, Mrs Eileen Bryant, Mr David Bryant.

Amateur: Miss M. P. Bryant.

73
MRS KATE BUCKETT, Upham
Postal: **Woodlocks Down Farm, Upham, Bishops Waltham, Hampshire, SO32 1JN**
Contacts: PHONE (01962) 777557

  1 **BOARDWALK EMPIRE (IRE)**, 11, b g Overbury (IRE)—Mighty Mandy (IRE) **Mrs K. A. Buckett**
  2 **JOIN THE NAVY**, 13, b g Sea Freedom—Join The Parade **Mrs K. A. Buckett**
  3 **UPHAM RUNNING (IRE)**, 10, b g Definite Article—Tara Brooch **Mrs K. A. Buckett**

Jockey (NH): Mark Grant. **Amateur:** Miss Chloe Boxall.

74
MR BOB BUCKLER, Bridgwater
Postal: **Gibb Hill, Courtway, Spaxton, Bridgwater, Somerset, TA5 1DR**
Contacts: **PHONE (01278) 671268 MOBILE (07785) 773957**
E-MAIL rbuckler@btconnect.com WEBSITE www.robertbucklerracing.co.uk

  1 **ALL KINGS (IRE)**, 9, b g Milan—Rilmount (IRE) **Avalon Surfacing & Construction Co Ltd**
  2 **BALLYEGAN (IRE)**, 13, b g Saddlers' Hall (IRE)—Knapping Princess (IRE) **R. H. Buckler**
  3 **GIBB HILL**, 4, ch g Frozen Fire (GER)—River Reine (IRE) **Mrs D Gamble & R H Buckler**
  4 **HOO BALLY DIVA (IRE)**, 7, b m Scorpion (IRE)—Dr Sandra (IRE) **Golden Cap**
  5 **NOSPER (FR)**, 6, b g Whipper (USA)—Nostaltir (FR) **Mrs J. M. Mills**
  6 **REGAL FLOW**, 11, b g Erhaab (USA)—Flow **Mrs H. R. Dunn**

MR BOB BUCKLER - Continued

    7 SAY MY NAME (IRE), 7, ch g Fleetwood (IRE)—River Reine (IRE) **Mr T. S. Macdonald & Mr R. H. Buckler**
    8 UNWIN VC, 4, b g Black Sam Bellamy (IRE)—Becky B **Golden Cap**

Other Owners: Mrs D. R. Gamble, Mr T. S. Macdonald, Mrs H. E. Shane.

Head Lad: Giles Scott (07774) 033246

Jockey (NH): Liam Heard.

---

75   MR DAI BURCHELL, Ebbw Vale
Postal: **Drysiog Farm, Briery Hill, Ebbw Vale, Gwent, NP23 6BU**
Contacts: **PHONE (01495) 302551 MOBILE (07980) 482860**

    1 APPROACHING STAR (FR), 7, ch m New Approach (IRE)—Madame Arcati (IRE) **Mr A. P. Shinton**
    2 BLUE TOP, 9, b g Millkom—Pompey Blue **B. M. G. Group**
    3 COOPERESS, 5, b m Sixties Icon—Vilnius **J. Parfitt**
    4 CROPLEY (IRE), 9, gr g Galileo (IRE)—Niyla (IRE) **Miss S. Carter**
    5 FACT FLOW (IRE), 9, br g Whitmore's Conn (USA)—Beaver Run (IRE) **The Bill & Ben Partnership**
    6 FURIOUSLY FAST (IRE), 6, b g Fast Company (IRE)—Agouti **Exors of the Late C. J. Friel**
    7 TYROLEAN, 5, b g Raven's Pass (USA)—Alessandria **B. M. G. Group**

Other Owners: Mr P. G. Amos, Mr T. G. Brooks, Mrs A. Davies, Mr W. R. A. Davies, Mr T. G. Williams.

Assistant Trainer: Ruth Burchell

Jockey (NH): Robert Dunne, Alan Johns. **Amateur:** Miss Jodie Hughes.

---

76   MR PAUL BURGOYNE, Wincanton
Postal: **Trainer did not wish details of his string to appear**

---

77   MR K. R. BURKE, Leyburn
Postal: **Spigot Lodge, Middleham, Leyburn, North Yorkshire, DL8 4TL**
Contacts: **PHONE (01969) 625088 FAX (01969) 625099 MOBILE (07778) 458777**
E-MAIL karl@karlburke.co.uk WEBSITE www.karlburke.co.uk

    1 ANGEL PALANAS, 4, b g Mayson—Scottish Exile (IRE) **Mr Mark Bates & Mrs E Burke**
    2 BARON RUN, 8, ch g Bertolini (USA)—Bhima **Mr Eric Burke & Partner**
    3 BORN TO BE ALIVE (IRE), 4, b g Born To Sea (IRE)—Yaria (IRE) **Mr T Dykes & Mrs E Burke**
    4 BOURNVILLE (IRE), 4, b f Casamento (IRE)—Passaggio **Ontoawinner, J Farmer & Mrs E Burke**
    5 CHAMPAGNE PINK (FR), 4, b f Teofilo (IRE)—Carruba (IRE) **Nick Bradley Racing 2 & Mrs E Burke**
    6 COPPER BAKED (FR), 4, b f I Never On Sunday (FR)—Shakila **Nick Bradley Racing 5 & E Burke**
    7 DAISY BERE (FR), 5, b m Peer Gynt (JPN)—Jackette (USA) **Mrs E. M. Burke**
    8 ENGLAND EXPECTS, 4, b f Mount Nelson—Fanny's Fancy **Tim Dykes & Jon Hughes**
    9 FOUR KINGDOMS (IRE), 4, b g Lord Shanakill (USA)—Four Poorer (IRE) **Mr D Simpson & Mrs E Burke**
   10 FRONTLINE PHANTOM (IRE), 11, b g Noverre (USA)—Daisy Hill **Mr Eric Burke & Partner**
   11 GEORGIAN BAY (IRE), 8, b g Oratorio (IRE)—Jazzie (FR) **Market Avenue Racing Club & Mrs E Burke**
   12 KELLY'S DINO (FR), 5, b g Doctor Dino (FR)—Sabolienne (FR) **Mr Liam Kelly & Mrs E Burke**
   13 LADY CRISTAL (IRE), 4, b f Footstepsinthesand—Scarborough Lily **Hope Eden & Mrs E Burke**
   14 LONDON PROTOCOL (FR), 5, ch g Muhtathir—Troiecat (FR) **Ontoawinner, Mr R McKeown & E Burke**
   15 LOST AT SEA, 4, b g Dutch Art—Tahlia Ree (IRE) **Mrs Z. Wentworth**
   16 MADE OF HONOUR (IRE), 4, ch f Casamento (IRE)—Bonne **Ontoawinner, Mr D Mackay & Mrs E Burke**
   17 MEDICI BANCHIERE, 4, ch g Medicean—Fairy Shoes **Global Racing Club & Mrs E Burke**
   18 MY AMIGO, 5, gr g Stimulation (IRE)—Blue Crest (FR) **Mr J. E. Dance**
   19 PEARL CASTLE (IRE), 8, b g Montjeu (IRE)—Ghurra (USA) **New Approach Racing Limited**
   20 RIVIERE ARGENTEE (FR), 4, gr f Hurricane Cat (USA)—River Trebor (USA) **Global Racing Club & Mrs E Burke**
   21 SEDUCE ME, 4, b f Dutch Art—Deep Bleu **Ontoawinner, Mr R McKeown & E Burke**
   22 TESTBOURNE (IRE), 4, b g Big Bad Bob (IRE)—Magnificent Bell **Mr T. J. Dykes**
   23 TRAP QUEEN (IRE), 5, b m Nayef (USA)—Quiritis **Mrs E. M. Burke**
   24 TWIZZELL, 4, b f Equiano (FR)—Greensand **Mr J. E. Dance**
   25 YOU'RE FIRED (IRE), 7, b g Firebreak—My Sweet Georgia (IRE) **Market Avenue Racing Club & Tim Dykes**

MR K. R. BURKE - Continued

THREE-YEAR-OLDS

26 **ASHLAR**, b c Mayson—Jillolini **Mr J. E. Dance**
27 **ASSIMILE (IRE)**, b c Dabirsim (FR)—Ascot Memory (IRE) **Hambleton Racing Ltd III & E Burke**
28 **BLUE HARMONY**, b f Bahamian Bounty—Fascination Street (IRE) **Middleham Park Racing LXVIII & Mrs Burke**
29 **BROKEN FORCE (USA)**, ch g Broken Vow (USA)—New Girlfriend (IRE) **Mr J Henderson & Mrs E Burke**
30 **BROKEN TIME (IRE)**, b f Iffraaj—Miranda Frost (IRE) **Mr J. E. Dance**
31 **CHANTRESSE (IRE)**, b f Holy Roman Emperor (IRE)—Woodland Chant (USA) **Owners For Owners: Chantresse**
32 **CIRRUS MINOR (FR)**, b f George Vancouver (USA)—Porza (FR) **Mrs Z. Wentworth**
33 **CROWN VALLARY (FR)**, b f Manduro (GER)—Troiecat (FR) **Ontoawinner, Mr R McKeown & E Burke**
34 **DIZZY G (IRE)**, b f Red Jazz (USA)—Altogether (IRE) **Mrs M. Bryce**
35 **DOUBLE REFLECTION**, b f Showcasing—Green And Bleue **Ontoawinner, SDH, James Pak & E Burke**
36 **DUBAI CLASSIC (IRE)**, b f Fast Company (IRE)—Dubai Pearl (IRE) **Hambleton Racing Ltd XXXV & E Burke**
37 **ELEMENTS QUEST (IRE)**, b f Elzaam (AUS)—Sweet Chilli (IRE) **Ontoawinner, J Farmer & Mrs E Burke**
38 **ELLTHEA (IRE)**, b f Kodiac—Tropical Lady (IRE) **Mrs M. Gittins**
39 **EMERALD ROCKET (IRE)**, b g Society Rock (IRE)—
                       Lady From Limerick (IRE) **Hambleton Racing Ltd III & E Burke**
40 **ENZO'S LAD (IRE)**, b g Society Rock (IRE)—Geht Fasteur (IRE) **Mrs M Gittins & Mrs E Burke**
41 **FABELLA BERE (FR)**, b f Peer Gynt (JPN)—L'ete (CHI) **Middleham Park Racing CVIII & Mrs Burke**
42 **GOLDEN GUIDE**, b f Havana Gold (IRE)—Blonde (IRE) **Ontoawinner 9 & Mrs E Burke**
43 **GRAND COMPANY**, ch f Fast Company (IRE)—Grand Zafeen **Partnership Terminated**
44 **GUVENOR'S CHOICE**, ro g Intikhab (USA)—Exempt **Mr I McInnes, Dr M Glaze & E Burke**
45 **HAVANA GREY**, gr c Havana Gold (IRE)—Blanc de Chine (IRE) **Global Racing Club & Mrs E Burke**
46 **HAVANA MARIPOSA**, b f Havana Gold (IRE)—Critical Path (IRE) **Hope Eden & Mrs E Burke**
47 **HELEN SHERBET**, br f Makfi—Clifton Dancer **S Lock, J Craft & E Burke**
48 **HUMBLE GRATITUDE**, ch g Foxwedge (AUS)—Gilt Linked **Mrs E. M. Burke**
49 B g Mayson—Inchcoonan **Mrs E. M. Burke**
50 **JENOOW (IRE)**, b f Tobougg (IRE)—Raspberry Beret (IRE) **Mr M. R. D. Fleming**
51 **LAURENS (FR)**, b f Siyouni (FR)—Recambe (IRE) **Mr J. E. Dance**
52 **LINE HOUSE**, ch f Kheleyf (USA)—Wood Fairy **Nick Bradley Racing 28**
53 **LORD OBERON**, b c Mayson—Fairy Shoes **Mr D J MacKay & Mrs E Burke**
54 **LUMI (IRE)**, b f Canford Cliffs (IRE)—Ravish **Mr J. E. Dance**
55 **MAGIC MARK**, b g Helmet (AUS)—Silken Aunt **Ontoawinner, SDH, James Pak & E Burke**
56 **MAMETZ WOOD (IRE)**, b g Elzaam (AUS)—Shaanbar (IRE) **Ontoawinner 14, James Pak & Mrs E Burke**
57 **MAXIMILION**, b g Dream Ahead (USA)—Maid A Million **K. A. Dasmal**
58 **MAYFAIR ROCK (IRE)**, ch f Society Rock (IRE)—Tara Too (IRE) **The Tara Five**
59 **MIDSUMMER KNIGHT**, b g Dream Ahead (USA)—High Spice (USA) **K. A. Dasmal**
60 **MOUNT ARARAT (IRE)**, b c Sea The Stars (IRE)—Divine Authority (IRE) **Mr H Strecker & Mrs E Burke**
61 **MYBOYHENRY (IRE)**, b g Footstepsinthesand—Renaissance Rio (IRE) **Mrs M. Gittins**
62 **PLAN AHEAD**, b f Dream Ahead (USA)—Poly Blue (IRE) **K. A. Dasmal**
63 **PROGRESSIVE JAZZ (IRE)**, b g Red Jazz (USA)—Kind Regards (IRE) **Mrs E. M. Burke**
64 **RAGGS AND RICHES (IRE)**, b f Wootton Bassett—
                       Scottish Exile (IRE) **Ontoawinner 14, James Pak & Mrs E Burke**
65 **RAYDIANCE**, b c Mayson—Iridescence **Ontoawinner 14 & Mrs E Burke**
66 **REMNANT (IRE)**, b g Dawn Approach (IRE)—Arbaah (USA) **Mr H Strecker & Mrs E Burke**
67 **RIZZLE DIZZLE**, b f Foxwedge (AUS)—Greensand **Mr J. E. Dance**
68 B f Holy Roman Emperor (IRE)—Sheer Glamour (IRE) **Mr H Strecker & Mrs E Burke**
69 **SNOW DIAMOND (IRE)**, b f Swiss Spirit—Early Morning Rain (IRE) **Market Avenue Racing Club Ltd**
70 **STAR OF ZAAM (IRE)**, br g Elzaam (AUS)—Golconda (IRE) **Hambleton Racing Ltd III & E Burke**
71 **STAY IN THE LIGHT**, b f Showcasing—Starlight Walk **Mr H Strecker & Mrs E Burke**
72 **UNFORTUNATELY (IRE)**, b c Society Rock (IRE)—Unfortunate **Cheveley Park Stud Limited**
73 **UNWRITTEN**, b g Poet's Voice—Passata (FR) **Lease Terminated**
74 **VALDOLOBO (IRE)**, b g Lope de Vega (IRE)—Eucharist (IRE) **Mr J. E. Dance**
75 **WAX AND WANE**, b c Maxios—Moonavvara **Mr T. J. Dykes**
76 **WUNDERBAR**, ch f Havana Gold (IRE)—Wunders Dream (IRE) **Mr H Strecker & Mrs E Burke**

TWO-YEAR-OLDS

77 B f 19/3 Kodiac—Affability (IRE) (Dalakhani (IRE)) (38095) **Mr J. E. Dance**
78 B c 17/2 Poet's Voice—African Plains (Oasis Dream) **Hambleton Racing Ltd III & E Burke**
79 Gr f 2/2 Rajsaman (FR)—Angel Rose (IRE) (Definite Article)
80 B f 4/2 Charm Spirit (IRE)—Bijou A Moi (Rainbow Quest (USA)) (100000) **Mr J. E. Dance**
81 Ch c 11/2 Havana Gold (IRE)—Blanc de Chine (IRE) (Dark Angel (IRE)) (140000)
82 Ro c 22/3 Alhebayeb (IRE)—Caerella (IRE) (Alzao (USA)) (10000)
83 **CHAINS OF LOVE (IRE)**, b f 16/3 Society Rock (IRE)—
                       Sportsticketing (IRE) (Spectrum (IRE)) (13837) **Ontoawinner 9 & Mrs E Burke**
84 **CONSTANT**, ch c 17/2 Dutch Art—West of The Moon (Pivotal) (70000) **Cheveley Park Stud Limited**

MR K. R. BURKE - Continued

85 Ch c 9/5 Dawn Approach (IRE)—
Danat Al Atheer (Shamardal (USA)) (8000) **Hambleton Racing Ltd XXXV & E Burke**
86 DARK HAVANA (IRE), b c 23/3 Havana Gold (IRE)—
Top of The Art (IRE) (Dark Angel (IRE)) (42328) **Mr D J MacKay & Mrs E Burke**
87 B f 7/3 Siyouni (FR)—Dawn To Dance (IRE) (Selkirk (USA)) (120000) **Mr J. E. Dance**
88 DIVINITY, b f 6/3 Dutch Art—Elysian (Galileo (IRE)) **Cheveley Park Stud Limited**
89 Gr f 22/2 Dark Angel (IRE)—Dulcian (Shamardal (USA)) (75000) **Mr J. E. Dance**
90 EXALTED ANGEL (FR), b c 9/2 Dark Angel (IRE)—
Hurryupharriet (IRE) (Camacho) (122100) **Mr D J MacKay & Mrs E Burke**
91 GEORGE HASTINGS, gr c 26/4 Gregorian (IRE)—
Pachanga (Inchinor) (32560) **Middleham Park Racing Lxxxix & E Burke**
92 B c 21/3 Holy Roman Emperor (IRE)—
Great Joy (IRE) (Grand Lodge (USA)) (28490) **Nick Bradley Racing 33 & Mrs E Burke**
93 Ch c 22/3 Mukhadram—Hoh Chi Min (Efisio) (28571) **Ontoawinner 14 & Mrs E Burke**
94 B f 26/2 Gale Force Ten—Issarose (IRE) (Ishiguru (USA)) (13024) **Hope Eden & Mrs E Burke**
95 Ch f 18/4 Manduro (GER)—Jolie Laide (IRE) (Sakhee (USA)) (12210) **Ontoawinner, SDH Project Services Ltd 1**
96 B f 19/4 Dandy Man (IRE)—Lisfannon (Bahamian Bounty) **Mr J. E. Dance**
97 Ch c 4/2 French Fifteen (FR)—Madeenh (IRE) (Pivotal) (32560) **Middleham Park Racing Lxxiii & E Burke**
98 Gr f 7/2 Alhebayeb (IRE)—Mary Pekan (IRE) (Sri Pekan (USA)) (23809) **Mr J. E. Dance**
99 B c 18/3 Mayson—Marysienka (Primo Dominie) (120000) **K. A. Dasmal**
100 B c 27/3 George Vancouver (USA)—
Memoire (FR) (Sadler's Wells (USA)) (21164) **Hambleton Racing Ltd III & E Burke**
101 B c 7/4 Heeraat (IRE)—Mimi Mouse (Diktat) (16280) **Ontoawinner, SDH Project Services Ltd 1**
102 B c 30/1 Morpheus—Miss Glitters (IRE) (Chevalier (IRE)) (12210) **Ontoawinner, SDH Project Services Ltd 1**
103 Gr c 1/3 Helmet (AUS)—My Girl Lisa (IRE) (With Approval (CAN)) (33333) **Ontoawinner 9 & Mrs E Burke**
104 B c 17/2 Swiss Spirit—Mysterious Girl (IRE) (Teofilo (IRE)) (41904) **Titanium Racing Club**
105 B c 15/4 Anodin (IRE)—Nebraska (FR) (Octagonal (NZ)) (14652) **Nick Bradley Racing 16 & Burke**
106 B f 8/3 Kodiac—One Giant Leap (IRE) (Pivotal) (80000) **Mr H. J. Strecker**
107 B c 5/3 Kingman—Parisi (Rahy (USA)) **Mr J. E. Dance**
108 B f 22/2 Kodiac—Payphone (Anabaa (USA)) (67000) **Mr H Strecker,A F O'Callaghan & E Burke**
109 B c 6/4 Siyouni (FR)—Pearl Away (FR) (Gold Away (IRE)) (18722) **Mr J. E. Dance**
110 B f 4/3 Swiss Spirit—Perfect Pursuit (Pastoral Pursuits) (12209) **Ontoawinner 14 & Mrs E Burke**
111 PRAXIDICE, b f 30/4 Toronado (IRE)—
Cross My Heart (Sakhee's Secret) (16000) **Ontoawinner, Mr R McKeown & E Burke**
112 B f 19/2 Garswood—Primo Lady (Lucky Story (USA)) (45000) **Nick Bradley 35, Strecker & Burke**
113 Br c 28/2 Footstepsinthesand—Secret Friend (IRE) (Royal Applause) (7500) **Ontoawinner 14 & Mrs E Burke**
114 SELF ASSESSMENT (IRE), b c 23/2 Elzaam (AUS)—
Little Miss Diva (IRE) (Diktat) (16280) **Hold Your Horses Racing & Mrs E Burke**
115 Ch f 4/2 Burwaaz—She's So Pretty (IRE) (Grand Lodge (USA)) (4571) **Hope Eden & Mrs E Burke**
116 B f 20/4 George Vancouver (USA)—Sienna Bella (Anabaa (USA)) (10582) **The Mount Racing Club & Mrs E Burke**
117 B c 10/3 Showcasing—Swan Wings (Bahamian Bounty) (60000) **Ontoawinner, Strecker & Burke**
118 SWEET DREAMER, br f 5/3 Harbour Watch (IRE)—Unasuming (IRE) (Orpen (USA))
119 B c 19/1 Kodiac—Throne (Royal Applause) (45714) **Mr J. E. Dance**
120 B c 19/3 Makfi—Troiecat (FR) (One Cool Cat (USA)) (24420) **Hambleton Racing Ltd III & E Burke**
121 B c 2/3 Slade Power (IRE)—Varnish (Choisir (AUS)) (70000) **K. A. Dasmal**
122 Ch f 7/4 Shamardal (USA)—Viola da Braccio (IRE) (Vettori (IRE)) (105000) **Mr H. J. Strecker**
123 B c 15/4 Farhh—Windlass (IRE) (Teofilo (IRE)) (10000) **Nick Bradley Racing 17 & Mrs E Burke**
124 B f 22/4 Zoffany (IRE)—Xaloc (IRE) (Shirocco (GER)) (40000)
125 B c 18/2 Mayson—Xtrasensory (Royal Applause) (47619) **Mrs E. M. Burke**
126 Bl f 17/3 Excelebration (IRE)—Yin (Dansili) (40000) **Ontoawinner 14 & Mrs E Burke**

Other Owners: Ontoawinner 14, James Pak, Mr D. C. Bacon, Mr M. Bates, Mr N. Bradley, Mr S. Bridge, Mr E. J. Burke, Mr J. P. Craft, Mr T. Dal, Mr P. Doughty, Mr A. N. Eaton, Dr C. I. Emmerson, Dr M. E. Glaze, Global Racing Club, Hambleton Racing Ltd, Hambleton Racing Ltd XXXIII, Hambleton Racing Ltd XXXV, Mr J. Henderson, Hold Your Horses Racing, Mr G. W. Holden, Miss S. Holden, Hope Eden Racing Limited, Mr E J. Hughes, Mrs J. Hughes, Mr L. Kelly, Mrs S. J. Keniry, Mr S. Lock, Mr D. J. MacKay, Mr A. R. W. Marsh, I. McInnes, Mr R. C. McKeown, Mr D. P. Meagher, Middleham Park Racing LXVIII, Middleham Park Racing LXXIII, Middleham Park Racing LXXXIX, Nick Bradley Racing 16, Nick Bradley Racing 17, Nick Bradley Racing 2, Nick Bradley Racing 33, Nick Bradley Racing 35, Nick Bradley Racing 5, Mr J. Nolan, Mr N. J. O'Brien, A. F. O'Callaghan, Ontoawinner 14, Ontoawinner 9, Ontoawinner, J. Farmer, Ontoawinner, SDH Project Services Ltd, Ontoawinner, SDH, James Pak, T. S. Palin, M. Prince, D. Simpson, Mr S. R. H. Turner.

Assistant Trainers: Mrs E. Burke, Mrs K. A. Voy, Miss L. Burke

Jockey (flat): Martin Harley, Joey Haynes, P. J. McDonald. **Apprentice:** Russell Harris, Clifford Lee, Patrick O'Hanlon.

78 MR HUGH BURNS, Alnwick
Postal: **Rose Cottage, Hedgeley Hall, Powburn, Alnwick, Northumberland, NE66 4HZ**
Contacts: **PHONE (01665) 578647 MOBILE (07503) 539571**
E-MAIL hughburns123@hotmail.co.uk

1 **CANADIAN JOSIE (IRE)**, 6, b m Definite Article—The Munyabure **Mr H. Burns**
2 **COUNTRY DELIGHTS (IRE)**, 5, b m Mahler—Nadwell (IRE) **Mr H. Burns**
3 5, Gr m Double Eclipse (IRE)—Leavemealoneawhile (IRE) **Mr H. Burns**
4 **MARBETH (IRE)**, 5, b m Frozen Power (IRE)—Suddenly **Mr H. Burns**
5 **MYLITTLEOULBUDDY (IRE)**, 5, br m Darsi (FR)—She Will Return (IRE) **Mr H. Burns**
6 **SLANEY CRAIGLEGACY (IRE)**, 6, b m Craigsteel—Slaney Legacy (IRE) **Mr H. Burns**
7 5, B br m Court Cave (IRE)—The Great O'malley (IRE) **Mr H. Burns**
8 **ZAMBEZI TIGER (IRE)**, 9, b g Tiger Hill (IRE)—Johannesburg Cat (USA) **Mr H. Burns**

79 MR OWEN BURROWS, Lambourn
Postal: **Kingwood House Stables Ltd, Lambourn Woodlands, Hungerford, Berkshire, RG17 7RS**
Contacts: **PHONE (01488) 73144**

1 **AKHLAAQ**, 4, b c New Approach (IRE)—Misheer **Mr Hamdan Al Maktoum**
2 **ALFAWARIS**, 4, b c Frankel—Kareemah (IRE) **Mr Hamdan Al Maktoum**
3 **ALWAATHEQ (IRE)**, 4, ch c Frankel—Tariysha (IRE) **Mr Hamdan Al Maktoum**
4 **ASBAAB (USA)**, 8, ch g Jazil (USA)—Alsaabeqa (USA) **Mr Hamdan Al Maktoum**
5 **AZALY (IRE)**, 4, ch g Sepoy (AUS)—Azzoom (IRE) **Mr Hamdan Al Maktoum**
6 **EHTIRAAS**, 5, b g Oasis Dream—Kareemah (IRE) **Mr Hamdan Al Maktoum**
7 **HATHIQ (IRE)**, 4, b g Exceed And Excel (AUS)—Madany (IRE) **Mr Hamdan Al Maktoum**
8 **JAAZEM (IRE)**, 4, b g Dark Angel (IRE)—Miss Indigo **Mr Hamdan Al Maktoum**
9 **KHAMRY**, 5, b g Poet's Voice—Poppets Sweetlove **Mr Hamdan Al Maktoum**
10 **LARAAIB (IRE)**, 4, b c Pivotal—Sahool **Mr Hamdan Al Maktoum**
11 **MAFAAHEEM (IRE)**, 4, b c Shamardal (USA)—Hammiya (IRE) **Mr Hamdan Al Maktoum**
12 **MASSAAT (IRE)**, 5, b h Teofilo (IRE)—Madany (IRE) **Mr Hamdan Al Maktoum**
13 **MEZEL**, 7, b g Tamayuz—Mumayeza **Mr Hamdan Al Maktoum**
14 **NAJASHEE (IRE)**, 4, gr c Invincible Spirit (IRE)—Tonnara (IRE) **Mr Hamdan Al Maktoum**
15 **OKOOL (FR)**, 4, b g Cape Cross (IRE)—Seschat (IRE) **Mr Hamdan Al Maktoum**
16 **QULOOB**, 4, b c New Approach (IRE)—Jadhwah **Mr Hamdan Al Maktoum**
17 **THAMMIN**, 4, gr c Dark Angel (IRE)—Gimme Some Lovin (IRE) **Mr Hamdan Al Maktoum**

THREE-YEAR-OLDS
18 **AJDDARR (IRE)**, b c Iffraaj—Naalatt (IRE) **Sheikh Ahmed Al Maktoum**
19 **ALAFLAAK (USA)**, b f War Front (USA)—Lahudood **Mr Hamdan Al Maktoum**
20 **ALFARQAD (USA)**, b br c War Front (USA)—Love And Pride (USA) **Mr Hamdan Al Maktoum**
21 **ALTHAAQIB (USA)**, b c War Front (USA)—Prize Catch (USA) **Mr Hamdan Al Maktoum**
22 **ALYAMAAMA (USA)**, ch f Kitten's Joy (USA)—Sarayir (USA) **Mr Hamdan Al Maktoum**
23 **ANAAKEED**, ch f Dubawi (IRE)—Daymooma **Mr Hamdan Al Maktoum**
24 **ANASHEED**, b f Frankel—Hathrah (IRE) **Mr Hamdan Al Maktoum**
25 **BAWAASIL**, b c Oasis Dream—Hedaaya (IRE) **Mr Hamdan Al Maktoum**
26 **ELWAZIR**, ch c Frankel—Dash To The Front **Mr Hamdan Al Maktoum**
27 **ENJAZAAT**, b c Acclamation—Miliika **Mr Hamdan Al Maktoum**
28 **ETISALAT**, gr c Lethal Force (IRE)—Chalet Girl **Mr Hamdan Al Maktoum**
29 **FAKHOOR (IRE)**, b c Oasis Dream—Darajaat (USA) **Mr Hamdan Al Maktoum**
30 **GANAYEM (IRE)**, gr f Frankel—Rose of Summer (USA) **Mr Hamdan Al Maktoum**
31 **HAADER (FR)**, ch c Sepoy (AUS)—Idle Tears **Mr Hamdan Al Maktoum**
32 **HABUB (USA)**, b c War Front (USA)—Sweet Lulu (USA) **Mr Hamdan Al Maktoum**
33 **HANAAN (IRE)**, b f Sea The Stars (IRE)—Mahaatheer (IRE) **Mr Hamdan Al Maktoum**
34 **JAALBOOT**, b g Invincible Spirit (IRE)—Selinka **Mr Hamdan Al Maktoum**
35 **KASAYID (IRE)**, ch f Pivotal—Serious Dowth (IRE) **Mr Hamdan Al Maktoum**
36 **KASBAAN**, br c Dansili—Aghareed (USA) **Mr Hamdan Al Maktoum**
37 **KATLEEN (USA)**, b f Lonhro (AUS)—Nasmatt **Sheikh Ahmed Al Maktoum**
38 **KITAABAAT**, b c Dansili—Ausus (USA) **Mr Hamdan Al Maktoum**
39 **MANTHOOR (IRE)**, gr c Swiss Spirit—Enchanting Way **Mr Hamdan Al Maktoum**
40 **MASRUR (IRE)**, b g Sea The Stars (IRE)—Elle Woods (IRE) **Mr Hamdan Al Maktoum**
41 **MODHAFARAH**, ch f Dubawi (IRE)—Kareemah (IRE) **Mr Hamdan Al Maktoum**

MR OWEN BURROWS - Continued

42 **MOKAATIL**, br c Lethal Force (IRE)—Moonlit Garden (IRE) **Mr Hamdan Al Maktoum**
43 **MONTSHI**, b c Dubawi (IRE)—Tantshi (IRE) **Sheikh Ahmed Al Maktoum**
44 **MOTAJAASID (IRE)**, b br g Harbour Watch (IRE)—Cape Joy (IRE) **Mr Hamdan Al Maktoum**
45 **MOTARAABET**, b c Dansili—Hawaafez **Mr Hamdan Al Maktoum**
46 **MUKTASHIF (IRE)**, ch g Shamardal (USA)—Silent Secret (IRE) **Mr Hamdan Al Maktoum**
47 **MURAAHIN**, ch c Teofilo (IRE)—Fatanah (USA) **Mr Hamdan Al Maktoum**
48 **MUTAAQEB**, b c Invincible Spirit (IRE)—Mejala (IRE) **Mr Hamdan Al Maktoum**
49 **MUTAFARRID (IRE)**, gr g Dark Angel (IRE)—Margarita (IRE) **Mr Hamdan Al Maktoum**
50 **MUTANAQEL**, b c Havana Gold (IRE)—Audaz **Mr Hamdan Al Maktoum**
51 **NAQAAWA (IRE)**, b f Shamardal (USA)—Hammiya (IRE) **Mr Hamdan Al Maktoum**
52 **ORIENTAL SONG (IRE)**, ch f Shamardal (USA)—Oriental Melody (IRE) **Hadi Al-Tajir**
53 **RAHAABA (IRE)**, b br f Dubawi (IRE)—Muthabara (IRE) **Mr Hamdan Al Maktoum**
54 **SAWWAAH**, b c New Approach (IRE)—Mudaaraah **Mr Hamdan Al Maktoum**
55 **SHABAABY**, b c Kyllachy—On The Brink **Mr Hamdan Al Maktoum**
56 **SHUROOQ**, gr f Dubawi (IRE)—Natagora (FR) **Mr Hamdan Al Maktoum**
57 **SUNOOF (IRE)**, ch f Raven's Pass (USA)—Arwaah (IRE) **Mr Hamdan Al Maktoum**
58 **TABDEED**, b c Havana Gold (IRE)—Puzzled (IRE) **Mr Hamdan Al Maktoum**
59 **TAMKEEN**, ch c Kyllachy—Regatta (IRE) **Mr Hamdan Al Maktoum**
60 **TASHAABOH (IRE)**, gr c Lethal Force (IRE)—Rush **Mr Hamdan Al Maktoum**
61 **THAAYER**, b c Helmet (AUS)—Sakhya (IRE) **Mr Hamdan Al Maktoum**
62 **WADILSAFA**, b c Frankel—Rumoush (USA) **Mr Hamdan Al Maktoum**
63 **WARSAAN**, b c Oasis Dream—Tanfidh **Mr Hamdan Al Maktoum**
64 **WOHILEH**, b f Cape Cross (IRE)—Saadatt **Sheikh Ahmed Al Maktoum**
65 **ZAAJER**, b c Shamardal (USA)—Zahoo (IRE) **Mr Hamdan Al Maktoum**

TWO-YEAR-OLDS

66 B c 7/4 Kingman—Anna's Rock (IRE) (Rock of Gibraltar (IRE)) **Mr Hamdan Al Maktoum**
67 B f 8/2 Sea The Moon (GER)—Anqooda (USA) (Oasis Dream) **Mr Hamdan Al Maktoum**
68 Ch f 4/3 Shamardal (USA)—Arwaah (IRE) (Dalakhani (IRE)) **Mr Hamdan Al Maktoum**
69 B f 26/2 Dubawi (IRE)—Atayeb (USA) (Rahy (USA)) **Mr Hamdan Al Maktoum**
70 Ch c 9/2 New Approach (IRE)—Ausus (USA) (Invasor (ARG)) **Mr Hamdan Al Maktoum**
71 **BAALBEK (USA)**, b c 19/2 Elusive Quality (USA)—Nasmatt (Danehill (USA)) **Sheikh Ahmed Al Maktoum**
72 **BUSTAAN (USA)**, b f 28/3 Distorted Humor (USA)—Aryaamm (IRE) (Galileo (IRE)) **Sheikh Ahmed Al Maktoum**
73 B f 20/3 Oasis Dream—Daymooma (Pivotal) **Mr Hamdan Al Maktoum**
74 B f 5/3 Dawn Approach (IRE)—Enfijaar (IRE) (Invincible Spirit (IRE)) **Mr Hamdan Al Maktoum**
75 B f 6/2 Dawn Approach (IRE)—Estidraaj (USA) (Medaglia d'oro (USA)) **Mr Hamdan Al Maktoum**
76 B c 28/2 War Front (USA)—Fascinating (USA) (Smart Strike (CAN)) **Mr Hamdan Al Maktoum**
77 Ch f 19/5 Poet's Voice—Ghandoorah (USA) (Forestry (USA)) **Mr Hamdan Al Maktoum**
78 B f 17/4 Kingman—Hathrah (IRE) (Linamix (FR)) **Mr Hamdan Al Maktoum**
79 B c 9/4 Dark Angel (IRE)—La Reine de Pearls (IRE) (Dubawi (IRE)) (95238) **Mr Hamdan Al Maktoum**
80 B c 3/5 Kodiac—Madany (IRE) (Acclamation) **Mr Hamdan Al Maktoum**
81 B c 6/5 Shamardal (USA)—Mahaatheer (IRE) (Daylami (IRE)) **Mr Hamdan Al Maktoum**
82 **MAKHLOOQ**, b c 20/4 Dubawi (IRE)—Zahoo (IRE) (Nayef (USA)) **Mr Hamdan Al Maktoum**
83 **MOTFAEL (IRE)**, b c 12/4 Invincible Spirit (IRE)—
                    Fidelite (IRE) (In The Wings) (240000) **Sheikh Ahmed Al Maktoum**
84 **MUHAARAR'S NEPHEW**, b c 27/2 Mukhadram—Rufoof (Zamindar (USA)) **Hadi Al-Tajir**
85 **MULTAMIS (IRE)**, gr c 1/2 Charm Spirit (IRE)—Dabista (IRE) (Highest Honor (FR)) **Mr Hamdan Al Maktoum**
86 **MURAAD (IRE)**, gr c 27/2 Dark Angel (IRE)—Hidden Girl (IRE) (Tamayuz) **Mr Hamdan Al Maktoum**
87 B c 31/3 Kitten's Joy (USA)—Nereid (USA) (Rock Hard Ten (USA)) (348432) **Mr Hamdan Al Maktoum**
88 **NOOR DUBAI**, br f 4/3 Invincible Spirit (IRE)—Beach Frolic (Nayef (USA)) (650000) **Mr Hamdan Al Maktoum**
89 **OJOOBA**, b f 5/5 Dubawi (IRE)—Rumoush (USA) (Rahy (USA)) **Mr Hamdan Al Maktoum**
90 B c 10/5 War Front (USA)—Prize Catch (USA) (A P Indy (USA)) (309717) **Mr Hamdan Al Maktoum**
91 Ch c 14/4 Havana Gold (IRE)—Raggiante (IRE) (Rock of Gibraltar (IRE)) (110000) **Mr Hamdan Al Maktoum**
92 **RAHEEB (IRE)**, b f 1/3 Kodiac—Dream Date (IRE) (Oasis Dream) **Mr Hamdan Al Maktoum**
93 **RAJWAA**, gr f 25/2 Dark Angel (IRE)—The Thrill Is Gone (Bahamian Bounty) (190476) **Mr Hamdan Al Maktoum**
94 B c 23/3 Daaher (CAN)—Sablah (USA) (Distorted Humor (USA)) **Mr Hamdan Al Maktoum**
95 B f 1/3 Kodiac—Samaah (IRE) (Cape Cross (IRE)) **Mr Hamdan Al Maktoum**
96 B f 18/3 Arch (USA)—Saraama (USA) (Bahri (USA)) **Mr Hamdan Al Maktoum**
97 B f 10/2 Mukhadram—Shadow Dancing (Unfuwain (USA)) (75000) **Mr Hamdan Al Maktoum**
98 B brc 18/4 Elzaam (AUS)—So Blissful (IRE) (Cape Cross (IRE)) (78095) **Mr Hamdan Al Maktoum**
99 Ch f 24/4 Speightstown (USA)—Special Me (USA) (Unbridled's Song (USA)) (425861) **Mr Hamdan Al Maktoum**
100 B c 28/3 War Front (USA)—Stanwyck (USA) (Empire Maker (USA)) (580720) **Mr Hamdan Al Maktoum**
101 B f 17/3 Dark Angel (IRE)—Surrey Storm (Montjeu (IRE)) (100000) **Mr Hamdan Al Maktoum**
102 **TANQEEB**, b c 26/1 Garswood—Oasis Mirage (Oasis Dream) **Mr Hamdan Al Maktoum**
103 B f 23/3 Shamardal (USA)—Umseyat (USA) (Arch (USA)) **Mr Hamdan Al Maktoum**

MR OWEN BURROWS - Continued

104 B f 24/2 Iffraaj—Uroobah (USA) (Dynaformer (USA)) **Mr Hamdan Al Maktoum**
105 USTATH, ch c 5/2 Exceed And Excel (AUS)—Adorn (Kyllachy) (260000) **Mr Hamdan Al Maktoum**

Assistant Trainer: Robert McDowall

---

80 MR JOHN BUTLER, Newmarket

Postal: **The Cottage, Charnwood Stables, Hamilton Road, Newmarket, Suffolk, CB8 7JQ**
Contacts: MOBILE **(07764) 999743**
E-MAIL johnbutler1@btinternet.com

1 ABSOLUTELY AWESOME, 4, ch g Choisir (AUS)—Milton of Campsie **Mr M. Mckay**
2 CAT ROYALE (IRE), 5, b g Lilbourne Lad (IRE)—Call This Cat (IRE) **Whiterok Ltd**
3 COME ON DAVE (IRE), 9, b g Red Clubs (IRE)—Desert Sprite (IRE) **Royale Racing Syndicate**
4 CONNEMARA QUEEN, 5, ch m Major Cadeaux—Cashleen (USA) **Northumbria Leisure Ltd**
5 DECLAMATION (IRE), 8, ch g Shamardal (USA)—Dignify (IRE) **Mr J. Butler**
6 DELEYLL, 4, ch g Sepoy (AUS)—Strings **Tramore Tree**
7 DENMEAD, 5, b g Champs Elysees—Glorious Dreams (USA) **John O'Donnell & Noel Kelly**
8 FALCAO (IRE), 6, br g Majestic Missile (IRE)—Cafe Lassere (USA) **Power Geneva Ltd**
9 FASHAAK (IRE), 5, b g Starspangledbanner (AUS)—Szabo (IRE) **Mr J. Butler**
10 GENUINE APPROVAL (IRE), 5, ch m Approve (IRE)—Genuinely (IRE) **Madeira Racing**
11 JOYFUL DREAM (IRE), 4, ch f Dream Ahead (USA)—Tearsforjoy (USA) **Mr G. Dolan**
12 KATALAN (GER), 5, b g Adlerflug (GER)—Kalla **Miss A. Haynes**
13 KATIE'S SURPRISE (IRE), 4, b f Famous Name—Lamh Eile (IRE) **6468 Racing**
14 KING CRIMSON, 6, ch g Captain Gerrard (IRE)—Elegant Lady **Power Geneva Ltd**
15 KINGSLEY KLARION (IRE), 5, b g Arcano (IRE)—May Day Queen (IRE) **Madeira Racing**
16 LADY OF STEEL, 4, b f Sir Percy—Steel Free (IRE) **Recycled Products Limited**
17 LORD REASON, 6, b g Sixties Icon—Luck Will Come (IRE) **Greenstead Hall Racing Ltd**
18 MADRINHO (IRE), 5, ch g Frozen Power (IRE)—Perfectly Clear (USA) **Royale Racing Syndicate**
19 MIME DANCE, 7, b g Notnowcato—Encore My Love **Tramore Tree**
20 OUR KIM (IRE), 4, b g Lawman (FR)—Kayd Kodaun (IRE) **Exors of the Late S. Brown**
21 PIAZON, 7, br g Striking Ambition—Colonel's Daughter **Royale Racing Syndicate**
22 RED INVADER (IRE), 8, b g Red Clubs (IRE)—Tifariti (USA) **6468 Racing**
23 SAYEDAATI SAADATI (IRE), 5, b g Montjeu (IRE)—Guessing (USA) **Miss A. Haynes**
24 SO LONELY (IRE), 4, b f So You Think (NZ)—Via Aurelia (IRE) **Mr J. Butler**
25 SPECULATOR, 6, gr g Bahamian Bounty—Swift Dispersal **Power Geneva Ltd**
26 SPLASH AROUND, 4, ch c Nathaniel (IRE)—Splashdown **Mr N. Buresli**
27 SPRYT (IRE), 6, b g Invincible Spirit (IRE)—Out of Thanks (IRE) **Mr J. Annable**
28 STAR LINKS (USA), 12, b g Bernstein (USA)—Startarette (USA) **Mr G. Dolan**
29 STAR OF THE STAGE, 6, b g Invincible Spirit (IRE)—Enact **Get On The Bunny**
30 TEST RIDE (IRE), 4, b g Rip Van Winkle (IRE)—Easter Fairy (USA) **Mr J. Butler**
31 TIME TO SEA (IRE), 4, b g Born To Sea (IRE)—Eastern Glow **C Benham/ D Whitford/ L Quinn/ K Quinn**
32 TOOFI (FR), 7, b g Henrythenavigator (USA)—Silver Bark **Northumbria Leisure Ltd & C. H. McGhie**
33 TORCH, 5, b g Paco Boy (IRE)—Singed **Tramore Tree**
34 UNFORGIVING MINUTE, 7, b g Cape Cross (IRE)—Ada River **Power Geneva Ltd**
35 WANEEN (IRE), 5, b g Approve (IRE)—Million All Day (IRE) **Mr J. Butler**
36 WELOOF (FR), 4, b g Redoute's Choice (AUS)—Pointed Song (USA) **Mr J. Butler**
37 ZAIN ARION (IRE), 5, b m Danehill Dancer (IRE)—Shaanara (IRE) **Mr A. Al Banwan**
38 ZAIN STAR (IRE), 4, b c Shamardal (USA)—Astrologie (FR) **Mr A. Al Banwan**
39 ZIG ZAG GIRL, 4, b f Sixties Icon—Mistic Magic (IRE) **Mr M. Mckay**

THREE-YEAR-OLDS

40 ELUSIVE SHOW (USA), b c Elusive Quality (USA)—Daisyago (USA) **Mr J. Butler**
41 FATHER AILBE (IRE), b g Excelebration (IRE)—Ms Sophie Eleanor (USA) **Mr J. Browne**
42 HAVEONEYERSELF (IRE), b c Requinto (IRE)—Charismas Birthday (IRE) **M McKay & T Cassidy**
43 NATIONAL ANTHEM, ch c Intikhab (USA)—Song of Passion (IRE) **M McKay & T Cassidy**
44 TIGER LYON (USA), b c Kitten's Joy (USA)—Hold It (USA) **M McKay & T Cassidy**

Other Owners: Mr C. F. Benham, Mr T. Cassidy, Mr G. Dunphy, Mr A. Fellowes, Mrs S. Horne, Mr W. E. N Kelly, Mrs A. M. Kirby, C. H. McGhie, Mr J. O'Donnell, L. M. Power, K. J. Quinn, Mr L. M. Quinn, Mr W. J. Salthouse, Mr D. M. Standring, Mr D. L. Whitford.

Assistant Trainer: Alice Haynes (07585) 558717

81 MR PADDY BUTLER, Lewes
Postal: **Homewood Gate Racing Stables, Novington Lane, East Chiltington, Lewes, East Sussex, BN7 3AU**
Contacts: **PHONE/FAX (01273) 890124 MOBILE (07973) 873846**
E-MAIL **homewoodgate@aol.com**

1 **ALL OR NOTHIN (IRE),** 9, b g Majestic Missile (IRE)—
Lady Peculiar (CAN) **Miss M P Bryant, David & Eileen Bryant**
2 **ATHENIAN GARDEN (USA),** 11, b m Royal Academy (USA)—Webee (USA) **Homewoodgate Racing Club**
3 **ELUSIVE COWBOY (USA),** 5, ch g Elusive Quality (USA)—Sarmad (USA) **Mrs E. Lucey-Butler**
4 **ESTIBDAAD (IRE),** 8, b g Haafet (IRE)—Star of Siligo (USA) **Miss M. P. Bryant**
5 **FLOWERS ON VENUS (IRE),** 6, ch g Raven's Pass (USA)—Chelsea Rose (IRE) **Miss M. P. Bryant**
6 **HILAND OSCAR (IRE),** 9, b g Oscar (IRE)—Be My Treasure (IRE) **Mrs E. Lucey-Butler**
7 **MERCERS,** 4, b f Piccolo—Ivory's Joy **Homewoodgate Racing Club**
8 **MY LORD,** 10, br g Ishiguru (USA)—Lady Smith **Miss M. P. Bryant**
9 **ROYAL RETTIE,** 4, br m Royal Applause—Bended Knee **TWT Racing Club I**
10 **SPICE BOAT,** 6, ch g Shamardal (USA)—Frizzante **C. W. Wilson**
11 **SWEET PICCOLO,** 8, ch g Piccolo—Quality Street **Mrs E. Lucey-Butler**

Other Owners: Mr D. Bryant, Mrs E. Bryant, Mr B. Merritt.

Assistant Trainer: Mrs E Lucey-Butler

Amateur: Miss M. Bryant, Miss J. Oliver.

82 MRS BARBARA BUTTERWORTH, Appleby
Postal: **Bolton Mill, Bolton, Appleby-in-Westmorland, Cumbria, CA16 6AL**
Contacts: **PHONE (01768) 361363 MOBILE (07778) 104118**

1 **AGE OF GLORY,** 9, b g Zamindar (USA)—Fleeting Moon **Miss E. Butterworth**
2 **BROTHER SCOTT,** 11, b g Kirkwall—Crimson Shower **Miss E. Butterworth**
3 **CHERRY PRINCESS,** 8, gr m Act One—Francia **Mrs B. Butterworth**
4 **IT'S A LONG STORY (IRE),** 7, b g Court Cave (IRE)—Rockholm Girl (IRE) **Mrs B. Butterworth**
5 **MINNIE MILAN (IRE),** 9, b m Milan—Shiminnie (IRE) **Miss E. Butterworth**
6 **SNOWED IN (IRE),** 9, gr g Dark Angel (IRE)—Spinning Gold **Miss E. Butterworth**

Assistant Trainer: Miss Elizabeth Butterworth

Jockey (NH): Sean Quinlan. **Amateur:** Miss Elizabeth Butterworth.

83 MISS JULIE CAMACHO, Malton
Postal: **Star Cottage, Welham Road, Norton, Malton, North Yorkshire, YO17 9QE**
Contacts: **PHONE (01653) 696205 FAX (01653) 696205 MOBILE (07779) 318135 / (07950) 356440**
E-MAIL **julie@jacracing.co.uk** WEBSITE **www.juliecamacho.com**

1 **BINT ARCANO (FR),** 5, ch m Arcano (IRE)—Rosa Mundi **G. B. Turnbull Ltd**
2 **BROCKHOLES,** 5, ch m Equiano (IRE)—Rivalry **Mr D. W. Armstrong**
3 **BURTONWOOD,** 6, b g Acclamation—Green Poppy **Judy & Richard Peck & Partner**
4 **CHARTBUSTER (IRE),** 4, b g Mastercraftsman (IRE)—Gift Dancer **Owners Group 015**
5 **CHOSEN WORLD,** 4, b g Intikhab (USA)—Panoptic **The Kirkham Partnership**
6 **DANDY BIRD (IRE),** 4, b f Dandy Man (IRE)—Labba **Judy & Richard Peck & Partner**
7 **DEANSGATE (IRE),** 5, b g Dandy Man (IRE)—Romarca (IRE) **Axom LXIII**
8 **DREAMOFDISCOVERY (IRE),** 4, b g Henrythenavigator (USA)—Dreamwriter (USA) **Miss J. A. Camacho**
9 **ECCLESTON,** 7, b g Acclamation—Miss Meggy **Mr D. W. Armstrong**
10 **JUDICIAL (IRE),** 6, b g Iffraaj—Marlinka **Elite Racing**
11 **KIRKHAM,** 5, b g Pastoral Pursuits—Royal Grace **The Kirkham Partnership**
12 **MAJESTIC STONE (IRE),** 4, b g Casamento (IRE)—Pretty Majestic (IRE) **Majestic Stone Partnership**
13 **MARSEILLE (IRE),** 4, b f Excelebration (IRE)—Marlinka **Elite Racing Club**
14 **MEDIA WORLD (IRE),** 5, ch g Medicean—Panoptic **Judy & Richard Peck & Partner**
15 **MYTHICAL SPIRIT (IRE),** 4, b f Dragon Pulse (IRE)—Call This Cat (IRE) **Miss J. A. Camacho**
16 **PLANETARIA (IRE),** 5, b g Lilbourne Lad (IRE)—Red Planet **Owners Group 020**
17 **ROUBLES (USA),** 4, b f Speightstown (USA)—Soviet Song (IRE) **Elite Racing Club**
18 **SANTAFIORA,** 4, b f Poet's Voice—Acquifer **Judy & Richard Peck & Partner**
19 **SPIRIT OF WEDZA (IRE),** 6, b g Footstepsinthesand—Sampers (IRE) **Owners Group 005**

MISS JULIE CAMACHO - Continued

20 SWAHEEN, 6, b g Lawman (FR)—Whole Grain **Judy & Richard Peck**
21 WILDE EXTRAVAGANCE (IRE), 5, ch g Dandy Man (IRE)—Castanetta (IRE) **Judy & Richard Peck**

THREE-YEAR-OLDS

22 I KNOW HOW (IRE), b g Epaulette (AUS)—Blue Crystal (IRE) **Judy & Richard Peck & Partner**
23 B g Thewayyouare (USA)—Joint Destiny (IRE) **G. & S. Turnbull**
24 LANGHO (IRE), gr g Dark Angel (IRE)—Merrymaking **Mr D. W. Armstrong**
25 MADISON, b f Mastercraftsman (IRE)—Kalinova (Marju (IRE)) **Elite Racing**
26 MAKANAH, b g Mayson—Diane's Choice **Axom LXXI**
27 PARIS DIXIE, b f Champs Elysees—Last of The Dixies **G. B. Turnbull Ltd**
28 ROYAL PROSPECT (IRE), b g Thewayyouare (USA)—Jillian (USA) **G. & S. Turnbull**

TWO-YEAR-OLDS

29 KUREDU, b c 8/4 Intello (GER)—Wait It Out (USA) (Swain (IRE)) (6000) **Julie Camacho**
30 LORETTA (IRE), b f 24/4 Iffraaj—Marlinka (Marju (IRE)) **Elite Racing**
31 LORTON, b f 22/3 Sepoy (AUS)—Oilinda (Nayef (USA)) (18000) **G. B. Turnbull**
32 MARVEL, b g 8/5 Poet's Voice—Baralinka (AИ) (Barathea (IRE)) **Owner's Group**
33 B f 20/4 Epaulette (AUS)—Shesastar (Bahamian Bounty) **Julie Camacho**
34 B f 20/5 Cape Cross (IRE)—
        Thousandkissesdeep (IRE) (Night Shift (USA)) (28000) **Mr N. O'Keefe & Mrs D. Camacho**

Other Owners: Axom, Miss Julie Camacho, Mrs Debbiella Camacho, Mr R. Dean, Mr Dan Downie, Mr Tony Hill, Mr B. M. Hillier, Miss M. Noden, Mr Richard Peck, Mrs Judy Peck, Mrs Rosemary Pritchard, Mrs D. Rush, Mr Cliff Verity.

Assistant Trainer: Mr S. Brown

Jockey (flat): Joe Doyle.

---

84 | **MR MARK CAMPION, Malton**
Postal: **Whitewell House Stables, Whitewall, Malton, North Yorkshire, YO17 9EH**
Contacts: PHONE **(01653) 692729** FAX **(01653) 600066** MOBILE **(07973) 178311**
E-MAIL **info@markcampion-racing.com** WEBSITE **www.markcampion-racing.com**

1 ASK SHANROE (IRE), 6, b g Ask—Lady Quesada (IRE)
2 6, Ch m Getaway (GER)—Founding Daughter (IRE)
3 SADDLERS' SECRET (IRE), 13, b m Saddlers' Hall (IRE)—Birdless Bush (IRE)
4 7, Ch g Proclamation (IRE)—Tish Too
5 TROIS BON AMIS (IRE), 4, gr g Lilbourne Lad (IRE)—Vanozza (FR)

Other Owners: Mr V. B. Coleman.

Assistant Trainer: Mrs F. Campion

---

85 | **MS JENNIE CANDLISH, Leek**
Postal: **Basford Grange Racing Stables, Basford, Leek, Staffordshire, ST13 7ET**
Contacts: PHONE **(07889) 413639 (07976) 825134** FAX **(01538) 360324**
E-MAIL **jenniecandlish@yahoo.co.uk** WEBSITE **www.jenniecandlishracing.co.uk**

1 AENGUS (IRE), 8, b g Robin des Champs (FR)—Which Thistle (IRE) **Mr V. A. Healy**
2 AL DESTOOR, 8, ch g Teofilo (IRE)—In A Silent Way (IRE) **Glen's Fools 2**
3 AQUA LIBRE, 5, b m Aqlaam—Be Free **Mrs D. Hopkins**
4 ARTHUR'S REUBEN, 5, b g Malinas (GER)—Ambitious Annie **Mr A. J. White**
5 ASTAROLAND (FR), 8, b g Astarabad (USA)—Orlandaise (FR) **Mr B. W. Verinder**
6 BASFORD BEN, 10, b g Trade Fair—Moly (FR) **Mr A. J. Baxter**
7 BEEVES (IRE), 11, b g Portrait Gallery (IRE)—Camas North (IRE) **Mr & Mrs Paul & Clare Rooney**
8 BRIDANE REBEL (IRE), 7, b m Milan—Rebel Dream (IRE) **Ms J. Candlish**
9 BRYDEN BOY (IRE), 8, b g Craigsteel—Cailin Vic Mo Cri (IRE) **Alan Baxter & Brian Hall**
10 CANDLELIGHT STORY, 8, b m Kayf Tara—Foehn Gale (IRE) **Mrs F. M. Draper**
11 COSHESTON, 5, ch g Black Sam Bellamy (IRE)—Rare Ruby (IRE) **Mrs J. M. Ratcliff**
12 COSTA PERCY, 4, b g Sir Percy—Costa Brava (IRE) **Mr & Mrs Paul & Clare Rooney**
13 CROSS OF STEEL (IRE), 5, b g Craigsteel—Gaelic Million (IRE) **Mr P. & Mrs G. A. Clarke**
14 DOUGALSTAR (FR), 9, b g Layman (USA)—Concert House (IRE) **Mr A. J. White**
15 FOR JIM (IRE), 6, gr g Milan—Dromhale Lady (IRE) **Mr V. A. Healy**

MS JENNIE CANDLISH - Continued

16 GRANDADS HORSE, 12, br g Bollin Eric—Solid Land (FR) **Whites of Coventry Limited**
17 GRANVILLE VARNER (IRE), 11, b g Flemensfirth (USA)—Fox Glen **Mr P. & Mrs G. A. Clarke**
18 GREENWORLDSOLUTION, 6, b g Lucarno (USA)—Basford Lady (IRE) **Brian Hall, Jen Candlish & Alan Baxter**
19 GROVE SILVER (IRE), 9, gr g Gamut (IRE)—Cobbler's Well (IRE) **Mr A. J. Baxter**
20 IRIS'S PROMISE, 6, gr m Black Sam Bellamy (IRE)—Cheeky Mare **Mr R. Lester**
21 LUCKY ELLEN (IRE), 4, b f Elusive Pimpernel (USA)—Dona Alba (IRE) **Mr V. A. Healy**
22 MANKALA (IRE), 8, b g Flemensfirth (USA)—Maracana (IRE) **Mr & Mrs Paul & Clare Rooney**
23 MAOI CHINN TIRE (IRE), 11, b g Mull of Kintyre (USA)—Primrose And Rose **Ms J. Candlish**
24 MICK THE POSER (IRE), 4, b g Art Connoisseur (IRE)—Naked Poser (IRE) **Matt Barrett & Alan Baxter**
25 OUTCROP (IRE), 4, b g Rock of Gibraltar (IRE)—Desert Sage **Alan Baxter & Brian Hall**
26 QUICK PICK (IRE), 7, b g Vinnie Roe (IRE)—Oscars Arrow (IRE) **4 Left Footers & A Blewnose**
27 RAINBOW LEGEND, 5, b g Midnight Legend—Princess Rainbow (FR) **Mr P. & Mrs G. A. Clarke**
28 RED GIANT (IRE), 7, ch g Beneficial—Barrack Star **Mr V. A. Healy**
29 RED TORTUE (IRE), 9, b g Turtle Island (IRE)—Howrwedoin (IRE) **Whites of Coventry Limited**
30 SECRETSISTA, 6, b m Presenting—Princess Rainbow (FR)
31 SHOW PALACE, 5, ch g Showcasing—Palais Polaire **Mr P. & Mrs G. A. Clarke**
32 SLEEPY HAVEN (IRE), 8, b g Indian Haven—High Society Girl (IRE) **Mr A. J. Baxter**
33 SPIRIT OF HALE (IRE), 7, ch g Stowaway—Roseboreen (IRE) **Mrs A. V. Hall**
34 STAR ASCENDING (IRE), 6, ch g Thousand Words—Sakaka **Mr P. Wright-Bevans**
35 SUNSHINEANDBUBBLES, 5, b m Multiplex—Dockside Strike **Amazing Racing**
36 TANARPINO, 7, ch g Tobougg (IRE)—Got Tune (FR) **Mr P. & Mrs G. A. Clarke**
37 THE HORSECHESNUT (IRE), 10, ch g Definite Article—Ballinahowliss (IRE) **Mr M. M. Allen**
38 THEFLYINGPORTRAIT (IRE), 9, gr g Portrait Gallery (IRE)—Skule Hill Lass (IRE) **The Mere Partnership**
39 TOMMY THE RASCAL, 8, b g Multiplex—Tina Gee **Mr A. J. White**
40 ZOLFO (IRE), 6, gr g Cloudings (IRE)—Hardy Lamb (IRE) **Mr P. & Mrs G. A. Clarke**

Other Owners: Mr D. S. Allan, Mr M. Barrett, Mrs P. M. Beardmore, Mr D. C. Byrne, Mr P Clarke, Mrs G. A. Clarke, Mr B. J. Hall, Mr P. McKeown, Mr K. J. Mulville, Mrs C. Rooney, Mr P. A. Rooney, Mrs P. A. Smith, J. White.

Assistant Trainer: Alan O'Keeffe

Jockey (flat): Joe Fanning, Paul Hanagan.

---

86 **MR HENRY CANDY, Wantage**
Postal: **Kingstone Warren, Wantage, Oxfordshire, OX12 9QF**
Contacts: **PHONE** (01367) 820276 / 820514 **FAX** (01367) 820500 **MOBILE** (07836) 211264
E-MAIL henrycandy@btconnect.com

1 CAPTON, 5, b g Cape Cross (IRE)—Flavian **Mr W. P. Wyatt**
2 CHAIN OF DAISIES, 6, b m Rail Link—Puya **Girsonfield Ltd**
3 DIMITRE, 4, gr g Showcasing—Devoted (IRE) **Landmark Racing Limited**
4 EULA VARNER, 4, b f Showcasing—Tremelo Pointe (IRE) **Andrew Whitlock Racing Ltd**
5 GREENSIDE, 7, b g Dubawi (IRE)—Katrina (IRE) **Clayton, Frost, Kebell & Candy**
6 KING OF NEPAL, 4, b g Sepoy (AUS)—Empress Anna (IRE) **First Of Many**
7 LET RIP (IRE), 4, b g Rip Van Winkle (IRE)—Al Ihsas (IRE) **Mr P. G. Jacobs**
8 LIMATO (IRE), 6, b g Tagula (IRE)—Come April **P. G. Jacobs**
9 MADELEINE BOND, 4, ch f Monsieur Bond (IRE)—Spin A Wish **Candy, Pritchard & Thomas**
10 OLAUDAH, 4, b g Equiano (FR)—Bookiesindexdotnet **Mr A. Davis**
11 PAST MASTER, 5, gr g Mastercraftsman (IRE)—Millestan (IRE) **Mr D B Clark/Mr A R Bentall/Mr H Candy**
12 QUEEN OF TIME, 4, b f Harbour Watch (IRE)—Black Belt Shopper **First Of Many**
13 REBECCA ROCKS, 4, b f Exceed And Excel (AUS)—Rebecca Rolfe **Hunscote Stud**
14 SON OF AFRICA, 6, b g Equiano (FR)—Generously Gifted **One Too Many Partners**
15 STOIC BOY, 6, ch g Paco Boy (IRE)—Dramatic Turn **Mr David Blackburn & Mr M. Blackburn**
16 TURNPIKE TRIP, 4, b g Champs Elysees—Neqaawi **Mrs D. Blackburn**
17 UDZUNGWA FOREST, 4, ch f Power—Uvinza **Mrs A. Ruggles**
18 UELE RIVER, 6, b m Refuse To Bend (IRE)—Baddi Heights (FR) **Mrs A. Ruggles**
19 VIBRANT CHORDS, 5, b g Poet's Voice—Lovely Thought **P. G. Jacobs**

THREE-YEAR-OLDS

20 ALIZETI (IRE), b f Dutch Art—Ushindi (IRE) **First Of Many And Turner**
21 BE MY ANGEL, b br f Dark Angel (IRE)—Mullein **Landmark Racing Limited**
22 BLAZING TUNDER (IRE), gr c Casamento (IRE)—La Chita Bonita (IRE) **Qatar Racing Limited**

MR HENRY CANDY - Continued

23 **CHOOSEY (IRE),** ch g Choisir (AUS)—Petit Chou (IRE) **Mr T Frost & Mr H Candy**
24 **CLAUDINE (IRE),** b f Zoffany (IRE)—Hamalka (IRE) **Henry Candy & Partners III**
25 **CLEVERLEY (IRE),** gr f Mastercraftsman (IRE)—Turning Point **Bloomsbury Stud**
26 **COLLATE,** b f Oasis Dream—Homepage **W. Tillett**
27 **CONSTANCEA (IRE),** b f High Chaparral (IRE)—Starfly (IRE) **M Hughes & A Frost**
28 **CUBAN SPIRIT,** b g Harbour Watch (IRE)—Madam Mojito (USA) **Candy, Pritchard & Thomas**
29 **EXPLOITATION (IRE),** b f Excelebration (IRE)—Reclamation (IRE) **Sir E. J. Loder**
30 **GOSCOTE,** ch f Pivotal—Gosbeck **Major M. G. Wyatt**
31 **GREAT MIDGE,** b c Kyllachy—Super Midge **E. Penser**
32 **HEDONISM (IRE),** b f Excelebration (IRE)—Knapton Hill **Chris Humber & Amanda Brudenell**
33 **HIDDEN AFFAIR,** b g Equiano (FR)—Love Action (IRE) **Cheveley Park Stud Limited**
34 **HOLDING MY BREATH,** b f Bated Breath—Dramatic Turn **Mrs D. Blackburn**
35 **I CAN (IRE),** b g So You Think (NZ)—Walk On Water **Bloomsbury Stud**
36 **JUPITER,** b g Finjaan—Medicea Sidera **Girsonfield Ltd**
37 **KATIE LEE (IRE),** b f Camacho—Katherine Lee (IRE) **M D Poland & H Candy**
38 **MARBLE BAR,** b f Makfi—Presbyterian Nun (IRE) **The Earl Cadogan**
39 **MT AUGUSTUS,** b g Champs Elysees—In Secret **The Earl Cadogan**
40 **NOEL (IRE),** b g Requinto (IRE)—Santacus (IRE) **The Noel Racing Partnership**
41 **ORD RIVER,** b f Intello (GER)—Free Offer **The Earl Cadogan**
42 **ORNAMENTAL,** b c Iffraaj—Tulipe Rose (FR) **Cheveley Park Stud Limited**
43 **ORTIZ,** ch f Havana Gold (IRE)—Almatinka (IRE) **P. G. Jacobs**
44 **RAINCALL,** b f Pivotal—Lone Rock (AUS) **Rockcliffe Stud**
45 B f Mastercraftsman (IRE)—Rakiza (IRE) **Mrs P. J. Burns**
46 **ROSE HIP,** b f Acclamation—Poppy Seed **Lady Whent**
47 **SARSTEDT,** b g Sixties Icon—Saluem **Mr Henry Candy & Mr David Altham**
48 **SHARP INNTAKE (IRE),** b f Bated Breath—Fidelio's Miracle (USA) **Mr J. A. Wetherald**
49 **SOVEREIGN DUKE (GER),** b c Jukebox Jury (IRE)—Shadow Queen (GER) **One Too Many Partners**
50 **TAOISEACH,** b c Roderic O'connor (IRE)—Munaa's Dream **Mr C. Humber**
51 **THRAVE,** b c Sir Percy—Feis Ceoil (IRE) **T. Barr**
52 **TWILIGHT THYME,** b g Bahamian Bounty—Twilight Mistress **Mr G. Wilson**
53 **VERVE (IRE),** b br f Epaulette (AUS)—Onomatomania (USA) **Mr C. Humber**
54 **WEAR IT WELL,** b f Kodiac—Choosey Girl (IRE) **Andrew Whitlock Racing Ltd**

TWO-YEAR-OLDS

55 **ADONIJAH,** b c 24/3 Sea The Stars (IRE)—Meeznah (USA) (Dynaformer (USA)) (325000) **T. Barr**
56 **ALFRED BOUCHER,** gr c 29/2 Aussie Rules (USA)—Policy Term (IRE) (Authorized (IRE)) **Mr R. Allcock**
57 **ALL RIGHT,** b f 25/4 Intello (GER)—Alice Alleyne (IRE) (Oasis Dream) **Major M. G. Wyatt**
58 **CANAL ROCKS,** br c 8/3 Aussie Rules (USA)—In Secret (Dalakhani (IRE)) **The Earl Cadogan**
59 B c 16/4 Sir Percy—Cheviot Heights (Intikhab (USA)) (16190) **Simon Broke & Partners**
60 **DELCIA,** b f 6/2 Delegator—Fiducia (Lawman (FR)) (761) **Mr P. G. Jacobs**
61 B f 21/2 Kuroshio (AUS)—Easy To Imagine (USA) (Cozzene (USA)) **Hot To Trot Racing**
62 **FOUR FEET (IRE),** b c 28/3 Harbour Watch (IRE)—Royal Connection (Bahamian Bounty) (7326) **Mr H. Candy**
63 **IFTON,** b c 4/5 Iffraaj—Flambeau (Oasis Dream) (42000) **Major M. G. Wyatt**
64 B f 18/2 Assertive—Layla's Oasis (Oasis Dream) **Lady Whent**
65 **LONICERA,** br f 27/3 Lethal Force (IRE)—Puya (Kris) **Girsonfield Ltd**
66 **MAIDEN CASTLE,** b c 12/5 Nayef (USA)—Danae (Dansili) **Girsonfield Ltd**
67 Ch f 11/2 Champs Elysees—Moonlight Mystery (Pivotal) **Mr A Frost & Mr C Brandon**
68 B f 30/4 Kyllachy—Night Affair (Bold Edge) (40000) **Six Too Many**
69 Ch c 4/4 Camacho—Pashmina (IRE) (Barathea (IRE)) (68000) **Thurloe Thoroughbreds XLV**
70 B f 30/3 Rock of Gibraltar (IRE)—Peach Bloom (Cape Cross (IRE)) **Mr A. Davis**
71 **QUARRY BEACH,** b f 29/3 Dutch Art—Free Offer (Generous (IRE)) **The Earl Cadogan**
72 **SALVE ETOILES (IRE),** b f 5/4 Sea The Stars (IRE)—Salve Diana (GER) (Dalakhani (IRE)) **Hunscote Stud**
73 **SEASCAPE (IRE),** b f 19/3 Sea The Moon (GER)—Feis Ceoil (IRE) (Key of Luck (USA)) **Mr R. Allcock**
74 **SOLDIER'S SON,** b c 13/3 Epaulette (AUS)—Elsie's Orphan (Pastoral Pursuits) (5238) **Mr H. Candy**
75 B c 3/2 Heeraat (IRE)—Sound of Life (IRE) (Cape Cross (IRE)) (19535) **Mr A. Davis**
76 B c 22/4 Showcasing—Veiled Intrigue (Pastoral Pursuits) **Mr A. Penfold**

Other Owners: Mr David Altham, Mr A. Bentall, Mr Mark Blackburn, Mrs T. Brudenell, Mr Henry Candy, Mr D. B. Clark, Mr A. Davis, Mrs Amanda Dixon, Mr D. J. Erwin, Mr M. Eves, Mr Richard Farquhar, Mr Alexander Frost, Mr T. A. F. Frost, Mr Martin Hughes, Mr J. Kebell, Mr D. Norris, Mr Michael Poland, Mrs C. M. Poland, Mr Roy Pritchard, Mrs L. A. Smith, Mr S. M. Smith, Mrs Jenny Snowball, Mr J. A. B. Stafford, Mr Gerry Thomas.

Assistant Trainer: Amy Scott

87 MR GRANT CANN, Lower Hamswell
Postal: Park Field, Hall Lane, Lower Hamswell, Bath, Gloucestershire, BA1 9DE
Contacts: PHONE (01225) 891674 MOBILE (07968) 271118

1 ASTER'S APPROVAL, 8, b g With Approval (CAN)—Aster (IRE) **P. J. Cave**
2 BERTIE MY BOY (IRE), 9, b g Millenary—Slievemhuire (IRE) **J. G. Cann**
3 GOOSEN MAVERICK (IRE), 7, b g Morozov (USA)—Bonny River (IRE) **Mrs H. L. Stoneman**
4 HOW'S MY FRIEND, 13, b g Karinga Bay—Friendly Lady **The Hussey's Hustlers**
5 JOHN DANIELL, 13, b g Overbury (IRE)—Hottentot **The Hussey's Hustlers**
6 SAVE THE PENNIES (IRE), 7, ch m Shantou (USA)—Penny Fiction (IRE) **J. G. Cann**

Other Owners: Miss A. M. Bush.

88 MR DON CANTILLON, Newmarket
Postal: 63 Exeter Road, Newmarket, Suffolk, CB8 8LP
Contacts: PHONE (01638) 668507 MOBILE (07709) 377601

1 CANBERRA CLIFFS (IRE), 4, b f Canford Cliffs (IRE)—Gloved Hand **Mrs C. Reed**
2 HINT OF GREY (IRE), 5, gr m Mastercraftsman (IRE)—Anamarka **Mrs C. Reed**
3 HOLLYWOOD ROAD (IRE), 5, b g Kodiac—Rinneen (IRE) **Mrs C. Reed**
4 STORMINGIN (IRE), 5, gr g Clodovil (IRE)—Magadar (USA) **Mrs C. Reed**
5 WESTERN WAY (IRE), 9, b g Westerner—Faucon **D. E. Cantillon**
6 WHATS NOT TO LIKE (GER), 7, b g Saddex—Wild Girl (GER) **D. E. Cantillon**

THREE-YEAR-OLDS
7 NAVARRA PRINCESS (IRE), b f Intense Focus (USA)—Navarra Queen **D. E. Cantillon**

89 MRS LOUISA CARBERRY, Senonnes
Postal: Les Fosses, 53390 Senonnes, France
Contacts: PHONE (0033) 624866369 (0033) (02) 249801795
E-MAIL louisacarberryracing@gmail.com WEBSITE www.carberry-racing.com

1 A POSTERIORI (FR), 8, ch g Michel Georges—Kinshasac (FR) **Tony Killoran, Mark Flood**
2 AL MUSHEER (FR), 7, gr g Verglas (IRE)—Canzonetta (FR) **Louisa Carberry**
3 ANCHORMAN (FR), 5, b g Smadoun (FR)—Go Lison (FR) **Louisa Carberry**
4 BAYFIELD (IRE), 5, b m Robin des Champs (FR)—Canitellyou (IRE) **Jameina Scarisbrick**
5 BETISE BEAUCHENE (FR), 7, b m Peer Gynt (JPN)—Adria de Clermont (FR) **Louisa Carberry**
6 BLETCHLEY (FR), 5, b m Saint des Saints (FR)—Royale Sulawesie (FR) **George Vergette**
7 CABARET DANCER (FR), 5, b m Montmartre (FR)—Allez Loulou (FR) **Fabien Cailler**
8 CELEBRE D'ALLEN (FR), 6, ch g Network (GER)—Revoltee (FR) **Allan Stennett**
9 CIEL DE PARIS, 6, b m Vale of York (IRE)—Absolute Precision (USA) **Louisa Carberry**
10 COMO COTTAGE (IRE), 5, b m Yeats (IRE)—Talinas Rose (IRE) **Martin Donovan**
11 DELONIX DE BERCE (FR), 5, b g Coastal Path—Maracay (FR) **Boultbee Brooks (Clive Brooks)**
12 DINETTE DE BALLON (FR), 6, b m Doctor Dino (FR)—Nile Altesse (FR) **Mrs Robert Gasche-Luc**
13 DOCTEUR DE BALLON (FR), 6, ch g Doctor Dino (FR)—Nile Breeze (FR) **Mrs Robert Gasche-Luc**
14 DOURDOUR (FR), 6, b g Redback—La Bezizais (FR) **Luc Monnet**
15 HUDSON RIVER (FR), 6, gr g Turgeon (USA)—Heritage River (FR) **Mrs Henri Devin**
16 INNOVATE (FR), 6, ch m Full of Gold (FR)—Ryde (FR) **George Vergette**
17 IT'S JENNIFER (FR), 6, b m Martaline—Shanxi Girl **Timothy Johnson**
18 JOE DE CLERMONT (IRE), 7, b g Westerner—Joe's Dream Catch (IRE) **Louisa Carberry**
19 MAKAMBA PASSION (FR), 5, b m Miesque's Son (USA)—Seven Brides (FR) **Ursula Toole**
20 MONEY MART (FR), 5, b m Martaline—Shanxi Girl **Timothy Johnson**
21 OURO FINO (FR), 6, b g Full of Gold (FR)—My Fabuleuse (FR) **George Vergette**
22 POKER DE BALLON (FR), 5, b g Doctor Dino (FR)—Nile Altesse (FR) **Mrs Robert Gasche-Luc**
23 REALM KEEPER (USA), 5, b g Arch (USA)—La Lodola (USA) **John Riley**
24 REWARD (IRE), 4, b g Pour Moi (IRE)—Elusive Legend (USA) **John Riley**
25 ROYAL GRINE (MOR), 4, ch c Montmartre (FR)—Royal Tiara (UAE) **M'hammed Karimine**
26 SURDOUE DE BALLON (FR), 5, gr g Turgeon (USA)—Nile Breeze (FR) **Mrs Robert Gasche-Luc**
27 TECTONA (IRE), 7, b m Shirocco (GER)—Too Marvelous (FR) **John Robert Powell**
28 TURLOUGH (FR), 6, gr g Turgeon (USA)—Vanilla Sky (FR) **Mrs Henri Devin**

MRS LOUISA CARBERRY - Continued

THREE-YEAR-OLDS
29 **FLOUANE (FR)**, b f Secret Singer (FR)—Roulmapoule (FR) **Louisa Carberry**
30 **FURTIVE (FR)**, b f Masterstroke (USA)—Anecdotique (FR) **Didier Blot**
31 **GIZA MKUU (FR)**, b g Manduro (GER)—Russian Beauty (USA) **David Alexander Reynolds**

Assistant Trainer: Philip Carberry

---

90 MRS RUTH CARR, Stillington
Postal: Mowbray House Farm, Easingwold Road, Stillington, York, North Yorkshire, YO61 1LT
Contacts: PHONE (01347) 823776 (home) (01347) 821683 (yard) MOBILE (07721) 926772
E-MAIL ruth@ruthcarrracing.co.uk WEBSITE www.ruthcarrracing.co.uk

1 **ABUSHAMAH (IRE)**, 7, b g Nayef (USA)—Adaala (USA) **Grange Park Racing VIII & Mrs R Carr**
2 **ADVENTUREMAN**, 6, b g Kyllachy—Constitute (USA) **The Venturers & Mrs R Carr**
3 **BE PERFECT (USA)**, 9, b g Street Cry (IRE)—Binya (GER) **The Beer Stalkers & Ruth Carr**
4 **BOBBY JOE LEG**, 4, ch g Pastoral Pursuits—China Cherub **Mrs A. Clark**
5 **CALVINIST**, 5, b g Holy Roman Emperor (IRE)—Sharp Relief (IRE) **Sohi & Sohi**
6 **CHAPLIN BAY (IRE)**, 6, b g Fastnet Rock (AUS)—
        Green Castle (USA) **Miss B Houlston, Mrs M Chapman & Mrs R Carr**
7 **COSMIC CHATTER**, 8, b g Paris House—Paradise Eve **Grange Park Racing VII**
8 **CUPID'S ARROW (IRE)**, 4, b g Majestic Missile (IRE)—Kiss And Don'tell (USA) **Miss Vanessa Church**
9 **DANISH DUKE (IRE)**, 7, ch g Duke of Marmalade (IRE)—Bridge Note (USA) **Mr Michael Hill**
10 **DISTANT PAST**, 7, b g Pastoral Pursuits—Faraway Lass **Mrs Marion Chapman & Mrs Ruth A. Carr**
11 **EXPLAIN**, 6, ch g Kyllachy—Descriptive (IRE) **The Beer Stalkers & Ruth Carr**
12 **FOXTROT KNIGHT**, 6, b g Kyllachy—Rustam **Grange Park Racing XIII & Ruth Carr**
13 **FOXY REBEL**, 4, ch g Cockney Rebel (IRE)—Foxholes Lodge **Mr G. Scruton & Mr D. Williamson**
14 **KATHEEFA (USA)**, 4, gr g Street Cry (IRE)—Wid (USA) **Grange Park Racing XIV & Ruth Carr**
15 **KIBAAR**, 6, b g Pastoral Pursuits—Ashes (IRE) **Mrs S Hibbert & Mrs R Carr**
16 **KING'S COINAGE (IRE)**, 4, b g Holy Roman Emperor (IRE)—Seducing (IRE) **Cragg Wood Racing**
17 **KINGSTREET LADY**, 5, b m Royal Applause—Intellibet One **Mr G. E. Amey**
18 **LEXINGTON PLACE**, 8, ch g Compton Place—Elidore **Mrs Marion Chapman & Mrs Ruth A. Carr**
19 **LEXINGTON TIMES (IRE)**, 6, b g Paco Boy (IRE)—Fuaigh Mor (IRE) **Middleham Park Racing C**
20 **LIBERATUM**, 4, b g Paco Boy (IRE)—Fine Lady **RHD**
21 **MAGICAL EFFECT (IRE)**, 6, ch g New Approach (IRE)—Purple Glow (IRE) **Miss Vanessa Church**
22 **MELANIEMILLIE**, 4, gr f Hellvelyn—Real Diamond **J. H. Sissons**
23 **MESHARDAL (GER)**, 8, b g Shamardal (USA)—Melody Fair (IRE) **The Hollinbridge Partnership & Ruth Carr**
24 **MUTAMADED (IRE)**, 5, b g Arcano (IRE)—Sahaayeb (IRE) **The Bottom Liners & Mrs R. Carr**
25 **MUTARAKEZ (IRE)**, 6, ch g Fast Company (IRE)—Nightswimmer (IRE) **The Bottom Liners & Paul Saxton**
26 **ORIENTAL SPLENDOUR (IRE)**, 6, br g Strategic Prince—Asian Lady **Mr J. A. Swinburne & Mrs Ruth A. Carr**
27 **OWER FLY**, 5, b g Pastoral Pursuits—Contrary Mary **Paul Saxton & The Bottom Liners**
28 **PIPERS NOTE**, 8, b g Piccolo—Madam Valentine **Cragg Wood Racing**
29 **RACQUET**, 5, br g Pastoral Pursuits—Billie Jean **Reach For The Moon & Mrs R Carr**
30 **RADJASH**, 4, b g Shamardal (USA)—White Moonstone (USA) **The Beer Stalkers & Ruth Carr**
31 **RAFFLE KING (IRE)**, 4, b g Kodiac—Tap The Dot (IRE) **6 Bit Racing**
32 **ROZY BOYS**, 4, b g Kyllachy—Responsive **Mr J Berry, Mrs M Chapman, Mrs R Carr**
33 **SOVEREIGN DEBT (IRE)**, 9, gr g Dark Angel (IRE)—Kelsey Rose **Lady O'Reilly, J P Hames & T Dorman**
34 **SUREYOUTOLDME (IRE)**, 4, ch g Tamayuz—Place de Moscou (IRE) **Mr Michael Hill**
35 **SUWAAN (IRE)**, 4, ch g Exceed And Excel (AUS)—Janina **Mr J. A. Swinburne & Mrs Ruth A. Carr**
36 **TADAANY (IRE)**, 6, b g Acclamation—Park Haven (IRE) **Mrs R. A. Carr**
37 **VALLARTA (IRE)**, 8, b g Footstepsinthesand—Mexican Miss (IRE) **Mr D Renton & Mrs R Carr**
38 **WASM**, 4, ch g Exceed And Excel (AUS)—Finchley **Ged Martin Nick & Mrs R Carr**
39 **ZEBULON (IRE)**, 4, gr g Zebedee—Novelina (IRE) **Bruce Jamieson, Barbara Dean, Ruth Carr**

THREE-YEAR-OLDS
40 **BRIAN RYAN**, b c Finjaan—Touching (IRE) **Franconson Partners**
41 **CARDAW LILY (IRE)**, b f Lawman (FR)—Chervil **British Racing Club**
42 Ch f Haathd—China Cherub **Mrs A. Clark**
43 **ERASTUS**, b g Swiss Spirit—Blakeshall Rose **Mrs R. A. Carr**
44 **FINSBURY PARK**, b g Finjaan—Fonnie (IRE) **RHD**
45 **IMPULSIVE FORCE (IRE)**, gr g Lethal Force (IRE)—A Mind of Her Own (IRE) **Mr P. K. Spencer**
46 **LOULIN**, ch g Exceed And Excel (AUS)—Wimple (USA) **G. Murray**
47 Ch g Haathd—Mandarin Lady **Mrs A. Clark**
48 **SKITO SOLDIER**, b g Sepoy (AUS)—Kotsi (IRE) **G Scruton, D Williamson & R Carr**

MRS RUTH CARR - Continued

TWO-YEAR-OLDS

49 GLORYELLA, b f 4/4 Yorgunnabelucky (USA)—Ceiriog Valley (In The Wings)

Other Owners: The Beer Stalkers, J. Berry, The Bottom Liners, T. J. E. Brereton, Mrs M. Chapman, Miss V. A. Church, Mr A. D. Crombie, Mrs D. Curran, D. Curran, Mr T. W. Deadman, Mrs B. I. Dean, Mr T. M. Dorman, Mr C. Dufferwiel, Mr F. H. Eales, Mr R. J. Fowler, Mrs B. S. Fowler, Ged Martin Nick, Grange Park Racing VIII, Grange Park Racing X1V, Grange Park Racing XIII, J. P. Hames, Mr A. R. G. Harris, Mrs S. Hibbert, Michael Hill, Hollinridge Partnership, Miss B. J. Houlston, Dr K. Howard, Mrs P. Howard, Mr A. B. Jamieson, Mr D. R. Kelly, Mr D. G. Neri, Mr P. Newell, Lady C. J. O'Reilly, T. S. Palin, M. Prince, R J H Limited, RHD Research Limited, Racing Club Ltd, D. C. Renton, A. Riaz, Mr P. A. Saxton, Mr G. Scruton, Mr G. A. Shields, Mr T. J. Snaith, Mr K. Sohi, Mr J. Sohi, Mr S. A. Sowray, Mr E. T. Surr, Mr J. A. Swinburne, Mr D. J. Williamson, Mr R. W. Wilson.

Assistant Trainer: Mrs M. Chapman

Jockey (flat): James Sullivan. **Amateur:** Miss Serena Brotherton.

---

91 MR DECLAN CARROLL, Malton

Postal: **Norton Grange Stables, Park Road, Malton, North Yorkshire, YO17 9EA**
Contacts: PHONE **(01653) 698517** MOBILE **(07801) 553779**
E-MAIL **declancarrollracing@gmail.com**

1 **BOLD SPIRIT,** 7, b g Invincible Spirit (IRE)—Far Shores (USA) **Mrs S. A. Bryan**
2 **BUONARROTI (IRE),** 7, b g Galileo (IRE)—Beauty Is Truth (IRE) **D. Hardy**
3 **GOD WILLING,** 7, b g Arch (USA)—Bourbon Ball (USA) **Bee Health Ltd**
4 **JUSTANOTHERBOTTLE (IRE),** 4, ch g Intense Focus (USA)—Duchess K (IRE) **Mr Steve Ryan & Mr M J Tedham**
5 **LIGHTS,** 4, b f Delegator—Sirenuse (IRE) **Mrs B. J. Sands**
6 **MONSIEUR JIMMY,** 6, ch g Monsieur Bond (IRE)—
Artistic License (IRE) **Mr Mr Ray Flegg & Mr John Bousfield.**
7 **MOTAHASSEN (IRE),** 4, b g Lonhro (AUS)—Journalist (IRE) **Mrs S. A. Bryan**
8 **MUSHARRIF,** 6, b g Arcano (IRE)—Cefira (USA) **Ray Flegg & John Bousfield**
9 **MUSIC SEEKER (IRE),** 4, b g Henrythenavigator (USA)—Danehill Music (IRE) **Mrs S. A. Bryan**
10 **SAIGON CITY,** 8, b g Mount Nelson—Hoh Chi Min **C H Stephenson,Tate,Flegg & Bousfield**
11 **SAVE THE BEES,** 10, b g Royal Applause—Rock Concert **Mr S. P. Ryan**
12 **SHEARIAN,** 8, b g Royal Applause—Regal Asset (IRE) **Mrs S. A. Bryan**
13 **STONEBOAT BILL,** 6, ch g Virtual—Applauding (IRE) **Mr D. J. O'Reilly**
14 **TILLY TROTTER (IRE),** 4, b f Kodiac—Inourthoughts (IRE) **Mr F. Gillespie**
15 **TITUS,** 4, b g Dansili—Mirror Lake **Steve Ryan & the Bramblers**

THREE-YEAR-OLDS

16 **ABEL HANDY (IRE),** b c Arcano (IRE)—Belle Isle **Mr F. Gillespie**
17 **BEA RYAN (IRE),** b f Dream Ahead (USA)—Kimola (IRE) **Mr S. P. Ryan**
18 **BEE MACHINE (IRE),** b g Footstepsinthesand—Lady Royale **Mr S. P. Ryan**
19 **HONEY GG,** b f Mayson—Local Fancy **The Commissioning Team**
20 **MACHREE (IRE),** b f Lord Shanakill (USA)—Faleena (IRE) **Yenilecas Syndicate**
21 **MAGOJIRO (USA),** b g Hat Trick (JPN)—Rebuke (USA) **John Blackburn & Andy Turton**
22 **NALAINI (IRE),** b f Holy Roman Emperor (IRE)—Lanark Belle **Yenilecas Syndicate**
23 **SHAY C,** b c Foxwedge (AUS)—Sirenuse (IRE) **Steve Ryan & The Bay Horse**

TWO-YEAR-OLDS

24 **ALOTABOTTLE,** ch c 28/1 Mukhadram—Lady Tabitha (IRE) (Tamayuz) (50000) **Gordon Bulloch & Steve Ryan**
25 **DEEBEE,** ch c 22/2 Dawn Approach (IRE)—Tooraweenah (Notnowcato) (60000) **Mr S. P. Ryan**
26 **HOUSE DEPOSIT,** ch c 24/1 Sepoy (AUS)—
Rosaceous (Duke of Marmalade (IRE)) (30000) **Lewis Ryan & Gordon Bulloch**
27 **LANGHOLM (IRE),** b c 30/1 Dark Angel (IRE)—
Pindrop (Exceed And Excel (AUS)) (81400) **Mr Steve Ryan & Mr M J Tedham**
28 **RAYPETEAFTERME,** ch c 24/3 Harbour Watch (IRE)—
Trump Street (First Trump) (4523) **Ray Flegg & John Bousfield**
29 B c 1/1 Harbour Watch (IRE)—Sirenuse (IRE) (Exceed And Excel (AUS)) **Miss Emily Carroll**
30 **TOBEEORNOTTOBEE,** ch c 3/3 Coach House (IRE)—
Lady Le Quesne (IRE) (Alhaarth (IRE)) (17142) **Ray Flegg, John Bousfield & Steve Ryan**

MR DECLAN CARROLL - Continued

Other Owners: Mr S. R. Bean, Mr J. N. Blackburn, Mr H. J. Bousfield, Mr G. Bulloch, D. Carroll, R. J. Flegg, Mr E. H. M. Frost, Mrs Y. Lavin, Mrs L. Maher, Mrs N. McDonnell, Mr A. Middlehurst, Ms C. Mulrennan, Ms S. O'Dowd, Mr L. Ryan, Mr M. B. Spence, C. H. Stephenson, Mr D. Tate, Mr M. J. Tedham, Mr A. Turton, Mr H. E. Wigan.

Apprentice: Phil Dennis, Ger O'Neil.

---

92   **MR TONY CARROLL, Cropthorne**
Postal: **Mill House Racing, Cropthorne, Pershore, Worcs**
Contacts: **PHONE (01386) 861020 FAX (01386) 861628 MOBILE (07770) 472431**
E-MAIL **a.w.carroll@btconnect.com** WEBSITE **www.awcarroll.co.uk**

1 ADMIRABLE ART (IRE), 8, b g Excellent Art—Demi Voix **Mr D. S. G. Morgan**
2 ALCANAR (USA), 5, ch g Teofilo (IRE)—Badalona **Contubernium Racing**
3 ALLIGATOR, 4, ch g Sepoy (AUS)—See You Later **Neville Statham & Family**
4 ALTAIRA, 7, b g Dubawi (IRE)—Peach Pearl **Mrs S. R. Keable**
5 ARYA STARK, 4, b f Piccolo—Night Affair **Lady Whent**
6 ASSERTOR, 4, b f Assertive—Blue Goddess (IRE) **G. A. Wilson**
7 ASTONE MAN (FR), 4, gr c Rajsaman (FR)—Astonia (FR) **Mr S. N. A. Al Romaithi**
8 BALTIC PRINCE (IRE), 8, b g Baltic King—Brunswick **Mr A. Mills**
9 BEAU MISTRAL (IRE), 9, ch m Windsor Knot (IRE)—Carpet Lover (IRE) **Mr A. Mills**
10 BLACK BUBLE (FR), 5, b g Valanour (IRE)—Miss Bubble Rose (FR) **Northway Lodge Racing**
11 BLISTERING DANCER (IRE), 8, b g Moss Vale (IRE)—Datura **Mrs E. Madden**
12 BOOM THE GROOM (IRE), 7, b g Kodiac—Ecco Mi (IRE) **Mr B. J. Millen**
13 BOSTON BLUE, 11, b g Halling (USA)—City of Gold (IRE) **Mr B. J. Millen**
14 BROTHER IN ARMS (IRE), 4, b g Kodiac—Cool Cousin (IRE) **Cover Point Racing**
15 CAPTAIN CAT (IRE), 9, b br g Dylan Thomas (IRE)—Mother of Pearl (IRE) **Seasons Holidays**
16 CLOUD NINE (FR), 5, b m Sakhee (USA)—Heaven **Wedgewood Estates**
17 COMPTON POPPY, 4, b f Compton Place—Miss Poppy **Mr P. A. Downing**
18 DE VEGAS KID (IRE), 4, ch c Lope de Vega (IRE)—Fravolina (USA) **The Rebelle Boys**
19 DEMI'S QUEST, 4, b f Roderic O'connor (IRE)—Demi Voix **Mr A. W. Carroll**
20 DOC SPORTELLO (IRE), 6, b g Majestic Missile (IRE)—Queen of Silk (IRE) **George Nixon & Mr W McLuskey**
21 EL DEGUELLO, 5, b m Shirocco (GER)—Competa
22 ELVIZ, 4, b g Medicean—Estrela **Seasons Holidays**
23 ESSAKA (IRE), 6, b g Equiano (FR)—Dream Vision (USA) **Mrs J. Carrington**
24 EVANESCENT (IRE), 9, b g Elusive City (USA)—Itsanothergirl **Mr A. W. Carroll**
25 FORESEE (GER), 5, b g Sea The Stars (IRE)—Four Roses (FR) **Millen & Cooke**
26 FRANCISCO, 6, b g Paco Boy (IRE)—Blue Goddess (IRE) **G. A. Wilson**
27 FRANTICAL, 6, b g Observatory (USA)—Quest For Freedom **Mr J. M. Wall**
28 GORGEOUS (FR), 5, b m Assertive—Agent Kensington **Wedgewood Estates**
29 HAVANA BEAT (IRE), 8, b g Teofilo (IRE)—Sweet Home Alabama (IRE) **Northway Lodge Racing**
30 HENRY CROFT, 5, b g Dubawi (IRE)—Karen's Caper (USA) **Mr B. J. Millen**
31 HEURTEVENT (FR), 9, b br g Hold That Tiger (USA)—Sybilia (GER) **L. T. Cheshire**
32 ILHABELA FACT, 4, b gr c High Chaparral (IRE)—Ilhabela (IRE) **Cooke & Millen**
33 IMBUCATO, 4, b g Paco Boy (IRE)—L'invitata **Mr D. Page**
34 JEREMY'S JET (IRE), 7, b g Jeremy—Double Vie (IRE) **Mrs P. J. Clark**
35 KATH'S BOY (IRE), 4, b g Bushranger (IRE)—Elayoon (USA) **Mr C. J. Wheeler**
36 KINGS CROSS (FR), 8, b br g King's Theatre (IRE)—Ladies Choice (FR) **Mr A. W. Carroll**
37 KINGSTON (GER), 9, br g Dylan Thomas (IRE)—Katy Carr **Three Counties Racing**
38 MAN OF THE NORTH, 5, b h And Beyond (IRE)—Latin Beauty (IRE) **Last Day Racing Partnership**
39 MISTER MUSIC, 9, b g Singspiel (IRE)—Sierra **Mr A Sergent & Partner**
40 MR JIM, 9, b g Fraam—Coddington Susie **Mr C. J. Wheeler**
41 NOUVELLE ERE, 7, b g Archipenko (USA)—Sinister Ruckus (USA) **Mr M. C. Palmer**
42 OCEAN BENTLEY (IRE), 6, b g Amadeus Wolf—Bentley's Bush (IRE) **Mr A. W. Carroll**
43 OEIL DE TIGRE (FR), 7, b g Footstepsinthesand—Suerte **Mr A. W. Carroll**
44 PAPA DELTA, 4, b g Makfi—Step Softly **Mr P. A. Downing**
45 POETIC FORCE (IRE), 4, ch g Lope de Vega (IRE)—Obligada (IRE) **W McLuskey & S Barton**
46 POUR LA VICTOIRE (IRE), 8, b g Antonius Pius (USA)—Lady Lucia (IRE) **Curry House Corner**
47 PRAIRIE TOWN (IRE), 7, b g High Chaparral (IRE)—Lake Baton **Cooke & Millen**
48 PREROGATIVE (IRE), 4, b g Rock of Gibraltar (IRE)—Tedarshana **Six Pack**
49 PROMINNA, 8, ch g Proclamation (IRE)—Minnina (IRE) **Mayden Stud**
50 RED ALERT, 4, b g Sleeping Indian—Red Sovereign **Mr A. A. Byrne**
51 RIGHTWAY (IRE), 7, b g Cockney Rebel (IRE)—Caeribland (IRE) **Mr B. J. Millen**
52 RIVER DART (IRE), 6, ch g Dutch Art—Sky Galaxy (USA) **Mr B. J. Millen**
53 ROWLESTONERENDEZVU, 5, b m Rail Link—Charmante Femme **The Rowlestone Racing Club**

MR TONY CARROLL - Continued

54 **SIR JAMIE,** 5, ch g Monsieur Bond (IRE)—First Dawn **Mayden Stud**
55 **SPIRITOFTOMINTOUL,** 9, gr g Authorized (IRE)—Diamond Line (FR) **The Sunday Players**
56 **SUNI DANCER,** 7, b m Captain Gerrard (IRE)—Sunisa (IRE) **Mr I. Furlong**
57 **TIME MEDICEAN,** 12, gr g Medicean—Ribbons And Bows (IRE) **Mr A. W. Carroll**
58 **TONI'S A STAR,** 6, b m Avonbridge—Canina **A Star Recruitment Limited**
59 **WEDGEWOOD ESTATES,** 7, ch m Assertive—Heaven **Wedgewood Estates**
60 **WEDGEWOOD WONDER,** 4, b f Medicean—Katya Kabanova **Wedgewood Estates**
61 **WINDSORLOT (IRE),** 5, ch g Windsor Knot (IRE)—Majestic Jenny (IRE) **SF Racing Club**

THREE-YEAR-OLDS

62 **EESHA SAYS (IRE),** b f Fast Company (IRE)—Admire The View (IRE) **Mr A. W. Carroll**
63 **HOLD YOUR BREATH,** b f Bated Breath—Chittenden (USA) **D Boocock & Childswickham Partnership**

TWO-YEAR-OLDS

64 **BRING US PARADISE,** b c 24/4 Zoffany (IRE)—Paradise Way (Elusive Quality (USA)) (12000) **Mr D. Boocock**
65 B f 21/1 Sayif (IRE)—Dubawi's Spirit (IRE) (Dubawi (IRE)) (3333) **Mill House Racing Syndicate**
66 B f 27/1 Stimulation (IRE)—Miss Poppy (Averti (IRE)) (3809) **Mill House Racing Syndicate**
67 B c 20/2 Rip Van Winkle (IRE)—Serenity Spa (Excellent Art) **Seasons Holidays**

Other Owners: Mr G. E. Amey, Mr S. Barton, Mr D. R. Blake, Mr D. Boddy, N. A. Brimble, Mr C. E. Carroll, Mr M. S. Cooke, Mr J. R. Daniell, J. A. Dewhurst, Mrs D. S. Dewhurst, Mrs E. M. Juckes, Mr B. Kelleher, Mr R. J. Lanchbury, Mr J. Lawrence, Mr W. McLuskey, Mr J. McMahon, Mr R. J. Millen, Mr D.J. Morris, Mr M. Nichol, Mr W. G. Nixon, Dr A. D. Rogers, Mr N. Scanlan, Mr A. W. Sergent, Mr N. J. Statham, Mrs P. Statham, Mr J. A. Sullivan, Mr J. D. Taylor, Mr L. C. Thomas, Mr S. F. Whitehouse.

Jockey (flat): George Downing. **Jockey (NH):** Lee Edwards. **Conditional:** Josh Hamer.

---

93 **MR TONY CARSON, Newmarket**
Postal: **Southgate Stables, Hamilton Road, Newmarket**
Contacts: **PHONE (01638) 660947 MOBILE (07837) 601867**
E-MAIL southgatestables@outlook.com

1 **AMBLE INN,** 6, b m Sulamani (IRE)—Distant Florin **Mr C. T. Dennett**
2 **CAINHOE STAR,** 5, ch g Pivotal—Celeste **Hugh & Mindi Byrne & W H Carson**
3 **CURIOUS FOX,** 5, b m Bertolini (USA)—Doric Lady **Carson, Francis, Ghauri & Percy**
4 **GULLAND ROCK,** 7, b g Exceed And Excel (AUS)—Sacre Coeur **W. F. H. Carson**
5 **HAWATIF (IRE),** 5, b m Royal Applause—Excellerator (IRE) **W. F. H. Carson**
6 **MOSSY'S LODGE,** 5, b m High Chaparral (IRE)—Tee Cee **MacAttack**
7 **SEA DWELLER,** 5, b m Royal Applause (IRE)—Langoustine (AUS) **Dave Newman & Minster Stud**
8 **SEA TEA DEA,** 4, b f Archipenko (USA)—Half Sister (IRE) **Mr C. T. Dennett**
9 **SMALL MERCY,** 4, ch f Medicean—Munchkin **W. F. H. Carson**
10 **SWILLY SUNSET,** 5, b g Kyllachy—Spanish Springs (IRE) **Alderson Carson Francis Hart**
11 **TIME CONSTRAINTS (USA),** 4, b g Gio Ponti (USA)—Escape To Victory **P. D. Rogers**
12 **TULIP DRESS,** 5, ch m Dutch Art—White Dress (IRE) **Hugh & Mindi Byrne & Minster Stud**

THREE-YEAR-OLDS

13 **PAMMI,** b f Poet's Voice—Bright Girl (IRE) **Mr C. T. Dennett**

Other Owners: P. S. Alderson, Mr H. M. Byrne, Mrs M. D. Byrne, Mrs E. Carson, Mr A. T. Carson, Mr M. R. Francis, Mr A. S. Hart, Mr T. J. McLoughlin, Mr D. J. Newman, Mr A. Percy.

Assistant Trainer: Graham Carson

Jockey (flat): William Carson. **Amateur:** Mr Graham Carson.

---

94 **MR LEE CARTER, Epsom**
Postal: **The Old Yard, Clear Height Stables, Epsom, Surrey, KT18 5LB**
Contacts: **PHONE (01372) 740878 FAX (01372) 740898 MOBILE (07539) 354819**
E-MAIL leecarterracing@aol.co.uk WEBSITE www.leecarterracing.com

1 **BRIDGE OF SIGHS,** 6, ch g Avonbridge—Ashantiana **Ewell Never Know**
2 **CADEAUX BOXER,** 5, ch g Major Cadeaux—Ashantiana **SN Racing VII**

MR LEE CARTER - Continued

3 **FAIRWAY TO HEAVEN (IRE)**, 9, b g Jeremy (USA)—Luggala (IRE) **Wackey Racers Harefield**
4 **FIRST EXPERIENCE**, 7, b m Tamayuz—Lolla's Spirit (IRE) **Clear Racing With SMD Investments**
5 **FOLLOW ME (IRE)**, 4, b f Zoffany (IRE)—Flower of Kent (USA) **Clear Racing & Mrs S A Pearson**
6 **GERRY THE GLOVER (IRE)**, 6, b g Approve (IRE)—Umlani (IRE) **N. Boyce**
7 **GOLD CLUB**, 7, b g Multiplex—Oceana Blue **Tattenham Corner Racing IV**
8 **IXELLES DIAMOND (IRE)**, 7, br m Diamond Green (FR)—Silk Point (IRE) **Clear Racing**
9 **JUST FAB (IRE)**, 5, b m Canford Cliffs (IRE)—Unlock (IRE) **Bevington Salads With Clear Racing**
10 **MUNSARIM (IRE)**, 11, b g Shamardal (USA)—Etizaaz (USA) **Wackey Racers Harefield**
11 **SALEH (IRE)**, 5, b g Iffraaj—Pellinore (USA) **Only One Bid Partnership**
12 **SPIRITUAL STAR (IRE)**, 9, b g Soviet Star (USA)—Million Spirits (IRE) **Wackey Racers Harefield**

Other Owners: Mrs K. T. Carter, Miss N. F. Davey, Mr J. D. A. Gordon, Mrs M. M. Greening, Mr B. J. Greening, Mr G. Marshall, Mr S. Nunn, Mr J. O'Hara, Mrs S. A. Pearson, SMD Investments Ltd, Mr D. Wood.

---

95 MR BEN CASE, Banbury

Postal: **Wardington Gate Farm, Edgcote, Banbury, Oxfordshire, OX17 1AG**
Contacts: **PHONE (01295) 750959 FAX (01295) 758840 MOBILE (07808) 061223**
E-MAIL info@bencaseracing.com WEBSITE www.bencaseracing.com

1 **BALLELA MAGIC (IRE)**, 7, b m Kalanisi (IRE)—Glen's Magic (IRE) **Wardington Hopefuls**
2 **COCHINILLO (IRE)**, 9, b g Shantou (USA)—Nut Touluze (IRE) **Mr B. I. Case**
3 **CODED MESSAGE**, 5, b m Oscar (IRE)—Ring Back (IRE) **Mrs A. P. B. Allen**
4 **CROCO BAY (IRE)**, 11, b g Croco Rouge (IRE)—April Thistle (IRE) **Lady Jane Grosvenor**
5 **CROOKSTOWN (IRE)**, 11, b g Rudimentary (USA)—Millview Lass (IRE) **Mrs C. Wallace**
6 4, B f Shantou (USA)—Dabiyra (IRE) **Case Racing Partnership**
7 **DAKKAR COLLONGES (FR)**, 5, br g Network (GER)—Karesse Collonges (FR) **Mrs C. Kendrick**
8 **DUBAI OR NOT DUBAI (IRE)**, 5, b g Dubai Destination (USA)—Silk Affair (IRE) **Mrs C. Kendrick**
9 **FIRST DRUM (IRE)**, 7, ch g Generous (IRE)—Supreme Cove **Mrs C. Kendrick**
10 **FREE TRAVEL (IRE)**, 7, b g Stowaway—Janet Lindup **Mr T W Moore & Mrs Wendy Moore**
11 **GINGER FIZZ**, 11, ch m Haafhd—Valagalore **Mrs A. D. Bourne**
12 **GRACEFUL LEGEND**, 7, b m Midnight Legend—Clover Green (IRE) **Mrs A. P. B. Allen**
13 **HUGO'S REFLECTION**, 6, b g Robin des Champs (FR)—Dawn Court **Mrs S. R. Bailey**
14 **J'AI FROID (IRE)**, 5, b g Flemensfirth (USA)—Park Wave (IRE) **Mrs K. Bromley**
15 **KILBROE BOY (IRE)**, 5, b g Stowaway—Bean Ki Moon (IRE) **Lady Jane Grosvenor**
16 **KINGS TEMPTATION**, 6, b g King's Theatre (IRE)—Temptation (FR) **Lady Jane Grosvenor**
17 **MAZURATI (IRE)**, 9, b g Definite Article—Mazuma (IRE) **Mrs C. Kendrick**
18 **MIDNIGHT JAZZ**, 8, b m Midnight Legend—Ring Back (IRE) **Mrs A. P. B. Allen**
19 **MIDNIGHT MONSOON**, 5, gr m Midnight Legend—Another Storm
20 **MONAR ROSE**, 6, b m Yeats (IRE)—Rhapsody Rose **Mrs A. P. B. Allen**
21 **OKSANA**, 5, b m Midnight Legend—La Harde (FR) **N. S. Hutley**
22 **OSKI (IRE)**, 6, b g Oscar (IRE)—Mossville (FR) **Mrs C. Kendrick**
23 **PHARE ISLE (IRE)**, 13, b g Turtle Island (IRE)—Pharenna (IRE) **Moore, Moore & Kendrick**
24 **PRINCESS ROXY**, 5, ch m Midnight Legend—Royal Roxy **Swanee River Partnership**
25 **PULP FICTION (IRE)**, 6, b g Robin des Champs (FR)—Bean Ki Moon (IRE) **Swanee River Partnership**
26 **SHANROE SAINT**, 6, b g Saint des Saints (FR)—Aconit (FR) **The Polk Partnership**
27 **SHANTY ALLEY**, 4, b g Shantou (USA)—Alexander Road (IRE) **Jerry Wright Adam Lucock Patricia Murray**
28 **SHARP GETAWAY (IRE)**, 6, b g Getaway (GER)—Thanks Noel (IRE) **Mrs C. Kendrick**
29 **SILENT ENCORE (IRE)**, 6, ch g Curtain Time (IRE)—What Can I Say (IRE) **North & South Racing Partnership**
30 4, Ch c Golden Lariat (USA)—Stability Treaty (IRE)
31 **TEMPLEPARK**, 5, b g Phoenix Reach—Kenny's Dream **Mrs C. Kendrick**
32 **THEMANFROM MINELLA (IRE)**, 9, b g Shantou (USA)—Bobormy (IRE) **Mrs C. Kendrick**
33 **WISECRACKER**, 5, br g Sageburg (IRE)—Folie Lointaine (FR) **Lady Jane Grosvenor**
34 **WISH IN A WELL (IRE)**, 9, b g Gamut (IRE)—Lady Bellingham (IRE) **Case Racing Partnership**
35 **ZARA'S REFLECTION**, 5, b m Midnight Legend—Twoy's Reflection **N. S. Hutley**

THREE-YEAR-OLDS

36 B g Great Pretender (IRE)—Madame Bleue **Mrs A. P. B. Allen**

MR BEN CASE - Continued

Other Owners: D. Baines, C. Beaumont, M. Beesley, N. Biggs, Mr T. Boylan, Mrs S. Case, A. Case, A. Charlton, Mr C K Crossley Cooke, O. Denny, J. English, E. Gladden, A. Gladden, P Grindlay, R. Harper, J. Harrison, S. Harrison, R & J Howlett, Mrs M. Howlett, Mr Neil Hutley, C. Ilsley, P Jackson, B. Joice, Mrs Carolyn Kendrick, H. Loggin, Mr Adam Lucock, A. Lush, P Lush, M. Marshall, M. Matthews, E. Middleton, Mrs Wendy Moore, Mr T. W. Moore, Miss Pat Murray, G. Nicholson, C. Nixey, J. Nowell-Smith, M. Okninski, R. Palmer, D. Payne, K. Perrem, Mr James Polk, Mr John Polk, D. Scott, J. Shaw, Mr R. I. Sims, Mrs F. Sims, I. Smith, R. Stevens, J. & M. Sullivan, D. Turberville, Mr Jerry Wright.

Jockey (NH): Daryl Jacob, Kielan Woods. **Conditional:** Max Kendrick. **Amateur:** Mr Charlie Case.

---

96 MR PATRICK CHAMINGS, Basingstoke
Postal: **Inhurst Farm Stables, Baughurst, Tadley, Hampshire, RG26 5JS**
Contacts: **PHONE (01189) 814494 FAX (01189) 820454 MOBILE (07831) 360970**
E-MAIL **chamingsracing@talk21.com**

1 CHARLES MOLSON, 7, b g Monsieur Bond (IRE)—Arculinge **Trolley Action**
2 CHURCH LEAP (IRE), 7, gr g High Chaparral (IRE)—Alambic **Robinson,Wiggin,Hayward-Cole,Roberts**
3 DOURADO (IRE), 4, b c Dark Angel (IRE)—Skehana (IRE) **Mrs A. J. Chandris**
4 EMJAYEM, 8, ch g Needwood Blade—Distant Stars (IRE) **Mr I. Beach**
5 FOXFORD, 7, b m Clodovil (IRE)—Pulau Pinang (IRE) **The Foxford House Partnership**
6 HAABIS (USA), 5, b br g Super Saver (USA)—Raise Fee (USA) **Mr I. Beach**
7 HARLEQUIN ROSE (IRE), 4, ch f Dutch Art—Miss Chaussini (IRE) **G E Bassett & P R Chamings**
8 MISTER FREEZE (IRE), 4, ch g Frozen Power (IRE)—Beacon of Hope (IRE) **G N Hunt, G E Bassett**
9 MORACHE MUSIC, 10, b g Sleeping Indian—Enchanted Princess **The Berks & Hants Racing Partnership**
10 REGAL MISS, 6, b m Royal Applause—Pretty Miss **The Foxford House Partnership**
11 SCOTTISH GLEN, 12, ch g Kyllachy—Dance For Fun **The Foxford House Partnership**
12 TOGETHERNESS (IRE), 5, b g Pour Moi (IRE)—Madeira Mist (IRE) **Paul Jenkins & Partners**
13 WHAT A WELCOME, 4, ch g Nathaniel (IRE)—Hometime **Mrs K. J. Meredith**
14 WILD DANCER, 5, b m Mawatheeq (USA)—Pretty Miss **The Foxford House Partnership**

THREE-YEAR-OLDS

15 COPILOT, b f Harbour Watch (IRE)—Perfect Flight **Dr Bridget Drew & Partners**
16 HIGHWAY BESS, br f Dick Turpin (IRE)—Bob's Princess **The Foxford House Partnership**
17 PRETTY MARYS, b f Royal Applause—Pretty Miss **Mrs B. Powell**
18 SPANISH STAR (IRE), b g Requinto (IRE)—Rancho Star (IRE) **Shirley Symonds & Fred Camis**
19 SPEEDY LOST SOCK, b g Erhaab (USA)—Jilmah (IRE) **Mr N. Zayani**

TWO-YEAR-OLDS

20 Br f 6/2 Harbour Watch (IRE)—Elegant Times (IRE) (Dansili) (5000) **F. D. Camis**

Other Owners: Mr G. E. Bassett, Mr P R. Chamings, Dr S. B. Drew, Miss P.B. Drew, Mrs N. Hayward-Cole, Mr G. N. Hunt, Mr P Jenkins, Mrs M. Roberts, Mr N. R. Robinson, Mr M. R. Stewart, Mrs S. A. Symonds, K. W. Tyrrell, Mr D. P. Wiggin, Mr W. Womersley.

Assistant Trainer: Phillippa Chamings

---

97 MR MICK CHANNON, West Ilsley
Postal: **West Ilsley Stables, West Ilsley, Newbury, Berkshire, RG20 7AE**
Contacts: **PHONE (01635) 281166 FAX (01635) 281177**
E-MAIL **mick@mick-channon.co.uk/susan@mick-channon.co.uk WEBSITE www.mickchannon.tv**

1 BARD OF BRITTANY, 4, b g Sayif (IRE)—Lily Le Braz **M. R. Channon**
2 BUILDMEUPBUTTERCUP, 4, ch f Sixties Icon—Eastern Paramour (IRE) **Mr J. Turner**
3 CARAVELA (IRE), 4, b f Henrythenavigator (USA)—Stella Point (IRE) **Jon & Julia Aisbitt**
4 CHICAGO STAR, 4, b f Exceed And Excel (AUS)—Librettista (AUS) **Partnership Terminated**
5 DOCK OF THE BAY, 4, b g Sixties Icon—Kaylianni **Mr W. A. Harrison-Allan**
6 ELIDOR, 8, br g Cape Cross (IRE)—Honorine (IRE) **Jon & Julia Aisbitt**
7 ETTIE HART (IRE), 5, b m Bushranger (IRE)—Miss Megs (IRE) **M. R. Channon**
8 FITZWILLY, 8, b g Sixties Icon—Canadian Capers **Mr Peter Taplin & Mr M. Channon**
9 GLEN FORSA (IRE), 6, b g Mahler—Outback Ivy (IRE) **Mr T. P. Radford**
10 HATS OFF TO LARRY, 4, b g Sixties Icon—Highland Jig **Mr W. A. Harrison-Allan**
11 HEYDOUR (IRE), 5, br g Presenting—Our Lucky Venture (IRE) **Mr T. P. Radford**
12 I'M A BELIEVER, 4, b f Sixties Icon—Fascinatin Rhythm **Mr W. A. Harrison-Allan**

MR MICK CHANNON - Continued

13 **ICONIC BELLE**, 4, ch f Sixties Icon—Five Bells (IRE) **The Sweet Partnership**
14 **KOEMAN**, 4, b c Dutch Art—Angelic Note (IRE) **Taplin & Bunney Partnership**
15 **LINCOLN (IRE)**, 7, b g Clodovil (IRE)—Gilt Linked **Mr W. G. Parish**
16 **MISTER WHITAKER (IRE)**, 6, b g Court Cave (IRE)—Benbradagh Vard (IRE) **Mr T. P. Radford**
17 **MOBSTA (IRE)**, 6, b h Bushranger (IRE)—Sweet Nicole **Lease Terminated**
18 **OCTOBER STORM**, 5, br g Shirocco (GER)—Cyber Star **Jon & Julia Aisbitt**
19 **OPAL TIARA (IRE)**, 5, b m Thousand Words—Zarafa **The Filly Folly & Sweet Partnership**
20 **PATTIE**, 4, ch f Sixties Icon—Excellent Day (IRE) **M. R. Channon**
21 **RIPPLING WATERS (FR)**, 4, b f Areion (GER)—Pepples Beach (GER) **Mr T. P. Radford**
22 **ROSE CROWN**, 4, b f New Approach (IRE)—Silver Touch (IRE) **M. R. Channon**
23 **SAYESSE**, 4, b g Sayif (IRE)—Pesse (IRE) **Lord Ilsley Racing (Steele Syndicate)**
24 **SUMMER ICON**, 5, b m Sixties Icon—Summer Cry (USA) **Allen, Porter, Voute Partnership 1**
25 **ZOLTAN VARGA**, 4, b g Sayif (IRE)—Mar Blue (FR) **Mr T. P. Radford**

THREE-YEAR-OLDS

26 **ADORABLE (IRE)**, b f Kodiac—Caffe Latte (IRE) **Mr M. Al-Qatami & Mr K. M. Al-Mudhaf**
27 **ANN WITHOUT AN E**, b f Rip Van Winkle (IRE)—Visanilla (FR) **Barry Walters Catering**
28 **APPLE ANNI (IRE)**, b f Fast Company (IRE)—Common Cause **Mrs T. Burns**
29 **BANKSY'S ART**, b c Sixties Icon—Outside Art
30 **BEER WITH THE BOYS**, b c Nathaniel (IRE)—Bathilde (IRE) **G. D. P. Materna**
31 **BILLY RAY**, b c Sixties Icon—Fiumicino **Mr P. Trant**
32 B g Sepoy (AUS)—Bold Bidder
33 **CALENDIMAGGIO (IRE)**, b c Invincible Spirit (IRE)—Three Days In May **Mrs T Burns & Partners**
34 **CAN CAN SIXTY TWO**, b f Sixties Icon—Natalie Jay **M. R. Channon**
35 **CHARMING GUEST (IRE)**, b f Kodiac—Na Zdorovie **John Guest Racing Ltd**
36 **CHIKOKO TRAIL**, ch c Sixties Icon—Search Party **Dave & Gill Hedley**
37 **DAN'S DREAM**, br f Cityscape—Royal Ffanci **Hunscote,Watt,Peckham,Botham & Edwards**
38 **DARK BLUE (IRE)**, b f Dark Angel (IRE)—Lapis Blue (IRE) **Mrs A. C. Black**
39 **DIAMOND DOUGAL (IRE)**, b g Zebedee—Blue Saphire **Lease Terminated**
40 **DUBA PLAINS**, b g Sixties Icon—Selinda **Dave & Gill Hedley**
41 **DUSTY**, ch f Paco Boy (IRE)—Hairspray **Box 41 Racing 1**
42 **EDEN ROSE**, b f Dansili—Gallic Star (IRE) **Jon & Julia Aisbitt**
43 Ch f Approve (IRE)—Ella Fitzgerald (IRE) **M. R. Channon**
44 **FADING ICON**, b f Sixties Icon—Fading Away **P. Taplin**
45 **FANNIE BY GASLIGHT**, b f Sixties Icon—Inffiraaj (IRE) **Aston Bloodstock**
46 **FINANCIAL CRIME (IRE)**, b g Red Jazz (USA)—Clodilla (IRE) **Regulatory Finance Solutions Limited**
47 **HELVETIAN**, b c Swiss Spirit—Lucky Dip **Box 41**
48 **HIGHLIFE FLYER**, b g Medicean—Floating **The Highlife Racing Club**
49 **JAZEEL (IRE)**, b c Roderic O'connor (IRE)—Simla Bibi **Mr A. Al-Abdulrazzaq**
50 **KENNY GEORGE**, b g Mawatheeq (USA)—One For Philip **S W Group Logistics Limited**
51 B g Sixties Icon—Lakaam
52 **MACHO MOVER (IRE)**, b c Camacho—Fanciful Dancer **Box 41 Racing**
53 **MAKSAB (IRE)**, b br c Makfi—Azeema (IRE) **Mr M. Al-Qatami & Mr K. M. Al-Mudhaf**
54 **MARIETTA ROBUSTI (IRE)**, b f Equiano (FR)—La Tintoretta (IRE) **M. R. Channon**
55 **MEDESS**, ch f Medicean—Essell **Mr & Mrs D. D. Clee**
56 **NEOLA**, b f Foxwedge (AUS)—Effie B **Bastian Family**
57 **POUCOR**, b g Pour Moi (IRE)—Corinium (IRE) **Mr & Mrs D. D. Clee**
58 **ROCKY SHORES (IRE)**, b c Canford Cliffs (IRE)—Josphiel (IRE) **Mr J Mitchell**
59 **SECTION ONESIXSIX (IRE)**, b f Dandy Man (IRE)—The Last Laugh **Regulatory Finance Solutions Limited**
60 **SO NEAR SO FARHH**, ch f Farhh—Protectress **Mrs N. Murray**
61 **TELLTALE**, ch g Monsieur Bond (IRE)—Yarn **R. C. Tooth**
62 **THE NIGHT KING**, b g Arcano (IRE)—Semplicita (IRE) **M. R. Channon**
63 **THE NIGHT PORTER**, b g Sixties Icon—La Gifted
64 **TRICKSY SPIRIT**, b f Lethal Force (IRE)—Spritzeria **Mr J Mitchell**
65 **TROGON (IRE)**, ch g Leroidesanimaux (BRZ)—Savanna Days **Jon & Julia Aisbitt**
66 **TRUMPS UP**, b c Cape Blanco (IRE)—Zeva **Mr D. M. FitzGerald**
67 **VAILLANCE**, gr g Sinndar (IRE)—Vayasa (FR) **M. R. Channon**
68 **WESTBROOK BERTIE**, b c Sixties Icon—Evanesce **The Further Folly Partnership 1**
69 **WHY WE DREAM (IRE)**, b f Al Kazeem—Sandreamer (IRE) **Jon & Julia Aisbitt**
70 **ZAIN CITY (IRE)**, b c Lope de Vega (IRE)—On My Kness (FR) **Mr A. Al Banwan**

TWO-YEAR-OLDS

71 B f 22/3 Fast Company (IRE)—Acushladear (IRE) (Tagula (IRE)) (19000)
72 **AFTER JOHN**, b c 31/3 Dutch Art—
　　　　　　Rosacara (Green Desert (USA)) (30000) **Mrs John Lee, Alf Heaney, Alec Tuckerman**

MR MICK CHANNON - Continued

73 B gr f 27/2 Gregorian (IRE)—Altona (IRE) (Redback) **Bastian Family I**
74 B gr c 29/4 Gregorian (IRE)—Blakeshall Rose (Tobougg (IRE)) **Bastian Family**
75 Ch c 4/3 Zebedee—Blond Beauty (USA) (Theatrical (5500) **M. R. Channon**
76 B c 4/3 Slade Power (IRE)—Bound Copy (USA) (Street Cry (IRE)) (27000)
77 B f 19/3 Gregorian (IRE)—Bridie Ffrench (Bahamian Bounty)
78 Gr c 14/3 Clodovil (IRE)—Broadway Musical (IRE) (Exceed And Excel (AUS)) (11000) **M. R. Channon**
79 B f 12/5 Society Rock (IRE)—Bronze Baby (USA) (Silver Charm (USA)) (55238) **John Guest Racing Ltd**
80 CERTAIN LAD, b c 29/4 Clodovil (IRE)—Chelsey Jayne (IRE) (Galileo (IRE)) (13000) **Mr C. R. Hirst**
81 CITY WANDERER (IRE), b c 18/4 Kodiac—
                                    Viletta (GER) (Doyen (IRE)) (120000) **George Materna & Roger Badley**
82 B f 15/3 Mukhadram—Classical Dancer (Dr Fong (USA)) (13000)
83 B f 28/3 Bungle Inthejungle—Common Cause (Polish Patriot (USA)) (8500) **Mrs T. Burns**
84 B c 27/3 Sixties Icon—Crazee Diamond (Rock of Gibraltar (IRE)) (11395)
85 B f 24/4 Moohaajim (IRE)—Easee On (IRE) (Hawk Wing (USA)) (813)
86 B f 10/2 Champs Elysees—Effie B (Sixties Icon) **Bastian Family**
87 EQUIPPED, b f 17/4 Equiano (FR)—Marjong (Mount Nelson) **Mr J. L. Marsden**
88 B c 8/3 Most Improved (IRE)—Evening Sunset (GER) (Dansili) (4761)
89 B c 8/5 Zebedee—Fiuise (IRE) (Montjeu (IRE)) (24420) **M. R. Channon**
90 B c 2/3 Sixties Icon—Good Morning Lady (Compton Place)
91 B f 26/4 Sixties Icon—Hairspray (Bahamian Bounty) **Norman Court Stud**
92 B c 6/2 Lethal Force (IRE)—Holberg Suite (Azamour (IRE)) (68571) **John Guest Racing Ltd**
93 B f 9/4 Sixties Icon—Inffiraaj (IRE) (Iffraaj)
94 Ch c 22/3 Dragon Pulse (IRE)—Itaya (IRE) (Namid) (23809) **Mr J. Turner**
95 JUNGLE INTHEBUNGLE (IRE), ch c 10/3 Bungle Inthejungle—Princess Banu (Oasis Dream) (6512) **Mrs T. Burns**
96 B c 12/2 Nathaniel (IRE)—Junia Tepzia (IRE) (Rock of Gibraltar (IRE)) (23000)
97 KARALINI (IRE), b f 4/3 Es Que Love (IRE)—
                                    Lucky Leigh (Piccolo) (26666) **Mrs John Lee, Alf Heaney, Alec Tuckerman**
98 Ch f 21/3 Presenting—Lakaam (Danzero (AUS))
99 B f 18/4 Society Rock (IRE)—Liscoa (IRE) (Foxhound (USA)) (16280) **M. R. Channon**
100 Ch f 20/2 Sixties Icon—Madame Hoi (IRE) (Hawk Wing (USA)) (10000) **Norman Court Stud**
101 B c 6/3 Rip Van Winkle (IRE)—Miss Lahar (Clodovil (IRE)) **Barry Walters Catering**
102 B f 4/4 Pour Moi (IRE)—Ms Cordelia (USA) (Anabaa (USA)) **R. C. Tooth**
103 B f 26/4 Sixties Icon—Nadinska (Doyen (IRE))
104 Br f 6/5 Gregorian (IRE)—Natalie Jay (Ballacashtal (CAN))
105 B f 10/4 Gregorian (IRE)—Petaluma (Teofilo (IRE))
106 B f 9/3 Acclamation—Phillippa (IRE) (Galileo (IRE)) (40700) **Mr T. P. Radford**
107 RED HANDED, ch f 26/4 Sixties Icon—Outside Art (Excellent Art)
108 B c 22/3 Mazameer (IRE)—Remix (IRE) (Oratorio (IRE))
109 B f 24/4 Bungle Inthejungle—Riymaisa (IRE) (Traditionally (USA)) (26047)
110 Ch f 3/5 Sixties Icon—Rose Cheval (USA) (Johannesburg (USA))
111 B f 12/2 Sixties Icon—Rough Courte (IRE) (Clodovil (IRE))
112 B f 3/4 Heeraat (IRE)—Saona Island (Bahamian Bounty)
113 Bl gr c 3/4 Clodovil (IRE)—Shemissa (IRE) (Fairy King (USA)) (34285) **Box 41**
114 B f 28/3 Sixties Icon—Shrimpton (Cadeaux Genereux)
115 SOUTHERN SONG (IRE), ch f 16/1 Slade Power (IRE)—Katchy Lady (Kyllachy) (110000) **Jon & Julia Aisbitt**
116 B c 11/4 Society Rock (IRE)—Spirit of Success (Invincible Spirit (IRE)) (22000) **John & Zoe Webster**
117 Br f 6/2 Bungle Inthejungle—Splashofchocolate (IRE) (Intikhab (USA)) (7619)
118 B f 8/3 Sepoy (AUS)—Spritzeria (Bigstone (IRE))
119 B c 23/4 Harbour Watch (IRE)—Steal The Curtain (Royal Applause) (10000)
120 STORTING, b c 27/3 Iffraaj—Stella Point (IRE) (Pivotal) **Jon & Julia Aisbitt**
121 Ch c 12/3 Sixties Icon—Tanojin (IRE) (Thousand Words) (800)
122 B c 20/4 Sixties Icon—The Screamer (IRE) (Insan (USA))
123 VALENTINO SUNRISE, b c 14/2 Sixties Icon—Leleyf (IRE) (Kheleyf (USA)) **P. Taplin**
124 VENUSTA (IRE), b f 4/3 Medicean—Grevillea (IRE) (Admiralofthefleet (USA)) **Mr N. J. Hitchins**
125 B f 6/4 Cacique (IRE)—Vespasia (Medicean) (7000)

Other Owners: Mrs J. M. Aisbitt, J. R. Aisbitt, K. M. Al-Mudhaf, Mohammed Jasem Al-Qatami, Mr T. J. Allen, Mr R. Badley, Mr E. I. R. Bastian, Mr R. W. Bastian, Mrs S. G. Bunney, D. D. Clee, Mrs J. P Clee, Mr T. V. Drayton, The Filly Folly Partnership, Ms G. H. Hedley, Irish National Stud, Mrs A. M. Jones, Mr A. S. L. Leader, Mike Channon Bloodstock Ltd, Mr J. M. Mitchell, S. M. Smith, Mrs L. A. Smith, Mrs T. G. Trant, Mrs G. Voute, Mrs Z. J. Webster, Mr J. Webster, Mr J. A. Williams.

98 MR MICHAEL CHAPMAN, Market Rasen
Postal: **Woodlands Racing Stables, Woodlands Lane, Willingham Road, Market Rasen, Lincolnshire, LN8 3RE**
Contacts: **PHONE/FAX (01673) 843663 MOBILE (07971) 940087**
E-MAIL woodlands.stables@btconnect.com WEBSITE www.woodlandsracingstables.co.uk

1 6, B g Bushranger (IRE)—Cayambe (IRE) **Mrs M. M. Chapman**
2 **DUC DE SEVILLE (IRE)**, 6, b g Duke of Marmalade (IRE)—Splendid (IRE) **Mrs M. M. Chapman**
3 **FEELING PECKISH (USA)**, 14, ch g Point Given (USA)—Sunday Bazaar (USA) **J. E. Reed**
4 **HAMELIN POOL**, 4, b g High Chaparral (IRE)—Presbyterian Nun (IRE) **Quench Racing Partnership**
5 **KHESKIANTO (IRE)**, 12, b m Kheleyf (USA)—Gently (IRE) **F. A. Dickinson**
6 **L'ES FREMANTLE (FR)**, 7, b g Orpen (USA)—Grand Design **Mrs M. M. Chapman**
7 **MONZINO (USA)**, 10, b br g More Than Ready (USA)—Tasso's Magic Roo (USA) **Mrs M. M. Chapman**
8 **PEAK SEASONS**, 15, ch g Raise A Grand (IRE)—Teresian Girl (IRE) **J. E. Reed**
9 **PORT LAIRGE**, 8, b g Pastoral Pursuits—Stylish Clare (IRE) **Mrs M. M. Chapman**
10 **STRIKING NIGELLA**, 8, b m Striking Ambition—Fiona Fox **F. A. Dickinson**
11 **TAYARAT (IRE)**, 13, b g Noverre (USA)—Sincere (IRE) **Mrs M. M. Chapman**
12 **THE SOCIETY MAN (IRE)**, 11, ch g Moscow Society (USA)—Redruth (IRE) **Mrs M. M. Chapman**
13 **VOLCANIC JACK (IRE)**, 10, b g Kodiac—Rosaria Panatta (IRE) **Mrs M. M. Chapman**

Other Owners: Mr B. Downard, Mr M. Preedy.

Assistant Trainer: Mrs M. Chapman

99 MS JANE CHAPPLE-HYAM, Newmarket
Postal: **Rose Cottage, The Street, Dalham, Newmarket, Suffolk, CB8 8TF**
Contacts: **PHONE (01638) 500451 FAX (01638) 661335 MOBILE (07899) 000555**
E-MAIL janechapplehyam@hotmail.co.uk / janechapplehyamracing@outlook.com

1 **BULLINGTON BEAR (FR)**, 5, b g Youmzain (IRE)—Maternelle (FR) **Mr Bryan Hirst & Jane Chapple-Hyam**
2 **DALGARNO (FR)**, 5, b h Sea The Stars (IRE)—Jakonda (USA) **Mrs Fiona Carmichael**
3 **HOW'S LUCY**, 4, b f Approve (IRE)—Murielle **The Green Diamond Partnership**
4 **MISS TENACITY**, 5, b m Rail Link—Desert Secrets (IRE) **Jane Chapple-Hyam**
5 **STAMFORD RAFFLES**, 5, b g Champs Elysees—Romantic Retreat **Jane Chapple-Hyam & Mr Bryan Hirst**
6 **TOMMY'S SECRET**, 8, gr g Sakhee's Secret—La Gessa **Jane Chapple-Hyam**
7 **UBER COOL (IRE)**, 4, b g Born To Sea (IRE)—My Uptown Girl **Mrs Fiona Carmichael & Jane Chapple-Hyam**
8 **WICKER**, 4, b f Myboycharlie (IRE)—Lady Berta **Mrs T Brudenell & Jane Chapple-Hyam**

THREE-YEAR-OLDS

9 **AMOURICE (IRE)**, b f Authorized (IRE)—Amancaya (GER) **Jane Chapple-Hyam & Essex Racing Club**
10 **BANJO'S VOICE**, ch g Poet's Voice—La Jwaab **Chapple-Hyam, Peacock, Hirst**
11 **BIGSHOTTE**, b g Champs Elysees—Humility **Mrs E A Cyzer**
12 **ECHO COVE (IRE)**, ch c Roderic O'connor (IRE)—Russian Rave **Mrs H. H. Morriss**
13 **GLORIOUS ROSE**, b f Cityscape—Where I Be **Mrs E A Cyzer**
14 **MARLOR**, b g Sixties Icon—Indian Story (IRE) **Andy Brown & Russell Read**
15 **MOCHALOV**, b g Denounce—Awesome Asset (USA) **Jane Chapple-Hyam**
16 **NAVAL INTELLIGENCE (USA)**, b g War Front (USA)—Say (IRE) **The Look Partnership**
17 **NOBLE GESTURE**, b g Finjaan—Bexandella **A. McCabe, A. Brown & R. Reed**

TWO-YEAR-OLDS

18 B g 10/4 Hallucinate (USA)—Bedouin Bride (USA) (Chester House (USA)) **Jane Chapple-Hyam**
19 **BULLINGTON BOY (FR)**, b c 19/1 Canford Cliffs (IRE)—
Borgia Gold (IRE) (Cape Cross (IRE)) (47212) **Mr Bryan Hirst**
20 **FLAUNT IT (IRE)**, b f 3/2 Mukhadram—Labisa (High Chaparral (IRE)) (66666) **Mrs Fiona Carmichael**
21 **PUSHMI PULLYU (IRE)**, b f 7/4 Roderic O'connor (IRE)—
Russian Rave (Danehill Dancer (IRE)) (5697) **C Harding & Jane Chapple-Hyam**
22 **SLOWPOKE RODRIGUEZ (IRE)**, b c 15/4 Fast Company (IRE)—
Spring Will Come (IRE) (Desert Prince (IRE)) (9523) **Jane Chapple-Hyam**
23 **SUNG CHOI BAO**, b f 22/2 Casamento (IRE)—
Six Diamonds (Exceed And Excel (AUS)) **Mr Bryan Hirst & Jane Chapple-Hyam**

Other Owners: Mr S. Brewster, Mrs A. J. Brudenell, Essex Racing Club, Mr B. J. Hirst, The Hon A. S. Peacock, Mrs J. P. Root, Mr R. B. Root.

Assistant Trainer: Abigail Harrison

100 **MR PETER CHAPPLE-HYAM, Newmarket**
Postal: Trainer did not wish details of his string to appear

101 **MR GEORGE CHARLTON, Stocksfield**
Postal: **Mickley Grange Farm, Stocksfield, Northumberland, NE43 7TB**
Contacts: **PHONE (01661) 843247 MOBILE (07808) 955029**
E-MAIL george@georgecharltonracing.co.uk

1 **BALIVERNIER**, 12, b g Beat All (USA)—Keep Ikis
2 **BALLYVOQUE (IRE)**, 12, b g Revoque (IRE)—Timissa (IRE) **J. I. A. Charlton**
3 **BONCHESTER**, 7, b g Tikkanen (USA)—Golden Aureole **Mr G. A. G. Charlton**
4 **FAIRLEE BLUE**, 6, b g Alflora (IRE)—Listen Tarablue **J. L. Gledson**
5 **FAIRLEE PEARL**, 8, b m Fair Mix (IRE)—Cloudy Pearl **J. L. Gledson**
6 **FORBIDDING (USA)**, 5, ch g Kitten's Joy (USA)—La Coruna (USA) **Northumbria Leisure Ltd**
7 **HUBAL (POL)**, 6, b g Safety Wire (IRE)—Hebra (POL) **Mr G. A. G. Charlton**
8 **ITALIAN COUSIN (IRE)**, 8, b g Milan—Cousin Kizzy (IRE) **Miss A. McMahon**
9 **MONASHEE (IRE)**, 13, b br g Monashee Mountain (USA)—On The Bridle (IRE)
10 **REGISTAN (IRE)**, 6, b g Darsi (FR)—Hannabelle (IRE) **Mr G. A. G. Charlton**
11 **ROCKY ONE**, 8, br g Beat All (USA)—Bonnie Rock (IRE) **Mr G. A. G. Charlton**
12 **SHANNAGARRY (IRE)**, 12, b g Presenting—Tikrara (USA)
13 **SHANTOU THEATRE (IRE)**, 8, ch g Shantou (USA)—As Lathair (IRE) **Mr G. A. G. Charlton**

Assistant Trainer: Mr J. I. A. Charlton

Jockey (NH): Jan Faltejsek.

102 **MR ROGER CHARLTON, Beckhampton**
Postal: **Beckhampton House, Marlborough, Wiltshire, SN8 1QR**
Contacts: **OFFICE (01672) 539533 HOME (01672) 539330 FAX (01672) 539456**
MOBILE (07710) 784511
E-MAIL office@beckhamptonstables.com WEBSITE www.rogercharlton.com

1 **ALMODOVAR (IRE)**, 6, b g Sea The Stars (IRE)—Melodramatic (IRE) **Bjorn Nielsen**
2 **ATTY PERSSE (IRE)**, 4, b g Frankel—Dorcas Lane **Godolphin**
3 **BLAKENEY POINT**, 5, b g Sir Percy—Cartoon **Axom**
4 **CASEMENT (IRE)**, 4, b g Casamento (IRE)—Kirk Wynd **Beckhampton Racing**
5 **COUNTERMEASURE**, 6, b g American Post—Namaskar **K. Abdullah**
6 **CRIBBS CAUSEWAY (IRE)**, 4, b f Rip Van Winkle (IRE)—Bristol Fashion **Bradley Racing**
7 **DAWN CHOIR**, 4, b f Fastnet Rock (AUS)—Heavenly Dawn **Michael Jackson & John Law**
8 **KAZAWI (IRE)**, 4, ch g Dubawi (IRE)—Kazeem **D. J. Deer**
9 **MAGELLAN (IRE)**, 4, b g Sea The Stars (IRE)—Hector's Girl **Mrs D. Swinburn**
10 **MAKZEEM**, 5, b h Makfi—Kazeem **D. J. Deer**
11 **PETITIONER (IRE)**, 4, b g Dansili—Reflective (USA) **Bjorn Nielsen**
12 **PROJECTION**, 5, b g Acclamation—Spotlight **Royal Ascot Racing Club**
13 **ROAR (IRE)**, 4, b g Pour Moi (IRE)—Evening Rushour (IRE) **P Inglett, J Basquill & E Frost**
14 **SECOND STEP (IRE)**, 7, b g Dalakhani (IRE)—My Dark Rosaleen **Merry Fox Stud Ltd**
15 **WITHHOLD**, 5, b g Champs Elysees—Coming Back **Tony Bloom**

THREE-YEAR-OLDS

16 **AL KHERB**, b g Al Kazeem—Perfect Spirit (IRE) **Al Shaqab**
17 **ALLEGIANT (USA)**, b g City Zip (USA)—Preferential **K. Abdullah**
18 **ALUCINADO**, b f Henrythenavigator (USA)—Estrela **Seasons Holidays**
19 **ANTAGONIST**, b c Dansili—Melodramatic (IRE) **Bjorn Nielsen**
20 **ASPETAR (FR)**, b c Al Kazeem—Bella Qatara (IRE) **Sheikh Mohammed bin Khalifa Al Thani**
21 **BLUE MIST**, ch g Makfi—Namaskar **K. Abdullah**
22 **BREATHLESS TIMES**, b c Bated Breath—Bea Menace (USA) **Sheikh Juma Dalmook Al Maktoum**
23 **BUFFER ZONE**, b c Bated Breath—Buffering **K. Abdullah**
24 **BURGUNDY (IRE)**, b f Holy Roman Emperor (IRE)—China Tea (USA) **Elite Racing**
25 **CHIPPIE HILL (IRE)**, b f Camacho—With Colour **Michael Pescod**
26 **CLAIRETTE (IRE)**, b f Al Kazeem—Petit Calva (FR) **D. J. Deer**

MR ROGER CHARLTON - Continued

27 **CRAFTINESS**, b f Al Kazeem—Artful (IRE) **Her Majesty The Queen**
28 **DABBLE (IRE)**, b gr f Mastercraftsman (IRE)—Dolma (FR) **Lady Rothschild**
29 **DIVINE ACT (IRE)**, ch f Frankel—Ramruma (USA) **Clipper Logistics**
30 **EXTRA ELUSIVE**, ch c Mastercraftsman (IRE)—Nessina (USA) **Saleh Al Homaizi & Imad Al Sagar**
31 **FASHION WORLD**, b f Dubawi (IRE)—Icon Project (USA) **Andrew Rosen**
32 **FLEETING VIEW**, b f Sixties Icon—Flash of Gold **Her Majesty The Queen**
33 **GALILEO SILVER (IRE)**, gr g Galileo (IRE)—Famous (IRE) **Walters Plant Hire & Mr & Mrs Potter**
34 **GAVOTA**, b f Bated Breath—Ombre **K. Abdullah**
35 **GIOVANNI ACUTO (IRE)**, ch g Kendargent (FR)—Maybe (GER) **Michael Pescod**
36 **GREAT BEYOND**, b c Dansili—Solar Pursuit **K. Abdullah**
37 **GUILD**, ch c Frankel—Arrive **K. Abdullah**
38 **HERCULEAN**, ch c Frankel—African Rose **K. Abdullah**
39 **IT'S NOT UNUSUAL**, b f Exceed And Excel (AUS)—Welsh Anthem **Clipper Logistics**
40 **KASSAR (IRE)**, b g Exceed And Excel (AUS)—Inchiri **Al Shaqab**
41 **KING TUT (USA)**, b c Animal Kingdom (USA)—St Malo's Gate (USA) **Team Valor**
42 **KOLO TAMAM**, b c Al Kazeem—Sensiz (IRE) **Saleh Al Homaizi & Imad Al Sagar**
43 **L'EXPLORA (USA)**, b f War Front (USA)—Damson (IRE) **Sheikh Mohammed bin Khalifa Al Thani**
44 **LOGAN'S CHOICE**, b g Redoute's Choice (AUS)—Bright Morning (USA) **Paul Hearson**
45 B c Oasis Dream—Loulwa (IRE) **Saleh Al Homaizi & Imad Al Sagar**
46 **LOW PROFILE**, ch c Galileo (IRE)—Dynaforce (USA) **Brook Farm Bloodstock**
47 **LUMEN**, ch g Rip Van Winkle (IRE)—Luminance (IRE) **Beckhampton Stables**
48 **PASSIONATE LOVE (IRE)**, b f Bated Breath—Magic Nymph (IRE) **A. E. Oppenheimer**
49 **PERPETRATOR (IRE)**, b c Shamardal (USA)—Palmeraie (USA) **Bjorn Nielsen**
50 **PERSIAN RHAPSODY**, b g Camelot—Hector's Girl **Dr Jamal Ahmadzadeh**
51 **PESCEDORA (IRE)**, b f So You Think (NZ)—Poisson d'or **Fishdance**
52 **PILOT WINGS (IRE)**, b g Epaulette (AUS)—Intaglia (GER) **P Inglett & Partners**
53 **POLISH**, b c Teofilo (IRE)—Polygon (USA) **Lady Rothschild**
54 **REGINA PACIS (IRE)**, b f Acclamation—Galileos Daughter (IRE) **Sahara Bloodstock**
55 **SALVE HELENA (IRE)**, b f Soldier Hollow—Salve Diana (GER) **Hunscote Stud**
56 **SAVAANAH (IRE)**, b f Olden Times—Tanouma (USA) **Prince A A Faisal**
57 **SCOOTER (IRE)**, gr g Iffraaj—Cassandra Go (IRE) **Trevor Stewart**
58 B f High Chaparral (IRE)—Seaham Hall **Seasons Holidays**
59 **SIMBIRSK**, ch g Al Kazeem—Oulianovsk (IRE) **D. J. Deer**
60 **SISTER CELINE (IRE)**, b f Al Kazeem—Quan Yin (IRE) **D. J. Deer**
61 **TIADARGENT (FR)**, b br f Kendargent (FR)—Restia (FR) **K. Abdullah**
62 **TIMESPAN**, b f Al Kazeem—All Time **K. Abdullah**
63 **TINSMITH**, gr ro c Mastercraftsman (IRE)—Catopuma (USA) **Lady Rothschild**
64 **TRUE DESTINY**, ch g Mastercraftsman (IRE)—Holy Dazzle **H.R.H. Sultan Shah**
65 **UNIVERSAL COMMAND**, b g Delegator—Telescopic **D Hunt & E Markham**
66 **WINSTON (GER)**, gr g Soldier Hollow—Wilddrossel (GER) **Bjorn Nielsen**

TWO-YEAR-OLDS

67 Ch f 7/4 Frankel—Ascot Family (IRE) (Desert Style (IRE)) **Andrew Rosen**
68 **BASILISK (USA)**, ch c 22/4 Speightstown (USA)—Treat Gently (Cape Cross (IRE)) **K. Abdullah**
69 Br c 17/3 Le Havre (IRE)—Bella Qatara (IRE) (Dansili) **Sheikh Mohammed bin Khalifa Al Thani**
70 **BLOWING DIXIE**, b c 1/4 Dubawi (IRE)—Time Control (Sadler's Wells (USA)) **Merry Fox Stud**
71 **CASUAL REPLY**, b f 23/1 Frankel—Passing Parade (Cape Cross (IRE)) **Merry Fox Stud**
72 **COCHISE**, b c 10/3 Intello (GER)—Ship's Biscuit (Tiger Hill (IRE)) **Philip Newton**
73 B c 12/2 Dansili—Could It Be (IRE) (Galileo (IRE)) **Sheikh Mohammed bin Khalifa Al Thani**
74 B c 14/2 Exceed And Excel (AUS)—Crysdal (Dalakhani (IRE)) (90000) **Brook Farm Bloodstock**
75 **DOUBLY BEAUTIFUL (IRE)**, ch c 1/3 Born To Sea (IRE)—Bella Bella (IRE) (Sri Pekan (USA)) (40000) **Paul Inglett**
76 B c 30/4 Champs Elysees—Dylanesque (Royal Applause) (12000) **Tony Bloom**
77 Br c 29/1 Oasis Dream—Ferevia (IRE) (Motivator) **Sheikh Mohammed bin Khalifa Al Thani**
78 B f 23/3 Dansili—Fleur de Cactus (IRE) (Montjeu (IRE)) **Sheikh Mohammed bin Khalifa Al Thani**
79 B f 14/3 Charm Spirit (IRE)—Garanciere (FR) (Anabaa (USA)) **Seasons Holidays**
80 Ch c 31/1 Intello (GER)—Hazy Dancer (Oasis Dream) **Willie Carson & Partners**
81 **HEADMAN**, b c 21/3 Kingman—Deliberate (King's Best (USA)) **K. Abdullah**
82 **HYMN**, b f 16/3 Nayef (USA)—
            Merayaat (IRE) (Darshaan) (90000) **Highclere Thoroughbred Racing - Waddesdon**
83 **IMPERIUM (IRE)**, ch c 14/6 Frankel—Ramruma (USA) (Diesis) (81400) **Weston, Brook Farm and Bromfield**
84 **INFUSE (IRE)**, b f 29/2 Lope de Vega (IRE)—Fusion (IRE) (Cape Cross (IRE)) **Duke of Roxburgh**
85 **LADY ADELAIDE (IRE)**, b f 23/2 Australia—Confusion (FR) (Anabaa (USA)) **Fishdance**
86 Ch f 5/4 Exceed And Excel (AUS)—
            Magic Nymph (IRE) (Galileo (IRE)) (200000) **Sheikh Juma Dalmook Al Maktoum**
87 **MERLIN'S MAGIC (IRE)**, b c 3/2 Camelot—Poisson d'or (Cape Cross (IRE)) **Fishdance**

MR ROGER CHARLTON - Continued

88 **MIDPORT (IRE)**, b c 9/2 Dabirsim (FR)—Monspa (Monsun (GER)) (90000) **P Inglett & P Hearson**
89 **MISTER MERLIN**, gr c 1/2 Dark Angel (IRE)—
   Rosehill Artist (IRE) (Excellent Art) (80000) **Paul Inglett & Simon de Zoete**
90 **MOMKIN (IRE)**, b c 20/2 Bated Breath—Contradict (Raven's Pass (USA)) **Prince A A Faisal**
91 **ORCHIDIA (IRE)**, ch f 17/4 Bated Breath—
   New Orchid (USA) (Quest For Fame) (97680) **Glentree Pastoral Pty. Ltd**
92 **RED IMPRESSION**, gr f 22/4 Dark Angel (IRE)—Purissima (USA) (Fusaichi Pegasus (USA)) **K. Abdullah**
93 B c 3/2 Teofilo (IRE)—Rosa Muscosa (USA) (Dixie Union (USA)) (60000) **Sheikh Juma Dalmook Al Maktoum**
94 B f 3/3 Camelot—Rosie Probert (Dylan Thomas (IRE)) **Seasons Holidays**
95 **SAILING (GER)**, b f 13/4 Lope de Vega (IRE)—Sail (IRE) (Sadler's Wells (USA)) (230000) **K. Abdullah**
96 B c 18/3 Rip Van Winkle (IRE)—Sarawati (IRE) (Haafhd) (40700) **Nick Bradley 19**
97 **SHE'S APPLES (IRE)**, b f 22/2 Redoute's Choice (AUS)—
   Steal The Show (NZ) (High Chaparral (IRE)) **Bloomsbury Stud**
98 **SHORE (USA)**, b c 26/5 First Defence (USA)—Romantica (Galileo (IRE)) **K. Abdullah**
99 B c 16/4 Mukhadram—Skyrider (IRE) (Dalakhani (IRE)) (90000) **Paul Inglett & Simon de Zoete**
100 **TATSIA**, b f 24/3 Showcasing—Ombre (Galileo (IRE)) **K. Abdullah**
101 **TAVUS (IRE)**, b c 30/4 Pour Moi (IRE)—La Persiana (Daylami (IRE)) (65000) **Tony Bloom**
102 **TEMPUS**, b c 5/4 Kingman—Passage of Time (Dansili) **K. Abdullah**
103 Ch f 21/2 Australia—Terre du Vent (FR) (Kutub (IRE)) (50000) **Simon Clarke**
104 **WEST NEWTON**, b c 6/2 Kitten's Joy (USA)—Queen's Prize (Dansili) **Her Majesty The Queen**
105 **YIMKIN (IRE)**, b f 10/3 Kingman—Orpha (New Approach (IRE)) **Prince A A Faisal**
106 B br f 17/3 So You Think (NZ)—Zongoraora (FR) (Bering) (46398) **Nick Bradley 14**

Assistant Trainers: Harry Charlton, Tom Charlton

---

103 **MR HARRY CHISMAN, Stow-on-the-Wold**
Postal: **The Retreat Stables, Maugersbury, Cheltenham, Gloucestershire, GL54 1HP**
Contacts: PHONE (07787) 516723
WEBSITE www.harrychisman.co.uk

1 **ALL RILED UP**, 10, b m Dr Massini (IRE)—Martha Reilly (IRE) **P Baker D Wood M Flint D Welch**
2 **CAPTAIN KENDALL (IRE)**, 9, b g Clodovil (IRE)—Queen's Lace (IRE) **S Kirkland D Welch**
3 **FOYLESIDEVIEW (IRE)**, 6, b g Dark Angel (IRE)—Showerproof **Mr P Baker, Wendy Summers, Debra Spencer**
4 **LEGENDOIRE (IRE)**, 4, b g Fast Company (IRE)—Last Shaambles (IRE) **Steven Kirkland David Welch**

Other Owners: Mr P. M. Baker, Mr Harry Chisman, Mr Michael Flint, Mr S. Kirkland, Mrs D. Spencer, Wendy Summers, Mr D. Welch, Mr Duncan Wood.

Assistant Trainer: G. Charles-Jones.

Jockey (flat): Robert Havlin. **Jockey (NH):** Tom O'Brien, Sean Quinlan, Andrew Tinkler. **Conditional:** Daniel Hiskett.
Amateur: Mr A. Hark.

---

104 **MR TOM CLOVER, Newmarket**
Postal: **White Yard, Wroughton House Stables, Newmarket, Suffolk, CB8 8DT**
Contacts: PHONE (07795) 834960 (01638) 660055
E-MAIL thomaspwclover@gmail.com WEBSITE www.tomcloverracing.com

1 **ARCHIE (IRE)**, 6, b g Fast Company (IRE)—Winnifred **Mrs G. A. S. Jarvis**
2 **BALGAIR**, 4, ch g Foxwedge (AUS)—Glencal **Mr J. T. Habershon-Butcher**
3 **CASTLE TALBOT (IRE)**, 6, b g Rock of Gibraltar (IRE)—Louve Sacree (USA) **Mrs J. I. Clover**
4 **MAESTRO MAC (IRE)**, 5, b g Roderic O'connor (IRE)—Union City Blues (IRE) **C Holmes, B Keane & S Nugent**

THREE-YEAR-OLDS

5 **CHAMBER MAID**, b f Nathaniel (IRE)—Maid To Dream **Unregistered Syndicate**
6 B c Mayson—Fit To Burst **J. C. S. Wilson**
7 B c Acclamation—Galistic (IRE) **D Proos, F H Lee & T Clover**
8 **GO FOX**, ch g Foxwedge (AUS)—Bling Bling (IRE) **R & S Marchant, J Allen & G Jarvis**
9 **HUNNI**, b f Captain Gerrard (IRE)—Lady O Malley (IRE) **The Hunni Partnership**
10 **LE MAHARAJAH (FR)**, b c Cacique (IRE)—Sign of Life **Mr Raj Matharu & Egerton House Racing**
11 **OBRIGADA**, b f Worthadd (IRE)—Oblige **Miss K. Rausing**
12 Ch g Bahamian Bounty—Oceana Blue **The C H F Partnership**
13 **PHEIDIPPIDES**, ch c Sepoy (AUS)—Bounty Box **Dr O. Rangabashyam**

MR TOM CLOVER - Continued

14 **PIVELLO**, ch g Intello (GER)—Pivotting **The Pivello Partnership**
15 **VIENTO DE CONDOR (IRE)**, b g Dragon Pulse (IRE)—Polska (USA) **Dr O. Rangabashyam**

TWO-YEAR-OLDS

16 B f 6/4 Society Rock (IRE)—Cape Mystery (Cape Cross (IRE)) (19000) **Nick Bradley Racing 39**
17 B c 28/4 Gale Force Ten—City Vaults Girl (IRE) (Oratorio (IRE)) (38000) **Mr A. Signy**
18 **GYPSY SPIRIT**, b f 22/3 Gregorian (IRE)—
Romany Gypsy (Indesatchel (IRE)) (6000) **The Gypsy Spirit Partnership**
19 **HANBURY DREAMS**, b f 10/4 Heeraat (IRE)—Lady O Malley (IRE) (Oratorio (IRE)) **B Keane & S Nugent**
20 B f 4/3 Swiss Spirit—Harryana To (Compton Place) (10476) **C. V. Wentworth**
21 B c 25/2 Archipenko (USA)—Kinetica (Stormy Atlantic (USA)) (20349) **R & S Marchant, D Fawdon & G Jarvis**
22 B c 12/4 Coach House (IRE)—Minnola (Royal Applause) (20952) **Mr C. F. E. Hill**
23 **MONSIEUR LAMBRAYS**, b c 6/3 Champs Elysees—
Windermere Island (Cadeaux Genereux) (27000) **Mr J. T. Habershon-Butcher**
24 B f 25/4 Equiano (FR)—Peace And Love (IRE) (Fantastic Light (USA)) (10000) **The North South Syndicate**
25 **SAMARITAINE**, ch f 29/4 Archipenko (USA)—Samando (FR) (Hernando (FR)) **Miss K. Rausing**
26 Ch c 9/2 Casamento (IRE)—Stunned Silence (USA) (Officer (USA)) (36630) **H Moorhead, C Fahy & J Collins**

Other Owners: Mrs J. A. Allen, Mr N. Bradley, Mr T. P. Clover, Mr J. A. Collins, Mr C. J. Fahy, Mr D. Fawdon, C. H. Fischer, K. H. Fischer, Mrs S. Hamilton, M. G. H. Heald, Mr A. M. H. Heald, Mrs M. E. Holdcroft, Miss S. Holden, Mr C. R. Holmes, Mrs A. H. Jordan, Mr B. A. Keane, Mr F. H. Lee, Mr A. Linnett, Mr S. Marchant, Mr R. P. Marchant, Mr R. S. Matharu, Mr S. Nugent, D. M. Proos.

---

105 MR DENIS J. COAKLEY, West Ilsley
Postal: **Keeper's Stables, West Ilsley, Newbury, Berkshire, RG20 7AH**
Contacts: PHONE (01635) 281622 MOBILE (07768) 658056
E-MAIL racing@deniscoakley.com WEBSITE www.deniscoakley.com

1 **HORS DE COMBAT**, 7, ch g Mount Nelson—Maid For Winning (USA) **Chris van Hoorn Racing**
2 **KEEPER'S CHOICE (IRE)**, 4, ch f Intikhab (USA)—Crossing **Keeper's 12**
3 **MAARIT (IRE)**, 4, b f Harbour Watch (IRE)—Atamana (IRE) **J. C. Kerr**
4 **PETER STUYVESANT (IRE)**, 4, b g Elusive City (USA)—Dream For Life (FR) **Chris van Hoorn Racing**
5 **POWER HOME (IRE)**, 4, ch f Power—Ascendancy **Count Calypso Racing**
6 **SAUMUR**, 6, b m Mawatheeq (USA)—Sparkling Montjeu (USA) **Sparkling Partners**
7 **SHEILA'S ROCK (IRE)**, 4, b f Fastnet Rock (AUS)—Crystal Curling (IRE) **R. J. Styles**
8 **STAFFA (IRE)**, 5, b m Rock of Gibraltar (IRE)—Gabriellina Klon (IRE) **Mrs B. Coakley**
9 **TIAR NA NOG (IRE)**, 6, b m Ask—Carmencita **Mrs B. Coakley**
10 **YOGIYOGIYOGI (IRE)**, 4, ch f Finsceal Fior (IRE)—Zelloof (USA) **Mr J. G. Mountford**

THREE-YEAR-OLDS

11 **BRILLIANT RIPOSTE**, b g Rip Van Winkle (IRE)—Waldena (USA) **Poachers' Dozen**
12 **CONNAUGHT RANGER (IRE)**, ch g Finsceal Fior (IRE)—Mona Brown (IRE) **Mr A. Killoran**
13 **ELECTRIC LANDLADY (IRE)**, b f Red Jazz (USA)—Margie (USA) **PMC Syndicate**
14 **GIVEPEACEACHANCE**, b f Declaration of War—Mount Crystal (IRE) **Chris van Hoorn Racing**
15 **LILY OF YEAR (FR)**, b f Siyouni (FR)—Arpagone (FR) **Mountford & Styles**
16 **SHEILA ROSE (IRE)**, b f Rip Van Winkle (IRE)—Al Ihsas (IRE) **R. J. Styles**
17 **SWEET CHARITY**, b f Mount Nelson—Fanny May **Chris van Hoorn Racing**
18 **VANITY VANITY (USA)**, ch f Kitten's Joy (USA)—Blue Grass Music (USA) **Chris van Hoorn Racing**

TWO-YEAR-OLDS

19 **BARTIMAEUS (IRE)**, b c 14/2 Nathaniel (IRE)—Zora Seas (IRE) (Marju (IRE)) (10000) **West Ilsley Racing**
20 B f 18/1 Toronado (IRE)—Fanny May (Nayef (USA)) **Chris van Hoorn Racing**
21 B c 5/3 Showcasing—Loreto Rose (Lahib (USA)) **R. J. Styles**
22 B f 31/3 War Command (USA)—Megaspiel (Singspiel (IRE)) (14000)
23 **ROCKSTAR MAX (GER)**, b c 19/4 Maxios—
Remote Romance (USA) (Irish River (FR)) (11000) **Melbourne 10 Racing**
24 **SONNETINA**, b f 12/2 Poet's Voice—Tebee's Oasis (Oasis Dream) (9500) **The Good Mixers**

Other Owners: Mr Richard Barnes, Mr Ian Barratt, Mrs C. Barratt, Mr Alan Bloor, Mr R. J. Bolam, Mrs Barbara Coakley, Mr James Kerr, Mr Patrick MacKenzie-Charrington, Mr J. G. Mountford, Mr Graham Oakley, Mr John Ross, Mr Ray Styles, Miss A. D. Swift, Mr Chris van Hoorn.

106 MR PAUL COLE, Whatcombe

Postal: Whatcombe Estate, Whatcombe, Wantage, Oxfordshire, OX12 9NW
Contacts: PHONE (01488) 638433 FAX (01488) 638609
E-MAIL admin@paulcole.co.uk WEBSITE www.paulcole.co.uk

1 **ARCTIC SEA**, 4, b br c Oasis Dream—Rainbow Dancing **P. F. I. Cole Ltd**
2 **ASSASSINATE (IRE)**, 4, b g Tagula (IRE)—Ten Spot (IRE) **Mrs Josephine Green & PFI Cole LTD**
3 **AUCKLAND (IRE)**, 4, b c Galileo (IRE)—Airwave **Mrs F. H. Hay**
4 **BARON BOLT**, 5, b g Kheleyf (USA)—Scarlet Royal **Asprey Wright Evans PJL Racing Wilcock**
5 **BLACK SEA (IRE)**, 5, b g Galileo (IRE)—Christmas Kid (USA) **King Power Racing Co Ltd**
6 **MEDIEVAL (IRE)**, 4, b g Kodiac—Quickstyx **Mrs F. H. Hay**
7 **MR POCKET (IRE)**, 4, b c Acclamation—Midnight Martini **Gatley & Baines**
8 **PORT DOUGLAS (IRE)**, 5, b g Galileo (IRE)—Walzerkoenigin (USA) **King Power Racing Co Ltd**
9 **ROTHERWICK (IRE)**, 6, ch g Starspangledbanner (AUS)—Pivotalia (IRE) **P. F. I. Cole Ltd**
10 **SHAKERATTLENROLL (IRE)**, 5, b g Intikhab (USA)—Carolxaar (IRE) **Mr Chris Wright & PFI Cole Ltd**
11 **SPIRIT OF BELLE**, 4, b g Sir Percy—Yensi **King Power Racing Co Ltd**
12 **STORMBOUND (IRE)**, 9, b g Galileo (IRE)—A Footstep Away (USA) **P. F. I. Cole Ltd**
13 **TUSCANY (IRE)**, 4, ch g Poet's Voice—Avril Rose (IRE) **P. F. I. Cole Ltd**
14 **UPSTAGING**, 6, b g Mount Nelson—Corndavon (USA) **P. F. I. Cole Ltd**

THREE-YEAR-OLDS

15 **BLACK MEDUSA (IRE)**, b c Canford Cliffs (IRE)—Dancer's Leap **Mr C. S. Norman**
16 **BLUE MOTION**, b g Cityscape—Bluebelle **Mr C. M. Budgett**
17 **CAPITAL FLIGHT (IRE)**, ch g Zoffany (IRE)—Mackenzie's Friend **Mrs F. H. Hay**
18 **DOCTOR KNOX (IRE)**, b c Dawn Approach (IRE)—Queen of Carthage (USA) **Mrs F. H. Hay**
19 **MAY REMAIN**, b g Mayson—Ultimate Best **PJL Racing, Asprey, Wilcock, Wright, Meyrick**
20 **MUSICAL ART (IRE)**, ch f Dutch Art—Musical Bar (IRE) **Mrs F. H. Hay**
21 **PINK PHANTOM**, b f Oasis Dream—Pink Symphony **Mrs F. H. Hay**
22 **PLUNGER**, ch c Helmet (AUS)—Percolator **A. H. Robinson**
23 **ROGUE HERO (IRE)**, b g Oasis Dream—Pink Damsel (IRE) **Mrs F. H. Hay**
24 **SECRET EYE (IRE)**, ch f Street Cry (IRE)—What A Treasure (USA) **Mr H. A. Lootah**
25 **SUMMER THUNDER (USA)**, b f Street Cry (USA)—Satulagi (USA) **Mrs F. H. Hay**
26 **TOWELRADS BOY (IRE)**, b c Red Jazz (USA)—
                                      Mystery Hill (USA) **Clive S. Norman, Paul Hamilton, Alan J. Simpson**
27 **UNITED KINGDOM**, b g Equiano (FR)—Lucky Legs (IRE) **P.F.I. Cole & James Gaffney**
28 **ZORAYA (FR)**, b f Zoffany (IRE)—Aztec Queen **The Fairy Story Partnership**

TWO-YEAR-OLDS

29 B c 18/4 Foxwedge (AUS)—Astrantia (Dansili) (25000) **P. F. I. Cole Ltd**
30 **CATHOLIC POETRY (IRE)**, ch f 23/4 Lope de Vega (IRE)—Tinaheely (IRE) (Intikhab (USA)) (48000) **Mr F. P. Stella**
31 **CELTIC CLASSIC (IRE)**, b c 10/4 Cacique (IRE)—
                        Dabtiyra (IRE) (Dr Devious (IRE)) (40000) **Evans Wright Asprey PJL Racing Wilcock**
32 Ch c 18/4 Dawn Approach (IRE)—Echo River (USA) (Irish River (FR)) (42000) **Mrs F. H. Hay**
33 **HAZE**, b f 10/3 Oasis Dream—Dorelia (IRE) (Efisio) **Denford Stud Limited**
34 B c 18/2 Zoffany (IRE)—Lexy May (USA) (Lear Fan (USA)) (24420) **P. F. I. Cole Ltd**
35 Br c 14/3 Poet's Voice—Lily Again (American Post) (36000) **P. F. I. Cole Ltd**
36 **MAJESTIC DAWN (IRE)**, ch c 15/2 Dawn Approach (IRE)—
                        Jolie Chanson (FR) (Mount Nelson) (40000) **Green & Norman**
37 **MELYA**, b f 13/4 Equiano (FR)—Percolator (Kheleyf (USA)) **A. H. Robinson**
38 **NGUNI**, ch f 6/3 Mount Nelson—Flashbang (Dubawi (USA)) **A. H. Robinson**
39 **OVER THE GUNS (IRE)**, b c 18/3 Garswood—Princess Rose (Royal Applause) (15000) **P. F. I. Cole Ltd**
40 B c 2/4 Acclamation—Precipitous (IRE) (Indian Ridge) (146520) **Mrs F. H. Hay**
41 **PTARMIGAN**, gr f 11/3 Mastercraftsman (IRE)—Arabescatta (Monsun (GER)) **Denford Stud Limited**
42 **SASSOON**, ch c 24/3 Poet's Voice—Seradim (Elnadim (USA)) **The Fairy Story Partnership**
43 **SELOUS (IRE)**, b c 30/3 Showcasing—Miss Lacey (IRE) (Diktat) (105820) **Mrs F. H. Hay**
44 **SHIR KHAN**, ch c 28/2 Leroidesanimaux (BRZ)—
                        Sterling Sound (USA) (Street Cry (IRE)) (50000) **Arbib, Robinson & Cole**
45 **SO STRICTLY**, b c 21/5 So You Think (NZ)—Salsa Steps (USA) (Giant's Causeway) **Ben & Sir Martyn Arbib**
46 **VOLTAIC**, ch c 12/4 Power—Seramindar (Zamindar (USA)) **The Fairy Story Partnership**
47 **WALKMAN (IRE)**, b c 5/4 War Command (USA)—Mooching Along (IRE) (Mujahid (USA)) (90476) **Mr A. Altazi**
48 Ch c 18/4 Australia (IRE)—Winesong (IRE) (Giant's Causeway (USA)) (219780) **Mrs F. H. Hay**
49 B c 26/1 Lope de Vega (IRE)—With Your Spirit (FR) (Invincible Spirit (IRE)) (105820) **Mrs F. H. Hay**

MR PAUL COLE - Continued

Other Owners: M. Arbib, Mr B. G. Arbib, Miss Emily Charlotte Asprey, Mr T. R. Baines, Mr G. Baker, Mrs C. E. S. Baker, T. M. Bird, Mr P. F. I. Cole, Sir C. Evans, Mr J. Gaffney, Mr J. Gatley, E. R. Goodwin, Mrs J. Green, Miss C. S. Scott-Balls, Mr N. Wilcock, Mr C. N. Wright.

Assistant Trainer: Oliver Cole

---

107 | **MR PAUL COLLINS, Saltburn**
Postal: **1 Longthwaite Close, Skelton-In-Cleveland, Saltburn, Cleveland, TS12 2WP**
Contacts: **MOBILE (07779) 794684**

1 DICA (FR), 12, ch g Kapgarde (FR)—Easy World (FR) **Mr P. Collins**
2 DREAM REVIVAL, 5, br m Captain Gerrard (IRE)—Passkey **Mr P. Collins**
3 ROYS DREAM, 4, b f Monsieur Bond (IRE)—Velvet Jaguar **Mrs A. Pickering**
4 SOLID STRIKE, 10, b g Sir Harry Lewis (USA)—Solid Land (FR) **Mr P. Collins**

---

108 | **MR STUART COLTHERD, Selkirk**
Postal: **Clarilawmuir Farm, Selkirk, Selkirkshire, TD7 4QA**
Contacts: **PHONE (01750) 21251 FAX (01750) 21251 MOBILE (07801) 398199**
E-MAIL **wscoltherd@gmail.com**

1 ACHILL ROAD BOY (IRE), 9, b g Morozov (USA)—
Presenting Katie (IRE) **Farming Army Newitt Flannigan Findlater**
2 AVONDHU PEARL (IRE), 7, ch m Beneficial—Ballinapierce Lady (IRE) **Jeffrey Hall Martino Mitchell Cawkwell**
3 BUDARRI, 5, b g Supreme Sound—Amtaar **Cruikshank Coltherd**
4 CAPTAIN BLACK, 6, b g Black Sam Bellamy (IRE)—
Midlem Melody **Scotgiliesandersonswintoncampbelmckirgan**
5 CAPTAIN REDBEARD (IRE), 9, ch g Bach (IRE)—Diesel Dancer (IRE) **W. S. Coltherd**
6 CASIMIR DU CLOS (FR), 6, b g Blue Bresil (FR)—Cyrienne du Maine (FR) **Newitt Flannigan Coltherd**
7 FAIRLEE GRACE, 7, b m Fair Mix (IRE)—Halo Flora **J. L. Gledson**
8 FELIX MENDELSSOHN (IRE), 7, b g Galileo (IRE)—Ice Queen (IRE) **Shire Dreamers**
9 GRAYSTOWN (IRE), 6, b g Well Chosen—Temple Girl (IRE) **The Farming Army**
10 KANTURK BANK (IRE), 8, b g Carlo Bank (IRE)—
Kanturk Belle (IRE) **WhyteScottSwintonGillieHoodSandersonSmail**
11 POETIC PRESENCE (IRE), 8, b m Presenting—Johnston's Crest (IRE) **W. S. Coltherd**
12 POOKIE PEKAN (IRE), 5, b g Putra Pekan—Shii-Take's Girl **W. S. Coltherd**
13 RYLESTONE, 7, ch m Presenting—Silver Monument **Mr I. D. Stark**
14 SHANAWAY (IRE), 7, b g Stowaway—Shannagh Run (IRE) **Coltherd Whyte**
15 SHARNEY SIKE, 12, ch g And Beyond (IRE)—Squeeze Box (IRE) **Mrs C. Hogg**
16 SPORTING MILAN (IRE), 7, b g Milan—Sports Leader (IRE) **Mr A. G. Whyte**
17 SUPRISE VENDOR (IRE), 12, ch g Fath (USA)—Dispol Jazz **Mercer Campbell Coltherd**
18 TIBBIE TAMSON, 7, b m Josr Algarhoud (IRE)—Midlem Melody **W. S. Coltherd**

Other Owners: Mrs J. Campbell, Mr D. T. Campbell, Mr S. F. Cawkwell, Mr N. J. Cruikshank, Mrs G. De Martino, Mr G. Findlater, Mr R. Flannigan, Mr I. R. Flannigan, Mr E. Gillie, Mr D. A. Gray, Mr I. Hall, Mr M. J. Hood, J. B. Jeffrey, Mr M. G. M. MacDonald, Mrs S. M. McKirgan, Mr K. Mercer, Mr I. A. J. Mitchell, Mrs S. C. Newitt, Mr D. Reive, Mr S. Sanderson, Mr M. J. Scott, Mr J. D. R. Smail, Mr S. Swinton.

Jockey (NH): Danny Cook. **Conditional:** Sam Coltherd.

---

109 | **MRS SUSAN CORBETT, Otterburn**
Postal: **Girsonfield, Otterburn, Newcastle upon Tyne, Tyne and Wear, NE19 1NT**
Contacts: **PHONE (01830) 520771 FAX (01830) 520771 MOBILE (07713) 651215**
E-MAIL **girsonfield@outlook.com** WEBSITE **www.girsonfield.co.uk**

1 AHEAD OF THE CURVE (FR), 6, b g Ballingarry (IRE)—Jasla (FR) **Mr T. H. J. Green**
2 BAHRIKATE, 5, b m Bahri (USA)—Dispol Katie **Mr L. Richards**
3 COOLMEEN HILL (IRE), 7, b g Bahri (USA)—Hazel's Tisrara (IRE) **Mr T. H. J. Green**
4 DARCEY'S PENNY, 5, b m Bahri (USA)—Penteli **Girsonfield Racing Club**
5 EBONY ROSE, 6, br m Kalanisi (IRE)—Cogolie (FR) **The Nelson Racing Club**
6 FERNGROVE (USA), 7, gr g Rockport Harbor (USA)—Lucky Pipit **Green, Chapman, Corbett**
7 FOREWARNING, 4, b g Cacique (IRE)—Buffering **Ms J. E. Maggs**

MRS SUSAN CORBETT - Continued

8 **HARRISONS PROMISE,** 6, b m Westerner—Hello My Lovely **Mr W. F. Corbett**
9 **HEARTASIA (IRE),** 5, b m Danehill Dancer (IRE)—Big Heart **Corbett & McMahon**
10 **HILLS OF CONNEMARA (IRE),** 6, gr m Tikkanen (USA)—Desirable Rhythm (IRE) **Mr F. W. W. Chapman**
11 **LOMHARA,** 4, b f Bahri (USA)—Moonshine Malt **Hassle-Free Racing**
12 **LUVLY BOY BLUE,** 7, b g Blueprint (IRE)—Mellouise **C. R. Green**
13 **MAGNUM (IRE),** 5, gr g Lawman (FR)—Coventina (IRE) **Mr T. H. J. Green**
14 **MAMDOOD (IRE),** 4, gr g Clodovil (IRE)—Fact **Mr T. H. J. Green**
15 **MORNING WITH IVAN (IRE),** 8, b m Ivan Denisovich (IRE)—Grinneas (IRE) **Mr L. Richards**
16 **MR KITE,** 7, b g Sixties Icon—Mar Blue (FR) **TWT Racing Club 2**
17 **MY BROWN EYED GIRL,** 5, b m Ferrule (IRE)—Chalosse **Mr G. Satchwell**
18 **REIVERS LODGE,** 6, b m Black Sam Bellamy (IRE)—Crystal Princess (IRE) **Mr F. W. W. Chapman**
19 **RIPONIAN,** 8, ch g Trade Fair—Dispol Katie **Girsonfield Racing Club**
20 **ROSE TREE (IRE),** 5, b m Yeats (IRE)—Isaballareine (GER) **Mr T. H. J. Green**
21 **RUSSIANTOM (IRE),** 7, b m Dylan Thomas (IRE)—Russian Roubles (IRE) **Mr T. H. J. Green**
22 **SATIS HOUSE,** 4, b f Bahri (USA)—Ex Mill Lady **Castle View Racing**
23 **SHESTHEBUSINESS,** 7, b m Midnight Legend—Sabreflight **Mrs J. L. Corbett**
24 **SODOI,** 5, b m Millkom—Island Path (IRE) **The Nelson Racing Club**
25 **STAIGUE FORT,** 10, b g Kirkwall—Mulberry Wine **Mr W. F. Corbett**
26 **TOARMANDOWITHLOVE (IRE),** 10, ch m Choisir (AUS)—Deadly Buzz (IRE) **Ms R. Enright**
27 **VIOGNIER,** 6, ch m Black Sam Bellamy (IRE)—Noun de La Thinte (FR) **Castle View Racing**
28 **WOR VERGE,** 5, b g Virtual—Hanover Gate **TWT Racing Club 2**

THREE-YEAR-OLDS

29 **GOWANBUSTER,** b g Bahri (USA)—Aahgowangowan (IRE) **Hassle-Free Racing**

Other Owners: Mr D. O. Chapman, Mr D. J. Clarke, Mrs S. Corbett, Mr M. D. Foden, Mr G. Foley, Mr I. Galletley, Mr S. Humphries, Miss H. M. McMahon, Mrs J. Pringle, Mr L. Waugh.

Assistant Trainer: Mr J. Corbett

Conditional: James Corbett. **Amateur:** Mr Dillan Hurst, Mr Ross Wilson.

---

110 **MR JOHN CORNWALL, Melton Mowbray**
Postal: **April Cottage, Pasture Lane, Hose, Melton Mowbray, Leicestershire, LE14 4LB**
Contacts: **PHONE (01664) 444453 FAX (01664) 444754 MOBILE (07939) 557091**
E-MAIL johncornwall7@gmail.com

1 **FLICHITY (IRE),** 13, br g Turtle Island (IRE)—Chancy Gal **Mr J. R. Cornwall**
2 **NEXT EXIT (IRE),** 13, b g Exit To Nowhere (USA)—Pilgrim Star (IRE) **Mr J. R. Cornwall**
3 **OUR THOMAS (IRE),** 6, b g Dylan Thomas (IRE)—Sinamay (USA) **Mr J. R. Cornwall**
4 **THAT'S THE DEAL (IRE),** 14, b br g Turtle Island (IRE)—Sister Swing **Mr J. R. Cornwall**
5 **THE JUGOPOLIST (IRE),** 11, b g Oscar (IRE)—Chance My Native (IRE) **Mr J. R. Cornwall**

---

111 **MISS JACQUELINE COWARD, Sheriff Hutton**
Postal: **Low Moor Farm, Dalby, Yorkshire, YO60 6PF**
Contacts: PHONE (01653) 628995

1 **CHISWICK BEY (IRE),** 10, b g Elusive City (USA)—Victoria Lodge (IRE) **Mr M. J. Macleod**
2 **COVIGLIA (IRE),** 4, ro c Invincible Spirit (IRE)—Bright Snow (USA) **Mr J. N. Blackburn**
3 **MY DISTANT MURPHY,** 4, b g Distant Peak (IRE)—So Cannie **Mr E. C. Wilkin**
4 **TAPIS LIBRE,** 10, b g Librettist (USA)—Stella Manuela (FR) **Mrs S. E. Mason**

---

112 **MR ROBERT COWELL, Newmarket**
Postal: **Bottisham Heath Stud, Six Mile Bottom, Newmarket, Suffolk, CB8 0TT**
Contacts: **PHONE (01638) 570330 MOBILE (07785) 512463**
E-MAIL robert@robertcowellracing.co.uk WEBSITE www.robertcowellracing.co.uk

1 **ALWAYS AMAZING,** 4, ch g Kyllachy—Amazed **Mr A. Al Mansoori**
2 **BAHAMIAN HEIGHTS,** 7, b g Bahamian Bounty—Tahirah **Mrs J Morley & Mr A Rix**
3 **BLUE DE VEGA (GER),** 5, b h Lope de Vega (IRE)—Burning Heights (GER) **Blue De Vega Partnership**

MR ROBERT COWELL - Continued

4 **DESERT SPORT (USA)**, 4, b g Hat Trick (JPN)—Desert Sky (IRE) **Mr M. Al Shafar**
5 **ENCORE D'OR**, 6, b g Oasis Dream—Entente Cordiale (IRE) **Mrs Morley, G Johnson & Newsells Park Stud**
6 **EVERGATE**, 4, b g Exceed And Excel (AUS)—Lion Forest (USA) **The Ever Hopeful Partnership**
7 **GOLDREAM**, 9, br g Oasis Dream—Clizia (IRE) **Mr J Sargeant & Mrs J Morley**
8 **GREEN DOOR (IRE)**, 7, b g Camacho—Inourhearts (IRE) **Mrs A Henry & Partner**
9 **INDIAN TINKER**, 9, b g Sleeping Indian—Breakfast Creek **Bottisham Heath Stud**
10 **JUMIRA BRIDGE**, 4, b g Invincible Spirit (IRE)—Zykina **Mrs M. J. Morley**
11 **LEO MINOR (USA)**, 4, b c War Front (USA)—Kissed (IRE) **Mr T. W. Morley**
12 **OCELOT**, 4, b f Poet's Voice—Desert Lynx (IRE) **Manor Farm Stud (Rutland)**
13 **OUTBACK TRAVELLER (IRE)**, 7, b g Bushranger (IRE)—Blue Holly (IRE) **Lordship Stud & Mrs J Morley**
14 **PEACE DREAMER (IRE)**, 4, b f Sir Prancealot (IRE)—See Nuala (IRE) **Mrs J. Hadida**
15 **RAUCOUS**, 5, b g Dream Ahead (USA)—Shyrl **Mr T. W. Morley**
16 **ROCKING RUDOLPH (USA)**, 5, b m Discreetly Mine (USA)—Empire Spring (USA) **Mr G. M. C. Johnson**
17 **ROMANTIC STORY**, 4, ch f Poet's Voice—Scallywag (IRE) **Mr N. Al Habtoor**
18 **SIR ROBERT CHEVAL**, 7, b g Green Desert (USA)—Aunt Ruby (USA) **Heart of the South Racing 102**
19 **SOUTHERN BELLE (IRE)**, 5, b m Aqlaam—Areyaam (USA) **Mr A. Alharbi**
20 **STORM OVER (IRE)**, 4, b c Elnadim (USA)—Stormy View (USA) **Mr A. Al Mansoori**
21 **VISIONARY (IRE)**, 4, b g Dream Ahead (USA)—Avodale (IRE) **K. A. Dasmal**
22 **ZAMJAR**, 4, b g Exceed And Excel (AUS)—Cloud's End **Mrs M. J. Morley**

THREE-YEAR-OLDS

23 **BOBBY'S CHARM (USA)**, b g Shanghai Bobby (USA)—Magic Charm (USA) **The Cool Silk Partnership**
24 **CALEDONIA EARL**, b g Rip Van Winkle (IRE)—Granuaile O'malley (IRE) **Isla & Colin Cage**
25 **COOL BABY**, b f Intense Focus (USA)—Dead Cool **K. A. Dasmal**
26 **COWBOY SOLDIER (IRE)**, b c Kodiac—Urgele (FR) **Mrs F. H. Hay**
27 **DAZZLE GOLD (USA)**, b c Lemon Drop Kid (USA)—Tustarta (USA) **Mr S. Pan**
28 **DOLLAR VALUE (USA)**, gr g Exchange Rate (USA)—Makoma (USA) **K. A. Dasmal**
29 **DREAM FOR LIFE**, b f Dream Ahead (USA)—Everlasting Dream **K. A. Dasmal**
30 **DUBAI SILK**, ch f Helmet (AUS)—Silken Express (IRE) **Malih L. Al Basti**
31 **EMPHATIC (IRE)**, b br c Epaulette (AUS)—Wild Ocean **Cheveley Park Stud Limited**
32 **EXPEDIATE**, ch g Bahamian Bounty—Welanga **Gough, Henry, Read & Swinburn**
33 **FOREVER IN LOVE**, ch f Dutch Art—Ardent **Cheveley Park Stud Limited**
34 **FRENCH SPARKLE**, b f Swiss Spirit—Chantilly Jewel (USA) **Bottisham Heath Stud**
35 **GRANDFATHER TOM**, b c Kheleyf (USA)—Kassuta **Mr J. Sargeant**
36 **L'AGE D'OR**, b f Iffraaj—Goleta (IRE) **C. Humphris**
37 **MADAM DEVIOUS**, b f Dutch Art—Bouyrin (IRE) **Saleh Al Homaizi & Imad Al Sagar**
38 **MASTER POET**, b c Poet's Voice—Lilli Marlane **Heart Of The South Racing**
39 **MOLLY BLOOM (FR)**, b f Royal Applause—Farnesina (FR) **C. Humphris**
40 **NOMORECALLS (IRE)**, b g Dawn Approach (IRE)—Semayyel (IRE) **M. Alharbi**
41 **SENSORY (IRE)**, gr f Dream Ahead (USA)—Dookus (IRE) **Cheveley Park Stud Limited**
42 **TROPICAL WATERS (IRE)**, b f Acclamation—Hurricane Havoc (USA) **Mr A. Al Mansoori**
43 **VICTORS LADY (IRE)**, b f Society Rock (IRE)—Novat (IRE) **Mr P. Hunt**
44 **WARRIOR GODDESS**, b f Henrythenavigator (USA)—Azenzar **Saleh Al Homaizi & Imad Al Sagar**

TWO-YEAR-OLDS

45 **ADAM TILER (USA)**, b c 14/2 Justin Phillip (USA)—
           Moneygrabber (USA) (Awesome Again (CAN)) (73557) **Mr T. W. Morley**
46 B f 14/3 Mayson—Chantilly Jewel (USA) (Century City (IRE))
47 B f 27/2 Kodiac—Dance Bid (Authorized (IRE)) (300000) **Mr S. Pan**
48 B f 28/2 Pastoral Pursuits—Dutch Girl (Dutch Art) **Bottisham Heath Stud**
49 **HESSEL**, ch c 15/3 Dutch Art—Cantal (Pivotal) (37000) **Cheveley Park Stud Limited**
50 **HOOFLEAP (IRE)**, b c 1/3 Gale Force Ten—Hflah (IRE) (Dubawi (IRE)) (57142) **The Cool Silk Partnership**
51 B f 3/4 Foxwedge (AUS)—Instructress (Diktat) **Bottisham Heath Stud**
52 B c 2/4 Sir Percy—Kassuta (Kyllachy) **Mr J. Sargeant**
53 B c 22/4 Oxbow—Lady Melesi (USA) (Colonial Affair (USA)) (166473) **K. A. Dasmal**
54 B f 16/1 Born To Sea (IRE)—Madame Boulangere (Royal Applause) (25000) **D Tunmore & Partner**
55 B c 1/4 Kodiac—Pale Orchid (IRE) (Invincible Spirit (IRE)) (146520) **Mrs F. H. Hay**
56 **POCKET DYNAMO (USA)**, b c 29/3 Dialed In (USA)—
           Little Bit Tiny (USA) (Cuvee (USA)) (27100) **Mr T. W. Morley**
57 B c 4/5 Central Banker (USA)—
           Quietly Elegant (USA) (Quiet American (USA)) (28648) **Nick Bradley Racing 21 & Partner**
58 **REEVES**, b c 5/2 Tamayuz—Mania (IRE) (Danehill (USA)) (95000) **Mrs F. H. Hay**
59 B f 22/2 Swiss Spirit—Royal Award (Cadeaux Genereux) (9000) **J Sargeant, B Rose & Partner**
60 B f 19/4 Blame—Royal Parisian (Royal Applause) (20905) **K. A. Dasmal**
61 Ch f 19/3 Congrats (USA)—Smart Dancer (USA) (Smart Strike (CAN)) (54200) **Mr T. W. Morley**

MR ROBERT COWELL - Continued

62 B c 15/4 Dawn Approach (IRE)—Step Lightly (IRE) (Danehill Dancer (IRE)) **Mr N. Al Habtoor**
63 **SUPERSTITION,** b f 1/3 Swiss Spirit—School Fees (Royal Applause)

Other Owners: Mrs E. Adamski, Mr Malih Al Basti, Mr Nasser Al Habtoor, Mr Al Mansoori, Mr Al Shafer, Sheikh Khalifa Al Thani, Sheikh Suhaim Al Thani, Mr Imad Al-Sagar, BGC Racing VI, Bottisham Heath Stud, Mrs I. Cage, Mr C. J. Cage, Mr S. A. Cawkwell, Mr A. Chapman, Cheveley Park Stud, Cool Silks Partnership, Mr K. Dasmal, Mrs A. C. Finster, Mrs S. J. Hadida, T. F. Harris, Mrs E. A. Harris, Mrs Fitri Hay, Heart Of The South Racing, Mrs A. Henry, Mr Carl Hodgson, Miss S. Holden, Saleh Al Homaizi, Mr C. Humphris, Mr P. Hunt, Mr M. Jaber, Mr G Johnson, Lordship Stud, Manor Farm Stud, Mr J. Mellon, Mrs J. Morley, Mr T. W. Morley, Newsells Park Stud Limited, Nick Bradley Racing, Mr S. Pan, Mr J. R. Penny, Qatar Racing Limited, Mr Allen Rix, Dr B. Rose, Mr J Sargeant, P. Swann, Mr D. Tunmore, Mr Richard Ward, Mrs B. E. Wilkinson, Mrs S. Wright, Mr R. R. Wright.

Assistant Trainer: Mr Ross Studholme

Apprentice: Jonathon Fisher, Eoin Walsh.

---

113 **MR PAUL COWLEY, Banbury**
Postal: Lodge Farm, Culworth, Banbury, Oxfordshire, OX17 2HL
Contacts: PHONE (01295) 768998 MOBILE (07775) 943346
E-MAIL paulcowleyequine@yahoo.co.uk

1 BUSY BARO (IRE), 8, ch g Acambaro (GER)—Miss Busy Lizzy (IRE) **The BMWs**
2 FRONTLINE (IRE), 10, b g King's Theatre (IRE)—Thunder Road (IRE) **Tower Hamlets Partnership**
3 GLENDERMOT (IRE), 9, b g Portrait Gallery (IRE)—Native Bandit (IRE) **George Beyts & Stan West**
4 GORTNAGIRL (IRE), 6, b m Mahler—Rebel Flyer (IRE)
5 NEXT LEVEL (IRE), 7, b g Mahler—Molly Be **Tower Hamlets Partnership**
6 NICOLOSIO (IRE), 8, b g Peintre Celebre (USA)—Nicolaia (GER) **Tower Hamlets Partnership**
7 SANOK (POL), 6, b g Jape (USA)—Sun Queen (POL) **Tower Hamlets Partnership**

Other Owners: Mr R. J. Batchelor, Mr G. Beyts, Mr P. E. Cowley, Mrs A. Cowley, Mr D. J. Leadbeater, S. G. West, D. E. Wilson.

---

114 **MR CLIVE COX, Hungerford**
Postal: Beechdown Farm, Sheepdrove Road, Lambourn, Hungerford, Berkshire, RG17 7UN
Contacts: OFFICE (01488) 73072 FAX (01488) 73500 MOBILE (07740) 630521
E-MAIL clive@clivecox.com WEBSITE www.clivecox.com

1 BOBBY WHEELER (IRE), 5, b g Pivotal—Regal Rose **Mr Peter Ridgers**
2 COME ON COME ON (IRE), 4, br c Lord Shanakill (USA)—Maridiyna (IRE) **Paul & Clare Rooney**
3 CRUMBLECREEK (IRE), 4, b f Sir Prancealot (IRE)—Larkfield Empress (IRE) **Clive Cox Racing Ltd**
4 DARK POWER (IRE), 4, gr g Dark Angel (IRE)—Sixfields Flyer (IRE) **Mr Alan G. Craddock**
5 DELILAH PARK, 4, b f Delegator—Sarah Park (IRE) **Mr & Mrs DE & J Cash and Mr P Turner**
6 FINAL FRONTIER (IRE), 5, b g Dream Ahead (USA)—Polly Perkins (IRE) **Mr Vimal Khosla**
7 GRAPHITE STORM, 4, gr g Delegator—Ice Haven (IRE) **Mrs Olive Shaw**
8 GREY GALLEON (USA), 4, gr g Mizzen Mast (USA)—Floresta (USA) **BA Racing & R G Levin**
9 HARRY ANGEL (IRE), 4, b c Dark Angel (IRE)—Beatrix Potter (IRE) **Godolphin**
10 KHALIDI, 4, br c High Chaparral (IRE)—Bezique **Mr Nizar Anwar**
11 KODILINE (IRE), 4, b g Kodiac—Kris Spring **Martin McHale & Partner**
12 LITTLE PALAVER, 6, b g Showcasing—Little Nymph **Mr Trevor Fox**
13 LOUIE DE PALMA, 6, b h Pastoral Pursuits—Tahirah **Mr Peter Ridgers**
14 NOW CHILDREN (IRE), 4, ch c Dragon Pulse (IRE)—Toberanthawn (IRE) **Paul & Clare Rooney**
15 PERFECT CRACKER, 10, ch g Dubai Destination (USA)—Perfect Story (IRE) **Mildmay Racing**
16 PERFECT LADY, 4, b f Excelebration (IRE)—Theladyinquestion (IRE) **Mildmay Racing & D. H. Caslon**
17 PUTTO (IRE), 4, gr g Dark Angel (IRE)—Fair Sailing (IRE) **Mr Anthony Rogers**
18 SEEKING MAGIC, 10, b g Haafhd—Atnab (USA) **The Seekers**
19 THE JEAN GENIE, 4, b br f Lawman (FR)—Miracle Seeker **Mr D. J. Burke & Mr P Alderson**
20 TIS MARVELLOUS, 4, b g Harbour Watch (IRE)—Mythicism **Miss J. Deadman & Mr S. Barrow**
21 ZONDERLAND, 5, ch h Dutch Art—Barynya **Cheveley Park Stud**

THREE-YEAR-OLDS

22 AL JELLABY, b c Exceed And Excel (AUS)—Dolphina (USA) **AlMohamediya Racing**
23 ARABIAN FAIRYTALE, b f Mawatheeq (USA)—Tattercoats (FR) **Mondial Racing**
24 ASK THE DUDE (IRE), ch g Dutch Art—Sharp Crisp Air (IRE) **Miss J. Deadman & Mr S. Barrow**

MR CLIVE COX - Continued

25 **ASTROLOGIST (IRE)**, b c Sea The Stars (IRE)—Jumooh **Syder, Whateley, Murphy, Burke**
26 **AUTUMN LEAVES**, b f Helmet (AUS)—Jadwiga **JT & KM Thomas**
27 **AWESOME**, ch f Bahamian Bounty—Ballymore Celebre (IRE) **Carmel Stud**
28 **BALKHASH (IRE)**, b g Champs Elysees—Balatoma (IRE) **Mr Nurlan Bizakov**
29 **CASIMA**, b f Dark Angel (IRE)—Caskelena (IRE) **Mr Nurlan Bizakov**
30 **CHAGATAI (IRE)**, b g Kodiac—Golden Shine **AlMohamediya Racing**
31 **CONNECT**, b c Roderic O'connor (IRE)—Robema **Mr A. D. Spence**
32 **CRACK ON CRACK ON**, ch c Havana Gold (IRE)—Almunia (IRE) **Paul & Clare Rooney**
33 **CUBAN HEEL**, gr g Havana Gold (IRE)—Tipping Over (IRE) **Kennet Valley Thoroughbreds VII**
34 **DEVA DANDY (USA)**, ch c Midshipman (USA)—Yankee Belle (USA) **Mr David Russell**
35 **DOCTOR WONDERFUL**, ch c Medicean—Wonderful Desert **Castle Down Racing**
36 **DYAGILEV**, ch c Kheleyf (USA)—Dancemetothemoon **Miss Harriet Loder**
37 **ELSE APPROACH**, b c Dawn Approach (IRE)—Elle Shadow (IRE) **Mr Nizar Anwar**
38 **EXISTENTIAL (IRE)**, br f Lethal Force (IRE)—Fascination (IRE) **Mr J Shack & Mr G Barnard**
39 **FIELDS OF PLAY (USA)**, b c Kitten's Joy (USA)—Elite **Prince A. A. Faisal**
40 **GET BACK GET BACK (IRE)**, b c Lord Shanakill (USA)—Bawaakeer (USA) **Paul & Clare Rooney**
41 **GHAZAN (IRE)**, ch c Iffraaj—Sweet Firebird (IRE) **AlMohamediya Racing**
42 **GO ROO**, br c Kyllachy—Cross My Heart **Paul & Clare Rooney**
43 **GRAND KOONTA (IRE)**, gr c Dark Angel (IRE)—Wrong Key (IRE) **China Horse Club International Limited**
44 **HEARTACHE**, b f Kyllachy—Place In My Heart **The Hot to Trot Syndicate - Heartache**
45 **HIT THE BEAT**, br f Fast Company (IRE)—Dance Express (IRE) **Clive Cox Racing Ltd**
46 **HULCOTE**, b f Frankel—Polly's Mark (IRE) **Mr F. Anstock**
47 **ICART POINT**, br g Poet's Voice—Maziona **Miss Italia J. Keogh**
48 **ISLE OF MAN**, b c Exceed And Excel (AUS)—One So Marvellous **Mr Lee Tze Bun Marces**
49 **IT'S A WISH**, b f Invincible Spirit (IRE)—Sun Bittern (USA) **Prince A. A. Faisal**
50 **KICK ON KICK ON**, b c Swiss Spirit—Catmint **Paul & Clare Rooney**
51 **KING'S SLIPPER**, b c Leroidesanimaux (BRZ)—Last Slipper **D B Clark & A R Bentall**
52 **KODITIME (IRE)**, b g Kodiac—Eponastone (IRE) **Martin McHale & Partner**
53 B c Invincible Spirit (IRE)—La Grande Zoa (IRE) **Clipper Logistics**
54 **LETHAL LUNCH**, gr c Lethal Force (IRE)—Pin Cushion **The Rat Pack Partnership 2017**
55 **LETHAL SPIRIT**, b g Lethal Force (IRE)—Emmuska **Mr Alan G. Craddock**
56 **LILBOURNE STAR (IRE)**, b g Lilbourne Lad (IRE)—Make Amends (IRE) **The Fifth Amendment**
57 **LITTLE MISS LILLY**, b f Lethal Force (IRE)—Malilla (IRE) **Clive Cox Racing Ltd**
58 **MAID OF SPIRIT (IRE)**, br f Invincible Spirit (IRE)—Indian Maiden (IRE) **Mr Con Harrington**
59 **MANDUKHAI (IRE)**, b f Pivotal—Danelissima (IRE) **AlMohamediya Racing**
60 **MOON SONG**, gr f Lethal Force (IRE)—West of The Moon **Cheveley Park Stud**
61 **OSKEMEN**, gr g Mastercraftsman (IRE)—Ollie Olga (USA) **Mr Nurlan Bizakov**
62 **PERFECT CLARITY**, b f Nathaniel (IRE)—Clarietta (IRE) **Dr B Drew & Mr David J Keast**
63 **PERFECT REFUGE**, gr f Champs Elysees—Perfect Haven **Hants & Herts**
64 **PRINCE AHWAHNEE**, b c Harbour Watch—Ahwahnee **The Watchmen**
65 **PRINCE OF THE DARK**, gr c Lethal Force (IRE)—Fanrouge (IRE) **Mr Alan G. Craddock**
66 **RECKLESS DREAM (IRE)**, b f Reckless Abandon—Regal Fairy (IRE) **Miss J. Deadman & Mr S. Barrow**
67 **SALUTE THE SOLDIER (GER)**, br c Sepoy (AUS)—Street Fire (IRE) **Mr & Mrs P Hargreaves & Mr A D Spence**
68 **SHAHEREZADA (IRE)**, b f Dutch Art—Shabyt **Mr Nurlan Bizakov**
69 **SILCA MISTRESS**, ch f Dutch Art—Strictly Silca **Windmill Racing II**
70 **SIMPLY BREATHLESS**, b f Bated Breath—Darling Grace **The Hold Your Breath Syndicate**
71 **SNAZZY JAZZY (IRE)**, b c Red Jazz—Bulrushes **Mrs Olive Shaw**
72 **SUPEREGO**, ch f Sepoy (AUS)—Ego **Mildmay Racing and Mr R A Farmiloe**
73 **SWISS CHILL**, b c Swiss Spirit—Littlemisssunshine (IRE) **Mrs Olive Shaw**
74 **TAMERLANE (IRE)**, b c Dark Angel (IRE)—Coy (IRE) **AlMohamediya Racing**
75 Ch g Approve (IRE)—Timbre **Clive Cox Racing Ltd**
76 **TWIST (IRE)**, b c Invincible Spirit (IRE)—Kahira (IRE) **Mr A D Spence**
77 **TWO WEEKS**, ch f Mayson—Laurena (GER) **Apple Tree Stud**
78 **VERDIGRIS (IRE)**, b f Intense Focus (USA)—Nimboo (USA) **Ms Gillian Khosla**

TWO-YEAR-OLDS

79 B c 31/3 Es Que Love (IRE)—Ajig Dancer (Niniski (USA)) (59047) **Mr Peter Ridgers**
80 B c 29/4 Invincible Spirit (IRE)—Alumni (Selkirk (USA)) (97680) **China Horse Club International Limited**
81 **ASAATIER (IRE)**, b f 29/2 War Front (USA)—
Spring In The Air (CAN) (Spring At Last (USA)) (300000) **Prince A. A. Faisal**
82 B c 30/1 George Vancouver (USA)—Ascot Glory (IRE) (Kheleyf (USA)) (21164) **Ahmad Abdulla Al Shaikh**
83 Ch c 24/4 Dutch Art—Barynya (Pivotal) (180000) **Cheveley Park Stud**
84 **DERRY BOY**, b c 14/4 Havana Gold (IRE)—Steppe By Steppe (Zamindar (USA)) **Paul & Clare Rooney**
85 **DESIGNATED**, ch f 8/4 Dutch Art—Entitled (Pivotal) **Cheveley Park Stud**
86 Gr c 18/1 Dark Angel (IRE)—Djinni (IRE) (Invincible Spirit (IRE)) (40700) **Mr J. Goddard**

MR CLIVE COX - Continued

87 B c 6/3 Lethal Force (IRE)—Fanrouge (IRE) (Red Clubs (IRE)) **Mr Alan G. Craddock**
88 B c 30/1 Iffraaj—Fig Roll (Bahamian Bounty) (180952) **China Horse Club International Limited**
89 **GETCHAGETCHAGETCHA,** b c 18/4 Champs Elysees—Paella (Oasis Dream) (48840) **Paul & Clare Rooney**
90 B c 4/3 Oasis Dream—Gothic Dance (IRE) (Dalakhani (IRE)) (61050) **Mrs Olive Shaw**
91 **HERITAGE,** b f 2/3 Garswood—Inheritance (Oasis Dream) **Cheveley Park Stud**
92 B f 13/3 Camacho—Ibecke (Exceed And Excel (AUS)) (43809) **Mr Peter Ridgers**
93 Gr c 18/4 Dark Angel (IRE)—Lady Alexander (IRE) (Night Shift (USA)) (100000) **Mr Noel O'Callaghan**
94 B c 17/3 Dark Angel (IRE)—Lady Duxyana (Most Welcome) (45000) **Mr Trevor Fox**
95 Ch f 1/2 Exceed And Excel (AUS)—Leopard Hunt (USA) (70000) **Mildmay Racing & D. H. Caslon**
96 B c 8/2 Dream Ahead (USA)—Lookslikeanangel (Holy Roman Emperor (IRE)) **Carmel Stud**
97 B c 3/3 Lethal Force (IRE)—Lostintheclouds (Firebreak) (24420) **B Allen, G Hill & N Wagland**
98 B c 9/2 Dark Angel (IRE)—Love In The Desert (Lemon Drop Kid (USA)) (227920) **Mr Lee Tze Bun Marces**
99 B br f 20/4 No Nay Never (USA)—
        Love Over Gold (FR) (Peintre Celebre (USA)) (52000) **Mr J Shack & Mr G Barnard**
100 B c 13/3 Lethal Force (IRE)—Malilla (IRE) (Red Clubs (IRE)) **Clive Cox Racing Ltd**
101 B c 22/2 Zebedee—Miss Smilla (Red Ransom (USA)) (26666) **New Syndicate**
102 **NOT OFTEN WRONG (IRE),** b f 5/5 Lethal Force (IRE)—Hip (Pivotal) (21163) **Paul & Clare Rooney**
103 B f 5/3 Bated Breath—Park Melody (IRE) (Refuse To Bend (IRE)) (22857) **Mr Peter Ridgers**
104 Ch f 29/2 Showcasing—Perfect Star (Act One) **Mildmay Racing**
105 B f 27/3 Showcasing—Place In My Heart (Compton Place) **The Hot To Trot Syndicate**
106 B c 2/3 Lethal Force (IRE)—Poetic Dancer (Byron) **Mr Alan G. Craddock**
107 **POUR ME A DRINK,** ch c 27/3 Nathaniel (IRE)—
        Euroceleb (IRE) (Peintre Celebre (USA)) (26000) **Paul & Clare Rooney**
108 **QUICK ON THE DRAW (IRE),** b f 26/2 Charm Spirit (IRE)—
        Olympic Medal (Nayef (USA)) (22792) **Simon Hope & Jonathan Shack**
109 B c 13/1 Lope de Vega (IRE)—Redoutable (IRE) (Invincible Spirit (IRE)) (50000) **Mr Alan Spence**
110 **REGAL AMBITION,** ch f 27/1 Pivotal—Regal Salute (Medicean) **Cheveley Park Stud**
111 B f 6/2 Lethal Force (IRE)—Sadaharu (FR) (Dansili) (19047) **Kennett Valley Thoroughbreds VI**
112 B f 24/1 Nathaniel (IRE)—Scent of Roses (IRE) (Invincible Spirit (IRE)) (36630) **Mr S. Hope & Mr S. Barrow**
113 B c 15/4 Dark Angel (IRE)—Secrets Away (IRE) (Refuse To Bend (IRE)) (130000) **Mr Alan Spence**
114 Br c 7/3 Zebedee—Silk Fan (IRE) (Unfuwain (USA)) (90476) **Miss J. Deadman & Mr S. Barrow**
115 Gr c 18/3 Lethal Force (IRE)—Soar (Danzero (AUS)) (85000) **AlMohamediya Racing**
116 B c 2/4 Showcasing—Starfly (IRE) (Invincible Spirit (IRE)) (187220) **Mr Malik L. Al Basti**
117 B c 2/4 Xtension (IRE)—Subtle Affair (IRE) (Barathea (IRE)) (56980) **Mr Li Fung Luck**
118 B f 26/3 Es Que Love (IRE)—Tallassee (Indian Ridge) (9523) **Dan Tunmore & GB Horseracing Services**
119 B c 26/1 Poet's Voice—Three Sugars (AUS) (Starcraft (NZ)) (58000) **Olivia Hoare & Simon de Zoete**
120 B f 13/4 Garswood—Wedding Party (Oasis Dream) **Apple Tree Stud**
121 B c 3/3 Bated Breath—Welsh Anthem (Singspiel (IRE)) (48840) **Mr Malik L. Al Basti**
122 B f 10/3 Bungle Inthejungle—Witnessed (Authorized (IRE)) (44769) **Mr S. Barrow & Mr S. Hope**
123 B c 9/4 Foxwedge (AUS)—Woolfall Rose (Generous (IRE)) (6666) **New Syndicate**

Other Owners: Mr W. P. Aitkenhead, Sheikh N. M. H. Al Khalifa, Sheikh N. Al Khalifa, Mr Peter Alderson, Miss Barbara Allen, BA Racing, G. M. Barnard, Mr Stephen W. Barrow, Mr A. Bentali, Mr Paul Blaydon, Mr D. J. Burke, Mrs Valda Burke, Mrs J. Dermot Cantillon, Mr D. E. Cash, Mrs J. Cash, Mr D. H. Caslon, Mr D. B. Clark, Miss Julie Deadman, Dr Bridget Drew & Partners, Miss Pippa Drew, Dr Bridget Drew, Mr N. R. R. Drew, Mr P. J. Dunkley, Mrs Denise Dunkley, Mr P. Grimes, Mr and Mrs P. Hargreaves, Mrs R. J. Hargreaves, Mr P. K. Hargreaves, Mr C. J. Harper, Mr P. Harper, Mr Geoff Hill, Mr S. Hill, Mr S. R. Hope, Mr R. S. Hoskins, Mr D. J. Keast, Mrs Sabina Kelly, Mr Richard Levin, L. Lillingston, Mr Martin McHale, Mildmay Racing, Mrs M. E. Morgan, P. H. Morgan, Mr Aiden Murphy, Mr Nicolas Patsalides, Mr Phil Robinson, Mr N. J. F. Robinson, Mrs C. Rooney, Mr P. A. Rooney, Mrs Susan Scargill, Mr P. J. Scargill, J. Shack, Mrs M. E. Slade, Tim Syder, The Hot To Trot Syndicate, Mrs K. M. Thomas, Mr J. T. Thomas, Mr D. Tunmore, Mr P. J. Turner, Mr Nigel Wagland, Mr M. Weinfeld, Mrs Diana L. Whateley.

Jockey (flat): Sam Hitchcott, Adam Kirby. **Apprentice:** Amelia Glass.

115 **MR TONY COYLE, Norton**
Postal: **Long Row Stables, Beverley Road, Norton, Malton, North Yorkshire, YO17 9PJ**
Contacts: MOBILE **(07976) 621425**
E-MAIL tonycoyleracing@hotmail.co.uk

1 **CALLALOO,** 4, ch f Rip Van Winkle (IRE)—In The Soup (USA) **Miss V. L. Wood**
2 **CANDELISA (IRE),** 5, br g Dream Ahead (USA)—Vasilia **Gap Personnel Franchises Limited**
3 **CASPIAN PRINCE (IRE),** 9, ch g Dylan Thomas (IRE)—Crystal Gaze (IRE) **Mr S. Louch**
4 **CORNWALLVILLE (IRE),** 6, ch h Makfi—Morinqua (IRE) **Mr S. Louch**
5 **COROBEREE (IRE),** 5, b g Dansili—Cabaret (IRE) **Craig Buckingham & Tony Coyle**

MR TONY COYLE - Continued

6 **EXCELLENT WORLD (IRE)**, 5, b m Excellent Art—Granny Kelly (USA) **Mr A. C. Coyle**
7 **HAROON (IRE)**, 4, ch c Lope de Vega (IRE)—Hazarista (IRE) **Mr S. Louch**
8 **LITTLE PIPPIN**, 5, b m Sir Percy—Lady Le Quesne (IRE) **Mr A. C. Coyle**
9 **MAUREB (IRE)**, 6, br m Excellent Art—Almost Blue (USA) **Gap Personnel & Tony Coyle**
10 **MICHELE STROGOFF**, 5, b g Aqlaam—Maschera d'oro **Mr S. Louch**
11 **NEWGATE DUCHESS**, 4, b f Haafhd—Arctic Queen **W. P. S. Johnson**
12 **NEWGATE SIOUX**, 4, b f Sleeping Indian—Rio's Girl **W. P. S. Johnson**
13 **TAN**, 4, b g Aqlaam—Sunburnt **Mr S. Louch**
14 **THATCHERITE (IRE)**, 10, gr g Verglas (IRE)—Damiana (IRE) **Mr Brian Kerr & Mr Tony Coyle**
15 **TOWN CHARTER (USA)**, 4, gr c Lonhro (AUS)—Summer Fete (IRE) **The Renaissance Partnership**
16 **UNOBTAINABLE**, 4, b f Malinas (GER)—Sharwakom (IRE) **Mr A. C. Coyle**
17 **WISHMAKER**, 4, b g Raven's Pass (USA)—Wedding March (IRE) **Mr C. Buckingham**
18 **ZAPPER CASS (FR)**, 5, b br g Elusive City (USA)—Moonlight Cass (USA) **Mr S. Louch**

THREE-YEAR-OLDS

19 **CUM SPIRO SPERO (IRE)**, ch f Casamento (IRE)—Bon Ton Roulet **Mr A. C. Coyle**
20 **EAST WIND**, b f Dick Turpin (IRE)—Angel Rays **Heather Raw & Tony Coyle**
21 **SHADES OF MIST**, b g Lilbourne Lad (IRE)—Talqaa **Mr C. Buckingham**
22 Ch f Malinas (GER)—Sharwakom (IRE) **Mr A. C. Coyle**

TWO-YEAR-OLDS

23 Br f 17/3 Canford Cliffs (IRE)—Almost Blue (USA) (Mr Greeley (USA)) (9523)
24 B c 10/4 Harbour Watch (IRE)—Cesseras (IRE) (Cape Cross (IRE)) (7326)
25 Ch f 6/3 Dragon Pulse (IRE)—Dreamaway (IRE) (Oasis Dream) (22792) **Mr C. Buckingham**
26 B f 16/3 Swiss Spirit—Hasten (USA) (Lear Fan (USA)) (9523)
27 B f 12/3 Dandy Man (IRE)—Krynica (USA) (Danzig (USA)) (7732)
28 Ch c 16/2 Zoffany (IRE)—Looker (Barathea (IRE)) (6512)
29 B c 18/3 Lilbourne Lad (IRE)—Maid To Order (IRE) (Zafonic (USA)) (4883) **Mr C. Buckingham**
30 B c 8/3 Pastoral Pursuits—My Pretty Girl (Arakan (USA)) (9523) **Morecool Racing**
31 B f 19/3 Sir Percy—Shirocco Passion (Shirocco (GER)) **P. D. Smith Holdings Ltd**
32 B f 17/3 Dick Turpin (IRE)—Tarneem (USA) (Zilzal (USA))

Other Owners: Mr D. F. L. Bishop, Mr S. Bland, Mr M. Kay, Mr B. Kerr, Mrs H. B. Raw, Mr M. Sykes.

Jockey (flat): Barry McHugh. **Amateur:** Miss Harriet Dukes.

 MR RAY CRAGGS, Sedgefield
Postal: **East Close Farm, Sedgefield, Stockton-On-Tees, Cleveland, TS21 3HW**
Contacts: **PHONE (01740) 620239 FAX (01740) 623476**

1 **AMOURI CHIEF**, 4, b g Sleeping Indian—Tour d'amour (IRE) **R. Craggs**
2 **CORAL QUEEN**, 7, b m Desideratum—Queen's Lodge (IRE) **R. Craggs**
3 **FLEURTILLE**, 9, b m Tillerman—Miss Fleurie **R. Craggs**
4 **GALLEY GREY (IRE)**, 7, gr m Great Palm (USA)—Sabi Sand **R. Craggs**
5 **PARK HOUSE**, 9, b g Tillerman—Rasin Luck **R. Craggs**
6 **TARA TIARA**, 6, b m Kayf Tara—Royal Roxy (IRE) **R. Craggs**

THREE-YEAR-OLDS

7 **AMOURI GLEAM**, b f Arabian Gleam—Tour d'amour (IRE) **R. Craggs**

Assistant Trainer: Miss J N Craggs

---

117 **MR PETER CRATE, Newdigate**
Postal: **Springfield Farm, Parkgate Road, Newdigate, Dorking, Surrey, RH5 5DZ**
Contacts: **MOBILE (07775) 821560**
E-MAIL peterdcrate@jandjfranks.com

1 **SANDFRANKSKIPSGO**, 9, ch g Piccolo—Alhuloof (USA) **P. D. Crate**

MR PETER CRATE - Continued

THREE-YEAR-OLDS

  2 B f Foxwedge (AUS)—Alhufoof (USA) **P. D. Crate**

Jockey (flat): Shane Kelly. **Amateur:** Mr George Crate.

---

118 **MR SIMON CRISFORD, Newmarket**
Postal: **Kremlin House Stables, Fordham Road, Newmarket, Suffolk, CB8 7AQ**
Contacts: **PHONE (01638) 662661**
E-MAIL office@crisfordracing.com Instagram: crisford_racing Twitter: @crisfordracing

  1 AFRICAN RIDE, 4, b c Candy Ride (ARG)—Paiota Falls (USA)
  2 ARCHETYPE (FR), 4, b br c Le Havre (IRE)—Angel Rose (IRE)
  3 CELEBRATION DAY (IRE), 5, b g Raven's Pass (USA)—Bunting
  4 CENTURY DREAM (IRE), 4, b c Cape Cross (IRE)—Salacia (IRE)
  5 EAGLE CREEK (IRE), 4, b g Raven's Pass (USA)—Blue Angel (IRE)
  6 FIRST SELECTION (SPA), 5, b g Diktat—Villa Sonata
  7 MAAKAASIB, 4, b g Equiano (FR)—Majoune (FR)
  8 MORDIN (IRE), 4, b g Invincible Spirit (IRE)—Bryanstown (IRE)
  9 MUTAWATHEA, 7, b g Exceed And Excel (AUS)—Esteemed Lady (IRE)
10 PERCY'S WORD, 4, b g Sir Percy—Laverre (IRE)
11 RED ENSIGN (IRE), 4, b g Dark Angel (IRE)—Rayon Rouge (IRE)
12 RODAINI (USA), 4, ch g Exchange Rate (USA)—Blessings Count (USA)
13 SAROOG, 4, b g Nathaniel (IRE)—Bahama Bay (GER)
14 STANHOPE, 4, b g Equiano (FR)—Nicoise (IRE)
15 TIME TO BLOSSOM, 5, b m Cape Cross (IRE)—Time Over

THREE-YEAR-OLDS

16 B f Iffraaj—Abbagnato
17 AFFINA (IRE), b f Kodiac—Epistoliere (IRE)
18 AL AMIR, b c Frankel—Emirates Queen
19 AL OZZDI, b g Acclamation—Zibeling (IRE)
20 ALLEYFA (IRE), b f Shamardal (USA)—Hall Hee (IRE)
21 ALWASMIYA, b f Kyllachy—Miss Bunter
22 AWALII (FR), b c Dabirsim (FR)—Elusive Feeling (USA)
23 BOBBY K (IRE), br g Dabirsim (FR)—Shanjia (GER)
24 CAPE LIBERTY (IRE), b f Cape Cross (IRE)—Sharqawiyah
25 CITY LIGHTS, ch c Cityscape—Tipsy Girl
26 CRAVING (IRE), b c Equiano (FR)—Pretty Bonnie
27 CUBAN FIRE (IRE), ch f Teofilo (IRE)—Sharareh
28 B c Dutch Art—Dare To Dream
29 DARK LIBERTY (IRE), gr f Dark Angel (IRE)—Extricate (IRE)
30 DARK ROSE ANGEL (IRE), b f Dark Angel (IRE)—Roseraie (IRE)
31 ENTHAAR, ch c Sepoy (AUS)—Caledonia Princess
32 EYECATCHER (IRE), b g Camelot—For Joy
33 FANAN, ch g Iffraaj—Paradise Isle
34 FARD, b g Dutch Art—Rose Blossom
35 FOUZ, b f Iffraaj—Bronwen (IRE)
36 GLOBAL CONQUEROR, b c Dubawi (IRE)—Nargys (IRE)
37 HONEY MAN (IRE), ch c Dawn Approach (IRE)—Whisp (GER)
38 HOW FAR (IRE), b c Kodiac—Akuna Magic (IRE)
39 IRON DOVE (IRE), gr f Dark Angel (IRE)—I'm So Glad
40 JADEYRA, b br f Dubawi (IRE)—Modeyra
41 JATHI (IRE), b br c Lawman (FR)—Manieree (IRE)
42 Ch g Teofilo (IRE)—Lady Zonda
43 MAHFOODH, b c Invincible Spirit (IRE)—Scarborough Fair
44 MATCH MAKER (IRE), b c Declaration of War (USA)—I'm In Love (USA)
45 MOVED (IRE), ch c Iffraaj—Amber Romance (IRE)
46 MUTADAAWEL (IRE), b g Invincible Spirit (IRE)—Elshabakiya (IRE)
47 MUTAFANI, b c Exceed And Excel (AUS)—Hokkaido
48 NASQ (IRE), b f Teofilo (IRE)—Eldalil
49 NAUTICAL MILE (IRE), b g Sir Prancealot (IRE)—Three Knots (IRE)
50 NOBLEMAN'S NEST, br c Poet's Voice—Tamzin
51 OSTILIO, ch c New Approach (IRE)—Reem Three

MR SIMON CRISFORD - Continued

52 **PERSIAN SUN**, b c Dansili—Khor Sheed
53 **POINT OF HONOUR (IRE)**, b g Lope de Vega (IRE)—Shamayel
54 **PRIDE'S GOLD (USA)**, b f Animal Kingdom (USA)—Royal Order (USA)
55 B f Cacique (IRE)—Quiza Quiza Quiza
56 **RECONCILE (IRE)**, b g Kodiac—Solace (USA)
57 **RED MIST**, b c Frankel—Red Dune (IRE)
58 **REGAL DIRECTOR (IRE)**, b c New Approach (IRE)—Dubai Queen (USA)
59 **REVOLUTIONARY MAN (IRE)**, b c Exceed And Excel (AUS)—Bint Almukhtar (IRE)
60 **ROMAANA**, b f Iffraaj—Baheeja
61 **ROSE SAPPHIRE (USA)**, ch f Congrats (USA)—Lillybuster (USA)
62 **SAJANJL**, ch f Iffraaj—Soraaya (IRE)
63 **SHAMLAHAR**, b f Shamardal (USA)—Miss Lahar
64 **SHARP SUITED**, b c Dansili—Appearance
65 **SHAWAAF AL NIJOOM (IRE)**, b c Sea The Stars (IRE)—Kithonia (FR)
66 **SHIKOBA (IRE)**, b f Kodiac—Shoshoni Wind
67 **SHREWD APPROACH (IRE)**, ch f Dawn Approach (IRE)—Al Sharood
68 **SIMPLE THOUGHT (IRE)**, b f Teofilo (IRE)—Punita (USA)
69 **SMART CHAMPION**, b c Teofilo (IRE)—Soryah (IRE)
70 **SUN HAT (IRE)**, ch f Helmet (AUS)—Bright Water
71 **VOW OF PRESENCE**, b g Showcasing—Your Word
72 **WAZIN**, b f Dutch Art—Azameera (IRE)
73 **WE KNOW (IRE)**, b c Teofilo (IRE)—Yellow Rosebud (IRE)
74 **WELL SUITED (IRE)**, ch c Dandy Man (IRE)—Dame d'honneur (IRE)

TWO-YEAR-OLDS

75 **AKWAN (IRE)**, b c 5/5 Camacho—Saytara (IRE) (Nayef (USA)) (45000)
76 **AL MORTAJAZ (FR)**, b c 25/4 Camacho—Danse En Soiree (USA) (Cat Thief (USA)) (28000)
77 B f 15/1 Dark Angel (IRE)—Angelic Air (Oasis Dream) (60000)
78 Ch c 29/2 Dawn Approach (IRE)—Bint Almukhtar (IRE) (Halling (USA))
79 Ch f 19/4 Kyllachy—Bravo (Indian Charlie (USA)) (18000)
80 B c 20/5 Cape Cross (IRE)—Bright Water (Refuse To Bend (IRE))
81 B f 11/4 Farhh—Bronwen (IRE) (King's Best (USA))
82 **BUNIANN (IRE)**, b c 7/4 Tamayuz—Darajaat (USA) (Elusive Quality (USA))
83 B c 30/1 Cape Cross (IRE)—Buntingford (IRE) (Manduro (GER))
84 B c 28/1 Kingman—Cubanita (Selkirk (USA)) (40700)
85 Gr f 9/2 Mukhadram—Deire Na Sli (IRE) (Aussie Rules (USA)) (20000)
86 B f 9/2 Shamardal (USA)—Dreaming Beauty (Oasis Dream)
87 B f 7/3 Invincible Spirit (IRE)—Dubai Queen (USA) (Kingmambo (USA))
88 **EBBRAAM**, b f 9/3 Teofilo (IRE)—Oojooba (Monsun (GER))
89 B c 18/2 Pivotal—Fashion Line (Cape Cross (IRE))
90 Ch c 29/2 Lope de Vega (IRE)—Harem Lady (FR) (Teofilo (IRE)) (179080)
91 B c 3/4 Dansili—I Am Beautiful (IRE) (Rip Van Winkle (IRE)) (340000)
92 **JASH (IRE)**, b c 18/3 Kodiac—Miss Azeza (Dutch Art) (185000)
93 B f 3/3 Shamardal (USA)—Jathabah (IRE) (Singspiel (IRE))
94 B c 27/2 Dubawi (IRE)—Joys of Spring (IRE) (Invincible Spirit (IRE))
95 B c 25/4 New Approach (IRE)—Lady Zonda (Lion Cavern (USA))
96 Ch f 25/1 Teofilo (IRE)—Local Spirit (USA) (Lion Cavern (USA))
97 **MAAMORA (IRE)**, b f 25/1 Dubawi (IRE)—Zoowraa (Azamour (IRE))
98 **MANNAAL (IRE)**, b f 1/3 Dubawi (IRE)—Soraaya (IRE) (Elnadim (USA))
99 **MANNGUY**, b c 17/2 Oasis Dream—Galaxy Highflyer (Galileo (IRE)) (280000)
100 B c 7/3 Pivotal—Masarah (IRE) (Cape Cross (IRE))
101 B c 3/4 Cape Cross (IRE)—Matauri Pearl (IRE) (Hurricane Run (IRE)) (475000)
102 B c 2/3 Alhebayeb (IRE)—Mistress of Rome (Holy Roman Emperor (IRE)) (52380)
103 **MOFAAJI**, ch c 4/4 Animal Kingdom (USA)—My Dubai (IRE) (Dubai Millennium)
104 B f 9/5 Quality Road (USA)—Mufajaah (USA) (Tapit (USA))
105 **NEESAAN**, b f 30/3 New Approach (IRE)—Red Dune (IRE) (Red Ransom (USA))
106 B f 7/3 Farhh—Pencarrow (Green Desert (USA))
107 B f 4/2 Shamardal (USA)—Prime Run (Dansili)
108 B f 3/4 Dubawi (IRE)—Reem Three (Mark of Esteem (IRE))
109 **SALAD DAYS (FR)**, gr c 5/3 Dalakhani (IRE)—Naive (IRE) (Nayef (USA)) (13024)
110 Ch f 3/4 No Nay Never (USA)—Saturn Girl (IRE) (Danehill Dancer (IRE))
111 Ch f 12/2 Exceed And Excel (AUS)—Shama's Crown (IRE) (New Approach (IRE))
112 B c 17/4 Authorized (IRE)—Soryah (IRE) (Shamardal (USA))
113 Ch f 24/3 More Than Ready (USA)—Tabreed (Sakhee (USA)) (65120)
114 B c 25/4 Dawn Approach (IRE)—Tea Cup (Danehill Dancer (IRE)) (50000)

MR SIMON CRISFORD - Continued

115 B c 21/2 Cape Cross (IRE)—Trikala (IRE) (High Chaparral (IRE)) (32000)
116 Ch c 1/2 Poet's Voice—Umneyati (Iffraaj) (50000)
117 **WALLAA,** b f 22/4 Dawn Approach (IRE)—Shuhra (IRE) (Marju (IRE))
118 B f 4/4 Dubawi (IRE)—Zeeba (IRE) (Barathea (IRE))

---

119 | **MR GAVIN CROMWELL, Co. Meath**
Postal: **Danestown, Balrath, Navan, Co. Meath, Ireland**
Contacts: MOBILE (00353) 86 2693388
E-MAIL admin@gavincromwellracing.com WEBSITE www.gavincromwellracing.com

1 **A PLACE APART (IRE),** 4, b g Power—Simadartha (USA) **GBLOGBD Ltd**
2 **AS DE PIQUE (IRE),** 13, b g Woods of Windsor (USA)—Casheral **The Pique Syndicate**
3 **BENTHAM (IRE),** 4, b g Jeremy (USA)—Detonante (FR) **Brendan Higgins, Conor Irwin, Willie Murphy**
4 **BIDDY THE BOSS (IRE),** 5, b m Doyen (IRE)—Thiarnathoir (IRE) **Kilbrien's Syndicate**
5 **CALLTHEBARMAN (IRE),** 4, b g Lord Shanakill (USA)—African Scene (IRE) **Killian McDonnell**
6 **CHARLIE'S CHARM (IRE),** 6, b g Golan (IRE)—Ben's Turn (IRE) **The Pique Syndicate**
7 **CLASSICAL ROSE,** 6, b m Amadeus Wolf—Monaazalah (IRE) **Tony Cromwell**
8 4, B c Scorpion (IRE)—Clonleigh Lady (IRE) **John Keegan**
9 **CRESENDO (IRE),** 5, b g Vocalised (USA)—Rachida (IRE) **Gavin Cromwell Racing Club**
10 **DAMUT I'M OUT (IRE),** 8, b g Gamut (IRE)—Five Cents More (IRE) **Eoin Hughes**
11 **DEBURRAFIELD (IRE),** 5, b br g Kalanisi (IRE)—Santa's Girl (IRE) **Enda Kerley**
12 **EJAYTEEKAY,** 5, b m Big Bad Bob (IRE)—Lovely Dream (IRE) **Brian Poots**
13 **ELUSIVE IVY (IRE),** 8, b m Elusive City (USA)—Just Like Ivy (CAN) **Alymer Stud**
14 **ESPOIR D'ALLEN (FR),** 4, b g Voix du Nord (FR)—Quadanse (FR) **J. P. McManus**
15 **FAMOUS MILLY (IRE),** 4, b f Famous Name—Gilah (IRE) **Nigel Kirkwood**
16 **FUWAIRT (IRE),** 6, b g Arcano (IRE)—Safiya Song (IRE) **Kimberley Racing Syn.**
17 **GETAFLYER (IRE),** 5, b g Getaway (GER)—Knapping Princess (IRE) **P. McGuiness, Willie Murphy**
18 **GUNMAKER (IRE),** 4, b g Canford Cliffs (IRE)—Can Dance **Gibirish Syndicate**
19 **HIGHLAND FLING (IRE),** 6, br g Country Reel (USA)—High Fun (FR) **Eoin Hughes**
20 **JEREMYS FLAME (IRE),** 4, b f Jeremy (USA)—Supreme Beneficial (IRE) **Flushfarm Syndicate**
21 **KILLASSER BOY,** 5, b g Authorized (IRE)—Tidal **Gerry Blake**
22 **LADY ISCHIA (IRE),** 6, b m Getaway (GER)—Summer Flight (FR) **James O'Rourke**
23 **MURGAN,** 6, b g Galileo (IRE)—Approach **Sean Mac An Bhaird**
24 4, B f Milan—No Time For Tears (IRE) **Mr John Quinn**
25 **POLITICAL POLICY (IRE),** 7, b g Bushranger (IRE)—Alexander Express (IRE) **F. Lynch Snr**
26 **PROSPECTUS,** 5, b g Sakhee (USA)—Some Sunny Day **McAlpine Syndicate**
27 **RAZ DE MAREE (FR),** 13, ch g Shaanmer (IRE)—Diyala III (FR) **James Swan**
28 **SIEMPRE AMIGOS (IRE),** 5, gr m Fast Company (IRE)—Zamiyla (IRE) **M. Dunphy & Ian Reilly**
29 **SPADES ARE TRUMPS (IRE),** 5, b g Yeats (IRE)—Sway (FR) **J. P. McManus**

THREE-YEAR-OLDS

30 **AASLEAGH FAWN (IRE),** b f Kalanisi (IRE)—Aasleagh Lady (IRE) **M. Rowland**
31 B c Urban Poet (USA)—Eritrea **Keith Brazil**
32 **KNUCKLES MCGINTY,** ch c Helmet (AUS)—Sadowa Destination **Andrew Lynch**
33 **WAVEPOINT,** b g Swiss Spirit—Easy To Love (USA) **Alymer Stud**

TWO-YEAR-OLDS

34 B c 29/2 Garswood—Authoritative (Diktat) (8140) **Yard**

Other Owners: P. Bamford, Mr J. M. Binns, Mr W. D. Corless, Mr R. G. Fell, Mr M. P. Gibbens, Mrs J. M. Simcock, Mr D. M. I. Simcock, A. J. Stone.

Jockey (flat): Ronan Whelan. **Jockey (NH):** Ger Fox, Andrew Lynch. **Conditional:** Breen Kane.
Apprentice: Conor Heavey. **Amateur:** Mr Anthony Fox.

---

120 | **MR ANDREW CROOK, Leyburn**
Postal: **Ashgill Stables (Yard 2), Tupgill Park, Coverham, Middleham, North Yorkshire, DL8 4TJ**
Contacts: PHONE (01969) 640303 MOBILE (07764) 158899
E-MAIL andycrookracing@gmail.com WEBSITE www.andrewcrookracing.co.uk

1 **ALONG CAME THEO (IRE),** 8, b g Vertical Speed (FR)—Kachina (IRE) **The 100 Club**
2 **BAH LAMB,** 7, ch m Sakhee (USA)—Lucinda Lamb **Mrs D. S. Wilkinson**

MR ANDREW CROOK - Continued

3 **CRAKEHALL LAD (IRE)**, 7, ch g Manduro (GER)—My Uptown Girl **Mrs K. M. Savage**
4 **CYRANO STAR (FR)**, 6, gr g Martaline—Quezac du Boulay (FR) **Leeds Plywood & Doors Ltd**
5 **DISTURB**, 6, ch g Halling (USA)—Ataraxy **David Carter**
6 **DIZZY CHIEF**, 6, b m Erhaab (USA)—Dizzy Whizz **Miss M. Hodgson**
7 **DUDETTE**, 6, ch m Apple Tree (FR)—Whatagale **Dudettes Quartet**
8 **E SI SI MUOVE (IRE)**, 6, b g Galileo (IRE)—Queen of France (USA) **David Carter**
9 **EARLY BOY (FR)**, 7, b g Early March—Eclat de Rose (FR) **R. P. E. Berry**
10 **EMPORTEPARLAFOULE (FR)**, 4, gr g Smadoun (FR)—Sempiternelle (FR) **David Carter**
11 **IDEAL ANGEL (IRE)**, 4, b g Dark Angel (IRE)—Irishstone (IRE) **David Carter**
12 **JACARNO**, 6, ch g Lucarno (USA)—Sparkling Jewel **The 100 Club**
13 **JUST CALL ME JENNI**, 7, b m Alflora (IRE)—Fairlie **Miss M. Hodgson**
14 **K O KENNY**, 7, b g Apple Tree (FR)—Cool Island (IRE) **Mr Kevin Heilbron**
15 **LADY BABS**, 4, br f Malinas (GER)—Jontys'lass **Ashgill Stud**
16 **LISKEARD**, 6, b g Dansili—Quest To Peak (USA) **Hodgson & Looney**
17 **LORD FRANKLIN**, 9, ch g Iceman—Zell (IRE) **Jolly Boys Racing Club**
18 **RACEMAKER**, 4, b g Stimulation (IRE)—Sophies Heart **Mrs Helen Sinclair**
19 **ROBERTTOWN ROSE (IRE)**, 5, b m Milan—Windfola (FR) **Mrs Sj Beddis & Steven Padgett**
20 **SIGNIFY (FR)**, 5, b m Laveron—Signature (FR) **R. P. E. Berry**
21 **VENTUREPREDEMENTIA**, 7, b g Indian Danehill (IRE)—Sounds Familiar (IRE) **Elite Ladies Racing Club**
22 **YOREDOINGWELL (IRE)**, 5, b g Mount Nelson—Local Abbey (IRE) **The 100 Club**

THREE-YEAR-OLDS

23 B f Havana Gold (IRE)—Kisses For Me (IRE) **Andrew Crook**
24 **RED SEEKER**, ch g Red Jazz (USA)—Purepleasureseeker (IRE) **Mr Brian Valentine**

TWO-YEAR-OLDS

25 **JAGERBOND**, ch g 4/2 Monsieur Bond (IRE)—
Velvet Jaguar (Hurricane Run (IRE)) (5714) **Jolly Boys Racing Club**
26 **SAMBUCCA SPIRIT**, b g 27/2 Charm Spirit (IRE)—Hokkaido (Street Cry (IRE)) (3000) **Jolly Boys Racing Club**

Other Owners: Mrs Sally Archard, Mrs S. J. Beddis, Mr Carl Chapman, Mrs Rosie Donmall, Miss D. Gabbitas, Mr Wayne Henderson, Dr Kieran Looney, Mr S. J. Padgett, Mr R. Parks, Mrs Kath Savage, Ms Sandra Trewhitt, Mrs Margaret Wood, Mr Tom Wooldridge, Mrs Claudette Yarrow.

Assistant Trainer: Amy Crook

Jockey (flat): Kevin Stott. **Jockey (NH):** Henry Brooke. **Conditional:** Ross Turner. **Apprentice:** Phil Dennis.

---

121 MR LUCA CUMANI, Newmarket
Postal: **Bedford House Stables, Bury Road, Newmarket, Suffolk, CB8 7BX**
Contacts: **PHONE (01638) 665432 FAX (01638) 667160 MOBILE (07801) 225300**
E-MAIL luca@lucacumani.com WEBSITE www.lucacumani.com

1 **ALJEZEERA**, 4, b f Frankel—Dynaforce (USA) **Al Shaqab Racing UK Limited**
2 **ALWAYSANDFOREVER (IRE)**, 4, b f Teofilo (IRE)—
Deep Winter **Mr M.Tabor, Mrs John Magnier, Mr Derrick Smith**
3 **BUXTED DREAM (USA)**, 4, gr g Dream Ahead (USA)—America Nova (FR) **Buxted Partnership**
4 **CORTADO**, 4, bl c Pivotal—Contredanse (IRE) **Mr S. A. Stuckey**
5 **EL VIP (IRE)**, 5, b g Pivotal—Elle Danzig (GER) **Al Shaqab Racing UK Limited**
6 **GOD GIVEN**, 4, b f Nathaniel—Ever Rigg **St Albans Bloodstock Limited**
7 **GORGEOUS NOORA (IRE)**, 4, b f Raven's Pass (USA)—Aneedah (IRE) **Saleh Al Homaizi & Imad Al Sagar**
8 **HIGHFALUTING (IRE)**, 4, b g High Chaparral (IRE)—Walk On Water **Stilvi, Boorer, Booth**
9 **LA RAV (IRE)**, 4, b g Footstepsinthesand—Swift Acclaim (IRE) **Mr S. P. Capon**
10 **PLEASANT SURPRISE (IRE)**, 4, b g Mastercraftsman (IRE)—Ibiza Dream **Gerry Mordaunt & Partners**
11 **SHEMDA (IRE)**, 4, b f Dutch Art—Shamooda (IRE) **Mr P Stokes & Mr S Krase**
12 **STYLISH DANCER**, 4, b f Nathaniel—Hazy Dancer **Mr Michael & Mrs Michelle Morris**
13 **WARSAW ROAD (IRE)**, 4, ch g Zebedee—Warda **Ventura Racing 1 & Partners**

THREE-YEAR-OLDS

14 **ALEXANDRIA**, gr f Oasis Dream—Amarillo Starlight (IRE) **OTI Racing & Mrs L Cumani**
15 B f Fastnet Rock (AUS)—Ambria (GER) **E. I. Mack**
16 **ASHINGTON**, b g Canford Cliffs (IRE)—Kadoma **Bengough, Boorer, Booth, Stilvi**
17 **BESSIE WARFIELD**, b f Oasis Dream—Wallis **Fittocks Stud**
18 **COOLONGOLOOK**, b c Invincible Spirit (IRE)—Cascata (IRE) **Mr S. A. Stuckey**

MR LUCA CUMANI - Continued

19 **DRAP D'OR (FR)**, ch c Nathaniel (IRE)—Doggerbank (IRE) **Mr G. Schoeningh**
20 **DRILL**, b c Dansili—Pongee **Fittocks Stud**
21 **EDELLINE (IRE)**, b f Cape Cross (IRE)—Brigitta (IRE) **Mrs D. A. Tabor**
22 **FAIRLIGHT (IRE)**, b g Lope de Vega (IRE)—Flaming Song (IRE) **OTI Racing & Mrs L Cumani**
23 **FAREWELL TO YOU**, ch f Leroidesanimaux (BRZ)—You Too **Helena Springfield Ltd**
24 **FLORIA TOSCA (IRE)**, b f Shamardal (USA)—Islington (IRE) **Fittocks Stud**
25 **FOUR WHITE SOCKS**, ch f Lope de Vega (IRE)—Peppermint Green **Mr S. A. Stuckey**
26 **HARBOUR VIEW (FR)**, b c Le Havre (IRE)—Icky Woo **OTI Racing & Mrs L Cumani**
27 B f Shamardal (USA)—Kitty Wells **Mr Uyan Yap**
28 **MAYER**, b c Nathaniel (IRE)—Paisley **Fittocks Stud**
29 **MERSEYBEAT**, b f New Approach (IRE)—Hippy Hippy Shake **Helena Springfield Ltd**
30 **MSAIKAH (IRE)**, b f Galileo (IRE)—Light Quest (USA) **Al Shaqab Racing UK Limited**
31 **OUTLANE**, b f Camelot—Batik (IRE) **Aston House Stud**
32 **PINKSTER**, b f Nathaniel (IRE)—Puce **Newsells Park Stud Limited**
33 **PLENTIFUL**, ch c Makfi—Ever Rigg **St Albans Bloodstock Limited**
34 **PYRMONT**, b g High Chaparral (IRE)—Puzzling **OTI Racing & Mrs L Cumani**
35 **RECOLLECT**, b c Invincible Spirit (IRE)—Forgotten Dreams (IRE) **Fittocks Stud**
36 **SAVING GRACE**, b f Mastercraftsman (IRE)—Lady of Everest (IRE) **Fittocks Stud**
37 **SPIRIT OF BUXTED**, b c Equiano (FR)—London Welsh **Buxted Partnership**
38 **VALYRIAN**, b c Dansili—Victoire Finale **Mr S. A. Stuckey**
39 **WILSON (IRE)**, b g Born To Sea (IRE)—Alkhawarah (USA) **Stilvi, Boorer, Booth, Bengough**

TWO-YEAR-OLDS

40 B c 27/4 Cape Cross (IRE)—Allegheny Creek (IRE) (Teofilo (IRE)) (47000)
41 B c 2/3 Intello (GER)—Angelic Note (IRE) (Excellent Art) (60000) **Dahab Racing**
42 B br c 4/2 Oasis Dream—Astorgs Galaxy (Galileo (IRE)) (47000)
43 **AVENUE FOCH**, b c 2/3 Champs Elysees—Kindu (Pivotal) **Fittocks Stud**
44 **CAFTAN**, b gr f 21/3 Mount Nelson—Kassiyra (IRE) (Kendor (FR)) (22000) **Fittocks Stud**
45 B c 18/4 Dansili—Cascata (IRE) (Montjeu (IRE)) **Mr S. A. Stuckey**
46 B c 10/5 Showcasing—Dream Vision (USA) (Distant View (USA)) (80000)
47 **ERNEST ALDRICH**, b c 22/4 Oasis Dream—Wallis (King's Best (USA))
48 **FELIX**, ch c 27/3 Lope de Vega (IRE)—Luminance (IRE) (Danehill Dancer (IRE)) (32000) **Fittocks Stud**
49 B f 19/2 Sir Percy—Forest Express (AUS) (Kaaptive Edition (NZ)) (37000) **Jonathan Shack & Friends**
50 B f 28/2 Camelot—Gameday (Zamindar (USA)) **Mr P. Stokes & Partners**
51 **HIGH GLOSS**, b f 20/4 Invincible Spirit (IRE)—So Silk (Rainbow Quest (USA)) **Fittocks Stud & Mr A Bengough**
52 B f 11/5 Kingman—Hippy Hippy Shake (Danehill Dancer (IRE)) (180000) **Helena Springfield Ltd**
53 **HONFLEUR (IRE)**, ch f 15/5 Le Havre (IRE)—Galistic (IRE) (Galileo (IRE)) (72000) **Fittocks Stud**
54 B f 18/4 Dubawi (IRE)—Love Divine (Diesis) **Lordship Stud**
55 B f 20/4 Alhebayeb (IRE)—Mount Lavinia (IRE) (Montjeu (IRE)) (48000)
56 **PREJUDICE**, ch c 30/4 Dubawi (IRE)—
                            Ever Rigg (Dubai Destination (USA)) (525000) **St Albans Bloodstock Limited**
57 B c 16/2 Iffraaj—Represent (IRE) (Exceed And Excel (AUS)) (57000)
58 B c 4/5 Dark Angel (IRE)—Rougette (Red Ransom (USA)) (50000) **Dahab Racing**
59 Ch f 12/5 Australia—Sense of Style (USA) (Thunder Gulch (USA)) **Mr M Tabor**
60 **SWANSDOWN**, ch f 20/4 Dubawi (IRE)—Pongee (Barathea (IRE)) (210000) **Fittocks Stud**
61 B c 2/5 Dansili—Victoire Finale (Peintre Celebre (USA)) **Mr S. A. Stuckey**

Other Owners: Mrs Emma Agostini, Mr Paolo Agostini, Mr Imad Al-Sagar, Mr A. N. C. Bengough, Mr C. Bird, Mr Daniel Boorer, Mr P. Booth, Mrs Emma Capon, Mrs Luca Cumani, Mrs H. S. Ellingsen, Mr D. Graham, Mr Jim Hanifin, Mr T. Henderson, Mr Saleh Al Homaizi, Mr Scott D. Krase, Mrs John Magnier, Mr L. Marinopoulos, Mr G. C. Mordaunt, Mr M. Morris, Mrs Michelle Morris, Mr S. O'Donnell, O.T.I. Racing, Mrs J. Ruthven, Mr J. Shack, Mrs Angie Silver, Mr Derrick Smith, Mr Peter Stokes, Mr M. Tabor, Ms Sylvia Vrska, Mr M. Weinfeld, Mr N. J. Wingfield Digby.

Assistant Trainer: Freddie Eccles-Williams

---

122 **MR KEN CUNNINGHAM-BROWN, Stockbridge**
Postal: Danebury Place, Stockbridge, Hampshire, SO20 6JX
Contacts: **PHONE** (01264) 781061 **FAX** (01264) 781061 **MOBILE** (07802) 500059
E-MAIL kcb@danebury.co.uk

1 **ALLOFMELOVESALLOFU**, 4, ch g Sakhee's Secret—La Palma **Danebury Racing Stables**
2 **AYE AYE SKIPPER (IRE)**, 8, b g Captain Marvelous (IRE)—Queenfisher **Mr J. F. Pearl**
3 **BULLETPROOF (IRE)**, 12, b g Wareed (IRE)—Laura's Native (IRE) **Danebury Racing Stables & David Henery**
4 **DRAMATIC VOICE**, 5, ch m Poet's Voice—Darwinia (GER) **Mrs E. A. Bass**

MR KEN CUNNINGHAM-BROWN - Continued

5 **HALLINGHAM**, 8, b g Halling (USA)—In Luck **Mr D. F. Henery**
6 **INDIAN CHARLIE**, 6, b m Compton Place—Emerald Fire **Danebury Racing Stables**
7 **LOVING YOUR WORK**, 7, b g Royal Applause—Time Crystal (IRE) **Danebury Racing Stables**
8 **MISS GERONIMO**, 6, b m Hellvelyn—Churn Dat Butter (USA) **Danebury Racing David Henery John Pearl**
9 **RED TYCOON (IRE)**, 6, b g Acclamation—Rugged Up (IRE) **Mr D. F. Henery**
10 **SECRET STRIKER**, 6, ch m Sakhee's Secret—Silver Purse **Danebury Racing Stables & David Henery**
11 **SUFI**, 4, ch g Pivotal—Basanti (USA) **Mr J. F. Pearl**
12 **VINCENZO COCCOTTI (USA)**, 6, gr ro g Speightstown (USA)—Ocean Colors (USA) **Mr D. F. Henery**
13 **WASEEM FARIS (IRE)**, 9, b g Exceed And Excel (AUS)—Kissing Time **Danebury Racing Stables**

Other Owners: Mrs V. E. Cunningham-Brown, Mr K. Cunningham-Brown.

Assistant Trainer: Tony Charlton

Jockey (flat): Dane O'Neill. **Jockey (NH):** Tom Cannon.

---

123 MISS REBECCA CURTIS, Newport
Postal: **Fforest Farm, Newport, Pembrokeshire, SA42 0UG**
Contacts: **PHONE (01348) 811489 MOBILE (07970) 710690**
E-MAIL rebcurtis@hotmail.com

1 **ABSOLUTE POWER**, 7, b g Flemensfirth (USA)—Crystal Ballerina (IRE) **Mark Sherwood & Spencer Gammond**
2 **DROVERS LANE (IRE)**, 6, b g Oscar (IRE)—Minnie Turbo (IRE) **Hyde, Hill, Moran, Outhart & Curtis**
3 **GEORDIE DES CHAMPS (IRE)**, 7, br g Robin des Champs (FR)—Kilcoleman Lady (IRE) **Mr J. P. McManus**
4 **HIDDEN IMPACT (IRE)**, 7, br g Oscar (IRE)—Maiden Flight (IRE) **Hyde, Hill, Moran, Outhart & Curtis**
5 **IRISH CAVALIER (IRE)**, 9, gr g Aussie Rules (USA)—Tracker **Mr A. McIver**
6 **JESSIE WEBSTER (IRE)**, 9, b m Kayf Tara—Blueberry Bramble (IRE) **Miss R. Curtis**
7 **JOE FARRELL (IRE)**, 8, b g Presenting—Luck of The Deise (IRE) **M Sherwood, N Morris & R Curtis**
8 **JOUEUR BRESILIEN (FR)**, 6, b g Fuisse (FR)—Fille du Bresil (FR) **Inthewayboy Group**
9 **JUST A THOUGHT (IRE)**, 6, ch m Stowaway—Carrig Lucy (IRE) **Hyde, Outhart, Moran & Hill**
10 **LIBBY T VALANCE (IRE)**, 7, b m Scorpion (IRE)—Dipp In The Dark (IRE) **Mr A. McIver**
11 **LOCKER ROOM TALK (IRE)**, 5, b g Beneficial—Whistling Gypse (IRE) **Miss R. Curtis**
12 **MYSTICAL KNIGHT**, 9, b g Kayf Tara—Dark Diva **Mr J. P. McManus**
13 **NIGH OR NEVER (IRE)**, 4, b g Excelebration (IRE)—Nigh (IRE) **Miss R. Curtis**
14 **O'FAOLAINS BOY (IRE)**, 11, b g Oscar (IRE)—Lisa's Storm (IRE) **Hyde, Roddis, Outhart, Hill & Curtis**
15 **O'HANRAHAN BRIDGE (IRE)**, 6, b g Gold Well—Greenacre Mandalay (IRE) **Mr M. Kelly**
16 **ONE TERM (IRE)**, 11, b g Beneficial—One Edge (IRE) **Miss L Reid & Mr G Costelloe**
17 **PAUL (FR)**, 7, b g Boris de Deauville (FR)—Bartjack (FR) **Mr N. D. Morris**
18 **POTTERS CROSS**, 11, b g Alflora (IRE)—Teeno Nell **Conyers, O'Reilly, Roddis, Zeffman**
19 **RELENTLESS DREAMER (IRE)**, 9, br g Kayf Tara—Full of Elegance (FR) **Mr N. D. Morris**
20 **SUMMER NAME (IRE)**, 6, b g Duke of Marmalade (IRE)—Summer's Eve **Ramsden, Morecombe & JCM Retail**
21 **SUNSET SHOWDOWN (IRE)**, 5, b g Flemensfirth (USA)—Sunset Queen (IRE) **Mr J. P. McManus**
22 **THEGIRLFROMMILAN (IRE)**, 8, b m Milan—Legendsofthefall (IRE) **Conyers, O'Reilly, Roddis, Zeffman**

Other Owners: Mr J. Conyers, Mr G. Costelloe, Mr M. Davis, Fishlake Commercial Motors Ltd, Mr G. S. Gammond, Mr I. Glendenning, Mr. Hill, Mr R. Hyde, JCM Retail Equipment Ltd, Mr R. J. Line, Mr B. Merrett, Ms J. A. Moran, Mr R. H. W. Morecombe, Mr J. P O'Reilly, A. J. Outhart, Mrs L. E. Ramsden, Miss L. Reid, Mr N. M. Roddis, Mr M. A. Sherwood, Mr A. Spencer, D. C. Zeffman.

Assistant Trainer: Paul Sheldrake

---

124 MR THOMAS CUTHBERT, Brampton
Postal: **Woodlands, Cowranbridge, How Mill, Brampton, Cumbria, CA8 9LH**
Contacts: **PHONE (01228) 560822 FAX (01228) 560822 MOBILE (07747) 843344**
E-MAIL cuthbertracing@gmail.com

1 **RED FOREVER**, 7, ch g Major Cadeaux—Spindara (IRE) **T. A. K. Cuthbert**
2 **YAIR HILL (IRE)**, 10, b g Selkirk (USA)—Conspiracy **T. A. K. Cuthbert**

Assistant Trainer: Helen Cuthbert

Amateur: Miss H. Cuthbert.

125 MR PAUL D'ARCY, Newmarket
Postal: **Charnwood Stables, Hamilton Road, Newmarket, Suffolk, CB8 7JQ**
Contacts: **PHONE (01638) 662000 MOBILE (07768) 807653**
E-MAIL pauldarcyracingltd@gmail.com WEBSITE www.pauldarcyracing.com

1 CALEDONIAN GOLD, 5, b m Acclamation—Moonlight Rhapsody (IRE) **Dr J. S. Kinnear**
2 NOREENA, 4, b f Medicean—Nurai **Mr K. Snell**
3 SHADOW WARRIOR, 4, b g Born To Sea (IRE)—Dolcetto (IRE) **Mrs Jan Harris & Mrs M. Doyle**
4 SPRING LOADED (IRE), 6, gr g Zebedee—Nisriyna (IRE) **Rowley Racing**

THREE-YEAR-OLDS
5 ASHEENA, gr f Lethal Force (IRE)—Meddle **Mr K. Snell**
6 MISTY BREESE (IRE), b f Zebedee—Geordie Iris (IRE) **Rowley Racing**

TWO-YEAR-OLDS
7 B f 15/3 Poet's Voice—Meddle (Diktat) (15000) **Mr K. Snell**
8 ZEEBAD (IRE), gr c 18/4 Zebedee—Love Intrigue (IRE) (Marju (IRE)) (26862) **Mr P. W. D'Arcy**

Other Owners: Mr Paul D'Arcy, Mrs Sue D'Arcy, Mrs M. Doyle, Mrs Jan Harris.

Assistant Trainer: Sue D'Arcy

Apprentice: Oliver Daykin. Amateur: Mrs Rachel Wilson.

126 MR LUKE DACE, Billingshurst
Postal: **Copped Hall Farm and Stud, Okehurst House, Okehurst Lane, Billingshurst, West Sussex,
RH14 9HR**
Contacts: **FAX (01403) 612176 MOBILE (07949) 401085**
E-MAIL lukedace@yahoo.co.uk WEBSITE www.lukedace.co.uk

1 BELEAVE, 5, gr m Avonbridge—Grezie **R. L. Page**
2 RAVENOUS, 7, b g Raven's Pass (USA)—Supereva (IRE) **I Farminer,Hilary&C Barrett,Farminer Dev**
3 THE SECRETS OUT, 4, bl g Sakhee's Secret—Brooksby **Mr G. Collacott**

THREE-YEAR-OLDS
4 AIGLETTE, b f Foxwedge (AUS)—Falcon In Flight **R. L. Page**

Other Owners: Mrs H. A. Barrett, Mr C. Barrett, Farminer Developments Ltd, Mr I. E. J. Farminer.

Assistant Trainer: Mrs L Dace

Amateur: Mr J. Doe.

127 MR KEITH DALGLEISH, Carluke
Postal: **Belstane Racing Stables, Carluke, Lanarkshire, ML8 5HN**
Contacts: **PHONE (01555) 773335**
E-MAIL dalgleish.racing@outlook.com

1 ACKER BILK (IRE), 4, ch g Rip Van Winkle (IRE)—Portentous **Thats My Boys**
2 AMY BLAIR, 5, b g Captain Gerrard (IRE)—Shalal'or **Mr J. Fyffe**
3 ARTFUL ROGUE (IRE), 7, b g Excellent Art—Szabo (IRE) **Mr R. McCulloch**
4 BUTOOLAT, 4, b f Oasis Dream—Handassa **Mr J. P. Hayes**
5 CE LA VIE, 4, ch f Dutch Art—Chase The Lady (USA) **Weldspec Glasgow Limited**
6 CHANCEANOTHERFIVE (IRE), 6, b g Dubai Destination (USA)—Ryhall (IRE) **Mr R. McCulloch**
7 CHOOKIE ROYALE, 10, ch g Monsieur Bond (IRE)—Lady of Windsor (IRE) **Raeburn Brick Limited**
8 CLIFF BAY (IRE), 4, b g Elzaam (AUS)—Lost Highway (IRE) **D. L. McKenzie**
9 COBALTY ISLE (IRE), 4, b g Kodiac—Shamarlane **Middleham Park Racing CIII**
10 COMPRISE, 4, b g Pivotal—Constitute (USA) **Weldspec Glasgow Limited**
11 CORTON LAD, 8, b g Refuse To Bend (IRE)—Kelucia (IRE) **Mr J. J. Hutton**
12 CRAZY TORNADO (IRE), 5, b g Big Bad Bob—All Day (CHI) **Mr J. K. McGarrity**
13 DARK DEFENDER, 5, b g Pastoral Pursuits—Oh So Saucy **Prestige Thoroughbred Racing**
14 DARK PROFIT (IRE), 6, gr g Dark Angel (IRE)—Goldthroat (IRE) **Weldspec Glasgow Limited**
15 DEFINITELY MAYBE (IRE), 4, b g Elusive Quality (USA)—Ebony Street (USA) **Weldspec Glasgow Limited**
16 DELEGATE, 8, ch g Robin des Champs (FR)—As You Leave (FR) **The Gilbert's & Mr Campbell**

MR KEITH DALGLEISH - Continued

17 **DESERT POINT (FR)**, 6, b g Le Havre (IRE)—Bonne Mere (FR) **Straightline Bloodstock**
18 **DIRTY RANDY (IRE)**, 4, b g Notnowcato—Regal Fairy (IRE) **Straightline Bloodstock**
19 **EDGAR BALTHAZAR**, 6, b g Pastoral Pursuits—Assistacat (IRE) **Middleham Park Racing XXII**
20 **EEZ EH (IRE)**, 5, b g Jeremy (USA)—Step With Style (USA) **Weldspec Glasgow Limited**
21 **EL HOMBRE**, 4, ch c Camacho—Nigella **Weldspec Glasgow Limited**
22 **ENEKO (FR)**, 4, bl g Laverock (IRE)—Kaline Collonges (FR) **Straightline Bloodstock**
23 **EURO NIGHTMARE (IRE)**, 4, b f Kodiac—Kilakey (IRE) **J. S. Morrison**
24 **EYE OF THE STORM (IRE)**, 8, ch g Galileo (IRE)—Mohican Princess **J. S. Morrison**
25 **EYREBORN (IRE)**, 4, b f Born To Sea (IRE)—Eyrecourt (IRE) **Mr K. W. Dalgleish**
26 **FALCON'S FIRE (IRE)**, 5, ch g Thewayyouare (USA)—Matadora (USA) **Mr R. Docherty**
27 **FOREVER A LADY (IRE)**, 5, b m Dark Angel (IRE)—Unicamp **Mr J. K. McGarrity**
28 **FREDERIC**, 7, b g Zamindar (USA)—Frangy **Mr & Mrs Paul & Clare Rooney**
29 **GLENGARRY**, 5, b g Monsieur Bond (IRE)—Lady McBeth (IRE) **Mrs J. M. MacPherson**
30 **GOLIATH (IRE)**, 6, br g Golan (IRE)—Lady Shanakill (IRE) **Adamson, Bell, Etheridge**
31 **HARDROCK DAVIS (FR)**, 7, b br g Saint des Saints (FR)—Trumpet Davis (FR)
32 **I'M TO BLAME (IRE)**, 5, b g Winged Love (IRE)—Swap Shop (IRE) **Mr & Mrs Paul & Clare Rooney**
33 **INGLORIOUS**, 4, gr g Kheleyf (USA)—Impulsive Decision (IRE) **Weldspec Glasgow Limited**
34 **JACK BLANE**, 4, br g Kheleyf (USA)—Blane Water (USA) **Mr R. Docherty**
35 **JACOB BLACK**, 7, b g Amadeus Wolf—First Eclipse (IRE) **Mr D. C. Moat**
36 **KENSINGTON STAR**, 5, b g Pivotal—Wild Silk **Straightline Bloodstock**
37 **LADY MOLLY (IRE)**, 4, b f Kodiac—Beth **Ken McGarrity & Partner**
38 **LEONIDAS (IRE)**, 4, b g Dalakhani (IRE)—Marque Royale **J. S. Morrison**
39 **LOMU (IRE)**, 4, ch g Dandy Man (IRE)—Miss Me **S. J. Macdonald**
40 **MAC N CHEESE (IRE)**, 8, b g Milan—Fox Burrow (IRE) **Straightline Bloodstock**
41 **MAULESDEN MAY (IRE)**, 5, b m Dark Angel (IRE)—Jemima's Art **The County Set (Two)**
42 **MIRSAALE**, 8, ch g Sir Percy—String Quartet (IRE) **Mr J. Fyffe**
43 4, B g Oscar (IRE)—Mission Hills **Mr J. C. Higgins**
44 **MISTER SHOWMAN**, 5, b g Showcasing—Theatre Royal **Richard & Katherine Gilbert**
45 **MIXBOY (FR)**, 8, gr g Fragrant Mix (FR)—Leston Girl (FR) **Mr & Mrs Paul & Clare Rooney**
46 **MYSTIKANA**, 5, ch m Sir Percy—Peintre d'argent (IRE) **Mr J. Kelly**
47 **NEW ABBEY ANGEL (IRE)**, 5, gr g Dark Angel (IRE)—Alinda (IRE) **Mr A. G. MacLennan**
48 **NICEANDEASY (IRE)**, 5, b g Kalanisi (IRE)—High Priestess (IRE) **Straightline Bloodstock**
49 **PADDYPLEX**, 5, b g Multiplex—Turtle Bay **G & J Park**
50 **PICTURE PAINTER (IRE)**, 5, gr g Zoffany (IRE)—Sisceal **Thats My Boys**
51 **PLAY WITH ME**, 4, ch f Captain Gerrard (IRE)—Plead (FR) **Derrick Mossop & Partner**
52 **QASR**, 4, b c Exceleration (IRE)—Blur **Weldspec Glasgow Limited**
53 **QUIET MOMENT (IRE)**, 4, b f Dandy Man (IRE)—Easee On (IRE) **We're Electric**
54 **RAINING STARS**, 4, b g Sea The Stars (IRE)—Sayyedati Symphony (USA) **Thats My Boys**
55 **REIMAGINE (IRE)**, 4, br g Teofilo (IRE)—Aguinaga (IRE)
56 **RITA'S MAN (IRE)**, 4, b c Lawman (FR)—French Fern (IRE) **Middleham Park Racing XX**
57 **ROCK N ROLLA (IRE)**, 4, ch g Intikhab (USA)—Fantastic Opinion (IRE) **Weldspec Glasgow Limited**
58 **SAINT EQUIANO**, 4, b g Equiano (FR)—St Athan **Mr & Mrs Paul & Clare Rooney**
59 **SCARPACH**, 4, b g Pastoral Pursuits—Bijan (IRE) **Mr A. G. MacLennan**
60 **SEBASTIAN'S WISH (IRE)**, 5, b g Aqlaam—Swish (GER) **Two Goldfish & A Balloon**
61 **SENOR LOMBARDY (IRE)**, 5, b g Milan—Killoughey Babe (IRE) **Straightline Bloodstock**
62 **SILVER CONCORDE**, 10, b g Dansili—Sacred Pearl (IRE) **Straightline Bloodstock**
63 **SOMNAMBULIST**, 4, b g Rip Van Winkle (IRE)—Sister Moonshine **The Sleepwalkers**
64 **SOUND ADVICE**, 9, b g Echo of Light—Flylowflylong (IRE) **A. R. M. Galbraith**
65 **SPORTING PRESS (IRE)**, 5, b g Flemensfirth (USA)—Rudy Renata (IRE)
66 **STARPLEX**, 8, b g Multiplex—Turtle Bay **G & J Park**
67 **TAKE THE HIGH ROAD**, 4, b g Kyllachy—China Tea (USA) **Straightline Bloodstock**
68 **TAXMEIFYOUCAN (IRE)**, 4, b g Beat Hollow—Accounting **Straightline Bloodstock**
69 **TECTONIC (IRE)**, 9, b g Dylan Thomas (IRE)—Pine Chip (USA) **Mrs L. A. Ogilvie**
70 **TOMMY DOCC (IRE)**, 6, b g Thewayyouare (USA)—Liturgy (IRE) **Mr R. Docherty**
71 **UPTOWN FUNK (IRE)**, 4, b g Galileo (IRE)—All's Forgotten (USA) **Mr J. Fyffe**
72 **WAR DEPARTMENT (IRE)**, 5, b g Frozen Power (IRE)—On My Kness (FR) **Weldspec Glasgow Limited**
73 **WHAT'S THE STORY**, 4, b c Harbour Watch (IRE)—Spring Fashion (IRE) **Weldspec Glasgow Limited**
74 **WHATSTHEMESSAGE (IRE)**, 4, b f Bushranger (IRE)—Fatwa (IRE) **Mr R. Docherty**
75 **ZORAVAN (USA)**, 5, ch g More Than Ready (USA)—Zaralanta (IRE) **Ontoawinner 8 & Partner**

THREE-YEAR-OLDS

76 **ALABANZA**, b g Big Bad Bob (IRE)—Tahfeez (IRE) **Mr R. C. Hyndman**
77 **ALRIGHT SUNSHINE (IRE)**, b c Casamento (IRE)—Miss Gibraltar **Mr & Mrs Paul & Clare Rooney**
78 **BROKEN WINGS (IRE)**, b f Canford Cliffs (IRE)—Moss Top (IRE) **Middleham Park Racing LXXVII**
79 Ch f Sir Percy—Camp Fire (IRE) **Straightline Bloodstock**

MR KEITH DALGLEISH - Continued

80 **CANADIAN GEORGE (FR)**, b c George Vancouver (USA)—Connaissance (IRE) **Middleham Park Racing CVII**
81 **CHARNIERE**, b g Pivotal—Miss Corniche **Straightline Bloodstock**
82 **CHE BELLA (IRE)**, gr f Holy Roman Emperor (IRE)—Satwa Ruby (FR) **Weldspec Glasgow Limited**
83 **CHEESEANDPICKLE**, ch f Helmet (AUS)—Branston Gem **Equus I**
84 **CHOOKIE DUNEDIN**, b c Epaulette (AUS)—Lady of Windsor (IRE) **Raeburn Brick Limited**
85 **COBBLER QUINN (IRE)**, b g Tagula (IRE)—Skyscape **Mrs J. M. MacPherson**
86 **CORTON LASS**, gr f Showcasing—Elbow Beach **Mr J. J. Hutton**
87 **CUILLIN HILLS**, ch g Pastoral Pursuits—Justbetweenfriends (USA) **Mr K. W. Dalgleish**
88 B g Clodovil (IRE)—Delphica (IRE)
89 B f Dandy Man (IRE)—Diksie Dancer **Weldspec Glasgow Limited**
90 **DROVER**, ch g Foxwedge (AUS)—Brooksby **Weldspec Glasgow Limited**
91 **DUSCHAFFSTDASSCHON (IRE)**, b c Zoffany (IRE)—Cant Hurry Love **Mr M. Beaumont**
92 **EVA DOCC (IRE)**, ch f Dandy Man (IRE)—La Rochelle (IRE) **Mr R. Docherty**
93 B g Medicean—Flylowflylong (IRE) **G L S Partnership**
94 **GERMAN BIGHT (IRE)**, br f Makfi—Saint Lucia (IRE) **Mr M. Beaumont**
95 **GOOD BOY ALFIE**, b g Showcasing—Costa Brava (IRE) **Mr & Mrs Paul & Clare Rooney**
96 **HANDSOME BOB (IRE)**, b g Most Improved (IRE)—Beautiful Dreamer **Weldspec Glasgow Limited**
97 **HERE IN THE DARK**, b g Harbour Watch (IRE)—Behest **Prestige Thoroughbred Racing**
98 **I'M IMPROVING (IRE)**, b c Most Improved (IRE)—Shebelia (GER) **Mr & Mrs Paul & Clare Rooney**
99 **ICONIC CODE**, ch f Sixties Icon—Silca Key **Sir Ian Good & Mr C Anderson**
100 **IRON SKY**, b g Showcasing—Addiena **Weldspec Glasgow Limited**
101 B f Zebedee—Jeannie Galloway (IRE)
102 **KIKINI BAMALAAM (IRE)**, b f Society Rock (IRE)—Crimson Sunrise (IRE) **Middleham Park Racing LXXXII**
103 **KIRBEC (IRE)**, b f Lord Shanakill (USA)—Monsusu (IRE) **From The Front Racing**
104 B c Kodiac—Knock Stars (IRE)
105 **MI CAPRICHO (IRE)**, b c Elzaam (AUS)—Mavemacullen (IRE) **Prestige Thoroughbred Racing**
106 **MISS BAR BEACH (IRE)**, b f Choisir (AUS)—Whitegate Way **Middleham Park Racing CXV**
107 B c Sir Percy—Mookhlesa **Weldspec Glasgow Limited**
108 **MOVE IT MOVE IT**, gr c Lethal Force (IRE)—Madam Valentine **Mr & Mrs Paul & Clare Rooney**
109 B f Nathaniel (IRE)—Peace Signal (USA) **Weldspec Glasgow Limited**
110 Ch c Champs Elysees—Procession **Weldspec Glasgow Limited**
111 **RAY PURCHASE**, b g Lethal Force (IRE)—Raggle Taggle (IRE) **Middleham Park Racing LXXI**
112 **RIVERSIDE WALK**, b f Showcasing—Distant Waters **Clipper Group Holdings Ltd**
113 **SHPADOINKLE DAY (IRE)**, ch g Champs Elysees—Idle Chatter (IRE) **Mr G. R. Leckie**
114 **SOLDIER'S MINUTE**, b c Raven's Pass (USA)—Hadba (IRE) **Weldspec Glasgow Limited**
115 **SPARK OF WAR (IRE)**, b c Declaration of War (USA)—Acts of Grace (USA) **Mr F. Brady**
116 **TASTE OF PARADISE (IRE)**, b f Zoffany (IRE)—Bounty Star (IRE) **Mr J. E. Dance**
117 **TOUGH REMEDY (IRE)**, b g Tough As Nails (IRE)—Remediate (USA) **Titanium Racing Club**
118 **UP STICKS AND GO**, gr c Equiano (FR)—Reaching Ahead (USA) **Mr & Mrs Paul & Clare Rooney**
119 **WARDADDY (IRE)**, b g Worthadd (IRE)—Let Your Love Flow (IRE) **Weldspec Glasgow Limited**
120 B g Red Jazz (USA)—Yours Faithfully (IRE)

TWO-YEAR-OLDS

121 B f 14/2 Kyllachy—Al Joudha (FR) (Green Desert (USA)) (24761) **Weldspec Glasgow Limited**
122 Ch c 8/3 Havana Gold (IRE)—Bounty Box (Bahamian Bounty) (52380)
123 Ch c 19/2 Camacho—Dame d'honneur (IRE) (Teofilo (IRE)) (44769) **Weldspec Glasgow Limited**
124 Ch f 14/1 Dandy Man (IRE)—Don't Tell Bertie (Bertolini (USA)) (4285) **Mr R. Docherty**
125 B c 12/4 Red Jazz (USA)—Faithfulbond (IRE) (Elbio) (9523) **Middleham Park Racing XXVII**
126 B f 4/3 Sir Prancealot (IRE)—Fayreway (IRE) (Strategic Prince) (7142)
127 B c 13/2 War Command (USA)—Final Opinion (IRE) (King's Theatre (IRE)) (11395)
128 Ch c 1/3 Poet's Voice—Good Health (Magic Ring) (33000) **Mrs J. M. MacPherson**
129 **IRON MIKE**, gr c 5/3 Gregorian (IRE)—Regal Velvet (Halling (USA)) (48840) **Weldspec Glasgow Limited**
130 B f 23/3 Epaulette (AUS)—Jackline (Diktat) (11428)
131 B gr f 27/3 Alhebayeb (IRE)—Kowara (IRE) (Kodiac) (9767)
132 B f 9/3 Camacho—La Estatua (Lope de Vega (IRE)) (6500)
133 **LET ME BE (IRE)**, b c 28/2 Gale Force Ten—Peryzat (IRE) (Mastercraftsman (IRE)) (6918)
134 B c 25/3 Requinto (IRE)—Mattinata (Tiger Hill (IRE)) (28571)
135 B c 15/4 Battle of Marengo (IRE)—Mikes Baby (IRE) (Key of Luck (USA)) (17907) **J. S. Morrison**
136 B c 24/3 Battle of Marengo (IRE)—
    Misrepresent (USA) (Distorted Humor (USA)) (69189) **Weldspec Glasgow Limited**
137 Ch c 30/4 Tagula (IRE)—Muffin (UAE) (Halling (USA)) (23809)
138 **PEARL OF NIGHT (FR)**, b f 18/1 Wootton Bassett—
    Joyce (GER) (Chato (USA)) (20350) **Middleham Park Racing CXI**
139 B c 8/4 War Command (USA)—
    Ponte Sanangelo (FR) (Authorized (IRE)) (34188) **Middleham Park Racing LXXXIV**

MR KEITH DALGLEISH - Continued

140 B f 8/3 Dandy Man (IRE)—Rugged Up (IRE) (Marju (IRE)) (38095) **Middleham Park Racing LII**
141 B f 10/2 Morpheus—Silver Cache (USA) (Silver Hawk (USA)) (7000)
142 B f 17/2 Footstepsinthesand—Summer Dream (IRE) (Oasis Dream) (5290) **Mr R. Docherty**
143 B f 8/4 No Nay Never (USA)—Tamazug (Machiavellian (USA)) (36190) **Middleham Park Racing XVI**
144 WOODSIDE WONDER, br c 22/4 Camacho—
                                   Cambridge Duchess (Singspiel (IRE)) (19047) **Middleham Park Racing XIV**

Other Owners: Mr G. G. Adamson, C. Anderson, Mr A. Bell, Mr S. Bridge, Mr K. P. Bucas, Mr W. Burke, A. Cadger, Mr J. J. Campbell, Mr D. Duncan, Mr Gary Etheridge, Mr S. Franks, Mr A. N. Gargan, Mr R. P. Gilbert, Mrs K. E. Gilbert, G. Godsman, Sir Ian Good, E. D. Haggart, Mr A. W. Henderson, Mrs S. J. Keniry, R. Kent, Mr J. S. Lessells, Robert Macgregor, Mr J. M. Mcintyre, Mr M. G. Mellor, D. Mossop, Mr N. J. O'Brien, Ontoawinner 8, T. S. Palin, Mr G. Park, Miss J. Park, M. Prince, Mr S. C. Reay, Mrs C. Rooney, Mr P. A. Rooney, Mr A. Savage, Exors of the Late Mr D. G. Savala, A. W. Sinclair, Miss M. M. Smith, Straightline Construction Ltd, Mr D. A. Walker.

Assistant Trainer: Kevin Dalgleish

Conditional: Callum Bewley. **Apprentice:** Rowan Scott.

---

128 MR HENRY DALY, Ludlow
Postal: Trainer did not wish details of his string to appear

---

129 MR PHILLIP DANDO, Peterston-Super-Ely
Postal: Springfield Court, Peterston-Super-Ely, Cardiff, South Glamorgan, CF5 6LG
Contacts: PHONE (01446) 760012 MOBILE (07872) 965395

1 DRIFTWOOD HAZE, 10, b g Nomadic Way (USA)—Kristal Haze **P. C. Dando**
2 MOONTRIPPER, 9, b m Doyen (IRE)—Moon Spinner **Mr H. A. Brown**
3 RAINBOW HAZE, 12, b g Rainbow High—Kristal Haze **P. C. Dando**
4 RIVER HAZE, 8, b g Lucarno (USA)—Kristal Haze **P. C. Dando**
5 SAHARA HAZE, 9, b m Rainbow High—Gypsy Haze **P. C. Dando**

Assistant Trainer: Mrs Rebecca Davies

---

130 MR VICTOR DARTNALL, Barnstaple
Postal: Higher Shutscombe Farm, Charles, Brayford, Barnstaple, Devon, EX32 7PU
Contacts: PHONE (01598) 710280 FAX (01598) 710708 MOBILE (07974) 374272
E-MAIL victordartnall@gmail.com WEBSITE www.victordartnallracing.com

1 ADMIRAL'S SECRET, 7, b g Kayf Tara—Bobs Bay (IRE) **The Whacko Partnership**
2 AMBION LANE (IRE), 8, b g Scorpion (IRE)—Thrilling Prospect (IRE) **Mr O. C. R. Wynne & Mrs S. J. Wynne**
3 BINDON MILL, 9, b g Tamure (IRE)—Singing Cottage **Mrs E. S. Weld**
4 BOLVING (IRE), 7, b g Stowaway—Kiniohio (FR) **Mrs C. M. Barber**
5 DANCING SHADOW (IRE), 9, b rg Craigsteel—Be My Shadow (IRE) **The Dancing Shadows**
6 DARLOA (IRE), 9, b g Darsi (FR)—Lady Lola (IRE) **Mr S. W. Campbell**
7 EXMOOR MIST, 10, gr g Kayf Tara—Chita's Flora **Exmoor Mist Partnership**
8 GET WISHING (IRE), 6, b g Getaway (GER)—Third Wish (IRE) **Edge Of Exmoor**
9 HELUVAGOOD, 6, b g Helissio (FR)—Cape Siren **Mr Dennis & Mr Mark Blight**
10 HOWARDIAN HILLS (IRE), 5, b g Vale of York (IRE)—Handsome Anna (IRE) **Mrs C Carter & Mr V Dartnall**
11 MAHLER'S FIRST (IRE), 6, b g Mahler—Fridays Folly (IRE) **First Brayford Partnership**
12 MINNIE ESCAPE, 6, b m Getaway (GER)—Minnie Hill (IRE) **The Second Brayford Partnership**
13 MY MATADOR (IRE), 7, b g Kandahar Run—My Special (IRE) **Mr V. R. A. Dartnall**
14 RIVER BRAY (IRE), 5, ch g Arakan (USA)—Cill Fhearga (IRE) **The River Bray Syndicate**
15 RUN TO MILAN (IRE), 6, b g Milan—Run Supreme (IRE) **Barber, Birchenhough, De Wilde**
16 SHUTSCOMBE HILL, 6, b g Arvico (FR)—Storm Kitten **Edge Of Exmoor**
17 SWEET ADARE (IRE), 5, b m Getaway (GER)—The Adare Woman (IRE) **G. D. Hake**
18 UT MAJEUR AULMES (FR), 10, ch g Northern Park (USA)—My Wish Aulmes (FR) **Mrs S. De Wilde**
19 WEE SAXON, 9, b g Kayf Tara—Countess Point **Exors of the Late Mrs J. E. Purdie**

MR VICTOR DARTNALL - Continued

Other Owners: Mrs K. Birchenhough, Mr M. Blight, Mr D. P. Blight, Ms C. Carter, Mrs P. Cunliffe, Mr B. C. Dallyn, Mr G. Dartnall, Mrs J. Dartnall, Miss Alison Delve, Mr J. Edelman, N. P. Haley, Mrs S. M. Hall, Mr C. W. M. Herbert, Mr M. E. Nicholls, Mr M. W. Richards, Mr P. A. Roberts, Mrs T. M. Scott, Mr L. Singleton, A. P. Staple, Mr R. Willcocks, O. C. R. Wynne, Mrs S. J. Wynne.

Assistant Trainer: G. A. Dartnall

---

131 **MR TOM DASCOMBE, Malpas**
Postal: **Manor House Stables, Malpas, Cheshire, SY14 8AD**
Contacts: **PHONE (01948) 820485 FAX (01948) 820495 MOBILE (07973) 511664**
E-MAIL tom@manorhousestables.com WEBSITE www.manorhousestables.com

1 **ARCANADA (IRE)**, 5, ch g Arcano (IRE)—Bond Deal (IRE) **The Arcanada Partnership**
2 **AZARI (IRE)**, 6, b g Azamour (IRE)—Atasari (IRE) **Mr D Ward & Partner**
3 **BARNABY BROOK (CAN)**, 8, b g North Light (IRE)—Mascara (USA) **Mr T. G. Dascombe**
4 **CALDER PRINCE (IRE)**, 5, gr g Dark Angel (IRE)—Flame of Ireland (IRE) **Mr P. G. Birbeck**
5 **CHEERFILLY (IRE)**, 4, br f Excelebration (IRE)—Classic Remark (IRE) **Mr L. A. Bellman**
6 **CHOSEN CHARACTER (IRE)**, 10, b g Choisir (AUS)—Out of Thanks (IRE) **Aykroyd & Sons Limited**
7 **FIRE DIAMOND**, 5, b g Firebreak—Diapason (IRE) **Mr J. D. Brown**
8 **KACHY**, 5, b h Kyllachy—Dubai Bounty **Mr D. J. Lowe**
9 **MAC O'POLO (IRE)**, 4, b g Henrythenavigator (USA)—Topka (FR) **Macguire's Bloodstock Ltd**
10 **MICKEY (IRE)**, 5, b g Zoffany (IRE)—Enchantment **Mrs Janet Lowe & Mr Tom Dascombe**
11 **MR CHRISTOPHER (IRE)**, 6, b g Bahamian Bounty—Embassy Pearl (IRE) **Mrs M. C. Antrobus**
12 **PUNKAWALLAH (IRE)**, 4, b g Sepoy (AUS)—Max One Two Three (IRE) **Laurence Bellman & Chasemore Farm**
13 **REFLEKTOR (IRE)**, 5, ch g Bahamian Bounty—Baby Bunting **David Lowe & Miss Amber Lowe**
14 **SIMPLY ME**, 5, b m New Approach (IRE)—Ego **Mr L. A. Bellman**
15 **TEODORO (IRE)**, 4, ch g Teofilo (IRE)—Altesse Imperiale (IRE) **Laurence Bellman & Caroline Ingram**

THREE-YEAR-OLDS

16 **A LITTLE ACTION (IRE)**, b f Mastercraftsman (IRE)—Lace (IRE) **Lease Terminated**
17 **ADMIRAL SPICE (IRE)**, gr g Lethal Force (IRE)—Rustam **Mr D. R. Passant**
18 **AMARONE RED (IRE)**, ch f Harbour Watch (IRE)—Lisa's Strong (IRE) **Denis Barry & Manor House Stables Llp**
19 **BIG TIME MAYBE (IRE)**, b g Dandy Man (IRE)—Divine Design (IRE) **Jones', Langfords' & Owens'**
20 **CAPOMENTO (IRE)**, b f Casamento (IRE)—Satin Cape (IRE) **Deva Racing Casamento Partnership**
21 **CASHEL (IRE)**, b c Sepoy (AUS)—Snow Dust **Laurence Bellman & David Ward**
22 **CELESTIAL FORCE (IRE)**, b c Sea The Stars (IRE)—Aquarelle Bleue **Mr J. E. Dance**
23 **CHARLIE D (USA)**, b c Animal Kingdom (USA)—Ocicat (USA) **Mr D. R. Passant & Mr T. Dascombe**
24 **CRIMSON SKIES (IRE)**, b c Declaration of War (USA)—Emily Blake (IRE) **Bob & Pauline Scott & Partner**
25 **DANCE ON THE DAY (IRE)**, b f Epaulette (AUS)—Skeleton (IRE) **G. A. Lowe**
26 **DIAMOND SET**, b c Dutch Art—Asaawir **Russell Jones & David Lowe**
27 **DRAGONS TAIL (IRE)**, b c Dragon Pulse (IRE)—Mastoora (IRE) **Goss Hyden Jones Owen**
28 **ENDLESS TANGENT (IRE)**, b f Lawman (FR)—Passion Planet (IRE) **Mr J. E. Dance**
29 **EPAULEMENT (IRE)**, b g Epaulette (AUS)—Little Whisper (IRE) **Deva Racing Epaulette Partnership**
30 **FANCIFUL MISS**, b f New Approach (IRE)—Fann (USA) **The Forty Three Partnership**
31 **FINNISTON FARM**, b c Helmet (AUS)—Logic **The Famous Five Partnership**
32 **FIRE TO THE REIGN**, b f Showcasing—Adele Blanc Sec (FR) **Lowe Mchale Jackson Singh Kavanagh & Co**
33 **FORMIDABLE KITT**, b f Invincible Spirit (IRE)—Ceiling Kitty **Chasemore Farm LLP**
34 **FOUR CHAMPS**, gr g Champs Elysees—Lana Jolie (GER) **Dodd, O'Halloran, Satchell & Towns**
35 **GINBAR (IRE)**, b c Kodiac—Double Fantasy (GER) **The BGW Partnership**
36 **GLORIOUS PLAYER (IRE)**, b g Kyllachy—Playwithmyheart **Kangyu International Racing (HK) Limited**
37 **HARRY CALLAHAN (IRE)**, b g Dutch Art—Sovana (IRE) **Chelsea Thoroughbreds - Dirty Harry**
38 **KRAKA (IRE)**, b g Dark Angel (IRE)—Manuelita Rose (ITY) **Jones, Mound, Trowbridge**
39 **NEW DAY DAWN (IRE)**, ch f Dawn Approach (IRE)—Roo **Laurence Bellman & David Ward**
40 **NO I'M EASY (IRE)**, b c Zoffany (IRE)—Caribbean Queen (IRE) **The Groundhog Day Partnership**
41 **POPPY LOVE**, br f Harbour Watch (IRE)—Don't Tell Mary (IRE) **Keith & Mary Trowbridge**
42 **PORCHY PARTY (IRE)**, ch g Dragon Pulse—Shawaaty (IRE) **R. F. H. Partnership 1**
43 **PROSCHEMA (IRE)**, ch c Declaration of War (USA)—Notable **Empire State Racing Partnership**
44 **QUANTATMENTAL (IRE)**, ch g New Approach (IRE)—Anayid **Mr J. E. Dance**
45 **RED FORCE ONE**, ro g Lethal Force (IRE)—Dusty Red **Done Ferguson Mason**
46 **ROCK FORCE (IRE)**, b c Fastnet Rock (AUS)—Sweepstake (IRE) **Laurence Bellman & David Ward**
47 **SHA LA LA LA LEE**, b c Helmet (AUS)—Shamara (IRE) **Nigel and Sharon Mather & Charles Ledigo**
48 **SILVER CHARACTER (IRE)**, gr c Camelot—Convocate (USA) **Aykroyd & Sons Limited**
49 **SOCIETY SECRET (IRE)**, ch c Society Rock (IRE)—Bond Deal (IRE) **Wilmshurst, Cronshaw & Attenborough**

MR TOM DASCOMBE - Continued

50 **THIS GIRL**, b f Nathaniel (IRE)—Fibou (USA) **Mr D. J. Lowe**
51 **ZOFFALEE (FR)**, ch c Zoffany (IRE)—Senderlea (IRE) **Mr D. R. Passant**

TWO-YEAR-OLDS

52 Ch c 30/4 Frankel—Adoration (USA) (Honor Grades (USA)) (100000) **Cleverley Clyne Dance Mound**
53 B c 24/3 Dansili—Anticipation (FR) (Muhtathir) (85470) **Timothy Storey & Roofing Consultants Gp**
54 **ARTHUR KITT**, b c 24/2 Camelot—Ceiling Kitty (Red Clubs (IRE)) **Chasemore Farm LLP**
55 **ARTISTIC STREAK**, b f 1/2 New Approach (IRE)—Artisti (Cape Cross (IRE)) **Mr D. M. Shaw**
56 B f 23/2 Rip Van Winkle (IRE)—Awjila (Oasis Dream) **Manor House Stables LLP**
57 Ch f 19/3 Lope de Vega (IRE)—Ballymore Celebre (IRE) (Peintre Celebre (USA)) (155000) **Mr J. E. Dance**
58 **BARRISTAN THE BOLD**, b c 10/3 Excelebration (IRE)—
                                Cradle of Life (IRE) (Notnowcato) (35000) **Chasemore Farm & Mr Kevin Costello**
59 B f 31/3 Helmet (AUS)—Bawaakeer (USA) (Kingmambo (USA)) (33374) **Mr J. E. Dance**
60 B c 7/4 Kodiac—Burstingdalak (IRE) (Dalakhani (IRE)) (52000) **Manor House Stables LLP**
61 B c 7/2 Dark Angel (IRE)—Clear Impression (IRE) (Danehill (USA)) (76190) **The Famous Five Partnership**
62 B c 13/4 No Nay Never (USA)—Conniption (IRE) (Danehill Dancer (IRE)) (60000) **Mr D. Ward**
63 B f 27/1 Exceed And Excel (AUS)—Coral Mist (Bahamian Bounty) (133333) **Mr J. E. Dance**
64 **DARK THUNDER (IRE)**, gr c 7/4 Alhebayeb (IRE)—
                                Call This Cat (IRE) (One Cool Cat (USA)) (40000) **Birbeck Burke Goss Hyden Jones**
65 B f 2/2 Dandy Man (IRE)—Disko (IRE) (Kodiac) (22792) **Mike Nolan & Partner**
66 Ch f 23/2 Bated Breath—Don't Tell Mary (IRE) (Starcraft (NZ)) **Keith & Mary Trowbridge**
67 **DROGON (IRE)**, b c 19/4 Zoffany (IRE)—Flames To Dust (GER) (Oasis Dream) (45000) **APCC Limited**
68 **FOOTSTEPSINTHEMIST (IRE)**, br c 10/3 Footstepsinthesand—
                                Highland Miss (USA) (Theatrical) (48840) **Peter Birbeck & Alan & Sue Cronshaw**
69 **GUANDI (USA)**, ch c 5/4 Declaration of War (USA)—
                                Hoh Buzzard (IRE) (Alhaarth (IRE)) (73260) **Empire State Racing Partnership**
70 Ch c 5/5 Siyouni (FR)—Hill of Grace (Desert Prince (IRE)) (65120) **Fdcholdings Rutherford Witheridge**
71 **ICONIC CHOICE**, ch f 31/1 Sixties Icon—Adorable Choice (IRE) (Choisir (AUS)) (4285) **Mr J. D. Brown**
72 **JACKSTAR (IRE)**, gr c 3/2 Dark Angel (IRE)—
                                Starbright (IRE) (Duke of Marmalade (IRE)) (114285) **Mrs C. L. Ingram**
73 **JENSUE (IRE)**, b f 7/4 Red Jazz (USA)—Gold Tobougg (Tobougg (IRE)) (12380) **Alan & Sue Cronshaw**
74 **KATIESHEIDINLISA**, b f 8/4 Camelot—
                                Spritza (IRE) (Spectrum (IRE)) (75000) **Mr D.R Passant & Hefin Williams**
75 B c 19/3 Requinto (IRE)—La Rosiere (USA) (Mr Greeley (USA)) (2380) **Empire State Racing Partnership**
76 Gr f 22/3 Iffraaj—Lady's Art (FR) (Verglas (IRE)) (35000) **Manor House Stables LLP**
77 **LIGHT MY FIRE (IRE)**, ch f 17/3 Dragon Pulse (IRE)—
                                Shawaaty (IRE) (Monsun (GER)) (18722) **The Light My Fire Partnership**
78 B c 20/2 Dark Angel (IRE)—
                                Majestic Alexander (IRE) (Bushranger (IRE)) (87619) **Birbeck Mound Trowbridge & Partner**
79 **METATRON (IRE)**, gr c 10/3 Dark Angel (IRE)—
                                Orikawa (FR) (Gold Away (IRE)) (114285) **Burns Smyth Studholme**
80 B c 28/2 Kodiac—Minwah (IRE) (Oasis Dream) (80952) **The Famous Five Partnership**
81 **MOGSY (IRE)**, br c 17/5 Dandy Man (IRE)—Dictatrice (IRE) (Anabaa (USA)) (30000) **Satchell Moran Solicitors**
82 B c 4/3 Alhebayeb (IRE)—Mokama (Motivator) (35000) **The Famous Five Partnership**
83 Gr c 7/4 Dark Angel (IRE)—Moonvoy (Cape Cross (IRE)) (65120) **Mr D. R. Passant**
84 B c 9/3 Kodiac—Motion Lass (Motivator) (45714) **Mr R. Jones**
85 B c 7/3 Zoffany (IRE)—Mount Crystal (IRE) (Montjeu (IRE)) (100000) **Mr A. E. Peterson**
86 **NAVIGATE BY STARS**, br f 9/5 Sea The Stars (IRE)—Bitooh (Diktat) (28490) **The Wilmshurst Partnership**
87 B c 11/4 Zoffany (IRE)—Pink Moon (IRE) (Namid) (24420) **Manor House Stables LLP**
88 **RED DRAGONESS (IRE)**, ch f 4/5 Dragon Pulse (IRE)—
                                Salydora (FR) (Peintre Celebre (USA)) (17908) **Mr R. J. Lennon**
89 **SESAME (IRE)**, b f 21/4 Slade Power (IRE)—
                                Tiger Spice (Royal Applause) (42327) **Laurence Bellman & Caroline Ingram**
90 **SMOKI SMOKA (IRE)**, ch c 23/2 Dragon Pulse (IRE)—
                                Creating Speed (IRE) (Lord Shanakill (USA)) (32380) **Duncan, Dunnington & Shaw**
91 B c 17/2 Sea The Stars (IRE)—Starlit Sands (Oasis Dream) (73260) **Mr L. A. Bellman**
92 B c 12/4 Helmet (AUS)—Sweet Home Alabama (IRE) (Desert Prince (IRE)) (26000) **The Famous Five Partnership**
93 **TIDAL POINT (IRE)**, br c 20/3 Sea The Moon (GER)—Centred (IRE) (Dalakhani (IRE)) (5000) **Sleeve It Ltd**
94 B c 3/2 Sir Prancealot (IRE)—
                                Victoria Lodge (IRE) (Grand Lodge (USA)) (32560) **Deva Racing Sir Prancealot P/ship**
95 B f 28/1 Elusive Quality (USA)—Wall of Sound (Singspiel (IRE)) **Chasemore Farm LLP**
96 B c 24/2 Sixties Icon—Wansdyke Lass (Josr Algarhoud (IRE)) (50000) **Manor House Stables LLP**
97 B c 15/4 Iffraaj—Welsh Cake (Fantastic Light (USA)) (47619) **FDCHoldings Nolan RCG Rutherford**
98 **WILD EDRIC**, ch c 7/2 Equiano (FR)—Lady Red Oak (Medicean) (6190) **Mr D. R. Passant**

MR TOM DASCOMBE - Continued

Other Owners: Mrs Sandra G. E. Arkwright, Major P. W. F. Arkwright, Mr N. B. Attenborough, Mr D. J. Barry, Mr M. Batters, Mrs A. Biles, Mrs J. E. Black, A. W. Black, Mr C. T. Broadbent, Mr L. Burke, Mr S. Burns, Chelsea Thoroughbreds Ltd, Mr T. W. Cleverley, Mr N. Clyne, Mr P. G. Cooke, Mr K. Costello, Mrs M. Coxon, Mrs S. P. Cronshaw, Mr A. Cronshaw, Mr P. E. Done, Mr D. Duncan, Mr N. C. Dunnington, FDC Holdings Ltd, Sir A. Ferguson, Mr R. B. Foskett, Mr M. D. Foster, Mrs J. Foster, Mrs J. Fuller, Ms J. L. Gibson, Mr G. S. Goss, C. E. R. Greenway, Mrs C. I. Hesketh, Mrs L. C. Hyden, Mr A. Jackson, Mr M. A. Jones, Mrs A. G. Kavanagh, Mr P. M. Langford, Mr C. Ledigo, Mrs J. Lowe, Miss A. J. Lowe, G. A. Mason, Mrs S. E. Mather, Mr N. P. Mather, Mr C. McHale, Mrs J. P. Melia, Mr T. J. Moran, Mr S. N. Mound, M. F. Nolan, Mr M. O'Halloran, Mr M.J Owen, Mr L. T. Owen, Owen Promotions Limited, Mr C. D. Pritchard, Roofing Consultants Group, L. M. Rutherford, Mr M. Satchell, Mrs P. M. Scott, Mr & Mrs R. Scott, R. Scott, Mr J. Singh, Mr M. Smyth, Mr T. J. Storey, Mr D. Studholme, Mrs M. C. Trowbridge, K. P. Trowbridge, Mr H. Williams, Mr C. J. Wilmshurst, Mr M. Wilmshurst, Mr R. L. K. Witheridge, Ms J. C. Woodall.

Assistant Trainer: Colin Gorman

Jockey (flat): Richard Kingscote. **Apprentice:** Elisha Whittington. **Amateur:** Miss Alyson Deniel.

---

132 **MR TRISTAN DAVIDSON, Carlisle**
Postal: **Bellmount, Laversdale, Irthington, Carlisle, Cumbria, CA6 4PS**
Contacts: **MOBILE (07789) 684290**

1 **ASKGARMOR (IRE)**, 6, b g Ask—Karmafair (IRE) **E G Tunstall, Mr G. Etheridge, Mr J. Reay**
2 **CHICORIA (IRE)**, 9, ch g Presenting—Coco Girl **Carlisle Poker Club & Mr P S Nicholson**
3 **LEANNA BAN**, 11, b g Afflora (IRE)—Gurleigh (IRE) **E G Tunstall, P Nicholson, S M Grice**
4 **NAILER (IRE)**, 8, b g Coroner (IRE)—Celtic Serenade (IRE) **G E Davidson, S M Grice, M McManus**

Other Owners: Mr G. G. Adamson, Carlisle Poker Club, Mr Gordon E. Davidson, Mr Gary Etheridge, Mr S. M. Grice, Mr Dean Lamonby, Mr M. McManus, Mr P. S. Nicholson, Mr J. Reay, Mr E. G. Tunstall.

---

133 **MR JOHN DAVIES, Darlington**
Postal: **Denton Grange, Piercebridge, Co. Durham, DL2 3TZ**
Contacts: **PHONE (01325) 374366 MOBILE (07746) 292782**
E-MAIL johndavieshorses@live.co.uk WEBSITE www.johndaviesracing.com

1 **ALFRED RICHARDSON**, 4, ch g Dapper—Vera Richardson (IRE) **K Kirkup & J Davies**
2 **EXCELLENT STORY**, 4, b g Excelebration (IRE)—Storyland (USA) **Mr & Mrs R. Scott**
3 **IM DAPPER TOO**, 7, b g Dapper—Lonely One **Mr C. W. Davies**
4 **MAJOR ROWAN**, 7, b g Captain Gerrard (IRE)—Julie's Gift **J. J. Davies**
5 **MANGO CHUTNEY**, 5, ch g Sleeping Indian—Crimson Topaz **The Sexy Fish Partnership**
6 **MAYDALE**, 5, ch m Monsieur Bond (IRE)—Jaldarshaan (IRE) **T. B. Tarn**
7 **MCVICAR**, 9, b g Tobougg (IRE)—Aries (GER) **Ms D. Nicholson**
8 **MONTYDARKDESTROYER**, 7, b g Lucarno (USA)—Markila (FR) **Mrs M. S. Stone**

THREE-YEAR-OLDS

9 **FREEWAY**, b g Henrythenavigator (USA)—Sky Crystal (GER) **J. J. Davies**
10 **LIME PICKLE**, b g Major Cadeaux—Ocean Grove (IRE) **The Sexy Fish Partnership**
11 **MARCONI**, ch g Monsieur Bond (IRE)—Tamara Bay **Mr & Mrs R Scott & J Davies**
12 B f Mount Nelson—Sambarina (IRE) **J. J. Davies**
13 **SEXYFISH (FR)**, b g Authorized (IRE)—Honorable Love **Mr P. Taylor**
14 **THE HOPPINGS**, b f Kyllachy—Rosa Bud **The Maroon Stud**

TWO-YEAR-OLDS

15 Ch f 13/3 Doncaster Rover (USA)—Davana (Primo Valentino (IRE)) **T. B. Tarn**
16 Gr g 4/4 Swiss Spirit—Firoza (FR) (King's Best (USA)) (17142) **Ms D. Nicholson**
17 B g 25/3 Dick Turpin (IRE)—Vera Richardson (IRE) (Dutch Art) **K. Kirkup**

Other Owners: Mr K. Borrett, Mr A. Dickman, L. L. Dickman, Mr P. Dunnill, Mrs P. M. Scott, R. Scott.

Jockey (flat): Phillip Makin.

134 MISS SARAH-JAYNE DAVIES, Leominster

Postal: **The Upper Withers, Hundred Lane, Kimbolton, Leominster, Herefordshire, HR6 0HZ**
Contacts: **PHONE** (01584) 711780 **MOBILE** (07779) 797079
E-MAIL sjdracing@live.co.uk WEBSITE www.sjdracing.co.uk

1 **ACCESSALLAREAS (IRE)**, 13, ch g Swift Gulliver (IRE)—Arushofgold (IRE) **Withers Winners**
2 **ALBERT GEORGE**, 4, ch g Paco Boy (IRE)—Avonrose
3 **ALL DOLLED UP (IRE)**, 6, b m Aussie Rules (USA)—All On Sugar (GER) **Mr A. J. Gough**
4 **ARVICO'S LIGHT**, 4, b g Arvico (FR)—Miss Lightning **Mrs S. M. Davies**
5 **BAILEYS GALAXY (FR)**, 5, b g Elusive City (USA)—Kosmic View (USA) **John Priday, Mike Mifflin & Wyn Owen**
6 **CAMLAD KINGFISHER**, 6, ch g Sulamani (IRE)—Val de Fleurie (GER) **Mrs C. J. Davies**
7 **CHANKILLO**, 9, ch g Observatory (USA)—Seasonal Blossom (IRE) **Mr A. J. Gough**
8 **DEADLY APPROACH**, 7, b g New Approach (IRE)—Speirbhean (IRE) **Quadriga Racing**
9 **ELECTORAL (IRE)**, 5, b g Rip Van Winkle (IRE)—Sumingasefa **Steve Mace, Paul Whilock & Mark Hammond**
10 **GUYBOY**, 5, b g Like A Boy—Left Nostril (IRE) **L. T. Woodhouse**
11 **HIGGS (IRE)**, 5, b g Scorpion (IRE)—Captain Supreme (IRE) **Pump & Plant Services Ltd**
12 **HONOURABLE HENRY**, 8, b g Kayf Tara—Kingara **K. E. Stait**
13 6, Ch m Recharge (IRE)—Island Hopper **Mr A. J. Gough**
14 **PASSING FIESTA**, 9, b m Passing Glance—Clarice Starling **Mr A. J. Gough**
15 **PEMBROKE HOUSE**, 11, gr g Terimon—Bon Coeur **Sarah-jayne Davies & Steve Mace**
16 **PEPPERDEW (USA)**, 4, ch g Street Cry (IRE)—Spice Island (USA) **Pump & Plant Services Ltd**
17 **PERCY THROWER (IRE)**, 4, ch g Sir Percy—Dayrose **The Cannon Club**
18 **RED EMPEROR (IRE)**, 4, b g Holy Roman Emperor (IRE)—Rougette **Miss S. J. Davies**
19 **RED FOUR**, 8, ch m Singspiel (IRE)—Protectorate **Miss N. Thompson**
20 **RING EYE (IRE)**, 10, b g Definite Article—Erins Lass (IRE) **Mr A. J. Gough**
21 **ROYAL ACT**, 6, br g Royal Anthem (USA)—Native's Return **Moorland Racing**
22 **SEQUINSATDAWN**, 6, ch m Tobougg (IRE)—Two Aye Em **Mrs S. M. Davies**
23 **TIMS CRUSADER (IRE)**, 10, ch g Fruits of Love (USA)—Duiske Abbey (IRE) **Miss S. J. Davies**
24 **WHOS DE BABY (IRE)**, 10, gr g Bienamado (USA)—Beaus Rose (IRE) **Mrs C. J. Davies**

Other Owners: M. P. Bass, Mr M. J. Hammond, Mrs A. M. Mace, S. A. Mace, Mr T. M. Mifflin, Mr D. W. Owen, J. Priday, Mrs C. Tucker, Mr J. F. Vincent, Mr P. R. Whilock.

Jockey (NH): Robbie Dunne. **Conditional:** Charlie Hammond.

135 MISS JOANNA DAVIS, East Garston

Postal: **1 Parson Close Stables, School Lane, East Garston, Hungerford, Berkshire, RG17 7HR**
Contacts: **PHONE** (01488) 649977 **FAX** (01488) 649977 **MOBILE** (07879) 811535
E-MAIL davisjo_007@hotmail.com WEBSITE www.jodavisracing.com

1 4, Ch g Malinas (GER)—Bright Spangle (IRE) **Mrs M. Davis**
2 **CAPELLIAN CRUSADER (IRE)**, 9, b g Cape Cross (IRE)—Llia **Mrs P. M. Brown**
3 **FREE ONE (IRE)**, 6, b g Fast Company (IRE)—Tatamagouche (IRE) **Mrs Patricia Brown & Jo Davis**
4 **GALLIC DESTINY (IRE)**, 7, b g Champs Elysees—Cross Your Fingers (USA) **Mrs P. Brown**
5 **HE'S A TOFF (IRE)**, 4, br g Dandy Man (IRE)—Prevarication (IRE) **Mrs C. G. Cruddace**
6 **HEROES OR GHOSTS (IRE)**, 9, br g Indian River (FR)—Awomansdream (IRE) **Tony Worth & Vic Bedley**
7 **JOHN BISCUIT (IRE)**, 10, ch g Hawk Wing (USA)—Princess Magdalena **Mrs P. M. Brown**
8 **KEN'S WELL (IRE)**, 7, b g Trans Island—Tiergarten (IRE) **Mrs P. M. Brown**
9 **MARMONT**, 5, ch g Winker Watson—Five Bells (IRE) **Mrs J. S. Davis**
10 **MR FITZROY (IRE)**, 8, ch g Kyllachy—Reputable **Mrs P. M. Brown**
11 **OSCARS LEADER (IRE)**, 5, b g Oscar (IRE)—Lead'er Inn (IRE) **J. L. Marriott**
12 **STAR FOOT (IRE)**, 7, b g Soviet Star (USA)—On The Backfoot (IRE) **J. L. Marriott**
13 **TOUCHY SUBJECT (IRE)**, 5, br g Tikkanen (USA)—Legal Lodge (IRE) **J. L. Marriott**
14 **TUPPENCE COLOURED**, 4, br f Oasis Dream—No Frills (IRE) **Mrs P. M. Brown**

Other Owners: Mr V. R. Bedley, Mrs Patricia Brown, Miss J. Davis, Mrs M. A. Davis, Mr Tony Worth.

136 MISS ZOE DAVISON, East Grinstead
Postal: **Shovelstrode Racing Stables, Shovelstrode Lane, Ashurstwood, East Grinstead, West Sussex, RH19 3PN**
Contacts: **PHONE** (01342) 300319 **MOBILE** (07970) 839357 & (07812) 007554
E-MAIL andy01031976@yahoo.co.uk **WEBSITE** www.shovelstroderacing.co.uk

1 BEAUFORT BOY (IRE), 9, b g Heron Island (IRE)—What A Mewsment (IRE) **The Secret Circle Racing Club**
2 BROTHER BENNETT (FR), 8, gr g Martaline—La Gaminerie (FR) **The Secret Circle & Chris Sowerby**
3 DYLANSEOGHAN (IRE), 9, b g Pierre—Sabbatical (IRE) **The Lump O'Clock Syndicate**
4 FINNEGAN'S GARDEN (IRE), 9, b g Definite Article—Tri Folene (FR) **Mr K. Corke**
5 FRANK N FAIR, 10, br m Trade Fair—Frankfurt (GER) **The Secret Circle Racing Club**
6 GEORGIESHORE (IRE), 10, b g Turtle Island (IRE)—Pride of St Gallen (IRE) **The Lump O'Clock Syndicate**
7 GUSTAV (IRE), 8, b g Mahler—Pakaradyssa (FR) **The Plum Merchants**
8 KILINAKIN (IRE), 8, ch g Definite Article—Topanberry (IRE) **The Lump O'Clock Syndicate**
9 PIAZZA SAN PIETRO, 12, ch g Compton Place—Rainbow Spectrum (FR) **Mr K. Corke**
10 RACE TIME (USA), 5, b br m Street Sense (USA)—Well At The Top (IRE) **Mrs S. E. Colville**
11 THE GAME IS A FOOT (IRE), 11, b g Oscar (IRE)—Cooksgrove Rosie (IRE) **The Secret Circle Racing Club**
12 THE GOLDEN HOUR (IRE), 8, b m Gold Well—Kirktonmoor Katie (IRE) **Mr N. D. Sharp**
13 VENETIAN PROPOSAL (IRE), 4, b f Fast Company (IRE)—Ide Say (IRE) **Mr & Mrs C Sowerby**

THREE-YEAR-OLDS
14 DEVIOUS DICKS DAME, b f Dick Turpin (IRE)—Bridal White **Mr R. Devereux**
15 OPEN HANDED, b g Sakhee (USA)—Naemi (GER) **Mr R. Devereux**
16 B g Mayson—Wenden Belle (IRE) **Mr R. Devereux**

Other Owners: S. J. Clare, Mr A. C. Clift, Miss Z. C. Davison, Mr A. J. Irvine, T. M. Santry, The Secret Circle, Mr C. F. Sowerby, Mrs S. Sowerby, Mr A. N. Waters.

Assistant Trainer: A. Irvine

Amateur: Mr M. G. Miller.

137 MR WILLIAM DE BEST-TURNER, Swindon
Postal: **8 North End, Calne, Wiltshire, SN11 9DQ**
Contacts: **PHONE** (01249) 811944 **HOME** (01249) 813850 **MOBILE** (07977) 910779
E-MAIL debestracing@hotmail.co.uk

1 CHICAGO SOCKS, 8, b h Catcher In The Rye (IRE)—Sachiko **W. de Best-Turner**
2 NELSON'S HILL, 8, b g Mount Nelson—Regal Step **Debestracing**

THREE-YEAR-OLDS
3 B f Tiger Groom—Maylan (IRE)
4 B g Tiger Groom—Sachiko **W. de Best-Turner**
5 B f Dream Eater (IRE)—Spartaculous **Debestracing**

Other Owners: Miss S J Slade.

Assistant Trainer: Mrs I. De Best

138 MR ED DE GILES, Ledbury
Postal: **Lilly Hall Farm, Little Marcle, Ledbury, Herefordshire, HR8 2LD**
Contacts: **PHONE** (01531) 637369 **MOBILE** (07811) 388345
E-MAIL ed@eddegilesracing.com **WEBSITE** www.eddegilesracing.com

1 AKAVIT (IRE), 6, b g Vale of York (IRE)—Along Came Molly **Simon Treacher & Partner**
2 ARQUUS (IRE), 5, b g Lilbourne Lad (IRE)—Charaig **Mr E. B. de Giles**
3 BOMBERO (IRE), 4, b g Dragon Pulse (IRE)—Mathool (IRE) **Woodham Walter Partnership**
4 BREEZE UP, 4, b g Shirocco (GER)—Lucky Breeze (IRE) **Mr C. C. Shand Kydd & Partner**
5 4, B f Mount Nelson—Candle **Mr E. B. de Giles**
6 CLASSIFIED (IRE), 4, b f Lope de Vega (IRE)—Crossbreeze (USA) **Mrs S. Powell**
7 COACHELLA (IRE), 4, gr g Kyllachy—Indian Belle (IRE) **Clarissa Casdagli & Simon Treacher**
8 CROQUEMBOUCHE (IRE), 9, b g Acclamation—Wedding Cake (IRE) **Mr P. J. Manser**
9 DELIRIUM (IRE), 4, b f Tamayuz—Coeur de La Mer (IRE) **Mrs S. Powell**
10 GO NANI GO, 12, b g Kyllachy—Go Between **Tight Lines Partnership**

MR ED DE GILES - Continued

11 **INCUS**, 5, b g Bertolini (USA)—Cloudchaser (IRE) **Mange Tout II**
12 **LESANTI**, 4, b g Royal Applause—Kammaan **The LAM Partnership**
13 **LUCY THE PAINTER (IRE)**, 6, b m Excellent Art—Royal Bounty (IRE) **Mr J. P. Carrington**
14 **OPERATIVE**, 5, ch g Pastoral Pursuits—Gilt Linked **Gwyn & Samantha Powell & Partner**
15 **OVERHAUGH STREET**, 5, b g Bahri—Bom Chicka Wah Wah (USA) **Sharron & Robert Colvin**
16 **PIKE CORNER CROSS (IRE)**, 6, b g Cape Cross (IRE)—Smart Coco (USA) **Mrs Yvonne Fleet & Partner**
17 **PRENDERGAST HILL (IRE)**, 6, b g Raven's Pass (USA)—Daraliya (IRE) **Gwyn & Samantha Powell**
18 **QUANTUM DOT (IRE)**, 7, ch g Exceed And Excel (AUS)—Jeed (IRE) **Mrs Yvonne Fleet & Partner**
19 **SHADES OF SILVER, (IRE)**, 8, b g Dansili—Silver Pivotal (IRE) **The Champion Family**
20 **SWANTON BLUE (IRE)**, 5, b g Kodiac—Cabopino (IRE) **Mr E. B. de Giles**
21 **THREE'S A CROWD (IRE)**, 4, br g Vocalised (USA)—Tense (IRE) **Mange Tout II**
22 **TREACHEROUS**, 4, b g Paco Boy (IRE)—Black Baroness **Woodham Walter Partnership**
23 **VINCENT'S FOREVER**, 5, b g Pour Moi (IRE)—Glen Rosie (IRE) **Mange Tout**
24 **WASSAIL**, 5, b m Shamardal (USA)—Gower Song **Simon Treacher & Partner**
25 **WIND IN MY SAILS**, 6, b g Footstepsinthesand—Dylanesque **Mr P. J. Manser**
26 **ZAMORANO (IRE)**, 6, b m Teofilo (IRE)—Petit Calva (FR) **Mr E. B. de Giles**
27 **ZLATAN (IRE)**, 5, b g Dark Angel (IRE)—Guard Hill (USA) **Gwyn Powell & Richard Meakes**

THREE-YEAR-OLDS

28 **A CHANCE TO BE ME**, b f Showcasing—Miss Meticulous **The LAM Partnership**
29 **BOMBASTIC (IRE)**, ch c Raven's Pass (USA)—Star of The West **The Philistines**
30 **BOREAGH LASS (IRE)**, b f Fast Company (IRE)—Jalasaat (USA) **North Yorkshire Bloodstock Racing**
31 **CATCH THE PIGEON (IRE)**, ch f Paco Boy (IRE)—Jasmick (IRE) **Tight Lines Partnership**
32 **FITZROVIA**, br c Poet's Voice—Pompey Girl **Simon Treacher & Clarissa Casdagali**
33 **LIBERISQUE**, b f Equiano (FR)—Jane Austen (IRE) **Andrew Bengough & Partners**
34 **PLENTY IN THE TANK (IRE)**, b c Champs Elysees—Lunathea (IRE) **Simon Treacher & Partner**
35 **PRETTY LETHAL**, ch f Lethal Force (IRE)—Pretty Primo (IRE) **Simon Treacher & Clarissa Casdagali**
36 **SALSA VERDE (IRE)**, b g Canford Cliffs (IRE)—Bridal Dance (IRE) **John Manser & Simon Treacher**
37 **SEXY BEAST**, b c Teofilo (IRE)—Wadaat **Spear Family**
38 **SWEETEST SMILE (IRE)**, b f Champs Elysees—Scorn (USA) **The LAM Partnership**

TWO-YEAR-OLDS

39 B c 25/1 Nathaniel (IRE)—Linda (FR) (Tamayuz) (65000)
40 B c 21/2 Paco Boy (IRE)—Lucky Breeze (IRE) (Key of Luck (USA)) **Mr C. C. Shand Kydd & Partner**
41 B c 16/4 Lope de Vega (IRE)—The Shrew (Dansili) (35000) **Mr E. B. de Giles**

Other Owners: Mr G. Barot, Mr A. N. C. Bengough, Mrs B. Blair, Mrs A. Buchanan, Mrs C. R. Casdagli, Mr S. N. Champ, Mrs A. P. Champion, Mr N. C. Champion, R. Colvin, Mrs S. Colvin, Mrs Y. Fleet, Dr M. F. Ford, Mr J. C. Golder, Mr N. Griffith, Mr G. A. Holmes, Mr T. D. J. Marshall, Mr R. Meakes, Ms L. M. Mulcahy, G. E. Powell, Mr P. R. Sercombe, C. C. Shand Kydd, Mr A. Spear, Mr P. Spear, Mr S. Treacher, A. J. Viall, Mrs C. R. de Giles.

---

139 MR GEOFFREY DEACON, Compton
Postal: **Hamilton Stables, Hockham Road, Compton, Newbury, Berkshire, RG20 6QJ**
Contacts: **MOBILE (07967) 626757**
E-MAIL geoffdeacon@aol.com **WEBSITE** www.geoffreydeacontraining.com

1 4, B f Phenomena—Attishoe **Mrs A. Wood**
2 **CAPTAIN RYAN**, 7, b g Captain Gerrard (IRE)—Ryan's Quest (IRE) **Andy Lomax, Boyd Mortimer**
3 **CHERISHED (IRE)**, 3, b f Kodiac—Marasem **Mrs E. F. Clarke**
4 4, Gr f Hellvelyn—Elderberry **Geoffrey Deacon Racing**
5 **HEPIJEU (FR)**, 7, b g Palace Episode (USA)—Helenjeu **Mr D. & Mrs H. Woodhall**
6 **IZZY PICCOLINA (IRE)**, 10, b m Morozov (USA)—Chloara (IRE) **Geoffrey Deacon Racing Club**
7 **MAGS WELL (IRE)**, 4, gr f Thewayyouare (USA)—Sliabh Aniaran (IRE) **Mr J. J. Kelly**
8 **PICKET LINE**, 6, b g Multiplex—Dockside Strike **Homegrown Partnership**
9 5, Ch m Tobougg (IRE)—Queen of The Bees (IRE) **Mrs S. Roe**
10 **RAHMAH (IRE)**, 6, b g Vale of York (IRE)—Sweet Home Alabama (IRE) **Business Moves Group & Partners**
11 **SUITSUS**, 7, b g Virtual—Point Perfect **Suitsus Partnership**
12 **SUTTONWOOD SALLY**, 4, b f Delegator—Hip Hip Hooray **Sutton Wood Partnership**

THREE-YEAR-OLDS

13 **MIRROR MAGIC**, b f Nathaniel (IRE)—Mirror Effect (IRE) **Mr S. K. McPhee**
14 **WOGGLE (IRE)**, ch f Camacho—Radio Wave **Hearty Racing**

MR GEOFFREY DEACON - Continued

TWO-YEAR-OLDS

15 **DEE DEE DOTTIE**, b f 24/3 Delegator—Pantita (Polish Precedent (USA)) **Sutton Wood Partnership**
16 **FROSTY TERN**, gr f 20/3 Aussie Rules (USA)—
                       Frosty Welcome (USA) (With Approval (CAN)) **Sutton Wood Partnership**
17 B f 2/3 Gale Force Ten—Hadya (IRE) (Teofilo (IRE))
18 B f 27/3 Born To Sea (IRE)—Khajool (IRE) (Haafhd)

Assistant Trainer: Sally Duckett

140	**MR DAVID DENNIS**, Hanley Swan

Postal: **Tyre Hill Racing Stables, Hanley Swan, Worcester, Worcestershire, WR8 0EQ**
Contacts: PHONE **(01684) 310565 MOBILE (07867) 974880**
E-MAIL **david@daviddennistrainer.co.uk** WEBSITE **www.ddracing.co.uk**

1 **BALLYEGAN WARRIOR (IRE)**, 6, b g Getaway (GER)—Sweet Empire (IRE) **Corbett Stud**
2 **BEHRANELL**, 4, b f Paco Boy (IRE)—Behra (IRE) **The David Dennis Racing Club**
3 **BLACKMILL (IRE)**, 7, b g Kalanisi (IRE)—Lady of The Mill (IRE) **Mrs J. Hitchings**
4 **BROKEN QUEST (IRE)**, 6, b g Ask—Broken Thought (IRE) **Wright Morgan Ltd & Partner**
5 **CRANK EM UP (IRE)**, 7, b g Royal Anthem (USA)—Carrawaystick (IRE) **Favourites Racing (Syndication) Ltd 12**
6 **CYCLOP (IRE)**, 7, b g King's Theatre (IRE)—Tasmani (FR) **DD Racing & Professor L P Hardwick**
7 **DANECASE**, 5, ch g Showcasing—Yding (IRE) **Professor L P Hardwick & Partner**
8 **DEAUVILLE DANCER (IRE)**, 7, b g Tamayuz—Mathool (IRE) **Favourites Racing (Syndication) Ltd 10**
9 **DIAMOND JOEL**, 6, b g Youmzain (IRE)—Miss Lacroix **Mrs N. S. Harris**
10 **DOITFORJOE (IRE)**, 8, ch g Vinnie Roe (IRE)—Native Kin (IRE) **B & S Vaughan & Rose Farm Developments**
11 **FINAL NUDGE (IRE)**, 9, b g Kayf Tara—Another Shot (IRE) **Corbett Stud**
12 **FLYING VERSE**, 6, b g Yeats (IRE)—Flight Sequence **Tyre Hill Farm Ltd**
13 **INDY FIVE (IRE)**, 6, b g Vertical Speed (FR)—Beesplease (IRE) **The Dobbin Club**
14 **INNISFREE LAD (IRE)**, 6, b g Yeats (IRE)—Tasmani (FR) **Rees, Hardwick, Vaughan, Allum & Saville**
15 **JAUNE ET BLEUE (FR)**, 6, gr m Al Namix (FR)—Jaune de Beaufai (FR) **Taylormaid**
16 **JUST SO COOL (IRE)**, 7, gr g Acambaro (GER)—Lauras Dote (IRE) **B & S Vaughan & Rose Farm Developments**
17 **LUCKY JIM**, 7, b g Lucky Story (USA)—Lateralle (IRE) **DD Racing & Professor L P Hardwick 2**
18 **MARQUIS OF CARABAS (IRE)**, 8, b br g Hurricane Run (IRE)—Miss Otis Regrets (IRE) **Favourites Racing Ltd**
19 **MR WASHINGTON (IRE)**, 5, b g Vinnie Roe (IRE)—Anna Bird (IRE) **Mrs J. Hitchings**
20 **NEETSIDE (IRE)**, 6, b m Getaway (GER)—Lady Wagtail (IRE) **Mrs J. E. Dennis**
21 4, Ch g Schiaparelli (GER)—Norma Hill **Mr G. Lloyd**
22 **NORSE LIGHT**, 7, ch g Norse Dancer (IRE)—Dimelight **The David Dennis Racing Club**
23 **PEPPAY LE PUGH (IRE)**, 7, b g Arakan (USA)—Pinaflore (FR) **Mr D. R. Dennis**
24 **PHOENIX PARK (GER)**, 6, b g Sholokhov (IRE)—Piercetown (IRE) **Mr D. R. Dennis**
25 **ROMAN FLIGHT (IRE)**, 10, b g Antonius Pius (USA)—Flight Sequence **Favourites Racing Ltd**
26 **SARANAPOUR**, 7, b m Shirocco (GER)—Samrana (FR) **No Fools And Horses Racing Club**
27 **SCHNABEL (IRE)**, 6, b g Ask—Velsatis (IRE) **Professor L P Hardwick & Partner**
28 **SEVEN KINGDOMS (IRE)**, 6, b g Yeats (IRE)—Valrhona (IRE) **Professor L P Hardwick & Partner**
29 **SHANTY TOWN (IRE)**, 9, b g Zagreb (USA)—Rapsan (IRE) **Mrs E. C. Stewart**
30 **STEEL SUMMIT (IRE)**, 9, b g Craigsteel—B Greenhill **B & S Vaughan**
31 4, B g Getaway (GER)—Stormy Breeze (IRE) **Clan McNeil**
32 **ZEE MAN (FR)**, 4, b g Soldier of Fortune (IRE)—Sky High Flyer **B & S Vaughan**

THREE-YEAR-OLDS

33 Br g Avonbridge—Encore du Cristal (USA) **Tyre Hill Farm Ltd**
34 Ch g Harbour Watch (IRE)—Honesty Pays **Tyre Hill Farm Ltd**
35 **KINGFAST (IRE)**, b g Fast Company (IRE)—Monarchy (IRE) **Tyre Hill Farm Ltd**
36 **MY SOCIETY (IRE)**, b g Society Rock (IRE)—Greek Easter (IRE) **Mr D. R. Dennis**
37 Br g Jeremy (USA)—Phantom Waters **Tyre Hill Farm Ltd**
38 **SWISSAL (IRE)**, b c Swiss Spirit—Al Gharrafa (IRE) **Tyre Hill Farm Ltd**

Other Owners: Mr R. Allum, Miss A. Bryan, Mr G. Bryan, Mr M. J. S. Cockburn, Mr D. W. Doolittle, Favourites Racing (Syndication) Ltd, J. R. Hall, Prof L. P. Hardwick, Mr M. N. Higgs, M. Hingley, Mr J. McNeil, Mr P. J. McNeil, Mrs J. Rees, Rose Farm Developments (UK) Ltd, Mr G. A. S. Saville, Mrs Ann Taylor, Mr B. D. Vaughan, Mrs S. A. Vaughan.

141 MR ROBIN DICKIN, Alcester

Postal: **Alne Park, Park Lane, Great Alne, Alcester, Warwickshire, B49 6HS**
Contacts: PHONE **(01789) 488148** (01789) **488388** MOBILE (07979) **518593** / (07979) **518594**
E-MAIL **claire@robindickinracing.org.uk** WEBSITE **www.robindickinracing.org.uk**

1 **ALL IS GOOD (IRE)**, 6, b g Scorpion (IRE)—Peinture Rose (IRE) **The Tricksters & The Goodies**
2 **BALLY LAGAN (IRE)**, 10, gr g Kalanisi (IRE)—Rose Palma (FR) **Park Lane Partnership**
3 **BELLE'S SPIRIT**, 5, b m Kutub (IRE)—Dickies Girl **The Happy Horse Partnership**
4 **BETTERLATETHANNEVA (IRE)**, 7, b m Albano (IRE)—Acqua Pesante (IRE) **Ms G. P. C. Howell**
5 **BLACK COUNTRY BOY**, 6, b g Black Sam Bellamy (IRE)—Simple Glory (IRE) **E. R. C. Beech & B. Wilkinson**
6 **BLAZING GOLD**, 5, b m Fair Mix (IRE)—Playing With Fire (IRE) **Mrs A. L. Merry**
7 **CELESTIAL CHIMES (IRE)**, 7, ch m Mahler—Celestial Rose (IRE) **Mrs C. M. Dickin**
8 **CHEER'S DELBOY (IRE)**, 5, ch g Golan (IRE)—Lindy Lou **Just 4 Fun**
9 **DAN'S QUEST**, 8, b g Kalanisi (IRE)—Piedmont (UAE) **Mr M. J. James**
10 **DONTMINDDBOYS (IRE)**, 9, gr g Portrait Gallery (IRE)—Native Ocean (IRE) **EPDS Racing Partnership 7**
11 **FUTURE BOY (IRE)**, 6, b g Beneficial—Money Clip (IRE) **Mrs C. M. Dickin**
12 **GALACTIC POWER (IRE)**, 8, ch g Gamut (IRE)—Celtic Peace (IRE) **EPDS Racing Twitterati Partnership**
13 **KADDYS DREAM**, 7, b m Kadastrof (FR)—Symbiosis **Shaw Racing & Tim Greig**
14 **LA FILLE FRANCAISE (FR)**, 5, b m Kapgarde (FR)—Pondimari (FR) **Mrs Louise Merry & Mrs Julia Venvell**
15 **LARA TROT (IRE)**, 6, b m Scorpion (IRE)—Honour Own (IRE) **Mrs C. M. Dickin**
16 **MYROUNDORURS (IRE)**, 8, b g Arakan (USA)—Six Bob (IRE) **John Nicholls (Trading) Ltd**
17 **NETHERTON BOY**, 5, b g Black Sam Bellamy (IRE)—Simple Glory (IRE) **E. R. C. Beech & B. Wilkinson**
18 **ONEIDA TRIBE (IRE)**, 9, b g Turtle Island (IRE)—Glory Queen (IRE) **John Nicholls (Trading) Ltd**
19 **SOME FINISH (IRE)**, 9, b g Kayf Tara—Kylie Kaprice (GER) **Mrs C Dickin & The Some Finish Partners**
20 **TARA WELL (IRE)**, 8, b m Kayf Tara—Miss Baden (IRE) **Mrs C. M. Dickin**
21 **THE LION MAN (IRE)**, 8, b g Let The Lion Roar—Just Smart (IRE) **Mrs M A Cooper & Mr J R Cooper**
22 **THOMAS CRAPPER**, 11, b g Tamure (IRE)—Mollycarrs Gambul **Apis.uk.com**
23 **THREE BULLET GATE (IRE)**, 5, b g Touch of Land (FR)—Brave Hope (IRE) **The Point Of Attack Partnership**
24 **TIMON'S TARA**, 9, gr m Kayf Tara—Princess Timon **Mr M. J. James**
25 **TWYCROSS WARRIOR**, 6, b g Cockney Rebel (IRE)—Gaelic Roulette (IRE) **Graham & Lynn Knight**
26 **UNDER THE PHONE (IRE)**, 9, b g Heron Island (IRE)—Theo On The Bench (IRE) **The Tricksters**
27 **VOCALISER (IRE)**, 6, b g Vocalised (USA)—Bring Back Matron (IRE) **The Songsters**
28 **WILDMOOR BOY**, 7, b g Midnight Legend—Simple Glory (IRE) **E. R. C. Beech & B. Wilkinson**
29 **YOUNG LOU**, 9, b m Kadastrof (FR)—Wanna Shout **E. R. C. Beech & B. Wilkinson**

THREE-YEAR-OLDS

30 **AFTERTHISONE**, ch g Pastoral Pursuits—Mandolin Wind **Mr & Mrs A Thompson**

Other Owners: E. R. C. Beech, Mrs C. H. Borghoff, Mr H. Brown, Mr R. A. Cockrell, Mrs M. A. Cooper, J. R. Cooper, Mr C. J. Dickin, Mrs A. Field, Mr M. F. FitzGerald, The Goodies, Mr T. L. Greig, D. J. Hern, Mr S. P. J. Kirby, Mrs L. C. Knight, G. Knight, Mr J. S. Porter, Mr J. R. Powell, Shaw Racing, Miss T. Sloan, Ms C. L. Spencer-Herbert, Mr A. Thompson, Mrs A. W. Thompson, Mrs J. C. Venvell, Mr P. Whitehead, B. Wilkinson.

Assistant Trainer: Claire Dickin

Jockey (NH): Charlie Poste, Jack Quinlan. **Amateur:** Mr James Martin.

---

142 MR JOHN DIXON, Carlisle

Postal: **Moorend, Thursby, Carlisle, Cumbria, CA5 6QP**
Contacts: PHONE **(01228) 711019**

1 **PISTOL (IRE)**, 9, b g High Chaparral (IRE)—Alinea (USA) **Mrs S. F. Dixon**
2 **PRESENCE FELT (IRE)**, 10, br g Heron Island (IRE)—Faeroe Isle (IRE) **Mrs S. F. Dixon**

Amateur: Mr J. J. Dixon.

143 **MR SCOTT DIXON, Retford**
Postal: **Haygarth House Stud, Haygarth House, Babworth, Retford, Nottinghamshire, DN22 8ES**
Contacts: **PHONE** (01777) 869300 (01777) 869079/701818 **FAX** (01777) 869326
MOBILE (07976) 267019
E-MAIL scottdixon1987@hotmail.com / mrsyvettedixon@gmail.com
WEBSITE www.scottdixonracing.com

1 **ALBERT BOY (IRE)**, 5, ch g Falco (USA)—Trumbaka (IRE) **Mr J. Radford**
2 **BEST TAMAYUZ**, 7, ch g Tamayuz—Pink Ivory **Winning Connections Racing**
3 **BOOGEY WONDERLAND**, 4, b f Paco Boy (IRE)—
                Western Eyes (IRE) **Mrs Mary Anne Parker & Mrs Yvette Dixon**
4 **BOOTS AND SPURS**, 9, b g Oasis Dream—Arctic Char **Mr S. E. Chappell**
5 **BREAK THE SILENCE**, 4, b g Rip Van Winkle (IRE)—In A Silent Way (IRE) **Winning Connections Racing**
6 **CHEZ VEGAS**, 5, gr g Hellvelyn—Lola Sapola (IRE) **Chesterfield Estates**
7 **COISTE BODHAR (IRE)**, 7, b g Camacho—Nortolixa (FR) **Yvonne Lowe & W A Robinson**
8 **CROSSE FIRE**, 6, b g Monsieur Bond (IRE)—Watersilk (IRE) **Paul J Dixon & Darren Lucas**
9 **DARK SHOT**, 5, b g Acclamation—Dark Missile
10 **DELIGHTFULSURPRISE**, 4, b f Delegator—Surprise Statement **Mr D Sharp and Partners**
11 **EBITDA**, 4, b f Compton Place—Tipsy Girl **Chesterfield Estates**
12 **FILLE THE FORCE**, 4, b f Sakhee's Secret—Coup de Torchon (FR) **Homecroft Wealth Racing & Partner**
13 **HUGIE BOY (IRE)**, 6, b g Art Connoisseur (IRE)—Piece Unique **Mr J. Radford**
14 **KRYSTALLITE**, 5, ch m Kheleyf (USA)—Chrystal Venture (IRE) **Paul J Dixon & The Chrystal Maze Ptn**
15 **LAKESKI**, 4, b f Sir Percy—Floating **Showstoppers Racing**
16 **LE LAITIER (FR)**, 7, b g Milk It Mick—La Brigitte **Ms Yvonne Lowe, P J Dixon & Partners**
17 **MEDICI MOON**, 4, ch g Medicean—Cockney Fire **Mr D Sharp and Partners**
18 **NELLIE'S DANCER**, 4, b f Mount Nelson—Xaphania **Winning Connections Racing**
19 **PEARL NOIR**, 8, b g Milk It Mick—Cora Pearl (IRE) **Winning Connections Racing**
20 **PENNY DREADFUL**, 6, b m Piccolo—Trina's Pet **Sexy Six Partnership**
21 **RED DOUGLAS**, 4, ch c Sakhee (USA)—Chrystal Venture (IRE) **Paul J Dixon & The Chrystal Maze Ptn**
22 **SANS SOUCI BAY**, 4, b c Medicean—Cumana Bay **The Sans Souci Bay Partnership**
23 **SARABI**, 5, b m Rip Van Winkle (IRE)—Xaphania **Paul J Dixon & Yvonne Lowe**
24 **SILKEN MOONLIGHT**, 4, b f Aqlaam—Silks (IRE) **Starlighters**
25 **SIR GEOFFREY (IRE)**, 12, b g Captain Rio—Disarm **General Sir Geoffrey Howlett/Mr Paul J. Dixon**
26 **SOCIALITES RED**, 5, ch m Sakhee's Secret—Tipsy Girl **J Melo Racing**
27 **THUNDERBELL**, 4, ch f Haafhd—Trustthunder **P. J. Dixon**
28 **TILLY DEVINE**, 4, gr f Aussie Rules (USA)—Cora Pearl (IRE) **Winning Connections Racing**

THREE-YEAR-OLDS

29 **CHICA DA SILVA**, b f Kheleyf (USA)—Cora Pearl (IRE) **Winning Connections Racing**
30 **IPCRESS FILE**, ch g Sixties Icon—Solmorin **Showstoppers Racing**
31 **JAFFAR**, b g Mawatheeq (USA)—Velvet Jaguar **P. J. Dixon**
32 **KATHY**, b f Bated Breath—Lolita Lebron (IRE) **Ian Buckley**
33 **LOVE RAT**, b g Mawatheeq (USA)—Watersilk (IRE) **Jilly Cooper & Friends**
34 **OPTIMICKSTICKHILL**, gr f Milk It Mick—Stylistickhill (IRE) **P. J. Dixon**
35 **SAMOVAR**, b g Finjaan—Chrystal Venture (IRE) **Paul J Dixon & The Chrystal Maze Ptn**
36 **SHORTBACKANDSIDES (IRE)**, b g Fast Company (IRE)—Whatagoodcatch (IRE) **L Bond-R Johnson**
37 **TEA RATTLE**, b f Finjaan—Scrooby Baby **Winning Connections Racing**
38 **THUNDERCLOUD**, gr f Aussie Rules (USA)—Trustthunder **P. J. Dixon**
39 Ch f Milk It Mick—Totally Trusted **The Doncaster Racing Club**

TWO-YEAR-OLDS

40 B f 4/3 Kyllachy—Blue Lyric (Refuse To Bend (IRE)) (32000) **Anglo Irish Partners**
41 B c 24/4 Showcasing—Freedom Pass (USA) (Gulch (USA)) (35000) **Anglo Irish Partners**

Other Owners: Mr A. D. Baker, Mr L. Bond, The Chrystal Maze Partnership, Mrs Y. Dixon, Dr A. J. F. Gillespie, Homecroft Wealth Racing, General Sir G. H. W. Howlett, Mr R. F. Johnson, Mrs M. Lingwood, Miss Y. Lowe, Mr D. R. Lucas, Mr J. Melo, Mrs M. Parker, Mr B. Pettis, Mr S. J. Piper, Mr W. A. Robinson, Mr D. Sharp, Mr A. C. Timms, Mrs S. Woodcroft.

Assistant Trainer: Mr K. Locking (07835 360125)

Amateur: Mr Kevin Locking.

144 MR STEVEN DIXON, Salisbury
Postal: **Apple Tree Barn, Livery Road, Winterslow, Nr Salisbury, Wiltshire, SP5 1RJ**
Contacts: **PHONE (01980) 862930 MOBILE (07771) 963011**
E-MAIL **sarahjdixon@hotmail.co.uk**

1 **I'LL BE YOUR CLOWN (IRE)**, 7, b g Aqlaam—Lady Avenger (IRE) **Mr S. D. Dixon**
2 **SHADOW BLUE (IRE)**, 9, br g Blueprint (IRE)—Rosie Belle (IRE) **Mr S. D. Dixon**

Assistant Trainer: Mrs Sarah Dixon

145 MRS ROSE DOBBIN, Alnwick
Postal: **South Hazelrigg Farm, Chatton, Alnwick, Northumberland, NE66 5RZ**
Contacts: **PHONE (01668) 215395 (office) (01668) 215151 (house) FAX (01668) 215114**
MOBILE (07969) 993563
E-MAIL **hazelriggracing1@btconnect.com WEBSITE www.rosedobbinracing.co.uk**

1 **ATTENTION PLEASE (IRE)**, 8, b g Kalanisi (IRE)—
Dangerous Dolly (IRE) **Mr Ronnie Jacobs & Mrs Rose Dobbin**
2 **BAKO DE LA SAULAIE (FR)**, 7, b g Balko (FR)—Krickette (FR) **Mr & Mrs Duncan Davidson**
3 **BIGIRONONHISHIP (IRE)**, 7, b g Beneficial—Portobello Lady (IRE) **Mr & Mrs Duncan Davidson**
4 **CANT PAY WONT PAY (IRE)**, 10, b g Flying Legend (USA)—Kadastrofs Prize (IRE) **Mr G. Delahunt**
5 **CLASSICAL SOUND (IRE)**, 6, b g Mahler—Sovienne (IRE) **M Hunter, J Matterson & R Jacobs**
6 4, b g Arcadio (GER)—Clover Pearl (IRE) **Mrs R. Dobbin**
7 **COOLE HALL (IRE)**, 6, b g Flemensfirth (USA)—Coole Assembly (IRE) **Mr & Mrs Duncan Davidson**
8 **DOKTOR GLAZ (FR)**, 8, b g Mount Nelson—Deviolina (IRE) **Mr & Mrs D Davidson & The Friday Lions**
9 **FINAL FLING (IRE)**, 7, b g Milan—Supreme Singer (IRE) **J. M. & Mrs M. R. Edwardson**
10 **HEATHER BURNING (IRE)**, 7, b g Mountain High (IRE)—Go To Blazes (IRE) **The Friday Lions 2**
11 **JACK DEVINE (IRE)**, 6, b g Kalanisi (IRE)—Sybil Says (IRE) **Mr & Mrs Duncan Davidson**
12 **JONNIESOFA (IRE)**, 8, b g Well Made (GER)—Lucky Sarah (IRE) **Mr R & Mrs A Houghton & Mr A Houghton**
13 **LADY LONDON (IRE)**, 7, b m Beneficial—Torduff Storm (IRE) **Miss C. L. Jones**
14 **LE GAVROCHE (IRE)**, 5, b g Flemensfirth (USA)—Knockieran (IRE) **Mr. Ronnie Jacobs & Mr. Albert Roux**
15 **LOG ON (IRE)**, 7, b g Scorpion (IRE)—Go Girl (IRE) **R. Jacobs, S. Davidson, R. & T. Dobbin**
16 **MINELLA SUITE (IRE)**, 7, br g Oscar (IRE)—Ballymaguirelass (IRE) **Mr & Mrs Duncan Davidson**
17 **MISTER DON (IRE)**, 8, br g Presenting—Spring Flower (IRE) **Mr Ronnie Jacobs & Mrs Rose Dobbin**
18 **MONFASS (IRE)**, 7, b g Trans Island—Ajo Green (IRE) **Mrs Dobbin & The Dimhorns**
19 **PERMISSION GRANTED (IRE)**, 6, b g Oscar (IRE)—Ask The Misses (IRE) **Jacobs & Dobbin**
20 **PLANET NINE (IRE)**, 6, b g Flemensfirth (USA)—Old Moon (IRE) **Mr & Mrs Duncan Davidson**
21 **PROFESSOR PLUM (IRE)**, 8, b g Kalanisi (IRE)—Miss Plum **Mr & Mrs Duncan Davidson**
22 **PURCELL'S BRIDGE (FR)**, 11, b g Trempolino (USA)—
Theatrical Lady (USA) **Mr John Dickson & Mrs Sarah Davidson**
23 **ROCKING BLUES (FR)**, 13, b g Lavirco (GER)—Herbe de La Roque (FR) **Partnership Terminated**
24 **ROMULUS DU DONJON (FR)**, 7, gr g Stormy River (FR)—
Spring Stroll (USA) **Major General C. Ramsay & Mr. R Roberts**
25 **SLANELOUGH (IRE)**, 6, b g Westerner—Tango Lady (IRE) **Miss J. Matterson & Mrs D. Davidson**
26 **SMUGGLER'S STASH (IRE)**, 8, ch g Stowaway—Sweetasanu (IRE) **Mr & Mrs Duncan Davidson**
27 **SOME REIGN (IRE)**, 7, b g Kayf Tara—Bridge Love (FR) **Mr & Mrs Duncan Davidson**
28 **SWEET AS CANDY (IRE)**, 6, b g Morozov (USA)—Sweet Nancy (IRE) **Mr & Mrs Duncan Davidson**
29 **VINTAGE GLEN (IRE)**, 6, b g Ask—Rare Vintage (IRE) **Mr T. J. Hemmings**
30 **WITNESS TIME (IRE)**, 6, b g Witness Box (USA)—Emotional Melody (IRE) **Mr T. J. Hemmings**

Other Owners: Mrs S. K. Davidson, D. H. Davidson, Mr J. L. Dickson, Mr L. Dimsdale, Mr A. G. Dobbin, J. M. Edwardson, Mrs M. R. Edwardson, Mr R. Houghton, Mrs A. M. Houghton, Mr A. Houghton, M. S. Hunter, Mr R. A. Jacobs, J. R. Jeffreys, Miss J. G. K. Matterson, Exors of the Late Maj-Gen Sir C. A. Ramsay, Mr R. Roberts, Mr A. H. Roux, Mr D. A. C. Spencer-Churchill.

Assistant Trainer: Tony Dobbin (07775) 680894

Jockey (NH): Craig Nichol. **Conditional:** Lorcan Murtagh.

146 **MR MICHAEL DODS, Darlington**

Postal: **Denton Hall Farm, Piercebridge, Darlington, Co. Durham, DL2 3TY**
Contacts: PHONE **(01325) 374270** FAX **(01325) 374020** MOBILE **(07860) 411590/
(07773) 290830 C Dods**
E-MAIL **dods@michaeldodsracing.co.uk** WEBSITE **www.michaeldodsracing.co.uk**

1 **APRICOT SKY**, 8, ch g Pastoral Pursuits—Miss Apricot **The Wayward Lads**
2 **ARCHI'S AFFAIRE**, 4, ch g Archipenko (USA)—Affaire d'amour **D. Neale**
3 **DAKOTA GOLD**, 4, b g Equiano (FR)—Joyeaux **Doug Graham & Ian Davison**
4 **DAVY'S DILEMMA**, 4, b g Sixties Icon—Wansdyke Lass **D. Neale**
5 **FUMBO JUMBO (IRE)**, 5, b m Zebedee—Baraloti (IRE) **Sekura Trade Frames Ltd**
6 **GET KNOTTED (IRE)**, 6, ch g Windsor Knot (IRE)—Genuinely (IRE) **D. Neale**
7 **GRINTY (IRE)**, 4, b g Elnadim (USA)—Fire Line **Mr J. N. Blackburn**
8 **INTENSE ROMANCE (IRE)**, 4, b f Intense Focus (USA)—Hedera (USA) **Mr H. M. Linsley**
9 **KINGS GOLD (IRE)**, 5, ch g Excellent Art—Party Feet (IRE) **Mr Peter Appleton & Mr M. J. K. Dods**
10 **KIWI BAY**, 13, b g Mujahid (USA)—Bay of Plenty (FR) **Kiwi Racing**
11 **LE CHAT D'OR**, 10, b g One Cool Cat (USA)—Oh So Well (IRE) **Dr Anne J. F. Gillespie/Mr M. J. K. Dods**
12 **MININGGOLD**, 5, b m Piccolo—Rosein **Mrs C. E. Dods**
13 **MISTER BELVEDERE**, 4, b g Archipenko (USA)—Diablerette **Mr Allan Mcluckie & Mr M. J. K. Dods**
14 **MOOLTAZEM (IRE)**, 4, b g Elzaam (AUS)—Whisper Dance (USA) **Mr M. D. Pearson**
15 **MUSTAQBAL (IRE)**, 6, b g Invincible Spirit (IRE)—Alshamatry (USA) **M. J. K. Dods**
16 **MY NAME IS RIO (IRE)**, 8, ch g Captain Rio—Walk In My Shadow (IRE) **K. Kirkup**
17 **OCEAN SHERIDAN (IRE)**, 6, b g Starspangledbanner (AUS)—
Endless Night (GER) **Mr J Blackburn & Mr A Turton**
18 **PROUD ARCHI (IRE)**, 4, b g Archipenko (USA)—Baharah (USA) **Eagle Racing**

THREE-YEAR-OLDS

19 **ADMIRAL ROOKE (IRE)**, b g Rock of Gibraltar (IRE)—Qenaa **M Pearson & S Lowthian**
20 **ARCAVALLO (IRE)**, ch c Arcano (IRE)—Pashmina (IRE) **Mr P Appleton & Mrs Anne Elliott**
21 **BYRON'S CHOICE**, b g Poet's Voice—Byrony (IRE) **Exors of Mr Wynn Williams & Mr D Graham**
22 **CAMACHO CHIEF (IRE)**, b g Camacho—Passage To India (IRE) **Davison & Drysdale**
23 **FARHH AWAY**, ch g Farhh—Bukhoor (IRE) **D Neale & Exors of JA Wynn-Williams**
24 **FRENCH FLYER (IRE)**, b g Pour Moi (IRE)—Leavingonajetplane (IRE) **D. Neale**
25 **HEIRSLOOKINGATYOU**, b g Maxios—Souvenance **STS Racing**
26 **ILIKEYOUALOT (IRE)**, b f Swiss Spirit—Timeless (USA) **STS Racing**
27 **JACKONTHEROCKS**, b g Bated Breath—Desert Kiss **Mr V Spinks & Partner**
28 **JOHN KIRKUP**, ch g Assertive—Bikini **Mrs Suzanne Kirkup & Mr Kevin Kirkup**
29 **MECCA'S MINSTREL (IRE)**, b f Poet's Voice—Hairy Rocket **D J Metcalfe & M Dods**
30 **MECCA'S SPIRIT (IRE)**, gr f Dark Angel (IRE)—Wiltshire Life (IRE) **D J Metcalfe & M Dods**
31 **RUMSHAK (IRE)**, ch g Arcano (IRE)—Scarlet Rosefinch **Mrs C. Dods & Mr D Stone**
32 **SUPER MAJOR (IRE)**, b g Sir Prancealot—Majestic Alexander (IRE) **Mrs C Hewitson, Mr M Dods**
33 **TEAM SHOWME**, b f Harbour Watch (IRE)—Straitjacket **Champagne Charlies Club**
34 **TEBAY (IRE)**, b g Elzaam (AUS)—Maid of Ale (IRE) **Mr David W. Armstrong & Mr M. J. K. Dods**
35 **TOOHOTTOTOUCH**, b g Hellvelyn—Soft Touch (IRE) **Denton Hall Racing Ltd**
36 **WAHOO**, b g Stimulation (IRE)—Shohrah (USA) **Mr J Blackburn & Mr A Turton**
37 **WHAT DO YOU THINK (IRE)**, b f Excelebration (IRE)—Dama'a (IRE) **Bolton Grange**

TWO-YEAR-OLDS

38 B g 23/3 Epaulette—Baylini (Bertolini (USA)) (18000) **M. J. K. Dods**
39 B c 31/1 Zoffany (IRE)—Change Course (Sadler's Wells (USA)) (6250) **Mr Peter Appleton & Mr M. J. K. Dods**
40 **DANCIN BOY**, br c 6/3 Gregorian (IRE)—La Gifted (Fraam) (17908) **Mr R. R. D. Saunders**
41 B c 7/3 War Command (USA)—Emeralds Spirit (Rock of Gibraltar (IRE)) (16000) **T. A. Scothern**
42 **FLINT HILL**, ch c 2/2 Excelebration (IRE)—Modify (New Approach (IRE)) (29523) **Mr T. P. Curry**
43 Ch f 31/3 Dutch Art—Maremmadiavola (IRE) (Kheleyf (USA)) (35000) **Mr D W Armstrong & Mr M J K Dods**
44 Br c 9/3 Epaulette (AUS)—Miaplacidus (IRE) (Shamardal (USA)) (10000) **Mr G Thompson & Mr M Dods**
45 B f 13/3 Es Que Love (IRE)—
Onomatomania (USA) (Mr Greeley (USA)) (28000) **Mr P Appleton & Mrs Anne Elliott**
46 B g 20/2 Clodovil (IRE)—Sabaidee (IRE) (Beat Hollow) (8140) **Mr J Sagar & Mr M Dods**
47 Ch f 29/2 Kyllachy—Samasana (IRE) (Redback) (30476) **Redgate Bloodstock**
48 B c 26/1 Bated Breath—Sea Pink (Oasis Dream) (40000) **Mr David W. Armstrong & Mr M. J. K. Dods**

Other Owners: Mr P. Appleton, Mr D. W. Armstrong, Mr C. Banister, Mr I. Bennett, Mr Ian Davison, Mr M. Dixon, Mr A. Drysdale, Mrs A. E. Elliott, J. A. Ellis, Miss E. A. Ellis, Mr D. C. Flynn, Miss E. Foley, Dr A. J. F. Gillespie, Mr D. R. Graham, Mr C. D. Harrison, Mrs C. M. Hewitson, Mrs S. Kirkup, Mr S. R. Lowthian, Mr A. McLuckie, D. T. J. Metcalfe, Mrs S. Peacock, STS Racing Limited, Mr J. Sagar, Mr S. R. Skinns, V. J. Spinks, Mr D. Stone, Mr M. W. Syme, Mr P. A. Taylor, Mr G. C. Thompson, Mr A. Turton, Mr M. J. Waite, D. Watts.

MR MICHAEL DODS - Continued

Assistant Trainers: Carole Dods, Steve Alderson (07533) 401887

Jockey (flat): Connor Beasley, Paul Mulrennan. **Apprentice:** Callum Rodriguez. **Amateur:** Miss Chloe Dods, Miss Sophie Dods.

---

147 **MR CONOR DORE, Frampton Fen**
Postal: **Barford Farm, Swineshead Road, Frampton Fen, Boston, Lincolnshire, PE20 1SG**
Contacts: **PHONE (01775) 822747 MOBILE (07984) 609170**
E-MAIL dores@supanet.com

1 CERTIFICATE, 7, ch g Pivotal—Graduation **A. N. Page**
2 CHELWOOD GATE (IRE), 8, gr g Aussie Rules (USA)—Jusoor (USA) **Louise Marsh & Mike Fitzsimons**
3 MININGROCKS (FR), 6, b g Lawman (FR)—Fashion School **C. D. Marsh**
4 NAG'S WAG (IRE), 5, b m Approve (IRE)—Street Kitty (IRE) **Mrs Jennifer Marsh & Mrs Louise Marsh**
5 ROYAL BEEKEEPER, 5, ch g Champs Elysees—Lasso **Mrs J. R. Marsh**
6 TOWERING (IRE), 9, b g Catcher In The Rye (IRE)—Bobs Article (IRE) **Mrs L. J. Marsh**
7 TRAPPER PEAK (IRE), 9, b g Westerner—Banningham Blaze **Mrs Jennifer Marsh & Mrs Louise Marsh**
8 VIVAT REX (IRE), 7, b g Fastnet Rock (AUS)—Strawberry Roan (IRE) **C. D. Marsh**
9 YASIR (USA), 10, b g Dynaformer (USA)—Khazayin (USA) **Mrs Jennifer Marsh & Mrs Louise Marsh**

TWO-YEAR-OLDS

10 B f 20/4 Toronado (IRE)—Daysiwaay (IRE) (Daylami (IRE)) (7500) **Mrs L. J. Marsh**
11 B f 25/1 Heeraat (IRE)—Say A Prayer (Indesatchel (IRE)) (6000) **Mrs J. R. Marsh**

Other Owners: Mr M. Fitzsimons.

---

148 **MR SIMON DOW, Epsom**
Postal: **Clearheights Stables, Derby Stables Road, Epsom, Surrey, KT18 5LB**
Contacts: **PHONE (01372) 721490 MOBILE (07860) 800109**
E-MAIL simon@simondow.co.uk WEBSITE www.simondow.co.uk Twitter: @SimonDowRacing

1 CHICA DE LA NOCHE, 4, b f Teofilo (IRE)—Welsh Cake **Mr R. J. Moss**
2 EMENEM, 4, b g Sir Percy—Kahalah (IRE) **Robert Moss & Damien Brennan**
3 FORCEFUL APPEAL (USA), 10, b b g Successful Appeal (USA)—Kinetic Force (USA) **Mr M. McAllister**
4 GALINTHIAS, 6, b g Sixties Icon—Tidie France (USA) **Ms S Snell & Mr S Dow**
5 HOMBRE ROJO (IRE), 5, b g Intikhab (USA)—Sidney Girl **Mr R. J. Moss**
6 HURRICANE ROCK, 5, ch g Rock of Gibraltar (IRE)—Seasonal Cross **Malcolm & Alicia Aldis**
7 LE TORRENT, 6, ch g Sir Percy—Cinnas Ransom **P. G. Jacobs**
8 LICENSE TO THRILL (USA), 4, b g Mizzen Mast (USA)—Mystic Miracle **Mr R. E. Anderson**
9 MR SCARAMANGA, 4, b c Sir Percy—Lulla Cigala (IRE) **Robert Moss & Damien Brennan**
10 NATIVE FIGHTER (IRE), 4, b c Lawman (FR)—Night of Magic (IRE) **Mr M. J. Convey**
11 REGAL GAIT (IRE), 5, b g Tagula (IRE)—Babylonian **P. G. Jacobs**
12 ROUNDABOUT MAGIC (IRE), 4, ch c Zebedee—Cayo Largo (IRE) **Six Mile Hill Racing**
13 ROYAL APPROACH (GER), 4, ch g New Approach (IRE)—Royal Dubai (GER)
14 SPARKALOT, 4, br c Bated Breath—Three Wrens (IRE) **R Moss, D Brennan, H Redknapp**

THREE-YEAR-OLDS

15 ALBISHR (IRE), b c Clodovil (IRE)—Casual Remark (IRE) **Robert Moss & Damien Brennan**
16 BOBBY BISCUIT (USA), b c Scat Daddy (USA)—Poupee Flash (USA) **Robert Moss & Damien Brennan**
17 BROGANS BAY (IRE), b f Born To Sea (IRE)—Sister Sylvia **R. A. Murray-Obodynski**
18 CHACACHACARE (IRE), b g Power—Half-Hitch (USA) **Chua, Ong, Persad & Dow**
19 CORAZON ESPINADO (IRE), b c Iffraaj—Three Decades (IRE) **Mr R. J. Moss**
20 EL BORRACHO (IRE), br g Society Rock—Flame of Hibernia (IRE) **Mr R. J. Moss**
21 OJALA (IRE), b c Epaulette (AUS)—Sonny Sunshine **Mr R. J. Moss**
22 PASTORAL DREAMS, b c Pastoral Pursuits—Engaging **Mr C Cooley, Mrs T Kelly, Mr T Wickins**
23 PRINCE ROCK (IRE), ch g Society Rock—She's A Queen (IRE) **Mr M. McAllister**
24 SARGENTO, b g Dick Turpin (IRE)—Vezere (USA) **Mr R. J. Moss**

Other Owners: Mr M. S. Aldis, Mrs A. Aldis, Mr D. Brennan, Mr C. G. J. Chua, Mr C. I. Cooley, S. L. Dow, Mrs T. Kelly, Mr F. Ong, Mr R. Persad, Mr H. Redknapp, Ms S. A. Snell, Mr T. Wickins.

149 **MR CHRIS DOWN, Cullompton**
Postal: Upton, Cullompton, Devon, EX15 1RA
Contacts: **PHONE** (01884) 33097 **FAX** (01884) 33097 **MOBILE** (07828) 021232
E-MAIL cjdownracing@gmail.com

1 ANNIE PROBUS, 5, ch m Geordieland (FR)—Probus Lady **Mr E. G. M. Beard**
2 BILLY DUTTON, 12, ch g Sir Harry Lewis (USA)—Tinoforty (FR) **Upton Racing 2**
3 BILLY MY BOY, 9, b g Volochine (IRE)—Key West (FR) **Mr J. B. Radford**
4 CULM COUNSELLOR, 9, ch g Erhaab (USA)—Miss Counsel **Culm Valley Racing**
5 FOXY ACT, 7, ch m Act One—Brown Fox (FR) **C. J. Down**
6 GAELIC FLOW, 7, ch g With The Flow (USA)—Gaelic Lime **The Jack High Racing Partnership**
7 ICE TRES, 9, br m Iceman—Tup Tim **C. J. Down**
8 4, ch f Shantou (USA)—Kingara **C. J. Down**
9 LADIES DANCING, 12, b g Royal Applause—Queen of Dance (IRE) **C. J. Down**
10 MAX FORTE (IRE), 8, br g Indian River (FR)—Brook Forte **P Holland, JT Measures, MA Kerr, V Holland**
11 MOTTS CROSS (IRE), 7, b g Scorpion (IRE)—Rainy Season (IRE) **S. Trump**
12 ORDENSRITTER (GER), 10, ch g Samum (GER)—Dramraire Mist **Red Baron Racing**
13 PAHASKA (GER), 5, b m Saddex—Pacific Cun (GER) **P. Holland, V. Holland, J. Measures**
14 SCRUPULEUX (FR), 7, b g Laveron—Rouge Folie (FR) **Mrs M. Trueman & Mr A O Neill**
15 STARLIT NIGHT, 6, b m Nayef (USA)—Perfect Night **C. J. Down**

Other Owners: Mr H. J. W. Davies, Dr Mark Dixon, Mr C. J. Down, Mrs Jacqui Elliott, Mr Norman Elliott, Mr A. D. Hill, Mr P. Holland, Mrs V. Holland, Ms M. A. Kerr, Mrs Hazel Leeves, Mr J. T. Measures, Mr A. G. O'Neill, Mrs M. Trueman.

Jockey (NH): James Davies, Richard Johnson, Tom Scudamore. **Conditional:** Kieron Edgar, Ciaran Gethings.
Amateur: Miss P. Fuller.

150 **MR CLIVE DREW, Rampton**
Postal: Fox End Stables, 83 King Street, Rampton, Cambridgeshire, CB24 8QD
Contacts: **PHONE/FAX** (01954) 250772 **MOBILE** (07917) 718127
E-MAIL polly.drew@googlemail.com

1 MAISON BRILLET (IRE), 11, b g Pyrus (USA)—Stormchaser (IRE) **C. Drew**
2 MONSIEUR ROYALE, 8, ch g Monsieur Bond (IRE)—Bond Royale **C. Drew**
3 MR SNIPS, 5, b g Indian Haven—Madam'x **C. Drew**

Assistant Trainer: Miss Polly Drew

151 **MR DAVID W. DRINKWATER, Redmarley**
Postal: Chapel Farm, Chapel Lane, Redmarley, Gloucester, Gloucestershire, GL19 3JF
Contacts: **PHONE** (07766) 011007 (07973) 193771
E-MAIL drinkys35@outlook.com

1 ASHPAN SAM, 9, b g Firebreak—Sweet Patoopie **Advantage Chemicals Holdings Ltd**
2 DEAR BRUIN (IRE), 6, b m Kodiac—Namu **Advantage Chemicals Holdings Ltd**
3 DLTRIPLESEVEN (IRE), 5, gr g Dark Angel (IRE)—Namu **Advantage Chemicals Holdings Ltd**
4 MAHNA MAHNA (IRE), 4, b g Kodiac—Namu **Advantage Chemicals Holdings Ltd**
5 MISS DUSKY DIVA (IRE), 6, gr m Verglas (IRE)—Dispol Veleta **Advantage Chemicals Holdings Ltd**
6 TABLE BLUFF (IRE), 9, ch g Indian Haven—Double Deal **Advantage Chemicals Holdings Ltd**

Assistant Trainer: Rachel Tudor

Jockey (flat): William Carson. **Jockey (NH):** Nico De Boinville.

152 **MR SAMUEL DRINKWATER, Strensham**
Postal: The Granary, Twyning Road, Strensham, Worcester, Worcestershire, WR8 9LH
Contacts: **MOBILE** (07747) 444633
E-MAIL samdrinkwater@gmail.com

1 BIGCHEXTOCASH (IRE), 6, b g Stowaway—Monakeeba (IRE) **P. Drinkwater**
2 BILLY HICKS, 7, b g Kayf Tara—Michelle's Ella (IRE) **P. Drinkwater**
3 CHATELIER (FR), 6, ch g Network (GER)—Elza III (FR) **The Lucky Seven**

MR SAMUEL DRINKWATER - Continued

4 **COME ON TEDDY (IRE)**, 4, b g Fame And Glory—Theatre View (IRE) **Mr N T Griffith & H M Haddock**
5 **FIRST DU CHARMIL (FR)**, 6, ch g Ballingarry (IRE)—Famous Member (FR) **Mr N T Griffith & H M Haddock**
6 **GENERAL CONSENSUS**, 6, br g Black Sam Bellamy (IRE)—Charlottes Webb (IRE) **Mrs K. Drinkwater**
7 5, B g Geordieland (FR)—Je Ne Sais Plus (FR)
8 **KAUTO LINGARRY (FR)**, 6, ch g Ballingarry (IRE)—Kauto Luisa (FR) **Mrs J. Drinkwater**
9 **MAXIMUS MARIDIUS**, 7, br g Fair Mix (IRE)—Dutch Czarina **Mr R. E. Bailey**
10 6, B g Black Sam Bellamy (IRE)—Mimi Equal **Mr K. Kane**
11 **NORTHANDSOUTH (IRE)**, 8, ch g Spadoun (FR)—Ennel Lady (IRE) **Strensham Stragglers**
12 **PRAY FOR A RAINBOW**, 7, b g Rainbow High—Blackchurch Lass (IRE) **Kevin & Anne Glastonbury**
13 **RIF RAFTOU (IRE)**, 8, b m Shantou (USA)—Sanadja (IRE) **P. Drinkwater**
14 **RIGHT ON ROY**, 8, b g Double Trigger (IRE)—One Wild Night **Mr R. E. Bailey**
15 **RUSSIAN SERVICE**, 6, b g Robin des Champs (FR)—Just Kate **Mr N T Griffith & H M Haddock**
16 **SAMARETTO**, 6, b g Black Sam Bellamy (IRE)—Amaretto Rose **Mr K. Kane**
17 **SERGEANT BRODY**, 7, ch g Black Sam Bellamy (IRE)—Ardent Bride **Mrs K. Drinkwater**
18 **SPITFIRE REGGIE**, 5, b g Flying Legend (USA)—Angie Marinie **Mr D. P. Drinkwater**
19 **TOP DECISION (IRE)**, 5, ch g Beneficial—Great Decision (IRE) **Prestbury Racing Club**
20 **TOUR DE PUB (IRE)**, 4, ch g Aizavoski (IRE)—Gallant Express (IRE)
21 4, Ch g Sulamani (IRE)—Wychwoods Legend

Other Owners: R. J. Clarke, Mr K. J. Glastonbury, Mrs A. J. Glastonbury, Mr N. Griffith, Mrs H. M. Haddock, C. D. Massey, Mr M. Pearse, Mr N. J. Witts-Hewinson.

---

153 **MISS JACKIE DU PLESSIS, Saltash**
Postal: **Burell Farm, Longlands, Saltash, Cornwall, PL12 4QH**
Contacts: **PHONE (01752) 842362 MOBILE (07970) 871505**
E-MAIL ziggerson@aol.com

1 **ARTHUR BURRELL**, 9, ch g With The Flow (USA)—Kingsmill Quay **Miss J. M. du Plessis**
2 **CAILLEACH ANNIE (IRE)**, 9, b m Blueprint (IRE)—Graineuaile (IRE) **Miss J. M. du Plessis**
3 **DRAGON'S DEN (IRE)**, 11, b g Antonius Pius (USA)—Tallassee **G. R. Waterman**
4 **ERICAS LAD**, 7, b g Mutazayid (IRE)—Kingsmill Quay **Miss J. M. du Plessis**
5 **FEAR GLIC (IRE)**, 12, b g Dr Massini (IRE)—Graineuaile (IRE) **Miss J Du Plessis & Mr G Waterman**
6 **FRANCE DU LUKKA (FR)**, 4, bl f Kap Rock (FR)—Orlamonde Queen (FR) **The Cornish Barmies**
7 **LADY KINGSMILL**, 7, b m Bandmaster (USA)—Kingsmill Lake **Miss J. M. du Plessis**
8 **MEXICAN BORDER (GER)**, 9, b g Sholokhov (IRE)—Moricana (GER) **Miss J. M. du Plessis**
9 **POLO THE MUMM (FR)**, 8, b g Great Journey (JPN)—Maido (FR) **Mrs R. Welch**
10 **RUPERT VALENTINO**, 5, gr g Schiaparelli (GER)—Magic Valentine **The Cornish Barmies**
11 **SEA PRESENT (IRE)**, 6, b m Presenting—Nautical Lady (IRE) **Miss J. M. du Plessis**
12 **ST ERNEY**, 7, ch g Kadastrof (FR)—Ticket To The Moon **Miss J. M. du Plessis**
13 **THEATRE MARS**, 5, gr m Fair Mix (IRE)—Theatre Diva (IRE) **Miss J. M. du Plessis**
14 **TREHAN CROSS**, 9, b m Bandmaster (USA)—Halton Quay **Miss J. M. du Plessis**
15 **WINNING SPARK (USA)**, 11, b g Theatrical—Spark Sept (FR) **Miss J. M. du Plessis**

Other Owners: Miss S. Pridham.

---

154 **MRS ANN DUFFIELD, Leyburn**
Postal: **Sunhill Racing Ltd, Sun Hill Farm, Constable Burton, Leyburn, North Yorkshire, DL8 5RL**
Contacts: **PHONE (01677) 450303 FAX (01677) 450993 MOBILE (07802) 496332**
E-MAIL ann@annduffield.co.uk WEBSITE www.annduffield.co.uk

1 **ARNOLD**, 4, b g Equiano (FR)—Azurinta (IRE) **Shewring, Marshall, Craig, Fantoni**
2 **CHANT (IRE)**, 8, b g Oratorio (IRE)—Akarita (IRE) **Mrs Ann Starkie & Mrs I. Starkie**
3 **HIGHLY FOCUSSED (IRE)**, 4, b g Intense Focus (USA)—Mood Indigo (IRE) **The Duchess of Sutherland**
4 **HILARY J**, 5, b m Mount Nelson—The Terrier **E & R Stott**
5 **MIMIC'S MEMORY**, 4, b f Sayif (IRE)—Blue Crest (FR) **Peter Wilson & Partner**
6 **MISS BATES**, 4, b f Holy Roman Emperor (IRE)—Jane Austen (IRE) **The Duchess of Sutherland**
7 **NIFTY NIECE (IRE)**, 4, gr f Zebedee—Hasty Harriet (IRE) **The Duchess of Sutherland**
8 **RED CHARMER (IRE)**, 8, b g Red Clubs (IRE)—Golden Charm (IRE) **Mr I Farrington & Mr R Chapman**
9 **ROSINA**, 5, b m Showcasing—Mondovi **Ms J. F. Bianco**
10 **SUGAR BEACH (FR)**, 4, b f Canford Cliffs (IRE)—Aktia (IRE) **Mrs S Bianco & Ms J Bianco**
11 **UNCLE CHARLIE (IRE)**, 4, b g Vale of York (IRE)—Velvet Kiss (IRE) **Mr David Barker & Partner**

MRS ANN DUFFIELD - Continued

THREE-YEAR-OLDS

12 **BALMEC (IRE)**, bl g Society Rock (IRE)—Crossreadh (USA) **Rasio Cymru Racing 1 & Iboxit Ltd**
13 **BIBBIDIBOBBIDIBOO (IRE)**, b f Red Jazz (USA)—Provence **Ms J. F. Bianco**
14 **CANFORD'S JOY (IRE)**, b g Canford Cliffs (IRE)—Joyful (IRE) **Mr J. R. Dwyer**
15 **COTTON SOCKS (IRE)**, b g Dream Ahead (USA)—Kartella (IRE) **Mrs Ann Starkie & Partner**
16 **CUPPACOCO**, b f Stimulation (IRE)—Glen Molly (IRE) **C A Gledhill & Partner**
17 **FASCINATOR**, ch f 21/3 Hoderic O'connor (IRE)—Mary Read **E & R Stott**
18 **GORSE (IRE)**, b g Zebedee—Golden Flower **The Duchess of Sutherland**
19 **I'M YER MAN**, b g Foxwedge (AUS)—Coffee Cup (IRE) **The Birrafun Partnership**
20 **KYLIE RULES**, bl f Aussie Rules (USA)—Africa's Star (IRE) **Mr J. A. Knox and Mrs M. A. Knox**
21 **LADY LINTERA (IRE)**, b f Lilbourne Lad (IRE)—Lintera (GER) **The Gathering Partnership & Partner**
22 **LUNA LADY**, ch f Paco Boy (IRE)—Tamara Moon (IRE) **The Duchess of Sutherland**
23 **SALIRE (IRE)**, b f Intense Focus (USA)—Gariepa (GER) **Iboxit Ltd & Partner**
24 **SUNHILL LAD (IRE)**, gr g Lilbourne Lad (IRE)—Gris Ladera (IRE) **Mr Alan Court & Partner**
25 **SYMPHONIC**, b f Mayson—Musical Moonlight **D J & S A Shewring & Partner**
26 **TROOP**, gr g Lethal Force (IRE)—Bendis (GER) **Shewring, Craig, Allison, Patterson**

TWO-YEAR-OLDS

27 B f 21/3 Hoderic O'connor (IRE)—Fleeting Affair (USA) (Gone West (USA)) (14285) **Mr Joe Richardson**
28 Ch f 8/3 Kyllachy—India Spirit (Dr Fong (USA)) (28571) **Mr P Bamford & Ms J Bianco**
29 B c 9/4 Bungle Inthejungle—Mirandassister (IRE) (Titus Livius (FR)) (12210)
30 **MISS SABINA**, ch f 13/2 Mayson—Some Diva (Dr Fong (USA)) (15238) **Stephen Bradley**
31 **SILS MARIA**, gr f 28/4 Swiss Spirit—Snow Cover (Verglas (IRE)) (19047) **Solo Syndicate**
32 B c 27/1 Kingsbarns (IRE)—Sweet Namibia (IRE) (Namid) (14000)
33 B f 21/2 Stimulation (IRE)—Ziefhd (Haafhd) (5000)

Other Owners: Mr D. K. Allison, P. Bamford, D. K. Barker, Mrs S. Bianco, Mr R. P. Chapman, Mr B. J. Connolly, Mr A. Court, Mr B. Craig, Mr A. C. Davies, Mr A. W. Ellis, Mr P. M. Fagan, Mr F. Fantoni, Mr I. J. Farrington, The Gathering, Mrs C. A. Gledhill, Mr R. Hamilton, Mrs M. A. Knox, Mr J. A. Knox, Mr D. A. Marshall, Mr L. S. Patterson, Mr J. D. Pierce, Rasio Cymru Racing 1, Mr J. Richardson, Mr D. J. Shewring, Mrs S. A. Shewring, Mrs A. Starkie, Mrs I. L. A. Starkie, Miss E. Stott, Miss R. Stott, Mr M. C. P. Suddards, Mr P. L. Wilson, iBoxit Ltd.

---

155 **MR BRENDAN W. DUKE, The Curragh**
Postal: Fenway House, Pollardstown, Curragh, Co. Kildare, Ireland
Contacts: PHONE (00353) 45 521104 MOBILE (00353) 85 8189724
E-MAIL brendanwduke@hotmail.com

1 **BALANCED APPROACH (IRE)**, 5, b g New Approach (IRE)—Soilse Na Cathrach (IRE) **Mrs Jackie Bolger**
2 **GALUMINOUS (IRE)**, 4, b f Intense Focus (USA)—Luminous One (IRE) **Mrs Jackie Bolger**
3 **GREAT UNCLE (IRE)**, 4, ch c Intense Focus (USA)—Abigail's Aunt **Mrs Jackie Bolger & June Judd**
4 **LET THE HEIRS WALK (IRE)**, 4, b g Vocalised (USA)—Heir Today (IRE) **Mrs Jackie Bolger**
5 **LITTLE MISS WILLOW (IRE)**, 4, b f Footstepsinthesand—Carakiysa (IRE) **Gary and Sharon Davis**
6 **MOUNTMELLICK GIRL (IRE)**, 6, b m Beneficial—Dream Witness (FR) **Martin Hayes, Peter Slezak**
7 **OSTAIOCHT (IRE)**, 4, b g Vocalised (USA)—Aeraiocht (IRE) **Mrs Jackie Bolger**
8 **PUNCH BAG (IRE)**, 7, ch g Teofilo (IRE)—Heir Today (IRE) **Martin Hayes, Peter Slezak**
9 **QUI BONO (IRE)**, 7, gr g Beneficial—Dream Witness (FR) **Fenway Syndicate**

THREE-YEAR-OLDS

10 **CALLANACH (IRE)**, b g Vocalised (USA)—Lily Marette (IRE) **Mrs Jackie Bolger**
11 **CHICA BUENA (IRE)**, b f Thewayyouare (USA)—Easter Parade **Fenway Syndicate**
12 **CHIRPY (IRE)**, b f Vocalised (USA)—Farida (IRE) **Mrs Jackie Bolger**
13 **FEISTY KATERINA (IRE)**, b f Vocalised (USA)—Miss Ekaterina (IRE) **Mrs Jackie Bolger**
14 Ch f Notnowcato—Hayward's Heath **Mrs Angela Duke**
15 **ULURU PARK (IRE)**, b f So You Think (NZ)—I'm Sheikra (IRE) **Brendan W. Duke & Linda Rodriguez**
16 **VOCATIO (IRE)**, b f Vocalised (USA)—Dancing On Turf (IRE) **Mrs Jackie Bolger**

TWO-YEAR-OLDS

17 Ch c 17/4 Casamento (IRE)—Casina Valadier (IRE) (Fath (USA)) (8140) **Brendan W. Duke Racing**
18 **CLEMENCIA (IRE)**, b c 31/5 Pour Moi (IRE)—Cleofila (Teofilo (IRE)) (4070) **Mrs Jackie Bolger**
19 B c 8/3 So You Think (NZ)—I'm Sheikra (IRE) (Captain Rio) **Brendan W. Duke**
20 **MACKEN (IRE)**, b c 12/2 Kendargent (FR)—Salorina (USA) (A P Indy (USA)) (4070) **Brendan W. Duke Racing**

MR BRENDAN W. DUKE - Continued

21 B f 16/4 Battle of Marengo (IRE)—Shamora (FR) (Oratorio (IRE)) **Fenway Syndicate**
22 **VOCAL DUKE (IRE)**, b c 9/5 Vocalised (USA)—Heir Today (IRE) (Princely Heir (IRE)) **Mrs Jackie Bolger**

Jockey (flat): Rory Cleary, Kevin Manning, Ronan Whelan. **Jockey (NH):** Andrew Lynch. **Apprentice:** D. Redmond.

---

156   **MR IAN DUNCAN, Coylton**
Postal: **Sandhill Farm, Coylton, AYR, Ayrshire, KA6 6HE**
Contacts: **PHONE (01292) 571118 FAX (01292) 571118 MOBILE (07731) 473668**
E-MAIL jennyclose86@googlemail.com

1 BIENNIAL (IRE), 6, ch g Bienamado (USA)—Midnight Orchid (IRE) **Alan & Barry Macdonald**
2 CYPRUS AVENUE, 6, b m Kayf Tara—Za Beau (IRE) **Dr S. Sinclair**
3 FINAGHY AYR (IRE), 10, ch g Lahib (USA)—Ali Ankah (IRE) **Mr A. J. R. Lilley**
4 IMPERIAL PRINCE (IRE), 9, b g Subtle Power (IRE)—Satco Rose (IRE) **Mr A. J. R. Lilley**
5 IRISH FASHION, 6, gr m Demetrius (IRE)—Flying Fashion (IRE) **I. A. Duncan**
6 JESSIEMAC (IRE), 4, br f Sholokhov (IRE)—All Our Blessings (IRE) **Alan & Barry Macdonald**
7 LOCHNELL (IRE), 9, br m Winged Love (IRE)—Nothing For Ever (IRE) **Alan & Barry Macdonald**
8 MILBOROUGH (IRE), 12, b g Milan—Fox Burrow (IRE) **The Milborough Boys**
9 NO NO MAC (IRE), 5, b g Oscar (IRE)—Whatdoyouthinkmac (IRE) **B H McFadzean & A L Gregg**
10 OLLISU LAD (IRE), 9, b g Westerner—Nick's Jule (IRE) **I. A. Duncan**
11 SPRING OVER (IRE), 12, ch m Samraan (USA)—Superswap (IRE) **I. A. Duncan**
12 5, B br m Oscar (IRE)—Za Beau (IRE) **Dr S. Sinclair**

Other Owners: Mr J. Boyce, Mr C. Davidson, Mr A. L. Gregg, Mr G. Hammersley, Mr B. N. MacDonald, Mr A. G. MacDonald, Mr B. McFadzean, Mr D. Mitchell, Mr J. Payne.

---

157   **MR NIGEL DUNGER, Pulborough**
Postal: **17 Allfrey Plat, Pulborough, West Sussex, RH20 2BU**
Contacts: **PHONE (07494) 344167 MOBILE (07790) 631962**
E-MAIL debdunger05@gmail.com

1 HIER ENCORE (FR), 6, ch g Kentucky Dynamite (USA)—Hierarchie (FR) **N. A. Dunger**
2 HIT THE HEADLINES (IRE), 12, b g Flemensfirth (USA)—Heather Breeze (IRE) **N. A. Dunger**

Assistant Trainer: Mrs D Dunger

---

158   **MR ED DUNLOP, Newmarket**
Postal: **La Grange Stables, Fordham Road, Newmarket, Suffolk, CB8 7AA**
Contacts: **PHONE (01638) 661998 FAX (01638) 667394 MOBILE (07785) 328537**
E-MAIL edunlop@eddunlopracing.co.uk WEBSITE www.edunlop.com

1 AL NAFOORAH, 4, b f Bated Breath—Cat O' Nine Tails **Mr Mohammed Jaber**
2 AMAZING RED (IRE), 5, b g Teofilo (IRE)—Artisia (IRE) **The Hon R. J. Arculli**
3 AMLAD (IRE), 4, ch g Lope de Vega (IRE)—Pietra Dura **Mr Abdullah Saeed Al Naboodah**
4 APEX KING (IRE), 4, b g Kodiac—Rainbowskia (FR) **Mr Mohammed Jaber**
5 ARNARSON, 4, b c Exceed And Excel (AUS)—Islandia (USA) **Mr C. Gan**
6 COLOURFUL CAREER (USA), 4, b br g More Than Ready (USA)—Rainbow Luck (USA) **Britannia Thoroughbreds**
7 DARK RED (IRE), 5, b g Dark Angel (IRE)—Essexford (IRE) **The Hon R. J. Arculli**
8 GLOBAL APPLAUSE, 4, b c Mayson—Crown (IRE) **Dr Johnny Hon**
9 KING KEVIN, 4, b g Holy Roman Emperor (IRE)—Annalina (USA) **Mr E. A. L. Dunlop**
10 MANJAAM (IRE), 5, ch g Tamayuz—Priory Rock (IRE) **Mr Mohammed Jaber**
11 MUDALLEL (IRE), 4, b g Invincible Spirit (IRE)—Lixirova (FR) **Mr Abdullah Saeed Al Naboodah**
12 PERLA BLANCA (USA), 4, gr f Dalakhani (IRE)—Trend Line (IRE) **Mrs C. L. Smith**
13 RED VERDON (USA), 5, ch h Lemon Drop Kid (USA)—Porto Marmay (IRE) **The Hon R. J. Arculli**
14 SANAM, 4, b c Oasis Dream—Seta **Mr Abdullah Saeed Al Naboodah**
15 SIR GNET (IRE), 4, b c Galileo (IRE)—Ecoutila (USA) **Mr Quenten Zheng**
16 SPARTE QUERCUS (IRE), 5, b g Canford Cliffs (IRE)—Khaizarana **Mr Hui Sai Fun**
17 SPORTING TIMES, 4, ch g Sir Percy—Queen of Iceni **Mrs I. H. Stewart-Brown & Mr M. J. Meacock**
18 WARRIOR PRINCE, 5, ch g Sakhee (USA)—Queen of Iceni **Mrs I. H. Stewart-Brown & Mr M. J. Meacock**

MR ED DUNLOP - Continued

THREE-YEAR-OLDS

19 **AGAR'S PLOUGH,** ch g Dutch Art—Cloud's End **The Old Etonian Racing Syndicate II**
20 **ALHRAM,** b c Intello (GER)—Whazzis **Mr Mohammed Jaber**
21 **ALTERNATIVE FACT,** b c Dalakhani (IRE)—O Fourlunda **Alternative Lot**
22 **AMPLIFICATION (USA),** b g Lonhro (AUS)—Our Drama Queen (IRE) **Mr Hui Sui Fun**
23 **ARMUM (IRE),** b f Society Rock (IRE)—Good Clodora (IRE) **Mr C. Gan**
24 **BAASHA,** b g Havana Gold (IRE)—Tawaasul **Mr Mohammed Jaber**
25 **BAWAADER (IRE),** gr c Dark Angel (IRE)—Aspen Falls (IRE) **Sheikh Hamdan bin Rashid Al Maktoum**
26 **BELLE DE NEIGE (IRE),** b br f Elusive Pimpernel (USA)—Snow Fairy (IRE) **Anamoine**
27 **CANIMAR,** b f Havana Gold (IRE)—Acquifer **Serendipity Partnership**
28 **CONFLAGRATION,** b c Exceed And Excel (AUS)—Please Sing **Mr Hui Sui Fun**
29 **CREEK HARBOUR (IRE),** b c Kodiac—Allegheny Creek (IRE) **Mr Mohammed Jaber**
30 **CUE'S FOLLY,** b f Nathaniel (IRE)—Island Odyssey **Mrs Janice Quy**
31 **DAGUENEAU (IRE),** b g Champs Elysees—Bright Enough **Mr A. Gemmell**
32 **DECORATION OF WAR (IRE),** b g Declaration of War (USA)—Sea Paint (IRE) **OTI and Partners**
33 **DUBAI FRAME,** b c Sixties Icon—Strictly Lambada **Mr Mohammed Jaber**
34 **FAAY (IRE),** gr f Dark Angel (IRE)—Folga **Mr Abdullah Saeed Al Naboodah**
35 **FABULOUS RED,** b f Red Jazz (USA)—Red Fantasy (IRE) **The Hon R. J. Arculli**
36 **GARSINGTON,** b c Intello (GER)—Ruse **Mrs Susan Roy**
37 **GLOBAL ANGEL,** b c Dark Angel (IRE)—Authoritarian **Dr Johnny Hon**
38 **GLOBAL ART,** b c Dutch Art—Constant Dream **Dr Johnny Hon**
39 **GLOBAL EXCEED,** b c Exceed And Excel (AUS)—Blue Maiden **Dr Johnny Hon**
40 **GLOBAL GIANT,** b c Shamardal (USA)—Aniseed (IRE) **Dr Johnny Hon**
41 **GLOBAL HUMOR (USA),** b c Distorted Humor (USA)—In Bloom (USA) **Dr Johnny Hon**
42 **GLOBAL SPIRIT,** b c Invincible Spirit (IRE)—Centime **Dr Johnny Hon**
43 **GLOBAL STYLE (IRE),** b c Nathaniel (IRE)—Danaskaya (IRE) **Dr Johnny Hon**
44 **GLOBAL WEALTH,** b g Havana Gold (IRE)—Inner Sea (USA) **Dr Johnny Hon**
45 **GLOBAL WONDER (IRE),** b g Kodiac—Traveller's Tales **Dr Johnny Hon**
46 **GRANDSCAPE,** b c Lemon Drop Kid (USA)—Unnatural (USA) **Mr Mohammed Jaber**
47 **HARLESTONE FINALE,** b f Olden Times—Harlestone Lady **Mr E. A. L. Dunlop**
48 **HAZARFAN,** b c Frankel—Debonnaire **Mr Mohammed Jaber**
49 **HIGHCASTLE (IRE),** b g High Chaparral (IRE)—Green Castle (IRE) **Frank Kaszynski**
50 **INDIAN WARRIOR,** b g Sepoy (AUS)—Night Gypsy **The Hope Partnership**
51 **MAGHROOM (IRE),** b c Iffraaj—French Fern (IRE) **Sheikh Hamdan bin Rashid Al Maktoum**
52 **MELODIES,** ch f Iffraaj—Singersongwriter **Cliveden Stud**
53 **MOASHER (USA),** b g Lonhro (AUS)—But for Money (USA) **Mr Abdullah Saeed Al Naboodah**
54 **MR GENT (IRE),** b c Society Rock (IRE)—Furnival (USA) **Mr Quenten Zheng**
55 **MURAADEF,** b g Kodiac—Dominatrix **Sheikh Hamdan bin Rashid Al Maktoum**
56 **NAVAJO SQUAW,** ch f Sir Percy—Navajo Charm **G. Bishop & E. Dunlop**
57 **QAARAAT,** b g Acclamation—Ladyship **Sheikh Hamdan bin Rashid Al Maktoum**
58 **QASWARAH (IRE),** b f Nayef (USA)—Katoom (USA) **Sheikh Hamdan bin Rashid Al Maktoum**
59 **QAWAMEES (IRE),** b c Exceed And Excel (AUS)—Jabhaat (USA) **Sheikh Hamdan bin Rashid Al Maktoum**
60 **SAGENESS (IRE),** b f Most Improved (IRE)—Saga Celebre (FR) **The Sagacious Lot**
61 **TADLEEL,** b c Dark Angel (IRE)—Quelle Affaire **Sheikh Hamdan bin Rashid Al Maktoum**
62 **TAJARROB (IRE),** b c Intikhab (USA)—Maany (USA) **Sheikh Hamdan bin Rashid Al Maktoum**
63 **TEENAGE GAL (IRE),** b f Acclamation—Bobbie Soxer (IRE) **Windflower Overseas Holdings Inc.**
64 **VISION CLEAR (GER),** br g Soldier Hollow—Vive Madame (GER) **Mr Mohammed Jaber**

TWO-YEAR-OLDS

65 **ALAMEERY,** b c 26/3 Kingman—
Zacheta (Polish Precedent (USA)) (160000) **Sheikh Hamdan bin Rashid Al Maktoum**
66 B c 28/4 Tertullian (USA)—Anatola (GER) (Tiger Hill (IRE)) (65120) **OTI Racing**
67 Gr c 23/1 Kodiac—Cland di San Jore (IRE) (Lando (GER)) (33500) **Mr Patrick Milmo**
68 **DANCINGWITHWOLVES (IRE),** b c 23/2 Footstepsinthesand—
Clodovina (Rock of Gibraltar (IRE)) (101750) **Mrs Susan Roy**
69 B c 28/3 Data Link (USA)—
Don't Cry For Me (USA) (Street Cry (IRE)) (47000) **The Old Etonian Racing Syndicate III**
70 **GLOBAL ACCLAMATION,** b c 19/4 Acclamation—
High Luminosity (USA) (Elusive Quality (USA)) (114285) **Dr Johnny Hon**
71 **GLOBAL COMMAND (IRE),** b c 24/3 War Command (USA)—Parsley (IRE) (Zebedee) (71428) **Dr Johnny Hon**
72 **GLOBAL DESTINATION (IRE),** b c 6/3 Slade Power (IRE)—
Silk Trail (Dubai Destination (USA)) (260000) **Dr Johnny Hon**
73 **GLOBAL EXPRESS,** ch c 16/2 New Approach (IRE)—All For Laura (Cadeaux Genereux) (175000) **Dr Johnny Hon**
74 **GLOBAL FREEDOM,** b c 3/4 Maxios—Modesty's Way (Giant's Causeway (USA) (105820) **Dr Johnny Hon**
75 **GLOBAL GIFT,** b c 10/2 Invincible Spirit (IRE)—Special Gift (IRE) (New Approach (IRE)) (162800) **Dr Johnny Hon**

MR ED DUNLOP - Continued

76 **GLOBAL LIGHT (IRE)**, b f 6/2 Excelebration (IRE)—Lucina (Machiavellian (USA)) (200000) **Dr Johnny Hon**
77 **GLOBAL MYTH**, b c 9/5 Scat Daddy (USA)—Excelente (IRE) (Exceed And Excel (AUS)) (260480) **Dr Johnny Hon**
78 **GLOBAL ROCK**, b c 18/3 Siyouni (FR)—Baino Rock (FR) (Rock of Gibraltar (IRE)) (130240) **Dr Johnny Hon**
79 **GLOBAL STORM (IRE)**, b c 8/5 Shamardal (USA)—Amathia (IRE) (Darshaan) (145000) **Dr Johnny Hon**
80 **GLOBAL WARNING**, ch c 19/4 Poet's Voice—Persario (Bishop of Cashel) (155000) **Dr Johnny Hon**
81 **HALLALULU**, b f 18/2 Kyllachy—Cat O' Nine Tails (Motivator) (48840) **Mr Mohammed Jaber**
82 **INSPIRATIONAL (IRE)**, b f 17/4 Slade Power (IRE)—
　　　　　　　Refuse To Give Up (IRE) (Refuse To Bend (IRE)) (82000) **Cliveden Stud**
83 **JABALALY (IRE)**, b c 4/4 Moohaajim (IRE)—
　　　　　　　Bahati (IRE) (Intikhab (USA)) (80952) **Sheikh Hamdan bin Rashid Al Maktoum**
84 **JEBEL (IRE)**, b c 14/4 Dark Angel (IRE)—Jo Bo Bo (IRE) (Whipper (USA)) (110000) **Sheikh Hamdan bin Rashid Al Maktoum**
85 **KHANMURJAN (USA)**, b c 11/4 Scat Daddy (USA)—
　　　　　　　Late Day Sun (Montjeu (IRE)) (130000) **Mr Mohammed Jaber**
86 **LIGHT OF INDIA**, b f 20/1 Sepoy (AUS)—Light Fantastic (Acclamation) **Racing Fillies Syndicate**
87 **MAP OF AUSTRALIA**, ch c 20/1 Australia—Map of Heaven (Pivotal) (70000) **Racing Fillies Syndicate**
88 **MAQAADEER**, b c 23/1 Mukhadram—
　　　　　　　Burnt Fingers (IRE) (Kheleyf (USA)) **Sheikh Hamdan bin Rashid Al Maktoum**
89 **MAWSOOL (IRE)**, b c 9/4 Kodiac—Habaayib (Royal Applause) **Sheikh Hamdan bin Rashid Al Maktoum**
90 **MAY JUNE (IRE)**, b f 22/1 Mukhadram—Subsequently (FR) (Dalakhani (IRE)) (26000) **Mrs Emma Capon**
91 **MUTARAAMY**, b f 28/3 Slade Power (IRE)—Musharakaat (IRE) (Iffraaj) **Sheikh Hamdan bin Rashid Al Maktoum**
92 B f 1/4 Charm Spirit (IRE)—Navajo Rainbow (Rainbow Quest (USA)) **Mr Geoffrey Bishop**
93 B c 27/4 Lemon Drop Kid (USA)—Parley (USA) (Street Cry (IRE)) (80000) **The Hon R. J. Arculli**
94 **PERIQUE**, b c 29/5 Cacique (IRE)—Meetyouthere (IRE) (Sadler's Wells (USA)) (30000) **Will Wyatt**
95 B c 24/2 Toronado (IRE)—Rawoof (IRE) (Nayef (USA)) (39071)
96 **ROXY ART (IRE)**, ch f 27/4 Dutch Art—Chicago Girl (IRE) (Azamour (IRE)) (175000) **Mrs Susan Roy**
97 **SAN SEBASTIAN (IRE)**, b c 21/2 Iffraaj—
　　　　　　　Invincible Cara (IRE) (Invincible Spirit (IRE)) **Windflower Overseas Holdings**
98 Ch f 9/4 Zoffany (IRE)—Serengeti Day (USA) (Alleged (USA)) (36629) **Mr Paul Shanahan**
99 **SHAWAAHEQ (IRE)**, b c 24/3 Tamayuz—
　　　　　　　Jabhaat (USA) (Hard Spun (USA)) **Sheikh Hamdan bin Rashid Al Maktoum**
100 B f 1/3 No Nay Never (USA)—Sheba's Humor (USA) (Distorted Humor (USA)) (47619) **Milmo, Sturgess, White**
101 **SINJAARI (IRE)**, b c 19/3 Camelot—Heavenly Song (IRE) (Oratorio (IRE)) (110000) **Mr Mohammed Jaber**
102 **SNAHFEE**, ch c 11/4 Dutch Art—Point of Control (Pivotal) (113960) **Mr Mohammed Jaber**
103 B br f 17/2 Medaglia d'oro (USA)—Strathnaver (Oasis Dream) **St Albans Bloodstock**
104 B f 26/3 Intello (GER)—Tahirah (Green Desert (USA)) (15000) **Colin Murfitt, Edwin Lee**
105 **THIN ICE (IRE)**, br f 3/4 Dandy Man (IRE)—Elusive Ice (IRE) (Elusive City (USA)) (6000) **Bengough, Brown**
106 **TRIPLE GENIUS (IRE)**, b c 7/4 Mastercraftsman (IRE)—
　　　　　　　Three Moons (IRE) (Montjeu (IRE)) (28490) **M. Wilmshurst and Friends**
107 **VALENCE**, b c 23/4 Oasis Dream—Independence (Selkirk (USA)) (40000) **MHS Partnership**
108 **VENEDEGAR (IRE)**, b c 10/5 Dubawi (IRE)—
　　　　　　　Cara Fantasy (IRE) (Sadler's Wells (USA)) **Windflower Overseas & J L Dunlop OBE**
109 **YOUARESTAR**, b c 20/2 Sea The Stars (IRE)—Alumna (USA) (Mr Greeley (USA)) (145000) **Mr Mohammed Jaber**

Other Owners: Mr Austin Allison, Anglo Australian Racing, Mr G. S. Bishop, Mr P. A. Deal, J. L. Dunlop, Mrs Edward Dunlop, Mr C. Gordon-Watson, Mr R. I. Hambury, Mr T. Henderson, Mr David Hicken, Mr Colin Linney, M. J. Meacock, Mr Trevor Milner, Mrs S. O'Donnell, Mr Richard Pilkington, Mrs J. Stewart-Brown, Mr J. R. Weatherby, Mrs Oriana Wilmott, Mr Eamonn Wilmott, Mr Michael Wilmshurst.

Amateur: Miss Sophie Smith.

159　**MR HARRY DUNLOP, Lambourn**
Postal: **Windsor House Stables, Crowle Road, Lambourn, Hungerford, Berkshire, RG17 8NR**
Contacts: PHONE (01488) 73584 MOBILE (07880) 791895
E-MAIL info@harrydunloprracing.com WEBSITE www.harrydunlopracing.com

1 **ASSANILKA (FR)**, 4, b f Diamond Green (FR)—Regal Step **The Three Musketeers**
2 **COASTAL CYCLONE**, 4, b g Canford Cliffs (IRE)—Seasonal Cross **Malcolm & Alicia Aldis**
3 **EARLY MORNING (IRE)**, 7, gr g New Approach (IRE)—Summer's Eve **Early Risers**
4 **FLIGHT OF FANTASY**, 4, b f Nathaniel (IRE)—Luminda (IRE) **P. A. Deal & G. Lowe**
5 **JUST AN IDEA (IRE)**, 4, b g Lilbourne Lad (IRE)—Emreliya (IRE) **Love Lambourn**
6 **MY ILLUSIONIST**, 4, b g Kheleyf (USA)—Shimoni **The Thrower Family**
7 **ROBIN OF NAVAN (FR)**, 5, ch h American Post—Cloghran (FR) **Cross, Deal, Foden, Sieff**
8 **STAR GYPSY (FR)**, 4, br g Myboycharlie (IRE)—Melandia (IRE) **Haven't A Pot, D. MacAuliffe & Anoj Don**

MR HARRY DUNLOP - Continued

THREE-YEAR-OLDS

9 BILLIE FLYNN, b f Lawman (FR)—Lyric Art (USA) **Crimbourne Stud**
10 BULLETIN (IRE), b g Bullet Train—Dixiedoodledandy (IRE) **Mrs James Blyth Currie & Sir Philip Wroughton**
11 CHILLALA (IRE), b f Requinto (IRE)—Positive Step (IRE) **Daniel MacAuliffe & Anoj Don**
12 DUTCH STRANGER, b f Dutch Art—Passing Stranger (IRE) **Mrs Susan Roy**
13 FIGHTING IRISH (IRE), b c Camelot—Quixotic **Daniel MacAuliffe & Anoj Don**
14 GRAND ACCLAIM (IRE), ch g Monsieur Bond (IRE)—Endless Applause **The Nigel Bennett Partnership**
15 INVINCIBLE PEACE, b c Declaration of War (USA)—Invincible Cara (IRE) **Windflower Overseas Holdings Inc**
16 JACKFINBAR (FR), b c Whipper (USA)—Anna Simona (GER) **Haven't A Pot**
17 JUST ANOTHER IDEA (IRE), ch g Casamento (IRE)—Emreliya (IRE) **Harry Dunlop Racing Partnership**
18 KNIGHT TO BEHOLD (IRE), b c Sea The Stars (IRE)—Angel Of The Gwaun (IRE) **Mr L. N. Jones**
19 LOOKING FOR CARL, b g Lope de Vega (IRE)—Dam Beautiful **Haven't A Pot**
20 MAYAMOUR, b f Mayson—Amour Fou (IRE) **Nigel & Carolyn Elwes & John Troy**
21 PACT OF STEEL, ch c Declaration of War (USA)—She's My Dandy (USA) **Daniel MacAuliffe & Anoj Don**
22 PIRATE KING, br c Farhh—Generous Diana **Daniel MacAuliffe & Anoj Don**
23 RAVEN'S SONG (IRE), b f Raven's Pass (USA)—Lyric of Fife (IRE) **Foxtrot Racing: Raven's Song & Partner**
24 ROMAN WARRIOR, b c Holy Roman Emperor (IRE)—Meet Marhaba (IRE) **Daniel MacAuliffe & Anoj Don**
25 SHEHASSPENTTHELOT (IRE), b f Kodiac—Jenlen (USA) **Haven't A Pot**
26 SPACE TALK, b f High Chaparral (IRE)—Retake **Mr M. Kurt**
27 STAR OF VENDOME (FR), gr f Style Vendome (FR)—Celestina Agostino (USA) **Mr R. P. Foden**
28 WHISPERING SANDS (IRE), ch f Dubawi (IRE)—Roses For The Lady (IRE) **Mr L. N. Jones**
29 WILLINGFORSHILLING (IRE), br f Dabirsim (FR)—Anavera (GER) **Haven't A Pot**

TWO-YEAR-OLDS

30 B c 10/3 Hannouma (IRE)—
    Alta Stima (IRE) (Raven's Pass (USA)) (32560) **D. MacAuliffe, Anoj Don & Etreham Partnership**
31 B c 2/5 Maxios—Alyssandre (IRE) (Oasis Dream) (24420)
32 BALLET RED (FR), ch f 12/2 Rio de La Plata (USA)—Beriosova (FR) (Starborough) (7733) **The Ascot 9**
33 B f 27/2 Kingman—Bourbonella (Rainbow Quest (USA)) **Mr & Mrs David Hearson**
34 BROOKLYN BOY, b c 1/3 Camelot—Tan Tan (King's Best) (USA) (68000) **Daniel MacAuliffe & Anoj Don**
35 CRANEUR, ch c 24/1 Showcasing—Paris Winds (IRE) (Galileo (IRE)) (12500) **Be Hopeful Partnership**
36 B c 31/3 Whipper—Ellary (FR) (Equerry (USA)) (23606)
37 FLYING MAIDEN (GER), b br c 1/1 Sea The Moon (GER)—Finity (USA) (Diesis) (22792) **Crimbourne Stud**
38 GORA BERE (FR), b br c 30/4 Pedro The Great (USA)—
    Monatora (FR) (Hector Protector (USA)) (21978) **Emma Hunter**
39 B f 11/2 Equiano (FR)—Iridescence (Dutch Art) (14000) **Emma Hunter**
40 KYAT KHAN (FR), b c 28/1 Palace Episode (USA)—Kensita (FR) (Soviet Star (USA)) (16280)
41 B f 8/3 Dutch Art—Lottie Dod (IRE) (Invincible Spirit (IRE)) (16280) **Velocity Racing**
42 B br f 21/3 Iffraaj—Merry Diva (Bahamian Bounty) (20000) **Windsor House Stables Partnership**
43 Ch f 6/2 Australia—Peace Palace (Archipenko (USA)) (22000)
44 B f 19/4 Rock of Gibraltar (IRE)—Seasonal Cross (Cape Cross (IRE)) **Malcolm & Alicia Aldis**
45 B c 20/3 Big Bad Bob (IRE)—Velvetina (IRE) (Barathea (IRE)) (1220) **Windflower Overseas Holdings Inc**
46 B g 24/2 Camelot—Zelloof (IRE) (Kheleyf (USA)) (65120) **Daniel MacAuliffe & Anoj Don**

Other Owners: Mrs J. K. Bennett, Mr N. A. Bennett, Mr L. A. Bolingbroke, Mr G. Freeman, Mr K. C. Freeman, Mrs E. J. Gregson-Williams, Mr R. W. Gregson-Williams.

Pupil Assistant: Rachel Davies

160
MRS ALEXANDRA DUNN, Wellington
Postal: **The Gallops, West Buckland, Wellington, Somerset, TA21 9LE**
Contacts: **MOBILE (07738) 512924**
WEBSITE www.alexandradunnracing.com

1 ARGUS (IRE), 6, b g Rip Van Winkle (IRE)—Steel Princess (IRE) **Mr N. McCloskey**
2 BLACK NARCISSUS (IRE), 9, b m Westerner—Arcanum (IRE) **Team Dunn**
3 BROKE AWAY (IRE), 6, br m Stowaway—Not Broke Yet (IRE) **Mr D. R. Arthur**
4 CHASING HEADLIGHTS, 6, b g Getaway (GER)—Could Do **S. Towens & W.B.B.**
5 CHORUS OF LIES, 6, b g Teofilo (IRE)—Cherry Orchard (IRE) **Dave Arthur & W.B.B.**
6 CORRUPTION, 4, b f Malinas (GER)—Blue Ride (IRE) **Four Quarters**
7 DEFINITE RIDGE (IRE), 11, ch g Definite Article—Do The Right Thing **West Buckland Bloodstock Ltd**
8 DIAMOND REFLECTION (IRE), 6, b g Oasis Dream—Briolette (IRE) **The Jas Club**
9 ENMESHING, 5, ch g Mastercraftsman (IRE)—Yacht Club (USA) **The Crafty Six**
10 GAMBLING GAMUT (IRE), 6, ch g Gamut (IRE)—Red Promise (IRE) **J.B. & W.B.B.**

MRS ALEXANDRA DUNN - Continued

11 **GANG WARFARE**, 7, b g Medicean—Light Impact (IRE) **Gangbusters & Partner**
12 **GENI JOHNSON (IRE)**, 6, b m Mountain High (IRE)—Garrymohrs (IRE) **West Buckland Bloodstock Ltd**
13 **GOLD MOUNTAIN (IRE)**, 8, b g Gold Well—La Belle de Serk (IRE) **Mr J. Burley**
14 **GOONJIM (IRE)**, 7, ch g Beneficial—Clogga Native (IRE) **The Profile Partnership**
15 **GUARACHA**, 7, ch g Halling (USA)—Pachanga **West Buckland Bloodstock Ltd**
16 **HELIUM (FR)**, 13, b g Dream Well (FR)—Sure Harbour (SWI) **West Buckland Bloodstock Ltd**
17 **HOW ABOUT IT (IRE)**, 9, b g Kayf Tara—Midnight Gift (IRE) **The Dunn Club**
18 **KUBLAI (FR)**, 8, b g Laveron—Java Dawn (IRE) **N Berbillion & West Buckland Bloodstock**
19 **LADY JAMESON (IRE)**, 7, b m Whitmore's Conn (USA)—Corbetstown Queen (IRE) **Mr W. A. Thomas**
20 **MILLEN DOLLAR MAN (IRE)**, 9, b g Milenary—Rare Dollar (IRE) **West Buckland Bloodstock Ltd**
21 **MINELLA VOUCHER**, 7, b g King's Theatre (IRE)—All Rise (GER) **Blue Blood Syndications & W. B. B.**
22 **PACK IT IN (IRE)**, 5, br g Big Bad Bob (IRE)—Evening Dress **A Game Pair**
23 **RED CON ONE (IRE)**, 8, b m Gold Well—Speedy Tactics (IRE) **R P B Michaelson & D Fitzgerald**
24 **ROYAL CHIEF (IRE)**, 9, gr g Royal Anthem (USA)—Help Yourself (IRE) **The Game Birds**
25 **SANDRO BOTTICELLI (IRE)**, 6, b g Galileo (IRE)—Ask For The Moon (FR) **The Primaveras**
26 **SEVEN NATION ARMY (IRE)**, 9, gr g Rock of Gibraltar (IRE)—Crepe Ginger (IRE) **The Dunn Army**
27 **SHINGHARI (IRE)**, 6, br g Cape Cross (IRE)—Sindiyma (IRE) **West Buckland Bloodstock Ltd**
28 **SPINY NORMAN**, 5, ch g Malinas (GER)—Helen Wood **The Time Enough Stud Partnership**
29 **SPRING STEEL (IRE)**, 9, b g Dushyantor (USA)—Fieldtown (IRE) **N Berbillion & West Buckland Bloodstock**
30 **SWEET OBSESSION (IRE)**, 6, b m Getaway (GER)—Dual Obsession
31 **TACTICAL MANOEUVRE (IRE)**, 7, b g Marienbard (IRE)—Pride O'fleet (IRE) **The Tacticians**
32 **THAHAB IFRAJ (IRE)**, 5, ch g Frozen Power (IRE)—Penny Rouge (IRE) **The Dunnitalls & Partner**
33 **TORRENT DES MOTTES (FR)**, 7, gr g Montmartre (FR)—Wavy (FR) **West Buckland Bloodstock Ltd**
34 **TRAFALGAR ROCK**, 7, b g Mount Nelson—Helter Helter (USA) **Mrs K. R. Smith-Maxwell**
35 **TRIPTICO (FR)**, 12, gr g Turgeon (USA)—All Kicks (FR) **R. J. Smith-Maxwell & W.B.B.**
36 **TRUCKERS TANGLE (IRE)**, 6, b g Tajraasi (USA)—Lodge Tangle (IRE) **Blue Blood Syndications & W. B. B.**
37 **TSUNDOKU (IRE)**, 7, ch m Medicean—Toberanthawn (IRE) **Dave Arthur & W.B.B.**
38 **WESTERNER OCEAN (IRE)**, 6, gr m Westerner—Silver Proverb
39 **WINGED EXPRESS (IRE)**, 9, b g Winged Love (IRE)—
Zaffaran Express (IRE) **Mr J. Burley & West Buckland Bloodstock**

Other Owners: Mrs Y. Bennett, Mr N. Berbillion, M. J. Bevan, Blue Blood Syndications, Mr F. Clothier, Mr T. H. Dunn, The Dunnitalls, Mr V. P Finn, Mr D. J. Fitzgerald, Gangbusters, R. P. B. Michaelson, Mr J. Rees, Miss R. J. Smith-Maxwell, Mr N. Towens, Mr D. Trueman, Mr T. Wheatley, Mrs C. M. Wheatley, Mr A. G. S. Wiltshire, Mr R. G. Wiltshire, Mr S. W. H. Winfield, Mrs J. Winfield.

---

161 MRS CHRISTINE DUNNETT, Norwich

Postal: **College Farm, Hingham, Norwich, Norfolk, NR9 4PP**
Contacts: PHONE **(01953) 850596** MOBILE **(07775) 793523**
E-MAIL **christine@christinedunnett.com** WEBSITE **www.christinedunnett.com**

1 **ARRYZONA**, 7, b g Phoenix Reach (IRE)—Southwarknewsflash **Christine Dunnett Racing (Arryzona)**
2 **BEATISA**, 4, b f Intikhab (USA)—Bea Menace (USA) **One For All**
3 **CLASSIC FLYER**, 6, b g Stimulation (IRE)—Tranquil Flight **Christine Dunnett Racing (Arryzona)**
4 **COACH MONTANA (IRE)**, 9, b g Proud Citizen (USA)—Market Day
5 **DANZOE (IRE)**, 11, br g Kheleyf (USA)—Fiaba **Mrs C. A. Dunnett**
6 **DROP KICK MURPHI (IRE)**, 4, b g Sir Prancealot (IRE)—Rindiseyda (IRE) **Mr T. Milner**
7 **GIVE US A BELLE (IRE)**, 9, b g Kheleyf (USA)—Bajan Belle (IRE) **Mr F Butler & Mrs C Dunnett**
8 **HERE I GO AGAIN (IRE)**, 4, b g Fast Company (IRE)—Jaldini (IRE) **Mr P. D. West**
9 **HUMOUR (IRE)**, 7, b g Invincible Spirit (IRE)—Hucking Hot **The Humourites**
10 **ONE FOR ALL**, 5, b g Pivotal—Midpoint (USA) **Partnership Terminated**
11 **PERCY TOPLIS**, 4, b g Kheleyf (USA)—West Lorne (USA) **One For All**
12 **PROUD KATE**, 4, b f Proud Citizen (USA)—Oceans Apart **Mr & Mrs Alan Barnard**
13 **RATHEALY (IRE)**, 7, b g Baltic King—Baltic Belle (IRE) **Mr P. D. West**
14 **RIPPER STREET (IRE)**, 4, b g Big Bad Bob (IRE)—Caster Sugar (USA) **Mr T. Milner**
15 **SHYARCH**, 4, b g Archipenko (USA)—Coconut Shy **Mr P. D. West**
16 **ZAM I AM**, 5, b g Zamindar (USA)—Prayer (IRE) **Mr C. R. Moore**

THREE-YEAR-OLDS

17 **AGENT OF FORTUNE**, ch f Kheleyf (USA)—Royal Bloom (IRE) **Mr A. Machin & Mrs C. Dunnett**
18 **COLLEGE KING**, b g Baltic King—Flaming Telepath **Christine Dunnett Racing (Arryzona)**
19 **FATA MORGANA**, b f Society Rock (IRE)—Life's A Whirl **College Farm Stud**
20 **HIDDEN DREAM (IRE)**, b f Casamento (IRE)—Anything (IRE) **Machin, Milner, Sparkes & Dunnett**

MRS CHRISTINE DUNNETT - Continued

21 **JONATHANS GIRL,** b f Equiano (FR)—Jewelled **Jonathan Butcher & Christine Dunnett**
22 **PATIENCEISAVIRTUE,** b f Libranno—Patience **Mr P. D. West**

Other Owners: Mr P. Amey, Mrs K. M. Barnard, Mr A. Barnard, Mr D. G. Burt, Mr J. G. Butcher, Mr F. G. Butler, Mr A. S. Machin, Mr B. R. Martin, Mr E. N. Sparkes.

---

162 **MR SEAMUS DURACK, Upper Lambourn**
Postal: **The Croft Stables, Upper Lambourn, Hungerford, Berkshire, RG17 8QH**
Contacts: PHONE **(01488) 491480** MOBILE **(07770) 537971**
E-MAIL **sd.111@btinternet.com** WEBSITE **www.seamusdurack.com**

1 **BALLINAHINCH (IRE),** 6, b g Oscar (IRE)—Before (IRE) **Clan McNeil**
2 **BARCA (USA),** 4, b c War Front (USA)—Magnificent Honour (USA) **The Barca Partnership**
3 **CAYIRLI (FR),** 6, b g Medicean—Clarinda (FR) **S. P. Tucker**
4 **DE CORONADO (USA),** 5, b h Street Cry (IRE)—Vertigineux (USA) **Miss S. J. Beddoes**
5 **HIGH WELLS,** 4, b g High Chaparral (IRE)—Valencha **Ownaracehorse & Stephen Tucker**
6 **LINGUINE (FR),** 8, ch g Linngari (IRE)—Amerissage (USA) **Mrs A. Cowley**
7 **NEVER FOLDING (IRE),** 4, b f Requinto (IRE)—Sarella Loren (IRE) **Mrs A. Cowley**
8 **NICELY DONE (IRE),** 5, b m Mahler—Rare Dollar (IRE) **Ownaracehorse & Looksarnteverything**
9 **PEDESTAL (IRE),** 4, b c Invincible Spirit (IRE)—Ashley Hall (USA) **Mrs A. Cowley**
10 **PIPES OF PEACE (IRE),** 4, b c Galileo (IRE)—Coachella **Egan Waste Services Ltd**
11 **SEAPORT,** 7, ch g Champs Elysees—Cochin **Mrs Pao, Mr Stafford & Mr Tucker**
12 **SPANISH HISTORY (USA),** 4, b g Street Cry (IRE)—Infanta **Andrew Wyke & Ownaracehorse**
13 **VALITOP,** 5, b g Pivotal—Songeria **S. P. Tucker**

THREE-YEAR-OLDS

14 **APEX PREDATOR (IRE),** b c Acclamation—Key Girl (IRE) **Mrs A. Cowley**
15 **CLAN MCGREGOR (IRE),** b c Dragon Pulse (IRE)—Riymaisa (IRE) **P McNeil, J McNeil, L Brady, I Thomson**
16 **DARK CROCODILE (IRE),** b c Dark Angel (IRE)—Heaven's Vault (IRE)
17 **GIOVANNI MEDICI,** b c Medicean—Hadeeya **Stafford, McCormack, Budgett & Tucker**
18 **PARA MIO (IRE),** b c Pour Moi (IRE)—Malaspina (IRE) **Tucker Stafford & McCormack**
19 B f Havana Gold (IRE)—Rose Ransom (IRE)
20 **THE GREAT DANDINI (IRE),** b c Dandy Man (IRE)—Monivea (IRE) **S. P. Tucker**
21 **ZENITH ONE (IRE),** br c Footstepsinthesand—Gemini Diamond (IRE) **Mrs A. Cowley**

Other Owners: Mr R. T. Bateman, Mr W. L. Brady, Mr C. M. Budgett, P. Dean, Ms M. Delaney, Mr M. F. FitzGerald, Mr S. J. Lee, Looksarnteverything Partnership, E. McCormack, Mr C. A. M. McMillan, Mr J. McNeil, Mr P. J. McNeil, Ownaracehorse Ltd, Mrs A. Pao, Mr D. Parkinson, Mr N. J. Stafford, Mr I. C. Thomson, Mr A. P. D. Wyke.

Assistant Trainer: Sam Beddoes

Jockey (flat): Oisin Murphy, Timmy Murphy. **Jockey (NH):** Conor O'Farrell.

---

163 **MR CHRIS DWYER, Newmarket**
Postal: **Grooms Cottage, Brickfield Stud, Exning Road, Newmarket, Suffolk, CB8 7JH**
Contacts: PHONE **(01638) 578651** MOBILE **(07831) 579844**
E-MAIL **getadwyer@aol.com**

1 **ANNIE SALTS,** 5, b m Zebedee—Dazzling View (USA) **Mrs S. Dwyer**
2 **ARCANISTA (IRE),** 5, ch m Arcano (IRE)—Cattiva Generosa **Mr & Mrs J Harris**
3 **ARZAAK (IRE),** 4, br g Casamento (IRE)—Dixieland Kiss (USA) **Mr M. M. Foulger**
4 **BINT DANDY (IRE),** 7, b m Dandy Man (IRE)—Ceol Loch Aoidh (IRE) **Mr M. M. Foulger**
5 **DARK SIDE DREAM,** 6, b g Equiano (FR)—Dream Day **Mr M. M. Foulger & Mrs Shelley Dwyer**
6 **ERISSIMUS MAXIMUS (FR),** 4, b c Holy Roman Emperor—Tegan (IRE) **Mr P. Venner**
7 **FLOWER CUP,** 5, b m Acclamation—Amber Queen (IRE) **Mrs S. Dwyer**
8 **FOIE GRAS,** 8, b g Kyllachy—Bint Zamayem (IRE) **Mrs S. Dwyer**
9 **PRECIOUS PLUM,** 4, b f Equiano (FR)—Miss Polly Plum **Mrs J. V. Hughes**
10 **RIGHT ABOUT NOW (IRE),** 4, b g Famous Name—Right Reason (IRE) **Mr M. M. Foulger**
11 **ROSE BERRY,** 4, b f Archipenko (USA)—Desert Berry **Strawberry Fields Stud**
12 **SAVED MY BACON (IRE),** 7, b m Camacho—Sally Green (IRE) **Mrs J. Hughes & Mrs C. Kemp**
13 **THE LACEMAKER,** 4, b f Dutch Art—Sospel **Drakenstein Stud Proprietary Limited**

MR CHRIS DWYER - Continued

THREE-YEAR-OLDS

14 BAILEYS EXCEL, b g Exceed And Excel (AUS)—Baileys Jubilee G. R. Bailey Ltd (Baileys Horse Feeds)
15 ROCK ON BAILEYS, ch f Rock of Gibraltar (IRE)—Ring For Baileys G. R. Bailey Ltd (Baileys Horse Feeds)
16 TURQUOISE BAY (USA), b g Lonhro (AUS)—Torre Di Pisa (USA) Mr H. K. Tang

TWO-YEAR-OLDS

17 CASARUBINA (IRE), br f 29/4 Casamento (IRE)—
                                    Mi Rubina (IRE) (Rock of Gibraltar (IRE)) (8000) Mr & Mrs J Harris

Other Owners: Mrs P. A. Harris, Mr J. E. Harris, Mrs C. J. Kemp, G. F. L. Robinson, Exors of the Late Mr F. B. B. White.

Assistant Trainer: Shelley Dwyer (07949) 612256

164

MISS CLAIRE DYSON, Evesham
Postal: **Froglands Stud Farm, Froglands Lane, Cleeve Prior, Evesham, Worcestershire, WR11 8LB**
Contacts: **PHONE (07803) 720183 (01789) 774000 FAX (01789) 774000**
E-MAIL cdyson@live.co.uk WEBSITE www.clairedysonracing.co.uk

1 BLACK BANJO (IRE), 9, br g Hawkeye (IRE)—Corkscrew Hill (IRE) FSF Racing
2 CAP'N (IRE), 7, b g Gamut (IRE)—Dawn Princess (IRE) Ishtar
3 CHEAT THE CHEATER (IRE), 11, ch f Flemensfirth (USA)—Ballyclough Gale Pink Fizz Fillies
4 CLASSIC TUNE, 8, b g Scorpion (IRE)—Classic Fantasy D. J. Dyson
5 CLASSULA, 6, b g Sulamani (IRE)—Classic Fantasy D. J. Dyson
6 HER DREAM (IRE), 6, b m Yeats (IRE)—High Benefit (IRE) Miss L. J. Rogers
7 HOLY CROSS (IRE), 7, b g Yeats (IRE)—Bleu Ciel Et Blanc (FR) FSF Racing
8 MIDNIGHT OWLE, 8, ch g Midnight Legend—Owlesbury Dream (IRE) FSF Racing
9 OVER MY HEAD, 10, gr g Overbury (IRE)—Altesse de Sou (FR) FSF Racing
10 PASSAM, 6, b g Black Sam Bellamy (IRE)—One Wild Night FSF Racing
11 YOU NEVER KNOW, 7, ch m Apple Tree (FR)—Capricorn Princess B & S Vaughan & Partner

Other Owners: Miss C. Dyson, B & S Vaughan, Mr B. D. Vaughan, Mrs S. A. Vaughan, Dr M. Viegas.

Jockey (NH): Brendan Powell.

165

MR SIMON EARLE, Warminster
Postal: **Little Croft, Tytherington, Warminster, Wiltshire, BA12 7AD**
Contacts: PHONE (01985) 840450 FAX (01985) 840450 MOBILE (07850) 350116
E-MAIL simon@simonearleracing.com WEBSITE www.simonearleracing.com

1 GOLDEN HOUR (USA), 4, b g Medaglia d'oro (USA)—Morrow R. L. Dacombe
2 KAVANAGHS CORNER (IRE), 9, b g Coroner (IRE)—Annacarney (IRE) Mrs B. O'Flynn
3 4, B g Sakhee (USA)—Madame Mozaik (USA)
4 WATER RAIL, 9, b g Manipulator (IRE)—Madame Mozaik (USA) Mr S. A. Earle

Conditional: Alice Mills.

166

MR MICHAEL EASTERBY, Sheriff Hutton
Postal: **New House Farm, Sheriff Hutton, York, North Yorkshire, YO60 6TN**
Contacts: PHONE (01347) 878368 FAX (01347) 878204 MOBILE (07831) 347481
E-MAIL enquiries@mickeasterby.co.uk WEBSITE www.mickeasterby-racing.co.uk

1 AELIUS, 4, ch g Sepoy (AUS)—Syvilla M. W. Easterby
2 ALBERT'S BACK, 4, b g Champs Elysees—Neath Golden Ratio P'ship & Mr S Winter
3 ALDRETH, 7, b g Champs Elysees—Rowan Flower (IRE) Mr A. Morse & Stittenham Racing
4 APALIS (FR), 6, gr m Mastercraftsman (IRE)—Parcimonie Mr J Blackburn Racing
5 ARROWTOWN, 6, b m Rail Link—Protectress S Hollings L Folwell S Hull M Bannister
6 BABOUSKA, 4, b f Monsieur Bond (IRE)—Prices Lane Mr M A G BLack & Mr M Burrows
7 BALLYNARRY LADY (IRE), 4, b f Desert Millennium (IRE)—Shone Island (IRE) Mr Gerard McMullan
8 BANNY'S LAD, 9, ch g Osorio (GER)—Skytrial (USA) Mr M. J. R. Bannister/Stittenham Racing
9 BOP IT, 9, b g Misu Bond (IRE)—Forever Bond R. C. Bond
10 BOSHAM, 8, b g Shamardal (USA)—Awwal Malika (USA) P. Easterby

MR MICHAEL EASTERBY - Continued

11 **BOUCLIER (IRE)**, 8, ch h Zamindar (USA)—Bastet (IRE) **Mr M. Chung**
12 **BOWSON FRED**, 6, b g Monsieur Bond (IRE)—Bow Bridge **Mrs A. Jarvis**
13 **CARLTON FRANKIE**, 4, b f Equiano (FR)—Valiant Runner **Padgett Hollings Hull Fielding Hoskins**
14 **CARLTON RYAN (IRE)**, 10, b g Morozov (USA)—Dante's Arrow (IRE) **Mr S Hollings & Partner**
15 **CHASMA**, 8, b m Kayf Tara—Luneray (FR) **Mr N Bannister Racing**
16 **CHAUCER'S TALE**, 4, b g Poet's Voice—Grand Slam Maria (FR) **Mr A. N. C. Bengough & Stittenham Racing**
17 **CURZON LINE**, 9, b g Dubawi (IRE)—Polska (USA) **The Golden Ratio Partnership**
18 **DECIMA (IRE)**, 4, b f Dream Ahead (USA)—Snowtime (IRE)
19 **DESERT DREAM**, 4, b c Oasis Dream—Rosika **P. Easterby**
20 **DIFFERENT JOURNEY**, 5, b g Poet's Voice—Vintage Gardenia **Mrs C Daurge, Mr S Hull & Mr S Winter**
21 **DUSTY BLUE**, 6, ch m Medicean—Jazz Jam **Mr M. Chung**
22 **ENLIGHTEN**, 4, b g Kayf Tara—Rapturous **R S Cockerill Farms**
23 **FLYMETOTHESTARS**, 5, b g Sea The Stars (IRE)—Precious Gem (IRE) **Middleham Park Racing & S Hull**
24 **GANBEI**, 12, ch g Lomitas—Native Ring (FR) **Mr N. W. A. Bannister**
25 **GULF OF POETS**, 6, b g Oasis Dream—Sandglass **Mr J Blackburn Mr A Pollock Mr A Turton**
26 **HERNANDO TORRES**, 10, b g Iffraaj—Espana **Mr C. D. Sigsworth**
27 **HOLIDAY MAGIC (IRE)**, 7, gr g Dark Angel (IRE)—Win Cash (IRE) **Mr A. Saha**
28 **HOOF IT**, 11, b g Monsieur Bond (IRE)—Forever Bond **Mr A Chandler Racing**
29 **IMPERIAL STATE**, 5, b g Holy Roman Emperor (IRE)—Seldemosa **S Winter, Mrs L. Folwell, J. Blackburn**
30 **INGS PASTURE**, 4, ch f Midnight Legend—Won More Night **Mr B. Burdett**
31 **ITLAAQ**, 12, b g Alhaarth (IRE)—Hathrah (IRE) **M. W. Easterby**
32 **KIMBERLEY BOY**, 5, b g Distant Peak (IRE)—Marsh Run **Mr Stewart A Lewis Racing**
33 **LADIES FIRST**, 4, b f Monsieur Bond (IRE)—Forever Bond **R. C. Bond**
34 **MAGIC CITY (IRE)**, 9, b g Elusive City (USA)—Annmarie's Magic (IRE) **A Turton J Blackburn & Mrs L Folwell**
35 **MALDONADO (FR)**, 4, ch g Rio de La Plata (USA)—Spanish Winner (IRE) **Mr A. Saha**
36 **MANON**, 4, b f Malinas (GER)—La Creole (FR) **Mr N Wrigley, Mrs J Lukas & Mr B Guerin**
37 **MELGATE MELODY**, 5, b g Royal Applause—Maeander (FR) **Mr B Hoggarth & Mr S Hull**
38 **MISS SHERIDAN (IRE)**, 4, br f Lilbourne Lad (IRE)—
Sues Surprise (IRE) **Mr J Blackburn & Mr A Turton & Partner**
39 **NOVELTY SEEKER (USA)**, 9, b g Street Sense (USA)—Nawaiet (USA) **Mr B. Padgett & Stittenham Racing**
40 **PERFECT PASTURE**, 8, b g Pastoral Pursuits—Word Perfect **S Hull & S Hollings**
41 **PURPLE ROCK (IRE)**, 6, b g Fastnet Rock (AUS)—Amethyst (IRE) **Mr M Blades, Mr S Hollings & Mr S Hull**
42 **QAFFAAL (USA)**, 7, b g Street Cry (IRE)—Wasseema (USA) **Michael Burrows, Calam & Holdsworth**
43 **QUICK LOOK**, 5, b g Kheleyf (USA)—Weqaar (USA) **Golden Ratio, Hull, Hollings & Winter**
44 **QUIXOTE (GER)**, 8, b h Pivotal—Quebrada (IRE) **Mr M. Chung**
45 **RAPID APPLAUSE**, 6, b g Royal Applause—Madam Ninette **A. Morse, S. Winter, Mrs L. Folwell, H. Mulryan**
46 **REAR ADMIRAL (IRE)**, 12, b g Dushyantor (USA)—
Ciaras Charm (IRE) **Mr S Hollings Mr A Turton Mr D Fielding**
47 **ROBERO**, 6, b g Piccolo—Ceilidh Band **Mr A. H. L. Zheng**
48 **ROLLER**, 5, b g Rail Link—Buffering **Irkroy Racing & Mr Andrew Pollock**
49 **ROYCANO**, 8, ch g Lucarno (USA)—Royal Distant (USA) **Mr M. J. R. Bannister/Stittenham Racing**
50 **SAINTS AND SINNERS (IRE)**, 10, b g Gold Well—How Provincial (IRE) **Mr N Wrigley & Mrs J Lukas**
51 **SAM'S GUNNER**, 5, ch g Black Sam Bellamy (IRE)—Falcon's Gunner **Falcon's Line Ltd**
52 **SELECTION (FR)**, 5, ch g Siyouni (FR)—Perspective (FR) **S Hull, S Davis**
53 **SPACE WAR**, 11, b g Elusive City (USA)—Princess Luna (GER) **The Laura Mason Syndicate**
54 **STEEL CITY**, 10, gr g Act One—Serraval (FR) **J. T. Brown**
55 **STUBYTUESDAY**, 4, b g Dick Turpin (IRE)—Just Dreams **Mr Stuart Daynes & Stittenham Racing**
56 **SWANSWAY**, 5, ch g Showcasing—Spring Stroll (USA) **W. H. & Mrs J. A. Tinning**
57 **TORRID**, 7, ch g Three Valleys (USA)—Western Appeal (USA) **J Blackburn, Mrs A Bartram & S Winter**
58 **TOWN HEAD**, 5, ch g Archipenko (USA)—Forever Loved **Mr M. J. R. Bannister/Stittenham Racing**
59 **UP TEN DOWN TWO (IRE)**, 9, b g Hurricane Run (IRE)—Darabela (IRE) **Mrs C. Daurge**
60 **WILD AL EMARAT**, 6, b g Dubawi (USA)—Spirit of Dubai (IRE) **Imperial Racing Partnership No.8**

THREE-YEAR-OLDS

61 **AIRGLOW (IRE)**, b g Invincible Spirit (IRE)—Pearl Grey **S Hull & S Davis**
62 **APHAEA**, b f Farhh—Wood Chorus **Mr B. Padgett**
63 **ASTRAEA**, b f Cityscape—Rapid Revelation (USA) **Mr B Padgett Racing**
64 **BAD DOG**, ch g Pastoral Pursuits—Movie Star (IRE) **Mr J. N. Blackburn & Stittenham Racing**
65 **BEGGING BOWL**, br f Pastoral Pursuits—Bow Bridge **Mrs A. Jarvis**
66 **CALL DAWN**, b f Helmet (AUS)—Authoritative **Mr A Morgans Racing**
67 **CARLTON THOMAS**, b g Pastoral Pursuits—Word Perfect **S Hollings, S Hull & D Swales**
68 **DAFFY GREY (IRE)**, ro g Zebedee—Pahokee (IRE) **Mr D. A. Fielding**
69 **DAHIK (IRE)**, ch c Society Rock (IRE)—Bishop's Lake **Mr A. Saha**
70 **FEEBS**, ch g Assertive—Fujakka (IRE) **J Blackburn, S Winter & D Fielding**
71 **FURZE LADY**, b f Dick Turpin (IRE)—Baymist **Mrs Linda Folwell Racing**

MR MICHAEL EASTERBY - Continued

72 **GANTON PAR,** b g Frozen Power (IRE)—Sheer Indulgence (FR) **S Hollings, S Hull & D Fielding**
73 **GLEAMING SUN,** b g Arabian Gleam—Cara's Delight (AUS) **K. Wreglesworth**
74 **HARVEST DAY,** b f Harbour Watch (IRE)—Miss Wells (IRE) **Mrs C E Mason & Partner**
75 **KANNAPOLIS (IRE),** b g Makfi—Alta Definizione (IRE) **Mr A Stott & Mr E Brook**
76 **LYRICAL PURSUIT,** ch f Poet's Voice—Crinklelini **Imperial Racing P'Ship & Mr J Blackburn**
77 **MISS WOLVERINE,** b f Amadeus Wolf—Mille Etoiles (USA) **Mr A Morgans Racing**
78 **NUNNERY LANE,** b g Mazameer—Prices Lane **Mr A G Black Racing**
79 **ROLLADICE,** ch g Bated Breath—Selkirk Sky **A Pollock, J Blackburn & B Burdett**
80 **WHERE'S JEFF,** b g Haafhd—Piece of Magic **M W Easterby Racing**

TWO-YEAR-OLDS

81 B g 21/2 Rip Van Winkle (IRE)—Amallna (Green Desert (USA)) (28000) **Sheep As A Lamb Syndicate**
82 Br f 12/5 Heerat (IRE)—Black Annis Bower (Proclamation (IRE)) **Mrs A Jarvis**
83 B f 4/2 Henrythenavigator (USA)—Bouyrin (IRE) (Invincible Spirit (IRE)) **The Laura Mason Syndicate**
84 Ch f 29/3 Mayson—Brave Mave (Daylami (IRE)) (19047) **J Munroe**
85 Ch g 5/2 Champs Elysees—Combustible (IRE) (Halling (USA)) (10476) **Imperial Racing**
86 B c 6/3 Nathaniel (IRE)—Dance East (Shamardal (USA)) (40000) **B Padgett**
87 Ch c 22/2 Lope de Vega (IRE)—Date With Destiny (IRE) (George Washington (IRE)) (48000) **B Padgett**
88 Ch g 29/2 Mukhadram—Divine Power (Kyllachy) (16190) **B Padgett**
89 B f 14/2 Burwaaz—El Molino Blanco (Royal Applause) **D Scott**
90 Ch g 1/3 Equiano (FR)—Faldal (Falbrav (IRE)) (12000) **S Davis, Mrs L Folwell, S Hull**
91 Br c 5/3 Havana Gold (IRE)—Fine Lady (Selkirk (USA)) (22000) **D F Spence**
92 B g 14/4 Lope de Vega (IRE)—Forces of Darkness (IRE) (Lawman (FR)) (40000) **J Blackburn, Imperial Racing**
93 **GEORGE RIDSDALE,** ch g 10/4 Ruler of The World (IRE)—
                                   Cape Rising (Cape Cross (IRE)) (21000) **J Blackburn, Imperial Racing**
94 B g 14/5 Heerat (IRE)—Hoof's So Lucky (Compton Place)
95 B g 24/1 Mukhadram—Illandrane (IRE) (Cape Cross (IRE)) (8000) **E A Brook**
96 **JACK BERRY HOUSE,** b g 17/2 Harbour Watch (IRE)—Dularame (IRE) (Pivotal) (11428) **L Vaessen**
97 B g 22/3 Archipenko (USA)—Kibini (Galileo (IRE)) (2604) **Imperial Racing**
98 **KIMBERLEY GIRL,** b f 10/4 Heerat (IRE)—Black Baccara (Superior Premium) (4761) **Stewart A Lewis**
99 **MAJOR SNUGFIT,** ch g 19/3 Ruler of The World (IRE)—Bridle Belle (Dansili) (7619) **Mr A Greenwood**
100 **MELGATE MAGIC,** ch g 24/2 Harbour Watch (IRE)—
                                   Corn Rigs (Exceed And Excel (AUS)) (20000) **B Hoggarth, D Scott**
101 **MELGATE MAJEURE,** br c 26/3 Lethal Force (IRE)—Ambrix (IRE) (Xaar) (9500) **B Hoggarth**
102 Ch f 19/2 Champs Elysees—Modern Art (New Approach (IRE)) **Imperial Racing**
103 B g 8/5 Burwaaz—On Holiday (Dubai Destination (USA))
104 B g 10/2 Poet's Voice—Our Faye (College Chapel) (12500) **S Hull, Mrs L Folwell, S Davis**
105 Ch g 5/4 Phoenix Reach (IRE)—Pavia (Alflora (IRE))
106 B g 20/2 Archipenko (USA)—Rowlestone Express (Rail Link) (2034) **Imperial Racing**
107 **SHE'S AWAKE,** b f 23/3 Iffraaj—Porthcawl (Singspiel (IRE)) **The Laura Mason Syndicate**

Other Owners: Mr N. W. A. Bannister, Mr M. J. R. Bannister, Mrs Ann Bartram, Mr A. N. C. Bengough, Mr A. G. Black, Mr J. N. Blackburn, Mr Michael Blades, Mrs Y. Blunt, Mr David Blunt, David & Yvonne Blunt, Mr J. E. Bray, Mr E. A. Brook, Mr Barry Burdett, Mr Michael Burrows, Mr T. Calam, Mr Andrew Chandler, Mr A. Courtine, Mrs Christine Daurge, David Scott and Co (Pattern Makers) Ltd, Mr Stuart Daynes, Mr M. W. Easterby, Mr Dean Fielding, Mrs L. S. Folwell, Mr B. Guerin, Mr Bernard Hoggarth, Mr P. Holdsworth, Mr S. A. Hollings, Mr R. S. Hoskins, Mr Steve Hull, Imperial Racing Partnership, Mr Stewart Lewis, Mrs Julia Lukas, Mrs C. E. Mason, Middleham Park Racing Lll, Mr E. A. R. Morgans, Mr A. Morse, Mr B. Padgett, Mr A. G. Pollock, Mr Ian A. Robinson, Miss Michelle Robinson, Mr David Scott, Stittenham Racing, Mr A. F. Stott, Mr D. Swales, Mrs J. A. Tinning, Mr W. H. Tinning, Mr Andrew Turton, Mrs L. F. Wei, Mr S. J. Winter, Mr K. Wreglesworth, Mr N. H. T. Wrigley.

Assistant Trainer: D. M. Easterby.

Jockey (flat): Nathan Evans, Paul Mulrennan, James Sullivan. **Jockey (NH):** Harry Bannister.
Apprentice: Harrison Shaw. **Amateur:** Miss S. Brotherton, Miss Joanna Mason.

---

167 | **MR TIM EASTERBY, Malton**
Postal: **Habton Grange, Great Habton, Malton, North Yorkshire, YO17 6TY**
Contacts: **PHONE (01653) 668566 FAX (01653) 668621**
E-MAIL easterby@btconnect.com WEBSITE www.timeasterby.co.uk

1 **AASHEQ (IRE),** 5, b g Dubawi (IRE)—Beach Bunny (IRE) **Ryedale Partners No1**
2 **ALICE LISLE,** 4, ch f Flemensfirth (USA)—Twilight Affair **Ryedale Partners No 4**
3 **APPOINTED,** 4, b f Delegator—Celestial Harmony **Mr M. J. Macleod & Partner**

MR TIM EASTERBY - Continued

4 **ASSURE**, 4, b g Aussie Rules (USA)—Salut **Mr R. Ellis**
5 **ATTENTION SEAKER**, 8, b m Bollin Eric—Pay Attention **Ryedale Partners No 6**
6 **AUTUMN SURPRISE (IRE)**, 5, b m Yeats (IRE)—Septembers Hawk (IRE) **Mr T. J. Hemmings**
7 **BALESTRA**, 4, b g Bated Breath—Nimble Thimble (USA) **Habton Farms**
8 **BOLLIN ACE**, 7, b g Bollin Eric—Bollin Annabel **Ryedale Partners No 3**
9 **BOLLIN TED**, 4, b g Haafhd—Bollin Greta **Mr Neil Arton & Partner**
10 **BOSSIPOP**, 5, ch g Assertive—Opopmil (IRE) **A. R. Turnbull**
11 **BREAKWATER BAY (IRE)**, 4, b g Lilbourne Lad (IRE)—Aqualina (IRE) **Reality Partnerships III**
12 **BROTHER MCGONAGALL**, 4, b r Equiano (FR)—Anatase **Reality Partnerships VI**
13 **C'EST DEJA CA (FR)**, 6, ch g Dano-Mast—Ou Es Tu (FR) **Habton Farms**
14 **COMPUTABLE**, 4, ch g Compton Place—Kummel Excess (IRE) **Mr B Guerin Mrs E J Wills & Habton Farms**
15 **COPPER KNIGHT (IRE)**, 4, b g Sir Prancealot (IRE)—Mystic Dream **Ventura Racing (Copper) & Partner**
16 **DANCE KING**, 8, ch g Danehill Dancer (IRE)—One So Wonderful **Mr Ambrose Turnbull & Partner**
17 **DELLAGUISTA (IRE)**, 4, gr f Sea The Stars (IRE)—Lady Springbank (IRE) **David & Yvonne Blunt**
18 **DEW POND**, 6, b g Motivator—Rutland Water (IRE) **Ashfield Caravan Park**
19 **DIG A BIT DEEPER**, 5, b g Duke of Marmalade (IRE)—Dayia (IRE) **Mr Ambrose Turnbull & Partner**
20 **DUKE OF YORKSHIRE**, 8, b g Duke of Marmalade (IRE)—Dame Edith (FR) **Habton Farms**
21 **EAST STREET REVUE**, 5, ch g Pastoral Pursuits—Revue Princess (IRE) **Mr S. A. Heley & Partner**
22 **EXCESSABLE**, 5, ch g Sakhee's Secret—Kummel Excess (IRE) **Mr B Guerin & Habton Farms**
23 **FASHION THEORY**, 4, b f Dubawi (IRE)—Lady's Purse **Habton Farms**
24 **FATHER BERTIE**, 6, b g Firebreak—Magical Music **Mr J. R. Saville**
25 **FLYING PURSUIT**, 5, ch g Pastoral Pursuits—Choisette **Ontoawinner, M Hulin & Partner**
26 **FOREST FUSION (IRE)**, 4, b g Flemensfirth (USA)—Qui Plus Est (FR) **The Hon Mrs E. J. Wills**
27 **FROZEN OUT (IRE)**, 5, b g Frozen Power (IRE)—Liscoa (IRE) **Habton Farms**
28 **GHAYYAR (IRE)**, 4, b g Power—Al Ihtithar (IRE) **CDM Developments (North West) Ltd & Ptr**
29 **GIVE IT SOME TEDDY**, 4, b g Bahamian Bounty—Croeso Cariad **Mr L. Bond**
30 **GOGO BALOO**, 6, b m Schiaparelli (GER)—Tarabaloo **R. W. Metcalfe**
31 **GOLDEN APOLLO**, 4, ch g Pivotal—Elan **Mr David Scott & Partner**
32 **HIGH JINX (IRE)**, 10, b g High Chaparral (IRE)—Leonara (GER) **Mr & Mrs W. J. Williams**
33 **ICEFALL (IRE)**, 5, b g Frozen Power (IRE)—Silvertine (IRE) **Ryedale Partners No. 10**
34 **IFANDBUTWHYNOT (IRE)**, 12, b g Raise A Grand (IRE)—
Cockney Ground (IRE) **Claire Hollowood & Henry Dean**
35 **INTHEDEAL**, 4, b g Multiplex—Chebsey Belle (IRE) **Habton Farms**
36 **JUST HISS**, 5, b g Lawman (FR)—Feather Boa (IRE) **The Sandmoor Partnership**
37 **KENNY THE CAPTAIN (IRE)**, 7, ch g Captain Rio—Kelso Magic (USA) **Reality Partnerships V**
38 **KING OF THE CELTS (IRE)**, 10, b g Celtic Swing—Flamands **Habton Farms**
39 **KNIGHTS TABLE**, 5, b g Sir Percy—Whole Grain **Ventura Racing 2 & Partner**
40 **MAJOR MINUS**, 4, b g Sir Percy—Eminencia **Habton Farms**
41 **MEDINA SIDONIA (IRE)**, 6, b g Montjeu (IRE)—Valdara **Mr M. Stewart**
42 **MIDNIGHT MALIBU (IRE)**, 5, b m Poet's Voice—Midnight Martini **Mr D. A. West & Partner**
43 **MIKMAK**, 5, b g Makfi—Rakata (USA) **Habton Farms**
44 **MILLY BALOO**, 7, b m Desideratum—Tarabaloo **R. W. Metcalfe**
45 **MISCHIEF MANAGED (IRE)**, 4, ch g Tagula (IRE)—Cape Clear **Dubelem (Racing) Limited**
46 **MUKHAYYAM**, 6, b g Dark Angel (IRE)—Caster Sugar (USA) **Mr T. A. Scothern & Partner**
47 **MULTELLIE**, 6, b g Multiplex—Bollin Nellie **Mr David Scott & Partner**
48 **MUNTHANY (USA)**, 4, b g Raven's Pass (USA)—Safarjal (IRE) **Habton Farms**
49 **MURAABIT**, 6, ch g Makfi—Ho Hi The Moon (IRE) **Major Sir E. Brook & Mr A Stott**
50 **MY DICE (IRE)**, 5, b g Approve (IRE)—Spirit of The Nile (FR) **Mr T. J. Hemmings**
51 **MY REWARD**, 5, b g Rail Link—Tarot Card **Mr M. J. Macleod**
52 **NUNS WALK**, 4, ch f Sleeping Indian—Dance Card **Mr Ambrose Turnbull & Partner**
53 **OFF ART**, 8, ch g Dutch Art—Off Camera **Mr D B & Mrs C Lamplough**
54 **ORION'S BOW**, 7, ch g Pivotal—Heavenly Ray (USA) **Mr T. J. Swiers**
55 **OUR CHARLIE BROWN**, 4, b g American Post—Cordoba **Ontoawinner, SDH Project Services Ltd 2**
56 **PAROLE (IRE)**, 4, b g Mastercraftsman (IRE)—Leniency (USA) **Habton Farms**
57 **PARYS MOUNTAIN (IRE)**, 4, gr g Dark Angel (IRE)—Muzdaan (USA) **Reality Partnerships XII**
58 **PRONTO TONTO (IRE)**, 5, b g Thousand Words—Island Sun (IRE) **Mr Tom Ford & Mr C P Magnier**
59 **RANDY PIKE (IRE)**, 8, b g Mahler—Niamh's Leader (IRE) **Reality Partnerships II**
60 **RASHEEQ (IRE)**, 5, b g Vale of York (IRE)—Limber Up (IRE) **Ventura Racing (Rasheeq) & Partner**
61 **REGAL MIRAGE (IRE)**, 4, ch g Aqlaam—Alzaroof (USA) **Ryedale Partners No 7**
62 **RELIGHT MY FIRE**, 8, ch g Firebreak—Making Music **J. Gill**
63 **SECRET MELODY**, 5, b g Sakhee's Secret—Montjeu's Melody (IRE) **The Mount Fawcus Partnership**
64 **SHERIFF GARRETT (IRE)**, 4, b g Lawman (FR)—Few Are Chosen (IRE) **Ontoawinner 10 & Partner 4**
65 **SILVERY MOON (IRE)**, 11, gr g Verglas (IRE)—Starry Night **Mrs D Stevens & Partner**
66 **STING IN HIS TAIL (IRE)**, 5, b g Scorpion (IRE)—Glory Queen (IRE) **Mrs E J Wills & Partner**
67 **STORM AHEAD (IRE)**, 5, b g Iffraaj—Loose Julie (IRE) **A. R. Turnbull**

MR TIM EASTERBY - Continued

68 **STORMIN TOM (IRE)**, 6, b g Dylan Thomas (IRE)—She Storm (IRE) **Three Jolly Farmers**
69 **SUITCASE 'N' TAXI**, 4, br g Major Cadeaux—Finalize **Ontoawinner 10 & Partner 3**
70 **TARA FORCE**, 4, b f Kayf Tara—Whizz Back (IRE) **Reality Partnerships VIII**
71 **VERY FIRST TIME**, 6, b g Champs Elysees—Like A Virgin (IRE) **Mr T. J. Hemmings**
72 **VIVE LA DIFFERENCE (IRE)**, 4, b g Holy Roman Emperor (IRE)—Galaxie Sud (USA) **Ryedale Partners No 5**
73 **WHAT A GAME (IRE)**, 7, ch g Milan—Moscow Mo Chuisle (IRE) **Dubelem (Racing) Limited**
74 5, B m Bollin Eric—Willows World **Habton Farms**

THREE-YEAR-OLDS

75 **AIRPLANE (IRE)**, b g Pour Moi (IRE)—Abyssinie (IRE) **Mr M. Stewart**
76 **ANGELS**, b gr f Dark Angel (IRE)—Magic Eye (IRE) **Clipper Group Holdings Ltd**
77 **BAYELSA BOY (IRE)**, b g Elzaam (AUS)—Extraordinary (IRE) **Ontoawinner, SDH Project Services Ltd 3**
78 **BIDDY BRADY (USA)**, ch f Street Boss (USA)—October Tempest (USA) **Mr F. Gillespie**
79 B f Multiplex—Bollin Annabel **Habton Farms**
80 **BOLLIN JOAN**, b f Mount Nelson—Bollin Greta **Habton Farms**
81 **BREATHABLE**, b g Bated Breath—Cassique Lady (IRE) **Mr B Guerin Mr J Westoll & Habton Farms**
82 **CHEERS MONSIEUR**, ch g Monsieur Bond (IRE)—Cheers For Thea (IRE) **Habton Farms**
83 **CONTREBASSE**, b g Champs Elysees—Viola da Braccio (IRE) **The Harmonious Lot & Partner**
84 **DANGEROUS LADY**, b f Bahamian Bounty—Purple Silk **Reality Partnerships XI**
85 **EL BERTIE (IRE)**, b g Elzaam (AUS)—Emily Jane (IRE) **Mr J. R. Saville**
86 **EXCELLENT TIMES**, b f Excelebration (IRE)—Al Janadeirya **Times Of Wigan Ltd**
87 B g Holy Roman Emperor (IRE)—Fairy Wings (USA) **Partnership Terminated**
88 **FASTALONG (IRE)**, b f Fastnet Rock (AUS)—Nidina (IRE) **Mr Craig Wilson & Partner**
89 **FINNION FOX**, b g Foxwedge (AUS)—Chushka **Mr F. Gillespie**
90 **FOXY'S SPIRIT**, b f Foxwedge (AUS)—Jessie's Spirit (IRE) **The Belton Boys**
91 **GRAPHITE GIRL (IRE)**, gr f Kodiac—My Girl Lisa (USA) **CDM Developments (North West) Limited**
92 **GULLANE ONE (IRE)**, ch g Dream Ahead (USA)—Shamsalmaidan (IRE) **Mount Pleasant Racing**
93 B c Desideratum—Gwyre (IRE) **Habton Farms**
94 **HYANNA**, b f Champs Elysees—Highly Spiced **Mr G. C. Vibert**
95 B c Epaulette (AUS)—Ice On Fire **Habton Farms**
96 **KODEINE (IRE)**, br f Kodiac—Jamary (IRE) **Habton Farms**
97 **LEVER DU SOLEIL (FR)**, b g Le Havre (IRE)—Morning Dust (IRE) **Mr & Mrs J. D. Cotton**
98 **LIFE FOR RENT**, b g Sleeping Indian—Sea Flower (IRE) **Reality Partnerships**
99 B g Thewayyouare (USA)—Ma Nikitia (IRE) **Habton Farms**
100 **MAY SYMPHONIC**, b f Mayson—Symphonic Dancer (USA) **Mr Julian Ball & Partner**
101 **MR GREENLIGHT**, b g Bahamian Bounty—Nos Da **R. Taylor & Mr P. Hebdon**
102 **NORTH ROAD REVUE**, b f Dick Turpin (IRE)—Revue Princess (IRE) **Mr S A Heley & Partner**
103 **PACO BLEUE**, b f Paco Boy (IRE)—Poulaine Bleue **CDM Developments (North West) Ltd & Ptr**
104 **PHOEBELLAS ANGEL**, ch f Equiano (FR)—Oasis Breeze **G Sunley, D & A Wilsdon & Partner**
105 **POET'S DAWN**, ch f Poet's Voice—Dudley Queen (IRE) **Mr Timothy O'Gram & Partner**
106 **POWER SAIL**, gr g Frozen Power (IRE)—Gone Sailing **Habton Farms**
107 **REVENGE**, b g Arcano (IRE)—Queens Revenge **HP Racing Revenge 1**
108 **RYEDALE ENCORE**, b f Canford Cliffs (IRE)—Jackie's Opera (FR) **Ryedale Partners No 8**
109 **SCENIC RIVER**, ch f Dutch Art—Camp Riverside (USA) **Mr & Mrs Lamplough & Partner**
110 **SCOUNDREL**, b g Dick Turpin (IRE)—Royal Punch **Habton Farms**
111 **SE YOU**, b g Sepoy (AUS)—Lady Hestia (USA) **R. Taylor & Mr P. Hebdon**
112 **SILVER STARLIGHT**, gr f Showcasing—Pendulum **Reality Partnerships I**
113 **SIR DERRICK (IRE)**, ch g Sir Prancealot (IRE)—Alexander Confranc (IRE) **Reality Partnerships IX**
114 **STAXTON**, b c Equiano (FR)—Snake's Head **Ontoawinner 10 & Partner**
115 **SUPAULETTE (IRE)**, b f Epaulette (AUS)—Supreme Spirit (IRE) **Mr Ambrose Turnbull & Partner**
116 **SURRENDER**, b g Sixties Icon—Mango Music **Habton Farms**
117 **SYMPOSING (IRE)**, b g Casamento (IRE)—Firecross (IRE) **Major Sir E. Brook & Mr A Stott**
118 **THE KNOT IS TIED (IRE)**, b g Casamento (IRE)—Really Polish (USA) **Mr E. A. Brook & Partner**
119 **TRAVEL LIGHTLY**, b f Showcasing—Upton Seas **E. A. Brook**
120 **VENTURA CREST (IRE)**, b g Elzaam (AUS)—Ms Cromby (IRE) **Ventura Racing (Crest) & Partner**
121 **VOGUELA (IRE)**, b f Arcano (IRE)—Trading Places **Nick Bradley Racing 4 & Partner**
122 **WELLS FARHH GO (IRE)**, b c Farhh—Mowazana (IRE) **Mr S A Heley & Partner**

TWO-YEAR-OLDS

123 B c 15/3 Kodiac—Airline Hostess (IRE) (Sadler's Wells (USA)) (15000) **Mr Tom Ford & Partner**
124 B f 1/2 Lethal Force (IRE)—Barleycorn Lady (IRE) (Nayef (USA)) (13333) **Habton Farms**
125 Gr c 5/4 Zebedee—Benedicte (IRE) (Galileo (IRE)) (28571) **Ontoawinner 10 & Partner**
126 **BIG ACE**, b c 21/1 Kuroshio (AUS)—Speedy Utmost Meg (Medicean) (14285) **Mr M. J. Macleod**
127 B c 3/3 Heeraat (IRE)—Blades Princess (Needwood Blade) (9523) **Habton Farms**
128 **CEMETRY WALL**, br c 18/4 Kuroshio (AUS)—Las Vital Spark (IRE) (Verglas (IRE)) (3809) **Mr M. J. Macleod**

MR TIM EASTERBY - Continued

129 Ch c 8/5 Havana Gold (IRE)—Diksie Dancer (Diktat) (17000) **Habton Farms**
130 Ch c 2/3 Pivotal—Fondled (Selkirk (USA)) (30000) **Mr David Scott & Partner**
131 **GREMOBOY,** ch c 14/2 Mayson—Largo (Selkirk (USA)) (9523) **Gremot Racing**
132 Ch c 27/3 Reliable Man—Hamloola (Red Ransom (USA)) (30000) **Qatar Racing Limited**
133 B c 15/2 Coach House (IRE)—
                    Kummel Excess (IRE) (Exceed And Excel (AUS)) (22857) **Ontoawinner 8 & Partner 2**
134 B c 9/2 Dream Ahead (USA)—Little Annie (Compton Place) (10000) **Ventura Racing 3 & Partner**
135 B c 27/2 Alhebayeb (IRE)—Manaka (FR) (Falco (USA)) (15000) **Habton Farms**
136 B f 12/1 Camacho—Mary Mortell (High Chaparral (IRE)) (8095) **Middleham Park Racing XLVII & Partner**
137 **MYTHICAL PURSUITS,** ch f 7/4 Pastoral Pursuits—Magic Myth (IRE) (Revoque (IRE)) **Ryedale Partners No 9**
138 B c 11/2 War Command (USA)—Natural Choice (Teofilo (IRE)) (24761) **Reality Partnerships IV**
139 Br c 5/3 Epaulette (AUS)—Neila (GER) (Diktat) (22000) **Habton Farms**
140 Gr c 16/3 Zebedee—Nippy (FR) (Anabaa (USA)) (20952) **Habton Farms**
141 B c 6/4 Harbour Watch (IRE)—Perfect Act (Act One) (12000) **Habton Farms**
142 B c 4/3 Swiss Spirit—Perfect Practice (Medicean) (11000) **Habton Farms**
143 B c 4/2 Dream Ahead (USA)—Pernica (Sir Percy) (66666) **Mr & Mrs J. D. Cotton**
144 Ch c 3/3 Dream Ahead (USA)—Picture of Lily (Medicean) (31000) **Ryedale Partners No. 2**
145 B gr f 24/3 Mastercraftsman (IRE)—Portraitofmylove (IRE) (Azamour (IRE)) (3000) **Habton Farms**
146 Br f 13/3 Swiss Spirit—Positivity (Monsieur Bond (IRE)) (13333)
147 Ch c 7/3 Sepoy (AUS)—Poyle Meg (Dansili) (26666) **Habton Farms**
148 Ch c 6/3 Camacho—Practicallyperfect (IRE) (King Charlemagne (USA)) (22857) **Middleham Park LXIX & Partner**
149 **PRINGLE,** ch f 16/5 Monsieur Bond (IRE)—Amethyst Dawn (IRE) (Act One) **Mr D. A. West & Partner**
150 B gr c 5/3 Gregorian (IRE)—Purple Silk (Holy Roman Emperor (IRE)) (11428) **Reality Partnerships VII**
151 Br gr c 10/4 Gregorian (IRE)—Raajis (IRE) (Dark Angel (IRE)) (23000) **Habton Farms**
152 B f 12/3 Mayson—Ride The Wind (Cozzene (USA)) (30476) **Ontoawinner 10 & Partner**
153 Ch c 24/4 Firebreak—Rosabee (IRE) (No Excuse Needed) (8571) **Habton Farms**
154 **SDH DREAM TEAM,** b c 11/2 Epaulette (AUS)—
                    Donatia (Shamardal (USA)) (9000) **Ontoawinner, SDH Project Services Ltd 2**
155 **SE GREEN,** b f 9/2 Sepoy (AUS)—Nos Da (Cape Cross (IRE)) **R. Taylor & Mr P. Hebdon**
156 **VINTAGE BRUT,** b c 30/1 Dick Turpin (IRE)—Traditionelle (Indesatchel (IRE)) **Lovely Bubbly Racing**
157 B f 26/1 Requinto (IRE)—Zuccini Wind (IRE) (Revoque (IRE)) (23809) **Reality Partnerships X**

Other Owners: Mr S. C. Appelbee, Armstrong Richardson & Co Ltd, Mr N. F. Arton, Mr J. Ball, Mrs Y. Blunt, Mr D. Blunt, Mr N. Bradley, Mr S. Bridge, Mr S. N. Bulmer, Mrs B. Cotton, J. D. Cotton, Mr H. T. H. Dean, Mr T. Denham, Mr T. D. Easterby, M. H. Easterby, Mrs S. J. Easterby, Mrs M. W. Fawcus, Mr D. S. Fawcus, T. E. Ford, Mr G. Fox, A. J. J. Gompertz, Mr J. H. Green, Mr B. M. P. R. Guerin, HP Racing Revenge, Mr P. F. Hebdon, S. A. Heley, Miss S. Holden, Mrs C. Hollowood, Mr M. A. S. Hulin, Mr N. E. M. Jones, Mrs D. Lamplough, D. B. Lamplough, Mr C. P Magnier, Martyn Macleod Racing, Middleham Park Racing LXIX, P. H. Milmo, Mr J. E. Mott, Nick Bradley Racing 4, Mr P. E. Nodding, Mr N. J. O'Brien, Dr M. J. O'Brien, T. J. O'Gram, Ontoawinner 10, Ontoawinner 8, Ontoawinner, SDH Project Services Ltd, T. S. Palin, Mr M. Pearson, Mr W. H. Ponsonby, Mr J. Preston, M. Prince, Mr A. H. Raby, T. A. Scothern, D. Scott, Mrs D. Stevens, Mr A. F. Stott, Mr G. Sunley, Mr R. Taylor, Miss S. J. Turner, Ventura Racing 2, Ventura Racing 3, Mr K. D. Watkins, D. A. West, Mr James Westoll, Mrs M. Williams, W. J. Williams, Mrs A. Wilsdon, D. E. Wilsdon, Mr C. Wilson.

Jockey (flat): Rachel Richardson. **Amateur:** Mr W. Easterby.

168	**MR BRIAN ECKLEY,** Brecon

MR BRIAN ECKLEY, Brecon
Postal: **Closcedi Farm, Llanspyddid, Brecon, Powys, LD3 8NS**
Contacts: **PHONE (01874) 622422 MOBILE (07891) 445409**
E-MAIL brian.eckley@live.co.uk

1 **JAUNTY CLEMENTINE,** 6, b m Lucario (USA)—Jaunty Spirit **B. J. Eckley**
2 **JAUNTY SORIA,** 5, ch m Malinas (GER)—Jaunty Spirit **B. J. Eckley**
3 **JAUNTY VELOCITY,** 5, b m Sulamani (GER)—Jaunty Walk **B. J. Eckley**
4 **LIBERTY BELLA,** 4, b f Librettist (USA)—Classy Crewella **B. J. Eckley**
5 4, B g Librettist (USA)—Somethingaboutmary (IRE) **B. J. Eckley**
6 4, B g Librettist (USA)—Timeforagin **B. J. Eckley**

169 MR ROBERT EDDERY, Newmarket
Postal: **Robert Eddery Racing, Heywood Place Stables, Hamilton Road, Newmarket, Suffolk, CB8 7JQ**
Contacts: **PHONE (01638) 428001 MOBILE (07938) 898455**
E-MAIL **info@robertedderyracing.com** WEBSITE **www.robertedderyracing.com**

1 **CHARLIE CHAPLIN (GER)**, 4, b g Lope de Vega (IRE)—Campina **Graham & Lynn Knight**
2 **DONNCHA (IRE)**, 7, br g Captain Marvelous (IRE)—Seasonal Style (IRE) **Mr D. Bannon**
3 **EQUIMOU**, 4, ch f Equiano (IRE)—Culture Queen **E. S. Phillips**
4 **FIRE PALACE**, 4, b f Royal Applause—Inflammable **E. S. Phillips**
5 **GRACEFUL LADY**, 5, b m Sixties Icon—Leitzu (IRE) **Graham & Lynn Knight**
6 **ROSS RAITH ROVER**, 5, b g Oasis Dream—Baqah (IRE) **Mrs Pamela Aitken & Mr Ian Anderson**
7 **SEVENTII**, 4, b f Medicean—Lowndes **Graham & Lynn Knight**
8 **TYNECASTLE PARK**, 5, b g Sea The Stars (IRE)—So Silk **Mr I Anderson**

THREE-YEAR-OLDS

9 **ADMISSIBLE**, b g Excelebration (IRE)—Admirable Spirit **Longview Stud & Bloodstock Ltd**
10 **ALDBURY LASS (IRE)**, b f Dark Angel (IRE)—Heeby Jeeby **R. J. Creese**
11 **BONIFACE (IRE)**, b c Born To Sea (IRE)—Sassy (FR) **Mr D. Bannon**
12 **FIERY BREATH**, br c Bated Breath—Sunset Kitty (USA) **E. S. Phillips**
13 **PRETTY PEARL**, b f Canford Cliffs (IRE)—Hijab **Robert's Rogues**
14 **TRAVELLERS JOY**, b f Equiano (FR)—Travelling **Longview Stud & Bloodstock Ltd**

TWO-YEAR-OLDS

15 **ALBAN'S DREAM**, gr ro f 2/3 Lethal Force (IRE)—
　　　　Piping Dream (IRE) (Approve (IRE)) (13809) **Mr Graham & Mrs Lynn Knight & Mrs Pamela Aitken**
16 **ELSIE VIOLET (IRE)**, ch f 7/3 Gale Force Ten—Kuaicoss (IRE) (Lujain (USA)) (16280) **E. S. Phillips**
17 **EVENTURA**, ch f 13/1 Lope de Vega (IRE)—Demi Voix (Halling (USA)) **Longview Stud & Bloodstock Ltd**
18 **FLOURISHABLE**, ch f 21/2 Equiano (FR)—
　　　　Choral Rhythm (IRE) (Oratorio (IRE)) (7619) **Longview Stud & Bloodstock Ltd**
19 **FORMALLY**, ch c 7/1 Showcasing—Adaptability (Mastercraftsman (IRE)) **Longview Stud & Bloodstock Ltd**
20 **FORTHWITH**, b f 17/4 Footstepsinthesand—
　　　　Admirable Spirit (Invincible Spirit (IRE)) (2000) **Longview Stud & Bloodstock Ltd**
21 **FREEDREAMS**, b f 20/2 Born To Sea (IRE)—Sinaadi (IRE) (Kyllachy) (2000) **Longview Stud & Bloodstock Ltd**
22 **Gr f** 10/4 Zebedee—Grey Again (Unfuwain (USA)) **E. S. Phillips**
23 **HORNETS JOY**, b f 22/1 Swiss Spirit—Kelamita (IRE) (Pivotal) **B.G.C. Racing**
24 **SHOWU**, b f 10/4 Showcasing—Travelling (Dubai Destination (USA)) (35000) **Longview Stud & Bloodstock Ltd**

Other Owners: Mrs Pam Aitken, Mr Ian Anderson (Edinburgh), Mr Robert Eddery, Mrs L. C. Knight, Mr G. Knight, Mrs Millicent Mathews, Mr R. Ward.

Jockey (flat): Andrea Atzeni. **Apprentice:** Darragh Keenan.

170 MR STUART EDMUNDS, Newport Pagnell
Postal: **6 Fences Farm, Tyringham, Newport Pagnell, Buckinghamshire, MK16 9EN**
Contacts: **PHONE (01908) 611406 Office (01908) 611369 FAX (01908) 611255**
MOBILE (07778) 782591
E-MAIL **Trishandstu@aol.com**

1 **APASIONADO (GER)**, 7, ch g Mamool (IRE)—Api Sa (IRE) **The Tyringham Partnership**
2 **BLACKBIRD**, 5, b m Black Sam Bellamy (IRE)—Daurica **Mr P. D. Robeson**
3 **CAMARO (FR)**, 6, b g Khalkevi (IRE)—Pricamarie (FR) **Nick Brown Racing**
4 **CHANDOS BELLE (GER)**, 5, b m Mamool (IRE)—Chandos Rose (IRE) **The Chicheley Partnership**
5 **CLASSIC BEN (IRE)**, 5, b g Beneficial—Dark Daisy (IRE) **The Lavendon Partnership**
6 **CLONDAW NATIVE (IRE)**, 6, b g Golan—Great Outlook (IRE) **KTDA Consultancy Limited**
7 **CLOONACOOL (IRE)**, 9, b g Beneficial—Newhall (IRE) **Nick Brown Racing**
8 **DOMESDAY BOOK (USA)**, 8, br g Street Cry (IRE)—Film Script **Mr J. Humberstone**
9 **HILLCREST FIRE (IRE)**, 4, b f Fast Company (IRE)—Firecrest (IRE) **Mr J. Humberstone**
10 **KALOCI (IRE)**, 6, b m Stowaway—Eye And Ear (IRE) **Nick Brown Racing**
11 **KAYLA**, 8, b m Kayf Tara—Palila **Mr P. D. Robeson**
12 **LAND LEAGUE (IRE)**, 7, b g Touch of Land (FR)—Be My Sunset (IRE) **Nick Brown Racing**
13 **MARIA'S BENEFIT (IRE)**, 6, b m Beneficial—Youngborogal (IRE) **Mr P. D. Wells**
14 **MOLLY CHILDERS (IRE)**, 6, b m Stowaway—Hushaby (IRE) **The Ravenstone Partnership**
15 **MY NAME IS JEFF**, 4, b g Mount Nelson—Vale of Belvoir (IRE) **Mr & Mrs G. Bhatti**

MR STUART EDMUNDS - Continued

16 **NOW MCGINTY (IRE)**, 7, b g Stowaway—Western Whisper (IRE) **The Garratt Family**
17 **PINE WARBLER**, 9, b g Pilsudski (IRE)—Cetti's Warbler **Mr P. D. Robeson**
18 **PULL TOGETHER (IRE)**, 6, b g Curtain Time (IRE)—Whos To Know (IRE) **The Oakley Partnership**
19 **QUEENOHEARTS (IRE)**, 5, ch m Flemensfirth (USA)—Chars (IRE) **The Sherington Partnership**
20 **REYNO**, 10, b g Sleeping Indian—Tereyna **Mr P. D. Robeson**
21 **SNEAKING BUDGE**, 6, b g Nayef (USA)—Ikat (IRE) **Nick Brown Racing**
22 **THECLOCKISTICKING (IRE)**, 6, br g Gamut (IRE)—Curragheen (IRE) **Asphalt Reinforcement Services Ltd**
23 **VINEGAR HILL**, 9, b g Kayf Tara—Broughton Melody **Theshouldhavehadabiggerbudgetgroup**

THREE-YEAR-OLDS

24 **BLACKFINCH**, ch g Black Sam Bellamy (IRE)—Grassfinch **Mr P. D. Robeson**
25 **SAN SEB (GER)**, br g Mamool (IRE)—Sunshine Story (IRE) **Riverport Racehorse Association**

TWO-YEAR-OLDS

26 **DUNEFINCH**, b g 23/3 Dunaden (FR)—Grassfinch (Generous (IRE)) **Mr P. D. Robeson**
27 **MARSH WREN**, b f 31/3 Schiaparelli (GER)—Carolina Wren (Sir Harry Lewis (USA)) **Mr P. D. Robeson**

Other Owners: Mr G. Bhatti, Mrs C. J. Bhatti, T. L. Brooks, Mr N. J. Brown, Mr A. C. Garratt, Mrs A. A. Garratt, Mr S. E. Tate, Mr B. H. Turner, Mr S. J. Winter, D. Yates.

171
MR GORDON EDWARDS, Minehead
Postal: **Summering, Wheddon Cross, Minehead, Somerset, TA24 7AT**
Contacts: **PHONE (01643) 831549 FAX (01643) 831549 MOBILE (07970) 059297**
E-MAIL angelaedwards549@gmail.com

1 **SHANANN STAR (IRE)**, 12, br m Anshan—Baile An Droichid (IRE) **G. F. Edwards**

Amateur: Mr D. Edwards.

172
MISS LUCINDA EGERTON, Malton
Postal: **Flint Hall, Brawby, Malton, North Yorkshire, YO17 6PZ**
Contacts: **PHONE (01944) 768233 MOBILE (07900) 458666**
E-MAIL lucy@legertonracing.co.uk WEBSITE www.legertonracing.co.uk

1 **AMBITIOUS ICARUS**, 9, b g Striking Ambition—Nesting Box **Jigsaw Racing**
2 **BOLLIN LINE**, 11, b g Bollin Eric—Leading Line **Reassuringly Racy Club**
3 **DRAGONFLI**, 6, b g Revoque (IRE)—Chiddingfold Chick **P. Robinson, D. Woodhead & L. Egerton**
4 **ETAAD (USA)**, 7, b g Intidab (USA)—Red's Lucky Lady (USA) **Mrs R. Robinson**
5 **OROBAS (IRE)**, 6, b g Dark Angel (IRE)—Miss Mujadil (IRE) **Northern Belles**
6 **PATIENCE TONY (IRE)**, 7, b g Windsor Knot (IRE)—Johar Jamal (IRE) **P. Robinson, D. Woodhead & L. Egerton**
7 **RAID STANE (IRE)**, 12, b g Morozov (USA)—Rashhattan (IRE) **Miss L. Egerton**
8 **TAEL O' GOLD**, 4, ch f Zoffany (IRE)—Wedding Dream **L Egerton & Mrs Debbie Raven**
9 **TRADE FLOW (FR)**, 6, b g Danehill Dancer (IRE)—Dubai Rose **Miss L. Egerton**
10 **WELSH RAREBIT**, 5, b g Dylan Thomas (IRE)—Chelsey Jayne (IRE) **P Robinson & J Gill**

Other Owners: Mrs C. M. Egerton, Mr A. K. Escott, J. Gill, Mr K. J. Raven, Mrs D. S. Raven, Mr P. Robinson, Mr D. A. Woodhead.

173
MISS CLARE ELLAM, Market Drayton
Postal: **Lostford Manor Stables, Mickley, Tern Hill, Market Drayton, Shropshire, TF9 3QN**
Contacts: **MOBILE (07974) 075042**
E-MAIL clareellam@btinternet.com WEBSITE www.clareellamracing.com

1 **AMBER FLUSH**, 9, b m Sir Harry Lewis (USA)—Sari Rose (FR) **Mr R. P. Clarke**
2 **ARCHIE STEVENS**, 8, b g Pastoral Pursuits—Miss Wells (IRE) **Miss Clare L. Ellam**
3 **ARCHIPENTURA**, 6, b m Archipenko (USA)—Bookiesindex Girl (IRE) **Miss Clare L. Ellam**
4 **MONSIEUR JAMIE**, 10, b g Monsieur Bond (IRE)—Primula Bairn **Miss Clare L. Ellam**
5 **PADDOCKS LOUNGE (IRE)**, 11, b g Oscar (IRE)—Sister Rosza (IRE) **Mr John Wilcox**
6 **PARISIAN STAR**, 6, ch m Champs Elysees—Cavallo da Corsa **Miss Clare L. Ellam**

MISS CLARE ELLAM - Continued

THREE-YEAR-OLDS

7 **KINTYRELYUPTOYOU,** b c Champs Elysees—Kintyre **Miss C. Y. Wootten**

Assistant Trainer: Amy Myatt

---

174 **MR GORDON ELLIOTT, Co. Meath**
Postal: **Cullentra House, Longwood, Co. Meath, Ireland, A83 XF20**
Contacts: **PHONE (00353) 46 9555051 MOBILE (00353) 86 2495453**
E-MAIL zoe@gordonelliottracing.com WEBSITE www.gordonelliottracing.com

1 **A SHIN IMPALA (IRE),** 5, b g Evasive—Muzayadah **Call It What You Like Syndicate**
2 **A TOI PHIL (FR),** 8, b g Day Flight—Lucidrile (FR) **Gigginstown House Stud**
3 **ABACADABRAS (FR),** 4, b g Davidoff (GER)—Cadoubelle des As (FR) **Gigginstown House Stud**
4 **ACRONYM (IRE),** 5, b g Flemensfirth (USA)—Turtle Lamp (IRE) **Gigginstown House Stud**
5 **AL KHAFJI,** 5, ch g New Approach (IRE)—Wadaat **Gordon Elliott**
6 **ANGE D'OR JAVILEX (FR),** 8, b g Puit d'or (IRE)—Ixia de Menil (FR) **Thomas R. Coleman**
7 **ANYWORDONQUINCY (IRE),** 5, ch m Arakan (USA)—History of Rome (IRE) **Don't Tell The Woman Syndicate**
8 **APPLE'S JADE (FR),** 6, b m Saddler Maker (IRE)—Apple's For Ever (FR) **Gigginstown House Stud**
9 **ASKARI,** 5, b g Sea The Stars (IRE)—Loulwa (IRE) **Lee Power**
10 **AZUA EMERY (FR),** 4, b f Califet (FR)—Take Emery (FR) **Gigginstown House Stud**
11 **BACK BAR (IRE),** 6, b br g Brian Boru—Howrwedoin (IRE) **Gigginstown House Stud**
12 **BALL D'ARC (FR),** 7, b g Network (GER)—Pretty Moon (FR) **Gigginstown House Stud**
13 **BALLELA BOY (IRE),** 7, b g Golan—Oscar Road (IRE) **Gigginstown House Stud**
14 **BARRA (FR),** 7, b m Vendangeur (IRE)—Oasaka (FR) **Gigginstown House Stud**
15 **BATTLEOVERDOYEN (IRE),** 5, b g Doyen (FR)—Battle Over (FR) **Gigginstown House Stud**
16 **BEN DUNDEE (IRE),** 6, ch g Beneficial—Miss Dundee (IRE) **C. Jones**
17 **BETTATOGETHER,** 9, b g Fair Mix (IRE)—Ella Falls (IRE) **Gordon Elliott Racing Club**
18 **BILKO (FR),** 7, b g Balko (FR)—Moriany (FR) **Gigginstown House Stud**
19 **BLESS THE WINGS (IRE),** 13, b g Winged Love (IRE)—Silva Venture (IRE) **Adrian Butler**
20 **BLOW BY BLOW (IRE),** 7, ch g Robin des Champs (FR)—Shean Rose (IRE) **Gigginstown House Stud**
21 **BOOT CAMP (IRE),** 5, b g Milan—Derravaragh Native (IRE) **Gigginstown House Stud**
22 **BRELADE,** 6, b g Presenting—Polivalente (FR) **Mr P. Sharkey**
23 **BURREN LIFE (IRE),** 6, br g Pelder—Burren Valley (IRE) **Gigginstown House Stud**
24 **CALTEX (FR),** 6, bl g Network (GER)—Qomposita (FR) **Gigginstown House Stud**
25 **CAMPEADOR (FR),** 6, gr g Gris de Gris (FR)—Royale Video (FR) **Mr John P. McManus**
26 **CARA'S WAY (IRE),** 5, br m Robin des Champs (FR)—Dare To Venture (IRE) **Gigginstown House Stud**
27 **CARRIG CATHAL,** 7, b g Fair Mix (IRE)—Blackwater Bay (IRE) **Mr T. Doran**
28 **CARTWRIGHT,** 5, b g High Chaparral (IRE)—One So Marvellous **Readytorun Syndicate**
29 **CAUSE OF CAUSES (USA),** 10, b g Dynaformer (USA)—Angel In My Heart (FR) **Mr John P. McManus**
30 **CECIL CORBETT,** 11, b g Bollin Eric—Cadoutene (FR) **Mr Liam J. Clancy**
31 **CHARMIX (FR),** 8, br g Laveron—Open Up (FR) **Mr J. Fyffe**
32 **CHESAPEAKE (FR),** 6, br m Network (GER)—Somosierra (FR) **Gigginstown House Stud**
33 **CLARCAM (FR),** 8, b g Califet (FR)—Rose Beryl (FR) **Gigginstown House Stud**
34 **CLASSIC ESCAPE (IRE),** 5, b g Golan—Seana Ghael (IRE) **F. Donnelly**
35 **COCKTAILS AT DAWN,** 10, b g Fair Mix (IRE)—Fond Farewell (IRE) **George P. Mahoney**
36 **COEUR DE BEAUCHENE (FR),** 6, br g Peer Gynt (JPN)—Iris de Beauchene (FR) **Gigginstown House Stud**
37 **COLONEL MAXIMUS (IRE),** 5, gr g Zebedee—Lella Beya **Nick Bradley Racing Club**
38 **COMMENTARIOLUS (IRE),** 4, b g Frankel—Apsara (FR) **M. Booth**
39 **COUNT SIMON (IRE),** 4, b g Rip Van Winkle (IRE)—Wedding Cake (IRE) **Mrs P. Sloan**
40 **CRACK OF THUNDER (IRE),** 9, b g September Storm (GER)—Keep Hunting (IRE) **Gordon Elliott Racing Club**
41 **CRACKING SMART (FR),** 6, b g Great Pretender (FR)—Maya du Frene (FR) **Gigginstown House Stud**
42 **CREADAN BELLE (IRE),** 5, b m Vinnie Roe (IRE)—Aliceaneileen (IRE) **James W. Power**
43 **CREZIC (FR),** 5, b g Califet (FR)—Valmasque (FR) **Gigginstown House Stud**
44 **CUBOMANIA (IRE),** 5, gr ro g Halling—Surrealism **Cubomania Syndicate**
45 **DE PLOTTING SHED (IRE),** 8, b g Beneficial—Lady Willmurt (IRE) **Daniel Ives**
46 **DEFI BLEU (FR),** 5, b g Saddler Maker (IRE)—Glycine Bleue (FR) **Gigginstown House Stud**
47 **DELTA WORK (FR),** 5, br g Network (GER)—Robbe (FR) **Gigginstown House Stud**
48 **DESTIN D'AJONC (FR),** 5, b g Martaline—Fleur d'ajonc (FR) **Mr John P. McManus**
49 **DIAMOND CAUCHOIS (FR),** 7, b g Crillon (FR)—Diamond Turtle (FR) **D. Charlesworth**
50 **DIAMOND KING (IRE),** 10, b g King's Theatre (IRE)—Georgia On My Mind (FR) **Mrs Diana L. Whateley**
51 **DIAMOND TURF (FR),** 5, b g Diamond Boy (FR)—Lovely Turf (FR) **Gigginstown House Stud**
52 **DINARIA DES OBEAUX (FR),** 5, b m Saddler Maker (IRE)—Indiana Jaune (FR) **Gigginstown House Stud**
53 **DINONS (FR),** 5, b g Balko (FR)—Beni Abbes (FR) **T. O'Driscoll**

MR GORDON ELLIOTT - Continued

54 **DOCTOR PHOENIX (IRE)**, 10, br g Dr Massini (IRE)—Lowroad Cross (IRE) **Nick Bradley Racing Club**
55 **DORTMUND PARK (FR)**, 5, b g Great Pretender (IRE)—Qena (IRE) **Gigginstown House Stud**
56 **DORYDALIS (FR)**, 5, b g Saddler Maker (IRE)—Kento Green (FR) **Gigginstown House Stud**
57 **DOUBLE PORTRAIT (IRE)**, 6, b g Portrait Gallery (IRE)—Dummy Run (IRE) **T. J. Doran**
58 **DOUNIKOS (FR)**, 7, b g Smadoun (FR)—Baby Sitter (FR) **Gigginstown House Stud**
59 **DUCA DE THAIX (FR)**, 5, b g Voix du Nord (FR)—Nouca de Thaix (FR) **Gigginstown House Stud**
60 **EDENE D'ARC (FR)**, 4, b f Maresca Sorrento (FR)—Pretty Moon (FR) **Fergies On A Sunday Morning Syndicate**
61 **EMPIRE BURLEQUE (IRE)**, 6, b g Cape Cross (IRE)—Mowazana (IRE) **Gigginstown House Stud**
62 **EMPIRE OF DIRT (IRE)**, 11, b g Westerner—Rose of Inchiquin (IRE) **Gigginstown House Stud**
63 **ENZANI (IRE)**, 7, b g Cape Cross (IRE)—Eytarna (IRE) **Shane Reville**
64 **ESHTIAAL (USA)**, 8, b g Dynaformer (USA)—Enfiraaj (USA) **Mr W. Salthouse**
65 **EXTRAPOLATE (IRE)**, 5, ch g Muhtathir—Sahabah (USA) **Gigginstown House Stud**
66 **FAGAN**, 8, ro g Fair Mix (IRE)—Northwood May **R. A. Bartlett**
67 **FAIRY FLUTE (IRE)**, 6, b m Peintre Celebre (USA)—Easter Fairy (USA) **Gordon Elliott Racing Club**
68 **FALAK (IRE)**, 5, b g Teofilo (IRE)—Family (USA) **Brendan Scully**
69 **FARCLAS (FR)**, 4, gr g Jukebox Jury (IRE)—Floriana (GER) **Gigginstown House Stud**
70 **FELIX DESJY (FR)**, 5, ch g Maresca Sorrento (FR)—Lamadoun (FR) **Gigginstown House Stud**
71 **FILUDO (FR)**, 4, b g Linngari (IRE)—First Light (GER) **Nick Bradley Racing Club**
72 **FIRE IN HIS EYES (IRE)**, 7, br g Stowaway—Carrigeen Kohleria (IRE) **Gigginstown House Stud**
73 **FLAWLESS ESCAPE**, 5, gr g Sagamix—Sainte Kadette (FR) **T. O'Driscoll**
74 **FLAXEN FLARE (IRE)**, 9, ch g Windsor Knot (IRE)—Golden Angel (USA) **Mrs P. Sloan**
75 **FOLSOM BLUE (IRE)**, 11, b g Old Vic—Spirit Leader (IRE) **Michael Canning**
76 **FOOLS AND KINGS**, 4, b br g Sakhee (USA)—Mookhlesa **Nick Bradley Racing Club**
77 **FULLASTHESEA**, 5, b g Champs Elysees—Pentatonic **Michael Goff**
78 **GENERAL PRINCIPLE (IRE)**, 9, b g Gold Well—How Provincial (IRE) **Gigginstown House Stud**
79 **GER'S LAD (IRE)**, 6, b g Kalanisi (IRE)—Mill Lady (IRE) **John F. Doyle**
80 **GETAWAY JOHN (IRE)**, 5, ch g Getaway (GER)—Present Your Own (IRE) **John F. Doyle**
81 **GIRLEY TALK (IRE)**, 5, ch m Whitmore's Conn (USA)—Fallacy **Mrs B. Dillon**
82 **GLENLOE (IRE)**, 7, br g Kayf Tara—Mandys Native (IRE) **Mr John P. McManus**
83 **GLOBAL JACKPOT**, 5, b g Flying Legend (USA)—A Fistful of Euros **KTDA Consultancy Limited**
84 **GOODTHYNEMILAN (IRE)**, 8, b m Milan—Calling Classy (IRE) **Barstool Prophets Syndicate**
85 **GRAINEYHILL (IRE)**, 7, b g Craigsteel—Inca Hill (IRE) **Mr T. Kenny**
86 **GREY EXCHANGE (IRE)**, 5, gr g Apple Tree (FR)—Pems Gift **Adrian Butler**
87 **GUN DIGGER (IRE)**, 6, ch g Stowaway—Booley Bay (IRE) **Gigginstown House Stud**
88 **HARDLINE (IRE)**, 6, b g Arcadio (GER)—Hidden Reserve (IRE) **Gigginstown House Stud**
89 **HERITAGE QUAY (IRE)**, 5, ch m Presenting—Ouro Preto **Mrs Caren Walsh**
90 **HOLLOW TREE (IRE)**, 9, b g Beat Hollow—Hesperia **Middleham Park Racing Ireland**
91 **ICARIO (FR)**, 5, ch g Soldier of Fortune (IRE)—Indianapolis (USA) **Gigginstown House Stud**
92 **INVINCIBLE CAVE (IRE)**, 5, b g Court Cave (IRE)—Bespoke Baby (IRE) **Gigginstown House Stud**
93 **ISLE OF DESTINY (IRE)**, 5, b m Gold Well—Young Amelie (IRE) **John F. Doyle**
94 **ISODON (FR)**, 6, b g Martaline—Between You And Me (FR) **Gigginstown House Stud**
95 **JAUNTY WARRIOR (IRE)**, 6, b g Lucarno (USA)—Jaunty Walk **Gigginstown House Stud**
96 **JETSTREAM JACK (IRE)**, 8, b g Beneficial—Westgrove Berry (IRE) **Mrs Diana L. Whateley**
97 **JOCK TALK (IRE)**, 4, b g Famous Name—Katdogawn **Ballygowan Ramblers Syndicate**
98 **JURY DUTY (IRE)**, 7, b g Well Chosen—Swan Heart (IRE) **Sideways Syndicate**
99 **KAYF THOU**, 7, br g Kayf Tara—Labelthou (FR) **D. Charlesworth**
100 **KISS ME KAYF (IRE)**, 5, b m Kayf Tara—Volverta (IRE) **Mrs Caren Walsh**
101 **KURAKA**, 4, b g Cacique (IRE)—Puzzling **Susan Frost**
102 **LACKANEEN LEADER (IRE)**, 6, b m Oscar (IRE)—Shandora (IRE) **Mrs Caren Walsh**
103 **LADY V (IRE)**, 4, b f Jeremy—Daly (IRE) **KTDA Consultancy Limited**
104 **LAST MINUTE MAN (IRE)**, 6, b g Yeats (IRE)—Ella Watson (IRE) **Paul A. Rooney**
105 **LIEUTENANT COLONEL**, 9, br g Kayf Tara—Agnese **Gigginstown House Stud**
106 **LORD SCOUNDREL (IRE)**, 9, b g Presenting—Noble Choice **Gigginstown House Stud**
107 **MAJOR MITCHELL (IRE)**, 5, b g Gold Well—Cooper's Rose (IRE) **Alexander McGregor**
108 **MALA BEACH (IRE)**, 10, b g Beneficial—Peppardstown **C. Jones**
109 **MASTER OF TARA (FR)**, 5, b g Kayf Tara—Ryme Bere (FR) **Gigginstown House Stud**
110 **MENGLI KHAN (IRE)**, 5, b g Lope de Vega (IRE)—Danielli (IRE) **Gigginstown House Stud**
111 **MICK JAZZ (FR)**, 7, b g Blue Bresil (FR)—Mick Maya (FR) **Mr George P. Mahoney**
112 **MIDNIGHT ESCAPE (IRE)**, 6, b g Milan—Special Case (IRE) **Grant Mercer**
113 **MILSEAN (IRE)**, 8, b g Milan—Boro Supreme (IRE) **Gigginstown House Stud**
114 **MINELLA TILL DAWN (IRE)**, 6, br g Shantou (USA)—Have At It (IRE) **Mr John P. McManus**
115 **MIRACLE IN MEDINAH**, 7, b g Milan—Annaghbrack (IRE) **Mr John P. McManus**
116 **MIRO (IRE)**, 6, b g Rock of Gibraltar (IRE)—Mission Secrete (IRE) **Don't Tell The Woman Syndicate**
117 **MISSY TATA (FR)**, 6, b m Astarabad (USA)—Queen Running (USA) **Simon Munir**
118 **MITCHOUKA (FR)**, 4, b g Creachadoir (IRE)—Minnaloushe (FR) **Gigginstown House Stud**

MR GORDON ELLIOTT - Continued

119 **MONASTERY (IRE)**, 6, b m Presenting—Princess Gaia (IRE) **Gigginstown House Stud**
120 **MONATOMIC (IRE)**, 5, b g Arcadio (GER)—Star Island (IRE) **Gigginstown House Stud**
121 **MONBEG NOTORIOUS (IRE)**, 7, b g Milan—Borleagh Princess (IRE) **Gigginstown House Stud**
122 **MONBEG WORLDWIDE (IRE)**, 6, b g Lucarno (USA)—Molly Duffy (IRE) **Gigginstown House Stud**
123 **MONITION (IRE)**, 5, b g Stowaway—Forever Bubbles (IRE) **Gigginstown House Stud**
124 **MONKSHOOD (IRE)**, 6, br g Stowaway—Flirthing Around (IRE) **Gigginstown House Stud**
125 **MOONLIGHT ESCAPE (IRE)**, 5, b m Court Cave (IRE)—Festival Leader (IRE) **Mr F. Donnelly**
126 **MORATORIUM (IRE)**, 5, b g Presenting—Shuil Oilean (IRE) **Gigginstown House Stud**
127 **MORGAN (IRE)**, 6, br g Big Bad Bob (IRE)—Gilt Ridden (IRE) **Gigginstown House Stud**
128 **MOSSBACK (IRE)**, 6, b g Yeats—Sejour (IRE) **Gigginstown House Stud**
129 **MR LINGO (IRE)**, 5, b g Curtain Time (IRE)—Pharlingo (IRE) **Gigginstown House Stud**
130 **NEARLY MAN (FR)**, 5, b g Turgeon (USA)—La Loute (FR) **Paul A. Rooney**
131 **NED STARK (IRE)**, 10, b g Wolfe Tone (IRE)—Last Moon (IRE) **Noel Moran**
132 **NOBLE ENDEAVOR (IRE)**, 9, b g Flemensfirth (USA)—Old Moon (IRE) **Mr C. Jones**
133 **OCEAN CREST (IRE)**, 5, ch g Beneficial—Simply Bellingham (IRE) **Mr D. P. Sharkey**
134 **OSMOTIC (IRE)**, 5, b g Fracas (IRE)—Miss Pickering (IRE) **Gigginstown House Stud**
135 **OUT SAM**, 9, b g Multiplex—Tintera (IRE) **D. Charlesworth**
136 **OUTLANDER (IRE)**, 10, b g Stowaway—Western Whisper (IRE) **Gigginstown House Stud**
137 **PALLASATOR**, 9, b g Motivator—Ela Athena **Qatar Racing Limited**
138 **PARK PADDOCKS (IRE)**, 4, b g Sea The Stars (IRE)—Dream of The Hill (IRE) **Gigginstown House Stud**
139 **PAT'S OSCAR (IRE)**, 7, b m Oscar (IRE)—Coming Home (FR) **Pioneer Racing**
140 **PEARL DRAGON (FR)**, 7, b g Nicobar—La Marlia (FR) **Pearl Bloodstock Ltd**
141 **PERCY (IRE)**, 4, b gr g Kodiac—Bysshe **George Turner**
142 **PETE SO HIGH (GER)**, 4, b g High Chaparral (IRE)—Paulaya (GER) **Gigginstown House Stud**
143 **PETER SILVER (FR)**, 7, b g Silver Cross (FR)—Sainte Mante (FR) **Twenty Syndicate**
144 **POLI ROI (FR)**, 6, b g Poliglote—Belle du Roi (FR) **Gigginstown House Stud**
145 **POORMANS HILL (IRE)**, 7, ch g Stowaway—Sharps Express (IRE) **Vincent Caldwell**
146 **PRESENT IN COURT (IRE)**, 5, b g Court Cave (IRE)—Present Line (IRE) **Pearl Bloodstock Ltd**
147 **PRESENTING JULIO (IRE)**, 10, b g Presenting—Ouro Preto **D. Charlesworth**
148 **PRINCE OF SCARS (IRE)**, 8, b g Flemensfirth (USA)—Spirit Leader (IRE) **Gigginstown House Stud**
149 **RAKHINE STATE (IRE)**, 5, b g Arakan (USA)—Oiselina (FR) **Martin Millar**
150 **RAPID ESCAPE (IRE)**, 5, ch g Doyen (IRE)—Kenzie (IRE) **Gigginstown House Stud**
151 **RAVENHILL (IRE)**, 8, b g Winged Love (IRE)—Rhythm Hill (IRE) **Try Ravenhill Syndicate**
152 **REALT MOR (IRE)**, 13, b g Beneficial—Suez Canal (FR) **Mrs P. Sloan**
153 **RIAN THOMAS (IRE)**, 5, b g Bushranger (IRE)—Stratospheric **Mrs Emer O'Brien**
154 **RIGHTDOWNTHEMIDDLE (IRE)**, 10, b g Oscar (IRE)—Alternative Route (IRE) **Dove Coat Syndicate**
155 **RINGLEADER**, 4, b g New Approach (IRE)—Banks Hill **Nick Bradley Racing Club**
156 **ROARING BULL (IRE)**, 5, b g Milan—Gift of Freedom (IRE) **Gigginstown House Stud**
157 **ROBIN DES MANA (IRE)**, 7, br g Robin des Pres (FR)—Kokopelli Mana (IRE) **Brendan Scully**
158 **ROI DES FRANCS (IRE)**, 9, b g Poliglote—Grande Souveraine (FR) **Gigginstown House Stud**
159 **ROUNDSTONE (IRE)**, 6, b g Flemensfirth (USA)—Kestral Heights (IRE) **C. Jones**
160 **SAFFRON AND GREY (IRE)**, 5, br g Robin des Champs (FR)—Tambourine Davis (FR) **Gigginstown House Stud**
161 **SAMCRO (IRE)**, 6, ch g Germany (USA)—Dun Dun (IRE) **Gigginstown House Stud**
162 **SANTANA PLESSIS (FR)**, 4, b g Saint des Saints (FR)—La Passeroie (FR) **D. Charlesworth**
163 **SAVANNAH STORM**, 5, b g Dubawi (IRE)—Savannah Belle **Mrs M. Gittins**
164 **SCHINDLERS ARK (USA)**, 4, gr g Exchange Rate (USA)—
Sweet Science (USA) **Mighty Ha 'Ward Union' Syndicate**
165 **SHADOW CATCHER**, 10, ch g Haafhd—Unchain My Heart **Mrs P. Sloan**
166 **SHATTERED LOVE (IRE)**, 7, b m Yeats (IRE)—Tracker **Gigginstown House Stud**
167 **SHIRLEYS GOLD WELL (IRE)**, 5, b m Gold Well—Shirleys Hill (IRE) **Gordon Elliott Racing Club**
168 **SIR CARNO (FR)**, 5, ch g Lucarno (USA)—Orlana (FR) **Gigginstown House Stud**
169 **SIRE DU BERLAIS (FR)**, 6, b g Poliglote—Royale Athenia (FR) **Mr John P. McManus**
170 **SOMETIME SOON (IRE)**, 5, b g Shantou (USA)—Back Log (IRE) **Gigginstown House Stud**
171 **SOMETIMES A FOX**, 4, b g Foxwedge (AUS)—Crooked Wood (USA) **Gigginstown House Stud**
172 **SOUL KALIBER (IRE)**, 8, b g Marienbard (IRE)—Rosie Bee (IRE) **Gigginstown House Stud**
173 **SPACE CADET (IRE)**, 8, b g Flemensfirth (USA)—Shuil A Hocht (IRE) **Mr C. Jones**
174 **SQUOUATEUR (FR)**, 7, gr g Martaline—Samansonnienne (FR) **Mr John P. McManus**
175 **STEAMBOAT QUAY (IRE)**, 7, b g Milan—Sunny Native (IRE) **Mr John P. McManus**
176 **STOOSHIE (IRE)**, 5, b g Fracas (IRE)—Misty Native (IRE) **Mrs Caren Walsh**
177 **SUTTON MANOR (IRE)**, 7, b g Gold Well—Nighty Bless (IRE) **Gigginstown House Stud**
178 **SUTTON PLACE (IRE)**, 7, b g Mahler—Glebe Beauty (IRE) **Mr John P. McManus**
179 **SWEETLIGHT D'OROUX (FR)**, 5, b m Balko (FR)—Moonlight Shadows (FR) **Gigginstown House Stud**
180 **SWINGBRIDGE (IRE)**, 10, b g Milan—Creative Approach (IRE) **Mr Noel Moran**
181 **SYNOPSIS**, 6, b m Azamour (IRE)—Censored **David Spratt**
182 **TAGLIETELLE**, 9, b g Tagula (IRE)—Averami **Olduvai Syndicate**

MR GORDON ELLIOTT - Continued

183 **TAKEITTOTHELIMITS (IRE)**, 6, br m Stowaway—A Plus Ma Puce (FR) **Mr John P. McManus**
184 **TAPENADE (IRE)**, 4, br g Scorpion (IRE)—Corravilla (IRE) **Gordon Elliott Racing Club**
185 **TELL US MORE (IRE)**, 9, b g Scorpion (IRE)—Zara's Victory (IRE) **Gigginstown House Stud**
186 **THE BIG LENSE (IRE)**, 5, b g Court Cave (IRE)—Megans Joy (IRE) **Mr John P. McManus**
187 **THE GAME CHANGER (IRE)**, 9, b g Arcadio (GER)—Gilt Ridden (IRE) **Gigginstown House Stud**
188 **THE SHEARERS WIFE (IRE)**, 5, ch g Beneficial—Constant Approach (IRE) **Alexander McGregor**
189 **THE STORYTELLER (IRE)**, 7, ch g Shantou (USA)—Bally Bolshoi (IRE) **Mrs P. Sloan**
190 **THIRD OPINION (IRE)**, 10, b g Zagreb (USA)—Toulon Pass (IRE) **T. Howley Jnr**
191 **THREE SWALLOWSNICK (IRE)**, 7, b m Westerner—Sitges (IRE) **Gigginstown House Stud**
192 **TIGER ROLL (IRE)**, 8, b g Authorized (IRE)—Swiss Roll (IRE) **Gigginstown House Stud**
193 **TIMIYAN (USA)**, 7, b g Ghostzapper (USA)—Timarwa (IRE) **Mr John P. McManus**
194 **TINTANGLE (IRE)**, 5, b m Yeats (IRE)—Connaught Hall (IRE) **Gigginstown House Stud**
195 **TOMBSTONE (IRE)**, 8, ch g Robin des Champs (FR)—Connaught Hall (IRE) **Gigginstown House Stud**
196 **TOUCH BASE (IRE)**, 6, b g Robin des Champs (FR)—Badawi Street **Mr John P. McManus**
197 **TURANGA LILLY (IRE)**, 5, b m Flemensfirth (USA)—Gilah (IRE) **Kaniz Bloodstock Investments Limited**
198 **TYCOON PRINCE (IRE)**, 8, b g Trans Island—Downtown Train (IRE) **Gigginstown House Stud**
199 **UCELLO CONTI (FR)**, 10, b g Martaline—Gazelle Lulu (FR) **Mr Simon Munir**
200 **VANISHING POINT**, 5, b g Pivotal—Hyperspectra **Martin Millar**
201 **VEINARD (FR)**, 9, ch g Shaanmer (IRE)—Ombline (FR) **T D Howley Jnr**
202 **VENEER OF CHARM (IRE)**, 4, b g Fast Company (IRE)—Nova Tor (IRE) **M. J. Wasylocha**
203 **VENGEFUL (FR)**, 5, b g Zoffany (IRE)—Miss Bex (IRE) **Gigginstown House Stud**
204 **WARLIKE INTENT (IRE)**, 6, ch g Stowaway—Native Mistress (IRE) **Gigginstown House Stud**
205 **WESTERN COMMAND (IRE)**, 6, b g Westerner—Mighty Millie (IRE) **Liam Quinn**
206 **WHISTLE DIXIE (IRE)**, 8, b m Kayf Tara—Fairy Blaze (IRE) **Gigginstown House Stud**
207 **WHISTLING BILLY (IRE)**, 4, b g Shantou (USA)—Lisacul Queen (IRE) **Mrs P. Sloan**
208 **WOODFORD ISLAND (IRE)**, 7, b br g Trans Island—Toulon Breeze (IRE) **T. J. Doran**
209 **WOODS WELL (IRE)**, 7, ch g Fleetwood (IRE)—Millbrook Marble (IRE) **Gigginstown House Stud**
210 **YOUGHAL BY THE SEA (IRE)**, 5, b g Milan—Down By The Sea (IRE) **Mr J. P. Russell**

THREE-YEAR-OLDS

211 **CALDBECK**, b g Dark Angel (IRE)—Geesala (IRE) **Mrs Caroline Fitzpatrick**
212 **SMILING ELIZA (IRE)**, b f Rock of Gibraltar (IRE)—Gift Dancer **Mrs D. P. Magnier**

Assistant Trainer: Oliver Murphy & Ian Amond

---

175 MISS JOEY ELLIS, Newmarket
Postal: **Georgia House Stud, Bradley Road, Burrough Green, Newmarket, Suffolk, CB8 9NH**
Contacts: **PHONE (07827) 316360**
E-MAIL georgiahousestud@btinternet.com

1 **AUTUMN GLOW**, 4, b f Sir Percy—Steady Rain **Georgia House Racing Club**
2 **DANICA ASHTON**, 4, b f Fast Company (IRE)—Spirit of Success **Georgia House Racing Club**
3 **MARBOOH (IRE)**, 5, b g Dark Angel (IRE)—Muluk (IRE) **Mrs A. B. Ellis**
4 **MOONLIGHT SECRET**, 4, gr f Black Sam Bellamy (IRE)—Scrupulous **Mrs A. B. Ellis**
5 **SHANAKILL STAR (IRE)**, 4, b f Lord Shanakill (USA)—Lola Rosa (IRE) **Mr B Edwards & Mr L Doolan**

THREE-YEAR-OLDS

6 **BELLMAID**, b f Champs Elysees—Never Enough (GER) **Mrs A. B. Ellis**
7 **FIFTYSHADESOFNEIGH (IRE)**, b f Sleeping Indian—Sceilin (IRE)
8 **TWILIGHT CAPER**, ch f Captain Gerrard (IRE)—Blades Princess **Georgia House Racing Club**

TWO-YEAR-OLDS

9 B c 12/4 Compton Place—Apple Sauce (Prince Sabo) **Mrs A. B. Ellis**
10 **BREATHTAKING VIEW**, b f 25/4 Bated Breath—Morning View (North Light (IRE)) **Mr Brian Edwards**
11 **MISS MISCHIEF**, b f 10/3 Epaulette (AUS)—Just Alice (Bertolini (USA)) **Mrs A. B. Ellis**
12 **RAINBOW PANACEA**, b c 24/5 Monsieur Bond (IRE)—Parsonagehotelyork (IRE) (Danehill (USA)) **Mrs A. B. Ellis**
13 B c 17/3 Epaulette (AUS)—Topflight Princess (Cockney Rebel (IRE)) **Mrs A. B. Ellis**

Other Owners: Mr Linton Doolan, Miss J. Ellis, Mr Howard Foster, Mrs Foster, Mr J. Rogers, Miss C. Rogers.

Assistant Trainer: Angela Ellis

Jockey (flat): Stevie Donohoe. **Apprentice:** Rosie Jessop.

176 MR BRIAN ELLISON, Malton

Postal: **Spring Cottage Stables, Langton Road, Norton, Malton, North Yorkshire, YO17 9PY**
Contacts: OFFICE (01653) 690004 FAX (01653) 690008 MOBILE (07785) 747426
E-MAIL office@brianellisonracing.co.uk WEBSITE www.brianellisonracing.co.uk

1 ALWAYS RESOLUTE, 7, b g Refuse To Bend (IRE)—Mad Annie (USA) **Market Avenue Racing Club Ltd**
2 ANDYS GIRL (IRE), 5, gr m Clodovil (IRE)—Fishy **Mr Andrew Dawson & Mr Andrew Wainwright**
3 ANGEL IN THE SNOW, 5, ch g Haafhd—Chilly Filly (IRE) **Mr D. R. Gilbert**
4 APROVADO (IRE), 6, b g Approve (IRE)—Aldburgh **Hanson, McKiver, Percival**
5 APTERIX (FR), 8, b g Day Flight—Ohe Les Aulmes (FR) **Mr P. J. Martin**
6 ARCHIVE (IRE), 8, b g Sulamani (IRE)—Royale Dorothy (FR) **Brian Ellison Racing Club**
7 BAL DE RIO (FR), 5, b g Vertigineux (FR)—Baldoranic (FR) **Mr P. J. Martin**
8 BALLYCRYSTAL (IRE), 7, b g Oscar (IRE)—Musical Madam (IRE) **Mr P. J. Martin**
9 BALLYVIC BORU (IRE), 6, b g Brian Boru—Thedoubledee (IRE) **Mr P J Martin & Partner**
10 BARON DE MIDLETON (IRE), 5, b g Brian Boru—Present Climate (IRE) **Mr P. J. Martin**
11 BARRYS JACK (IRE), 8, b g Well Chosen—Theatre Fool (IRE) **D Gilbert, M Lawrence, A Bruce**
12 BIG TIME DANCER (IRE), 5, b g Zoffany (IRE)—Final Opinion (IRE) **Andy Bell Anna Noble Arnie Flower**
13 BORDEAUX BILL (IRE), 7, b g Craigsteel—Laura Croft (IRE) **Mrs J. A. Martin**
14 BUTHELEZI (USA), 10, b g Dynaformer—Ntombi (USA) **Mr Wayne Hawkes & Brian Ellison**
15 CARTHAGE (IRE), 7, b g Mastercraftsman (IRE)—Pitrizzia (IRE) **Mr D. Foster**
16 CHATEAU MARMONT (IRE), 5, b g Flemensfirth (IRE)—Sliabh Geal Gcua (IRE) **Mr P. J. Martin**
17 CHOSEN THEATRE (IRE), 7, b g Well Chosen—Theatre Fool (IRE) **Miss J. J. Bell**
18 CONTRE TOUS (FR), 6, b g Forestier (FR)—Orphee de Vonnas (FR) **Personal Racehorse Owners 2**
19 CPM FLYER, 4, b g Aqlaam—Zennor **S & S Racing**
20 CRACKDELOUST (FR), 6, b g Daramsar (FR)—Magic Rose (FR) **Mr P. J. Martin**
21 DANDYS DENOUEMENT, 4, b g Pastoral Pursuits—Engaging **Mr D. Padgett**
22 DEFINITLY RED (IRE), 9, ch g Definite Article—The Red Wench (IRE) **Mr P. J. Martin**
23 DIAMANT DE L'OUEST (FR), 5, b g Epalo (GER)—Ortezia (FR) **Mr J. A. Hall & Mr Brian Ellison**
24 DOMINADA (IRE), 6, b g Mastercraftsman (IRE)—Red Blossom (USA) **Julie & Keith Hanson**
25 EASTERN RACER (IRE), 6, b g Bushranger (IRE)—Queen Cobra (IRE) **Mrs J. A. Martin**
26 EYES OF A TIGER (IRE), 7, ch g Golan (IRE)—Backtothekingsnest (IRE) **Mr P. J. Martin**
27 FAIR LOCH, 10, gr g Fair Mix (IRE)—Ardentinny **Mrs J. A. Martin**
28 FOREST BIHAN (FR), 7, ch g Forestier (FR)—Katell Bihan (FR) **Mr P. J. Martin**
29 GENERAL MAHLER (IRE), 8, b g Mahler—High Dough (IRE) **Mr P. J. Martin**
30 GREEN LIGHT, 7, b g Authorized (IRE)—May Light **Mr C Lowther & Mr B Ellison**
31 HAULANI (USA), 4, ch g Algorithms (USA)—License To Speed (USA) **D Gilbert, M Lawrence, A Bruce**
32 INSTANT REPLAY (IRE), 6, ch g Fruits of Love (USA)—Ding Dong Belle **Mr P. J. Martin**
33 IT'S YOUR MOVE (IRE), 6, b g Flemensfirth (IRE)—Jeruflo (IRE) **Mr P. J. Martin**
34 ITS PANDORAMA (IRE), 8, b g Misternando—Gretchen's Castle (IRE) **Brian Ellison Racing Club**
35 JAMACHO, 4, ch g Camacho—Obsessive Secret (IRE) **Mrs J. A. Martin**
36 LITTLE JO, 4, b g Major Cadeaux—Discoed **Mr Ian & Tom Pallas & The Mackem 2**
37 MAHLERDRAMATIC (IRE), 8, br g Mahler—Image of Vermont (IRE) **Mr P. J. Martin**
38 MANITOWOC COUNTY (IRE), 6, b g Darsi (FR)—Murphys Appeal (IRE) **Mr P. J. Martin**
39 MIDAS GOLD (IRE), 6, b g Rip Van Winkle (IRE)—Hespera **Mr P. J. Martin**
40 MISS RANGER (IRE), 6, gr m Bushranger (IRE)—Remiss (IRE) **Jane Greetham & Victoria Greetham**
41 MISTER MANDURO (FR), 4, ch g Manduro (GER)—Semenova (FR) **Brian Ellison Racing Club**
42 4, B f Clodovil (IRE)—Mugazala (IRE) **Mr K. Brown**
43 NEW LIST, 5, ch g Pivotal—Angel's Tears **S & S Racing & Partner**
44 NEWSTART (IRE), 7, br g Stowaway—Joes Annie (IRE) **Brian Ellison Racing Club**
45 NIETZSCHE, 5, ch g Poet's Voice—Ganga (IRE) **D Gilbert, M Lawrence, A Bruce, G Wills**
46 NORTHGATE LAD (IRE), 6, gr g Dark Angel (IRE)—Canosa (IRE) **Mrs J. A. Martin**
47 OSCAR BLUE (IRE), 8, gr g Oscar (IRE)—Blossom Rose (IRE) **Mr P. J. Martin**
48 OUR KYLIE (IRE), 6, b m Jeremy (USA)—Prakara (IRE) **Morecool & Cool Racing**
49 PEA SHOOTER, 9, b g Piccolo—Sparkling Eyes **Mrs A. M. Mallinson**
50 PICKETT'S CHARGE, 5, b g Clodovil (IRE)—Chelsea Morning (USA) **Cool Racing 2**
51 PISTOL PARK (FR), 7, b g Poliglote—Pistolera (GER) **Brian's Mates**
52 POINT THE WAY (IRE), 7, br g Brian Boru—Caslain Og (IRE) **Mr P. J. Martin**
53 RACING EUROPE (IRE), 9, b g Kayf Tara—Titanic Quarter (IRE) **Mr P. J. Martin**
54 RAVENHILL ROAD (IRE), 7, ch g Exit To Nowhere (USA)—Zaffarella (IRE) **Mr P. J. Martin**
55 RIVERSIDE BRIDGE (IRE), 6, gr g Rugby (USA)—Sahara Gold (IRE) **Brian Ellison Racing Club**
56 ROYAL FLAG, 8, b g New Approach (IRE)—Gonbarda **Dean Woodhouse & Brian Ellison**
57 SAM'S ADVENTURE, 6, b g Black Sam Bellamy (IRE)—My Adventure (IRE) **Mrs J. A. Martin**
58 SEAMOUR (IRE), 7, b g Azamour (IRE)—Chifney Rush **Mr P. J. Martin**
59 SECRET PASSENGER (IRE), 5, ch g Stowaway—Mtpockets (IRE) **Brian Ellison Racing Club**
60 SEEBRING (IRE), 4, b g Tagula (IRE)—Sunlit Romance (IRE) **Mr John James & Brian Ellison**
61 SERENITY NOW (IRE), 10, b g Key of Luck (USA)—Imdina (IRE) **Brian Ellison Racing Club**

MR BRIAN ELLISON - Continued

62 **SHEARLING**, 5, b m Rail Link—Casual **Mr Brian Ellison**
63 **SIANNES STAR (IRE)**, 5, b g Arakan (USA)—Musical Madam (IRE) **Mrs J. A. Martin**
64 **SMART TALK (IRE)**, 8, b m Hubbly Bubbly—Belon Breeze (IRE) **Mrs J. A. Martin**
65 **SNOOKERED (IRE)**, 4, b g Born To Sea (IRE)—Secret Quest **Brian Ellison Racing Club**
66 **SOLDIER BLUE (FR)**, 4, ch g Sepoy (AUS)—Kocooning (IRE) **S & S Racing**
67 **SUGARLOAF MOUNTAIN (IRE)**, 5, b g Fastnet Rock (AUS)—
Cherry Hinton **Andy Bell Anna Noble Arnie Flower 1**
68 **SUMNER BEACH**, 4, ch g Aqlaam—Cosmic Song **Mr K. Brown**
69 **TALLINSKI (IRE)**, 4, ch g Mayson—Estonia **Mrs J. A. Martin**
70 **THE KING OF MAY (FR)**, 4, b g High Rock (IRE)—Waltzing (IRE) **Mr P. J. Martin**
71 **TICKERTY BOO (IRE)**, 6, gr m Tikkanen (USA)—La Fille d'or (IRE) **Mrs J. A. Martin**
72 **TOMNGERRY (IRE)**, 8, b g Craigsteel—Lady Vic (IRE) **Mrs J. A. Martin**
73 **TOP NOTCH TONTO (IRE)**, 8, ch g Thousand Words—Elite Hope (USA) **Mr K. Brown**
74 **TOTALIZE**, 9, b g Authorized (IRE)—You Too **D Gilbert, M Lawrence, A Bruce**
75 **TRAVELTALK (IRE)**, 4, b g Fast Company (IRE)—Laheen (IRE) **Mr John James & Brian Ellison**
76 **VIENS CHERCHER (IRE)**, 7, b g Milan—La Zingarella (IRE) **Mr P. J. Martin**
77 **VOLVALIEN (FR)**, 9, b g Network (GER)—Josvalie (FR) **Mr Ashley Carr & Partners**
78 **WEAKFIELD (IRE)**, 5, b g Court Cave (IRE)—Thats The Lot (IRE) **Mr P. J. Martin**
79 **WINDSOR AVENUE (IRE)**, 6, b g Winged Love (IRE)—Zaffarella (IRE) **Mr P. J. Martin**
80 **XIN CHAO**, 5, b m Showcasing—Nelly's Glen **Mr Brian Ellison**
81 **ZAIDIYN (FR)**, 8, b g Zamindar (USA)—Zainta (IRE) **Mr P. J. Martin**

THREE-YEAR-OLDS

82 **BASILDON**, b g Champs Elysees—Casual **Mr D. R. Gilbert**
83 **BURN SOME DUST (IRE)**, b g Shirocco (GER)—Chilly Filly (IRE) **Mr D. R. Gilbert**
84 B f Frozen Power (IRE)—Go Maggie Go (IRE) **Mr K. Brown**
85 **HARRY CRUMB**, b g Sulamani (IRE)—Ananda Kanda (USA) **Brian Ellison & Kristian Strangeway**
86 **MOLTOIR (IRE)**, b g Vocalised (USA)—Gleigeal (USA) **Mr D. R. Gilbert**
87 **NORTHERN QUEEN (IRE)**, gr f Dark Angel (IRE)—
Queen Bodicea (IRE) **Northern Water Services & Graham Lund**
88 **SKYVA**, b g Dick Turpin (IRE)—Skylla **Facts & Figures**
89 **TALE OF TAILS (IRE)**, b g Rip Van Winkle (IRE)—Salute To Seville (IRE) **Mr K. Brown**
90 B c Jeremy (USA)—Tarziyma (IRE) **Mr P. J. Martin**

TWO-YEAR-OLDS

91 **ANTICO LADY (IRE)**, b f 29/2 Dandy Man (IRE)—
Former Drama (USA) (Dynaformer (USA)) (45000) **Julie & Keith Hanson**
92 B c 22/1 Harbour Watch (IRE)—Bahamamia (Vettori (IRE)) (19000)
93 **BISCUIT QUEEN**, br f 27/1 Harbour Watch (IRE)—Ginger Cookie (Bold Edge) (15238) **Brian Ellison Racing Club**
94 **JUALS SPIRIT (IRE)**, b f 4/4 Raven's Pass (USA)—
Bahama Spirit (IRE) (Invincible Spirit (IRE)) (42000) **K & J Hanson & A Dawson**
95 **KALISSI**, b f 26/3 Mayson—Dance Card (Cape Cross) (20952)
96 **LITTLE LEGS**, b f 29/3 Captain Gerrard (IRE)—
Livia Drusilla (IRE) (Holy Roman Emperor (IRE)) **Brian Ellison Racing Club**
97 B f 25/3 Finsceal Fior (IRE)—Lost Icon (Intikhab (USA)) (16280) **Mr K. Brown**
98 B c 15/3 Gale Force Ten—Luxuria (IRE) (Kheleyf (USA)) (17142)
99 B c 10/3 Casamento (IRE)—Mia Madonna (Motivator) (16280)
100 Gr f 17/4 Footstepsinthesand—Musical Molly (IRE) (Mastercraftsman (USA)) **Mrs J. A. Martin**
101 B f 19/3 Gregorian (IRE)—Peneia (USA) (Nureyev (USA)) (7000)
102 B c 17/4 Equiano (FR)—Procession (Zafonic (USA)) (10476)
103 **QUICKLY DOES IT**, b f 14/4 Havana Gold (IRE)—Mylington Maid (Dubai Destination (USA))
104 B f 30/3 Power—Redona (IRE) (Le Vie Dei Colori) (4069) **Mr K. Brown**
105 B f 2/2 Gregorian (IRE)—Sitting Pritty (Compton Place) (14285) **Mr D. Padgett**
106 B f 25/2 Captain Gerrard (IRE)—Striking Cat (Striking Ambition)
107 Ch c 28/4 Zoffany (IRE)—Winning Sequence (FR) (Zafonic (USA)) (4069) **Mr K. Brown**

Other Owners: Mr A. Bell, Mr S. Bland, A. Carr, Mr J. J. Cosgrove, Mr A. Dawson, Mr M. N. Dennis, Mrs C. L. Ellison, Mr S. A. Flower, Mrs J. Forsyth, Mrs J. Greetham, Miss V. Greetham, Mr J. A. Hall, J. P. Hames, Mr K. Hanson, Mrs J. Hanson, Mr W. D. Hawkes, Mr C. S. Heaps, Mr S. T. Hoare, J. James, Mr M. Lawrence, C. P. Lowther, Mr G. Lund, Mr N. P. Lyons, Morecool Racing, Mr T. D. Nield, Mrs A. M. Noble, Northern Water Services Limited, Mr G. Pickering, Mr B. Robe, Mr P. A. Saxton, Mr R. J. T. Smillie, Mr P. M. Stacey, Mr K. J. Strangeway, Mr M. Sykes, Mr A. Wainwright, Mrs J. Ward, Westbourne Consultants Ltd, Mr G. Wills, Mr D. Woodhouse.

MR BRIAN ELLISON - Continued

Assistant Trainer: Jessica Bell, Mobile (07939) 480860

Jockey (flat): Ben Curtis. **Jockey (NH):** Henry Brooke, Danny Cook, Brian Hughes. **Conditional:** Connor King, Nathan Moscrop. **Apprentice:** Ben Robinson.

---

177 **MR DAVID ELSWORTH, Newmarket**
Postal: Kings Yard, Egerton House Stables, Cambridge Road, Newmarket, Suffolk, CB8 0TH
Contacts: **PHONE** (01638) 665511 **FAX** (01638) 665310 **MOBILE** (07540) 750424
E-MAIL office@drcelsworth.com

1 AY AY (IRE), 4, b g Pour Moi (IRE)—Chatline (IRE) **Mr D. R. C. Elsworth**
2 BRANCASTER (IRE), 4, ch c Casamento (IRE)—Makheelah **C Benham/ D Whitford/ L Quinn/ K Quinn**
3 BURNING THREAD (IRE), 11, b g Captain Rio—Desert Rose **Mr D. R. C. Elsworth**
4 COUNTRY'N'WESTERN (FR), 6, b g Samum (GER)—Cracking Melody **Mr D. R. C. Elsworth**
5 DANCE TEACHER (IRE), 4, ch f Lope de Vega (IRE)—Fairnilee **Simon Lockyer & Tim Clark**
6 DASH OF SPICE, 4, br c Teofilo (IRE)—Dashiba **J. C. Smith**
7 JUSTICE LADY (IRE), 5, br m Dream Ahead (USA)—Celestial Dream (IRE) **Mr R. Ng**
8 MARK HOPKINS, 6, b g Mount Nelson—Halska **Mrs J. McCreery**
9 MASTER THE WORLD (IRE), 7, gr g Mastercraftsman (IRE)—Zadalla **K. Quinn/ C. Benham**
10 MISS HERITAGE (IRE), 4, b f Pour Moi (IRE)—Haretha (IRE) **Mark Venus & David Elsworth**
11 RIPP ORF (IRE), 4, b g Rip Van Winkle (IRE)—Barzah (IRE) **C Benham/K Quinn/L Quinn/D Elsworth**
12 SIR DANCEALOT (IRE), 4, b g Sir Prancealot (IRE)—
                    Majesty's Dancer **C Benham/ D Whitford/ L Quinn/ K Quinn**
13 SPECULATIVE BID (IRE), 7, b g Excellent Art—Barzah (IRE) **K. Quinn/ C. Benham**
14 TISBUTADREAM (IRE), 4, ch f Dream Ahead (USA)—Choose Me (IRE)

THREE-YEAR-OLDS

15 Ch g Champs Elysees—Agrippina **Mr D. R. C. Elsworth**
16 COSMOPOLITAN QUEEN, ch f Dubawi (IRE)—Barshiba (IRE) **J. C. Smith**
17 ENZEMBLE (IRE), b c Zoffany (IRE)—Fifer (IRE) **Mr B. C. M. Wong**
18 GALLOWAY HILLS, b c Kyllachy—Bonnie Brae **Li, Munnelly, Quinn, Benham & Whitford**
19 ICONIC BOY, b c Cape Cross (IRE)—Snoqualmie Girl (IRE) **J. C. Smith**
20 LADY DANCEALOT (IRE), b f Sir Prancealot (IRE)—Mayorstone (IRE) **K. J. Quinn**
21 MAKE HASTE SLOWLY, ch c Medicean—Skara Brae **Elsworth & Nettlefold**
22 MERLIN MAGIC, b c Camelot—Seattle Ribbon (USA) **J. C. Smith**
23 MORNING HAS BROKEN (IRE), ch f Dawn Approach (IRE)—Romie's Kastett (GER) **Mr D. R. C. Elsworth**
24 POLAR LIGHT, b f Norse Dancer—Dimelight **J. C. Smith**
25 POSSIBLY SO (IRE), br g Cacique (IRE)—Tango Tonic (IRE) **S. O'Sullivan**
26 B g Declaration of War (USA)—Three Moons (IRE) **Mr D. R. C. Elsworth**
27 B f Declaration of War (USA)—Turning Top (IRE) **Mrs D. A. Tabor**

TWO-YEAR-OLDS

28 Ch c 28/2 New Approach (IRE)—Barshiba (IRE) (Barathea (IRE)) **J. C. Smith**
29 DANDHU, ch f 25/2 Dandy Man (IRE)—Poldhu (Cape Cross (IRE)) (75000) **Mrs Anne Coughlan**
30 ENDEAVOURING (IRE), b c 4/2 Shamardal (USA)—
                    La Divina (IRE) (Sadler's Wells (USA)) (80000) **Mr B. C. M. Wong**
31 B c 14/3 Acclamation—Gift of Music (IRE) (Cadeaux Genereux) **J. C. Smith**
32 HARRY THE NORSEMAN, ch c 21/3 Norse Dancer (IRE)—Titled Lady (Sir Percy) (5238) **Elsworth & Nettlefold**
33 B f 12/3 Tamayuz—Lovers Peace (IRE) (Oratorio (IRE)) (21000) **Mr D. R. C. Elsworth**
34 C 15/4 Swiss Spirit—Moment In The Sun (Dubai Destination (USA)) **Roscommon Syndicate**
35 B c 20/2 Alhebayeb (IRE)—Peacemaker (IRE) (High Chaparral (IRE)) (40000) **Mr D. R. C. Elsworth**
36 Ch f 9/4 Norse Dancer (IRE)—Premier Prize (Selkirk (USA)) **J. C. Smith**
37 ROCKET ACTION, b c 6/4 Toronado (IRE)—Winning Express (IRE) (Camacho) **Mr R. Ng**
38 Ch c 14/3 Champs Elysees—Sailors Path (New Approach (IRE)) **G. B. Partnership**
39 B c 9/4 Australia—Snoqualmie Girl (IRE) (Montjeu (IRE)) **J. C. Smith**
40 SONGKRAN (IRE), b c 13/4 Slade Power (IRE)—
                    Choose Me (IRE) (Choisir (AUS)) (81400) **King Power Racing Co Ltd**

Other Owners: Mr Chris Benham, M. G. H. Heald, Mr A. M. H. Heald, Mr R. S. Hoskins, Mr Gordon Li, Mr Luke Lillingston, Mr Phil Munnelly, Mr Julian Nettlefold, Mr Leo Quinn, The Hot To Trot Syndicate, Mr M. Venus, Mr D. Whitford.

178 MISS SARA ENDER, Malton
Postal: **Swallows Barn, East Heslerton, Malton, North Yorkshire, YO17 8RN**
Contacts: **PHONE** (01653) 228758 **MOBILE** (07983) 462314
E-MAIL seequineservices@hotmail.com **WEBSITE** www.nevilleender.wix.com/enderracing

1 **BOLD PRINCE RUPERT (IRE)**, 8, br g Royal Anthem (USA)—Fortune And Favour (IRE) **Mr N. P. Ender**
2 **CASTLEY LANE**, 12, b g Dapper—Holly **Mr N. P. Ender**
3 **EASTER HUNT (IRE)**, 9, br g Kalanisi (IRE)—Easter Day (IRE) **Mr N. P. Ender**
4 **GREY MONK (IRE)**, 10, gr g Alderbrook—Thats The Bother (IRE) **Mr N. P. Ender**
5 **IVOR THE FOX**, 6, b g Sakhee (USA)—Florie **Mr N. P. Ender**
6 **MISTER KALANISI (IRE)**, 9, b g Kalanisi (IRE)—Maxis Girl (IRE) **Mr N. P. Ender**
7 **MOORLANDS MIST**, 11, gr g Fair Mix (IRE)—Sandford Springs (USA) **Mr N. P. Ender**
8 **ROYALE'S CHARTER**, 12, ch g Karinga Bay—Royale De Vassy (FR) **Mr N. P. Ender**

179 MRS SAM ENGLAND, Guiseley
Postal: **Brentwood, Manor Farm, Guiseley, Leeds, West Yorkshire, LS20 8EW**
Contacts: **MOBILE (07921) 003155**

1 **ALZAMMAAR (USA)**, 7, b g Birdstone (USA)—Alma Mater **The Sandmoor Partnership 2**
2 **ASK PADDY (IRE)**, 6, ch g Ask—Dalzenia (FR) **Gremot Racing 2**
3 **BROWN TRIX (IRE)**, 8, b g Flemensfirth (USA)—Five Trix **Itsnotabadlife**
4 **CHOOCHOOBUGALOO**, 6, b m Rail Link—Charmante Femme **Mrs S. A. England**
5 **GENTLEMAN JACK**, 6, gr g Great Palm (USA)—Queen of Diamonds (IRE) **Mrs J. E. Drake**
6 **HOLLINS HILL**, 8, b g Lucarno (USA)—Bonnie Buttons **Mr Gary Smith & Mrs J. Drake**
7 **MAGIC OF MILAN (IRE)**, 5, b m Milan—Laughing Lesa (IRE) **On the Road Again**
8 **MANWELL (IRE)**, 8, b g Gold Well—Roborette (FR) **Sam England Racing Club**
9 **MURCHISON RIVER**, 4, b g Medicean—Free Offer **The Atkin Partnership**
10 **MY RENAISSANCE**, 8, b br g Medicean—Lebenstanz **Lynne Pearson, Diane Mulcahy & Partners**
11 **NINEPOINTSIXTHREE**, 8, b g Bertolini (USA)—Armada Grove **Mr G. Smith**
12 **RAIN IN THE FACE**, 5, b g Naaqoos—Makaaseb (USA) **Mrs J. E. Drake**
13 **RAKTIMAN (IRE)**, 11, ch g Rakti—Wish List (IRE) **Mr J C England and Valerie Beattie**
14 **SIMPLY BUSINESS (FR)**, 5, b m Maresca Sorrento (FR)—Fabulous Darling (FR) **Mrs S. A. England**
15 **STAR PRESENTER (IRE)**, 10, b g Presenting—Star Councel (IRE) **Mrs J. E. Drake**
16 **THE LINKSMAN (IRE)**, 6, b g Westerner—Lost Link (IRE) **Mrs S. A. England**
17 **WINDY WRITER (IRE)**, 8, br g Rudimentary (USA)—Hardabout (IRE) **Guess What Racing**

Other Owners: T. J. Atkin, J. A. Atkin, Mr P. H. Ayre, Mrs V. A. Beattie, J. R. Bewley, Mr J. Birtles, Mr D. Brooks, Mr A. J. Cooper, Mr T. K. Davis, Mr J. C. England, Mr G. Fox, Mr D. N. French, Mr J. H. Green, Mr I. Janotta, Mr J. E. Mott, Mrs D. Mulcahy, Mrs L. E. Pearson, Mr M. J. Roche, Mr J. J. Wilkinson.

180 MR JAMES EUSTACE, Newmarket
Postal: **Park Lodge Stables, Park Lane, Newmarket, Suffolk, CB8 8AX**
Contacts: **PHONE** (01638) 664277 **FAX** (01638) 664156 **MOBILE** (07802) 243764
E-MAIL jameseustace@tiscali.co.uk **WEBSITE** www.jameseustace.com

1 4, B f Rail Link—Al Rayanah **Mr M. Bartram**
2 **APACHE SONG**, 4, ch m Mount Nelson—Pantita **Mr Andrew Mcgladdery & Mrs James Eustace**
3 **AVIATOR (GER)**, 10, br g Motivator—Amore (GER) **The MacDougall Two**
4 **BUSKIN RIVER (IRE)**, 4, b g Kodiac—Miss Smilla **Mr David Batten & Mrs James Eustace**
5 **CAPTAIN FELIX**, 6, b g Captain Gerrard (IRE)—Sweet Applause (IRE) **Mr M. Bartram**
6 **COVERHAM (IRE)**, 4, b g Bated Breath—Mark Too (IRE) **Blue Peter Racing 15**
7 **DEBACLE**, 5, b g Bach (IRE)—De Blanc (IRE) **J. P. Hancock**
8 **DEDUCE (FR)**, 5, b m Iffraaj—Count The Cost (USA) **T. H. Barma & Ian Rushby**
9 **ENVOY**, 4, gr g Delegator—La Gessa **H. R. Moszkowicz**
10 **FATHER MCKENZIE**, 4, b g Sixties Icon—Queen of Narnia **The MacDougall Two**
11 **FOLLY BERGERE (IRE)**, 5, ch m Champs Elysees—
Rainbow Queen (FR) **Mr & Mrs R Scott & Mrs James Eustace**
12 **GLENDUN (USA)**, 4, b g First Defence (USA)—La Mina (USA) **The MacDougall Two**
13 **ICE SLICE (IRE)**, 7, b g Dark Angel (IRE)—Ice Rock (IRE) **The MacDougall Two**
14 **LONGSIDE**, 6, b g Oasis Dream—Hypoteneuse (IRE) **Mrs G. R. Eustace**
15 **MACKSVILLE (IRE)**, 5, gr g Mastercraftsman (IRE)—Fairest of All (IRE) **G Carstairs & R Marker**
16 **QUEEN MONTOYA**, 4, b f High Chaparral (IRE)—Rainbow Queen (FR) **Mr & Mrs R. Scott**

MR JAMES EUSTACE - Continued

17 **SEE THE CITY (IRE),** 4, b f Lawman (FR)—Cedar Sea (IRE) **The MacDougall Two**
18 **WIND PLACE AND SHO,** 6, b g Shirocco (GER)—Coh Sho No **Mr Harold Nass**

THREE-YEAR-OLDS

19 **ALL ROUND,** b f Champs Elysees—Alice Alleyne (IRE) **Major M. G. Wyatt**
20 **BLUE WHISPER,** ch g Bated Breath—Vivid Blue **J. C. Smith**
21 **DIRECTORY,** b g Oasis Dream—Minority **Blue Peter Racing 16**
22 **KILLER PUNCH,** gr f Lethal Force (IRE)—La Gessa **Henry Moszkowicz & Upperwood Farm Stud**
23 **MEDIAN,** b f Medicean—Gale Green **Major M. G. Wyatt**
24 **NORDIC FLIGHT,** b g Norse Dancer (IRE)—Winged Diva (IRE) **J. C. Smith**

TWO-YEAR-OLDS

25 B c 14/3 Delegator—Bahama Blue (Bahamian Bounty) **J. C. Smith**
26 **POSTIE,** b f 7/3 Medicean—Postage Stampe (Singspiel (IRE)) **Major M. G. Wyatt**
27 **REASONED (IRE),** ch f 30/4 Intello (GER)—
                        Do The Honours (IRE) (Highest Honor (FR)) (13000) **Park Lodge Racing**
28 Ch f 19/3 Champs Elysees—Somersault (Pivotal) (7500) **Mr G. N. Carstairs**
29 **STERLING PRICE,** b c 27/2 War Command (USA)—Chantry (Galileo (IRE)) (14000) **Scott, Rushby, Charter**

Other Owners: Mr R. P. Abel, Mr D. F. Ballheimer, T. H. Barma, Mr D. H. Batten, P. F. Charter, Mr B. M. Cimmering, C. Z. Curtis, Mr T. E. Dyke, Mr J. M. P. Eustace, Mr A. C. Frost, Mr S. J. Gibson, Mrs J. A. Gibson, Mrs L. R. Lawson, R. J. T. Marker, Mr A. J. McGladdery, H. D. Nass, Mr G. Parsons, Mr I. L. Rushby, R. Scott, Mrs P. M. Scott, Mr R. J. Uzupris.

---

181 **MR DAVID EVANS, Abergavenny**
Postal: **Ty Derlwyn Farm, Pandy, Abergavenny, Monmouthshire, NP7 8DR**
Contacts: **PHONE** (01873) 890837 (07834) 834775 E. Evans **FAX** (01873) 890837
MOBILE (07860) 668499
E-MAIL pdevansracing@btinternet.com WEBSITE www.pdevansracing.co.uk

1 **AL'S MEMORY (IRE),** 9, b g Red Clubs (IRE)—Consensus (IRE) **Mrs R. L. Dawson**
2 **ATHASSEL,** 9, ch g Dalakhani (IRE)—Hope Island (IRE) **Mrs E. Evans**
3 **AWESOME ALLAN (IRE),** 4, b g Acclamation—Spring Approach **Mr A Cooke & Mr K McCabe**
4 **BLACK DAVE (IRE),** 8, b g Excellent Art—Miss Latina (IRE) **Mrs E. Evans**
5 **DAILY TRADER,** 4, ch g Medicean—Danehill Destiny **Mrs Penny Keble-white & Mr B J Mould**
6 **DIBLOAM (USA),** 5, ch g Hard Spun (USA)—Nuqoosh **Diamond Racing Ltd**
7 **DOUGAN,** 6, b g Dutch Art—Vive Les Rouges **Shropshire Wolves**
8 **ESSENAITCH (IRE),** 5, b g Zoffany—Karlisse (IRE) **Spiers & Hartwell Ltd & Mrs E. Evans**
9 **GRACIOUS JOHN (IRE),** 5, b g Baltic King—Dorn Hill **T. Reffell**
10 **HARRY BEAU,** 4, ch g Kheleyf (USA)—Lovellian **H. M. W. Clifford**
11 **HERM (IRE),** 4, b g Bushranger (IRE)—School Holidays (USA) **T. H. Gallienne**
12 **LETMESTOPYOUTHERE (IRE),** 4, b g Sir Prancealot (IRE)—Romanylei (IRE) **Mike Nolan & John Abbey**
13 **PRINCESS WAY (IRE),** 4, gr f Zebedee—Stef's Girl (IRE) **Mrs I. M. Folkes**
14 **SARK (IRE),** 5, b g Zoffany (IRE)—Breezeway (IRE) **T. H. Gallienne**
15 **SATCHVILLE FLYER,** 7, ch g Compton Place—Palinisa (FR) **Mr A Cooke & P D Evans**
16 **SEA FOX (IRE),** 4, b g Kodiac—City Maiden (USA) **Eric Griffiths & P D Evans**
17 **SHEER INTENSITY (IRE),** 5, ch m Dutch Art—Sheer Elegance (IRE) **Three Generations**
18 **SONNETIST,** 4, b g Poet's Voice—Society Rose **H. M. W. Clifford**
19 **SWIFT CEDAR (IRE),** 8, ch g Excellent Art—Ravish **J. E. Abbey**
20 **WORDINESS,** 10, br g Dansili—Verbose (USA) **Mrs E. Evans**
21 **ZIRCON (IRE),** 5, gr g Zebedee—Miss Glitters (IRE) **Dave & Emma Evans**

THREE-YEAR-OLDS

22 **BOND ANGEL,** gr f Monsieur Bond (IRE)—Angel Grigio **M. W. Lawrence**
23 **BROCKEY RISE (IRE),** ch g Zebedee—Age of Diplomacy **Power Geneva Ltd & John Abbey**
24 **CHERUBIC,** gr f Dark Angel (IRE)—Doula (USA) **R. Kent**
25 **COURTEOUS CROWN,** ch f Helmet (AUS)—Speak Softly To Me (USA) **H. M. W. Clifford**
26 **FELISA,** b f Multiplex—Limegrove **King Power Racing Co Ltd**
27 **GIVE EM A CLUMP (IRE),** b c Camacho—Pixie's Blue (IRE) **Power Geneva Ltd & Partner**
28 **ISTANBUL PASHA (IRE),** b g Fast Company (IRE)—Red Red Rose **Dave & Emma Evans**
29 **JOEGOGO (IRE),** b g Approve—Joyfullness (USA) **H. M. W. Clifford**
30 **KHELEYF'S GIRL,** br f Kheleyf (USA)—Handsome Molly **Mr J. A. Wilcox**
31 **LASTONEFORTHECRAIC (IRE),** b f Red Jazz (USA)—Charming Vista **Dukes Head Racing**
32 **LOPE DE LOOP (IRE),** b f Lope de Vega (IRE)—Patroller (USA) **H. M. W. Clifford**

MR DAVID EVANS - Continued

33 **LOS CAMACHOS (IRE)**, b c Camacho—Illuminise (IRE) **Mr A. L. Al Zeer**
34 **MOUCHEE (IRE)**, b c Zebedee—Nashaat **E. R. Griffiths**
35 **MR TOP HAT**, b c Helmet (AUS)—Tut (IRE) **Mr B McCabe & Mrs E Evans**
36 **RENNY'S LADY (IRE)**, ch f Excelebration (IRE)—Moriches (IRE) **Mrs I. M. Folkes**
37 **SHOVEL IT ON (IRE)**, br c Elusive Pimpernel (USA)—Fitrah (IRE) **Power Geneva & Bruce Williams**
38 **STAR GIRL**, ch f Dutch Art—Crossmolina (IRE) **H. M. W. Clifford**
39 **TEARDROP ISLAND (USA)**, b f Distorted Humor (USA)—Princess Sinead (IRE) **Mrs I. M. Folkes**

TWO-YEAR-OLDS

40 B f 1/2 Toronado (IRE)—Angus Newz (Compton Place) (19047) **Mrs R. L. Dawson**
41 B f 25/4 Kodiac—Annus Iucundus (IRE) (Desert King (IRE)) (13024) **Mr Naser Buresli & P D Evans**
42 **AWAKE IN ASIA**, ch c 18/4 Dragon Pulse (IRE)—
        Gladiatrix (Compton Place) (61904) **Mr Simon Munir & Mr Isaac Souede**
43 **DISRUPTOR (FR)**, ch c 29/1 Siyouni (FR)—
        Ultradargent (FR) (Kendargent (FR)) (49523) **Mr Simon Munir & Mr Isaac Souede**
44 Ch c 27/2 Olympic Glory (IRE)—Heaven's Sake (Cape Cross (IRE)) (72000) **H. M. W. Clifford**
45 **KG COURAGE (IRE)**, b f 2/3 Casamento (IRE)—
        Snapped (IRE) (Camacho) (17094) **Mr K McCabe & Mr P D Evans**
46 **KG PASSION (IRE)**, ch f 22/1 Bungle Inthejungle—
        Hustle Bustle (IRE) (Elusive City (USA)) (16280) **Mr K McCabe & Mr P D Evans**
47 Ch c 11/4 Mayson—Kodiac Island (Kodiac) (28000) **T. H. Gallienne**
48 **LADY PRANCEALOT (IRE)**, b f 9/2 Sir Prancealot (IRE)—
        Naqrah (IRE) (Haatef (USA)) (7732) **Dukes Head Racing**
49 B f 5/4 Delegator—Lovellian (Machiavellian (USA)) **H. M. W. Clifford**
50 B c 27/1 Morpheus—River Beau (IRE) (Galileo (IRE)) (10000)
51 **SIONA'S BOY (IRE)**, b c 15/4 Lilbourne Lad (IRE)—Snap Music (USA) (Mutakddim (USA)) (3809) **T. Reffell**
52 B f 12/3 Heeraat (IRE)—Sophie'jo (Agnes World (USA)) (4761) **H. M. W. Clifford**
53 **TEMPLE OF WONDER (IRE)**, b c 2/2 Clodovil (IRE)—
        Noble Fantasy (GER) (Big Shuffle (USA)) (41904) **Mr Simon Munir & Mr Isaac Souede**
54 **TWPSYN (IRE)**, b c 2/5 Es Que Love (IRE)—
        Gold Blended (GER) (Goldmark (USA)) (20952) **Rob Emmanuelle, T Burns & P D Evans**

Other Owners: Mr J. Babb, Mr N. Buresli, Mrs T. Burns, J. L. Collins, Mr A. D. Cooke, Mr P. G. Dalton, Mr R. Emmanuel, P. D. Evans, Mrs B. B. Grainger, Mr T. M. Grainger, Mrs P. Keble-White, Mr K. McCabe, Mr B. McCabe, Mr B. J. Mould, S. E. Munir, M. F. Nolan, Power Geneva Ltd, R. Simpson, Mr I. Souede, Spiers & Hartwell Ltd, Mr J. R. B. Williams.

Assistant Trainer: Mrs Emma Evans

Jockey (flat): Fran Berry, John Egan. **Apprentice:** Katherine Glenister, Philip Prince. **Amateur:** Miss E. McKenzie.

---

182 **MR JAMES EVANS, Kinnersley**
Postal: **Kinnersley Racing Stables, Kinnersley, Severn Stoke, Worcester, WR8 9JR**
Contacts: **MOBILE (07813) 166430**
E-MAIL **herbie_evans@hotmail.com** WEBSITE **www.hjamesevans.co.uk**

1 **ALPHA INDI (IRE)**, 7, b br g Oscar (IRE)—High Park Lady (IRE) **Mr S. D. Faiers**
2 **AMIRAL COLLONGES (FR)**, 8, ch g Dom Alco (FR)—Idole Collonges (FR) **Mr S. D. Faiers**
3 **CRY WOLF**, 5, ch g Street Cry (IRE)—Love Charm **Mr S. D. Faiers**
4 **DESILVANO**, 9, b g Desideratum—Cruz Santa **International Plywood (Importers) Ltd**
5 **FRIENDSHIP BAY**, 14, b g Midnight Legend—Friendly Fairy **Mrs J. Evans**
6 **LORD GETAWAY (IRE)**, 6, b g Getaway (GER)—Terre d'orient (FR) **Mr B. W. Preece**
7 **MALINDI BAY (FR)**, 5, b m Malinas (GER)—La Grande Villez (FR) **Mr S. D. Faiers**
8 **MOSSING**, 6, br m Passing Glance—Missy Moscow **James Evans Racing**
9 **NIGHTSWIFT**, 6, b g Midnight Legend—Sharbasia (IRE) **Mr S. D. Faiers & Mrs J. Evans**
10 **NOBEL LEADER (IRE)**, 8, b g Alflora (IRE)—Ben Roseler (IRE) **Mr S. D. Faiers**
11 **OPTIMISTIC BIAS (IRE)**, 9, b g Sayarshan (FR)—Dashers Folly (IRE) **Elegant Clutter Ltd**
12 **PRINCE OF STEAL (IRE)**, 8, b g Craigsteel—Princess Gloria (IRE) **The Cheltenham Flyers**
13 **SANDS COVE (IRE)**, 11, b g Flemensfirth (USA)—Lillies Bordello (IRE) **James Evans & The Harlequins Racing**
14 **SHARAINA**, 4, b f Yorgunnabelucky (USA)—Sharbasia (IRE)
15 **SWEET SHIRLEEN (IRE)**, 8, br m Kris Kin (USA)—
        Dashers Folly (IRE) **James Evans Racing & the Gmw Syndicate**

Other Owners: Mrs J. Evans, Mr James Evans, Mr S. D. Faiers, Mr Nigel Goodger, The Harlequins Racing, Mr A. J. Pidgeon, Mr Paul M. Smith, The GMW Syndicate.

MR JAMES EVANS - Continued

Assistant Trainer: Mrs Jane Evans

Amateur: Miss Emma Yardley.

---

183 **MRS MARY EVANS, Haverfordwest**
Postal: **Hengoed, Clarbeston Road, Haverfordwest, Pembrokeshire, SA63 4QL**
Contacts: **PHONE (01437) 731336**

1 **HOLD COURT (IRE)**, 11, br g Court Cave (IRE)—Tipsy Miss (IRE) **Mary & Billy Evans**
2 **MOUNTAIN OF ANGELS**, 9, b m Midnight Legend—Landsker Missile **Mary & Billy Evans**
3 **PRU**, 10, br m Weld—Floranz

Other Owners: W. J. Evans, Mrs M. Evans.

Assistant Trainer: W J Evans

---

184 **MRS NIKKI EVANS, Abergavenny**
Postal: **Penbiddle Farm, Penbidwal, Pandy, Abergavenny, Gwent, NP7 8EA**
Contacts: **(01873) 890957 FAX (01873) 890957 MOBILE (07977) 753437**
E-MAIL nikki@penbiddle.fsnet.co.uk WEBSITE www.nikki-evans-racing.co.uk

1 **AGREEMENT (IRE)**, 8, b g Galileo (IRE)—Cozzene's Angel (USA) **Nikki Evans Racing**
2 **ALLOW DALLOW (IRE)**, 11, b g Gold Well—Russland (GER) **Mr J. Berry**
3 **ANTON CHIGURH**, 9, b g Oasis Dream—Barathiki **Mr Matt Watkinson & Dare To Dream Racing**
4 **ARISTOCLES (IRE)**, 5, b g High Chaparral (IRE)—Amathusia **East Grinstead Scaffolding**
5 **LATE SHIPMENT**, 7, b g Authorized (IRE)—Time Over **Mrs M. E. Gittings-Watts**
6 **MAROC**, 5, b g Rock of Gibraltar (IRE)—Zietory **Dare To Dream & Mr P Green**
7 **PACO FILLY**, 4, b f Paco Boy (IRE)—Respectfilly **Mr G. M. Jones**
8 **PENNY RED**, 4, ch f Medicean—Peintre d'argent (IRE) **Mr J. Berry**
9 **POLKADOT PRINCESS (IRE)**, 4, b f Sir Prancealot (IRE)—Miriam's Song **L Gibbs, C Filsell, Nikki Evans Racing**
10 5, B m Jeremy (USA)—Right Reason (IRE) **Mrs N. S. Evans**
11 **SKYLARK LADY (IRE)**, 5, ch m Tamayuz—Allegrissimo (IRE) **Mrs M. E. Gittings-Watts**
12 **SMART MOVER (IRE)**, 5, b m Fast Company (IRE)—Alltherightmoves (IRE) **Mrs M. E. Gittings-Watts**
13 **SUE BE IT (IRE)**, 7, b m Presenting—Runaround Sue (IRE) **Hanford's Chemist Ltd**
14 **SWORD OF THE LORD**, 8, b g Kheleyf (USA)—Blue Echo **Mrs D. C. Scott**
15 **TAKBEER (IRE)**, 6, b g Aqlaam—Precious Secret (IRE) **Mrs M. E. Gittings-Watts**
16 **TIME FOR CHAMPERS (IRE)**, 8, b m Robin des Champs (FR)—Someone Told Me (IRE) **Hanford's Chemist Ltd**
17 **TURNBURY**, 7, b g Azamour (IRE)—Scottish Heights (IRE) **Dare To Dream Racing**
18 **WHAT A SCORCHER**, 7, b m Authorized (IRE)—Street Fire (IRE) **Mrs M. E. Gittings-Watts**

THREE-YEAR-OLDS

19 **CAVIAR ROYALE**, b g Royal Applause—Precious Secret (IRE) **Mrs M. E. Gittings-Watts**

Other Owners: P. T. Evans, Mr C. Filsell, Mr L. R. Gibbs, Mr P. T. Green, Mr I. Sharrock, Mr W. Smith, Mr A. N. Waters, Mr M. Watkinson.

Assistant Trainer: Mr P. T. Evans

---

185 **MR JAMES EWART, Langholm**
Postal: **James Ewart Racing Limited, Craig Farm, Westerkirk, Langholm, Dumfriesshire, DG13 0NZ**
Contacts: **PHONE (01387) 370707 MOBILE (07786) 995073**
E-MAIL office@jeracing.co.uk WEBSITE www.jamesewartracing.com

1 **ANGE DES MALBERAUX (FR)**, 8, b g Michel Georges—Petite Baie (FR) **The Craig Farm Syndicate**
2 **ARISTO DU PLESSIS (FR)**, 8, b g Voix du Nord (FR)—J'aime (FR) **Mrs J. E. Dodd**
3 **ASCOT DE BRUYERE (FR)**, 8, b br g Kapgarde (FR)—Quid de Neuville (FR) **The Steel Bonnets**
4 **BERING UPSUN**, 7, b g And Beyond (IRE)—Bering Up (FR) **The Craig Farm Syndicate**
5 **BETANCOURT (IRE)**, 8, ch g Refuse To Bend (IRE)—Orinoco (IRE) **Mrs S. J. Keniry**
6 **BILL D'ARON (FR)**, 7, ch g Dom Alco (FR)—Nobless d'aron (FR) **Mrs Hugh Fraser**
7 **BLACK PIRATE**, 6, b g Black Sam Bellamy (IRE)—Proper Posh **Leeds Plywood & Doors Ltd**
8 **BULLION (FR)**, 5, ch g Full of Gold (FR)—Ryde (FR) **Mrs Hugh Fraser**

MR JAMES EWART - Continued

9 **CALACH (FR)**, 6, gr g Fragrant Mix (IRE)—Nobless d'aron (FR) **Mr Graham & James Westoll**
10 **CALIX DELAFAYETTE (FR)**, 6, b g Caballo Raptor (CAN)—Obepinedelafayette (FR) **Mrs J. E. Dodd**
11 **CELLAR VIE**, 4, gr g Tikkanen (USA)—Branceilles (FR)
12 **CHARMANT (FR)**, 6, b g Balko (FR)—Ravissante (FR) **Mr A Phillips & Mr&Mrs Sperling**
13 **CIVIL UNREST (IRE)**, 12, ch g Blueprint (IRE)—Yore (FR) **Ancrum CFS Carruthers Palmer Galashan**
14 **DETONATE (FR)**, 5, gr g Al Namix (FR)—Tadorna (FR) **J. D. Gordon**
15 **DRENEK (FR)**, 5, gr g Turgeon (USA)—Sireva (FR) **Mr James Westoll**
16 **DURBANVILLE**, 6, b g Black Sam Bellamy (IRE)—Kealshore Lass **Mrs S. J. Keniry**
17 **EMPIRE DE MAULDE (FR)**, 4, b g Spanish Moon (USA)—Ondine de Brejoux (FR) **Mr J. Ewart**
18 **ETTILA DE SIVOLA (FR)**, 4, gr g Noroit (GER)—Wild Rose Bloom (FR) **Mr Phillips, Mrs Humbert & Mr Ogilvie**
19 **GILMER (IRE)**, 7, b g Exceed And Excel (AUS)—Cherokee Rose (IRE) **Mrs S. J. Keniry**
20 **GREEN TIKKANA**, 5, gr m Tikkanen (USA)—Think Green **The Craig Farm Syndicate**
21 **GROUND CONTROL (FR)**, 4, b g Al Namix (FR)—Gobeline (FR)
22 **HERMANUS (FR)**, 6, ch m Golan (IRE)—Almost Trumps **M. R. Johnson**
23 **INTO THE BREACH (FR)**, 5, b g Al Namix (FR)—Arvicaya **N. M. L. Ewart**
24 **IT'S NEVER ENOUGH**, 4, b g Equiano (FR)—Swynford Pleasure **J. D. Gordon**
25 **JASSAS (FR)**, 6, ch g Fuisse (FR)—Sylverina (FR) **Mrs J. E. Dodd**
26 **KINDLER**, 4, b g Firebreak—Neardown Beauty (IRE) **Mr & Mrs G. Turnbull**
27 **LORD WISHES (IRE)**, 11, b g Milan—Strong Wishes (IRE) **Leeds Plywood & Doors Ltd**
28 **LYCIDAS (GER)**, 9, b g Zamindar (USA)—La Felicita **J. D. Gordon**
29 **MAROCCHINO (FR)**, 5, gr g Tikkanen (USA)—Mocha (FR) **Mr J. Ewart**
30 **MULTIPEDE**, 6, b g Multiplex—Playful Lady **Mrs Hugh Fraser**
31 4, Gr b g Tikkanen (USA)—Pocahontas (FR) **Mr J. Ewart**
32 **SAO MAXENCE (FR)**, 5, b g Saint des Saints (FR)—Primadona (FR) **Mrs J. E. Dodd**
33 **SKY FULL OF STARS (IRE)**, 8, b g Mahler—Gold Flo (IRE) **J. D. Gordon**
34 **SLEEP IN FIRST (FR)**, 12, b br g Sleeping Car (FR)—First Union (FR) **First Sleepers, Craig Farm**
35 **STRIKE THE POSE (FR)**, 6, b m Saint des Saints (FR)—Royale Sulawesie (FR) **The Craig Farm Syndicate**
36 **UEUETEOTL (FR)**, 10, gr g Tikkanen (USA)—Acushladear (IRE) **Dodd, Graham & Sperling**
37 **UN GUET APENS (FR)**, 10, b g Enrique—Belisama (FR) **Drew, Sperling, Graham, Carruthers**
38 **UNDISPUTED (FR)**, 4, gr g Al Namix (FR)—Arvicaya

THREE-YEAR-OLDS

39 **AQUITAINE BOY (FR)**, b g Walk In The Park (IRE)—Dolce Vita Yug **Mrs J. E. Dodd**
40 B f Lucarno (USA)—Ballinargh Girl (IRE)
41 **BURNS SUPPER (IRE)**, ch g Poet's Voice—Charming (IRE) **The Craig Farm Syndicate**
42 **FEETRONIE DE KERVI (FR)**, b f No Risk At All (FR)—Malandra **N. M. L. Ewart**
43 **FOXEY**, b g Foxwedge (AUS)—Blue Lyric
44 **I AM DANDY (IRE)**, b c Dandy Man (IRE)—Acushladear (IRE) **Mr J. Ewart**
45 **LEAHCAR**, b f Delegator—Certral **Mr K. J. Strangeway**

Other Owners: Mr J. D. Allen, Mr R. Carruthers, Mrs L. J. Drew, Mr C. D. Dunnachie, Mr R. Galashan, Mr D. Graham, Mrs P. A. Graham, W. Graham, Mrs A. G. Humbert, Dr C. M. Kesson, Mr A. Kirkpatrick, Mr P. M. Ogilvie, Dr R. A. Palmer, Mrs J. D. Percy, Mr A. M. Phillips, Mr D. I. Rolinson, Mr R. E. Smith, Mrs J. Sperling, Mr N. A. Sperling, Mr D. R. Stanhope, Mrs S. E. Turnbull, Mr G. Turnbull.

Assistant Trainer: Briony Ewart

Conditional: Steven Fox.

---

186 **MR LES EYRE, Beverley**
Postal: Ivy House Stables, Main Street, Catwick, Beverley, North Humberside, HU17 5PJ
Contacts: MOBILE (07864) 677444
E-MAIL leseyreracing@hotmail.co.uk

1 **BLAGGER**, 5, ch g Major Cadeaux—Brogue Lanterns (IRE) **Miss V. Shaw**
2 **COSMIC RAY**, 6, b g Phoenix Reach (IRE)—Beat Seven **Over The Moon Racing III**
3 **COTE D'AZUR**, 5, ch g Champs Elysees—Florentia **Billy Parker & Steven Parker**
4 **DAWAALEEB (IRE)**, 4, b c Invincible Spirit (IRE)—Plaza **Billy Parker & Steven Parker**
5 **DETACHMENT**, 5, b g Motivator—Argumentative **Mr M. J. Rozenbroek**
6 **EL PRINCIPE**, 5, b g Strategic Prince—Shamrock Lady (IRE) **Mr M. J. Rozenbroek**
7 **GOLDEN GUEST**, 4, ch g Bated Breath—Si Belle (IRE) **Mr R. Peel**
8 **HIGHLY SPRUNG (IRE)**, 5, b g Zebedee—Miss Donovan **Mr A. Turton**
9 **INTENSE STYLE (IRE)**, 6, ch g Intense Focus (USA)—Style Queen (IRE) **RP Racing Ltd**
10 **MAKE ON MADAM (IRE)**, 6, b m Captain Rio—Rye (IRE) **Mr G Parkinson & Baz Gibson**

MR LES EYRE - Continued

11 **MARMION**, 6, b g Cape Cross (IRE)—Margarula (IRE) **RP Racing Ltd**
12 **PRAZERES**, 4, b g Sepoy (AUS)—Sewards Folly **Mr J. N. Blackburn**
13 **RONNIE THE ROOSTER**, 4, b g Captain Gerrard (IRE)—Piranha **J A Campbell & A Tattersall**
14 **SANDRA'S SECRET (IRE)**, 5, gr m Zebedee—Good For Her **Sunpak Potatoes**
15 **VALLEY OF FIRE**, 6, b g Firebreak—Charlie Girl **Billy Parker & Steven Parker**
16 **VAN GERWEN**, 5, ch g Bahamian Bounty—Disco Ball **Sunpak Potatoes**

THREE-YEAR-OLDS

17 **AISLIN MOON (IRE)**, b f Sleeping Indian—Shamrock Lady (IRE) **Personal Racehorse Owners**
18 **MAGICHULL**, ch f Dabbers Ridge (IRE)—The Pen **Mr G. Parkinson**
19 **QUEEN OF KALAHARI**, b f Lethal Force (IRE)—Aromatherapy **Billy Parker & John Blackburn**

TWO-YEAR-OLDS

20 B c 25/3 Bungle Inthejungle—Testa Unica (ITY) (Nordance (USA)) (6666)

Other Owners: Mr J. N. Blackburn, Mr James Arthur Campbell, Mr J. L. Eyre, Mr Baz Gibson, Mr Stephen Hackney, Mr C. S. Heaps, Mr C. Loughnane, Mr Billy Parker, Mr Steven Parker, Mr G. Parkinson, Mr A. Tattersall, Mrs S. J. Yates, Mr Tony Yates.

Assistant Trainer: Tracy Johnson

---

187 **MR RICHARD FAHEY, Malton**
Postal: RF Racing Ltd, Mews House, Musley Bank, Malton, North Yorkshire, YO17 6TD
Contacts: PHONE (01653) 698915 FAX (01653) 699735 MOBILE (07713) 478079
E-MAIL enquiries@richardfahey.com WEBSITE www.richardfahey.com

1 **ANDOK (IRE)**, 4, b g Elzaam (AUS)—My Causeway Dream (IRE) **Mr N. O'Keeffe**
2 **ANOTHER TOUCH**, 5, b g Arcano (IRE)—Alsalwa (IRE) **Nicholas Wrigley & Kevin Hart**
3 **BALLYMORE CASTLE (IRE)**, 6, br g Invincible Spirit (IRE)—
Ballymore Lady (USA) **Middleham Park Racing XXVI**
4 **BILLY BOND**, 6, b g Monsieur Bond (IRE)—Princess Cocoa (IRE) **Mr & Mrs P. Ashton**
5 **BOUNDSY (IRE)**, 4, ch g Dandy Man (IRE)—Chiba (UAE) **Kevin Mercer & Partner**
6 **CARNAGEO (FR)**, 5, b g Pivotal—Sudarynya (IRE) **The Up For Anything Syndicate**
7 **DARK DEVIL (IRE)**, 5, gr g Dark Angel (IRE)—Ride For Roses (IRE) **Dr M. B. Q. S. Koukash**
8 **DOCTOR CROSS (IRE)**, 4, b g Cape Cross (IRE)—Doctrine **Havelock Racing**
9 **DOSE**, 5, b m Teofilo (IRE)—Prescription **Richard Fahey Ebor Racing Club Ltd**
10 **FOREST RANGER (IRE)**, 4, b c Lawman (FR)—Alava (IRE) **Mrs H. Steel**
11 **GABRIAL (IRE)**, 9, b g Dark Angel (IRE)—Guajira (FR) **Dr M. B. Q. S. Koukash**
12 **GABRIAL'S STAR**, 9, b g Hernando (FR)—Grain Only **Dr M. B. Q. S. Koukash**
13 **GALLIPOLI (IRE)**, 5, b g Compton Place—Altadena Lady (IRE) **P. Timmins**
14 **GEOFF POTTS (IRE)**, 5, ch g Zebedee—Our Sheila **Mr J. Hart**
15 **GEORGE BOWEN (IRE)**, 5, b g Dark Angel (IRE)—Midnight Oasis **M. A. Scaife**
16 **GIN IN THE INN (IRE)**, 5, b g Alfred Nobel (IRE)—Nose One's Way (IRE) **Mr D. Hardman & Mrs S. Hardman**
17 **GOLCONDA PRINCE (IRE)**, 4, b g Arcano (IRE)—Mujarah (IRE) **Dr G. Davies**
18 **GRANDAD'S WORLD (IRE)**, 6, b g Kodiac—Nose One's Way (IRE) **Mr D. Hardman & Mrs S. Hardman**
19 **HEAVEN'S GUEST (IRE)**, 8, b g Dark Angel (IRE)—Bakewell Tart (IRE) **Mr J. K. Shannon & Mr M. A. Scaife**
20 **INAAM (IRE)**, 5, b g Camacho—Duckmore Bay (IRE) **Yorkshire Connections Ltd**
21 **INGLEBY SPRING (IRE)**, 6, br m Zebedee—Jouel (FR) **Percy Green Racing 3**
22 **JUDGE EARLE (IRE)**, 6, b g Court Cave (IRE)—Louis's Teffia (IRE) **D&D Armstrong Limited**
23 **KHELMAN (IRE)**, 8, b g Kheleyf (USA)—Mandolin (IRE) **Morebrooke Limited**
24 **KIMBERELLA (IRE)**, 8, b g Kyllachy—Gleam of Light (IRE) **Mr C. J. Titcomb**
25 **LA SIOUX (IRE)**, 4, ch f Casamento (IRE)—Dakota Sioux (IRE) **Mrs U. Towell**
26 **LADY IN QUESTION (IRE)**, 4, b f Elzaam (AUS)—Black Meyeden (FR) **Amie Canham I**
27 **LIQUID GOLD (IRE)**, 4, b f Nathaniel (IRE)—Northern Mischief (USA) **Mrs H. Steel**
28 **LUIS VAZ DE TORRES (IRE)**, 6, b g Tagula (IRE)—Tekhania (IRE) **Lets Go Racing 1**
29 **MARIE OF LYON**, 4, b f Royal Applause—Virginia Hall **Clipper Group Holdings Ltd**
30 **MEGAN LILY**, 4, b f Dragon Pulse (IRE)—Nebraas **Nick Bradley Racing 1**
31 **MUSTAAQEEM (USA)**, 6, b g Dynaformer (USA)—Wasseema (USA) **Merchants and Missionaries**
32 **NORMANDIE LADY**, 5, b m Kheleyf (USA)—Normandie Art **Mr A. B. Phipps**
33 **NORTHWEST FRONTIER (IRE)**, 4, b g Galileo (IRE)—Francesca d'gorgio (USA) **Sir R. Ogden C.B.E., LLD**
34 **PADDY POWER (IRE)**, 5, ch g Pivotal—Rag Top (IRE) **M Scaife & R A Fahey**
35 **PENWORTHAM (IRE)**, 5, b g Dandy Man (IRE)—Portofino Bay (IRE) **Dr M. B. Q. S. Koukash**
36 **PRIVATE MATTER**, 4, b g Mayson—Privacy Order **Richard Fahey Racing Club**
37 **PRYING PANDORA (FR)**, 5, b m Dark Angel (IRE)—Leniency (IRE) **Middleham Park Racing X**

MR RICHARD FAHEY - Continued

38 **PUDDING CHARE (IRE)**, 4, b g Arcano (IRE)—Rosy Dudley (IRE) **Havelock Racing 2 & Partner**
39 **QUILL ART**, 6, b g Excellent Art—Featherweight (IRE) **P. S. Cresswell & Mrs P. A. Morrison**
40 **RAJAR**, 4, b f Archipenko (USA)—Barnezet (GR) **Nick Bradley Racing 26**
41 **RENE MATHIS (GER)**, 8, ch g Monsieur Bond (IRE)—Remina (GER) **Dr M. B. Q. S. Koukash**
42 **RIGHT ACTION**, 4, b g Dandy Man (IRE)—Rockaby Baby (IRE) **Middleham Park Racing LVII & Partner**
43 **RIGHT TOUCH**, 8, b g Royal Applause—Amira **Nicholas Wrigley & Kevin Hart**
44 **ROYAL CONNOISSEUR (IRE)**, 7, b g Art Connoisseur (IRE)—Valferno (IRE) **Morebrooke Limited**
45 **ROYAL COSMIC**, 4, b f Wootton Bassett—Cosmic Case **The Cosmic Cases**
46 **RUBIS**, 5, ch m Monsieur Bond (IRE)—Princess Cocoa (IRE) **Mr & Mrs P. Ashton**
47 **SCOFFLAW**, 4, b g Foxwedge (AUS)—Belle des Airs (IRE) **P. Timmins & A. Rhodes Haulage**
48 **SCOTCH MYST**, 4, gr g Sepoy (AUS)—Shena's Dream (IRE) **Mrs V. C. Macdonald**
49 **SIR REGINALD BROWN**, 4, b g Archipenko (USA)—Elusive Sue (USA) **P. D. Smith Holdings Ltd**
50 **SOCIETY RED**, 4, ch g Arcano (IRE)—Idonea (CAN) **Mr M. J. Macleod**
51 **STAMP HILL (IRE)**, 5, b g Zoffany (IRE)—Edelfa (IRE) **Merchants and Missionaries**
52 **STARLIGHT ROMANCE (IRE)**, 4, b f Excelebration (IRE)—Takizada (IRE) **Mrs H. Steel**
53 **SUEGIOO (FR)**, 9, ch g Manduro (GER)—Mantesera (IRE) **Dr M. B. Q. S. Koukash**
54 **SUNNIA (IRE)**, 5, gr m Dark Angel (IRE)—Island Sunset (IRE) **Richard Fahey Ebor Racing Club Ltd**
55 **TATLISU (IRE)**, 8, b g Red Clubs (IRE)—Zwadi (IRE) **Middleham Park Racing LIV**
56 **THE FEATHERED NEST (IRE)**, 4, b f Dragon Pulse (IRE)—Jorum **Dr M. B. Q. S. Koukash**
57 **THIRD TIME LUCKY (IRE)**, 6, gr g Clodovil (IRE)—Speckled Hen (IRE) **The Musley Bank Partnership & Partner**
58 **TRUE COLORS**, 4, b g Sir Percy—Shesells Seashells **Smarden Thoroughbreds**
59 **WITHERNSEA (IRE)**, 7, b g Dark Angel (IRE)—Charlene Lacy (IRE) **Tiffin Sandwiches Limited & Partner**

THREE-YEAR-OLDS

60 **ALJADY (FR)**, b c Bated Breath—No Truth (IRE) **Al Shaqab Racing UK Limited**
61 **AMADEUS (IRE)**, gr c Fastnet Rock (AUS)—Alegra **Sir R. Ogden C.B.E., LLD**
62 **AMAZING MICHELE (FR)**, gr f Mastercraftsman (IRE)—Holy Freud (USA) **Nick Bradley Racing 40 & Partner**
63 **ARCTIC TREASURE (IRE)**, b g Iffraaj—Street Star (USA) **Percy / Green Racing 2**
64 **BENGALI BOYS (IRE)**, gr c Clodovil (IRE)—Caherassdotcom **Bardsley, Hyde & Tattersall**
65 **BRISK TEMPO (FR)**, b g Dabirsim (FR)—Allegro Vivace (FR) **Mr J. E. Dance**
66 **CAMEO STAR (IRE)**, ch g Camacho—Passionforfashion (IRE) **Let's Go Racing 2**
67 **CHIEF JUSTICE**, b g Acclamation—Freedom Pass (USA) **Cheveley Park Stud Limited**
68 **CHINGACHGOOK**, b c Al Kazeem—Natty Bumppo (IRE) **Mr W. A. Tinkler**
69 **CLUBBABLE**, b f Mayson—Invitee **Cheveley Park Stud Limited**
70 **CROTCHET**, gr f Lethal Force (IRE)—Humouresque **Cheveley Park Stud Limited**
71 **CROWNTHORPE**, b g Monsieur Bond (IRE)—Normandy Maid **Richard Fahey Ebor Racing Club Ltd**
72 **DANEHILL DESERT (IRE)**, b c Clodovil (IRE)—Misplace (IRE) **Percy/Green Racing**
73 **DAZE OUT (IRE)**, b f Acclamation—Maid To Order (IRE) **Johnson, Thornton, Thwaites**
74 **DELPH CRESCENT (IRE)**, gr g Dark Angel (IRE)—Zut Alors (IRE) **Tiffin Sandwiches Limited**
75 **DONTGIVEUPONBOB**, b g Pastoral Pursuits—Parsonagehotelyork (IRE) **P. D. Smith Holdings Ltd**
76 **DUBAI ACCLAIM (IRE)**, b c Acclamation—Bahati (IRE) **S & G Clayton**
77 **ENROLMENT**, b f Equiano (FR)—Enrol **Cheveley Park Stud Limited**
78 **FOOL FOR YOU (IRE)**, b f Lawman (FR)—Bosphorus Queen (IRE) **Mr J. E. Dance**
79 **FURZIG**, b g Monsieur Bond (IRE)—Princess Cocoa (IRE) **Mr & Mrs P. Ashton**
80 **GABRIAL THE SAINT (IRE)**, ch g Society Rock (IRE)—Green Briar (FR) **Dr M. B. Q. S. Koukash**
81 **GANGLAND**, gr g Lethal Force (IRE)—Miss Dutee **Merchants and Missionaries**
82 **GIVEN NAME**, b g Nathaniel (IRE)—Poly Pomona **Mr W. A. Tinkler**
83 **GREAT PROSPECTOR (IRE)**, b c Elzaam (AUS)—Guana (IRE) **Mr & Mrs J. D. Cotton**
84 **GRISE LIGHTNING (FR)**, gr f Wootton Bassett—Tenepia (FR) **Middleham Park Racing CXIX**
85 **I WAS ONLY JOKING (IRE)**, ch f Helmet (AUS)—Lady Angele (FR) **Middleham Park Racing XXXIV & K Sohi**
86 **INDOMENEO**, b c Piccolo—Cherrycombe-Row **Middleham Park Racing LX**
87 **INTERNATIONAL MAN**, b g Epaulette (AUS)—Right Answer **P. D. Smith Holdings Ltd**
88 **LADY NOORAH**, ch f Nathaniel (IRE)—Vital Statistics **M. Abdullah**
89 **MABO**, gr c Aussie Rules (USA)—Crochet (IRE) **Mr A. J. Ryan**
90 **MAGGIES ANGEL (IRE)**, b f Dark Angel (IRE)—Last Bid **P. D. Smith Holdings Ltd**
91 **MAYBRIDE**, b f Mayson—Wedding Party **Cheveley Park Stud Limited**
92 **MILITIA**, b c Equiano (FR)—Sweet As Honey **Middleham Park Racing CXVI & Partner**
93 **NARCOS (IRE)**, bl g Lethal Force (IRE)—Western Eyes (IRE) **Mr R. J. Arculli**
94 **NORMANDY BLUE**, b g Le Havre (FR)—Ballerina Blue (IRE) **Titanium Racing Club**
95 **OCEAN VOYAGE (IRE)**, b f Most Improved (IRE)—Minshar **Mr A. Harte**
96 **ODDS ON OLI**, b g Camelot—Red Blooded Woman (USA) **Mr Mike Browne & Mrs Dee Howe 1**
97 **OUR KID (IRE)**, b g Elnadim (USA)—Red Shoe **The Market Men**
98 **PARAMOUNT LOVE**, b f Pivotal—Portraitofmylove (IRE) **Mr H. Dalmook Al Maktoum**
99 **REGULATOR (IRE)**, b g Acclamation—Rasana **Cheveley Park Stud Limited**
100 **SANDS OF MALI (FR)**, b c Panis (USA)—Kadiania (FR) **The Cool Silk Partnership**

MR RICHARD FAHEY - Continued

101 **SAXONROAD BOY (USA)**, b g Mastercraftsman (IRE)—Good Strike (USA) **Mr Darren Barton & Partner**
102 **SEMPRE PRESTO (IRE)**, b f Nathaniel (IRE)—Flandre (USA) **Mrs H. Steel**
103 **SHOWMETHEDOUGH**, ch g Showcasing—Silver Purse **Dr M. B. Q. S. Koukash**
104 **SIOUX FRONTIER (IRE)**, b g Excelebration (IRE)—Sioux Rising (IRE) **Mrs U. Towell**
105 **SOSIAN**, b f Showcasing—Leonica **H. J. P. Farr**
106 **SPANISH MANE (IRE)**, b f Havana Gold (IRE)—Kiva **Mrs H. Steel**
107 **STREET SENSATION (IRE)**, b c Street Cry (IRE)—Sweet Hope (USA) **Titanium Racing Club**
108 **SUGAR COATING**, b f Dutch Art—Muscovado (USA) **Cheveley Park Stud Limited**
109 **SWISS BELLE**, b f Swiss Spirit—Belatorio (IRE) **Racegoers Club Owners Group**
110 **THE NAVIGATOR**, gr g Mastercraftsman (IRE)—Blessing (USA) **Sir R. Ogden C.B.E., LLD**
111 **THE RIGHT CHOICE (IRE)**, ch g Choisir (AUS)—Expedience (USA) **The Fairweather Foursome**
112 **TOMMY SHELBY (FR)**, b g Dabirsim (FR)—Interior (USA) **Nick Bradley Racing 34 & Partner**
113 **VENTURA DRAGON (IRE)**, ch g Dragon Pulse (IRE)—
                                           Dancing Duchess (IRE) **Middleham Park Racing XLII & Partner**
114 **VENTURA GOLD (IRE)**, b g Red Jazz (USA)—Desert Shine (IRE) **Middleham Park Racing XLVIII & Partner**
115 **WILDE OSCAR (IRE)**, b g Poet's Voice—Forthefirstime **Richard Fahey Ebor Racing Club Ltd**
116 **WINDSOR CROSS (IRE)**, gr g Camacho—Lizzy's Township (USA) **Mr A. Harte**
117 **WIRRAL GIRL (IRE)**, b f Kodiac—Ursula (IRE) **Ms A. Quinn**
118 **ZAP**, b g Mayson—Moonglow **P. Timmins**
119 **ZIP ALONG (IRE)**, b f Iffraaj—Wizz Up (IRE) **S. Ali**

Trainer did not wish details of his two-year-olds to appear

Other Owners: A. Rhodes Haulage Ltd, Mr W. P. Aitkenhead, Mrs P. Ashton, Mr P. Ashton, Mr D. Bardsley, Mr Darren Barton, Mr N. Bradley, Mr Steve Bradley, Mr Mike Browne, Mr I. T. Buchanan, Ms Amie Canham, Mr A. Clark, Mrs M. Clark-Wright, Mr Steven Clayton, Mrs G. A. Clayton, Mr E. Coll, Mr S. C. Corbett, Mr A. E. Corbett, Mr J. D. Cotton, Mrs B. Cotton, Mr M. Cressey, Mr P. S. Cresswell, Mr Garry Cuthbert, Mr John Dance, Mrs Christine Daurge, Mr Bernard Drinkall, Mr Sam Ellis, Facility Solutions Management Limited, Mr R. A. Fahey, Mr M. Feneron, Mrs Hilary Fitzsimons, Mr Brian W. Goodall, Mr J. D. Gordon, Mr David A. Green, Mrs Stella Hardman, Mr Dean Hardman, Mr David Harrison, Mr Roger Hart, Mr Kevin Hart, Havelock Racing 2, Miss S. Holden, Mr D. Holgate, Mrs Dee Howe, Mr K. Hubery, Mr G. R. Hunnam, Mr G. Hyde, Mr R. F. Johnson, Mrs Stef Keniry, Mr S. A. Kershaw, Mr N. D. Kershaw, Mr D. M. Knaggs, Mr P. Longstaff, Mr P.D. Macintosh, Mrs J Malcolmson, Ms Nicola Meese, Mr K. Mercer, Merchants and Missionaries, Middleham Park Racing CXVI, Middleham Park Racing XLVIII, Mrs P. A. Morrison, Mrs Margaret Nelson, Nick Bradley Racing 34, Nick Bradley Racing 40, Mr T. S. Palin, Mr M. Prince, Mr J. Rhodes, Mr Mel Roberts, Mr M. A. Scaife, Mr J. K. Shannon, Mr Jim Struth, Mr Peter Swann, Mr A. Tattersall, Mr P. Thompkins, Mr R. Thornton, Mr C. Thwaites, Tiffin Sandwiches Limited, Mr Peter Timmins, Mr Andrew Tinkler, Mr John Wicks, Mr David Wild, Mrs B. E. Wilkinson, Mr N. H. T. Wrigley.

Assistant Trainers: Robin O'Ryan, Jessica McLernon

Jockey (flat): Tony Hamilton, Paul Hanagan, Paddy Mathers, Barry McHugh, Jack Garritty, David Nolan.
Jockey (NH): Brian Hughes. Conditional: Jamie Hamilton. Apprentice: Connor Murtagh, Sebastian Woods.
Amateur: Miss Emily Bullock, Miss Fionn McSharry, Mr Matt Ennis.

---

188   MR CHRIS FAIRHURST, Middleham
Postal: **Glasgow House, Middleham, Leyburn, North Yorkshire, DL8 4QG**
Contacts: **PHONE/FAX (01969) 622039 MOBILE (07889) 410840**
E-MAIL cfairhurst@tiscali.co.uk

1 **CROWN AND GLORY (IRE)**, 11, b g Turtle Island (IRE)—Monteleena (IRE) **Mr & Mrs W. H. Woods**
2 **DANZELLA**, 6, b m Desideratum—Danzatrice **980 Racing**
3 **FLORENZA**, 5, b m Haafhd—Danzatrice **980 Racing**
4 **KATY ROYAL**, 6, b m King's Theatre (IRE)—Water Stratford (IRE) **Hugh T. Redhead**
5 **KAZOEY**, 5, b m Stimulation (IRE)—Dubawi's Spirit (IRE) **Mr A. Davies**
6 **SILVER GLEAM (IRE)**, 4, gr f Zoffany (IRE)—Gleaming Silver (IRE) **Miss B. C. Duxbury**
7 **SIXTIES STAR**, 4, b g Sixties Icon—Songbook **Mrs A. M. Leggett**
8 **SUPER CHARGE**, 6, ch g Recharge (IRE)—Arctic Ring **Mr & Mrs W. H. Woods**
9 **THACKERAY**, 11, b g Fasliyev (USA)—Chinon (IRE) **Mrs C. Arnold**
10 **THE ARMED MAN**, 5, b g Misu Bond (IRE)—Accamelia **Mrs C. Arnold**

THREE-YEAR-OLDS

11 **BENADALID**, b g Assertive—Gambatte **Mrs S. France**
12 **FRENCH SILK**, b f Pour Moi (IRE)—Green Silk (IRE) **The PQD Partnership**
13 **MOUNTAIN BREATH**, b f Bated Breath—Araminte **Mrs R. D. Peacock**
14 **THE GINGERBREADMAN**, b g Misu Bond (IRE)—Accamelia **Mrs C. Arnold**

MR CHRIS FAIRHURST - Continued

TWO-YEAR-OLDS

15 **FEEBI**, b f 28/4 Pour Moi (IRE)—Scorn (USA) (Seeking The Gold (USA)) (9000) **Mr A. Davies**

Other Owners: Mr M. D. Tozer, Mr J. M. Tozer, Mr W. H. Woods, Mrs G. H. Woods.

---

189 **MR JAMES R. FANSHAWE, Newmarket**
Postal: **Pegasus Stables, Snailwell Road, Newmarket, Suffolk, CB8 7DJ**
Contacts: **PHONE (01638) 664525 FAX (01638) 664523**
E-MAIL james@jamesfanshawe.com
WEBSITE www.jamesfanshawe.com / www.fredarcherracing.com

1 **COLONIAL CLASSIC (FR)**, 5, br m Dansili—Flame of Hestia (IRE) **Merry Fox Stud Limited**
2 **DEEP SEA (JPN)**, 4, b f Deep Impact (JPN)—Shamrocker (NZ) **Qatar Racing Limited**
3 **ENVISAGING (IRE)**, 4, b g Zoffany (IRE)—Star of Stars (IRE) **Mr Ben C. M. Wong**
4 **FLAMING MARVEL (IRE)**, 4, b g Redoute's Choice (AUS)—Flame of Hestia (IRE) **Merry Fox Stud Limited**
5 **GREAT WHITE SHARK (FR)**, 4, gr f Le Havre (IRE)—Trip To Fame (FR) **Mr Malcolm C. Denmark**
6 **HIGHER POWER**, 6, b g Rip Van Winkle (IRE)—Lady Stardust **Mrs Martin Armstrong**
7 **KNIGHT OWL**, 8, b g Rock of Gibraltar (IRE)—Miss Ivanhoe (IRE) **Miss Annabelle Condon**
8 **LADY BERGAMOT (IRE)**, 4, gr f Mastercraftsman (IRE)—Mahima (FR) **Andrew & Julia Turner**
9 **LORD GEORGE (IRE)**, 5, gr g Sir Percy—Mahima (FR) **Fred Archer Racing - Bend Or**
10 **MAGICAL DREAMER (IRE)**, 4, b f Acclamation—Double Fantasy (GER) **Fred Archer Racing - Ladylove**
11 **MASTER ARCHER (IRE)**, 4, gr g Mastercraftsman (IRE)—Kinigi (IRE) **Fred Archer Racing - Atlantic**
12 **MAZZINI**, 5, ch g Exceed And Excel (AUS)—Firenze **Mr & Mrs P Hopper, Mr & Mrs M Morris**
13 **MOD**, 4, b f Sixties Icon—Panna **Lord Halifax**
14 **NOBLE STAR (IRE)**, 5, b g Acclamation—Wrong Answer **Mr Tang Wai Bun Tony**
15 **POINTEL (FR)**, 5, b h Le Havre (IRE)—Polysheba (FR) **Swinburn, Godfrey & French**
16 **PTARMIGAN RIDGE**, 4, b g Kyllachy—Joshua's Princess **Fred Archer Racing - Energy**
17 **REGICIDE (IRE)**, 5, b g Archipenko (USA)—Armoise **Chris Van Hoorn Racing**
18 **SCOONES**, 4, ch g Sepoy (AUS)—Hannda (IRE) **Mr T R G Vestey**
19 **SITAR**, 4, b f Aqlaam—Soundwave **Manor Farm Stud & John Rose**
20 **STONEY BROKE**, 5, b m Dansili—Alvee (IRE) **Merry Fox Stud Limited**
21 **THE TIN MAN**, 6, b g Equiano (FR)—Persario **Fred Archer Racing - Ormonde**
22 **TRIBUTE ACT**, 4, b f Exceed And Excel (AUS)—Sister Act **Elite Racing Club**
23 **WARM OASIS**, 4, gr g Oasis Dream—Warling (IRE) **The Cool Silk Partnership**
24 **WOOTYHOOT (FR)**, 4, b g Wootton Bassett—Orlena (USA) **The Macaroni Beach Society**
25 **ZEST (IRE)**, 5, b m Duke of Marmalade (IRE)—Affinity **Elite Racing Club**

THREE-YEAR-OLDS

26 **ABEL SEAMAN**, b g Henrythenavigator (USA)—Helter Helter (USA) **Chris Van Hoorn Racing**
27 **BLUE REFLECTION**, br f Dansili—Alvee (IRE) **Merry Fox Stud Limited**
28 **BOMBYX**, ch c Sir Percy—Bombazine (IRE) **Mr and Mrs A. E. Pakenham**
29 **CHARLES FOX**, b g Power—Jouet **Mrs Mary Slack**
30 **CHETWYND ABBEY**, b f Nathaniel (IRE)—Chetwynd (IRE) **Mr Guy S Shropshire**
31 **CLOSE FOR COMFORT**, b c Dawn Approach (IRE)—Close At Hand **Normandie Stud Ltd**
32 **CUILLIN (USA)**, b f Arch (USA)—Zahrah (USA) **Dr J. P. Ryan**
33 **DESTINATA**, b f Canford Cliffs (IRE)—Hurricane Lady (IRE) **Mr Borgatti & Mr Moir**
34 **DUCHESS OF AVON**, ch f Dutch Art—Avon Lady **Meon Valley Stud**
35 **EXCELLERATION (IRE)**, b g Excelebration (IRE)—Lulawin **Fred Archer Racing-Trappist**
36 **FEARN'S PIPPIN**, b f Dubawi (IRE)—Flawly **Apple Tree Stud**
37 **FONDEST**, b f Mayson—Fondled **Cheveley Park Stud**
38 B f Siyouni (FR)—Gipson Dessert (USA) **Mr Malcolm C. Denmark**
39 **HARRY'S BAR**, ch c Exceed And Excel (AUS)—Firenze **Jan and Peter Hopper**
40 B c Mastercraftsman (IRE)—Herboriste **Mr Malcolm C. Denmark**
41 **HYPERACTIVE**, b f Rip Van Winkle (IRE)—Miss Dashwood **Helena Springfield Ltd**
42 **INDIAN TYGRESS**, b f Sepoy (AUS)—Persario **Elizabeth Grundy & Rosie Manning**
43 **INSURGENCE**, ch g Sepoy (AUS)—Isis (USA) **Dr Catherine Wills & Frederik Tylicki**
44 **IRISH MADAM**, ch f Equiano (FR)—Irish Light (USA) **Newsells Park Stud & Mrs Emma Capon**
45 **LILYPAD (IRE)**, b f New Approach (IRE)—Vow **Mrs A. M. Swinburn**
46 **LOVED SO MUCH**, b f Dansili—Wannabe Loved **Normandie Stud Ltd**
47 **MAGISTRATE (IRE)**, b c Cape Cross (IRE)—Marlinka **Elite Racing Club**
48 **MAINSAIL ATLANTIC (USA)**, b c Speightstown (USA)—Minakshi (FR) **Mrs Amelie Ehrnrooth**
49 **MANTOVANI (FR)**, b g High Chaparral (IRE)—Ripley (GER) **Qatar Racing Limited**
50 **MERCHANT OF VENICE**, b c Bated Breath—Isola Verde **Mr & Mrs P Hopper, Mr & Mrs M Morris**

MR JAMES R. FANSHAWE - Continued

51 **PEGASUS KID**, ch g Motivator—Caribbean Pearl (USA) **Mr Mohamed Obaida**
52 **PRAXEDIS**, b f Dutch Art—Angel Song **Mr P S Ryan**
53 **PREENING**, b f Dutch Art—Striving (IRE) **Cheveley Park Stud**
54 **SLEEPING LION (USA)**, ch c Teofilo (IRE)—Flame of Hestia (IRE) **Merry Fox Stud Limited**
55 **SOCIETY PRINCE (IRE)**, b g Society Rock (IRE)—Princess Atoosa (USA) **Fred Archer Racing - Melton**
56 **SPANISH ARCHER (FR)**, b g Lope de Vega (IRE)—Parcelle Perdue (FR) **Fred Archer Racing - Iroquois**
57 **SPORTING BELLE (IRE)**, b c Society Rock (IRE)—Pandoras Secret (IRE) **Mr Simon Gibson**
58 **TEASER**, b c Dansili—Tottie **Mr J H Richmond-Watson**
59 **THE HIEROPHANT**, b g Exceed And Excel (AUS)—Queen of Pentacles (IRE) **Normandie Stud Ltd**
60 **THE PINTO KID (FR)**, b g High Chaparral (IRE)—Lake Palace **Fred Archer Racing - Bruce**
61 **VISOR**, b g Helmet (AUS)—Entitlement **Dr Catherine Wills & Frederik Tylicki**
62 **VOLUMINOUS**, b f Nathaniel (IRE)—Capacious **Cheveley Park Stud**

TWO-YEAR-OLDS

63 B f 8/3 Dream Ahead (USA)—
　　　　　　Badr Al Badoor (IRE) (Acclamation) (38000) **Fred Archer Racing - Wheel of Fortune**
64 **CARNIVAL ROSE**, b f 24/2 Harbour Watch (IRE)—Gypsy Carnival (Trade Fair) **Evelyn, Duchess of Sutherland**
65 B c 24/4 Fast Company (IRE)—Chirkova (USA) (Sadler's Wells (USA)) (75000) **Mrs A. M. Swinburn**
66 B c 8/2 Sea The Moon (GER)—Diablerette (Green Desert (USA)) (80000) **Mr Hubert Strecker**
67 B f 27/1 Dawn Approach (IRE)—Dubai Cyclone (Bernardini (USA)) (45000) **Mr Mohamed Obaida**
68 **EDIFICE**, b f 9/4 Dutch Art—Palatial (Green Desert (USA)) **Cheveley Park Stud**
69 **ENTRUSTING**, b c 18/4 Nathaniel (IRE)—
　　　　　　Royal Empress (IRE) (Holy Roman Emperor (IRE)) (110000) **Mr Ben C. M. Wong**
70 **EXCELLED (IRE)**, b f 6/1 Exceed And Excel (AUS)—
　　　　　　Elle Woods (IRE) (Lawman (FR)) (81400) **Fred Archer Racing - Spinaway**
71 **GASLIGHT**, br f 28/3 Aussie Rules (USA)—Isis (USA) (Royal Academy (USA)) **Dr Catherine Wills**
72 B f 21/4 Wootton Bassett—Green Bananas (FR) (Green Tune (USA)) (101750) **Mrs A. M. Swinburn**
73 B f 26/2 Archipenko (USA)—Green Room (FR) (In The Wings) **Nigel & Carolyn Elwes**
74 **KEYHAVEN**, b f 10/4 Raven's Pass (USA)—New Nforest (Oasis Dream) **Elite Racing Club**
75 **KNOWING**, b c 23/3 Pour Moi (IRE)—Wedding Speech (IRE) (Acclamation) **G and Mrs L G Marney**
76 Ch f 28/2 Excelebration (IRE)—Mahima (FR) (Linamix (FR)) (36630) **Andrew & Julia Turner**
77 **OLYMPIC CONQUEROR (IRE)**, b c 12/4 Olympic Glory (IRE)—
　　　　　　Queen's Conquer (King's Best (USA)) (85000) **The Cool Silk Partnership**
78 **PAMPER**, b f 21/1 Lethal Force (USA)—Cosseted (Pivotal) **Cheveley Park Stud**
79 **SINCERITY**, b f 25/3 Iffraaj—Affinity (Sadler's Wells (USA)) **Elite Racing Club**
80 **SKERRYVORE**, gr b 15/3 Toronado (IRE)—Succinct (Hector Protector (USA)) (15000) **Dr Catherine Wills**
81 **SWEET PROMISE**, b f 18/1 Intello (GER)—Penny Rose (Danehill Dancer (IRE)) (65000) **Mr A. Boyd-Rochfort**
82 **VIBRANCE**, b f 1/2 Nathaniel (IRE)—Park Crystal (IRE) (Danehill (USA)) (37000) **Cheveley Park Stud**

Other Owners: Mr Geoffrey Baber, Mr Michael Beaumont, Mrs Denise Beetles, Mrs Mary Benjafield, Mrs Tina Blockley, Mr John Bodie, Mr Robert Boyce, The Hon Mrs Penny Butler, Mr Isidore Carivalis, Ms Emma Coutts, Mr Alex Davidson, Mrs Olivia Davidson, Mrs Tessa Deriziotis, Mr Roy Eady, Mrs Libby Fanshawe, Mr Brian Fanshawe, Mrs Georgie Fanshawe, Mr Patrick Forward, Mr Tony Francis, Mrs Susan French, Mr Colin Gilbert, Mrs Gillian Godfrey, Mr Haydn Gott, Mr Guy Gredley, Mr Robert Grove, Mr Terry Hart, Mr Steve Hewitt, Mrs Sue Human, Mr Mike King, Mrs Jenny King, Mrs Sarah King, Mr Arne Korsbakken, Mr Tim Law, Mr Bill Lemon, Mr Niall Lynch, Mr Dan Marney, Mr A Massen, Mr S Massen, Ms Lee Masters, Mr Michael McDonnell, Mr & Mrs John Mitchell, Mr Gordon Papworth, Mr Ian Pittaway, Mr Bill Rogerson, Mrs Pat Rowley, Ms Sarah Russell, Mr David Russell, Mr William Russell, Mr Ulf Ryden, Ms Hermione Scrope, Mr Nigel Smith, Mr Rob Stevens, Mr Richard Stevens, Mrs Camilla Stroud, Mr Peter Tarrant, Mr Tam Murray Thriepland, Mr Tom Trew Smith, The Lady Vestey.

Assistant Trainer: Kevin Philippart De Foy

Apprentice: George Wood.

---

190 | **MR JOHNNY FARRELLY, Midford**
Postal: Upper Twinhoe Farm, Midford, Bath, Avon, BA2 8QX
Contacts: **PHONE (01278) 671782 MOBILE (07811) 113363**

1 **ABLAZING (IRE)**, 7, b g Mastercraftsman (IRE)—Moore's Melody (IRE) **Hanford's Chemist Ltd**
2 **ALI THE HUNTER (IRE)**, 5, ch m Papal Bull—Polish Spring (IRE) **Mr J. Farrelly**
3 **ALL TOGETHER (FR)**, 7, ch g Zambezi Sun—Mareha (IRE) **Mrs Z. Wentworth**
4 **AMBRE DES MARAIS (FR)**, 8, ch m Network (GER)—Fee des Marais (FR) **Monday Boys Partnership**
5 **AND THE NEW (IRE)**, 7, b g Kalanisi (IRE)—Wheredidthemoneygo (IRE) **Mr P. A. Randall**
6 **ASCENDANT**, 12, ch g Medicean—Ascendancy **F. A. Clegg**

MR JOHNNY FARRELLY - Continued

7 **BATHWICK BRAVE (IRE)**, 11, b g Westerner—Dorans Grove **Mr J. Farrelly**
8 **BEAST**, 4, b g Makfi—Wunders Dream (IRE) **Top Hat Racing Club**
9 **BERMEO (IRE)**, 7, b g Definite Article—Miss Blueyes (IRE) **Mr R. E. Stuart-Jervis**
10 **BIG OPTION**, 6, b g Recharge (IRE)—Just Jenny (IRE) **Mr F. Walsh**
11 **BLACK FRANKS ANGEL**, 8, b m Black Sam Bellamy (IRE)—City of Angels **R. S. Brookhouse**
12 **BLUE N YELLOW (IRE)**, 5, b g Jeremy (USA)—Bluemamba (USA) **R. S. Brookhouse**
13 **COEUR DE BRUME (FR)**, 6, b g Saint des Saints (FR)—Mabelle Lescribaa (FR) **Mrs Z. Wentworth**
14 **CROWN HILL (IRE)**, 8, b g Definite Article—Silver Prayer (IRE) **Hanford's Chemist Ltd**
15 **D'PINESFLYER (IRE)**, 6, b m Westerner—Diskretion (GER) **Mr J. McMahon**
16 **DALASIRI (IRE)**, 9, gr g Dylan Thomas (IRE)—Dalataya (IRE) **Ms E. Reidy**
17 **DRIVE ON LOCKY (IRE)**, 11, b g Milan—Husyans Beauty (IRE) **Mr P. M. Tosh**
18 **FINISH THE STORY (IRE)**, 12, b g Court Cave—Lady of Grange (IRE) **Top Hat Racing Club**
19 **FOOL TO CRY (IRE)**, 5, ch m Fast Company (IRE)—
                      Islandagore (IRE) **Market Avenue Racing Club & Brian Dunn**
20 **GINGILI**, 8, b g Beat All (USA)—Gentian **Mr & Mrs Paul & Clare Rooney**
21 **JUMP AND JUMP (IRE)**, 8, br m Oscar (IRE)—My Twist (IRE) **Market Avenue Racing Club Ltd**
22 **JUSTICE SUPER (IRE)**, 5, b g Jeremy (USA)—Supercat (IRE) **BG Racing Partnership**
23 **KALASKADESEMILLEY**, 6, b m Myboycharlie (IRE)—Congressional (IRE) **C. Cheesman**
24 **LADY MAKFI (IRE)**, 6, b m Makfi—Dulcet Tones (IRE) **Mr J. McMahon**
25 **LAKE SHORE DRIVE (IRE)**, 6, b g Thewayyouare (USA)—Labrusca **Mr P. M. Tosh**
26 **LILLIPUT LANE (IRE)**, 6, b m Yeats (IRE)—Charade (IRE) **Mr J. Farrelly**
27 **LOVE THE LEADER (IRE)**, 10, b g Fruits of Love (USA)—Suelena (IRE) **Mr J. Farrelly**
28 **MAGNUS ROMEO**, 7, b g Manduro (GER)—Chili Dip **Mr R. E. Stuart-Jervis**
29 **MARVELLOUS MONTY (IRE)**, 8, br m Oscar (IRE)—Montys Miss (IRE) **Hanford's Chemist Ltd**
30 **MONEY FOR NOTHING**, 9, b g Kayf Tara—Top of The Dee **Top Hat Racing Club**
31 **MR LANDO**, 9, b g Shirocco (GER)—Capitana (GER) **The Lansdowners**
32 **PENSION MADNESS (IRE)**, 5, b g Vocalised (USA)—Grinneas (IRE) **F. A. Clegg**
33 **PINKIE BROWN (FR)**, 6, gr g Gentlewave (IRE)—Natt Musik (FR) **B. Dunn**
34 **POLISHED ROCK (IRE)**, 8, ch g Rock of Gibraltar (IRE)—Where We Left Off **Mr J. McMahon**
35 **RETRIEVE (AUS)**, 11, b g Rahy (USA)—Hold To Ransom (USA) **Tim & Liz Heal**
36 **SANDFORD CASTLE (IRE)**, 8, b g Norwich—Pegs Polly (IRE) **Live The Life**
37 **SPARKLING DAWN**, 6, gr m Sulamani (IRE)—Clotted Cream (USA) **Live The Life - Atlas**
38 **SPORTING BOY (IRE)**, 10, b g Barathea (IRE)—Sportsticketing (IRE) **H. M. W. Clifford**
39 **SYNDEX (IRE)**, 5, b m Frozen Power (IRE)—Zankara (FR) **Boys In Orange**
40 **VALSE AU TAILLONS (FR)**, 5, b m Montmartre (FR)—Eyaelle (FR) **Hanford's Chemist Ltd**
41 **WESTERN SUNRISE (IRE)**, 9, b m Westerner—Presenting Gayle (IRE) **Mr D. J. Adams**
42 **YOURE ALWAYS RIGHT (IRE)**, 5, b m Pour Moi (IRE)—Zaraba (IRE) **Mr & Mrs Paul & Clare Rooney**
43 **ZERO GRAND (IRE)**, 7, b g Thousand Words—Ellistown Lady (IRE) **H. M. W. Clifford**

Other Owners: J. F. Baldwin, Mrs S. L. Boyle, Mr P. Boyle, Mr P. Duffy, Mr D. Goodman, Mr T. Heal, Mrs E. A. Heal, Mr G. R. Heapy, Mr A. Knowles, Mr P. McGuinness, Mr P. A. Rooney, Mrs C. Rooney, Mr T. Rowsell, Mr M. A. Watson, R. T. Wilkins.

191 MS DEBORAH FAULKNER, Newport
Postal: **Craig-Y-Ceiliog Farm, Bettws, Newport, Gwent, NP20 7AE**

1 **BEALLANDENDALL (IRE)**, 10, b g Beneficial—Railstown Lady (IRE) **Ms D. C. Faulkner**
2 **COURTINTHEMIDDLE (IRE)**, 7, b g Court Cave—Kilmessan (IRE) **T. P. Faulkner**
3 **DINO BOY (FR)**, 5, b g Diamond Boy (FR)—Odeline (FR) **T. P. Faulkner**
4 **GOLDANBLEU (IRE)**, 5, b g Gold Well—Lisa Bleu (IRE) **T. P. Faulkner**
5 **GUN SHY (IRE)**, 10, b g Norwich—Debbies Scud (IRE) **T. P. Faulkner**
6 **OUTSMARTIN (IRE)**, 6, b br g Marienbard (IRE)—Fair Gina (IRE) **T. P. Faulkner**
7 **POLYMATH (IRE)**, 7, ch g Stowaway—Godlylady (IRE) **T. P. Faulkner**
8 **SPIN THE BEAT**, 8, b g Beat All (USA)—Little Red Spider **Ms D. C. Faulkner**
9 **STANZA BOY (IRE)**, 6, b g Stowaway—Lisa Bleu (IRE) **T. P. Faulkner**
10 **THOMAS CROWN (IRE)**, 4, b g Helmet (AUS)—Picture of Lily **T. P. Faulkner**
11 **UNION JACK D'YCY (FR)**, 10, b g Bonnet Rouge (FR)—Jacady (FR) **T. P. Faulkner**

192 MISS JULIA FEILDEN, Newmarket

Postal: Harraton Stud, Laceys Lane, Exning, Newmarket, Suffolk, CB8 7HW
Contacts: PHONE (01638) 577040 FAX (01638) 577040 MOBILE (07974) 817694
E-MAIL juliafeilden@aol.com WEBSITE www.juliafeildenracing.com

1 BEST EXAMPLE (USA), 6, ch g King's Best (USA)—Born Something (IRE) The Fourth Sector Pathfinders
2 CANDESTA (USA), 8, b g First Defence (USA)—Wandesta Mrs J. E. Lambert
3 CHAMPAGNE REEF, 4, gr f Literato (FR)—Kritzia Mrs C. T. Bushnell
4 GATILLO, 5, gr g Showcasing—Crystal Gale (IRE) Jakes Family
5 GO ON GAL (IRE), 5, b m Approve (IRE)—Jeritza Go On Gal Partnership
6 LIMERICK LORD (IRE), 6, b g Lord Shanakill (USA)—Hollow Green (IRE) Steve Clarke & Partner
7 MAAZEL (IRE), 4, b g Elzaam (AUS)—Laylati (IRE) Newmarket Equine Tours Racing Club
8 MAJESTIC MOON (IRE), 8, b g Majestic Missile (IRE)—Gala Style (IRE) Ahamed Farook & Partners
9 OCEANUS (IRE), 4, b g Born To Sea (IRE)—Alkhawarah (USA) Good Company Partnership
10 OUD METHA BRIDGE (IRE), 4, ch g Helmet (AUS)—Central Force In It To Win Partnership
11 OUR CILLA, 4, gr f Sixties Icon—Kinetix Mrs Carol Bushnell
12 PITCH HIGH (IRE), 4, br g Requinto (IRE)—Distant Skies Stowstowquickquickstow Partnership
13 SECRET STRATEGY (IRE), 4, b g Kodiac—Shall We Tell The Strategists
14 SPIRIT OF SARWAN (IRE), 4, b g Elzaam (AUS)—Hidden Heart Mr & Mrs G. Bhatti
15 SUNSET BOUNTY, 4, b f Bahamian Bounty—Sunset Kitty (USA) Steve Clarke & Partners 3
16 TALLULAH'S QUEST (IRE), 4, b f Tagula (IRE)—Sarin Dubhe (IRE) The Sultans of Speed

THREE-YEAR-OLDS

17 BOXATRICKS (IRE), b g Arakan (USA)—Million To One (IRE) Million To One Partnership
18 CASEY BANTER, b br f Holy Roman Emperor (IRE)—
                                        Sinister Ruckus (USA) Newmarket Equine Tours Racing Club
19 GAS MONKEY, b g Cityscape—Bavarica Newmarket Equine Tours Racing Club
20 LULU STAR (IRE), b f Oasis Dream—Jeanie Johnston (IRE) T. Healy
21 SIR FRED (IRE), gr c Born To Sea (IRE)—Diamond Line (FR) Mrs C. T. Bushnell
22 TERRI RULES (IRE), b f Camacho—Hawaiian Storm Raymond Treacy & Partner

TWO-YEAR-OLDS

23 B f 22/2 Paco Boy (IRE)—Amy Winehorse (Reset (AUS)) (3500) A Partnership
24 DELL'S BOY, b c 24/5 Epaulette (AUS)—
                                  Bushy Dell (IRE) (King Charlemagne (USA)) (571) Newmarket Equine Tours Racing Club
25 HIGHWAY ROBBERY, gr g 11/3 Dick Turpin (IRE)—Minty Fox (Dalakhani (IRE)) (5000) Mrs Carol Bushnell
26 PAINTBALL WIZARD (IRE), ch c 28/4 Mastercraftsman (IRE)—
                                  Dance Avenue (IRE) (Sadler's Wells (USA)) (10500) Mrs Carol Bushnell & Partners
27 RAHA, b f 1/4 Mukhadram—Cefira (USA) (Distant View (USA)) (3000) Ahamed Farook & Julia Feilden

Other Owners: Mr George Bhatti, Mrs Caroline Bhatti, Mr R. Birkett, Mr J. Birkett, Mr S. Clarke, Mr Ahamed Farook, Mr Jeremy Jakes, Mrs Tonie Jakes, Mr Chris Page, Mr Eddie Partridge, Ms Hannah Ranner, Mrs A. S. Styles, Mr R. Treacy, Mr R. Weston, Mr Tony Wideson, Mr R. Wright.

Assistant Trainer: Ross Birkett

Jockey (flat): Adam Beschizza. Apprentice: Shelley Birkett. Amateur: Mr R. Birkett.

193 MR ROGER FELL, Nawton

Postal: Arthington Barn House, Highfield Lane, Nawton, York, North Yorkshire, YO62 7TU
Contacts: PHONE (01439) 770184

1 BEADLAM (IRE), 5, ch m Frozen Power (IRE)—Pivotal Role Smarty Socks Racing
2 BURNT SUGAR (IRE), 6, b g Lope de Vega (IRE)—Lady Livius (IRE) Middleham Park Racing XL & Partner
3 CLUB WEXFORD (IRE), 7, b g Lawman (FR)—Masnada (IRE) Mr R. G. Fell
4 DAPPER MAN (IRE), 4, b g Dandy Man (IRE)—Gist (IRE) Mr R. G. Fell
5 ELUSIVE HEIGHTS (IRE), 5, b g Elusive Pimpernel (USA)—
                                        Berg Bahn (IRE) Middleham Park Racing LXI & Partner 2
6 FLORENCIO, 5, b g Equiano (FR)—Mary Pekan (USA) Colne Valley Racing & Partner
7 GUARDIA SVIZZERA (IRE), 4, b g Holy Roman Emperor (IRE)—
                                        Winged Harriet (IRE) Ventura Racing 7 & Partner
8 HAROME (IRE), 4, ch g Bahamian Bounty—Clytha Mr R. G. Fell
9 IMAGINE IF (IRE), 4, br g Dream Ahead (USA)—Bogini (IRE) High Hopes 2017
10 INNER CIRCLE (IRE), 4, b c Choisir (AUS)—Eternity Ring Ventura Racing 6 & Partner
11 JUSTICE PLEASING, 5, b g Kodiac—Spangle Mr R. G. Fell

MR ROGER FELL - Continued

12 **KODY RIDGE (IRE)**, 4, b g Kodiac—Top Of The Ridge (IRE) **Northern Marking Ltd & Partners**
13 **KUPA RIVER (IRE)**, 4, b g Big Bad Bob (IRE)—Lamanka Lass (USA) **Middleham Park Racing LXXII & Partner**
14 **LOZAH**, 5, b m Lawman (FR)—Princess Luna (GER) **Trendy Ladies**
15 **MEMORIES GALORE (IRE)**, 6, b g Invincible Spirit (IRE)—Persian Memories (IRE) **High Hopes 2017**
16 **MUATADEL**, 5, b g Exceed And Excel (AUS)—Rose Blossom **Mr R. G. Fell**
17 **MULLIGATAWNY (IRE)**, 5, b g Lope de Vega (IRE)—Wild Whim (IRE) **Middleham Park Racing LI & Partner**
18 **MUNTADAB (IRE)**, 6, b g Invincible Spirit (IRE)—Chibola (ARG) **Fell & High Hopes Partnership**
19 **MUQARRED (USA)**, 6, b br g Speightstown (USA)—Bawaara (FR) **Mr R. G. Fell**
20 **PRESIDENTIAL (IRE)**, 4, b g Invincible Spirit (IRE)—Poetical (IRE) **Mr R. G. Fell**
21 **SHERIFF OF NAWTON (IRE)**, 7, b g Lawman (FR)—Pivotal Role **Mr R. G. Fell**
22 **TADAAWOL**, 5, b g Kyllachy—Bright Edge **Fell, Hamilton & Smeaton**
23 **TWO FOR TWO (IRE)**, 10, b g Danehill Dancer (IRE)—D'articleshore (IRE) **Fell & Kelvin**
24 **URBAN SPIRIT (IRE)**, 4, b g Born To Sea (IRE)—Rose of Mooncoin (IRE) **Mr & Mrs G. Turnball**
25 **ZIHAAM**, 4, ch g Dutch Art—Hymnsheet **Nick Bradley Racing 29 & Partner**
26 **ZODIAKOS (IRE)**, 5, b g Kodiac—Zonic **Mr C Varley & Mr R G Fell**
27 **ZYLAN (IRE)**, 6, ch g Kyllachy—Belgique (IRE) **Mr R. G. Fell**

THREE-YEAR-OLDS

28 **AMERICAN RUBY (USA)**, b f Data Link (USA)—Fifth Avenue Doll (USA) **Mr R. G. Fell**
29 **CAMDEN TOWN (IRE)**, ch g New Approach (IRE)—Antique (IRE) **The First Of May Crew**
30 **CHEF UNITED**, b f Swiss Spirit—Eurolinka (IRE) **BGC Racing Xiv & Partner**
31 **ELIXSOFT (IRE)**, b f Elzaam (AUS)—Grandegrandegrande (IRE) **Middleham Park Racing CXIII & Partner**
32 **MOLLY MAYHEM**, ch f Casamento (IRE)—Inez **Nick Bradley Racing 42**
33 B f Teofilo (IRE)—Ninja Lady **Nick Bradley Racing 41**
34 **PLANSINA**, b f Planteur (IRE)—Sina (GER) **Miss V. Greetham**
35 **SHEF WEDSNEIGH (IRE)**, b f Choisir (AUS)—Tullawadgeen (IRE) **BGC Racing & Partner 1**
36 **SIENNA SAYS**, b f Bated Breath—Broughtons Charm (IRE) **BGC Racing**

TWO-YEAR-OLDS

37 Ch c 22/4 Dawn Approach (IRE)—Antique (IRE) (Dubai Millennium) (4069) **Mr R. G. Fell**
38 B c 8/3 Bungle Inthejungle—Magical Bupers (IRE) (Intikhab (USA)) (12209)
39 B f 31/3 Zebedee—Novelina (IRE) (Fusaichi Pegasus (USA)) (3662) **Mr R. G. Fell**
40 **STYLE DANCER (IRE)**, b f 14/4 Style Vendome (FR)—Dansalong (IRE) (Azamour (IRE))
41 B c 4/2 Sir Prancealot (IRE)—Sunny Harbor (IRE) (Indian Haven) (10000) **Mr R.G. Fell & Mr K Hamilton**
42 **THE GABBA (IRE)**, b c 15/4 Vocalised (USA)—
                                        Style Queen (IRE) (Galileo (IRE)) (13837) **Mr S Greenhalgh & Northern Marking Ltd**

Other Owners: Mrs P. M. A. Avison, BGC Racing XIV, Mr N. Bradley, Mr L. H. Christie, Colne Valley Racing, Mr T. Denham, Mr M. P. Glass, Mr S. Greenhalgh, Mr K. Hamilton, Miss S. Holden, Mrs M. Ireland, Mr A. S. Kelvin, Mr P. M. Lockwood, Middleham Park Racing CXIII, Middleham Park Racing LI, Middleham Park Racing LXI, Middleham Park Racing LXXII, Middleham Park Racing XL, Nick Bradley Racing 29, Northern Marking Ltd, T. S. Palin, M. Prince, Mr R. J. Smeaton, Mrs N. J. Smith, Mr D. Smith, Mr M. Taylor, Mrs S. E. Turnball, Mr G. Turnball, Mr C. J. Varley, Ventura Racing 6, Ventura Racing 7, Mr R. Ward, Mr I. K. White.

---

194 MR CHARLIE FELLOWES, Newmarket

Postal: St. Gatien Cottage, Vicarage Road, Newmarket, Suffolk, CB8 8HP
Contacts: **PHONE** (01638) 666948 **MOBILE** (07968) 499596
E-MAIL charlie@charliefellowesracing.co.uk **WEBSITE** www.charliefellowesracing.co.uk

1 **ACCESSION (IRE)**, 9, b g Acclamation—Pivotal's Princess (IRE) **Lady De Ramsey**
2 **BUCKLAND BEAU**, 7, b g Rock of Gibraltar—Heavenly Whisper (IRE) **Mr P. S. McNally**
3 **CAROLINAE**, 5, ch m Makfi—You Too **The Dalmunzie Devils Partnership**
4 **CHIEFOFCHIEFS**, 5, b g Royal Applause—Danvers **M. L. Ayers**
5 **CRIMSON ROSETTE (IRE)**, 4, b f Teofilo (IRE)—Crimson Ribbon (USA) **A. E. Oppenheimer**
6 **FEATHERY**, 4, b f Teofilo (IRE)—Huma Bird
7 **FIRE TREE (IRE)**, 5, b g Cacique (IRE)—Monicalew **Never So Bold**
8 **FRENZIFIED**, 6, b m Yeats (IRE)—Librettista (USA) **Mr D. Pearson**
9 **LIGHT LAUGHTER (IRE)**, 4, ch f Distorted Humor (USA)—
                                        Sense of Purpose (IRE) **Mr D. O'Callaghan Yeomanstown Stud**
10 **LOVE ME AGAIN**, 4, b f Kheleyf (USA)—Midnight Allure **M. L. Ayers**
11 **MIA TESORO (IRE)**, 5, b m Danehill Dancer (IRE)—Souter's Sister (IRE) **Mr D. Pearson**
12 **OOTY HILL**, 5, gr g Dubawi (IRE)—Mussoorie (FR) **A. E. Oppenheimer**
13 **PRINCE OF ARRAN**, 5, b g Shirocco (GER)—Storming Sioux **Mr S. M. bel Obaida**

MR CHARLIE FELLOWES - Continued

14 **REPERCUSSION,** 5, b g Manduro (GER)—Summertime Legacy **Seventh Lap Racing & Partners**
15 **SPUN GOLD,** 4, ch g Exceed And Excel (AUS)—Victoire Celebre (USA) **Joe Soiza & Mason Soiza**

THREE-YEAR-OLDS

16 **BUBBLY,** b f Excelebration (IRE)—Baralinka (IRE) **Elite Racing Club**
17 **BUCKLAND BOY (IRE),** b c Bated Breath—Rancho Montoya (IRE) **Mr P. S. McNally**
18 **CARNWENNAN (IRE),** b c Cacique (IRE)—Slieve **Mr K. F. V. Kong**
19 **ESCALATOR,** b c Cape Cross (IRE)—Sayyedati Symphony (USA) **Mr S. M. bel Obaida**
20 **FREEROLLING,** ch c Exceed And Excel (AUS)—Overturned **Three Of A Kind**
21 **HAVERLAND (IRE),** b g Big Bad Bob (IRE)—Pivotal's Princess (IRE) **Lady De Ramsey**
22 **IN DEMAND (IRE),** b c Dalakhani (IRE)—Fleur de Cactus (IRE) **The Yes Men**
23 **JEREMIAH,** ch c Kheleyf (USA)—Tessie **M. L. Ayers**
24 **LADY AL THUMAMA,** gr f Leroidesanimaux (BRZ)—Mrs Micawber **Al Thumama Racing**
25 **LADY OF ARAN (IRE),** b f Sir Prancealot (IRE)—
                                    Tipperary Boutique (IRE) **O'Callaghan Bengough Horsford Capon**
26 **LADY SAFEARA,** b f Holy Roman Emperor (IRE)—Empress Anna (IRE) **Al Thumama Racing**
27 **MACGREGOR'S PAL,** b c Royal Applause—Bridge Pal **Miss E. G. MacGregor**
28 **PACO'S PRINCE,** b c Paco Boy (IRE)—Equitissa (IRE) **Stewart Turner & Amanda Wilson-Martin**
29 **PASSEGIATA,** b f Mastercraftsman (IRE)—Souter's Sister (IRE) **Mr D. Pearson**
30 **RAMSBURY,** b g Dansili—Disco Volante **A. E. Oppenheimer**
31 **THE BEARFIGHTER (IRE),** b g Society Rock (IRE)—Absolute Fun (IRE) **The Bearfighters**
32 **TREASURE ME,** b f Poet's Voice—Treasured Dream **Normandie Stud Ltd**
33 **VICE MARSHAL (IRE),** b c Wootton Bassett—Celsius Degre (IRE) **M Hughes, A Frost & P Gauthier**
34 **WISE FOX,** gr g Foxwedge (AUS)—Daheeya **Biddestone Racing XVI**

TWO-YEAR-OLDS

35 **CRIMEAN QUEEN,** b f 15/2 Iffraaj—Victoria Cross (IRE) (Mark of Esteem (IRE)) **A. E. Oppenheimer**
36 **GARRYOWEN,** b c 20/3 Garswood—
                        Lomapamar (Nashwan (USA)) (17000) **Mrs Emma Capon, Tom Wilson, John Eastwood**
37 Ch c 6/2 Showcasing—Moving Sea (IRE) (Rock of Gibraltar (IRE)) (58000) **Never so Bold & Sohi**
38 B c 15/3 Famous Name—Neutral (Beat Hollow) (17907) **Never so Bold - Aquino**
39 **RUDY LEWIS (IRE),** b c 27/1 Excelebration (IRE)—Bless You (Bahamian Bounty) (36629)
40 B c 20/4 Epaulette (AUS)—Sarah Park (IRE) (Redback) (20000) **Never so Bold - Aquino**
41 B c 18/3 Charm Spirit (IRE)—Sassy Gal (IRE) (King's Best (USA)) (42000) **Ed Player Whatton Manor Stud**
42 B f 23/2 Kodiac—Tilthe End of Time (IRE) (Acclamation) (32560) **HighclereT'Bred Racing-JustWannaHaveFun**
43 Ch f 4/2 Toronado (IRE)—Tipsy Me (Selkirk (USA)) (32560) **Joe Soiza & Mason Soiza**
44 **URBAN SCENE,** b f 11/3 Cityscape—Fashionable Gal (Galileo (IRE)) **Mr J. C. Webb**

Other Owners: Mr A. A. A. Al Muslimani, Mr J. M. Basquill, Mr O. S. W. Bell, Mr A. N. C. Bengough, Mrs G. P. Bostwick, T. P. Bostwick, Mr S. P. Capon, Mr J. R. Eastwood, Mr C. H. Fellowes, Mr A. S. F. Frost, Mr E. H. M. Frost, Mr P. Hernon, Highclere Thoroughbred Racing Ltd, Mr A. J. Hill, G. Horsford, Mr M. B. Hughes, Miss M. Noden, Mr M. R. Soiza, Mr J. Soiza, Mr M. B. Spence, Mr S. J. A. Turner, Ms A. V. Wilson-Martin.

---

195 **MR DOMINIC FFRENCH DAVIS, Lambourn**
Postal: **College House, 3 Oxford Street, Lambourn, Hungerford, Berkshire, RG17 8XP**
Contacts: **YARD** (01488) 73675 **Home** (01488) 72342 **FAX** (01488) 73675 **MOBILE** (07831) 118764
E-MAIL ffrenchdavis@btinternet.com **WEBSITE** www.ffrenchdavis.com

1 **ANONYMOUS JOHN (IRE),** 6, gr g Baltic King—Helibel (IRE) **Mr R. F. Haynes**
2 **CHILL IN THE WOOD,** 9, br m Desert King (IRE)—Zaffaranni **Mr D. G. Cramm**
3 **JELLY MONGER (IRE),** 6, b m Strategic Prince—Royal Jelly **Gary Black & Mark Duthie**
4 **KNOCKALONGI,** 12, b g Fair Mix (IRE)—Understudy **Partnership Terminated**
5 **LOOE BAY,** 6, b m Kirkwall—Dragon Blue **Mr J. Hughes**
6 **MAJBOOR (IRE),** 4, ch g Dragon Pulse (IRE)—City Vaults Girl (IRE) **Marchwood Recycling Ltd**
7 **MANSON,** 5, ch g Equiano (FR)—Swain's Gold (USA) **The Agincourt Partnership**
8 **MIDNIGHT MOOD,** 5, b m Aqlaam—Inflammable **D. J. S. Ffrench Davis**
9 **MONDAY CLUB,** 5, ch g Strategic Prince—Support Fund (IRE) **Faber, Ffrench Davis & Taylor**
10 **ROLLING DICE,** 7, b g Rail Link—Breathing Space (USA) **D. J. S. Ffrench Davis**
11 **SMART GETAWAY (IRE),** 6, b m Getaway (GER)—Legendsofthefall (IRE) **D. J. S. Ffrench Davis**
12 **VAN HUYSEN (IRE),** 6, br g Excellent Art—Tara Too (IRE) **Prof C. D. Green**
13 **WHATTHEBUTLERSAW (IRE),** 9, br g Arcadio (GER)—
                            Phar From Men (IRE) **Mrs P Ffrench Davis & Mr D Ffrench Davis**

MR DOMINIC FFRENCH DAVIS - Continued

THREE-YEAR-OLDS
14 **DISTANT APPLAUSE (IRE)**, b g Acclamation—Spacecraft (USA) **S. J. Edwards**
15 Ch f Champs Elysees—Lasting View (IRE) **D. J. S. Ffrench Davis**

Other Owners: Mr G. H. Black, Mr J. O. Chapman, Mr M. Duthie, Mr E. S. G. Faber, Mr N. A. Fenn, Mrs P. Ffrench Davis, Mr T. G. Holroyd, Mrs J. E. Taylor.

Assistant Trainer: Avery Ffrench Davis

Jockey (NH): Mark Grant.

---

196 **MR GUISEPPE FIERRO, Hednesford**
Postal: **Bentley Brook House, Rawnsley Road, Hednesford, Cannock, Staffordshire, WS12 1RB**
Contacts: **HOME/YARD (01543) 879611 MOBILE (07976) 321468**

1 **JUST LIKE BETH,** 10, b m Proclamation (IRE)—Just Beth **G. Fierro**
2 **LITTLE DOTTY,** 9, br m Erhaab (USA)—Marsh Marigold **G. Fierro**
3 **RAMBLING RIVER,** 7, b g Revoque (IRE)—Just Beth **G. Fierro**
4 **SUNDANCE BOY,** 9, gr g Proclamation (IRE)—Just Beth **G. Fierro**

Assistant Trainer: M Fierro

---

197 **MRS MARJORIE FIFE, Stillington**
Postal: **White Thorn Farm, Stillington, Easingwold, York, YO61 1LT**
Contacts: **PHONE (01347) 822012 MOBILE (07890) 075217**
E-MAIL wfife10416@aol.com

1 **AFRICAN FRIEND (IRE)**, 5, b g Equiano (FR)—Fontanally Springs (IRE) **Mr T. W. Fife**
2 **B FIFTY TWO (IRE)**, 9, br g Dark Angel (IRE)—Petite Maxine **Fat Badger Racing**
3 **BARRACUDA BOY (IRE)**, 8, b g Bahamian Bounty—Madame Boulangere **Mr L. A. Bellman**
4 **BLUE MEDICI**, 4, b g Medicean—Bluebelle **Laurence Bellman & David Ward**
5 **CLASSIC SENIORITY**, 6, b g Kyllachy—Dramatic Solo **HuggyMac Racing**
6 **CONTROL CENTRE (IRE)**, 4, b g Dragon Pulse (IRE)—Margaux Magique (IRE) **Mr R. W. Fife**
7 **DARK FOREST**, 5, b g Iffraaj—Through The Forest (USA) **Mr D. J. Haddrell**
8 **GABRIAL'S STAR**, 9, b g Hernando (FR)—Grain Only **The Maverick Racing Partnership**
9 **INEXES**, 6, gr g Exceed And Excel (AUS)—Likeable **21st Century Racing**
10 **INTERLINK (USA)**, 5, b g Kitten's Joy (USA)—Seattle Tac (USA) **Mr C. Buckingham**
11 **LUV U UNDERWATER**, 8, b g Needwood Blade—Lady Suesanne (IRE) **Mr T. W. Fife**
12 **PALINDROME (USA)**, 5, b g Poet's Voice—Hi Dubai **Fat Badger Racing**
13 **PALMERSTON**, 5, b g Oasis Dream—Marywell **Mr C. Buckingham**
14 **PERFECT WORDS (IRE)**, 8, ch g Thousand Words—Zilayah (USA) **Green Lane**
15 **ROYAL HOLIDAY (IRE)**, 11, ch g Captain Rio—Sunny Slope **Mrs M. Turner**
16 **SAMTU (IRE)**, 7, b g Teofilo (IRE)—Samdaniya **B. W. Parren**
17 **SOLDIER'S FORTUNE (IRE)**, 4, b g Helmet (AUS)—Kerrys Requiem (IRE) **Mr C. Buckingham**

THREE-YEAR-OLDS
18 **ALLNITE (IRE)**, b g Arcano (IRE)—Paint The Town (IRE) **Mr L. A. Bellman**
19 **HOT JAZZ (IRE)**, b g Red Jazz (USA)—Pelican Waters (IRE) **Mr L. A. Bellman**
20 **MAKE IT SIMPLE**, ch g Compton Place—It's Complicated **Mr L. A. Bellman**
21 **UNCOVERED**, b g Helmet (AUS)—Caritas **Mr L. A. Bellman**

Other Owners: Mrs B. Catterall, A. W. Catterall, Mr A. Huggins, Mr J. Mcalpine, Mr C. R. Piercy, Mr A. J. Shaw, Mr D. Ward.

198 | MR TIM FITZGERALD, Malton
Postal: **Norton Grange, Norton, Malton, North Yorkshire, YO17 9EA**
Contacts: **OFFICE** (01653) 228456 **MOBILE** (07950) 356437
E-MAIL fitzgeraldracing@hotmail.com

1 **COMPETENT**, 6, b g Compton Place—Pantita **Dukes Racing 1**
2 **HE'S MAGIC**, 7, b g Court Masterpiece—Lady Magician **Mrs M. Lingwood**
3 **WARFARE**, 9, b g Soviet Star (USA)—Fluffy **Dukes Racing 1**

Other Owners: Mrs K. Dukes, O. R. Dukes.

Amateur: Miss H. Dukes.

199 | MR JOHN FLINT, Bridgend
Postal: **Woodland Lodge,, Waunbant Road,, Kenfig Hill, Bridgend, Mid-Glamorgan, CF33 6FF**
Contacts: **FAX** (01656) 744347 **MOBILE** (07581) 111471
E-MAIL johnflint900@gmail.com **WEBSITE** www.johnflintracing.com

1 **AARYAM (FR)**, 6, b g Dylan Thomas (IRE)—Selinea (FR) **Mr L. H. & Mrs T. Evans**
2 **AIR OF YORK (IRE)**, 6, b g Vale of York (IRE)—State Secret **Mrs L. A. Cullimore**
3 **ARIAN (IRE)**, 6, b m King's Theatre (IRE)—Brave Betsy (IRE) **Mr D. M. Mathias**
4 **AYLA'S EMPEROR**, 9, b m Holy Roman Emperor (IRE)—Ayla (IRE) **Mr L. H. & Mrs T. Evans**
5 **BAZ'S BOY**, 5, b g Compton Place—Spunger **Partnership Terminated**
6 5, B m Beat Hollow—Brave Betsy (IRE) **Mr D. M. Mathias**
7 **CILLIAN'S WELL (IRE)**, 8, b g Trans Island—Live A Lot (IRE) **Robert Aplin & Belly's Heroes**
8 **COURT DUTY (IRE)**, 6, b g Court Cave (IRE)—Easter Duties (IRE) **Davies & Price**
9 **CRINDLE CARR (IRE)**, 4, ch g Compton Place—Arley Hall **J. L. Flint**
10 **EBEN DUBAI (IRE)**, 6, b g New Approach (IRE)—Eldalil **J. L. Flint**
11 **EDDIEMAURICE (IRE)**, 7, ch g Captain Rio—Annals **Mr D. M. Mathias**
12 **ENGLISH PALE (IRE)**, 5, b g Elusive Pimpernel (USA)—Terme Cay (USA) **Westerwood (WG) Global Limited**
13 **FIELD OF VISION (IRE)**, 5, b g Pastoral Pursuits—Grand Design **Paul Duffy, David Semmens, Viv Williams**
14 **KAYF MOSS**, 10, b g Kayf Tara—Madam Mosso **Mr L. H. & Mrs T. Evans**
15 **KHISMET**, 5, b m Kheleyf (USA)—Bisaat (USA) **Mr D. M. Mathias**
16 **LAC SACRE (FR)**, 9, b g Bering—Lady Glorieuse (FR) **Mr L. H. & Mrs T. Evans**
17 **LOVE AND BE LOVED**, 4, b f Lawman (FR)—Rightside **J. L. Flint**
18 **MOOJANED (IRE)**, 7, b g Raven's Pass (USA)—Mufradat (IRE) **Mr R. Emmanuel**
19 **NATIVE SOLDIER (IRE)**, 4, b g Sepoy (AUS)—Electra Star **Burnham Plastering & Drylining Ltd**
20 **OUTER SPACE**, 7, b g Acclamation—Venoge (IRE) **J. L. Flint**
21 **PACOFILHA**, 4, b f Paco Boy (IRE)—Seradim **Burnham Plastering & Drylining Ltd**
22 **RUMOR**, 5, ch g Windsor Castle—Whispering Wind (IRE) **Burnham Plastering & Drylining Ltd**
23 **SADHBH (IRE)**, 4, b f Lilbourne Lad (IRE)—Stoney Cove (IRE) **Katchar Racing**
24 **SAHALIN**, 5, b m Red Rocks (IRE)—Tamathea (IRE) **Mr D. M. Mathias**
25 4, Ch f Dylan Thomas (IRE)—Silva Flint **John Flint**
26 **WINKLEMANN (IRE)**, 6, br g Rip Van Winkle (IRE)—Kykuit (IRE) **Mr D. M. Mathias**
27 **WITH PLEASURE**, 5, b g Poet's Voice—With Fascination (USA) **Burnham Plastering & Drylining Ltd**

THREE-YEAR-OLDS
28 **JUST RIGHT**, ch f Medicean—Rightside **Mr D. A. Poole**
29 B g Midnight Legend—One For Joules (IRE)

TWO-YEAR-OLDS
30 **JUST CHAMPION**, b c 11/5 Dunaden (FR)—Koliakhova (FR) (Literato (FR))

Other Owners: Mr R. J. Aplin, Mr P. D. Bell, Belly's Heroes, R. A. Davies, Mr D. P. Duffy, Mr L. H. Evans, Mrs T. Evans, Mr A. G. Price, Mrs T. J. Raymond, Mr S. A. Raymond, Mr D. M. Semmens.

Assistant Trainer: Mrs Martine Louise Flint (07968) 044487

Jockey (NH): Rhys Flint.

200 **MR DAVID FLOOD, Hungerford**
Postal: **15 High Street, Chiseldon, Swindon, Wiltshire, SN4 0NG**
Contacts: PHONE **(07919) 340619**
E-MAIL **davidflood1@hotmail.co.uk**

1 BAZOOKA (IRE), 7, b g Camacho—Janadam (IRE) **Mrs A. Cowley**
2 STOPDWORLDNLETMEOF, 4, b g Piccolo—Dilli Dancer **Flood Family Racing Limited**

THREE-YEAR-OLDS

3 KENDERGARTEN KOP (IRE), ch g Kendargent (FR)—Elsa T (IRE) **Mrs A. Cowley**

201 **MR STEVE FLOOK, Leominster**
Postal: **The Granary Stables, Downwood Farm, Shobdon, Leominster, Herefordshire, HR6 9NH**
Contacts: MOBILE **(07811) 511566**
E-MAIL **lwallace@btinternet.com**

1 BLACK JACK JAXON, 6, gr g Fair Mix (IRE)—No Virtue **S. M. Flook**
2 BLACKJACKTENNESSEE, 4, b g Fair Mix (IRE)—No Virtue **S. M. Flook**
3 BROWN REVEL, 9, b m Revoque (IRE)—Brown Seal **Mrs P. Corbett**
4 CENTREOFEXCELLENCE (IRE), 7, b g Oscar (IRE)—Calm Approach (IRE) **Mrs P Corbett & Mrs A Thomas**
5 DUBAI MISSION (IRE), 5, b g New Approach (IRE)—Al Joza **G. Byard**
6 GRANDIOSO (IRE), 11, b g Westerner—Champagne Warrior (IRE) **Foxhunters In Mind**
7 HIGHLAND LIFE, 8, b m Trans Island—High Life **Mr F. J. A. Morgan**
8 NAZZAA (IRE), 5, b g Shamardal (USA)—Multicolour Wave (IRE) **G. Byard**
9 OPERA BUFFA (IRE), 5, b m Exceed And Excel (AUS)—Dubai Opera (USA) **S. M. Flook**
10 PRINCE CARN, 7, b g Lucarno (USA)—Broadbrook Lass **Mr B. J. Mould**
11 VICTOR LEUDORUM (IRE), 11, b g Wareed (IRE)—Rock Garden (IRE) **Mr & Mrs J Duggan**
12 VIKEKHAL (FR), 9, b g Khalkevi (IRE)—Gesse Parade (FR) **Chasing Charlie Syndicate**

Other Owners: R. O. Addis, Mrs J. F. Duggan, Mr J. W. T. Duggan, Mr P. E. Jones, Mrs A. P. Thomas, Miss L. Wallace.

Assistant Trainer: Lynn Wallace

202 **MR TONY FORBES, Uttoxeter**
Postal: **Hill House Farm, Poppits Lane, Stramshall, Uttoxeter, Staffordshire, ST14 5EX**
Contacts: PHONE **(01889) 562722** MOBILE **(07967) 246571**
E-MAIL **tony@thimble.net**

1 BENISSIMO (IRE), 8, b g Beneficial—Fennor Rose (IRE) **Mr A. L. Forbes**
2 MEDIEVAL BISHOP (IRE), 9, b g Bachelor Duke (USA)—On The Backfoot (IRE) **Mr A. L. Forbes**
3 TINGO IN THE TALE (IRE), 9, b g Oratorio (IRE)—Sunlit Skies **Mr A. L. Forbes**

Assistant Trainer: Mr Tim Eley

203 **MRS PAM FORD, Hereford**
Postal: **Stone House Stables, Preston Wynne, Hereford, Herefordshire, HR1 3PB**
Contacts: HOME/FAX **(01432) 820604** MOBILE **(07733) 152051**
E-MAIL **pam_ford@hotmail.co.uk**

1 APACHE CHIEF, 10, b g Tikkanen (USA)—Dara's Course (IRE) **K. R. Ford**
2 DIGI (IRE), 5, b m Baltic King—Lorena (IRE) **K. R. Ford**
3 5, B h Fantastic Spain (USA)—Elegant Accord (IRE)
4 RUNNING SQUAW, 10, ch m Denounce—Georgie McTaggart **Miss V. A. M. Davies**

Assistant Trainer: Mr K Ford

Jockey (flat): Royston Ffrench. **Jockey (NH):** James Davies.

204 | MRS RICHENDA FORD, Blandford Forum
Postal: Garlands Farm, The Common, Okeford Fitzpaine, Blandford Forum, Dorset, DT11 0RT
Contacts: MOBILE (07800) 634846
E-MAIL richendasnook@hotmail.co.uk

1 BREAKING GROUND (IRE), 6, b g Echo of Light—Mayfair **Mr & Mrs K. B. Snook**
2 DAYS AHEAD (IRE), 11, ch g Kheleyf (USA)—Hushaby (IRE) **Mr & Mrs K. B. Snook**
3 DONT BE ROBIN (IRE), 6, b g Robin des Pres (FR)—Rainbow Times (IRE)
4 GOLD FLASH, 6, b g Kheleyf (USA)—My Golly **Miss L. Weinreb**
5 HURRY HENRY (IRE), 9, b g Blueprint (IRE)—Tower Princess (IRE) **Mr & Mrs K. B. Snook**
6 NENERGY'S QUEST, 7, b m Pasternak—Coolers Quest **Mr & Mrs K. B. Snook**
7 5, B h Ask—Rose Island
8 SUSTAINABLE STAR (IRE), 7, gr g Winged Love (IRE)—
Fooling Around (IRE) Neil Budden, Steven Hosie & Ian Cahill
9 TELMADELA (IRE), 8, b g Definite Article—Miss Pickering (IRE) **Mr & Mrs K. B. Snook**
10 THEATRE MILL (IRE), 10, b g King's Theatre (IRE)—River Mill (IRE) **Mr & Mrs K. B. Snook**

Other Owners: Mr N. Budden, Mr I. A. Cahill, Mr S. Hosie, Mrs M. Snook, K. B. Snook.

205 | MR BRIAN FORSEY, Taunton
Postal: Three Oaks, Ash Priors, Taunton, Somerset, TA4 3NQ
Contacts: PHONE (01823) 433914 MOBILE (07747) 392760
E-MAIL forsey2001@yahoo.com

1 BARISTA (IRE), 10, b g Titus Livius (FR)—Cappuccino (IRE) **Three Oaks Racing & Mrs P Bosley**
2 BLACKTHORN STICK (IRE), 9, b g Elusive City (USA)—Hi Lyla (IRE) **Mr K. C. Jago**
3 DROPZONE (USA), 9, b g Smart Strike (CAN)—Dalisay (IRE) **Mr Alan Stevens & Mr Brian Forsey**
4 EDDIES PEARL (IRE), 8, b m Craigsteel—Florida Bay (IRE) **Mrs S. Smyth-Ribeiro**
5 GEORGIEZAR, 5, ch m Winker Watson—Quaker Parrot **Mrs K. C. Jago**
6 RAINBOW EMPRESS, 6, ch m Hamairi (IRE)—Court Empress **P. D. Purdy**
7 THE IBBSTER (IRE), 8, b g Shantou (USA)—Annalisa (IRE) **Mrs S. Smyth-Ribeiro**

Other Owners: Mrs P. M. Bosley, B. Forsey, A. G. Stevens.

Assistant Trainer: Susan Forsey

206 | MISS SANDY FORSTER, Kelso
Postal: Halterburn Head, Yetholm, Kelso, Roxburghshire, TD5 8PP
Contacts: PHONE/FAX (01573) 420615 FAX (01573) 420615 MOBILE (07880) 727877 or (07976) 587315
E-MAIL clivestorey@btinternet.com

1 CHARLIE SNOW ANGEL, 9, b g Overbury (IRE)—Sister Seven (IRE) **C. Storey**
2 HERE COMES HOVIS, 7, br g Fair Mix (IRE)—Granary House **Halterburn Head Racing**
3 LASTIN' MEMORIES, 6, b g Overbury (IRE)—Dusky Rua (IRE) **Dave Skeldon & Sandy Forster**
4 4, B f Fame And Glory—Liss Rua (IRE) **Mr M. H. Walton**
5 LOWANBEHOLD, 11, gr g Cloudings (IRE)—Marble Quest (IRE) **C. Storey**
6 MISS QUEST, 6, b m Urgent Request (IRE)—Flighty Mist **J. R. Jeffreys**

Other Owners: Miss S. E. Forster, Mr D. A. Skeldon.

Assistant Trainer: C. Storey

Jockey (NH): Adrian Lane.

207 | MISS JOANNE FOSTER, Ilkley
Postal: Brookleigh Farm, Burley Road, Menston, Ilkley, West Yorkshire, LS29 6NS
Contacts: PHONE (07980) 301808 MOBILE (07980) 301808
E-MAIL info@jofosterracing.co.uk WEBSITE www.jofosterracing.co.uk

1 ARMOROUS, 7, b g Generous (IRE)—Armorine (FR) **Mad For Fun & Partners (2)**
2 BROTHERLY COMPANY (IRE), 6, b g Fast Company (IRE)—Good Lady (IRE) **The Reign It In Partnership**
3 CHASE THE WIND (IRE), 9, ch g Spadoun (FR)—Asfreeasthewind (IRE) **Mr J. Nixon**

MISS JOANNE FOSTER - Continued

   4 **FRANKIE BALLOU (IRE)**, 9, br g Norwich—One Up (IRE) **The Yorkshire Racing Partnership**
   5 **HOUNDSCOURT (IRE)**, 11, b g Court Cave (IRE)—Broken Rein (IRE) **The Berry Syndicate**
   6 **LAMMTURNER (IRE)**, 6, b m Brian Boru—Deploy Or Die (IRE) **Mr E. C. Wilkin**
   7 **LANSDOWNE ROAD (IRE)**, 10, b g Bienamado (USA)—
                              Ballinamona Wish (IRE) **Mrs Amanda Benson & J Foster**
   8 **LEOPARD (IRE)**, 4, b g Iffraaj—Appletreemagic (IRE) **Mad For Fun & Partners (2)**
   9 **NOBLE CALL (IRE)**, 10, b g King's Best (USA)—Really (IRE) **Mr P Foster & Partners**
 10 **SIGURD (GER)**, 6, ch g Sholokhov (IRE)—Sky News (GER) **Mrs E. A. Verity**
 11 **URBAN GALE (IRE)**, 13, b g City Honours (USA)—Margale (IRE) **P. Foster**

Other Owners: Mr J. Batty, Mrs A. C. Benson, J. Berry, Miss J. E. Foster, Mr S. A. Hollings, Mrs C. Potter, Mr M. J. Roche, Mr P. Thompson, J. Townson.

Assistant Trainer: P. Foster

---

208 **MR JIMMY FOX, Marlborough**
Postal: **Highlands Farm Stables, Herridge, Collingbourne Ducis, Marlborough, Wiltshire, SN8 3EG**
Contacts: **PHONE (01264) 850218 (07931) 724358 MOBILE (07702) 880010**
E-MAIL jcfoxtrainer@aol.com

   1 **ACT ACCORDINGLY**, 5, gr g Sagamix (FR)—Anns Girl **Mrs J. A. Cleary**
   2 **CAPTAIN MARMALADE (IRE)**, 6, gr g Duke of Marmalade (IRE)—Elisium **Mrs S. J. Fox**
   3 **CATHERINETHEGRACE (IRE)**, 4, gr f Duke of Marmalade (IRE)—
                              Little Miss Gracie **Abacus Employment Services Ltd**
   4 **FRANKIE**, 7, gr g Firebreak—Winterbourne **R. E. Kavanagh**
   5 **GRACEFUL JAMES (IRE)**, 5, ch g Rock of Gibraltar (IRE)—Little Miss Gracie **Abacus Employment Services Ltd**
   6 **GRACIOUS GEORGE (IRE)**, 8, b g Oratorio (IRE)—Little Miss Gracie **Mrs B. A. Fuller**
   7 **HENRY GRACE (IRE)**, 7, b g Oratorio (IRE)—Little Miss Gracie **Barbara Fuller & Claire Underwood**
   8 **MEDICEAN EL DIABLO**, 5, b g Medicean—Al Joudha (FR) **Sugar Syndicate**
   9 **MILLIE MAY**, 4, b f Sixties Icon—Maydream **The Dancing Partners**
 10 **OUR RUTH**, 5, ch m Assertive—My Jeanie (IRE) **R. E. Kavanagh**
 11 **WILD FLOWER (IRE)**, 6, b m Approve (IRE)—Midsummernitedream (GER) **Mrs S. J. Fox**

THREE-YEAR-OLDS

 12 **BILLY STAR**, b g Sixties Icon—Appreciative **Sugar Syndicate**
 13 **SWEET AND DANDY (IRE)**, b f Dandy Man (IRE)—Translator (IRE) **Mrs S. J. Fox**

Other Owners: Mr M. Dolnik, Mr D. S. Estall, Mrs E. Estall, Mr P. Ondrcka, Mrs C. C. Underwood.

Assistant Trainer: Sarah-Jane Fox

Jockey (flat): Pat Dobbs.

---

209 **MISS SUZZANNE FRANCE, Norton on Derwent**
Postal: **Cheesecake Hill House, Highfield, Beverley Road, Norton on Derwent, North Yorkshire, YO17 9PJ**
Contacts: **PHONE (01653) 691947 FAX (01653) 691947 MOBILE (07904) 117531**
E-MAIL suzzannemunchie@talk21.com
WEBSITE www.suzzannefranceracing.com / www.newstartracing.co.uk

   1 **AD VITAM (IRE)**, 10, ch g Ad Valorem (USA)—Love Sonnet **Newstart Partnership**
   2 **FLY TRUE**, 5, b m Raven's Pass (USA)—Have Faith (IRE) **Stuart & Kate Dobb, Newstart Partnership**
   3 **GEORGE BAILEY (IRE)**, 6, b g Zebedee—Zuzu (IRE) **Newstart Partnership**
   4 **LUATH**, 5, ch g Archipenko (USA)—Delaware Dancer **Miss Kate Dobb & Mr Stuart Dobb**
   5 **STAMP DUTY (IRE)**, 10, b g Ad Valorem (USA)—Lothian Lass (IRE) **Newstart Partnership**
   6 **WHISPERING WOLF**, 5, b m Amadeus Wolf—Ashover Amber **Newstart Partnership**

THREE-YEAR-OLDS

   7 **MOUNTAIN OF STARS**, b g Equiano (FR)—Ivory Silk **Stuart Dobb & Kate Dobb**

Other Owners: Mr S. Dobb, Miss K. M. Dobb, Mrs P. France.

Assistant Trainer: Mr Aaron James

Amateur: Mr Aaron James.

210 MR DEREK FRANKLAND, Brackley
Postal: **Springfields, Mixbury, Brackley, Northamptonshire, NN13 5RR**
Contacts: **FAX (01280) 847334 MOBILE (07763) 020406**
E-MAIL dsfrankland@aol.com

1 **DREAM EMPRESS**, 5, gr m Naaqoos—Daheeya **D. S. Frankland & D. J. Trott**
2 **STINGGREY (IRE)**, 5, gr g Scorpion (IRE)—Northinn Lady (IRE) **D. S. Frankland & D. J. Trott**

Other Owners: D. S. Frankland, Mr D. J. Trott.

211 MR JAMES FROST, Buckfastleigh
Postal: **Hawson Stables, Buckfastleigh, Devon, TQ11 0HP**
Contacts: **YARD (01364) 642267 HOME (01364) 642332 FAX (01364) 643182**
MOBILE (07860) 220229

1 **ARCHIE RICE (USA)**, 12, b g Arch (USA)—Gold Bowl (USA) **Frost Racing Club**
2 **BACCALAUREATE (FR)**, 12, b g High Chaparral (FR)—Rose d'or (IRE) **Frost Racing Club**
3 **BEE AN ARISTOCRAT (IRE)**, 9, b g Flemensfirth (USA)—Windy Bee (IRE) **Mrs E. Lane**
4 **BOGOSS DU PERRET (FR)**, 7, b br g Malinas (GER)—Lady Paques (FR) **Mrs J. Bury**
5 **FINDUSATGORCOMBE**, 6, b g Tobougg (IRE)—Seemma **Mr P. R. Meaden**
6 **FLIGHTY FILIA (IRE)**, 6, gr m Raven's Pass (USA)—Coventina (IRE) **The Flighty Five**
7 **GILLY GRACE**, 8, b m Morpeth—Miss Grace **Frost Racing Club**
8 **GOLAN DANCER (IRE)**, 10, b g Golan (IRE)—Seductive Dance **Frost Racing Club**
9 **GRISSOM (FR)**, 10, ch g Sabrehill (USA)—Nuit de Chine (FR) **J. D. Frost**
10 **ICE KONIG (FR)**, 9, gr g Epalo (GER)—Isarwelle (GER) **J. D. Frost**
11 **KRISTJANO (GER)**, 6, b g Nayef (USA)—Kalahari Dancer **Mr T. Saye**
12 **MONET MOOR**, 9, b m Morpeth—Miracle Monarch **Frost Racing Club**
13 **QUINTO**, 8, ch g Desideratum—Cruz Santa **Share My Dream**
14 **RED PENNY (IRE)**, 11, b m Definite Article—Hurricane Dawn (IRE) **Miss M. E. Sherrington**
15 **SANGRAM (IRE)**, 11, b g Blueprint (IRE)—Margeno's Fountain (IRE) **Mr T. Saye**
16 **SILVER QUAY (IRE)**, 6, gr g Dark Angel (IRE)—She Runs (FR) **C & Mrs A Jones**
17 **SUGAR GLIDER**, 6, b m Morpeth—Definite Lynn (IRE) **J. D. Frost**
18 **TRIPLE CHIEF (IRE)**, 7, b br g High Chaparral (FR)—Trebles (IRE) **G. D. Thompson**

Other Owners: Mr C. Coward, Mrs J. A. Jones, Mr C. Jones, Mr M. Kay, Mr C. W. Mather, Mr B. A. G. Robarts, Mr P. M. Tosh.

Assistant Trainer: G. Frost

Conditional: Bryony Frost.

212 MR KEVIN FROST, Butterton
Postal: **Butterton Racing Stables, Park Road, Butterton, Newcastle, Staffordshire, ST5 4DZ**
Contacts: **(07748) 873092 MOBILE (07919) 370081**
E-MAIL info@kevinfrostracing.co.uk WEBSITE www.kevinfrostracing.co.uk

1 **ALL SET TO GO (IRE)**, 7, gr g Verglas (IRE)—Firecrest (IRE) **C & D Racing**
2 **ARROWZONE**, 7, b g Iffraaj—Donna Giovanna **C & D Racing**
3 **BORN TO REASON (IRE)**, 4, b g Born To Sea (IRE)—Laureldean Lady (IRE) **Mr R. Carroll**
4 **CHIEFTAIN'S CHOICE (IRE)**, 9, b g King's Theatre (IRE)—Fairy Native (IRE) **Curzon House Partnership**
5 **DOC PENFRO**, 6, b g Dr Massini (IRE)—Prescelli (IRE) **Doc Redemption**
6 **HURRICANE DYLAN (IRE)**, 7, b g Brian Boru—Definetly Sarah (IRE) **Mr J. Stimpson**
7 **JOEY'S DESTINY (IRE)**, 8, ch g Kheleyf—Maid of Ailsa (USA) **Mrs A. Frost**
8 **MY BROTHER MIKE (IRE)**, 4, b g Bated Breath—Coming Back **Mr J. Stimpson**
9 **PERSHING**, 7, gr g Mount Nelson—La Gandilie (FR) **Mr K. Frost**
10 **REDEMPTION SONG (IRE)**, 6, gr m Mastercraftsman (IRE)—Humilis (IRE) **Doc Redemption**
11 **SHAMLAN (IRE)**, 6, br g Shamardal (USA)—Atamana (IRE) **Mr W. L. B. Smith**
12 **SHOWDANCE KID**, 4, b g Showcasing—Maid To Dance **Mr K. Frost**
13 **SOPHISTICATED HEIR (IRE)**, 8, b g New Approach (IRE)—My Girl Sophie (USA) **Mr K. Frost**
14 **STEAL THE SCENE (IRE)**, 6, b g Lord Shanakill (USA)—Namoos (IRE) **Mrs A. Frost**
15 **TOPLINE DIVA**, 6, b m Top Line Dancer (IRE)—Sita (IRE) **Miss D. S. Crewe**
16 **TORONTO SOUND**, 4, b g Aussie Rules (USA)—Caribana **Mr K. Frost**

MR KEVIN FROST - Continued

THREE-YEAR-OLDS

17 **BROADWAY ANGEL**, ch f Medicean—Quinzey's Best (IRE) **BGC Racing V**
18 **CHARLIE DOVE**, gr g Champs Elysees—Skyrider (IRE) **BGC Racing II**
19 **DUGGARY**, b g Champs Elysees—Waitingonacloud **BGC Racing IV**
20 **HOLTE END**, ch f Stimulation (IRE)—Ellway Queen (USA) **BGC Racing III**
21 **MY TOWN CHICAGO (USA)**, b c Medaglia d'oro (USA)—Say You Will (IRE) **Mr J. Stimpson**
22 **POPPY JAG (IRE)**, b f Kodiac—Jacquelin Jag (IRE) **Curzon House Partnership**
23 **THE FETTLER (IRE)**, ch g Rock of Gibraltar (IRE)—Green Empire (IRE) **Curzon House Partnership**
24 **THE THROSTLES**, b g Poet's Voice—Stylish Dream (USA) **BGC Racing I & Carl Hodgson**

Other Owners: Mr R. Carroll, Mr Dennis Coles, Ms D. Crewe, Mr S. W. Dunn, Mrs A. Frost, Mr C. Hodgson, Miss J. Jones, Mr Harold Jones, Mr D. L'Honore, Mr J. H. Mills, Mrs M. A. Moore, Mr C. Owen, Mr M. Roberts, Mr W. Smith, Mr J. T. Stimpson, Mr Richard Ward.

Jockey (NH): Brian Hughes.

---

213 **MR HUGO FROUD, Bruton**
Postal: **Redlynch Farm, Redlynch, Nr Bruton, Somerset, BA10 0NH**
Contacts: **MOBILE (07590) 413550**
E-MAIL hugo.froud@hugofroudracing.com WEBSITE www.hugofroudracing.com

1 **BEAUCHAMP VIKING**, 14, b g Compton Admiral—Beauchamp Jade **Mrs M. S. Emery**
2 **GIFT FROM GOD**, 5, b g Teofilo (IRE)—Piffling **The Gift From God Syndicate**
3 **LADY LYDIA (IRE)**, 7, b m Kheleyf (USA)—Piece Unique **The Lady Lydia Syndicate**
4 9, B m General Gambul—Vitinsel

Other Owners: P. E. Froud, Mr H. C. Froud.

---

214 **MR HARRY FRY, Seaborough**
Postal: **Flat 1, Manor Farm, Seaborough, Beaminster, Dorset, DT8 3QY**
Contacts: **PHONE (01308) 868192 FAX (01308) 867512**
E-MAIL info@harryfryracing.com WEBSITE www.harryfryracing.com

1 **ACTING LASS (IRE)**, 7, b g King's Theatre (IRE)—Darrens Lass (IRE) **Nigel & Barbara Collison**
2 **AIR HORSE ONE**, 7, gr g Mountain High (IRE)—Whisky Rose (IRE) **The Dons**
3 **ALL HANDS ON DECK (IRE)**, 5, b m Flemensfirth (USA)—On Galley Head (IRE) **Mr A. D. Polson**
4 **AMERICAN (FR)**, 8, b g Malinas (GER)—Grande Sultane (FR) **The Jago Family Partnership**
5 **AMERICAN GIGOLO**, 6, b g Azamour (IRE)—Sadie Thompson (GER) **Mr D. A. Olver**
6 **ANY DRAMA (IRE)**, 7, b g Gamut (IRE)—Oak Lodge (IRE) **N. G. Cooper**
7 **ART OF PAYROLL (GER)**, 9, b g Shirocco (GER)—Anna Maria (GER) **Bishopsgate Syndicate**
8 **AS I SEE IT**, 6, b g King's Theatre (IRE)—Chomba Womba (IRE) **Mrs Clare Clifford & Mrs Diana Goodall**
9 **ASTUTE BOY (IRE)**, 4, b g Arcano (IRE)—Spa **Astute Partnership**
10 **BAGS GROOVE (IRE)**, 7, b g Oscar (IRE)—Golden Moment (IRE) **M. Pescod**
11 **BEHIND TIME (IRE)**, 7, b g Stowaway—She's Got To Go (IRE) **Mr J. P. McManus**
12 **BLACK MISCHIEF**, 6, b g Black Sam Bellamy (IRE)—Miss Mitch (IRE) **Tom Chadney and Friends**
13 **BULLIONAIRE (IRE)**, 5, b g Gold Well—Dontcallerthat (IRE) **Phil Fry & Charlie Walker -Osborne House**
14 **CANELIE (FR)**, 6, b m Gentlewave (IRE)—Medjie (FR) **Mr J. P. McManus**
15 **CAPTAIN DRAKE (IRE)**, 5, b g Getaway (GER)—Julika (GER)
16 **CARIBERT (FR)**, 5, b g Ballingarry (IRE)—Cardamine (FR) **Phil Fry & Charlie Walker -Osborne House**
17 **CHALONNIAL (FR)**, 6, ch g Protektor (GER)—Kissmirial (FR) **N. G. Cooper**
18 **COCKNEY WREN**, 5, b m Cockney Rebel (IRE)—Compose **P. E. Atkinson**
19 **DASHING OSCAR (IRE)**, 8, b g Oscar (IRE)—Be My Leader (IRE) **Andy & Sharon Measham**
20 **DEADRINGERFORLOVE**, 4, b f Black Sam Bellamy (IRE)—
                                              La Perrotine (FR) **Mayoh, Callan, Beese & the Dennys**
21 **DESERT QUEEN**, 10, b m Desert King (IRE)—Priscilla **The Jago Family Partnership**
22 **DRUMCLIFF (IRE)**, 4, b g Presenting—Dusty Too **Mr J. P. McManus**
23 **ELEANOROFAQUITAINE (IRE)**, 5, b m Flemensfirth (USA)—
                                              Misty Heather (IRE) **Dolan-Abrahams & Fry Families**
24 **ENA BAIE (FR)**, 4, b f Crillon (FR)—Trema Baie (FR) **Mr J. P. McManus**
25 **EROS (FR)**, 4, b g Diamond Boy (FR)—Madame Lys (FR) **Sullivan Bloodstock Limited**
26 **FIRMAGE BURG (FR)**, 4, b f Sageburg (FR)—Firmini (FR) **Mr J. P. McManus**
27 **FLETCHERS FLYER (IRE)**, 10, b g Winged Love (IRE)—Crystal Chord (IRE) **Masterson Holdings Limited**

MR HARRY FRY - Continued

28 **FOREST GENERAL,** 5, gr g Geordieland (FR)—Mollycarrs Gambul **Mr John Pemberton & Ms Susan Evans**
29 **GENERAL GINGER,** 8, ch g Generous (IRE)—Nuzzle **Hazard Chase Racing**
30 **GOLDEN BIRTHDAY (FR),** 7, b g Poliglote—Gold Or Silver (FR) **G. C. Stevens**
31 **GOODNITESWEETHEART,** 7, b m Midnight Legend—Over To Charlie **The Twelfth Man Partnership III**
32 **GREEN DOLPHIN (IRE),** 4, b g Oscar (IRE)—Shamrock Miss (IRE) **M. Pescod**
33 **HELL'S KITCHEN,** 7, b g Robin des Champs (FR)—Mille Et Une (FR) **Mr J. P. McManus**
34 **HENRYVILLE,** 10, b g Generous (IRE)—Aquavita **R P B Michaelson & E M Thornton**
35 **IF THE CAP FITS (IRE),** 6, b g Milan—Derravaragh Sayra (IRE) **Mr & Mrs Paul & Clare Rooney**
36 **INNOCENT GIRL (IRE),** 9, b m King's Theatre (IRE)—Belle Innocence (FR) **Coral Champions Club**
37 **ISHKHARA LADY,** 4, b f Scorpion (IRE)—Loxhill Lady **The Horse Flys Partnership**
38 **JEREMIAH JAMES (IRE),** 4, b g Jeremy (USA)—Lougholly Native (IRE) **Dr Caroline Fry & Susie Dilhorne**
39 **JOLLY'S CRACKED IT (FR),** 9, b g Astarabad (USA)—Jolly Harbour **GDM Partnership**
40 **JUST A STING (IRE),** 6, b g Scorpion (IRE)—Shanann Lady (IRE) **Nigel & Barbara Collison**
41 **JUSTAPUZZLE,** 6, ch m Apple Tree (FR)—Gaelic Gold (IRE) **Happy Days Racing**
42 **KYLEMORE LOUGH,** 9, b g Revoque—One of The Last **M J McMahon & Denis Gallagher**
43 **LADY OF LAMANVER,** 8, b m Lucarno (USA)—Lamanver Homerun **Dr D. Christensen**
44 **LAMANVER ODYSSEY,** 6, b m Lucarno (USA)—Lamanver Homerun **Dr D. Christensen**
45 **LAMANVER PIPPIN,** 5, b g Apple Tree (FR)—Lamanver Homerun **Dr D. Christensen**
46 **LEGENDE DE MINUIT,** 4, br g Midnight Legend—Chilla Cilla **The Eyre Family**
47 **LITTERALE CI (FR),** 5, b m Soldier of Fortune (FR)—Cigalia **Mr J. P. McManus**
48 **MELROSE BOY (FR),** 6, b g Saint des Saints (FR)—Pollypink (FR) **Mr & Mrs Paul & Clare Rooney**
49 **MESOPHERE,** 4, ch g Exceed And Excel (AUS)—Monturani (IRE) **Mrs Rebecca Philipps & John Troy**
50 **MINELLA AWARDS (IRE),** 7, b g Oscar (IRE)—Montys Miss (IRE) **Masterson Holdings Limited**
51 **MISTERTON,** 7, gr g Sagamix (FR)—Mighty Splash **Wilkin, Orr, Boileau and Sim**
52 **MISTY WHISKY,** 4, gr f Stowaway—Whisky Rose (IRE) **Distillery Stud**
53 **MR ONE MORE (IRE),** 6, b g Asian Heights—Norah's Quay (IRE) **Mr J. P. McManus**
54 **MR WEST COAST (IRE),** 5, b g Dubai Destination (USA)—Camas North (IRE) **West Coast Haulage Limited**
55 **ONEFORTHEROADTOM,** 5, gr g Fair Mix (IRE)—Ifni du Luc (FR) **Mr J. P. McManus**
56 **OPENING BATSMAN (IRE),** 12, b g Morozov (USA)—Jolly Signal (IRE) **The Twelfth Man Partnership**
57 **OUTOFTHISWORLD (IRE),** 5, b br m Shantou (USA)—Mystic Music (IRE) **Chasing Gold Limited**
58 **OVER TO SAM (IRE),** 6, b g Black Sam Bellamy (IRE)—Lady Brig **The Jago Family Partnership**
59 **OVERTOWN EXPRESS (IRE),** 10, br g Overbury (IRE)—Black Secret **Lorna Squire & Richard Metherell**
60 **REALITY BITES (IRE),** 7, b g Mahler—Seeds of Doubt (IRE) **Masterson Holdings Limited**
61 **RISE OF AN EMPIRE (IRE),** 8, b g Stowaway—Kymin (IRE) **Gigginstown House Stud**
62 **RITAS BID (IRE),** 5, b m Oscar (IRE)—Present Bid (IRE) **Mrs R. O'Callaghan**
63 **ROSEMARY RUSSET,** 6, b m Midnight Legend—Apple Days **Somerset Racing**
64 **RUBY BEAR (IRE),** 4, b g Gold Well—Noble Nell (IRE) **Brian & Sandy Lambert**
65 **RUFIO,** 4, b g Schiaparelli (GER)—Mole End **The Lost Boys**
66 **SAM I (FR),** 5, gr g Lord du Sud (FR)—Blue Girl Star (FR) **Seuss Racing**
67 **SAMARQUAND,** 4, b br g Malinas (GER)—Samandara (FR) **Phil Fry & Charlie Walker -Osborne House**
68 **SECRET DOOR (IRE),** 7, b m Stowaway—Cellar Door (IRE) **Mrs C. Fry**
69 **SEROSEVSKY (IRE),** 5, b g Morozov (USA)—Be My Rainbow (IRE) **Brian & Sandy Lambert**
70 **SHALL WE GO NOW,** 5, b g Midnight Legend—Suave Shot **Mr & Mrs Paul & Clare Rooney**
71 **SHUIL ROYALE (IRE),** 13, b g King's Theatre (IRE)—Shuil Na Lee (IRE) **R. P. Fry**
72 **SIR IVAN,** 8, b g Midnight Legend—Tisho **The Eyre Family**
73 **SPACE ODDITY (IRE),** 7, b br g Al Namix (FR)—Schoune (FR) **The Rate Chasers**
74 **STATUS QUO (IRE),** 5, b g Thewayyouare (USA)—Again Royale (IRE) **Coral Champions Club**
75 **STEEL BOB (IRE),** 6, b g Craigsteel—Lady Kamando **The Steel Bob Partnership**
76 **TANGLEY,** 6, b m Black Sam Bellamy (IRE)—All Rise (GER) **Mahon Racing**
77 **THOMAS BROWN,** 9, b g Sir Harry Lewis—Tentsmuir **The Corse Lawners**
78 **TIGER SKY (IRE),** 5, br m Milan—Standfast (IRE) **Thornton, Gibbs, Cameron & Fry**
79 **TOODLEPIP (IRE),** 4, b f Robin des Champs (FR)—Shannon Theatre (IRE) **Mrs J. A. Thomas**
80 **UNOWHATIMEANHARRY,** 10, b g Sir Harry Lewis (USA)—Red Nose Lady **Mr J. P. McManus**
81 **VIVANT,** 5, gr m Shirocco (GER)—Sisella (IRE) **P. E. Atkinson**
82 **VIVANT POEME (FR),** 9, b g Early March—Hasta Manana (FR) **Andy & Sharon Measham**
83 **VOIX D'EAU (FR),** 8, b g Voix du Nord (FR)—Eau de Chesne (FR) **Harry Fry Racing - Voix D'Eau Syndicate**
84 **WHATAKNIGHT,** 9, b g Midnight Legend—What A Mover **J. M. Dare, T. Hamlin, J. W. Snook**
85 **WINNINGSEVERYTHING (IRE),** 4, b g Flemensfirth (USA)—Baliya (IRE) **Mr & Mrs Paul & Clare Rooney**
86 **WOTZIZNAME (IRE),** 8, b g Fruits of Love (USA)—Native Beau (IRE) **Mr C. J. Horton**
87 5, B m Alflora (IRE)—Wychnor Dawn (IRE) **Unregistered Syndicate**
88 **ZIPPLE BACK (IRE),** 6, b g Sendawar (IRE)—With Conviction (IRE) **Masterson Holdings Limited**

THREE-YEAR-OLDS

89 **DUKE OF DORSET,** b c Sepoy (AUS)—Zuleika Dobson **Mrs R Philipps & Mrs F Mahony**
90 **ZOUTOISE (FR),** b f Enrique—Belle Yepa (FR)

MR HARRY FRY - Continued

TWO-YEAR-OLDS

91 BURROWS TREAT (FR), b f 21/5 Muhtathir—La Vie de Boitron (FR) (Lavirco (GER)) (16280)

Other Owners: Mr S. W. Barrow, Mr J. D. Beese, Mr C. Blackburn, Mrs H. L. Boileau, P. H. Boss, Mrs J. Calder, G. Calder, Mr I. P. Callan, Mrs S. Cameron, Mr D. M. Cameron, Mrs V. J. Chadney, T. H. Chadney, Mr D. Charlesworth, G. Charlesworth, S. J. Clare, Mrs C. M. Clifford, Mr N. Collison, Mrs B. Collison, K. J. Corcoran, Mr S. Cullum, Mr J. M. Dare, D. J. B. Denny, R. B. Denny, Mr M. R. Dentten, Viscountess S. J. Dilhorne, Mrs P. E. Dolan-Abrahams, Mr E. J. Dolan-Abrahams, Mr J. N. I. Edwards, Ms S. L. Evans, Miss R. E. Eyre, Mr H. Eyre, Mrs C. A. Eyre, Mr C. G. S. Eyre, Dr C. E. Fry, R. A. Fry, Mr Denis Gallagher, Mr R. Gibbs, Mrs D. J. Goodall, T. Hamlin, Mr T. Hanrahan, Mrs H. Harding, Mrs R. G. Hillen, Mr A. G. Hipgrave, Mr F. C. A. Jago, Miss M. L. A. Jago, Miss S. J. L. Jago, Mr P. J. A. Jago, Miss J. K. Keech, Mr I. N. Kingham, Mr B. Lambert, Mr R. F. Magrath, Mr D. Magrath, Mr D. J. Mahon, Mrs F. Mahony, Dr B. Mayoh, Mr G. W. McCausland, Mr T. F. McGowan, Mr M. J. McMahon, Mrs S. M. Measham, Mr A. R. Measham, Mr A. R. Measham, R. J. Metherell, R. P. B. Michaelson, Mr P. A. Munnelly, Mrs S. Orr, Mr H. T. Pelham, Mr J. L. Pemberton, Mrs R. Philipps, Mr M. Powell, R. Robinson, Mrs Margaret Robinson, Mrs C. Rooney, Mr P. A. Rooney, A. G. Sim, Mr M. Smith, J. W. Snook, Mrs L. Squire, Mr G. M. Thornton, Mr E. M. Thornton, Mr J. M. Troy, Mr J. P. G. Turner, C. C. Walker, Mr P. M. Warren, Mr J. C. Whiting, Mr R. C. Wilkin, Mr E. Wilson.

Assistant Trainers: Ciara Fry, Mike Legg

Jockey (NH): Noel Fehily, Niall P. Madden. Conditional: Kieron Edgar. Amateur: Mr M. Legg, Miss A. B. O'Connor.

---

215 **MISS CAROLINE FRYER, Wymondham**
Postal: **Browick Hall Cottage, Browick Road, Wymondham, Norfolk, NR18 9RB**
Contacts: **PHONE (01953) 601257 MOBILE (07783) 056076**
E-MAIL caroline@carolinefryerracing.co.uk / c.fryer528@btinternet.com
WEBSITE www.carolinefryerracing.co.uk

1 CATMYGIRL, 4, b f Kayf Tara—Katmai (IRE) Mr P. J. Edwards
2 GOODNIGHT CHARLIE, 8, gr m Midnight Legend—Over To Charlie Miss C. Fryer
3 HIGH WHEELER (IRE), 7, b g Kalanisi (IRE)—Penny Farthing Miss C. Fryer
4 KINGSTON COLLEGE (IRE), 8, b g King's Theatre (IRE)—Princesse Ira (FR) Mrs S. Fryer
5 MIDNIGHT BLISS, 8, b m Midnight Legend—Violet Elizabeth Miss C. Fryer
6 NEW HORIZONS (IRE), 8, b g Presenting—Namloc (IRE) Mr A. & Mrs P. Hurn
7 NICHEINTHEMARKET (IRE), 6, b m Oscar (IRE)—Supreme Kellycarra (IRE) Mr J. D. Ward
8 RIDDLESTOWN (IRE), 11, b g Cloudings (IRE)—Gandi's Dream (IRE) Mr J. D. Ward
9 SCHAP, 6, ch m Schiaparelli (GER)—Royal Keel Miss C. Fryer
10 THE BLUE BOMBER, 6, b g Stimulation (IRE)—Mar Blue (FR) C J Underwood & Caroline Fryer
11 VOLCAN SURPRISE (FR), 10, b g Dom Alco (FR)—Invitee Surprise (FR) Miss C. Fryer

Other Owners: A. Hurn, The Hon Mrs A. Hurn, C. J. Underwood.

---

216 **MR IVAN FURTADO, Wiseton**
Postal: **Flat 2, Wiseton Stables, Wiseton, Doncaster, South Yorkshire, DN10 5AE**
Contacts: **MOBILE (07783) 520746**
E-MAIL ivanfurtado@hotmail.co.uk

1 AFRICAN SHOWGIRL, 5, ch m Showcasing—Georgie The Fourth (IRE) Miss V. Ohlidalova
2 AFRICAN TRADER (USA), 5, b br g Lonhro (AUS)—Nasaieb (IRE) Mr D. H. Slater
3 AVAGO JOSH, 4, ch g Aqlaam—Heart Stopping (USA) The Giggle Factor Partnership
4 BORN IN THORNE, 5, b m Haafhd—Royal Nashkova The Giggle Factor Partnership
5 CHECK 'EM TUESDAY (IRE), 5, b m Kodiac—Wait Watcher (IRE) Mr D. H. Slater
6 FRANK'S LEGACY, 4, ch g Aqlaam—Quite A Thing The Giggle Factor Partnership
7 FREDRICKA, 7, ch m Assertive—Vintage Steps (IRE) Mr J. Melo
8 GLORIOUS ASSET, 6, b g Aqlaam—Regal Asset (USA) The Giggle Factor Partnership
9 GREY CHARLIE, 4, gr g Hellvelyn—Phoenix Rising BGC Racing & Partner
10 HELIOBLU BARELIERE (FR), 5, b g Heliostatic (IRE)—Lonia Blue (FR) The Giggle Factor Partnership
11 HUDDERSFILLY TOWN, 4, b f Major Cadeaux—Mortitia BGC Racing Xi & Partner
12 ILLUSTRISSIME (USA), 5, b g Mizzen Mast (USA)—Ghost Friendly (USA) Mr C. Hodgson
13 MALASPINA (ITY), 6, b m Pounced (USA)—Modern Goddess (USA) BGC Racing, C Hodgson & Giggle Factor
14 MISS UPPITY, 5, ch m Notnowcato—Instructress Mr J. Melo
15 MURDANOVA (IRE), 5, gr g Zebedee—Agnista (IRE) Mr P. Slater
16 NORMAL EQUILIBRIUM, 8, b g Elnadim (USA)—Acicula (IRE) J. L. Marriott
17 RAVEN BANNER (IRE), 5, b m Raven's Pass (USA)—Ask Annie (IRE) Mr D. H. Slater

MR IVAN FURTADO - Continued

18 **ROMAN DE BRUT (IRE)**, 6, ch g Rock of Gibraltar (IRE)—Nesmeh (USA) **Mr Phil Slater**
19 **RULED BY THE MOON**, 4, b g Mawatheeq (USA)—Hallingdal (UAE) **The Giggle Factor Partnership**
20 **SCRIBNER CREEK (IRE)**, 5, b g Roderic O'connor (IRE)—Nebraska Lady (IRE) **Mr D. H. Slater**
21 **SHELNEVERWALKALONE**, 4, b f Captain Gerrard (IRE)—Rabarama **BGC Racing X & Partner**
22 **SIR OTTOMAN (FR)**, 5, b g Excellent Art—Hali Layali **Mr C. Hodgson**
23 **SKI BLAST**, 7, ch g Three Valleys (USA)—Chasing Stars **The Giggle Factor Partnership**
24 **SWORD EXCEED (GER)**, 4, b g Exceed And Excel (AUS)—
Sword Roche (GER) **21st Century Racing, C Hodgson & BGC**
25 **THATSTHEWAYTODOIT (IRE)**, 5, ch m Lord Shanakill (USA)—Van de Cappelle (IRE) **Mr D. H. Slater**
26 **VAN GROGAN (IRE)**, 4, ch g Rip Van Winkle (IRE)—Metaphor (USA) **Mr P. Slater**
27 **WILLIAM BOOTH (IRE)**, 4, b g Born To Sea (IRE)—Chaguaramas (IRE) **H/J Racing**
28 **ZAEEM**, 9, b g Echo of Light—Across (ARG) **21st Century Racing & Nigel Sennett**

THREE-YEAR-OLDS

29 **ALLLEEDSAREN'TWE**, b g Havana Gold (IRE)—Minnola **BGC Racing VIII**
30 **BLACKLOOKS (IRE)**, b g Society Rock (IRE)—Mosaique Beauty (IRE) **J. L. Marriott**
31 **EQUILIBRIUM**, b f Equiano (FR)—Piste **BGC Racing,Trisha Keane & Giggle Factor**
32 **FEEL THE WRATH (IRE)**, b c Arcano (IRE)—Takaliya (IRE) **Mr Phil Slater**
33 **FILBERT STREET**, ch c Poet's Voice—Tinnarinka **BGC Racing Vi & Carl Hodgson**
34 **FOLLOWTHESTEPS (IRE)**, b g Footstepsinthesand—Excellent Mariner (IRE) **J. L. Marriott**
35 **GEMBARI**, b g Denounce—Zagarock **Mr R. Hull**
36 **ITSUPFORGRABSNOW (IRE)**, b f Footstepsinthesand—Rye Rhythm (IRE) **BGC Racing VII**
37 **JASI (IRE)**, b g Kodiac—Late Night Movie (IRE) **Mr A. Almutairi**
38 **LAITH ALAREEN**, b g Invincible Spirit (IRE)—Bewitchment **21st Century Racing & Nigel Sennett**
39 **ONEROA (IRE)**, b f Dandy Man (IRE)—Alexander Express (IRE) **H/J Racing**
40 **SHEEDY**, b f Sir Percy—Purest **BGC Racing & Partner**
41 **SWISSIE**, br g Swiss Spirit—Princess Pivotal **Ms J. A. French**

TWO-YEAR-OLDS

42 B c 22/3 Epaulette (AUS)—Destiny of A Diva (Denounce) (10476) **Mr Ron Hull**
43 B c 7/3 Sir Prancealot (IRE)—Monsusu (IRE) (Montjeu (IRE)) (19047) **J. L. Marriott**
44 B c 30/4 Zebedee—No Way (IRE) (Rainbows For Life (CAN)) (14285) **Mr P. Slater**
45 B c 31/3 Epaulette (AUS)—Zagarock (Rock of Gibraltar (IRE)) (17142) **Mr Ron Hull**

Other Owners: 21st Century Racing, BGC Racing, BGC Racing VI, BGC Racing X, BGC Racing XI, Mrs B. Catterall, A. W. Catterall, Mr J. R. Holt, Mr S. G. Hope, Mr K. W. Jarvis, Ms T. Keane, Mr N. P. Sennett, Mr R. Ward.

---

217 **MR JOHN GALLAGHER, Moreton-In-Marsh**
Postal: Grove Farm, Chastleton, Moreton-In-Marsh, Gloucestershire, GL56 0SZ
Contacts: PHONE (01608) 674492 MOBILE (07780) 972663
E-MAIL john@gallagherracing.com WEBSITE www.gallagherracing.com

1 **ANDALUSITE**, 5, br m Equiano (FR)—Kammaan **The LAM Partnership**
2 **BAHAMIAN SUNRISE**, 6, ch g Bahamian Bounty—Tagula Sunrise (IRE) **Caveat Emptor Partnership**
3 **BELLA'S VENTURE**, 5, gr m Hellvelyn—Fayre Bella **John Gallagher**
4 **HARRISON STICKLE**, 6, gr g Hellvelyn—Hollybell **Ms A. Clifford**
5 **ILEY BOY**, 4, b g Delegator—Menha **John Gallagher**
6 **JUNOESQUE**, 4, b f Virtual—Snake Skin **The Juniper Racing Club Ltd**
7 **LA GOULUE**, 4, ch f Kheleyf (USA)—Quotation **Mr D. A. Clark**
8 **LADWEB**, 8, ch g Bertolini (USA)—Adweb **The Juniper Racing Club & Andrew Bell**
9 **LUNGARNO PALACE (USA)**, 7, b g Henrythenavigator (USA)—
Good Time Sally (USA) **Caveat Emptor Partnership**
10 **MAJOR PUSEY**, 6, ch g Major Cadeaux—Pusey Street Lady **C. R. Marks (Banbury)**
11 **OOLOGIST**, 7, gr g Proclamation (IRE)—Orchid's Silver **Mr Charles Stone & Mr Trevor Beeches**
12 **OUR YOUNG UN**, 5, b g Native Ruler—Dani (IRE) **J & L Wetherald - M & M Glover**
13 **QUENCH DOLLY**, 4, gr f Hellvelyn—Hollybell **Quench Racing Partnership**
14 **RIVAS ROSE MARIE**, 4, b f Archipenko (USA)—Rivas Rhapsody (IRE) **Mr D. H. L. Jones**

THREE-YEAR-OLDS

15 **CRUEL CLEVER CAT**, b f Bated Breath—Satin Braid **Noreen & Don Clark**
16 **FIT TO FLY**, b f Mount Nelson—Pusey Street Lady **Caveat Emptor Partnership**
17 **GOWER GOLD**, b f Mayson—Mistressofthelake (IRE) **John Gallagher**
18 **GREEN POWER**, b c Kheleyf (USA)—Hakuraa (IRE) **Nino's Partnership**

MR JOHN GALLAGHER - Continued

19 **NO EQUALISERS**, b g Vale of York (IRE)—Rose Season **Mr R Bedford & Mr P Bedford**
20 **RIVAS ROB ROY**, ch g Archipenko (USA)—Rivas Rhapsody (IRE) **Mr D. H. L. Jones**

TWO-YEAR-OLDS

21 **BLUE BATTALION**, ch c 10/2 Cityscape—Hollybell (Beveled (USA)) (17142) **Mr R. Little**
22 **FOXY FEMME**, ch f 22/2 Foxwedge (AUS)—Pusey Street Vale (Moss Vale (IRE))
23 **MAHUIKA**, b f 25/2 Firebreak—Adweb (Muhtarram (USA)) **The Juniper Racing Club & Andrew Bell**
24 **MAID FROM THE MIST**, gr f 18/2 Hellvelyn—
                     Ball Burst (IRE) (Imperial Ballet (IRE)) (4761) **M. C. S. D. Racing Partnership**
25 **Gra** g 23/3 Archipenko (USA)—Rivas Rhapsody (IRE) (Hawk Wing (USA)) **Mr D. H. L. Jones**
26 **SWISS MISS**, b f 25/2 Swiss Spirit—Miss Meticulous (Bahamian Bounty) **The LAM Partnership**
27 **TOMAHAWK RIDGE (IRE)**, gr c 16/3 Alhebayeb (IRE)—
                     Low Cut Affair (IRE) (Fast Company (IRE)) (11428) **Max Europe Limited**

Other Owners: Mr P. N. Bedford, Mr R. J. Bedford, Mr T. A. Beeches, Mr A. Bell, Mrs N. Clark, Mr B. Downard, Dr M. F. Ford, Mrs A. J. Forde, M. P. Glover, Ms M. E. Glover, Mr M. W. Goodall, Mr J. N. Greenley, Mr C. F. Little, J. F. Long, Mrs B. A. Long, B. J. McClean, Mrs M. B. McClean, Ms L. M. Mulcahy, Mr M. Preedy, Mr M. T. Rigby, Mr C. Stone, Mrs L. T. Wetherald, Mr J. A. Wetherald.

Assistant Trainer: Mrs R. J. Gallagher

---

218   MRS ILKA GANSERA-LÉVÊQUE, Newmarket
Postal: **St Wendred's, Hamilton Road, Newmarket, Suffolk, CB8 7JQ**
Contacts: **PHONE (01638) 454973 MOBILE (07855) 532072**
E-MAIL **office@gansera-leveque.com** WEBSITE **www.gansera-leveque.com**

1 **ANNOUSHKA**, 5, b m Proclamation (IRE)—Anapola (GER) **Strawberry Fields Stud**
2 **ROBBIE ROO ROO**, 5, br m Kheleyf (USA)—Haiti Dancer **Mrs I. Gansera-Leveque**

THREE-YEAR-OLDS

3 **Gr g** Lethal Force (IRE)—Cool Catena
4 **EZZ (IRE)**, b c Intello (GER)—Looby Loo **Al Nujaifi Racing Ltd**
5 **MIDNIGHT IN PARIS**, b f Champs Elysees—Midnight Ransom **Mrs E. A. P. Haynes**
6 **PASS MARK**, b g Raven's Pass (USA)—Examinee (GER) **The Kathryn Stud Limited**
7 **RISING SEAS**, b g Mount Nelson—Puya **Mrs I. Gansera-Leveque**
8 **THAMA**, b f Finjaan—It's The War (USA) **Mr H. M. K. Al Mehairi**

TWO-YEAR-OLDS

9 **Ch f** 17/3 Intello (GER)—Portrait (Peintre Celebre (USA)) (8000) **Mr S. P. Hussain**

Other Owners: Mrs Kathy Kroll-Smoke, Mr G. F. L. Robinson, Graf. Stauffenberg, Exors of the Late Mr Basil White.

Assistant Trainer: Stephane Lévêque

Jockey (flat): Adam Beschizza, Saleem Golam.

---

219   MRS SUSAN GARDNER, Longdown
Postal: **Woodhayes Farm, Longdown, Exeter**
Contacts: **PHONE/FAX (01392) 811213 MOBILE (07936) 380492**
E-MAIL **woodhayesstudfarm@btinternet.com** WEBSITE **www.suegardnerracing.co.uk**

1 **BREDON HILL LAD**, 11, ch g Kirkwall—Persian Clover **Mr & Mrs R W & Mrs J M Mitchell**
2 **COEUR BLIMEY (IRE)**, 7, b br g Winged Love (IRE)—Eastender **Keith Harris & Tom Gardner**
3 **EDDY**, 9, b g Exit To Nowhere (USA)—Sharway Lady **J. F. Panvert**
4 **HERE'S HERBIE**, 10, b g Classic Cliche (IRE)—Tyre Hill Lilly **Mr P. A. Tylor & Mr D V Gardner**
5 **HOOLA HULA**, 5, br m Yeats (IRE)—Dancing Dasi (IRE) **Mr D. V. Gardner**
6 4, B g Winged Love (IRE)—Lady Oakwell (IRE) **Mr D. V. Gardner**
7 **LAPFORD LAD**, 6, ch g Arvico (FR)—State of Grace **Mr A. I. Leach**
8 **NYMET ROWLAND LAD**, 7, ch g With The Flow (USA)—State of Grace **Mr A. I. Leach**
9 **ONLY GORGEOUS (IRE)**, 9, b g Vertical Speed (FR)—Pure Beautiful (IRE) **Miss Jane Edgar & Mr D. V. Gardner**
10 **PEDULIA ALBA (FR)**, 5, b m Beat Hollow—Parthenia (IRE) **Mr J. L. Lightfoot**
11 **QUICK N' EASY (IRE)**, 8, ch g Vertical Speed (FR)—Tarmons Duchess (IRE) **Mr D. V. Gardner**
12 **RAFAFIE**, 10, b g Kayf Tara—Florie **Mr D. V. Gardner**

MRS SUSAN GARDNER - Continued

13 **SNAZZ MAN**, 8, b g Beat All (USA)—Ela d'argent (IRE) **Jason Brooke & Partner**
14 **TEA TIME FRED**, 9, b g Kayf Tara—Darjeeling (IRE) **Mr D. V. Gardner**
15 **THE IMITATION GAME**, 5, b m Yeats (IRE)—Katmai (IRE) **Mr W. Belcher**
16 **TRANS EXPRESS (IRE)**, 8, br g Trans Island—Hazel Fastrack **Mr D. V. Gardner**
17 **WOULDUADAMANDEVEIT (IRE)**, 5, b g Stowaway—Figlette **Keith Harris & Tom Gardner**

Other Owners: Mr J. J. Brooke, Miss J. E. Edgar, Mr T. A. Gardner, Mr K. T. Harris, R. W. Mitchell, Mrs J. M. Mitchell, P. A. Tylor.

Assistant Trainer: D. V. Gardner

Jockey (NH): Aidan Coleman, Lucy Gardner, Micheal Nolan.

---

220 **MRS ROSEMARY GASSON, Banbury**
Postal: **Alkerton Grounds, Balscote, Banbury, Oxfordshire, OX15 6JS**
Contacts: **PHONE (01295) 730248 MOBILE (07769) 798430**
E-MAIL arb@aqf.myzen.co.uk

1 **BIGNORM (IRE)**, 6, b g Mahler—Merry Heart (IRE) **Mrs R. Gasson**
2 **CROCO MISTER (IRE)**, 11, ch g Croco Rouge (IRE)—Nimrods Dream (IRE) **Mrs R. Gasson**
3 **DRAGON KHAN (IRE)**, 9, b g Dr Fong (USA)—Desert Magic (IRE) **Mrs R. Gasson**
4 **IRISH OCTAVE (IRE)**, 8, b g Gamut (IRE)—Fairytaleofnewyork (IRE) **Mrs R. Gasson**
5 **JUSTTHEGREY (IRE)**, 6, gr g Getaway (GER)—Line White (FR) **Mrs R. Gasson**
6 **KALA LORD (IRE)**, 7, b g Kalanisi (IRE)—Eimears Pet (IRE) **Mrs R. Gasson**
7 **KILCASCAN**, 14, b g Alflora (IRE)—Peasedown Tofana **Mrs R. Gasson**
8 **MR MCGUINESS (IRE)**, 8, b g Kalanisi (IRE)—Maig Mandy (IRE) **Mrs R. Gasson**
9 **SCARTARE (IRE)**, 7, br g Trans Island—La Speziana (IRE) **Mrs R. Gasson**

Jockey (NH): Ben Poste.

---

221 **MR JONATHAN GEAKE, Marlborough**
Postal: **Harestone House, East Kennett, Marlborough, Wiltshire, SN8 4EY**
Contacts: **PHONE (01672) 861784 MOBILE (07768) 350738**
E-MAIL jageake@yahoo.co.uk

1 **A LASTING JOY**, 7, b m Refuse To Bend (IRE)—Sir Kyffin's Folly **Mrs A. Leftley**
2 **BONDI MIST (IRE)**, 9, gr m Aussie Rules (USA)—Akoya (IRE) **Mrs A. Leftley**
3 **CORNELIUS (FR)**, 6, b g Country Reel (USA)—Dinaha (FR) **Mrs S. A. Geake**
4 **FIDELITY**, 6, b g Halling (USA)—Sir Kyffin's Folly **Mrs A. Leftley**
5 **GLENS WOBBLY**, 10, ch g Kier Park (IRE)—Wobbly **Mr R. G. Symes**
6 **HEEZARARITY**, 10, b g Librettist (USA)—Extremely Rare (USA) **Miss E. Tanner**
7 **MICQUUS (IRE)**, 9, b g High Chaparral (IRE)—My Potters (USA) **Mrs A. Leftley**
8 **PRINCE OF CARDAMOM (IRE)**, 6, b g Nayef (USA)—Tiger Spice **Mrs P. D. Gulliver**
9 **SACRAMENTO KING (IRE)**, 9, gr g Desert King (IRE)—Kindle Ball (FR) **Mrs P. D. Gulliver**
10 **SHOT IN THE DARK (IRE)**, 9, ch g Dr Fong (USA)—Highland Shot **Mrs P. D. Gulliver**

Assistant Trainer: Mrs S. A. Geake **Pupil Assistant:** Mr Sam Geake

---

222 **MISS KAREN GEORGE, Crediton**
Postal: **Higher Eastington Stables, Lapford, Crediton, Devon, EX17 6NE**
Contacts: **PHONE (01363) 83092 FAX (01363) 83092 MOBILE (07917) 007892**
E-MAIL eastington1@yahoo.com WEBSITE www.eastingtonracing.co.uk

1 **HAZELL BERRY (IRE)**, 4, b f Big Bad Bob (IRE)—Mudalalah (IRE) **Miss K. M. George**
2 **I SHOULD COCO**, 5, b m With The Flow (USA)—Follow The Dream **P. J. H. George**
3 **LOG OFF (IRE)**, 4, b f Sir Prancealot (IRE)—Dolphin Stamp (IRE) **P. J. H. George**
4 **NETLEY ABBEY**, 4, b g Myboycharlie (IRE)—Ana Style (FR) **Henacre Racing Club Ltd**
5 **QUINTUS CERIALIS (IRE)**, 6, b g Vale of York (IRE)—Red Fox (IRE) **Clare Smith & Karen George**
6 **SECRET RETURN (IRE)**, 5, ch m Roderic O'connor (IRE)—Quick Return **Martin Vaughan & Karen George**

MISS KAREN GEORGE - Continued

THREE-YEAR-OLDS

7 **POLLY'S GOLD (IRE)**, ch f Havana Gold (IRE)—Keyta Bonita (IRE) **Mrs V. James**

TWO-YEAR-OLDS

8 Ch f 22/3 Harbour Watch (IRE)—Clifton Dancer (Fraam) (9500)
9 B c 18/4 Battle of Marengo (IRE)—Margie (IRE) Marju (IRE)) (4500)
10 Ch f 6/3 Dawn Approach (IRE)—Samdaniya (Machiavellian (USA)) (6000)
11 Ch f 23/2 Mukhadram—Today's The Day (Alhaarth (IRE)) (2000) **Henacre Racing Club Ltd**
12 B f 29/4 Mayson—Warden Rose (Compton Place) (3000)

Other Owners: Mrs C. E. Smith, Mr M. Vaughan.

Assistant Trainers: Mr P. George, Mr R. E. Baskerville.

---

223 **MR TOM GEORGE, Slad**
Postal: **Down Farm, Slad, Stroud, Gloucestershire, GL6 7QE**
Contacts: **PHONE (01452) 814267 MOBILE (07850) 793483**
E-MAIL tom@trgeorge.com WEBSITE www.tomgeorgeracing.co.uk

1 **AIR NAVIGATOR**, 7, b g Yeats (IRE)—Lox Lane (IRE) **Lady Cobham & Doone Hulse**
2 **ANOTHER STOWAWAY (IRE)**, 6, b g Stowaway—Another Pet (IRE) **H Stephen Smith & Family Gabbertas**
3 **BABY KING (IRE)**, 9, b g Ivan Denisovich (IRE)—Burn Baby Burn (IRE) **About Two Weeks**
4 **BALLINVARIG (IRE)**, 11, b g Beneficial—Leos Holiday (IRE) **Simon Clarke & Sisters**
5 **BARAZA (FR)**, 7, gr g Smadoun (FR)—Gerbora (FR) **Mr S. W. Clarke**
6 **BATTLE OF SHILOH (IRE)**, 9, b g Shantou (USA)—Realt Na Ruise (IRE) **Mr & Mrs Paul & Clare Rooney**
7 **BENI LIGHT (FR)**, 7, b g Crossharbour—Or Light (FR) **Crossed Fingers Partnership**
8 **BEST TO COME (IRE)**, 5, b g Stowaway—Nippy Nora (IRE) **Mr & Mrs Paul & Clare Rooney**
9 **BIGPIPENOTOBACEEE (IRE)**, 7, b br g King's Theatre (IRE)—
Another Dollar (IRE) **PP Control & Automation Limited**
10 **BLACK OP (IRE)**, 7, br g Sandmason—Afar Story (IRE) **R. S. Brookhouse**
11 **BOAGRIUS (IRE)**, 6, ch g Beneficial—Greenhall Rambler (IRE) **The MerseyClyde Partnership**
12 **BORN FOR WAR (IRE)**, 6, ch g Wareed (IRE)—Oscar Bird (IRE) **Mr & Mrs Paul & Clare Rooney**
13 **BOYHOOD (IRE)**, 7, b g Oscar (IRE)—Glen Dubh (IRE) **H Stephen Smith & The Gabbertas Family**
14 **BRANDON HILL (IRE)**, 10, b g Beneficial—Annesbanker (IRE) **Mr N T Griffith & H M Haddock**
15 **BRAVENTARA**, 7, b m Kayf Tara—L'aventure (FR) **Mr C. J. Harriman**
16 **BROOM TIP (IRE)**, 6, b g Flemensfirth (USA)—Norabelle (FR) **Mr S. W. Clarke**
17 **BUN DORAN (IRE)**, 7, b g Shantou (USA)—Village Queen (IRE) **Crossed Fingers Partnership**
18 **CALL ME VIC (IRE)**, 11, b g Old Vic—Call Me Dara (IRE) **Mr C. B. Compton**
19 **CERNUNNOS (IRE)**, 8, b g Della Francesca (USA)—Jackette (USA) **Mr J. P. McManus**
20 **CHAMPAGNE CITY**, 5, ch g Tobougg (IRE)—City of Angels **R. S. Brookhouse**
21 **CLONDAW CASTLE (IRE)**, 6, b g Oscar (IRE)—Lohort Castle (IRE) **J French, D McDermott, S Nelson, T Syder**
22 **COPPER WEST (IRE)**, 7, b g Westerner—Printing Copper (IRE) **The MerseyClyde Partnership**
23 **CRUISEAWEIGH (IRE)**, 7, b g Oscar (IRE)—Triptoohan (IRE) **Mr S. W. Clarke**
24 **DANDY DUKE (IRE)**, 7, b g Duke of Marmalade (IRE)—
Quest For Eternity (IRE) **Dermot O'Donohoe & Sharon C Nelson**
25 **DARLING DU LARGE (FR)**, 5, b m Kapgarde (FR)—Dissidente (FR) **Mr S. W. Clarke**
26 **DEXCITE (FR)**, 7, b br g Authorized (IRE)—Belle Alicia (FR) **Crossed Fingers Partnership**
27 **DOCTOR DEX (IRE)**, 5, b g Oscar (IRE)—Larnalee (IRE) **Crossed Fingers Partnership**
28 **DOUBLE SHUFFLE (IRE)**, 8, b g Milan—Fiddlers Bar (IRE) **Crossed Fingers Partnership**
29 **DRILL BABY DRILL**, 7, b m Black Sam Bellamy (IRE)—Tulipa (POL) **Mrs Sharon C. Nelson**
30 **DRUMLEE SUNSET (IRE)**, 8, br g Royal Anthem (USA)—Be My Sunset (IRE) **R. S. Brookhouse**
31 **FORGOT TO ASK (IRE)**, 6, b g Ask—Lady Transcend (IRE) **Miss J. A. Hoskins**
32 **GET RHYTHM (IRE)**, 8, b g Kayf Tara—Ninna Nanna (FR) **Miss J. A. Hoskins**
33 **GOD'S OWN (IRE)**, 10, b g Oscar (IRE)—Dantes Term (IRE) **Crossed Fingers Partnership**
34 **GORSKY ISLAND**, 10, b g Turtle Island (IRE)—Belle Magello (FR) **Silkword Racing Partnership**
35 **HATTAAB (IRE)**, 5, b g Intikhab (USA)—Sundus (USA) **Mr N T Griffith & H M Haddock**
36 **KILBREE KID (IRE)**, 11, b g Cloudings (IRE)—Bustingoutallover (USA) **Five Valleys Racing Partnership**
37 **KK LEXION (IRE)**, 7, b g Flemensfirth (USA)—Kiloradante (IRE) **Perry, Lawson, Waller, Rea, McDermott**
38 **MASSINI MAN**, 5, b g Dr Massini (IRE)—Alleged To Rhyme (IRE) **Mrs E. A. Fletcher**
39 **MAX WARD (IRE)**, 9, b g Milan—Made Easy (IRE) **Mr N T Griffith & H M Haddock**
40 **MICK MAESTRO (FR)**, 5, b br g Air Chief Marshal (USA)—Mick Maya (FR) **Crossed Fingers Partnership**
41 **MINELLA ARIS (IRE)**, 7, b g King's Theatre (IRE)—Liss Rua (IRE) **Mr S. W. Clarke**
42 **MINELLA FOR ME (IRE)**, 8, b g King's Theatre (IRE)—Irish Mystics (IRE) **Mr S. W. Clarke**
43 **MISS FLEMING**, 6, b m Flemensfirth (USA)—Uppermost **Quartet**

MR TOM GEORGE - Continued

44 MISS NIGHT OWL, 8, ch m Midnight Legend—Moyliscar Capt & Mrs John George
45 MOSS ON THE MILL, 10, b g Overbury (IRE)—Mimis Bonnet (FR) Mr R. T. Cornock
46 MZUZU (IRE), 6, b g Oscar (IRE)—Tempest Hill (IRE) Mr N T Griffith & H M Haddock
47 NEEDS FURTHER (IRE), 5, ch g Doyen (IRE)—My Linda (IRE) Mr & Mrs Paul & Clare Rooney
48 NET DE TREVE (FR), 5, b g Network (GER)—Dame de Treve (FR) O'Donohoe, Cavanagh, Robinson, Nelson
49 NEVER GO SHORT, 6, ch m Midnight Legend—Tulipa (POL) Sharon C. Nelson & Dermot O'Donohoe
50 NO DUFFER, 11, ch g Karinga Bay—Dolly Duff Mr D. C. Robey
51 NOW LOOK AT ME (IRE), 4, ch g Shantou (USA)—Similan (IRE) Mr & Mrs Paul & Clare Rooney
52 O MAONLAI (IRE), 10, b g Oscar (IRE)—Another Gaye (IRE) Mr C. H. Perry
53 ON PAROLE (IRE), 5, b g Kayf Tara—Ain't Misbehavin (IRE) Syder, Whateley, Murphy, Burke
54 OSCAR BRAVO (IRE), 7, br g Oscar (IRE)—Brave Commitment (IRE) Mr C. B. Compton
55 OTTER MOON, 6, b g Midnight Legend—Highland Dawn Mr & Mrs M C Houghton
56 OVERAWED, 7, b m Overbury (IRE)—Alleged To Rhyme (IRE) Mrs E. A. Fletcher
57 ROCKLANDER (IRE), 9, b g Oscar (IRE)—Rua Lass (IRE) Mr D O'Donohoe, J Cavanagh, S Nelson
58 SAINT ARE (FR), 12, b g Network (GER)—Fortanea (FR) Mr D. W. Fox
59 SEDDON (IRE), 5, b g Stowaway—Andreas Benefit (IRE) McNeill Family Ltd
60 SINGLEFARMPAYMENT, 8, b g Milan—Crevamoy (IRE) Mr N T Griffith & H M Haddock
61 SMUGGLER'S BLUES (IRE), 6, b g Yeats (IRE)—Rosy de Cyborg (FR) Mr N T Griffith & H M Haddock
62 SOME ARE LUCKY (IRE), 7, b g Gold Well—Foreign Estates (IRE) PP Control & Automation Limited
63 SONG SAA, 8, b m Midnight Legend—Mystere (IRE) Sharon C. Nelson & Georgie McGrath
64 STAMP YOUR FEET (IRE), 6, b g Galileo (IRE)—Nausicaa (USA) Mr J. P. McManus
65 STOP THE WORLD (IRE), 5, b g Oscar (IRE)—Coolsilver (IRE) McNeill Family Ltd
66 STRIKE IN MILAN (IRE), 6, b g Milan—Great Days (IRE) R. S. Brookhouse
67 SUMKINDOFKING (IRE), 7, br g King's Theatre (IRE)—Shannon Rose (IRE) PP Control & Automation Limited
68 SUMMERVILLE BOY (IRE), 6, b g Sandmason—Suny House R. S. Brookhouse
69 SUPER SID (IRE), 6, b g Westerner—Super Sammy Mr N T Griffith & H M Haddock
70 THE BIG BITE (IRE), 5, b g Scorpion (IRE)—Thanks Noel (IRE) Mr N T Griffith & H M Haddock
71 THE ROMFORD PELE (IRE), 11, b g Accordion—Back And Fore (IRE) Racing Ventures 2014
72 THE WORLDS END (IRE), 7, b g Stowaway—Bright Sprite (IRE) McNeill Family Ltd
73 TRUCKERS LODGE (IRE), 6, b g Westerner—Galeacord (IRE) Gordon & Su Hall
74 UNTIL WINNING (FR), 10, b g Kapgarde (FR)—Fripperie (FR) Thoroughbred Ladies 1
75 VALSEUR DU GRANVAL (FR), 9, b g Della Francesca (USA)—La Grande Vallee (FR) Mr S. W. Clarke
76 WESTERN WAVE (FR), 6, b g Westerner—Kaprissima (FR) Quartet
77 WILD WEST WIND (IRE), 9, b g Westerner—Mhuire Na Gale (IRE) Mr S. W. Clarke
78 WUFF (IRE), 10, b g Beneficial—Dummy Run (IRE) R. S. Brookhouse

Other Owners: Mr Andrew Brown, Mr J. Cavanagh, Mr Simon W. Clarke, Lady Cobham, Mr J. M. Fawbert, Mr J. French, Mr R. K. Gabbertas, Mrs S. Gabbertas, Mr Mark Gabbertas, Mrs C. M. George, Mr T. R. George, Capt. J. A. George, Mrs S. P. George, Mrs Jane Gerard-Pearse, Mr N. Griffith, Heather Haddock, Mr Gordon Hall, Mrs Su Hall, Mrs Sally Hayward, Miss Julie Hoskins, Mrs H. J. Houghton, Mr M. C. Houghton, Mrs Doone Hulse, Mr John B. Lawson, Mrs Mary MacGregor, Mr David McDermott, Mrs Georgie McGrath, Ms J. Moran, Mr Aiden Murphy, Mrs Sharon C. Nelson, Mr D. J. O'Donohoe, Mr Tony Outhart, Mr Colin Perry, Mr David Rea, Mr Nick Rieger, Mrs Vicki Robinson, Mrs C. Rollings, Mrs C. Rooney, Mr P. A. Rooney, Mr P. Ryan, Mrs Susie Saunders, Ms Virginia Slaymaker, Mr H. Stephen Smith, Tim Syder, Thoroughbred Ladies, Mr C. R. Trembath, Mr R. F. Tromans, Mr Alan Waller, Mrs Diana L. Whateley, Mr Richard Wilkin, Mr Nicholas Williamson.

Assistant Trainers: John Cullinan & Ciaran McKee

Jockey (NH): Adrian Heskin. Conditional: Ciaran Gethings. Amateur: Mr Noel George.

224
MR NICK GIFFORD, Findon
Postal: The Downs, Stable Lane, Findon, West Sussex, BN14 0RT
Contacts: OFFICE (01903) 872226 MOBILE (07940) 518077
E-MAIL downs.stables@btconnect.com WEBSITE www.nickgiffordracing.co.uk

1 ALKA STEP (IRE), 7, gr g Alkaadhem—D'ibbbys Step (IRE) Mr J E Burrows & Mrs V C Burrows
2 BEACH DANCER (IRE), 4, b g Footstepsinthesand—All Night Dancer (IRE) Mrs D. A. Willis
3 BLACK LIGHTNING (IRE), 5, br g Whitmore's Conn—Annie May (IRE) D. G. Trangmar
4 BROWN BEAR (IRE), 7, b g Yeats (IRE)—Moray Firth (UAE) The Bear Necessities
5 CANYOURINGMEBACK (IRE), 6, b br g Robin des Pres (FR)—Hunters Bar (IRE) Mr T. C. McKeever
6 CASHANOVA (IRE), 7, b g Arcadio (GER)—Starshade (IRE) C.Mehta J.Brooks Mr&Mrs Lovell C.Bray
7 4, Br f Robin des Champs (FR)—Cruising Katie (IRE) J. R. Hulme
8 DAYLIGHT KATIE (FR), 5, b m Bonbon Rose (FR)—Sirani (FR) Coldunell Limited
9 DIDTHEYLEAVEUOUTTO (IRE), 5, ch g Presenting—Pretty Puttens (IRE) Mr J. P. McManus

MR NICK GIFFORD - Continued

10 **FAIRWAY FREDDY (IRE)**, 5, b g Elusive Pimpernel (USA)—
Silent Supreme (IRE) **Kyle, Shepherd and Andrea & Graham Wylie**
11 4, B f Sans Frontieres (IRE)—Free Dreamer (IRE) **Nick Gifford Racing Club**
12 **GIVE HIM TIME**, 7, b g Kalanisi (IRE)—Delayed (FR) **Mrs T. J. Stone-Brown**
13 **GLEN ROCCO**, 7, ch g Shirocco (GER)—Adees Dancer **J Kyle, G Mason, D Stevens**
14 **JEBS GAMBLE (IRE)**, 7, b g Dubai Destination (USA)—
Gentle Caribou (IRE) **Mrs C Gamble, JEB & Mrs R Gifford**
15 **MARKET COURT (IRE)**, 7, b g Court Cave (IRE)—Piepowder **B. Noakes & Baroness S. Noakes**
16 **MINUTESTOMIDNIGHT (IRE)**, 7, b m Vinnie Roe (IRE)—Midnight Reel (IRE) **Coldunell Limited**
17 **NOTRE AMI (IRE)**, 7, br g Kalanisi (IRE)—Shuilan (IRE) **The Morpheus Partnership**
18 **ODEN**, 4, ch g Lope de Vega (IRE)—Dashing (IRE) **Mrs S. Cotty**
19 **PADDY'S POEM**, 7, b g Proclamation (IRE)—Ashleys Petale (IRE) **Mrs T. J. Stone-Brown**
20 **PARTY ROYAL**, 8, b g Royal Applause—Voliere **Coldunell Limited**
21 **PROJECT MARS (IRE)**, 6, b g Presenting—Molly Massini (IRE) **Project Mars Racing Partnership**
22 **PROUTS PUB (IRE)**, 9, b g Catcher In The Rye (IRE)—A Woman In Love **Nick Gifford Racing Club**
23 **PUPPET WARRIOR**, 6, ch g Black Sam Bellamy (IRE)—Rakajack **Mrs Philippa Wates**
24 **REAR GUARD (IRE)**, 4, b g Oscar (IRE)—Kahysera **The Brooks, Stewart Families & J. Kyle**
25 **SNOWY OSCAR (IRE)**, 5, b g Oscar (IRE)—Reedsbuck (FR) **Mr M. K. O'Shea**
26 **SOLAR GLORY (IRE)**, 4, b g Fame And Glory—Cashalass (IRE)
27 **SWIFT NATIVE (IRE)**, 6, br m Mahler—Hasty Native (IRE) **Nick Gifford Racing Club**
28 **THE MIGHTY DON (IRE)**, 6, ch g Shantou (USA)—Flying Answer (IRE) **Golden Rose Partnership**
29 **THEO'S CHARM (IRE)**, 8, b g Presenting—Kates Charm (IRE) **Mr M. K. O'Shea**

Other Owners: Mr J. P. M. Bowtell, Mrs L. Bowtell, Mr G. F. Brooks, Mr J. R. Brooks, Mr J. E. Burrows, Mrs V. C. Burrows, Mr M. T. Forbes-Wood, Mrs C. A. Foster, Mr G. Gamble, Mrs R. E. Gifford, Mr J. Kyle, G. A. Mason, Mr C. F. Mehta, C. B. Noakes, Baroness S. Noakes, Mr M. A. C. Rudd, Exors of the Late F. W. Shepherd, Mr D. J. Stevens, Mrs J. A. Stewart, Mr A. Stewart, The Stewart Family, Mr M. J. Tracey, Mr P. R. Tymms, Mrs L. Wolfe, Mr A. W. G. Wylie, Mrs A. Wylie.

Jockey (NH): Leighton Aspell, Tom Cannon.

MR MARK GILLARD, Sherborne
Postal: **Hawkes Field Farm, Hilton, Blandford Forum, Dorset, DT11 0DN**
Contacts: PHONE (01963) 23026 (01258) 881111 FAX (01963) 23297 MOBILE (07970) 700605
E-MAIL Mark@thegillards.co.uk WEBSITE www.markgillardracing.com

1 **AVITHOS**, 8, b m Kayf Tara—Digyourheelsin (IRE) **Mr N J McMullan & Mr T Winzer**
2 **BLACKADDER**, 6, b g Myboycharlie (IRE)—Famcred **Mr S. J. Garnett**
3 **CORSECOMBE**, 6, ch g Norse Dancer (IRE)—Digyourheelsin (IRE) **Miss Kay Russell**
4 **DARTMOOR GIRL (IRE)**, 4, b f So You Think (NZ)—Preveza (FR) **Mr B. R. Rudman**
5 **INDIGO STAMP**, 7, b g Rainbow High—Philatelic Lady (IRE) **N. J. McMullan & S. H. Bryant**
6 **KARL MARX (IRE)**, 8, b g Red Clubs (IRE)—Brillano (FR) **Mr S. Bartlett**
7 **KINGSTON MIMOSA**, 6, b g Kheleyf (USA)—Derartu (AUS) **Mrs P. M. R. Gillard**
8 **KOSTAQUARTA (IRE)**, 11, ch g Beneficial—Aclare Thyne (IRE) **Mrs Julie Whatley & Mrs Sandra Boggon**
9 **MADAME CLAUD**, 5, ch m Champs Elysees—Change Partners (IRE) **McMullan, Garnett & Rybaruk**
10 **NO NO CARDINAL (IRE)**, 9, ch g Touch of Land (FR)—Four Moons (IRE) **T. J. C. Seegar**
11 **ORBIT LIGHT (IRE)**, 7, b m Echo of Light—Niobe **Miss Kay Russell**
12 **SAINT HELENA (IRE)**, 10, b m Holy Roman Emperor (IRE)—Tafseer (IRE) **Mr A. K. Hosie**
13 **TOUCH SCREEN (IRE)**, 8, b g Touch of Land (FR)—Capard Lady (IRE) **T. L. Morshead**

THREE-YEAR-OLDS

14 **AMENHOTEPTHETHIRD**, b c Motivator—Autumn Wealth (IRE) **Mr I. T. Booth**

Other Owners: Mrs S. B. Boggon, S. H. Bryant, N. J. McMullan, Mr D. Rybaruk, Mrs J. Whatley, T. O. Winzer.

Assistant Trainer: Pippa Grace

MR JAMES GIVEN, Willoughton
Postal: **Mount House Stables, Long Lane, Willoughton, Gainsborough, Lincolnshire, DN21 5SQ**
Contacts: PHONE (01427) 667618 FAX (01427) 667734 MOBILE (07801) 100496
E-MAIL james@jamesgivenracing.com WEBSITE www.jamesgivenracing.com

1 **ALFONSO MANANA (IRE)**, 4, ch g Dutch Art—Chance For Romance **Mrs Stephanie Oliver & Mr Ron Spore**
2 **DUSKY MAID (IRE)**, 4, b f Dark Angel (IRE)—Dream Scape **The Cool Silk Partnership**

MR JAMES GIVEN - Continued

3 **POPPY MAY (IRE)**, 4, b f Zoffany (IRE)—Lara Amelia (IRE) **Team Given 1**
4 **ROYAL BAJAN (USA)**, 10, gr ro g Speightstown (USA)—Crown You (USA) **The Cool Silk Partnership**
5 **SANDS CHORUS**, 6, b g Footstepsinthesand—Wood Chorus **The Cool Silk Partnership**
6 **TAWNY PORT**, 4, ch g Arcano (IRE)—Tawaasul **Tawny Port Ptners & Lovely Bubbly Racing**
7 **TRUE ROMANCE (IRE)**, 4, gr g Mastercraftsman (IRE)—Full of Love (IRE) **Suzanne & Nigel Williams**

THREE-YEAR-OLDS

8 **BECKER**, b c Delegator—Mosa Mine **T. P. Bostwick**
9 **BLYTON LASS**, ch f Havana Gold (IRE)—Cesseras (IRE) **Mr A. Clarke**
10 **COOL SPIRIT**, b g Swiss Spirit—Marmot Bay (IRE) **The Cool Silk Partnership**
11 **DORCAS**, b f Havana Gold (IRE)—Mortitia **Mrs S. Oliver**
12 **G EYE JOE**, ch g Lethal Force (IRE)—Winifred Jo **The Cool Silk Partnership**
13 **GIFT IN TIME (IRE)**, b g Society Rock (IRE)—Gift of Time **The Cool Silk Partnership**
14 **MISS MOLLIE**, b f Havana Gold (IRE)—Erebis **Ingram Racing**
15 **MISTRESS OF VENICE**, b f Bated Breath—Rohlindi **The Cool Silk Partnership**
16 **MOUNT VICTORIA (IRE)**, b f Arakan (USA)—Salingers Star (IRE) **D Gibbons T Gaunt Partnership**
17 **REACTIVE**, ch c Cityscape—Hollowina **Mr P. Onslow**
18 **TEATRO (IRE)**, b c Shamardal (USA)—Airline Hostess (IRE) **Mr A. Owen**

TWO-YEAR-OLDS

19 **ENIDOFTHEAMAZON (IRE)**, ch f 4/2 Bungle Inthejungle—
                                Malory Towers (Giant's Causeway (USA)) (5714) **Enid's Army**
20 **FAROL**, br f 22/3 Kuroshio (AUS)—Spate Rise (Speightstown (USA)) **Mr P. Onslow**
21 **GARSBAY**, ch c 4/3 Garswood—Marmot Bay (IRE) (36190) **The Cool Silk Partnership**
22 Gr f 12/3 Zebedee—Gone Sailing (Mizzen Mast (USA)) (24761) **Roy Tozer & Team Given 2**
23 **JUST JOSEPHINE (IRE)**, b f 1/4 Arakan (USA)—
                                Salingers Star (IRE) (Catcher In The Rye (IRE)) **D Gibbons T Gaunt Partnership**
24 **MENDELEEV**, b g 13/2 Hellvelyn—Wightgold (Golden Snake (USA)) (4285) **Team Given 1**
25 **ORANGE BLOSSOM**, ch f 29/1 Showcasing—Satsuma (Compton Place) (61904) **The Cool Silk Partnership**
26 **PIPOCA**, ch f 27/3 Archipenko (USA)—Trick Or Treat (Lomitas) **Mr P. Onslow**
27 **RUSSIAN RUM**, b c 25/2 Archipenko (USA)—Bebe de Cham (Tragic Role (USA)) **Lovely Bubbly Racing**
28 **SANTANA SLEW**, gr f 19/2 Gregorian (IRE)—Saratoga Slew (IRE) (Footstepsinthesand) **Dachel Stud**
29 **SIRIUS SLEW**, b c 16/4 Epaulette (AUS)—Slewtoo (Three Valleys (USA)) (15238) **Dachel Stud**
30 **SISTER OF THE SIGN (IRE)**, b f 30/3 Kodiac—
                                Summer Magic (IRE) (Desert Sun) (58000) **The Cool Silk Partnership**
31 B f 9/4 Havana Gold (IRE)—Sunseek (Rail Link) (1428) **C. G. Rowles Nicholson**
32 **THE LAST UNICORN**, b c 2/3 Bated Breath—Rohlindi (Red Ransom (USA)) (125000) **The Cool Silk Partnership**
33 **TINAYA**, gr f 8/3 Gregorian (IRE)—Alushta (Royal Applause) (11428) **R. C. Spore**

Other Owners: Mr S. C. Appelbee, Mr C. G. R. Booth, Mrs T. Gaunt, Mr M. Gibbons, James Given, Mrs C. Goddard, Mr N. P. Hardy, Mr P. A. Horton, Mr I. Jackson, O. H. Kingsley, Mr J. Mullin, Mrs R. J. Norman, Dr M. J. O'Brien, P. Swann, Tawny Port Partnership, Team Given 2, Mr R. C. L. Tozer, Mrs B. E. Wilkinson, Mrs S. E. Williams, Mr N. Williams.

---

227 **MR JIM GOLDIE, Glasgow**
Postal: Libo Hill Farm, Uplawmoor, Glasgow, Lanarkshire, G78 4BA
Contacts: **PHONE (01505) 850212 MOBILE (07778) 241522**
WEBSITE www.jimgoldieracing.com

1 **ANNA'S LEGACY**, 5, b m Shirocco (GER)—Gargoyle Girl **Mr J. S. Goldie**
2 **ARIZONA BOUND (IRE)**, 6, b g Presenting—Loyal Gesture (IRE) **Mr J. Fyffe**
3 **BOOGIE LIFE**, 7, b m Tobougg (IRE)—Life Is Life (FR) **Mr & Mrs Raymond Anderson Green**
4 **BRAES OF LOCHALSH**, 7, b g Tiger Hill (IRE)—Gargoyle Girl **Johnnie Delta Racing**
5 **CHEENI**, 6, ch m Orientor—Class Wan **Mrs V. C. Macdonald**
6 **ETERNALIST**, 5, ch m Equiano (FR)—Eternal Instinct **Mr J. S. Goldie**
7 **FINTRY FLYER**, 4, ch f Compton Place—Primo Heights **Fyffe, Robinson & Goldie**
8 **GOLDEN STEPS (FR)**, 7, b g Footstepsinthesand—Kocooning (IRE) **Mrs M. Craig**
9 **GONINODAETHAT**, 10, b g Proclamation (IRE)—Big Mystery (IRE) **Mr G E Adams & Mr J S Goldie**
10 **GREAT FIGHTER**, 8, b g Street Cry (IRE)—Evil Empire (GER) **Mr J. Fyffe**
11 **HUGOIGO**, 4, b g Sulamani (USA)—Gargoyle Girl **Johnnie Delta Racing**
12 **INSURPLUS (IRE)**, 5, b g Bushranger (IRE)—Emly Express (IRE) **Mr & Mrs G Grant & Partner**
13 **JESSIE ALLAN (IRE)**, 7, b m Bushranger (IRE)—Ishimagic **Mr R. W. C. McLachlan**
14 5, B m Mawatheeq (USA)—Linnet (GER)
15 **LOTARA**, 6, b m Monsieur Bond (IRE)—Cheviot Heights **Mrs L. B. K. Bone**

MR JIM GOLDIE - Continued

16 **NUOVA SCUOLA**, 5, b m Mount Nelson—La Vecchia Scuola (IRE) **Mr J. S. Goldie**
17 **ORIENTAL LILLY**, 4, ch f Orientor—Eternal Instinct **Mr J. S. Goldie**
18 **RIOJA DAY (IRE)**, 8, b g Red Clubs (IRE)—Dai E Dai (USA) **Ayrshire Racing & Partner**
19 **SCOTS SONNET**, 4, b g Poet's Voice—Jabbara (IRE) **W. M. Johnstone**
20 **SIR CHAUVELIN**, 6, b g Authorized (IRE)—Jabbara (IRE) **Mr J. Fyffe, Mrs M. Craig, Mr G. Thomson**
21 **STAR CRACKER (IRE)**, 6, ch g Starspangledbanner (AUS)—Champagne Cracker **The Vital Sparks**
22 **STRATHY**, 5, b g Mount Nelson—Rose Street (IRE) **Mr & Mrs Raymond Anderson Green**
23 **TESTA ROSSA (IRE)**, 8, b g Oratorio (IRE)—Red Rita (IRE) **Mr & Mrs Gordon Grant**
24 **THEGLASGOWWARRIOR**, 4, b g Sir Percy—Sweet Cando (IRE) **Mrs L. B. K. Bone**
25 **THELLO**, 6, b g Arcano (IRE)—Silca Destination **Mr J. Gaffney**
26 **THORNTOUN LADY (USA)**, 8, b m Henrythenavigator (USA)—Valery Lady (ARG) **Mrs M. Craig & Mr J. S. Goldie**
27 **TIGER JIM**, 8, b g Tiger Hill (GER)—Quintrell **Johnnie Delta Racing**
28 **TITUS BOLT (IRE)**, 9, b g Titus Livius (FR)—Megan's Bay **I. G. M. Dalgleish**
29 **TOMMY G**, 5, ch g Makfi—Primo Heights **Johnnie Delta Racing**

THREE-YEAR-OLDS

30 **JEFFREY HARRIS**, b g Orientor—Theatrical Dancer **Unregistered Syndicate**
31 B f Sulamani (IRE)—La Vecchia Scuola (IRE) **Mrs V. C. Macdonald**
32 **LORD OF THE GLEN**, ch g Orientor—Glenlini **Johnnie Delta Racing**
33 **ONE LAST HUG**, b g Orientor—Gargoyle Girl **The Reluctant Suitor's**
34 **PARTY FEARS TOO (IRE)**, b c Society Rock (IRE)—Comedic Art (IRE) **Mr S. Fyffe**
35 **PRIMO'S COMET**, g g Orientor—Primo Heights **The Reluctant Suitor's**

TWO-YEAR-OLDS

36 B c 3/3 Orientor—Gargoyle Girl (Be My Chief (USA))
37 B c 9/4 Orientor—Glenlini (Bertolini (USA))
38 **LADY SEBASTIAN**, b f 12/4 Morpheus—
        Starburst (Fantastic Light (USA)) **Stuart & Emma Earley & Valerie Lampard**

Other Owners: Mr G. Adams, Mr N. Boyle, Mrs E. Earley, Mr S. D. Earley, Mrs L. Goldie, Mrs D. I. Goldie, Mr G. R. Grant, Mrs C. H. Grant, Mrs A. Green, R. A. Green, Mrs V. A. Lampard, Mr D. W. McIntyre, Mr W. Robinson, G. M. Thomson.

Assistant Trainers: James Goldie, George Goldie

Jockey (flat): P. J. McDonald. **Conditional:** Callum Bewley. **Apprentice:** Phil Dennis, Sean Mooney.

MR ROBERT GOLDIE, Kilmarnock
Postal: **Harpercroft, Old Loans Road, Dundonald, Kilmarnock, Ayrshire, KA2 9DD**
Contacts: **PHONE (01292) 314306 FAX (01292) 313585 MOBILE (07801) 922552**
E-MAIL **harpercroft@yahoo.co.uk**

1 **ALFRED OATS**, 14, b g Alflora (IRE)—Easter Oats **R. H. Goldie**
2 **FIRTH OF BAVARD**, 11, b g Flemensfirth (USA)—Ice Bavard **R. H. Goldie**
3 **LAST OF THE OATS**, 10, b g Luso—Easter Oats **R. H. Goldie**

Assistant Trainer: Mrs R H Goldie

229

MR STEVE GOLLINGS, Louth
Postal: **Highfield House, Scambleby, Louth, Lincolnshire, LN11 9XT**
Contacts: **YARD (01507) 343204 HOME/FAX (01507) 343213 MOBILE (07860) 218910**
E-MAIL **stevegollings@aol.com WEBSITE www.stevegollings.com**

1 **ARTIC MILAN (IRE)**, 6, b g Milan—Arctic Rose (IRE) **Northern Bloodstock Racing**
2 **CAGED LIGHTNING (IRE)**, 8, b g Haatef (USA)—Rainbow Melody (IRE) **Four Men & A Little Lady**
3 **EURATO (FR)**, 8, ch g Medicean—Double Green (IRE) **Mr L. Martell**
4 **HANDIWORK**, 8, ch g Motivator—Spinning Top **Mr C. A. Johnstone**
5 **MAKE ME A FORTUNE (IRE)**, 10, b g Heron Island (IRE)—Biora Queen (IRE) **Mr P W Baxter & Mr R C Key**
6 **NEVADA**, 5, gr g Proclamation (IRE)—La Columbina **Northern Bloodstock Racing**
7 **ONE FOR JODIE (IRE)**, 7, ch g Majestic Missile (IRE)—Tough Chic (IRE) **Northern Bloodstock Racing**
8 **ROCOCO STYLE**, 5, b m Shirocco (GER)—Akdara (IRE) **Tensational**
9 **SUBLIMATION (IRE)**, 8, ch g Manduro (GER)—Meon Mix **David & Ros Chapman**

MR STEVE GOLLINGS - Continued

10 TROOPINGTHECOLOUR, 12, b g Nayef (USA)—Hyperspectra **Mrs Jayne M. Gollings**
11 WITH HINDSIGHT (IRE), 10, b g Ad Valorem (USA)—Lady From Limerick (IRE) **Northern Bloodstock Racing**
12 ZAMOYSKI, 8, ch g Dutch Art—Speech **I. S. Naylor**

Other Owners: Mr P. W. Baxter, Mrs R. M. H. Chapman, Mr D. O. Chapman, Mr S. Chapman, S. Gollings, Miss N. J. Gollings, Mr R. C. Key, Mr S. T. Powell, Mr S. Stockdale, Mr P. G. Taiano.

Assistant Trainer: Mrs J M Gollings

Jockey (flat): Jamie Spencer. **Jockey (NH):** Keith Mercer, Brian Hughes, Tom Scudamore.

---

230 | **MR CHRIS GORDON, Winchester**
Postal: **Morestead Farm Stables, Morestead, Winchester, Hampshire, SO21 1JD**
Contacts: **PHONE (01962) 712774 FAX (01962) 712774 MOBILE (07713) 082392**
E-MAIL chrisgordon68@hotmail.co.uk WEBSITE www.chrisgordonracing.com

1 ALKETIOS (GR), 7, b g Kavafi (IRE)—Mazea (IRE) **Mrs J. L. Gordon**
2 BADDESLEY KNIGHT (IRE), 5, b g Doyen (IRE)—Grangeclare Rhythm (IRE) **Mr Richard & Mrs Carol Cheshire**
3 BADDESLEY PRINCE (IRE), 4, b g Doyen (IRE)—Norabella (IRE) **Mr R. Cheshire**
4 BALLYHEIGUE BAY (IRE), 11, b g Rudimentary (USA)—Terinka (IRE) **E. J. Farrant**
5 BE DARING (FR), 7, gr g Dom Alco (FR)—Quinine (FR) **Gilbert & Gamble**
6 BOL D'AIR (FR), 7, b g Blue Bresil (FR)—Holding (FR) **Mr P. Hernon**
7 BUGSIE MALONE (IRE), 8, b g Mahler—The Irish Whip **A. C. Ward-Thomas**
8 CADMAR, 4, b g Shirocco (GER)—Raitera (FR) **Mr R. Cheshire**
9 COMMANCHE RED (IRE), 5, ch g Mahler—Auntie Bob **Mr Richard & Mrs Carol Cheshire**
10 DON'T TELL GEORGE (FR), 5, b g Enrique—Anowa (FR) **Mrs K. Digweed**
11 ESTHERS RANSOM, 5, b m Tobougg (IRE)—Yemeni Princess (IRE) **Chris Gordon Racing Club**
12 HIGHWAY ONE O ONE (IRE), 6, br g Stowaway—High Accord (IRE) **A. C. Ward-Thomas**
13 HOWLONGISAFOOT (IRE), 9, b g Beneficial—Miss Vic (IRE) **Mr D. S. Dennis**
14 JIMMY, 5, ch g Norse Dancer (IRE)—Isintshelovely (IRE) **L. Gilbert**
15 JUMPING JACK (IRE), 4, b g Sir Prancealot (IRE)—She's A Character **Broadsword Group Ltd**
16 KING CNUT (FR), 4, ch g Kentucky Dynamite (USA)—Makadane **Mrs J. L. Gordon**
17 KING UTHER, 8, b g Master Blade—Cadbury Castle **A. C. Ward-Thomas**
18 LADOFASH, 4, b g Canford Cliffs (IRE)—Curras Spirit **Gander & Gamble**
19 LOVES DESTINATION, 7, b m Dubai Destination (USA)—Bijou Love (USA) **Chris Gordon Racing Club**
20 MELLOW BEN (IRE), 5, b g Beneficial—Mellowthemoonlight (IRE) **Broadsword Group Ltd**
21 MUSIKEL (IRE), 4, ch g Frankel—Musical Treat (IRE) **Mrs K. Digweed**
22 NEYJA BLUE (FR), 6, gr g Blue Bresil (FR)—Laura's Dream (FR) **A.B.C. Partnership**
23 NIGHT GENERATION (GER), 6, ch g Sholokhov (IRE)—Night Woman (GER) **Party People**
24 RAMORE WILL (IRE), 7, gr g Tikkanen (USA)—Gill Hall Lady **E. J. Farrant**
25 REMILUC (FR), 9, b g Mister Sacha (FR)—Markene de Durtal (FR) **Gilbert & Gamble**
26 ROB ROBIN (IRE), 8, b g Robin des Champs (FR)—Ashwell Lady (IRE) **The Select Syndicate**
27 ROPARTA AVENUE, 11, b g Nomadic Way (USA)—Miss Fizz **Chris Gordon Racing Club**
28 ROTHMAN (FR), 8, b g Michel Georges—Bravecentadj (FR) **Mr Roger Alwen Mrs Heather Alwen**
29 SEA WALL (FR), 10, b g Turgeon (USA)—Si Parfaite (FR) **Draper Edmonds Draper**
30 SHUT THE BOX (IRE), 4, ch g Doyen (IRE)—Bond Holder (IRE) **Shut The Box Partnership**
31 TARA BRIDGE, 10, b g Kayf Tara—Annie Greenlaw **B. J. Champion**
32 TARSEEKH, 5, b g Kyllachy—Constitute (USA) **Broadsword Group Ltd**
33 ULVA FERRY (IRE), 6, ch g Stowaway—Lisacul Queen (IRE) **Mr & Mrs Michael Coates**
34 VICENZO MIO (FR), 8, b g Corri Piano (FR)—Sweet Valrose (FR) **Mrs J. L. Gordon**

Other Owners: Mrs Heather Alwen, Mr Roger Alwen, Mr Luke Axel-Berg, Mrs Sarah Bullen, Mr R. Cheshire, Mrs C. L. Cheshire, Mr Michael Coates, Mrs Michael Coates, Mr M. J. Draper, Mr J. Draper, Mr T. W. Edmonds, Mr Julian Gamble, Mr L. Gilbert, Mr C. Gordon, Mr Steve Hobbs, Mr C. Leafe, Miss Juliet E. Reed, Mr Richard Venn, Mr Steve Windsor.

Assistant Trainer: Jenny Gordon

Jockey (NH): Tom Cannon, David Noonan.

231 MR J. T. GORMAN, Curragh
Postal: **Maddenstown Lodge, Maddenstown, Curragh, Co Kildare, Ireland**
Contacts: **PHONE (00 353) 87 2599603**
E-MAIL jt.gorman1@hotmail.com

1 **ATHENRY BOY (IRE)**, 6, br g Excellent Art—Dancing With Stars (IRE) **P. Reilly**
2 **BUSY BUSH (IRE)**, 6, b m Bushranger (IRE)—Candela Bay (IRE) **Andrews Syndicate**
3 **CAITIE (IRE)**, 5, b m Canford Cliffs (IRE)—The Shrew **Mrs Margaret Comer**
4 **DONT QUIT (IRE)**, 5, b g Bushranger (IRE)—Elitista (FR) **Andrews Syndicate**
5 **ITS HARRYS GIRL (IRE)**, 6, b m Kodiac—Ufallya (IRE) **Andrews Syndicate**
6 **JOELY (IRE)**, 4, b f Bushranger (IRE)—Callanish **Andrews Syndicate**
7 **KILLDUNNE (IRE)**, 11, b g Hawk Wing (USA)—Trigger Happy (IRE) **Andrews Syndicate**
8 **SIXTIES SUE**, 5, gr m Sixties Icon—Rose Cheval (USA) **Mrs Margaret Comer**
9 **SNAP CLICK (IRE)**, 7, b g Kodiac—Happy Hour (GER) **P. Reilly**
10 **VERBOSITY (IRE)**, 5, b m Vocalised (USA)—Stitch Night (IRE) **Mrs J. Bolger**
11 **VISTA STEPPE**, 4, b f Dutch Art—Rare Ransom **Luke Comer**

Other Owners: Mrs T. G. Trant, Mr P. Trant.

Jockey (flat): Rory Cleary, Kevin Manning, Ronan Whelan. Jockey (NH): Ronan Shortt. Amateur: Mr Cathal Gorman.

232 MR JOHN GOSDEN, Newmarket
Postal: **Clarehaven, Bury Road, Newmarket, Suffolk, CB8 7BY**
Contacts: **PHONE (01638) 565400 FAX (01638) 565401**
E-MAIL jhmg@johngosden.com

1 **CORONET**, 4, gr f Dubawi (IRE)—Approach
2 **CRACKSMAN**, 4, b c Frankel—Rhadegunda
3 **DREAMFIELD**, 4, b c Oasis Dream—Izzi Top
4 **ENABLE**, 4, b f Nathaniel (IRE)—Concentric
5 **GARRICK**, 4, b c Galileo (IRE)—Rimth
6 **GLENCADAM GLORY**, 4, b g Nathaniel (IRE)—Lady Grace (IRE)
7 **LAUGH ALOUD**, 5, ch m Dubawi (IRE)—Opera Comique (FR)
8 **MAVERICK WAVE (USA)**, 7, ch h Elusive Quality (USA)—Misty Ocean (USA)
9 **MONARCHS GLEN**, 4, b g Frankel—Mirabilis (USA)
10 **MUNTAHAA (IRE)**, 5, gr g Dansili—Qertaas (IRE)
11 **POUVOIR MAGIQUE (FR)**, 4, b c Le Havre (IRE)—Barmaid (FR)
12 **PRECIOUS RAMOTSWE**, 4, b f Nathaniel (IRE)—Miss Pinkerton
13 **REMARKABLE**, 5, b g Pivotal—Irresistible
14 **ROYAL LINE**, 4, ch c Dubawi (IRE)—Melikah (IRE)
15 **SAMHARRY**, 4, b g Exceed And Excel (AUS)—Ballymore Celebre (IRE)
16 **STRADIVARIUS (IRE)**, 4, ch c Sea The Stars (IRE)—Private Life (FR)
17 **TAQDEER (IRE)**, 5, ch g Fast Company (IRE)—Brigantia
18 **TRICORN (IRE)**, 4, b g Helmet (AUS)—Special Dancer
19 **UTMOST (USA)**, 4, ch c Giant's Causeway (USA)—Fugitive Angel (USA)
20 **WEEKENDER**, 4, b c Frankel—Very Good News (USA)

THREE-YEAR-OLDS
21 **AIM OF ARTEMIS (IRE)**, ch f Leroidesanimaux (BRZ)—Justlookdontouch (IRE)
22 **ALMOGHARED (IRE)**, b c Dansili—Ezima (IRE)
23 **ANBAA (IRE)**, b f Lope de Vega (IRE)—Biswa (USA)
24 **ANTONIAN**, b c Intello (GER)—Highest
25 **ARGENTELLO (IRE)**, b c Intello (GER)—Evita
26 **AWARD WINNING (IRE)**, ch f Dubawi (IRE)—Hit The Sky (IRE)
27 **BELLE RIVIERE (USA)**, b f Frankel—Winsili
28 **BEN VRACKIE**, b c Frankel—Kinnaird (IRE)
29 **BOLD REASON (GER)**, b c Invincible Spirit (IRE)—Bufera (IRE)
30 **BOWDITCH (IRE)**, b c Nathaniel (IRE)—Kate The Great
31 **CASEY JONES (IRE)**, b c Casamento (IRE)—Balamiyda (IRE)
32 **CASSINI (IRE)**, b c Galileo (IRE)—Chrysanthemum (IRE)
33 **CERAMIST**, gr f Mastercraftsman (IRE)—Dalasyla (IRE)
34 **CHIEFDOM (USA)**, gr c The Factor (USA)—Sultana (USA)
35 **CHLORIS**, b f Dansili—Primevere (IRE)

MR JOHN GOSDEN - Continued

36 **COMPLETELY (IRE)**, b f Invincible Spirit (IRE)—Teeky
37 **CORELLI (USA)**, b c Point of Entry (USA)—Vignette (USA)
38 **COURT HOUSE (IRE)**, b c Dawn Approach (IRE)—Crossanza (IRE)
39 **CROSSED BATON**, b c Dansili—Sacred Shield
40 **CULPABILITY (USA)**, b c Blame (USA)—Princess Consort (USA)
41 **DERRYMORE (IRE)**, b f Dark Angel (IRE)—Slieve Mish (IRE)
42 **DIVE FOR GOLD**, b c Dubawi (IRE)—State Treasure (USA)
43 **DOLCISSIMO (IRE)**, b f Dark Angel (IRE)—Beneventa
44 **ELHAFEI (USA)**, br c Speightstown (USA)—Albamara
45 **EMARAATY**, b c Dubawi (IRE)—Zee Zee Top
46 **EMBLAZONED (IRE)**, b c Invincible Spirit (IRE)—Sendmylovetorose
47 **ENBIHAAR (IRE)**, b f Redoute's Choice (AUS)—Chanterelle (FR)
48 **FENNAAN (IRE)**, b c Footstepsinthesand—Sanadaat
49 **FIRST ELEVEN**, b c Frankel—Zenda
50 **FLYING DEMON**, gr c Nathaniel (IRE)—Gossamer Seed (IRE)
51 **FOR NOW (IRE)**, b f Lawman (FR)—Aricia (IRE)
52 **GAUDI (IRE)**, b c Invincible Spirit (IRE)—Alava (IRE)
53 **GEORGE VILLIERS (IRE)**, b c Dubawi (IRE)—Comic (IRE)
54 **GHALYOON**, b c Invincible Spirit (IRE)—Swiss Lake (USA)
55 **GLENCADAM MASTER**, gr c Mastercraftsman (IRE)—Coquet
56 **GRAFFITI MASTER**, b c Dubawi (IRE)—Independence
57 **GUARDSMAN (IRE)**, b c More Than Ready (USA)—Dundalk Dust (USA)
58 **GUMRIYAH**, b f Shamardal (USA)—Yummy Mummy
59 **HALF DOLLAR (USA)**, ch f Street Cry (IRE)—Star Silver (USA)
60 **HAMEEM**, br f Teofilo (IRE)—Tres Ravi (GER)
61 **HIGHGARDEN**, b f Nathaniel (IRE)—Regalline (IRE)
62 **HINDE STREET (USA)**, gr g Giant's Causeway (USA)—Marylebone (USA)
63 **HIPSTER BOY**, b c Dubawi (IRE)—Mandellicht (IRE)
64 **IL PRIMO SOLE**, b c Raven's Pass (USA)—Sweet Alabama
65 **JAMIH**, ch c Intello (GER)—Hannda (IRE)
66 **JAWWAAL**, ch c Bahamian Bounty—Avenbury
67 **JULIET CAPULET (IRE)**, b f Dark Angel (IRE)—Capulet Monteque (IRE)
68 **KELTIE**, ch f Giant's Causeway (USA)—Fugitive Angel (USA)
69 **KINGS SHIELD (USA)**, b c Scat Daddy (USA)—Gender Dance (USA)
70 **KITE WING**, ch c Pivotal—Gull Wing (USA)
71 **LADY LIVONIA (IRE)**, ch f Frankel—Lady Vettori
72 **LAH TI DAR**, b f Dubawi (IRE)—Dar Re Mi
73 **LARADEEF (IRE)**, b c Shamardal (USA)—Lanansaak (IRE)
74 **LAST PEARL**, ch f Sepoy (AUS)—Swain's Gold (USA)
75 **MAIN STREET**, b c Street Cry (IRE)—My Special J's (USA)
76 **MARECHAL NEY**, b c Frankel—Hidden Hope
77 **MERWEB (IRE)**, ch c Shamardal (USA)—Ashley Hall (USA)
78 **MILITARY LAW**, b c Dubawi (IRE)—Marine Bleue (IRE)
79 **MISTER AMBASSADOR (IRE)**, b c Scat Daddy (USA)—Excelente (IRE)
80 **MOMTALIK (USA)**, b c Point of Entry (USA)—Sacred Feather (USA)
81 **MR MARRAKECH**, b c Scat Daddy (USA)—Morocco Moon
82 **MSAYYAN (IRE)**, b c Camelot—Elusive Girl (USA)
83 **MYTHICAL QUEEN**, b f Camelot—L'ile Aux Loups (IRE)
84 **NASSYA**, b f Dubawi (IRE)—Gemstone (IRE)
85 **NATCH**, b c Nathaniel (IRE)—Angara
86 **NAWASSI**, b f Dubawi (IRE)—Maqaasid
87 **ODE TO AUTUMN**, b g Showcasing—Turning Leaf (IRE)
88 **OSCAR'S RIDGE (IRE)**, b c Galileo (IRE)—Posterity (IRE)
89 **OSTORA (IRE)**, b f Sea The Stars (IRE)—Mooakada (IRE)
90 **PERFECTION**, ch f Dutch Art—Cantal
91 **PETIT PALAIS**, ch c Champs Elysees—Galicuix
92 **PHOTOGRAPHER**, b c New Approach (IRE)—Approach
93 **PLAYFULL SPIRIT**, b f Invincible Spirit (IRE)—Annabelle's Charm (IRE)
94 B c War Front (USA)—Praise (USA)
95 B g Sea The Stars (IRE)—Precious Gem (IRE)
96 **PURSER (USA)**, b c Mizzen Mast (USA)—Solo Piano (USA)
97 **RAWAAF (IRE)**, gr f Dark Angel (IRE)—Prodigal Daughter
98 **RAY OF SUNSHINE**, ch f Dawn Approach (IRE)—Crimson Ribbon (USA)
99 **RHODE ISLAND (IRE)**, ch c Galileo (IRE)—Native Force (IRE)
100 **ROARING LION (USA)**, gr c Kitten's Joy (USA)—Vionnet (USA)

MR JOHN GOSDEN - Continued

101 ROCOCO, b f Dubawi (IRE)—Intrigued
102 ROUDHA (IRE), b f Galileo (IRE)—Melito (AUS)
103 SACRED PATH, b f Galileo (IRE)—All's Forgotten (USA)
104 SCOTTISH JIG (USA), ch f Speightstown (USA)—Light Jig
105 SEEING STARS (USA), ch c Tapit (USA)—Rainbow View (USA)
106 SEVENNA STAR (IRE), b c Redoute's Choice (AUS)—Sevenna (FR)
107 SOPHIE GRAY (IRE), b f Dansili—Susan Stroman
108 STAR OF BENGAL, b c Oasis Dream—Stage Presence (IRE)
109 STARSCAPE (IRE), b f Cape Cross (IRE)—Star Studded
110 STEALTH, b c Kodiac—White Dress (IRE)
111 STREAM SONG, gr f Mastercraftsman (IRE)—Montare (IRE)
112 STYLEHUNTER, ch c Raven's Pass (USA)—Sunday Bess (JPN)
113 SUPPORTER, b f Dubawi (IRE)—Very Good News (USA)
114 SURYA, b c Frankel—Sariska
115 TAMADDON, b g Al Kazeem—Request
116 THE MUMS, b f Holy Roman Emperor (IRE)—Ballyalla
117 TIFFIN TOP, gr c Oasis Dream—Mussoorie (FR)
118 TIVOLI (IRE), b f Dark Angel (IRE)—Fluvial (IRE)
119 TOBRUK (IRE), b f Declaration of War (USA)—Slow Sand (USA)
120 TRIARIA (USA), b f War Front (USA)—State (USA)
121 UNCHAINED (IRE), b f Dansili—Take the Ribbon (USA)
122 VERANDAH, b f Medicean—Palatial
123 WELL YES (IRE), ch f Galileo (IRE)—Faraday Light (IRE)
124 WHITLOCK, ch c Dutch Art—Barynya
125 WISSAHICKON (USA), ch c Tapit (USA)—No Matter What (USA)
126 WITHOUT PAROLE, b c Frankel—Without You Babe (USA)

Trainer did not wish details of his two-year-olds to appear

Jockey (flat): L. Dettori, Nicky Mackay, Robert Havlin.

233	**MRS HARRIET GRAHAM, Jedburgh** Postal: **Strip End, Jedburgh, Roxburghshire, TD8 6NE** Contacts: **PHONE (01835) 840354 MOBILE (07843) 380401** E-MAIL hgrahamracing@aol.com

1 ANDANOTHER, 4, b g And Beyond (IRE)—Catriona **H G Racing**
2 AYE RIGHT (IRE), 5, b g Yeats (IRE)—Gaybric (IRE) **Mr G. F. Adam**
3 BELL OFTHE BONGATE (IRE), 4, b f Sakhee (USA)—Peace Lily **Mr M McGovern & Partner**
4 JUSTADREAMYEKEN, 6, b g Scorpion (IRE)—Loxhill Lady **Mr G. F. Adam**
5 4, B g Gold Well—Presenteea (IRE) **Mr G. F. Adam**
6 RHYMERS STONE, 10, b g Desideratum—Salu **Mr G. F. Adam**
7 ROCKET MAN RODNEY, 5, b g Black Sam Bellamy (IRE)—Miss Quickly (IRE) **H G Racing**
8 SCOTSWELL, 12, b g Endoli (USA)—Tofino Swell **H G Racing**
9 SUDSKI STAR (IRE), 10, br g Pilsudski (IRE)—Mogen's Star (IRE) **Mr G. F. Adam**

THREE-YEAR-OLDS

10 Br c Bollin Eric—Miss Quickly (IRE) **H G Racing**

TWO-YEAR-OLDS

11 B f 16/2 Black Sam Bellamy (IRE)—Minimum (Terimon) (857) **H G Racing**

Other Owners: Mrs H. O. Graham, Mr R. D. Graham, Mr M. J. McGovern.

Assistant Trainer: R D Graham

Jockey (NH): Lucy Alexander, Danny Cook. **Conditional:** Calum Bewley, Tommy Dowson.

234 **MR CHRIS GRANT, Billingham**
Postal: **Low Burntoft Farm, Wolviston, Billingham, Cleveland, TS22 5PD**
Contacts: PHONE **(01740) 644054** MOBILE **(07860) 577998**
E-MAIL **chrisgrantracing@gmail.com** WEBSITE **www.chrisgrantracing.co.uk**

1 **ACDC (IRE)**, 8, b g King's Theatre (IRE)—Always Alert (IRE) **D&D Armstrong Limited**
2 **AN LAOCH (IRE)**, 6, b g Flemensfirth (USA)—Petite Ballerina (IRE) **D&D Armstrong Limited**
3 **ASK CAITLIN (IRE)**, 4, b f Ask—Bold Cailin (IRE) **Mrs H. N. Eubank**
4 **BLUNDER BUSS (IRE)**, 5, b g Court Cave (IRE)—Shantou Rose (IRE) **D&D Armstrong Limited**
5 **BROADWAY BELLE**, 8, b m Lucarno (USA)—Theatre Belle **C. Grant**
6 **CASTLE ON A CLOUD (IRE)**, 7, b g Flemensfirth (USA)—Ifyoucouldseemenow (IRE) **C. Grant**
7 **COLBY (IRE)**, 5, b g Witness Box (USA)—Wet And Dry (IRE) **Mr T. J. Hemmings**
8 **DONNA'S DIAMOND (IRE)**, 9, gr g Cloudings (IRE)—Inish Bofin (IRE) **D&D Armstrong Limited**
9 **DONNAS DREAM (IRE)**, 5, b m Kalanisi (IRE)—Gerarda (IRE) **D&D Armstrong Limited**
10 **DRUMS OF WAR (IRE)**, 6, b g Youmzain (IRE)—Min Asl Wafi (IRE) **J. Wade**
11 **HAIGHALL (IRE)**, 6, b g Scorpion (IRE)—Longwhitejemmy (IRE) **Mr T. J. Hemmings**
12 **HEY BOB (IRE)**, 6, br g Big Bad Bob (IRE)—Bounty Star (IRE) **Miss Alison P. Lee & Mr Chris Grant**
13 **KALANITI (IRE)**, 7, b m Kalanisi (IRE)—Miss Twinkletoes (IRE) **Mrs S. Sunter**
14 **KNOCKKING (IRE)**, 4, b g Baltic King—Lady of Knock (IRE) **C. Grant**
15 4, B f Getaway (GER)—Mary Kate O'brien **C. Grant**
16 **MISTER KIT**, 10, gr g Tikkanen (USA)—Rosie Mist **Mrs H. N. Eubank**
17 **OUTNUMBERED (IRE)**, 5, b g Stowaway—Back Market Lass (IRE) **Mr N. E. M. Jones**
18 **PARKWARDEN (IRE)**, 4, b g Bushranger (IRE)—Honour And Obey (IRE) **C. Grant**
19 **PHANTOM ISLE**, 5, b g Teofilo (IRE)—Antillia **John Wade & A K Collins**
20 **PIKES PEAK (IRE)**, 9, br g Kutub (IRE)—Accordionline (IRE) **Miss A. P. Lee**
21 **QUADRIGA (IRE)**, 8, b g Acclamation—Turning Light (GER) **Mr L. M. Hall**
22 **REAPLEE**, 5, ch g Recharge (IRE)—Chant de L'aube (FR) **Miss A. P. Lee**
23 **RED OCHRE**, 5, b g Virtual—Red Hibiscus **C. Grant**
24 **ROBINS LEGEND (IRE)**, 6, b g Robin des Pres (FR)—Lemons Legend **J. Wade**
25 **TAKING AIM (IRE)**, 6, b g Acambaro (GER)—Sharp Missile (IRE) **C. Grant**
26 **THE HARD SHOULDER (IRE)**, 5, gr g Cloudings (IRE)—Our Witness (IRE) **D&D Armstrong Limited**
27 **THEATRE ACT**, 7, ch m Act One—Theatre Belle **Division Bell Partnership**
28 **THEATRE LEGEND**, 5, b g Midnight Legend—Theatre Belle **Division Bell Partnership**
29 **YELOW BIRD**, 4, b g Power—Aiaam Al Wafa (IRE) **Mr J. Hamilton**
30 **ZAKETY ZAK**, 7, b g Overbury (IRE)—Jeanne d'arc **Mr D. M. Wordsworth**

Other Owners: A. K. Collins, T. Cunningham, A. Meale, A. D. Wright.

Assistant Trainer: Mrs S. Grant

Jockey (NH): Brian Hughes. **Conditional:** Callum Bewley.

---

235 **MR M. C. GRASSICK, Curragh**
Postal: **Fenpark House, Pollardstown, Curragh, Co. Kildare, Ireland**
Contacts: MOBILE **(00353) 86 3648829**
E-MAIL **mcgrassick@hotmail.com** WEBSITE **www.michaelcgrassick.com**

1 **KING OF ARAN (IRE)**, 11, b br g Val Royal (FR)—Innishmore (IRE) **M. C. Grassick**
2 **MALIBU MAGIC (IRE)**, 4, b f Rip Van Winkle (IRE)—Awjila **T. Geary**
3 **RENAISSANCE MAN (IRE)**, 4, b c Galileo (IRE)—My Renee (USA) **M. C. Grassick**
4 **TEXAS ROCK (IRE)**, 7, b g Rock of Gibraltar (IRE)—Vestavia (IRE) **J. Keeling**
5 **VARTAN (IRE)**, 4, br g Rock of Gibraltar (IRE)—Vestavia (IRE) **J. Keeling**

THREE-YEAR-OLDS

6 **EADBHARD (IRE)**, b g Elzaam (AUS)—Only Exception (IRE) **J. Keeling**
7 Ch g Lord Shanakill (USA)—Princess Nicole (IRE) **M. McRedmond**
8 **SILVRETTA SCHWARZ (IRE)**, b gr f Silver Frost (IRE)—Perruche Grise (FR) **S. Eade**
9 **VERHOYEN**, b g Piccolo—Memory Lane **P. Cullen**

TWO-YEAR-OLDS

10 B f 19/4 Intense Focus (USA)—Apple Blossom Time (IRE) (Invincible Spirit (IRE)) **J. Keeling**
11 Ch f 13/4 Arakan (USA)—Blaenavon (Cadeaux Genereux) **Chris Grassick**

MR M. C. GRASSICK - Continued

12 B f 15/2 Slade Power (IRE)—Blueberry Gal (IRE) (Bushranger (IRE)) **J. Keeling**
13 Ch c 25/2 Excelebration (IRE)—Livia Galilei (IRE) (Galileo (IRE)) **K. Molloy**
14 B c 13/4 Henrythenavigator (USA)—Only Exception (IRE) (Jeremy (USA)) (813) **Roisin Walshe**
15 Gr f 30/4 Raven's Pass (USA)—Perruche Grise (FR) (Mark of Esteem (IRE)) (9767) **T. Geary**
16 B f 22/4 Elzaam (AUS)—Showmesomething (IRE) (Mujadil (USA)) (2441) **P. Cullen**

Assistant Trainer: David Flynn

Jockey (flat): W J Lee, Niall McCullagh. **Jockey (NH):** Kevin Coleman, Danny Mullins.

---

236 MR CARROLL GRAY, Bridgwater
Postal: **The Little Glen, Peartwater Road, Spaxton, Bridgwater, Somerset, TA5 1DG**
Contacts: **MOBILE (07989) 768163**

1 **ARTHUR'S QUEEN (FR)**, 7, b m Soldier of Fortune (IRE)—Tintagel **Riverdance Consortium**
2 **BELLAMY'S GREY**, 6, gr g Black Sam Bellamy (IRE)—Lambrini Queen **Riverdance Consortium 2**
3 **BREAN GOLF BIRDIE**, 6, br m Striking Ambition—Straight As A Die **Unity Farm Holiday Centre Ltd**
4 **CAUTIOUS KATE (IRE)**, 11, b m Witness Box (USA)—Cautious Leader **Mr L. & Mrs J. Waring**
5 **IN THE TUB (IRE)**, 9, b g Kutub (IRE)—County Classic **Mr L & Mrs J Waring & Mr S Reeves**
6 **TIS WONDERFUL (IRE)**, 4, b g Casamento (IRE)—Cosenza **Riverdance Consortium 3**
7 **WILLIE MCLOVIN (IRE)**, 6, b g Apple Tree (FR)—Kiss Me du Cochet (FR) **Mr B. J. Masters**

Other Owners: Mr M. J. Colenutt, Mr R. Napper, Mr S. Reeves, Mrs J. Waring, Mr L. Waring, Mr M. Wright.

Assistant Trainer: Mrs C. M. L. Gray

Jockey (NH): Micheal Nolan. **Conditional:** R. Hawker. **Apprentice:** W. Cox

---

237 MR WARREN GREATREX, Upper Lambourn
Postal: **Uplands, Upper Lambourn, Hungerford, Berkshire, RG17 8QH**
Contacts: **PHONE (01488) 670279 FAX (01488) 72193 MOBILE (07920) 039114**
E-MAIL **info@wgreatrexracing.com** WEBSITE **www.wgreatrexracing.com**

1 **AARDWOLF (USA)**, 4, b g Cape Cross (IRE)—Desert Gazelle (USA) **Little Roberts Dowley & Turner**
2 **ALOOMOMO (FR)**, 8, b g Tirwanako (FR)—Kayola (FR) **The Large G & T Partnership**
3 **ANOTHER EMOTION (FR)**, 6, gr g Turgeon (USA)—Line Perle (FR) **Weatherbys Racing Club**
4 **ARTICLE FIFTY (IRE)**, 5, b g Doyen (IRE)—Annie Go (IRE) **Swanee River Partnership**
5 **ATTEST**, 5, b g Cacique (IRE)—Change Course **Bolingbroke Bartram Flatt Molony Sutton**
6 **BEGBIE (IRE)**, 5, b g Scorpion (IRE)—Ben's Pride **Mr T. J. Hemmings**
7 **BOB MAHLER (IRE)**, 6, b g Mahler—Cooladurragh (IRE) **Bolingbroke, Bunch, Howard & Sutton**
8 **BOITE (IRE)**, 8, b g Authorized (IRE)—Albiatra (USA) **Mrs T. J. Stone-Brown**
9 **BON ENFANT (FR)**, 7, gr g Saint des Saints (FR)—Montanara Paris (FR) **Mrs T. Greatrex**
10 **BRIANSTORM (IRE)**, 6, b g Brian Boru—Coco Moon (IRE) **G. B. Firmager & G. H. Firmager**
11 **BRIGHT TOMORROW (IRE)**, 7, b g Robin des Pres (FR)—Gweedara (IRE) **ROA Arkle Partnership**
12 **CARNSPINDLE (IRE)**, 6, b m Ask—Whistling Gypse (IRE) **Fitorfat1 Racing**
13 **CEANN SIBHEAL (IRE)**, 9, b g Flemensfirth (USA)—Imperial Award (IRE) **The High Kites**
14 **CHEF D'OEUVRE (FR)**, 7, b g Martaline—Kostroma (FR) **McNeill Family Ltd**
15 **CLASH OF D TITANS (IRE)**, 5, b g Gold Well—Give Us A Look (IRE) **Million in Mind Partnership**
16 **COLE HARDEN (IRE)**, 9, b g Westerner—Nosie Betty (IRE) **Mrs Jill Eynon & Mr Robin Eynon**
17 **D'GENTLE REFLEXION (FR)**, 5, b g Gentlewave (IRE)—Reflexion (FR) **Yorton Racing**
18 **DESERTER (IRE)**, 7, ch g Tagula (IRE)—Lady Van Gogh **Bolingbroke Flatt Howard Sutton Turner**
19 **DICOSIMO (IRE)**, 7, b g Laveron—Coralisse Royale (FR) **Mrs Jill Eynon & Mr Robin Eynon**
20 **DON DES FOSSES (FR)**, 5, b g Denham Red (FR)—Sara des Fosses (FR) **Mr A. M. Gibbons**
21 **DON'T ASK (IRE)**, 5, b g Ask—Outback Ivy (IRE) **Walters Plant Hire & James & Jean Potter**
22 **DORY (IRE)**, 5, br m Westerner—Papal Princess (IRE) **Mr C. S. Hinchy**
23 **DREAM BROTHER (IRE)**, 6, b g Oscar (IRE)—Warmley's Gem (IRE) **Mr W. J. Greatrex**
24 **ECTOR (FR)**, 4, b g Coastal Path—Evane (FR) **McNeill Family Ltd**
25 **EMITOM (IRE)**, 4, b g Gold Well—Avenging Angel (IRE) **The Spero Partnership Ltd**
26 **FINAL CHOICE (IRE)**, 5, b g Makfi—Anasazi (IRE) **Jockey Club Ownership (SW 2016) Limited**

MR WARREN GREATREX - Continued

27 **FLEMENSKILL (IRE)**, 6, b g Flemensfirth (USA)—Nivalf **Middleham Park Racing XXXVIII**
28 **FLY DU CHARMIL (FR)**, 7, b g Saint des Saints (FR)—Famous Member (FR) **McNeill Family Ltd**
29 **GREAT RETURN**, 5, b g New Approach (IRE)—Under The Rainbow **Fitorfat Racing**
30 **GROUNDUNDERREPAIR (IRE)**, 7, b g Milan—Discerning Air **No Dramas Partnership 1**
31 **GVS IRPORTENSA (IRE)**, 6, ch m Trans Island—Greenfield Noora (IRE) **P Molony & J da Mata**
32 **HUNT POLITICS**, 6, b g Black Sam Bellamy (IRE)—Jaunty Flight **Fitorfat Racing**
33 **INDIAN HERCULES (IRE)**, 6, b br g Whitmore's Conn (USA)—Carrawaystick (IRE) **Excel Racing**
34 **INVISIBLE CLOUDS (IRE)**, 5, gr g Cloudings (IRE)—Go My Dream **Mr T. J. Hemmings**
35 **JAMMIN MASTERS (IRE)**, 7, b g Sinndar (IRE)—Zara Million (ITY) **No Dramas**
36 **KEEPER HILL (IRE)**, 7, b g Westerner—You Take Care (IRE) **McNeill Family Ltd**
37 **LA BAGUE AU ROI (FR)**, 7, b m Doctor Dino (FR)—
                                          Alliance Royale (FR) **Mrs Julien Turner & Mr Andrew Merriam**
38 4, B f Doyen (IRE)—Lady Zephyr (IRE)
39 4, B g Shirocco (GER)—Love Train (IRE) **Mr W. J. Greatrex**
40 **LOVENORMONEY (IRE)**, 7, br g Winged Love (IRE)—Dixies Gem (IRE) **Mr T. D. J. Syder**
41 4, B f Malinas (GER)—Madam Jolie (IRE) **Mr W. J. Greatrex**
42 **MAHLERVOUS (IRE)**, 5, b g Mahler—Brook Style (IRE) **The Marvellous Partnership**
43 **MAJINGILANE (IRE)**, 6, b g Winged Love (IRE)—Kiora Lady (IRE) **Urban Cookie Collective**
44 **MAJOR DAVIS (FR)**, 6, b g Vision d'etat (FR)—Majorica Sancta (IRE) **Fromthestables.Com & Partner**
45 **MASTER CARD**, 5, ch g Presenting—Subtilty **Shropshire Wanderers**
46 **MISS HONEY RYDER (IRE)**, 5, b m Stowaway—Seesea (IRE) **The Albatross Club**
47 **MISSED APPROACH (IRE)**, 8, b g Golan (IRE)—Polly's Dream (IRE) **Alan & Andrew Turner**
48 **MONTHYNE**, 7, ch g Nomadic Way (USA)—Captivating Tyna (IRE) **Mr W. Tilley**
49 **MULCAHYS HILL (IRE)**, 6, b g Brian Boru—Belsalsa (FR) **McNeill Family and Prodec Networks Ltd**
50 **MYTHICAL PRINCE (IRE)**, 6, b g Beneficial—Conker Nails (IRE) **Mr L. A. Bolingbroke**
51 4, B g Oscar (IRE)—North Star Poly (IRE) **Mr W. J. Greatrex**
52 **ODELLO**, 7, b m King's Theatre (IRE)—Isabello (IRE) **J.N.G-M Racing**
53 **OSCAR MOR (IRE)**, 6, b g Oscar (IRE)—Gran Chis (IRE) **Swanee River Partnership**
54 **PATGARY (FR)**, 6, b g Ballingarry (IRE)—Maylady Pat (FR) **Mrs D. J. Fleming**
55 **PECULIAR PLACES (IRE)**, 6, b g Presenting—Blu Louisiana (IRE) **Highclere T'Bred Racing - Louisiana**
56 **PENN LANE (IRE)**, 7, b g Scorpion (IRE)—Belsalsa (FR) **Alan & Andrew Turner**
57 **PENNYWELL (IRE)**, 8, b m Gold Well—Boyne Bridge (IRE) **The Silo Syndicate**
58 4, B g Malinas (GER)—Persian Forest **Mr W. J. Greatrex**
59 **PETTICOAT TAILS**, 6, b m Presenting—Theatre Girl **Wynnstay Wanderers**
60 **PORTRUSH TED (IRE)**, 6, b g Shantou (USA)—Village Queen (IRE) **McNeill Family Ltd**
61 4, B g Great Pretender (IRE)—Precious Lucy (FR) **Mr W. J. Greatrex**
62 **RAMBLING RECTOR (IRE)**, 6, ch g Bonbon Rose (FR)—Califea (FR) **Robert Aplin & Swanee River**
63 **ROCK MY STYLE (IRE)**, 6, b g Marienbard (IRE)—Meara Trasna (IRE) **Alan & Andrew Turner**
64 **ROCKPORTIAN (IRE)**, 8, b br g Definite Article—Wilmott's Fancy **N.W.A. Bannister & M.J.R. Bannister**
65 **ROSE OF CIMARRON (IRE)**, 5, b m Westerner—Sharp Single (IRE) **The Munificent Seven**
66 **SANDHURST LAD (IRE)**, 7, b g Presenting—Off She Goes (IRE) **Nigel & Barbara Collison**
67 **SAVOY COURT (IRE)**, 7, b g Robin des Champs (FR)—North Star Poly (IRE) **Mrs T. J. Stone-Brown**
68 **SHANTOU BOB (IRE)**, 10, b g Shantou (USA)—Bobset Leader (IRE) **Fallon, Shipp & Bolingbroke**
69 **SPIN A YARN (IRE)**, 5, b g Flemensfirth (USA)—Keeps Sake (IRE) **Miss C. S. D. Shipp**
70 **THE BLACK SQUIRREL (IRE)**, 5, br g Craigsteel—Terra Lucida (IRE) **Fitorfat Racing**
71 **THE BUTCHER SAID (IRE)**, 5, b g Robin des Champs (FR)—Georgina Valleya (IRE) **McNeill Family Ltd**
72 **THE MISSUS**, 7, b m Presenting—Violet Express (FR) **Mr R. B. Waley-Cohen**
73 **THE NIPPER (IRE)**, 7, b m Scorpion (IRE)—Sharp Single (IRE) **Smith, Ratcliffe & Bowring**
74 **THE WOLF (FR)**, 4, ch g Kapgarde (FR)—Ges (FR) **McNeill Family and Prodec Networks Ltd**
75 **THEATRE TERRITORY (IRE)**, 8, b m King's Theatre (IRE)—Specifiedrisk (IRE) **Mr R. B. Waley-Cohen**
76 **THELUNARSCHOONER (IRE)**, 5, b m Milan—Garden City (IRE) **Mr M. Fennessy**
77 **UP TO NO GOOD (IRE)**, 5, b g Oscar (IRE)—You Take Care (IRE) **E. M. G. Roberts**
78 **VINCIAETTIS (FR)**, 7, b g Enrique—Over The Sea (FR) **Mrs J & Miss C Shipp**
79 **WELL SMITTEN (IRE)**, 6, b g Gold Well—The Dark One (IRE) **Edwards & Flatt**
80 **WESTERN RYDER (IRE)**, 6, b g Westerner—Seesea (IRE) **Albatross Club/Bryan Drew & Friends**

THREE-YEAR-OLDS

81 **BODES WELL (IRE)**, b g Rock of Gibraltar (IRE)—Gypsie Queen (IRE) **Mr W. J. Greatrex**
82 **FENISA'S HOOK**, ch g Lope de Vega (IRE)—Islandia (USA) **Bolingbroke, Freeman & Friends**

MR WARREN GREATREX - Continued

Other Owners: Mr R. J. Aplin, R. K. Aston, Mr C. Austin, J. Baldwin, Mr N. W. A. Bannister, Mr M. J. R. Bannister, Mr M. Bartram, J. R. Bayer, Mr D. S. Bowring, Mr T. E. Boylan, A. R. Bromley, Bryan Drew and Friends, Mrs P. M. Bunch, N. J. Chamberlain, Mrs B. Collison, Mr N. Collison, Mr N. D. Craven, Mr C. K. Crossley Cooke, Mr J. P. Da Mata, Mr P. A. Deal, Mr K. J. Dowley, Mr B. J. C. Drew, G. K. Duncan, Mrs K. D. Edwards, Mr C. J. Edwards, Mrs S. Evans, R. A. F. Eynon, Mrs J. M. Eynon, Mrs G. E. Fallon, Mr G. H. Firmager, Mr G. B. Firmager, Mr P. Fisher, Mrs G. Fisher, Mr D. R. Flatt, Mr K. C. Freeman, Fromthestables.Com Racing, Mr D. Futter, Mr N. J. A. Gifford-Mead, G. F. Goode, R. A. Green, Mr R. Gurney, Highclere Nominated Partner Limited, Highclere Thoroughbred Racing Ltd, Mr J. D. Horgan, Mr G. P. Howard, S. Hurst, James & Jean Potter, Mr S. M. Little, Mr I. G. Martin, A. W. K. Merriam, Mr W. D. C. Minton, Mrs J. M. Minton, Mr P. Molony, Mrs A. J. Murphy, Mrs D. C. Nicholson, Mr S. C. Oelkers, Palatinate Thoroughbred Racing Limited, T. S. Palin, Mr B. Panton, Mr S. J. Piper, Mr N. Pogmore, J. E. Potter, Mrs M. J. Potter, M. Prince, Prodec Networks Ltd, Mr J. Ratcliffe, Mr D. A. Roberts, Mr A. M. D. Robertson, Mr S. R. Roper, Mr S. W. Salkeld, Mrs J. Shipp, Mr W. L. Smith, Mrs K. A. Stuart, Mr C. J. Sutton, Mr J. S. E. Turner, Mrs N. C. Turner, Mr S. Turner, Mr D. A. Turner, Mr A. R. Turner, Mr A. M. Turner, Mrs M. Vaughan-Fowler, Walters Plant Hire Ltd, I. F. White, Mr W. J. Wood.

Assistant Trainer: Olly Kozak **Head Lads:** Trigger Plunkett, Graham Baines.

Racing Secretaries: Oriana-Jane Baines, Karen Dooley

Jockey (NH): Gavin Sheehan. **Conditional:** Harry Bannister, Tom Greatrex, Ben Hicks.
Amateur: Mr A Elias, Mr S Sainsbury.

---

238 | **MR OLIVER GREENALL, Malpas**
Postal: Stockton Hall Farm, Oldcastle, Malpas, Cheshire, SY14 7AE
Contacts: PHONE (01948) 861207 MOBILE (07771) 571000
E-MAIL ocg@stocktonhall.co.uk WEBSITE www.olivergreenall.co.uk

1 ALDERSON, 5, b g Zamindar (USA)—Claradotnet **Mr G. D. Kendrick**
2 AMERICAN LIFE (FR), 11, b br g American Post—Poplife (FR) **American Life Partnership**
3 ASKING QUESTIONS (IRE), 6, b g Ask—Just Sara (IRE) **Salmon Racing**
4 BRONZALLURE (IRE), 5, b g Dubai Destination (USA)—Satco Street (IRE) **Evason, Walsh & Appleton**
5 CAVE TOP (IRE), 6, b g Court Cave (IRE)—Cyrils Top Girl (IRE) **Lord Daresbury & Jocelyn Rosenburg**
6 CHRISTO, 8, ch g Areion (GER)—Chantra (GER) **Dewhurst, Michaelson & Hewitt**
7 COME ON LOUIS, 10, b g Grape Tree Road—Seamill (IRE) **Mr O. C. Greenall**
8 FIRST UP (IRE), 4, b g Rip Van Winkle (IRE)—Doregan (IRE) **S Burns, M Smyth & D Studholme**
9 FORT JEFFERSON, 5, br g Passing Glance—Florida Heart **Racing Spirit Fort Jefferson Owners**
10 HELF (IRE), 4, b c Helmet (AUS)—Causeway Song (USA)
11 JAUNTY THOR, 8, b g Norse Dancer (IRE)—Jaunty Walk **Daresbury, Green Wilson**
12 KATEBIRD (IRE), 4, gr f Dark Angel (IRE)—She Basic (IRE) **Mrs J. P. Rosenberg**
13 KIKIMORA, 5, gr m Malinas (GER)—Tikk Tokk (IRE) **Aston, Bostock, Fox, Goodall, Pollard**
14 LESKINFERE (IRE), 5, b g Darsi (FR)—Taipans Girl (IRE) **Racing Spirit Leskinfere Owners Group**
15 LINCOLN COUNTY, 7, b g Authorized (IRE)—Lane County (USA) **Faithful Followers**
16 LORD COUNTY (FR), 4, gr g Lord du Sud (FR)—County County (USA) **Brook, Daresbury & Clayeux**
17 LOS CERRITOS (SWI), 6, ch g Dr Fong (USA)—La Coruna (SWI) **Emdells Limited**
18 MR YOUNG (FR), 4, ch g Mr Sidney (USA)—Young Majesty (USA) **Mr D. C. Mercer**
19 NEVER A WORD (USA), 4, br g Lonhro (AUS)—Janetstickettocats (USA) **Mr G. Dewhurst**
20 4, Bl f Fame And Glory—Peinture Rose (IRE)
21 QUIDS IN (IRE), 5, b g Pour Moi (IRE)—Quixotic **Daresbury, MacEchern & Lee Baldwin**
22 ROCK WARBLER (IRE), 5, ch g Raven's Pass (USA)—
Rare Tern (IRE) **Mr R A Royle, Mr S Evason, Mr M Appleton**
23 SPIRIT OF WATERLOO, 4, b c Malinas (GER)—Warm Front **Salmon Racing**
24 TITAN, 4, b g Lawman (FR)—Dragonera **Preston Lodge Stud, Champneys**
25 TOUCH OF STEEL (IRE), 9, b g Craigsteel—Tourmaline Girl (IRE) **T.O.S Of A Coin**
26 TWOTWOTHREE (IRE), 5, b g Shantou (USA)—Sibury (IRE) **S. J. Allwood**
27 VERANO (GER), 9, ch g Lord of England (GER)—Vive La Vie (GER) **R. J. Hewitt**
28 WESTERN MORNING (IRE), 5, b g Westerner—Gweedara (IRE) **Faithful Followers**
29 ZALVADOS (FR), 5, ch g Soldier of Fortune (IRE)—Zariyana (IRE) **Mr D. C. Mercer**

THREE-YEAR-OLDS

30 ARTY BUT POOR, b g Dutch Art—Libys Dream (IRE) **E. A. Brook**

Other Owners: Mr M. Appleton, R. K. Aston, Mrs J. L. Baldwin, Mrs B. A. Bostock, Mrs S. E. Brown, Mr S. Burns, Mr E. Clayeux, Dr J. D. Dalton, Lord Daresbury, Mrs D. Dewbery, Mr S. Evason, Miss S. Fox, Mr D. Goodall, Ms M. M. L. Green, G. M. MacEchern, R. P. B. Michaelson, Mr J. P. Naylor, Mr J. Pollard, S. J. Purdew, Mr R. A. Royle, Mrs Lynn Salmon, Mr D. B. Salmon, Mr M. W. Salmon, Mr M. Smyth, Mr D. Studholme, Mr S. M. Walsh, Mr J. R. Weatherby, Mr J. F. Wilson, Mrs L. Winrow-Campbell.

MR OLIVER GREENALL - Continued

Assistant Trainer: J. Guerriero

Jockey (flat): Kevin Stott. **Jockey (NH):** Ian Popham. **Amateur:** Mr Edward Glassonbury.

---

239 **MR TOM GRETTON, Inkberrow**
Postal: **C/o Gretton & Co Ltd, Middle Bouts Farm, Bouts Lane, Inkberrow, Worcester**
Contacts: **PHONE (01386) 792240 FAX (01386) 792472 MOBILE (07866) 116928**
E-MAIL tomgretton@hotmail.co.uk WEBSITE www.tomgrettonracing.com

1 APPLETREE LANE, 8, b m Croco Rouge (IRE)—Emmasflora **T. R. Gretton**
2 ARMEDANDBEAUTIFUL, 10, b m Oscar (IRE)—Grey Mistral **Not The Peloton Partnership**
3 ART LOOKER (IRE), 6, b g Excellent Art—Looker **Mrs L. Gretton**
4 BIT OF A GEORDIE, 5, br m Geordieland (FR)—Gaelic Gold (IRE) **Mr B. P. Keogh**
5 CALLAGHAN (GER), 5, b g Cacique (IRE)—
                                  Cent Cheveux Blanc (GER) **Tom Gretton Racing II & Ownaracehorse**
6 FAFA, 7, b g Westerner—Ifuseehersayhello **Coldunell Limited**
7 JACKTHEJOURNEYMAN (IRE), 9, b g Beneficial—Maslam (IRE) **Mr E. B. O'Reilly Hyland**
8 KAUTO RIKO (FR), 7, b g Ballingarry (IRE)—Kauto Relstar (FR) **Mr & Mrs J.Dale & Partners**
9 5, B m Milan—La Dame Brune (FR) **Mr J. R. Hynes**
10 LICKPENNY LARRY, 7, gr g Sagamix (FR)—Myriah (IRE) **Mr A. S. Clarke**
11 LITTLE JIMMY, 11, br g Passing Glance—Sementina (USA) **Tom Gretton Racing & Ownaracehorse Ltd**
12 PRIMO ROSSI, 9, b g Primo Valentino (IRE)—Flaming Rose (IRE) **Ownaracehorse Ltd & Mr T. R. Gretton**
13 SNOW RESCUE (IRE), 6, gr g Stowaway—Annilogs Palm (IRE) **Ian Powell & Ownarachorse Ltd**
14 TEN IN THE HAT (IRE), 4, b g Sir Prancealot (IRE)—Vampire Queen (IRE) **Three Bags Of Sand Syndicate**
15 YOURHOLIDAYISOVER (IRE), 11, ch g Sulamani (IRE)—Whitehaven **G1 Racing Club Ltd**

Other Owners: Mr B. J. Brennan, Mr J. W. Dale, Mrs J. S. Dale, Mr B. Dennehy, Ownaracehorse Ltd, Mr G. C. Parkins, Mr I. Powell, Mr T. Rees.

Assistant Trainer: Laura Gretton (07789) 754806

---

240 **MR DAVID C. GRIFFITHS, Bawtry**
Postal: **Martin Hall, Martin Common, Bawtry, Doncaster, South Yorkshire, DN10 6DA**
Contacts: **PHONE (01302) 714247 MOBILE (07816) 924621**
E-MAIL davidgriffiths250@hotmail.com WEBSITE www.davidgriffithsracing.co.uk

1 AGUEROOO (IRE), 5, b g Monsieur Bond (IRE)—Vision of Peace (IRE) **Ontoawinner 8**
2 ARCHIMEDES (IRE), 5, b g Invincible Spirit (IRE)—Waveband **Ladies & The Tramps**
3 BROTHER TIGER, 9, b g Singspiel (IRE)—Three Secrets (IRE) **Norcroft Park Stud**
4 CYFLYMDER (IRE), 12, b g Mujadil (USA)—Nashwan Star (IRE) **Mr D. C. Griffiths**
5 DUKE OF FIRENZE, 9, ch g Pivotal—Nannina **Adlam,Damary-Thompson,Wilson,Griffiths**
6 FIELDSMAN (USA), 6, b g Hard Spun (USA)—R Charlie's Angel (USA) **Gallop Racing**
7 HUNTSMANS CLOSE, 8, b g Elusive Quality (USA)—Badminton **Mr D. C. Griffiths**
8 LUCKY BEGGAR (IRE), 8, gr g Verglas (IRE)—Lucky Clio (IRE) **Eros Bloodstock**
9 MARYLEBONE, 5, b g Shamardal (USA)—Mary Boleyn (IRE) **Wentdale Limited**
10 MILLYBOND, 4, b f Misu Bond (IRE)—Noble Attitude **Fishlake Commercial Motors Ltd**
11 ORNATE, 5, b g Bahamian Bounty—Adorn **Cheveley Park Stud Limited**
12 PEARL ACCLAIM (IRE), 8, b g Acclamation—With Colour **Ontoawinner 2 & Partner**
13 SIEGE OF BOSTON (IRE), 5, ch g Starspangledbanner (AUS)—Milton of Campsie **Mr M. Mckay**
14 STORM KING, 9, b g Shamardal (USA)—Tarandot (USA) **Norcroft Park Stud**
15 TAVENER, 6, b g Exceed And Excel (AUS)—Sea Chorus **Baker, Hensby, Longden, Baker**

THREE-YEAR-OLDS

16 ANGEL FORCE (IRE), ch f Lethal Force (IRE)—Indian Angel **Mr P. Baker**
17 ELEGANT JOAN, ch f Assertive—Fangfoss Girls **Abacus Bloodstock Racing Club**
18 KEYNOTE (IRE), b g Dragon Pulse (IRE)—Taalluf (USA) **David Poulton & Griffiths**
19 MAGIC PULSE (IRE), b f Dragon Pulse (IRE)—Invincible Magic (IRE) **Mr C. Buckingham**
20 MENDALI, b g Multiplex—Future Regime (USA) **Wurlyburly Partnership**
21 MYSTICAL MOON (IRE), ch f Excelebration (IRE)—Boast **Mr M. Smith**
22 WARRIOR'S VALLEY, b c Mayson—Sand And Deliver **RPB Michaelson N Davies D Clarke**

MR DAVID C. GRIFFITHS - Continued

TWO-YEAR-OLDS

23 Ch c 31/3 Arakan (USA)—Ambonnay (Ashkalani (IRE)) (8571) **Mr D. C. Griffiths**
24 B f 28/2 Epaulette (AUS)—Precious Secret (IRE) (Fusaichi Pegasus (USA)) (9523) **Mr D. C. Griffiths**
25 B f 11/2 Delegator—Rock Candy (IRE) (Rock of Gibraltar (IRE)) **Eros Bloodstock**

Other Owners: Mr J. P. Adlam, Mr R. Baker, Mr P. Birley, Mr S. Bridge, Mr D. J. Clarke, Miss H. A. Damary-Thompson, Mr
N. J. Davies, Mrs S. E. Griffiths, Mr G. D. Hensby, Mr A. J. Hollis, Mr D. M. Hollis, Mr A. R. Lavender, Mr S. J. Matheson,
R. P. B. Michaelson, Mr N. J. O'Brien, Mr D. J. Poulton, Mr R. Walker, Miss A. M. Walker, Mr L. Wilson, Mrs J. Worley.

Assistant Trainer: Mrs S. E. Griffiths

Apprentice: Alistair Rawlinson.

---

241 | **MR SIRRELL GRIFFITHS, Carmarthen**
Postal: **Rwyth Farm, Nantgaredig, Carmarthen, Dyfed, SA32 7LG**
Contacts: **PHONE (01267) 290321/290120**

1 COUSIN RITA, 6, b m Black Sam Bellamy (IRE)—Aunt Rita (IRE) **S. G. Griffiths**

Assistant Trainer: Martyn Roger Griffiths

---

242 | **MRS DIANA GRISSELL, Robertsbridge**
Postal: **Brightling Park, Robertsbridge, East Sussex, TN32 5HH**
Contacts: **PHONE (01424) 838241 MOBILE (07950) 312610**
E-MAIL digrissell@aol.com WEBSITE www.brightlingpark.com

1 BALLINTARA (IRE), 6, b g Getaway (GER)—Miltara (IRE) **Cockerell Cowing Racing**
2 CANYOUHEARMENOW (IRE), 7, b g Trans Island—First of April (IRE) **Mr P.S.Wardle & Mr.J.N.Allen**
3 DE CLARE MAN, 9, b g Kayf Tara—Douce Maison (IRE) **Mr C. Ballenden**
4 HERE I AM (IRE), 11, br g Presenting—The Last Bank (IRE) **Nigel & Barbara Collison**
5 JAPPELOUP (IRE), 9, b br g Presenting—Crackin' Liss (IRE) **Partnership Terminated**
6 MICKIEBLUEEYES (IRE), 6, b g Dilshaan—Killerig Park **Mr K. M. Dilworth**

Other Owners: Mr J. N. Allen, B. J. Cockerell, Mrs B. Collison, Mr N. Collison, A. Cowing, P. S. Wardle.

Jockey (NH): Marc Goldstein. **Amateur:** Mr O. Wedmore.

---

243 | **MR JOHN GROUCOTT, Much Wenlock**
Postal: **Dairy Cottage, Bourton, Much Wenlock, Shropshire, TF13 6QD**
Contacts: **PHONE (01746) 785603**

1 BATTLEBRAVE (IRE), 5, b g Fracas (IRE)—Silly Mille (IRE) **Mrs B. Clarke**
2 BATTLEFIELD (IRE), 6, b g Central Park (IRE)—Silly Mille (IRE) **Mrs B. Clarke**
3 EL SCORPIO (IRE), 6, b g Scorpion (IRE)—El Monica (IRE) **Mrs B. Clarke**
4 HEAVENLY PROMISE (IRE), 7, ch m Presenting—Ambrosia's Promise (IRE) **Geoff Hubbard Racing**
5 LADY RED OAK, 7, ch m Medicean—Nuit Sans Fin (FR) **Mr D. R. Passant**
6 MIDNIGHT TARGET, 8, b m Midnight Legend—Right On Target (IRE) **Mr E. P. Parkes**
7 NELLEMANI, 6, ch m Sulamani (IRE)—Send Me An Angel (IRE) **The Heartbreakers**
8 NEWERA, 6, ch g Makfi—Coming Home **Mr D. R. Passant**
9 SHININSTAR (IRE), 9, b g Westerner—Shiny Button **Mrs B. Clarke**
10 SIDSTEEL (IRE), 7, b g Craigsteel—Clare Hogan (IRE) **Mrs B. Clarke**
11 4, B f Malinas (GER)—Sunnyland
12 THE TOOJUMPA, 5, b m Midnight Legend—Sunnyland **Lord C. D. Harrison**
13 TRUCKERS HIGHWAY (IRE), 9, b g Rudimentary (USA)—Countessdee (IRE) **C. J. Tipton**

TWO-YEAR-OLDS

14 B f 15/2 Schiaparelli (GER)—Sunnyland (Sovereign Water (FR))

Other Owners: Mr P. R. D'Amato, Mr J. E. H. Reader, Mrs J. Reader.

244 MR RAE GUEST, Newmarket

Postal: **Chestnut Tree Stables, Hamilton Road, Newmarket, Suffolk, CB8 0NY**
Contacts: **PHONE (01638) 661508 FAX (01638) 667317 MOBILE (07711) 301095**
E-MAIL raeguest@raeguest.com WEBSITE www.raeguest.com

1 **BERRYESSA (IRE)**, 4, b f Dandy Man (IRE)—Carrauntoohil (IRE) **RGRL Syndicate 2**
2 **DEFINING MOMENT**, 4, b f Camacho—Elfine (IRE) **Mr Derek J. Willis**
3 **LUNAR MIST**, 4, b f Bated Breath—Time Will Show (FR) **Mr Ross Carson**
4 **MIDNIGHTLY**, 4, b f Acclamation—Midnight Shift (IRE) **Bradmill Ltd**
5 **MIRZA**, 11, b g Oasis Dream—Millyant **Mr C. J. Mills**
6 **ODE TO GLORY**, 4, b f Poet's Voice—Blue Lyric **The Reprobates**
7 **SALT WHISTLE BAY (IRE)**, 4, b c Royal Applause—Quantum (IRE) **The Hightailers & Rae Guest**
8 **SHOW STEALER**, 5, ch m Showcasing—Winifred Jo **Mr Colin Joseph**
9 **THE EAGLE'S NEST (IRE)**, 4, ch g Lope de Vega (IRE)—Follow My Lead **The Eagle Has Landed Syndicate**

THREE-YEAR-OLDS

10 **ALASKAN BAY (IRE)**, b f Kodiac—Party Appeal (USA) **Reprobates Too**
11 **DAME NELLIE**, b f Aussie Rules (USA)—Eminencia **Ms Kirsten Rausing**
12 **DANCE LEGEND**, b f Camelot—Syvilla **Tim Cooper**
13 **DASH OF ORANGE**, br f Lethal Force (IRE)—Princess of Orange **Mr Colin Joseph**
14 **ETERNAL DESTINY**, b f Poet's Voice—Mrs Mogg **4G Racing**
15 **INCH PINCHER**, b f Captain Gerrard (IRE)—Elfine (IRE) **Mr Derek J. Willis**
16 **KACHUMBA**, b f Mayson—Native Nickel (IRE) **The Storm Again Syndicate**
17 **ROMAN SPINNER**, ch f Intikhab (USA)—Pompeia **Reprobates Too**
18 **TIARA GOLD**, ch f Poet's Voice—Dress Code (IRE) **BB Bloodstock & Rae Guest**
19 **WALLFLOWER (IRE)**, b f Thewayyouare (USA)—Gaselee (USA) **Paul Smith & Rae Guest**
20 **WINTER WALTZ**, b f Frozen Power (IRE)—Quail Landing **Reprobates Too**

TWO-YEAR-OLDS

21 Ch f 20/2 Sir Percy—Blush's Gift (Cadeaux Genereux) (7000) **Mr Enno Albert**
22 B f 15/4 Roderic O'connor (IRE)—California Rose (Oratorio (IRE)) (4000)
23 **DEPTFORD MICK (IRE)**, br c 5/4 Bated Breath—Be Joyful (Teofilo (IRE)) (11000) **Mr Derek J. Willis**
24 **FEEL THE NOIZE**, br f 12/2 Slade Power (IRE)—
Sugar Free (IRE) (Oasis Dream) (14000) **The Storm Again Syndicate**
25 B c 11/4 Camelot—Gaselee (USA) (Toccet (USA)) **Paul Smith & Rae Guest**
26 **MOUNTAIN DOG**, b c 10/5 Mount Nelson—The Blue Dog (IRE) (High Chaparral (IRE)) (10000) **Mr Ross Carson**
27 B f 20/4 Born To Sea (IRE)—Rhapsodize (Halling (USA)) (6000) **The Reprobates**
28 B f 10/4 Bated Breath—Ruffled (Harlan's Holiday (USA)) **Mr Colin J. Murfitt**

Other Owners: BB Bloodstock, Mr A. P. Davies, Mr E. P Duggan, Mr John Fullick, Mr R. T. Goodes, Mr Rae Guest, Mr R. H. Jennings, Mrs L. M. Lambert, Mr Perry Martin, Mr D. G. Raffel, Mr Stephen Russell, Mr Paul J. Smith, Mr Barry Stewart.

245 MR RICHARD GUEST, Ingmanthorpe

Postal: **Ingmanthorpe Racing Stables, Ingmanthorpe Grange Farm, Ingmanthorpe, Wetherby, West Yorkshire, LS22 5HL**
Contacts: **PHONE 0800 2988088 (07715) 516072 (07713) 132577 MOBILE (07715) 516071**
E-MAIL enquiries@richardguestracing.co.uk WEBSITE www.richardguestracing.co.uk

1 **AMAZING GRAZING (IRE)**, 4, b g Intense Focus (USA)—North Light Rose (USA) **A. R. Barnes**
2 **BILLY ROBERTS (IRE)**, 5, b g Multiplex—Mi Amor (IRE) **www.primelawns.co.uk**
3 **BOLLIHOPE**, 6, ch g Medicean—Hazy Dancer **Mr S. Lockyer**
4 **BREATHOFFRESHAIR**, 4, b g Bated Breath—Stormy Weather **Alfa Site Services Ltd/Mrs Alison Guest**
5 **CAPTAIN SCOOBY**, 12, b g Captain Rio—Scooby Dooby Do **The Captain Scooby Syndicate**
6 **CRAGGAKNOCK**, 7, b g Authorized—Goodie Twosues **Alfa Site Services Ltd**
7 **HEDIDDODINTHE (IRE)**, 4, gr g Kendargent (FR)—Damoiselle (USA) **Mrs A. L. Guest**
8 **ISNTSHESOMETHING**, 6, br m Assertive—Princess Almora **Mr C. J. Penney**
9 **LADY JOANNA VASSA (IRE)**, 5, ch m Equiano (FR)—Lady Natilda **www.primelawns.co.uk**
10 **LOUGH SALT (IRE)**, 7, b g Brian Boru—Castlehill Lady (IRE) **Mr J Toes & Mr J O'Loan**
11 **MR COOL CASH**, 6, b g Firebreak—Cashleen (USA) **Mr I. Lawson**
12 **MR POTTER**, 5, ch g Assertive—Enclave (USA) **A. Turton, A. Rhodes & Mrs Alison Guest**
13 **MY GIRL MAISIE (IRE)**, 4, b f Fast Company (IRE)—
Queen Al Andalous (IRE) **Alfa Site Services Ltd, Mrs Alison Guest**
14 **OUTLAW TORN (IRE)**, 9, ch g Iffraaj—Touch And Love (IRE) **Mr J Toes & Mr J O'Loan**
15 **POLAR FOREST**, 8, br g Kyllachy—Woodbeck **Mr R. C. Guest**

MR RICHARD GUEST - Continued

16 **TELLOVOI (IRE)**, 10, b g Indian Haven—Kloonlara (IRE) **Mrs A. L. Guest**
17 **UDONTDODOU**, 5, b g Fastnet Rock (AUS)—Forever Times **Mrs A. L. Guest**
18 **WEDIDDODONTWE**, 4, b g Equiano (FR)—Vodka Shot (USA) **Ian Guise & Partner**

THREE-YEAR-OLDS

19 **ANOTHER SITUATION (USA)**, ch f Trappe Shot (USA)—
Return The Jewel (USA) **Alfa Site Services Ltd & Daniel Newett**
20 **CARNAGE**, b g Holy Roman Emperor (IRE)—Sylvestris (IRE) **Franconson Partners**
21 **FINK HILL (USA)**, b g The Factor (USA)—Matroshka (IRE) **Morecool & Cool Racing 2**
22 **FOXRUSH TAKE TIME (FR)**, b g Showcasing—Stranded **Alfa Site Services Ltd & Partner**
23 **GISELE'S ANGEL**, gr f Dark Angel (IRE)—Lovely Thought **Mrs A. L. Guest**
24 **HOCUS FOCUS (IRE)**, b c Intense Focus (USA)—Hedera (USA) **Mr P Sutherland & Mr A Barnes**
25 **MOREMONEYMOREPARTY (IRE)**, b f Epaulette (AUS)—Three Times **Mr S. Lockyer**
26 **SAVANNAH'S SHOW**, b f Showcasing—Grandmas Dream **Mrs Alison Guest**
27 **SQUIRRELHEED**, b g Finjaan—Valjarv (IRE) **Mr Simon Lockyer & Partner**
28 **WHATWOULDYOUKNOW (IRE)**, b g Lope de Vega (IRE)—Holamo (IRE) **Dearing Plastics Ltd & Partner**
29 **WYNFAUL THE WIZARD (USA)**, b c Bodemeister (USA)—Red Dot (USA) **Alfa Site Services Ltd & Partner**

TWO-YEAR-OLDS

30 B f 16/3 Finjaan—Chapellerie (IRE) (Acclamation)
31 **CLOUDY DANCER**, gr f 13/3 Invincible Spirit (IRE)—Ronaldsay (Kirkwall) (119047)
32 B f 3/2 Verrazano (USA)—J J's Pattern (USA) (Langfuhr (CAN)) (7742)
33 B c 30/4 Fast Company (IRE)—Lady's Locket (IRE) (Fasliyev (USA)) (48840)
34 Gr ro c 17/3 Exchange Rate (USA)—Lastroseofsummer (IRE) (Haafhd) **Alfa Site Services Ltd**
35 B f 11/3 Equiano (FR)—Modern Lady (Bertolini (USA))

Other Owners: Mr A. Barnes, Mr S. Bland, Dearing Plastics Ltd, Mr Ian Guise, Mr Simon Lockyer, Mr D. G. Newett, Mr T. D. Nield, Mr J. O'Loan, Mr A. Rhodes, Mr P. Sutherland, Mr M. Sykes, Mr J. Toes, Mr Andrew Turton.

Jockey (flat): Connor Beasley.

246
MS POLLY GUNDRY, Ottery St Mary
Postal: **Holcombe Brook, Holcombe Lane, Ottery St. Mary, Devon, EX11 1PH**
Contacts: **PHONE (01404) 813053 MOBILE (07932) 780621**
E-MAIL **pollygundrytraining@live.co.uk**

1 **BIG TIME FRANK (IRE)**, 7, b g Bienamado (USA)—Pure Spirit (IRE) **N Allen & P Bowler**
2 **DAWSON CITY**, 9, b g Midnight Legend—Running For Annie **Ian Payne & Kim Franklin**
3 **HOLD ME TIGHT (IRE)**, 4, b g Zoffany (IRE)—All Embracing (IRE) **Mrs W. J. Jarrett**
4 4, B g High Chaparral (IRE)—Lindeman (IRE) **Mr & Mrs R. G. Kelvin-Hughes**
5 **MOOR FREEDOM**, 5, b m Beat Hollow—Line Freedom (FR)
6 **QUITE RIGHT**, 7, b m Lucarno (USA)—Thebelloftheball **Mr J. P. Selby**
7 **SIR DYLAN**, 9, b g Dylan Thomas (IRE)—Monteleone (IRE) **M James & S Jarrett**
8 **SWINCOMBE SCORCHIO**, 8, b g Scorpion (IRE)—Lady Felix **Holcombe Hopefuls**
9 **TICKET TO RIDE (FR)**, 5, b g Al Namix (FR)—Eightdaysaweek **R. G. Kelvin-Hughes**

Other Owners: Mr N. G. Allen, Mr P. O. Bowler, Mr S. A. Evans, Miss K. M. Franklin, Mr P. G. Gibbins, Mr M. James, Mr S. H. Jarrett, Mrs E. A. Kelvin-Hughes, Mr I. T. Payne.

Assistant Trainer: Edward Walker

Jockey (flat): Liam Keniry. **Jockey (NH):** James Best, Nick Schofield. **Amateur:** Mr William Biddick.

247
MR WILLAM HAGGAS, Newmarket
Postal: **Somerville Lodge, Fordham Road, Newmarket, Suffolk, CB8 7AA**
Contacts: **PHONE (01638) 667013 FAX (01638) 660534 MOBILE (07860) 282281**
E-MAIL **william@somerville-lodge.co.uk** WEBSITE **www.somerville-lodge.co.uk**

1 **ACROSS DUBAI**, 4, b g Cape Cross (IRE)—Saadiah (IRE) **Sheikh Juma Dalmook Al Maktoum**
2 **ADDEYBB (IRE)**, 4, ch g Pivotal—Bush Cat (USA) **Sheikh Ahmed Al Maktoum**
3 **ALFARRIS (FR)**, 4, b g Shamardal (USA)—Rose Et Noire (IRE) **Mr Hamdan Al Maktoum**

MR WILLAM HAGGAS - Continued

4 **CALL TO MIND**, 4, b c Galileo (IRE)—Memory (IRE) **Her Majesty The Queen**
5 **CRYSTAL RIVER**, 4, b f Dubawi (IRE)—Inner Secret (USA) **Somerville Lodge Ltd**
6 **DAL HARRAILD**, 5, ch g Champs Elysees—Dalvina **St Albans Bloodstock Ltd**
7 **DIAGNOSTIC**, 4, b c Dutch Art—Holistic **Cheveley Park Stud**
8 **DYNAMIC**, 4, b f Teofilo (IRE)—White Cay **Michael & Michelle Morris**
9 **HAKEEM**, 4, b g Exceed And Excel (AUS)—Khazeena **Mr Hamdan Al Maktoum**
10 **HUMBLE HERO (IRE)**, 4, b g High Chaparral (IRE)—Alamouna (IRE) **Coolmore & Jooste**
11 **IMPORTANT MISSION (USA)**, 4, b br g More Than Ready (USA)—
Laura's Pleasure (USA) **Sheikh Juma Dalmook Al Maktoum**
12 **MAM'SELLE (IRE)**, 4, b f Teofilo (IRE)—Coquette Rouge (IRE) **Highclere Thoroughbred Racing**
13 **MOJITO (IRE)**, 4, b c Requinto (IRE)—Narva (USA) **Carmichael Jennings**
14 **MUBTASIM (IRE)**, 4, b g Arcano (IRE)—Start The Music (USA) **Sheikh Rashid Dalmook Al Maktoum**
15 **MUTHMIR (IRE)**, 8, b g Invincible Spirit (IRE)—Fairy of The Night (IRE) **Mr Hamdan Al Maktoum**
16 **ONE MASTER**, 4, b f Fastnet Rock (AUS)—Enticing (IRE) **Lael Stable**
17 **ORIGINAL CHOICE (IRE)**, 4, ch g Dragon Pulse (IRE)—Belle Watling (IRE) **Mr Albert Goodman**
18 **REVEREND JACOBS**, 4, b g Nathaniel (IRE)—Light Impact (IRE) **Mr B. Kantor**
19 **SECOND THOUGHT (IRE)**, 4, b c Kodiac—Bobby Jane (IRE) **Mr L. Sheridan**
20 **SENIORITY**, 4, ch g Dubawi (IRE)—Anna Palarva (IRE) **Her Majesty The Queen**
21 **SMASHED (IRE)**, 5, b g Beat Hollow—Sel **Mr B. Haggas**
22 **TARTE TROPÉZIENNE (IRE)**, 4, b f Nathaniel (IRE)—High Heel Sneakers **Stratford Place Stud**
23 **TASLEET**, 5, b h Showcasing—Bird Key **Mr Hamdan Al Maktoum**
24 **THE GRAND VISIR**, 4, b c Frankel—Piping (IRE) **Saleh Al Homaizi & Imad Al Sagar**
25 **TIRANIA**, 4, b f Pivotal—Tiriana **Yvonne Jacques**
26 **URBAN FOX**, 4, b f Foxwedge (AUS)—Lomapamar **Barnane Stud**
27 **VICTORY BOND**, 5, b g Medicean—Antebellum (FR) **Duke Of Bedford**
28 **WHAT A HOME (IRE)**, 4, b f Lope de Vega (IRE)—Inchmahome **Sunderland Holding Inc.**

THREE-YEAR-OLDS

29 **AL MUFFRIH (IRE)**, b c Sea The Stars (IRE)—Scarlet And Gold (IRE) **Sheikh Juma Dalmook Al Maktoum**
30 **ALEXANA**, b f Al Kazeem—Dolores **Normandie Stud Ltd**
31 **ALEXANDERTHEGREAT (FR)**, b c Redoute's Choice (AUS)—Garota da Ipanema (FR) **Cheveley Park Stud**
32 **ALGAFFAAL (USA)**, ch c Speightstown (USA)—Rockcide (USA) **Mr Hamdan Al Maktoum**
33 **ALLIEYF**, b c New Approach (IRE)—Sajjhaa **Sheikh Ahmed Al Maktoum**
34 **AWESOMETANK**, br f Intense Focus (USA)—Janey Muddles (IRE) **Mr Lee Yuk Lun Alan**
35 **BARTON MILLS**, b c Iffraaj—Balladonia **Abdulla Al Mansoori**
36 **BEAUTY FILLY**, b f Invincible Spirit (IRE)—Miss Delila (USA) **Sheikh Juma Dalmook Al Maktoum**
37 **BERMUDA TRIANGLE (IRE)**, b c Sea The Stars (IRE)—Sea of Heartbreak (IRE) **Mohamed Obaida**
38 **BESHAAYIR**, b f Iffraaj—Bahia Breeze **Sheikh Rashid Dalmook Al Maktoum**
39 **CAVATINA**, b f Lethal Force (IRE)—Piano **Cheveley Park Stud**
40 **CINTRA (IRE)**, b f Camacho—Bordighera (USA) **Lael Stable**
41 **CLOUDLAM**, b f Arch (USA)—Sharnberry **St Albans Bloodstock Ltd**
42 **COHEN**, b c Poet's Voice—Musical Sands **Helena Springfield Ltd**
43 **COMPLETION (IRE)**, b c Arch (USA)—Minute Limit (IRE) **Cheveley Park Stud**
44 **COSMIC LOVE**, ch f Sea The Stars (IRE)—Soodad **St Albans Bloodstock Ltd**
45 **CRISTAL SPIRIT**, b f Nathaniel (IRE)—Celestial Girl **Roberts/Green/Savidge/Whittal-Williams**
46 **DRAMATIC QUEEN (USA)**, ch f Kitten's Joy (USA)—Midnight Music (IRE) **Sheikh Juma Dalmook Al Maktoum**
47 **ERTIYAD**, b f Dark Angel (IRE)—Lily Again **Sheikh Juma Dalmook Al Maktoum**
48 **EXTRA LARGE**, b c Dubawi (IRE)—Check the Label (USA) **Lael Stable**
49 **FELINE GROOVY (USA)**, ch f Kitten's Joy (USA)—Element of Truth (USA) **Mr Chris Wright**
50 **FIELD GUN (USA)**, b br g More Than Ready (USA)—D'wild Beach (USA) **Mr Isa Salman**
51 **FLAMENCO**, b f Showcasing—Astrantia **Highclere Thoroughbred Racing**
52 **FRENCH HEROINE**, b f Redoute's Choice (AUS)—Hasaiyda (FR) **Clipper Logistics**
53 **GIVE AND TAKE**, b f Cityscape—Grace And Glory (IRE) **Mr N. Jones**
54 **HATEEL (IRE)**, b f Kodiac—Vee Gita (IRE) **Mr Hamdan Al Maktoum**
55 **HEADWAY**, b c Havana Gold (IRE)—On Her Way **Royal Ascot Racing Club**
56 **HUMBOLT CURRENT**, b c Fastnet Rock (AUS)—Humdrum **Her Majesty The Queen**
57 **IMPROVE (IRE)**, b f Iffraaj—Choose Me (IRE) **Yvonne Jacques**
58 **INTANGIBLE STAR**, b c Sea The Stars (IRE)—Wosaita **Sunderland Holding Inc.**
59 **ISTANBUL SULTAN (IRE)**, gr g Zoffany (IRE)—Far Away Eyes (IRE) **Simon Munir & Isaac Souede**
60 **JAHAAFEL (FR)**, gr c Style Vendome (FR)—Irisijana (GER) **Mr Hamdan Al Maktoum**
61 **JURRAN**, b c Bated Breath—Bahamian Music (IRE) **Mr Hamdan Al Maktoum**
62 **JUTHOOR (IRE)**, ch c Shamardal (USA)—Dehbanu (IRE) **Mr Hamdan Al Maktoum**
63 **KLASSIQUE**, b f Galileo (IRE)—Chachamaidee (IRE) **Yvonne Jacques**
64 **LIBERTY LYNX**, b f High Chaparral (IRE)—Stella Point (IRE) **Jon & Julia Aisbitt**

MR WILLAM HAGGAS - Continued

65 **LIFE ON EARTH (USA)**, br f Animal Kingdom (USA)—Cukee (USA) **Qatar Racing**
66 **MAGICAL SIGHT**, b c Sea The Stars (IRE)—Sentaril **Lael Stable**
67 **MASHAHEER**, b g Dutch Art—Faustinatheyounger (IRE) **Mr Hamdan Al Maktoum**
68 **MONEEBB (IRE)**, b g Street Cry (IRE)—Alzerra (UAE) **Sheikh Ahmed Al Maktoum**
69 **MOSSEYB (IRE)**, b g Epaulette (AUS)—Allegrissimo (IRE) **Sheikh Ahmed Al Maktoum**
70 **MOVE SWIFTLY**, b f Farhh—Hurricane Harriet **Sheikh Rashid Dalmook Al Maktoum**
71 **MUNEYRA**, b f Dubawi (IRE)—Birjand **Sheikh Ahmed Al Maktoum**
72 **MY LORD AND MASTER (IRE)**, ch c Mastercraftsman (IRE)—Affability (IRE) **Mr Tim Bridge**
73 **NICKLAUS**, ch g Exceed And Excel (AUS)—Nianga (GER) **Mr M. J. Jooste**
74 **NOMOATHAJ (IRE)**, b f Dubawi (IRE)—Jadhwah **Mr Hamdan Al Maktoum**
75 **PERFECT THOUGHT**, ch f Dawn Approach (IRE)—Masaya **Mr Liam Sheridan**
76 **PRABENI**, ch c Teofilo (IRE)—Nyarhini **Mr A. E. Oppenheimer**
77 **PRETTY BABY (IRE)**, b f Orpen (USA)—Premiere Danseuse **Sheikh Rashid Dalmook Al Maktoum**
78 **RED CYMBAL**, b c Pivotal—Red Baton **Cheveley Park Stud**
79 **REGINA NOSTRA**, b f Pivotal—Regina **Cheveley Park Stud**
80 **REIFFA (IRE)**, b f Epaulette (AUS)—Phi Phi (IRE) **Abdulla Al Khalifa**
81 **RESTIVE SPIRIT**, b c Intello (GER)—Hooray **Messrs B Kantor & MJ Jooste**
82 **RHIGOLTER ROSE (IRE)**, ch f Leroidesanimaux (BRZ)—Landela **Mr Tim Bridge**
83 **ROUND THE BUOY**, b c Henrythenavigator (USA)—Key Point (USA) **Her Majesty The Queen**
84 **SAINT DIANA (JPN)**, b f Heart's Cry (JPN)—Realisatrice (FR) **Silvestro Thoroughbreds**
85 **SEA OF CLASS (IRE)**, ch f Sea The Stars (IRE)—Holy Moon (IRE) **Sunderland Holding Inc.**
86 **SHARAMM (IRE)**, b c Shamardal (USA)—Oojooba **Sheikh Ahmed Al Maktoum**
87 **SHAREET**, b g Raven's Pass (USA)—Estedaama (IRE) **Mr Hamdan Al Maktoum**
88 **SNOW WIND (IRE)**, b f High Chaparral (IRE)—Soul Mountain (IRE) **Royal Ascot Racing Club**
89 **SOCIETY POWER (IRE)**, b c Society Rock (IRE)—Yajala **Sheikh Rashid Dalmook Al Maktoum**
90 **SPICED**, b f Dansili—Superstar Leo (IRE) **Lael Stable**
91 **STRATEGIST (IRE)**, b g Shamardal (USA)—Snow Powder (IRE) **Her Majesty The Queen**
92 **SWEET NATURE (IRE)**, b f Canford Cliffs (IRE)—High Figurine (IRE) **Mr D. I. Scott**
93 **TALAAQY (IRE)**, b f Dansili—Shabiba (USA) **Mr Hamdan Al Maktoum**
94 **TALLOW (IRE)**, b f Kodiac—Flames **Cheveley Park Stud**
95 **TANSEEQ**, b c Havana Gold (IRE)—Roslea Lady (IRE) **Mr Hamdan Al Maktoum**
96 **TARAAYEF (IRE)**, b f Teofilo (IRE)—Shuhra (IRE) **Mr Hamdan Al Maktoum**
97 **THREE WEEKS (USA)**, gr c Tapit (USA)—Midnight Thoughts (USA) **Appletree Stud**
98 **UMAIMAH (USA)**, b f Speightstown (USA)—Soohaad (USA) **Mr Hamdan Al Maktoum**
99 **UMMALNAR**, ch f Shamardal (USA)—Royal Secrets (IRE) **Mohammed Jaber**
100 **VALIDATOR**, b f Kodiac—Enact **Cheveley Park Stud**
101 **WITCHING TIME**, b f Dubawi (IRE)—Carabosse **Her Majesty The Queen**
102 **WITH A START (IRE)**, b c Sea The Stars (IRE)—Sudden Blaze (IRE) **Sunderland Holding Inc.**
103 **YAJOOLL**, b c Invincible Spirit (IRE)—Tafiya **Sheikh Ahmed Al Maktoum**
104 **YOUNG RASCAL (FR)**, b c Intello (GER)—Rock My Soul (IRE) **Mr B. Kantor**

TWO-YEAR-OLDS

105 **A NOUS LA LIBERTE (FR)**, b f 22/1 Siyouni (FR)—Amerique (IRE) (Galileo (IRE)) **Mr Hamdan Al Maktoum**
106 **ALKAAMEL**, b c 19/2 Havana Gold (IRE)—
          Grace And Glory (IRE) (Montjeu (IRE)) (250000) **Mr Hamdan Al Maktoum**
107 B c 6/5 Sea The Moon (GER)—
          Angeleno (IRE) (Belong To Me (USA)) (50000) **Sheikh Hamed Dalmook Al Maktoum**
108 B f 8/3 Camelot—Ayshea (Mr Greeley (USA)) (100000) **Highclere Thoroughbred Racing**
109 B f 26/3 Slade Power (IRE)—Bedouin Dancer (IRE) (Pivotal) (85000) **Sheikh Juma Dalmook Al Maktoum**
110 B c 7/2 Charm Spirit (IRE)—Beldale Memory (IRE) (Camacho) **Qatar Racing**
111 **BIBLIC (IRE)**, b f 24/1 New Approach (IRE)—
          Savannah Belle (Green Desert (USA)) (210000) **Graham Smith-Bernal**
112 B c 29/4 Dubawi (IRE)—Birjand (Green Desert (USA)) **Sheikh Ahmed Al Maktoum**
113 **BOERHAN**, b c 15/5 Sea The Stars (IRE)—
          Greenisland (IRE) (Fasliyev (USA)) (270000) **Sheikh Ahmed Al Maktoum**
114 **BREAK OF DAY**, b f 31/1 Shamardal (USA)—Dawn Glory (Oasis Dream) **Her Majesty The Queen**
115 **CAPPTOO (IRE)**, b c 19/4 Dark Angel (IRE)—
          Charlotte Rua (IRE) (Redback) (120000) **Sheikh Ahmed Al Maktoum**
116 B c 23/2 Dandy Man (IRE)—Celtic Lynn (IRE) (Celtic Swing) (110000) **Sheikh Rashid Dalmook Al Maktoum**
117 B c 26/2 Sea The Stars (IRE)—Chiosina (IRE) (Danehill Dancer (IRE)) (310000) **Fiona Carmichael**
118 B f 29/3 Charm Spirit (IRE)—Columella (Kyllachy) **Qatar Racing**
119 B c 4/4 Camelot—Coppertop (Exceed And Excel (AUS)) (62000) **Mr B. Kantor**
120 Br c 17/2 Dark Angel (IRE)—Coquette Rouge (IRE) (Croco Rouge (IRE)) (220000) **Sheikh Ahmed Al Maktoum**
121 **COUP DE GOLD (IRE)**, br c 12/2 Maxios—Astroglia (USA) (Montjeu (IRE)) (126170) **Sunderland Holding Inc.**

MR WILLAM HAGGAS - Continued

122 **DALAALAAT (IRE)**, b c 16/5 Kingman—Gile Na Greine (IRE) (Galileo (IRE)) **Mr Hamdan Al Maktoum**
123 B c 22/4 Nathaniel (IRE)—Dalvina (Grand Lodge (USA)) **St Albans Bloodstock Ltd**
124 Br f 23/4 Showcasing—Dance Pearl (Danehill Dancer (IRE)) (330000) **Mike & Michelle Morris**
125 **DASHWOOD BEAU (IRE)**, b f 5/4 Kodiac—
                                    High Dasher (IRE) (High Chaparral (IRE)) (22792) **Sheikh Juma Dalmook Al Maktoum**
126 B f 12/3 Cacique (IRE)—Desert Bloom (IRE) (Pilsudski (IRE)) (70000) **OTI Racing**
127 **DESERT CARAVAN**, b c 12/3 Oasis Dream—Sequence (IRE) (Selkirk (USA)) **Her Majesty The Queen**
128 B c 10/2 Epaulette (AUS)—Desert Royalty (IRE) (Alhaarth (IRE)) (18000) **Mr & Mrs Ian Beard**
129 **DESTINATION**, b c 25/2 Mukhadram—Danehill Destiny (Danehill Dancer (IRE)) **Cheveley Park Stud**
130 B c 27/4 Shamardal (USA)—Estiqaama (USA) (Nayef (USA)) **Mr Hamdan Al Maktoum**
131 **EXOPTABLE**, b gr f 11/2 Dark Angel (IRE)—Executrix (Oasis Dream) **Cheveley Park Stud**
132 **EYELOOL (IRE)**, b c 7/2 Dragon Pulse (IRE)—Lady Heartbeat (Avonbridge) (80000) **Sheikh Ahmed Al Maktoum**
133 **FANAAR (IRE)**, b c 12/3 Dark Angel (IRE)—
                                    Inca Trail (USA) (Royal Academy (USA)) (228571) **Mr Hamdan Al Maktoum**
134 **FAYLAQ**, b c 2/3 Dubawi (IRE)—Danedream (GER) (Lomitas) (1500000) **Mr Hamdan Al Maktoum**
135 B f 14/3 Dubawi (IRE)—Ferdoos (Dansili) **Sheikh Ahmed Al Maktoum**
136 **FIVE DIAMONDS**, b f 4/3 Mukhadram—Felwah (Aqlaam) **Khalil Al Sayegh**
137 B c 6/2 Garswood—Flare of Firelight (USA) (Birdstone (USA)) (85000) **Kemal Kurt**
138 **FLAREPATH**, b f 3/2 Exceed And Excel (AUS)—Fiery Sunset (Galileo (IRE)) **Her Majesty The Queen**
139 Gr f 4/4 Galileo (IRE)—Fork Lightning (USA) (Storm Cat (USA)) (280000) **Sheikh Juma Dalmook Al Maktoum**
140 **FRANKELLINA**, ch f 27/1 Frankel—Our Obsession (IRE) (Shamardal (USA)) **Mr A. E. Oppenheimer**
141 B c 20/1 No Nay Never (USA)—Gilded Vanity (IRE) (Indian Ridge) (210000) **Sheikh Juma Dalmook Al Maktoum**
142 **HAMISH**, b c 3/2 Motivator—Tweed (Sakhee (USA)) **Mr B. Haggas**
143 B f 24/2 Toronado (IRE)—Henties Bay (IRE) (Cape Cross (IRE)) (100000) **Sheikh Rashid Dalmook Al Maktoum**
144 B f 19/4 War Command (USA)—High Figurine (IRE) (High Chaparral (IRE)) **Mr D. I. Scott**
145 **ICE GALA**, b f 18/3 Invincible Spirit (IRE)—Ice Palace (Polar Falcon (USA)) **Cheveley Park Stud**
146 **IMPETUS (IRE)**, br f 14/4 Tamayuz—Dancing Jest (IRE) (Averti (IRE)) (81400) **Yvonne Jacques**
147 **INCREDULOUS**, b f 30/3 Intello (GER)—Fantasize (Groom Dancer (USA)) **Cheveley Park Stud**
148 **JAHBATH**, ch f 26/2 Mukhadram—Oulianovsk (IRE) (Peintre Celebre (USA)) **Mr Hamdan Al Maktoum**
149 **JIRNAAS**, ch c 16/2 Showcasing—Stresa (Pivotal) **Mr Hamdan Al Maktoum**
150 B f 2/5 Shamardal (USA)—Khazeena (Oasis Dream) **Mr Hamdan Al Maktoum**
151 B f 27/3 Oasis Dream—Lacarolina (FR) (Charge d'affaires) (50000) **Ivis Size**
152 **LUXOR**, b c 22/1 Oasis Dream—Eminently (Exceed And Excel (AUS)) (180952) **Highclere Thoroughbred Racing**
153 **MAGNETIC CHARM**, b f 27/4 Exceed And Excel (AUS)—
                                    Monday Show (USA) (Maria's Mon (USA)) **Her Majesty The Queen**
154 **MAKTABBA**, b f 9/3 Dansili—Mudaaraah (Cape Cross (IRE)) **Mr Hamdan Al Maktoum**
155 **MALBAS**, b c 3/2 Mukhadram—Violet (IRE) (Mukaddamah (USA)) (85000) **Mr Hamdan Al Maktoum**
156 Gr f 16/4 Dark Angel (IRE)—Mamma Morton (IRE) (Elnadim (USA)) (68000) **Mike & Michelle Morris**
157 **MARMARR**, b f 6/3 Dubawi (IRE)—Anaamil (IRE) (Darshaan) **Sheikh Ahmed Al Maktoum**
158 **MARMOOQ (USA)**, ch c 12/2 Tamayuz—Bashoosha (USA) (Distorted Humor (USA)) **Mr Hamdan Al Maktoum**
159 B c 6/2 Lope de Vega (IRE)—Mickleberry (IRE) (Desert Style (IRE)) (125000) **Fiona Carmichael**
160 B f 2/4 Kodiac—Miss Queen (USA) (Miswaki (USA)) **Abdulla Al Khalifa**
161 **MOFTRIS**, b c 25/2 Iffraaj—Baheeja (Dubawi (IRE)) **Sheikh Ahmed Al Maktoum**
162 **MONTZAR**, b c 8/3 Dansili—Nahrain (Selkirk (USA)) **Sheikh Ahmed Al Maktoum**
163 Ch f 6/4 More Than Ready (USA)—Mujannada (USA) (Jazil (USA)) **Mr Hamdan Al Maktoum**
164 **NAPLES (IRE)**, b c 27/4 Clodovil (IRE)—
                                    Annamanamoux (USA) (Leroidesanimaux (BRZ)) (65000) **Graham Smith-Bernal**
165 **NEWTON'S ANGEL (IRE)**, b f 30/1 Dark Angel (IRE)—
                                    Newton's Night (IRE) (Galileo (IRE)) **Sunderland Holding Inc.**
166 **PAY COURT**, b f 1/5 Motivator—Courting (Pursuit of Love) **Cheveley Park Stud**
167 B c 28/2 Camelot—Politesse (USA) (Barathea (IRE)) **Mr B. Kantor**
168 **QUEEN OF BURGUNDY**, b f 5/2 Lethal Force (IRE)—Empress Adelaide (Pivotal) **Cheveley Park Stud**
169 B c 22/2 Kodiac—Queen of Mean (Pivotal) (100000) **Sheikh Rashid Dalmook Al Maktoum**
170 **RAFFLE**, b c 1/4 Iffraaj—Raymi Coya (CAN) (Van Nistelrooy (USA)) **Her Majesty The Queen**
171 **RED HUT RED (IRE)**, b f 4/4 Kodiac—Happy Land (Refuse To Bend (IRE)) (60000) **Mr Tim Bridge**
172 B c 20/3 Gale Force Ten—
                                    Sapphire Spray (IRE) (Viking Ruler (AUS)) (33000) **Roberts/Green/Savidge/Whittal-Williams**
173 **SEA WINGS**, ch c 1/3 Sea The Stars (IRE)—Infallible (Pivotal) **Cheveley Park Stud**
174 B br f 8/1 Shamardal (USA)—Sentaril (Danehill Dancer (IRE)) **Lael Stable**
175 **SENZA LIMITI (IRE)**, ch c 1/3 Lope de Vega (IRE)—
                                    Senza Rete (IRE) (Barathea (IRE)) (100000) **Simon Munir & Isaac Souede**
176 **SKARDU**, ch c 1/4 Shamardal (USA)—Diala (IRE) (Iffraaj) **Abdulla Al Khalifa**
177 **SPACE WALK**, b c 29/3 Galileo (IRE)—Memory (IRE) (Danehill Dancer (IRE)) **Her Majesty The Queen**
178 **SPOTTON (IRE)**, b c 31/3 Tamayuz—
                                    Farbenspiel (IRE) (Desert Prince (IRE)) (330000) **Sheikh Ahmed Al Maktoum**

MR WILLAM HAGGAS - Continued

179 **SQUELCH**, b f 13/3 Dark Angel (IRE)—Blancmange (Montjeu (IRE)) **Mr B. Haggas**
180 **STARKERS**, ch f 30/1 Mukhadram—Undress (IRE) (Dalakhani (IRE)) **Mr B. Haggas**
181 B f 13/4 Oasis Dream—Swiss Lake (USA) (Indian Ridge) **Lordship Stud**
182 **TAPISSERIE**, ch f 11/4 Le Havre (IRE)—Miss Work of Art (Dutch Art) (130000) **Isa Salman**
183 **THE NIGHT WATCH**, b c 4/5 Dutch Art—Scarlet Runner (Night Shift (USA)) **Mr Nicholas Jones**
184 **TIANADARGENT (FR)**, b f 22/3 Kendargent (FR)—Restia (FR) (Montjeu (IRE)) **Guy Pariente**
185 B c 23/1 Harbour Watch (IRE)—Tickle Me (GER) (Halling (USA)) (17142) **Somerville Lodge Ltd**
186 **TWO BIDS**, b c 8/4 Dalakhani (IRE)—Echelon (Danehill (USA)) (375000) **Sheikh Ahmed Al Maktoum**
187 B c 10/2 Camacho—Venetian Rhapsody (IRE) (Galileo (IRE)) (90476) **Abdulla Al Mansoori**
188 **WINGREEN (IRE)**, ch f 19/1 Lope de Vega (IRE)—
                                Relation Alexander (IRE) (Dandy Man) (71631) **Mr Isa Salman**
189 Ch f 14/4 Australia—Wurfklinge (GER) (Acatenango (GER)) (122100) **Bjande Minde-Minde**

Other Owners: Mrs Julia Aisbitt, Mr Jon Aisbitt, Mr Imad Al-Sagar, Mr M. Z. Almutairi, Mr Musaad Almutairi, Mr Ian Beard, Mrs Christine Beard, Mr Ian Carmichael-Jennings, Mrs Fiona Carmichael-Jennings, China Horse Club International Limited, Mr P.J. Dunkley, Mrs Denise Dunkley, Highclere Nominated Partner Limited, Highclere Thoroughbred Racing Ltd, Mr Saleh Al Homaizi, Mrs G. S. Jackson, Mr R. Jackson, Mr Bernard Kantor, Mr Michael Kerr-Dineen, Mr D. I. Scott, Somerville Lodge Limited, Mr C. N. Wright.

Assistant Trainers: Harry Eustace, Jason Favell

Apprentice: Georgia Cox.

---

248 MR ALEX HALES, Edgecote
Postal: **Trafford Bridge Stables, Edgecote, Banbury, Oxfordshire, OX17 1AG**
Contacts: **PHONE** (01295) 660131 **FAX** (01295) 660128 **MOBILE** (07771) 511652
E-MAIL alex@alexhalesracing.co.uk **WEBSITE** www.alexhalesracing.co.uk

1 **BIG JIM**, 9, b g Revoque (IRE)—Chilly Squaw (IRE) **Gumbrills Racing Partnership**
2 **BURNER (IRE)**, 6, b g High Chaparral (IRE)—Breathe (FR) **The Backburners**
3 **CEARA BE (IRE)**, 5, b m Oscar (IRE)—Pearl's A Singer (IRE) **Mr P. J. Byrne**
4 **CLIFFMEENA (IRE)**, 5, b m Canford Cliffs (IRE)—Yasmeena (USA) **Mr A. M. Hales**
5 **CRAFTY ROBERTO**, 10, ch g Intikhab (USA)—Mowazana (IRE) **S Brown H Steele D Fitzgerald**
6 **CRYSTAL SUNSTONE**, 4, b g Henrythenavigator (USA)—Crystal Power (USA) **Mr A. M. Hales**
7 **DANDILION (IRE)**, 5, b m Dandy Man (IRE)—Free Angel (USA) **The Golden Horse Racing Club**
8 **DARTAGNAN LE DUN (FR)**, 5, b g Kapgarde (FR)—Silvazeyra (FR) **All For One And One For All**
9 **DUEL AT DAWN (IRE)**, 8, b g Presenting—Phillis Hill **The Duel At Dawn Partnership**
10 **FLORRIE KNOX (IRE)**, 5, gr g Gold Well—Miss Orphan (FR) **The Fortune Hunters**
11 **HUNTSMAN SON (IRE)**, 8, b g Millenary—Daly Lady (IRE) **C. W. Booth**
12 **INDIAN NATIVE (IRE)**, 8, b m Oscar (IRE)—Roman Native (IRE) **C. W. Booth**
13 **ISAAC BELL (IRE)**, 10, b g Fruits of Love (USA)—Oso Well (IRE) **Mr S Brown & Mr D Raftery**
14 **MAGGIES LEGEND**, 5, b m Midnight Legend—Very Special One (IRE) **Gumbrills Racing Partnership**
15 **MAYBELL**, 7, b m Black Sam Bellamy (IRE)—Chilly Squaw (IRE) **Gumbrills Racing Partnership**
16 **METHAG (IRE)**, 5, b m Pour Moi (IRE)—Kyria **The One For Us**
17 **MINELLAFORLEISURE (IRE)**, 10, br g King's Theatre (IRE)—Dame Foraine (FR) **The Patient Partnership**
18 **PANKO (IRE)**, 5, b g Iffraaj—Engraving **S Mullaney, S Brown, D & V Jones**
19 **QUARRY LEADER (IRE)**, 7, b g Darsi (FR)—Pollys Leader (IRE) **The Patient Partnership**
20 **RUNNING WOLF (IRE)**, 7, b g Amadeus Wolf—Monet's Lady (IRE) **The Wolfgangers**
21 **SAMALARR (IRE)**, 6, gr m Ask—Sika Trix (IRE) **Premier Plastering (UK) Limited**
22 **SHAZZAMATAZ (IRE)**, 6, br m Presenting—Dame O'neill (IRE) **Edging Ahead**
23 **SHINOOKI (IRE)**, 11, br g Blueprint (IRE)—Rapid Response (IRE) **Mrs A. P. B. Allen**
24 **SHIROCCODEE (IRE)**, 5, b m Shirocco (GER)—La Marianne **The Golden Horse Racing Club**
25 **STEPOVER**, 7, b m Midnight Legend—Ring Back (IRE) **Mrs A. P. B. Allen**
26 **TAKE TWO**, 9, b g Act One—Lac Marmot (FR) **Edging Ahead**
27 **THE OTMOOR POET**, 5, b g Yeats (IRE)—Kristalette (IRE) **The Of-Ten Racing Partnership**
28 **TINKER TIME (IRE)**, 10. b g Turtle Island (IRE)—Gypsys Girl (IRE) **Mr B. E. Brackenbury**
29 **TOPPER THORNTON (IRE)**, 9, ch g Double Eclipse (IRE)—Gailybay Ellen (IRE) **Old Stoic Racing Club**
30 **TOWER OF ALLEN (IRE)**, 7, b g Beneficial—Baile An Droichid (IRE) **The Hexagon Racing Partnership**
31 **ULTIMATUM DU ROY (FR)**, 10, b g Brier Creek (USA)—La Fleur du Roy (FR) **Mrs A. P. B. Allen**

Other Owners: Miss S. A. Baxter, Mr S. Brown, Miss S. E. Burnell, Mr J. Cleary, Mrs K. A. Fry, J. S. C. Fry, Mr H. Kimbell, Ms L. Langford, R. E. Morris-Adams, Mrs H. Steele, Mr B. Tait, Mrs C. Taylor, Mrs J. Wood, Mr C. J. Woods.

249 MR MICHAEL HALFORD, Kildare

Postal: Copper Beech Stables, Doneaney, Kildangan Road, Kildare, Co. Kildare, Ireland
Contacts: PHONE (00 353) 45 526119 FAX (00 353) 45 526157 MOBILE (00 353) 87 2579204
E-MAIL info@michaelhalford.com WEBSITE www.michaelhalford.com

1 **AHLAN BIL ZAIN (FR)**, 4, b br g Elusive City (USA)—Fall View **Mr Richard McNally**
2 **AMBASSADORIAL (USA)**, 4, b g Elusive Quality (USA)—Tactfully (IRE) **Godolphin**
3 **CASTLE GUEST (IRE)**, 9, b g Rock of Gibraltar (IRE)—Castelletto **Paul Rooney**
4 **CIRCLING MOON (IRE)**, 4, b g Lope de Vega (IRE)—Jebel Musa (IRE) **Mr Patrick Woods**
5 **CLAREGATE STREET (IRE)**, 4, b f Helmet (AUS)—Eaton Street **River Syndicate**
6 **GOUGANE BARRA (IRE)**, 4, b br g First Defence (USA)—Beiramar (IRE) **Paul Rooney**
7 **INVINCIBLE RYKER (IRE)**, 4, b c Invincible Spirit (IRE)—Cabaret (IRE) **Eric Koh & Mr Yuesheng Zhang**
8 **KATIYMANN (IRE)**, 6, b g Shamardal (USA)—Katiyra (IRE) **Paul Rooney**
9 **KIRK'S DANCER (USA)**, 4, ch f Dunkirk (USA)—Mycatcandance (USA) **E. Koh**
10 **LADY DE VESCI (IRE)**, 5, ch m Approve (IRE)—La Bandola (GER) **Mr Frank Sommer**
11 **LIBERATIO (IRE)**, 4, b g Invincible Spirit (IRE)—Alshahbaa (IRE) **Cregg Castle Stud**
12 **LUNA'S LUCK (IRE)**, 4, b g Vale of York (IRE)—Over The Tylery (IRE) **James Matthews**
13 **MASSIF CENTRAL (IRE)**, 4, b g Arcano (IRE)—Melaaya (USA) **Paul Rooney**
14 **MISS SNOSSYBOOTS (IRE)**, 4, ch f Rip Van Winkle (IRE)—Nick's Nikita (IRE) **N. Hartery**
15 **PADDY THE CELEB (IRE)**, 12, ch g Peintre Celebre (USA)—On The Razz (USA) **Dr Paul J. McMahon**
16 **PETTICOAT**, 4, b f Cape Cross (IRE)—Minidress **Godolphin**
17 **REHANA (IRE)**, 4, b f Dark Angel (IRE)—Rayka (IRE) **H. H. Aga Khan**
18 **RUMMAGING (IRE)**, 10, ch g Chineur (FR)—Roundabout Girl (IRE) **P. E. I. Newell**
19 **RUSSIAN SOUL (IRE)**, 10, b g Invincible Spirit (IRE)—Russian Hill **Mrs A. G. Kavanagh**
20 **SALTONSTALL (IRE)**, 4, ch g Pivotal—Macleya (GER) **Godolphin**
21 **SHADAGANN (IRE)**, 8, b g Invincible Spirit (IRE)—Shamadara (IRE) **Paul Rooney**
22 **SHANNON SOUL (IRE)**, 6, b g Shamardal (USA)—Paimpolaise (IRE) **Cregg Castle Stud**
23 **STANDING ROCK (IRE)**, 4, b f Fastnet Rock (AUS)—Great Hope (IRE) **Mrs P Shanahan**
24 **STORM RYKER (USA)**, 4, ch c Proud Citizen (USA)—Maria's Storm (USA) **Eric Koh**
25 **SURROUNDING (IRE)**, 5, b m Lilbourne Lad (IRE)—Roundabout Girl (IRE) **Mr Evan Newell**
26 **TIRMIZI (FR)**, 5, b g Sea The Stars (IRE)—Timabiyra (IRE) **Paul Rooney**
27 **TONKINESE**, 5, b g Authorized (IRE)—Honky Tonk Sally **Godolphin**
28 **YAMATO (IRE)**, 5, b g Big Bad Bob (IRE)—Himiko (IRE) **T. Kimura**

THREE-YEAR-OLDS

29 **ADALIYA (IRE)**, b f Footstepsinthesand—Adjaliya (IRE) **H. H. Aga Khan**
30 **ALISADA (IRE)**, b c Dark Angel (IRE)—Alaiyma (IRE) **H. H. Aga Khan**
31 **ANDESH (IRE)**, ch c Medicean—Adelfia (IRE) **H. H. Aga Khan**
32 **ARCANEARS (IRE)**, b g Arcano (IRE)—Ondeafears (IRE) **Mrs C. Roper**
33 **BLACKGOLD FAIRY (USA)**, b br f More Than Ready (USA)—London Bid (USA) **Y. Zhang**
34 **CLOAK OF DARKNESS (IRE)**, b c Iffraaj—Cape of Night (IRE) **Godolphin**
35 **COCKALORUM (IRE)**, b c Cape Cross (IRE)—Opinionated (IRE) **Godolphin**
36 **DIAMOND (IRE)**, ch f Camacho—True Crystal (IRE) **Kaniz Bloodstock**
37 **ERENKAYA (IRE)**, b f Thewayyouare (USA)—Erdiyna (IRE) **H. H. Aga Khan**
38 Ch f Intello (GER)—Idilic Calm (IRE) **Forenaughts Racing**
39 **INTERMEDIA (IRE)**, ch f Intello (GER)—Dubai Smile (USA) **Godolphin**
40 B f Kodiac—Jiran (IRE) **Mr P. E. I. Newell**
41 **KALAXANA (IRE)**, b f Rock of Gibraltar (IRE)—Kaladena (IRE) **H. H. Aga Khan**
42 **KARAKOUR (IRE)**, gr c Dalakhani (IRE)—Karamaya (IRE) **H. H. Aga Khan**
43 **KOTTAYAM (IRE)**, b c Declaration of War (USA)—Katiyra (IRE) **H. H. Aga Khan**
44 **LA NOVIA (IRE)**, b f Casamento (IRE)—Mas A Fuera (IRE) **Mrs Anne McDonald**
45 **LOOMING (IRE)**, b f Shamardal (USA)—Await So **Godolphin**
46 **LUMINIST (IRE)**, b f Teofilo (IRE)—Bright Morning **Godolphin**
47 **PECCARY**, b f Teofilo (IRE)—Opera Gloves **Godolphin**
48 **PIENTA (IRE)**, b c Liaison (USA)—Belen (USA) **Mrs Wendy O'Leary**
49 **PLATINUM WARRIOR (IRE)**, br c Galileo (IRE)—Laugh Out Loud **Y. Zhang**
50 **PORT LIONS (IRE)**, b c Kodiac—Cold Cold Woman **Godolphin**
51 **PORTALLY COVE (IRE)**, b f Farhh—Cherika (IRE) **Knockenduff Stud**
52 **RAZOUL (IRE)**, b c Mastercraftsman—Saree **Ballygallon Stud**
53 **RIYAZAN (IRE)**, b c Iffraaj—Riyaba (IRE) **H. H. Aga Khan**
54 **SLIEVENABROCK (IRE)**, b g Epaulette (AUS)—Beguiler **Paul Rooney**
55 **SMART CRAFT (IRE)**, b c Mastercraftsman (IRE)—Velvet Flicker (IRE) **Imperial Racing Syndicate**
56 **TERZETTO (IRE)**, ch f Iffraaj—Calando (USA) **Godolphin**
57 **VIVIANITE (IRE)**, b f Teofilo (IRE)—Crystany (IRE) **Ballygallon Stud**

MR MICHAEL HALFORD - Continued

58 **WOMAN'S COMPANY (IRE)**, b g Fast Company (IRE)—Witchy Woman **Mr Colm Griffin**
59 **ZARIYFA (IRE)**, b f Zoffany (IRE)—Zariziyna (IRE) **H. H. Aga Khan**

TWO-YEAR-OLDS

60 Bl c 5/3 Bated Breath—Adelfia (IRE) (Sinndar (IRE)) (61050) **Copper Beech Racing Partnership**
61 B c 30/4 Canford Cliffs (IRE)—Alaiyma (IRE) (Refuse To Bend (IRE)) **H. H. Aga Khan**
62 Ch c 8/3 Motivator—Aliyama (IRE) (Red Ransom (USA))
63 B f 2/3 Iffraaj—Bahia Breeze (Mister Baileys) (42328) **Y. Zhang**
64 B f 24/5 Slade Power (IRE)—Buffalo Berry (IRE) (Sri Pekan (USA)) (24420) **Y. Zhang**
65 B c 23/2 Iffraaj—Burke's Rock (Cape Cross (IRE)) (32560) **Knockenduff Stud**
66 B f 29/2 Acclamation—Delira (IRE) (Namid) (85470) **Imperial Racing Syndicate**
67 **HAZRAN (IRE)**, b c 13/2 Lope de Vega (IRE)—Hazaraba (IRE) (Oasis Dream) **H. H. Aga Khan**
68 B f 23/4 Olympic Glory (IRE)—Hideaway Heroine (IRE) (Hernando (FR)) (69190) **Imperial Racing Syndicate**
69 B c 15/4 Ruler of The World (IRE)—Himiko (IRE) (Aussie Rules (USA)) **Mr T. Kimura**
70 B c 1/3 So You Think (NZ)—Karawana (IRE) (King's Best (USA)) **H. H. Aga Khan**
71 Br c 3/3 Rip Van Winkle (IRE)—Kastania (USA) (Gone West (USA)) **H. H. Aga Khan**
72 Ch c 30/3 Excelebration (IRE)—Kerisa (IRE) (Azamour (IRE)) **H. H. Aga Khan**
73 **KERLA (IRE)**, b f 6/2 Zoffany (IRE)—Kerania (IRE) (Daylami (IRE)) **H. H. Aga Khan**
74 Ch c 30/4 Nathaniel (IRE)—Lurina (IRE) (Lure (USA)) **Godolphin**
75 Ch f 18/3 Frankel—Maids Causeway (IRE) (Giant's Causeway (USA)) **Godolphin**
76 Ch f 1/3 Pivotal—Modern Ideals (New Approach (IRE)) **Godolphin**
77 Br c 4/4 Power—Money Penny (ITY) (Montjeu (IRE)) (29304) **Copper Beech Racing Syndicate**
78 B c 29/4 Mount Nelson—Morning After (Emperor Jones (USA)) (10988) **Mr Michael Halford**
79 B f 2/5 Dubawi (IRE)—My Renee (USA) (Kris S (USA)) (122100) **Mr Y. Zhang**
80 Ch f 30/4 Raven's Pass (USA)—Nadia (Nashwan (USA)) **Godolphin**
81 B f 12/3 Swiss Spirit—One Night In May (IRE) (Choisir (AUS)) (17094) **Copper Beech Racing Partnership**
82 B c 6/4 Shamardal (USA)—Patent Joy (IRE) (Pivotal) **Godolphin**
83 Ch c 16/4 Farhh—Philae (USA) (Seeking The Gold (USA)) **Godolphin**
84 B c 1/4 Elzaam (AUS)—Playamongthestars (AUS) (Galileo (IRE)) (32560) **Copper Beech Racing Partnership**
85 Gr c 12/2 Lethal Force (IRE)—Privet (IRE) (Cape Cross (IRE)) (40700) **Mr Sammy Ma**
86 B f 14/5 Shamardal (USA)—Raw Silk (USA) (Malibu Moon (USA)) **Godolphin**
87 Gr f 4/4 Dark Angel (IRE)—Riyaba (IRE) (Dalakhani (IRE)) **H. H. Aga Khan**
88 B f 29/4 Kodiac—Salmon Rose (IRE) (Iffraaj) (61049) **Knockenduff Stud**
89 B c 20/1 Lope de Vega (IRE)—Shamooda (IRE) (Azamour (IRE)) **H. H. Aga Khan**
90 Ch c 24/2 Rip Van Winkle (IRE)—Shebella (IRE) (Dubai Destination (USA)) **H. H. Aga Khan**
91 Gr f 19/3 Dark Angel (IRE)—Sinaniya (USA) (More Than Ready (USA)) **H. H. Aga Khan**
92 B c 3/4 Poet's Voice—Talkative (Oasis Dream) (14651) **Copper Beech Racing Partnership**
93 B f 26/5 Dream Ahead (USA)—Tanzania (IRE) (Alzao (USA)) (69189) **Mr Y. Zhang**
94 Ch f 24/1 Tamayuz—Tarziyna (IRE) (Raven's Pass (USA)) **H. H. Aga Khan**
95 B c 2/4 Rulership (JPN)—Triple Pirouette (USA) (Sunday Silence (USA)) **Godolphin**
96 B c 9/5 Siyouni (FR)—Virana (IRE) (King's Best (USA)) **H. H. Aga Khan**
97 Ch c 23/4 Camelot—Zerkeriya (IRE) (Soviet Star (USA)) **H. H. Aga Khan**

Assistant Trainer: Fabian Burke

Jockey (flat): Conor Hoban, Niall McCullagh, Pat Smullen. **Apprentice:** Dean Curran. **Amateur:** Mr Evan Halford.

---

250 MRS DEBRA HAMER, Carmarthen
Postal: **Bryngors Uchaf, Nantycaws, Carmarthen, Dyfed, SA32 8EY**
Contacts: **HOME (01267) 234585 MOBILE (07980) 665274**
E-MAIL **hamerracing@hotmail.co.uk**

1 **BARNEY RUBBLE**, 9, b g Medicean—Jade Chequer **J. D. Cound**
2 **CORBETT COURT (IRE)**, 6, br g Court Cave (IRE)—Stefphonic (IRE) **Mr J. Rees**
3 **EASYONDEYE (IRE)**, 12, b g Beneficial—Lady of Appeal (IRE) **J. D. Cound**
4 **GLOI**, 7, b m Overbury (IRE)—Go Gwenni Go **Nick Youngman Nicola Cooper**
5 **LAYERTHORPE (IRE)**, 6, b bl g Vale of York (IRE)—Strobinia (IRE) **Mr C. A. Hanbury**
6 **LOOKS LIKE POWER (IRE)**, 8, ch g Spadoun (FR)—Martovic **Mr C. A. Hanbury**
7 **MAGICAL MAN**, 11, b br g Lahib (USA)—Majestic Di (IRE) **Mr C. A. Hanbury**
8 **PENNANT LEGEND**, 5, b m Flying Legend (USA)—Pennant Princess **Mr P. J. Woolley**
9 **SHANKS A LOT**, 11, b g Beat All (USA)—Florida Fact **BW & RE Mansell**
10 **SLICE OF LEMON**, 6, b m Dr Massini (IRE)—Lady Maranzi **Mr J. E. Rees**
11 **SUPER SCORPION (IRE)**, 8, b g Scorpion (IRE)—Nolagh Supreme (IRE) **Mrs J. M. Edmonds**

MRS DEBRA HAMER - Continued

12 **TOBEFAIR**, 8, b br g Central Park (IRE)—Nan **Down The Quay Club**
13 **WHO AM I**, 12, b br g Tamayaz (CAN)—Short Fuse (IRE) **W. J. Cole**

Other Owners: Mr M. J. Cole, Miss N. Y. Cooper, Mr B. W. Mansell, Mrs R. E. Mansell, Mr A. G. Pannell, Mr N. E. Youngman.

Assistant Trainer: Mr M. P. Hamer

251
MRS ALISON HAMILTON, Denholm
Postal: **Dykes Farm House, Hawick, Roxburghshire, TD9 8TB**
Contacts: **PHONE (01450) 870323 MOBILE (07885) 477349**
E-MAIL Alisonhamilton53@yahoo.com

1 **ASK JD (IRE)**, 5, b g Ask—Sara Cara (IRE) **J. P. G. Hamilton**
2 **DANEHILLS WELL (IRE)**, 10, b g Indian Danehill (IRE)—Collatrim Choice (IRE) **J. P. G. Hamilton**
3 **KILLONE (IRE)**, 9, gr g Flemensfirth (USA)—Ceol Tire (IRE) **Turnbull Boyce**
4 **MASTER RAJEEM (USA)**, 9, b br g Street Cry (IRE)—Rajeem **Hamilton Racing**
5 **PAINTERS LAD (IRE)**, 7, b g Fruits of Love (USA)—Great Cullen (IRE) **J. P. G. Hamilton**
6 **ROYAL SUMMIT**, 7, b g Kayf Tara—Nas Na Riogh (IRE) **J. M. Nicholson**
7 **SUNSET MARQUIS (IRE)**, 7, b m Kayf Tara—Miss Abrahnovic (IRE) **J. P. G. Hamilton**
8 **THE ICE FACTOR**, 10, b g Iceman—Kiruna **J. P. G. Hamilton**
9 **TOWERBURN (IRE)**, 9, b g Cloudings (IRE)—Lady Newmill (IRE) **J. P. G. Hamilton**
10 **WAYUPINTHESKY (IRE)**, 11, gr g Cloudings (IRE)—Riancoir Alainn **J. P. G. Hamilton**
11 **WHAT A DREAM**, 12, ch g Supreme Sound—Ben Roseler (IRE) **Mr & Mrs D. S. Byers**

Other Owners: Mrs M. A. Bowie, Mr J. Boyce, D. S. Byers, Mrs M. J. Byers, Mrs A. C. Hamilton, Mr A. Turnbull.

Assistant Trainer: Mr G. Hamilton

252
MR ANDREW HAMILTON, Carluke
Postal: **Nellfield House, Braidwood, Carluke, Lanarkshire, ML8 4PP**
Contacts: (01555) 771502 MOBILE (07974) 744421
E-MAIL andrewhamiltoncoach@btinternet.com

1 **LETEMGO (IRE)**, 10, b g Brian Boru—Leteminletemout (IRE) **Mr A. B. Hamilton**
2 **SOUTHSEA ISLAND (IRE)**, 10, b g Heron Island (IRE)—Southsea Lady (IRE) **Mr A. B. Hamilton**
3 **ZACHARO**, 5, b g Zamindar (USA)—Winter Silence **Mr A. B. Hamilton**

253
MRS ANN HAMILTON, Newcastle Upon Tyne
Postal: **Claywalls Farm, Capheaton, Newcastle Upon Tyne, Tyne and Wear, NE19 2BP**
Contacts: **PHONE (01830) 530219 MOBILE (07704) 670704**
E-MAIL annhamilton1952@hotmail.com

1 **LITTLE BAVINGTON**, 5, b g Strategic Prince—Vanilla Delight (IRE) **Mr I. Hamilton**
2 **NUTS WELL**, 7, b g Dylan Thomas (IRE)—Renada **Mr I. Hamilton**
3 **OAK VINTAGE (IRE)**, 8, b g Fruits of Love (USA)—Brandam Supreme (IRE) **Mr I. Hamilton**
4 5, B m Oscar (IRE)—Renada **Mr I. Hamilton**
5 **TRUST THOMAS**, 10, ch g Erhaab (USA)—Yota (FR) **Mr I. Hamilton**
6 **WAR JOEY (IRE)**, 5, b g Primary (USA)—Wake Me Gently (IRE) **Mr I. Hamilton**

Assistant Trainer: Ian Hamilton

254 MR MICKY HAMMOND, Middleham
Postal: **Oakwood Stables, East Witton Road, Middleham, Leyburn, North Yorkshire, DL8 4PT**
Contacts: **PHONE** (01969) 625223 **MOBILE** (07808) 572777
E-MAIL mickyhammondracing@hotmail.com **WEBSITE** www.mickyhammondracing.co.uk

1 **ALCHIMIX (FR)**, 8, b g Al Namix (FR)—Julie Noire (FR) **Mr I. Barran & Mr M. D. Hammond**
2 **ALDERBROOK LAD (IRE)**, 12, ch g Alderbrook—Alone Tabankulu (IRE) **Ian Barran, Rita Butler & Gemma Hogg**
3 **ALLFREDANDNOBELL (IRE)**, 5, b g Alfred Nobel (IRE)—Its In The Air (IRE) **The Oakwood Nobels**
4 **ALMUNTHER (IRE)**, 5, b g Invincible Spirit (IRE)—Adaala (USA) **Mr Richard Howard & Mr Ben Howard**
5 **APPLAUS (GER)**, 6, b g Tiger Hill (IRE)—All About Love (GER) **Mr Joe Buzzeo & Partner**
6 **ART OF SUPREMACY (IRE)**, 6, b g Milan—Marble Desire (IRE) **Mr L. Horvath**
7 **BAMBYS BOY**, 7, b g Lucarno (USA)—Bamby (IRE) **Mrs S. P. Granger**
8 **BECKY THE THATCHER**, 5, b m Mastercraftsman (IRE)—Fairmont (IRE) **McGoldrick Racing**
9 **BIG THUNDER**, 8, gr g Dalakhani (IRE)—Charlotte O Fraise (IRE) **The Big Thunderbirds**
10 **BLUE HUSSAR (IRE)**, 7, b g Montjeu (IRE)—Metaphor (USA) **Mr Richard Howard & Mr Ben Howard**
11 **BULKOV (FR)**, 6, b g Zambezi Sun—Say Say (FR) **Finch Porter Partnership**
12 **CALYPSO DELEGATOR (IRE)**, 5, b g Lilbourne Lad (IRE)—Amber Nectar (IRE) **Ms Sherene Ure & Partners**
13 **CAMILLAS WISH (IRE)**, 9, b m Presenting—Take Ine (FR) **D. M. Proos**
14 **CARALINE (IRE)**, 7, b m Martaline—Vie Ta Vie (IRE) **Give Every Man His Due**
15 **CHARIN' CROSS**, 6, ch g Cockney Rebel (IRE)—Lush Lady (IRE) **Tasker-Brown & Partners**
16 **CHRISTMAS TWENTY (IRE)**, 8, br g Zagreb (USA)—Celestial Gale (IRE) **The Uncles**
17 **CORNERSTONE LAD**, 4, b g Delegator—Chapel Corner (IRE) **Mrs B. M. Lofthouse**
18 **CREST**, 7, b g Kayf Tara—Maiden Voyage **Mike & Eileen Newbould, N Rust, J Carthy**
19 **DAKOTA GREY**, 7, gr g Fair Mix (IRE)—Miss Sassi **Still Game Associates**
20 **DARK VALLEY (IRE)**, 8, b g Lend A Hand—Glorys Flame (IRE) **The Snook Family & Partner**
21 **DEDIGOUT (IRE)**, 12, b g Bob Back (USA)—Dainty Daisy (IRE) **Masters of the Hall 3**
22 **FRANK THE SLINK**, 12, b g Central Park (IRE)—Kadari **The Three Tigers**
23 **INCHCOLM (IRE)**, 8, br g Presenting—Rose of Inchiquin (IRE) **Maybe The Last Time**
24 **INDIAN VISION (IRE)**, 4, ch g Iffraaj—Sweet Fairnando **The Futurists**
25 **IT'S ALL ABOUT ME (IRE)**, 6, b m King's Theatre (IRE)—Annie Spectrim (IRE) **Horizon**
26 **JUST BOBBY (IRE)**, 5, b g Black Sam Bellamy (IRE)—Blackwater Bay (IRE) **Mr & Mrs P. Chapman**
27 **JUST CAMERON**, 11, b g Kayf Tara—Miss Fencote **Mr & Mrs P. Chapman**
28 **JUSTFORJAMES (IRE)**, 9, ch g Dr Massini (IRE)—Over The Road (IRE) **J4J Partnership**
29 **KNOCKNAMONA (IRE)**, 7, b g Trans Island—Faraday Lady (IRE) **The Rat Pack Racing Club**
30 **L'ETOILE (IRE)**, 5, ch g Champs Elysees—Cross Your Fingers (USA) **Richard & Katherine Gilbert**
31 **MAC CENNETIG (IRE)**, 6, b g Brian Boru—Buslane (IRE) **Mrs B. M. Lofthouse**
32 **MAJOR RIDGE (IRE)**, 9, b g Indian Danehill (IRE)—Native Novel (IRE) **Oakwood Minions**
33 **ONLY ORSENFOOLSIES**, 9, b g Trade Fair—Desert Gold (IRE) **Foolsies**
34 **OSCAR O'SCAR (IRE)**, 10, b g Oscar (IRE)—Shining Lights (IRE) **Newroc 1**
35 **PADDLING (FR)**, 7, b g Walk In The Park (IRE)—Sea Mamaille (FR) **Masters Of The Hall 2**
36 **PERTUIS (IRE)**, 12, gr g Verglas (IRE)—Lady Killeen (IRE) **M.H.O.G.**
37 **QUOTELINE DIRECT**, 5, ch g Sir Percy—Queen's Pudding (USA) **JFW Properties Limited**
38 **RATHLIN**, 13, b g Kayf Tara—Princess Timon **Masters Of The Hall 2**
39 **RHYTHM OF SOUND (IRE)**, 8, ch g Mahler—Oscarvail (IRE) **Maybe The Last Time**
40 **ROCKLIFFE**, 5, b g Notnowcato—Hope Island (IRE) **R M & T Holdings Limited & Partners**
41 **ROXYFET (FR)**, 8, b g Califet (FR)—Roxalamour (FR) **Mr R. J. Ball & Partner**
42 **RUSSIAN ROYALE**, 8, b m Royal Applause—Russian Ruby (IRE) **Raypasha**
43 **SCHIEHALLION MUNRO**, 5, ch g Schiaparelli (GER)—Mrs Fawlty **Tennant, Lynch,Sharpe and Boston**
44 **SHAKE IT UP (IRE)**, 9, br g Presenting—Miss Fresher (FR) **D. M. Proos**
45 **SHALAMZAR (FR)**, 9, ch g Selkirk (USA)—Shamalana (IRE) **Maybe The Last Time**
46 **SILVER TASSIE (IRE)**, 10, b g Shantou (USA)—Silver Castor (IRE) **Mr R. M. Howard**
47 **SKYWARDS REWARD (IRE)**, 7, b g Dubawi (IRE)—Russian Society **The Cheltenham Trail**
48 **STRIKE WEST (IRE)**, 6, b g Westerner—Fuel Queen (IRE) **The Multi-Taskers**
49 **THE ROOF HUB**, 5, b g Dick Turpin (IRE)—Glen Molly (IRE) **D. M. Proos**
50 **TICKANRUN (IRE)**, 8, gr g Tikkanen (USA)—Dusty Lane (IRE) **Grange Park Racing XV**
51 **TICKENWOLF (IRE)**, 8, gr g Tikkanen (USA)—Emma's Choice (IRE) **Mr G. R. Orchard & Partner**
52 **TUSCAN GOLD**, 11, ch g Medicean—Louella (USA) **Littlethorpe Park Racing 1**
53 **TYRELL (IRE)**, 5, b g Teofilo (IRE)—Sleeveless (USA) **Mr C. Buckingham**
54 **VALGOR DU RONCERAY (FR)**, 9, gr g Al Namix (FR)—Malta de Ronceray (FR) **Grey Daze In Yorkshire**
55 **WHOSTOSAY (IRE)**, 6, br g Witness Box (USA)—Black N Amber (IRE) **The Rat Pack Racing Club**
56 **WIG WAM WIGGLE (IRE)**, 6, b g Mahler—Last Sunrise (IRE) **The Gilbert's & Mr Campbell**
57 **WISHING WELL**, 6, b m Bahri (USA)—Amourallis (IRE) **The Pennies Dropped Partnership**
58 **WITNESS (FR)**, 9, b g Astarabad (USA)—Belle Yepa (FR) **R J Ball & R M & T Holdings Ltd**

MR MICKY HAMMOND - Continued

THREE-YEAR-OLDS

59 **JO'S GIRL (IRE)**, b f Zebedee—Diamond Finesse (IRE) **Mr & Mrs I P Earnshaw**

Other Owners: Mr R. J. Ball, Mr I. Barran, Mr Richard Berry, Mr A. Bradley, Mrs Rita Butler, Mr Joe Buzzeo, Mr J. Campbell, Mr Justin Carthy, Mr Paul W. Chapman, Mrs Jean Chapman, Mr Alan D. Crombie, Mr Ian P. Earnshaw, Mrs Joanne Earnshaw, Mr James Finch, Richard & Katherine Gilbert, Mr R. P. Gilbert, Mrs Katherine Gilbert, Mr Richard Green, Mr M. D. Hammond, Mrs Gemma Hogg, Mr L. Horvath, Mr B. R. Howard, Mr R. M. Howard, Mr James M. Hughes, Mr David Hymas, Mrs A. Kane, Mr Malcolm Kent, Littlethorpe Park Racing, Mr Richard Longley, Mr Irvine Lynch, Mr J. McAllister, New Roc, Mrs E. E. Newbould, Mr Mike Newbould, Mr Graeme Newton, Mr G. R. Orchard, Mr John Pettit, Mr Andrew Phillips, Mr T. W. J. Porter, Mr Edward Price, R M & T Holdings Limited, Mr Nick Rust, Mr C. M. Sharpe, Mr Angus Smith, Mr Tom Snook, Mrs Victoria Snook, Mr Alan Stainton, Mr J. B. Stead, Mr John Tasker-Brown, Mr J. Tennant, Ms Sherene Ure, Mr K. Ward, Mr K. R. Weeks.

Assistant Trainer: Mrs. G. Hogg (07809) 428117

Jockey (NH): Joe Colliver. **Conditional:** Finian O'Toole, Hugo Thompson-Brown. **Apprentice:** Lauren Steade. **Amateur:** Miss R. Smith, Mr Joe Wright.

---

255 | **MR MIKE HAMMOND, Abberley**
Postal: **Cherry Ash, Bank Lane, Abberley, Worcester, Worcestershire, WR6 6BQ**
Contacts: **PHONE (01299) 896057 MOBILE 07894 050183**
E-MAIL mphatwellcottage@aol.com WEBSITE www.hammondracing.co.uk

1 **BROCKTON GANDT**, 6, br m Erhaab (USA)—Oyster Bay **Mrs C. M. Lockett**
2 **BURGESS VIEW (IRE)**, 8, b g Kayf Tara—Dahara (FR) **R Morgan Evans Ian Mercer**
3 **CHARLIE MON (IRE)**, 9, ch g Presenting—Prowler (IRE) **Mr R. M. Evans**
4 **CUT FLOWER**, 4, b f Mighty—Heather Mix
5 **HAPPY RING HOUSE (IRE)**, 9, b g Muhtathir—Pink Topaz (USA) **R. J. Hewitt**
6 **SACKFULLOFDREAMS (IRE)**, 5, b g Rock of Gibraltar (IRE)—Nymphaea Alba (IRE) **Mr R. M. Evans**
7 **WELSH DESIGNE**, 10, ch g Midnight Legend—Barton Dante **Mr I. Mercer**

Other Owners: Mr R. Brooke, Mr Royston Morgan Evans, Mr W. Hill, Mr I. Mercer.

Assistant Trainer: Zoe Hammond

Conditional: Charlie Hammond

---

256 | **MR MIKE HAMMOND (SATELLITE), Garstang**
Postal: **Lancashire Racing Stables, The Paddocks, Strickens Lane, Barnacre, Garstang, Lancashire, PR3 1UD**
Contacts: **Office (01995) 605790 MOBILE (07802) 764094 Mike: (07894) 050183**
E-MAIL paul@lancashireracingstables.co.uk WEBSITE www.lancashireracingstables.co.uk
Temporary licence granted until May 2018

1 **BINGO CONTI (FR)**, 7, b g Coastal Path—Regina Conti (FR) **The Four Aces**
2 **HOW MUCH IS ENOUGH (IRE)**, 7, b m Moon Ballet (IRE)—Silankka **Network Racing**
3 **LATE FOR THE SKY**, 4, b f Shirocco (GER)—China Lily (USA) **The Cataractonium Racing Syndicate**
4 **MELABI (IRE)**, 5, b g Oasis Dream—Briolette (IRE) **Mr J. H. Chrimes**
5 **MELANNA (IRE)**, 7, b m Camacho—Colour's End (IRE) **Brandsby Racing**
6 **MISSESGEEJAY**, 8, br m Beat All (USA)—Riverbank Rainbow **The Coz Syndicate**
7 6, B g Bertolini (USA)—Monica Geller (USA) **Betty's Brigade**
8 **MOUNT CHEIRON (USA)**, 7, b g Henrythenavigator (USA)—Chalamont (IRE) **The Style Council**
9 **ONDA DISTRICT (IRE)**, 6, b g Oasis Dream—Leocorno (IRE) **Messrs Chrimes, Winn & Wilson**
10 **PRINCE OF TIME**, 6, ch g Bahamian Bounty—Touching (IRE) **Mr B. Hartley**
11 6, B g Sulamani (IRE)—Riverbank Rainbow **Mrs S. E. Barclay**
12 **ROB ROYAL (IRE)**, 10, b g Royal Anthem (USA)—Shamble Street (IRE) **CCCNLP**
13 5, B m Captain Gerrard (IRE)—Rose Bounty **Mrs S. E. Barclay**
14 **WEDDING BREAKFAST (IRE)**, 4, ch f Casamento (IRE)—Fair Countenance (IRE) **Mr J. H. Chrimes**

THREE-YEAR-OLDS

15 **CALDER VALE**, ch g Captain Gerrard (IRE)—Lee Miller (IRE) **The Haydock Badgeholders**

MR MIKE HAMMOND (SATELLITE) - Continued

TWO-YEAR-OLDS
16 B g 15/5 Coach House (IRE)—Dulally (Dubawi (IRE)) **The Bounty Hunters**
17 B f 5/4 Swiss Spirit—Lee Miller (IRE) (Danehill Dancer (IRE)) **Mrs S. E. Barclay**

Other Owners: John Ball, Alan Appleton, Leo Aspinall, Tony Ball, Paul Bushell, John Calderbank, Andy Clarke, Gordon Frater, George Gibson, Steven Graham, John Greaves, Martin James, David Maitland-Price, Cayce Marsden, Sally Martin, Richard Mattinson, Geoff & Jan Metcalfe, Philip & Christine Metcalfe, Ken Muir, Brian Postlethwaite, David Price, Andy Rourke, John Rowlandson, Brenda Rowley, Paul Scott, Tony Tib, Trevor Willis, Paul Wrench.

Assistant Trainer: Stella Barclay

---

257 **MR GARY HANMER, Tattenhall**
Postal: **Church Farm, Harthill Lane, Harthill, Tattenhall, Chester, Cheshire, CH3 9LQ**
Contacts: **MOBILE (07737) 181165**

1 ALLBARNONE, 10, b g Alflora (IRE)—What A Gem **Girls Are Loud**
2 DEE LANE (IRE), 5, br g Oscar (IRE)—Royal Robin (IRE) **The Deeside Partnership**
3 DON'T HANG ABOUT, 13, ch g Alflora (IRE)—Althrey Flame (IRE) **F. Lloyd**
4 GAMBOLING GIGI, 6, ch m Black Sam Bellamy (IRE)—Gundreda **Mrs M. D. Ritson**
5 HIGH COUNSEL (IRE), 9, br g Presenting—The Bench (IRE) **Herongate Racers**
6 LOCH GARMAN ARIS (IRE), 8, b g Jammaal—See Em Aime (IRE) **Exors of Late George Brookes & Family**
7 O'GRADY'S BOY (IRE), 7, b g Kalanisi (IRE)—Jemima Jay (IRE) **Mr R. P. Davies-Cooke**
8 ORO REBELDE, 5, b g Cockney Rebel (IRE)—Corsa All Oro (USA) **P. S. Burke**
9 PACKETTOTHERAFTERS (IRE), 9, b g Craigsteel—Darazari River (IRE) **The Tunstall Green Partnership**
10 POINT OF DEPARTURE (IRE), 7, b g Mahler—Miranda's Lace (IRE) **F. Lloyd**

Other Owners: Mrs S. Archdale, G. E. Brookes, Mr S. P. Edkins, Mr L. Felstead, M. E. Green, Mr J. F. Hales, Mr W. R. Kinsey, Mrs J. Kinsey, J. M. Tomlinson, Mr N. P. Tunstall.

---

258 **MR RICHARD HANNON, Marlborough**
Postal: **Herridge Racing Stables, Herridge, Collingbourne Ducis, Wiltshire, SN8 3EG**
Contacts: **PHONE (01264) 850254 FAX (01264) 850076**
E-MAIL kevin@richardhannonracing.co.uk WEBSITE www.richardhannonracing.co.uk

1 ACROSS THE STARS (IRE), 5, b g Sea The Stars (IRE)—Victoria Cross (IRE)
2 ALMOREB (IRE), 4, b c Raven's Pass (USA)—Macadamia (IRE)
3 BILLESDON BESS, 4, br f Dick Turpin (IRE)—Coplow
4 BOYCIE, 5, b g Paco Boy (IRE)—Eve
5 BRISTOL MISSILE (USA), 4, b br c Kitten's Joy (USA)—Dearest Girl (IRE)
6 CONTRAST (IRE), 4, ch g Dutch Art—Israar
7 DANEHILL KODIAC (IRE), 5, b h Kodiac—Meadow
8 EUGINIO (IRE), 4, b c Fastnet Rock (AUS)—Starstone
9 FAST AND HOT (IRE), 5, gr g Fastnet Rock (AUS)—Hotelgenie Dot Com
10 GEORGE WILLIAM, 5, b g Paco Boy (IRE)—Basque Beauty
11 HIMSELF, 4, b g High Chaparral (IRE)—Self Centred
12 JUAN HORSEPOWER, 4, b g Foxwedge (AUS)—Elysee (IRE)
13 KHAFOO SHEMEMI (IRE), 4, b c Dark Angel (IRE)—Appleblossom Pearl (IRE)
14 MEDAHIM (IRE), 4, b g Kodiac—Novel Fun (IRE)
15 MOUILLE POINT, 4, b f Motivator—Turning Leaf (IRE)
16 MR TYRRELL (IRE), 4, b g Helmet (AUS)—Rocking
17 NAYEL (IRE), 6, b h Acclamation—Soliza (IRE)
18 OH THIS IS US (IRE), 5, b h Acclamation—Shamwari Lodge (IRE)
19 PEAK PRINCESS (IRE), 4, b f Foxwedge (AUS)—Foot of Pride (IRE)
20 PEPITA (IRE), 4, ch f Sir Prancealot (IRE)—Esterlina (IRE)
21 PROMISING (IRE), 4, b f Invincible Spirit (IRE)—Lethal Quality (USA)
22 REPTON (IRE), 4, b g Zebedee—African Moonlight (UAE)
23 SECOND PAGE, 4, b c Harbour Watch—Almunia (IRE)
24 SEE THE SEA (IRE), 4, b f Born To Sea (IRE)—Shahmina (IRE)
25 STERLING SILVA (IRE), 4, ch g Sakhee's Secret—Silicon Star (FR)
26 TAI HANG DRAGON (IRE), 4, b f Tamayuz—Give A Whistle (IRE)
27 TOMILY (IRE), 4, b g Canford Cliffs (IRE)—Cake (IRE)

MR RICHARD HANNON - Continued

28 **TONY CURTIS**, 5, b g Rock of Gibraltar (IRE)—Strawberry Lolly
29 **TUPI (IRE)**, 6, b g Tamayuz—Carioca (IRE)
30 **VENTURA BLUES (IRE)**, 4, b br f Bated Breath—Salmon Rose (IRE)
31 **WAHASH (IRE)**, 4, gr c Dark Angel (IRE)—Delira (IRE)
32 **WAR GLORY (IRE)**, 5, b g Canford Cliffs (IRE)—Attracted To You (IRE)

THREE-YEAR-OLDS

33 **ACCESSOR (IRE)**, b c Exceed And Excel (AUS)—Amarette (GER)
34 **AL BARG (IRE)**, b g Acclamation—Miss Hawai (FR)
35 **ALGAM (IRE)**, b g Kodiac—Evangeline
36 **ALL OUT**, b f Acclamation—Time Over
37 **AMBROISE (IRE)**, br c Zebedee—Sweet Irish
38 **ANCHISES**, b c Choisir (AUS)—Afrodita (IRE)
39 **ANNA NERIUM**, ch f Dubawi (IRE)—Anna Oleanda (IRE)
40 **ATEEM (FR)**, b c Dark Angel (IRE)—Jeu de Plume (IRE)
41 **BALLETOMANE**, b c Exceed And Excel (AUS)—Alexander Ballet
42 **BATHSHEBA BAY (IRE)**, b c Footstepsinthesand—Valamareha (IRE)
43 **BEZOS (IRE)**, b g Famous Name—Midnight Oasis
44 **BILLESDON BROOK**, ch f Champs Elysees—Coplow
45 **BIRTHRIGHT**, b c Mawatheeq (USA)—Pooka's Daughter (IRE)
46 **BLANCHEFLEUR (IRE)**, b f Camelot—Portrait of A Lady (IRE)
47 **BOING**, b c Bated Breath—Lomapamar
48 **BOMBSHELL BAY**, b g Foxwedge (AUS)—Cumana Bay
49 **BON SCOTTE (IRE)**, b c Kodiac—Bonne
50 **BREXITMEANSBREXIT**, b f Helmet (AUS)—Lady Scarlett
51 Gr f Zebedee—Bruno Maris (IRE)
52 **BULLINGDON**, b g Dansili—Rimth
53 **BURIDAN (FR)**, b c Choisir (AUS)—Lady McKell (IRE)
54 **CHEEKY RASCAL (IRE)**, b c Most Improved (IRE)—Bessie Lou (IRE)
55 **CULTURE SHOCK**, b f Zoffany (IRE)—No Song
56 **DAISY CHAIN (IRE)**, b f Fastnet Rock (AUS)—College Fund Girl (IRE)
57 **DANDIESQUE (IRE)**, b f Dandy Man (IRE)—Marigold (FR)
58 **DEPARTMENT OF WAR (IRE)**, ch c Declaration of War (USA)—Danetime Out (IRE)
59 **DOCTOR JAZZ (IRE)**, b c Most Improved (IRE)—Daliyana (IRE)
60 **DONO DI DIO**, b f Nathaniel (IRE)—Sweet Cecily (IRE)
61 **DOTTED SWISS (IRE)**, b f Swiss Spirit—Luxuria (IRE)
62 **DRAGON MOON (USA)**, b c Super Saver (USA)—Lunargal (USA)
63 **DRAKEFELL (IRE)**, b c Canford Cliffs (IRE)—Cake (IRE)
64 **ELYSIUM DREAM**, b f Champs Elysees—Dream of Wunders
65 **ETEFAAQ (IRE)**, b c Kodiac—Sheila Blige
66 **FIRE ORCHID**, gr f Lethal Force (IRE)—Ring of Love
67 **GENDARME (IRE)**, b c Lawman (FR)—Gravitation
68 **GHEPARDO**, b f Havana Gold (IRE)—Clincher
69 **GIVEN NAME**, b g Nathaniel (IRE)—Poly Pomona
70 **HAYLAH (IRE)**, b f Epaulette (AUS)—Pearls of Wisdom
71 **HESTERYA (IRE)**, b f Kodiac—Lady Avenger (IRE)
72 **JANE ROSE (IRE)**, b f Acclamation—Miss Champagne (FR)
73 **LAMYA (GER)**, b f Choisir (AUS)—Livia's Wake (IRE)
74 **LETSBE AVENUE (IRE)**, b g Lawman (FR)—Aguilas Perla (IRE)
75 **MAGHAWEER (IRE)**, ch c Dubawi (IRE)—Indian Ink (IRE)
76 **MAGNIFICENT**, b c Zebedee—Barathea Dancer (IRE)
77 **MAYPOLE**, ch c Mayson—Constitute (USA)
78 **MAYYASAH (USA)**, b f More Than Ready (USA)—Whipsaw City (FR)
79 **METKAIF**, b g Iffraaj—Martagon Lily
80 **MISS MO BROWN BEAR (IRE)**, b f Kodiac—Currentis (IRE)
81 **MODEL (FR)**, gr f Mastercraftsman (IRE)—Goddess of Love
82 **MOTOWN MICK (IRE)**, ch g Intikhab (USA)—Top Row
83 **MUSHTAQ (IRE)**, b g Zoffany (IRE)—Iamfine (IRE)
84 **NAHHAM (IRE)**, b c Dawn Approach (IRE)—Anna's Rock (IRE)
85 **NO MORE THRILLS**, ch f Dutch Art—The Thrill Is Gone
86 **OCEAN SIDE**, gr c Dark Angel (IRE)—Mundus Novus (USA)
87 **OLIVER REED (IRE)**, b c Footstepsinthesand—Montbretia
88 **ON A ROLL**, b f Swiss Spirit—Amary (IRE)
89 **ORANGE SUIT (IRE)**, b c Declaration of War (USA)—Guantanamera (IRE)
90 **PHYSICAL POWER (IRE)**, b f Power—Street Shaana (FR)

MR RICHARD HANNON - Continued

91 **POINT HOPE (IRE)**, b f Kodiac—Frosted
92 **POPSICLE (IRE)**, b f Acclamation—Katchy Lady
93 **QAYSAR (FR)**, b c Choisir (AUS)—Coco Demure (IRE)
94 **QUEEN OF ROME (GER)**, b f Holy Roman Emperor (IRE)—Quilita (GER)
95 **RAJAAM (IRE)**, b c Invincible Spirit (IRE)—Midnight Partner (IRE)
96 **RAYMOND TUSK (IRE)**, b c High Chaparral (IRE)—Dancing Shoes (IRE)
97 **RED STARLIGHT**, br f Pivotal—Star Chart (IRE)
98 **REGIMENTED (IRE)**, b c Epaulette (AUS)—Colour Coordinated (IRE)
99 **RESHAAN (IRE)**, b c Dark Angel (IRE)—Bluebell (IRE)
100 **ROBINSON CRUSOE (IRE)**, b c Footstepsinthesand—Corrozal (GER)
101 **ROGUE**, b g Epaulette (AUS)—Miskin Diamond (IRE)
102 **ROUNDHEAD**, ch c Helmet (AUS)—Blue Mistral (IRE)
103 **RUM RUNNER**, b c Havana Gold (IRE)—Thermopylae
104 **SALLAB (IRE)**, b c Havana Gold (IRE)—Waveband
105 **SCIMITAR (IRE)**, b c Fast Company (IRE)—Zahr Alyasmeen (IRE)
106 **SERGIO LEONE (IRE)**, b c Acclamation—Elizabelle (IRE)
107 **SETTING SUN (IRE)**, br f Kodiac—Fonseca (IRE)
108 **SHARG (IRE)**, b g Invincible Spirit (IRE)—Rain Flower (IRE)
109 **SHERZY BOY**, b c Champs Elysees—Sherzam
110 **SOPRANOS ROCK (IRE)**, b c Society Rock (IRE)—Honeymead (IRE)
111 **SOTOMAYOR**, b c Havana Gold (IRE)—No Frills (IRE)
112 **STAR OF SOUTHWOLD (FR)**, bl c Le Havre (IRE)—Into The Wild (FR)
113 **STORMER (IRE)**, b c Kodiac—Easee On (IRE)
114 **STRAIGHT ASH (IRE)**, gr g Zebedee—Blackangelheart (IRE)
115 **STRONGARM CHASER (IRE)**, b c Footstepsinthesand—Sarawati (IRE)
116 **SURFA ROSA**, b c Delegator—Beechnut (IRE)
117 **TAJAANUS (IRE)**, b f Arcano (IRE)—Rayaheen
118 **TANGLED (IRE)**, b c Society Rock (IRE)—Open Verse (USA)
119 **TATHMEEN (IRE)**, b c Exceed And Excel (AUS)—Deyaar (USA)
120 **TIG TOG (IRE)**, b f Dark Angel (IRE)—Deira Dubai
121 **TIGRE DU TERRE (FR)**, b c Le Havre (IRE)—Allmia (FR)
122 **VENTURA MAGIC**, b g Mount Nelson—Elle Desert (GER)
123 **VITAMIN (IRE)**, b f Camelot—True Verdict (IRE)
124 **WAFEER (IRE)**, b c Equiano (FR)—Star Approval (IRE)
125 **YAFTA**, gr c Dark Angel (IRE)—Swiss Dream
126 **ZABALETASWANSONG (GER)**, b g Maxios—Zavaala (IRE)
127 **ZALSHAH**, ch g Mayson—Regal Velvet

TWO-YEAR-OLDS

128 **ACTIVE POWER (FR)**, b f 9/1 Le Havre (IRE)—Sun Seeker (IRE) (Galileo (IRE)) (73260)
129 B c 27/4 Roderic O'connor (IRE)—Agnista (IRE) (Iffraaj) (15238)
130 **AIM POWER (FR)**, gr f 5/3 Zebedee—Montefino (FR) (Shamardal (USA)) (160000)
131 Br c 28/4 Dandy Man (IRE)—Air Maze (Dansili) (48840)
132 Ch f 16/2 No Nay Never (USA)—Alamouna (IRE) (Indian Ridge) (61864)
133 B c 24/2 Oasis Dream—Albisola (IRE) (Montjeu (IRE)) (50000)
134 B f 15/4 Kodiac—Alina (IRE) (Galileo (IRE)) (400000)
135 B c 11/2 Olympic Glory (IRE)—Almaardiyah (IRE) (High Chaparral (IRE))
136 **AMOROUSLY (IRE)**, b f 19/3 Australia—Know Me Love Me (IRE) (Danehill Dancer (IRE)) (69189)
137 B f 19/3 Dabirsim (FR)—Amour Eternel (IRE) (Elusive City (USA)) (407000)
138 B c 28/2 War Command (USA)—Archina (IRE) (Arch (USA)) (24761)
139 B f 17/2 War Command (USA)—Areeda (IRE) (Refuse To Bend (IRE)) (140000)
140 **AUBRETIA (IRE)**, ch f 8/1 Poet's Voice—Abilene (Samum (GER)) (65120)
141 **BADER**, b c 22/1 Elusive City (USA)—Golbahar (IRE) (Holy Roman Emperor (IRE)) (66666)
142 B c 25/4 Kodiac—Bailonguera (ARG) (Southern Halo (USA)) (227920)
143 Ch f 17/3 Nayef (USA)—Barnezet (GR) (Invincible Spirit (IRE))
144 **BEAT LE BON (FR)**, b c 23/2 Wootton Bassett—Frida La Blonde (FR) (Elusive City (USA)) (81400)
145 B f 22/1 Kodiac—Big Boned (USA) (Street Sense (USA)) (69189)
146 **BOITRON (FR)**, b c 3/1 Le Havre (IRE)—Belliflore (FR) (Verglas (IRE)) (36630)
147 **BRIAN EPSTEIN (IRE)**, b c 3/4 Dark Angel (IRE)—Jewel In The Sand (IRE) (Bluebird (USA)) (133333)
148 B c 19/2 Slade Power (IRE)—Cake (IRE) (Acclamation)
149 **CANTON QUEEN (IRE)**, b f 19/2 Shamardal (USA)—Hana Lina (Oasis Dream) (110000)
150 **CASTING (IRE)**, b c 12/4 Society Rock (IRE)—Suffer Her (IRE) (Whipper (USA)) (152380)
151 **CHATHAM HOUSE**, gr c 4/3 Dark Angel (IRE)—Timely (Pivotal)
152 **CHONBURI**, b f 3/4 Lawman (FR)—Expected Dream (IRE) (Galileo (IRE)) (55000)
153 **COCO CHEVAL (IRE)**, ch f 3/2 Kyllachy—Chant de Sable (IRE) (Oasis Dream) (46398)

MR RICHARD HANNON - Continued

154 B c 10/4 Heeraat (IRE)—Contenance (IRE) (Dansant) (26000)
155 COOL KITTY, b f 7/2 Kodiac—Ligeia (Rail Link) (35000)
156 B c 16/3 Kyllachy—Cumana Bay (Dansili)
157 B f 21/2 War Command (USA)—Deora De (Night Shift (USA)) (14000)
158 DOUGHAN ALB, b c 1/2 Havana Gold (IRE)—Sandtime (IRE) (Green Desert (USA)) (30000)
159 B f 5/4 Australia—Dusty In Memphis (USA) (Broken Vow (USA)) (54538)
160 EDDIE COCHRAN (IRE), bl c 2/4 Society Rock (IRE)—Crossreadh (USA) (Sahm (USA)) (35816)
161 ELSAABLQAAT, b f 21/3 Invincible Spirit (IRE)—Fleeting Smile (USA) (Distorted Humor (USA))
162 ENTERTAINING (IRE), b c 25/3 Dandy Man (IRE)—Letizia Sophia (IRE) (Shamardal (USA)) (92000)
163 EQUAL SUM, br f 6/3 Paco Boy (IRE)—Hypoteneuse (IRE) (Sadler's Wells (USA))
164 Ch c 2/3 Bungle Inthejungle—Fanditha (IRE) (Danehill Dancer (IRE)) (53333)
165 B f 9/3 Dandy Man (IRE)—Fiancee (IRE) (Pivotal) (22857)
166 FLOATING ARTIST, b c 29/2 Nathaniel (IRE)—Miss Kenton (IRE) (Pivotal) (80000)
167 FOX HAPPY (IRE), b c 18/4 Showcasing—Roo (Rudimentary (USA)) (150000)
168 FOX KASPER (IRE), ch c 25/2 Society Rock (IRE)—Easy Times (Nayef (USA)) (220000)
169 FOX POWER (IRE), gr c 4/4 Dark Angel (IRE)—Zenella (Kyllachy) (450000)
170 B f 11/4 Olympic Glory (IRE)—Fringe Success (IRE) (Selkirk (USA)) (40000)
171 Ch c 7/4 Kyllachy—Gerika (FR) (Galileo (IRE)) (19000)
172 GIANT BREAK (FR), b c 22/4 Sunday Break (JPN)—Mururoa (FR) (Great Journey (JPN)) (7326)
173 GINGER FOX, ch c 1/4 Iffraaj—Rimth (Oasis Dream)
174 GINGER NUT (IRE), ch f 13/3 Sir Prancealot (IRE)—Applauding (IRE) (Royal Applause) (21904)
175 GLORIOUS DANE, b c 25/4 Olympic Glory (IRE)—Kaminari (IRE) (Sea The Stars (IRE)) (69189)
176 GOOD LUCK FOX (IRE), b c 29/3 Society Rock (IRE)—Violet Ballerina (IRE) (Namid) (180000)
177 GRACEFUL (IRE), b f 21/3 Zoffany (IRE)—Tahara (IRE) (Caerleon (USA))
178 Ch c 12/3 Tagula (IRE)—Grotta Del Fauno (IRE) (Galileo (IRE)) (66666)
179 B c 8/4 Alhebayeb (IRE)—Heat (King's Best) (40700)
180 HERMOCRATES (FR), b c 26/3 Farhh—Little Shambles (Shamardal (USA)) (78095)
181 B c 8/3 Battle of Marengo (IRE)—How Sweet It Is (IRE) (Kodiac) (20000)
182 HUA HIN (IRE), ch c 6/2 Dandy Man (IRE)—Midnight Oasis (Oasis Dream) (56980)
183 B f 20/2 Zoffany (IRE)—Idle Curiosity (IRE) (Red Clubs (IRE)) (71428)
184 B f 16/1 Olympic Glory (IRE)—Idle Tears (Selkirk (USA)) (77330)
185 JAAYIZ (IRE), b c 31/3 Zoffany (IRE)—So Devoted (IRE) (Holy Roman Emperor (IRE)) (68000)
186 Ch f 29/2 Teofilo (IRE)—Katdogawn (Bahhare (USA)) (29304)
187 KHIBRAH, b f 27/4 Dark Angel (IRE)—Mi Anna (GER) (Lake Coniston (IRE)) (140000)
188 KINGS ROYAL HUSSAR (FR), b c 30/3 Zebedee—Ile Rouge (Red Ransom (USA)) (32560)
189 B f 14/1 Le Havre (IRE)—Kithonia (FR) (Sadler's Wells (USA)) (89540)
190 B c 29/2 Dark Angel (IRE)—Lady Marita (IRE) (Dandy Man (IRE)) (80000)
191 LADY SCATTERLEY (FR), ch f 17/2 No Nay Never (USA)—Camdara (FR) (Hawk Wing (USA))
192 B c 22/3 Nathaniel (IRE)—Langs Lash (IRE) (Noverre (USA)) (350000)
193 Ch f 16/2 Strong Mandate (USA)—Lavish Outlook (USA) (Smarty Jones (USA)) (127758)
194 Gr c 31/3 Alhebayeb (IRE)—Lawman's Lady (IRE) (Lawman (FR)) (13500)
195 LEOUBE (IRE), b f 24/2 Kodiac—Sojitzen (FR) (Great Journey (JPN)) (120000)
196 LEROY LEROY, b c 25/2 Compton Place—Small Fortune (Anabaa (USA)) (68571)
197 B c 16/2 Toronado (IRE)—Lily Link (Rail Link) (100000)
198 B f 31/3 Holy Roman Emperor (IRE)—Maghzaa (IRE) (Aqlaam) (40700)
199 B c 20/4 Footstepsinthesand—Masseera (IRE) (Alzao (USA)) (180000)
200 MERSEY (IRE), gr f 13/3 Kodiac—Wylye (Dalakhani (IRE))
201 B f 25/3 Charm Spirit (IRE)—Mill Guineas (Salse (USA)) (65120)
202 B c 19/3 Siyouni (FR)—Miss Elena (Invincible Spirit (IRE)) (60000)
203 B c 22/3 Charm Spirit (IRE)—Miss Plimsoll (Arch (USA)) (97680)
204 Br c 3/5 No Nay Never (USA)—Mixed Blessing (Lujain (USA)) (227920)
205 MOLAAHETH, b c 12/2 Heeraat (IRE)—All Fur Coat (Multiplex) (142857)
206 MONDAKHAR (IRE), b c 20/3 Battle of Marengo (IRE)—Lost Highway (IRE) (Danehill Dancer (IRE)) (80952)
207 MORDRED (IRE), b c 23/3 Camelot—Endure (IRE) (Green Desert (USA)) (175000)
208 MOSHARAKKA (IRE), b c 28/4 Alhebayeb (IRE)—Azia (IRE) (Desert Story (IRE)) (105000)
209 MOSTAWAA, ch c 4/3 Poet's Voice—Mumtaza (Nayef (USA))
210 MOTAFAAWIT (IRE), b br c 20/4 Intikhab (USA)—Rayaheen (Nayef (USA))
211 MOYASSAR, ch c 10/3 Tamayuz—Catwalk (IRE) (Pivotal)
212 MY BABYDOLL, b f 9/4 Slade Power (IRE)—Keilogue (IRE) (Invincible Spirit (IRE)) (44769)
213 B c 23/2 Kodiac—Nateeja (IRE) (Shamardal (USA)) (135000)
214 B f 7/4 Camacho—Oatcake (Selkirk (USA)) (26000)
215 OCTAVIA MINOR (USA), b f 5/3 Noble Mission—Laurel Lassie (IRE) (Shinko Forest (IRE)) (50000)
216 OUZO, b c 7/4 Charm Spirit (IRE)—Miss Meltemi (IRE) (Miswaki Tern (USA)) (95000)
217 OWER MAGIC, b f 6/3 Dick Turpin—Rebel Magic (Cockney Rebel (IRE))
218 PACINO, b c 10/3 Heeraat (IRE)—Ringtail (USA) (Street Cry (IRE)) (45714)

MR RICHARD HANNON - Continued

219 PESTO, br c 2/4 New Approach (IRE)—Pickle (Piccolo) (80000)
220 PIMLICO PLEASER (IRE), b f 14/4 Zebedee—Pretty Bonnie (Kyllachy) (32380)
221 B c 1/3 Oasis Dream—Pure Excellence (Exceed And Excel (AUS)) (85000)
222 B c 9/2 Gale Force Ten—Queen Myrine (IRE) (Oratorio (IRE)) (22792)
223 B c 27/3 Born To Sea (IRE)—Red Planet (Pivotal) (24420)
224 B c 25/3 Acclamation—Refusetolisten (IRE) (Clodovil (IRE)) (58000)
225 REGENT (IRE), b f 5/4 War Command—Regency Girl (IRE) (Pivotal) (90476)
226 B f 12/2 Gregorian (IRE)—Reveille (Sakhee's Secret) (16000)
227 Ch f 17/4 Garswood—Ring of Love (Magic Ring (IRE)) (98000)
228 RITCHIE VALENS (IRE), ch c 9/2 Helmet (AUS)—Miss Cape (IRE) (Cape Cross (IRE)) (47000)
229 ROONG ROONG (IRE), gr f 31/1 Dark Angel—Cut No Ice (IRE) (Verglas (IRE)) (825000)
230 B c 9/4 Dark Angel (IRE)—Rum Raisin (Invincible Spirit (IRE)) (63809)
231 B c 25/3 Frankel—Rumored (USA) (Royal Academy (USA)) (447700)
232 B c 20/3 Farhh—Salacia (IRE) (Echo of Light)
233 B c 16/5 Society Rock (IRE)—Scottish Exile (Ashkalani (IRE)) (46398)
234 B f 31/3 Camacho—Shamardyh (IRE) (Shamardal (USA)) (34188)
235 Ch c 13/4 Toronado (IRE)—Shotgun Gulch (USA) (Thunder Gulch (USA))
236 Gr f 3/4 Tin Horse (IRE)—Sienna May (USA) (Dixie Union (USA)) (12210)
237 B c 20/4 Red Jazz (USA)—Signora Lina (IRE) (High Chaparral (IRE)) (57142)
238 SIRINAPHA (IRE), b c 5/4 Alhebayeb (IRE)—Sassari (IRE) (Darshaan) (36629)
239 B c 19/3 Elzaam (AUS)—Smilelikeyoumeanit (Authorized (IRE)) (45000)
240 B f 5/2 Kodiac—Society Pearl (IRE) (Kheleyf (USA)) (75000)
241 SPELL, b f 18/2 Slade Power (IRE)—Jeanie Johnston (IRE) (One Cool Cat (USA)) (44761)
242 B c 25/2 Lethal Force (IRE)—Spontaneity (IRE) (Holy Roman Emperor (IRE)) (36190)
243 Gr c 26/3 Alhebayeb (IRE)—Summer Glow (IRE) (Exceed And Excel (AUS)) (56980)
244 B c 25/2 Slade Power (IRE)—Summer In February (Sixties Icon) (200000)
245 B c 5/3 Garswood—Swanky Lady (Cape Cross (IRE)) (70000)
246 SWIPER (IRE), b c 8/4 Clodovil (IRE)—Hawk Dance (IRE) (Hawk Wing (USA)) (38095)
247 SWISS CHIME, b f 5/3 Swiss Spirit—Dolly Daydreamer (Equiano (FR)) (22857)
248 B f 11/3 Olympic Glory (IRE)—The Giving Tree (IRE) (Rock of Gibraltar (IRE)) (13000)
249 B c 2/3 Heeraat (IRE)—Tomintoul Magic (IRE) (Holy Roman Emperor (IRE)) (45714)
250 TOPICAL, b c 4/4 Toronado (IRE)—Star Value (IRE) (Danehill Dancer (IRE))
251 Br c 6/2 Kyllachy—Triple Star (Royal Applause) (134309)
252 B c 11/2 Olympic Glory (IRE)—Updated (FR) (New Approach (IRE)) (30000)
253 URBAN ICON, b c 20/3 Cityscape—Fauran (IRE) (Shamardal (USA)) (21904)
254 B f 9/4 Zebedee—Violet Flame (IRE) (Kalanisi (IRE)) (7500)
255 WATER DIVINER (IRE), b c 10/3 Bungle Inthejungle—Khayrat (IRE) (Polar Falcon (USA)) (24420)
256 B f 24/4 Dark Angel (IRE)—Waveband (Exceed And Excel (AUS)) (65120)
257 WELL DONE FOX, b c 28/1 Acclamation—Excelette (IRE) (Exceed And Excel (AUS)) (255000)
258 B c 14/3 Lilbourne Lad (IRE)—Whatever You Do (IRE) (Barathea (IRE)) (9767)
259 Ch c 16/3 Archipenko (USA)—Whispering Wind (IRE) (Sunshine Street (USA))
260 YESTAAHEL, b c 22/3 Footstepsinthesand—Azenzar (Danehill Dancer (IRE)) (64761)
261 B c 17/2 Footstepsinthesand—Ziggy's Secret (Sakhee's Secret) (28571)

Assistant Trainer: Tom Ward

Jockey (flat): Tom Marquand, Sean Levey. **Apprentice:** Hollie Doyle, Rossa Ryan.

---

 259 **MR GEOFFREY HARKER, Thirsk**
Postal: Stockhill Green, York Rd, Thirkelby, Thirsk, North Yorkshire, YO7 3AS
Contacts: PHONE (01845) 501117 FAX (01845) 501614 MOBILE (07803) 116412/(07930) 125544
E-MAIL gandjhome@aol.com WEBSITE www.geoffharkerracing.com

1 BLING KING, 9, b g Haafhd—Bling Bling (IRE) **P. I. Harker**
2 CABAL, 11, br m Kyllachy—Secret Flame **P. I. Harker**
3 DREAM DESTROYER (IRE), 4, gr f Vale of York (IRE)—Lady Georgina **Mrs V. Thompson**
4 EXTRASOLAR, 8, b g Exceed And Excel (AUS)—Amicable Terms **The Twelve Minimum Partnership**
5 FAIR FOR ALL, 7, b g Fair Mix (IRE)—Falcons Theatre (IRE) **Miss S. J. Turner**
6 GRAPHITE (IRE), 4, ro g Galileo (IRE)—Simply Perfect **The Twelve Minimum Partnership**
7 MAMBILA (FR), 4, b g Rio de La Plata (USA)—Maka (FR)
8 MOCCASIN, 9, b g Green Tune (USA)—Museum Piece **The Crazy Gang**
9 SCOTTISH SUMMIT (IRE), 5, b g Shamardal (USA)—
Scottish Stage (IRE) **Sterling Racing, Mr P Downes, Geoff Harker**
10 SHAMAHEART (IRE), 8, b g Shamardal (USA)—Encouragement **A. S. Ward**

MR GEOFFREY HARKER - Continued

11 **SIMMO'S PARTYTRICK (IRE)**, 5, b h Baltic King—Goose Island (IRE) **J F S Racing**
12 **WENTWORTH FALLS**, 6, gr g Dansili—Strawberry Morn (CAN) **Stockhill Racing Partnership**

THREE-YEAR-OLDS

13 **ROYAL LIBERTY**, b c Acclamation—Anadolu (IRE) **P. I. Harker**

Other Owners: Mr Wayne Bavill, Mr Harry Bryson, Mr John Clydesdale, Mr Neil Burns, Mr P. Downes, Mr Mark Fowler, Mr G. A. Harker, Mrs F. H. Hay, Mrs S. Magnier, Mr N. McGarty-Wood, Mr James Noble, Mr A. J. Parish, Mr D. J. Pentney, D. Smith, Sterling Racing, Mrs D. A. Tabor, Mr Steven Taylor.

Assistant Trainer: Jenny Harker

Jockey (NH): W. T. Kennedy.

---

260   **MR RICHARD HARPER, Kings Sutton**
Postal: **Home Farm, Kings Sutton, Banbury, Oxfordshire, OX17 3RS**
Contacts: **PHONE (01295) 810997 FAX (01295) 812787 MOBILE (07970) 223481**
E-MAIL rharper@freeuk.com

1 **JUST SKITTLES**, 10, b g Storming Home—Miss Roberto (IRE) **R. C. Harper**
2 **POYNTZPASS (IRE)**, 8, ch g Gamut (IRE)—Play Trix (IRE) **R. C. Harper**

Assistant Trainer: C. Harper

---

261   **MRS JESSICA HARRINGTON, Kildare**
Postal: **Commonstown Stud, Moone, Co. Kildare, Ireland**
Contacts: **PHONE (00353) 5986 24153 MOBILE (00353) 8725 66129**
E-MAIL jessica@jessicaharringtonracing.com WEBSITE www.jessicaharringtonracing.com

1 **A SIZING NETWORK (FR)**, 8, ch g Network (GER)—Gemma (FR)
2 **ALE AMBROSIO (IRE)**, 6, br m Big Bad Bob (IRE)—Memorys of Madness (IRE)
3 **ALLETRIX (IRE)**, 5, b m Flemensfirth (USA)—Miracle Trix (IRE)
4 **ANOTHER BARNEY (IRE)**, 5, br g Scorpion (IRE)—Roseabel (IRE)
5 4, ch f Mastercraftsman (IRE)—Arabian Hideway (IRE)
6 **ARION SKY (IRE)**, 4, b f Jeremy (USA)—Dream Function (IRE)
7 **BEAUTIFUL MORNING**, 5, b m Galileo (IRE)—Date With Destiny (IRE)
8 **BENEFIT OF MAGIC (IRE)**, 6, b m Beneficial—Corraig Lady (IRE)
9 **BENNAWAY (IRE)**, 5, b g Stowaway—Benny's Marble (IRE)
10 **CHARMED LIFE (IRE)**, 4, b g Kalanisi (IRE)—Lady Bellingham (IRE)
11 **CLOSE SHAVE**, 7, b g Presenting—Knock Down (IRE)
12 4, B g Salutino (GER)—Collinstown Queen (IRE)
13 **CONRON (IRE)**, 4, b g Mastercraftsman (IRE)—Numbers Game
14 4, B g Flemensfirth (USA)—Cut 'n' Run (IRE)
15 **DON'T TOUCH IT (IRE)**, 8, b g Scorpion (IRE)—Shandora (IRE)
16 **EASY PASS (IRE)**, 5, br g Elusive Pimpernel (USA)—Shady Nook (IRE)
17 **EMILY MOON (IRE)**, 4, b f Beneficial—Wood Lily (IRE)
18 **EXIT POLL (IRE)**, 4, b g Elusive Pimpernel (USA)—Carolobrian (IRE)
19 **FINTARA (IRE)**, 6, b m Kayf Tara—Fine Fortune (IRE)
20 **FORGE MEADOW (IRE)**, 6, b m Beneficial—Ballys Baby (IRE)
21 **GEMMATTYMOLL (IRE)**, 6, b g Getaway (GER)—Rebel Diva (IRE)
22 **GIRLY GIRL (IRE)**, 9, b m Golan (IRE)—Clan Music (IRE)
23 4, B br g Ask—Good Thyne Jenny (IRE)
24 **GYMKHANA**, 5, ch g Equiano (FR)—Village Fete
25 **HYPERDRIVE (IRE)**, 4, ch g Mastercraftsman (IRE)—Dromod Mour (IRE)
26 **I'M SO FANCY (IRE)**, 4, b f Rajj (IRE)—Royal Jelly
27 **IMPACT FACTOR (IRE)**, 6, b g Flemensfirth (USA)—Hello Kitty (IRE)
28 **JELARA (IRE)**, 4, b f Milan—Jeree (IRE)
29 **JETEZ (IRE)**, 5, b g Getaway (GER)—Miss Squiff (IRE)
30 **JETT (IRE)**, 7, b g Flemensfirth (USA)—La Noire (IRE)
31 **JETZ (IRE)**, 6, b g Flemensfirth (USA)—Miss Squiff (IRE)
32 **JEZKI (IRE)**, 10, b g Milan—La Noire (IRE)
33 **JUDY'S OSCAR (IRE)**, 5, b m Oscar (IRE)—Home At Last (IRE)
34 **JULIESPADDOCKWALK (IRE)**, 5, b m Gold Well—Shuil Dorcha (IRE)

MRS JESSICA HARRINGTON - Continued

35 **LADY OF ELYSIUM (IRE)**, 4, br f Doyen (IRE)—Suzy Q (IRE)
36 **LESLEY DAWN (IRE)**, 5, b m Flemensfirth (USA)—Glen Empress (IRE)
37 **LIGHT THAT (IRE)**, 6, b g Echo of Light—Tucum (IRE)
38 **LITTLE PRINCESS (GER)**, 4, br f Kamsin (GER)—Little Wonder (GER)
39 **LOAD UP TIME (IRE)**, 4, br g Stowaway—Orinocco Blue (IRE)
40 **LOVE AND WISHES (IRE)**, 6, b br g Winged Love (IRE)—Dixies Gem (IRE)
41 4, B g Shirocco (GER)—Lovely Star (IRE)
42 **MADISON TO MONROE (IRE)**, 5, ro g Presenting—Caltra Princess (IRE)
43 **MAGIC OF LIGHT (IRE)**, 7, b m Flemensfirth (USA)—Quest of Passion (FR)
44 **MAKE IT HURRAH (IRE)**, 4, b g Intikhab (USA)—Pershaan (IRE)
45 **MAPLE LAWN (IRE)**, 5, b m Alkaadhem—Johnsons Coat (IRE)
46 **MARSHALL JENNINGS (IRE)**, 6, b g Lawman (FR)—Zuniga's Date (USA)
47 **MOONSHINE BAY (IRE)**, 5, b g Milan—Chantoue Royale (FR)
48 **NEVERUSHACON (IRE)**, 7, b g Echo of Light—Lily Beth (IRE)
49 4, B f Shantou (USA)—No One Tells Me
50 **NOT MANY LEFT (IRE)**, 5, b g Oscar (IRE)—Lasado (IRE)
51 4, Ch f Flemensfirth (USA)—Now Its My Turn (IRE)
52 **OSCAR SAM (IRE)**, 9, b g Oscar (IRE)—Good Thyne Jenny (IRE)
53 **OUR DUKE (IRE)**, 8, b g Oscar (IRE)—Good Thyne Jenny (IRE)
54 **PERES ET FILS (IRE)**, 4, br g Stowaway—Allthewhile (IRE)
55 **PINCHECK (IRE)**, 4, b g Invincible Spirit (IRE)—Arty Crafty (USA)
56 **POCKET DIAL (IRE)**, 5, b m Scorpion (IRE)—Aktress (IRE)
57 **POLISHED STEEL (IRE)**, 4, b g Jeremy (USA)—Chaperoned (IRE)
58 **PRESENT'N'CORRECT (IRE)**, 5, b g Presenting—Cut 'n' Run (IRE)
59 **PRESS CONFERENCE (IRE)**, 5, b g Getaway (GER)—Beautiful Tune (FR)
60 4, B g Fame And Glory—Princess Susan (IRE)
61 **RAPID RESPONSE (FR)**, 4, br f Network (GER)—La Grande Villez (FR)
62 **REBELION BOY (IRE)**, 8, b g Millenary—Native Vicky (IRE)
63 **RICKRACK (IRE)**, 4, b f Teofilo (IRE)—Arazena (USA)
64 **ROCK THE WORLD (IRE)**, 10, b g Örpen (USA)—Sue N Win (IRE)
65 **ROVETTA (FR)**, 4, b f So You Think (NZ)—Rosa Brett (ITY)
66 **SAM CHISOLM (IRE)**, 5, br g Getaway (GER)—Undecided Hall (IRE)
67 **SANDYMOUNT DUKE (IRE)**, 9, b g Hernando (FR)—Joleah (IRE)
68 **SIZING JOHN**, 8, b g Midnight Legend—La Perrotine (FR)
69 **SIZING POTTSIE (FR)**, 4, b g Kapgarde (FR)—Line Salsa (FR)
70 **SOMEDAY**, 6, b g Black Sam Bellamy (IRE)—Like Manner
71 **SPRING GARDEN (IRE)**, 4, b f Fastnet Rock (AUS)—Butterfly Blue (IRE)
72 **ST BRELADES BAY (IRE)**, 6, b g Camacho—Tides
73 **STEPHANIE SUNSHINE (IRE)**, 5, b m Dubai Destination (USA)—Shyanne (IRE)
74 **STORY OF FRIENDS (FR)**, 4, b g Kingsalsa (USA)—Royale Malinelle (FR)
75 **STOWIE BELLE (IRE)**, 5, b m Stowaway—Vast Consumption (IRE)
76 **SUPASUNDAE**, 8, b g Galileo (IRE)—Distinctive Look (IRE)
77 **TEXIE REXIE (IRE)**, 5, b g Scorpion (IRE)—Quel Bleu (IRE)
78 **THE BIRDIE CROWE (IRE)**, 7, b m Westerner—Be Mine Tonight (IRE)
79 **THE HOLY ONE (IRE)**, 5, b g Court Cave (IRE)—Vickate (IRE)
80 **THE PRINCETONIAN (IRE)**, 5, b m Oscar (IRE)—Stony View (IRE)
81 **THIRSTY WORK (IRE)**, 7, b g Robin des Champs (FR)—Koko Rose (IRE)
82 **TILLY'S CHILLI (IRE)**, 4, b f Excelebration (IRE)—Scotch Bonnet (IRE)
83 **TORCEDOR (IRE)**, 6, b g Fastnet Rock (AUS)—Magnolia Lane (IRE)
84 **WHISPERINTHEBREEZE (IRE)**, 5, gr ro g Kayf Tara—Silver Spinner
85 **WHYDAH**, 4, gr g Black Sam Bellamy (IRE)—Talk The Talk
86 **WINGS LIKE ARION (IRE)**, 6, b m Beneficial—Fruits de Mer (IRE)
87 **WISE DISGUISE (IRE)**, 4, b g Getaway (GER)—Native Craft (IRE)
88 **WOODLAND OPERA (IRE)**, 8, br g Robin des Champs (FR)—Opera Hat (IRE)

THREE-YEAR-OLDS

89 **ALPHA CENTAURI (IRE)**, gr f Mastercraftsman (IRE)—Alpha Lupi (IRE)
90 **BELLA FIGURA (IRE)**, b f Mastercraftsman (IRE)—Ebony Street (USA)
91 **BIT OF BANTER (IRE)**, b f Big Bad Bob (IRE)—Armoise
92 **BOHO (IRE)**, br g Big Bad Bob (IRE)—Are You Mine (IRE)
93 **BRICK BY BRICK (IRE)**, b g Big Bad Bob (IRE)—Pivka
94 **BROTHER BEAR (IRE)**, b c Kodiac—Hurricane Emma (USA)
95 **CRISTALE (IRE)**, ch f Dandy Man (IRE)—Radiant Energy (IRE)

MRS JESSICA HARRINGTON - Continued

96 **DANCE EMPEROR (IRE)**, b g Holy Roman Emperor (IRE)—Dance Avenue (IRE)
97 **DRAGON GIRL (IRE)**, ch f Dragon Pulse (IRE)—Raise Your Spirits (IRE)
98 **ECHO PARK (IRE)**, br f Elusive Pimpernel (USA)—Pershaan (IRE)
99 **EXTRASENSORY (IRE)**, b f Arcano (IRE)—Kindest
100 **FAUGHILL (IRE)**, gr f Lawman (FR)—Diamond Sky (IRE)
101 B c Elusive Quality (USA)—Fiesta Lady (ARG)
102 **HOUSE CALL (IRE)**, b f Clodovil (IRE)—Zalanga (IRE)
103 **ITS MY TURN (IRE)**, b f Dream Ahead (USA)—Majestic Dancer (IRE)
104 **KODI'S GIRL (IRE)**, b f Kodiac—Helen Wells (IRE)
105 **LANDSHARK**, b c Bated Breath—Tremelo Pointe (IRE)
106 **LOVELY MORNING (IRE)**, ch f Rip Van Winkle (IRE)—Inca Trail (USA)
107 **LOVING A BOOM (IRE)**, b g Acclamation—Elektra Marino
108 **MATTYMOLLS GAGA (IRE)**, ch c Dragon Pulse (IRE)—Clenaghcastle Lady (IRE)
109 **MINNIE HAHA (FR)**, gr f Style Vendome (FR)—Claveria (FR)
110 **NIKU (IRE)**, b f High Chaparral (IRE)—Strawberry Fledge (USA)
111 **PERSIAN LION (IRE)**, ch g Leroidesanimaux (BRZ)—Persian Memories (IRE)
112 **RISE OVER CLOUD (IRE)**, b f Raven's Pass (USA)—Mayenne (USA)
113 **SONG OF DUNES**, ch g Footstepsinthesand—English Ballet (IRE)
114 **STILL STANDING (IRE)**, ch c Mastercraftsman (IRE)—Il Palazzo (USA)
115 **SUMMERSEAT DREAM (IRE)**, b f Dream Ahead (USA)—Green Oasis (USA)
116 **THE KING (IRE)**, ch c Mastercraftsman (IRE)—Catch The Moon (IRE)
117 **TICKLED (IRE)**, b c Oasis Dream—Snowgal (IRE)
118 **WHIRLING DERVISH**, b c Camelot—Synergy (FR)
119 **WRITTEN WORD**, ch f Mount Nelson—Darmiana (USA)

TWO-YEAR-OLDS

120 **ALFONS WALDE (IRE)**, br c 17/2 Intikhab (USA)—Bobbie Soxer (IRE) (Pivotal) (2848)
121 B c 23/2 Acclamation—Always The Lady (Halling (USA)) (82000)
122 B f 13/3 Big Bad Bob (IRE)—Analysis (Dubai Destination (USA)) (22791)
123 B f 17/1 Mastercraftsman (IRE)—Apparel (IRE) (Cape Cross (IRE)) (81400)
124 B f 3/4 Kodiac—Arty Crafty (USA) (Arch (USA)) (146520)
125 **BOSTON BRUIN**, b c 2/3 Kodiac—Sovana (IRE) (Desert King (IRE)) (160000)
126 B c 10/2 Invincible Spirit (IRE)—Bratislava (Dr Fong (USA)) (244200)
127 B f 14/4 No Nay Never (USA)—Catch The Eye (IRE) (Oratorio (IRE)) (40700)
128 **CHICAS AMIGAS (IRE)**, b f 4/3 Dragon Pulse (IRE)—Veronica Falls (Medicean) (20350)
129 **DINGLE BAY (IRE)**, gr c 14/5 Alhebayeb (IRE)—Lady Rockfield (IRE) (Rock of Gibraltar (IRE)) (6511)
130 B f 10/2 Invincible Spirit (IRE)—Evita (Selkirk (USA)) (400000)
131 Br c 16/4 Kodiac—Fonda (USA) (Quiet American (USA)) (97680)
132 **FOR YOUR EYES**, b f 16/1 Iffraaj—Armoise (Sadler's Wells (USA))
133 B c 9/2 Showcasing—Golden Legacy (IRE) (Rossini (USA)) (65120)
134 B c 29/4 Dark Angel (IRE)—Gorband (USA) (Woodman (USA)) (130000)
135 B f 19/2 Acclamation—Irish Flower (IRE) (Zieten (USA)) (93609)
136 B c 2/2 Camelot—La Vinchina (GER) (Oasis Dream) (185000)
137 B f 14/5 Dragon Pulse (IRE)—Madda's Force (ITY) (Blu Air Force (IRE)) (25233)
138 Br c 2/5 Society Rock (IRE)—Maiepomai (IRE) (Kalanisi (IRE)) (34187)
139 **MARSHALL LAW (IRE)**, b c 17/3 Bated Breath—Art of Dance (Medicean) (72000)
140 B f 28/2 Australia—Mauralakana (FR) (Muhtathir)
141 **MR SECRETARY (IRE)**, b c 8/2 Sea The Stars (IRE)—Oui Say Oui (IRE) (Royal Applause) (183149)
142 B f 12/4 Dream Ahead (USA)—New Spirit (IRE) (Invincible Spirit (IRE))
143 B f 27/1 Invincible Spirit (IRE)—Night Fever (IRE) (Galileo (IRE)) (260000)
144 B f 3/5 Camelot—Notable (Zafonic (USA)) (61050)
145 B c 7/2 Kodiac—Oasis Sunset (IRE) (Oasis Dream) (220000)
146 B f 18/3 Dandy Man (IRE)—Ocean Myth (Acclamation) (24420)
147 B c 11/2 Bated Breath—Pennard (IRE) (High Chaparral (IRE)) (28000)
148 **PLANET VENUS (IRE)**, b f 15/2 Mastercraftsman (IRE)—Transhumance (IRE) (Galileo (IRE))
149 **POCOTALIGO**, b c 27/3 Helmet (AUS)—Pizzarra (Shamardal (USA)) (145000)
150 **PURSUIT OF MAGIC (IRE)**, b f 24/3 Kingman—Three Mysteries (IRE) (Linamix (FR))
151 B f 6/4 Toronado (IRE)—Rainbow's Edge (Rainbow Quest (USA)) (47211)
152 **RIDING THE STORM**, ch f 12/2 Fast Company (IRE)—Massada (Most Welcome)
153 B c 6/3 Invincible Spirit (IRE)—Rose de France (IRE) (Diktat) (126169)
154 B g 28/3 Zoffany (IRE)—Scripture (IRE) (Sadler's Wells (USA)) (16280)
155 **SNEAKY SNOOZE**, b f 12/5 Exceed And Excel (AUS)—Crossanza (IRE) (Cape Cross (IRE)) (32560)

MRS JESSICA HARRINGTON - Continued

156 Ch f 3/2 Born To Sea (IRE)—Snooze (IRE) (Marju (IRE)) (17907)
157 **SPARKLE'N'JOY (IRE),** ch f 27/3 Sepoy (AUS)—Silent Secret (IRE) (Dubai Destination (USA)) (32560)

Assistant Trainer: Mrs Emma Galway

---

262 **MISS GRACE HARRIS, Shirenewton**
Postal: **White House, Shirenewton, Chepstow, Gwent, NP16 6AQ**
Contacts: **MOBILE (07912) 359425**
E-MAIL gracehar ris90@gmail.com WEBSITE www.graceharrisracing.com

1 **BERRY DE CARJAC (FR),** 7, ch g Epalo (GER)—Miria Galanda (FR) **Mr C. Johnston**
2 **BOUTAN,** 5, gr m Tobougg (IRE)—High Tan **Mrs S. M. Maine**
3 **DIRTY DEXTER,** 7, b g Beat All (USA)—Redlands Charm **Wood Bank Racing**
4 **DOCTOR BONG,** 6, b g Sleeping Indian—Vax Rapide **Mr Ronald Davies & Mrs Candida Davies**
5 **FAINT HOPE,** 6, ch g Midnight Legend—Rhinestone Ruby **Mrs Elaine Tate & Partner**
6 **GRAMS AND OUNCES,** 11, b g Royal Applause—Ashdown Princess (IRE) **Grace Harris Racing**
7 **LIVING LEADER,** 9, b g Oasis Dream—Royal Jade **Ms M. Harris**
8 **MAGUIRE'S GLEN (IRE),** 10, b g Craigsteel—Next Venture (IRE) **Grace Harris Racing**
9 **MOOROVERTHEBRIDGE,** 4, b f Avonbridge—Spennymoor (IRE) **Grace Harris Racing**
10 **PADDY THE OSCAR (IRE),** 15, b g Oscar (IRE)—Parsonage **Michelle Harris & Deberah Lawton**
11 **STRAVINSKYS FLAME,** 5, b m Motivator—Firebird Rising (USA) **Wood Bank Racing**
12 **TALLY'S SONG,** 5, b m Piccolo—Talamahana **Paul & Ann de Weck**

THREE-YEAR-OLDS

13 Br f Avonbridge—Amazing Dream (IRE) **Grace Harris Racing**

TWO-YEAR-OLDS

14 B c 12/4 Burwaaz—Firebird Rising (USA) (Stravinsky (USA)) **Wood Bank Racing**

Other Owners: Mr R. I. D. Davies, Mrs C. M. Davies, Mrs A. De Weck, Miss G. Harris, Mrs D. L. S. Lawton, Mrs J. Maund-Powell, Mr T. J. Maund-Powell, Mrs E. Tate, P. L. de Weck.

Assistant Trainer: Michelle Harris

Jockey (NH): David England.

---

263 **MR RONALD HARRIS, Chepstow**
Postal: **Ridge House Stables, Earlswood, Chepstow, Monmouthshire, NP16 6AN**
Contacts: **PHONE (01291) 641689 FAX (01291) 641258 MOBILE (07831) 770899**
E-MAIL ridgehousestables.ltd@btinternet.com WEBSITE www.ronharrisracing.co.uk

1 **ALHABAN (IRE),** 12, gr g Verglas (IRE)—Anne Tudor (IRE) **Ridge House Stables Ltd**
2 **ARIZONA SNOW,** 6, b g Phoenix Reach (IRE)—Calgary **Ridge House Stables Ltd**
3 **BROADHAVEN HONEY (IRE),** 4, b f Harbour Watch (IRE)—
Honeymead (IRE) **M Doocey, S Doocey & P J Doocey**
4 **CASTANEA,** 6, ch g Pivotal—Invitee **Ridge House Stables Ltd**
5 **CORPORAL MADDOX,** 11, b g Royal Applause—Noble View (USA) **Ridge House Stables Ltd**
6 **DIAMOND VINE (IRE),** 10, b g Diamond Green (FR)—Glasnas Giant **Ridge House Stables Ltd**
7 **EYMET,** 6, m Avonbridge—Emma Peel **Mrs D. M. Barker**
8 **FANTASY JUSTIFIER (IRE),** 7, b g Arakan (USA)—Grandel **Ridge House Stables Ltd**
9 **GLAM'SELLE,** 4, b f Elnadim (USA)—Town And Gown **Robert & Nina Bailey**
10 **JUST GLAMOROUS (IRE),** 5, ch g Arcano (IRE)—Glamorous Air (IRE) **Robert & Nina Bailey**
11 **LADY MANGO (IRE),** 10, ch m Bahamian Bounty—Opera
12 **LIGHT FROM MARS,** 13, gr g Fantastic Light (USA)—Hylandra (USA) **Ridge House Stables Ltd**
13 **MAJESTIC HERO (IRE),** 6, b g Majestic Missile (IRE)—Xena (IRE) **Mrs Jackie Jarrett & Ridge House Stables**
14 **MARGARET BAKER,** 8, b m Windsor Castle—Daisy Leigh
15 **PEACE SEEKER,** 10, b g Oasis Dream—Mina **Ridge House Stables Ltd**
16 **POWERFUL DREAM (IRE),** 5, b m Frozen Power (IRE)—Noble View (USA) **Ridge House Stables Ltd**
17 **RAIN WIND AND FIRE (USA),** 6, ch g Eskendereya (USA)—Call Mariah (USA) **Ridge House Stables Ltd**
18 **RUPERTCAMBELLBLACK (IRE),** 4, b g Canford Cliffs (IRE)—Negotiate **Ridge House Stables Ltd**
19 **SECRET POTION,** 4, b g Stimulation (IRE)—Fiancee (IRE) **RHS Ltd, Mr R Fox, Mr P Charter**
20 **SELENA ROSE,** 5, b m Stimulation (IRE)—Dot Hill **Mr D. A. Evans**
21 **TEXAN NOMAD,** 6, ch g Nomadic Way (USA)—Texas Belle (IRE) **Mr J. W. Miles**

MR RONALD HARRIS - Continued

22 **THE DALEY EXPRESS (IRE)**, 4, b c Elzaam (AUS)—Seraphina (IRE) **The W.H.O. Society**
23 **TOP COP**, 9, b g Acclamation—Speed Cop **Ridge House Stables Ltd**
24 **UNDER THE COVERS**, 5, b m Stimulation (IRE)—Sakha **Ridge House Stables Ltd**
25 **UNION ROSE**, 6, b g Stimulation (IRE)—Dot Hill **Mr D. A. Evans**
26 **VET CERT (IRE)**, 10, b g Dr Massini (IRE)—Fernhill Queen (IRE) **Mr G. J. Barber**
27 **VINCENTTI (IRE)**, 8, b g Invincible Spirit (IRE)—Bint Al Balad (IRE) **Robert & Nina Bailey**
28 **VIOLA PARK**, 4, b g Aqlaam—Violette **Mr John & Margaret Hatherell & RHS Ltd**
29 **XCLUSIVE**, 8, b g Pivotal—Dance A Daydream **Monmouthshire Racing Club**

THREE-YEAR-OLDS

30 **ALRIGHT DAVE**, gr c Frozen Power (IRE)—Crazy Hazy (IRE) **Mrs A. Jones**
31 **BENTAYGA BOY**, gr c Hellvelyn—Lady Mango (IRE) **Mr L. Scadding**
32 **GLAMOROUS DREAM (IRE)**, b f Dark Angel (IRE)—Glamorous Air (IRE) **Robert & Nina Bailey**
33 **GLAMOROUS ROCKET (IRE)**, gr f Dark Angel (IRE)—Glamorous Spirit (IRE) **Robert & Nina Bailey**

TWO-YEAR-OLDS

34 B f 17/4 Elzaam (AUS)—Alinda (IRE) (Revoque (IRE)) (2034)
35 B gr f 25/2 Coach House (IRE)—Debutante Blues (USA) (Dubawi (IRE)) (3333)
36 B c 19/3 Lilbourne Lad (IRE)—Desert Location (Dubai Destination (USA)) (5697)
37 B f 4/1 Bungle Inthejungle—Fitrah (IRE) (Tamayuz) (6104)
38 B c 9/4 Camacho—Happy Talk (IRE) (Hamas (IRE)) (7732)
39 Gr c 18/4 Hellvelyn—Lady Mango (IRE) (Bahamian Bounty)
40 B c 28/2 Poet's Voice—Moon Over Water (IRE) (Galileo (IRE)) (14000) **H/J Racing**
41 B c 10/4 Dream Ahead (USA)—Queen Grace (IRE) (Choisir (AUS)) (23605)
42 B f 3/4 Alhebayeb (IRE)—Smokey Ryder (Bertolini) (10476)
43 B c 24/3 Foxwedge (AUS)—Violette (Observatory (USA)) (3500)

Other Owners: R. M. Bailey, Mrs J. H. Bailey, P. F. Charter, Mr J. C. Colley, Mr P. J. Doocey, Mr S. Doocey, Mr M. A. Doocey, Mr R. S. Fox, Mrs M. E. Hatherell, Mr R. A. J. Hatherell, Mr S. G. Hope, Mrs J. Jarrett, Mr K. W. Jarvis, Mr D. Thomas.

Jockey (flat): Luke Morris.

---

264   MR SHAUN HARRIS, Worksop
Postal: **Pinewood Stables, Carburton, Worksop, Nottinghamshire, S80 3BT**
Contacts: **PHONE** (01909) 470936 **FAX** (01909) 470936 **MOBILE** (07768) 950460
E-MAIL shaunharrisracing@yahoo.com **WEBSITE** www.shaunharrisracing.co.uk

1 **AZA RUN (IRE)**, 8, b g Hurricane Run (IRE)—Aza Wish (IRE) **Miss G. H. Ward**
2 **BARBARY PRINCE**, 6, ch g Dapper—La Vie Est Belle **C A Harris & Peter Dawson**
3 **CULLODEN**, 6, b g Kyllachy—Mamounia (USA) **Burflex (Scaffolding) Ltd**
4 **DELPHYNE**, 6, ch m Mount Nelson—Darmiana (USA) **Miss G. H. Ward**
5 **DOLPHIN VILLAGE (IRE)**, 8, b g Cape Cross (IRE)—Reform Act (USA) **Mr S. P. Giles**
6 **DUKE OF SONNING**, 6, ch g Duke of Marmalade (IRE)—Moonshadow **Miss G. H. Ward**
7 **HAY JAMES**, 7, gr g Proclamation (IRE)—Rose Bien **Mrs J. B. Gorman**
8 **HEAR THE CHIMES**, 9, b g Midnight Legend—Severn Air **Miss G. H. Ward**
9 **INVESTIGATION**, 4, gr g Rip Van Winkle—Syann (USA) **Mr B. P. Keogh**
10 **QUICK MONET (IRE)**, 5, b g Excellent Art—Clinging Vine (USA) **J. Morris**
11 **REALITY SHOW (IRE)**, 11, b g Cape Cross (IRE)—Really (IRE) **Miss G. H. Ward**
12 **ROB'S LEGACY**, 5, ch g Phoenix Reach (IRE)—Clumber Pursuits **www.nottinghamshireracing.co.uk (2)**
13 **ROY'S LEGACY**, 9, b h Phoenix Reach (IRE)—Chocolada **Notts Racing, S Mohammed & S Rowley**
14 **SHAW'S DILEMMA**, 4, bl f Sakhee (USA)—Donastrela (IRE) **Mr B. P. Keogh**
15 **SKATE ON**, 4, b gr f Malinas (GER)—Grainne Ni Maille **Mr B. P. Keogh**
16 **SONG OF LOVE (IRE)**, 6, b g Fastnet Rock (AUS)—Delicate Charm (IRE) **Burflex (Scaffolding) Ltd**

THREE-YEAR-OLDS

17 **HARBOUR SUNRISE**, b f Harbour Watch (IRE)—Nairobi (FR) **Mr C. Harris**

Assistant Trainer: Miss G. H. Ward

265 MISS LISA HARRISON, Wigton
Postal: **Cobble Hall, Aldoth, Nr Silloth, Cumbria, CA7 4NE**
Contacts: **PHONE (01697) 361753 FAX (01697) 342250 MOBILE (07725) 535554**
E-MAIL lisa@daharrison.co.uk

1 GINNY BRIG, 7, b m Great Palm (USA)—Royal Reference **Mrs E. Brockbank**
2 GREEN ZONE (IRE), 7, b g Bushranger (IRE)—Incense **T Hunter & D A Harrison Racing**
3 INSTINGTIVE (IRE), 7, b g Scorpion (IRE)—Fully Focused (IRE) **Abbadis Racing & D A Harrison Racing**
4 LADY VIVONA, 10, gr m Overbury (IRE)—Ladylliat (FR) **F Crone, T Hunter & D A Harrison Racing**
5 MILEVA ROLLER, 6, b m Multiplex—Alikat (IRE) **D A Harrison Racing**
6 MUWALLA, 11, b g Bahri (USA)—Easy Sunshine (IRE) **Bell Bridge Racing**
7 PRESENTED (IRE), 11, ch g Presenting—Rustic Court (IRE) **Abbadis Racing & D A Harrison Racing**
8 SOLWAY BERRY, 7, b m Overbury (IRE)—Solway Rose **D A Harrison Racing**
9 SOLWAY DANDY, 11, b g Danroad (AUS)—Solway Rose **D A Harrison Racing**
10 SOLWAY LARK, 7, b g Beat All (USA)—Solway Larkin (IRE) **D A Harrison Racing**
11 SOLWAY LIZZIE, 6, ch m Tobougg (IRE)—Solway Rose **D A Harrison Racing**
12 SOLWAY PALM, 8, gr g Great Palm (USA)—Solway Donal **D A Harrison Racing**
13 SOLWAY STORM (IRE), 8, gr g Indian River (FR)—The Grey Lady (IRE) **D A Harrison Racing**
14 SOLWAY SUNNY, 6, b m Double Trigger (IRE)—Solway Sunset **D A Harrison Racing**
15 SOLWAY TRIGGER, 9, b g Double Trigger (IRE)—Double Flight **Abbadis Racing & D A Harrison Racing**

Other Owners: Abbadis Racing Club, Mrs F. H. Crone, Mr D. Gillespie, Mr J. D. Graves, Mr R. A. Harrison, Mr W. H. Harrison, Mr T. Hunter, R. E. Jackson, Mrs L. Monkhouse, Mr J. H. Monkhouse.

266 MR BEN HASLAM, Middleham
Postal: **Castle Barn Cottage, Castle Hill, Middleham, Leyburn, North Yorkshire, DL8 4QW**
Contacts: **PHONE (01969) 624351 MOBILE (07764) 411660**
E-MAIL office@benhaslamracing.com WEBSITE www.benhaslamracing.com

1 CAMANCHE GREY (IRE), 7, gr g Camacho—Sense of Greeting (IRE) **Mrs C Barclay & Partners**
2 CASH AGAIN (FR), 6, br g Great Pretender (IRE)—Jeu de Lune (FR) **J. P. McManus**
3 CASTLE HILL CASSIE (IRE), 4, ch f Casamento (IRE)—
Angel Bright (IRE) **Ontoawinner, Trojan Horse, J Pak & Partner**
4 CUP FINAL (IRE), 9, ch g Presenting—Asian Maze (IRE) **J. P. McManus**
5 EPEIUS (IRE), 5, b g Arakan (USA)—Gilda Lilly (USA) **Ben Haslam Racing Syndicate**
6 EPONINA (IRE), 4, b f Zoffany (IRE)—Dame Rochelle (IRE) **Trojan Horse Partnership, Pak, Wellingham**
7 EVER SO MUCH (IRE), 9, b g Westerner—Beautiful World (IRE) **J. P. McManus**
8 FULL SHIFT (FR), 9, b g Ballingarry—Dansia (GER) **J. P. McManus**
9 GIANT REDWOOD (IRE), 6, b g Galileo (IRE)—Gwynn (IRE) **Mrs C. Barclay**
10 HI DANCER, 15, b g Medicean—Sea Music **Mr R A Tocher**
11 LADY LEKKI (IRE), 6, b m Champs Elysees—One Zero (USA)
12 MOON OVER RIO (IRE), 7, b m Captain Rio—Moonchild (GER) **Blue Lion Racing IX**
13 PRANCING OSCAR (IRE), 4, b g Sir Prancealot (IRE)—Beguiler **Middleham Park Racing**
14 REY LOOPY (IRE), 4, b g Lope de Vega (IRE)—Al Basar (USA) **Mr D Shapiro & Mrs C Barclay**
15 SAINT CUTHBERTS, 4, b g Shirocco (GER)—Gladys' Gal **Fishlake Commercial Motors**
16 THE DOORMAN (IRE), 9, b g King's Theatre (IRE)—Amber Light (IRE) **J. P. McManus**

THREE-YEAR-OLDS

17 CANUFEELTHELOVE, b f Sayif—Lady-Love **Blue Lion Racing IX**
18 CHERRY OAK (IRE), b f Society Rock (IRE)—Blue Holly (IRE) **Ontoawinner & Mr D Shapiro**
19 DISPLAYING AMBER, ch f Showcasing—Amber Lane **Middleham Park Racing**
20 ELYSEE STAR, b f Champs Elysees—Alushta **Go Alfresco Racing Partners**
21 FIRST BREATH, b g Bated Breath—Miss Rimex (IRE) **OnToAWinner & B Haslam**
22 FUNKADELIC, ch c Dandy Man (IRE)—Cape Elizabeth (IRE) **Mrs C Barclay, M T Buckley, K Cunningham**
23 LORD CAPRIO (IRE), b g Lord Shanakill (USA)—Azzurra du Caprio (IRE) **Blue Lion Racing IX**
24 MUSBAQ (USA), b g Union Rags (USA)—Eraada **Champagne Charlies Club**
25 PORRIMA (IRE), gr f Kodiac—El Morocco (USA) **Mr D Shapiro & Partners**
26 TIME FOR TREACLE, b f Sayif—Fiancee (IRE) **Mr D Shapiro, Michaelson, Milner, Rees**
27 Ch g Camacho—Zarara (USA) **Excel Racing**

TWO-YEAR-OLDS

28 B c 6/3 Lilbourne Lad (IRE)—Array of Stars (IRE) (Barathea (IRE)) (6190) **Mr R A Tocher**
29 Gr c 13/3 Gregorian (IRE)—Avoidance (USA) (Cryptoclearance (USA)) (32000) **Mr D Shapiro**

MR BEN HASLAM - Continued

30 B f 13/2 Nathaniel (IRE)—Hayyona (Multiplex) (30000) **Mr D Shapiro**
31 B c 22/4 Es Que Love (IRE)—Kathy Sun (IRE) (Intikhab (USA)) (35238)
32 B c 3/3 Zebedee—Sava Sunset (IRE) (Manduro (GER)) (12209) **Ben Haslam Racing Syndicate**
33 B c 6/4 Battle of Marengo (IRE)—Stereo Love (FR) (Champs Elysees) (28571) **Mr D Shapiro**
34 B c 5/3 Intikhab (USA)—The Oldladysays No (IRE) (Perugino (USA)) (9360) **Ben Haslam Racing Syndicate**

Other Owners: Mrs C. Barclay, Mrs S. J. Bosanko, Mr M. T. Buckley, Mr Kevin Cunningham, Miss Lynn Douglas, Mr John S. Feeney, Mrs J. M. Feeney, Mr C. D. Harrison, James Pak Racing, Mr R. P. B. Michaelson, Mrs S. Milner, Mr N. J. O'Brien, Mr James Pak, Mr T. S. Palin, Mr M. Prince, Mr Marcus Rees, Mr Daniel Shapiro, Mr P. A. Taylor, Mr G. Walker, Mrs N. J. C. Wellingham, Mr Geoff Wilson, Mr R. Young.

Assistant Trainer: Alice Haslam

---

267   **MR NIGEL HAWKE, Tiverton**
Postal: Thorne Farm, Stoodleigh, Tiverton, Devon, EX16 9QG
Contacts: PHONE (01884) 881666 MOBILE (07769) 295839
E-MAIL nigel@thornefarmracingltd.co.uk WEBSITE www.nigelhawkethornefarmracing.co.uk

1 **ALMINAR (IRE)**, 5, b g Arakan (USA)—Classic Magic (IRE) **Mr M. J. Phillips**
2 **ATLANTIC KING (GER)**, 5, b g King's Best (USA)—Atlantic High **Mr Jeff W. Hall & Thorne Farm Racing Ltd**
3 **BALLYMAGROARTY BOY (IRE)**, 5, b g Milan—Glazed Storm (IRE) **Nigel Hawke Racing Club & Partners**
4 **BLUE SIRE (FR)**, 7, b b g Day Flight—Hirlish (FR) **Mr M. J. Phillips**
5 **CALIN DU BRIZAIS (FR)**, 7, b g Loup Solitaire (USA)—Caline du Brizais (FR) **Pearce Bros Partnership**
6 **CAMRON DE CHAILLAC (FR)**, 6, br g Laverock (IRE)—Hadeel **Mrs K. Hawke & Mr William Simms**
7 **DEAUVILLE CRYSTAL (FR)**, 5, b m Raven's Pass (USA)—Top Crystal (IRE) **Mrs K. Hawke & Mr W. Simms**
8 **DECKERS DELIGHT**, 7, b m Tobougg (IRE)—Oleana (IRE) **Mr J A Vowles & Partners**
9 **DHAROOS (IRE)**, 5, ch g New Approach (IRE)—Cailiocht (USA) **Mr M. J. Phillips**
10 **FACTION**, 6, b g Champs Elysees—Belladera (IRE) **Mr J A Vowles & Partners**
11 **FARMER BOY (IRE)**, 5, b g Scorpion (IRE)—Absent Beauty (IRE) **Mrs K. Hawke & Mr W. Simms**
12 **GEORGINA JOY**, 5, b m Midnight Legend—First Katoune (FR) **Nigel Hawke Racing Club & Partners**
13 **GREYBOUGG**, 9, gr g Tobougg (IRE)—Kildee Lass **Di Vincenzo, Capps, Smith & Partner**
14 **HEART OF KERNOW (IRE)**, 6, b g Fruits of Love (USA)—Rathturtin Brief (IRE) **Mr K. Evans**
15 **JACK IN A BOX**, 8, b g Kayf Tara—La Dame Brune (FR) **Mr M. J. Phillips**
16 **JOHANOS (FR)**, 7, ch g Limnos (JPN)—Madame Johann (FR) **Mark Phillips & Partners**
17 **LADY MIX**, 5, gr m Fair Mix (IRE)—Et Voila **Mr & Mrs C Glover & Partners**
18 **LE MUSEE (FR)**, 5, b g Galileo (IRE)—Delicieuse Lady **Dragonfly Racing**
19 **LEVEL OF INTENSITY (IRE)**, 4, b c Intense Focus (USA)—Teofolina (IRE) **Milltown Racing & Partner**
20 **LORD BALLIM (FR)**, 8, ch g Balko (FR)—Lady Pauline (FR) **Mrjeffw.Hall,Mrsk.Hawke,Mrwilliamsimms**
21 **MEAD VALE**, 5, ch g Schiaparelli (GER)—Devon Peasant **Nigel Hawke Racing Club & Partners**
22 **MIDNIGHT REQUEST**, 6, b g Midnight Legend—Friendly Request **Midnight Request Partnership**
23 **MUTOONDRESDASHORSE**, 4, ch g Harbour Watch (IRE)—Mutoon (IRE) **Mutoondresdashorse Partnership**
24 **NACHI FALLS**, 5, ch g New Approach (IRE)—Lakuta (IRE) **Bryant,McMullan,Warren,Phillips&partner**
25 **NEROCHE STAR (FR)**, 5, b g Hannouma (IRE)—Cristal Springs (FR) **Thorne Farm Racing Limited**
26 **NIKAP (FR)**, 4, b f Kapgarde (FR)—Nika Glitters (FR)
27 **OURO BRANCO (FR)**, 5, b g Kapgarde (FR)—Dolce Vita Yug **Pearce Bros & Partner**
28 **PEARL ROYALE (IRE)**, 6, b m Robin des Champs (FR)—Dartmeet (IRE) **Air Cdre & Mrs M R Hallam & Partners**
29 **PETERGATE**, 7, b g Alhaarth (IRE)—Shamayel **Air Cdre & Mrs Martin Hallam**
30 **PHOENIX FIREBIRD**, 5, b m Flying Legend (USA)—Flamebird (IRE) **Air Cdre & Mrs Martin Hallam**
31 **PIROLO (IRE)**, 6, ch g Teofilo (IRE)—Zavaleta (IRE) **Twelfth Man Partnership 4 & Partner**
32 **POINT N SHOOT (IRE)**, 7, b g Broadway Flyer (USA)—Ali's Dipper (FR) **Mr J A Vowles & Partners**
33 **REJAAH**, 6, b m Authorized (IRE)—Dhan Dhana (IRE) **Mrs K. Hawke & Mr W. Simms**
34 **SAPPHIRE NOIRE (IRE)**, 5, b m Shantou (USA)—Cool Cool (FR) **Tomahawke**
35 **SCAFFOLD**, 5, ch g Apple Tree (IRE)—Ocarina Davis (FR) **Mr K Evans**
36 **SIENNA ROYALE (IRE)**, 4, b f Sholokhov (IRE)—Dartmeet (IRE) **Air Cdre & Mrs Martin Hallam**
37 **SIN SIN (IRE)**, 4, b f Intense Focus (USA)—Saor Sinn (IRE) **Mrs K. Hawke & Mr W. Simms**
38 **SIR MIX**, 5, gr g Fair Mix (IRE)—Highland Cherry **Mr & Mrs C Glover**
39 **SPEREDEK (FR)**, 7, b br g Kapgarde (FR)—Sendamagic (FR) **Kapinhand**
40 **STORMY BLUES**, 4, b g Sepoy (AUS)—Miss Brown To You (IRE) **Mr M. J. Phillips**
41 **TAKE A BREAK (FR)**, 7, b br g Sunday Break (JPN)—Popee (FR) **Pearce Bros Partnership**
42 **TEQUILA SECRET (IRE)**, 7, b m Kayf Tara—Jubilee Queen (IRE) **The Time Enough Stud Partnership**

MR NIGEL HAWKE - Continued

Other Owners: Mrs K. M. Brain, Mrs R. C. V. Brook, Mr S. C. Browne, S. H. Bryant, Mr M. G. Capps, Mr M. Di-Vincenzo, Mr P. A. Docker, Mr F. G. Flanagan, Mr C. S. Glover, Mrs K. J. Glover, Mr J. H. Gumbley, Mr J. W. Hall, Air Commodore M. R. Hallam, Mrs M. Hallam, Mrs K. Hawke, Mr N. J. Hawke, Mr W. M. Izaby-White, Mr T. B. James, Mrs H. M. Jefferies, Mr P. Mason, N. J. McMullan, Milltown Racing, The Nigel Hawke Racing Club, Mr D. A. Pearce, Mr M. Powell, Mr W. J. Simms, Mr P. A. Sims, Mrs D. E. Smith, Twelfth Man Partnership 4, Mr J. A. Vowles, Mrs J. J. A. J. D. Warren, Mr S. W. H. Winfield, Mrs J. Winfield.

Assistant Trainers: Katherine Hawke & Edward Buckley

Jockey (NH): James Best, Sean Bowen, Aidan Coleman, Danny Cook. **Conditional:** James Bowen, Ciaran Gethings. **Apprentice:** Tom Buckley. **Amateur:** Mr Kieran Buckley.

---

268 **MR MICHAEL HAWKER, Chippenham**
Postal: **Battens Farm, Allington, Chippenham, Wiltshire, SN14 6LT**

1 BETTY BATTENS, 5, ch m Tobougg (IRE)—Where's My Slave (IRE) **Mr M. R. E. Hawker**
2 CECILE DE VOLANGES, 10, ch m Kheleyf (USA)—Fyvie **Mr M. R. E. Hawker**
3 LEMONADE DRINKER, 5, gr g Fair Mix (IRE)—Sheknowsyouknow **Mr M. R. E. Hawker**

---

269 **MR RICHARD HAWKER, Frome**
Postal: **Rode Farm, Rode, Bath, Somerset, BA11 6QQ**
Contacts: **PHONE (01373) 831479**

1 BEAUJOLAIS BOB, 10, gr g Grape Tree Road—Charliebob **R. G. B. Hawker**
2 BILLY CONGO (IRE), 11, b br g Zagreb (USA)—Delicate Child (IRE) **Mr R. C. Williams**
3 GENTLEMAN FARMER, 6, ch g Tobougg (IRE)—Sweet Shooter **R. G. B. Hawker**
4 PARLOUR MAID, 7, gr m Dr Massini (IRE)—Charliebob **R. G. B. Hawker**

---

270 **MR JONATHAN HAYNES, Brampton**
Postal: **Cleugh Head, Low Row, Brampton, Cumbria, CA8 2JB**
Contacts: **PHONE (01697) 746253 MOBILE (07771) 511471**

1 BERTIELICIOUS, 10, b g And Beyond (IRE)—Pennepoint **J. C. Haynes**
2 BEYONDPERFECTION, 7, b m And Beyond (IRE)—Pennepoint **J. C. Haynes**
3 BEYONDTEMPTATION, 10, ch m And Beyond (IRE)—Tempted **J. C. Haynes**
4 BEYONDTHEFLAME, 8, b m And Beyond (IRE)—Flame of Zara **J. C. Haynes**
5 GETONSAM, 6, ch g Black Sam Bellamy (IRE)—Pennepoint **J. C. Haynes**

---

271 **MISS SALLY HAYNES, Richmond**
Postal: **Western House Stables, East Road, Melsonby, Richmond, North Yorkshire, DL10 5NF**
Contacts: **PHONE (01325) 339964 MOBILE (07711) 488341**

1 ANOTHER GO (IRE), 5, gr g Strategic Prince—Golden Rose (GER) **Mr J. A. Swinbank Racing**
2 ARAMIST (IRE), 8, gr g Aussie Rules (USA)—Mistic Sun **Mr R. C. Penney & Partner**
3 AUSTERITY (IRE), 5, br g Elnadim (USA)—Royal Reprieve (FR) **Bluegrass Thoroughbreds 4**
4 BAHKIT (IRE), 4, b g Intikhab (USA)—Pink Moon (IRE) **Mrs J. Porter**
5 BLUE VISION (FR), 5, ch g Loup Breton (IRE)—Blueprint **D. G. Clayton Racing**
6 BUSY STREET, 6, b g Champs Elysees—Allegro Viva (USA) **Mrs T. Blackett**
7 CODESHARE, 6, b g Dansili—Clepsydra **Mr J. A. Swinbank Racing**
8 DANCIN ALPHA, 7, ch g Bahamian Bounty—Phoebe Woodstock (IRE) **Partnership Terminated**
9 DARK RULER (IRE), 9, b g Dark Angel (IRE)—Gino Lady (IRE) **Kenneth Walters Racing**
10 DARKSIDEOFTARNSIDE (IRE), 4, b g Intense Focus (USA)—Beautiful Dancer (IRE) **Bluegrass Thoroughbreds 4**
11 DEEP RESOLVE (IRE), 7, b g Intense Focus (USA)—I'll Be Waiting **Panther Racing Ltd**
12 DIVINE PORT (USA), 8, b g Arch (USA)—Out of Reach **Mr J. A. Swinbank Racing**
13 DOMINANNIE (IRE), 5, b m Paco Boy (IRE)—English Rose (USA) **Mrs Mrs J. Forrest**
14 FIDRA BAY (IRE), 5, b m Roderic O'connor (IRE)—Halicardia **Partnership Terminated**
15 GO GEORGE GO (IRE), 5, gr g Zebedee—La Bella Grande (IRE) **Mr J. A. Swinbank Racing**

MISS SALLY HAYNES - Continued

16 **HAPPY HOLLOW**, 6, b g Beat Hollow—Dombeya (IRE) **Mr J. A. Swinbank Racing**
17 **INDIAN HARBOUR**, 5, b g Indian Haven—Hawait Al Barr **Kenneth Walters Racing**
18 **LAST CHANCE PADDY (USA)**, 4, gr g Paddy O'prado (USA)—
                              Mizzcan'tbewrong (USA) **Mr J. A. Swinbank Racing**
19 **LOPES DANCER (IRE)**, 6, b g Lope de Vega (IRE)—Ballet Dancer (IRE) **D. G. Clayton Racing**
20 **LOVE CANDY (IRE)**, 4, b f Canford Cliffs (IRE)—Love Thirty **Mr J. A. Swinbank Racing**
21 **MICKLEGATE RUN**, 7, b g Tiger Hill (IRE)—Mamoura (IRE) **Mr J. A. Swinbank Racing**
22 **MISSCARLETT (IRE)**, 4, b f Red Rocks (IRE)—Coimbra (USA) **Mrs J. Porter**
23 **ON THE ROX (IRE)**, 5, b g Fastnet Rock (AUS)—Dance Parade (USA) **Mr J. A. Swinbank Racing**
24 **SHULAMMITE MAN (IRE)**, 5, ch g Arcano (IRE)—Shulammite Woman (IRE) **Bluegrass Thoroughbreds 4**
25 **STANARLEY PIC**, 7, b g Piccolo—Harlestone Lady **The Twopin Partnership**
26 **STAR OF LANKA (IRE)**, 4, b g Zoffany (IRE)—Indian Bounty **Mr J. A. Swinbank Racing**
27 **STECCANDO (IRE)**, 5, b g Lawman (FR)—Second Act **Mrs J. Porter**
28 **TEN TREES**, 8, b m Millkom—Island Path (IRE) **Ray Spencer & Partner**
29 **VIRNON**, 7, b g Virtual—Freedom Song **Mrs J. Porter**
30 **YOUNG SUNSHINE (IRE)**, 5, b m Pour Moi (IRE)—Garra Molly (IRE) **Partnership Terminated**
31 **ZEALOUS (IRE)**, 5, br g Intense Focus (USA)—Velvet Kiss (IRE) **Mrs J. Porter**

THREE-YEAR-OLDS

32 **FINAL GO**, b g Equiano (FR)—Ipsa Loquitur **Mr J. A. Swinbank Racing**
33 B f High Chaparral (IRE)—Keystone Gulch (USA)
34 Ch g Nathaniel (IRE)—Perse

Other Owners: Mrs T. Blackett, Mr D. G. Clayton, Mrs J. Forrest, Miss S. R. Haynes, Panther Racing Limited, Mr R. C. Penney, Mrs J. Porter, Mr R. Spencer, Mr J. A. Swinbank, Mr I. S. Tweddall, Mr K. Walters, Miss P. A. Ware.

---

272 MISS GAIL HAYWOOD, Moretonhampstead
Postal: **Stacombe Farm, Doccombe, Moretonhampstead, Newton Abbot, Devon, TQ13 8SS**
Contacts: PHONE **(01647) 440826**
E-MAIL **gail@gghracing.com** WEBSITE **www.gghracing.com**

1 **AMOUR D'OR**, 7, b m Winged Love (IRE)—Diletia **Miss G. G. Haywood**
2 **CHICA RAPIDA**, 6, ch m Paco Boy (IRE)—Tora Bora **Mrs J. Bland**
3 **DANCING GREY**, 5, gr m Dream Eater (IRE)—State of Grace **Mrs J. B. Floyd-Walker & Mrs Jane Oliver**
4 **FLEUR DU WELD**, 10, ch m Weld—Midnight Walker **Mrs J. B. Floyd-Walker**
5 **HIJA**, 7, b m Avonbridge—Pantita **Haywood's Heroes**
6 **QUEENSLAND BETTY**, 10, b m Kayf Tara—Ruby Star (IRE) **Miss G. G. Haywood**
7 **RICHARDOFDOCCOMBE (IRE)**, 12, b g Heron Island (IRE)—Strike Again (IRE) **Phillip & Mary Creese**
8 **RUSSIAN'S LEGACY**, 6, b m Kayf Tara—Ruby Star (IRE) **Miss G. G. Haywood**
9 **SECRET PALACE**, 6, ch m Pastoral Pursuits—Some Sunny Day **Phillip & Mary Creese**

Other Owners: Gp Cpt M. W. Haywood MBE, Mr M. J. Haywood.

Assistant Trainer: William McColl

Conditional: Kieron Edgar.

---

273 MR PETER HEDGER, Eastergate
Postal: **Melcroft, Eastergate Lane, Eastergate, Chichester, West Sussex, PO20 3SJ**
Contacts: PHONE **(01243) 543863** FAX **(01243) 543913** MOBILE **(07860) 209448**
E-MAIL **hedgerlaura@hotmail.com**

1 **BRIDGE BUILDER**, 8, b g Avonbridge—Amazing Dream (IRE) **P C F Racing Ltd/Ron Smith Recycling Ltd**
2 **C'EST NO MOUR (GER)**, 5, b g Champs Elysees—C'est L'Amour (GER) **Mr D. Wilbrey**
3 **CONTINUUM**, 9, b br g Dansili—Clepsydra **P C F Racing Ltd**
4 **FRANCO'S SECRET**, 7, b g Sakhee's Secret—Veronica Franco **P C F Racing Ltd**
5 **KAAFEL (IRE)**, 9, b g Nayef (USA)—Tafaani (IRE) **P C F Racing Ltd**
6 **MR MAC**, 4, b g Makfi—Veronica Franco **P C F Racing Ltd**
7 **MUSICAL FIRE**, 4, b f Equiano (FR)—Music In Exile (USA) **P C F Racing Ltd**
8 **SHACKLED N DRAWN (USA)**, 6, b g Candy Ride (ARG)—
                          Cajun Flash (USA) **Ron Smith Recycling Ltd/Mr P. R. Hedger**

MR PETER HEDGER - Continued

9 **SILENT ECHO**, 4, b g Oasis Dream—Quiet **P C F Racing Ltd**
10 **TRALEE HILLS**, 4, b g Mount Nelson—Distant Waters **P C F Racing Ltd**
11 **WHIPCRACKAWAY (IRE)**, 9, b g Whipper (USA)—Former Drama (USA) **Mr P. R. Hedger & P C F Racing Ltd**

TWO-YEAR-OLDS

12 **SISTER'S ACT**, b f 23/1 Equiano (FR)—Sister Guru (Ishiguru (USA)) (5714) **Mr P. R. Hedger & P C F Racing Ltd**

Other Owners: P. R. Hedger, Ron Smith Recycling Ltd.

Assistant Trainer: Mr Shaun Keightley (01252) 850016

Jockey (flat): Charles Bishop. **Jockey (NH):** Leighton Aspell.

---

274 **MR NICKY HENDERSON, Lambourn**
Postal: **Seven Barrows, Lambourn, Hungerford, Berkshire, RG17 8UH**
Contacts: **PHONE (01488) 72259 MOBILE (07774) 608168**
E-MAIL nj.henderson@virgin.net

1 **ALPH (IRE)**, 4, b g Gold Well—She's Our Banker (IRE) **Mrs P. J. Pugh**
2 **ALTIOR (IRE)**, 8, b g High Chaparral (IRE)—Monte Solaro (IRE) **Mrs P. J. Pugh**
3 **APPLE'S SHAKIRA (FR)**, 4, b f Saddler Maker (IRE)—Apple's For Ever (FR) **Mr J. P. McManus**
4 **ARMAANS WISH (IRE)**, 7, ch g Presenting—Pretty Puttens (IRE) **Middleham Park Racing LXIII & K Sohi**
5 **BADEN (FR)**, 7, gr g Martaline—Ma Sonate (USA) **C. O. P. Hanbury**
6 **BALLINURE (IRE)**, 8, b g Alkaadhem—Christy's Pride (IRE) **Mrs M. Parker**
7 **BARDD (IRE)**, 6, b g Dylan Thomas (IRE)—Zarawa **Elite Racing Club**
8 **BARMAN (FR)**, 7, b g Racinger (FR)—Koscina (FR) **The Bartenders**
9 **BE THAT AS IT MAY**, 5, b m Milan—Darbela (IRE) **Mr J. P. McManus**
10 **BEAT THAT (IRE)**, 10, b g Milan—Knotted Midge (IRE) **Mr J. P. McManus**
11 **BEFORE MIDNIGHT**, 5, ch g Midnight Legend—Lady Samantha **Walters Plant Hire & James & Jean Potter**
12 **BEWARE THE BEAR (IRE)**, 8, b g Shantou (USA)—Native Bid (IRE) **G. B. Barlow**
13 **BEYONDTHESTORM (IRE)**, 5, b g Flemensfirth (USA)—Blue Gale (IRE) **Seven Barrows Limited**
14 **BIG ROBIN (IRE)**, 6, b m Robin des Champs—Melodique **Grech & Parkin**
15 **BRAIN POWER (IRE)**, 7, b g Kalanisi (IRE)—Blonde Ambition (IRE) **M. A. C. Buckley**
16 **BRAVE EAGLE (IRE)**, 6, b g Yeats—Sinful Pleasure (IRE) **R. M. Kirkland**
17 4, B f Getaway (GER)—Buck's Blue (FR) **Mrs M. Parker**
18 **BURBANK (IRE)**, 6, b g Yeats—Spring Swoon (IRE) **R. A. Bartlett**
19 **BURROWS EDGE (FR)**, 5, b g Martaline—La Vie de Boitron (FR) **M. A. C. Buckley**
20 **BUVEUR D'AIR (FR)**, 7, b g Crillon (FR)—History (FR) **Mr J. P. McManus**
21 **CALL ME LORD (FR)**, 5, b br g Slickly (FR)—Sosa (GER) **Mr Simon Munir & Mr Isaac Souede**
22 **CASABLANCA MIX (FR)**, 6, ch m Shirocco (GER)—Latitude (FR) **Rutland Rascals**
23 **CHAMP (IRE)**, 6, b g King's Theatre (IRE)—China Sky (IRE) **Mr J. P. McManus**
24 **CHAMPAGNE EXPRESS**, 8, b g Kalanisi (IRE)—Marvellous Dream (FR) **Owners Group 008**
25 **CHARLI PARCS (FR)**, 5, b g Anabaa Blue—Ella Parcs (FR) **Mr J. P. McManus**
26 **CHARMING ZEN (FR)**, 6, gr g Youmzain (FR)—Nioumoun (FR) **Sullivan Bloodstock Limited**
27 **CHEF DES OBEAUX (FR)**, 6, b g Saddler Maker (IRE)—O Dame de Gene (FR) **Sullivan Bloodstock Limited**
28 **CHRISTMAS IN APRIL (FR)**, 6, b g Crillon (FR)—Similaresisploldofa (FR) **Mr J. Palmer-Brown**
29 **CLAIMANTAKINFORGAN (FR)**, 6, b g Great Pretender (IRE)—Taquine d'estrees (FR) **Grech & Parkin**
30 **COLONIAL DREAMS (IRE)**, 6, b g Westerner—Dochas Supreme (IRE) **C. N. Barnes**
31 **COMELY**, 6, b m Midnight Legend—Belle Magello (FR) **Her Majesty The Queen**
32 **COMMANDER MILLER**, 4, b g Shirocco (GER)—Milliegait **HP Racing Commander Miller**
33 **COOL MACAVITY (IRE)**, 10, b g One Cool Cat (USA)—Cause Celebre (IRE) **C. O. P. Hanbury**
34 **COSMOS DES OBEAUX (FR)**, 6, b g Spanish Moon (USA)—Kore des Obeaux (FR) **Sullivan Bloodstock Limited**
35 **COUNTISTER (FR)**, 6, b m Smadoun (FR)—Tistairly (FR) **Mr J. P. McManus**
36 **CRACKING DESTINY (IRE)**, 5, b g Dubai Destination (USA)—Cracking Gale (IRE) **Grech & Parkin**
37 **CULTIVATOR**, 7, b g Alflora (IRE)—Angie Marinie **Kimmins Family & Friends**
38 **DAME DE COMPAGNIE (FR)**, 5, b m Lucarno (USA)—Programmee (FR) **Mr J. P. McManus**
39 **DAPHNE DU CLOS (FR)**, 5, b m Spanish Moon (USA)—Katarina du Clos (FR) **Sullivan Bloodstock Limited**
40 **DARIUS DES BOIS (FR)**, 5, b g Great Pretender (IRE)—Palafixe (FR) **Sullivan Bloodstock Limited**
41 **DAYS OF HEAVEN (FR)**, 8, b br g Saint des Saints (FR)—Daramour (FR) **Mrs G. M. Johnston**
42 **DIESE DES BIEFFES (FR)**, 5, gr g Martaline—Chanel du Berlais (FR) **Sullivan Bloodstock Limited**
43 **DIVINE SPEAR (IRE)**, 7, b g Oscar (IRE)—Testaway (IRE) **Middleham Park Racing LXII**
44 **DOUX PRETENDER (FR)**, 5, b g Great Pretender (IRE)—Lynnka (FR) **Sullivan Bloodstock Limited**

MR NICKY HENDERSON - Continued

45 **DOWNTOWN GETAWAY (IRE)**, 5, b g Getaway (GER)—Shang A Lang (IRE) **Mr John Turner**
46 **DU DESTIN (FR)**, 5, gr g Fuisse (FR)—Parenthese (FR) **Middleham Park Racing V**
47 **DUKE DEBARRY (IRE)**, 7, b g Presenting—Blue Dante (IRE) **Middleham Park Racing CIX**
48 **ESPOIR DE ROUHET (FR)**, 4, b g Special Kaldoun (IRE)—Kermesse d'estruval (FR) **Middleham Park Racing CIV**
49 **FIXE LE KAP (FR)**, 6, gr g Kapgarde (FR)—Lady Fix (FR) **Mr Simon Munir & Mr Isaac Souede**
50 **FLY AGAIN**, 4, ch f Malinas (GER)—Spring Flight **Her Majesty The Queen**
51 **FLY CAMP (IRE)**, 8, gr g Westerner—Pearlsforthegirls **The Blue Bar Partnership**
52 **FOLLOW THE BEAR (IRE)**, 6, b g King's Theatre—Mrs Dempsey (IRE) **G. B. Barlow**
53 **FOREVER FIELD (IRE)**, 8, b g Beneficial—Sarahs Reprive (IRE) **R. M. Kirkland**
54 **FRENCH CRUSADER (FR)**, 5, b g Kapgarde (FR)—Largesse (FR) **R. M. Kirkland**
55 **FULL BORE (IRE)**, 5, b g Milan—Senora Snoopy (IRE) **The Albatross Club**
56 **GALLAHERS CROSS (IRE)**, 6, b g Getaway (GER)—Raheen Lady (IRE) **Grech & Parkin**
57 **GANACHE (IRE)**, 5, b g Scorpion (IRE)—Spring Baloo (IRE) **Mr T. J. Hemmings**
58 **GOLD BLADE (IRE)**, 5, b g Gold Well—Supreme Evening (IRE) **Lady Dulverton**
59 **GOLD PRESENT (IRE)**, 8, br g Presenting—Ouro Preto **Mr & Mrs J. D. Cotton**
60 **GRAPEVINE (IRE)**, 5, b g Lilbourne Lad (IRE)—High Vintage (IRE) **Mrs J. K. Powell**
61 **HAUL AWAY (IRE)**, 5, b g Stowaway—Lisacul Queen (IRE) **R. M. Kirkland**
62 **I CAN'T EXPLAIN (IRE)**, 5, b g Getaway (GER)—Dr Sandra (IRE) **Julie & David R Martin & Dan Hall**
63 **IGOR**, 5, b g Presenting—Stravinsky Dance **MHankin CNoell MenHolding RWaley-Cohen**
64 **INDIAN HAWK (IRE)**, 6, b g Westerner—Yorkshire Girl (IRE) **Mr Simon Munir & Mr Isaac Souede**
65 **JEN'S BOY (IRE)**, 8, b g Malinas (GER)—Friendly Craic (IRE) **Middleham Park Racing CV**
66 **JENKINS (IRE)**, 6, b g Azamour (IRE)—Aladiyna (IRE) **Pump & Plant Services Ltd**
67 **JOSSES HILL (IRE)**, 10, b g Winged Love (IRE)—Credora Storm (IRE) **Mr Alan Spence**
68 4, B g Kalanisi (IRE)—Katariya (IRE) **Michael Buckley & Mark Blandford**
69 **KAYF GRACE**, 8, b m Kayf Tara—Potter's Gale (IRE) **James & Jean Potter**
70 **KEEN ON**, 4, b g Kayf Tara—Romantic Dream **Her Majesty The Queen**
71 **KILCREA VALE (IRE)**, 8, b g Beneficial—Inflation (IRE) **Mr Alan Spence**
72 **KINGS RYDE**, 6, b g King's Theatre (IRE)—Ryde Back **Miss R. C. Tregaskes**
73 **KNIGHTHOOD**, 4, b g Delegator—Love Roi (ITY) **Lady Tennant**
74 4, B c Milan—Knotted Midge (IRE) **Mr J. P. McManus**
75 **KOTKIKOVA (FR)**, 7, gr m Martaline—Kotkita (FR) **Mr J. P. McManus**
76 **KUPATANA (IRE)**, 5, b m Westerner—Kildea Cailin (IRE) **Grech & Parkin**
77 **L'AMI SERGE (IRE)**, 8, b g King's Theatre (IRE)—La Zingarella (IRE) **Mr Simon Munir & Mr Isaac Souede**
78 **LAUGHING LUIS**, 4, b g Authorized (IRE)—Leitzu (IRE) **J. C. Sillett**
79 **LAURIUM**, 8, ch g Gold Away (IRE)—Silver Peak (FR) **The Ten From Seven**
80 **LE DAUPHIN (IRE)**, 7, b g Robin des Champs (FR)—Miss Denman (IRE) **Lady Tennant**
81 **LIGNY (FR)**, 5, ch g Fuisse (FR)—Light Wave (FR) **Pump & Plant Services Ltd**
82 **LOUGH DERG FARMER (IRE)**, 6, b g Presenting—Maryiver (IRE) **Grech & Parkin**
83 **LOUGH DERG SPIRIT (IRE)**, 6, b g Westerner—Sno-Cat Lady (IRE) **Grech & Parkin**
84 **LOVEHERANDLEAVEHER (IRE)**, 6, b br m Winged Love (IRE)—Rowdy Exit (IRE) **Mr Alan Spence**
85 **LUST FOR GLORY (IRE)**, 5, b m Getaway (GER)—Maisie Presenting (IRE) **Grech & Parkin**
86 **MAESTRO ROYAL**, 9, b g Doyen (IRE)—Close Harmony **Mrs R. H. Brown**
87 **MALACHITE**, 5, gr g Malinas (GER)—Kali **Mr D. H. Low**
88 **MALTON ROSE (IRE)**, 7, b g Milan—Pharney Fox (IRE) **Galopp Syndicate Ltd**
89 4, Ch f Sholokhov (IRE)—Maryota (FR) **Liam Breslin & Jonathon Duffy**
90 **MELANGERIE**, 6, b m Fair Mix (IRE)—Angie Marinie **The Barrow Boys**
91 **MIGHT BITE (IRE)**, 9, b g Scorpion (IRE)—Knotted Midge (IRE) **The Knot Again Partnership**
92 **MILL GREEN**, 6, b g Black Sam Bellamy (IRE)—Ceilidh Royal **Mrs R. H. Brown**
93 **MISTER FISHER (IRE)**, 4, b g Jeremy (USA)—That's Amazing (IRE) **James and Jean Potter**
94 **MONBEG LEGEND**, 8, b g Midnight Legend—Reverse Swing **Eventmasters Racing**
95 **MONBEG ZENA (IRE)**, 6, ch m Flemensfirth (USA)—Mandys Gold (IRE) **Sullivan Bloodstock Limited**
96 **MORNING VICAR (IRE)**, 5, b g Beneficial—Mary's Little Vic (IRE) **The Parishioners**
97 **MR WHIPPED (IRE)**, 5, br g Beneficial—Dyrick Daybreak (IRE) **Grech & Parkin**
98 **MR WOODY (IRE)**, 4, b g Shantou (USA)—She's On The Case (IRE) **Mrs E. Roberts**
99 **MY TENT OR YOURS (IRE)**, 11, b g Desert Prince (IRE)—Spartan Girl (IRE) **Mr J. P. McManus**
100 **NO HIDING PLACE (IRE)**, 5, b g Stowaway—Subtle Gem (IRE) **HP Racing No Hiding Place**
101 **NONESUCH (IRE)**, 4, b f Shirocco (GER)—N'avoue Jamais (FR) **Mr R. B. Waley-Cohen**
102 **O O SEVEN (IRE)**, 8, b g Flemensfirth (USA)—Kestral Heights (IRE) **C. O. P. Hanbury**
103 **OK CORRAL (IRE)**, 8, b g Mahler—Acoola (IRE) **Mr J. P. McManus**
104 **ON THE BLIND SIDE (IRE)**, 6, b g Stowaway—Such A Set Up (IRE) **Mr Alan Spence**
105 **PACIFIC DE BAUNE (FR)**, 5, gr g Al Namix (FR)—Perle De Baune (FR) **Mr & Mrs Sandy Orr**
106 **PALIXANDRE (FR)**, 4, b g Kapgarde (FR)—Palmeriade (FR) **Seven Barrows Limited**
107 **PERCY STREET**, 5, br g Sir Percy—Star of Gibraltar **Grech & Parkin**
108 **POLLY'S PURSUIT (IRE)**, 6, br m Westerner—Miss Denman (IRE) **Lady Tennant**
109 **POUGNE BOBBI (FR)**, 7, b br g Protektor (GER)—Amicus **Mr J. Meyer**

MR NICKY HENDERSON - Continued

110 **PREMIER BOND**, 8, b g Kayf Tara—Celtic Native (IRE) **Middleham Park Racing XI**
111 **PROTEK DES FLOS (FR)**, 6, b g Protektor (GER)—Flore de Chantenay (FR) **Mr J. P. McManus**
112 **PYM (IRE)**, 5, b g Stowaway—Liss Rua (IRE) **Mrs P. J. Pugh**
113 **RATHER BE (IRE)**, 7, b g Oscar (IRE)—Irish Wedding (IRE) **Matt & Lauren Morgan**
114 **RATHHILL (IRE)**, 5, b g Getaway (GER)—Bella Venezia (IRE) **Mr J. P. McManus**
115 **REBEL COMMANDER (IRE)**, 6, b g Flemensfirth (USA)—Pharney Fox (IRE) **The Albatross Club**
116 **REIGNING SUPREME (IRE)**, 7, b g Presenting—Gli Gli (IRE) **M. A. C. Buckley**
117 **RIVER WYLDE (IRE)**, 7, b g Oscar (IRE)—Clarin River (IRE) **Grech & Parkin**
118 **ROYAL IRISH HUSSAR (IRE)**, 8, b g Galileo (IRE)—Adjalisa (IRE) **C. O. P. Hanbury**
119 **ROYAL RUBY**, 6, b g Yeats (IRE)—Close Harmony **Mrs R. H. Brown**
120 **SANTINI**, 6, b g Milan—Tinagoodnight (FR) **Mr & Mrs R. G. Kelvin-Hughes**
121 **SETTIE HILL (USA)**, 5, b g Cape Blanco (IRE)—Claire Soleil (USA) **Michael Buckley & Lord Vestey**
122 **SHANA TOVA**, 5, b m Shantou (USA)—Milanella (USA) **Orbit Performance**
123 **SIGN OF A VICTORY (IRE)**, 5, b g Kayf Tara—Irish Wedding (IRE) **Matt & Lauren Morgan**
124 **SIMONIA (IRE)**, 5, gr m Yeats (IRE)—Dusty Too **S. P. Tindall**
125 **SOUL EMOTION (FR)**, 5, b g Martaline—Second Emotion (FR) **Mr & Mrs J. D. Cotton**
126 **STORM OF INTRIGUE (IRE)**, 6, b g Oscar (IRE)—Storminoora (IRE) **Mr Oscar Singh & Miss Priya Purewal**
127 **STOWAWAY MAGIC (IRE)**, 7, b g Stowaway—Irish Mystics (IRE) **Grech & Parkin**
128 **STYLE DE GARDE (FR)**, 4, b g Kapgarde (FR)—Anowe de Jelois (FR) **Highclere Thoroughbred Racing - Style**
129 **SUGAR BARON (IRE)**, 8, b g Presenting—Shuil Oilean (IRE) **Anthony Speelman**
130 **SUNSHADE**, 5, b m Sulamani (IRE)—Spring Flight **Her Majesty The Queen**
131 **TAKE TO HEART**, 6, b g Sakhee (USA)—Romantic Dream **Her Majesty The Queen**
132 **TELL IT TO ME**, 6, b m Kayf Tara—Liberthine (FR) **Turf Club 2016 & R Waley-Cohen**
133 **TERREFORT (FR)**, 5, gr g Martaline—Vie de Reine (FR) **Mr Simon Munir & Mr Isaac Souede**
134 **THE BOTTOM BAR (IRE)**, 6, br g Stowaway—Serenade Leader (IRE) **Mr Simon Munir & Mr Isaac Souede**
135 **THE VOCALIST**, 6, b m Recharge (IRE)—Ivy Edith **Million in Mind Partnership**
136 **THEINVAL (FR)**, 8, b g Smadoun (FR)—Kinevees (FR) **Mr & Mrs Sandy Orr**
137 **THOMAS CAMPBELL**, 6, b g Yeats (IRE)—Hora **Mrs Van Geest & Mrs Kelvin Hughes**
138 **TOP NOTCH (FR)**, 7, b g Poliglote—Topira (FR) **Mr Simon Munir & Mr Isaac Souede**
139 **TRULL LA LA**, 4, ch f Flemensfirth (USA)—Chomba Womba (IRE) **Mr & Mrs R. G. Kelvin-Hughes**
140 **TURTLE WARS (FR)**, 5, b g Turtle Bowl (IRE)—Forces Sweetheart **Sullivan Bloodstock Limited**
141 **VERDANA BLUE (IRE)**, 6, b m Getaway (GER)—Blue Gallery (IRE) **Crimbourne Stud**
142 **VERSATILITY**, 4, b g Yeats (IRE)—Stravinsky Dance **The Barrow Boys 2**
143 **VIA DOLOROSA**, ...
143 **V**..., 8, b g Fame And Glory—Victorine (IRE) **Mrs S. Magnier**
144 **VOYAGE DE RETOUR (IRE)**, 6, b g Craigsteel—Taipers (IRE) **Mrs Robert Bingley**
145 **VYTA DU ROC (FR)**, 9, gr g Lion Noir—Dolce Vyta (FR) **Mr Simon Munir & Mr Isaac Souede**
146 **WALLACE SPIRIT (FR)**, 5, gr g Le Havre (IRE)—In Love New (FR) **Mr & Mrs Sandy Orr**
147 **WAR CREATION (IRE)**, 6, b m Scorpion (IRE)—Creation (IRE) **Mr T. J. Hemmings**
148 **WE HAVE A DREAM (FR)**, 4, b g Martaline—Sweet Dance (FR) **Mr Simon Munir & Mr Isaac Souede**
149 **WELSBY (IRE)**, 6, b g Gold Well—Stonehouse (IRE) **Mr T. J. Hemmings**
150 **WENYERREADYFREDDIE (IRE)**, 7, ch g Beneficial—Ware It Vic (IRE) **A. Speelman M. Speelman M. Landau**
151 **WHATSWRONGWITHYOU (IRE)**, 7, ch g Bienamado (USA)—
                                                                Greenfield Noora (IRE) **5 Hertford Street Racing Club**
152 **WHISPER (FR)**, 10, b g Astarabad (USA)—Belle Yepa (FR) **Walters Plant Hire Ltd**
153 **WILLIAM HENRY (IRE)**, 8, b g King's Theatre (IRE)—Cincuenta (IRE) **Walters Plant Hire Ltd**
154 **WITH DISCRETION (IRE)**, 7, b m Tiger Hill (IRE)—Discreet **Bloomsbury Stud**
155 **YELLOW DOCKETS (IRE)**, 6, ch m Getaway (GER)—Soft Skin (IRE) **The Three Princesses**

Other Owners: Mr M. R. Blandford, A. R. Bromley, Mr A. N. Cheyne, J. D. Cotton, Mrs B. Cotton, Mr D. Downie, Mr L. Garside-Beattie, G. F. Goode, Mr C. M. Grech, D. A. Hall, E. R. Hanbury, Mrs N. A. Hanbury, Ms N. C. Heath, N. J. Henderson, Highclere Nominated Partner Limited, Highclere Thoroughbred Racing Ltd, Mr A. J. Hill, Mr B. M. Hillier, J. Hornsey, J. F. Jarvis, R. G. Kelvin-Hughes, Mrs E. A. Kelvin-Hughes, Mr M. B. J. Kimmins, Mr C. Kimmins, M. R. Landau, Col A. J. E. Malcolm, Mrs J. M. T. Martin, D. R. Martin, Mr P Martin, Mr W. D. C. Minton, M. Morgan, Mrs L. K. Morgan, S. E. Munir, Mrs D. C. Nicholson, Miss M. Noden, Mr J. A. M. Orr, Mrs C. R. Orr, Palatinate Thoroughbred Racing Limited, T. S. Palin, Mr C. M. Parker, Mr S. J. Parkin, Mrs S. Parkin, Mr S. R. C. Philip, W. H. Ponsonby, Mrs M. J. Potter, J. E. Potter, Brig C. K. Price, Mr Prince, Miss P Purewal, Mrs D. Sheasby, Mr E. J. N. Sheasby, Mr A. Singh, Mr I. Souede, Mr M. Speelman, Mr D. F. Sumpter, Turf Club 2016, Mrs G. D. V. Van Geest, Lord Vestey, Mr S. Williams.

Jockey (NH): David Bass, Nico De Boinville, Barry Geraghty, Jeremiah McGrath. **Conditional:** Ned Curtis, Alan Doyle. **Amateur:** Mr Hugo Hunt.

275 MR PAUL HENDERSON, Whitsbury
Postal: **1 Manor Farm Cottage, Whitsbury, Fordingbridge, Hampshire, SP6 3QP**
Contacts: PHONE **(01725) 518113** FAX **(01725) 518113** MOBILE **(07958) 482213**
E-MAIL **phendersonracing@gmail.com**

1 **ABBEY STREET (IRE)**, 7, b g Asian Heights—Cnocbui Cailin (IRE) **Mr and Mrs J Baigent**
2 **ALICE PINK (IRE)**, 8, b m Milan—That's The Goose (IRE) **Runthatbymeagain**
3 **AMRON KALI (IRE)**, 8, b m Kalanisi (IRE)—Glacial Snowboard (IRE) **Mareildar Racing Part 1**
4 **ARGEM**, 8, br m Araafa (IRE)—Lekka Ding (IRE) **Mr M. Tilbrook**
5 **DOITFORTHEVILLAGE (IRE)**, 9, b g Turtle Island (IRE)—Last Chance Lady (IRE) **The Rockbourne Partnership**
6 **EASTER IN PARIS (IRE)**, 9, b m Bienamado (USA)—Easter Saturday (IRE) **Runthatbymeagain**
7 **FOR CARMEL (IRE)**, 8, b g Mr Dinos (IRE)—Bobalena (IRE) **The Rockbourne Partnership**
8 **GOOD MAN VINNIE (IRE)**, 7, ch g Vinnie Roe (IRE)—Pellerossa (IRE) **Sarah Habib & Ed Hawkings**
9 **HATCHET JACK (IRE)**, 6, b g Black Sam Bellamy (IRE)—
Identity Parade (IRE) **A J Pearson, Mark Jenner, Ed Hawkings**
10 **MINELLA GATHERING (IRE)**, 9, b g Old Vic—A Plus Ma Puce (FR) **Mr E. J. Hawkings**
11 **MINELLA TWEET (IRE)**, 10, b g King's Theatre (IRE)—Cara Mhaith (IRE) **Michael & Tracie Willis**
12 **MIRIAM VIOLET**, 4, b f Dick Turpin (IRE)—Velvet Band **Mr J. H. W. Finch**
13 **MONTYCRISTO**, 5, br g Motivator—Water Gipsy **Priesthawes Partnership**
14 **MOUNT VESUVIUS (IRE)**, 10, b g Spartacus (IRE)—Parker's Cove (USA) **Mr R. G. Henderson**
15 **MR MULLINER (IRE)**, 9, br g Millenary—Mrs Battle (IRE) **Miss J. Patten**
16 **MR SCAFF (IRE)**, 4, br g Vocalised (USA)—Nancy Rock (IRE) **M R Scaffolding Services Ltd**
17 **RAISING HOPE (IRE)**, 9, b m Turtle Island (IRE)—Jurado It Is (IRE) **Mrs J. L. Chappell**
18 **RING MINELLA (IRE)**, 7, b g King's Theatre (IRE)—Ring of Water (USA) **NHRE Racing Club**
19 **RUN DON'T HIDE (IRE)**, 7, b g High Chaparral (IRE)—Right Key (IRE) **Mareildar Racing Part 1**
20 **SIZING SAHARA**, 10, gr g Shirocco (GER)—Aristocratique **Mrs J. L. Chappell**
21 **TALK OF THE SOUTH (IRE)**, 9, b g Milan—Smalltowntale (IRE) **The Rockbourne Partnership**
22 **TREACY HOTELS BOY (IRE)**, 11, br g Overbury (IRE)—Bridgehotel Rose (IRE) **The Rockbourne Partnership**
23 **TURBAN (FR)**, 11, b g Dom Alco (FR)—Indianabelle (FR) **Turbanators**
24 **UN BEAU ROMAN (FR)**, 10, bl g Roman Saddle (FR)—Koukie (FR) **John H. W. Finch & The Romans**

Other Owners: Mr J. R. Baigent, Mr M. H. Bunting, Mr R. J. Galpin, Mrs S. J. Habib, Mr P. F. Henderson, Mr R. L. Henderson, Mr A. W. Hill, Mr R. Jackson, Mr M. E. Jenner, Mr A. Pearson, J. F. R. Stainer, Mr T. J. Stubbs, Mrs S. R. Wadman, Mr L. M. Weinstein, Mrs T. J. Willis, Mr M. R. Willis.

276 MR MICHAEL HERRINGTON, Thirsk
Postal: **Garbutt Farm, Cold Kirby, Thirsk, North Yorkshire, YO7 2HJ**
Contacts: PHONE **(01845) 400123** MOBILE **(07855) 396858**
E-MAIL **info@michaelherringtonracing.co.uk** WEBSITE **www.michaelherringtonracing.co.uk**

1 **CIRCUIT JUDGE**, 4, b g Lawman (FR)—Gimasha **Tony Culhane Racing Club**
2 **DAZEEKHA**, 5, b m Captain Gerrard (IRE)—Dazakhee **Mrs H. J. Lloyd-Herrington**
3 **DUKE COSIMO**, 8, ch g Pivotal—Nannina **Mr J. S. Herrington**
4 **HONEY BADGER**, 7, b br g Pastoral Pursuits—Taminoula (IRE) **Mrs D. J. Black**
5 **JAN VAN HOOF (IRE)**, 7, b g Dutch Art—Cosenza **Mrs H. J. Lloyd-Herrington**
6 **KAMRA (USA)**, 4, b g Stay Thirsty (USA)—Milliondollarbill (USA) **Iredale Racing & GG Thoroughbreds I**
7 **KOMMANDER KIRKUP**, 7, ch g Assertive—Bikini **Stuart Herrington & Pete Forster**
8 **MISHAAL (IRE)**, 8, ch g Kheleyf (USA)—My Dubai (IRE) **Kelvyn Gracie & Lawrence McCaughey**
9 **NEWSTEAD ABBEY**, 8, b g Byron—Oatcake **Tony Culhane Racing Club**
10 **STREET POET (IRE)**, 5, b g Poet's Voice—Street Star (USA) **Acorn Racing**
11 **TUKHOOM (IRE)**, 5, b g Acclamation—Carioca (IRE) **M. A. Leatham**

THREE-YEAR-OLDS

12 B f Delegator—Echo of Footsteps **H. M. Hurst**
13 **NADINE**, b f Nathaniel (IRE)—Opening Ceremony (USA) **H. M. Hurst**

TWO-YEAR-OLDS

14 **DELICATE FOOTSTEPS**, ch f 16/3 Medicean—Echo of Footsteps (Authorized (IRE)) (2380) **H. M. Hurst**
15 Ch g 7/2 Schiaparelli (GER)—Khandala (IRE) (Soviet Star (USA)) **Mrs H. J. Lloyd-Herrington**

Other Owners: Mr P. A. Culhane, Mr Peter Forster, GG Thoroughbreds I, Mr George Gill, Mr Kelvyn Gracie, Mr Stuart Herrington, Mr Antony Iredale, Mr Frank McAleavy, Mr Lawrence McCaughey, Ms B. A. Newton, Mr M. O'Connor, Mr Charlie Pigram.

Assistant Trainer: Helen Lloyd-Herrington

277 MR PETER HIATT, Banbury
Postal: **Six Ash Farm, Hook Norton, Banbury, Oxfordshire, OX15 5DB**
Contacts: **PHONE (01608) 737255 FAX (01608) 730641 MOBILE (07973) 751115**

1 **BAASHIQ (IRE)**, 4, b g New Approach (IRE)—Fatanah (IRE) **Mr Phil Kelly**
2 **BEAMING**, 4, b f Shamardal (USA)—Connecting **R. D. & R. G. Robinson**
3 **EQUALLY FAST**, 6, b g Equiano (FR)—Fabulously Fast (USA) **Mr P. W. Hiatt**
4 **IONA ISLAND**, 5, b m Dutch Art—Still Small Voice **Mr P. W. Hiatt**
5 **MONARCH MAID**, 7, b m Captain Gerrard (IRE)—Orange Lily **Mr C. Demczak**
6 **PETERS FOLLY**, 5, ch m Captain Gerrard (IRE)—Lipica (IRE) **Mr P. W. Hiatt**
7 **RAASHDY (IRE)**, 5, b g Intikhab (USA)—Maghya (USA) **Mr P. W. Hiatt**
8 **RAFAAF (IRE)**, 10, b g Royal Applause—Sciunfona (IRE) **Mr P. W. Hiatt**
9 **RED TEA**, 5, ch m Sakhee (USA)—Maimoona (IRE) **Mr K & Mrs I Read Mrs S Tucker T Logan**

THREE-YEAR-OLDS
10 **CRYSTAL BLADE**, b f Casamento (IRE)—Weood (IRE) **R. D. & R. G. Robinson**
11 **TAKIAH**, b f Arcano (IRE)—Elmaam **Mrs S. Tucker**

Other Owners: Mr P. W. Hiatt, Mr Ken Read.

Assistant Trainer: Mrs M. King

Jockey (flat): William Carson. **Amateur:** Miss M. Edden.

278 MR PHILIP HIDE, Nepcote
Postal: **Cissbury Stables, Nepcote, West Sussex, BN14 0SR**
Contacts: **MOBILE (07768) 233324**
WEBSITE www.philiphideracing.com

1 **ARCHIMENTO**, 5, ch g Archipenko (USA)—Caribana **Forever Optimists**
2 **AYR OF ELEGANCE**, 6, b m Motivator—Gaelic Swan (IRE) **Mr W. F. N. Davis**
3 **BLACK CAESAR (IRE)**, 7, b g Bushranger (IRE)—Evictress (IRE) **The Long Furlong**
4 **BUTTERFIELD (IRE)**, 5, b g Fastnet Rock (AUS)—Cozzene's Angel (USA) **Mr Y. O. Wong**
5 **BUZZ LIGHTYERE**, 5, b g Royal Applause—Lady Gloria **Tara Moon Partnership**
6 **DRAGONS VOICE**, 4, b g Poet's Voice—China **Heart of the South Racing 106**
7 **FINTECH (IRE)**, 4, b g Dark Angel (IRE)—Final Legacy (USA) **Bankers Folly**
8 **LIGHTLY SQUEEZE**, 4, b g Poet's Voice—Zuleika Dobson **Mr Y. O. Wong**
9 **LUCKY ACCORD**, 6, ch g Schiaparelli (GER)—Prissie Lucinda (IRE) **See You In The Cheltenham Partnership**
10 **ONEHELLUVATOUCH**, 5, gr m Hellvelyn—Soft Touch (IRE) **Heart of the South Racing 109**
11 **ROCKSETTE**, 4, b f Mount Nelson—Native Nickel (IRE) **Hide & Seekers**
12 **VIVRE POUR VIVRE (IRE)**, 5, b g Pour Moi (IRE)—Miss Quality (USA) **P. Turner & J. Davies**
13 **ZAMBEASY**, 7, b g Zamindar (USA)—Hanella (IRE) **Heart Of The South Racing**

THREE-YEAR-OLDS
14 B f Nathaniel (IRE)—Lively Sprite
15 **PHANTOM WARRIOR**, b g Intello (GER)—Vassaria (IRE)
16 **STORM AGAIN**, ch g Nathaniel (IRE)—Triveni (FR) **The Storm Again Syndicate**
17 **THISTIMELASTYEAR**, b f Cacique (IRE)—Despatch **The Storm Again Syndicate**
18 **VALERIE'S MEMORY**, b f Sixties Icon—Nadinska **Mr N. C. Jones**

TWO-YEAR-OLDS
19 B c 28/4 Charm Spirit (IRE)—Ruse (Diktat) (26000) **Mr Y. O. Wong**

Other Owners: Mrs E. Adamski, Mr I. S. Burgess, Mr J. Davies, Mr T. Francis, J. W. Fullick, R. T. Goodes, Mr P. E. Hide, Mr A. G. Hide, Mr Paul Jubert, Mr J. R. Penny, D. G. Raffel, Mr G. Reeves, Mr M. L. E. Schotness, Mr B. Stewart, Mrs G. O. Tourle, Mr M. H. Tourle, Mr P. Turner.

279 MRS LAWNEY HILL, Aston Rowant
Postal: **Woodway Farm, Aston Rowant, Watlington, Oxford, OX49 5SJ**
Contacts: PHONE **(01844) 353051** FAX **(01844) 354751** MOBILE **(07769) 862648**
E-MAIL lawney@lawneyhill.co.uk WEBSITE www.lawneyhill.co.uk

1 **CLONDAW WESTIE (IRE)**, 7, b g Westerner—You're A Native (IRE) **Mrs D. M. Caudwell**
2 **JUDGE JUDY (IRE)**, 5, b m Oscar (IRE)—The Bar Maid **F. R. Jarvey**
3 **LUCY SKYWALKER**, 5, b m Tobougg (IRE)—Zaffre Bleu (IRE) **Mrs D. Salmon**
4 **MISS MAYFAIR (IRE)**, 11, b m Indian Danehill (IRE)—Cocktail Party (USA) **Mr A. Hill**
5 **OLIVER'S HILL (IRE)**, 9, b g Shantou (USA)—River Rouge (IRE) **Mrs Frank Caudwell**
6 **ROYAL ETIQUETTE (IRE)**, 11, b g Royal Applause—Alpine Gold (IRE) **Mr A. Hill**
7 **SAMURAI SAM**, 5, b g Black Sam Bellamy (IRE)—Aspra (FR) **Mrs D. A. T. Salmon**
8 **SHIMBA HILLS**, 7, b g Sixties Icon—Search Party **Shimba Hills Partnership/Mr Alan Hill**

Other Owners: Ms G. H. Hedley, Mrs H. M. Munn, The Shimba Hills Partnership.

Jockey (NH): Aidan Coleman, Nick Scholfield. **Apprentice:** Megan Nicholls. **Amateur:** Mr Joe Hill.

280 MR MARTIN HILL, Totnes
Postal: **The Barn, Knaves Ash Stables, Nr Redpost, Littlehempston, Totnes, Devon, TQ9 6NG**
Contacts: PHONE **(01803) 813102** MOBILE **(07980) 490220**
E-MAIL info@martinhillracing.co.uk WEBSITE www.martinhillracing.co.uk

1 **AUDORA**, 7, b m Alflora (IRE)—Vixen Run (IRE) **British Racing Club**
2 **BADILOU (FR)**, 7, b br g Ballingarry (IRE)—Doumia (FR) **Mr M. E. Hill**
3 **CLENI WELLS (FR)**, 7, b g Poliglote—Kailasa (FR) **The Away Day Partnership**
4 **FS LOLA**, 4, ch f Arvico (FR)—Semi Colon (FR) **Mr M. E. Hill**
5 **POET'S CHARM (IRE)**, 4, b g Poet's Voice—Antillia **Mr M. Leach**
6 **PUZZLE CACHE**, 4, b f Phoenix Reach (IRE)—Secret Queen **Kittymore Racing**
7 **SCORPION STAR (IRE)**, 9, b g Scorpion (IRE)—Chapanga (FR) **Mr M. E. Hill**
8 **SLAYING THE DRAGON (IRE)**, 5, ch g Notnowcato—Empress Charlotte **Bestwork Racing**
9 **TREASURE THE RIDGE (IRE)**, 9, b g Galileo (IRE)—Treasure The Lady (IRE) **The French Connection**
10 **WATCOMBE HEIGHTS (IRE)**, 8, b g Scorpion (IRE)—Golden Bay **Mr M. E. Hill**

THREE-YEAR-OLDS
11 **HUCCABY**, b g Arvico (FR)—Burrator **Mr M. E. Hill**
12 **KIM'S LEGEND**, b f Midnight Legend—Kim Tian Road (IRE) **Mr M. E. Hill**

Other Owners: Mr P. J. Ash, British Racing Club, Mrs J. M. Cole, Mr S. Edmunds, Mr Rupert Fowler, Mrs Belinda Fowler, Mrs Amanda Hutchings, Mrs Elizabeth Mogford, Mrs Keith Pook, Mrs Christine Tibbetts, Mrs Anne Way, Mrs Patricia Wolfenden.

Assistant Trainer: Rachel Williams

Jockey (NH): Jeremiah McGrath. **Conditional:** Charlie Deutsch.

281 MR CHARLES HILLS, Lambourn
Postal: **Wetherdown House, Lambourn, Hungerford, Berkshire, RG17 8UB**
Contacts: PHONE **(01488) 71548** FAX **(01488) 72823**
E-MAIL info@charleshills.co.uk WEBSITE www.charleshills.com

1 **A MOMENTOFMADNESS**, 5, b g Elnadim (USA)—Royal Blush **Tony Wechsler & Ann Plummer**
2 **AFAAK**, 4, b c Oasis Dream—Ghanaati (USA) **Hamdan Al Maktoum**
3 **ALNASHAMA**, 6, b g Dubawi (IRE)—Ghanaati (USA) **Hamdan Al Maktoum**
4 **ANGEL OF DARKNESS**, 4, b f Dark Angel (IRE)—Chelsea Morning (USA) **D James, J Gompertz, S Jenkins**
5 **BATTAASH (IRE)**, 4, b g Dark Angel (IRE)—Anna Law (IRE) **Hamdan Al Maktoum**
6 **CARRY ME HOME**, 5, b g Dark Angel (IRE)—Toffee Vodka (IRE) **Gary & Linnet Woodward**
7 **DUTCH CONNECTION**, 6, ch h Dutch Art—Endless Love (IRE) **Godolphin**
8 **JALLOTA**, 7, b g Rock of Gibraltar (IRE)—Lady Lahar **Mrs Fitri Hay**
9 **MAGICAL MEMORY (IRE)**, 6, gr g Zebedee—Marasem **Kennet Valley Thoroughbreds I**
10 **MAGILLEN (IRE)**, 4, ch g Lope de Vega (IRE)—Lady Natilda **Julie Martin, David Martin & Rob Mayall**

MR CHARLES HILLS - Continued

11 **NEVER SURRENDER (IRE)**, 4, b g High Chaparral (IRE)—
Meiosis (USA) **D M James, Steve Jenkins, Maurice Mogg**
12 **PLUTONIAN (IRE)**, 4, b c Raven's Pass (USA)—Ripalong (IRE) **Mrs Fitri Hay**
13 **ROSARNO (IRE)**, 4, b c Fastnet Rock (AUS)—Jouet **Mr Abdulla Al Khalifa**
14 **SHANGHAI GLORY (IRE)**, 5, ch g Exceed And Excel (AUS)—Hecuba **Mrs Fitri Hay**
15 **SHANGHAI SILVER (IRE)**, 4, ch g Kendargent (FR)—Ispanka **Kangyu International Racing (HK) Limited**
16 **TAI SING YEH (IRE)**, 4, b g Exceed And Excel (AUS)—Cherry Orchard (IRE) **Mr Hon Kit Cheung**
17 **WAQAAS**, 4, b g Showcasing—Red Mischief (IRE) **Hamdan Al Maktoum**

THREE-YEAR-OLDS

18 **ARTHENIA (IRE)**, b f Camelot—Miss Intimate (USA) **D James, S Jenkins, Triermore, B Hills**
19 **ATHARY (IRE)**, b f Shamardal (USA)—Tarfah (USA) **Mr Abdulla Al Khalifa**
20 **AUTUMN WAR (IRE)**, ch c Declaration of War (USA)—Autumn Leaves (FR) **Mr Chi Un Fred Ma**
21 **BARTHOLOMEU DIAS**, b c Mount Nelson—Lady Francesca **Mr P. K. Siu**
22 **BE MINDFUL (IRE)**, b f Invincible Spirit (IRE)—Strawberry Roan (IRE) **Mr Dan Hall & Mr Steve Jenkins**
23 **BIN DAAHIR**, b c Exceed And Excel (AUS)—Beach Frolic **Hamdan Al Maktoum**
24 **CHAPARRAL PRINCE (IRE)**, b g High Chaparral (IRE)—Snow Gretel (IRE) **Mr & Mrs J. D. Cotton**
25 **CHRISELLAINE (IRE)**, b f Iffraaj—Janicellaine (IRE) **Ballylinch Stud**
26 **DARK SERAPHIM (IRE)**, b c Dark Angel (IRE)—Win Cash (IRE) **Tony Wechsler & Ann Plummer**
27 **DEFINITION**, ch c Pivotal—Neshla **Highclere T'bred Racing-Kelly Holmes**
28 **DEPENDABLE (GER)**, ch f Reliable Man—Dessau (GER) **Windmill Racing**
29 B f Red Jazz (USA)—Desert Drama (IRE) **Mr B. W. Hills**
30 **ELIZABETH BENNET (IRE)**, b f Acclamation—Littlepromisedland (IRE) **Mr & Mrs T O'Donohoe**
31 **EPIC FANTASY**, b c Invincible Spirit (IRE)—Impressionism (IRE) **Saleh Al Homaizi & Imad Al Sagar**
32 **EQUILATERAL**, b c Equiano (FR)—Tarentaise **Mr K. Abdullah**
33 **ERAAD (IRE)**, b c Dark Angel (IRE)—Tickled Pink (IRE) **Hamdan Al Maktoum**
34 **FARAWAY FIELDS (USA)**, b c First Defence (USA)—Faraway Flower (USA) **Mr K. Abdullah**
35 **GEMINI**, b f Makfi—Gaze **Dan Hall, D M James, Steve Jenkins**
36 **GLOBAL PASSION (FR)**, b g Penny's Picnic (USA)—Lili St Cyr (IRE) **Dr Johnny Hon**
37 **GLOBAL TANGO (IRE)**, gr g Zebedee—Beautiful Dancer (IRE) **Dr Johnny Hon**
38 **GLORIOUS WINGER**, ch g Raven's Pass (USA)—Emonoja (IRE) **Kangyu International Racing (HK) Limited**
39 **GROVEMAN**, b g Holy Roman Emperor—Raving Monsun **Mr P. K. Siu**
40 **HERE'S ALICE (IRE)**, b f Galileo (IRE)—Baraka (IRE) **International Plywood (Importers) Ltd**
41 **HULA GIRL**, gr f Oasis Dream—Tropical Paradise (IRE) **Mrs Tessa Winkworth**
42 **INDICIA**, b f Bated Breath—Indication **Mr K. Abdullah**
43 **INSTITUTION (IRE)**, ch c Zoffany (IRE)—Became (USA) **Mr S. F. Hui**
44 **IVALDI (IRE)**, ch f Dutch Art—Paris Winds (IRE) **Sangster Family & B V Sangster**
45 **JETSTREAM (IRE)**, b c Galileo (IRE)—Bewitched (IRE) **Mr R A Scarborough & Mrs John Magnier**
46 **JULIET FOXTROT**, b f Dansili—Kilo Alpha **Mr K. Abdullah**
47 **KAPOW (IRE)**, b c Cape Cross (IRE)—Prianca (GER) **The Kapow Partnership**
48 **KHAWAATEM (USA)**, ch c Smart Strike (CAN)—Charmed Gift (USA) **Hamdan Al Maktoum**
49 **KODINA**, b f Kodiac—Quan Am (FR) **The Better Together Partnership**
50 **LICINIUS**, b g Rock of Gibraltar (IRE)—Vespasia **Mrs Fiona Williams**
51 **LIFEBOAT (IRE)**, b g Born To Sea (IRE)—Mrs Seek **Kennet Valley Thoroughbreds VIII**
52 **LIVVYS DREAM (IRE)**, b f Declaration of War (USA)—Briolette (IRE) **International Plywood (Importers) Ltd**
53 **MAKAMBE (IRE)**, gr g Dark Angel (IRE)—Pink Diva (IRE) **Mrs Fitri Hay**
54 **MAPPED (USA)**, b c Mizzen Mast (USA)—Geographic (USA) **Mr K. Abdullah**
55 **METATRONS CUBE (IRE)**, b g Artie Schiller (USA)—Quiet Down (USA) **D M James & Steve Jenkins**
56 **MIDAS MAGGIE**, b f Archipenko (USA)—Algarade **Mr John C. Grant**
57 **MIRBAT**, ch c Dutch Art—Davie's Lure (USA) **Mrs Fitri Hay**
58 **MISS PARIS**, b f Champs Elysees—Bantu
59 **MOON OF BARODA**, gr c Dubawi (IRE)—Millennium Star (IRE) **Tony Wechsler & Ann Plummer**
60 **MUKHAATER**, ch g Bahamian Bounty—Dame Shirley **Hamdan Al Maktoum**
61 **MUTAKATIF (IRE)**, b c Acclamation—Gorband (USA) **Hamdan Al Maktoum**
62 **MYSTIQUE**, b f Oasis Dream—Hidden Brief **Mr Jeremy Gompertz & Mr Patrick Milmo**
63 **NEBO (IRE)**, b c Kodiac—Kindling **Mrs Julie Martin & David R. Martin**
64 **NEWBOROUGH**, b g Farhh—Comeraincomeshine (IRE) **Mrs Julie Martin & David R. Martin**
65 **ORDER OF THISTLE (IRE)**, b c High Chaparral (IRE)—Law of The Jungle (IRE) **Mrs Fitri Hay**
66 **PORTH SWTAN (IRE)**, b c Invincible Spirit (IRE)—Propaganda (IRE) **Julie Martin & David R Martin & Partners**
67 **PUDS**, br f Bated Breath—Missy Wassie Gal (USA) **Mr N. Martin**
68 **QAFILAH (IRE)**, ch f Arcano (IRE)—Janina **Hamdan Al Maktoum**
69 **RED ROMAN**, b c Holy Roman Emperor—Domitia **Mr John C. Grant & The Hon R. J. Arculli**
70 **REVALUE**, b f Dansili—Take The Hint **Mr K. Abdullah**
71 **REWAAYAT**, br c Pivotal—Rufoof **Hamdan Al Maktoum**
72 **RHOSNEIGR (IRE)**, ch c Iffraaj—Sadinga (IRE) **Julie Martin & David R. Martin & Partner**

MR CHARLES HILLS - Continued

73 **RIPLEY (IRE)**, b f Declaration of War (USA)—La Conquerante **Mr R. J. Tufft**
74 **ROCK OF ESTONIA (IRE)**, ch c Society Rock (IRE)—Estonia **Kangyu Int. Racing (HK) Ltd & Mr F Ma**
75 **SAFFAH (USA)**, br f More Than Ready (USA)—Elghayoor (USA) **Hamdan Al Maktoum**
76 **SCOTESIA (IRE)**, b f Galileo (IRE)—Regal Rose **Mrs Fitri Hay**
77 **SERVILIA**, gr f Lethal Force (IRE)—Cartimandua **Mrs Fiona Williams**
78 **SMOOTH SAILING**, b f Bated Breath—Royal Confidence **Mr D. M. James**
79 **SPHERIC**, b f Champs Elysees—Starfan (USA) **Mr K. Abdullah**
80 **SPOOF**, b g Poet's Voice—Filona (IRE) **Gary & Linnet Woodward**
81 **TAFAWOQ**, b f Oasis Dream—Raasekha **Hamdan Al Maktoum**
82 **TAMREER**, ch f New Approach (IRE)—Reyaadah **Hamdan Al Maktoum**
83 **TARBEYAH (IRE)**, ch f Teofilo (IRE)—Shamtari (IRE) **Hamdan Al Maktoum**
84 **TIME FOR A TOOT (IRE)**, b f Oasis Dream—Market Forces **Mr P. Winkworth**
85 **WAFY (IRE)**, br c Dubawi (IRE)—Ghanaati (USA) **Hamdan Al Maktoum**
86 **WITH GOOD GRACE (IRE)**, ch f Galileo (IRE)—
Withorwithoutyou (IRE) **Mrs J Magnier, Mr M Tabor & Mr D Smith**
87 **WUFUD**, b c Dubawi (IRE)—Tahrir (IRE) **Hamdan Al Maktoum**

TWO-YEAR-OLDS

88 Ch f 25/3 Garswood—Agrippina (Timeless Times (USA)) (35000)
89 B f 28/2 Charm Spirit (IRE)—Air Biscuit (IRE) (Galileo (IRE))
90 **ALANDALOS**, b f 23/4 Invincible Spirit (IRE)—Ghanaati (USA) (Giant's Causeway (USA))
91 B c 16/2 Moohaajim (USA)—Alhena (IRE) (Alhaarth (IRE)) (52380)
92 B f 7/2 New Approach (IRE)—Aqsaam (USA) (Dynaformer (USA))
93 B c 8/3 Heeraat (IRE)—Aquasulis (IRE) (Titus Livius (FR)) (31000)
94 B c 27/2 Mayson—Aromatherapy (Oasis Dream) (24761)
95 **BURNING LAKE (IRE)**, br c 2/2 Le Havre (IRE)—Baby Houseman (Oasis Dream) (252340)
96 B c 5/2 Le Havre (IRE)—Cape Magic (IRE) (Cape Cross (IRE)) (85000)
97 B c 25/2 War Command (USA)—Chatham Islands (USA) (Elusive Quality (USA)) (48840)
98 B c 7/3 Morpheus—Cheworee (Milk It Mick) (26666)
99 **CHUCK WILLIS (IRE)**, b c 10/3 Kodiac—Xinji (IRE) (Xaar) (44770)
100 **CLEMATIS (USA)**, b br f 4/3 First Defence (USA)—Faraway Flower (USA) (Distant View (USA))
101 **COOL POSSIBILITY (IRE)**, br c 6/3 Dark Angel (IRE)—Pink Diva (IRE) (Giant's Causeway (USA))
102 B c 23/2 Zebedee—Cute (Diktat) (30476)
103 **DELICIOUS**, gr f 15/2 Olympic Glory (IRE)—You Look So Good (Excellent Art) (68000)
104 **DEVILS ROC**, gr f 2/4 Lethal Force (IRE)—Ring For Baileys (Kyllachy) (18000)
105 B f 18/2 Dandy Man (IRE)—Dissonance (IRE) (Rossini (USA)) (15465)
106 **DRUMNADROCHIT**, b c 17/2 Coach House (IRE)—Blissamore (Kyllachy) (28000)
107 B f 31/1 Zebedee—Fonseca (IRE) (Red Clubs (IRE)) (38095)
108 **FOUR MILE BRIDGE (IRE)**, b c 27/2 Acclamation—Agent Allison (Dutch Art) (100000)
109 **FRAGRANT DAWN**, b f 2/4 Iffraaj—Festivale (IRE) (Invincible Spirit (IRE))
110 B c 28/3 Slade Power—French Fern (IRE) (Royal Applause) (71428)
111 B f 29/4 Acclamation—Glitter Baby (Danehill Dancer (IRE)) (42000)
112 **GLOBAL FALCON**, ch c 31/1 Siyouni (FR)—Maggi Fong (Dr Fong (USA)) (115000)
113 **GLOBAL QUALITY**, ch c 7/4 No Nay Never (USA)—Dynacam (USA) (Dynaformer (USA)) (80000)
114 **GLOBAL SHIFT (IRE)**, ch g 15/3 Dandy Man (IRE)—Am I (USA) (Thunder Gulch (USA)) (50000)
115 **GLORIOUS SUNSHINE (IRE)**, br c 25/2 Bated Breath—Brilliant Sunshine (Pivotal) (75000)
116 **GLORY FIGHTER**, b c 7/4 Kyllachy—Isola Verde (Oasis Dream) (95000)
117 B c 2/5 Zoffany (IRE)—Green Castle (IRE) (Indian Ridge) (37443)
118 B c 28/4 Exceed And Excel (AUS)—Hecuba (Hector Protector (USA)) (60000)
119 B f 13/2 Dark Angel (IRE)—Iffraaj Pink (IRE) (Iffraaj)
120 B f 14/2 Dark Angel (IRE)—Illuminating Dream (IRE) (High Chaparral (IRE)) (81400)
121 **INCHARGE**, b f 18/4 Kingman—Whirly Bird (Nashwan (USA)) (200000)
122 **KHAADEM (IRE)**, br c 18/4 Dark Angel (IRE)—White Daffodil (IRE) (Footstepsinthesand) (750000)
123 **KHILWAFY**, b c 10/4 Mukhadram—Almass (IRE) (Elnadim (USA))
124 B f 4/4 Dark Angel (IRE)—Littlepromisedland (IRE) (Titus Livius (FR)) (53333)
125 Br c 22/3 Magician (IRE)—Looks Like Rain (Medicean) (52909)
126 Ch f 15/2 Showcasing—Love And Cherish (IRE) (Excellent Art) (70000)
127 **MALAKOFF (USA)**, b c 10/4 Mizzen Mast (USA)—Hidden Face (USA) (Empire Maker (USA))
128 **MONYA (IRE)**, gr f 27/3 Dark Angel (IRE)—Bridal Dance (IRE) (Danehill Dancer (IRE)) (425000)
129 **MUNHAMEK**, br c 11/3 Dark Angel (IRE)—Cadenza (FR) (Dansili)
130 **MUTARAFFA**, b c 3/3 Acclamation—Excellent View (Shamardal (USA)) (70000)
131 **MUTAWAFFER (IRE)**, b c 15/4 Kodiac—Golden Flower (Royal Applause) (160000)
132 **NASSAM (IRE)**, br c 7/4 New Approach (IRE)—Moon's Whisper (USA) (Storm Cat (USA))
133 B c 16/2 Dark Angel (IRE)—Natty Bumppo (IRE) (Kheleyf (USA)) (200000)
134 **NUBOUGH (IRE)**, b c 14/1 Kodiac—Qawaasem (IRE) (Shamardal (USA))

MR CHARLES HILLS - Continued

135 **OCEAN PARADISE**, gr f 5/4 New Approach (IRE)—Tropical Paradise (IRE) (Verglas (IRE)) (115000)
136 **PENRHOS**, b c 25/2 Kodiac—Bereka (Firebreak) (70000)
137 **PHOENIX OF SPAIN (IRE)**, gr c 17/2 Lope de Vega (IRE)—Lucky Clio (IRE) (Key of Luck (USA)) (220000)
138 **QUTOB (IRE)**, b c 17/3 Acclamation—When Not Iff (IRE) (Iffraaj) (152380)
139 **RHYDWYN (IRE)**, b c 22/2 Kodiac—Pilates (IRE) (Shamardal (USA)) (170000)
140 **RING OUT THE BELLS (IRE)**, b f 9/1 Kodiac—Newlywed (IRE) (Authorized (IRE)) (75000)
141 **RISAALA**, br f 25/3 Mukhadram—Maayad (USA) (Jazil (USA))
142 B g 5/2 Charm Spirit (IRE)—Royal Confidence (Royal Applause)
143 B f 28/4 Camacho—Royal Majestic (Tobougg (IRE)) (35816)
144 **SAFEENAH**, b f 27/2 Oasis Dream—Raasekha (Pivotal)
145 Gr c 4/4 Exceed And Excel (AUS)—Satwa Ruby (FR) (Verglas (IRE)) (50467)
146 **SHANGHAI GRACE**, b c 18/2 Kyllachy—Lavinia's Grace (USA) (Green Desert (USA)) (68000)
147 B c 26/4 Invincible Spirit (IRE)—Sharapova (IRE) (Elusive Quality (USA)) (150000)
148 Br f 28/2 Kuroshio (AUS)—Sonnellino (Singspiel (IRE))
149 **TABASSOR (IRE)**, ch f 6/4 Raven's Pass (USA)—Thaahira (USA) (Dynaformer (USA))
150 **TADAABEER**, b f 7/4 Dubawi (IRE)—Thakafaat (IRE) (Unfuwain (USA))
151 Gr f 16/4 Sea The Stars (IRE)—Turning Point (Dalakhani (IRE)) (65000)
152 B c 12/4 Acclamation—Vision of Peace (IRE) (Invincible Spirit (IRE)) (75000)
153 B c 10/3 Kodiac—Whitefall (USA) (Street Cry (IRE)) (68000)
154 B f 1/1 Lemon Drop Kid (USA)—Yageen (Green Desert (USA))
155 **YNYS MON (IRE)**, b c 14/3 Olympic Glory (IRE)—Russian Spirit (Falbrav (IRE)) (85000)

Other Owners: Mr Imad Al-Sagar, Sheikh Abdullah Almalek Alsabah, The Hon R J Arculli, Mr R. A. Bartlett, Brightwalton Bloodstock Ltd., Chelsea Thoroughbreds Ltd, The Hon Mrs J. M. Corbett, The Hon Mrs J. M. Corbett, Mr J. D. Cotton, Mrs B. Cotton, Mr L. R. A. Godfrey, Mr Jeremy Gompertz, Mr John C. Grant, Mr Dan Hall, Mr Christopher Hanbury, Mrs Christopher Hanbury, Highclere Nominated Partner Limited, Highclere Thoroughbred Racing Ltd, Mrs B. W. Hills, Mr B. W. Hills, Mr Saleh Al Homaizi, Mr R. S. Hoskins, Irish National Stud Company Limited, Mr Steve Jenkins, Mr Hussain Alabbas Lootah, Mrs John Magnier, Mr Mick Mariscotti, Mrs Janice Mariscotti, Mrs Fiona Marner, Mr David R. Martin, Mrs Julie Martin, Mr R. C. Mayall, Mr Patrick Milmo, Mr Maurice Moogy, Mrs Eloise O'Donohoe, Mr Thomas O'Donohoe, Mr Charles Parker, Mrs Mary-Anne Parker, Mrs Richard Plummer, Mrs J K Powell, Qatar Racing Limited, Mr N. J. F. Robinson, Roc Steady Partnership, B. V. Sangster, G. E. Sangster, Mr R. A. Scarborough, Mrs Paul Shanahan, Mr Derrick Smith, Mr James Sumsion, Mr M. Tabor, Triermore Stud, Mr J. A. Wechsler, Mrs Linnet Woodward, Mr Gary Woodward, Mr C Wright, Mr Christopher Wright.

Assistant Trainers: Kevin Mooney, Matt Stanley

Apprentice: Callum Shepherd. **Amateur:** Mr K Lenihan.

---

282 **MR MARK HOAD, Lewes**
Postal: **Windmill Lodge Stables, Spital Road, Lewes, East Sussex, BN7 1LS**
Contacts: **PHONE (01273) 477124/(01273) 480691 FAX (01273) 477124 MOBILE (07742) 446168**
E-MAIL markhoad@aol.com

1 **DEW REWARD (IRE)**, 10, b g Aussie Rules (USA)—Shariyfa (FR)
2 **HURRICANE ALERT**, 6, b g Showcasing—Raggle Taggle (IRE) **Mr M. R. Baldry**
3 **MOVIE MAGIC**, 7, b m Multiplex—Alucica **Mr B Pay**
4 **SANTADELACRUZE**, 9, b g Pastoral Pursuits—Jupiters Princess **Mrs K. B. Tester**
5 **SEA'S ARIA (IRE)**, 7, b g Sea The Stars (IRE)—Speed Song **Mrs K. B. Tester**
6 **SEBS SENSEI (IRE)**, 7, ch g Art Connoisseur (IRE)—Capetown Girl **Mr Mr M. L. Waters**
7 **WILLSHEBETRYING**, 7, b m Act One—Precedence (IRE) **G. C. Brice**

THREE-YEAR-OLDS

8 **ISLA CATALINA**, ch f Libranno—Dispol Katie **Mrs K. B. Tester**

---

283 **MR PHILIP HOBBS, Minehead**
Postal: **Sandhill, Bilbrook, Minehead, Somerset, TA24 6HA**
Contacts: **PHONE (01984) 640366 FAX (01984) 641124 MOBILE (07860) 729795**
E-MAIL pjhobbs@pjhobbs.com WEBSITE www.pjhobbs.com

1 **ACTION REPLAY (IRE)**, 7, b g Milan—Mary Connors (IRE) **Mr J. P. McManus**
2 **ALLEE BLEUE (IRE)**, 8, ch g Mount Nelson—Murrieta **Mr A. L. Cohen**
3 **ANNDARROW (IRE)**, 5, b m Beat Hollow—Kim Hong (IRE) **Mr M. W. Pendarves**

MR PHILIP HOBBS - Continued

4 **ARTHUR MAC (IRE)**, 5, ch g Getaway (GER)—Orchardstown Moss (IRE) **The Vacuum Pouch Company Limited**
5 **AWAKE AT MIDNIGHT**, 6, b g Midnight Legend—Wakeful **Mrs S. L. Lloyd-Baker**
6 **BACCHANEL (FR)**, 7, b g Vendangeur (IRE)—Pardielle (FR) **Gold & Blue Limited**
7 **BALLOTIN (FR)**, 7, b g Enrique—Orphee de Vonnas (FR) **David Maxwell Racing Limited**
8 **BALLYGOWN BAY (IRE)**, 5, b g Flemensfirth (USA)—Star Shuil (IRE) **Mrs J. J. Peppiatt**
9 **BARBROOK STAR (IRE)**, 6, b g Getaway (GER)—Fille de Robin (FR) **Mrs B. A. Hitchcock**
10 **BARN HILL**, 6, b g Kayf Tara—Shuil Mavourneen (IRE) **Mr Tim Syder & Martin St Quinton**
11 **BEAU DU BRIZAIS (FR)**, 6, gr g Kapgarde (FR)—Belle du Brizais (FR) **Mrs C. Skan**
12 **BOOK DIRECT (IRE)**, 7, b g Kayf Tara—Sinnaja **Brocade Racing**
13 **BRADFORD BRIDGE (IRE)**, 6, b g Milan—Isis Du Berlais (FR) **Brocade Racing**
14 **CASPER KING (IRE)**, 7, b g Scorpion (IRE)—Princess Supreme (IRE) **The Brushmakers**
15 **CASTERLY ROCK (IRE)**, 6, b g King's Theatre (IRE)—Alderbrook Girl (IRE) **Diana Whateley & Tim Syder**
16 **CEDAR VALLEY (IRE)**, 4, b f Flemensfirth (USA)—Lunar Path (IRE) **Mrs Caren Walsh & Mrs Kathleen Quinn**
17 **CHEF D'EQUIPE (FR)**, 6, b g Presenting—Millesimee (FR) **David Maxwell Racing Limited**
18 **COME ON CHARLIE (FR)**, 6, b g Anzillero (GER)—End of Spring (FR) **Mr M. G. St Quinton**
19 **CONTENTED (IRE)**, 5, gr g Dalakhani (IRE)—Leo's Spirit (IRE) **Highclere Thoroughbred Racing-Contented**
20 **COPPER KAY**, 8, b m Kayf Tara—Presenting Copper (IRE) **Aiden Murphy & Alan Peterson**
21 **COTSWOLD WAY (IRE)**, 5, b g Stowaway—Rosies All The Way **Miss I. D. Du Pre**
22 **CRANSTAL (IRE)**, 5, b g Gold Well—Vincenta (IRE) **Mr T. J. Hemmings**
23 **CROOKS PEAK (IRE)**, 5, b g Arcadio (GER)—Ballcrina Girl (IRE) **Mr C. A. H. Tilley**
24 **DARK EPISODE (IRE)**, 4, b g Getaway (GER)—No Moore Bills **Louisville Syndicate Elite**
25 **DEFI DU SEUIL (FR)**, 5, b g Voix du Nord—Quarvine du Seuil (FR) **Mr J. P. McManus**
26 **DIPLOMATE SIVOLA (FR)**, 5, ch g Noroit (GER)—None de Sivola (FR) **David Maxwell Racing Limited**
27 **DUKE DES CHAMPS (IRE)**, 8, b g Robin des Champs (FR)—
                    Ballycowan Lady (IRE) **Diana Whateley & Tim Syder**
28 **EARTH MOOR (IRE)**, 4, ch g Ask—Merrylas (IRE) **Mrs C. E. Penny**
29 **EBONY GALE**, 4, br g Shirocco (GER)—Glenora Gale (IRE) **Mrs J. A. S. Luff**
30 **ELIXIR DE NUTZ (FR)**, 4, gr g Al Namix (FR)—Nutz (FR) **J. T. Warner**
31 **EMMPARA**, 4, ch g Black Sam Bellamy (IRE)—Maria Antonia (IRE) **Clear Racing**
32 **FOR GOOD MEASURE (IRE)**, 7, b g King's Theatre (IRE)—Afdala (IRE) **Mr J. P. McManus**
33 **FROM THE HEART (IRE)**, 4, b g Jeremy (USA)—Zephyr Lilly (IRE) **Mr R. Whitehorn**
34 4, B g Gold Well—Fugal Maid (IRE) **Mrs K. Quinn**
35 **GAELIC PRINCE (IRE)**, 6, b g Martaline—Gaelic Jane (FR) **Diana Whateley & Tim Syder**
36 **GARDE LA VICTOIRE (FR)**, 9, b g Kapgarde (FR)—Next Victory (FR) **Mrs D. L. Whateley**
37 **GAUCHO GIL (IRE)**, 5, b g Getaway (GER)—Ballys Baby (IRE) **Diana Whateley & Tim Syder**
38 **GOSHEVEN (IRE)**, 5, b g Presenting—Fair Choice (IRE) **The Grocer Syndicate**
39 **GREAT LOVER (IRE)**, 6, gr g Smadoun (FR)—Dominelle (FR) **Dr V. M. G. Ferguson**
40 **GUMBALL (FR)**, 4, gr g No Risk At All (FR)—Good Time Girl (FR) **J. T. Warner**
41 **HARDNESS (IRE)**, 5, b g Makfi—Hideaway (FR) **Mr C. A. H. Tilley**
42 **HURLSTONE POINT**, 5, br m Scorpion (IRE)—Dudeen (IRE) **The Vintage Hunters**
43 **I'M A GAME CHANGER (IRE)**, 6, b g Arcadio (GER)—Drinadaly (IRE) **Mr & Mrs Paul & Clare Rooney**
44 **ICE COOL CHAMPS (IRE)**, 7, ch g Robin des Champs (FR)—Last of Many (IRE) **West Coast Haulage Limited**
45 **IMPERIAL PRESENCE (IRE)**, 7, ch g Presenting—Penneyrose Bay **Sir Christopher & Lady Wates**
46 **JERRYSBACK (IRE)**, 6, b g Jeremy (USA)—Get A Few Bob Back (IRE) **Mr J. P. McManus**
47 **KALOOKI (GER)**, 4, b g Martaline—Karuma (GER) **Mr A. L. Cohen**
48 **KATY P**, 6, b m Ask—Kingara **P. E. Atkinson**
49 **KAYF ADVENTURE**, 7, b g Kayf Tara—My Adventure (IRE) **Louisville Syndicate**
50 **KEEP MOVING (FR)**, 6, b g Linda's Lad—Keeping Gold (FR) **The Country Side**
51 **KEEP ROLLING (IRE)**, 5, ch g Mahler—Kayles Castle (IRE) **Mick Fitzgerald Racing Club**
52 **LAMB OR COD (IRE)**, 11, ch g Old Vic—Princess Lizzie (IRE) **J. T. Warner**
53 **LARKBARROW LAD**, 5, b g Kayf Tara—Follow My Leader (IRE) **The Englands and Heywoods**
54 **LEAPAWAY (IRE)**, 6, b g Stowaway—Gisela (IRE) **Dr V. M. G. Ferguson**
55 **LITTLE MISS POET**, 6, b m Yeats (IRE)—R de Rien Sivola (FR) **M. J. Tuckey**
56 **LONGTOWN (IRE)**, 7, b g Scorpion (IRE)—Desirable Asset (IRE) **Mr T. J. Hemmings**
57 **LORD DUVEEN (IRE)**, 5, br g Doyen (IRE)—Afdala (IRE) **L Field, L Cognet, J Sigler & C Walsh**
58 **LOUIS' VAC POUCH (IRE)**, 6, b g Oscar (IRE)—Coming Home (FR) **The Vacuum Pouch Company Limited**
59 **MAJESTIC TOUCH (IRE)**, 7, br g Kalanisi (IRE)—Alexander Divine **N. R. A. Sutton**
60 **MASTER WORK (FR)**, 5, b g Network (GER)—Mascarpone (FR) **Mr B K Peppiatt & Mr D R Peppiatt**
61 **MELCHIOR KING (IRE)**, 4, br g Stowaway—Miss Ira Zarad (FR) **The Brushmakers**
62 **MELEKHOV (IRE)**, 4, b g Sholokhov (IRE)—Yorkshire Girl (IRE) **Owners For Owners: Melekhov**
63 **MENDIP EXPRESS (IRE)**, 12, br g King's Theatre (IRE)—Mulberry (IRE) **David Maxwell Racing Limited**
64 **MIDNIGHT GLORY**, 6, b m Midnight Legend—Land of Glory **Mrs L. R. Lovell**
65 **MOTUEKA (IRE)**, 6, b g King's Theatre (IRE)—Tchouina (FR) **Mrs D. L. Whateley**
66 **MUSICAL SLAVE (IRE)**, 5, b g Getaway (GER)—Inghwung **Mr J. P. McManus**
67 **NEW MILLENNIUM (IRE)**, 5, b g Galileo (IRE)—Banquise (IRE) **Mr D Symondson & Mrs L Roper**

MR PHILIP HOBBS - Continued

68 **NO COMMENT**, 7, br g Kayf Tara—Dizzy Frizzy **Mr J. P. McManus**
69 **OAKLEY (IRE)**, 5, b g Oscar (IRE)—Tirolean Dance (IRE) **Mr T. D. J. Syder**
70 **ONEFITZALL (IRE)**, 8, b g Indian Danehill (IRE)—Company Credit (IRE) **Mick Fitzgerald Racing Club**
71 **OZZIE THE OSCAR (IRE)**, 7, b g Oscar (IRE)—Private Official (IRE) **Bradley Partnership**
72 **PERFORM (IRE)**, 9, b g King's Theatre (IRE)—Famous Lady (IRE) **Merry Old Souls**
73 **PERSIAN SNOW (IRE)**, 12, b g Anshan—Alpine Message **David Maxwell Racing Limited**
74 **PINEAPPLE RUSH**, 5, b m Kayf Tara—Celtic Native (IRE) **Bradley Partnership**
75 **POINTED AND SHARP (IRE)**, 6, b g Scorpion (IRE)—Leamybe (IRE) **Tony Staple & George Giles**
76 **POPPY KAY**, 8, b m Kayf Tara—Double Red (IRE) **Aiden Murphy & Alan Peterson**
77 **PYRIOS (FR)**, 5, b g Heliostatic (IRE)—Nuance Tartare (FR) **Merry Old Souls**
78 **QUADRILLER (FR)**, 11, b g Lando (GER)—Tabachines (FR) **P. J. Hobbs**
79 **RESOLUTION BAY**, 6, br g Presenting—Parthenia (IRE) **Mrs D. L. Whateley**
80 **ROBBIN'HANNON (IRE)**, 7, ch g Robin des Champs (FR)—Culleen Lady (IRE) **The Mount Fawcus Partnership**
81 **ROCK THE KASBAH (IRE)**, 8, ch g Shirocco (GER)—Impudent (IRE) **Mrs D. L. Whateley**
82 **ROLL THE DOUGH (IRE)**, 9, b g Definite Article—High Dough (IRE) **The Kingpins**
83 **ROLLING DYLAN (IRE)**, 7, ch g Indian River (FR)—Easter Saturday (IRE) **Miss I. D. Du Pre**
84 **ROYAL REGATTA (IRE)**, 10, b g King's Theatre (IRE)—
            Friendly Craic (IRE) **Mrs Lesley Field & Mrs Eileen Murphy**
85 **SAMBURU SHUJAA (FR)**, 5, b g Poliglote—Girelle (FR) **R. & Mrs J. E. Gibbs**
86 **SGROPPINO (IRE)**, 6, b g Getaway (GER)—Boadicea **Louisville Syndicate II**
87 **SHOW ON THE ROAD**, 7, b g Flemensfirth (USA)—Roses of Picardy (IRE) **R. M. Penny**
88 **SNEAKY FEELING (IRE)**, 6, b g Oscar (IRE)—Shuil Aris (IRE) **Syder, Whateley, Murphy, Burke**
89 4, B g Yeats (IRE)—Solar Quest (IRE) **The Vacuum Pouch Company Limited**
90 **SPIRIT OF MENDIP (IRE)**, 5, b m Arakan (USA)—Afdale (IRE) **Mr C. A. H. Tilley**
91 **SPRINGTOWN LAKE (IRE)**, 6, b g Gamut (IRE)—Sprightly Gal (IRE) **Mr T. D. J. Syder**
92 **STEELY ADDITION (IRE)**, 6, b g Craigsteel—Blond's Addition (IRE) **Step By Step**
93 **THAT'S A GIVEN (FR)**, 4, b g Great Pretender (IRE)—Aulne River (FR) **Mr A. L. Cohen**
94 **THE MILAN GIRL (IRE)**, 4, b f Milan—En Vedette (FR) **Mr & Mrs Paul & Clare Rooney**
95 **THREE FACES WEST (IRE)**, 10, b g Dr Massini (IRE)—ArdnatAggle (IRE) **Mr & Mrs Paul & Clare Rooney**
96 **TIDAL FLOW**, 5, b g Black Sam Bellamy (IRE)—Mrs Philip **Brocade Racing**
97 **TURANGI**, 6, b g King's Theatre (IRE)—Bold Fire **Mrs D. L. Whateley**
98 **UMNDENI (IRE)**, 6, b g Balko (FR)—Marie Royale (FR) **St Quinton, D.L. Whateley & Syder**
99 **VANGO DE VAIGE (FR)**, 5, b g Great Pretender (IRE)—Yellow Park (FR) **M. Short**
100 **VERNI (FR)**, 9, ch g Sabrehill (USA)—Nobless d'aron (FR) **Mr & Mrs Paul & Clare Rooney**
101 **VICTARION (IRE)**, 6, b g Scorpion (IRE)—Gaye Preskina (IRE) **Mrs D. L. Whateley**
102 **VIEUX LILLE (IRE)**, 8, b g Robin des Champs (FR)—Park Athlete (IRE) **Louisville Syndicate III**
103 **VILLAGE VIC (IRE)**, 11, b g Old Vic—Etoile Margot (FR) **Mr A. E. Peterson**
104 **VODKA ALL THE WAY (IRE)**, 6, b g Oscar (IRE)—Fully Focused (IRE) **Bradley Partnership**
105 **WAIHEKE**, 5, ch m Black Sam Bellamy (IRE)—Its Meant To Be **Mrs S. A. White**
106 **WAIT FOR ME (FR)**, 8, b g Saint des Saints (FR)—Aulne River (FR) **Mr A. L. Cohen**
107 **WAR SOUND**, 9, b g Kayf Tara—Come The Dawn **The Englands and Heywoods**
108 **WESTEND STORY (IRE)**, 7, b g Westerner—Sarahall (IRE) **Mick Fitzgerald Racing Club**
109 **WHO'S MY JOCKEY (IRE)**, 5, b g Yeats (IRE)—Scandisk (IRE) **Mr & Mrs Paul & Clare Rooney**

Other Owners: Mrs A. E. M. Broom, Mr G. R. Broom, Mrs J. L. Buckingham, Mrs V. F. Burke, C. J. Butler, Mrs L. J. Cognet, Mr J. P. Cooper, Mr P. K. Davis, Mr A. D. England, Mrs E. England, Mr D. V. Erskine Crum, Mr D. S. Fawcus, Mrs M. W. Fawcus, Mrs L. H. Field, H. R. Gibbs, Mrs J. E. Gibbs, Mr G. R. Giles, Mr B. J. Greening, Mrs M. M. Greening, Mr T. M. Hailstone, J. R. Hall, Mr C. G. Hellyer, Mr A. S. Heywood, Mr A. H. Heywood, Highclere Nominated Partner Limited, Highclere Thoroughbred Racing Ltd, Mr J. R. Holmes, Mrs J. Hughes, Mr M. J. Hyson, Mr B. R. Ingram, Miss N. Martin, H. A. Murphy, Mrs E. Murphy, Mr T. E. Olver, B. K. Peppiatt, D. R. Peppiatt, Mr N. D. Peppiatt, D. A. Rees, Mr P. A. Rooney, Mrs C. Rooney, Mrs L. J. Roper, N. C. Savery, Mr J. Sigler, Mr J. Simpson, A. P. Staple, Step By Step Supporting Independence Ltd, M. C. Stoddart, Mr D. W. Symondson, C. J. M. Walker, Mrs C. J. Walsh, Mr M. D. Warner, Lady G. F. Wates, Sir Christopher Wates.

Assistant Trainer: Richard White

Jockey (NH): Richard Johnson, Micheal Nolan, Tom O'Brien, Conor Smith. **Conditional:** Tom Cheesman, Sean Houlihan. **Amateur:** Mr Jake Bament, Mr Stefan Kirwan, Mr Nick Lawton.

284 MISS CLARE HOBSON, Royston
Postal: **The Woolpack, London Road, Reed, Royston, Hertfordshire, SG8 8BB**
Contacts: **MOBILE (07966) 734889**
E-MAIL clarehobsonracing@gmail.com

1 **AZAMESSE (IRE)**, 6, b m Azamour (IRE)—Jeunesse Doree (IRE) **Greg Molen & Harry Hobson**
2 **CARRIE ON DUBAI**, 5, b g Dubai Destination (USA)—Carrie On **Mr G. Molen, Mr S. Klein & Mr H. Musaphia**
3 **CAZZA CAZAM**, 4, b f Malinas (GER)—Flo The Machine (IRE) **Mrs Rosemary E. Hobson**
4 4, Gr g Fair Mix (IRE)—Clever Liz **Mr H. R. Hobson**
5 **GOLD CLASS**, 7, ch g Firebreak—Silken Dalliance **The Fox and Duck syndicate**
6 **GOLDEN JET (IRE)**, 5, b g Golan (IRE)—Could Do **Mr H. R. Hobson**

Other Owners: Miss Clare Hobson, Mrs Rosemary Hobson, Mr Harry Hobson, Mr Steven Richard Klein, Mr G. Molen, Mr Harry Musaphia, Mr George Sherriff.

Assistant Trainer: Harry Hobson

285 MR RICHARD HOBSON, Stow-On-The-Wold
Postal: **19 Hart Close, Upper Rissington, Cheltenham, Gloucestershire, GL54 2PX**
Contacts: **PHONE (01451) 820535 MOBILE (07939) 155843**
E-MAIL hobson.r1@sky.com WEBSITE www.rhbloodstock.com

1 **ALLYSSON MONTERG (FR)**, 8, b g Network (GER)—Mellyssa (FR) **Mr D. W. Fox**
2 **CARLITA MORIVIERE (FR)**, 6, b m Balko (FR)—Halladine (FR) **Mr C. S. Hinchy**
3 **CEPORINE (FR)**, 6, gr g Cachet Noir (USA)—Cyclosporine (FR) **Carl Hinchy & Gregory Davies**
4 **CHIC NAME (FR)**, 6, b g Nickname (FR)—Vuelta Al Ruedo (FR) **Mr R. H. Hobson**
5 **DAME ROSE**, 5, b m Network (GER)—Ile Rose (FR) **Mr C. S. Hinchy**
6 **DISCKO DES PLAGES (FR)**, 5, b g Balko (FR)—Lady des Plages (FR) **Mr C. S. Hinchy**
7 **ECHO WATT (FR)**, 4, gr g Fragrant Mix (IRE)—Roxane du Bois (FR) **The Boom Syndicate**
8 **ETOO SPORT (FR)**, 4, b g Great Journey (JPN)—Theloune (FR) **Mr D. W. Fox**
9 **GOING GOLD (IRE)**, 6, b g Gold Well—Wednesday Girl (IRE) **Mr C. S. Hinchy**
10 **KAMPUR EMERY (FR)**, 4, b g Califet (FR)—Chic Et Zen (FR) **Mr C. S. Hinchy**
11 **PETIVILLE (FR)**, 6, gr g Montmartre (FR)—Aegle (FR) **Mr R. H. Hobson**
12 **RAMONEX (GER)**, 7, b g Saddex—Ramondia (GER) **Mr C. S. Hinchy**
13 **SHANTOU FLYER (IRE)**, 8, b g Shantou (USA)—Carrigmorna Flyer (IRE) **Mr C. S. Hinchy**
14 **SURF AND TURF (IRE)**, 12, ch g Beneficial—Clear Top Waltz (IRE) **Mr R. H. Hobson**
15 **VALADOM (FR)**, 9, gr g Dadarissime (FR)—Laurana (FR) **Mr R. H. Hobson**

Other Owners: Mr G. Davies, Mr G. C. Farr.

Assistant Trainer: Shirley Jane Becker

286 MR JOHN HODGE, Cumnock
Postal: **Corbie Lodge, Muirdyke Farm, Cumnock, Ayrshire, KA18 2SG**

1 **CELTIC POWER**, 6, b g Rail Link—Biloxi **J. M. C. Hodge**
2 **SCRIPTURIENT (IRE)**, 6, ch g Arakan (USA)—Kelso Magic (USA) **J. M. C. Hodge**

287 MR RON HODGES, Somerton
Postal: **Little Orchard, George Street, Charlton Adam, Somerton, Somerset, TA11 7AS**
Contacts: **PHONE (01458) 223922 MOBILE (07770) 625846**
E-MAIL mandyhodges@btconnect.com

1 **BE HAPPY TWO**, 4, b f Delegator—There's Two (IRE) **J & P Frampton R J Hodges**
2 **DAYLAMI KIRK (IRE)**, 7, b g Daylami (IRE)—Uptothefrontkirk (IRE) **P. L. Hart**
3 **DAYTIME AHEAD (IRE)**, 7, gr m Daylami (IRE)—Bright Times Ahead (IRE) **R J Hodges & C Mackenzie**
4 **DREAMS OF GLORY**, 10, ch g Resplendent Glory (IRE)—Pip's Dream **P. E. Axon**
5 **EVENING STARLIGHT**, 5, gr m Kyllachy—Night Haven **R. J. Hodges**
6 **GENERAL GIRLING**, 11, b g General Gambul—Gold Charm **The Yeovilton Flyers**
7 **HERE'S TWO**, 5, b m Hellvelyn—There's Two (IRE) **K Corcoran, C E Weare, R J Hodges**
8 **MET BY MOONLIGHT**, 4, b f Sakhee's Secret—Starlight Walk **P. E. Axon**

MR RON HODGES - Continued

    9 **MIDNIGHT MIDGE**, 4, b g Midnight Legend—Posh Emily **A Midgley, R J Hodges**
  10 **MISTER MUSICMASTER**, 9, b g Amadeus Wolf—Misty Eyed (IRE) **Mrs S G Clapp & R J Hodges**
  11 **OH DEAR OH DEAR**, 10, b m Pasternak—Post It **Mr J. M. Dare**
  12 **WILSPA'S MAGIC (IRE)**, g m Zebedee—Triple Zero (IRE) **The Gardens Entertainments Ltd&Mr Hodges**

TWO-YEAR-OLDS

  13 **LAWN MEET**, b f 16/2 Foxwedge (AUS)—Lane County (USA) (Rahy (USA)) **John Frampton & Paul Frampton**

Other Owners: Mrs S. G. Clapp, K. J. Corcoran, Mr J. L. Frampton, Mr Paul S. Frampton, The Gardens Entertainments Ltd, Ms Jane Girling, Mr John Knight (Somerset), Mr C. Mackenzie, Mr Andrew Midgley, Mr C. E. Weare.

---

288   MR HENRY HOGARTH, Stillington
Postal: New Grange Farm, Stillington, York
Contacts: **PHONE** (01347) 811168 **FAX** (01347) 811168 **MOBILE** (07788) 777044
E-MAIL harryhogarth@ymail.com

  1 **ALADDIN SANE (IRE)**, 4, b g Teofilo (IRE)—Aqua Aura (USA) **Hogarth Racing**
  2 **ALTO DES MOTTES (FR)**, 8, b g Dream Well (FR)—Omance (FR) **Hogarth Racing**
  3 **BOSS DES MOTTES (FR)**, 7, b g Califet (FR)—Puszta des Mottes (FR) **Hogarth Racing**
  4 **FIGHTING BACK**, 7, b g Galileo (IRE)—Maroochydore (IRE) **Hogarth Racing**
  5 **GRAND ENTERPRISE**, 8, b g Fair Mix (IRE)—Miss Chinchilla **Hogarth Racing**
  6 **GRIS DE PRON (FR)**, 5, b g Gris de Gris (FR)—Say Say (FR) **Hogarth Racing**
  7 **HATTONS HILL (IRE)**, 9, b g Pierre—Cluain Chaoin (IRE) **Hogarth Racing**
  8 **HERITAGE WAY**, 9, b g Tamayaz (CAN)—Morning Caller (IRE) **Hogarth Racing**
  9 **KILCULLEN LADY (IRE)**, 8, b m Scorpion (IRE)—Glittering Star (IRE) **Hogarth Racing**
  10 **LAKEFIELD REBEL (IRE)**, 12, b br g Presenting—River Mousa (IRE) **Hogarth Racing**
  11 **LENTEN ROSE (IRE)**, 6, b m Milan—Our Song **Hogarth Racing**
  12 **SUPER LUNAR (IRE)**, 9, b g Super Celebre (FR)—Kapricia Speed (FR) **Hogarth Racing**

Other Owners: Mr P. H. Hogarth, Mr H. P. Hogarth, Mr J. Hogarth, Mr J. L. Hogarth.

Jockey (NH): Tony Kelly. **Conditional:** Jamie Hamilton. **Amateur:** Miss Emma Todd.

---

289   MISS SARAH HOLLINSHEAD, Upper Longdon
Postal: **Lodge Farm, Upper Longdon, Rugeley, Staffordshire, WS15 1QF**
Contacts: **PHONE** (01543) 490298

  1 **BILASH**, 11, gr g Choisir (AUS)—Goldeva **Pyle & Hollinshead**
  2 **CASTLEREA TESS**, 5, ch m Pastoral Pursuits—Zartwyda (IRE) **Graham Brothers Racing Partnership**
  3 **CHASE ME (IRE)**, 7, b g Mahler—Collatrim Choice (IRE) **Mr Paul Shaw & Mr Mark Round**
  4 **FINAL ATTACK (IRE)**, 7, b g Cape Cross (IRE)—Northern Melody (IRE) **N. Chapman**
  5 **GEALACH GHORM (IRE)**, 4, b g Finsceal Fior (IRE)—
                                   Saintly Wish (USA) **The Mr R. Robinson & Sarah Hollinshead**
  6 **HANDSOME DAN (IRE)**, 12, b g Busy Flight—Beautiful City (IRE) **Graham Brothers Racing Partnership**
  7 **HEAD HIGH (IRE)**, 5, gr g Mastercraftsman (IRE)—Elisium **Mr P Shaw, Mr M Round, Mrs M Moore**
  8 **LACEY**, 9, b g Rail Link—Shamana (USA) **Mr N. S. Sweeney/Miss Sarah Hollinshead**
  9 **LOOKFORARAINBOW**, 5, b g Rainbow High—Look Here's May **The Giddy Gang**
  10 **MISTRESS VIZ (IRE)**, 4, gr f Mastercraftsman (IRE)—Vizean (IRE) **Mr J. A. Ashley**
  11 **MYSTERIOUS GLANCE**, 5, b m Cacique (IRE)—Largo (IRE) **S. L. Edwards**
  12 **MYSTERIOUS LOOK**, 5, ch m Sakhee's Secret—Look Here's Carol (IRE) **S. L. Edwards**
  13 **TESS GRAHAM**, 4, b f Pastoral Pursuits—Zartwyda (IRE) **Graham Brothers Racing Partnership**
  14 **UNCLE BERNIE (IRE)**, 8, gr g Aussie Rules (USA)—Alwiyda (USA) **Graham Brothers Racing Partnership**
  15 **WELL OWD MON**, 8, b g Vitus—Farina (IRE) **The Giddy Gang**
  16 **ZENAFIRE**, 9, b g Firebreak—Zen Garden **Mr R. J. R. Moseley**

THREE-YEAR-OLDS

  17 **FAIR ISLAND**, b f Trans Island—La Vie Est Belle **The Three R's 1**
  18 **JENNY REN**, b f Multiplex—Cherished Love (IRE) **Miss S. A. Hollinshead**
  19 **MADAME JO JO**, ch f Havana Gold (IRE)—Paradise Place **David Lockwood & Fred Lockwood**

Other Owners: Mr A. M. Graham, Mr M. P. Graham, Mr A. Lawrence, Mr F. M. Lockwood, D. J. Lockwood, Mrs M. A. Moore, M. J. F. Pyle, Mrs T. P. Pyle, R. Robinson, Mr M. D. Round, Mr P. A. Shaw, Mrs C. A. Stevenson, Mr N. S. Sweeney.

290 MRS STEPH HOLLINSHEAD, Rugeley

Postal: Deva House, Bardy Lane, Longdon, Rugeley, Staffordshire, WS15 4LJ
Contacts: PHONE (01543) 493656 MOBILE (07791) 385335
E-MAIL steph_hollinshead@hotmail.co.uk WEBSITE www.stephhollinsheadracing.com

1 BELLE EN NOIR, 6, b m Black Sam Bellamy (IRE)—Miss Holly **The Four Plus Two More Partnership**
2 BELLEDESERT, 5, b m Pastoral Pursuits—Ocean Blaze **K Meredith, D Hodson, The Ocean Four**
3 CAHAR FAD (IRE), 6, b g Bushranger (IRE)—Tarbiyah **D Hodson, K Meredith, N Sweeney**
4 CORAL CAYE, 4, b f Pastoral Pursuits—Vermilion Creek **M. A. N. Johnson**
5 FRANK THE BARBER (IRE), 6, gr g Zebedee—Red Rosanna **Mrs D. A. Hodson**
6 LADY EMMA, 5, b m Mount Nelson—Songbook **Sweeney, Hollinshead & Hawkins**
7 SNOWY DAWN, 8, gr g Notnowcato—Tereyna **Mrs C. A. Stevenson**
8 SPIRIT OF ROSANNA, 6, gr m Hellvelyn—Tharwa (IRE) **Mr J. Holcombe**
9 STONEYFORD LANE (IRE), 4, b g Bushranger (IRE)—Peace Talks **Ocean Four**

THREE-YEAR-OLDS

10 BILLIEBROOKEDIT, ch c Dragon Pulse (IRE)—Klang (IRE) **Mr M. Gavin**
11 BIRTHDAY CAKE, b g Denounce—Angel Cake (IRE) **W. Sewell**
12 ENCHANTING ENYA (IRE), ch f Champs Elysees—Miss Honorine **Mr M. Gavin**
13 GRANDMA TILLY, b f Hellvelyn—Sleep Dance **Mrs D. A. Hodson**
14 KYLIE STYLE, b f Aussie Rules (USA)—Stilettoesinthemud (IRE) **Proxygene Kylie Syndicate**
15 RUBY SOUND, b f Assertive—Vermilion Creek **Mr M. Johnson & Mrs L. A. Hollinshead**
16 SNOOKER JIM, b c Holy Roman Emperor (IRE)—Lucia de Medici **Mrs D. A. Hodson**
17 STOCKINGS LANE (IRE), ch c Excelebration (IRE)—Mubkera (IRE) **Christine Stevenson & Debbie Hodson**
18 THE GOLDEN CUE, ch g Zebedee—Khafayif (USA) **The Golden Cue Partnership**

TWO-YEAR-OLDS

19 CASTER SEMENYA, gr f 6/4 Albaasil (IRE)—Goldeva (Makbul) (5714) **Mr M & Mrs T Pyle & Longdon Stud**
20 B c 2/2 Finjaan—Girl of The Rain (IRE) (Refuse To Bend (IRE)) (4285) **Dash Bloodstock Ltd**
21 B f 9/1 Mukhadram—Green Poppy (Green Desert (USA)) (2000) **Dash Bloodstock Ltd**
22 Ch f 29/4 Nayef (USA)—Harriet's Girl (Choisir (AUS)) (4761) **Ray Bailey**
23 B f 30/1 Heeraat (IRE)—Matron (Bahamian Bounty) (7142) **MAGG Group & Richard Kent**
24 B f 30/3 Albaasil (IRE)—Mohair (Motivator) **Mrs Veronica Gilbert**
25 B c 5/4 Lethal Force (IRE)—Peace Talks (Pivotal) **Julia Howlett**
26 B f 5/2 Sepoy (AUS)—True Course (Dubawi (IRE)) (16190) **Mrs Debbie Hodson**
27 B c 8/4 Heeraat (IRE)—Word Perfect (Diktat) (7500) **Dash Bloodstock Ltd**

Other Owners: Mr D. J. Carter, Mr A. C. Gray, Mrs G. Gray, Mr G. Hancock, Mr A. Hawkins, Mrs S. C. Hawkins, Mr A. J. Highfield, Mrs L. A. Hollinshead, Mrs J. E. Howlett, K. S. Meredith, Mr G. T. Rowley, Mr N. S. Sweeney, Mr M. J. Upton.

Assistant Trainer: Adam Hawkins (07554) 008405

Jockey (flat): Adam Beschizza, Royston Ffrench. **Amateur:** Mr Liam Hamblett.

291 MR PATRICK HOLMES, Middleham

Postal: Little Spigot, Coverham, Middleham, Leyburn, North Yorkshire, DL8 4TL
Contacts: PHONE (01969) 624880 MOBILE (07740) 589857
E-MAIL patrick@foulriceparkracing.com WEBSITE www.foulriceparkracing.com

1 ANGUINO (FR), 5, b g Lucarno (USA)—Anguilla (GER) **Mrs C. M. Clarke**
2 ASYLO (IRE), 6, b g Flemensfirth (USA)—Escrea (IRE) **Mr A. L. Brooks**
3 AUXILIARY, 5, b g Fast Company (IRE)—Lady Xara (IRE) **Mrs C M Clarke, Foulrice Park Racing Ltd**
4 BIG CHUNKY (IRE), 5, b g Kalanisi (IRE)—Mystic Vic (IRE) **Mrs M. Hatfield & Mrs S. Kramer**
5 BOGARDUS (IRE), 7, b g Dalakhani (IRE)—Sugar Mint (IRE) **Peter Acheson & Foulrice Park Racing Ltd**
6 BUYER BEWARE (IRE), 6, br g Big Bad Bob (IRE)—Adoring (IRE) **Mr C. R. Stirling**
7 CAPTAIN PEAKY, 5, b g Captain Gerrard (IRE)—Multi-Loft **Foulrice Park Racing Limited**
8 CHARAVA (IRE), 6, br g Captain Marvelous (IRE)—Sweet Compliance **Oakfield Racing**
9 DUCK EGG BLUE (IRE), 4, b f Haatef (USA)—Sapphire Spray (IRE) **Foulrice Park Racing Limited**
10 FILLYDELPHIA (IRE), 7, b m Strategic Prince—Lady Fonic **FPR Syndicate 7**
11 FRAMLEY GARTH (IRE), 6, b g Clodovil (IRE)—Two Marks (USA) **FPR Yorkshire Syndicate**
12 LIFE KNOWLEDGE (IRE), 6, ch g Thewayyouare (USA)—
                                    Rosa Bellini (IRE) **Mrs C M Clarke, Foulrice Park Racing Ltd**

MR PATRICK HOLMES - Continued

13 **LUSO BENNY (IRE)**, 6, ch g Beneficial—Luas Luso (IRE) **J. B. Wallwin**
14 **MISSION TRIO (IRE)**, 6, b g Presenting—Miss Brandywell (IRE) **J. B. Wallwin**
15 **MUSICO (IRE)**, 4, b g Lilbourne Lad (IRE)—Viola da Gamba (FR) **Foulrice Park Racing Limited**
16 **OPTIMA PETAMUS**, 6, gr g Mastercraftsman (IRE)—
    In A Silent Way (IRE) **Mrs C M Clarke, Foulrice Park Racing Ltd**
17 **PRINCESS NEARCO (IRE)**, 4, b f Elzaam (AUS)—Royal Jubilee (IRE) **Mrs C M Clarke, Foulrice Park Racing Ltd**
18 **REFLATION**, 6, b g Stimulation (IRE)—Miss Poppy **Foulrice Park Racing Limited**
19 **SIR DOMINO (FR)**, 6, b g Evasive—Domino Queen (IRE) **Peter Acheson & Foulrice Park Racing Ltd**
20 **STORMBAY BOMBER (IRE)**, 9, b g September Storm (GER)—Top Tottie (IRE) **Mr P R Walker & Mr R Walker**
21 **TOMORROW'S LEGEND**, 8, b g Midnight Legend—Colvada **Mrs M. Hatfield & Mrs S. Kramer**

Other Owners: Mr P. Acheson, Mrs M. Hatfield, Mrs S. Kramer, Miss M. A. Stirling, Mrs A. M. Stirling, Mr R. J. Stirling, Mr P. R. Walker, Mr R. Walker.

Assistant Trainer: Liam Bailey

Jockey (NH): John Kington. **Apprentice:** Paula Muir.

---

292 **MR JOHN HOLT, Peckleton**
Postal: **Hall Farm, Church Road, Peckleton, Leicester, LE9 7RA**
Contacts: **PHONE/FAX (01455) 821972 MOBILE (07850) 321059**
E-MAIL **hallfarmracing@btconnect.com** WEBSITE www.hallfarmracing.co.uk

1 **BARNSDALE**, 5, b g Stimulation (IRE)—Seren Teg **Planters (Leicester) Limited**
2 **DREAM VOICE (IRE)**, 5, b m Approve (IRE)—Louve Sereine (FR) **J. R. Holt**
3 **GLYDER**, 4, b f Camacho—Blades Princess **Jobsworth Racing**
4 **GOADBY**, 7, gr m Kodiac—Gone Sailing **Cleartherm Glass Sealed Units Ltd**
5 **ICEAXE**, 5, b m Stimulation (IRE)—Laser Crystal (IRE) **J. R. Holt**
6 **MINI'S DESTINATION**, 10, b m Dubai Destination (USA)—Heather Mix **J. R. Holt**
7 **NOMADRUSH**, 8, b m Nomadic Way (USA)—Tanguero (IRE) **Mrs C. M. Tyler**
8 **NUMBER THEORY**, 10, b g Halling (USA)—Numanthia (IRE) **Mr M. S. Fonseka**

THREE-YEAR-OLDS

9 **MOCEAD CAPPALL**, b f Captain Gerrard (IRE)—All Fur Coat **Holt, Lynch, Mickley Stud**
10 **TIGGERHAPPY**, b f Native Ruler—Hikkaduwa **Mr M. S. Fonseka**

TWO-YEAR-OLDS

11 B f 16/3 Bated Breath—Sina (GER) (Trans Island) (2500)

Other Owners: Mr A. A. Ford, Mr M. P. Gavin, R. Kent, Mr M. G. Lynch.

Assistant Trainer: Jessica Holt

Apprentice: Megan Ellingworth.

---

293 **MR ANTHONY HONEYBALL, Beaminster**
Postal: **Potwell Farm, Mosterton, Beaminster, Dorset, DT8 3HG**
Contacts: **PHONE (01308) 867452 MOBILE (07815) 898569**
E-MAIL **anthony@ajhoneyballracing.co.uk** WEBSITE www.ajhoneyballracing.co.uk

1 **ACEY MILAN (IRE)**, 4, b g Milan—Strong Wishes (IRE) **Owners For Owners: Acey Milan**
2 **ACT NOW**, 9, br m Act One—Lady Turk (FR) **Barrow Hill**
3 **BLACK PRINCE (FR)**, 4, b g Falco (USA)—Thamara (USA) **Owners For Owners: Black Prince**
4 **CHILL FACTOR (IRE)**, 9, b g Oscar (IRE)—Glacial Princess (IRE) **Potwell Partners**
5 **CITY SUPREME (IRE)**, 8, b g Milan—Run Supreme (IRE) **San Siro Six**
6 **CLOUDY BOB (IRE)**, 11, gr g Cloudings (IRE)—Keen Supreme (IRE) **Men Of Stone**
7 **CRESSWELL BREEZE**, 8, b m Midnight Legend—Cresswell Willow (IRE) **Bright N Breezy**
8 **DON LAMI (FR)**, 5, ch g Honolulu (IRE)—Toutamie (FR) **Les Amis De Don**
9 **DOUBLE ACCORD**, 8, ch m Double Trigger (IRE)—Got Tune (FR) **R W Huggins & Atlantic Racing**
10 **DROPS OF JUPITOR (IRE)**, 6, gr m Dylan Thomas (IRE)—Fancy Intense **Mr & Mrs G Woodley**
11 **DUHALLOW GESTURE (IRE)**, 6, b m King's Theatre (IRE)—Rare Gesture (IRE) **Galveston Partners**

MR ANTHONY HONEYBALL - Continued

12 **EAST WING (IRE)**, 6, b g Winged Love (IRE)—Eastender **Geegeez.co.uk PA**
13 4, B f Double Trigger (IRE)—Encore du Cristal (USA) **Mr R. W. Huggins**
14 **ENNISTOWN**, 8, b g Authorized (IRE)—Saoirse Abu (USA) **Jones, Kelly & Whittle**
15 **EVERLANES**, 5, br m Shirocco (GER)—Good Thinking **Barrow Hill**
16 **HIDEAWAY VIC (IRE)**, 5, b g Stowaway—Cailin Vic Mo Cri (IRE) **Michael & Angela Bone**
17 **INDIAN BRAVE (IRE)**, 7, b g Definite Article—Fridays Folly (IRE) **Mr D. J. Bridger**
18 **JUKEBOX JIVE (FR)**, 4, b g Jukebox Jury (IRE)—Sweetheart **Mr R. W. Huggins**
19 **LE COEUR NET (FR)**, 6, ch g Network (GER)—Silverwood (FR) **The Potwell Optimists**
20 **LECHLADE MAGICIAN (IRE)**, 5, b g Getaway (GER)—Run Supreme (IRE) **Mr M. R. Chapman**
21 **MIDNIGHT TUNE**, 7, b m Midnight Legend—Harmonic Motion (IRE) **The Park Homes Syndicate**
22 **MOZO**, 7, b m Milan—Haudello (FR) **Anthony Honeyball Racing Club Ltd**
23 **MS PARFOIS (IRE)**, 7, ch m Mahler—Dolly Lewis **Mr M. R. Chapman**
24 **MY DANCE**, 6, b m Kayf Tara—My Petra **Geegeez.co.uk PA**
25 **NOCTURNAL MYTH**, 5, b g Midnight Legend—Gan On **The Night Shifters**
26 **OUR SOX (IRE)**, 9, b g September Storm (GER)—Winning Sally (IRE) **Anthony Honeyball Racing Club Ltd**
27 **PORT ROYALE, (IRE)**, b m King's Theatre (IRE)—Easibrook Jane **Barrow Hill**
28 **PURE VISION (IRE)**, 7, b g Milan—Distillery Lane (IRE) **Mr J. P. McManus**
29 **REBOUND (IRE)**, 5, b g Big Bad Bob (IRE)—Shine Silently (IRE) **Mr P. P. Thorman**
30 **REGAL ENCORE (IRE)**, 10, b g King's Theatre (IRE)—Go On Eileen (IRE) **Mr J. P. McManus**
31 **REPRESENTED (IRE)**, 5, b g Presenting—Lunar Path (IRE) **One Small Step**
32 **SAM BROWN**, 6, b g Black Sam Bellamy (IRE)—Cream Cracker **Mr T. C. Frost**
33 **SHAPIRO**, 5, b m Schiaparelli (GER)—Lady Turk (FR) **Burley, Buckingham, Chapman & Cobbett**
34 **SOJOURN (IRE)**, 5, b g Getaway (GER)—Toscar (IRE) **Jon & Jacqueline Hughes**
35 **SOLSTICE SON**, 9, b g Haafhd—Karasta (IRE) **The Summer Solstice**
36 **SOLSTICE TWILIGHT**, 6, b m Milan—Twilight Eclipse (IRE) **Gill Langford & Dorothy Ritzema**
37 **SOULSAVER**, 6, ch g Recharge (IRE)—Lapina (IRE) **R. J. Matthews**
38 **TACENDA (IRE)**, 6, b m Flemensfirth (USA)—Tordasia (IRE) **Return Ta Senda**
39 **URCA DE LIMA**, 5, b m Black Sam Bellamy (IRE)—Dame Fonteyn **R. W. Devlin**

THREE-YEAR-OLDS

40 Br f Midnight Legend—Carrigeen Queen (IRE) **Ms G. S. Langford**

Other Owners: Atlantic Racing Limited, Mr M. Bisogno, Mr J. F. Blackburn, Mr M. J. Bone, Mrs A. P. Bone, Mrs M. H. Bowden, D. F. Briers, Mrs J. L. Buckingham, Mr J. Burley, Mr J. Cannon, Mr A. J. Chapman, Mr C. R. Cobbett, Mr A. G. Craig, Mr T. Dal, Mr P. K. Davis, Mr I. Dickson, Mr J. Fairrie, Mr M. S. Green, Mr R. Guest, Mr A. Honeyball, Mr E. J. Hughes, Mrs J. Hughes, Mr E. Jones, Mr B. Jones, Mr N. Kelly, Mr P. D. Lloyd, N. J. McMullan, Mr L. Moody, Mrs S. M. Morley, M. C. Pipe, Mrs D. J. Ritzema, Mr J. P. Romans, Mrs W. A. Shuttleworth, Mr A. J. Smith, R. G. Tizzard, Mrs S. L. Tizzard, Mr J. S. Whittle, Mrs D. Woodley, Mr G. R. Woodley.

Assistant Trainer: Rachael Honeyball (07813) 984418

Jockey (NH): Aidan Coleman, David Noonan.

---

294 **MRS JO HUGHES, Lambourn**
Postal: **Hill House Stables, Folly Road, Lambourn, Hungerford, Berkshire, RG17 8QE**
Contacts: **PHONE** (01488) 71444 **FAX** (01488) 71103 **MOBILE** (07900) 680189
E-MAIL johughes3@aol.co.uk WEBSITE www.johughesracing.co.uk

1 **CALEDONIA DUCHESS**, 5, b m Dutch Art—Granuaile O'malley (IRE) **Isla & Colin Cage**
2 **CALEDONIA LAIRD**, 7, b g Firebreak—Granuaile O'malley (IRE) **Isla & Colin Cage**
3 **COMPASS HILL (USA)**, 6, ch g Mizzen Mast (USA)—Zamindarling (USA) **Mrs C. C. Regalado-Gonzalez**
4 **DALAVIDA (FR)**, 4, gr f Kendargent (FR)—Dalawysa (FR) **Mickley Stud & Derrick Mossop**
5 **DIABLO DE ROUHET (FR)**, 5, b g Great Pretender (IRE)—Querelle d'estruval (FR) **Business Moves Group Ltd**
6 **IGNACIO ZULOAGA (IRE)**, 4, ch g Lope de Vega (IRE)—Indian Express **Mrs C. C. Regalado-Gonzalez**
7 **LEFORTOVO (FR)**, 5, b g Arcano (IRE)—Lorientaise (IRE) **Mrs C. C. Regalado-Gonzalez**
8 **RIP VAN SUZY (IRE)**, 5, br m Rip Van Winkle (IRE)—Suzy Bliss **Mr R. P. Phillips**
9 **ROCK ICON**, 5, b g Sixties Icon—Monashee Rock (IRE) **Mr M. Black**
10 **SILVER MAN**, 11, gr g Silver Patriarch (IRE)—Another Mans Cause (FR) **T. J. Wardle**

MRS JO HUGHES - Continued

THREE-YEAR-OLDS

 11 **ALONSO CANO (IRE)**, b c High Chaparral (IRE)—Awjila **Mrs C. C. Regalado-Gonzalez**
 12 **CAPE GRECO (USA)**, b g Cape Blanco (IRE)—High Walden (USA) **Joe Smith, Jimmy Smith, Jo Hughes**
 13 **CAPTAIN KISSINGER**, b g Captain Gerrard (IRE)—Nigella **Mrs J. F. Hughes**
 14 **CELTIC RAIDER (FR)**, ch c Siyouni (FR)—Madawaska (USA) **Mr R. P. Phillips**
 15 **DIAMOND PURSUIT**, b f Pastoral Pursuits—Broughtons Jewel (IRE) **David Klein & Jo Hughes**
 16 **FLOR DE SEDA (FR)**, b f George Vancouver (USA)—Toile de Soie (FR) **J Melo & J Hughes**
 17 **GET EVEN**, b f Multiplex—Retaliator **Richard Kent & Jo Hughes**
 18 **JONA'S ECLIPSE**, ch f Showcasing—Newkeylets **Miss L. Ormsby**
 19 **LLAMREI**, b f Multiplex—Nalear (FR) **Church Racing Partnership & Jo Hughes**
 20 **MAJOR PEIRSON (IRE)**, b g Society Rock—Snowtime (IRE) **Mrs C C Regalado-Gonzalez & Jo Hughes**
 21 **PEGGY'S ANGEL**, b f Captain Gerrard (IRE)—Dora's Sister (IRE) **Dalwhinnie Bloodstock Limited**
 22 **PURAMENTE**, ch g Pastoral Pursuits—Sahend (IRE) **Mr H. S. Maan**
 23 **WHITE FEATHER**, ch g Bated Breath—Just Wood (IRE) **J. Smith**

TWO-YEAR-OLDS

 24 Ch g 17/2 Evasive—Only For Fun (IRE) (Kheleyf (USA)) **M Ali & A Cordero**

Other Owners: Mr M. Ali, Mr A. Bibi Cordero, J. E. Bone, Mrs I. Cage, Mr C. J. Cage, Church Racing Partnership, J. Kavanagh, R. Kent, Mr D. A. Klein, Mr J. Melo, D. Mossop, Mr J. D. A. Smith.

Assistant Trainer: Paul Blockley (07778 318295)

---

295 MR RICHARD HUGHES, Upper Lambourn
Postal: **Weathercock House, Upper Lambourn, Hungerford, Berkshire, RG17 8QT**
Contacts: **PHONE (01488) 71198 MOBILE (07768) 894828**
E-MAIL **office@richardhughesracing.co.uk** WEBSITE **www.richardhughesracing.co.uk**

 1 **AMITIE WALTZ (FR)**, 6, b g Sinndar (IRE)—Lia Waltz (FR) **Third Time Lucky**
 2 **ANGEL'S QUEST (FR)**, 4, b f Dark Angel (IRE)—Lilac Charm (IRE) **HP Racing Angel's Quest**
 3 **BARYE**, 7, b g Archipenko (USA)—Oblige **Mr Anthony Hogarth**
 4 **BEEPEECEE**, 4, b g Henrythenavigator (USA)—Roedean (IRE) **BPC Partnership**
 5 **BELIEVE IT (IRE)**, 6, b h Rip Van Winkle (IRE)—Have Faith (IRE) **Richard Hughes Racing Club**
 6 **DR JULIUS NO**, 4, b g Dick Turpin (IRE)—Royal Assent **Gallagher Bloodstock Limited**
 7 **GETBACK IN PARIS (IRE)**, 5, ch g Galileo (IRE)—Elusive Wave (IRE) **Mr G. B. Firmager & G. H. Firmager**
 8 **GOLDEN WOLF (IRE)**, 4, b br g Big Bad Bob (IRE)—Jeunesse Doree (IRE) **Aristotle's Elements**
 9 **JASHMA (IRE)**, 4, b g Power—Daganya (IRE) **M Clarke, S Geraghty, J Jeffries**
 10 **KATH'S LEGACY**, 5, ch m Cockney Rebel (IRE)—It's Dubai Dolly **Mr Merv Cox**
 11 **MR MINERALS**, 4, ch g Poet's Voice—River Song (USA) **Mr R. P. Gallagher**
 12 **PACO'S ANGEL**, 4, b f Paco Boy (IRE)—Papabile (USA) **Biddestone Racing Partnership XIII**
 13 **PLANT POT POWER (IRE)**, 4, b c Lawman (FR)—Featherweight (IRE)
 14 **SEE OF ROME**, 4, gr g Pour Moi (IRE)—Balandra **John & Jordan Lund**
 15 **SOGHAN (IRE)**, 4, b g Cape Cross (IRE)—Quiet Dream (USA) **The Queens**
 16 **STANLEY**, 5, b g Sea The Stars (IRE)—Deirdre **Normandie Stud Ltd**
 17 **TWENTY TIMES (IRE)**, 4, b f Dream Ahead (USA)—Mad Existence (IRE) **True Reds**

THREE-YEAR-OLDS

 18 **ACQUIRER (IRE)**, b g Zoffany (IRE)—See Emily Play (IRE) **Top Trumps Partnership**
 19 **APPENZELLER (USA)**, gr g Mizzen Mast (USA)—Uforia (USA) **Mrs D J Fleming & Partner**
 20 **BIG BRAVE BOB**, b c Big Bad Bob (IRE)—Namaadhej (USA) **Biddestone Racing Partnership XIII**
 21 **CARRICKLANE**, b f Zoffany (IRE)—New River (IRE) **The New River Partnership**
 22 **ELLEN GATES**, b f Mayson—Mrs Greeley **Prime Suspects**
 23 **FAYROUZ ROSE (IRE)**, b f Epaulette (AUS)—Very Nice **Mr Jaber Abdullah**
 24 **GEORGE OF HEARTS (FR)**, gr c Kendargent (FR)—Bugie d'amore **Mr D. Campbell & Mr D. Waters**
 25 **GLENDEVON (USA)**, ch c Scat Daddy (USA)—Flip Flop (FR) **Cheveley Park Stud, Campbell & Waters**
 26 **GOLD FILIGREE (IRE)**, b f Dark Angel (IRE)—Gold Lace (IRE) **Galloway, Lawrence, Merritt & Mrs Blake**
 27 **HOLLYDAZE (IRE)**, b f Big Bad Bob (IRE)—Fashionable **Mr P. D. Merritt**
 28 **INUK (IRE)**, b f Kodiac—Elkmait **Mrs Fiona Young**
 29 **JACK TAYLOR (IRE)**, b c Invincible Spirit (IRE)—Glory Power (IRE) **Mr Anthony Hogarth**
 30 **KATH'S LUSTRE**, b f Dick Turpin (IRE)—It's Dubai Dolly **Mr Merv Cox**
 31 **KENDAR ROUGE (FR)**, b f Kendargent (FR)—Lune Rouge (IRE) **Top Trumps Partnership**
 32 **MARIE FRANCE**, b f Sepoy (AUS)—Maria Letizia **Normandie Stud Ltd**
 33 **NAPOLEONICA**, gr f Dalakhani (IRE)—Napoleon's Sister (IRE) **Normandie Stud Ltd**

MR RICHARD HUGHES - Continued

34 **NOTEWORTHY (IRE)**, b f Acclamation—Church Melody **Rosenblatt, Mandell & Margolis**
35 **ODYSSA (IRE)**, b f Kodiac—Deliziosa (IRE) **The Low Flyers**
36 **POLLYISSIMO**, ch f Nathaniel (IRE)—Fleurissimo **M Flitton, K Lawrence & Partner**
37 **RAGSTONE RIDGE (FR)**, ch g Choisir (AUS)—Almogia (USA) **Gallagher Bloodstock Limited**
38 **RAGSTONE ROAD (IRE)**, b c Kodiac—Greenflash **Gallagher Bloodstock Limited**
39 **ROYAL GOLDIE (IRE)**, b f Havana Gold (IRE)—Dream Maker (IRE) **Mr Jaber Abdullah**
40 **RUSTANG (FR)**, b g Holy Roman Emperor (IRE)—Oppamattox (FR) **White Beech Farm**
41 **SECRATARIO (FR)**, ch g Kendargent (FR)—Amoa (USA) **The Queens**
42 **TWILIGHT WAR (IRE)**, b g Declaration of War (USA)—Special Assignment (USA) **Fourth Time Lucky**
43 **YAA MOUS**, b f Farhh—Sweet Lilly **Mr Jaber Abdullah**
44 **ZAPATEADO**, b f Zoffany (IRE)—Ziggy Zaggy **Mr Don Churston & Mr Ray Greatorex**

TWO-YEAR-OLDS

45 **AMBITION**, ch f 18/3 Dubawi (IRE)—Talent (New Approach (IRE)) **Mr Mark Dixon & Mr J Roswell**
46 **ANTIDOTE (IRE)**, gr c 13/3 Dark Angel (IRE)—Mood Indigo (IRE) (Indian Ridge) (100000) **Mr Anthony Hogarth**
47 B c 3/5 War Command (USA)—Aurelia (Rainbow Quest (USA)) (33000) **M Clarke, P Munnelly & D Waters**
48 **BALLYLEMON (IRE)**, b c 11/4 Champs Elysees—
           Athreyaa (Singspiel (IRE)) (75000) **Graham Doyle & Hazel Lawrence**
49 B c 21/3 Le Havre (IRE)—Bugie d'amore (Rail Link) (40700) **Mr Danny Waters**
50 **CANFORD DANCER**, b f 25/2 Canford Cliffs (IRE)—
           Petite Nymphe (Golan (IRE)) (25000) **The Lakota Partnership & Mrs J. Blake**
51 **DANDY LAD (IRE)**, b c 5/5 Dandy Man (IRE)—Lucky Pipit (Key of Luck (USA)) (32000) **Mr Peter Crane**
52 B f 18/3 Kuroshio (AUS)—Doris Souter (IRE) (Desert Story (IRE)) **Mr P. D. Merritt**
53 B c 11/2 Swiss Spirit—Encore Encore (FR) (Royal Applause) (35000)
54 B c 9/3 Lethal Force (IRE)—Garraun (IRE) (Tamayuz) (30117) **John & Jordan Lund**
55 B f 22/3 Paco Boy (IRE)—Goldamour (IRE) (Fasliyev (USA)) **Richard Hughes Racing Club**
56 B c 29/1 Mayson—Jessie's Spirit (IRE) (Clodovil (IRE)) (16190)
57 **KADIZ (IRE)**, b f 14/4 Lope de Vega (IRE)—Looby Loo (Kyllachy) (47619) **The High Flyers**
58 **LIGHT UP OUR STARS (IRE)**, b c 7/3 Rip Van Winkle (IRE)—
           Shine Like A Star (Fantastic Light (USA)) (30000) **Dereck Boocock**
59 **LILLE**, b f 1/4 Equiano (FR)—Interlace (Pivotal) **Cheveley Park Stud Limited**
60 Ch f 7/2 Showcasing—Magic Art (IRE) (Nayef (USA)) (48840) **C. McHale & The Rat Pack Partnership**
61 B c 19/1 Kendargent (FR)—Meandra (IRE) (Dubawi (IRE)) (22792) **Mr John Henwood**
62 Ch c 19/2 Kyllachy—Miss Bond (IRE) (Danehill Dancer (IRE)) (44769) **H. Robin Heffer**
63 B c 5/3 Olympic Glory (IRE)—Miss Hygrove (IRE) (Exceed And Excel (AUS)) (25234) **H. Robin Heffer**
64 **MORE THAN LIKELY**, b f 5/4 Coach House (IRE)—
           Moss Likely (IRE) (Clodovil (IRE)) (8571) **H Pinniger & Peter Cook**
65 B f 17/3 Kodiac—Mysteriousness (FR) (Beat Hollow) (40700)
66 B c 28/3 Dark Angel (IRE)—Mythicism (Oasis Dream) (48000) **M Clarke, P Munnelly & D Waters**
67 B f 8/5 Harbour Watch (IRE)—New River (IRE) (Montjeu (IRE)) **The New River Partnership**
68 B f 14/2 Society Rock (IRE)—Pareia (GER) (Areion (GER)) (15000) **Mr Jaber Abdullah**
69 **PRETTY EYES (IRE)**, b f 15/2 Kodiac—
           Maoin Dor (GER) (Manduro (GER)) (66666) **Cedar Investments Ltd & Mr M Burke**
70 **PUZZLE**, b g 10/3 Paco Boy (IRE)—Appleton Drove (USA) (Street Cry (IRE)) **Her Majesty The Queen**
71 **QUEEN SHAAHD (IRE)**, b f 28/4 Kodiac—Cherika (IRE) (Cape Cross (IRE)) (38095) **Mr Jaber Abdullah**
72 **RATTLE ALONG (IRE)**, b c 3/5 Dansili—Paramita (FR) (Galileo (IRE)) **Niarchos Family**
73 **RENNEH**, ch f 31/3 Mukhadram—Wish You Luck (Dubai Destination (USA)) (14285) **Mr Jaber Abdullah**
74 **SAEDI SHAAHD**, ch c 20/3 Coach House (IRE)—Martha (IRE) (Alhaarth (IRE)) (15238) **Mr Jaber Abdullah**
75 **SCATTERBRAINED (USA)**, ch c 1/5 Scat Daddy (USA)—
           Cool Ghoul (USA) (Silver Ghost (USA)) (20350) **H Pinniger, Peter Cook & Partner**
76 B f 3/5 No Nay Never (USA)—
           Sparkling Rock (Rock of Gibraltar (IRE)) (34187) **M Clarke, P Munnelly & D Waters**
77 Ch c 11/4 Sir Prancealot (IRE)—Sunny Hollow (Beat Hollow) (8571) **Mr Jaber Abdullah**
78 B c 29/1 Slade Power (IRE)—
           Three Decades (IRE) (Invincible Spirit (IRE)) (140000) **Gallagher Bloodstock Limited**
79 **TOROLIGHT**, b c 25/1 Toronado (IRE)—Tuscan Light (Medicean) **Mr D. Thorpe**
80 **TWENTY YEARS ON**, b c 7/2 Rip Van Winkle (IRE)—Distinctive (Tobougg (IRE)) (25000) **HP Racing**
81 **UM SHAMA (IRE)**, ch f 22/3 Helmet (AUS)—Night Club (Mozart (IRE)) (8571) **Mr Jaber Abdullah**
82 **UNCLE JERRY**, b c 27/3 Kyllachy—News Desk (Cape Cross (IRE)) (20000) **Thames Boys**
83 **WINTER LIGHT**, ch f 14/2 Bated Breath—Moonglow (Nayef (USA)) **Cheveley Park Stud Limited**

MR RICHARD HUGHES - Continued

Other Owners: Mr D. Barrett, Mr Aaron Bhadra, Mrs J. A. Blake, Mr S. Blight, Mrs G. P. Bostwick, T. P. Bostwick, Mr M. H. Burke, Mr David Campbell, Mr J. P. Carrington, Cedar Investments Limited, Mr Don Churston, Mr Martin Clarke, Mr P. Cook, Mr Paul Cousins, Mr F. Deely, Mr J. Devine, M. H. Dixon, Mr Graham Doyle, Sir A. Ferguson, Mr G. H. Firmager, Mr G. Firmager, Mrs D. J. Fleming, Mr M. R. Flitton, Mr Ivan Forster, Mr Rupert Fowler, Mrs Belinda Fowler, Mr B. S. Galloway, Mr S. Geraghty, Mr R. E. Greatorex, Mr J. Gwyther, Mr Richard Hughes, Mr James Jeffries, Mr J. L. Langridge, Mr Ken Lawrence, Miss Hazel Lawrence, Countess of Lonsdale, Mr J. E. Lund, Mr J. E. Lund, Mrs P. J. Makin, Mr S. Malone, Mr N. M. Mandell, Mr Stuart J. Marchant, Mr R. P. Marchant, D. Margolis, G. A. Mason, Mr J. McGarry, Mr Martin Mitchell, Munnelly Support Services Limited, Mr P. G. O'Sullivan, Mr S. Padmanabhan, Mr James Pak, Ms H. N. Pinniger, Racing Club Ltd, Mr J. J. Reddington, Mr R. J. Rexton, Ms F. E. Rogers, Mr H. Rosenblatt, J. L. Rowsell, Star Pointe Ltd, Mr Graham P Triefus, Mr T. W. Wellard, Mr R. M. Whitby, Mrs Fiona Young.

Assistant Trainer: Patrick McEwan

Jockey (flat): Shane Kelly. **Apprentice:** Stephen Cummins, Nicola Currie, Finley Marsh.

---

296 MS N. M. HUGO, Newmarket
Postal: **Flat 2 Harraton Court Stables, Church Lane, Exning, Newmarket, Suffolk, CB8 7HF**
Contacts: **MOBILE (07736) 360550**
E-MAIL nickyhugo1@gmail.com

1 **DREAM OF SUMMER (IRE)**, 5, b g Canford Cliffs (IRE)—
  Danehill's Dream (IRE) **Happy Valley Racing & Breeding Limited**
2 6, B h Great Pyramid (IRE)—Fleur A Lay (USA)
3 4, B f Court Cave (IRE)—She's A Venture (IRE) **Ms N. M. Hugo**
4 **SIEGE OF CORINTH (FR)**, 5, b m Astronomer Royal (USA)—Final Overture (FR) **Ms N. M. Hugo**
5 **THE GOLDEN ONE (IRE)**, 4, ch f New Approach (IRE)—Punita (USA) **Ms N. M. Hugo**

TWO-YEAR-OLDS
6 B c 25/4 Anodin (IRE)—Katsya (FR) (Sinndar (IRE)) (3256)
7 B f 10/2 Dream Ahead (USA)—One Pixel (Primo Valentino (IRE)) (3809) **Ms N. M. Hugo**
8 B f 9/3 Mayson—Veni Bidi Vici (Horse Chestnut (SAF)) (952) **Ms N. M. Hugo**

Assistant Trainer: Mr Linas Balciunas

---

297 MRS SARAH HUMPHREY, West Wratting
Postal: **Yen Hall Farm, West Wratting, Cambridge, Cambridgeshire, CB21 5LP**
Contacts: **PHONE (01223) 291445 MOBILE (07798) 702484**
E-MAIL sarah@yenhallfarm.com WEBSITE www.sarahhumphrey.co.uk

1 **BRECON HILL (IRE)**, 5, b g Arcano (IRE)—Bryanstown Girl (IRE) **The Brecon Hill Partnership**
2 **CALL ME TJ**, 4, b g Mawatheeq (USA)—Silver Lily (IRE) **Mr G. Thomas, Mr J. Thomas, Dr R. Britton**
3 **FARE THEE WELL (IRE)**, 8, b g Duke of Marmalade (IRE)—Bowstring (IRE) **Yen Hall Farm Racing**
4 **HIDDEN PASSAGE (IRE)**, 6, b m Stowaway—More Hope (IRE) **Mrs S. J. Humphrey**
5 **HIGHWAY STAR (FR)**, 6, b g Vision d'etat (FR)—Lyli Rose (FR) **Mrs S. J. Humphrey**
6 **KNIGHT'S PARADE (IRE)**, 8, b g Dark Angel (IRE)—Toy Show (IRE) **Yen Hall Farm Racing**
7 **LEGENDOFTHEKNIGHT (IRE)**, 6, b g Midnight Legend—Pentasilea **Mrs S. J. Humphrey**
8 **LOCAL SHOW (IRE)**, 10, br g Oscar (IRE)—Loughaderra Rose (IRE) **The Friday Lunch Club**
9 **LOUIS P**, 4, b g Pastoral Pursuits—Freedom Song **The Louis P Partnership**
10 **POSTBRIDGE (IRE)**, 7, br m Robin des Pres (FR)—Dartmeet (IRE) **Yen Hall Farm Racing**
11 **STONEBRIGG LEGEND**, 6, b m Midnight Legend—Forget The Ref (IRE) **Robert Abrey & Ian Thurtle**
12 **THE HAPPY CHAPPY (IRE)**, 7, b g Flemensfirth (USA)—Native Design (IRE) **The Happy Folders**
13 **WHO YOU FOR (IRE)**, 8, b g Craigsteel—Knappogue Honey (IRE) **The Doc Partnership**

THREE-YEAR-OLDS
14 Gr g Mawatheeq (USA)—Silver Lily (IRE) **Mr G. Thomas, Mr J. Thomas, Mrs L. Thomas**

TWO-YEAR-OLDS
15 Ch f 3/3 Nayef (USA)—Kompete (Komaite (USA))

Other Owners: Mr R. Abrey, Mr J. Bone, Dr R. Britton, Mr P. Darlington, Mr P. Denley, Mr A. Eaton, Mr L. Greenlees, Mrs L. Greenlees, Mrs S. J. Humphrey, Mr A. R. Humphrey, Mr D. F. Nott, Mrs E. Reid, Mrs L. Thomas, Mr G. Thomas, Mr J. Thomas, Mr Ian Thurtle.

MRS SARAH HUMPHREY - Continued

Assistant Trainer: Mr A. R. Humphrey

Jockey (NH): Aidan Coleman, Daryl Jacob, Jack Quinlan, Nick Scholfield. **Conditional:** Graham Carson.
Amateur: Mr W. Humphrey.

---

298 **MR KEVIN HUNTER, Natland**
Postal: **Larkrigg, Natland, Cumbria, LA9 7QS**
Contacts: **PHONE (01539) 560245**

1 CATACLYSM (IRE), 8, b g Captain Rio—Marilaya (IRE) **J. K. Hunter**
2 FAIR OAKS, 6, gr m Fair Mix (IRE)—School Days **J. K. Hunter**
3 TRILLERIN MINELLA (IRE), 10, b g King's Theatre (IRE)—Eva Fay (IRE) **J. K. Hunter**

---

299 **MISS LAURA HURLEY, Kineton**
Postal: **Kineton Grange Farm, Kineton, Warwick, Warwickshire, CV35 0EE**
Contacts: **PHONE (01926) 640380**

1 CANDYMAN CAN (IRE), 8, b g Holy Roman Emperor (IRE)—Palwina (FR) **Mrs R. E. Hurley**
2 CATCHIN TIME (IRE), 10, b g Chineur (FR)—Lady Dane (IRE) **Mrs R. E. Hurley**
3 PRINCE KUP (IRE), 7, ch g High Rock (IRE)—Lockup (IRE) **Mrs R. E. Hurley**

---

300 **MRS CAROLE IKIN, Sutton In The Elms**
Postal: **Walton Lodge Farm, Sutton In The Elms, Leicestershire, LE9 6RB**
Contacts: **PHONE (01455) 282321 MOBILE (07850) 278491**
E-MAIL nevagree@yahoo.co.uk WEBSITE www.equinespa.co.uk

1 RIME AVEC GENTIL (FR), 13, b g Kapgarde (FR)—Quenice (FR) **Mrs C. J. Ikin**
2 RUNITAGAINSAM, 7, b m Samraan (USA)—Hollywood **Mrs C. J. Ikin**

Assistant Trainer: Mr P. J. Ikin

---

301 **MR ROGER INGRAM, Epsom**
Postal: **Wendover Stables, Burgh Heath Road, Epsom, Surrey, KT17 4LX**
Contacts: **PHONE (01372) 748505 or (01372) 749157 FAX (01372) 748505**
MOBILE (07773) 665980 / (07715) 993911
E-MAIL roger.ingram.racing@virgin.net WEBSITE www.rogeringramracing.com

1 AWESOME ROCK (IRE), 9, ch g Rock of Gibraltar (IRE)—Dangerous Diva (IRE) **Mr M. F. Cruse**
2 BALLESTEROS, 9, ch g Tomba—Flamenco Dancer **Mr M. F. Cruse**
3 CHARLIE ALPHA (IRE), 4, b g Dandy Man (IRE)—Maroussies Rock **Mr P. J. Burton**
4 DRAGON DREAM (IRE), 4, b f Dragon Pulse (IRE)—Night Scent (IRE) **Drag On Funds**
5 DUKES MEADOW, 7, b g Pastoral Pursuits—Figura **The Stargazers**
6 ENCAPSULATED, 8, b g Zamindar (USA)—Star Cluster **Mrs E. N. Nield**
7 QUEBEC, 7, b g Dansili—Milford Sound **Mr K. Tollick**
8 SILVER SPRINGS (IRE), 5, gr m Zebedee—Charming Vista **Hallam, Swift & Tollick**
9 ZARLIMAN (IRE), 8, ch g Zamindar (USA)—Zarlana (IRE) **Mr Steve Robinson & Miss Heather Best**

THREE-YEAR-OLDS

10 ARGENT BLEU, b c Steele Tango (USA)—Silver Marizah (IRE) **Burgh Heath Associates**
11 CRISTAL PALLAS CAT (IRE), b g Kodiac—Flower of Kent (USA) **Titan Partnership**
12 B f Captain Gerrard (IRE)—Dilys Maud **Sharon Ingram**
13 MAISON WIX, b f Mayson—Petit A Petit (IRE) **Wix Hill Partnership**

TWO-YEAR-OLDS

14 B f 17/4 Heeraat (IRE)—Silver Marizah (IRE) (Manduro (GER)) **Sharon Ingram**

MR ROGER INGRAM - Continued

Other Owners: Mr M. A. Allen, Mr Stephen Appleyard, Miss Heather Best, Mr Toby Duthie, Mrs Claire Edwards, Miss C. C. Fagerstrom, Mrs Annie Gerrard, Mrs C. Hallam, Mr David Hazelton, Mr Michael Joy, Mr Connor Kelly, Mrs C. J. Lowman, Mr Simon Milner, Mr Steve Robinson, Mr D. Ross-Watt, Mr Shaun Steele, Ms Wenche Swift, Mr Keith Tollick.

Assistant Trainer: Sharon Ingram

Apprentice: Rhiain Ingram.

---

302 MR DEAN IVORY, Radlett
Postal: **Harper Lodge Farm, Harper Lane, Radlett, Hertfordshire, WD7 7HU**
Contacts: **PHONE (01923) 855337 FAX (01923) 852470 MOBILE (07785) 118658**
E-MAIL **deanivoryracing@gmail.com** WEBSITE **www.deanivoryracing.co.uk**

1 **BADENSCOTH**, 4, b g Foxwedge (AUS)—Twice Upon A Time **P. J. Skinner**
2 **BLAZE OF HEARTS (IRE)**, 5, b g Canford Cliffs (IRE)—Shesthebiscuit **Mr R. Beadle**
3 **BOBBY VEE**, 4, ch g Camacho—Miss Lesley **Mr Roger S Beadle & Radlett Racing**
4 **CAPPANANY CON**, 4, gr g Zebedee—Fairmont (IRE) **Jim Biggane, John Waterfall & Dean Ivory**
5 **DARK MAGIC**, 4, b g Invincible Spirit (IRE)—Dark Promise **Heather & Michael Yarrow**
6 **DOR'S LAW**, 5, b m Lawman (FR)—Law of Chance **Mrs D. A. Carter**
7 **ELJADDAAF (IRE)**, 7, b g Shamardal (USA)—Almansoora (USA) **Wentdale Ltd & Mrs L A Ivory**
8 **FIGHTING TEMERAIRE (IRE)**, 5, b g Invincible Spirit (IRE)—Hot Ticket (IRE) **Michael & Heather Yarrow**
9 **FOREVER YOURS (IRE)**, 5, b g Canford Cliffs (IRE)—Gilded (IRE) **Mr A. Chapman**
10 **HARLEQUIN STRIKER (IRE)**, 6, b g Bahamian Bounty—Air Maze **Harlequin Direct Ltd & Mr D Bloy**
11 **HIGGY'S HEARTBEAT**, 4, b g Acclamation—Adorn **K. T. Ivory**
12 **I'M RIGHT ON TIME**, 4, ch g Dutch Art—Euroceleb (IRE) **Mr A. L. Cohen**
13 **INCREDIBLE DREAM (IRE)**, 5, b g Vale of York (IRE)—Finnmark **Black Star Racing**
14 **KADRIZZI (FR)**, 5, ch g Hurricane Cat (USA)—Kadiania (FR) **Mr A Chapman & Wentdale Limited**
15 **LANCELOT DU LAC (ITY)**, 8, b g Shamardal (USA)—Dodie Mae (USA) **Michael & Heather Yarrow**
16 **LIBRISA BREEZE**, 6, gr g Mount Nelson—Bruxcalina (FR) **Mr A. G. Bloom**
17 **LOTHARIO**, 4, gr g Dark Angel (IRE)—Kisses For Me (IRE) **Michael & Heather Yarrow**
18 **LUCYMAI**, 5, b m Multiplex—Miss Lesley **Mr R. Beadle**
19 **NEZAR (IRE)**, 7, ch g Mastercraftsman (IRE)—Teddy Bears Picnic **Black Star Racing & Dean Ivory**
20 **NICKY BABY (IRE)**, 4, gr g Dark Angel (IRE)—Moon Club (IRE) **Mrs D. A. Carter**
21 **SOARING SPIRITS (IRE)**, 8, ch g Tamayuz—Follow My Lead **Mrs D. A. Carter**
22 **STAKE ACCLAIM (IRE)**, 6, b g Acclamation—Golden Legacy (IRE) **Mr M. J. Yarrow**
23 **TANGRAMM**, 6, b br g Sakhee's Secret—Tripti (IRE) **Mr J. L. Marsden**
24 **TROPICS (USA)**, 10, ch g Speightstown—Taj Aire (USA) **Mr D. K. Ivory**
25 **USSEGLIO**, 4, b g Kyllachy—Pingus **Mr A. L. Cohen**
26 **VARSOVIAN**, 8, ch g Refuse To Bend (IRE)—Queen of Poland **Radlett Racing**
27 **VILLETTE (IRE)**, 4, b f Sixties Icon—Spinning Lucy (IRE) **Mr D. K. Ivory**

THREE-YEAR-OLDS

28 **ANGEL OF THE SOUTH (IRE)**, gr f Dark Angel (IRE)—Oeuvre d'art (IRE) **Heather & Michael Yarrow**
29 **BEST COMPANY (IRE)**, b g Fast Company (IRE)—Story **K. T. Ivory**
30 **CLASSIC CHARM**, b f Rip Van Winkle (IRE)—Classic Lass **Gracelands Stud Partnership**
31 **DADDY'S DAUGHTER (CAN)**, b f Scat Daddy (USA)—Golden Stripe (CAN) **Heather & Michael Yarrow**
32 **DON'T LOOK DOWN**, gr c Aussie Rules (USA)—Miss Katmandu (IRE)
33 **EIRENE**, b f Declaration of War (USA)—Za Za Zoom (IRE) **Mr M. J. Yarrow**
34 **FANTASTIC FLYER**, br f Harbour Watch (IRE)—Lucky Flyer **Mrs K. M. Young**
35 **HELLO GIRL**, ch f Bated Breath—Elysee (IRE) **Mr A. Chapman**
36 **MADAM DRAGONFLY (IRE)**, b f Intello (GER)—Caelis **Heather & Michael Yarrow**
37 **MIMRAM**, b f Kheleyf (USA)—Tobaranama (USA) **Mrs L. A. Ivory**
38 **OLIVE MABEL**, b f Captain Gerrard (IRE)—Shembara (FR) **A. Stennett**
39 **ONE COOL DADDY (USA)**, b c Scat Daddy (USA)—Coup (USA) **Michael & Heather Yarrow**
40 **SIR PRIZE**, b g Sir Percy—Three Sugars (AUS) **Michael & Heather Yarrow**
41 **SPRING ROMANCE (IRE)**, b br g Zebedee—Love And Devotion **Solario Racing (Berkhamsted)**
42 **YIMOU**, b g Kodiac—Heroine Chic (IRE)
43 **YOLO STAR (IRE)**, br f Society Rock (IRE)—Pearly Brooks **Heather & Michael Yarrow**

TWO-YEAR-OLDS

44 **ARCHDEACON**, b c 21/4 Archipenko (USA)—Akdarena (Hernando (FR)) (30000) **K T Ivory & Michael Yarrow**
45 B c 18/2 Sea The Moon (GER)—Classic Lass (Dr Fong (USA)) (19000) **Gracelands Stud Partnership**
46 Ch f 4/3 Bated Breath—Fisadara (Nayef (USA)) **Wood Hall Stud Limited**
47 B f 16/4 Gregorian (IRE)—Jackie's Opera (FR) (Indian Ridge) (9523)

MR DEAN IVORY - Continued

48 B f 23/1 Lethal Force (IRE)—Love Me Tender (Green Desert (USA))
49 B c 2/2 Archipenko (USA)—Lucky Flyer (Lucky Story (USA)) (21000) **Gracelands Stud Partnership**
50 **PENNIESFROMHEAVEN (IRE),** gr f 18/3 Lethal Force (IRE)—
Dittander (Exceed And Excel (AUS)) (16190) **K. T. Ivory**
51 B f 28/3 Exceed And Excel (AUS)—Sues Surprise (IRE) (Montjeu (IRE)) (50000) **Heather & Michael Yarrow**
52 Ch f 24/3 Compton Place—Vitta's Touch (USA) (Touch Gold (USA)) (6666) **It's Your Lucky Day**

Other Owners: Mr Roger S. Beadle, Mr J. Biggane, Mr Derrick Bloy, Mr S. T. J. Broderick, Mr A. Chapman, Dean Ivory Racing Ltd, Mr Simon K. I. Double, Mr J. Gunnell, Harlequin Direct Ltd, Mrs L. A. Ivory, Mr N. A. Rooney, Mr John B. Waterfall, Wentdale Limited, Mrs Heather Yarrow, Mr M. J. Yarrow, Mrs K. M. Young, Mr Bob Young.

Assistant Trainer: Chris Scally

Apprentice: Jack Duern.

---

303 **MISS TINA JACKSON, Loftus**
Postal: Tick Hill Farm, Liverton, Loftus, Saltburn, Cleveland, TS13 4TG
Contacts: **PHONE (01287) 644952 MOBILE (07774) 106906**

1 **ARIZONA SUNRISE,** 5, b g Sakhee's Secret—Phoenix Rising **Mr H. L. Thompson**
2 **GRIMTHORPE,** 7, ch g Alflora (IRE)—Sally Scally **Mr H. L. Thompson**
3 **IVORS INVOLVEMENT (IRE),** 6, b g Amadeus Wolf—Summer Spice (IRE) **Mr H. L. Thompson**
4 **JAN DE HEEM,** 8, ch g Dutch Art—Shasta **H L Thompson & D Tucker**
5 **KHITAAMY (IRE),** 4, b g Approve (IRE)—Halliwell House **Peter Jeffers & Howard Thompson**
6 **KING'S REALM (IRE),** 11, ch g King's Best (USA)—Sweet Home Alabama (IRE) **Mr H. L. Thompson**
7 **POINT OF WOODS,** 5, b g Showcasing—Romantic Myth **Mr H. L. Thompson**
8 **PURPLE HARRY,** 10, gr g Sir Harry Lewis (USA)—Ellfiedick **Mr H. L. Thompson**
9 **ROSY RYAN (IRE),** 8, b m Tagula (IRE)—Khaydariya (IRE) **Mr H. L. Thompson**
10 **SORY,** 11, b g Sakhee (USA)—Rule Britannia **Mr H. L. Thompson**
11 **THOMAS CRANMER (USA),** 4, b g Hard Spun (USA)—
House of Grace (USA) **Peter Jeffers & Howard Thompson**
12 **YOUNOSO,** 7, b g Alflora (IRE)—Teeno Nell **Mr H. L. Thompson**

THREE-YEAR-OLDS

13 **GLACEON (IRE),** b f Zoffany (IRE)—Ihtiraam (IRE) **Peter Jeffers & Howard Thompson**

TWO-YEAR-OLDS

14 **HAVANA BAY,** b c 11/3 Havana Gold (IRE)—Bisou (Tiger Hill (IRE)) **Mr H. L. Thompson**

Other Owners: Mr P. Jeffers, Mr D. Tucker.

---

304 **MRS VALERIE JACKSON, Newcastle Upon Tyne**
Postal: Edge House, Belsay, Newcastle Upon Tyne, Tyne and Wear, NE20 0HH
Contacts: **PHONE (01830) 530218 MOBILE (07808) 812213**

1 **BLUE CANNON (IRE),** 10, b g High Chaparral (IRE)—Blushing Barada (USA) **Mrs V. S. Jackson**
2 **KNICK KNACK (IRE),** 8, b g Kalanisi (IRE)—Full Imperatrice (FR) **Mrs V. S. Jackson**
3 **PADDY'S YARN (IRE),** 8, ch g Houmayoun (FR)—Deidamia (USA) **Mrs V. S. Jackson**

---

305 **MISS HANNAH JAMES, Malvern**
Postal: The Merries Farm, Rye Street, Birtsmorton, Malvern, Worcestershire, WR13 6AS

1 **SPROGZILLA,** 9, gr m Fair Mix (IRE)—Gentle Approach **Miss H. L. James**

306 MR LEE JAMES, Malton
Postal: **Cheesecake Stables, Beverley Road, Norton, North Yorkshire, YO17 9PJ**
Contacts: PHONE **(01653) 699466** FAX **(01653) 699581** MOBILE **(07732) 556322**

1 BILLY TEAL, 13, ch g Keen—Morcat **Mr C. I. Ratcliffe**
2 EXCELLENT ADDITION (IRE), 8, ch g Excellent Art—Race The Wild Wind (USA) **Mr Ian Johnson & Partner**
3 JACKMAN, 4, gr g Aussie Rules (USA)—Fit To Burst **Mr Ian Johnson & Partner**
4 KEEN'S TOKEN, 12, b g Keen—Bella Mary **Mr C. I. Ratcliffe**
5 LILLY BALLERINA (IRE), 4, b f Lilbourne Lad (IRE)—Entrechat **Mrs C. Lloyd James**
6 MA PETIT LUMIER, 8, b g Echo of Light—Alisdanza **L. R. James**
7 8, B m Dubai Destination (USA)—Palisandra (USA) **L. R. James**
8 STRIKEMASTER (IRE), 12, b g Xaar—Mas A Fuera (IRE) **Mrs C. Lloyd James**
9 TEALS LAD, 9, b g Kayf Tara—Derry Ann **Mr C. I. Ratcliffe**

Other Owners: Mr Ian Johnson (North Yorkshire).

Assistant Trainer: Carol James

307 MR IAIN JARDINE, Carrutherstown
Postal: **Paddock House, Hetlandhill Farm, Carrutherstown, Dumfriesshire, DG1 4JX**
Contacts: PHONE **(01387) 840347** MOBILE **(07738) 351232**
E-MAIL **iainjardineracing@outlook.com**

1 AKKADIAN EMPIRE, 4, b g Arabian Gleam—Floral Beauty **Alex & Janet Card**
2 ANGEL'S ENVY, 6, b m Yeats (IRE)—Caoba **Distillery Racing Club**
3 ANIMORE, 5, b m Sulamani (IRE)—More Likely **Mrs A. F. Tullie**
4 ARCHIPELIGO, 7, b g Archipenko (USA)—Red Slew **Top Of The Hill Racing Club**
5 ATKINSON GRIMSHAW (FR), 4, ch g Rio de La Plata (USA)—Cosabawn (IRE) **Mr I. Jardine**
6 ATLANTIC DANCER (IRE), 5, b m Waky Nao—Sarika (IRE) **The Big Hats**
7 BEDROCK, 5, b g Fastnet Rock (AUS)—Gemstone (IRE) **The Risk Takers Partnership**
8 BENNY THE MIXER, 8, gr g Fair Mix (IRE)—See My Girl **Mr J. Duckworth**
9 BRUICHLADDICH, 6, b g Westerner—Highland Cherry **Distillery Racing Club**
10 CARRICKCROSS BOYE (IRE), 8, b g Trans Island—Ellie Forte **M Russell & D Monteith**
11 COLOUR CONTRAST (IRE), 9, b g Rock of Gibraltar (IRE)—Colour Coordinated (IRE) **Kildonan Gold Racing**
12 COOL MIX, 6, gr g Fair Mix (IRE)—Lucylou (IRE) **D&D Armstrong Limited**
13 DIMPLE (FR), 7, gr g Montmartre (FR)—Dynella (FR) **D&D Armstrong Limited**
14 GOLDEN JEFFREY (SWI), 5, b g Soldier Hollow—Ange Doree (FR) **Mrs Jo Tracey**
15 HOUDINI JACK, 5, ch g Daylami (IRE)—Stravaigin **Drew & Ailsa Russell**
16 JABBAAR, 5, ch g Medicean—Echelon **Let's Be Lucky Racing 11**
17 KASHMIRI SUNSET, 7, b g Tiger Hill (IRE)—Sagamartha **Mr & Mrs Paul & Clare Rooney**
18 KEEP THE RIVER, 4, b f Scorpion (IRE)—River Alder
19 L'INGANNO FELICE (FR), 8, br g Librettist (USA)—Final Overture (FR) **Mr A. Dawson & Mrs K. Campbell**
20 LA BACOUETTEUSE (FR), 13, b g Miesque's Son (USA)—Toryka **Miss S. A. Booth & Mr I. J. Jardine**
21 LOUD AND CLEAR, 7, b g Dalakhani (IRE)—Whispering Blues (IRE) **The Dregs Of Humanity**
22 MAYLEAF SHINE (IRE), 4, b f Mayson—Let Me Shine (USA) **Mr R S Solomon & Partner**
23 MY JAMAICAN GUY (IRE), 5, b g Duke of Marmalade (IRE)—Mustique Dream **Suzanne & Nigel Williams**
24 NAKEETA, 7, b g Sixties Icon—Easy Red (IRE) **Alex & Janet Card**
25 NEWMARKET WARRIOR (IRE), 7, b g Dalakhani (IRE)—Heavens Peak **Ms S A Booth & Partner**
26 ORIENTAL TIGER, 7, b g Tiger Hill (IRE)—Cal Norma's Lady (IRE) **Mr A. Barclay**
27 PECHEURS DE PERLES (IRE), 4, b g Pour Moi (IRE)—Annacloy Pearl (IRE) **C. H. McGhie**
28 PLUS JAMAIS (FR), 11, b g Caballo Raptor (CAN)—Branceilles (FR) **A Crawford & Partner**
29 RAINY CITY (IRE), 8, b g Kalanisi (IRE)—Erintante (IRE) **Mr I. Jardine**
30 RESTIVE (IRE), 5, b g Rip Van Winkle (IRE)—I Hearyou Knocking (IRE) **Mr I. Jardine**
31 RIVER ICON, 6, b m Sixties Icon—River Alder **Mr M Friel, Mr T Reid & Mr K Wilson**
32 ROO ROO (IRE), 4, b g Court Cave (IRE)—Shuil Sionnach (IRE) **Mr & Mrs Paul & Clare Rooney**
33 ROSEMAY (FR), 4, b f Mayson—Maine Rose **Lease Terminated**
34 SFUMATO, 4, br g Bated Breath—Modern Look **J. A. Rattigan**
35 SMUGGLERS CREEK (IRE), 4, b g Medicean—Crystany (IRE) **Mr A. McLuckie**
36 SO SATISFIED, 7, b g Aqlaam—Pirouetting **Wharton, Nixon, Jardine**
37 SOMETHING BREWING (FR), 4, gr g Clodovil (IRE)—Talwin (IRE) **Mrs C Brown & Partner**
38 STONE THE CROWS, 4, b g Cape Cross (IRE)—Stars In Your Eyes **Mr R. D. Rainey**
39 STONEHAM, 7, b m Sixties Icon—Cibenze **Mr I. Jardine**
40 THE DELRAY MUNKY, 6, b m Overbury (IRE)—Delray Beach (FR) **The Twelve Munkys**
41 THORNTOUN CARE, 7, b g Rail Link—Thorntoun Piccolo **Alba-Eire Syndicate**
42 TOE JEFFREY, 5, b h Sulamani (IRE)—Minouchka (FR) **Mr M. P. Wares**

MR IAIN JARDINE - Continued

43 **TOKARAMORE**, 6, b m Sulamani (IRE)—More Likely **Mrs A. F. Tullie**
44 **TOR**, 4, ch g Orientor—Dance In The Sun **Mr I. Wilson**
45 **TRADITIONAL DANCER (IRE)**, 6, b g Danehill Dancer (IRE)—Cote Quest (USA) **I. G. M. Dalgleish**
46 **TWIGGY**, 4, b f Sixties Icon—Queen's Pudding (IRE) **Mr R. J. Sommerville**
47 **YES YOU (IRE)**, 4, ch f Choisir (AUS)—Mexican Milly **Taco Partners**
48 **YOUNOYOUNOYOUNO**, 5, b g Overbury (IRE)—Ceiriog Valley **Mr & Mrs Paul & Clare Rooney**

THREE-YEAR-OLDS

49 **FALMOUTH LIGHT (FR)**, b g Cape Cross (IRE)—Wonderous Light (IRE) **Mr I. Jardine**
50 **KYLLACHY DRAGON (IRE)**, b g Dragon Pulse (IRE)—Lafayette (GER) **Mr S. R. Middleton**
51 **LADY GRIGIO (IRE)**, gr f Casamento (IRE)—Park Approach (IRE) **Big Teeree Racing**
52 **MABLE LEE (IRE)**, ch f Zoffany (IRE)—Mexican Milly (IRE) **Dunedin Castle Rock Partnership**
53 **MARNIE JAMES**, b g Camacho—Privy Garden (IRE) **James Property Ltd**
54 **MEARING**, b g Aussie Rules (USA)—Director's Dream (IRE) **Let's Be Lucky Racing 14**
55 **MISS DD (IRE)**, b f Dandy Man (IRE)—Dynaperformer (IRE)
56 **MISS T STAR (IRE)**, gr f Clodovil (IRE)—March Star (IRE) **Mr I. Jardine**
57 **SONG OF SUMMER**, ch f Choisir (AUS)—Height of Summer (IRE) **Unregistered Syndicate**
58 **SUPER FLORENCE (IRE)**, gr f Zebedee—Top of The Ridge (IRE) **Mr B. Miller**

TWO-YEAR-OLDS

59 B f 20/1 Harbour Watch (IRE)—Akhila (IRE) (Dalakhani (IRE)) (9523)
60 **GOD OF DREAMS**, b c 17/2 Morpheus—Bella Chica (IRE) (Bigstone (IRE)) **Mr I. Jardine**
61 Gr c 5/3 Gregorian (IRE)—Green Vision (IRE) (Green Desert (USA)) (13837) **Mr I. Jardine**
62 B f 22/2 Morpheus—Idyllic Star (IRE) (Choisir (AUS))
63 B c 12/2 Fast Company (IRE)—Kyrielle (Medicean) (14651) **Mr I. Jardine**
64 B c 24/3 Morpheus—Lovegood (IRE) (Desert Style (IRE))
65 Ch c 28/2 Coach House—Mandy Layla (IRE) (Excellent Art) (20952) **Mr I. Jardine**
66 Ch f 8/2 Compton Place—Miss Trish (IRE) (Danetime (IRE)) (6000) **C. H. McGhie**
67 **MUST SEE THE DOC**, b c 19/4 Sea The Moon (GER)—
Kong Moon (FR) (Hernando (FR)) **Mr & Mrs Paul & Clare Rooney**
68 **MY LITTLE ORPHAN**, b c 26/2 Heeraat (IRE)—
Costa Brava (IRE) (Sadler's Wells (USA)) **Mr & Mrs Paul & Clare Rooney**
69 **PLAY IT BY EAR (IRE)**, ch c 17/4 Dragon Pulse (IRE)—
Seriously (FR) (Sinndar (IRE)) (19047) **Mr & Mrs Paul & Clare Rooney**
70 Ch f 15/3 Orientor—Rafta (IRE) (Atraf) **Mr J. Fyffe**
71 B f 30/4 Camelot—Za'hara (IRE) (Raven's Pass (USA)) (32560)

Other Owners: Mr R. M. S. Allison, Miss S. A. Booth, Mrs C. Brown, Mr C. A. Burness, Mrs K. Campbell, Mrs J. A. Card, Mr A. M. Card, Mr A. S. Crawford, A. Dawson, Mr J. Doherty, Mr M. Friel, Mr R. J. Goodfellow, Mr S. T. Gorrie, Mr R. A. Gorrie, E. Graham, A. G. Guthrie, Mr J. A. Hay, Mr D. T. Irving, Mr D. I. B. Livingstone, Mr A. Manson, Mr S. R. Mckenzie, Mr B. Melrose, Mrs D. M. Monteith, G. R. S. Nixon, Mr J. Parkes, Mr C. T. Reid, R. Robinson, Mr P. A. Rooney, Mrs C. Rooney, A. J. R. Russell, Mrs A. Russell, Mr M. R. Russell, R. S. Solomon, Mr R. E. Wharton, Mrs S. E. Williams, Mr N. Williams, Mr K. A. Wilson, Mr J. Wright.

Jockey (flat): David Nolan. **Jockey (NH):** Henry Brooke. **Conditional:** Ross Chapman. **Apprentice:** Jamie Gormley, Callum Rodriguez. **Amateur:** Mr Bruce Lynn.

---

308 | **MR WILLIAM JARVIS, Newmarket**
Postal: **Phantom House Stables, Fordham Road, Newmarket, Suffolk, CB8 7AA**
Contacts: **OFFICE (01638) 669873 HOME (01638) 662677 FAX (01638) 667328**
E-MAIL mail@williamjarvis.com WEBSITE www.williamjarvis.com

1 **ARCADIAN SEA (IRE)**, 4, b g Born To Sea (IRE)—Drombeg Dawn (IRE) **The Arcadian Sea Partnership**
2 **COLD SNAP (IRE)**, 5, b g Medicean—Shivering **P. C. J. Dalby & R. D. Schuster**
3 **FANG**, 5, b g Lawman (FR)—Desert Tigress (USA) **Mr David Batten**
4 **GIRL SQUAD**, 4, b f Intikhab (USA)—Foxtrot Alpha (IRE) **The Raceology Partnership**
5 **JUANITO CHICO (IRE)**, 4, br g Pour Moi (IRE)—Miss Kittyhawk (IRE) **Mr Tony Verrier**
6 **KERRE (IRE)**, 4, b f Pour Moi (IRE)—Double Green (IRE) **Mr Kevin Hickman**
7 **MONTICELLO (IRE)**, 4, b g Teofilo (IRE)—Towards (USA) **Dr Jim Walker**
8 **ONWARDSANDUPWARDS**, 5, b g Multiplex—Turn Back **The Willie Robertson Partnership**
9 **PORT PARADISE**, 5, gr b g Paco Boy (IRE)—Yacht Woman (USA) **Mr William Jarvis**
10 **SLOW TO HAND**, 4, ch g Sepoy (AUS)—One Giant Leap (IRE) **Rupert Villiers & Sally Hall**
11 **WIMPOLE HALL**, 5, b g Canford Cliffs (IRE)—Sparkling Eyes **Ms E. L. Banks**

MR WILLIAM JARVIS - Continued

THREE-YEAR-OLDS

12 **ARIGATO**, b g Poet's Voice—Xtrasensory **Ms E. L. Banks**
13 **BEDIVERE**, b c Camelot—Foreign Language (USA) **P. C. J. Dalby & R. D. Schuster**
14 **CHIEF IRONSIDE**, b c Lawman (FR)—Moment of Time **Mr Clive Washbourn**
15 **KNIGHT ERRANT (IRE)**, b c So You Think (NZ)—Lamanka Lass (USA) **Mr R C C Villers & Partner**
16 **MRS GALLAGHER**, b f Oasis Dream—A Huge Dream (IRE) **Ms E. L. Banks**
17 **QUEEN TOMYRIS**, b f Declaration of War (USA)—Caphene **Ms E. L. Banks**
18 **TILGHMAN (IRE)**, b c Lawman (FR)—Poppet's Lovein **Mr Clive Washbourn**

TWO-YEAR-OLDS

19 Gr f 31/1 Nathaniel (IRE)—All Hallows (IRE) (Dalakhani (IRE)) (113960) **Mr Kevin Hickman**
20 Ch f 5/3 Starspangledbanner (AUS)—Alpine Belle (NZ) (Rock of Gibraltar (IRE)) **Mr Kevin Hickman**
21 B c 23/1 War Command (USA)—Divisme (USA) (Elusive Quality (USA)) (52000) **A Partnership**
22 **GREAT SUSPENSE**, b c 31/1 Bated Breath—Gimasha (Cadeaux Genereux) (52000) **Mr Clive Washbourn**
23 B f 21/4 Sir Percy—Katy O'hara (Komaite (USA)) **Mrs S. E. Hall**
24 **LESTRADE**, b c 7/4 Lawman (FR)—Ninas Rainbow (Rainbow Quest (USA)) (65000) **Mr Clive Washbourn**
25 B f 7/3 Acclamation—Lovely Thought (Dubai Destination (USA)) (200000) **Ms E. L. Banks**
26 B c 4/5 Equiano (FR)—Luanshya (First Trump) (16000) **The Marine Team**
27 B f 22/4 Nathaniel (IRE)—Maglietta Fina (IRE) (Verglas (IRE)) (82000) **Ms E. L. Banks**
28 **NO THANKS**, b c 21/3 Pour Moi (IRE)—Miss Fifty (IRE) (Whipper (USA)) (40000) **P. C. J. Dalby & R. D. Schuster**
29 B f 8/3 Holy Roman Emperor (IRE)—Quilita (GER) (Lomitas) (73260) **Mr Kevin Hickman**
30 B c 25/3 War Command (USA)—Todber (Cape Cross (IRE)) (52000) **The Music Makers**

Other Owners: Mr D. H. Batten, W. F. Charnley, P.C. J. Dalby, A. Foster, Miss M. V. Greenwood, Mr R. M. Harris, Mr S. A. Herbert, Mr M. Hunter, The Lime Street Partnership, Miss J. D. Margossian, Mr P. J. Merton, R. D. Schuster, L. G. Straszewski, Mr J. A. R. Toller, R. C. C. Villers.

Assistant Trainer: James Toller

---

309 **MISS RUTH JEFFERSON, Malton**
Postal: **Newstead Cottage Stables, Norton, Malton, North Yorkshire, YO17 9PJ**
Contacts: **PHONE (01653) 697225 MOBILE (07976) 568152**
E-MAIL newsteadracing@btconnect.com WEBSITE www.malcolmjefferson.co.uk

1 **BALLY CONOR (IRE)**, 5, b g Presenting—Soliya (FR) **Drew & Ailsa Russell**
2 **BALLYBEN (IRE)**, 10, ch g Beneficial—I'm Maggy (NZ) **Drew & Ailsa Russell**
3 **BLACK EBONY**, 4, b g Malinas (GER)—Our Ethel **The Mount Fawcus Partnership**
4 **BLACK IVORY**, 6, b g Revoque (IRE)—Annie's Gift (IRE) **The Mount Fawcus Partnership**
5 **BOY NAMED SIOUX**, 7, b g Indian Danehill (IRE)—Annie's Gift (IRE) **The Corse Lawners**
6 **BRANSTON DOYEN**, 5, b m Doyen (IRE)—Julatten (IRE) **Mr J. D. Abell**
7 **CATHAL'S STAR**, 5, ch g Malinas (GER)—Hand Inn Glove **Charlie Doocey / Cathal Doocey**
8 **CHILLY MISS**, 9, b m Iceman—Fairlie **Racegoers Club Owners Group**
9 **CLOUDY DREAM (IRE)**, 8, gr g Cloudings (IRE)—Run Away Dream **Mr T. J. Hemmings**
10 **CYRUS DARIUS**, 9, b g Overbury (IRE)—Barton Belle **Mr & Mrs G Calder & Mr P M Warren**
11 **CYRUS KEEP (IRE)**, 5, b g Doyen (IRE)—Overbranch **Newstead Racing Partnership**
12 **DOUBLE W'S (IRE)**, 8, ch g Fruits of Love (USA)—Zaffre (IRE) **Wharton & Wilson**
13 **DUBAI ANGEL (IRE)**, 7, b g Dubai Destination (USA)—Just Another Penny (IRE) **Mrs D. W. Davenport**
14 **FENCOTE BELLE**, 5, b m Presenting—Hannigan's Lodger (IRE) **Mrs K. M. Richardson**
15 **FIRTH OF THE CLYDE**, 13, b g Flemensfirth (USA)—Miss Nel **R. H. Goldie**
16 **FOUR MILE BEACH**, 5, gr g Dalakhani (IRE)—Rappel **J. M. Jefferson**
17 **HELLO BERTIE**, 6, b g Kayf Tara—I'm Delilah **Mr C. S. Johnston & Mr T. Ambler**
18 **HELMSLEY LAD**, 7, gr g Fair Mix (IRE)—Wuchowsen (IRE) **Derek Gennard & Gillian Gennard**
19 **KICK ON DOTTIE (IRE)**, 5, ch m Getaway (GER)—Oddly Presented (IRE) **Mrs D W Davenport & Mr D Obank**
20 **MAYO STAR (IRE)**, 6, b g Stowaway—Western Whisper (IRE) **Charlie Doocey / Cathal Doocey**
21 **MOUNT MEWS (IRE)**, 7, b g Presenting—Kneeland Lass (IRE) **Mr T. J. Hemmings**
22 **MOUNTAIN HAWK (IRE)**, 6, b g Mountain High (IRE)—Septembers Hawk (IRE) **Mr T. J. Hemmings**
23 **MR MONOCHROME**, 8, gr g Indian Danehill (IRE)—Our Ethel **Mr & Mrs G Calder & Mr P M Warren**
24 **NAUTICAL TWILIGHT**, 8, gr m Proclamation (IRE)—Anabranch **Capt M. S. Bagley**
25 **NORTHERN SOUL**, 5, ch g Presenting—Our Ethel **The Northern Triangle**
26 **ONLY ORVIETO (IRE)**, 7, b m Kayf Tara—Vigna Maggio (FR) **Mr D. M. Gibbons**
27 **PRINCESS TARA (IRE)**, 8, b m Kayf Tara—Oscars Vision (IRE) **Chris Perkins & Toby Becton**
28 **RETURN TICKET (IRE)**, 5, b g Getaway (GER)—Capelvenere (IRE) **Mr R. Collins**
29 **ROBBING THE PREY (IRE)**, 7, b g Robin des Pres (FR)—Derravarra Lady (IRE) **The Bells Steakhouse Ltd**
30 **ROWDY ROBIN**, 6, b g Revoque (IRE)—Youamazeme **C. N. Richardson**

MISS RUTH JEFFERSON - Continued

31 **RYEDALE RACER**, 7, b g Indian Danehill (IRE)—Jontys'lass **Derek Gennard & Gillian Gennard**
32 **SAMMAMISH (IRE)**, 5, b m Oscar (IRE)—Issaquah (IRE) **Racegoers Club Owners Group**
33 **SCHIAPARANNIE**, 6, b m Schiaparelli (GER)—Annie's Answer (IRE) **Can't Last Won't Last**
34 **SECRETE STREAM (IRE)**, 9, ch g Fruits of Love (USA)—Bonny River **Mrs M. E. Dixon**
35 **SHEPHERD'S BIGHT (IRE)**, 6, b g Court Cave (IRE)—Orador Sur Glane (IRE) **Mrs S. M. Wood**
36 **SPECIAL CATCH (IRE)**, 11, b g Catcher In The Rye (IRE)—Top Quality **M. F. Browne**
37 **SUN CLOUD (IRE)**, 11, b g Cloudings (IRE)—Miss Melrose **Boundary Garage (Bury) Limited**
38 **TAYZAR**, 7, b g Kayf Tara—Matilda Too (IRE) **C. D. Carr**
39 **TEMPLE MAN**, 6, b g Sulamani (USA)—Altogether Now (IRE) **Mrs I C Straker & Steven Key**
40 **WAITING PATIENTLY (IRE)**, 7, b g Flemensfirth (USA)—Rossavon (IRE) **Mr R. Collins**
41 **YORVIK**, 4, b g Yeats (IRE)—Overbranch **Mr & Mrs G. Calder**

Other Owners: Mr W. P. Aitkenhead, Mr Tony Ambler, Mr Toby Becton, Mrs J. Calder, Mr G. Calder, Mrs D. W. Davenport, Mrs E. J. Dolan-Abrahams, Mr E. J. Dolan-Abrahams, Mr Cathal Doocey, Mr Charles Doocey, Mrs M. W. Fawcus, Mr D. S. Fawcus, Mr Derek Gennard, Mrs Gillian Gennard, Mr C. S. Johnston, Mr S. Key, Mr R. G. Makin, Mr D. R. Obank, Mr S. Oldroyd, Mr Chris Perkins, Mrs Ailsa Russell, Mr Drew Russell, Mrs I. C. Straker, Mr P. M. Warren, Mr R. Wharton, Mr J. H. Wilson.

Jockey (NH): Brian Hughes. **Conditional:** Aiden Blakemore.

---

310 MR J. R. JENKINS, Royston
Postal: **Kings Ride, Baldock Road, Royston, Hertfordshire, SG8 9NN**
Contacts: **PHONE (01763) 241141 (01763) 246611 FAX (01763) 248223 MOBILE (07802) 750855**
E-MAIL john@johnjenkinsracing.co.uk WEBSITE www.johnjenkinsracing.co.uk

1 **ACE CHEETAH (USA)**, 4, b c Kitten's Joy (USA)—Imagistic (USA) **Ms A. Juskaite**
2 **ALSHAN FAJER**, 8, ch g Lemon Drop Kid (USA)—Illuminise (IRE) **The Alshan Fajer Partnership**
3 **BELROG**, 7, ch g New Approach (IRE)—Millennium Dash **Mrs C. Goddard**
4 **BILLY'S BOOTS**, 4, ch g Winker Watson—Solmorin **Mr F. Qadir**
5 **BRAVE RICHARD (IRE)**, 7, b g Jeremy (USA)—Certainly Brave **Partnership Terminated**
6 **BUBBLY BAILEY**, 8, b g Byron—Night Gypsy **Mrs S. Bowmer & Mrs Wendy Jenkins**
7 **CLEVER DIVYA**, 5, b m Archipenko (USA)—Clever Omneya (USA) **Ms A. Juskaite**
8 **COMPTON BRAVE**, 4, b g Compton Place—Willmar (IRE) **Compton Brave Partnership**
9 **COOL ECHO**, 4, b f Mount Nelson—Ellcon (IRE) **Mr M. Turner**
10 **DALKADAM (FR)**, 7, gr g Martaline—Cadoudane (FR) **Mrs S. F. Hadida**
11 **DIORE LIA (IRE)**, 4, b f Yeats (IRE)—Cyclonic Storm **Ms M. Todd**
12 **DOLLYWAGGON PIKE**, 4, b f Hellvelyn—Once Removed **Amazing Racing IV & Partner**
13 **EYE BURNER**, 4, ch g Equiano (FR)—Tilly's Dream **Mr R. Sival**
14 **FREDDY WITH A Y (IRE)**, 8, b g Amadeus Wolf—Mataji (IRE) **Mr A. J. Taylor**
15 **GALUPPI**, 7, b g Galileo (IRE)—La Leuze (IRE) **Mrs W. A. Jenkins**
16 **GRANNY FRANKHAM**, 5, b m Authorized (IRE)—Faldal
17 **KARAM ALBAARI (IRE)**, 10, b h King's Best (USA)—Lilakiya (IRE) **Mr Mark Goldstein & Mrs Wendy Jenkins**
18 **LEWISHAM**, 8, b g Sleeping Indian—Almunia (IRE) **Mr M. J. Benton**
19 **LITTLE INDIAN**, 8, b g Sleeping Indian—Once Removed **Mrs W. A. Jenkins**
20 **ONLY TEN PER CENT (IRE)**, 10, b g Kheleyf (USA)—Cory Everson (IRE) **Mrs W. A. Jenkins**
21 **PRETTY BUBBLES**, 9, b m Sleeping Indian—Willmar (IRE) **Mr Mark Goldstein & Mrs Wendy Jenkins**
22 **PURPLE SPECTRUM**, 7, gr g Verglas (IRE)—Rainbow's Edge **Roldvale Ltd G Pascoe Barry Silkman**
23 **REBEL SKY**, 5, b m Cockney Rebel (IRE)—Sakhacity **Mr Barry Polkey & Mrs Wendy Jenkins**
24 **SAGA SPRINT (IRE)**, 5, b m Excellent Art—Queen of Malta (IRE) **Saga Sprint Partnership**
25 **SAMMY'S CHOICE**, 6, ch g Pastoral Pursuits—Diane's Choice **Mr A. J. Taylor**
26 **SILVER MOUNTAIN**, 7, gr g Sir Percy—Pearl Bright (FR) **Ms A. Juskaite**
27 **SLIPALONGTREVASKIS**, 5, b g Kheleyf (USA)—Tilly's Dream **VSN Ltd**
28 **ST PATRICK'S DAY (IRE)**, 6, b g Fastnet Rock (AUS)—
Race For The Stars (USA) **The Boys From Roscommon Syndicate**
29 **TASTY GINGER (IRE)**, 5, ch g Tamayuz—Secret Fashion **B. S. P. Dowling**
30 **THE FIRM (IRE)**, 9, b g Acclamation—Aspen Falls (IRE) **Mr D. J. Nestorovic**
31 **TILSWORTH LUKEY**, 5, b g Sixties Icon—Chara **Michael Ng & Phyllis Hutchins**
32 **WALLY'S WISDOM**, 6, b g Dutch Art—Faldal **Mr R. Cooper**
33 **WE WIN**, 4, b f Hellvelyn—Pink Champagne **Mr R. Sival**
34 **WHALEWEIGH STATION**, 7, b g Zamindar (USA)—Looby Loo **Mr J. Melo**
35 **WILLOW TIGER LILY**, 4, ch f Sakhee's Secret—Tinkerbell Will **Mrs S. Bambridge**

MR J. R. JENKINS - Continued

THREE-YEAR-OLDS

36 CHLOELLIE, b f Delegator—Caramelita **Mrs Veronica Bullard & Mrs Wendy Jenkins**
37 MAGIC BUDDY, ch f Captain Gerrard (IRE)—Magic By Bell **Mr M. Turner**
38 POORAULDJOSEPHINE, ch f Piccolo—Moment In The Sun **The Boys From Roscommon Syndicate**
39 RAISE A LITTLE JOY, b f Pastoral Pursuits—Ray of Joy **Mr R. Stevens**
40 ZAHRAANI, b c Mount Nelson—Mediterranean Sea (IRE) **Mr F. Qadir**

Other Owners: Mr D. S. Allan, Mrs S. Bowmer, Mrs V. Bullard, Mr M. D. Goldstein, Mrs I. C. Hampson, Mr G. Higgins, Mr S. Higgins, Mrs P. E. E. Hutchins, Michael Ng, G. J. Pascoe, Mr B. L. Polkey, Roldvale Ltd, B. Silkman.

311

MR ALAN JESSOP, Chelmsford
Postal: **Flemings Farm, Warren Road, South Hanningfield, Chelmsford, Essex, CM3 8HU**
Contacts: **PHONE (01268) 710210 MOBILE (07718) 736482**

1 BLAZING GLEN (IRE), 10, ch g Beneficial—Kofiyah's Rose (IRE) **Mrs G. Jessop**
2 CHORAL BEE, 9, b m Oratorio (IRE)—Chief Bee **Mrs G. Jessop**
3 MAX MILANO (IRE), 13, b g Milan—Stellissima (IRE) **Mrs G. Jessop**
4 OUTLAW JACK (IRE), 6, b g Mr Dinos—Bonus Issue (IRE) **Mrs G. Jessop**

312

MR F. JESTIN, Wigton
Postal: **Hilltop, Brocklebank, Wigton, Cumbria, CA7 8DL**
Contacts: **PHONE (01697) 478439**
E-MAIL fejestin@icloud.com

1 COOTE STREET (IRE), 10, b g Winged Love (IRE)—Unknown Quality **F. Jestin**
2 HOMBRE DE HIERRO (IRE), 10, b g Winged Love (IRE)—Dama De Seda (IRE) **F. Jestin**

313

MRS LINDA JEWELL, Maidstone
Postal: **Southfield Stables, South Lane, Sutton Valence, Maidstone, Kent, ME17 3AZ**
Contacts: **PHONE (01622) 842788 MOBILE (07856) 686657**
E-MAIL lindajewell@hotmail.com WEBSITE www.lindajewellracing.co.uk

1 BREDEN (IRE), 8, b g Shamardal (USA)—Perfect Touch (USA) **The Breden Racing Partnership**
2 CLONUSKER (IRE), 10, b g Fasliyev (USA)—Tamburello (IRE) **Mr David Yeadon & Mrs Linda Jewell**
3 COCKNEY SEAGULL (IRE), 5, b g Watar (IRE)—Acountry Lane (IRE) **CS Partnership**
4 DUE SOUTH (IRE), 7, b g City Honours (USA)—Lady Shackleton (IRE)
5 EASYONTHEEYE (IRE), 7, br m Kalanisi (IRE)—Lady Bernie (IRE) **P. A. Oppenheimer**
6 HAB SAB (IRE), 6, b g Papal Bull—Tamburello (IRE) **Mr T. Betteridge**
7 HECTON BAY (IRE), 7, b g Trans Island—Reserve The Right (IRE) **Mr H J Jarvis & Mrs P Jarvis**
8 INDISPENSABELLE, 9, b m Passing Glance—Belle Largesse **Mr R. Churcher**
9 ITOLDYOU (IRE), 12, ch g Salford Express (IRE)—Adisadel (IRE) **Valence Racing Too**
10 5, Ch g Fruits of Love (USA)—Jilly Jaffa Cake (IRE)
11 JOLLY JET (IRE), 6, b m Arcadio (GER)—Boarding Pass (IRE) **Mrs S. M. Stanier**
12 KAYFLIN (FR), 10, b m Kayf Tara—Flinders **Mr Dick Churcher Racing**
13 MAB DAB (IRE), 7, b g Papal Bull—Pret A Porter (UAE) **Mr T. Betteridge**
14 MADAM ANNA (IRE), 5, b m Papal Bull—Melaaya (USA) **Mr T. Betteridge**
15 MISS MALARKY (IRE), 5, b m Presenting—The Shan Gang (IRE) **Mr R. Dean**
16 MONEYSTOWN (IRE), 8, b m Touch of Land (FR)—Karinga Duff **Mr H J Jarvis & Mrs P Jarvis**
17 MR JACK (IRE), 6, ch g Papal Bull—Miss Barbados (IRE) **The Breden Racing Partnership**
18 OUR GIRL ACORN, 4, b f Bushranger—Dominatrix **From Little Acorns**
19 ROYAL CONCORDE (IRE), 7, br g Kalanisi (IRE)—Talinas Rose (IRE) **Mr R. B. Morton**
20 TOPOTHEHILL (IRE), 6, b m Papal Bull—Maid of Ale (IRE) **Mr R. Dean**
21 WATAR DAY, 4, b f Watar (IRE)—Hopeshedoes (USA) **Martin Boutcher/Linda Jewell**
22 WONTSTOPMENOW (IRE), 5, b g Scorpion (IRE)—Jodi (IRE) **Valence Racing**

THREE-YEAR-OLDS

23 Ch c Spot On Remarque—Princess Matthews
24 Ch f Watar (IRE)—She's Humble (IRE)

MRS LINDA JEWELL - Continued

Other Owners: Mr C. G. Benford, Mr M. J. Boutcher, Mr M. R. Charlton, Mr C. M. Couldrey, Mrs L. J. Felstead, Mrs S. M. Fitzjohn, Mr M. G. Fitzjohn, Mrs A. P. Giggins, Mr W. Giggins, Miss S. E. Haughton, Mr B. J. Hensman, H. J. Jarvis, Mrs P. Jarvis, Mrs L. C. Jewell, Mr K. Pinder, Mr J. J. Saxton, Mr J. C. Webb, Mr D. N. Yeadon, R. I. B. Young.

Assistant Trainer: Karen Jewell

Jockey (flat): Robert Havlin, Robert Winston. **Jockey (NH):** Leighton Aspell, Tom Cannon.
Conditional: Tom Garner, Jack Sherwood.

---

314 **MR BRETT JOHNSON, Epsom**
Postal: **The Durdans Stables, Chalk Lane, Epsom, Surrey, KT18 7AX**
Contacts: **MOBILE (07768) 697141**
E-MAIL thedurdansstables@googlemail.com WEBSITE www.brjohnsonracing.co.uk

1 **CAYUGA,** 9, b g Montjeu (IRE)—Ithaca (USA) **B. R. Johnson**
2 **CLANDON,** 5, b g Sakhee's Secret—Whassup (FR) **Mrs A. M. Upsdell**
3 **COMPTON ABBEY,** 4, b f Compton Place—Bolsena (USA) **J. Daniels**
4 **DANGEROUS ENDS,** 4, b g Monsieur Bond (IRE)—Stolen Glance **Mr C. Westley**
5 **HERON (USA),** 4, b c Quality Road (USA)—Dreamt **O1 Racing Partnership**
6 **JACKBLACK,** 6, b g Crosspeace (IRE)—Saharan Royal **B. R. Johnson**
7 **LACAN (IRE),** 7, b g New Approach—Invincible Isle (IRE) **Mr C. Westley**
8 **LADY MARITIME (IRE),** 4, b f Delegator—No Song **Mr C. Westley**
9 **RAKEMATIZ,** 4, ch g Pivotal—Regal Velvet **Mr C. Westley**
10 **VERY HONEST (IRE),** 5, b m Poet's Voice—Cercle d'amour (USA) **Omni Colour & B R Johnson**
11 **VIOLET'S LADS (IRE),** 4, b f Myboycharlie (IRE)—Cape Violet (IRE) **The Savy Group**

THREE-YEAR-OLDS

12 **IRVING'S GIRL,** b f Rip Van Winkle (IRE)—High Cross (IRE) **Tann & Mr N Jarvis**
13 B g Poet's Voice—Mexicali (IRE) **J Daniels, Omni, D Sparks, C Westley**

TWO-YEAR-OLDS

14 Ch c 23/3 Dawn Approach (IRE)—Remarkable Story (Mark of Esteem (IRE)) (22000) **Mr C. Westley**
15 Gr c 27/3 Archipenko (USA)—She Is Great (IRE) (Dalakhani (IRE)) (15000) **Mr C. Westley**

Other Owners: Mr M. Cumins, Mr N. Hale, Mr S. Hills, Mr N. A. Jarvis, Omni Colour Presentations Ltd, Mrs S. Rutherford, Mr D. Sparks, Mr G. Tann, Mr B. D. Townsend, Miss L. Wilde.

Assistant Trainer: Vanessa Johnson

---

315 **MISS EVE JOHNSON HOUGHTON, Blewbury**
Postal: **Woodway, Blewbury, Didcot, Oxfordshire, OX11 9EZ**
Contacts: **PHONE (01235) 850480 (01235) 850500 (Home) FAX (01235) 851045**
MOBILE (07721) 622700
E-MAIL Eve@JohnsonHoughton.com WEBSITE www.JohnsonHoughton.com

1 **ACCIDENTAL AGENT,** 4, b c Delegator—Roodle **Mrs F. M. Johnson Houghton**
2 **BAHAMADAM,** 4, b f Bahamian Bounty—Pelagia (IRE) **Mr J. P. Repard**
3 **BE BE KING (IRE),** 4, b g Bated Breath—Champion Place **G. C. Stevens**
4 **BECCA CAMPBELL (IRE),** 5, b m Roderic O'connor (IRE)—Scottendale **Eden Racing Club**
5 **COUNT CALABASH (IRE),** 4, b g Big Bad Bob (IRE)—Tinaheely (IRE) **Trish Hall & Colin Fletcher**
6 **DESERT EXPLORER (IRE),** 4, b g Henrythenavigator (USA)—Bee Eater (IRE) **The Pantechnicons VI**
7 **FAVOURITE ROYAL (IRE),** 4, b f Acclamation—Affirmative **J Cross, M Duckham, L Godfrey, P Wollaston**
8 **FRANK BRIDGE,** 5, b g Avonbridge—First Among Equals **Mr J. Dyer**
9 **GOLDEN WEDDING (IRE),** 6, b g Archipenko (USA)—Peace Lily **Mrs F. M. Johnson Houghton**
10 **GORING (GER),** 6, b g Areion (GER)—Globuli (GER) **G. C. Stevens**
11 **HEDGING (IRE),** 4, gr ro g Mastercraftsman (IRE)—Privet (IRE) **The Picnic Partnership**
12 **ICE AGE (IRE),** 5, b g Frozen Power (IRE)—Incendio **Eden Racing III**
13 **KIRKLAND FOREVER,** 4, ch f Sakhee (USA)—Maystock **Mrs M. Fairbairn & P. Dean**
14 **MISS INGA SOCK (IRE),** 6, ch m Tagula (IRE)—Support Fund (IRE) **The Ascot Colts & Fillies Club**
15 **NEW RICH,** 8, b g Bahamian Bounty—Bling Bling (IRE) **Eden Racing Club**
16 **ON TO VICTORY,** 4, b g Rock of Gibraltar (IRE)—Clouds of Magellan (USA) **HP Racing On To Victory**
17 **SIX STRINGS,** 4, b g Requinto (IRE)—Island Music (IRE)
18 **SUPER JULIUS,** 4, ch g Bated Breath—Paradise Isle **Mr B. Miller**

MISS EVE JOHNSON HOUGHTON - Continued

19 **VIXEN (IRE)**, 4, b f Kodiac—Radio Wave **Mrs Jennifer Simpson Racing**
20 **WHAT ABOUT CARLO (FR)**, 7, b g Creachadoir (IRE)—Boccatenera (GER) **Mr A. J. Pye-Jeary**

THREE-YEAR-OLDS

21 **CAIYA**, b f Casamento (IRE)—Louverissa (IRE) **Blyth Currie & Royle**
22 **CAMOMILE LAWN (IRE)**, b f Camelot—Endure (IRE) **Biddestone Racing Partnership IX**
23 **DORELLA (GER)**, b f Reliable Man—Diacada (GER) **Mrs A. G. Kavanagh**
24 **DOWNTOWN MOMBASA (IRE)**, b f Lord Shanakill (USA)—Mattinata **Partnership Terminated**
25 **DUKEOFWALLINGFORD**, b g Equiano (FR)—Hazelberry **J. H. Widdows**
26 **FERIK (IRE)**, b g Arcano (IRE)—Love And Laughter (IRE) **Mr Simon Munir & Mr Isaac Souede**
27 **FROSTBITE**, gr g Lethal Force (IRE)—Red Sovereign **G. C. Stevens**
28 **GENERAL JACK (IRE)**, br c Society Rock (IRE)—City Dazzler (IRE) **Ms E. Chivers & Merlin Racing**
29 **GLORIA TUA**, b f Dutch Art—Short Affair **Aston House Stud**
30 **GREAT VIZIER**, b g Sir Percy—Special Green (FR) **Mr Simon Munir & Mr Isaac Souede**
31 **JACK CROW**, b c Bahamian Bounty—Here To Eternity (USA) **Mrs Jennifer Simpson Racing**
32 **JUNGLE QUEEN (IRE)**, ch f Leroidesanimaux (BRZ)—Elusive Gold (IRE) **Eden Racing**
33 **KEY PLAYER**, ch g Kheleyf (USA)—My Pretty Girl **Raw, Reeve & Wollaston**
34 **LADY MARIGOLD (IRE)**, b f Intense Focus (USA)—Peace Lily **The Ascot Revellers**
35 **LADY OF PETRA**, b f Compton Place—Aqaba **Wood Street Syndicate & Partner**
36 **LAST ENCHANTMENT (IRE)**, b f Camelot—Illandrane (IRE) **Mrs Whitehall, Spiegelberg & Everett**
37 **MAGNOLIA SPRINGS (IRE)**, b f Shamardal (USA)—Rainbow City (IRE) **Anthony Rogers & Mrs Sonia Rogers**
38 **MARY ELISE (IRE)**, b f Mastercraftsman (IRE)—Je T'adore (IRE) **Elaine Chivers & Merlin Racing**
39 **OPTIMUM TIME (IRE)**, b g Manduro (GER)—Mypreciousblue **The Picnic Partnership**
40 **ROSER MOTER (IRE)**, b f Motivator—Rosia Bay
41 **RUNNING CLOUD (IRE)**, b g Cacique (IRE)—Nimbus Star **HP Racing Running Cloud**
42 **SAFE WATERS**, ch f Helmet (AUS)—Golden Waters **Mr R Crutchley & Mr B McNamee**
43 **SCENERY**, ch g Elnadim (USA)—Widescreen (USA) **Mr S McPhee, Mrs E Rice, Mrs C Whitehall**
44 **SKYDIVING**, b c Al Kazeem—How High The Sky (IRE) **P D Player & R J Cornelius**
45 **SO CRAFTY**, ch f Mastercraftsman (IRE)—Mea Parvitas (IRE) **Lionel Godfrey & Peter Wollaston**
46 **STATUARIO**, b g Helmet (AUS)—Cat Hunter **Mr Michael G Cohen & Mr David Cohen**
47 **TOUR DE PARIS (IRE)**, b g Champs Elysees—Disco Lights **HP Racing Tour de Paris**

TWO-YEAR-OLDS

48 B c 23/4 No Nay Never (USA)—City Dazzler (IRE) (Elusive City (USA)) **Elaine Chivers**
49 B f 22/4 Charm Spirit (IRE)—Coventina (IRE) (Daylami (IRE)) (11000) **Mr Khalifa Dasmal**
50 **DARYANA**, b f 12/2 Dutch Art—Darysina (USA) (Smart Strike (CAN)) (20000) **Lionel Godfrey & Peter Wollaston**
51 **DOUBLE ESPRIT**, b c 20/3 Invincible Spirit (IRE)—
      Nature Spirits (FR) (Beat Hollow) (100000) **Mr Simon Munir & Mr Isaac Souede**
52 **DREAM MANOEUVRE**, b c 5/3 Oasis Dream—
      Jostle (USA) (Brocco (USA)) (15000) **Simon Munir & Isaac Souede**
53 B f 15/3 Kodiac—Funday (Daylami (IRE)) (50000) **Mrs J. Blyth Currie**
54 Gr f 14/2 Aussie Rules (USA)—Garabelle (IRE) (Galileo (IRE)) **Mrs H. Raw**
55 **GARRISON COMMANDER (IRE)**, b c 6/3 Garswood—Malea (IRE) (Oratorio (IRE)) (30476) **HP Racing**
56 **GIN PALACE**, b c 25/2 Swiss Spirit—
      Regal Curtsy (Royal Applause) **Mrs Z. Campbell-Harris & The Hon. A. Barker**
57 B c 7/3 Dutch Art—Guajara (GER) (Montjeu (IRE)) (52000) **Mr A. Pye-Jeary**
58 Ch f 6/4 Showcasing—Heading North (Teofilo (IRE)) **Hot To Trot Syndicate**
59 **JUMEIRAH (IRE)**, b f 5/1 Acclamation—Scarlet Plum (Pivotal) (33000) **Mr S. Almuhairi**
60 Gr c 31/3 Clodovil (IRE)—Lizzy's Township (USA) (Delaware Township (USA)) (10582)
61 **LYRICAL WATERS**, b c 20/3 Poet's Voice—Golden Waters (Dubai Destination (USA))
62 **MASTER MILLINER (IRE)**, ch c 8/4 Helmet (AUS)—
      Aqualina (IRE) (King's Theatre (IRE)) (21164) **Mrs Jennifer Simpson Racing**
63 B f 25/3 Acclamation—Meet Marhaba (IRE) (Marju (IRE)) (24761) **Biddestone Racing**
64 B c 25/2 Sepoy (AUS)—My Golly (Mozart (IRE)) (5000)
65 **MY STYLE (IRE)**, bl gr c 8/3 Holy Roman Emperor (IRE)—That's My Style (Dalakhani (IRE)) (30000)
66 B f 26/3 Toronado (IRE)—Myth And Magic (IRE) (Namid) (40000) **Galloway Page Pritchard Hobson & Thomas**
67 B c 1/2 Charm Spirit (IRE)—Nickels And Dimes (IRE) (Teofilo (IRE)) (26666) **Nick Bradley Racing**
68 **OVER THE RIVER**, b f 8/4 Avonbridge—First Among Equals (Primo Valentino (IRE)) **Mr J. Dyer**
69 **PARISEAN ARTISTE (IRE)**, ch f 21/2 Zoffany (IRE)—Meeting In Paris (IRE) (Dutch Art) **Mr A. R. W. Marsh**
70 **PEGASUS BRIDGE**, b c 8/4 Camacho—Fire Line (Firebreak) (33333) **HP Racing**
71 **RESOLUTE BAY**, b f 4/2 Showcasing—Confusing (Refuse To Bend (IRE)) (30000) **Mrs Jennifer Simpson Racing**
72 Ch f 12/2 Mastercraftsman (IRE)—Rivara (Red Ransom (USA)) (20952) **The Chriselliam Partnership**
73 B f 24/2 Champs Elysees—Roodle (Xaar) **Mrs R. F. Johnson Houghton**

MISS EVE JOHNSON HOUGHTON - Continued

74 **SMITH (IRE)**, ch c 16/1 Dawn Approach (IRE)—Alazeya (IRE) (Shirocco (GER)) (32000) **Mr A. J. Pye-Jeary**
75 Ch f 3/3 Poet's Voice—Sunday Bess (JPN) (Deep Impact (JPN)) **Chasemore Farm**
76 B f 3/5 Frozen Power (IRE)—Support Fund (IRE) (Intikhab (USA)) (761) **Eden Racing Club**
77 B f 5/4 Havana Gold (IRE)—Tamalain (USA) (Royal Academy (USA)) **Mr & Mrs R. Scott**
78 **TIN HAT (IRE)**, ch c 20/3 Helmet (AUS)—Precautionary (Green Desert (USA)) (30000) **Eden Racing III**

Other Owners: T. Al-Mazeedi, Mrs James Blyth Currie, Mrs G. P. Bostwick, T. P. Bostwick, Mr N. Bradley, Mr P. A. Brend, Mr Richard Bryan, Mr J. A. Bryan, Mr S. Calton, Ms Lauren Chivers, Ms Elaine Chivers, Miss Charlotte Chivers, Mr David Cohen, Mr Michael Cohen, Mr R. J. Cornelius, Mr Gordon Cosburn, Mr Jonathan Cross, Mr R. Crutchley, Mr S. M. Dibb, Mr Mark Duckham, Mr Guy Everett, Mr Colin Fletcher, Mr B. S. Galloway, Mr Lionel Godfrey, Ms Trish Hall, Mr J. Hobson, Miss S. Holden, Mrs R. F. Johnson Houghton, Miss E. Johnson Houghton, Mr R. F. Johnson Houghton, Mr Charles Liverton, Mr B. P. McNamee, Mr Stuart McPhee, Mr J. A. McWilliam, S. E. Munir, Mr M. E. Page, Mr P. D. Player, W. H. Ponsonby, Mr R. Pritchard, Mrs H. Raw, Mr Robert Reeve, Mrs E. Rice, Mrs S. M. Rogers, A. P. Rogers, Mrs Heather Royle, Mr W. H. Simpson, Mrs Jennifer Simpson, Mr I. Souede, Mr G. A. Thomas, Mr J. R. Wallis, Mrs C. Whitehall, Mr F. Wintle, Mr P. Wollaston, Wood Street Syndicate.

Assistant Trainer: R. F. Johnson Houghton

Jockey (flat): Charles Bishop, Edward Greatrex.

---

316 | **MR KENNY JOHNSON, Newcastle Upon Tyne**
Postal: **Grange Farm, Newburn, Newcastle Upon Tyne, Tyne and Wear, NE15 8QA**
Contacts: **PHONE (0191) 2674464 (01388) 721813 MOBILE (07774) 131121**
E-MAIL kennyjohnson68@hotmail.co.uk WEBSITE www.johnsonracing.co.uk

1 **BEAU SANCY (FR)**, 6, b g Blue Bresil (FR)—Touquette (FR) **Mr L Armstrong & Partner**
2 **BYGONES FOR COINS (IRE)**, 10, ch m Danroad (AUS)—Reservation (IRE) **Carter Thompson Associates**
3 **CAPTAIN SHARPE**, 10, ch g Tobougg (IRE)—Helen Sharp **Carter Thompson Associates Racing**
4 **KING GOLAN (IRE)**, 7, b g Golan (IRE)—Crimson Bow (GER) **I. Blacklock, K. Johnson**
5 **MAHLER BAY (IRE)**, 8, b g Mahler—Belalzao (IRE) **Blacklock Simpson**
6 **MR WITMORE (IRE)**, 8, b g Whitmore's Conn (USA)—Bright Future (IRE) **Blacklock Simpson**
7 **NOTONEBUTTWO (IRE)**, 11, b g Dushyantor (USA)—Daiquiri (IRE) **Mr N. Taylor**
8 **POLITELYSED**, 12, ch m Courteous—Allegedly Red **Partnership Terminated**
9 **PSYCHOLOGY**, 5, b g Shamardal (USA)—Emotion Parade (ARG) **Mr R C Whitelock & Partner**
10 **ROSQUERO (FR)**, 13, ch g Blushing Flame (USA)—Kingsgirl (FR) **Dave Bamlet Racing**
11 **UNDER THE RED SKY (IRE)**, 11, ch g Insatiable (IRE)—
Official Secret **Mr Robert C. Whitelock/Mr Kenny Johnson**
12 **VECHEKA (IRE)**, 7, b g Lawman (FR)—Lidanski (IRE) **John Caldow & Kenny Johnson**
13 **VODKA RED (IRE)**, 10, b g Ivan Denisovich (IRE)—Begine (IRE) **Carter Thompson Associates**

Other Owners: J. L. Armstrong, Mr D. Bamlet, Mr I. M. Blacklock, Mr J. R. Caldow, Mr A. Carter, Mr K. Johnson, Mr I. Simpson, Mr S. Thompson, R. C. Whitelock.

Conditional: Callum Bewley, Tommy Dowson. **Amateur:** Mr Kane Yeoman.

---

317 | **MRS SUSAN JOHNSON, Madley**
Postal: **Carwardine Farm, Madley, Hereford**
Contacts: **PHONE (01981) 250214 FAX (01981) 251538**

1 **THE LAST BRIDGE**, 11, b g Milan—Celtic Bridge **I. K. Johnson**

Jockey (NH): Richard Johnson.

---

318 | **MR MARK JOHNSTON, Middleham**
Postal: **Kingsley House Racing Stables, Middleham, Leyburn, North Yorkshire, DL8 4PH**
Contacts: **PHONE (01969) 622237 FAX (01969) 622484**
E-MAIL mark@markjohnstonracing.com WEBSITE www.markjohnstonracing.com

1 **ABAREEQ**, 5, ch g Haatef (USA)—Hafawa (IRE) **Mr A D Spence & Mr M B Spence**
2 **ACLIMATISE**, 4, b g Acclamation—Favourita **Mark Johnston Racing Ltd**

MR MARK JOHNSTON - Continued

3 **ADDICTED TO YOU (IRE)**, 4, ch g Medicean—Adalawa (IRE) **M. W. Graff**
4 **CAPE COAST**, 4, b c Cape Cross (IRE)—Famusa **A. Saeed**
5 **DOMINATING (GER)**, 4, ch g Jukebox Jury (IRE)—Dominante (GER) **Mr Alan Spence**
6 **FINAL**, 6, b g Arabian Gleam—Caysue **C. H. Greensit & W. A. Greensit**
7 **FIRE FIGHTING (IRE)**, 7, b g Soldier of Fortune (IRE)—Savoie (FR) **Mr Alan Spence**
8 **FRANKUUS (IRE)**, 4, gr c Frankel—Dookus (IRE) **Hussain Lootah & Ahmad Al Shaikh**
9 **HOCHFELD (IRE)**, 4, b g Cape Cross (IRE)—What A Charm (IRE) **Sheikh Hamdan Bin Mohammed Al Maktoum**
10 **JAFETICA**, 4, ch f New Approach (IRE)—Fann (USA) **Mr A D Spence & Mr M B Spence**
11 **KHAMAARY (IRE)**, 4, br f Tamayuz—Nufoos **Hamdan bin Rashid Al Maktoum**
12 **KILMAH**, 4, b f Sepoy (AUS)—Perfect Star **Mr A. Al Mansoori**
13 **LOVE DREAMS (IRE)**, 4, b c Dream Ahead (USA)—Kimola (IRE) **Crone Stud Farms Ltd**
14 **LOVE OASIS**, 4, b f Oasis Dream—Pickle **Crone Stud Farms Ltd**
15 **MAMBO DANCER (IRE)**, 4, b g So You Think (NZ)—Mambo Halo (USA) **Kingsley Park 9**
16 **MASHAM STAR (IRE)**, 4, b g Lawman (FR)—Croisiere (USA) **3 Batterhams and a Reay**
17 **MISS DANBY (IRE)**, 4, gr f Mastercraftsman (IRE)—Dunbrody (FR) **Kingsley Park Owners Club**
18 **POET'S SOCIETY**, 4, ch g Poet's Voice—Rahiyah (USA) **Kingsley Park 9**
19 **RAINBOW REBEL (IRE)**, 5, b g Acclamation—Imperial Quest **Owners Group 004**
20 **RAVENHOE (IRE)**, 5, ch g Bahamian Bounty—Breathless Kiss (USA) **Kingsley Park Owners Club**
21 **SOFIA'S ROCK (FR)**, 4, b g Rock of Gibraltar (IRE)—Princess Guria (UAE) **Mezzone Family 1**
22 **SOLDIER IN ACTION (FR)**, 5, ch g Soldier of Fortune (IRE)—Ripley (GER) **Mr Alan Spence**
23 **STAR OF THE EAST (IRE)**, 4, b g Cape Cross (IRE)—
                                           Serenity Star **Sheikh Hamdan Bin Mohammed Al Maktoum**
24 **TARTAN BUTE**, 5, b g Azamour (IRE)—On A Soapbox (USA) **Mr F. Bird**
25 **THE LAST DEBUTANTE**, 4, b f Henrythenavigator (USA)—Lady Eclair (IRE) **Netherfield House Stud**
26 **TIME TO STUDY (FR)**, 4, ch c Motivator—Dissertation (FR) **Mr A. Al Mansoori**
27 **TITI MAKFI**, 4, b f Makfi—Titivation **Mr & Mrs Paul & Clare Rooney**
28 **WATERSMEET**, 7, gr g Dansili—Under The Rainbow **Mr J. A. Barson**
29 **X RATED (IRE)**, 4, gr g Exceed And Excel (AUS)—Screen Star (IRE) **Kingsley Park Owners Club**
30 **YORKIDDING**, 6, b m Dalakhani (FR)—Claxon **Mr P. R. York**

THREE-YEAR-OLDS

31 **AGADEER**, ch f Sepoy (AUS)—Xtra Special **Mr H. Dalmook Al Maktoum**
32 **ALHAWDAJ (USA)**, ch f Speightstown (USA)—Baragah (USA) **Hamdan bin Rashid Al Maktoum**
33 **ANGELINA D'OR (GER)**, ch f Casamento (IRE)—Ange Doree (FR) **M. W. Graff**
34 **AQUARIUM**, ch c Leroidesanimaux (BRZ)—Caribana **Mark Johnston Racing Ltd**
35 **ARCH GOLD (USA)**, b c Arch (USA)—Trepidation (USA) **Mr H. A. Lootah**
36 **AUSTIN POWERS (IRE)**, ch g Power—My Lass **Excel Racing VII**
37 **AUSTRIAN SCHOOL (IRE)**, b c Teofilo (IRE)—Swiss Roll (IRE) **Dr J. Walker**
38 **BAGHDAD (FR)**, b c Frankel—Funny Girl (IRE) **Mr M. B. H. K. Al Attiya**
39 **BAILEYS EXCELERATE (FR)**, gr c Excelebration (IRE)—
                                           Cruel Sea (USA) **G. R. Bailey Ltd (Baileys Horse Feeds)**
40 **BARBARA VILLIERS**, b f Champs Elysees—Frances Stuart (IRE) **Lowther Racing Iv**
41 **BIG KITTEN (USA)**, ch c Kitten's Joy (USA)—Queen Martha (USA) **Mr H. A. Lootah**
42 **BIRDETTE (IRE)**, b f Epaulette (AUS)—Madam Ninette **Mr F. Bird**
43 **BOOK OF DREAMS (IRE)**, b g Dream Ahead (USA)—Moonbi Ridge (IRE) **The Passionate Partnership**
44 **BRANSCOMBE**, b g Invincible Spirit (IRE)—Lacily (USA) **Sheikh Hamdan Bin Mohammed Al Maktoum**
45 **BURGONET (IRE)**, b c Helmet (AUS)—Dragonera **Mark Johnston Racing Ltd**
46 **CARDSHARP**, b c Lonhro (AUS)—Pure Illusion (USA) **Sheikh Hamdan Bin Mohammed Al Maktoum**
47 **CLARAMARA (IRE)**, b f Epaulette (AUS)—Yaqootah (USA) **Mezzone Family**
48 **COMMUNIQUE (IRE)**, ch c Casamento (IRE)—
                                           Midnight Line (USA) **Sheikh Hamdan Bin Mohammed Al Maktoum**
49 **DALILEO (IRE)**, b c Galileo (IRE)—Snow Queen (IRE) **Mr H. A. Lootah**
50 **DANZAY (IRE)**, b c Raven's Pass (USA)—La Chapelle (IRE) **Sheikh Hamdan Bin Mohammed Al Maktoum**
51 **DARK HONEY (IRE)**, b g Epaulette (AUS)—Manuka Magic (IRE) **Mr J. D. Abell**
52 **DEE EX BEE**, b c Farhh—Dubai Sunrise **Sheikh Hamdan Bin Mohammed Al Maktoum**
53 **DOWITCHER (USA)**, b f Lonhro (AUS)—Danelagh (AUS) **Sheikh Hamdan Bin Mohammed Al Maktoum**
54 **DR RICHARD KIMBLE (IRE)**, b c Lawman (FR)—Aoife Alainn (IRE) **Garrett J Freyne Racing**
55 **DREAM TODAY (IRE)**, b c Dream Ahead (USA)—Macheera (IRE) **Barbara & Alick Richmond**
56 **ELARQAM**, b c Frankel—Attraction **Hamdan bin Rashid Al Maktoum**
57 **ELEGIAC**, b c Farhh—Lamentation **Browne Boyce Richards & Richards**
58 **EMILIA JAMES**, ch f Poet's Voice—Dozy (IRE) **James Property Ltd**
59 **FAITHFUL PROMISE**, b f Acclamation—Devotion (IRE) **S. Manana**
60 **FIRLINFEU**, b g New Approach (IRE)—Antara (GER) **Sheikh Hamdan Bin Mohammed Al Maktoum**
61 **FRANCOPHILIA**, b f Frankel—Lady Jane Digby **Miss K. Rausing**
62 **GALITELLO**, b g Intello (GER)—Coventina (IRE) **Kingsley Park 6**

MR MARK JOHNSTON - Continued

63 **GEMOLOGIST (IRE)**, b f Sir Percy—Tiffany Diamond (IRE) **Kingsley Park Owners Club**
64 **GO NOW GO NOW (IRE)**, b g Kodiac—Ms Mary C (IRE) **Mr & Mrs Paul & Clare Rooney**
65 **ILLUSIONAL**, b g Bernardini (USA)—Illustrious Miss (USA) **Sheikh Hamdan Bin Mohammed Al Maktoum**
66 **INDIAN ADMIRAL**, ch c Sepoy (AUS)—Love And Cherish (IRE) **Mr A. Al Mansoori**
67 **JUNEAU (IRE)**, b f Dubawi (IRE)—Snow Rose (USA) **Sheikh Hamdan Bin Mohammed Al Maktoum**
68 **JUST WAIT (IRE)**, b f Teofilo (IRE)—Winesong (IRE) **Mr A. Al Mansoori**
69 **KALAGIA (IRE)**, b f Kodiac—Esuvia (IRE) **Mrs J. E. Newett**
70 **KING'S PROCTOR (IRE)**, b c Cape Cross (IRE)—Alimony (IRE) **Sheikh Hamdan Bin Mohammed Al Maktoum**
71 **KIT MARLOWE (IRE)**, b g Poet's Voice—La Nuit Rose (FR) **Sheikh Hamdan Bin Mohammed Al Maktoum**
72 **KITTILEO (IRE)**, b c Galileo (IRE)—Kittens **Mr H. A. Lootah**
73 **KNIGHT IN ARMOUR (IRE)**, b g Camelot—Madeira Mist (IRE) **Atlantic Racing & R. W. Huggins**
74 **KNOCKOUT BLOW**, b g Lethal Force (IRE)—Elidore **Mr Alan Spence**
75 **LAKE VOLTA (IRE)**, b g Raven's Pass (USA)—Ghanaian (FR) **Sheikh Hamdan Bin Mohammed Al Maktoum**
76 **LOVE SUMMER NIGHTS**, b c Intello (GER)—Summer Night **Mr M. Doyle**
77 **LUCKY DEAL**, ch c Mastercraftsman (IRE)—Barter **K. F. Leung**
78 **LYNWOOD GOLD (IRE)**, ro c Mastercraftsman (IRE)—Witch of Fife (USA) **Mr J. A. Barson**
79 **MAKING MIRACLES**, b g Pivotal—Field of Miracles (IRE) **Acorn, Brown, Parker & Scott**
80 Ch g Zoffany (IRE)—Marasima (IRE) **G. R. Bailey Ltd (Baileys Horse Feeds)**
81 **MATTERHORN (IRE)**, b c Raven's Pass (USA)—Tanaghum **Sheikh Hamdan Bin Mohammed Al Maktoum**
82 **MILDENBERGER**, b c Teofilo (IRE)—Belle Josephine **Sheikh Hamdan Bin Mohammed Al Maktoum**
83 **MISS VAN WINKLE**, b f Rip Van Winkle (IRE)—Lasso **Holleyhead, Ross, White & Johnston**
84 **MOAKKAD**, b g Helmet (AUS)—Generously Gifted **Hamdan bin Rashid Al Maktoum**
85 **NINE ELMS (USA)**, ch g Street Cry (IRE)—Nawaiet (USA) **Sheikh Hamdan Bin Mohammed Al Maktoum**
86 **NYALETI (IRE)**, b f Arch (USA)—America Nova (FR) **3 Batterhams and a Reay**
87 **ONE SECOND**, b f Intello (GER)—Albavilla **Mr A. Al Mansoori**
88 **POET'S PRINCE**, b c Poet's Voice—Palace Affair **Mr J. D. Abell**
89 **POETIC AFFAIR**, ch c Poet's Voice—Wendylina (IRE) **A. Saeed**
90 **POETIC STEPS (IRE)**, ch f Poet's Voice—Step This Way (USA) **Kingsley Park 6**
91 **PRESTBURY PARK (USA)**, br g Shamardal—Sutra (USA) **Sheikh Hamdan Bin Mohammed Al Maktoum**
92 **RAMPANT LION (IRE)**, b c Bahamian Bounty—Mamma Morton (IRE) **Dr J. Walker**
93 **RASTACAP**, ch f Helmet (AUS)—Caribbean Dancer (USA) **Mr H. C. Hart**
94 **READY TO IMPRESS (USA)**, b g More Than Ready (USA)—Menekineko (USA) **Mr A. Al Mansoori**
95 **REBEL ASSAULT (IRE)**, b f Excelebration (IRE)—Naomh Geileis (USA) **Mrs Christine E Budden & Partners**
96 **RIVER GLADES**, b c Cape Cross (IRE)—Everglades **Sheikh Hamdan Bin Mohammed Al Maktoum**
97 **ROYAL KING (IRE)**, b c Teofilo (IRE)—Imperialistic Diva (IRE) **J. Alharbi**
98 **RUFUS KING**, ch g Iffraaj—Mosqueras Romance **Garrett J Freyne Racing**
99 **SEA YOUMZAIN (IRE)**, b f Sea The Stars (IRE)—Chantilly Pearl (USA) **J. Alharbi**
100 **SHATHARAAT (IRE)**, b c Kodiac—Party Whip (IRE) **Hamdan bin Rashid Al Maktoum**
101 **SHOWROOM (FR)**, b c Motivator—Lemon Twist (IRE) **Highclere T'bred Racing- Nick Skelton**
102 **SNAX**, b f High Chaparral (IRE)—Cosmodrome (USA) **T T Bloodstocks**
103 **STARLIGHT MYSTERY (IRE)**, b br f Iffraaj—Electra Star **A. Saeed**
104 **SUNBREAK (IRE)**, b g Dawn Approach (IRE)—
                        Carry On Katie (USA) **Sheikh Hamdan Bin Mohammed Al Maktoum**
105 **TAIFBALADY (IRE)**, b g Dark Angel (IRE)—Tartiflette **Hamdan bin Rashid Al Maktoum**
106 **TAJDEED (IRE)**, br c Teofilo (IRE)—Nufoos **Hamdan bin Rashid Al Maktoum**
107 **THE BRITISH LION (IRE)**, b c Power—Mala Mala (IRE) **John Brown & Megan Dennis**
108 **THE JUNGLE VIP**, b c Leroidesanimaux (BRZ)—Alakananda **Kingsley Park Owners Club**
109 **THE LINCOLN LAWYER**, b g Lawman (FR)—Adventure Seeker (FR) **John Brown & Megan Dennis**
110 **THREADING (IRE)**, b f Exceed And Excel (AUS)—
                        Chaquiras (USA) **Sheikh Hamdan Bin Mohammed Al Maktoum**
111 **TIGHT LINES**, b f Fastnet Rock (AUS)—Dusty Answer **The Duke Of Roxburghe & Mr D. Burke**
112 **TRAVELCARD (USA)**, b f Iffraaj—Central Line (USA) **Sheikh Hamdan Bin Mohammed Al Maktoum**
113 **VALE OF KENT (IRE)**, b g Kodiac—Red Vale (IRE) **Sheikh Hamdan Bin Mohammed Al Maktoum**
114 **VENTURA KNIGHT (IRE)**, b c Casamento (IRE)—Alltherightmoves (IRE) **Middleham Park Racing XXXVII**
115 **VICTORIA DRUMMOND (IRE)**, b f Sea The Stars (IRE)—Rezyana (AUS) **Mr P. F. M. D. Carmo**
116 **VILLA TORA**, b f Excelebration (IRE)—Tatora **Kingsley Park 6**
117 **VISCOUNT LOFTUS (IRE)**, b g Clodovil (IRE)—Melpomene **Mrs Christine E Budden & Partners**
118 **WADACRE GIGI**, ch f Martaline—Glenreet
119 **WINGED SPUR (IRE)**, ch f Motivator—Mark of An Angel (IRE) **Kingsley Park Owners Club**
120 **ZADORRA (IRE)**, b f Iffraaj—Vitoria (IRE) **Sheikh Hamdan Bin Mohammed Al Maktoum**

TWO-YEAR-OLDS

121 **ACCORDANCE**, b f 28/1 Archipenko (USA)—Moi Aussi (USA) (Mt Livermore (USA)) **Miss K. Rausing**
122 **ADAALAH**, b f 22/4 Oasis Dream—Muteela (Dansili) **Hamdan bin Rashid Al Maktoum**

MR MARK JOHNSTON - Continued

123 Ch f 12/4 Exceed And Excel (AUS)—
Adriana (GER) (Poliglote) (65120) **Sheikh Hamdan Bin Mohammed Al Maktoum**
124 B c 25/5 War Command (USA)—Aguinaga (IRE) (Machiavellian (USA)) (6000) **Kingsley Park 10**
125 B c 9/4 Farhh—Al Mahmeyah (Teofilo (IRE)) (10000) **Mr H. R. Bin Ghedayer**
126 B c 14/2 Born To Sea (IRE)—Albarouche (Sadler's Wells (USA)) (30000) **J. Alharbi**
127 ASIAN ANGEL (IRE), b c 17/2 Dark Angel (IRE)—Chiang Mai (IRE) (Sadler's Wells (USA)) (36630) **Dr J. Walker**
128 Ch c 26/3 Universal (IRE)—Assabiyya (IRE) (Cape Cross (IRE)) (11000) **Mr A. Al Mansoori**
129 B c 28/2 Jukebox Jury (IRE)—Attima (Zafonic (USA)) (17907) **Mr Alan Spence**
130 AXEL JACKLIN, b c 14/2 Iffraaj—Reroute (IRE) (Acclamation) (20000)
131 B c 12/4 Slade Power (IRE)—
Bergamask (USA) (Kingmambo (USA)) **Sheikh Hamdan Bin Mohammed Al Maktoum**
132 B f 13/2 Pivotal—Betimes (New Approach (IRE)) **Sheikh Hamdan Bin Mohammed Al Maktoum**
133 B f 17/1 Galileo (IRE)—Bewitched (IRE) (Dansili) (162800) **Mr H. A. Lootah**
134 B c 16/2 Dream Ahead (USA)—Black Dahlia (Dansili) (15000) **Kingsley Park 10**
135 B c 4/5 Exceed And Excel (AUS)—
Bluefire (Distorted Humor (USA)) **Sheikh Hamdan Bin Mohammed Al Maktoum**
136 B c 4/2 Slade Power (IRE)—Boadicee (Aqlaam) (20000) **Sheikh Hamdan Bin Mohammed Al Maktoum**
137 B f 1/3 Animal Kingdom (USA)—
Braided (USA) (Elusive Quality (USA)) **Sheikh Hamdan Bin Mohammed Al Maktoum**
138 B f 2/3 Dawn Approach (IRE)—Calando (USA) (Storm Cat (USA)) **Sheikh Hamdan Bin Mohammed Al Maktoum**
139 CAPLIN, b c 26/3 Cape Cross (IRE)—Party Line (Montjeu (IRE)) **S. R. Counsell**
140 B c 12/5 Lethal Force (IRE)—Caribbean Dancer (USA) (Theatrical) **Mr H. C. Hart**
141 B c 21/2 Mastercraftsman (IRE)—Chinese White (IRE) (Dalakhani (IRE)) (13024) **A. Saeed**
142 DAME FREYA STARK, ch f 28/2 Leroidesanimaux (BRZ)—Lady Jane Digby (Oasis Dream) **Miss K. Rausing**
143 DANCING ON A DREAM (IRE), b f 26/2 Dream Ahead (USA)—
Slip Dance (IRE) (Celtic Swing) (21163) **P. D. Savill**
144 B c 13/4 Oasis Dream—Demisemiquaver (Singspiel (IRE)) (32000) **Mr J. D. Abell**
145 B f 4/3 Australia—Dingle View (IRE) (Mujadil (USA)) (32560) **Mr A. Al Mansoori**
146 B c 16/3 Invincible Spirit (IRE)—
Discourse (USA) (Street Cry (IRE)) **Sheikh Hamdan Bin Mohammed Al Maktoum**
147 B c 22/1 Dream Ahead (USA)—Double Diamond (FR) (Muhtathir) (77000) **Mark Johnston Racing Ltd**
148 B c 8/3 Tamayuz—Elopa (GER) (Tiger Hill (IRE)) (14652) **A. Al Shaikh**
149 B c 26/3 Slade Power (IRE)—Embassy (Cadeaux Genereux) **Sheikh Hamdan Bin Mohammed Al Maktoum**
150 EMIRATES EMPIRE (IRE), b c 30/3 Authorized (IRE)—Ana Shababiya (IRE) (Teofilo (IRE)) **A. Al Shaikh**
151 B f 27/4 Camelot—Flawless Beauty (Excellent Art) (45000) **Mr H. R. Bin Ghedayer**
152 B c 4/5 Showcasing—Flora Trevelyan (Cape Cross (IRE)) (16000) **Mr B. Yeardley**
153 B f 20/1 Charm Spirit (IRE)—Galactic Heroine (Galileo (IRE)) (16000) **Mr H. Dalmook Al Maktoum**
154 B c 14/4 Dansili—Gaze (Galileo (IRE)) (100000) **China Horse Club**
155 Ch c 4/3 Pivotal—Ghostflower (IRE) (Dansili) (170000) **Hamdan bin Rashid Al Maktoum**
156 Ch f 15/4 Nathaniel (IRE)—Gossamer Seed (IRE) (Choisir (AUS)) (18000) **Mark Johnston Racing Ltd**
157 B f 4/2 Dream Ahead (USA)—Greannmhar (USA) (Distorted Humor (USA)) (7000) **Kingsley Park 8**
158 GRENADIER GUARD (IRE), ch c 16/5 Australia—
Another Storm (USA) (Gone West (USA)) (125000) **Mr J. A. Barson**
159 Ch f 22/4 Australia—Healing Music (FR) (Bering) (32000) **Mr H. Dalmook Al Maktoum**
160 B f 13/2 Iffraaj—Honky Tonk Sally (Dansili) (250000) **Sheikh Hamdan Bin Mohammed Al Maktoum**
161 Ch c 2/2 Helmet (AUS)—Hush Money (CHI) (Hussonet (USA)) **Sheikh Hamdan Bin Mohammed Al Maktoum**
162 I AM A DREAMER, b c 27/2 Dream Ahead (USA)—Alexander Ballet (Mind Games) (62000) **Mr M. Doyle**
163 B br 18/1 Galileo (IRE)—Inca Princess (IRE) (Holy Roman Emperor (IRE)) (200000) **China Horse Club**
164 B f 10/3 Poet's Voice—Indian Petal (Singspiel (IRE)) **Sheikh Hamdan Bin Mohammed Al Maktoum**
165 Ch f 13/2 Animal Kingdom (USA)—
Ishitaki (ARG) (Interprete (ARG)) **Sheikh Hamdan Bin Mohammed Al Maktoum**
166 Ch c 7/2 Iffraaj—Jumeirah Palm Star (Invincible Spirit (IRE)) **Mr H. R. Bin Ghedayer**
167 B f 31/1 Slade Power (IRE)—Key To Peace (IRE) (Kheleyf (USA)) **Sheikh Hamdan Bin Mohammed Al Maktoum**
168 KILBARCHAN (GER), gr f 7/5 Jukebox Jury (IRE)—
Kellemoi de Pepita (Hawk Wing (USA)) (19536) **Dr J. Walker & Partner**
169 B c 18/3 Australia—Lady Eclair (IRE) (Danehill Dancer (IRE)) (73260) **Netherfield House Stud**
170 B f 29/2 Elusive Quality (USA)—
Letterfromamerica (USA) (Ghostzapper (USA)) (12000) **Mr H. Dalmook Al Maktoum**
171 B c 29/2 Cape Cross (IRE)—Lil's Jessy (Kris) (81400) **J. Alharbi**
172 B f 23/4 War Command (USA)—Lisselan Diva (IRE) (Barathea (IRE)) (14652)
173 LIVING LEGEND (IRE), b c 15/3 Camelot—Jazz Girl (IRE) (Johar (USA)) (22000) **Barbara & Alick Richmond**
174 LOVE KISSES (IRE), b c 16/4 Dream Ahead (USA)—
Coconut Kisses (Bahamian Bounty) (42328) **Mark Johnston Racing Ltd**
175 B c 7/4 Makfi—Lune Rose (High Chaparral (IRE)) (40000)
176 B f 29/1 Zoffany (IRE)—Maine Lobster (USA) (Woodman (USA)) (62000) **S. Ali**

MR MARK JOHNSTON - Continued

177 **MARIE'S DIAMOND (IRE)**, br c 21/3 Footstepsinthesand—Sindiyma (IRE) (Kalanisi (IRE)) (28489)
178 **MAYDANNY (IRE)**, b c 25/2 Dubawi (IRE)—Attraction (Efisio) (1350000) **Hamdan bin Rashid Al Maktoum**
179 **MITHMAAR (IRE)**, b br c 30/5 Sea The Stars (IRE)—Nufoos (Zafonic (USA)) **Hamdan bin Rashid Al Maktoum**
180 B c 7/5 Shamardal (USA)—Model Queen (USA) (Kingmambo (USA)) (100000) **K. F. Leung**
181 Ch c 1/4 Dubawi (IRE)—Mondalay (Monsun (GER)) **Sheikh Hamdan Bin Mohammed Al Maktoum**
182 B f 1/2 Hard Spun (USA)—Moojha (USA) (Forest Wildcat (USA)) (50000) **Mr H. A. Lootah**
183 B f 20/3 Invincible Spirit (IRE)—Moonlight Danceuse (IRE) (Bering) (40000) **Mr A. Al Mansoori**
184 **MOUNTAIN RULER**, ch c 7/2 Ruler Of The World (IRE)—Regal Fairy (Desert King (IRE))
185 **NATALIE'S JOY**, b f 2/4 Lope de Vega (IRE)—Semaphore (Zamindar (USA)) (35000) **Mark Johnston Racing Ltd**
186 **NAYEF ROAD (IRE)**, ch c 3/5 Galileo (IRE)—
                           Rose Bonheur (Danehill Dancer (IRE)) (100000) **Sheikh Mohammed Obaid Al Maktoum**
187 **NO LIPPY (IRE)**, b f 19/2 Oasis Dream—Freedonia (Selkirk (USA)) (35816) **Barbara & Alick Richmond**
188 B c 7/4 Excelebration (IRE)—Nuit Polaire (IRE) (Kheleyf (USA)) (24420) **J. Alharbi**
189 B c 19/2 Raven's Pass (USA)—Off Chance (Olden Times) (18000) **Mark Johnston Racing Ltd**
190 Ch f 10/2 Dawn Approach (IRE)—On The Dark Side (IRE) (Kheleyf (USA)) (27619)
191 **PANZANO**, b c 6/2 Dutch Art—Special Meaning (Mount Nelson) (68000) **P. D. Savill**
192 Ch c 4/3 Olympic Glory (IRE)—Party (IRE) (Cadeaux Genereux) (65000) **Sohi & Sohi**
193 B c 20/4 Exceed And Excel (AUS)—
                           Picture Hat (USA) (El Prado (IRE)) **Sheikh Hamdan Bin Mohammed Al Maktoum**
194 B c 27/1 Camelot—Plying (USA) (Hard Spun (USA)) (32000) **Mark Johnston Racing Ltd**
195 B c 22/3 Poet's Voice—Polar Circle (USA) (Royal Academy (USA)) (36000)
196 Ch c 15/2 Australia—Ponty Acclaim (IRE) (Acclamation) (105820) **Mr Alan Spence**
197 B c 17/2 Dutch Art—Privacy Order (Azamour (IRE)) (57000) **Mr A. Al Mansoori**
198 B c 23/1 Maxios—Psychometry (FR) (Danehill Dancer (IRE)) (50000) **Mark Johnston Racing Ltd**
199 **QUINTADA**, b f 30/4 Leroidesanimaux (BRZ)—Quiza Quiza Quiza (Golden Snake (USA)) **Miss K. Rausing**
200 B c 1/4 Holy Roman Emperor (IRE)—Raydaniya (IRE) (In The Wings) (21163) **Mark Johnston Racing Ltd**
201 B c 25/5 Archipenko (USA)—Robe Chinoise (Robellino (USA)) (25000) **The Originals**
202 **ROCHESTER HOUSE (IRE)**, ch c 28/2 Galileo (IRE)—
                           Kalla (Monsun (GER)) (61050) **John Brown & Megan Dennis**
203 B f 29/4 Lawman (FR)—Rose of Mooncoin (IRE) (Brief Truce (USA)) (18000) **Kingsley Park 8**
204 B f 20/5 Iffraaj—Sarmad (USA) (Dynaformer (USA)) (10000) **Mr H. Dalmook Al Maktoum**
205 B c 7/4 Sea The Stars (IRE)—Sassenach (IRE) (Night Shift (USA)) (120000) **J. Alharbi**
206 B f 15/4 Shamardal (USA)—Say No Now (IRE) (Refuse To Bend (IRE)) (50000) **Jane Newett & Dougie Livingston**
207 Ch c 10/4 Shamardal (USA)—Sexy Lady (GER) (Danehill Dancer (IRE)) (12000) **Kingsley Park 10**
208 Ch c 1/3 Dubawi (IRE)—Shumoos (USA) (Distorted Humor (USA)) (350000) **Mr A. Al Mansoori**
209 B c 11/4 Oasis Dream—Silkwood (Singspiel (IRE)) **Sheikh Hamdan Bin Mohammed Al Maktoum**
210 **SIR RON PRIESTLEY**, ch c 11/3 Australia—Reckoning (IRE) (Danehill Dancer (IRE)) (70000) **P. Dean**
211 Ch c 28/4 Sea The Moon (GER)—Songerie (Hernando (FR)) (1000) **The Originals**
212 B f 6/3 Iffraaj—Sri Kandi (Pivotal) (65000) **Owners Group 004**
213 B f 14/5 Iffraaj—Sweet Lilly (Tobougg (IRE)) (24420) **Mr A. Al Mansoori**
214 **TANAAWOL**, b c 2/4 Dansili—Eshaadeh (USA) (Storm Cat (USA)) **Hamdan bin Rashid Al Maktoum**
215 B c 30/3 Dark Angel (IRE)—Tender Is Thenight (IRE) (Barathea (IRE)) (56980) **Jane Newett & Dougie Livingston**
216 B c 31/3 Toronado (IRE)—Trust The Wind (Dansili) (62000) **Sheikh R. D. Al Maktoum**
217 B f 15/3 Sepoy (AUS)—Vista Bella (Diktat) **Godolphin Management Company Ltd**
218 Ch f 3/4 Dutch Art—Walk On Bye (IRE) (Danehill Dancer (IRE)) (25000) **Mark Johnston Racing Ltd**
219 B f 8/2 Charm Spirit (IRE)—Water Fountain (Mark of Esteem (IRE)) (11396) **Mark Johnston Racing Ltd**
220 Ch f 8/4 New Approach (IRE)—West Wind (Machiavellian (USA)) **Godolphin Management Company Ltd**
221 B c 16/5 Raven's Pass (USA)—White Star (IRE) (Darshaan) **Godolphin Management Company Ltd**

Other Owners: Mr Ahmad Abdulla Al Shaikh, Atlantic Racing Limited, Mrs R. F. Batterham, Mr C. M. Batterham, Mr R. Batterham, Mr I. Boyce, Mr E. Brierley, Mr J. M. Brown, Mrs Christine Brown, Brown & Parker, Mr N. N. Browne, Mr M. Budden, Mr Matthew Budden, Mrs Christine E. Budden, Mr D. J. Burke, David Scott and Co (Pattern Makers) Ltd, Mr Paul Dean, Mrs Megan Dennis, Mr Dan Downie, Excel Racing, Mrs Lisa Fellows, Mr P. Fisher, Mr Garrett J. Freyne, Mr A. Greenhalgh, Mr C. H. Greensit, Mr Jason Hathorn, Highclere Nominated Partner Limited, Highclere Thoroughbred Racing Ltd, Robin Holleyhead, Holleyhead, Ross & White, Mr R. W. Huggins, Mrs Deirdre Johnston, Mr R. Kent, Mrs Julie Lightbody, Mr M. Lightbody, Mr Douglas Livingston, Countess of Lonsdale, Mr M. R. Lonsdorfer, Mr Hussain Alabbas Lootah, Manor Farm Stud (Rutland), Mark Johnston Racing Ltd, Mrs N. J. McGrath, Mr Graham Mezzone, Mrs S. M. Mezzone, Mr L. Mezzone, Mrs Jane Newett, Mr T. S. Palin, Mr A. F. Parker, Mr O. J. W. Pawle, Mr M. Prince, Mrs J. Reay, Mrs Stevie Richards, Mr Stevie Richards, Mrs Barbara Richmond, Mr A. Richmond, Mr Ian Robinson, Mrs C. Rooney, Mr P. A. Rooney, Mr William Ross, Duke of Roxburghe, Mr M. B. Spence, Mr A. D. Spence, Mr J. A. B. Stafford.

Assistant Trainers: Deirdre Johnston, Charlie Johnston & Jock Bennett.

Jockey (flat): Joe Fanning, Franny Norton. **Apprentice:** Sharna Armstrong, Andrew Breslin, Oli Stammers.
Amateur: Miss Emma Bedford.

319 MR ALAN JONES, Timberscombe
Postal: **East Harwood Farm, Timberscombe, Minehead, Somerset, TA24 7UE**
Contacts: **FAX 01633 680232 MOBILE (07901) 505064**
E-MAIL heritageracing@btconnect.com WEBSITE www.alanjonesracing.co.uk

1 BOBBITS WAY, 13, b g Overbury (IRE)—Bit of A Chick **Mr A. E. Jones**
2 DUHALLOW LAD (IRE), 6, b g Papal Bull—Macca Luna (IRE) **Burnham Plastering & Drylining Ltd**
3 5, B g Craigsteel—Glenair Lucy (IRE)
4 HUMBEL BEN (IRE), 15, br g Humbel (USA)—Donegans Daughter **Burnham Plastering & Drylining Ltd**
5 LADY AVERY (IRE), 6, b m Westerner—Bobs Article (IRE) **Burnham Plastering & Drylining Ltd**
6 MA'IRE RUA (IRE), 11, ch g Presenting—Long Acre **Mr A. E. Jones**
7 MISSMEBUTLETMEGO, 8, b g With The Flow (USA)—Bay Bianca (IRE) **Mr A. E. Jones**
8 POKARI (FR), 6, ch g Bonbon Rose (FR)—Pokara (FR) **Mr A. E. Jones**
9 QUALANDO (FR), 7, b g Lando (GER)—Qualite Controlee (FR) **Mrs K. A. Stuart**
10 STAND BY ME (FR), 8, b g Dream Well (FR)—In Love New (FR) **Mr A. E. Jones**
11 TIQUER (FR), 10, b g Equerry (USA)—Tirenna (FR) **Burnham Plastering & Drylining Ltd**

THREE-YEAR-OLDS

12 B c Arvico (FR)—A Nun With A Gun (IRE)
13 B g Midnight Legend—Dancing Emily (IRE) **Burnham Plastering & Drylining Ltd**

TWO-YEAR-OLDS

14 B c 16/5 Bollin Eric—Rest And Be (IRE) (Vinnie Roe (IRE))

Assistant Trainer: Miss A. Bartelink

Jockey (NH): Richard Johnson, Paddy Brennan, Tom O' Brien.

320 MR MALCOLM JONES, Treharris
Postal: **Pant-Y-Ffynnon House, Bedlinog, Treharris, Mid Glamorgan**

1 ASHTOWN (IRE), 11, b g Westerner—Christmas River (IRE) **M. G. Jones**
2 BUTLERSBRIDGE (IRE), 9, b g Heron Island (IRE)—Vivre Aimer Rire (FR) **M. G. Jones**
3 TA HA (IRE), 10, br g Posidonas—Euro Dancer (IRE) **M. G. Jones**
4 VALLEYOFTHEFOX, 8, b g Petrovich (USA)—Ruby Dante (IRE) **M. G. Jones**

321 MR MARTIN KEIGHLEY, Cheltenham
Postal: **Condicote Stables, Luckley, Moreton-In-Marsh, Gloucestershire, GL56 0RD**
Contacts: **MOBILE (07767) 472547**
E-MAIL keighleyracing@btinternet.com WEBSITE www.martinkeighleyracing.com

1 ASK ALICE, 5, b m Robin des Champs (FR)—Viva Victoria **Martin Keighley Racing Club**
2 BACK ON THE LASH, 4, b g Malinas (GER)—Giovanna **M. Boothright**
3 BALLYMOUNTAIN BOY (IRE), 7, b g Mountain High (IRE)—Minoras Return (IRE) **The Chameleons**
4 BOBBLE EMERALD (IRE), 10, ch g Rudimentary (USA)—Aunt Emeralds (IRE) **D Bishop, C Bowkley & M Parker**
5 BRILLARE MOMENTO (IRE), 7, b m Milan—Sunshine Leader (IRE) **Mr O. F. Ryan**
6 BUCKLE STREET, 5, br g Cacique (IRE)—Rose Row **The Condicote Clan**
7 CUL DE POULE, 6, b g Multiplex—Madam Blaze **Mr & Mrs R. Allsop**
8 CUP OF AMBITION (IRE), 6, b g Vinnie Roe (IRE)—Sparkling Gem (IRE) **Martin Keighley Racing Club**
9 CUT AND RUN, 5, b m Getaway (GER)—Somethinaboutmolly (IRE) **Mrs Z. A. E. Tindall**
10 DR DUNRAVEN, 7, b g Dr Massini (IRE)—Bajan Girl (FR) **Owners For Owners Dr Dunraven**
11 FAIRMOUNT, 7, gr g Fair Mix (IRE)—Miss Chinchilla **J B Property Investments (Midlands) Ltd**
12 HARTSHORNE ABBIE (IRE), 5, ch m Getaway (GER)—Lala Nova (IRE) **Mr J. Abernethy**
13 LADY VITESSE, 5, b m Rail Link—Sainte Gig (FR) **Brick Kiln Farming,Coulson,Gent,Poore**
14 LERICHI BELLE (IRE), 7, b m King's Theatre (IRE)—Lerichi (IRE) **The Transporters**
15 LORD CONDI (IRE), 6, b g Papal Bull—Wings To Soar (USA) **Owners for Owners Lord Condi**
16 MADAME FIONA, 6, gr m Overbury (IRE)—Roslin **Mr & Mrs R. Allsop**
17 MISTER VALENTINE, 5, b g Aflfora (IRE)—Aberdeen Park **The Lucky Seven**
18 MORNING HERALD, 7, br m Lucky Story (USA)—Wakeful **Mrs S. L. Lloyd-Baker**
19 MR MAFIA (IRE), 9, b g Zerpour (IRE)—Wizzy (IRE) **Three Counties Racing**
20 MY LAD PERCY, 10, b g Central Park (IRE)—Only Millie **The Almost Hopeful Partnership**

MR MARTIN KEIGHLEY - Continued

21 **OSCAR WORLD (IRE)**, 6, b m Oscar (IRE)—Maresin **P. R. Armour**
22 **POMME DE NUIT**, 5, b m Midnight Legend—Apple Days **Martin Keighley Racing Partnership 4**
23 **RAVING BONKERS**, 5, ch g Notnowcato—Harriet's Girl **What In Heavens Partnership**
24 **SOLSTICE STAR**, 8, b g Kayf Tara—Clover Green (IRE) **E & G Racing Partnership**
25 **SOMEWHERE TO BE (IRE)**, 6, ch g Golan (IRE)—Somethinaboutmolly (IRE) **P. R. Armour**
26 **SPICE GIRL**, 5, ch m Black Sam Bellamy (IRE)—Karmest **Mr Richard Davies & Mr Mark Holland**
27 **SPORTY YANKEE (USA)**, 5, gr g Paddy O'prado (USA)—I Insist (USA) **Martin Keighley Racing Partnership 2**
28 **TWENTYONEBLACKJACK (IRE)**, 6, b g Robin des Pres (FR)—Grove Juliet (IRE) **Mr R. M. E. Wright**
29 **VIKING MISTRESS**, 10, b m Bollin Eric—Mistress Caramore (IRE) **Martin Keighley Racing Club**
30 **WEYBURN (IRE)**, 7, gr g September Storm (GER)—Saffron Pride (IRE) **The Gang of Three**
31 **YOUNG PHOENIX (IRE)**, 6, b g Robin des Pres (FR)—Lady Phoenix (IRE) **The Four Tops**

THREE-YEAR-OLDS

32 **COTSWOLD PRINCE (IRE)**, b g Elzaam (AUS)—Kalinjara (IRE) **Martin Keighley Racing Partnership 3**
33 **ENFORCEMENT (IRE)**, b g Lawman (FR)—Elodie **Mr E. J. Hughes**

Other Owners: Mr D. Abraham, Mr R. Allsop, Mrs Y. E. Allsop, Mr M. S. Anderson, D. Bishop, Mr C. Bowkley, N. A. Brimble, Mr A. J. A. Cole, Mr M. D. Coulson, R. A. Davies, Mr R. Davies, Mr P. K. Davis, Mr J. A. Digby, Mr J. Fairrie, J. A. Gent, Mr J. M. Gibbs, Mrs C. F. Godsall, Mr I. H. Goldsmith, Mr N. J. Guttridge, S. R. Harman, B. G. Hellyer, Mr M. A. Holland, Mrs J. Hughes, Mrs B. J. Keighley, Mr A. S. Martin, C. D. Massey, Mr M. D. Parker, Miss J. Pimblett, Mr C. W. D. Poore, Mr S. C. Prowting, Mr N. Scanlan, Mr B. D. Smith, Ms K. H. Smith, Mr N. J. Statham, Mr G. M. Thornton, Mr J. E. S. Tufts, Mr M. K. Warren, Mr N. J. Witts-Hewinson.

Assistant Trainer: Mr Jamie Goldstein

---

322 **MR CHRISTOPHER KELLETT, Lathom**
Postal: Blythe Stables, Blythe Hall, Blythe Lane, Lathom, Lancashire, L40 5TY
Contacts: PHONE (01704) 643775 MOBILE (07966) 097989
E-MAIL CNKellett@outlook.com WEBSITE www.chriskellettracing.co.uk

1 **ARGENT KNIGHT**, 8, gr g Sir Percy—Tussah **Blythe Stables LLP**
2 **BITHYNIA (IRE)**, 4, b f Kodiac—Alexander Confranc (IRE) **Blythe Stables LLP**
3 **BLYTHE PRINCE**, 6, b g Dutch Art—Arculinge **Blythe Stables LLP**
4 **DREAMLINER**, 5, b g Samraan (USA)—Oklahoma **Mr R. Kernohan**
5 **ECHO SPRINGS**, 8, b g Kayf Tara—Mrs Malt (IRE) **Blythe Stables LLP**
6 **KODIMOOR (IRE)**, 5, b g Kodiac—Victoria Lodge (IRE) **Blythe Stables LLP**
7 **SIR LUKE ARNO**, 7, b g Lucarno (USA)—Never Lost **J. E. Titley**
8 **SOLAR IMPULSE (FR)**, 8, b g Westerner—Moon Glow (FR) **Andy Bell & Fergus Lyons**

TWO-YEAR-OLDS

9 **BLISTERING BARNEY (IRE)**, b c 27/3 Sir Prancealot (IRE)—
Eternal View (IRE) (Pivotal) (18000) **Andy Bell & Fergus Lyons**
10 **CARLOW BOY (IRE)**, b c 17/4 Elzaam (AUS)—
Whitershadeofpale (IRE) (Definite Article) (20000) **Andy Bell & Fergus Lyons**
11 **DECONSO**, b c 19/1 Dandy Man (IRE)—Tranquil Flight (Oasis Dream) (24000) **Andy Bell & Fergus Lyons**
12 **SHOWSHUTAI**, b c 15/4 Showcasing—Sleeper (Rail Link) (15000) **Andy Bell & Fergus Lyons**

Other Owners: Mrs T. Bell, Mr A. J. Bell, Mr F. Lyons, Mrs C. Lyons.

---

323 **MISS GAY KELLEWAY, Newmarket**
Postal: Queen Alexandra Stables, 2 Chapel Street, Exning, Newmarket, Suffolk, CB8 7HA
Contacts: PHONE (01638) 577778 MOBILE (07974) 948768
E-MAIL gaykellewayracing@hotmail.co.uk WEBSITE www.gaykellewayracing.com

1 **COSMELLI (ITY)**, 5, b g Mr Vegas (IRE)—Victorian Girl (GER) **Marc Walker & Gay Kelleway**
2 **ELITE TREATY**, 4, b g Mawatheeq (USA)—Silver Elite **Mr A. P. Griffin**
3 **LINDA DORIS (IRE)**, 4, b f Art Connoisseur (IRE)—Kai Mook **Miss L. S. McIntosh**
4 **MIDNIGHT MAN (FR)**, 4, ch g Evasive—Moon Tree (FR) **Miss G. M. Kelleway**
5 **PASTIME**, 4, b g Pastoral Pursuits—Piddies Pride (IRE) **Countrywide Classics Ltd**
6 **REEDANJAS (IRE)**, 4, b f Sir Prancealot (IRE)—Blue Holly (IRE) **Mr G. Kerr**
7 **ROYAL MARSKELL**, 9, b g Multiplex—Socialise **Miss C. Y. Wootten**
8 **SEPTEMBER ISSUE**, 5, b g Dutch Art—Alexander Ballet

MISS GAY KELLEWAY - Continued

9 **STOSUR (IRE)**, 7, b m Mount Nelson—Jules (IRE) **B. C. Oakley**
10 **TEA EL TEE (IRE)**, 4, b g Holy Roman Emperor (IRE)—Mayenne (USA) **Logistics Terminal LLP**
11 **TOPMEUP**, 4, ch f Mayson—Ambrix (IRE) **Mortlock & Kelleway**
12 **UBLA (IRE)**, 5, ch g Arcano (IRE)—Manuelita Rose (ITY) **Mr P. Petrovic**
13 **VETTORI RULES**, 5, gr g Aussie Rules (USA)—Vettori Loose (IRE) **Mr Marc Walker & Partners**
14 **VROOM (IRE)**, 5, ch g Poet's Voice—Shivaree **Buy, Clarke, Sparham & Presland**
15 **WHAT A PARTY (IRE)**, 6, ch m Windsor Knot (IRE)—Tarziyma (IRE) **Mr M. M. Foulger**
16 **YEAH BABY YEAH (IRE)**, 5, b m Art Connoisseur (IRE)—Royal Interlude (IRE) **Winterbeck Manor Stud Ltd**

THREE-YEAR-OLDS

17 **BILLY BOOTH (IRE)**, br g Big Bad Bob (IRE)—Lady Natilda **Ontoawinner, Scandrett & Short**
18 **CAPLA DEMON**, b g Kodiac—Namu **Classic Racing (Capla Demon)**
19 **CRYSTAL DEAUVILLE (FR)**, b g Equiano (FR)—Crystal Plum (IRE) **iBoxit Ltd & Partner 2**
20 **ELITE SHADOW**, gr g Finjaan—Silver Elite **Mr A. P. Griffin**
21 **ELITE WARRIOR**, b g Finjaan—Minstrell Tygeress **Mr A. P. Griffin**
22 **ERETOKA (FR)**, ch f Style Vendome (FR)—Territorial **C. V. Wentworth**
23 **FAIRY TALE (IRE)**, b g Kheleyf (USA)—Singapore Fairy (FR) **Winterbeck Manor Stud & Gay Kelleway**
24 **GLOBAL ACADEMY (IRE)**, b g Zebedee—Lady Meagan (IRE) **Dr J. Hon**
25 **GLOBAL HEIGHTS**, b g Epaulette (AUS)—Uvinza **Dr J. Hon**
26 **GLOBAL HOPE (IRE)**, b c Oasis Dream—Classic Remark (IRE) **Dr J. Hon**
27 **GLOBAL ROSE (IRE)**, b f Dark Angel (IRE)—Classic Falcon (IRE) **Dr J. Hon**
28 **JOHNI BOXIT**, ch g Sakhee's Secret—Pink Supreme **iBoxit Ltd**
29 **LOST ON YOU**, b f Lord Shanakill (USA)—If Or When (IRE) **Chris Peach & Partners**
30 **MAJOR REACHER**, b g Phoenix Reach (IRE)—Chocolada **Winterbeck Manor Stud Ltd**
31 **OSWALD (IRE)**, gr c Mastercraftsman (IRE)—Tough Chic (IRE) **Dr J. Hon**
32 **ROBSDELIGHT (IRE)**, br g Harbour Watch (IRE)—Silca Boo **Graham Parr**

TWO-YEAR-OLDS

33 B gr c 28/4 Lethal Force (IRE)—Fairmont (IRE) (Kingmambo (USA)) (13333) **Gay Kelleway**
34 **GLOBAL GODDESS (IRE)**, b f 9/3 Morpheus—Church Mice (IRE) (Petardia) (16190) **Dr J. Hon**
35 **INDUCT**, br c 18/3 Pastoral Pursuits—Local Honey (Diktat) (4761) **iBoxit Ltd**
36 B c 29/2 Phoenix Reach (IRE)—Pink Supreme (Night Shift (USA)) **Gay Kelleway, Winterbeck Manor Stud Ltd**
37 Gr c 2/3 Dark Angel (IRE)—Silca Boo (Efisio) (52909) **Gay Kelleway**

Other Owners: Mr Michael Brown, Mr Shane Buy, Mr Robert P. Clarke, Classic Racing (Namu), Miss Patricia Crook, Mrs E. F. Harte, Mr A. J. Moore, Mr Ralph Mortlock, Mr Richard Newbold, Mr N. J. O'Brien, Mr Paul Presland, Mr N. S. Scandrett, Mr M. J. Short, Mr Ian J. Sparham, Mr Marc Walker.

Assistant Trainer: Anne-Sophie Crombez **Head Girl:** Liz Mullin

---

324 MR NICK KENT, Brigg
Postal: **Newstead House, Newstead Priory, Cadney Road, Brigg, Lincolnshire, DN20 9HP**
Contacts: **PHONE (01652) 650628 MOBILE (07710) 644428**
E-MAIL **nick@nickkent.co.uk** WEBSITE **www.nickkent.co.uk**

1 **BOWIE (IRE)**, 11, br g Pelder (IRE)—La Fenice (IRE) **Cynthia Commons,Marina Kent,Nick Kent**
2 **BRIGHTS PARK (IRE)**, 6, b g Mahler—Ellesmere (IRE) **Mr A. R. P. Parkin**
3 **CIBOIR (FR)**, 6, gr g Fragrant Mix (IRE)—Fleche Noir II (FR) **Nick Kent Racing Club II**
4 **DUFFY ALLEN (FR)**, 5, b g Lucarno (USA)—Parade (FR) **Mrs M Pinney, N Kent**
5 **GONALSTON CLOUD (IRE)**, 11, gr g Cloudings (IRE)—Roseoengus (IRE) **Mr R. J. Jackson**
6 **LOST IN NEWYORK (IRE)**, 11, b g Arakan (USA)—Lace Flower **Mr J. N. Kent**
7 **MUSTANG ON**, 8, b g Croco Rouge (IRE)—More To Life **Mr J. N. Kent**
8 **NOT AN OSCAR**, 6, b g Wareed (IRE)—High Dough (IRE) **Mr J. N. Kent**
9 **OREGON GOLD (FR)**, 5, b g Confuchias (IRE)—Gold Wine (FR) **Newstead Priory Racing Club**
10 **PICKNICK PARK**, 6, b g Sulamani (IRE)—Eva's Edge (IRE) **Mr Andy Parkin, Nick Kent**
11 **POP THE CHAMPERS (IRE)**, 7, b g Scorpion (IRE)—Manesbil (IRE) **C W Booth, W Wesley, N Kent**
12 4, B br g Sulamani (IRE)—Returning
13 **SPENDAJENNIE (IRE)**, 9, b m Old Vic—American Jennie (IRE) **Partnership Terminated**
14 **THE GRINDER (IRE)**, 6, b g Arcadio (GER)—Bincas Beauty (IRE) **Mrs Wendy Wesley, Mr Nick Kent**
15 **THEBIGCLEANUP (IRE)**, 6, b g Milan—Newcastlebeauty (IRE) **C. W. Booth**

MR NICK KENT - Continued

THREE-YEAR-OLDS

16 B f Watar (IRE)—Durango (IRE)
17 B f Bollin Eric—Linen Line **C. Commons, N. Kent**

Other Owners: Mr C. W. Booth, Miss C. Commons, Mr Nick Kent, Mrs Marina Kent, Mr Andy Parkin, Mrs M. A. Pinney, Mrs Wendy Wesley.

Assistant Trainer: Mrs Jane Kent

Jockey (NH): Adam Wedge. **Conditional:** Tom Broughton.

---

325 **MR LEONARD KERR, Irvine**
Postal: **Annick Lodge, Irvine, Ayrshire, KA11 2AN**

1 CHICAGO OUTFIT (IRE), 13, b g Old Vic—Lambourne Lace (IRE) **Mr L. B. Kerr**
2 HAVANA JACK (IRE), 8, b g Westerner—Hackler Poitin (IRE) **Mr L. B. Kerr**

---

326 **MR ALAN KING, Barbury Castle**
Postal: **Barbury Castle Stables, Wroughton, Wiltshire, SN4 0QZ**
Contacts: **PHONE (01793) 815009 FAX (01793) 845080 MOBILE (07973) 461233**
E-MAIL alanking.racing@virgin.net WEBSITE www.alankingracing.co.uk

1 AMADEUS ROX (FR), 4, b g Falco (USA)—Vittoria Vetra **Mr A. Gemmell**
2 AWESOME ROSIE, 7, b m Midnight Legend—
                     Awesome Aunt (IRE) **Mrs Meacham, Withyslade & Mrs A L Davies**
3 AZZERTI (FR), 6, b g Voix du Nord (FR)—Zalagarry (FR) **McNeill Family and Prodec Networks Ltd**
4 BALLYWOOD (FR), 4, b g Ballingarry (IRE)—Miss Hollywood (FR) **Highclere Thoroughbred Racing -Ballywood**
5 BASTIEN (FR), 7, b br g Panoramic—Que du Charmil (FR) **The Sandy Lodge Syndicate**
6 BENEAGLES (IRE), 6, b g Milan—Liss Rua (IRE) **Lady Horn-Smith & Godfrey Wilson**
7 BIG CHIEF BENNY (IRE), 7, ch g Beneficial—Be Airlie (IRE) **Oitavos Partnership**
8 BOARD OF TRADE, 7, ch g Black Sam Bellamy (IRE)—Realms of Gold (USA) **Ian Payne & Kim Franklin**
9 BRIGADE OF GUARDS (IRE), 4, b g Presenting—Lasado (IRE) **C Dingwall, N Farrell & J Murray**
10 BULFIN ISLAND (IRE), 9, b g Milan—Tournore Court (IRE) **Alan King**
11 CAJUN FIDDLE (IRE), 7, b m Robin des Champs (FR)—Silk Style **Mickleton Racing Club**
12 CANELO (IRE), 5, ch g Mahler—Nobody's Darling (IRE) **Million in Mind Partnership**
13 CHATEZ (IRE), 7, b g Dandy Man (IRE)—Glory Days (GER) **Mrs P. Andrews**
14 CHATO (FR), 6, ch g Malinas (GER)—Queen Bruere (FR) **The Barbury Lions**
15 CHOSEN PATH (IRE), 5, b g Well Chosen—Karsulu (IRE) **McNeill Family and Prodec Networks Ltd**
16 CHOSEN WELL (IRE), 9, b g Well Chosen—Killmaleary Cross (IRE) **Keirle, Love, Sullivan & Holmes**
17 CITY DREAMER (IRE), 4, ch g Casamento (IRE)—Cadescia (IRE) **Mr A. R. W. Marsh**
18 COEUR DE LION, 5, b g Pour Moi (IRE)—Hora **The Barbury Lions 2**
19 COGBURN, 6, ch g Black Sam Bellamy (IRE)—Realms of Gold (USA) **Mrs Sue Welch & Alan King**
20 COLDITZ CASTLE (IRE), 4, ch g Getaway (GER)—Stowaway Sue (IRE) **Charles Dingwall & Tony Morris**
21 COLONEL MILLER, 4, b g Multiplex—Legion of Merit **HP Racing Colonel Miller**
22 COSMEAPOLITAN, 5, b g Mawatheeq (USA)—Cosmea **Kingston Stud**
23 CRIQ ROCK (FR), 7, ch g Kap Rock (FR)—Criquetot (FR) **The Trouble Partnership**
24 CRUSHED (IRE), 4, b g Beat Hollow—Sel **Wright, Jervis & Whitestonecliff Racing**
25 DESIRABLE COURT (IRE), 5, b m Court Cave (IRE)—
                     Desirable Rhythm (IRE) **Mr Simon Munir & Mr Isaac Souede**
26 DESIREMOI D'AUTHIE (FR), 5, b g Cachet Noir (USA)—Toietmoi d'authie (FR) **Sullivan Bloodstock Limited**
27 DEYRANN DE CARJAC (FR), 5, b g Balko (FR)—Queyrann (FR) **Mr J. A. Law**
28 DINGO DOLLAR (IRE), 6, ch g Golden Lariat (USA)—
                     Social Society **M Warren J Holmes R Kidner & J Wright**
29 DINO VELVET (FR), 5, b g Naaqoos—Matgil (FR) **McNeill Family & Niall Farrell**
30 DOCTOR BARTOLO (IRE), 4, gr g Sir Prancealot (IRE)—Operissimo **Mrs E. A. Prowting**
31 DUSKY LEGEND, 8, b m Midnight Legend—Tinagoodnight (IRE) **Mr & Mrs R. G. Kelvin-Hughes**
32 ELGIN, 6, b g Duke of Marmalade (IRE)—China Tea (USA) **Elite Racing Club**
33 ENDLESS RIVER, 5, b m Tobougg (IRE)—Blaeberry
34 FIDUX (FR), 5, b g Fine Grain (JPN)—Folle Tempete (FR) **Axom LXVIII**
35 FIELDS OF FORTUNE, 4, b g Champs Elysees—Widescreen (USA) **HP Racing Fields Of Fortune**
36 FIRST MOHICAN, 10, ch g Tobougg (IRE)—Mohican Girl **HP Racing First Mohican**

MR ALAN KING - Continued

37 **FORGETTHESMALLTALK (IRE)**, 6, b g Flemensfirth (USA)—
Mylane du Charmil (FR) **Tim Leadbeater & Barry Winfield**
38 **GIVEAWAY GLANCE**, 5, br m Passing Glance—Giving **Pitchall Stud Partnership**
39 **GIVING BACK**, 4, br gr f Midnight Legend—Giving **Pitchall Stud Partnership & Mrs Pat Toye**
40 **GOOD MAN PAT (IRE)**, 5, b g Gold Well—Basically Supreme (IRE) **Mr D. J. S. Sewell**
41 **HARAMBE**, 5, b g Malinas (GER)—Crystal Princess (IRE) **Niall Farrell & Friends**
42 **HAREFIELD (IRE)**, 5, b g Doyen (IRE)—Bobbi's Venture (IRE) **Mr A. Charity**
43 **HEREWEGO HEREWEGO (IRE)**, 7, b g Kalanisi (IRE)—Downtown Train **Mr J. P. McManus**
44 **HIDDEN CARGO (IRE)**, 6, b g Stowaway—All Heart **Mr T. D. J. Syder**
45 **HOLLOW PENNY**, 10, b g Beat Hollow—Lomapamar **Mr D. J. S. Sewell**
46 **HOTTER THAN HELL (FR)**, 4, ch f No Risk At All (FR)—Ombrelle (FR) **The Devil's Advocates**
47 **HURRICANE MINNIE**, 5, b m Authorized (IRE)—Hurricane Milly (IRE) **John J. Murray & Niall Farrell**
48 **I WILL FOLLOW HER**, 4, b f Schiaparelli (GER)—Katess (IRE) **Mrs M. C. Sweeney**
49 **INN THE BULL (GER)**, 5, ch g Lope de Vega (IRE)—Ile Rousse **Loose Cannon Racing**
50 **INNER DRIVE**, 10, b g Heron Island (IRE)—Hingis (IRE) **McNeill Family Ltd**
51 **JUST IN TIME**, 4, b g Excelebration (IRE)—Flying Finish (FR) **HP Racing Just In Time**
52 **KAREZAK (IRE)**, 7, b g Azamour (IRE)—Karawana (IRE) **McNeill Family Ltd**
53 **KEEP IN LINE (GER)**, 6, b g Soldier Hollow—Kastila (GER) **Mr & Mrs Paul & Clare Rooney**
54 **KERROW (IRE)**, 8, b g Mahler—Olives Hall (IRE) **Mr T. J. Hemmings**
55 **KIMBERLEY POINT**, 5, b m Sixties Icon—Kingara **P. E. Atkinson**
56 **KOZIER (GER)**, 4, ch g Muhtathir—Kasumi (GER) **The Barbury Lions 2**
57 **LABEL DES OBEAUX (FR)**, 7, b g Saddler Maker (IRE)—La Bessiere (FR) **David Sewell & Terry Warner**
58 **LADY PERSEPHONE (FR)**, 7, br m Sir Percy—Acenanga (GER) **All The Kings Ladies**
59 **LEXINGTON LAW (IRE)**, 5, b g Lawman (FR)—Tus Nua (IRE) **Middleham Park Racing XXXIX**
60 **LISP (IRE)**, 4, ch g Poet's Voice—Hora **Mr & Mrs R. G. Kelvin-Hughes**
61 **LONG SOCKS**, 4, ch g Notnowcato—Sienna Sunset (IRE) **R. Bailey**
62 **LORD HUNTINGDON**, 5, b g Lord of England (GER)—Marajuana **Mr & Mrs Paul & Clare Rooney**
63 **LORD WALSINGHAM**, 4, b g Shirocco (GER)—Glorious Twelfth (IRE) **C Dingwall, A Morris & S Kiss**
64 **MAHLERMADE (IRE)**, 5, ch g Mahler—Double Concerto **The Lesser Lights**
65 **MASTER BLUEYES (IRE)**, 5, gr g Mastercraftsman (IRE)—Miss Blueyes (IRE) **The Legends Partnership**
66 **MELODY OF SCOTLAND (FR)**, 4, b f Youmzain (IRE)—This Melody (FR) **Mr J. P. McManus**
67 **MESSIRE DES OBEAUX (FR)**, 6, b g Saddler Maker (IRE)—Madame Lys (FR)
68 **MIA'S STORM (IRE)**, 8, b m September Storm (GER)—Letitia's Gain (IRE) **The Maple Street Partnership**
69 **MIDNIGHT MAESTRO**, 6, b g Midnight Legend—Calamintha **Mr J. P. McManus**
70 **MIDNIGHT TOUR**, 8, br m Midnight Legend—Uppermost **James & Jean Potter**
71 **MIDNIGHTREFERENDUM**, 5, b m Midnight Legend—Forget The Ref (IRE) **Robert Abrey & Ian Thurtle**
72 **MILLE NAUTIQUE (FR)**, 7, b g Panis (USA)—Anoush (USA) **Mrs J. A. Watts**
73 **MINELLA CHARMER (IRE)**, 7, b g King's Theatre (IRE)—Kim Hong (IRE) **Mr D. J. S. Sewell**
74 **MISS CRICK**, 7, b m Midnight Legend—Kwaheri **Mr D. J. S. Sewell**
75 **MR PUMBLECHOOK**, 4, b g Midnight Legend—Definitely Red (IRE) **Mr D. J. S. Sewell**
76 **MYBOYSAM**, 4, b g Delegator—Fantastisch (IRE) **Mrs M. C. Sweeney**
77 4, Ch f Malinas (GER)—Mystery Lot (IRE) **Kingston Stud**
78 **MYSTICAL CLOUDS (IRE)**, 5, gr g Cloudings (IRE)—Silent Valley **Mr T. J. Hemmings**
79 **NATHAN**, 4, b g Nathaniel (IRE)—Maid To Treasure (IRE) **Normandie Stud Ltd**
80 **NAYATI (FR)**, 4, b g Spirit One (FR)—Smadouce (FR) **Grech & Parkin**
81 **NEWTOWN BOY (IRE)**, 5, b g Beneficial—Tanit Lady (IRE) **Mr & Mrs Paul & Clare Rooney**
82 **NYLON SPEED (IRE)**, 4, b g Campanologist (USA)—Neuquen (IRE) **Axom L**
83 **OCEANE (FR)**, 6, b g Kentucky Dynamite (USA)—Zahrana (FR) **McNeill Family Ltd**
84 **OUTOFTHEQUESTION**, 4, b g Delegator—Why Dubai (USA) **The Barbury Lions**
85 **PADDY BOSS (IRE)**, 6, ch g Gamut (IRE)—Agladora (FR) **McNeill Family Ltd**
86 **PASSING CALL**, 5, b m Passing Glance—Call Me A Legend **Pitchall Stud Partnership**
87 4, B f Flemensfirth (USA)—Peggies Run **Sir Christopher Wates**
88 **PEGGIES VENTURE**, 7, b m Presenting—Peggies Run **Sir Christopher & Lady Wates**
89 **PERFECT HARMONY (IRE)**, 6, b g Definite Article—Brandam Supreme (IRE) **Mrs E. A. Prowting**
90 **POTTERMAN**, 5, b g Sulamani (IRE)—Polly Potter **James & Jean Potter**
91 **RAINBOW DREAMER**, 5, b g Aqlaam—Zamhrear **The Maple Street Partnership**
92 **REALMS OF FIRE**, 5, ch g Malinas (GER)—Realms of Gold (USA) **Mrs S. C. Welch**
93 **REDICEAN**, 4, b g Medicean—Red Halo (IRE) **Apple Tree Stud**
94 **RIVER FROST**, 6, b g Silver Frost—River Test **Mr J. P. McManus**
95 **ROSA DAMASCENA (FR)**, 5, b m Kalanisi (IRE)—Rosewater (GER) **McNeill Family Ltd**
96 **ROYAL SUNDAY (FR)**, 4, gr g Never On Sunday (FR)—Royale Malaisie (FR) **The Barbury Lions 2**
97 **SAINT CONTEST (FR)**, 5, b g Air Chief Marshal (IRE)—Sainte Adresse **Mr & Mrs Paul & Clare Rooney**
98 **SALMANAZAR**, 10, b g Classic Cliche (IRE)—Leroy's Sister (FR) **Top Brass Partnership**
99 **SCARLET DRAGON**, 5, b g Sir Percy—Welsh Angel **HP Racing Scarlet Dragon**
100 **SCEAU ROYAL (FR)**, 6, b g Doctor Dino (FR)—Sandside (FR) **Mr Simon Munir & Mr Isaac Souede**

MR ALAN KING - Continued

101 **SECOND TIME AROUND**, 6, b g Midnight Legend—Silk Rope (IRE) **Mr & Mrs R. Scott**
102 **SEGO SUCCESS (IRE)**, 10, b g Beneficial—The West Road (IRE) **Mr E. T. D. Leadbeater**
103 **SENIOR CITIZEN**, 5, b g Tobougg (IRE)—Mothers Help **McNeill Family Ltd**
104 **SIR ANTONY BROWNE**, 6, ch g Black Sam Bellamy (IRE)—Shayaza **Incipe Partnership**
105 **SIXTY'S BELLE**, 4, b f Gold Well—Over Sixty **Mr & Mrs C. Harris**
106 **SKIN DEEP (IRE)**, 5, ch m Presenting—Maryota (FR) **Mr J. P. McManus**
107 **SMAD PLACE (FR)**, 11, gr g Smadoun (FR)—Bienna Star (FR) **Mrs P. Andrews**
108 **SMITH'S BAY**, 5, b g Midnight Legend—Takotna (IRE) **Ian Payne & Kim Franklin**
109 5, b g Black Sam Bellamy (IRE)—Star Ar Aghaidh (IRE) **Alan King**
110 **STOCKBURN (IRE)**, 5, b g Scorpion (IRE)—Hayabusa **Godfrey Keirle & Alan King**
111 **STYLISH MOMENT (IRE)**, 5, b g Milan—Up The Style (IRE) **Mr T. J. Hemmings**
112 **SULA ISLAND**, 4, ch f Sulamani (IRE)—Cosmea **Kingston Stud**
113 **TALKISCHEAP (IRE)**, 6, b g Getaway (GER)—Carrigmoorna Oak (IRE) **Mr C. B. J. Dingwall**
114 **TARA VIEW**, 7, b m Kayf Tara—Temptation (FR) **Mr D. J. Barry**
115 **THE BLUES MASTER (IRE)**, 4, gr g Mastercraftsman (IRE)—Catch The Blues (IRE) **HJW Partnership**
116 **THE DEVILS DROP (IRE)**, 5, b g Court Cave (IRE)—Concernforkillen (IRE) **Mr D. M. Mason**
117 **THE TOURARD MAN (IRE)**, 12, b g Shantou (USA)—Small Iron **Mr & Mrs F Bell,N Farrell, A Marsh**
118 **THE UNIT (IRE)**, 7, b g Gold Well—Sovana (FR) **International Plywood (Importers) Ltd**
119 **TILLYTHETANK (IRE)**, 5, b m Stowaway—All Heart **Mr T. D. J. Syder**
120 **TIMOTEO (FR)**, 5, b g Diamond Green (FR)—Goldnella (FR) **Million in Mind Partnership**
121 **TOP TUG (IRE)**, 7, ch g Halling (USA)—Top Romance (IRE) **Elite Racing Club**
122 **VALDEZ**, 11, ch g Doyen (IRE)—Skew **Riverdee Stable**
123 **VOIE DANS VOIE (FR)**, 5, br g Coastal Path—Peggy Pierji (FR) **R. & P. Scott & I. Payne & K. Franklin**
124 6, Ch g Kier Park (IRE)—Waheeba **Withyslade**
125 **WAR CHIEF**, 4, ch g Aqlaam—My Colleen (USA) **Andrews Farrell King McNeill Sullivan**
126 **WHO DARES WINS (IRE)**, 6, b g Jeremy (USA)—Savignano **HP Racing Who Dares Wins**
127 **WILDE BLUE YONDER (IRE)**, 9, b g Oscar (IRE)—Blue Gallery (IRE) **Maybe Only Fools Have Horses**
128 **WILDE SPIRIT (IRE)**, 4, b f Oscar (IRE)—Full of Spirit (IRE) **Mr & Mrs C. Harris**
129 **WILLIAM H BONNEY**, 7, b g Midnight Legend—Calamintha **Mr & Mrs R. Scott**
130 **WILLIAM HUNTER**, 6, b g Mawatheeq (USA)—Cosmea **Incipe Partnership**
131 **WINTER ESCAPE (IRE)**, 7, b g Robin des Pres (FR)—Saddleeruppat (IRE) **Mr J. P. McManus**
132 **YANWORTH**, 8, ch g Norse Dancer (IRE)—Yota (FR) **Mr J. P. McManus**
133 **YESANDNO (IRE)**, 5, b g Scorpion (IRE)—In Fact (IRE) **Mrs G. Meacham**
134 **ZIGA BOY (FR)**, 9, gr g Califet (FR)—Our Ziga (FR) **Axom LI**

THREE-YEAR-OLDS

135 **ANTIGUAN ROCK**, ch g Rock of Gibraltar (IRE)—Totally Millie **Mr & Mrs EJA Smith-Maxwell**
136 **BERINGER**, b g Sea The Stars (IRE)—Edaraat (USA) **L Field, B Cognet, N Farrell, J Spack**
137 **CASPAR THE CUB (IRE)**, ch g Casamento (IRE)—Esposa (IRE) **The Barbury Lions**
138 **DAVID**, gr c Dalakhani (IRE)—Ethel **Normandie Stud Ltd**
139 **ELYSEES (IRE)**, ch g Champs Elysees—Queen of Tara (IRE) **Elysees Partnership**
140 Ch c Champs Elysees—Fever Fever (USA) **Alan King**
141 **GAVI DI GAVI (IRE)**, b g Camacho—Blossom Deary (IRE) **L Field, N Farrell & B Cognet**
142 **GIVING GLANCES**, b f Passing Glance—Giving **Pitchall Stud Partnership**
143 **GRAVINA**, b f Havana Gold (IRE)—Dolcetto (IRE) **Mrs Lesley Field & Mr Aiden Murphy**
144 **KISMAT**, b f Sepoy (AUS)—Magic Destiny **R. Bailey**
145 **MANOR PARK**, b g Medicean—Jadeel **McNeill Family & Niall Farrell**
146 B c Youmzain (IRE)—Minnie's Mystery (FR) **McNeill Family & Niall Farrell**
147 **NEBUCHADNEZZAR (FR)**, b g Planteur (IRE)—Trexana **Top Brass 2**
148 **PARMENTER**, b f Dick Turpin (IRE)—Triple Cee (IRE) **Kingston Stud**
149 B f Shirocco (GER)—Penneyrose Bay **Sir Christopher & Lady Wates**
150 **PERFECT PREDATOR**, b g Passing Glance—Cosmea **Kingston Stud**
151 **SAFARHI**, b g Farhh—Swarm (IRE) **The Barbury Lions**
152 **SEABOROUGH (IRE)**, b g Born To Sea (IRE)—Nobilissima (IRE) **Nautical 5**

TWO-YEAR-OLDS

153 **GREEN ETOILE**, ch c 28/3 Nathaniel (IRE)—
      Myriades d'etoiles (IRE) (Green Tune (USA)) (22000) **Mr Simon Munir & Mr Isaac Souede**

MR ALAN KING - Continued

Other Owners: Mr R. Abrey, Mr D. J. Anderson, Axom Ltd, Mrs H. L. Bell, Mr F. D. Bell, Mr David Bond, Mr P. A. Boyle, A. R. Bromley, Mr N. S. G. Bunter, Mr R. J. Caddick, Mr S. Clancy, Mr N. Clyne, Mr B. R. Cognet, Mrs A. L. Davies, Mr D. Downie, Mr S. Dunkley, P. J. Dunkley, Mr N. Farrell, Mr S. Field, Mrs L. H. Field, Miss K. M. Franklin, Mr J. Frew, G. F. Goode, Mr C. M. Grech, Mr M. Grier, P. Hampshire, Mrs C. A. Harris, Mr C. I. K. Harris, Mr D. A. Heffer, Highclere Thoroughbred Racing Ltd, Mr D. F. Hill, Mr A. J. Hill, J. Holmes, Mrs K. Holmes, Mr D. Holmes, Lady E. Horn-Smith, Mr D. J. Jackson, Mr C. S. D. James, Mr P. Jervis, G. F. Keirle, R. G. Kelvin-Hughes, Mrs E. A. Kelvin-Hughes, Mr R. A. Kidner, Mrs R. J. King, Mr S. J. Kiss, Mr W. P. Ledward, Mr R. M. Levitt, S. Love, Miss K. A. Marsh, Mr W. D. C. Minton, Mr A. A. Morris, S. E. Munir, H. A. Murphy, Mr J. J. Murray, Mrs D. C. Nicholson, Miss M. Noden, Mr T. Nolan, Mr P. Nolan, T. S. Palin, Mr S. J. Parkin, Mr I. T. Payne, Miss H. Pease, W. H. Ponsonby, J. E. Potter, Mrs M. J. Potter, M. Prince, Prodec Networks Ltd, Mr S. J. Rogers, Mrs C. Rooney, Mr P. A. Rooney, R. Scott, Mrs P. M. Scott, Mrs S. J. Smith-Maxwell, Mr E. J. A. Smith-Maxwell, Mr I. Souede, Mrs J. A. Spack, Mr R. T. Sullivan, Mr I. R. Thurtle, Mr M. Townroe, Mrs C. Townroe, Mrs P. J. Toye, Mrs K. J. Tudor, Mr O. Vaughan, Mr E. C. J. W. Walsh, J. T. Warner, Mr M. K. Warren, Lady G. F. Wates, Whitestonecliffe Racing Partnership, G. A. Wilson, B. Winfield, J. Wright.

Assistant Trainers: Oliver Wardle, Dan Horsford

Jockey (NH): Wayne Hutchinson. **Conditional:** Tom Bellamy, Kevin Dowling, Will Featherstone, Jamie Insole.

327 **MR NEIL KING, Burderop**
Postal: **Upper Herdswick Farm, Hackpen, Burderop, Swindon, Wiltshire, SN4 0QH**
Contacts: **PHONE** (01793) 845011 **FAX** (01793) 845011 **MOBILE** (07880) 702325
E-MAIL neil@neil-king.co.uk **WEBSITE** www.neil-king.co.uk

1 BIG MEADOW (IRE), 7, br g Marienbard (IRE)—Lakyle Lady (IRE) **Mr P. M. H. Beadles**
2 CANYON CITY, 5, b g Authorized (IRE)—Colorado Dawn **A Whyte, J Bone, D Nott & B Smith**
3 CHIMES OF DYLAN (IRE), 5, b g Court Cave (IRE)—What A Princess (IRE) **Mr & Mrs James Blyth Currie**
4 COMANCHE CHIEFTAIN (CAN), 6, b g Broken Vow (USA)—
          Platinum Preferred (CAN) **Mr B Bell, Mr T Messom & Mrs P Sturgis**
5 CUBSWIN (IRE), 4, b f Zamindar (USA)—Moonlight Rhapsody (IRE) **Mr D Caldwell & Mr K Lawrence**
6 DIZZEY HEIGHTS (IRE), 6, b m Halling (USA)—
          Extreme Pleasure (IRE) **The Ridgeway Racing For Fun Partnership**
7 ELYSIAN PRINCE, 7, b g Champs Elysees—Trinkila (USA) **Mr D. S. Lee**
8 FFORBIDDEN LOVE, 4, b f Fastnet Rock (AUS)—Trinkila (USA) **Mr D. S. Lee**
9 HERDSWICK HOLLOA (IRE), 7, ch g Marienbard (IRE)—Cash A Lawn (IRE) **Mr Ken Lawrence & Mr Neil King**
10 HOLBROOK PARK, 8, b g Midnight Legend—Viciana **Mrs B. M. Chamberlain**
11 5, B m Milan—Island Walk (IRE) **Mrs H. M. Buckle**
12 LIL ROCKERFELLER (USA), 7, ch g Hard Spun (USA)—Layounne (USA) **Davies Smith Govier & Brown**
13 LITTLE MILLIE (IRE), 6, b m Milan—Sweetbitter (FR) **Mr A Whyte, Mr T Messom & Mrs P Sturgis**
14 LITTLE WINDMILL (IRE), 8, ch g Mahler—Ennismore Queen (IRE) **The Ridgeway Racing For Fun Partnership**
15 MAMOO, 5, ch g Sir Percy—Meredith **The Ridgeway Racing For Fun Partnership**
16 MARIENSTAR (IRE), 7, b m Marienbard (IRE)—Starofdonickmore (IRE) **Kevin Taylor & Garry Ambrose**
17 MERCERS COURT (IRE), 10, b g Court Cave (IRE)—
          Vikki's Dream (IRE) **David Nott, Ken Lawrence, Tim Messom**
18 MILANSBAR (IRE), 11, b g Milan—Ardenbar **Mr R. N. Bothway**
19 MYPLACEATMIDNIGHT, 6, b g Midnight Legend—Zahra's Place **SLIS Ltd & Mrs J K Buckle**
20 OH LAND ABLOOM (IRE), 8, b g King's Theatre (IRE)—Talinas Rose (IRE) **Milsom Baker Racing**
21 PRINCETON ROYALE (IRE), 9, br g Royal Anthem (USA)—Shelikesitsstraight (IRE) **D Nott, P Beadles, R Clarke**
22 REGULATION (IRE), 9, br g Danehill Dancer (IRE)—Source of Life (IRE) **D Caldwell, J Preuninger & N King**
23 SACKETT, 7, b g Midnight Legend—Gloriana
24 SHOULDAGONETOVEGAS (IRE), 6, b g Whitmore's Conn (USA)—
          Jennifers Guest (IRE) **Whyte, Coyne & Douglas**
25 TANKERTON BOY (IRE), 5, br g Marienbard (IRE)—Smashing Leader (IRE) **Mr P. M. H. Beadles**
26 THE BOSS's DREAM (IRE), 10, b g Luso—Mrs Kick (IRE) **SLIS Ltd, Mr M Gibbons & Mr D Nott**
27 THIRD ESTATE (IRE), 6, b g Suleiman (IRE)—Fizanni (IRE) **Lawrence, Govier & Brown**
28 WORKING LEATHER (IRE), 5, b g Teofilo (IRE)—Masnada (IRE)
29 ZEROESHADESOFGREY (IRE), 9, gr g Portrait Gallery (IRE)—Hazy Rose (IRE) **Mrs H. M. Buckle**

Other Owners: Mr G. P. Ambrose, Mr S. Baker, Mr Peter Beadles, Mr B. Bell, Mr James Blyth Currie, Mrs James Blyth Currie, Mr John Bone, Mr G. Brown, Mrs J. K. Buckle, Mr Donald Caldwell, Mr N. J. Catterwell, Mr Roy Clarke, Mr Mark Coyne, Mr John Davies, Mr Adrian Douglas, Mr Mike Gibbons, Mr P. T. Govier, Mr P. F. Govier, Mr Neil King, Mr Steven Langdon, Mr Ken Lawrence, Mr A. Maddox, Mr Tim Messom, Mr Gary Milsom, Mr D. F. Nott, Mr James Preuninger, Mr Bob W. Smith, Mr Andy Smith, Stephen Lower Insurance Services Ltd, Mrs Penny Sturgis, Mr K. A. Taylor, Mr A. A. Whyte.

MR NEIL KING - Continued

Assistant Trainer: Richie O'Dee **Head Lad:** Brian Scott. **Racing Secretary:** Jessica White

Jockey (flat): Adam Kirby. **Jockey (NH):** Trevor Whelan, Mark Grant, Richard Johnson, Jamie Moore, Jack Quinlan, Harry Skelton. **Conditional:** Bridget Andrews, Harry Teal.

---

328 **MR PHILIP KIRBY, Richmond**
Postal: Green Oaks Farm, East Appleton, Richmond, North Yorkshire, DL10 7QE
Contacts: PHONE (01748) 517337 MOBILE (07984) 403558
E-MAIL sharphillowners@gmail.com WEBSITE www.philipkirbyracing.co.uk

1 **ALLMYOWN (IRE)**, 7, b g Mr Combustible (IRE)—Cappard Ridge (IRE) **John Birtles & Bill Allan**
2 **ANIKNAM (FR)**, 8, b g Nickname (FR)—Kelle Home (FR) **Nobaj Ltd**
3 **ARCHIPPOS**, 5, b g Archipenko (USA)—Sparkling Clear **Well Oiled Partnership & Friend**
4 **ASUM**, 7, b g Kayf Tara—Candy Creek (IRE) **Bill Fraser & Adrian Pritchard**
5 **BARACALU (FR)**, 7, gr g Califet (FR)—Myragentry (FR) **SprayClad UK**
6 **BERTIE BLAKE (IRE)**, 5, b g Beneficial—Diandrina **The Kirby Club Partnership**
7 **BITUMEN BELLE (IRE)**, 6, b m Oscar (IRE)—Midnight Pond (IRE) **The Well Oiled Partnership**
8 **BOHERNAGORE (IRE)**, 9, b g Tajraasi (USA)—Brownies Haven (IRE) **Surefire Racing**
9 **CANFORD CHIMES (IRE)**, 5, b g Canford Cliffs (IRE)—Appleblossom Pearl (IRE) **The Well Oiled Partnership**
10 **CAPTAIN BOB (IRE)**, 7, b g Dark Angel (IRE)—Birthday Present **Malcolm Long & P Kirby**
11 **COURTOWN OSCAR (IRE)**, 9, b g Oscar (IRE)—Courtown Bowe VII **Nobaj Ltd**
12 **DARES TO DREAM (IRE)**, 4, br f Beneficial—Miss McGoldrick (IRE) **Ashley & Sue Clark & Clearabee Ltd**
13 **DISCAY**, 9, b g Distant Music (USA)—Caysue **John & Linda Oldroyd**
14 **DUBH DES CHAMPS (IRE)**, 6, br g Robin des Champs (FR)—Aneda Dubh (IRE) **Mr P. A. Kirby**
15 **EASTVIEW BOY**, 7, ch g Iktibas—Eastview Princess **Eastview Thoroughbreds 1**
16 **FINGAL'S CAVE (IRE)**, 6, ch g Fast Company (IRE)—Indiannie Moon **RedHotGardogs**
17 **GONN AWAY (IRE)**, 6, b m Mahler—Supreme Call (IRE) **Ramscove Ltd**
18 **GOOD TIME AHEAD (IRE)**, 4, b g Iffraaj—Good Time Sue (IRE) **Greenbank, Fairhurst & Fletcher**
19 **GRACIE STANSFIELD**, 4, ch f Peintre Celebre (USA)—Ex Gracia **Surefire Racing**
20 **HANGARD**, 6, b g Black Sam Bellamy (IRE)—Empress of Light **Daniel Blake & P Kirby**
21 **ICE GALLEY (IRE)**, 5, br g Galileo (IRE)—Ice Queen (IRE) **Mrs J. Sivills**
22 **IMPROVED (IRE)**, 8, ch g Rainwatch—Show Potential (IRE) **John Birtles & Colin Fletcher**
23 **KAYLEN'S MISCHIEF**, 5, ch g Doyen (IRE)—Pusey Street Girl **Mr M. E. Smith**
24 **KILCULLEN FLEM (IRE)**, 8, ch g Flemensfirth (USA)—
Cansalrun (IRE) **David Obree David McDermott Paul Betts**
25 **L'ATTENDUE (IRE)**, 4, br f Oscar (IRE)—Triptoshan (IRE) **Mr A. D. Bradshaw**
26 **LADY BUTTONS**, 8, b m Beneficial—Lady Chapp (IRE) **Mrs J. Sivills**
27 **LITTLE BRUCE (IRE)**, 6, b g Yeats (IRE)—Lady Rolfe (IRE) **The Gps Partnership**
28 **MANGATA (FR)**, 4, b g Cape Cross (IRE)—Kong Moon (FR) **The Philip Kirby Racing Partnership**
29 **MCKENZIE'S FRIEND (IRE)**, 7, b g Flemensfirth (IRE)—Escrea (IRE) **Mr P. A. Kirby**
30 **MINSTREL ROYAL**, 8, b g Kayf Tara—Close Harmony **The Gathering & P Kirby**
31 **NAUTICAL NITWIT (IRE)**, 9, b g Let The Lion Roar—Mrs Pugwash (IRE) **Birrafun 2**
32 **NEMEAN LION (IRE)**, 6, b g Mahler—Sandy Desert **The Well Oiled Partnership**
33 **NICELY INDEED (IRE)**, 8, b g Marienbard (IRE)—Rare Dollar (IRE) **Ownaracehorse Ltd**
34 **NORTHERN GIRL (IRE)**, 5, b m Westerner—Janebailey **Ownaracehorse & Topspec Partnership**
35 **PINEAPPLE CRUSH (IRE)**, 6, b br m Milan—Katie Snurge (IRE) **Mr L. Richards**
36 **PUMAFLOR (IRE)**, 6, b g Aussie Rules—Krasotka (IRE) **Resdev Ltd**
37 **RICHARD STRAUSS (IRE)**, 4, b br g Kheleyf (USA)—Symfony (IRE) **Zoe Hassall & George Hassall**
38 **ROCK OF LEON**, 7, b g Rock of Gibraltar (IRE)—Leonica **Surefire Racing**
39 **SAKHEE'S CITY (FR)**, 7, b g Sakhee (USA)—A Lulu Ofa Menifee (USA) **Mrs J. Sivills**
40 **SHINE BABY SHINE**, 4, b f Aqlaam—Rosewood Belle (USA) **David Gray & P Kirby**
41 **SKIPTHESCALES (IRE)**, 6, b g Winged Love (IRE)—Waterland Gale (IRE) **Mr L. Richards**
42 **STARGAZER (IRE)**, 5, b g Canford Cliffs (IRE)—Star Ruby (IRE) **Zoe Hassall & George Hassall & P Kirby**
43 **SUGGESTION**, 6, gr g Dansili—Jibboom (USA) **Red Cap Racing 1**
44 4, B g Scorpion (IRE)—Summertime Girl (IRE) **Mrs J. Sivills**
45 **THE RESDEV WAY**, 5, b g Multiplex—Lady Duxyana **Resdev Ltd**
46 **TOP VILLE BEN (IRE)**, 6, b g Beneficial—Great Decision (IRE) **Harbour Rose Partnership**
47 **TRANSIENT BAY (IRE)**, 8, b g Trans Island—Boarding Pass (IRE) **The Waking Ned Partnership**
48 **TRUE BALLEW (IRE)**, 4, b f Equiano (IRE)—Hula Ballew **The Jessies & P Kirby**
49 **WEMYSS POINT (IRE)**, 6, b g Champs Elysees—Wemyss Bay **The Green Oaks Partnership**
50 **ZIG ZAG (IRE)**, 5, b g Zoffany (IRE)—Le Montrachet **Mr & Mrs R G Capstick**

MR PHILIP KIRBY - Continued

THREE-YEAR-OLDS

51 **CAMPION,** b f Exceed And Excel (AUS)—Princess Janie (USA) **Mr P. A. Kirby**
52 B f Andorn (GER)—Cayman Sound
53 Br g Passing Glance—Epicurean **Red Cap Racing 1**
54 Br gr g Mastercraftsman (IRE)—French Friend (IRE) **Newton Racing**
55 **JAYCOLS STAR,** ch g Medicean—A Lulu Ofa Menifee (USA) **Jayne Sivills & Colin Fletcher**
56 **MR CARBONATOR,** b g Bated Breath—Diamond Lass (IRE) **Alan Fairhurst & Peter Sharp**
57 **RAYNA'S WORLD (IRE),** b f Poet's Voice—Salmon Rose (IRE) **Ace Bloodstock & Rayna Fitzgerald**
58 **ROBIN DES CHAPP (IRE),** b g Robin des Champs (FR)—Lady Chapp (IRE) **The Pinnacleplus Partnership**
59 **ROCCOCO (FR),** b g Shirocco (GER)—Lady Chloe
60 **SINCERELY RESDEV,** br g Rock of Gibraltar (IRE)—Sincerely **Resdev Ltd**
61 B f Teofilo (IRE)—Skid (IRE) **Ace Bloodstock Ltd**

TWO-YEAR-OLDS

62 B c 8/2 Fast Company (IRE)—Musikhani (Dalakhani (IRE)) (1904) **Ace Bloodstock Ltd**
63 B f 8/4 Archipenko (USA)—Sparkling Clear (Efisio) (5000) **Well Oiled Partnership & Friend**

Other Owners: Mr L. G. Aldsworth, Mr W. Allan, Mr J. A. Barber, Mr S. Beach, Mr J. K. Bell, Mr A. D. Bingham, Mr J. Birtles, Mr D. C. Blake, Mr S. Bocking, Mrs K. L. Capstick, R. G. Capstick, Mrs S. M. Clark, Mr A. G. Clark, Clearabee Limited, Mr E. L. Coates, Mr B. J. Connolly, Mr A. C. Davies, Mr B. H. Dolan, Eastview Thoroughbreds, Mr A. L. Ellison, Mr A. Fairhurst, Mrs R. Fitzgerald, Mr C. Fletcher, Mr I. Ford, W. R. Fraser, The Gathering, Mr D. W. Gray, Mr W. J. Greenbank, Mr R. Hamilton, Mr J. D. Hanson, Mr N. A. D. Hassall, Mrs Z. L. Hassall, Mr A. G. A. Hassall, Mr W. Hayler, The Jessies, Mrs P. R. Kirby, Mr M. A. Long, Mr W. D. Obree, Mr J. Oldroyd, Mrs L. M. Oldroyd, Mr A. Pritchard, Hugh T. Redhead, Mr A. J. Roberts, Mr R. P. Sharp, Mr J. G. R. Stent, The Topspec Partnership, Mr C. R. Trembath, Mr A. N. Waters.

Assistant Trainer: Simon Olley

Jockey (NH): Adam Nicol. **Conditional:** Thomas Dowson.

---

329 MR SYLVESTER KIRK, Upper Lambourn
Postal: Cedar Lodge Stables, Upper Lambourn, Hungerford, Berkshire, RG17 8QT
Contacts: PHONE (01488) 73215 FAX (01488) 670012 MOBILE (07768) 855261
E-MAIL info@sylvesterkirkracing.co.uk WEBSITE www.sylvesterkirkracing.co.uk

1 **CRICKLEWOOD GREEN (USA),** 7, ch g Bob And John (USA)—
B Berry Brandy (USA) **Mr Chris Wright & Mr Andy Macdonald**
2 **FAIR POWER (IRE),** 4, b g Power—Pitrizzia **Fairway Racing**
3 **FAMILY FORTUNES,** 4, ch g Paco Boy—Barawin (IRE) **Highclere Thoroughbred Racing**
4 **GAWDAWPALIN (IRE),** 5, b g Holy Roman Emperor (IRE)—Dirtybirdie **Mr H. Balasuriya**
5 **GOLDEN EYE,** 4, ch g Kheleyf (USA)—Gennie Bond **Sylvester Kirk**
6 **JAKEBOY,** 4, ch g Equiano (FR)—Teyateyaneng (IRE) **Mr J. Melo**
7 **PACOLITA (IRE),** 6, ch m Paco Boy (IRE)—Clara (IRE) **Mr G Dolan & Mr P Wheatley**
8 **PINK RIBBON (IRE),** 6, gr g Dark Angel (IRE)—My Funny Valentine (IRE) **Mr Tim Lock**
9 **SALOUEN (IRE),** 4, b c Canford Cliffs (IRE)—Gali Gal (IRE) **Mr H. Balasuriya**
10 **STAR GUIDE,** 4, b f Henrythenavigator (USA)—Exorcet (FR) **Mr J. C. Smith**
11 **WOODUKHELEYFIT,** 4, b g Kheleyf (USA)—Wood Chorus **Lady Suzannah O'Brien**

THREE-YEAR-OLDS

12 **AINNE,** ch f Cityscape—Ayun (USA) **Quantum Leap Racing**
13 **BOND DO TIGRAO,** b c Monsieur Bond (IRE)—Bahama Bay **Sylvester Kirk**
14 **DANCE ME (USA),** b f Bernardini (USA)—Stormy Saturday (USA) **Gerald Morrin & Sylvester Kirk**
15 **DEMONS AND WIZARDS (IRE),** b g Elnadim (USA)—Crystal Theatre (IRE) **Mr T. Pearson & Mr D. Barton**
16 **DORIES DELIGHT (IRE),** b g Dandy Man (IRE)—She's My Rock (IRE) **Mrs M. Cousins**
17 **GALLOPING HOGAN (IRE),** b g Most Improved (IRE)—Rapparee (USA) **The Goring Society**
18 **GEORGE (IRE),** b g Dragon Pulse (IRE)—Before The Storm **Mrs J K Powell**
19 **GIFT OF HERA,** ch f Nathaniel (IRE)—Premier Prize **Mr J. C. Smith**
20 **HOLDENHURST,** gr g Hellvelyn—Michelle Shift **Ansells Of Watford**
21 **KATHERINE PLACE,** b f Showcasing—Folly Drove **Ansells Of Watford**
22 **LYFORD (IRE),** ch g Intense Focus (USA)—Nurture (IRE) **Mr N. Pickett**
23 **MASTERS APPRENTICE (IRE),** ch g Mastercraftsman (IRE)—
Maghzaa (IRE) **The Old Enough To Know Better Partnership**
24 **MUSIC SOCIETY (IRE),** gr c Society Rock (IRE)—
Absolutely Cool (IRE) **Mr Des Kavanagh & Mr Derrick Murphy**
25 **MUSICAL DREAM,** ch f Dream Ahead (USA)—Gift of Music (IRE) **Mr J. C. Smith**

MR SYLVESTER KIRK - Continued

26 **PARTY DANCER,** b f Excelebration (IRE)—Indiana Blues **Mr J. C. Smith**
27 **REVERBERATION,** ch g Excelebration (IRE)—Echo Ridge (IRE) **Mr J. Melo**
28 **RIVER CAFE (IRE),** b f High Chaparral (IRE)—Dingle View (IRE) **Mr N Simpson & Mr P Shanahan**
29 **SAGUARO (IRE),** b f High Chaparral (IRE)—
             Plying (USA) **Mr M Gaffney, Mr T Gaffney, Mr D O'Loughlan, Mr J Casey**
30 **SASSIE (IRE),** b f Rip Van Winkle (IRE)—Star of Gibraltar **Mr N. Simpson**
31 **SAUCHIEHALL STREET (IRE),** b g Mastercraftsman (IRE)—
             Top Trail (USA) **The Old Enough To Know Better Partnership, Mr Colm McEvoy**
32 **SHE BELIEVES (IRE),** ch f Arcano (IRE)—African Moonlight (UAE) **Marchwood Recycling**
33 **SKY ROCKET,** b g Azamour (IRE)—Roseum **Thurloe Thoroughbreds XXX & Partner**
34 **TIME TO PERFECTION (IRE),** gr f Mastercraftsman (IRE)—Time Ahead **Homebred Racing**

TWO-YEAR-OLDS

35 Gr f 6/2 Gregorian (IRE)—Anazah (USA) (Diesis) (45000) **Mrs J. K. Powell**
36 B c 25/2 Battle of Marengo (IRE)—Autumn Tide (IRE) (Jeremy (USA)) (18000) **Mr S. Kirk**
37 **BENNY AND THE JETS (IRE),** ch c 29/3 Showcasing—
             Orange Pip (Bold Edge) (28571) **Deauville Daze Partnership**
38 B f 29/3 Foxwedge (AUS)—Chicklade (Firebreak) (6000) **Glebe Farm Stud**
39 Gr f 20/1 Tamayuz—Comfort In Sound (USA) (War Front (USA)) **Mr Christopher Wright**
40 **FIGHTING FINISH,** b f 29/3 War Command (USA)—
             Flying Finish (Priolo (USA)) (18000) **Mr D Boocock & Partner**
41 Ch c 10/4 Medicean—Giusina Mia (USA) (Diesis) (20000) **Mrs J. K. Powell**
42 B c 1/4 Zoffany (IRE)—Haven's Wave (IRE) (Whipper (USA)) (100000) **Mr H. Balasuriya**
43 **INVINCIBLE ONE (IRE),** b c 25/4 Invincible Spirit (IRE)—
             Photophore (IRE) (Clodovil (IRE)) (100000) **Mr R W Clothier & Miss J Gray**
44 B c 25/3 Norse Dancer (IRE)—King's Siren (IRE) (King's Best (USA)) **Mr J. C. Smith**
45 **MISSTRAL,** b f 17/2 Garswood—Presto Levanter (Rock of Gibraltar (IRE)) (6666) **Mr P Reglar & Mr R Gander**
46 **MR NICE GUY (IRE),** b c 20/2 Nathaniel (IRE)—
             Three Choirs (IRE) (Rock of Gibraltar (IRE)) (32560) **Deauville Daze Partnership & Mr G. Morrin**
47 **NAYSLAYER,** b c 7/4 No Nay Never (USA)—
             Elaflaak (USA) (Gulch (USA)) (28571) **Mr Neil Simpson & Mr Paul Shanahan**
48 **ROKA,** b c 29/4 Toronado (IRE)—Mullein (Oasis Dream) (10000) **Mr N. Simpson**
49 B f 23/2 Camelot—Star Search (Zamindar (USA)) (50000) **The Kathryn Stud**
50 Ch c 25/2 Footstepsinthesand—Winged Diva (IRE) (Hawk Wing (USA)) **Mr J. C. Smith**
51 B c 6/4 Noble Mission—Zaharias (USA) (Grand Slam (USA)) (24420) **Mr E. McCay**

Other Owners: Mrs L. M. Shanahan.

Assistant Trainer: Fanny Kirk

---

330 **MR STUART KITTOW, Cullompton**
Postal: Haynefield Farm, Blackborough, Cullompton, Devon, EX15 2JD
Contacts: HOME (01823) 680183 FAX (01823) 680601 MOBILE (07714) 218921
E-MAIL stuartkittowracing@hotmail.com WEBSITE www.stuartkittowracing.com

1 **AVOCADEAU (IRE),** 7, b g Lawman (FR)—Christmas Cracker (FR) **Mrs S. Clapp & Mrs L. Sharpe**
2 **BAKHT A RAWAN (IRE),** 6, b g Rip Van Winkle (IRE)—Foolish Ambition (GER) **Chris & David Stam**
3 **DILINGER,** 4, b g Equiano (FR)—Dilys **Cushing,Ingham,Boswell,Urquhart&Wilson**
4 **DORA'S FIELD (IRE),** 5, b m Rip Van Winkle (IRE)—Rydal Mount (IRE) **R. S. E. Gifford**
5 **EVERLASTING SEA,** 4, b f Harbour Watch (IRE)—Doliouchka **R. S. E. Gifford**
6 **INCENTIVE,** 4, b f Stimulation (IRE)—Folly Drove **The Incentive Partnership**
7 **MAD ENDEAVOUR,** 7, b g Muhtathir—Capelly **R. S. E. Gifford**
8 **NIGHTINGALE VALLEY,** 5, ch m Compton Place—Dancing Storm **M. E. Harris**
9 **NORDIC COMBINED (IRE),** 4, b g Haafhd—Chilly Filly (IRE) **Chris & David Stam**
10 **OUR FOLLY,** 10, b g Sakhee (USA)—Regent's Folly (IRE) **Midd Shire Racing**
11 **ROSIE LEA (FR),** 5, b m Manduro (GER)—Saralea (FR) **Mr J. R. Urquhart**
12 **TOBOUGGALOO,** 7, ch m Tobougg (IRE)—Let Alone **Dr G. S. Plastow**
13 **TROTTER,** 4, b g Piccolo—Vintage Steps (IRE) **Mr K. B. Hodges**
14 **WE'LL BE THERE,** 9, b m Kayf Tara—Teachmetotango **Pam Pengelly & David Lockwood**

THREE-YEAR-OLDS

15 **BEYOND EQUAL,** b g Kheleyf (USA)—Samasana (IRE) **Stuart Wood & Partner**
16 **COMSELLE,** b f Compton Place—M'selle (IRE) **The Comselle Partnership**
17 **GLOWETH,** b f Pastoral Pursuits—Dancing Storm **M. E. Harris**

MR STUART KITTOW - Continued

18 **ISABELLA MAYSON**, b f Mayson—Sydney Star **The Isabella Mayson Partnership**
19 **LILY JEAN**, ch f Makfi—Eastern Lily (USA)
20 **MOSTLY GREEN (IRE)**, b f Most Improved (IRE)—Green Green Grass **Mrs L. M. Francis**
21 B g Nathaniel (IRE)—Pan Galactic (USA) **Dr G. S. Plastow**
22 **PIEL CASTLE**, b g Camelot—Rydal Mount (IRE) **R. S. E. Gifford**
23 **SPIRIT OF ISHY**, b f Hellvelyn—Our Piccadilly (IRE) **Mrs G. R. Shire**
24 **YOUKAN (IRE)**, b g Choisir (AUS)—Ellikan (IRE) **Mrs L. M. Francis**

TWO-YEAR-OLDS

25 **MAYFAIR MADAME**, ch f 11/3 Mayson—Talqaa (Exceed And Excel (AUS)) (5714) **The Swells Syndicate**

Other Owners: John Boswell, Mrs S. G. Clapp, Mr H. A. Cushing, Mr A. R. Ingham, Mr M. J. Kennell, W. S. Kittow, Mr D. Lockwood, B. G. Middleton, The Hon Mrs R. Pease, Mrs P. J. Pengelly, Mrs R. J. M. Perry, Mrs L. Sharpe, A. J. Shire, Mr D. B. Stam, Dr C. Stam, Mr T. P. Wilson, Mr S. C. Wood.

Assistant Trainer: Mrs Judy Kittow

Jockey (NH): Paddy Brennan, Tom Scudamore.

---

331 MR WILLIAM KNIGHT, Angmering
Postal: Lower Coombe Racing Stables, Angmering Park, Littlehampton, West Sussex, BN16 4EX
Contacts: **PHONE** (01903) 871188 **FAX** (01903) 871184 **MOBILE** (07770) 720828
E-MAIL william@wknightracing.co.uk **WEBSITE** www.wknightracing.co.uk

1 **ARAB MOON**, 4, b g Elnadim (USA)—Albeed **Angmering Park Thoroughbreds IV**
2 **AUTHOR'S DREAM**, 5, gr g Authorized (IRE)—Spring Dream (IRE) **Mr & Mrs Conroy**
3 **BALLARD DOWN (IRE)**, 5, b g Canford Cliffs (IRE)—Mackenzie's Friend **Angmering Park Thoroughbreds I**
4 **BLOODSWEATANDTEARS**, 10, b g Barathea (IRE)—Celestial Princess **Canisbay Bloodstock**
5 **DELIBERATOR**, 4, b g Delegator—Purest **Mr & Mrs N. Welby & Fromthestables.com**
6 **GAVLAR**, 7, b g Gentlewave (IRE)—Shawhill **Canisbay Bloodstock**
7 **JACOB CATS**, 9, b g Dutch Art—Ballet **Canisbay Bloodstock**
8 **KINGSTON KURRAJONG**, 5, b g Authorized (IRE)—Kingston Acacia **Canisbay Bloodstock**
9 **NOBLE GIFT**, 8, ch g Cadeaux Genereux—Noble Penny **Canisbay Bloodstock**
10 **PROFESSOR**, 8, ch g Byron—Jubilee **Canisbay Bloodstock**
11 **SEA SHACK**, 4, b g Equiano (FR)—Folly Bridge **Seabrook Miller**
12 **SECRET ART (IRE)**, 8, ch g Excellent Art—Ivy Queen (IRE) **Art of Racing**
13 **SOLAR FLAIR**, 6, b g Equiano (FR)—Air Biscuit (IRE) **Art Of Racing & The Kimber Family**
14 **THE JUGGLER**, 5, b g Archipenko (USA)—Oblige **Mrs S. K. Hartley**
15 **UNIT OF ASSESSMENT (IRE)**, 4, b g Dragon Pulse (IRE)—Before The Storm **Mr A. Hetherton**

THREE-YEAR-OLDS

16 **AD VALOREM QUEEN (IRE)**, b f Dandy Man (IRE)—Herful Schnerful **Mr A. Hetherton**
17 Ch g Makfi—Albeed **Fromthestables.com & Apt II**
18 **FANFARE LADY (IRE)**, br f Society Rock (IRE)—Silk Fan (USA) **Angmering Park Thoroughbreds III**
19 **FORRICHERFORPOORER (IRE)**, gr g Casamento (IRE)—Ghedi (IRE) **Mr & Mrs Mark Tracey**
20 **GOODWOOD SHOWMAN**, b g Showcasing—Polly Floyer **Goodwood Racehorse Owners Group (24) Ltd**
21 **KOSHI**, b f Kyllachy—Espagnolette **Mrs E. C. Roberts**
22 **MAKIN IT**, b f North Light (IRE)—Saltpetre (IRE) **Chasemore Farm LLP**
23 **N OVER J**, b g Kodiac—Risk A Look **Mr A. Hetherton**
24 **PROGRESSIVE DAWN**, ch f Equiano (FR)—Foxtrot Alpha (IRE) **Progressive Racing I**
25 **QUEEN OF DREAMS (IRE)**, b f Epaulette (AUS)—Celestial Dream (IRE) **Mr T. G. Roddick**
26 **ROYAL WAVE**, b f Royal Applause—Air Biscuit (IRE) **Kennet Valley Thoroughbreds XIII**
27 **SEA MILLIONS**, b g Equiano (FR)—Folly Bridge **Seabrook Miller**
28 **SEINESATIONAL**, b g Champs Elysees—Kibara **One Day Rodney Partnership**
29 **SOTO SIZZLER**, b g Mastercraftsman (IRE)—Jalousie (IRE) **I. J. Heseltine**
30 **TESORINA (IRE)**, b f Lilbourne Lad (IRE)—Insieme (IRE) **Hot To Trot Syndicate & APT VI**
31 **TUSCAN PEARL**, b f Medicean—Western Pearl **Mr & Mrs N. Welby**
32 **VELVET MORN (IRE)**, b f Epaulette (AUS)—El Soprano **Mrs S. K. Hartley**

TWO-YEAR-OLDS

33 Ch c 9/4 Dragon Pulse (IRE)—Add Up (IRE) (Ad Valorem (USA)) (20349)
34 **CHINESE ALPHABET**, b c 20/2 Leroidesanimaux (BRZ)—
Kesara (Sadler's Wells (USA)) (30000) **Mr C. K. R. Cheung**
35 **DANCING WARRIOR**, b f 1/5 War Command (USA)—Corps de Ballet (IRE) (Fasliyev (USA)) **Mr T. G. Roddick**

MR WILLIAM KNIGHT - Continued

36 B f 14/2 Fast Company (IRE)—Elusive Gold (IRE) (Elusive City (USA)) (21978)
37 **ENGLISH HEROINE,** ch f 27/1 Nathaniel (IRE)—Merton Matriarch (Cadeaux Genereux) **Mr P. Winkworth**
38 **GOODWOOD SONNET (IRE),** b c 14/2 Lope de Vega (IRE)—
 Surface of Earth (USA) (Empire Maker (USA)) (48000) **Goodwood Racehorse Owners Group (25)**
39 B c 10/5 Born To Sea (IRE)—Kekova (Montjeu (IRE)) **Mr T. G. Roddick**
40 B c 14/3 Es Que Love (IRE)—
 Larghetto (USA) (Giant's Causeway (USA)) (8546) **Angmering Park Thoroughbreds V**
41 B f 13/3 Aussie Rules (USA)—Purest (Shamardal (USA)) **Mr & Mrs N. Welby**
42 B c 20/3 Sir Prancealot (IRE)—Street Kitty (IRE) (Tiger Hill (IRE)) (20350) **Kennet Valley Thoroughbreds XI**
43 **WINTER GLEAM (IRE),** b f 19/3 Kodiac—Boo Boo Bear (IRE) (Almutawakel) (55000) **Mrs E. Roberts**

Other Owners: Miss S. Bannatyne, Mrs J. E. Black, A. W. Black, Mrs H. G. Clinch, Mr C. Conroy, Mr N. A. Coster, Fromthestables.Com Racing, Mr P. Gregg, Mr R. S. Hoskins, Hot To Trot Racing Club, R. F. Kilby, Dr S. T. Kimber, Mrs C. Kimber, Mrs E. J. J. Knight, W. J. Knight, L. Lillingston, Mrs K. McCormack, Mrs M. E. A. Miller, Progressive Racing, Mr M. A. C. Rudd, Mr J. F. Seabrook, Miss M. E. Stopher, Mr L. A. Stoten, Ms L. Thompson, Mr M. J. Tracey, Mrs I. M. Tracey, Mrs N. J. Welby, Mr N. Welby, Mr R.J Wright.

---

332 **MR DANIEL KUBLER, Lambourn**
Postal: **High View Stables, Folly Road, Lambourn, Hungerford, Berkshire, RG17 8QE**
Contacts: **MOBILE (07984) 287254**
E-MAIL **daniel@kublerracing.com** WEBSITE **www.kublerracing.com**

1 **DIAMANTE (IRE),** 4, b f Big Bad Bob (IRE)—Miracle Steps (CAN) **Capture The Moment III**
2 **DISTINGUE,** 4, b g Sepoy (AUS)—Distinctive **Mr & Mrs G. Middlebrook**
3 **FIREBACK,** 11, b g Firebreak—So Discreet **Partnership Terminated**
4 **HOLYROMAN PRINCESS,** 4, b f Holy Roman Emperor (IRE)—Princess Ellen **Mr K. Taskiran**
5 **I WOULDN'T BOTHER,** 4, b g Captain Gerrard (IRE)—Dalmunzie (IRE) **Mr & Mrs Paul & Clare Rooney**
6 **MEDRANO,** 6, b g Archipenko (USA)—Trick Or Treat **Peter Onslow & Mr & Mrs Gary Middlebrook**
7 **MUTINEER,** 4, ch g Sepoy (AUS)—Violet (IRE) **Mr A Bell & Partners**
8 **OUTRAGE,** 6, ch g Exceed And Excel (AUS)—Ludynosa (USA) **D Blunt & G Middlebrook**
9 **PASSING STAR,** 7, b g Royal Applause—Passing Hour (USA) **Mr A. G. Bell**
10 **SENECA CHIEF,** 4, b g Invincible Spirit (IRE)—Albertine Rose **Mr & Mrs G. Middlebrook**
11 **SILENTLY,** 5, b m Zamindar (USA)—Quiet Elegance **Mr & Mrs G. Middlebrook**

THREE-YEAR-OLDS

12 **CHIZZ DE BIZ (IRE),** b f Zebedee—Chizzler (IRE) **Booth and Southworth**
13 B f Leroidesanimaux (BRZ)—Dance of Light (USA) **Mr & Mrs G. Middlebrook**
14 **DAWN COMMANDO,** ch c Dawn Approach (IRE)—Dynacam (USA) **Mr A. Stonehill**
15 **DISAPPROVAL (IRE),** b f Approve (IRE)—Disko (IRE) **Kubler Racing Ltd**
16 **FRONSAC,** ch c Frankel—Riberac **Mr & Mrs G. Middlebrook**
17 **INVOLVED,** b c Havana Gold (IRE)—Trick Or Treat **Peter Onslow & Gary Middlebrook**
18 **KIRKSTALL SPIRIT (IRE),** b br c Big Bad Bob (IRE)—Shine Silently (IRE) **Chris Greenall & Partner**
19 **NOT AFTER MIDNIGHT (IRE),** b br f Big Bad Bob (IRE)—Zenella **Mr & Mrs Paul & Clare Rooney**
20 **NYALA,** b f Vale of York (IRE)—Cio Cio San (IRE) **Ms V. O'Sullivan**
21 B g Born To Sea (IRE)—Valluga (USA) **David Blunt & Partner**

TWO-YEAR-OLDS

22 **CHAMOMILE,** b f 17/1 Teofilo (IRE)—Al Joza (Dubawi (IRE)) (85000) **Mr & Mrs G. Middlebrook**
23 Ch c 27/3 Paco Boy (IRE)—Free Falling (Selkirk (USA)) **A.C. Entertainment Technologies Limited**
24 B c 24/2 Toronado (IRE)—Jules (IRE) (Danehill (USA)) (26666)
25 Ch f 4/3 Havana Gold (IRE)—Secret Happiness (Cape Cross (IRE)) (20952)
26 B f 23/4 Kyllachy—Welsh Angel (Dubai Destination (USA)) (95000) **Newclose Properties Ltd**
27 **ZEPHYRINA (IRE),** b f 26/2 Big Bad Bob (IRE)—Western Sky (Barathea (IRE)) (10581) **Mr P. J. H. Whitten**

Other Owners: Mr D. Blunt, Mrs Y. Blunt, David & Yvonne Blunt, Mr K. Booth, Mr C. Greenall, Mrs C. E. Kubler, Mr G. Middlebrook, Mrs L. A. Middlebrook, Mr P. Onslow, Mr P. A. Rooney, Mrs C. Rooney.

Assistant Trainer: Claire Kubler

333 **MR TOM LACEY, Woolhope**
Postal: **Sapness Farm, Woolhope, Herefordshire, HR1 4RG**
Contacts: **MOBILE (07768) 398604**
E-MAIL tom@cottagefield.co.uk WEBSITE www.cottagefield.co.uk

1 **AMADOUE (FR)**, 5, b g Smadoun (FR)—Aimessa du Berlais (FR) **Mr N. C. Vowles**
2 **COLT LIGHTNING (IRE)**, 5, b g Flemensfirth (USA)—
Shannon Theatre (IRE) **Roberts, Churchward, Whittal-Williams**
3 **CONINGSBY**, 5, ch g Midnight Legend—Motcombe (USA) **Lady N. F. Cobham**
4 **DAVID'S PHOEBE (IRE)**, 5, br m Dubai Destination (USA)—
Miss Compliance (IRE) **Mrs Toni James & Mrs Ann Trotman**
5 **EQUUS AMADEUS (IRE)**, 5, b g Beat Hollow—Charade (IRE) **Galloping On The South Downs Partnership**
6 **FLASHING GLANCE**, 5, b g Passing Glance—Don And Gerry (IRE) **Barrett, Meredith, Panniers, Wilde**
7 **HE'S A GOER (IRE)**, 4, b g Yeats (IRE)—Tessas Girl (IRE) **Mr T. F. Lacey**
8 **JESTER JET**, 8, br m Overbury (IRE)—Hendre Hotshot **Mrs T. P. James**
9 **KATESON**, 5, gr g Black Sam Bellamy (IRE)—Silver Kate (IRE) **DavidMrichardsandRobertsCWhittalWilliams**
10 **KIMBERLITE CANDY (IRE)**, 6, b g Flemensfirth (USA)—Mandys Native (IRE) **Mr J. P. McManus**
11 **KING SPIRIT (IRE)**, 10, b g Fruits of Love (USA)—Tariana (IRE) **Mr J. J. King**
12 4, B g Winged Love (IRE)—Kiss Jolie (FR) **Galloping On The South Downs Partnership**
13 **LUCK OF THE LEGION (IRE)**, 5, b m Getaway (GER)—Grangeclare Flight (IRE) **Mrs S M Newell Mr T F Lacey**
14 **POLYDORA (IRE)**, 6, b g Milan—Mandysway (IRE) **P. J. H. Wills & J. J. King**
15 **SILK RUN (IRE)**, 5, b m Oscar (IRE)—Asian Alliance (IRE) **Silk Run Partnership**
16 **SIR EGBERT**, 5, b g Kayf Tara—Little Miss Flora **Mrs E. M. F. Cadbury**
17 **SNAPDRAGON FIRE (IRE)**, 5, b g Getaway (GER)—Global Diamond (IRE) **Mr J. J. King**
18 **SWORD OF FATE (IRE)**, 5, b g Beneficial—Beann Ard (IRE) **Galloping On The South Downs Partnership**
19 **THE LAST OF THEM**, 6, b g Kayf Tara—Marello **Mr & Mrs W. J. Williams**
20 **THOMAS PATRICK (IRE)**, 6, b g Winged Love (IRE)—Huncheon Siss (IRE) **Mr D. Kellett**
21 **TRIOPAS (IRE)**, 6, b g Stowaway—Aine Dubh (IRE) **Mr J. J. King**
22 **VADO FORTE (FR)**, 5, b g Walk In The Park (IRE)—Gloire (FR) **Roberts, Churchward, Whittal-Williams**

Other Owners: Mr P. L. Barrett, Mr T. W. C. Edwards, Mr P. A. Herbert, Mr J. Hinds, Mr G. J. Meredith, Mrs S. M. Newell, Mr N. J. Panniers, D. M. Richards, G. A. Roberts, Mrs E. V. A. Trotman, Mr M. C. Waddingham, Mr E. B. Whittal-Williams, Mr W. E. Wilde, W. J. Williams, Mrs M. Williams, Mr P. J. H. Wills.

Jockey (NH): Richard Johnson. **Amateur:** Mr Sam Burton, Mr Tommie O'Brien.

334 **MR CARLOS LAFFON-PARIAS, Chantilly**
Postal: **38, Avenue du General Leclerc, 60500 Chantilly, France**
E-MAIL ecuries.laffon.parias@wanadoo.fr

1 **ALIGNEMENT**, 5, b g Pivotal—Soldata (USA) **Wertheimer et Frere**
2 **ESPACE**, 4, b c Galileo (IRE)—Evaporation (FR) **Wertheimer et Frere**
3 **HAGGLE**, 5, ch m Pivotal—Barter **Wertheimer et Frere**
4 **ICEBERG (IRE)**, 6, b g Shamardal (USA)—Soft Ice (IRE) **Wertheimer et Frere**
5 **MILK MAN (USA)**, 4, ch c Kitten's Joy (USA)—Meteor Miracle (USA) **Wertheimer et Frere**
6 **ORIENTAL (JPN)**, 4, b c Smart Strike (CAN)—Iron Lips **Sarl Darpat France**
7 **RECOLETOS (FR)**, 4, b c Whipper (USA)—Highphar (FR) **Sarl Darpat France**

THREE-YEAR-OLDS

8 **ARECIBO (FR)**, b c Invincible Spirit (IRE)—Oceanique (USA) **Wertheimer et Frere**
9 **ARRIATE (FR)**, b c Shamardal (USA)—Briviesca **Sarl Darpat France**
10 **BALINAISE**, b f Dansili—Mydarshaan **Wertheimer et Frere**
11 **BIENVEILLANT**, b g Falco (USA)—Alfreda **Ecurie Mathieu Offenstadt**
12 **BOLSHINA**, b f Galileo (IRE)—Danzigaway (USA) **Wertheimer et Frere**
13 **BUSTER (FR)**, b c Invincible Spirit (IRE)—Comique (USA) **Wertheimer et Frere**
14 **CASTELLAR (FR)**, b f American Post—Highphar (FR) **Sarl Darpat France**
15 **CONTORTIONISTE**, ch c Pivotal—Distortion **Wertheimer et Frere**
16 **COURTESANA**, b f Cacique (IRE)—Casaca **Mme C. Laffon-Parias**
17 **DARIYA (USA)**, b f Include (USA)—Dubai (IRE) **Wertheimer et Frere**
18 **FOREIGN STAR**, b f Sea The Stars (IRE)—Foreign Tune **Wertheimer et Frere**
19 **GALUNPE (IRE)**, b c Camelot—Pop Art (USA) **P. Offenstadt**
20 **GRAVITAS (FR)**, b f Intello (GER)—Soldata (USA) **Wertheimer et Frere**
21 **HUMANISTE (IRE)**, b c Intello (GER)—Wingspan (USA) **Wertheimer et Frere**
22 **IVIRKA (FR)**, ch f Mastercraftsman (IRE)—Akrivi (IRE) **Ecurie Skymarc Farms**

MR CARLOS LAFFON-PARIAS - Continued

23 **LE MECENE (IRE)**, ch g Motivator—Aktia (IRE) **Ecurie Mathieu Offenstadt**
24 **LIPSTICK**, ch c Kendargent (FR)—Soft Lips **Wertheimer et Frere**
25 **MELODIENNE (USA)**, ch f Kitten's Joy (USA)—Melody Maiden (USA) **Wertheimer et Frere**
26 **MONTILLANA (FR)**, gr f Mastercraftsman (IRE)—Freedom Flashing (USA) **Sarl Darpat France**
27 **POLAR SEA**, b f Pivotal—Legerete (USA) **Wertheimer et Frere**
28 **SEJO (IRE)**, b c Nathaniel (IRE)—Amarysia (FR) **Bering SL**
29 **SOLESILI**, b c Dansili—Solemia (IRE) **Wertheimer et Frere**
30 **SOUSTRACTION (IRE)**, ch f Lope de Vega (IRE)—Mathematicienne (IRE) **Wertheimer et Frere**
31 **SPADAY (IRE)**, b f Exceed And Excel (AUS)—Beautifix (GER) **Wertheimer et Frere**
32 **ZAFFARAYA (FR)**, ch f Fuisse (FR)—Alrayihah (IRE) **Sarl Darpat France**
33 **ZANIBAR (FR)**, b f Invincible Spirit (IRE)—Flash Dance (IRE) **Wertheimer et Frere**
34 **ZIYAD**, b br g Rock of Gibraltar (IRE)—Arme Ancienne **Wertheimer et Frere**

TWO-YEAR-OLDS

35 **ARCMANIA (IRE)**, b f 6/4 Dansili—Solemia (IRE) (Poliglote) **Wertheimer et Frere**
36 B c 26/3 Dalakhani (IRE)—Campanillas (IRE) (Montjeu (IRE)) (16280) **Montojo**
37 **DOSILA**, b f 16/2 Galileo (IRE)—Stormina (USA) (Gulch (USA)) **Wertheimer et Frere**
38 **ECOLO (FR)**, b c 11/2 Invincible Spirit (IRE)—Never Green (IRE) (Halling (USA)) **Wertheimer et Frere**
39 **FLAMBEUR (USA)**, gr c 16/2 Mizzen Mast (USA)—Flamenba (USA) (Kingmambo (USA)) **Wertheimer et Frere**
40 **HAPPY BEAN (USA)**, bl f 3/3 Medaglia d'oro (USA)—
                                        Happy Week (USA) (Distorted Humor (USA)) **Wertheimer et Frere**
41 **MATEMATICA (GER)**, b f 14/3 Rock of Gibraltar (IRE)—
                                        Mathematicienne (IRE) (Galileo (IRE)) **Wertheimer et Frere**
42 B f 21/1 Anodin (IRE)—Minted (Mineshaft (USA)) **Wertheimer et Frere**
43 **NOSOLOW (FR)**, b c 26/3 Distorted Humor (USA)—Dubai (IRE) (Galileo (IRE)) **Wertheimer et Frere**
44 **PALOMBA (USA)**, b f 26/1 Lope de Vega (IRE)—Australienne (IRE) (Monsun (GER)) **Wertheimer et Frere**
45 Gr c 19/4 Iffraaj—Pearl Earrine (FR) (Kaldounevees (FR)) (24420) **Stilvi Compania Financiera**
46 **PLATANE**, f 22/4 Le Havre (IRE)—Modestie (FR) (Nayef (USA)) **Wertheimer et Frere**
47 **SHAMAN (IRE)**, ch c 8/4 Shamardal (USA)—Only Green (IRE) (Green Desert (USA)) **Wertheimer et Frere**
48 **STARIFIQUE (IRE)**, ch f 12/2 Sea The Stars (IRE)—
                                        Sapphire Pendant (IRE) (Danehill Dancer (IRE)) **Wertheimer et Frere**
49 **STARMANIAC**, b c 10/4 Sea The Stars (IRE)—Plumania (Anabaa (USA)) **Wertheimer et Frere**
50 **TOO LOUD (USA)**, b f 3/5 Arch (USA)—Quiet Royal (USA) (Royal Academy (USA)) **Wertheimer et Frere**
51 **TOP SPACE (USA)**, b c 9/2 Speightstown (USA)—Top Order (USA) (Dayjur (USA)) **Wertheimer et Frere**
52 **ULTIMATUM**, b c 12/2 Dutch Art—Danzigaway (USA) (Danehill (USA)) **Wertheimer et Frere**

---

335 MR DAVID LANIGAN, Newmarket
Postal: **Rathmoy Stables, Hamilton Road, Newmarket, Suffolk, CB8 0GU**
Contacts: PHONE **(01638) 664063** MOBILE **(07803) 257864**
E-MAIL **david@laniganracing.co.uk** WEBSITE **www.laniganracing.co.uk**

1 **EXPOSITION (IRE)**, 4, ch f Exceed And Excel (AUS)—Paramita (FR)
2 **LIGHT OF JOY (USA)**, 4, ch f Kitten's Joy (USA)—Light Blow (USA)
3 **RETRIBUTION**, 4, b g Iffraaj—The Giving Tree (IRE)
4 **TAKE A TURN (IRE)**, 4, b g Henrythenavigator (USA)—Satwa Pearl

THREE-YEAR-OLDS

5 **AMOLIKA (IRE)**, b f Kodiac—Dark Indian (IRE)
6 **APURA (IRE)**, gr f Oasis Dream—Three Mysteries (IRE)
7 **ATTICUS BOY (IRE)**, b c Cape Cross (IRE)—Satwa Pearl
8 **ELAPIDAE**, b c Helmet (AUS)—Al Cobra (IRE)
9 **EXCELABIT**, b c Exceed And Excel (AUS)—Saaboog
10 **GILTED PRINCESS (IRE)**, b f Farhh—Dabawiyah (IRE)
11 **HEAVENS ALIGN (IRE)**, b f Shamardal (USA)—Althea Rose (IRE)
12 **ISLAND ICON (IRE)**, b f Cape Cross (IRE)—Kerrys Requiem (IRE)
13 **LEXINGTON EMPIRE**, ch g Intello (GER)—Emperice (USA)
14 **NARODOWA**, ch f Iffraaj—Zacheta
15 **NOW SAY YES (IRE)**, b f Elusive Quality (USA)—Say No Now (IRE)
16 **PARADOX STATE (IRE)**, b g Camelot—Shine A Star
17 **PURPLEST**, b f Iffraaj—Purple Tiger (USA)
18 **ROUNDABOUT KITTEN (USA)**, ch g Kitten's Joy (USA)—Shining Jewel (USA)
19 **THUNDER NORTH (IRE)**, b c Dansili—Maidin Maith (IRE)
20 **TRANQUIL SOUL**, b f Farhh—Peaceful Soul (USA)

MR DAVID LANIGAN - Continued

21 **TRITONIX**, b f Nathaniel (IRE)—Triton Dance (IRE)
22 **WORTH WAITING**, b f Bated Breath—Salutare (IRE)

TWO-YEAR-OLDS

23 B f 19/3 Champs Elysees—Al Cobra (IRE) (Sadler's Wells (USA)) (30000)
24 Ch c 10/3 Lope de Vega (IRE)—Autumn Leaves (FR) (Muhtathir) (35000)
25 B f 31/5 Maxios—Burning Sunset (Caerleon (USA))
26 Ch c 4/5 Showcasing—Cockney Dancer (Cockney Rebel (IRE)) (20000)
27 Gr c 18/5 Lethal Force (IRE)—Dream Belle (Oasis Dream) (35000)
28 **DREAMINGOFDIAMONDS (IRE)**, b f 29/2 Alhebayeb (IRE)—Jemima's Art (Fantastic Light (USA)) (12857)
29 Ch f 4/4 Raven's Pass (USA)—Elegant Beauty (Olden Times) (60000)
30 B c 20/4 Archipenko (USA)—Goldrenched (IRE) (Montjeu (IRE)) (35000)
31 B c 26/4 Galileo (IRE)—Gooseberry Fool (Danehill Dancer (IRE)) (58072)
32 B f 3/2 Australia—Have Faith (IRE) (Machiavellian (USA)) (81400)
33 **IRISH ART (IRE)**, b c 2/2 Dutch Art—Slieve Mish (IRE) (Cape Cross (IRE)) (20000)
34 Ch f 29/1 Noble Mission—Kissin Party (IRE) (Kissin Kris (USA))
35 B c 7/2 Zoffany (IRE)—Millestan (IRE) (Invincible Spirit (IRE)) (130000)
36 B f 1/4 Universal (IRE)—Saaboog (Teofilo (IRE))
37 B f 25/1 Giant's Causeway (USA)—Sarah Lynx (IRE) (Montjeu (IRE))
38 Ch gr c 29/4 Mastercraftsman (IRE)—Satwa Pearl (Rock of Gibraltar (IRE))
39 Ch c 3/2 Iffraaj—Spirit Of Winning (Invincible Spirit (IRE))
40 Ch f 2/4 Slade Power (IRE)—Star Studded (Cadeaux Genereux) (28000)
41 B f 16/4 Mayson—Sunset Avenue (USA) (Street Cry (IRE)) (10000)
42 B f 2/2 Sepoy (AUS)—Threetimesalady (Royal Applause) (60000)

Owners: Abdulla Al-Mansoori, Saeed H Al-Tayer, Saif Ali, Mr Fergus Anstock, Mr Richard Bateman, Mr Ian Black, Mr Paul Brosnan, Mr Brian Cognet, Ms Madeleine Delaney, Diamond Racing, Flaxman Stables, The Kathryn Stud, Mr M. McMahon, Mr C. A. McMillan, Middleham Park, Niarchos Family, Mrs M. O'Malley, Mr T. S. Palin, Mr M. Prince, Promenade Bloodstock, Mrs S. K. Ramsey, Mr K. L. Ramsey, Mr Ben Sangster, Mr Chris Trigg, 21st Century Farms.

---

336 MISS EMMA LAVELLE, Marlborough

Postal: **Bonita Racing Stables, Ogbourne Maizey, Marlborough, Wiltshire, SN8 1RY**
Contacts: PHONE **(01672) 511544** FAX **(01672) 511544** MOBILE **(07774) 993998**
E-MAIL info@emmalavelle.com WEBSITE www.emmalavelle.com

1 **ACT OF SUPREMACY (IRE)**, 8, b g Presenting—Supreme Touch (IRE) **Equis (B) Partnership**
2 **ALLEZ JACQUES (IRE)**, 6, b g Robin des Champs (FR)—Crystal Stream (IRE) **Mr T. D. J. Syder**
3 **BALIBOUR (FR)**, 6, b g Policy Maker (IRE)—Saintheze (FR) **The High Altitude Partnership**
4 4, B g Shantou (USA)—Ballyguider Bridge (IRE) **T. Syder & N. Mustoe**
5 **BARLOW (IRE)**, 11, br g Beneficial—Carrigeen Kerria (IRE) **GDM Partnership**
6 **BELLE EMPRESS**, 7, b m Black Sam Bellamy (IRE)—Empress of Light **Mighty Acorn Stables**
7 **BLUSHING RED (FR)**, 4, ch g Le Havre (IRE)—Boliche **Mr R. J. Lavelle**
8 **BOOMARANG**, 4, b g Passing Glance—Materiality **Swanbridge Bloodstock Limited**
9 **BUSTER THOMAS (IRE)**, 7, b g Westerner—Awesome Miracle (IRE) **Axom LXVII**
10 **CASINO MARKETS (IRE)**, 10, br g Fruits of Love (USA)—Vals Dream (IRE) **Mighty Acorn Stables**
11 **CELTIC JOY (IRE)**, 5, b g Kayf Tara—No Time For Tears (IRE) **Hawksmoor Partnership**
12 **CHELSEA FLYER (IRE)**, 7, b g Westerner—Aktress (IRE) **Mrs Rosemary Luck & Mrs Deirdre Walker**
13 **CLOSING CEREMONY (IRE)**, 9, b g Flemensfirth (USA)—
                                    Supreme Von Pres (IRE) **The High Altitude Partnership**
14 **CUPID'S ICON**, 4, b f Sixties Icon—Flinders **Leith Hill Chasers**
15 **DARK MAHLER (IRE)**, 7, b g Mahler—Aries Rambler (IRE) **Axom LXVI**
16 **DE RASHER COUNTER**, 6, b g Yeats (IRE)—Dedrunknmunky (IRE) **Makin' Bacon Partnership**
17 **DEMOGRAPHIC (USA)**, 9, b g Aptitude (USA)—Private Line (USA) **British Racing Club**
18 **DISSAVRIL (FR)**, 5, gr m Balko (FR)—Odile (FR) **P. G. Jacobs**
19 **ENNISCOFFEY OSCAR (IRE)**, 6, b g Oscar (IRE)—Enniscoffey (IRE) **The Pick 'N' Mix Partnership**
20 **FIELD MASTER (IRE)**, 5, b g Doyen (IRE)—West Hill Rose (IRE) **Mrs C. L. Bonner**
21 **FLEMCARA (IRE)**, 6, b g Flemensfirth (USA)—Cara Mara (IRE) **Andy & The Frisky Fillies**
22 **FLYING SHADOW (GER)**, 6, b g Sholokhov (USA)—Fitness (IRE) **The Optimists**
23 **FONTSANTA (IRE)**, 5, b g Flemensfirth (USA)—Day's Over **Mr T. D. J. Syder**
24 **FORGET ME KNOT (IRE)**, 5, b m Presenting—J'y Reste (FR) **Swanbridge Bloodstock Limited**
25 **FORTUNATE GEORGE (IRE)**, 8, b g Oscar (IRE)—Fine Fortune (IRE) **The George Inn Racing Syndicate**
26 **FOX APPEAL (IRE)**, 11, b g Brian Boru—Lady Appeal (IRE) **The Hawk Inn Syndicate 3**
27 **FREEDOM RUN**, 5, ch m Presenting—Mathine (FR) **Bonita Racing Club**

MISS EMMA LAVELLE - Continued

28 **FRIZZLE**, 5, b m Rocamadour—Dizzy Frizzy **Bonita Racing Club**
29 **FULL IRISH (IRE)**, 7, b g Flemensfirth (USA)—Miss Kettlewell (IRE) **N. Mustoe**
30 **GUNFLEET (IRE)**, 6, b g Oscar (IRE)—Lady Lincon (IRE) **Mrs P. J. Travis**
31 **HAWK'S WELL (IRE)**, 4, b g Yeats (IRE)—Our Song **Mrs N. C. Turner**
32 **HIGH NOON (IRE)**, 6, b g Westerner—Seymourswift **N. Mustoe**
33 4, B g Flemensfirth (USA)—How Is Things (IRE) **T. Syder & N. Mustoe**
34 **I AM SAM**, 7, b g Black Sam Bellamy (IRE)—Flinders **Leith Hill Chasers**
35 **IRISH PROPHECY (IRE)**, 5, b g Azamour (IRE)—Prophets Honor (FR) **N. Mustoe**
36 **JAVERT (IRE)**, 9, b g Kayf Tara—Royalrova (FR) **Axom LII**
37 **JOYRIDER (IRE)**, 6, b g Stowaway—Aileen Supreme (IRE) **N. Mustoe**
38 **JUNCTION FOURTEEN (IRE)**, 9, b g King's Theatre—Chevet Girl (IRE) **Martin St. Quinton & Tim Syder**
39 **LADY MARKBY (IRE)**, 7, b m Oscar (IRE)—Leitrim Bridge (IRE) **Mrs S. Metcalfe**
40 **LETS HOPE SO**, 8, b m Generous (IRE)—Baily Mist (IRE) **Bonita Racing Club**
41 4, B g Authorized (IRE)—Linnet (GER) **The Bonhamie Partnership**
42 **MAJESTIC MOLL**, 6, b m King's Theatre—Artist's Muse (IRE) **Mustoe & Lavelle**
43 **MISTY BLOOM (IRE)**, 5, b m Yeats (IRE)—Misty Mountain (IRE) **Mr R. J. Lavelle**
44 **MOSSPARK (IRE)**, 10, b g Flemensfirth (USA)—Patio Rose **Mrs A. C. Lavelle**
45 **MR FENTON (IRE)**, 7, b g Trans Island—Carnagh Girl (IRE) **The Hawk Inn Syndicate**
46 **MYTHICAL LEGEND**, 7, ch m Midnight Legend—Materiality **British Racing Club**
47 **NAMIB DANCER (IRE)**, 4, b g Westerner—Derriana (IRE) **Mr W. P. L. Davies**
48 **NOT NORMAL (IRE)**, 5, b g Robin des Champs (FR)—Mardi Roberta (IRE) **Mighty Acorn Stables**
49 **PAISLEY PARK (IRE)**, 6, b g Oscar (IRE)—Presenting Shares (IRE) **Mr A. Gemmell**
50 **PARISH BUSINESS (IRE)**, 10, b br g Fruits of Love (USA)—Parkality (IRE) **N. Mustoe**
51 **PAWN STAR (IRE)**, 8, b g Beneficial—Missindependence (IRE) **Hawk Inn Syndicate 5**
52 **PEMBERLEY (IRE)**, 5, b g Darsi (FR)—Eyebright (IRE) **Laurie Kimber & Partners**
53 **PRIVATE MALONE (IRE)**, 5, b g Darsi (FR)—Native Artist (IRE) **Mrs Sarah Stevens & Mr P. Mitford-Slade**
54 **PROPHETS PRAYER (IRE)**, 4, b f Azamour (IRE)—Prophets Honor (FR) **N. Mustoe**
55 **ROOSTER COGBURN (IRE)**, 5, b g Westerner—Hollygrove (IRE) **N. Mustoe**
56 **RUGGIERO (IRE)**, 5, ch g Robin des Champs (FR)—Kayf Vera (IRE) **Mr T. D. J. Syder**
57 **SHIROCCAN ROLL**, 4, b g Shirocco (GER)—Folie Dancer **J. R. Lavelle & Dr Mark Scott**
58 **SHOTGUN PADDY (IRE)**, 11, b g Brian Boru—Awesome Miracle (IRE) **Axom (XXXVI)**
59 **SOUND INVESTMENT (IRE)**, 10, b g Dr Massini (IRE)—Drumcay Polly (IRE) **Owners Group 001**
60 **SWATOW**, 6, b m Shantou (USA)—Sudden Beat **G. C. Hartigan**
61 **THE DOMINO EFFECT (IRE)**, 4, b g Oscar (IRE)—Lively Lass (IRE) **Mighty Acorn Stables**
62 **THE SWEENEY (IRE)**, 6, b g Oscar (IRE)—Banningham Blaze **N. Mustoe**
63 **TRULY AMAZING (IRE)**, 5, br m Presenting—Asian Maze (IRE) **Swanbridge Bloodstock Limited**
64 **VENDREDI TROIS (FR)**, 9, b g Daarnsi (FR)—Legende Sacree (FR) **Awdry, Gemmell, Pomford & Williams**
65 **VIBRATO VALTAT (FR)**, 9, gr g Voix du Nord (FR)—La Tosca Valtat (FR) **Axom XLIII**
66 **VIVA VITTORIA (IRE)**, 4, b f Stowaway—La Fisarmonica (IRE) **Mr & Mrs A Millett**
67 **WATER WAGTAIL**, 11, b g Kahyasi—Kentford Grebe **D. I. Bare**
68 **WOOLSTONE ONE**, 6, b m Authorized (IRE)—Saralea (IRE) **P. G. Jacobs**

THREE-YEAR-OLDS

69 **BLISTERING BOB**, b g Big Bad Bob (IRE)—Kristalette (IRE) **Bex Design & Print Ltd**

Other Owners: Mr C. V. Awdry, Axom Ltd, Mr D. M. Bradshaw, Mr D. Charlesworth, G. Charlesworth, Mr D. Downie, Mr J. B. Duffy, Mrs B. S. Fowler, Mr R. J. Fowler, Mrs N. J. Haigh, Mrs C. D. Halpern, Mr S. Halpern, Mrs S. C. Hepworth, Mr A. J. Hill, Mr B. M. Hillier, Mr R. S. Keck, Mr L. G. Kimber, Mr M. Kirkby, Miss I. G. Langton, Mr J. R. Lavelle, Mrs R. A. Luck, Mr G. P. MacIntosh, Mrs J. Maltby, Mrs A. May, Mrs A. M. Millett, Mr A. J. Millett, P.B. Mitford-Slade, Mr P. Nicholls, Mr B. G. Pomford, Racing Club Ltd, K. P. Ryan, Mrs V. Scott, Dr M. J. Scott, Sir David Sieff, Mr J. Smee, Mr M. Smith, Mr M. G. St Quinton, Mrs S. V. M. Stevens, Mrs K. M. Taylor, Mrs J. C. Verity, Mrs V. A. Villers, Mrs D. Walker, Mr A. G. Weston, Mr P. R. Weston, Mrs P. H. Williams.

Assistant Trainer: Barry Fenton

---

337 **MR BARRY LEAVY, Stoke-on-Trent**
Postal: **Cash Heath Farm, Cash Heath, Forsbrook, Stoke-on-Trent, ST11 9DE**
Contacts: **HOME/FAX** (01782) 398591 **MOBILE** (07540) 806915
E-MAIL lauraleavy@hotmail.co.uk **WEBSITE** www.leavyracing.co.uk

1 **AKULA (IRE)**, 11, ch g Soviet Star (USA)—Danielli (IRE) **Mr B. Leavy**
2 **CLOCK ON TOM**, 8, b g Trade Fair—Night Owl **Mr F. W. Dronzek**
3 **FLOBURY**, 10, b m Overbury (IRE)—Miss Flora **Mrs L. M. Leavy**
4 **GEORGIAN FIREBIRD**, 8, b m Firebreak—Skovshoved (IRE) **Mrs E. A. Wilson**

MR BARRY LEAVY - Continued

    5 **HELAMIS**, 8, b m Shirocco (GER)—Alnoor (USA) **Mr F. W. Dronzek**
    6 **INFINITI (IRE)**, 5, b m Arcano (IRE)—Seraphina (IRE) **Mr Frank Dronzek & Mrs Susan Ashford**
    7 **KATARA BAY**, 7, b g Kayf Tara—De Blanc (IRE) **You Can Be Sure**
    8 **LUCY MC (IRE)**, 7, gr m Tikkanen (USA)—Careless Abandon (IRE) **Mr N. Heath**
    9 **MORE THAN TWO**, 8, b m Kayf Tara—Sweet Stormy (IRE) **Mr Frank Dronzek & Cops & Robbers**
   10 **REMEMBER NERJA (IRE)**, 4, ch f Lord Shanakill (USA)—Tequise (IRE) **Mr B. Leavy**
   11 **SCENT OF POWER**, 6, b m Authorized (IRE)—Aromatherapy **Mr B. Leavy**

THREE-YEAR-OLDS

   12 **FLO'S MELODY**, br f Swiss Spirit—Ginger Cookie **Mr F. W. Dronzek**

Other Owners: Dr M. Booth, Cops & Robbers, Dr C. Cowell, N. Heath, Mr N. A. Johnson, Mr D. Rowlinson, Mrs S. D. Williams-Ashford.

Assistant Trainer: Mrs L Leavy

---

338 MISS KERRY LEE, Presteigne
Postal: **Bell House, Byton, Presteigne, Powys, LD8 2HS**
Contacts: PHONE **(01544) 267672** MOBILE **(07968) 242663**
E-MAIL kerry@kerrylee.co.uk WEBSITE www.kerrylee.co.uk

    1 **ALFIE SPINNER (IRE)**, 13, b g Alflora (IRE)—Little Red Spider **Alan Beard & Brian Beard**
    2 **ALTIEPIX (FR)**, 8, ch g Fragrant Mix (IRE)—Naltiepy (FR) **Glass Half Full**
    3 **ASKNOTWHAT (IRE)**, 7, ch g Dylan Thomas (IRE)—Princess Roseburg (USA) **In It For The Crack No.1**
    4 **BISHOPS ROAD (IRE)**, 10, b g Heron Island (IRE)—Nice Resemblance (IRE) **Mr D. A. Halsall**
    5 **BRIGADIER BOB (IRE)**, 5, b g Excellent Art—Plausabelle **Mark E Smith & The Excellent Dees**
    6 **CINDERFELLA**, 7, gr g Sagamix (FR)—Firecracker Lady (IRE) **J.C.Harrison Lee & T.Howard Partnership**
    7 **DEFINITE FUTURE (IRE)**, 9, b g Definite Article—Miss Marilyn (IRE) **Mr R. L Baker & Mr Richard Lee**
    8 **DESTINED TO SHINE (IRE)**, 6, b g Dubai Destination (USA)—Good Shine (IRE) **Campbell-Mizen**
    9 **DUBLIN INDEMNITY**, 6, b g Presenting—Tazzarine (IRE) **Bailey-Carvill Equine**
   10 **EATON HILL (IRE)**, 6, b g Yeats (IRE)—Guilt Less (FR) **Mr & Mrs J. H. Watson**
   11 **EVERYDAY EVERYHOUR**, 7, b g Presenting—Candello **D. E. Edwards**
   12 **GASSIN GOLF**, 9, b g Montjeu (IRE)—Miss Riviera Golf **W. Roseff**
   13 **GINO TRAIL (IRE)**, 11, br g Perugino (USA)—Borough Trail (IRE) **Mrs J. Smith**
   14 **GOODTOKNOW**, 10, b g Presenting—Atlantic Jane **Burling Lee MacEchern Nolan Potter**
   15 **GREY GOLD (IRE)**, 13, gr g Strategic Choice (USA)—Grouse-N-Heather **Mrs M. A. Boden**
   16 **HAPPY DIVA (IRE)**, 7, b m King's Theatre (IRE)—Megans Joy (IRE) **W. Roseff**
   17 **JAYO TIME (IRE)**, 9, b g Morozov (USA)—Billythefilly (IRE) **Mrs B M Ayres, S R Holt & Mrs W Mole**
   18 **KING KAYF**, 9, b g Kayf Tara—Firecracker Lady (IRE) **J.C.Harrison Lee & T.Howard Partnership**
   19 **KINGS MONARCH**, 5, b g Schiaparelli (GER)—Monarch's View **Miss K. Lee**
   20 **KRACKATOA KING**, 10, b g Kayf Tara—Firecracker Lady (IRE) **J.C.Harrison Lee & T.Howard Partnership**
   21 **KRIS SPIN (IRE)**, 10, br g Kris Kin (USA)—Auditing Empress (IRE) **Six To Five Against**
   22 **MAGIC DANCER**, 6, b g Norse Dancer (IRE)—King's Siren (IRE) **Mark E Smith & The Magic Partnership**
   23 **MAHARI (IRE)**, 5, b g Duke of Marmalade (IRE)—Mission Secrete (IRE) **W. Roseff**
   24 **MR BACHSTER (IRE)**, 13, b g Bach (IRE)—Warrior Princess (IRE) **R. A. Lee**
   25 **MURPHY'S NAILS**, 6, b g Milan—Definite Artist (IRE) **Bailey-Carvill Equine**
   26 **RUSSE BLANC (FR)**, 11, wh g Machiavellian Tsar (FR)—Fleur de Mad (FR) **Mr M. R. H. Jackson**
   27 **SAGE MONKEY (IRE)**, 9, br g Craigsteel—Braw Lass **Miss K. Lee**
   28 **SCALES (IRE)**, 12, b g Bob Back (USA)—Mrs Avery (IRE) **A Beard B Beard S Ripley**
   29 **SHEAR ROCK (IRE)**, 8, b g Spadoun (FR)—Sleeping Diva (IRE) **Mr M. E. Smith**
   30 **SINAKAR (IRE)**, 7, br g Manduro (GER)—Siniyya (IRE) **Miss K. Lee**
   31 **SIR WILL (IRE)**, 7, b g Yeats (IRE)—Tinopasa (FR) **West Coast Haulage Limited**
   32 **STORM CONTROL (IRE)**, 5, b g September Storm (GER)—Double Dream (IRE) **W. Roseff**
   33 **TOP GAMBLE (IRE)**, 10, ch g Presenting—Zeferina (IRE) **Walters Plant Hire & James & Jean Potter**
   34 **TOWN PARKS (IRE)**, 7, b g Morozov (USA)—Outdoor Heather (IRE) **Mrs J. A. Beavan**
   35 **TREE OF LIBERTY (IRE)**, 6, ch g Stowaway—The Wrens Nest (IRE) **Mr M. E. Smith**

Other Owners: Mrs B. M. Ayres, Mr R. F. Bailey, Mr R. L. Baker, Mr B. Beard, Mr Alan Beard, Mr Patrick Burling, Mrs Roslyn Burling, Mr Daniel Campbell, Mr R. K. Carvill, The Excellent Dees, Mr G. T. Gilbert, Mr Stewart Harris, Ms J. C. Harrison-Lee, Mr R. L. C. Hartley, Mr M. R. Hawkins, Mr Simon Holt, Miss T. Howard, James and Jean Potter, Mr B. Knight, Mr Richard Lee, Mr Gavin MacEchern, The Magic Partnership, Mr P. Mizen, Mrs Wendy Mole, Ms L. E. Moore, Mr Paul B. Nolan, Mrs J. E. Potter, Mr J. E. Potter, Lady Susan Ripley, Mr Will Roseff, Mr Mark E. Smith, Walters Plant Hire Ltd, Mrs H. Watson, Mr J. H. Watson.

MISS KERRY LEE - Continued

Assistant Trainer: Richard Lee

Jockey (NH): Richard Johnson, Jamie Moore. **Conditional:** Richard Patrick.

339

MRS SOPHIE LEECH, Westbury-on-Severn
Postal: T/A Leech Racing Limited, Tudor Racing Stables, Elton Road, Elton, Newnham,
Gloucestershire, GL14 1JN
Contacts: PHONE (01452) 760691 MOBILE (07775) 874630
E-MAIL info@leechracing.co.uk WEBSITE www.leechracing.co.uk

1 **ANTEROS (IRE)**, 10, b g Milan—Sovereign Star (IRE) **K. W. Bell**
2 **BIRCH HILL (IRE)**, 8, b g Kalanisi (IRE)—Miss Compliance (IRE) **G. D. Thompson**
3 **BUONAROTTI BOY (IRE)**, 6, b g Galileo (IRE)—Funsie (FR) **Mr R. S. Liddington**
4 **DOTHRAKI RAIDER**, 7, b g Kayf Tara—French Spice **Mr M. J. Gorman**
5 **DUN SCAITH (IRE)**, 10, b g Vinnie Roe (IRE)—Scathach (IRE) **Leech Racing Platinum Club**
6 **FLANS O MAN (IRE)**, 8, b g Milan—Boro Supreme (IRE) **Leech Racing Platinum Club**
7 **HAZAMAR (IRE)**, 5, gr g Manduro (GER)—Hazarafa (IRE) **Mike Harris Racing Club & Partner**
8 **MAN OF PLENTY**, 9, ch g Manduro (GER)—Credit-A-Plenty **G. D. Thompson**
9 **MILROW (IRE)**, 5, b g Tamayuz—Cannikin (IRE) **John Cocks & Roger Liddington**
10 **MOSTLY BOB (IRE)**, 15, b g Bob Back (USA)—Town Gossip **C. J. Leech**
11 **PERFECT SYMPHONY (IRE)**, 4, b g Dandy Man (IRE)—Fields of Joy (GER) **Out Of Bounds Racing Club**
12 **RADMORES REVENGE**, 15, b g Overbury (IRE)—Harvey's Sister **CJ Leech & RS Liddington**
13 **RIVER MAIGUE (IRE)**, 11, b g Zagreb (USA)—Minor Tantrum (IRE) **C. J. Leech**
14 **SAMSON**, 7, ch g Black Sam Bellamy (IRE)—Riverine **The Cheltonians**
15 5, Ch h Anabaa Blue—Santoria (FR)
16 **SAXO JACK (FR)**, 8, b g King's Best (USA)—Gamma (FR) **Mike Harris Racing Club & Partner**
17 **SOIESAUVAGE (FR)**, 7, b m Lauro (GER)—Taffetas (FR) **Ms K. Neill & Mr W. Mackey**
18 **STEVE MEQUINE**, 5, ch g Native Ruler—Rabbit **Messrs M. E. & A. D. I. Harris**
19 **STUCCODOR (IRE)**, 9, b g Modigliani (USA)—Armilina (FR) **Cheltenham Racing Club**
20 **TAMARILLO GROVE (IRE)**, 11, b g Cape Cross (IRE)—Tamarillo **Cheltenham Racing Club**
21 **THROCKLEY**, 7, b g Passing Glance—Porcelain (IRE) **Out Of Bounds Racing Club**
22 **VASTLY (USA)**, 9, gr ro g Mizzen Mast (USA)—Valentine Band (USA) **Out Of Bounds Racing Club**
23 **WAHAAB (IRE)**, 7, ch g Tamayuz—Indian Ink (IRE) **Out Of Bounds & Mike Harris Racing Club**
24 **WALDEN PRINCE (IRE)**, 11, b g Saffron Walden (IRE)—Kahyasi Princess (IRE) **Mike Harris Racing Club**
25 **WEST WIZARD (FR)**, 9, b br g King's Theatre (IRE)—Queen's Diamond (GER) **J. O'Brien**
26 **WINDSHEAR**, 7, b g Hurricane Run (IRE)—Portal **G. D. Thompson**

Other Owners: Mr J. J. Cocks, Mr M. E. Harris, A. D. I. Harris, Mr M. D. Kilsby, Mr C. R. Leech, Mr W. Mackey, Ms K.
Neill, Mr C. Parkin, Mrs S. L. Wood.

Assistant Trainer: Christian Leech (07880) 788464

340

MISS TRACEY LEESON, Towcester
Postal: Earls Farm, Burcote Road, Towcester, Northamptonshire, NN12 6JW
Contacts: MOBILE (07761) 537672
E-MAIL traceyl31@hotmail.co.uk

1 **BLACKWELL SYNERGY (FR)**, 12, b g Antarctique (IRE)—Pyu (GER) **The Peter Partnership**
2 **DRAGON CITY**, 8, b g Elusive City (USA)—Oulianovsk (IRE) **The Nap Hand Partnership**
3 **JONJOELA (IRE)**, 7, b m Great Exhibition (USA)—Yorkshire Blade (IRE) **In The Pink Partnership**
4 **SAMIZDAT (IRE)**, 15, b g Soviet Star (USA)—Secret Account (FR) **Miss Tracey Leeson**
5 **SPYDER**, 10, b g Resplendent Glory (IRE)—Collect **The Marron Partnership**
6 **THEFRIENDLYGREMLIN**, 10, b g Vinnie Roe (IRE)—Queens Fantasy **The Nap Hand Partnership**

Other Owners: Mr M. H. Beesley, Mr D. Deveney, Mr J. L. Frampton, Mr J. D. Horgan, Mrs J. M. Letts, Miss K. J. Letts,
Mr M. E. White.

341 MRS SHEILA LEWIS, Brecon
Postal: **Mill Service Station, Three Cocks, Brecon, Powys, LD3 0SL**
Contacts: PHONE **(01497) 847081**
E-MAIL **sheilalewisracing1@gmail.com**

1 CHANGE UR TUNE (IRE), 6, br g Milan—Sunny Native (IRE) **Mr G. Wilson**
2 LISSYCASEY (IRE), 5, b g Rule of Law (USA)—Forever Mates (IRE) **Hopefully Not A Moose Partnership**
3 STRANGSMILL (IRE), 9, b m Beneficial—Sweet Vale (IRE) **G Wilson**
4 STUPID CUPID (IRE), 7, b m Beneficial—Supreme Arrow (IRE) **W. B. R. Davies**
5 THE FINAL WHISTLE (IRE), 5, ch g Approve (IRE)—Fairnilee **W. B. R. Davies**
6 TRY IT SOMETIME (IRE), 10, b g Milan—Lead'er Inn (IRE) **W. B. R. Davies**
7 WAY OF THE WORLD (IRE), 7, b g Flemensfirth (USA)—Night Heron (IRE) **W. B. R. Davies**

Other Owners: Mr R. Sheppard, Mr Graham Wilson, Mr S. J. Winter.

342 MR CLIFFORD LINES, Exning
Postal: **Hethersett House, Church House, Exning, Newmarket, Suffolk, CB8 7EH**
Contacts: PHONE **(01638) 608016** FAX **(01638) 608016** MOBILE **(07980) 120157**
E-MAIL **hethersetthouse@gmail.com**

1 CORNELIOUS (IRE), 6, b g Cape Cross (IRE)—Fantastic Spring (USA) **Prima Racing Partnership**
2 SIGNSEALDELIVERED, 4, b g Mawatheeq (USA)—Confluence **Prima Racing Partnership**
3 TYRSAL (IRE), 7, b g Jeremy (USA)—Blanchelande (IRE) **Prima Racing Partnership**

THREE-YEAR-OLDS
4 CATAPULT, b g Equiano (FR)—Alectrona (FR) **Prima Racing Partnership**

Other Owners: Ms S. Cawthorn, C. V. Lines

343 MR NICK LITTMODEN, Newmarket
Postal: **Red House Stables, Barn 2, Hamilton Road, Newmarket, Suffolk, CB8 0TE**
Contacts: MOBILE **(07770) 964865**
E-MAIL **nicklittmoden@icloud.com**

1 BY RAIL, 4, br g Rail Link—Soldata (USA) **Mr G. F. Chesneaux & Mr Nick Littmoden**
2 CANTABRO (FR), 7, gr g Stormy River (FR)—Dakota Go **Mr G. F. Chesneaux**
3 FEARSOME, 4, b c Makfi—Lixian **Mr G. F. Chesneaux**
4 FIGEAC (FR), 4, gr g Kendargent (FR)—Faviva (USA) **Mr G. F. Chesneaux & Mr Nick Littmoden**
5 HATEM (FR), 5, gr g Kendargent (FR)—Escolhida (IRE) **We Live In Norfolk Partnership**
6 HEAVEN HALL (FR), 5, b g Born King (JPN)—Sola Luna (FR) **G. Mulrooney, G. Chesneaux, N. Littmoden**
7 JOYCETICK (FR), 4, b g Myboycharlie (IRE)—Joyce (GER) **G. Chesneaux, N. Littmoden**
8 TORIANO, 5, ch g Equiano (FR)—Ticki Tori (IRE) **Chesneaux, Hassiakos & Littmoden**

THREE-YEAR-OLDS
9 B g Stimulation (IRE)—Betty Brook (IRE) **Ms P. Ferguson**

TWO-YEAR-OLDS
10 B f 12/3 Sepoy (AUS)—Betty Brook (IRE) (Refuse To Bend (IRE)) **Mr G. F. Chesneaux**
11 GLUTNFORPUNISHMENT, b c 15/2 Dawn Approach (IRE)—Oxsana (Dubawi (IRE)) (36000) **Mr A. A. Goodman**
12 GREYBYCHOICE (IRE), gr c 26/2 Dark Angel (IRE)—Khalice (Bahamian Bounty) (130000) **Mr A. A. Goodman**
13 Ch c 6/3 Le Havre (IRE)—Irish Cliff (IRE) (Marju (IRE)) (32000) **Mr N. P. Littmoden**

Other Owners: Mr G. F. Chesneaux, Mr S. Hassiakos, Mr A. Highfield, Mr Nick Littmoden, Mrs E. Littmoden, Mr G. Mulrooney, Mr Anthony Ringer.

344 **MR BERNARD LLEWELLYN, Bargoed**
Postal: **Ffynonau Duon Farm, Pentwyn, Fochriw, Bargoed, Mid-Glamorgan, CF81 9NP**
Contacts: **PHONE (01685) 841259 FAX (01685) 843838 MOBILE (07971) 233473/(07960) 151083**
E-MAIL bernard.llewellyn@btopenworld.com

1 **ARTY CAMPBELL (IRE)**, 8, b g Dylan Thomas (IRE)—Kincob (USA) **Mr Alex James & Mr B. J. Llewellyn**
2 **BIG FRED (IRE)**, 7, gr g Tikkanen (USA)—Whadouno (IRE) **Smerdon Tree Services Ltd**
3 **EARTHLY (USA)**, 4, b c Spring At Last (USA)—Geographic (USA) **Mr A. James**
4 **EDGE (IRE)**, 7, b g Acclamation—Chanter **Mr D Maddocks & Partner**
5 **FILATORE (IRE)**, 9, ch g Teofilo (IRE)—Dragnet (IRE) **B. J. Llewellyn**
6 **FLANAGANS FIELD (IRE)**, 10, b g Araafa (IRE)—Zvezda (USA) **G A Security**
7 **GLOBAL THRILL**, 9, b g Big Shuffle (USA)—Goonda **Mr Alex James & Mr B. J. Llewellyn**
8 **HANSUPFORDETROIT (IRE)**, 13, b g Zagreb (USA)—Golden Needle (IRE) **Mr Alex James & Mr B. J. Llewellyn**
9 **KASHGAR**, 9, b g Hernando (FR)—Miss Katmandu (IRE) **Mr Alex James & Mr B. J. Llewellyn**
10 **LET ME IN (IRE)**, 8, ch g Pivotal—I Hearyou Knocking (IRE) **B. J. Llewellyn**
11 **MARENGO**, 7, gr g Verglas (IRE)—Cloudchaser (IRE) **Mrs Beth Williams**
12 **NABHAN**, 6, b g Youmzain (IRE)—Danidh Dubai (IRE) **Gethyn Mills & Alex James**
13 **NEVER EQUALLED (IRE)**, 9, br g Brian Boru—Broken Thought (IRE) **Miss I. G. Tompsett**
14 **NORAB (GER)**, 7, b g Galileo (IRE)—Night Woman (GER) **B. J. Llewellyn**
15 **PETRIFY**, 8, b g Rock of Gibraltar (IRE)—Frigid **T. G. Price**
16 **PLYMOUTH SOUND**, 6, b g Fastnet Rock (AUS)—Shardette (IRE) **Mrs E. A. Llewellyn**
17 **TASTE THE WINE (IRE)**, 12, gr g Verglas (IRE)—Azia (IRE) **A. J. Williams**

Other Owners: Mr G. Anstee, Mr D. P. Maddocks, G. Mills.

Assistant Trainer: J L Llewellyn

Jockey (flat): Daniel Muscutt, David Probert. **Conditional:** Robert Williams. **Amateur:** Mr Jordan Williams.

345 **MISS NATALIE LLOYD-BEAVIS, East Garston**
Postal: **Parsonage Farm Stables, Newbury Road, East Garston, Hungerford, Berkshire, RG17 7ER**
Contacts: **PHONE (01488) 648347 MOBILE (07768) 117656**
E-MAIL nlbracing@gmail.com

1 **DEFTERA LAD (IRE)**, 6, b g Fast Company (IRE)—Speedbird (USA) **Mr Y. Mustafa**
2 **DOCTOR PARKES**, 12, b g Diktat—Lucky Parkes **Parsonage Racing Partnership**
3 **HIGHEST RED**, 9, ch g Byron—Honor Rouge (IRE) **Parsonage Racing Partnership**
4 **MADAME MIME ARTIST**, 7, b m Dutch Art—Silent Waters **Parsonage Racing Partnership**
5 **MY METEOR**, 11, b g Bahamian Bounty—Emerald Peace (IRE) **Parsonage Racing Partnership**

TWO-YEAR-OLDS

6 B f 21/4 Kuroshio (AUS)—Bold Love (Bold Edge) (761) **Parsonage Racing Partnership**

Other Owners: R. Eagle.

Jockey (NH): David Bass. **Apprentice:** Charlie Bennett.

346 **MR ALAN LOCKWOOD, Malton**
Postal: **Fleet Cross Farm, Brawby, Malton, North Yorkshire, YO17 6QA**
Contacts: **PHONE (01751) 431796 MOBILE (07747) 002535**

1 **AUTHENTICATION**, 9, b g Authorized (IRE)—Valley of Gold (FR) **A. J. Lockwood**
2 **BELLE PEINTURE (FR)**, 7, ch m Peintre Celebre (USA)—Grosgrain (USA) **A. J. Lockwood**
3 **PINDARIC**, 4, ch g Poet's Voice—Hunter's Fortune (USA) **Highgreen Partnership**

Other Owners: Mr M. Larkin, Mr J. Richardson, Mr Derek Wilson.

347 MR JOHN E. LONG, Brighton
Postal: **Southdown Stables, Bear Road, Brighton, East Sussex, BN2 6AB**
Contacts: MOBILE **(07958) 296945/(07815) 186085**
E-MAIL **winalot@aol.com**

1 **CHANDRAYAAN,** 11, ch g Bertolini (USA)—Muffled (USA) **R. D. John**
2 **MULTI QUEST,** 6, b m Multiplex—Ryan's Quest (IRE) **Mr Martin J. Gibbs & Mr R. D. John**
3 **TRUST ME BOY,** 10, gr g Avonbridge—Eastern Lyric **R. Pearson & J. Pearson**

THREE-YEAR-OLDS
4 **CATIVO RAGAZZO,** b c Multiplex—Sea Isle **Miss M. B. Fernandes**
5 B g Denounce—Ela d'argent (IRE) **Mr J. King**

Other Owners: Mr Martin J. Gibbs, Mr R. D. John, Mr R. Pearson, Miss J. Pearson.

Assistant Trainer: Miss S Cassidy

Jockey (flat): Robert Havlin, Franny Norton. **Amateur:** Miss E. Mackenzie.

348 MR CHARLIE LONGSDON, Chipping Norton
Postal: **Hull Farm Stables, Stratford Road, Chipping Norton, OX7 5QF**
Contacts: PHONE **(08450) 525264** FAX **(08450) 525265** MOBILE **(07775) 993263**
E-MAIL **charlie@charlielongsdonracing.com** WEBSITE **www.charlielongsdonracing.com**

1 **A VOS GARDES (FR),** 8, br g Kapgarde (FR)—Miscia Nera (FR) **The Rollright Stones**
2 **AUNTY ANN (IRE),** 7, b m Vinnie Roe (IRE)—On Good Advise (IRE) **Ms G. E. Morgan**
3 **AZURE FLY (IRE),** 10, br g Blueprint (IRE)—Lady Delight (IRE) **Girls Allowed**
4 **BALLYDINE (IRE),** 8, ch g Stowaway—Bealaha Essie (IRE) **Mr D. A. Halsall**
5 **BARTON ROSE,** 9, b m Midnight Legend—Barton Flower **Ms G. E. Morgan**
6 **BENTELIMAR (IRE),** 9, ch g Beneficial—Montel Girl (IRE) **Swanee River Partnership**
7 **BESTWORK (FR),** 7, bl g Network (GER)—Harmony (FR) **Mr R. J. Aplin**
8 **BOB TUCKER (IRE),** 11, b g Brian Boru—Acumen (IRE) **Mr N. Davies**
9 **BRADDAN HEAD,** 5, br g Recharge (IRE)—Solid Land (FR) **Mr T. J. Hemmings**
10 **CADEAUX'S FIRE,** 5, ch m Major Cadeaux—Confetti **Big Bucks Racing**
11 **CAPRICE D'ANGLAIS (FR),** 6, gr g Kapgarde (FR)—Odile de Neulliac (FR) **The Charlie Longsdon Racing Club**
12 **CARDIGAN BAY (FR),** 5, b m Turtle Bowl (IRE)—Nan's Catch (FR) **Henacre Racing Club Ltd**
13 **CASTAFIORE (USA),** 5, b m Street Cry (IRE)—Showlady (USA) **Slater Stockwood Nicholson Partnership**
14 **COOLOGUE (IRE),** 9, b g Helissio—Scolboa (IRE) **The New Club Partnership**
15 **DEFINITLY GREY (IRE),** 7, gr g Daylami (IRE)—Caroline Fontenail (IRE) **Jeromes Partnership**
16 **DJARKEVI (FR),** 5, b g Khalkevi (IRE)—Onvavoir (FR) **Mrs J. A. Wakefield**
17 **FLEMENSTRIX (IRE),** 5, b g Flemensfirth (USA)—Laurens Trix (IRE) **Mr D. A. Halsall**
18 **FLY HOME HARRY,** 9, b g Sir Harry Lewis (USA)—Fly Home **The Charlie Longsdon Racing Club**
19 **FORTH BRIDGE,** 5, b g Bernardini (USA)—Sally Forth **Her Majesty The Queen**
20 **FROZEN MOTION,** 6, b m Black Sam Bellamy (IRE)—Katys Jools **The Four Kings**
21 **HAMMERSLAKE (FR),** 10, b g Kapgarde (FR)—Loin de Moi (FR) **Mr R. J. Aplin**
22 **HEATHER SONG,** 4, b f Kayf Tara—Bella Macrae **Her Majesty The Queen**
23 **HIGHWAY GIRL,** 5, b m Kayf Tara—Whichway Girl **Mrs D. P. G. Flory**
24 **INDY ISLAND (IRE),** 9, gr m Indian Danehill (IRE)—Another Sparkle **The Charlie Longsdon Racing Club**
25 **JOLIE FRANCINE (IRE),** 6, gr m King's Theatre (IRE)—Belle Innocence (FR) **Mr Richard & Mrs Susan Perkins**
26 **JUST DON'T ASK (IRE),** 6, ch g Ask—Lucys Mate (IRE) **Robert Aplin & Swanee River Partnership**
27 **JUST YOUR TYPE (IRE),** 6, gr g Morozov (USA)—Enistar (IRE) **Mr T. Hanlon**
28 4, B f Sulamani (USA)—Karinga Madame
29 **KILLALA QUAY,** 11, b g Karinga Bay—Madam Bijou **Mr Richard & Mrs Susan Perkins**
30 8, B m Multiplex—Lady Jay Jay **Mr P. Bates**
31 **LAMBEAU FIELD (USA),** 5, b g Cape Blanco (IRE)—Xinji (IRE) **The Stewkley Shindiggers Partnership**
32 **LANGNESS (IRE),** 5, b g Milan—Bally Robin (IRE) **Mr T. J. Hemmings**
33 **LARGY PROSPECT (IRE),** 6, b g Stowaway—Thrilling Prospect (IRE) **Robert Aplin & Gavin Macechern**
34 **LEITH HILL LAD,** 8, b g Kayf Tara—Leith Hill Star **Mr & Mrs N. F. Maltby**
35 **LEITH HILL LEGASI,** 6, b m Kahyasi—Leith Hill Star **Mr & Mrs N. F. Maltby**
36 **LISDOONVARNA LAD (IRE),** 6, br g Westerner—Socialite Girl **Swanee River Partnership**
37 **LOOSE CHIPS,** 12, b g Sir Harry Lewis (USA)—Worlaby Rose **Barrels Of Courage**
38 **LOUSE TALK (IRE),** 6, b g Mahler—Foxy-Lady (IRE) **Mr C. E. Longsdon**
39 4, B f Malinas (GER)—Maiden Voyage
40 **MASTERPLAN (IRE),** 8, b g Spadoun (FR)—Eurolucy (IRE) **G. M. MacEchern**
41 **MIDNIGHT GEM,** 8, b m Midnight Legend—Barton Flower **Ms G. E. Morgan**

MR CHARLIE LONGSDON - Continued

42 **MIDNIGHT SHOT**, 8, b g Midnight Legend—Suave Shot **Mr D. A. Halsall**
43 **MIDNIGHT SONATA (IRE)**, 4, b g Big Bad Bob (IRE)—Symphonique (FR) **Mrs P. Pink**
44 **MONTY'S AWARD (IRE)**, 6, b g Oscar (IRE)—Montys Miss (IRE) **Mr D. A. Halsall**
45 **NIGHTFLY**, 7, br m Midnight Legend—Whichway Girl **Mrs D. P. G. Flory**
46 **NIGHTLINE**, 8, b g Midnight Legend—Whichway Girl **Mrs D. P. G. Flory**
47 **NO NO LEGEND**, 5, b m Midnight Legend—Karinga Madame **R. Jenner & J. Green**
48 **OLD JEROBOAM (IRE)**, 4, b g Jeremy (USA)—Old Line (IRE) **Mr Matthew Roberts & Simon Jessel**
49 **ORTENZIA (IRE)**, 4, b f Lawman (FR)—Ondoyante (FR) **Mr J. N. Greenley**
50 **OUR KAEMPFER (IRE)**, 9, b g Oscar (IRE)—Gra-Bri (IRE) **Swanee River Partnership**
51 **OVERWORKDUNDERPAID (IRE)**, 5, b g Getaway (GER)—Another Whiparound (IRE) **Mrs J. A. Wakefield**
52 **PENDRA (IRE)**, 10, ch g Old Vic—Mariah Rollins (IRE) **Mr J. P. McManus**
53 **PERLE'S AN ICON**, 4, b f Sixties Icon—Kahooting **Mr & Mrs N. F. Maltby**
54 **PETE THE FEAT (IRE)**, 14, b g King's Theatre (IRE)—Tourist Attraction (IRE) **Don Sebastiao Partnership**
55 **RAVISHED (IRE)**, 4, b g Oscar (IRE)—Fair Present (IRE) **Countrywide Vehicle Rentals Limited**
56 **READY TOKEN (IRE)**, 10, gr g Flemensfirth (USA)—Ceol Tire (IRE) **Foxtrot Racing: Ready Token**
57 **SAINT CAJETAN (FR)**, 6, b g Saint des Saints (FR)—Erivieve (FR) **Five Saints Racing**
58 **SCORPION PRINCESS (IRE)**, 7, b m Scorpion (IRE)—Cailin's Princess (IRE) **Mr J. N. Greenley**
59 **SHANROE IN MILAN (IRE)**, 6, b g Milan—Shanroe Scenario (IRE) **Mr D. M. Mason**
60 **SIMPLY THE WEST (IRE)**, 9, b g Westerner—Back To Stay (IRE) **Biddestone Racing XI**
61 **SOME AMBITION (IRE)**, 5, b g Westerner—Heath Heaven **Birch, Doel & Parker-Jervis**
62 **SOMMERVIEU (FR)**, 4, gr g Rajsaman (FR)—Simple Solution (USA) **Mrs J. A. Wakefield**
63 **STORM GODDESS (IRE)**, 4, br f Oscar (IRE)—Afasheen (IRE) **Don Sebastiao Partnership**
64 **STORMY MILAN (IRE)**, 5, b g Milan—Socialite Girl **Swanee River Partnership**
65 **TREACKLE TART (IRE)**, 6, b m Winged Love (IRE)—Battle Over (FR) **Bradley Partnership**
66 **VIVAS (FR)**, 7, b br g Davidoff (GER)—Lavircas (FR) **Mr N. Davies**
67 **VIVE LE ROI (IRE)**, 7, b g Robin des Pres (FR)—Cappard View (IRE) **Mr T. Richens**
68 **VOLT FACE (FR)**, 9, ch g Kapgarde (FR)—Jourenuit (FR) **Big Bucks Racing**
69 **WAY OUT WEST (IRE)**, 5, b g Westerner—Rose Vic (IRE) **Mrs C Djivanovic & Mr M Rose**
70 **WESTERN MILLER (IRE)**, 7, b g Westerner—Definite Miller (IRE) **The Pantechnicons IV**
71 **WILBERDRAGON**, 8, b g Kayf Tara—Swaythe (USA) **Don Sebastiao Partnership**

Other Owners: Mr D. Abraham, Mr G. H. S. Bailey, Mr N. M. Birch, Mrs G. P. Bostwick, T. P. Bostwick, Mr T. E. Boylan, Mr I. M. Brown, J. S. Cantrill, Mr A. J. Carter, Dr M. R. Clinch, Mr C. K. Crossley Cooke, Mrs C. J. Djivanovic, Mrs R. J. Doel, P. J. Donnison, Dr S. B. Drew, Mrs C. M. Du Pon, Mr F. S. W. Dudley, I. Dunbar, Mr P. A. Erskine, Mrs A. J. Green, Mr M. W. Gregory, Mr R. S. Jago, Ms R. A. Jenner, Mr S. R. J. Jessel, Mrs L. King, Mr D. P. King, G. J. Larby, Mrs S. J. Lavan, Mr C. O. A. Liverton, Mrs J. Maltby, Mr N. F. Maltby, Miss N. Martin, Mr J. W. Motson, J. M. Nicholson, Mrs E. H. Parker-Jervis, Mr M. A. Pausey, Mrs R. S. Perkins, R. A. H. Perkins, E. M. G. Roberts, Mr M. C. Rose, Mr J. Simpson, Mr P. J. Smith, Mrs S. Spencer-Jones, Mr S. Spencer-Jones, Mrs R. Steel, Mr J. Stockwood, Mr R. W. P. Weeks, Mr F. Wintle.

Assistant Trainer: Marcus Foley

Jockey (NH): Jonathan Burke. **Conditionals:** Paul O'Brien, Charlie Davies.

---

349 | **MR DANIEL MARK LOUGHNANE, Kidderminster**
Postal: Rock Farm, Rock Cross, Rock, Kidderminster, Worcestershire, DY14 9SA
Contacts: **MOBILE (07805) 531021**

1 **ALKASHAAF (USA)**, 4, b g More Than Ready (USA)—Abby Road (IRE) **Eclipse Horse Racing**
2 **BIG AMIGO (IRE)**, 5, b g Bahamian Bounty—Goldamour (IRE) **Worcester Young Farmers**
3 **BIG LACHIE**, 4, b g Camacho—Ryan's Quest (IRE) **A Tait & G&J Fernand**
4 **BINKY BLUE (IRE)**, 6, b m Approve—Sabander Bay (USA) **Mrs C. M. Loughnane**
5 **BOUNDERBY**, 4, b g Manduro (GER)—Most Charming (FR) **Shropshire Wolves**
6 **CHESTNUT FIRE**, 6, ch g Showcasing—Music In Exile (USA) **B. Dunn**
7 **CHOCOLATE BOX (IRE)**, 4, b c Zoffany (IRE)—Chocolate Mauk (USA) **Racing Facades Syndicate**
8 **COILLTE CAILIN (IRE)**, 8, b m Oratorio (IRE)—Forest Walk (IRE) **Mr P. Moran**
9 **DARK ALLIANCE (IRE)**, 7, b g Dark Angel (IRE)—Alinda (IRE) **Mrs C. M. Loughnane**
10 **DEELEY'S DOUBLE (FR)**, 5, ch g Makfi—Habilea (FR) **Shropshire Wolves**
11 **DRAGONITE (IRE)**, 4, ch g Dragon Pulse (IRE)—Glamorous (GER) **E Downey & C Loughnane**
12 **DREAM MAGIC (IRE)**, 4, b g Lord Shanakill (USA)—Pursuit of Passion **Mrs C. M. Loughnane**
13 **FETHIYE BOY**, 4, br g Pastoral Pursuits—Ocean Blaze **Mrs R. M. Serrell**
14 **GOLDEN SANDSTORM (IRE)**, 9, ch g Golden Tornado (IRE)—Killoughey Fairy (IRE) **Mr R. M. Brilley**
15 **4**, B f Gold Well—Hazel Mist (IRE) **Strutting Cockerels Syndicate**
16 **JOYS DELIGHT**, 4, b f Stimulation (IRE)—Lambadora **S & A Mares & A Potze**
17 **JUST FOR FEE (IRE)**, 4, b f Fame And Glory—Hakuna (IRE) **Concept Furniture International Limited**
18 **LITTLE MISS KODI (IRE)**, 5, b m Kodiac—Sensasse (IRE) **S. & A. Mares**

MR DANIEL MARK LOUGHNANE - Continued

19 **LORD MURPHY (IRE)**, 5, b g Holy Roman Emperor (IRE)—Tralanza (IRE) **The Goodwooders**
20 **ON A WHIM**, 6, b m Tamayuz—Love Me Tender **Mr R. M. Brilley**
21 **PENSAX BOY**, 6, b g Rail Link—Cyclone Connie **S. & A. Mares**
22 **PENSAX LADY (IRE)**, 5, b m Fast Company (IRE)—Aljafliyah **S & A Mares & M Millichamp**
23 **POUR L'AMOUR (IRE)**, 5, b m Aqlaam—Passion Fruit **Over The Moon Racing**
24 **SAM THE REBEL**, 4, b g Cockney Rebel (IRE)—Casablanca Minx (IRE) **Mr W. Hill**
25 **SOMEPINK (IRE)**, 5, b m Lilbourne Lad (IRE)—Cloonkeary **Mr R. M. Brilley**
26 **ST GEORGE'S OVAL (IRE)**, 5, b g Milan—Lisselton Lady **B. Dunn**
27 **TIGERWOLF (IRE)**, 5, br g Dream Ahead—Singing Field (IRE) **The Friday Morning Fourball**
28 **TOGA TIGER (IRE)**, 11, b g Antonius Pius (USA)—Minerwa (GER) **Jan Mead Kelly Gould**
29 **VIVA VERGLAS (IRE)**, 7, gr g Verglas (IRE)—Yellow Trumpet **Dining Chairs Uk Ltd & Partner**

THREE-YEAR-OLDS

30 **ANYTHINGWITHAPULSE (IRE)**, br f Dragon Pulse (IRE)—Mahatta (IRE) **The Half Past Seven Partnership**
31 B f Reliable Man—Costa Rica (IRE) **B. Dunn**
32 **DESTINYS ROCK**, b f Zoffany (IRE)—Special Destiny **Ladies of Rock**
33 **JOUST (IRE)**, b g Iffraaj—Thawrah (IRE) **Mrs R. M. Serrell**
34 **LOVELYSIMPLYLOVELY**, b f Firebreak—Spring Goddess (IRE) **Market Avenue Racing Club Ltd**
35 B c Fast Company (IRE)—Magical Bupers (IRE)
36 **MOXY MARES**, ch g Motivator—Privalova (IRE) **S. & A. Mares**
37 **ONEFOOTINFRONT**, b c Sir Percy—Anaya **2 Counties Racing**
38 **PONTBLYDDYN**, ch g Mount Nelson—Daring Damsel (IRE) **Mr R. M. Brilley**
39 **ROCK BOY GREY (IRE)**, gr g Dark Angel (IRE)—Encore View **The Likely Lads**
40 **RUSTY BLADE (IRE)**, ch g Zebedee—Flashing Blade **Mr R Brilley & Mrs A Townsend**
41 **SILVINGTON**, b g Firebreak—Millinsky (USA) **Mr M. Millichamp**
42 **STILL GOT IT**, b f Captain Gerrard (IRE)—Petaluma **Shropshire Wolves**
43 **TAKEONEFORTHETEAM**, b g Bahamian Bounty—Miss Bond (IRE) **S. & A. Mares**

TWO-YEAR-OLDS

44 B f 19/2 War Command (USA)—Causeway Queen (IRE) (Giant's Causeway (USA)) (28490) **S. & A. Mares**
45 **PRECISION PRINCE (IRE)**, b c 13/3 Dragon Pulse (IRE)—
Little Live Wire (IRE) (Dubawi (IRE)) (13023) **Precision Facades Ltd**
46 **SITTIN HANDY (IRE)**, ch c 5/4 Helmet (AUS)—Three Times (Bahamian Bounty) **Maximum Limit Syndicate**
47 B f 10/3 Swiss Spirit—Starlight Angel (IRE) (Dark Angel (IRE)) **S. & A. Mares**

Other Owners: Mr J. Babb, Mrs L. A. Cullimore, Mr D. A. Cullimore, Dining Chairs Uk Ltd, Mr E. Downey, Mr J. Fernand, Mr G. Fernand, S. P. Hackney, Mr S. Mares, Mrs A. Mares, Mr D. Mead, Mrs J. A. Mead, Mr M. Montague, Mr R. Morris, Ms A. S. Potze, R. Simpson, Mr P. Slater, Mr A. F. Tait, Mrs A. E. Townsend.

---

350 | MR DAVID LOUGHNANE, Tern Hill
Postal: Helshaw Grange, Warrant Road, Tern Hill, Shropshire
Contacts: **MOBILE (07527) 173197**
E-MAIL info@daveloughnaneracing.com WEBSITE www.daveloughnaneracing.com

1 **ALEJANDRO (IRE)**, 9, b g Dark Angel (IRE)—Carallia (IRE) **Lydonford Ltd**
2 **BERLUSCA (IRE)**, 9, b g Holy Roman Emperor (IRE)—Shemanikha (FR) **Mr P. Ball**
3 **BRITISH EMBASSY (IRE)**, 6, b g Clodovil (IRE)—
Embassy Belle (IRE) **The Golden Horse Racing Club & Syd Hosie**
4 **CRITICAL THINKING (IRE)**, 4, b g Art Connoisseur (IRE)—Cookie Cutter (IRE) **Mr J. Rocke**
5 **D'WATERSIDE**, 4, b g Sir Percy—Santorini Sunset **Mr J. Hughes**
6 **DEOLALI**, 4, b g Sleeping Indian—Dulally **The Most Wanted Partnership**
7 **KACHESS**, 4, b f Kyllachy—Fibou (USA) **Mr D. J. Lowe**
8 **MALPREEDY (IRE)**, 6, b m Mahler—Miles Apart (IRE) **Max Europe Limited**
9 **MRS ANGEL (IRE)**, 4, ch f Fast Company (IRE)—Sharakaat (IRE) **Sports 360**
10 **SANDY COVE**, 7, br g Oasis Dream—Maganda (IRE) **Miss S. L. Hoyland**
11 **SEAMSTER**, 11, ch g Pivotal—Needles And Pins (IRE) **Miss S. L. Hoyland**
12 **SHEPHERD'S PURSE**, 6, b g Pastoral Pursuits—Neyraan **Mr C. Greenall**
13 **SIGNORE PICCOLO**, 7, b g Piccolo—Piccolo Cativo **Mike and Eileen Newbould**
14 **STAR QUALITY (IRE)**, 4, b f Champs Elysees—Starfan (USA) **Miss S. L. Hoyland**
15 **THEODORICO (IRE)**, 5, b g Teofilo (IRE)—Yes Oh Yes (USA) **Mike and Eileen Newbould**

MR DAVID LOUGHNANE - Continued

THREE-YEAR-OLDS

16 **BAHUTA ACHA**, b g Captain Gerrard (IRE)—Rosein **Lancashire Lads Partnership**
17 **CALLING RIO (IRE)**, b f Canford Cliffs (IRE)—Rio's Pearl **Compas Racing**
18 **HARBOUR PILOT**, b c Harbour Watch (IRE)—Bountiful Girl **Ms J. A. French**
19 **HOGAR SEGURO (IRE)**, b f Casamento (IRE)—Gemma's Pearl (IRE) **Mr J. Hughes**
20 **ISLAND FOX**, gr ro f Foxwedge (AUS)—Emman Bee (IRE) **Mr J. Rocke**
21 B g Champs Elysees—Ja One (IRE) **Miss S. L. Hoyland**
22 **KARLYHAMILTON (IRE)**, b f Thewayyouare (USA)—All Embracing (IRE) **Max Europe Limited**
23 **MILAN REEF (IRE)**, br f Famous Name—Jagapaw (IRE) **Mr M. Godfrey**
24 **SNOOP**, b f Paco Boy (IRE)—Carafe **Mr H. Taylor**
25 **SUPERSYMMETRY (IRE)**, br f Kyllachy—Duniatty **Mr D. J. Lowe**
26 **VICEROY MAC**, b g Sepoy (AUS)—Tebee's Oasis **Macguire's Bloodstock Ltd**

TWO-YEAR-OLDS

27 B c 17/4 Big Bad Bob (IRE)—Baharah (USA) (Elusive Quality (USA)) (4500) **Miss S. L. Hoyland**
28 Ch c 22/4 Sir Prancealot (IRE)—
        Penny Serenade (IRE) (Lawman (FR)) (3333) **From the Front Racing & Darren Ryan**

Other Owners: Mrs S. E. Barclay, Mr P. M. Clarkson, Mr F. Frankland, Mr S. Franks, From The Front Racing, Mr A. N. Gargan, The Golden Horse Racing Club, Mr B. K. Haughey, Mr S. Hosie, Mr M. Keating, Mr J. M. Newbould, Mrs E. E. Newbould, Mr M. D. Orlandi, Mr D. Ryan, Mr B. Tait, Capt J. H. Wilson, Mr C. J. Woods.

---

351 | **MR SHAUN LYCETT, Witney**
Postal: **6 Mallard Crescent, Bourton-On-The-Water, Cheltenham, Gloucestershire, GL54 2RT**
Contacts: **PHONE (01451) 824143 MOBILE (07788) 100894**
E-MAIL **trainer@bourtonhillracing.co.uk** WEBSITE **www.bourtonhillracing.co.uk**

1 **A FALLING STAR**, 5, bl g Aeroplane—Westendview **C. M. Rutledge**
2 **AUMERLE**, 6, b g Authorized (IRE)—Succinct **D. Teevan**
3 **BARE NECESSITIES (IRE)**, 8, b g Sandmason—Marquante (IRE) **D Gilbert, M Lawrence, A Bruce**
4 **BOSTONIAN**, 8, b g Dubawi (IRE)—Bolshaya **Mr H E Peachey & Mr M J Snowdon**
5 **EXCELLENT PUCK (IRE)**, 8, b g Excellent Art—Puck's Castle **Bourton Racing**
6 **MONSART (IRE)**, 6, gr g Echo of Light—Monet's Lady (IRE) **L & M Atkins**
7 **NABATEAN (IRE)**, 7, b g Rock of Gibraltar (IRE)—Landinium (ITY) **Lord J. Blyth**
8 **NUTCRACKER PRINCE**, 7, b g Rail Link—Plum Fairy **D Gilbert, M Lawrence, A Bruce**
9 **OVERRIDER**, 8, b g Cockney Rebel (IRE)—Fustaan (IRE) **L & M Atkins**
10 **THE KING'S STEED**, 5, b g Equiano (FR)—King's Siren (IRE) **D Gilbert, J Lancaster, G Wills**
11 **TIKANITE (IRE)**, 7, b g Tikkanen (USA)—Scented Night (IRE) **L & M Atkins**
12 **TROY DEE KNEE**, 6, b g Rainbow High—Matthew's Bridey **The Golden Boys Partnership**
13 **WEEKLY GOSSIP (IRE)**, 7, br g Kalanisi—Mary's Little Vic (IRE) **L & M Atkins**

Other Owners: Mrs M. Atkins, Mr L. Atkins, Mr P. Davis, Mr D. R. Gilbert, Mr M. Lawrence, Mr M. Lovett, Mr H. E. Peachey, Mr M. J. Snowdon, Mr A. White.

---

352 | **MR JOHN MACKIE, Church Broughton**
Postal: **The Bungalow, Barton Blount, Church Broughton, Derby**
Contacts: **PHONE (01283) 585604/585603 FAX (01283) 585603 MOBILE (07799) 145283**
E-MAIL **jmackie@bartonblount.freeserve.co.uk**

1 **ART ECHO**, 5, b g Art Connoisseur (IRE)—Madhaaq (IRE) **Annwell Inn Syndicate**
2 **BARTON KNOLL**, 6, b g Midnight Legend—Barton Flower **Mr S. W. Clarke**
3 **BRIDAL MARCH**, 4, ch f Casamento (IRE)—Exultate Jubilate (USA) **Derbyshire Racing III**
4 **CAPTAIN SWIFT (IRE)**, 7, br g Captain Rio—Grannys Reluctance (IRE) **Mrs Sue Adams & Mr S. P. Adams**
5 **CUSTARD THE DRAGON**, 5, b g Kyllachy—Autumn Pearl **Derbyshire Racing**
6 **EBBISHAM (IRE)**, 5, b g Holy Roman Emperor (IRE)—Balting Lass (IRE) **P. Riley**
7 **ENGLISH HERO**, 5, b g Royal Applause—Merton Matriarch **Mr D. Ward**
8 **FIRE JET (IRE)**, 5, ch m Ask—Lightning Jet **Ladas**
9 **HALLSTATT (IRE)**, 12, ch g Halling (USA)—Last Resort **NSU Leisure & Mrs Carolyn Seymour**
10 **INFLEXIBALL**, 6, b m Refuse To Bend (IRE)—Sphere (IRE) **Derbyshire Racing II**
11 **INNISH MAN (IRE)**, 6, b g Fastnet Rock (AUS)—Super Gift (IRE) **Derbyshire Racing VII**
12 **JUST MILLY (IRE)**, 7, b m Milan—Out Performer (IRE) **The Mojan Partnership**
13 **KINGS ACADEMY (IRE)**, 4, ch g Mayson—Intrusion **Derbyshire Racing VI**

MR JOHN MACKIE - Continued

14 **LUNAR JET**, 4, ch g Ask—Lightning Jet **Ladas**
15 **MALINAS JACK**, 4, b g Malinas (GER)—Sphere (IRE) **Mr S. Smithurst**
16 **MANY TALES**, 6, b g Multiplex—All Three Fables **Mrs E. M. Mackie**
17 **MARMAS**, 9, ch g Sir Percy—Kitabaat (IRE) **Mrs E. M. Mackie**
18 **MONKS STAND (USA)**, 4, b g More Than Ready (USA)—Return The Jewel (USA) **Mr D. J. Haddrell**
19 **MOON JET (IRE)**, 6, b g Ask—Playwaki (USA) **Ladas**
20 **MUFFIN MCLAY**, 7, b g Lucky Story (USA)—Katie Savage **Mrs E. M. Mackie**
21 **OFF THE BEAT**, 4, ch g Black Sam Bellamy (IRE)—Off By Heart **G. B. Maher**
22 **ROCK SONG**, 9, b g Rock of Gibraltar (IRE)—Jackie's Opera (FR) **Mrs E. M. Mackie**
23 **TRENTMAN**, 6, ch g Denounce—Sharabosky **Mr T. M. Dorman**
24 **TRISTRAM**, 4, b g Sinndar (IRE)—Treasured Dream **The Tristram Syndicate**

THREE-YEAR-OLDS

25 **BERTOG**, ch g Sepoy (AUS)—Lucky Token (IRE) **Mr D. Ward**
26 Ch g Equiano (FR)—Lalina (GER)
27 **POLYPHONY (IRE)**, b f Power—Start The Music (IRE) **Mr D. Ward**

TWO-YEAR-OLDS

28 **AMBER JET (IRE)**, b f 17/2 Dream Ahead (USA)—Star Jet (IRE) (Teofilo (IRE)) **Ladas**

Other Owners: Mrs S. P. Adams, S. P. Adams, G. Bromley, Mr S. A. Flower, Mrs M. T. Mullin, Mr C. Mullin, NSU Leisure Ltd, Mr D. R. Penman, Mrs C. Seymour, Mr M. Skellett, Sotby Farming Company Limited.

---

353 **MR PETER MADDISON, Skewsby**
Postal: **5 West End Cottages, Skewsby, York, YO61 4SG**
Contacts: **PHONE (01347) 888385**

1 **KINGS OWN**, 4, b g Distant Peak (IRE)—Phoebe Nullis **P. Maddison**
2 **SGT BULL BERRY**, 11, b g Alflora (IRE)—Cede Nullis **P. Maddison**

Conditional: Jamie Hamilton.

---

354 **MR MICHAEL MADGWICK, Denmead**
Postal: **Forest Farm, Forest Road, Denmead, Waterlooville, Hampshire, PO7 6UA**
Contacts: **PHONE/FAX (02392) 258313 MOBILE (07835) 964969**

1 **GENERAL GERRARD**, 4, b g Captain Gerrard (IRE)—Dockside Strike **Mrs L. N. Harmes & Mr M. Madgwick**
2 **HI THERE SILVER (IRE)**, 4, gr g Clodovil (IRE)—Elaborate **Los Leader**
3 **JERSEY BULL (IRE)**, 6, b g Clodovil (IRE)—Chaguaramas (IRE) **Mrs Susan Bunney & Mr Peter Taplin**
4 **MULTIGIFTED**, 5, b m Multiplex—Attlongglast **Mrs L. N. Harmes**
5 **POYLE THOMAS**, 9, b g Rail Link—Lost In Lucca **Cecil and Miss Alison Wiggins**
6 **QUOTHQUAN (FR)**, 4, b g Myboycharlie (IRE)—Lonestar Spirit (IRE) **Los Leader**
7 **ROD OF IRON**, 5, br g Alkaased (USA)—Leading Star **Recycled Products Limited**
8 **TOMMYS GEAL**, 6, b m Halling (USA)—Steel Free (IRE) **Recycled Products Limited**

THREE-YEAR-OLDS

9 **MISS RECYCLED**, b f Royal Applause—Steel Free (IRE) **Recycled Products Limited**
10 **MULLION STAR**, b g Mullionmileanhour (IRE)—Leading Star **Mr M Madgwick, Mr P Taplin, Mrs S Bunney**
11 **RAVEN'S GIRL**, b f Raven's Pass (USA)—Ravenel (GER) **Los Leader**

TWO-YEAR-OLDS

12 **ARBUCKLE**, b c 2/4 Heeraat (IRE)—Attlongglast (Groom Dancer (USA)) **Mrs L. N. Harmes**
13 Ch c 17/3 Equiano (FR)—Kurtanella (Pastoral Pursuits) (1142) **M. Madgwick**

Other Owners: Mrs Susan Bunney, Mrs L. N. Harmes, Mr M. Madgwick, Mr Robert Oliver, Mr T. Smith, Mr Peter Taplin, Miss Alison Wiggins, Mr Cecil Wiggins.

Assistant Trainer: David Madgwick

Jockey (flat): Adam Kirby. **Jockey (NH):** Marc Goldstein. **Amateur:** Mr Lance Madgwick.

355 MRS HEATHER MAIN, Wantage

Postal: **Kingston Common Farm, Kingston Lisle, Wantage, Oxfordshire, OX12 9QT**
Contacts: **PHONE** (01367) 820124 **FAX** (01367) 820125
E-MAIL **heather.main@hotmail.com** WEBSITE **www.heathermainracing.com**

1 **AL KOUT**, 4, gr g Oasis Dream—Honorlina (FR) **John Rylands & Wetumpka Racing**
2 **BLUEGRASS BLUES (IRE)**, 8, gr g Dark Angel (IRE)—
                                                          Dear Catch (IRE) **Marcus Scott Russell & Wetumpka Racing**
3 **C NOTE (IRE)**, 5, b g Iffraaj—Alexander Queen (IRE) **G. C. Stevens**
4 **DASHING POET**, 4, b f Poet's Voice—Millisecond **Mr M. J. Moss**
5 **FAIR SELENE**, 4, b f Equiano—Jane Jubilee (IRE) **AndrewKnott,MrsPenelopeToll,MrLloyd**
6 **FIRST FLIGHT (IRE)**, 7, b g Invincible Spirit (IRE)—First of Many **Mr & Mrs D. R. Guest**
7 **ISLAND BRAVE (IRE)**, 4, b c Zebedee—Tip the Scale (USA) **D. M. Kerr**
8 **ISLAND CLOUD**, 4, b f Harbour Watch (IRE)—Cloud Illusions (USA) **D. M. Kerr**
9 **KESWICK**, 4, b c Dansili—Marywell **Lease Terminated**
10 **RAKE'S PROGRESS**, 4, b g Sir Percy—Cartoon **Coxwell Partnership**
11 **ROYAL MELODY**, 4, b f Royal Applause—Wannabe Free **Mr & Mrs D. R. Guest**
12 **TIFL**, 5, ch g Approve (IRE)—Isobel Rose (IRE) **Mrs Helen Adams & Wetumpka Racing**

THREE-YEAR-OLDS

13 **CHILDE HAROLD**, b c Thewayyouare (USA)—Byroness **The Haroldians**
14 **DE BEAU TANT**, b f Delegator—Miss Beaudacious (IRE) **Mrs H. Adams**
15 Ch c Thewayyouare (USA)—Gerardina
16 **ISLAND SOUND**, gr c Havana Gold (IRE)—Cloud Illusions (USA) **Mr Donald Kerr & Wetumpka Racing**
17 **LADY OF THE COURT (IRE)**, b f Camelot—Caserta **D. M. Kerr**
18 **MARSHAL DAN (IRE)**, b c Lawman (FR)—Aunt Nicola **Coxwell Partnership**
19 **SUPERMOSS**, b f Cacique—Fairy Moss (IRE) **Funboythree**

TWO-YEAR-OLDS

20 B f 9/6 Nayef (USA)—Byroness (Byron)
21 Gr c 15/4 Mount Nelson—Cloud Illusions (USA) (Smarty Jones (USA))
22 B f 29/4 Slade Power (IRE)—Dancer's Leap (Pivotal) **Wetumpka Racing**
23 **SONG OF THE ISLES (IRE)**, ch f 6/3 Tagula (IRE)—Musicology (USA) (Singspiel (IRE)) (15238) **D. M. Kerr**
24 B c 19/3 Zoffany (IRE)—Zadalla (Zaha (CAN)) (17907) **Llewelyn Yardley Runeckles**

Other Owners: Mr R. A. Fisher, Mr D. R. Guest, Mr P. B. Harrington, Mr A. Knott, G. I. D. Llewelyn, Mr P. M. A. Lloyd, Sir J. A. Mactaggart, J. P. M. Main, Mrs H. S. Main, Mr J. F. Runeckles, Mr J. M. C. Rylands, Mr M. Scott Russell, Mr M. R. Telfer, Mr P. A. Toll, Mr R. D. Walpole.

356 MRS ALYSON MALZARD, Jersey

Postal: **Les Etabl'yes, Grosnez Farm, St Ouen, Jersey, JE3 2AD**
Contacts: **MOBILE (07797) 738128**
E-MAIL **malzardracing@gmail.com**

1 **BOWL IMPERIOR**, 6, ch g Raven's Pass (USA)—Turtle Point (USA) **Geoff Somers**
2 **CARRERA**, 8, b g Sixties Icon—Aileen's Gift (IRE) **Malzard Racing**
3 **COUNTRY BLUE (FR)**, 9, bl g Country Reel (USA)—Exica (FR) **Tony Taylor**
4 **FLUTTERBEE**, 6, b m Equiano (FR)—Dunya **Geoff Somers**
5 **FOURNI (IRE)**, 9, ch m Rakti—Eckbeag (USA) **Ms J. Lowery**
6 **HARD TO HANDEL (IRE)**, 6, b g Stimulation (IRE)—Melody Maker **Jim Jamouneau & Matt Watkinson**
7 **HONCHO (IRE)**, 6, gr g Dark Angel (IRE)—Disco Lights **Sheikh A Leg Racing**
8 **ICE ROYAL (IRE)**, 5, b g Frozen Power (IRE)—Salford Princess (IRE) **Tony Taylor**
9 **MENDACIOUS HARPY (IRE)**, 7, b m Dark Angel (IRE)—Idesia (IRE) **Malzard Racing**
10 **NATIONAL SERVICE (USA)**, 7, b g War Chant (USA)—Cotton Club Ballet (USA) **Mr S. & Mrs F. Harrison-White**
11 **OCEAN CRYSTAL**, 8, gr m Stimulation (IRE)—Crystal Gale (IRE) **Channel Highland Racing**
12 **PAS D'ACTION**, 10, ch g Noverre (USA)—Bright Vision **Jim Jamouneau**
13 **PRINCESS KODIA (IRE)**, 5, b m Kodiac—Pixie's Blue (IRE) **Funboy 5**
14 **SAFIRA MENINA**, 6, b m Paco Boy (IRE)—Isla Azul (IRE) **Mr S. & Mrs F. Harrison-White**
15 **SPANISH BOUNTY**, 13, b g Bahamian Bounty—Spanish Gold **Malzard Racing**
16 **SPRING DIXIE (IRE)**, 6, gr m Zebedee—Dixie Jazz **Sheikh A Leg Racing**

Other Owners: Mr J. A. Osborne, Mr A. Taylor.

Jockey (flat): Paddy Aspell, Jemma Marshall. **Jockey (NH):** Mattie Batchelor. **Amateur:** Miss Michelle Hooper, Miss Victoria Malzard, Miss F. Tett.

357 MR JAMES JOSEPH MANGAN, Mallow
Postal: **Curraheen, Conna, Mallow, Co. Cork, Ireland**
Contacts: **PHONE (00 353) (0)87 2684611**

1 BANDON BRIDGE (IRE), 8, br g Presenting—Karen Mag (IRE) **Ms Karen O'Driscoll**
2 CASTLEBROOK (IRE), 5, b g Oscar (IRE)—Monty's Sister (IRE) **Ann & Alan Potts Ltd**
3 CONNA CROSS (IRE), 7, b g Lecroix (GER)—Country Time (IRE) **Hanford's Chemist Ltd**
4 LILY OF LEYSBOURNE, 5, b m Shirocco (GER)—Alegralil **C B Brooks**
5 MONTYS MEADOW (IRE), 10, b g Oscar (IRE)—Montys Miss (IRE) **Hanford's Chemist Ltd**

Assistant Trainer: Mary Mangan

358 MR CHARLIE MANN, Upper Lambourn
Postal: **Neardown, Upper Lambourn, Hungerford, Berkshire, RG17 8QP**
Contacts: **PHONE (01488) 71717 / 73118 FAX (01488) 73223 MOBILE (07721) 888333**
E-MAIL charlie@charliemann.info WEBSITE www.charliemannracing.com

1 BEAR VALLEY (IRE), 4, b g Manduro (GER)—Shane (GER) **Mr G. R. J. Jones**
2 CODY WYOMING, 12, b g Passing Glance—Tenderfoot **The Neardowners**
3 FIXED RATE, 5, b g Oasis Dream—Pretty Face **The Steeple Chasers**
4 GLORVINA (IRE), 4, b f Dragon Pulse (IRE)—Hawk Dance (IRE) **Mr G. R. J. Jones**
5 ILEWIN GEEZ, 8, ch g Generous (IRE)—Ilewin Janine (IRE) **T. J. Segrue**
6 LEORO (IRE), 4, ch g Campanologist (USA)—Ledicea (USA) **STG Racing Partnership**
7 LEX TALIONIS (IRE), 5, b g Thewayyouare (USA)—Dawn Air (USA) **Mrs Jill Mayo**
8 MAID OF MILAN (IRE), 7, br m Milan—Joes Lady (IRE) **The Neardowners**
9 MORNEY WING (IRE), 9, b g Antonius Pius (USA)—Tillan Fuwain (FR) **The Steeple Chasers**
10 OREGON GIFT, 6, b g Major Cadeaux—Dayville (USA) **Mrs S. P. B. Frosell**
11 ORIENTAL FLAME, 5, b m Norse Dancer (IRE)—Eastern Paramour (IRE) **Mr W. A. Harrison-Allan**
12 OSCAR CEREMONY (IRE), 7, b g Oscar (IRE)—Native Singer (IRE) **Racing Ventures 2014**
13 PICKAMIX, 7, gr g Sagamix (FR)—Star of Wonder (FR) **Racing Ventures 2014**
14 RAY'S THE MONEY (IRE), 4, b g Dragon Pulse (IRE)—Riymaisa (IRE) **Mr G. R. J. Jones**
15 ROYALS AND REBELS (IRE), 8, b g Robin des Pres (FR)—Native Deal (IRE) **The Neardowners**
16 SID HOODIE (IRE), 4, b f Rip Van Winkle (IRE)—Universe **Mr D. G. Christian**
17 SOME KINDA LAMA (IRE), 7, gr g Daylami (IRE)—Last Sunrise (IRE) **The Steeple Chasers**
18 THE DARLEY LAMA (IRE), 4, b g Carlotamix (FR)—Last Sunrise (IRE)
19 THE LION DANCER (IRE), 6, b g Let The Lion Roar—Shesadoll (IRE) **The 25 Club**
20 THE OGLE GOGLE MAN (IRE), 6, b g Yeats (IRE)—Miss Otis Regrets (IRE) **The 25 Club**
21 WELCOME POLLY (IRE), 6, br m Milan—Culmore Lady (IRE) **The 25 Club**
22 ZEN MASTER (IRE), 6, b g Shantou (USA)—Back Log (IRE) **The 25 Club**

Other Owners: Mr W. Brindle, Mr Charlie Mann, Mr A. J. McClafferty, Mr E. McClafferty, Ms J. Moran, Mr Tony Outhart, Mr Andy Stone, Major John Thorneloe, Mr C. R. Trembath.

Jockey (NH): Harry Bannister, Noel Fehily. **Conditional:** Angus Cheleda.

359 MR GEORGE MARGARSON, Newmarket
Postal: **Graham Lodge, Birdcage Walk, Newmarket, Suffolk, CB8 ONE**
Contacts: **PHONE (01638) 668043 MOBILE (07860) 198303**
E-MAIL george@georgemargarson.co.uk WEBSITE www.georgemargason.co.uk

1 CARIBBEAN SPRING (IRE), 5, b g Dark Angel (IRE)—Bogini (IRE) **Graham Lodge Partnership II**
2 DARING GUEST (IRE), 4, b g Fast Company (IRE)—Balm **John Guest Racing Ltd**
3 EXCELLENT AIM, 11, b g Exceed And Excel (AUS)—Snugfit Annie **Graham Lodge Partnership II**
4 HIPZ (IRE), 7, br m Intense Focus (USA)—Radha **Mr J. Melo**
5 SHYRON, 7, b g Byron—Coconut Shy **Mr F. G. Butler**
6 STORM RUNNER (IRE), 10, b g Rakti—Saibhreas (IRE) **Graham Lodge Partnership II**

THREE-YEAR-OLDS

7 BLAME CULTURE (USA), b c Blame (USA)—Pearl In The Sand (IRE) **Mangiacapra, Hill, Hook Partnership**
8 CITY GUEST (IRE), b g Epaulette (AUS)—Union City Blues (IRE) **John Guest Racing Ltd**
9 HEAVENLY GUEST (IRE), ch g Havana Gold (IRE)—Maid In Heaven (IRE) **John Guest Racing Ltd**
10 LORD GUEST (IRE), b g Lord Shanakill (USA)—Webcast (IRE) **John Guest Racing Ltd**
11 MACHO GUEST (IRE), b g Camacho—Alabama Grace (IRE) **John Guest Racing Ltd**

MR GEORGE MARGARSON - Continued

12 **MIDNIGHT GUEST (IRE),** b f Acclamation—Midnight Martini **John Guest Racing Ltd**
13 **PROTECTED GUEST,** b g Helmet (AUS)—Reem Star **John Guest Racing Ltd**
14 **SHYJACK,** ch g Archipenko (USA)—Coconut Shy **Mr F. G. Butler**
15 **TECHNOLOGICAL,** gr c Universal (IRE)—Qeethaara (USA) **Mr A. Al Mansoori**

TWO-YEAR-OLDS

16 B c 4/2 Swiss Spirit—Choisette (Choisir (AUS)) (42857) **John Guest Racing Ltd**
17 B c 1/2 Toronado (IRE)—Enliven (Dansili) (40000) **John Guest Racing Ltd**
18 Ch f 1/3 Showcasing—Looks All Right (IRE) (Danehill Dancer (IRE)) (135000) **John Guest Racing Ltd**
19 Ch c 22/2 Universal (IRE)—New Falcon (IRE) (New Approach (IRE)) (22000) **Mr A. Al Mansoori**
20 B f 22/3 Delegator—Red Larkspur (IRE) (Red Clubs (IRE)) **J. A. Khan**
21 Ch c 16/2 Universal (IRE)—Regal Sultana (New Approach (IRE)) (10000) **Mr A. Al Mansoori**

Other Owners: Mr R. Buckenham, Mr S. Hill, Mrs E. L. Hook, Mr J. G. Mangiacapra, G. G. Margarson.

Assistant Trainer: Katie Margarson

Apprentice: Jane Elliott. **Amateur:** Miss Katie Margarson.

---

360 | **MR ANDREW J. MARTIN, Chipping Norton**
Postal: Yew Tree Barn, Hook Norton Road, Swerford, Chipping Norton, Oxfordshire, OX7 4BF
Contacts: **PHONE (01608) 737288**

1 **GONEINAGLANCE,** 9, b m Passing Glance—It's Missy Imp **A. J. Martin**
2 **MIDNIGHT MUSTANG,** 11, b g Midnight Legend—Mustang Molly **A. J. Martin**
3 **MIGHTY MUSTANG,** 8, b g Passing Glance—Mustang Molly **A. J. Martin**
4 **MILITARIAN,** 8, b g Kayf Tara—Mille Et Une (FR) **A. J. Martin**
5 **SUNNY LEDGEND,** 13, b g Midnight Legend—Swordella **A. J. Martin**
6 **WORTHABOBORTWO,** 6, gr g Proclamation (IRE)—Bobs Bay (IRE) **A. J. Martin**

---

361 | **MISS NICKY MARTIN, Minehead**
Postal: Great Bradley, Withypool, Minehead, Somerset, TA24 7RS
Contacts: **PHONE (01643) 831175 MOBILE (07980) 269510**
E-MAIL nickymartin3@hotmail.co.uk

1 **ACCORDING TO HARRY (IRE),** 9, b g Old Vic—Cassilis (IRE) **Bradley Partnership**
2 **ALBEROBELLO (IRE),** 10, b g Old Vic—Tourist Attraction (IRE) **Bradley Partnership**
3 **BEER GOGGLES (IRE),** 7, br g Oscar (IRE)—Tynelucy (IRE) **Bradley Partnership**
4 **BODEKIN POINT (IRE),** 7, br g Robin des Pres (FR)—Countessdee (IRE) **Bradley Partnership**
5 **COLONEL CUSTARD (IRE),** 5, ch g Mahler—Criaire Princess (IRE)
6 **DAVE THE RAVE (IRE),** 8, b g Craigsteel—Coolharbour Lady (IRE) **Bradley Partnership**
7 **DONT EVEN GO THERE (IRE),** 7, b g Brian Boru—Foreal (IRE) **Bradley Partnership**
8 **INFAMOUS GROUSE (IRE),** 9, b g Oscar (IRE)—Big Daddy's Girl (IRE) **Bradley Partnership**
9 **JUST ANOTHER VODKA,** 6, gr g Double Trigger (IRE)—Par Excellence **Bradley Partnership**
10 4, Br g Robin des Champs (FR)—Lady Titanium (IRE)
11 **MOLE TRAP,** 7, b m Kayf Tara—Fairly High (IRE) **Bradley Partnership**
12 **ONE FOR THE GUV'NR (IRE),** 9, b g Oscar (IRE)—Wintry Day (IRE) **Bradley Partnership**
13 **PHOBIAPHILIAC (IRE),** 7, b g Beneficial—Denys Eyre (IRE) **Bradley Partnership**
14 **PISTOL SHOOT (IRE),** 6, b g Milan—Emesions Lady (IRE) **Bradley Partnership**
15 **POISON ARROW (IRE),** 4, b g Scorpion (IRE)—Lobatica (GER)
16 **PURE VODKA,** 5, b m Westerner—Fairly High (IRE)
17 4, B f Oscar (IRE)—Redwood Lady (IRE) **Bradley Partnership**
18 **ROCKIN ON THE MOOR (IRE),** 5, b g Oscar (IRE)—Montys Miss (IRE)
19 **SONOFTHEKING (IRE),** 10, b g King's Theatre (IRE)—Nikadora (FR) **Bradley Partnership**
20 **STEADY AWAY (IRE),** 4, b g Fame And Glory—Inch Pride (IRE) **Bradley Partnership**
21 **SYKES (IRE),** 9, b g Mountain High (IRE)—Our Trick (IRE) **Bradley Partnership**
22 **THE LIZARD KING (IRE),** 9, b g Indian River (FR)—Norwich Breeze (IRE) **Bradley Partnership**
23 **THE TWO AMIGOS (IRE),** 6, b g Midnight Legend—As Was **Bradley Partnership**

Other Owners: Miss N. Martin, Mr J. Simpson.

362 MR CHRISTOPHER MASON, Caerwent
Postal: **Whitehall Barn, Five Lanes, Caerwent, Monmouthshire**
Contacts: **PHONE (01291) 422172 FAX (01633) 666690 MOBILE (07767) 808082**
E-MAIL cjmason@tiscali.co.uk

1 BEYOND THE EDGE, 6, ch m Compton Place—Edge of Gold **Mr Christopher and Annabelle Mason Racing**
2 EDGED OUT, 8, b m Piccolo—Edge of Light **Mr Christopher and Annabelle Mason Racing**
3 JAGANORY (IRE), 6, b g Dylan Thomas (IRE)—Jacquelin Jag (IRE) **B. G. Hicks**

THREE-YEAR-OLDS
4 MASONS BELLE, b g Piccolo—Edge of Gold **Mr Christopher and Annabelle Mason Racing**
5 B f Compton Place—Superior Edge

TWO-YEAR-OLDS
6 B f 21/4 Havana Gold (IRE)—Bright Edge (Danehill Dancer (IRE)) **Mr Christopher and Annabelle Mason Racing**
7 B f 17/4 Harbour Watch (IRE)—Edge of Light (Xaar)
8 B f 24/4 Harbour Watch (IRE)—Elidore (Danetime (IRE)) **Mr Christopher and Annabelle Mason Racing**
9 GLAMOROUS CRESCENT, ch f 23/3 Stimulation (IRE)—
Go Glamorous (IRE) (Elnadim (USA)) **Robert & Nina Bailey**

Other Owners: R. M. Bailey, Mrs J. H. Bailey, C. J. Mason, Exors of the Late Mrs A. L. Mason.

Assistant Trainer: Annabelle Mason

363 MRS JENNIFER MASON, Cirencester
Postal: **Manor Farm, Ablington, Bibury, Cirencester, Gloucestershire, GL7 5NY**
Contacts: **PHONE (01285) 740445 MOBILE (07974) 262438**
E-MAIL pwmason2002@yahoo.co.uk WEBSITE www.jennifermasonracing.com

1 CALL ME SID, 6, b g Schiaparelli (GER)—Zolotaya **Mr N. G. Mills**
2 4, B f Midnight Legend—Love of Tara

THREE-YEAR-OLDS
3 Ch g Schiaparelli (GER)—Tenderfoot **Mrs J. S. Mason**

Assistant Trainer: Mr Peter W. Mason

Amateur: Mr Peter Mason.

364 MR ROBIN MATHEW, Burford
Postal: **Church Farm, Little Barrington, Burford, Oxfordshire, OX18 4TE**
Contacts: **PHONE (01451) 844311 MOBILE (07960) 990037**

1 DOODLE DANDY (IRE), 5, b m Starspangledbanner (AUS)—Grid Lock (IRE) **R. Mathew**
2 EMPEROR COMMODOS, 11, b g Midnight Legend—Theme Arena **R. Mathew**
3 SO HOITY TOITY, 4, ch f Harbour Watch (IRE)—Dignify (IRE) **R. Mathew**

Conditional: Richie Condon. **Amateur:** Mr Alan King.

365 MISS JANE MATHIAS, Llancarfan
Postal: **Crosstown, Llancarfan, Vale of Glamorgan, CF62 3AD**
Contacts: **MOBILE (07779) 382727**

1 DEFINATELY VINNIE, 8, ch g Vinnie Roe (IRE)—Sohapara **Mrs S. E. Mathias**

366 MR G. C. MAUNDRELL, Marlborough
Postal: Ogbourne Down, Ogbourne St Andrew, Marlborough, Wilts
Contacts: **PHONE (01672) 841202**

1 **DELINEATE (IRE)**, 9, b m Definite Article—New Line (IRE) **G. C. Maundrell**
2 **FLEUR DU POMMIER**, 5, br m Apple Tree (FR)—Jersey Countess (IRE) **G. C. Maundrell**
3 **TAMBURA**, 8, b m Tamure (IRE)—Singing Cottage **G. C. Maundrell**

Amateur: Mr Z. Baker.

367 MR PHILIP MCBRIDE, Newmarket
Postal: **Exeter House Stables, 33 Exeter Road, Newmarket, Suffolk, CB8 8LP**
Contacts: **PHONE/FAX (01638) 667841 MOBILE (07929) 265711**

1 **BLUFF CRAG**, 5, b g Canford Cliffs (IRE)—Camp Riverside (USA) **Mr P. S. Thompson**
2 **BROUGHTONS STORY**, 4, b g Royal Applause—News Desk **Broughton Thermal Insulations**
3 **CLAIRE'S SECRET**, 4, ch f Sakhee's Secret—Akathea **Mr Howard J. Cooke & Mr P. J. McBride**
4 **RITE TO REIGN**, 7, b g Tiger Hill (IRE)—Magical Cliche (USA) **Maelor Racing**
5 **ZACK MAYO**, 4, b g Air Chief Marshal (IRE)—White Wedding (IRE) **Mrs Sarah Hamilton & Mr Chris Budgett 1**

THREE-YEAR-OLDS
6 **BOND STREET BEAU**, ch g Dandy Man (IRE)—Loveleaves **Mr Chris Budgett & Mr P J McBride**
7 **IMAGE**, b f Sepoy (AUS)—The Terrier **Mrs R. J. Mitchell**
8 **MANDARIN PRINCESS**, b f Vale of York (IRE)—Little China **Mr Ian Pattle & P J McBride**
9 **ONEFOOTINPARADISE**, b f Footstepsinthesand—Sancai (USA) **PM Racing & P J McBride**
10 **PRISCILLA'S DREAM**, ch f Bated Breath—Be Free **Mr Chris Massie & Partners**
11 **RUBY'S GEM**, b f Havana Gold (IRE)—News Desk **Mrs Jacqui Barrs & P J McBride**

TWO-YEAR-OLDS
12 Br gr f 29/3 Lethal Force (IRE)—Falling Angel (Kylian (USA)) **Mr S. Agodino**
13 B f 3/3 Mayson—Handsome Molly (Halling (USA)) (6666) **Ten Fools & A Horse & Partner**
14 B f 29/2 Camacho—Heeby Jeeby (Lawman (FR)) (11000) **The Narc Partnership**

Other Owners: Mrs J. Barrs, Mr J. W. Blake, Mr C. M. Budgett, Mr A. D. Bunce, Mr G. P. Chapman, Mr H. J. Cooke, N. L. Davies, Mrs S. Hamilton, Mr D. L. Jackson, Mr C. Massie, P. J. McBride, Mr I. J. Pattle, Pmracing (Uk) Ltd, Mr R. Wilson.

368 MR DONALD MCCAIN, Cholmondeley
Postal: D McCain Racing Ltd, Bankhouse, Cholmondeley, Malpas, Cheshire, SY14 8AL
Contacts: **PHONE (01829) 720352/720351 MOBILE (07903) 066194**
E-MAIL info@donaldmccain.co.uk WEBSITE www.donaldmccain.co.uk

1 **ALWAYS DU CERISIER (FR)**, 5, b g Apsis—Tyr Elissa (FR) **Mr P. J. Byrne**
2 **ARCTIC DESTINATION (IRE)**, 7, b g Dubai Destination (USA)—Arctic Scale (IRE) **T. G. Leslie**
3 **ASKAMORE DARSI (IRE)**, 9, b g Darsi (FR)—Galamear **Deva Racing Darsi Partnership**
4 **BALLASALLA (IRE)**, 6, br g Presenting—Papoose (IRE) **Mr T. J. Hemmings**
5 **BANRION SCAIRP (IRE)**, 5, b m Scorpion (IRE)—Pairfree **Mr P J P Byrne & Mrs L E Byrne**
6 **BEACH BREAK**, 4, b g Cacique (IRE)—Wemyss Bay **Mr G. E. Fitzpatrick**
7 **BIRCH BANK**, 5, b g Multiplex—Dolly Duff **Birkdale Bloodstock**
8 **BIRCH VALE (IRE)**, 6, br m Presenting—Oscar Rebel (IRE) **Tim & Miranda Johnson**
9 **BLACK JACK ROVER (IRE)**, 9, b g Vinnie Roe (IRE)—Kilgefin Tina (IRE) **Deva Racing Black Jack Partnership**
10 **BREEZEMOUNT (IRE)**, 8, b g Flemensfirth (USA)—Hep To The Jive (FR) **D. R. McCain**
11 **CHARACTER ONESIE (IRE)**, 6, b g Dark Angel (IRE)—Flame Keeper (IRE) **Aykroyd & Sons Limited**
12 **CHICAGO LADY (IRE)**, 7, b m Stowaway—Gemmeus (IRE) **D. R. McCain**
13 **CHTI BALKO (FR)**, 6, br g Balko (FR)—Ina Scoop (FR) **Mr D. Carrington**
14 **CLASSIC IMPACT (IRE)**, 6, b m Witness Box (USA)—Tanya Thyne (IRE) **Mr T. J. Hemmings**
15 **CLONDAW DRAFT (IRE)**, 10, b g Shantou (USA)—Glen Ten (IRE) **T. G. Leslie**
16 **CLONDAW KAEMPFER (IRE)**, 10, b g Oscar (IRE)—Gra-Bri (IRE) **T Leslie & D Gorton**
17 **COUSIN OSCAR (IRE)**, 6, b g Oscar (IRE)—On The Jetty (IRE) **T. G. Leslie**
18 **COWSLIP**, 9, b m Tobougg (IRE)—Forsythia **Mrs I. I. Plumb**
19 **CRAIG STAR (IRE)**, 8, b g Craigsteel—Different Dee (IRE) **Hale Racing Limited**
20 **CULMINATION**, 6, b g Beat Hollow—Apogee **Tim & Miranda Johnson**
21 **DANCEINTOTHELIGHT**, 11, gr g Dansili—Kali **Mrs S. K. McCain**

MR DONALD MCCAIN - Continued

22 **DARK CONFIDANT (IRE)**, 5, b g Royal Applause—Sleek Gold **D. R. McCain**
23 **DARK SUNSET (IRE)**, 7, b m Scorpion (IRE)—Wilmott's Fancy **Penketh & Sankey Jech Racing Club 1**
24 **DEAR SIRE (FR)**, 6, gr g Al Namix (FR)—Polismith (FR) **Green Day Racing**
25 **DERINTOHER YANK (IRE)**, 7, b g Dubai Destination (USA)—
                                                    Anns Present **Don't Tell The Wife Racing Ltd P'Ship**
26 **DERRYNANE (IRE)**, 7, b g Oscar (IRE)—Tessano Queen (IRE) **T. G. Leslie**
27 **DIAMONDS A DANCING**, 4, ch g Delta Dancer—Zing **Mrs S. K. McCain**
28 **FAIR HIT**, 4, b g Fair Mix (IRE)—Double Hit **Dr G. M. Thelwall Jones**
29 **FEDERICI**, 9, b g Overbury (IRE)—Vado Via **Mr J. M. Glews**
30 **FIN AND GAME (IRE)**, 6, b g Oscar (IRE)—Miss Cilla (IRE) **T. G. Leslie**
31 **FIT FOR FIFTY**, 6, ch g Lucarno (USA)—Just For Jean (IRE) **Don't Tell The Wife Racing Limited**
32 **FLEMENS STORY (IRE)**, 7, b g Flemensfirth (USA)—Amelia Earhart (IRE) **T. G. Leslie**
33 **FREDDIES PORTRAIT (IRE)**, 9, gr g Portrait Gallery (IRE)—Phara (IRE) **T. G. Leslie**
34 **FRONT AT THE LAST (IRE)**, 8, b g Golan (IRE)—Kilgefin Tina (IRE) **Aykroyd & Sons Limited**
35 **GOLDEN INVESTMENT (IRE)**, 9, b g Gold Well—Mangan Pet (IRE) **T. G. Leslie**
36 **GOOD TRADITION (IRE)**, 7, b g Pivotal—Token Gesture (IRE) **Mr C. D. Stock**
37 **GRAY DAY (IRE)**, 7, gr g Daylami (IRE)—Carrigeen Diamond (IRE) **Dr G. M. Thelwall Jones**
38 **HANDY HOLLOW (IRE)**, 5, ch g Beat Hollow—Hesperia **Donald McCain Racing Club**
39 **HANNA HVAR**, 4, b f Pour Moi (IRE)—Visanilla (IRE) **Mr M. Jones**
40 5, B m Black Sam Bellamy (IRE)—Harringay **Mr B. J. Richardson**
41 **HENRY'S JOY (IRE)**, 5, b g Craigsteel—Shocona (IRE) **T. G. Leslie**
42 **HILLS OF DUBAI (IRE)**, 9, ch g Dubai Destination (USA)—Mowazana (IRE) **T. G. Leslie**
43 **HIT AND RUN (IRE)**, 6, b g Getaway (GER)—Arrive In Style (IRE) **Birkdale Bloodstock**
44 4, B f Beat Hollow—Holme Rose **T. G. Leslie**
45 **INK MASTER (IRE)**, 8, b g Whitmore's Conn (USA)—Welsh Connection (IRE) **Green Day Racing**
46 **INNISCASTLE LAD**, 6, b g Kyllachy—Glencal **Mrs B. E. McCain**
47 **IRISH HAWKE (IRE)**, 6, b g Montjeu (IRE)—Ahdaab (USA) **Sarah & Wayne Dale 1**
48 **IT'S GRAND (IRE)**, 5, b g Westerner—Calomeria **D. R. McCain**
49 **JARDIN DES PLANTES (FR)**, 8, ch g High Rock—Dear Marianne (FR) **Mrs S. K. McCain**
50 **KATACHENKO (IRE)**, 9, b g Kutub (IRE)—Karalee (FR) **Mr T. J. Hemmings**
51 **KILRONAN CASTLE**, 7, ch g Indian River (FR)—Greatest Friend (IRE) **Mr P. J. Byrne**
52 **KILTORMER (IRE)**, 6, b m Presenting—Lady Hillingdon **Donald McCain Racing Club**
53 **KNOCK HOUSE (IRE)**, 9, ch g Old Vic—Lady's Gesture (IRE) **T. G. Leslie**
54 **KNOCKROBIN (IRE)**, 7, b g Robin des Pres (FR)—Tudor Style (IRE) **Deva Racing Knockrobin Partnership**
55 **KNOW YOUR NAME**, 7, ch g Halling (USA)—Lady Agnes **Livvys Racing Group**
56 **LASTBUTNOTLEAST (IRE)**, 8, ch m Flemensfirth (USA)—Lakil Princess (IRE) **Sarah Leslie & Beryl McCain**
57 **LITTLE STEVIE**, 6, b g Overbury (IRE)—Candy's Room (IRE) **Mr J. M. Glews**
58 **LOFGREN**, 7, b g Multiplex—Sherry Darling (IRE) **Mr J. M. Glews**
59 **LOUGH DERG JEWEL (IRE)**, 7, b g Oscar (IRE)—River Valley Lady (IRE) **Mrs A. E. Strang Steel**
60 **MAHLER LAD (IRE)**, 8, b g Mahler—Sister Merenda (IRE) **T. G. Leslie**
61 **MAN LOOK**, 6, b g Nayef (USA)—Charlecote (IRE) **Mr M. J. Taylor**
62 **MIDDLEBROW (IRE)**, 7, b g Oscar (IRE)—O What A Girl (IRE) **T. G. Leslie**
63 **MIDNIGHT WALK (IRE)**, 8, b m Oscar (IRE)—Lady Belvedere (IRE) **Graham & Carole Worsley**
64 **MO CHAILIN (IRE)**, 7, b m Milan—Consultation (IRE) **Mrs Sarah Leslie & Mr D. McCain Jnr**
65 **MOVE TO THE GROOVE (IRE)**, 8, b g Catcher In The Rye (IRE)—Valley of Love (IRE) **D. R. McCain**
66 **MR MCGO (IRE)**, 7, b g Touch of Land (FR)—La Principal (IRE) **Mr J. M. Glews**
67 **NEFYN BAY**, 9, b g Overbury (IRE)—So Cloudy **Tim & Miranda Johnson**
68 **OFCOURSEIWILL (IRE)**, 6, b g Publisher (USA)—Camden Princess (IRE) **Mr N. Hartley**
69 **OUR DANCING DANDY (IRE)**, 8, b g Scorpion (IRE)—Woodsia **Deva Racing Scorpion Partnership**
70 **OUR DELBOY**, 6, gr g Multiplex—Dawn's Della **K. Benson**
71 **PARIYAN (FR)**, 6, b g Sinndar (IRE)—Pink And Red (USA) **D. R. McCain**
72 **PASTORAL MUSIC**, 5, b g Pastoral Pursuits—Jasmeno **D. R. McCain**
73 **PERFECT POISON (IRE)**, 10, b g Vinnie Roe (IRE)—
                                                    Noddys Confusion (IRE) **Mr John Gwynne & Mr D. McCain Jnr**
74 **PINCH OF GINGER (IRE)**, 7, ch g Golden Lariat—Espiritu Santo (IRE) **First Serve Solutions Ltd**
75 **PRINCE KHURRAM**, 8, b g Nayef (USA)—Saree **T. G. Leslie**
76 **PRINCESS MONONOKE (IRE)**, 7, b m Oscar (IRE)—Grande Solitaire (FR) **Donald McCain Racing Club**
77 **ROBERT DE BRUCE (IRE)**, 7, b g Brian Boru—Have At It (IRE) **Donald McCain Racing Club**
78 **ROCKALZARO (FR)**, 6, gr g Balko (FR)—Royale Wheeler (FR) **First Serve Solutions Ltd**
79 **SAME CIRCUS (IRE)**, 7, b m Brian Boru—Curragh Orpen (IRE) **Penketh & Sankey Jech Racing Club 1**
80 **SAN PIETRO (IRE)**, 10, b g Poliglote—Sainte Berinne (FR) **Mrs A. M. Lees-Jones**
81 **SEALOUS SCOUT (IRE)**, 10, b g Old Vic—Hirayna (IRE) **T. G. Leslie**
82 **SEAN BAN (IRE)**, 8, b g Flemensfirth (USA)—Galingale (IRE) **Mr M. J. Taylor**
83 **SECRET ESCAPE (IRE)**, 6, ch m Getaway (GER)—Portorosa (USA) **M Four Properties Partnership**
84 4, B f Multiplex—Seedless **R. Kent**

MR DONALD MCCAIN - Continued

85 SHANTALUZE (IRE), 6, b g Shantou (USA)—Nut Touluze (IRE) **Deva Racing Cheltenham Syndicate**
86 SNOUGAR (IRE), 5, b g Arakan (USA)—Thorbella **Tim & Miranda Johnson**
87 SONIC (IRE), 5, b g Vinnie Roe (IRE)—Bella's Bury **Special Piping Materials Ltd**
88 SPIN THE COIN (IRE), 5, b g Witness Box (USA)—Kempinski (IRE) **Mrs S. C. Leslie**
89 STAY IN TOUCH (IRE), 7, b g Touch of Land (FR)—Supreme Dancer (IRE) **Richard & Katherine Gilbert**
90 STONE QUERCUS (IRE), 5, b g Rock of Gibraltar (IRE)—Redglow (IRE) **D. R. McCain**
91 SUPER MAC (IRE), 6, b g Yeats (IRE)—Midnight Flirt (IRE) **Jon Glews & Brendan Richardson**
92 SWASHBUCKLE, 5, b g Dashing Blade—Inhibition **Mr M. J. Taylor**
93 TAILOR TOM (IRE), 6, b g Fruits of Love (USA)—Anfield Lady (IRE) **The Tailor 4**
94 TAWSEEF (IRE), 10, b g Monsun (GER)—Sahool **D. R. McCain**
95 TESTIFY (IRE), 7, b g Witness Box (USA)—Tanya Thyne (IRE) **Mr T. J. Hemmings**
96 THE CHARACTER (IRE), 7, b g Bushranger (IRE)—Operissimo **Aykroyd & Sons Limited**
97 THE CLOCK LEARY (IRE), 10, b g Helissio (FR)—Kiwi Babe **MIG Medical Installations Ltd**
98 THE GREAT GETAWAY (IRE), 6, b g Getaway (GER)—Park Mist (IRE) **Richard & Katherine Gilbert**
99 THE PIERRE LARK (IRE), 8, b g Pierre—Kyle Lark **D. R. McCain**
100 THE SOME DANCE KID (IRE), 5, b g Shantou (USA)—River Rouge (IRE) **The Blue Nuns**
101 THOMAS DO (IRE), 7, b g Flemensfirth (USA)—Loughaderra (IRE) **Deva Racing Persistence Partnership**
102 THYNE FOR GOLD (IRE), 7, b g Robin des Pres (FR)—My Name's Not Bin (IRE) **Livvys Racing Group**
103 TOBOGGAN'S FIRE, 5, b m Firebreak—Toboggan Lady **Grange Park Racing X, Mr T P & D McMahon**
104 TOBOGGAN'S GIFT, 6, b m Major Cadeaux—Toboggan Lady **Mr T. P. McMahon & Mr D. McMahon**
105 TWO JABS, 8, b g Teofilo (IRE)—Red Bravo (USA) **Mr M. J. Taylor**
106 UBALTIOUR (FR), 10, b g Balko (FR)—Ode Antique (FR) **T. G. Leslie**
107 UPPERTOWN PRINCE (IRE), 6, b g Strategic Prince—Tarrawarra (IRE) **T. G. Leslie**
108 UPSETTHEODDS (IRE), 6, b g Oscar (IRE)—Cruella de Vil **Clwydian Connections**
109 VENUE, 8, b g Beat Hollow—Shirley Valentine **David Lockwood & Peter Spencer**
110 VISERION, 6, ch g Tamayuz—Frivolity **Clwydian International**
111 VOLCANIC (FR), 9, br g Al Namix (FR)—Queen of Rock (FR) **Elite Racing Club**
112 WATERLORD, 7, b g Cape Cross (IRE)—Shell Garland (USA) **Mr M. J. Taylor**
113 WAZOWSKI, 9, b g Overbury (IRE)—Malay **D. R. McCain**
114 WELSH BARD (IRE), 9, ch g Dylan Thomas (IRE)—Delphinium (IRE) **George Tobitt & Richard Gurney**
115 WHAT HAPPENS NOW (IRE), 9, b g Dr Massini (IRE)—Euro Burden (IRE) **Deva Racing Dr Massini Partnership**
116 WHATDOESTHEFOXSAY (IRE), 9, ch m Vinnie Roe (IRE)—
She's The One (IRE) **Mrs Sarah Leslie & D McCain Jnr**
117 WHISKEY CHASER (IRE), 10, br g Flemensfirth (USA)—
Cregane Lass (IRE) **Deva Racing Flemensfirth Partnership**
118 WHITEOAK MOLLY, 4, b f Flemensfirth (USA)—Whiteoak (IRE) **Mr B. J. Richardson**
119 WHITEOAK STROLLER, 5, b m Shirocco (GER)—Whiteoak (IRE) **Mr B. J. Richardson**
120 WHITSUNDAYS (IRE), 9, b g Kutub (IRE)—Urdite's Vic (IRE) **Mrs L. Middleton**
121 WILLIAM OF ORANGE, 7, b g Duke of Marmalade (IRE)—Critical Acclaim **T W Johnson & G Maxwell**
122 WITNESS IN COURT (IRE), 11, b g Witness Box (USA)—Inter Alia (IRE) **T. G. Leslie**

THREE-YEAR-OLDS

123 ORMESHER, b g Sir Percy—Marakabei **Sarah & Wayne Dale**
124 THE CLIFF HORSE (IRE), b f Canford Cliffs (IRE)—Ballet School (IRE) **The Horse Watchers**
125 Br gr g Aussie Rules (USA)—Zarkavean **The Shinton Family**

TWO-YEAR-OLDS

126 B f 26/5 Milan—Miss Cilla (IRE) (Shernazar) (2848) **T. G. Leslie**

Other Owners: Mr A. D. Crombie, Mr W. R. Dale, Mrs S. J. Dale, Mr C. Dixon, Mr D. Duncan, Mr N. C. Dunnington, Mr W. A. Eastup, Mr M. Foster, Mrs J. Foster, Mr M. D. Foster, Mr R. P. Gilbert, Mrs K. E. Gilbert, D. M. Gorton, Grange Park Racing X, Mr R. Gurney, Mr R. J. Gwynne, Mr A. J. Hill, Mrs M. Johnson, Mr T. Johnson, Mr G. L. Joynson, Mrs K. F. Kent, Mr S. Kent, Mr F. M. Lockwood, D. J. Lockwood, M Four Properties Ltd, Mr G. Maxwell, Mr T. P. McMahon, Mr D. McMahon, Mr P. J. Mentha, Miss M. Noden, Mr E. Norris, Penketh & Sankey Jech Racing Club, Mr D. Rowe, Mr D. M. Shaw, M. H. Shinton, Mr A. P. Shinton, Mr J. M. Smart, Mr P. J. Spencer, Mr E. T. Surr, G. E. Tobitt, Mrs C. P. Worsley, Mr G. W. Worsley.

Assistant Trainer: Adrian Lane

Conditional: Aaron McGlinchey, Lorcan Murtagh. **Amateur:** Mr Theo Gillard, Miss Ella McCain, Miss Abbie McCain.

369 **MR TIM MCCARTHY, Godstone**
Postal: **Nags Hall Farm, Oxted Road, Godstone, Surrey, RH9 8DB**
Contacts: **PHONE (01883) 740379 MOBILE (07887) 763062**
E-MAIL tim@tdmccarthy.com

1 **ANNABELLA,** 5, b m Approve (IRE)—Ashlinn (IRE) **Mr W. Thornton**
2 **UNDERSTORY (USA),** 11, b g Forestry (USA)—Sha Tha (USA) **Homecroft Wealth Racing & T D McCarthy**
3 **WATER THIEF (USA),** 6, b g Bellamy Road (USA)—Sometime (IRE) **Surrey Racing Club**
4 **WHITE TOWER (IRE),** 4, b g Cape Cross (IRE)—Star Blossom (USA) **T. D. McCarthy**

THREE-YEAR-OLDS

5 **W G GRACE (IRE),** b c Exceed And Excel (AUS)—Ownwan (USA)

Other Owners: Homecroft Wealth Racing, Mrs C. V. McCarthy, Mr B. Pettis, Mr S. J. Piper.

Assistant Trainer: Mrs C.V. McCarthy

370 **MR PHIL MCENTEE, Newmarket**
Postal: **Racefield Stables, Carriageway, Hamilton Road, Newmarket, Suffolk, CB8 7JQ**
Contacts: **PHONE (01638) 662092 FAX (01638) 662092 MOBILE (07802) 663256**

1 **BERNIE'S BOY,** 5, b g Lilbourne Lad (IRE)—Stoney Cove (IRE) **T. D. Johnson**
2 **EMBER'S GLOW,** 4, ch g Sepoy (AUS)—Fading Light **T. D. Johnson**
3 **GENTLEMEN,** 7, ch g Ad Valorem (USA)—Stoney Cove (IRE) **T. D. Johnson**
4 **JUSTICE ROCK,** 5, b g Acclamation—Fashion Rocks (IRE) **Mr S. Jakes**
5 **LONDON (FR),** 5, b g Galileo (IRE)—Altana (USA) **T. D. Johnson**
6 **MALAYSIAN BOLEH,** 8, ch g Compton Place—Orlena (USA) **Miss R. B. McEntee**
7 **PEARL SPECTRE (USA),** 7, ch g Street Cry (IRE)—Dark Sky (USA) **Mr S. Jakes**
8 **RED MOHICAN,** 4, ch f Harbour Watch (IRE)—Magical Cliche (USA) **Eventmaker Racehorses**
9 **SPARE PARTS (IRE),** 4, b g Choisir (AUS)—Grandel **Mr S. Jakes**
10 **SWISS VINNARE,** 4, b g Arabian Gleam—Matilda Peace **Mr S. Jakes**
11 **TASAABOQ,** 7, b g Aqlaam—Seldemosa **Mrs R. L. Baker**

THREE-YEAR-OLDS

12 **CHARLES VANE (IRE),** b g Footstepsinthesand—Fair Adelaide (IRE) **T. D. Johnson**
13 B f Bated Breath—Grand Coral **T. D. Johnson**
14 **MOTHER OF DRAGONS (IRE),** ch f Society Rock (IRE)—Queen O'the Desert (IRE) **Mr S. Jakes**

TWO-YEAR-OLDS

15 **ANGEL DUNDEE,** ch f 31/3 Dunaden (FR)—Angel Cake (IRE) (Dark Angel (IRE))

Other Owners: Mr M. A. Humphris.

371 **MR MURTY MCGRATH, Maidstone**
Postal: **Galway Barn, Kiln Barn Road, East Malling, Kent, ME19 6BG**
Contacts: **PHONE (01732) 840173 MOBILE (07818) 098073**
E-MAIL mjmcgrath@hotmail.com

1 **DR JULIUS NO,** 4, b g Dick Turpin (IRE)—Royal Assent **Gallagher Bloodstock Limited**
2 **REZWAAN,** 11, b g Alhaarth (IRE)—Nasij (USA) **Gallagher Bloodstock Limited**

THREE-YEAR-OLDS

3 B f Champs Elysees—Freya Tricks **Mr R. P. Gallagher**
4 **LADY OF AUTHORITY,** b f Kheleyf (USA)—Miss Authority **Mr R. P. Gallagher**
5 **RAGSTONE RIDGE (FR),** ch g Choisir (AUS)—Almogia (USA) **Gallagher Bloodstock Limited**
6 **RAGSTONE ROAD (IRE),** b c Kodiac—Greenflash **Gallagher Bloodstock Limited**

Assistant Trainer: Heidi McGrath (07795) 178178

372 MRS JEAN MCGREGOR, Milnathort
Postal: **Wester Tillyrie Steading, Milnathort, Kinross-shire, KY13 0RW**
Contacts: PHONE **(01577) 861792 MOBILE (07764) 464299**
E-MAIL **purebred68@hotmail.co.uk**

1 **BURLINGTON BERT (FR)**, 7, b g Califet (FR)—Melhi Sun (FR) **The Good To Soft Firm**
2 **JACKOFHEARTS**, 10, b g Beat Hollow—Boutique **Mr S. Taylor**
3 **SIERRA OSCAR (IRE)**, 6, b g Robin des Champs (FR)—John's Eliza (IRE) **Tillyrie Racing Club**
4 **YORKSTERS PRINCE (IRE)**, 11, b g Beat Hollow—Odalisque (IRE) **Miss A. L. McGregor**

Other Owners: Mr R. Black, Mr M. Cameron, Mr S. Duffy, Mr A. McDonald, Mrs Jean McGregor, Mr J. Pickard, Mr J. Thomson, Mrs Dorothy Thomson.

Jockey (NH): Henry Brooke, Sean Quinlan.

373 MR LUKE MCJANNET, Newmarket
Postal: **Heath View Stables, Hamilton Road, Newmarket, Suffolk, CB8 0NY**
Contacts: PHONE: **(01638) 664505**

1 **AMHERST ROCK**, 4, ch g Exceed And Excel (AUS)—Frigid **Mr J. Ramadhan**
2 **DIANA LADY (CHI)**, 6, gr m Dunkirk (USA)—Lady Kitty Karson (USA) **Mr M. A. M. A. Al Falasi**
3 **OLD FASHIONED (CHI)**, 6, ch g Neko Bay (USA)—Hebrides (CHI) **Mr A. A. Saboosi & Mr M.M. Alamri**
4 **SCARLET THRUSH (IRE)**, 4, b f Kodiac—Reveal The Star (USA) **AlMohamediya Racing**
5 **SPRING OFFENSIVE (IRE)**, 6, b g Iffraaj—Night Sphere (IRE) **Mr J. Ramadhan**

Other Owners: Sheikh N. Al Khalifa, Sheikh N. M. H. Al Khalifa, Mr M. M. Alamri, Mr P. Harper, Mr A. A. Saboosi.

374 MS KAREN MCLINTOCK, Newcastle Upon Tyne
Postal: **The Byerley Stud, Ingoe, Newcastle-Upon-Tyne, NE20 0SZ**
Contacts: PHONE **(01661) 886356 MOBILE (07966) 776710**
E-MAIL **karen.mclintock@equiname.co.uk** WEBSITE **www.karenmclintock.co.uk**

1 **AVENUE OF STARS**, 5, b g Makfi—Clifton Dancer **Mr Alan Lamont & Mr Don Eddy**
2 **DIODORUS (IRE)**, 4, b g Galileo (IRE)—Divine Proportions (USA) **Mr G. Topham**
3 **DUBAWI FIFTY**, 5, b g Dubawi (IRE)—Plethora **Mr & Mrs Paul & Clare Rooney**
4 **EMPEROR SAKHEE**, 8, ch g Sakhee (USA)—Pochard **Mr D. Eddy**
5 **GOOD MAN (IRE)**, 5, ch g New Approach (IRE)—Garden City (FR) **Mr D. Eddy**
6 **GREY MIST**, 4, gr g Mastercraftsman (IRE)—Kekova **Mr Alan Lamont & Mr Brian Chicken**
7 **GURKHA BRAVE (IRE)**, 10, b g Old Vic—Honeyed (IRE) **Mr A. C. Lamont**
8 **GURKHA FRIEND**, 6, b g Showcasing—Parabola **Self Preservation Society & Don Eddy**
9 **JOHN MILTON (IRE)**, 5, b g Poet's Voice—Kelly Nicole (USA) **Self Preservation Society & Don Eddy**
10 **ROCKWOOD**, 7, b g Rock of Gibraltar (IRE)—Hannah Frank (IRE) **Mr I. R. Clements & Dr L. G. Parry**
11 **TAOPIX**, 6, b g Rip Van Winkle (IRE)—
Sinister Ruckus (USA) **Mr Roger Stockdale, Mr Don Eddy, Mr Alan Lamont**
12 **TRINITY STAR (IRE)**, 7, gr g Kheleyf (USA)—Zamiyla (IRE) **Trinity Racing**
13 **WEATHER FRONT (USA)**, 5, ch g Stormy Atlantic (USA)—Kiswahili **Mr Ken Eales & Mr Don Eddy**
14 **ZABEEL STAR (IRE)**, 6, ch g Arcano (IRE)—Deep Winter **The Self Preservation Society**

THREE-YEAR-OLDS

15 **BIG LES (IRE)**, b g Big Bad Bob (IRE)—Love Match **Mr G. R. Stockdale**
16 **BLACK FRIDAY**, b c Equiano (FR)—The Clan Macdonald **Mr A. C. Lamont**
17 **HELLO MY SUNSHINE**, ch c Captain Gerrard (IRE)—Dalmunzie (IRE) **Mr & Mrs Paul & Clare Rooney**
18 **HIGH FORT (IRE)**, b g Acclamation—Barracade (IRE) **Alan Lamont, Ian Clements & Don Eddy**
19 **STOPWATCH**, b g Harbour Watch (IRE)—Almond Branches **Mr A. C. Lamont**

Other Owners: B. Chicken, Mr I. R. Clements, Mr W. Cockcroft, Mr R. Cockcroft, Mr J. Cockcroft, Mr S. Cockcroft, Mr K. F. Eales, K. R. Elliott, Dr L. G. Parry, Mr P. A. Rooney, Mrs C. Rooney, Mr T. J. Whiting.

Assistant Trainer: Donald Eddy

375 | MR GRAEME MCPHERSON, Stow-On-The-Wold
Postal: **Martins Hill, Bledington Road, Stow-on-the-wold, Gloucestershire, GL54 1JH**
Contacts: **PHONE (01451) 830769 MOBILE (07815) 887360**
E-MAIL **info@mcphersonracing.co.uk** WEBSITE **www.mcphersonracing.co.uk**

1 **ALEXANDER THE GREY**, 7, gr g Fair Mix (IRE)—Cadourova (FR) **Mr Howard Burdett/Mr Graeme P. Mcpherson**
2 **AMI DESBOIS (FR)**, 8, b g Dream Well (FR)—Baroya (FR) **EPDS Racing Partnership 12 & Partner**
3 5, B g Robin des Pres (FR)—Another Vodka (IRE) **Mr J. Chamberlain**
4 **BALLINA LADY (IRE)**, 7, b m Royal Storm (IRE)—Tinas Friend **Mr G. P. McPherson**
5 **BENEFICIAL JOE (IRE)**, 8, b b g Beneficial—Joleen (IRE) **Mr & Mrs Paul & Clare Rooney**
6 **BOLDMERE**, 5, b g Multiplex—Pugnacious Lady **W. J. Odell**
7 **CHARLIE COOK (IRE)**, 9, b g Royal Anthem (USA)—Supreme Baloo (IRE) **Mrs K. Peto**
8 **CRANBROOK CAUSEWAY (IRE)**, 6, b g Mohaajir (USA)—Kingarriff Bell (IRE) **Nino's Partnership Ii**
9 **CUIL ROGUE (IRE)**, 10, b g Presenting—Coolshamrock (IRE) **Mr G. P. McPherson**
10 **DAHILLS HILL (IRE)**, 6, br m Mahler—Whites Cross (IRE) **Mr G. P. McPherson**
11 **DAYDREAM AULMES (FR)**, 5, b g Linda's Lad—My Wish Aulmes (FR) **Ms S. A. Howell**
12 **DELIRIOUS LOVE (IRE)**, 6, b g Definite Article—Grangeclare Lark (IRE) **Wildcat Syndicate**
13 **FOLLOW THE SWALLOW (IRE)**, 10, b g Dr Massini (IRE)—Old Chapel (IRE) **Mrs M. M. Gwillam**
14 5, B g Scorpion (IRE)—Fromrussiawithlove **Mr A. N. Clark**
15 **GENEROUS CHIEF (IRE)**, 10, br g Generous (IRE)—Yosna (FR) **The McPherson Racing Partnership**
16 **HARRY HUNT**, 11, b g Bertolini (USA)—Qasirah (IRE) **The Reserved Judgment Partnership**
17 **HEY BILL (IRE)**, 8, b g Indian Danehill (USA)—Grange More (IRE) **H Stephen Smith & Graeme McPherson**
18 **HOLLYWOOD ALL STAR (IRE)**, 9, b g Kheleyf (USA)—Camassina (IRE) **The McPherson Racing Partnership**
19 **IT'S FINE WINE**, 5, b g Multiplex—Reem Two **Mr & Mrs Paul & Clare Rooney**
20 **KAYF BLANCO**, 9, b g Kayf Tara—Land of Glory **Mrs L.Day, Mr H.Burdett & Mr G.McPherson**
21 **LONDONIA**, 6, gr g Paco Boy (IRE)—Snowdrops **EPDS Racing 16 & Partner**
22 **MY CHARITY (IRE)**, 7, b g King's Theatre (IRE)—Benefit Ball (IRE) **Captain McGarry and the Odd Foxes**
23 **NORMAN STANLEY (IRE)**, 6, b g Flemensfirth (USA)—Ballerina Laura (IRE) **Mr G. P. McPherson**
24 **PADDYS RUNNER**, 6, gr g Sir Percy—Frosty Welcome (USA) **Paddys Runner Partnership**
25 **PANDY WELLS**, 9, b m Kayf Tara—Alina Rheinberg (GER) **Mike & Linda Paul**
26 **POPERINGHE GINGER (IRE)**, 5, ch m Beneficial—Masamor (IRE) **The Reserved Judgment Partnership**
27 **RED ADMIRABLE (IRE)**, 12, b g Shantou (USA)—Eimears Pet (IRE) **The McPherson Racing Partnership**
28 **RIO BRAVO (IRE)**, 7, b g Westerner—Diaconate (USA) **Tony & Gillian Allen**
29 **SALLY CAN'T WAIT**, 5, b m Sulamani (IRE)—Kate Hill Dancer (IRE) **Mr G. P. McPherson**
30 **SAMMYLOU (IRE)**, 5, b g Beneficial—Carrigeen Diamond (IRE) **Chris Johnson & Family**
31 **SCOOBY (IRE)**, 7, b g Dubai Destination (USA)—Maggie Howard (IRE) **The Ladies Of Martins Hill**
32 **SERPICO (IRE)**, 7, b g Scorpion (IRE)—Call Her Again (IRE) **Anglia & Wolves**
33 **SHADY GLEN (IRE)**, 9, br g Dr Massini (IRE)—Poppins (IRE) **Mr G. P. McPherson**
34 **SILVA SAMOURAI**, 9, gr g Proclamation (IRE)—Ladykirk **Mrs S Gray, I Gray & G Gray**
35 **SKIPTHECUDDLES (IRE)**, 7, b g Westerner—Autumn Sky (IRE) **TyroneForSam**
36 **SWALEDALE LAD (IRE)**, 11, b g Arakan (USA)—Tadjnama (USA) **Chris Johnson & Friends**
37 **SYMPHONY OF ANGELS**, 6, b g Sulamani (IRE)—Flying Lion **Good Evans Racing Partnership**
38 **TELSON BARLEY (IRE)**, 5, b g Scorpion (IRE)—El Monica (IRE) **Mrs L. Day**
39 **TOUCH OF VELVETT**, 6, gr m Proclamation (IRE)—Rose Bien **Mr H. W. Wheeler**
40 **ZULU DAWN (IRE)**, 4, b g Fame And Glory—Maslam (USA) **Miss J. E. Sherrard**

Other Owners: Mrs G. P. Allen, Mr A. Allen, Mr M. Ball, Mr M. Barnett, Mr H. Burdett, Mr C. G. Burr, Mr R. Cunningham, EPDS Racing Partnership 12, Mr A. M. Elshout, Mr M. Evans, First With Mortgages Limited, Mrs A. J. Forde, Mr J. A. S. Fowke, Mr K. J. P. Gilmore, Mrs S. Gray, Mr I. J. B. Gray, Mr C. N. Johnson, Mr C. F. Little, Mrs S. M. McPherson, Mr K. J. N. Meek, Mrs L. C. Paul, Mr M. R. Paul, Mr J. R. Powell, Mr D. Richardson, Mr G. Rodgers, Mrs C. Rooney, Mr P. A. Rooney, Mr G. P. Sinclair, Miss T. Sloan, H. S. Smith.

Assistant Trainers: Mick Finn, Jodie Mogford

Jockey (NH): Daniel Hiskett, Kielan Woods.

376 | MR MARTYN MEADE, Manton
Postal: **The Manton Estate, Manton, Marlborough, Wiltshire, SN8 4HB**
Contacts: **PHONE (01638) 666100 MOBILE (07879) 891811**
E-MAIL **mmeade@martynmeaderacing.com** WEBSITE **www.martynmeaderacing.com**

1 **CARTOGRAPHER**, 4, b f Henrythenavigator (USA)—Right Answer
2 **CHELSEA LAD (IRE)**, 5, b g Clodovil (IRE)—Yali (IRE)
3 **DOLPHIN VISTA (IRE)**, 5, b g Zoffany (IRE)—Fiordiligi
4 **EMINENT (IRE)**, 4, b c Frankel—You'll Be Mine (USA)

MR MARTYN MEADE - Continued

  5 RAZZMATAZZ, 4, b f Monsieur Bond (IRE)—Tibesti
  6 SOLO HUNTER, 7, b g Sleeping Indian—Night Owl
  7 WILAMINA (IRE), 5, b m Zoffany (IRE)—Tropical Lake (IRE)

THREE-YEAR-OLDS

  8 ACCEPT (IRE), ch c Dawn Approach (IRE)—Aris (IRE)
  9 Ch f Pivotal—Adonesque (IRE)
10 B c Camelot—Brigid (USA)
11 CASCOVA (IRE), b c Casamento (IRE)—Sina Cova (IRE)
12 CHILEAN, b c Iffraaj—Childa (IRE)
13 COMMONWEALTH (IRE), b c Sea The Stars (IRE)—Night Fairy (IRE)
14 ENDLESSLY (IRE), b c Nathaniel (IRE)—What's Up Pussycat (IRE)
15 Ch f Raven's Pass (USA)—Fabia (IRE)
16 B g Style Vendome (FR)—Forewarned (IRE)
17 INFRASTRUCTURE, ch g Raven's Pass (USA)—Foundation Filly
18 LOYAL PROMISE (IRE), b c Teofilo (IRE)—Distorted Promise (USA)
19 MICHAEL CORLEONE (IRE), ch c Declaration of War (USA)—Needles And Pins (IRE)
20 MONOXIDE, b c Galileo (IRE)—Breathe (FR)
21 RAYITA (IRE), b f Raven's Pass (USA)—Minikin (IRE)
22 RISE HALL, b c Frankel—Forever Bond
23 SHIP OF THE FEN, b c Champs Elysees—Ruffled
24 SOCIOLOGIST (FR), ch c Society Rock (IRE)—Fabiola (GER)
25 SOLAR ECHO (IRE), b f Galileo (IRE)—Rose Bonheur
26 Ch f Mastercraftsman (IRE)—Station House (USA)
27 TUM TUM, ch c Dawn Approach (IRE)—Lalectra
28 YAYOON, ch c Dawn Approach (IRE)—Assabiyya (IRE)

TWO-YEAR-OLDS

29 Gr f 15/4 Dark Angel (IRE)—Abeille (IRE) (Alhaarth (IRE)) (24420)
30 AIRWAVES, b f 21/3 Monsieur Bond (IRE)—Forever Bond (Danetime (IRE))
31 Ch c 12/4 Iffraaj—Alabelle (Galileo (IRE)) (29304)
32 B c 22/2 Vale of York (IRE)—Almatlaie (USA) (Elusive Quality (USA)) (20350)
33 Br f 14/5 No Nay Never (USA)—Always A Way (Danehill Dancer (IRE)) (24420)
34 B f 10/3 Zoffany (IRE)—Arcangela (Galileo (USA)) (36630)
35 B c 14/5 Cape Cross (IRE)—Argent du Bois (USA) (Silver Hawk (USA)) (50000)
36 B f 29/3 Slade Power (IRE)—Aris (IRE) (Danroad (AUS))
37 Ch c 20/1 Mastercraftsman (IRE)—Arosa (IRE) (Sadler's Wells (USA)) (32560)
38 Ch f 25/3 Ruler of The World (IRE)—Bold Assumption (Observatory (USA)) (30000)
39 B c 6/5 Dubawi (IRE)—Casual Look (USA) (Red Ransom (USA))
40 Ch f 21/2 Monsieur Bond (IRE)—Chez Cherie (Wolfhound (USA))
41 B c 5/3 Iffraaj—Entre Nous (IRE) (Sadler's Wells (USA)) (38258)
42 FOX VARDY (USA), b c 17/1 Frankel—Dance With Another (IRE) (Danehill Dancer (IRE)) (210000)
43 B c 23/2 Showcasing—Furbelow (Pivotal) (57142)
44 Ch c 14/3 Champs Elysees—Galicuix (Galileo (IRE))
45 B f 10/1 Invincible Spirit (IRE)—Kissable (IRE) (Danehill Dancer (IRE)) (200000)
46 Ch f 4/4 Frankel—Ladies Are Forever (Monsieur Bond (IRE)) (171428)
47 B c 7/4 Havana Gold (IRE)—Luminous Angel (Fantastic Light (USA)) (50000)
48 B c 8/3 Dalakhani (IRE)—Montbretia (Montjeu (IRE)) (19536)
49 B f 27/4 Exceed And Excel (AUS)—Myrine (IRE) (Sadler's Wells (USA)) (22000)
50 B f 25/3 Lawman (FR)—Rising Wind (IRE) (Shirocco (GER)) (29303)
51 B c 10/3 Le Havre (IRE)—Santa Louisia (Highest Honor (FR)) (65120)
52 B c 11/4 Toronado (IRE)—Sparkling Eyes (Lujain (USA)) (34188)
53 B c 7/3 Exceed And Excel (AUS)—Tupelo Honey (IRE) (Sadler's Wells (USA)) (32000)
54 B c 2/4 Maxios—Unaided (Dansili) (40700)
55 Br gr f 29/1 Poet's Voice—White Wedding (IRE) (Green Desert (USA)) (30000)
56 B c 18/4 Acclamation—With Colour (Rainbow Quest (USA)) (63492)

Owners: The Below Reeve Partnership, C Bernick, Mr R C Bond, Canning Downs, Chelsea Thoroughbreds, W S Farish, Haras d'Etreham, S Heider, King Power Racing Co Ltd, Lordship Stud, Mrs John Magnier, P Makin, Mr C J Murfitt, Mr Y Nasib, Mrs Jane Newett, Mrs B V Sangster, Sefton Lodge (Thoroughbred Racing), The Snailwell Stud, Sun Bloodstock SARL, Sir Peter Vela.

Assistant Trainer: Freddie Meade (fmeade@martynmeaderacing.com)

377 **MR NOEL MEADE, Navan**
Postal: **Tu Va, Castletown-Kilpatrick, Navan, Co. Meath, Ireland**
Contacts: **PHONE (00 353) 46 905 4197 FAX (00 353) 46 905 4459 MOBILE (00 353) 87 256 6039**
E-MAIL tuvastables@gmail.com WEBSITE www.noelmeade.com

1 **A GENIE IN ABOTTLE (IRE)**, 7, b g Beneficial—Erkindale Miss (IRE)
2 **ACTIVE FORCE (IRE)**, 5, br g Oscar (IRE)—Terracotta Queen (IRE)
3 **ARCH STANTON (IRE)**, 5, b g Jeremy (USA)—Half-Hitch (USA)
4 **ART OF SECURITY (IRE)**, 8, b g High Chaparral (IRE)—Irish Wedding (IRE)
5 **ART OF SYNERGY (IRE)**, 7, b g Yeats (IRE)—Elizabeth Tudor (IRE)
6 **ATHENEAN (IRE)**, 5, b g Westerner—Cash And New (IRE)
7 **BALISKO (FR)**, 7, b g Day Flight—Ghostaline (FR)
8 5, B g Oscar (IRE)—Ballyknock Present (IRE)
9 **BEHIND THE CURTAIN (IRE)**, 4, br g Curtain Time (IRE)—Veronica's Gift (IRE)
10 **BEL AMI DE SIVOLA (FR)**, 7, b g Network (GER)—Notting Hill (FR)
11 **BILL HICKOK (IRE)**, 4, ch g Tobougg (IRE)—Jungle Jewel (IRE)
12 **BLACK ACE (IRE)**, 7, b g Yeats (IRE)—All Our Blessings (IRE)
13 **BONNY KATE (IRE)**, 8, ch m Beneficial—Peppardstown (IRE)
14 **BRACE YOURSELF (IRE)**, 5, ch g Mahler—Angelica Garnett
15 **BRIODY (IRE)**, 4, b g Azamour (IRE)—Estrelle (GER)
16 **BRONCO BILL (IRE)**, 8, b g Kalanisi (IRE)—Mill Lady (IRE)
17 **BUGSY SIEGEL (IRE)**, 6, b g Jeremy (USA)—Cant Hurry Love
18 **BURGAS (FR)**, 7, b br g Protektor (GER)—Tyrolienne Bleue (FR)
19 **CALICOJACK (IRE)**, 6, b g Beneficial—Ballyoscar (IRE)
20 **CASK MATE (IRE)**, 5, b g Kalanisi (IRE)—Littleton Liberty
21 **CHAMPOLEON (FR)**, 8, gr g Turtle Bowl (IRE)—Trasimene
22 **CHEROKEE BILL**, 7, b g Robin des Champs (FR)—Daizinni
23 **COKEY FLO (IRE)**, 4, br f September Storm (GER)—Outo'theblue (IRE)
24 **COTE TETE (FR)**, 6, b g Coastal Path—Liste En Tete (FR)
25 **CROWN OF THORNS**, 5, ch g Shirocco (GER)—Gaye Sophie
26 **CURLEY BILL (IRE)**, 10, b g Heron Island (IRE)—In Excelsis (GER)
27 **DALY TIGER (FR)**, 5, b g Tiger Groom—Reine Tresor (FR)
28 **DARKEST FLYER (IRE)**, 6, ch g Broadway Flyer (USA)—Dipp In The Dark (IRE)
29 **DE NAME ESCAPES ME (IRE)**, 8, ch g Vinnie Roe (IRE)—Heartlight (IRE)
30 4, Ch g Doyen (IRE)—Dew Drop
31 **DIS DONC (FR)**, 5, b g Kingsalsa (USA)—Skarina (FR)
32 **DISKO (FR)**, 5, gr g Martaline—Nikos Royale (FR)
33 **DREAM CONTI (FR)**, 5, br g Lauro (GER)—Posterite (FR)
34 **FAUGUERNON (FR)**, 4, b g Martaline—I'm Right (USA)
35 **FIRST APPROACH (IRE)**, 5, b g Robin des Champs (FR)—Manhattan Babe (IRE)
36 4, B f Arakan (USA)—First Battle (IRE)
37 **FRANKIEFIVEANGELS (IRE)**, 8, b g Indian River (FR)—Luck's A Lady (IRE)
38 **FREE RANGER (IRE)**, 4, b g Lope de Vega (IRE)—Purple Tigress
39 **GETAWAY KID (IRE)**, 6, ch g Getaway (GER)—Bambootcha (IRE)
40 **GRECO ROMAIN (FR)**, 7, b g Martaline—De Haute Lutte (USA)
41 **GUIDED BY YOU (IRE)**, 5, b g Getaway (GER)—Black Ouzel (IRE)
42 **HALF THE ODDS (IRE)**, 6, b m Flemensfirth (USA)—Technohead (IRE)
43 **HE'S NO MOLLY (IRE)**, 5, b g Beneficial—Violet Hill (IRE)
44 4, Ch g Mountain High—Heather Sue (IRE)
45 **HELL OR HIGH WATER (IRE)**, 5, ch g Robin des Champs (FR)—Boragh Thyme (IRE)
46 **HEROESANDVILLAINS**, 5, b g Beneficial—Keys Pride (IRE)
47 **IAMASTARTOO (IRE)**, 5, ch m Well Chosen—Lobinstown Girl (IRE)
48 **ICE COLD SOUL (IRE)**, 5, b g Stowaway—Western Whisper (IRE)
49 **IMPATIENT PARTNER (IRE)**, 5, b g Gold Well—Madmoiselle Etoile (IRE)
50 **ITSALLHAPPENING (IRE)**, 7, ch g Presenting—Niamh's Dream (IRE)
51 **JAKOBY (IRE)**, 4, b g Frozen Fire (GER)—Morning Rise (GER)
52 **KAGNEY (IRE)**, 7, br g Kalanisi (IRE)—Clondalee (IRE)
53 **KAMIL (GER)**, 5, ch g Sholokhov (IRE)—Kastoria (GER)
54 **KEARNEY**, 4, ch g Medicean—Moonlight Mystery
55 **LADYSINGSTHEBLUES (IRE)**, 6, b m Robin des Champs (FR)—Ghillie's Bay (IRE)
56 **LAVERTEEN (FR)**, 7, b g Laveron—Manson Teene (FR)
57 **LE MARTALIN (FR)**, 7, ch g Martaline—Hembra (FR)
58 **LILL SMITH (IRE)**, 5, b m Gold Well—Vivachi (IRE)
59 **LORD IN RED (GER)**, 6, ch g Noroit (GER)—Lady In Red (GER)
60 **MAD CAREW (IRE)**, 6, b g Getaway (GER)—Babygotback (IRE)
61 **MAJOR DESTINATION (IRE)**, 7, b g Dubai Destination (USA)—Clara Allen (IRE)

MR NOEL MEADE - Continued

62 MINELLA FAIR (IRE), 7, b g Flemensfirth (USA)—Bell Walks Run (IRE)
63 MOMUS (IRE), 5, b g Touch of Land (FR)—Accordion To Bob (IRE)
64 MONKSLAND (IRE), 11, b g Beneficial—Cush Jewel (IRE)
65 MONSTROSITY (IRE), 6, b g Mahler—Little Pearl (IRE)
66 MOULIN A VENT, 6, gr g Sagamix (FR)—Bahia Blanca (FR)
67 MOYROSS, 7, b g Kayf Tara—Dancing Dasi (IRE)
68 MUJADEL (FR), 5, b g Sinndar (IRE)—Pimprenelle
69 NARCISSISTIC (IRE), 6, b g Robin des Champs (FR)—Night Therapy (IRE)
70 4, B f Winged Love (IRE)—Nice Idea (IRE)
71 NIVEN (IRE), 5, b g Elusive Pimpernel (USA)—Ginger Lily (IRE)
72 PAT'S PICK (IRE), 4, b g Shantou (USA)—Lady Lenson (IRE)
73 RAGIN CAJUN (IRE), 5, b g Kalanisi (IRE)—Dipp In The Dark (IRE)
74 RAYNA JAYMES (IRE), 6, b m Darsi (FR)—Arts Theater (IRE)
75 RED JACK (IRE), 5, b g Mahler—Hollygrove Bonnie (IRE)
76 ROAD TO RESPECT (IRE), 7, ch g Gamut (IRE)—Lora Lady (IRE)
77 ROAD TO RICHES (IRE), 11, b g Gamut (IRE)—Bellora (IRE)
78 ROSENCRANTZ (IRE), 4, ch g Flemensfirth (USA)—Miss Brandywell (IRE)
79 ROSERIVER HAS (FR), 5, gr g Astarabad (USA)—Vaibuscar Has (FR)
80 RUSSIAN BILL (IRE), 8, b g Kalanisi (IRE)—Littleton Liberty
81 SCHOOL BOY HOURS (IRE), 5, b g Presenting—Trinity Alley (IRE)
82 SEEYOUINVINNYS (IRE), 4, b g Carlotamix (FR)—Deploy Or Die (IRE)
83 SHE'S A STAR (IRE), 6, br m Well Chosen—Lobinstown Girl (IRE)
84 SHEISDIESEL, 4, ch f Harbour Watch (IRE)—Rockme Cockney
85 SNOW FALCON (IRE), 8, b g Presenting—Flocon de Neige (IRE)
86 STONEFORD (IRE), 7, b g Beneficial—Hester Hall (IRE)
87 TECUMSEH SHERMAN (IRE), 6, gr g King's Theatre (IRE)—Drumrawn Lass (IRE)
88 TEXAS JACK (IRE), 12, b g Curtain Time (IRE)—Sailors Run (IRE)
89 THE CADDY ROSE (IRE), 4, br f Presenting—Las Princess (IRE)
90 THE CHOSEN APACHE (IRE), 5, b m Well Chosen—Apache Rose (IRE)
91 THE COMEDIOLOGIST, 7, b g Fair Mix (IRE)—Cashmere Lady
92 THE RORY STORY (IRE), 7, b g Flemensfirth (USA)—Phardester (IRE)
93 THREE QUEENS (IRE), 6, b m Getaway (GER)—Miss Platinum (IRE)
94 TIGER SAM (IRE), 8, ch g Beneficial—Colleen Donn
95 TIPP TOE (IRE), 5, b g Milan—Famous Lady (IRE)
96 TRAPPIST MONK (IRE), 5, b g Beneficial—Cush Jewel (IRE)
97 TULSA JACK (IRE), 9, b g Urban Ocean (FR)—Jessica's Pet (IRE)
98 TURFMANS DAUGHTER (IRE), 8, b m Flemensfirth (USA)—Atomic Winner (IRE)
99 UNE LAVANDIERE (FR), 7, b m Laveron—Nouvelle Donne (FR)
100 VALDIEU (FR), 5, b g Diamond Boy (FR)—Vamuna (FR)
101 VERSE OF LOVE (FR), 4, b g Diamond Green (FR)—Verseka (FR)
102 VILLAGE MYSTIC (FR), 7, b br g Saint des Saints (FR)—Mistica (FR)
103 VISION D'ETE (FR), 4, b g Vision d'etat (FR)—Vuelta Al Ruedo (FR)
104 WAXIES DARGLE, 9, b g Sakhee (USA)—Cup of Love (USA)
105 WHERE EAGLES DARE (IRE), 5, b g Mahler—Tariana (IRE)
106 WINGS OF AN EAGLE (IRE), 4, b f Winged Love (IRE)—Like A Bolt (IRE)
107 WOUNDED WARRIOR (IRE), 9, b g Shantou (USA)—Sparkling Sword
108 YOUNG TED (IRE), 4, b g Fame And Glory—Last of Many (IRE)

THREE-YEAR-OLDS

109 ART OF AMERICA, br g American Post—Marigay's Magic
110 ART OF UNITY, ch g Mazameer (IRE)—Vintage Steps (IRE)
111 COCOHULABABY (IRE), ch f Casamento (IRE)—Rockahoolababy (IRE)
112 MILLS ON TOUR (IRE), b f Lovelace—Headford View (IRE)
113 B g Canford Cliffs (IRE)—Vivachi (IRE)

TWO-YEAR-OLDS

114 B gr f 27/2 Intikhab (USA)—Ghost of A Girl (IRE) (Verglas (IRE)) (4883)
115 B g 16/4 Born To Sea (IRE)—Glorious Melody (FR) (Dylan Thomas (IRE)) (6918)
116 Br c 19/3 Dawn Approach (IRE)—Hairpin (USA) (Bernardini (USA)) (11396)
117 B c 4/5 Canford Cliffs (IRE)—Hollow Talk (Beat Hollow) (8546)
118 B f 5/4 Canford Cliffs (IRE)—Vivachi (IRE) (Red Ransom (USA))

Assistant Trainers: Paul Cullen, Damien McGillick, Emma Connolly.

MR NOEL MEADE - Continued

Jockey (NH): Sean Flanagan, Jonathan Moore. **Conditional:** Jorden Benson, Barry Reynolds. **Amateur:** Miss Nina Carberry, Mr Paddy Magee.

378 MR NEIL MECHIE, Leyburn
Postal: **55 The Springs, Middleham, Leyburn, North Yorkshire, DL8 4RB**

1 BEAUTIFUL MIX, 6, b m Fair Mix (IRE)—Just Beautiful (FR) **The Kerr and Mechie Families**
2 STEEL RUN, 6, gr g Sagamix (FR)—Safari Run (IRE) **N. Mechie**
3 TOMMY O'DWYER (IRE), 9, b g Milan—Always Present (IRE) **Mrs L. E. Mechie**
4 WANDAOVER, 6, b m Overbury (IRE)—Programme Girl (IRE) **N. Mechie**

379 MR BRIAN MEEHAN, Manton
Postal: **Trainer did not wish details of his string to appear**

380 MR DAVID MENUISIER, Pulborough
Postal: **Shinco Racing Limited, Coombelands Stables, Coombelands Lane, Pulborough, West Sussex, RH20 1BP**
Contacts: **MOBILE 07876 674095**
E-MAIL david@dmhorseracing.com WEBSITE www.dmhorseracing.com

1 CONTRAPPOSTO (IRE), 4, b c Cacique (IRE)—Interim Payment (USA) **Mr C. A. Washbourn**
2 PSYCHOTIC, 5, b g Nayef (USA)—Palatial **Mr C. A. Washbourn**
3 RAINBOW RISING (FR), 4, b f Henrythenavigator (USA)—Rainbow Goddess **Mr C. A. Washbourn**
4 SINFONIETTA (FR), 6, b g Sinndar (IRE)—Final Whistle (IRE) **Mr C. A. Washbourn**
5 SLUNOVRAT (FR), 7, b br g Astronomer Royal (USA)—Slewmamba (FR) **Shinco Racing Limited**
6 THE BEAR CAN FLY, 4, b f Pastoral Pursuits—Torrecilla **The Mrs S. Frost, Mrs A.Hollis & Mr W.Kenny**
7 THUNDERING BLUE (USA), 5, gr g Exchange Rate (USA)—Relampago Azul (USA) **Mr C. A. Washbourn**

THREE-YEAR-OLDS
8 ATALANTA'S BOY, b c Paco Boy (IRE)—Affirmatively **Mrs M. J. Borton**
9 BATTLE OF ISSUS (IRE), b c Declaration of War (USA)—Athenian Way (IRE) **Mr C. A. Washbourn**
10 BUXLOW BELLE (FR), gr f Authorized (IRE)—Steel Woman (IRE) **Mrs A. K. Oldfield**
11 CACOPHONOUS, b c Cacique (IRE)—Zee Zee Gee **Mr C. A. Washbourn**
12 CHANSON DE LA MER (IRE), b f Le Havre (IRE)—Easy To Sing **Mr S. K. McPhee**
13 CHIAVE DI VOLTA, ch c Intello (GER)—Silca Chiave **Mr C. A. Washbourn**
14 DANCETARIA (FR), b c Redoute's Choice (AUS)—Bal de La Rose (IRE) **Mr C. A. Washbourn**
15 DESERT TRIP (FR), b g Fuisse (FR)—Sea Life (FR) **M. H. Watt**
16 HISTORY WRITER (IRE), b c Canford Cliffs (IRE)—Abhasana (IRE) **Clive Washbourn & Partner**
17 LADY MERGANSER, b f Dick Turpin (IRE)—The Lady Lapwing **Felicity Veasey Star Partnership**
18 LUCKY KISSES (FR), b f Muhtathir—Kiss My Heart **Wedgewood Estates**
19 NUITS ST GEORGES (IRE), ch c Mount Nelson—Twelfth Night (IRE) **Boy George Partnership**
20 PLACE DES VOSGES (IRE), b f Rip Van Winkle (IRE)—Red Blossom (USA) **Shinco Racing Limited**
21 SEA THE SUNRISE, ro f Sea The Stars (IRE)—Tequila Sunrise **Wright, Macdonald, Creed & Creed**
22 STAR ATTRACTION (FR), b f Orpen (USA)—Heaven **Wedgewood Estates**
23 STRAWBERRY LACE, b f Sea The Stars (IRE)—Crying Lightening (IRE) **Mr C. A. Washbourn**
24 VINTAGER, ro c Mastercraftsman (IRE)—White And Red (IRE) **Gail Brown Racing (VIII)**

TWO-YEAR-OLDS
25 MIGRATION (IRE), b c 13/3 Alhebayeb (IRE)—
Caribbean Ace (IRE) (Red Clubs (IRE)) (72000) **Gail Brown Racing (ix)**
26 MOUSQUETAIRE (FR), b c 20/1 Anodin (IRE)—Cavaliere (FR) (Traditionally (USA)) (5698) **One For All Racing**

Other Owners: Mr L. Arstall, Mrs D. J. Arstall, Mr S. A. Ashley, Mrs L. Bullen-Smith, Mrs H. G. Clinch, J. R. Creed, Mrs S. Frost, Mrs A. Hollis, Mr W. Kenny, Mr J. J. Lancaster, Mr A. T. Macdonald, Macdonald & Creed, Mrs F. A. Veasey, Mr C. W. Wright, Mr R.J Wright.

381 MISS REBECCA MENZIES, Sedgefield
Postal: **Howe Hills, Sedgefield, Stockton-On-Tees, Cleveland, TS21 2HF**
Contacts: **MOBILE (07843) 169217**
E-MAIL rebeccaelizabeth.menzies@hotmail.co.uk   WEBSITE www.rebeccamenziesracing.com
TWITTER: @Rebeccaemenzies

1 **ALL HAIL CAESAR (IRE)**, 4, b g Nathaniel (IRE)—Ragiam (ITY) **The Top Silk Syndicate**
2 **ANIMATED HERO**, 5, b g Sakhee's Secret—Society (IRE) **Mr D. H. Slater**
3 **ANNE'S VALENTINO**, 8, b m Primo Valentino (IRE)—Annie's Gift (IRE) **The Magic Circle**
4 5, B h Malinas (GER)—Annie's Gift (IRE) **The Magic Circle**
5 **AZERT DE COEUR (FR)**, 8, b g Tiger Groom—Eden de Coeur (FR) **Gay & Peter Hartley**
6 **BERTUZZI**, 4, b g Mawatheeq (USA)—Camina **Heather Calzini**
7 **BLACK KETTLE (IRE)**, 8, b g Robin des Pres (FR)—Whistful Suzie (IRE) **Mr D. H. Slater**
8 **CALYPSO STORM (IRE)**, 7, b g Trans Island—Valin Thyne (IRE) **John Dance & Partner**
9 **CAPTAIN MOWBRAY**, 7, ch g Shami—Some Like It Hot **Premier Racing Partnerships**
10 **CELTIC ARTISAN (IRE)**, 7, ch g Dylan Thomas (IRE)—Perfectly Clear (USA) **EPDS Racing Partnership 11**
11 **CLEOFE**, 4, ch f Shirocco (GER)—Agnese **Heather Calzini**
12 **DULCE PANEM (FR)**, 6, ch g Panis (USA)—Danissima (FR) **Tony & Pauline Weight**
13 **ELZAWAY (IRE)**, 5, b m Stowaway—Elzahann (IRE) **Mr I. A. Todd & West Coast Racing**
14 **FAIR SHERIFF**, 4, gr f Fair Mix (IRE)—Sheriff's Falcon (IRE) **Falcon's Line**
15 **FALCOS (FR)**, 6, ch g Falco (USA)—Olvera (IRE) **Premier Racing Partnerships**
16 **GENRES**, 6, b g Champs Elysees—Musical Horizon (USA) **Liz Dixon & Shelagh Fagen**
17 **GEORDIE GEORGE (IRE)**, 6, b g Kodiac—Trika **Fletcher, Outhart, Moran & Maddison**
18 **HALCYON DAYS**, 9, b g Generous (IRE)—Indian Empress **Centaur Racing Club**
19 **LADY CLITICO (IRE)**, 7, b m Bushranger (IRE)—Villa Nova (IRE) **The Extra Time Partnership**
20 **LANDING NIGHT (IRE)**, 6, b g Kodiac—Night Delight (IRE) **Mr J. E. Dance**
21 **LEONARD THOMAS**, 8, b g Singspiel (IRE)—Monawara (IRE) **Mr W. A. Robinson**
22 **MY CHEROKEE**, 4, b f Sleeping Indian—Another Paris **Mr J. D. Spensley & Mrs M. A. Spensley**
23 **NORTONTHORPELEGEND (IRE)**, 8, b g Midnight Legend—Tanit **Miss M. D. Myco**
24 **PAIN AU CHOCOLAT (FR)**, 7, b g Enrique—Clair Chene (FR) **Mike and Eileen Newbould**
25 **PANTOMIME (IRE)**, 6, gr m Mastercraftsman (IRE)—Dama'a (IRE) **EPDS Racing & Partner**
26 **PEAK TIME**, 5, ch g Distant Peak (IRE)—Ruby Redwing **J. Wade**
27 **PORTO DU SUD (FR)**, 5, gr g Lord du Sud (FR)—Queen du Vallon (FR) **Mr S. A. Murrills**
28 **PRAIRIE IMPULSE**, 5, b m Major Cadeaux—Prairie Sun (GER) **ICM Racing**
29 **RETURN FLIGHT**, 7, b g Kayf Tara—Molly Flight (IRE) **Mike and Eileen Newbould**
30 **RONN THE CONN (IRE)**, 5, b g Whitmore's Conn (USA)—Speedy Fairy (IRE) **J. Wade**
31 **ROYAL MACNAB (IRE)**, 10, b g Beneficial—Tina McBride (IRE) **The Extra Time Partnership**
32 **ROYAL MANDATE (IRE)**, 6, ch g Manduro (GER)—Hesperia (GER) **Mike and Eileen Newbould**
33 **RUNNING IN HEELS (IRE)**, 9, br m September Storm (GER)—Ceo Draiochta (IRE) **Miss L. V. Horner**
34 **SEARANGER (USA)**, 5, b g U S Ranger (USA)—Baby Lets Cruise (USA) **ICM Racing**
35 **SKA RIDGE**, 6, b g Distant Peak (IRE)—Tandawizi **J. Wade**
36 **SMILING JESSICA (IRE)**, 8, ch m Golden Tornado (IRE)—Charlie's Mary (IRE) **Mr D. H. Slater**
37 **SOMEONE NEW (IRE)**, 6, ch m Getaway (GER)—Jill's Girl (IRE) **EPDS/MyRacing Partnership**
38 **SOVIET CASTLE (IRE)**, 5, b g Soviet Star—Castle Hope (IRE) **Miss M. D. Myco**
39 **STRIKE FEAR (IRE)**, 6, b g Scorpion (IRE)—Skatey Kate (IRE) **Mount Racing Club & Duncan Horton**
40 **TOMKEVI (FR)**, 7, b g Khalkevi (IRE)—Tamsna (FR) **Mr P J Howe & Mr R G Oliver**
41 **TRAUTMANN (IRE)**, 4, ch g Casamento (IRE)—Klang (IRE) **Mr D. H. Slater**
42 **VALZAN (FR)**, 6, b g Zanzibari (USA)—Victory Road (FR) **Mrs M. A. Thackray**
43 **VON BLUCHER (IRE)**, 5, ch g Zoffany (IRE)—Tropical Lady (IRE) **Mr J. E. Dance**
44 **XPO UNIVERSEL (FR)**, 9, b g Poliglote—Xanadu Bliss (FR) **Club Racing Partnership & A. Spittal**

THREE-YEAR-OLDS

45 **EVERLY (IRE)**, b f Acclamation—Academicienne (CAN) **Mr J. E. Dance**
46 **LUOLA**, b f Mullionmileanhour (IRE)—Cheap N Chic **Laurie Huntley**
47 **PHOENIX LIGHTNING (IRE)**, b c Lawman (FR)—Royal Fizz (IRE) **Panther Racing Limited**
48 B f Rip Van Winkle (IRE)—Velvet Ribbon (IRE) **Panther Racing Limited**

Other Owners: Mr Steve Avery, Mr John Dance, Liz Dixon, Liz Dixon & Shelagh Fagen 1, EPDS Racing Partnership 23, Mr A. N. Eaton, Miss Shelagh Fagen, Mrs Mary Feely, Ms Debra A. Fields, Mr Neil Fletcher, Mr M. Gornall, Miss Liz Hall, Mr I. Harle, Mrs P. A. H. Hartley, Mr P. A. H. Hartley, Mr G. W. Holden, Mr D. C. Horton, Mr P. J. Howe, ICM Racing, Mrs Stef Keniry, Miss R. E. A. Menzies, Mr P. Nelson, Mrs E. E. Newbould, Mr Mike Newbould, Mr R. G. Oliver, Mr Tony Outhart, Mr Gary Peacock, Mr John Powell, Miss T. Sloan, Mr J. D. Spensley, Mrs M. A. Spensley, Mr Robert Turner, Mr J. Veitch, Dr Pauline Weight, Mr Tony Weight, Mrs Sandra Windross.

Jockey (flat): Dougie Costello, Graham Lee, P. J. McDonald. **Jockey (NH):** Brian Hughes, Tony Kelly.
Conditional: Jamie Hamilton. **Apprentice:** Rowan Scott. **Amateur:** Mr Aaron Anderson.

382 MR PHIL MIDDLETON, Aylesbury
Postal: **Dorton Place, Dorton Park Farm, Dorton, Aylesbury, Buckinghamshire, HP18 9NR**
Contacts: **PHONE (01844) 237503 FAX (01844) 237503 MOBILE (07860) 426607**

1 **EXITAS (IRE)**, 10, b g Exit To Nowhere (USA)—Suntas (IRE) **Mr P. W. Middleton**
2 **GOLAN FORTUNE (IRE)**, 6, b g Golan (IRE)—Ballyknock Alainn (IRE) **P Middleton, M Lowther**
3 **HOLLY BUSH HENRY (IRE)**, 7, b g Yeats (IRE)—Maslam (IRE) **P Middleton, M Lowther**
4 **MISS ADVENTURE (IRE)**, 6, b m Brian Boru—Blue Fire Lady (IRE) **P Middleton, M Lowther**

Other Owners: Mr M. Lowther.

Assistant Trainer: Fausta Poskute

383 MR PAUL MIDGLEY, Westow
Postal: **Sandfield Farm, Westow, York, YO60 7LS**
Contacts: **Office (01653) 658790 FAX (01653) 658790 MOBILE (07976) 965220**
E-MAIL ptmidgley@aol.com **WEBSITE** www.ptmidgley.com

1 **ARAQEEL**, 5, b g Dutch Art—Alice Alleyne (IRE) **The Howarting's Partnership**
2 **ART OBSESSION (IRE)**, 7, b g Excellent Art—Ghana (IRE) **Pee Dee Tee Syndicate & T W Midgley**
3 **BUCCANEERS VAULT (IRE)**, 6, gr g Aussie Rules (USA)—Heaven's Vault (IRE) **Robert and Sheila Bradley**
4 **CAESAR'S COMET (IRE)**, 4, b g Acclamation—Star Now **Mr P. T. Midgley**
5 **CAPTAIN COLBY (USA)**, 6, b g Bernstein (USA)—Escape To Victory **Bob Bradley & P T Midgley**
6 **DESERT ACE (IRE)**, 7, ch g Kheleyf (USA)—Champion Place **Mr P. T. Midgley**
7 **DESERT LAW (IRE)**, 10, b g Oasis Dream—Speed Cop **Taylor's Bloodstock Ltd**
8 **DOWN TIME (USA)**, 8, b g Harlan's Holiday (USA)—Frappay (USA) **Mr P. T. Midgley**
9 **ELYSIAN FLYER (IRE)**, 6, b g Majestic Missile (IRE)—Starisa (IRE) **Robert and Sheila Bradley**
10 **FINAL VENTURE**, 6, b g Equiano (FR)—Sharplaw Venture **Taylor's Bloodstock Ltd**
11 **GAMESOME (FR)**, 7, b g Rock of Gibraltar (IRE)—Hot Coal (USA) **TA & PJ Stephenson,S Wibberley,R Bradley**
12 **GIANT SPARK**, 6, b g Orientor—Annie Gee **Mr F. Brady**
13 **GROUNDWORKER (IRE)**, 7, b g Tagula (IRE)—Notepad **Blackburn Family**
14 **HEE HAW (IRE)**, 4, b g Sleeping Indian—My American Beauty **Taylor's Bloodstock Ltd**
15 **LINE OF REASON (IRE)**, 8, br g Kheleyf (USA)—Miss Party Line (USA) **Taylor's Bloodstock Ltd**
16 **MANSHOOD (IRE)**, 5, b g Iffraaj—Thawrah (USA) **Taylor's Bloodstock Ltd**
17 **MERRY BANTER**, 4, b f Bated Breath—Merry Diva **Mr H. Thornton & Mr P. T. Midgley**
18 **MOVE IN TIME (IRE)**, 10, ch g Monsieur Bond (IRE)—Tibesti **A. Turton, J. Blackburn & R. Bond**
19 **MR ORANGE (IRE)**, 5, b g Paco Boy (IRE)—Shirley Blake (IRE) **Mr J Blackburn & Mr A Turton**
20 **NAGGERS (IRE)**, 7, ch g Excellent Art—Trika **Taylor's Bloodstock Ltd**
21 **NINJAGO**, 8, b g Mount Nelson—Fidelio's Miracle (USA) **Taylor's Bloodstock Ltd & PT Midgley**
22 **ONE BOY (IRE)**, 7, ch g Captain Gerrard (IRE)—Paris Song (IRE) **R Wardlaw & Partner**
23 **ORIENT CLASS**, 7, ch g Orientor—Killer Class **F Brady,A Williams,P Lindley,S Wibberley**
24 **ORVAR (IRE)**, 5, b g Dandy Man (IRE)—Roskeen (IRE) **Taylor's Bloodstock Ltd**
25 **PATRICK (IRE)**, 6, b g Acclamation—Red Liason (IRE) **Blackburn Family**
26 **PEGI BROWNE (IRE)**, 5, ch m Fast Company (IRE)—Alta Petens **Kildare Racing Club**
27 **RANTAN (IRE)**, 5, b g Kodiac—Peace Talks **Jolly Boy's Racing Club & Partner**
28 **RELATED (IRE)**, 8, b g Kheleyf (USA)—Balladonia **Taylor's Bloodstock Ltd**
29 **RUSSIAN REALM**, 8, b g Dansili—Russian Rhythm (USA) **The Guys & Dolls & Partner**
30 **SILVANUS (IRE)**, 13, b g Danehill Dancer (IRE)—Mala Mala (IRE) **Mr Colin Alton & Mr P. T. Midgley**
31 **START TIME (IRE)**, 5, b g Invincible Spirit (IRE)—Silca's Sister **Taylor's Bloodstock Ltd & PT Midgley**
32 **TANASOQ (IRE)**, 5, b g Acclamation—Alexander Youth (IRE) **Mr F Brady & Mr J S Morrison**
33 **TARBOOSH**, 5, b g Bahamian Bounty—Mullein **The Guys & Dolls & Sandfield Racing**
34 **TWENTYSVNTHLANCERS**, 5, b g Hellvelyn—Subtle Move (USA) **D Hopper & D Ellis**
35 **TYLERY WONDER (IRE)**, 8, ch g Choisir (AUS)—Over The Tylery (IRE) **Taylor's Bloodstock Ltd**
36 **WAR WHISPER (IRE)**, 5, b g Royal Applause—Featherweight (IRE) **Mr P. T. Midgley**
37 **YORKSHIREDEBUT (IRE)**, 4, ch f Sir Prancealot (IRE)—Yasmeena (USA) **Taylor's Bloodstock Ltd**

THREE-YEAR-OLDS

38 **CE DE NULLIS (IRE)**, ch f Dandy Man (IRE)—Plym **Taylor's Bloodstock Ltd**
39 **COASTAL DRIVE**, gr g Harbour Watch (IRE)—Added Attraction (USA) **Bob Bradley & P T Midgley**
40 **MOUNT HELLVELYN**, b g Hellvelyn—Sugar Mountain (IRE) **Jolly Boys Racing Club**
41 **NANJOE**, b f Helmet (AUS)—Hanella (IRE) **Frank & Annette Brady**
42 **ORIENT PRINCESS**, ch f Orientor—Killer Class **F Brady & The Guys & Dolls**
43 **PACO ESCOSTAR**, ch f Paco Boy (IRE)—Shesastar **Sandfield Racing**

MR PAUL MIDGLEY - Continued

44 **PALMER (IRE)**, b g Acclamation—Aneedah (IRE) **Ms D. Aldridge**
45 **ROCK HILL (IRE)**, br g Rock of Gibraltar (IRE)—Pascali **Mr H. Thornton & Mr P. T. Midgley**

TWO-YEAR-OLDS

46 Br f 20/2 Society Rock (IRE)—Dispol Kylie (IRE) (Kheleyf (USA)) (1142) **Mr W. B. Imison**
47 Br f 4/3 Lethal Force (IRE)—Dixey (Diktat) (1464) **Bob Bradley & P T Midgley**
48 B f 3/3 Lethal Force (IRE)—Isontonic (IRE) (Kodiac) (1301) **Sandfield Racing**
49 B c 4/4 Morpheus—Killer Class (Kyllachy) **Mr F. Brady**
50 Ch f 8/3 Zoffany (IRE)—Surrey Pink (FR) (Kyllachy) (8140) **Mr J. N. Blackburn**

Other Owners: Mr C. Alton, Mr P. Bateson, Mr A. B. Blackburn, Mrs G. I. Blackburn, R. C. Bond, Mrs S. Bradley, Mr R. Bradley, Mrs A. Brady, Mr D. Chapman, Mr C. Chapman, Mr L. Clarke, Mr P. W. Clifton, Mr D. B. Ellis, Miss D. Gabbitas, The Guys & Dolls Syndicate, Mr D. Hopper, Mr P. N. Lindley, Mr T. W. Midgley, J. S. Morrison, Mr F. O'Sullivan, Mr R. J. Parks, Peedeetee Syndicate, R. Standring, Mr P. J. Stephenson, T. A. Stephenson, Mr H. Thornton, Mr A. Turton, Mr A. D. Ward, Mr R. Wardlaw, Mr S. Wibberley, Mr A. Williams.

Assistant Trainer: Mrs W. E. Midgley

Amateur: Mr Tom Midgley.

---

384 MR ROD MILLMAN, Cullompton
Postal: The Paddocks, Dulford, Cullompton, Devon, EX15 2DX
Contacts: PHONE/FAX (01884) 266620 MOBILE (07885) 168447
E-MAIL rod.millman@ic24.net

1 **BIOTIC**, 7, b g Aqlaam—Bramaputra (IRE) **Mrs B. Sumner & Mr B. R. Millman**
2 **CHAMPAGNE CHAMP**, 6, b g Champs Elysees—Maramba **Five Horses Ltd**
3 **CONCUR (IRE)**, 5, ch g Approve (IRE)—Tradmagic (IRE) **Miss G. J. Abbey**
4 **DUKE OF BRONTE**, 4, b g Mount Nelson—Reaf **Perfect Match**
5 **GLORY OF PARIS (IRE)**, 4, b g Sir Prancealot (IRE)—Paris Glory (USA) **David Little The Links Partnership**
6 **HANDYTALK (IRE)**, 5, b g Lilbourne Lad (IRE)—Dancing With Stars (IRE) **Cantay Racing**
7 **HAWRIDGE FLYER**, 4, b g Sir Percy—Strictly Lambada **E. J. S. Gadsden**
8 **HAWRIDGE GLORY (IRE)**, 4, b g Royal Applause—Saint Lucia (IRE) **E. J. S. Gadsden**
9 **LANGLAUF (USA)**, 5, gr m Raven's Pass (USA)—Emirates Girl (USA) **Mr A. G. Bloom**
10 **MASTER CARPENTER (IRE)**, 7, ch h Mastercraftsman (IRE)—Fringe **David Little The Links Partnership**
11 **PENTITO RAP (USA)**, 4, b g Smart Strike (CAN)—Sing Like A Bird (USA) **J. Kelsey-Fry**
12 **SIR PLATO (IRE)**, 4, b g Sir Prancealot (IRE)—Dessert Flower (IRE) **The Sir Plato Partnership**
13 **SIR RODERIC (IRE)**, 5, b g Roderic O'connor (IRE)—
                                    Begin The Beguine (IRE) **David Little The Links Partnership**
14 **SIXTH OF JUNE**, 4, b f Crosspeace (IRE)—Eccentricity **Mrs B. C. Tucker**
15 **SWEET PURSUIT**, 4, b f Pastoral Pursuits—Sugar Beet **Always Hopeful Partnership**
16 **ZULU**, 4, b g Cockney Rebel (IRE)—Pantita **Howard Barton Stud**

THREE-YEAR-OLDS

17 **ACHIANNA (USA)**, ch f Gemologist (USA)—Adoradancer (USA) **Mr C. Demetriou**
18 **AIRSHOW**, ch g Showcasing—Belle des Airs (IRE) **Mrs H. I. Slade**
19 **CRYSTAL CASQUE**, ch f Helmet (AUS)—Crystal Moments **The Dirham Partnership**
20 **DADDIES GIRL (IRE)**, b f Elzaam (AUS)—La Cuvee **Daddies Girl Partnership**
21 **HASTENPLACE**, b f Compton Place—Hasten **Mr & Mrs J. F. S. Laws**
22 **LIVINGSTONES QUEST (IRE)**, b g Showcasing—Maramba **Five Horses Ltd**
23 **MASTER GREY (IRE)**, gr g Mastercraftsman (IRE)—Market Day **David Little The Links Partnership**
24 **RAGSTONE VIEW (IRE)**, b g Requinto (IRE)—Highland Miss (USA) **Rioja Raiders 04**
25 **RED MIRACLE**, b f Dylan Thomas (IRE)—Under Milk Wood **Seasons Holidays**
26 **RIO SANTOS**, ch g Casamento (IRE)—Midnight Flower (IRE) **The Rio Santos Partnership**
27 **SPOT LITE**, b g Compton Place—High Class Girl **Mr C. H. Saunders**

TWO-YEAR-OLDS

28 B c 29/2 Intello (GER)—Aneedah (IRE) (Invincible Spirit (IRE)) (75000) **E. J. S. Gadsden**
29 B f 5/4 Kuroshio (AUS)—Angry Bark (USA) (Woodman (USA)) **Howard Barton Stud**
30 B c 18/2 Champs Elysees—Aspasi (Dalakhani (IRE)) (26000) **David Little The Links Partnership**
31 B c 13/4 Roderic O'connor (IRE)—
                                    Begin The Beguine (IRE) (Peintre Celebre (USA)) **David Little The Links Partnership**
32 B f 12/3 Harbour Watch (IRE)—Bonnie Grey (Hellvelyn) **Howard Barton Stud**
33 B c 27/3 Dutch Art—Clorofilla (IRE) (Refuse To Bend (IRE)) (10000)

MR ROD MILLMAN - Continued

34 Ch c 31/3 Lethal Force (IRE)—Club Tahiti (Hernando (FR))
35 Gr c 29/3 Zebedee—Curl (IRE) (Duke of Marmalade (IRE)) (9523) **David Little The Links Partnership**
36 B c 17/3 Power—Eclat Royale (Royal Applause) **Five Horses Ltd**
37 B c 10/4 Sir Prancealot (IRE)—Hannah Greeley (USA) (Mr Greeley (USA)) (17142) **B. R. Millman**
38 MAWDE (IRE), ch f 20/1 Sir Prancealot (IRE)—Rise Up Lotus (IRE) (Zebedee) (7619)
39 Br c 17/2 Dalakhani (IRE)—Reaf (In The Wings)
40 SKI MIST, gr f 29/3 Hellvelyn—Piste (Falbrav (IRE)) (2857) **Miss G. J. Abbey**
41 SUFFICIENT, gr f 14/4 Showcasing—Good Enough (FR) (Mukaddamah (USA))

Other Owners: Mr R. K. Arrowsmith, P Bartlam, Mr T. Bennett, Mr N. A. Clark, Mrs J. A. Daly, Mr R. W. Daly, K. L. Dare, Mr A. S. P. Drake, Mr R. D. Gamlin, Mr P. C. W. Green, Mr R. Gudge, Mr S. J. Kattau, Mrs C. Knowles, Mr J. F. S. Laws, Mrs J. E. Laws, Mr M. Leach, V. B. Lewer, D. A. Little, Mr A. M. Nolan, Ms P. D. O'Sullivan, Mrs M. O'Sullivan, G. G. Payne, Mr S. M. Perry, Mrs B. Sumner, Mr M. J. Tidball, Mr T. Tompkins.

Assistant Trainers: Louise Millman, Pat Millman

Jockey (flat): William Carson, Oisin Murphy, Ryan Tate. **Amateur:** Mr Pat Millman.

385 **MR NICK MITCHELL, Dorchester**
Postal: **1 Racklands, Piddletrenthide, Dorchester, Dorset, DT2 7QP**
Contacts: **PHONE (01300) 348049 MOBILE (07770) 892085**
E-MAIL nick.mitch@btinternet.com **WEBSITE** www.nickmitchellracing.com

1 BUTNEY ISLAND (IRE), 8, b g Trans Island—Tash McGarry (IRE) **Mr N. R. Mitchell**
2 DANCE FLOOR KING (IRE), 11, b g Generous (IRE)—Strawberry Fool (FR) **Mr N. Elliott**
3 DRUMLEE CITY (IRE), 6, b g City Honours (USA)—Alentio (IRE) **Mr H. Redknapp**
4 FRED'S FILLY, 5, ch m Avonbridge—Regal Quest (IRE) **Mr A. F. Horsington**
5 JULLY LES BUXY, 8, b m Black Sam Bellamy (IRE)—Jadidh **Mr M. S. Rose**
6 LOUGH DERG MYSTERY (IRE), 7, b g Oscar (IRE)—Have To Go (IRE) **Mr N. Elliott**
7 MR MAGILL (FR), 6, b g Hamairi (IRE)—Marie Cuddy (IRE) **K B Racing**
8 SUMMER GETAWAY (IRE), 6, b g Getaway (GER)—Summer Crush (USA) **Mr N. Elliott**
9 SWALLOW DANCER, 4, b f Danehill Dancer (IRE)—Bay Swallow (IRE) **Glanvilles Stud Partners**
10 THIS IS IT (IRE), 6, b g Milan—Riviera Sands (IRE) **Three Kings Partnerships**
11 VIOLETS GIRL, 8, b m Black Sam Bellamy (IRE)—Sunshine Rays **Mr H. Redknapp**

Other Owners: Mr K. M. F. Burke, Dr G. W. Guy, Mr E. Pritchard, Mr W. D. Procter, Miss E. Rogers, Mr H. J. M. Wilson.

Jockey (NH): Daryl Jacob.

386 **MR RICHARD MITCHELL, Dorchester**
Postal: **East Hill Stables, Piddletrenthide, Dorchester, Dorset, DT2 7QY**
Contacts: **PHONE/FAX (01300) 348739 MOBILE (07775) 843136**
E-MAIL easthillstables@tiscali.co.uk

1 BENBECULA, 9, b g Motivator—Isle of Flame **Mr & Mrs Andrew May**
2 MACHIAVELIAN STORM (IRE), 6, gr m Dark Angel (IRE)—
Terri's Charmer (USA) **Mrs Harriet Naylor & Mr J. R. Boughey**
3 SHANKARA (IRE), 4, gr f Mastercraftsman (IRE)—White And Red (IRE) **J. R. Boughey**
4 TAGINE, 7, b m Deltic (USA)—Panhandle **Mrs E. Mitchell**
5 THUNDERING HOME, 11, gr g Storming Home—Citrine Spirit (IRE) **J. R. Boughey**

Other Owners: Mr J. R. Boughey, Mr Andrew May, Mrs Andrew May, Mrs Harriet Naylor.

Assistant Trainer: Mrs E. Mitchell

387 **MR RICHARD MITFORD-SLADE, Norton Fitzwarren**
Postal: **Pontispool Farm, Allerford, Norton Fitzwarren, Taunton, Somerset, TA4 1BG**
Contacts: **PHONE (01823) 461196 FAX (01823) 462945 MOBILE (07899) 994420**
E-MAIL rms@pontispool.com

1 APPLESOLUTELY, 7, b m Apple Tree (FR)—Allerford Annie (IRE) **R Mitford-Slade & Lucy Johnson**
2 DARK ASTER, 6, b m Alflora (IRE)—Westbourne (IRE) **R Mitford-Slade & Lucy Johnson**
3 IMPERIAL CIRCUS (IRE), 12, b g Beneficial—Aunty Dawn (IRE) **Mrs L. Fielding-Johnson**

MR RICHARD MITFORD-SLADE - Continued

4 **LAZY SUNDAY**, 4, b f Schiaparelli (GER)—Sari Rose (FR) **Mrs L. Fielding-Johnson**
5 **MASTER TRADESMAN**, 7, ch g Marienbard (IRE)—Tobeornotobe (IRE) **R. C. Mitford-Slade**
6 **RUBY FOOL**, 8, b m Apple Tree (FR)—Westbourne (IRE) **R. C. Mitford-Slade**
7 **SAMUEL JACKSON**, 6, b g Alflora (IRE)—Primitive Quest **R Mitford-Slade & Lucy Johnson**

---

388 **MR JAMES MOFFATT, Cartmel**
Postal: **Pit Farm Racing Stables, Cartmel, Grange-Over-Sands, Cumbria, LA11 6PJ**
Contacts: **PHONE (01539) 533808 FAX (01539) 536236 MOBILE (07767) 367282**
E-MAIL **jamesmoffatt@hotmail.co.uk** WEBSITE **www.jamesmoffatt.co.uk**

1 **ALTRUISM (IRE)**, 8, b g Authorized (IRE)—Bold Assumption **Mr V R Vyner-Brooks, Mr K Bowron**
2 **AMUSE ME**, 12, gr g Daylami (IRE)—Have Fun **Vilprano, Bowron & Beaumont**
3 **BOA ISLAND (IRE)**, 8, b g Trans Island—Eskimo Kiss (IRE) **Mrs P. Thompson**
4 **BON CHIC (IRE)**, 9, b m Presenting—Homebird (IRE) **Bowes Lodge Stables**
5 **BORUMA (IRE)**, 8, b g Brian Boru—Itlallendintears (IRE) **The Running In Rail Partnership**
6 **CAPTAIN BROWN**, 10, b g Lomitas—Nicola Bella (IRE) **Mr K. Bowron**
7 **DODGYBINGO (IRE)**, 5, b g Roderic O'connor (IRE)—Happy Flight (IRE) **The Clock Tower Partnership**
8 **FANTASY KING**, 12, b g Acclamation—Fantasy Ridge **Mr V. R. Vyner-Brooks**
9 **FIOSRACH (IRE)**, 8, b g Bachelor Duke (USA)—Saana (IRE) **The Sheroot Partnership**
10 **GOLDEN TOWN (IRE)**, 7, b g Invincible Spirit (IRE)—Princesse Dansante (IRE) **Bowes Lodge Stables**
11 **GOOD BOY JASPER**, 4, ch g Doncaster Rover (USA)—Mitchelland **Mr R. R. Whitton**
12 **HIGHLAND LODGE (IRE)**, 12, b g Flemensfirth (USA)—Supreme Von Pres (IRE) **Mrs P. Thompson**
13 **IDDER (IRE)**, 7, b g Authorized (IRE)—Epiphany **The Boom Boom Partnership**
14 **LOUGH KENT (IRE)**, 9, b g Barathea (IRE)—King's Doll (IRE) **Hadwin, Moffatt, Green, Chamberlain Bros**
15 **MORNING ROYALTY (IRE)**, 11, b g King's Theatre (IRE)—Portryan Native (IRE) **Mrs E. M. Milligan**
16 **MUNSAAB (IRE)**, 12, b g Alhaarth (IRE)—Claustra (FR) **Countrywide Vehicle Rentals Limited**
17 **NICOLAS CHAUVIN (IRE)**, 10, b g Saffron Walden (FR)—Kenzie (IRE) **Ladsdoracing**
18 **SMART RULER (IRE)**, 12, ch g Viking Ruler (AUS)—Celebrated Smile (IRE) **The Vilprano Partnership**
19 **STRONG RESEMBLANCE (IRE)**, 7, b g Tikkanen (USA)—Shenamar (IRE) **Countrywide Vehicle Rentals Limited**
20 **THE STEWARD (USA)**, 7, b g Street Cry (IRE)—Candlelight (USA) **Cartmel Six Pack**
21 **THINK AHEAD**, 7, b g Shamardal (USA)—Moonshadow **Mr V. R. Vyner-Brooks**
22 **WESTERN HONOUR (IRE)**, 6, b g Westerner—Cailins Honour (IRE) **Mrs D. Thompson**
23 **WOOD BREIZH (FR)**, 8, gr g Stormy River (FR)—Polynevees (FR) **Countrywide Vehicle Rentals Limited**

Other Owners: Mr Jim Beaumont, Mr James Boshier, Mr K. Bowron, Mr Keith Hadwin, Mr Peter J. Higham, Mr Peter A. Holt, Mr A. R. Mills, Mr D. J. Moffatt, Mr P. Porter, Mr Daniel Spencer, The Vilprano Partnership, Mr Varlien Vyner-Brooks, Mr Carl Waters, Mrs J. C. Wilson, Mr Simon Wilson.

Assistant Trainer: Nadine Moffatt

Jockey (NH): Henry Brooke, Brian Hughes. **Conditional:** Charlotte Jones. **Apprentice:** Polly Steele.

---

389 **MR ISMAIL MOHAMMED, Newmarket**
Postal: **Grange House Stables, Hamilton Road, Newmarket, Suffolk, CB8 0TE**
Contacts: **PHONE (01638) 669074 MOBILE (07766) 570271 / (07747) 191606**
E-MAIL **justina.stone@dubairacingclub.com**

1 **ALWAYS THANKFUL**, 4, b f Showcasing—Thankful **S. H. Altayer**
2 **AMAZOUR (IRE)**, 6, b g Azamour (IRE)—Choose Me (IRE) **Sheikh J. D. Al Maktoum**
3 **BIG SIGH (IRE)**, 4, ch g Raven's Pass (USA)—Sospira **Sheikh J. D. Al Maktoum**
4 **COUNTER SPIRIT (USA)**, 4, b f Invincible Spirit (IRE)—Counterclaim **S. H. Altayer**
5 **IFUBELIEVEINDREAMS (IRE)**, 4, b f Iffraaj—Oratrix (IRE) **Mr I. Mohammed**
6 **ITSAKINDAMAGIC**, 4, b g Mount Nelson—Carsulae (IRE) **Sheikh J. D. Al Maktoum**
7 **MONSIEUR BAY**, 4, b c Sir Percy—Pilcomayo (IRE) **S. Manana**
8 **NIBRAS AGAIN**, 4, b g Kyllachy—Regina **S. H. Altayer**
9 **STARSOVERTHERIVER (IRE)**, 4, b f Kodiac—River Style (IRE) **S. Manana**

THREE-YEAR-OLDS

10 **COMPORTA**, b c Iffraaj—Hot Wired **Mr A. Al Mansoori**
11 **MY HEART**, b f Universal (IRE)—Mazuna (IRE) **Mr A. Al Mansoori**
12 **NIBRAS GALAXY (IRE)**, b c Nathaniel (IRE)—Galaxy Dancer (USA) **S. H. Altayer**
13 **SHAYTOON (IRE)**, b g Sepoy (AUS)—Winner's Wish **Mr A. Al Mansoori**

MR ISMAIL MOHAMMED - Continued

TWO-YEAR-OLDS

14 B f 29/1 Dark Angel (IRE)—Aertex (IRE) (Exceed And Excel (AUS)) (35000)
15 B f 8/4 Slade Power (IRE)—Al Sharood (Shamardal (USA)) **A. Saeed**
16 B c 22/3 Le Havre (IRE)—Alice's Dancer (IRE) (Clodovil (IRE)) (60000)
17 B f 27/3 Dream Ahead (USA)—Beat As One (Medicean) **Saif Ali & Saeed H. Altayer**
18 B c 19/3 Australia—Blanche Dubawi (IRE) (Dubawi (IRE)) (65000) **S. Ali**
19 Ch c 20/2 Iffraaj—Blue Beacon (Fantastic Light (USA)) (100000)
20 B f 7/5 Slade Power (IRE)—Broadway Hit (Sadler's Wells (USA)) **Saif Ali & Saeed H. Altayer**
21 B f 19/2 Universal (IRE)—Eluding (Street Cry (IRE)) **A. Saeed**
22 B f 22/4 Iffraaj—Extreme Beauty (USA) (Rahy (USA)) **Dr A. Ridha**
23 B c 14/4 Farhh—Island Babe (USA) (Kingmambo (USA)) (75000)
24 B f 2/2 Slade Power (IRE)—Needles And Pins (IRE) (Fasliyev (USA)) (85000) **S. H. Altayer**
25 Ch c 20/2 Mukhadram—Pasithea (IRE) (Celtic Swing) **S. Ali**
26 B gr c 23/1 Universal (IRE)—Phoenix City (USA) (El Prado (IRE)) **A. Saeed**
27 B f 5/3 Dawn Approach (IRE)—Power of Light (IRE) (Echo of Light) **Dr A. Ridha**
28 B c 31/3 Dawn Approach (IRE)—Rainbow Desert (USA) (Dynaformer (USA))
29 Ch f 28/1 Sepoy (AUS)—Shafaani (Green Desert (USA)) (32000)
30 B br c 7/3 Dawn Approach (IRE)—Sparkling Smile (IRE) (Cape Cross (IRE)) (60000) **Saif Ali & Saeed H. Altayer**
31 B f 9/2 Dawn Approach (IRE)—Superior Charm (USA) (Elusive Quality (USA)) **Dr A. Ridha**
32 B f 27/4 Cape Cross (IRE)—Sweet Rose (New Approach (IRE)) **Sheikh J. D. Al Maktoum**
33 B f 19/4 Nathaniel (IRE)—Synergy (FR) (Victory Note (USA)) (55000)
34 B g 10/2 Mukhadram—Wolumla (IRE) (Royal Applause) (8000)

Other Owners: S. Ali.

Assistant Trainer: Mike Marshall

---

390 | **MRS LAURA MONGAN, Epsom**
Postal: **Condover Stables, Langley Vale Road, Epsom, Surrey, KT18 6AP**
Contacts: PHONE **(01372) 271494** FAX **(01372) 271494** MOBILE **(07788) 122942**
E-MAIL ljmongan@hotmail.co.uk WEBSITE www.lauramongan.co.uk

1 **ABLAZE**, 4, ch f Arcano (IRE)—Angry Bark (USA) **Mrs P. J. Sheen**
2 **ARDAMIR (FR)**, 6, b g Deportivo—Kiss And Cry (FR) **Mrs P. J. Sheen**
3 **EPSOM DAY (IRE)**, 5, b g Teofilo (IRE)—Dubai Flower **Mrs P. J. Sheen**
4 **FIGHT FOR LOVE (FR)**, 5, b g Fuisse (FR)—Love Affair (FR) **Mrs P. J. Sheen**
5 **FIRST AVENUE**, 13, b g Montjeu (IRE)—Marciala (IRE) **Mrs L. J. Mongan**
6 **FULLON CLARETS**, 6, ch g Equiano (IRE)—Palinisa (IRE) **Mrs L. J. Mongan**
7 **GOLDEN NECTAR**, 4, ch f Sakhee's Secret—Mildoura **Mrs P. J. Sheen**
8 **GOUTEZ MOI (FR)**, 5, b g Dragon Dancer—Titi Jolie (FR) **Mrs P. J. Sheen**
9 **KEPPEL ISLE (IRE)**, 9, b g Heron Island (IRE)—Wadi Khaled (IRE) **Mrs P. J. Sheen**
10 **MISS YEATS (IRE)**, 7, b m Yeats (IRE)—Mrs Wallensky (IRE) **Mrs P. J. Sheen**
11 **MORGAN'S BAY**, 13, b g Karinga Bay—Dubai Dolly (IRE) **Mrs L. J. Mongan**
12 **MY BOY JAMES (IRE)**, 6, br g Getaway (GER)—Parkallity (IRE) **Mrs P. J. Sheen**
13 **NAPOLEON (IRE)**, 5, b h Jeremy (USA)—Desert Drama (IRE) **Miss J. Frankham**
14 **NARJES**, 4, b f Sepoy (AUS)—Dubai Sea (USA) **Mr P. R. Howell**
15 **ORSM**, 11, b g Erhaab (USA)—Royal Roulette **Mrs P. J. Sheen**
16 **REEDWAY (IRE)**, 5, ch g Intikhab (USA)—Mistress Bailey (IRE) **Mrs J. A. Cornwell**
17 **RIVERMOUTH**, 13, ch g Karinga Bay—Rippling Brook **Mrs P. J. Sheen**
18 **SANDACRES**, 5, b g Frozen Power (IRE)—Lady Golan (IRE) **Condover Racing**
19 **SEA TIDE**, 4, b f Champs Elysees—Change Course **Mrs P. J. Sheen**
20 **SEAESTA**, 4, b f Harbour Watch (IRE)—Lady Golan (IRE) **Mrs J. A. Cornwell**
21 **SILVER TICKET (IRE)**, 7, gr g Tikkanen (USA)—Windmill View (IRE) **Mrs P. J. Sheen**
22 **TANZINA**, 6, b m Equiano (IRE)—Pilcomayo (IRE) **Mrs J. A. Cornwell**
23 **WITH APPROVAL (IRE)**, 6, b g Approve (IRE)—Kelsey Rose **Mrs P. J. Sheen**
24 **WOOFIE (IRE)**, 6, b g Duke of Marmalade (IRE)—Violet Ballerina (IRE) **Mrs P. J. Sheen**

THREE-YEAR-OLDS

25 **BELOVED KNIGHT**, ch c Sir Percy—Silent Decision (USA) **Hever Stud Farm Ltd**
26 **JETPAC**, b g Paco Boy (IRE)—Emperor's Hope (IRE) **Mr D. R. J. King**
27 **SNOW MOBILE**, ro f Lethal Force (IRE)—Run of The Day **Mr D. R. J. King**
28 **SPRING ABILITY (IRE)**, b g Oasis Dream—Because (IRE) **Mrs P. J. Sheen**
29 **YOUR CHOICE**, ch f Foxwedge (AUS)—Mildoura (FR) **Mrs P. J. Sheen**

MRS LAURA MONGAN - Continued

Assistant Trainer: Ian Mongan

Jockey (NH): Tom Cannon.

---

391 MR ARTHUR MOORE, Naas
Postal: **Dereens, Caragh, Naas, Co. Kildare, Ireland**
Contacts: PHONE **(00353) 4587 6292** MOBILE **(00353) 8725 52535**
E-MAIL **arthurlmoore@eircom.net**

1 **AT YOUR EASE (IRE)**, 5, b g Scorpion (IRE)—Victoria Bridge (IRE) **Mr J. P. McManus**
2 **BACK OFF MATE (IRE)**, 10, b g Old Vic—Flyhalf (IRE) **M. Beresford**
3 **CONNARD (IRE)**, 5, b g Shantou (USA)—Sparkling Sword **R. Bartlett**
4 **CROSSED MY MIND (IRE)**, 6, b g Beneficial—Coolvane (IRE) **Mr J. P. McManus**
5 **DANDRIDGE**, 9, ch g Doyen (IRE)—Arantxa **R. Bartlett**
6 **GENTLEMAN DUKE (IRE)**, 10, b g Bachelor Duke (USA)—Housekeeping **Mr J. P. McManus**
7 4, B g Where Or When (IRE)—Lady Terimond **Mrs A. L. T. Moore**
8 **LAURENCIN (IRE)**, 5, b m Peintre Celebre (USA)—Laren (GER) **S. Lanigan, O'Keeffe**
9 4, B f Stowaway—Market Niche (IRE) **Mrs A. L. T. Moore**
10 **ONTOPOFTHEWORLD (IRE)**, 9, ch g Desert King (IRE)—Zaffre (IRE) **Planets In Orbit Syndicate**
11 **ORGANISED SOLUTION (FR)**, 4, b g Azamour (IRE)—Phille Phuong (USA) **Mrs A. L. T. Moore**
12 **PRIVATE LEDGER (IRE)**, 6, b g Milan—Time For An Audit **T. Syder**
13 **SKELLIG ROCKS (FR)**, 7, b g Poliglote—Skellig Mist (FR) **Mrs T. K. Cooper**
14 **WHATS THE PLOT (IRE)**, 6, b g Alfred Nobel (IRE)—Hazarama (IRE) **D. Jones**

TWO-YEAR-OLDS

15 B f 2/3 Elusive Pimpernel (USA)—Hannah's Magic (IRE) (Lomitas) (3255) **Mrs A. L. T. Moore**

Assistant Trainer: J. D. Moore

Jockey (NH): D. Meyler.

---

392 MR GARY MOORE, Horsham
Postal: **Cisswood Racing Stables, Sandygate Lane, Lower Beeding, Horsham, West Sussex, RH13 6LR**
Contacts: HOME **(01403) 891997** YARD **(01403) 891912** MOBILE **(07753) 863123**
E-MAIL **garyjayne.moore@cisswood.com** WEBSITE **www.garymooreracing.com**

1 **AFRICAN QUEST**, 4, b f Air Quest—Pursuit of Purpose **Mr Michael Baldry**
2 **AGE OF WISDOM (IRE)**, 5, ch g Pivotal—Learned Friend (GER) **The 1901 Partnership**
3 **AIGUILLE ROUGE (FR)**, 4, ch f Falco (USA)—Avanguardia (GER) **The Winning Hand (Robin Brown)**
4 **AIRTIGHT**, 5, b g Proclamation (IRE)—Megasue **Galloping On The South Downs Partnership**
5 **ALL CURRENCIES (IRE)**, 6, b m Getaway (GER)—Splendid Presence (IRE) **Mr S. Riley**
6 **ALTAAYIL (IRE)**, 7, br g Sea The Stars (IRE)—Alleluia **Mr P. B. Moorhead**
7 **AMAJARI (FR)**, 4, b c Lonhro (AUS)—Angalia (IRE) **Mr Michael Baldry**
8 **ANTONY (FR)**, 8, b g Walk In The Park (IRE)—Melanie du Chenet (FR) **The Winning Hand**
9 **AR MAD (FR)**, 8, b g Tiger Groom—Omelia (FR) **Mr Ashley Head**
10 **AR MEST (FR)**, 5, bl g Diamond Boy (FR)—Shabada (FR) **Galloping On The South Downs Partnership**
11 **ARGYLE (IRE)**, 5, gr g Lawman—All Hallows (IRE) **Mr N. J. Roach**
12 **ART OF SWING (IRE)**, 6, b g Excellent Art—Shahmina (IRE) **Mr T Jacobs & Mr J E Harley**
13 **ASPASIUS (GER)**, 6, b g Desert Prince (IRE)—Aspasia Lunata (GER) **Mr Paul Mott**
14 **ATALANTA'S GOLD (IRE)**, 5, b m Arcadio (GER)—Sandy Desert **Pierce Molony**
15 **AUSSIE REIGNS (IRE)**, 8, b g Aussie Rules (USA)—Rohain (IRE) **Wicklow Bloodstock (Ireland) Ltd**
16 **BAD BOY DU POULDU (FR)**, 7, b g Loup Solitaire (USA)—Wild Flush (USA) **Cocktail Racing Partnership**
17 **BAGGING TURF (IRE)**, 8, b m Scorpion (IRE)—Monica's Story **Mrs M. Devine**
18 **BAN SHOOF**, 5, b g Shirocco (GER)—Pasithea (IRE) **Mr Tommy Ware & Mr Bob Pettett**
19 **BARON ALCO (FR)**, 7, ch g Dom Alco (FR)—Paula (FR) **Mr John Stone**
20 **BARRSBROOK**, 4, b g Doyen (IRE)—Sayrianna **Mr G. A. Jackman**
21 **BENATAR (IRE)**, 6, b g Beneficial—Carrigeen Lily (IRE) **Mr Ashley Head**
22 **BIGDEAL (FR)**, 5, gr g Montmartre (FR)—Rauxa **Redec Ltd & Mr G L Moore**
23 **BOLISTER (FR)**, 7, b g Le Balafre (FR)—Girlish (FR) **Past the Post Racing & Gary Moore**
24 **BRITANIO BELLO (FR)**, 7, b g Irish Wells (FR)—Tchi Tchi Bang Bang (FR) **Mr Ashley Head**
25 **BULLFROG (IRE)**, 5, b m Jeremy (USA)—Tramp Stamp (IRE) **Galloping On The South Downs Partnership**

MR GARY MOORE - Continued

26 **CASSE TETE (FR)**, 6, b g Poliglote—Ellapampa (FR) **Mr J. K. Stone**
27 **CHANDON ELYSEES**, 5, b m Champs Elysees—Upstream **Mr Michael Baldry**
28 **CHEQUE EN BLANC (FR)**, 6, b br g Bernebeau (FR)—Necossaise (FR) **Mrs E. A. Kiernan**
29 **CHRIS PEA GREEN**, 9, b g Proclamation (IRE)—
Another Secret **C Green & Galloping On The South Downs Partnership**
30 **CILAOS GLACE (FR)**, 5, br g Voix du Nord (FR)—Miss Glacee (FR) **Heart Of The South Racing**
31 **CLAYTON**, 9, b g Peintre Celebre (USA)—Blossom **Mr Ashley Head**
32 **COOLKING**, 11, b g King's Theatre (IRE)—Osocool **Sir Peter & Lady Forwood**
33 **CRYSTAL LAD (FR)**, 6, ch g Kapgarde (FR)—Qrystale Mag (FR) **Mr C. E. Stedman**
34 **DANCECRAFT**, 4, b f Mastercraftsman (IRE)—Samba Chryss (IRE) **Mr Robert E. Tillett**
35 **DAREBIN (GER)**, 6, ch g It's Gino (GER)—Delightful Sofie (GER) **Mr Chris Stedman & Mr Mark Albon**
36 **DAWN GODDESS**, 4, b f Dick Turpin (IRE)—Aurora Sky (IRE) **Mike & Sue Chandler**
37 **DEEBAJ (IRE)**, 6, b g Authorized (IRE)—Athreyaa **Phillips & Codell**
38 **DELL ORO (FR)**, 5, b g Walk In The Park (IRE)—Kallistea (FR) **Galloping On The South Downs Partnership**
39 **DIAKALI (FR)**, 9, gr g Sinndar (IRE)—Diasilixa (FR) **Wicklow Bloodstock (Ireland) Ltd**
40 **DISTINGO (IRE)**, 5, b g Smart Strike (CAN)—Distinctive Look (IRE) **Mr Alan Jamieson**
41 **EARLY DU LEMO (FR)**, 5, gr g Early March—Kiswa (FR) **Mr Ashley Head**
42 **EAST INDIES**, 5, b g Authorized (IRE)—Elan **Redec Ltd**
43 **EL HAGEB ROSE (FR)**, 4, b g Coastal Path—Ile Rose (FR) **Mr Jeremy Hinds**
44 **EMPTY MARMALADES (FR)**, 7, b g Poliglote—Arvicaya **Westbourne Racing Club & G L Moore**
45 **ERAGON DE CHANAY (FR)**, 4, b g Racinger (FR)—Rose Celebre (FR) **Five Star Racing Group**
46 **ET MOI ALORS (FR)**, 4, b g Kap Rock (FR)—Qui L'eut Cru (FR) **Mr Ashley Head**
47 **FAT SAM**, 4, ch g Denham Red (FR)—Emergence (FR) **Galloping On The South Downs Partnership**
48 **FLASHMAN**, 4, ch g Doyen (IRE)—Si Si Si **Mr Andrew Bradmore**
49 **GENTLEMAN'S DREAM (IRE)**, 6, b g Flemensfirth (USA)—Fair And Aisey (IRE) **Dedman Properties Limited**
50 **GERMAN WHIP**, 5, b g Zoffany (IRE)—Tan Tan **Mr G. L. Moore**
51 **GOLDSLINGER (FR)**, 6, b g Gold Away (IRE)—Singaporette (IRE)
52 **GOOD LUCK CHARM**, 9, b g Doyen (IRE)—Lucky Dice **Heart of the South Racing**
53 **GOOD MAN HUGHIE (IRE)**, 9, ch g Flemensfirth (USA)—Good Dawn (IRE) **Power Geneva Ltd**
54 **GORES ISLAND (IRE)**, 12, b g Beneficial—Just Leader (IRE) **Collins, Horsfall, Michael & O'Sullivan**
55 **GOSSIPING**, 6, b g Dubawi (IRE)—Gossamer **Mr G L Moore & Mr Ashley Carr**
56 **GRAASTEN (GER)**, 6, ch g Sholokhov (IRE)—Golden Time (GER) **Galloping On The South Downs Partnership**
57 **GRAND MYLA (IRE)**, 4, gr f Dark Angel (IRE)—Selfara **Jacobs Construction & Grand Holdings**
58 **GUARDS CHAPEL**, 10, b g Motivator—Intaaj (IRE) **Mr Andrew Bradmore**
59 **GUNS OF LEROS (USA)**, 5, b br g Cape Blanco (IRE)—Zappeuse (USA) **Mr Paul Hunt**
60 **HAVE THIS FOR NOW (IRE)**, 5, b g Daylami (IRE)—Annas Theatre **Mr Mick Coulson & Mr Colin Poore**
61 **HERMINIO (FR)**, 6, b g New Approach (IRE)—Histoire Sainte (FR) **Wicklow Bloodstock (Ireland) Ltd**
62 **HERMOSA VAQUERA (IRE)**, 8, b m High Chaparral (IRE)—Sundown **Mr Michael Baldry**
63 **IBALLISTICVIN**, 5, b g Rail Link—Guntakal (IRE) **Scuderia Vita Bella**
64 **ICONIC MUDDLE**, 5, gr g Sixties Icon—Spatham Rose **Saloop**
65 **IMARI KID (IRE)**, 5, b g Pour Moi (IRE)—Breathe (IRE) **Mr P. B. Moorhead**
66 **IT'S GOT LEGS (IRE)**, 5, b g Getaway (GER)—Lady Cadia (FR) **Galloping On The South Downs Partnership**
67 **JAY ARE (IRE)**, 9, b g Heron Island (IRE)—Vulpalm (IRE) **Ms Adrienne Gross**
68 **JUSTANOTHER MUDDLE**, 9, gr g Kayf Tara—Spatham Rose **Saloop Ltd**
69 **JUSTIFICATION**, 10, b g Montjeu (IRE)—Colorspin (FR) **Mrs Elizabeth Kiernan**
70 **KAFEEL (USA)**, 7, b g First Samurai (USA)—Ishraak (USA) **Mr Keith Johnson, Mr Kim Jessup**
71 **KAPDAD (FR)**, 4, ch g Kapgarde (FR)—Reveries (FR) **Galloping On The South Downs Partnership**
72 **KAVEMAN**, 6, b g Kayf Tara—Megalex **Galloping On The South Downs Partnership**
73 **KING COOL**, 7, b g King's Theatre (IRE)—Cool Spice **Mr P. T. Mott**
74 **KLOUD GATE (FR)**, 6, ch g Astronomer Royal (USA)—Talkata (IRE) **Hail Sargent Evans**
75 **KNOCKNANUSS (IRE)**, 8, b g Beneficial—Dato Vic (IRE) **Hail Sargent Evans**
76 **KRUGERMAC (IRE)**, 7, b br g Kalanisi (IRE)—Vindonissa (IRE) **Mr J. Hinds**
77 **LARRY**, 5, b g Midnight Legend—Gaspaisie (FR) **D. Bessell & Galloping On The South Downs Partnership**
78 **LE CAPRICIEUX (FR)**, 7, b g Alberto Giacometti (IRE)—Eria Flore (FR) **Mr A. Foreman & Mr G. L. Moore**
79 **LE PRECIEUX (FR)**, 5, b g Diamond Boy (FR)—Bab Khaldoun (FR) **Shark Bay Racing & Mr G L Moore**
80 **LEO LUNA**, 9, b g Galileo (IRE)—Eva Luna (USA) **Mr P. B. Moorhead**
81 **LIGHT OF AIR (FR)**, 5, b g Youmzain (IRE)—Height of Vanity (IRE) **Mr R. E. Anderson**
82 **LORD CLENAGHCASTLE (IRE)**, 4, b g Big Bad Bob (IRE)—Clenaghcastle Lady (IRE) **Mr Michael Baldry**
83 **LOUP DE LOUVE (FR)**, 6, b g Turtle Bowl (FR)—Signe de La Louve (FR) **Mr Ashley Head**
84 **LUCK'S BOY**, 5, b g Malinas (GER)—Mons Meg **Galloping On The South Downs Partnership**
85 **LUNA BEAR**, 4, b f Dick Turpin (IRE)—Royal Tavira Girl (IRE) **Scuderia Vita Bella**
86 **MAQUISARD (FR)**, 6, ch g Creachadoir (IRE)—Gioiosa Marea (IRE) **Mr M. K. George**
87 **MASTER OF SPEED (IRE)**, 6, ch g Mastercraftsman (IRE)—
Mango Groove (IRE) **Mr Ashley Head & Mr Garry Dreher**
88 **MICKEY BUCKMAN**, 5, b g Gleaming (IRE)—Mysaynoway **Mr & Mrs R Sage**

MR GARY MOORE - Continued

89 **MILKY WAY (IRE)**, 6, b g Galileo (IRE)—Beauty Bright (IRE) **Patterson Hinds & Curwen**
90 **MISTER CHOW**, 4, ch g Nathaniel (IRE)—Skimmia **Mr G. L. Moore**
91 **MR BOYCIE QUEST**, 4, gr c Air Quest—Salt Kettle **Mr Michael Baldry**
92 **MR FICKLE (IRE)**, 9, b g Jeremy (USA)—Mamara Reef **Gary Moore Racing**
93 **MR MUDDLE**, 11, gr g Imperial Dancer—Spatham Rose **Saloop**
94 **MULTITASK**, 8, b g Multiplex—Attlongglast **Power Geneva Ltd & Mr G. L. Moore**
95 **NALINKA DE LA MARE (FR)**, 5, gr m Martaline—
                          Fidji de La Mare (FR) **Galloping On The South Downs Partnership**
96 **NANNY PAT'S**, 5, b m Kayf Tara—Megalex **Galloping On The South Downs Partnership**
97 **NOT ANOTHER MUDDLE**, 7, b g Kayf Tara—Spatham Rose **Saloop**
98 **NOT NEVER**, 6, ch g Notnowcato—Watchoverme **Hail Sargent Evans**
99 **NOW LISTEN HERE (IRE)**, 6, b g Captain Marvelous (IRE)—Thanks Eileen **Mrs Ruth Arnold**
100 **NUMERO NEUF (FR)**, 5, b g Saint des Saints (FR)—Aimela (IRE) **Mr B. Siddle & Mr B. D. Haynes**
101 **PRIDE OF ANGELS**, 5, gr m Dark Angel (IRE)—Openness **Mr Michael Baldry**
102 **PROCRASTINATING (IRE)**, 6, gr g Acambaro (GER)—Another Dote (IRE) **Mr David Leon & Mr Jim Devine**
103 5, B h Kalanisi (IRE)—Queen Plaisir (IRE) **Dedman Properties Limited**
104 **REMAL DUBAI (USA)**, 4, b f Hard Spun (USA)—Chilukki's Song (USA) **Mr Tony Keeley**
105 **REMIND ME LATER (IRE)**, 9, b g Zerpour (IRE)—Two T'three Weeks **Mrs M. Devine**
106 **RIANNA STAR (IRE)**, 5, b m Haafhd—Sayrianna **Mrs J. Gawthorpe**
107 **RIGHT OLD TOUCH (IRE)**, 5, b g Stowaway—No Easy Way (IRE) **Galloping On The South Downs Partnership**
108 **ROLL OF THE DICE (IRE)**, 6, b g Publisher (USA)—Dinah B (IRE) **Mrs Ruth Arnold**
109 **ROYAL HALL (IRE)**, 6, b g Halling (USA)—Royal Fantasy (IRE) **Westbourne Racing Club**
110 **RYDAN (IRE)**, 7, ch g Intense Focus (USA)—Lough Mewin (IRE) **Jacobs Construction (Holdings) Ltd**
111 **RYEOLLIEAN**, 7, ch g Haafhd—Brave Mave **Mr Bryan Fry**
112 **SAN PEDRO DE SENAM (FR)**, 5, b g Saint des Saints (FR)—
                          Tetiaroa (FR) **Mrs Jane George & Mrs Helen Shelton**
113 **SCARLET COUTURE**, 5, b m Schiaparelli (GER)—Little Red Spider **Mr J. A. Jenkins**
114 **SEARCHING (IRE)**, 6, ro g Mastercraftsman (IRE)—Miracolia (IRE) **Mr Paul Chapman**
115 **SISANIA (IRE)**, 5, gr ro m Mastercraftsman (IRE)—Avril Rose **Heart Of The South Racing**
116 **STOICAL PATIENT (IRE)**, 9, b m Shantou (USA)—Dust Gale (IRE) **Westbourne Racing Club**
117 **SUSSEX RANGER (USA)**, 4, b g Hat Trick (JPN)—Purple (USA) **The Tongdean Partnership**
118 **TEMPLIER (IRE)**, 5, b g Mastercraftsman (IRE)—Tigertail (FR) **Mr Paul Chapman**
119 **THANK YOU BEFORE (FR)**, 5, b m Saddler Maker (IRE)—Before Royale (FR) **Mr G. L. Moore**
120 **THE FLYING SOFA (FR)**, 5, b g Sholokhov (IRE)—La Julie (IRE) **Galloping On The South Downs Partnership**
121 **THE GREEN OGRE**, 8, b g Dubai Destination (USA)—Takegawa **Past The Post Racing & Gary Moore**
122 **THOUNDER (FR)**, 4, b g Hurricane Cat (USA)—Meldown (FR) **Mr Tony Head**
123 **TOWIE (IRE)**, 4, br c Sea The Stars (IRE)—Epping **Mr Mark Albon**
124 **TRAFFIC FLUIDE (FR)**, 8, b g Astarabad (USA)—
                          Petale Rouge (FR) **Galloping On The South Downs Partnership**
125 **UBAK (FR)**, 10, b g Kapgarde (FR)—Gesse Parade (FR) **Mr N. J. Peacock**
126 **VINO GRIEGO (FR)**, 13, b g Kahyasi—Vie de Reine (FR) **Mr C. E. Stedman**
127 **WAIKIKI WAVES (FR)**, 5, b g Alexandros—Lulabelle Spar (IRE) **Heart Of The South Racing**
128 **WHINGING WILLIE (IRE)**, 9, b g Cape Cross (IRE)—Pacific Grove **Mr P. B. Moorhead**
129 **YUKON DELTA (IRE)**, 11, ch g Old Vic—Red Fern (IRE) **Mr Brian Homewood**
130 **ZANTE (FR)**, 6, ch g Zanzibari (USA)—Calling All Angels (FR) **Heart of the South Racing**

THREE-YEAR-OLDS

131 **BILLIE FLYNN**, b f Lawman (FR)—Lyric Art (USA) **Mrs Mary-Anne Parker**
132 **DREAM OF CAMELOT (IRE)**, b f Camelot—Definite Opinion (IRE) **Mrs S. Neville, Mr M. George & Mr N. Roach**
133 **HAMILTON ISLAND (IRE)**, b g So You Think (NZ)—Chatham Islands (USA) **Mr C. E. Stedman**
134 **IS IT OFF (IRE)**, b c Clodovil (IRE)—French Doll (IRE) **Power Geneva Ltd**
135 **KING OF THE SAND (IRE)**, ch c Footstepsinthesand—Lough Mewin (IRE) **Jacobs Construction & Mr J Harley**
136 **POMPEY CHIMES (IRE)**, b g Big Bad Bob (IRE)—Zamarelle **Mrs S Neville, Mr M George & Mr G Moore**
137 **RAGSTONE SAND (IRE)**, b g Footstepsinthesand—Speedy Storm (IRE) **Gallagher Bloodstock Limited**
138 **SING OUT LOUD (IRE)**, b g Vocalised (USA)—Tus Maith (IRE) **Mrs S Neville & Mr M George**
139 **SKY BANDIT**, gr f Dick Turpin (IRE)—Aurora Sky (IRE) **Mike & Sue Chandler**
140 **SWIFT FOX**, b g Foxwedge (AUS)—Amontillado (IRE) **Shark Bay Racing Syndicate**
141 **THECHILDREN'STRUST (IRE)**, br g Society Rock (IRE)—Estemaala (IRE) **Mr Ashley Head**

TWO-YEAR-OLDS

142 **BARBARA HEPWORTH (IRE)**, b f 6/4 Dark Angel (IRE)—
                        Muzdaan (IRE) (Exceed And Excel (AUS)) (93609) **Mr R. A. Green**
143 **CLARA PEETERS**, b f 26/3 Epaulette (AUS)—Musical Key (Key of Luck (USA)) (70000) **Mr R. A. Green**
144 **LADY MORPHEUS**, b f 4/3 Morpheus—Tatora (Selkirk (USA)) (IRE) **Mr P. B. Moorhead**
145 Ch c 3/3 Slade Power (IRE)—Lough Mewin (IRE) (Woodman (USA)) (48840) **Jacobs Construction & J Harley**

MR GARY MOORE - Continued

146 B c 14/5 Epaulette (AUS)—Lucky Dice (Perugino) (USA) **Heart of the South Racing**
147 B f 23/3 Mukhadram—Sablonne (USA) (Silver Hawk (USA)) **Mr C. E. Stedman**
148 **TATHRA,** b f 1/2 Harbour Watch (IRE)—Kameruka (Auction House (USA)) **Exors of the Late G. Pritchard-Gordon**

Other Owners: Mr D. R. Adam, Mrs E. Adamski, Mrs V. Baker, R. L. Brown, Rev L. M. Brown, A. Carr, Mr M. Chandler, Mrs S. J. Chandler, Mr J. A. Collins, Mr M. D. Coulson, Mr D. A. Cranfield, Mr S. Curwen, J. T. Devine, Mr G. C. Dreher, Mr D. L. Evans, Mr A. J. Foreman, Lady Forwood, Sir Peter Forwood, Mrs J. George, Mr L. Graffato, Grand Holdings Ltd, Mr C. Green, Ms A. R. Gross, Mr J. E. Hale, J. E. Harley, Mr M. A. Harris, B. D. Haynes, Heart of the South Racing 103, Mr P. A. Herbert, Ms L. M. Hess, Mr M. Hess, Mr A. D. S. Hodges, T. Jacobs, Jacobs Construction (Holdings) Limited, Mrs L. Jenkins, Mr K. P. Jessup, Mr K. W. Johnson, Mr A. Keeley, D. Leon, Mr S. A. Michael, Mr D. G. Moore, Mrs C. S. Muddle, Mrs S. C. Neville, Newco 1111 Ltd, Mr J. Norman, Past The Post Racing, Mr J. R. Penny, Mr R. Pettett, Mr C. W. D. Poore, Mr N. J. Roach, M. G. Rogers, Mrs T. J. Sage, Mr R. J. Sage, Mr R. D. Sargent, Mrs P. L. C. L. Sarzi-Braga, Mrs H. J. Shelton, R. M. Siddle, Mr M. T. Titterton, Mr M. C. Waddingham, T. Ware, Miss C. A. Webb, Mr M. K. Webb, Westbourne Consultants Ltd.

Assistant Trainers: David Wilson, Andrew Glassonbury

Jockey (flat): Ryan Moore. **Jockey (NH):** Andrew Glassonbury, Jamie Moore, Joshua Moore. **Conditional:** William Clarke, Jason Nuttall. **Apprentice:** Hector Crouch. **Amateur:** Miss Becky Butler, Miss Hayley Moore.

---

393 MR J. S. MOORE, Upper Lambourn
Postal: **Berkeley House Stables, Upper Lambourn, Hungerford, Berkshire, RG17 8QP**
Contacts: **PHONE (01488) 73887 FAX (01488) 73997 MOBILE (07860) 811127 / (07900) 402856**
E-MAIL jsmoore.racing@btopenworld.com WEBSITE www.stanmooreracing.co.uk

1 EVERKYLLACHY (IRE), 4, br f Kyllachy—Superfonic (FR) **Ever Equine & J. S. Moore**
2 POETIC PRINCIPLE (IRE), 4, b g Royal Applause—Lady Links **Mrs F. H. Hay**
3 SHEILA'S FANCY (IRE), 4, ch g Casamento (IRE)—Fancy Vivid (IRE) **Mr Ray Styles & J. S. Moore**

THREE-YEAR-OLDS
4 BOSS FOR A DAY, ch g Mastercraftsman (IRE)—Santa Agata (FR) **J S Moore Partnership**
5 BROCKAGH CAILIN, b f Helmet (AUS)—Step Softly **Gridline Racing**
6 CONTROVERSIAL LADY (IRE), b f Holy Roman Emperor (IRE)—
Eleanor Roosevelt (IRE) **Mrs Wendy Jarrett & J S Moore**
7 DADDY TYRRELL (USA), b c Scat Daddy (USA)—
My Hopeful Heart (USA) **James Lovett, Robert Tyrrell & J S Moore**
8 DEBUTANTE'S BALL (IRE), ch f Society Rock (IRE)—Query (USA) **Mrs Wendy Jarrett & J S Moore**
9 FAS LE FIOS (IRE), b f Epaulette (AUS)—Saffa Garden (IRE) **J. S. Moore & Partner**
10 LAS LOMAS BLANCA (FR), b g Planteur (IRE)—Parisian Princess (IRE) **Mr D G Pryde & J S Moore**
11 LENIN (IRE), gr c Arakan (USA)—Virginia Woolf **Mr Sean O'Sullivan & J S Moore**
12 POWER FROM ABOVE (IRE), br f Power—Aspasias Tizzy (USA) **J S Moore & Mr J Carr**
13 ROSE OF SHIRAZ, b f Mazameer (IRE)—Redeemed **Mr Eddie McGlinchey & J S Moore**
14 SAY ABOUT IT, b g Sayif (IRE)—Manaaber (USA) **C Instone, K Badger & J S Moore**
15 SHEILA'S EMPIRE (IRE), b f Holy Roman Emperor (IRE)—Silk Mascara (IRE) **Mr Ray Styles & J. S. Moore**
16 STYLISH GRACE (FR), gr f Style Vendome (FR)—
Conciliatory **Mrs Wendy Jarrett, Mrs June Newell-Smyth & Sara Moore**
17 UTHER PENDRAGON (IRE), b g Dragon Pulse (IRE)—Unreal **Mrs Wendy Jarrett & J S Moore**
18 ZOUCH, b g Sakhee's Secret—Sabrina Brown **Mr G V March & J S Moore**

TWO-YEAR-OLDS
19 B f 9/5 Requinto (IRE)—All Embracing (IRE) (Night Shift (USA)) (813)
20 ATHENA STAR, b f 12/5 War Command (USA)—Angie And Liz (IRE) (Spectrum (IRE))
21 B g 13/4 Coach House (IRE)—Ella Rosie (Dubai Destination (USA)) (12000)
22 EVER ROCK, b f 4/4 Society Rock (IRE)—Alhaadh (USA) (Diesis) (1627) **Ever Equine & J. S. Moore**
23 Gr f 18/2 Alhebayeb (IRE)—Flywheel (IRE) (Teofilo (IRE)) **J. S. Moore & Partner**
24 Ch f 18/4 Bungle Inthejungle—Lady Piste (IRE) (Ali-Royal (IRE))
25 MAGNETIC (IRE), b g 21/4 Alhebayeb (IRE)—
Telltime (IRE) (Danetime (IRE)) (6666) **Mrs Wendy Jarrett & J S Moore**
26 B g 11/2 Sayif (IRE)—Pose (IRE) (Acclamation) (3000) **The Moore The Merrier**
27 B f 25/2 Raven's Pass (USA)—Redinha (Dansili) **Mrs Patricia Walsh & J. S. Moore**
28 B f 8/1 Mastercraftsman (IRE)—
Rhiannon (IRE) (High Chaparral (IRE)) (12210) **Eventmasters Racing & J S Moore**
29 B g 29/2 Battle of Marengo (IRE)—Saffa Garden (IRE) (King's Best (USA)) **J. S. Moore & Partner**
30 B f 3/4 Bungle Inthejungle—Sayrah (Sakhee (USA)) **The Petticoat Government**

MR J. S. MOORE - Continued

31 B f 12/2 Sayif (IRE)—Shohrah (IRE) (Giant's Causeway (USA))
32 Ch f 20/4 Dalakhani (IRE)—Sky Colours (IRE) (Galileo (IRE)) (21164)
33 B f 4/4 Bungle Inthejungle—Tallawalla (IRE) (Oratorio (IRE))

Other Owners: Mr Kieron Badger, Mr Kevin Elliott, Ever Equine, Mr Ian J. Gray, Ms Caroline Instone, Mrs Sabina Kelly, Mr James Lovett, Mr G. V. March, Mr Nigel McGlinchey, Mr Eddie McGlinchey, Mr J. S. Moore, Mr Sean O'Sullivan, Mr Ray Styles, Mr Robert Tyrrell, Mr M. Winter.

Assistant Trainer: Mrs S. Moore

Apprentice: Georgia Dobie.

---

394 **MISS LAURA MORGAN, Waltham On The Wolds**
Postal: Foxfield Stud, Goadby Road, Waltham On The Wolds, Melton Mowbray, Leicestershire, LE14 4AG
Contacts: PHONE (01664) 464571 MOBILE (07817) 616622
E-MAIL lauramorg@hotmail.co.uk

1 **BORN A SAINT**, 5, ch g Phoenix Reach (IRE)—Kind Nell **Dr H. J. F. Why**
2 **FENJACK (IRE)**, 6, b g Jimble (FR)—Katie Baby (IRE) **Mrs A. M. Williams**
3 **GOLD FIELDS**, 4, b g Sakhee (USA)—Realms of Gold (USA) **Mrs M. J. Pepperdine**
4 **GRECIAN KING**, 5, b g Kheleyf (USA)—Grecian Air (FR) **Triumph In Mind**
5 **HAASAB (IRE)**, 5, b g Sakhee (USA)—Badweia (USA) **Roemex Ltd**
6 **HEADS UP CLEMMIE**, 5, b m Sulamani (IRE)—M'lady Rousseur (IRE) **The Rann Family**
7 **MUZAAHIM (IRE)**, 7, ch g Tamayuz—Elizabeth Swann **R. A. Jenkinson**
8 **RISING TIDE (IRE)**, 7, b g Dubai Destination (USA)—Erins Love (IRE) **Read & Pepperdine**
9 **RUN FOR EVA**, 5, b m Westerner—Glorybe (GER) **The Rann Family**
10 **SKIPPING ON (IRE)**, 9, b g Westerner—Skipping Along (IRE) **Laura Morgan Racing Club**
11 **TAQWAA (IRE)**, 5, ch h Iffraaj—Hallowed Park (IRE) **R. A. Jenkinson**
12 **TED'S BROTHER (IRE)**, 10, b g Fath (USA)—Estertide (USA) **Laura Morgan Racing Club**
13 **THE NEW PHARAOH (IRE)**, 7, b g Montjeu (IRE)—Out West (USA) **Paul Read & Mrs Anthea Williams**
14 **TOLETHORPE**, 7, ch g Halling (USA)—Tcherina (IRE) **Mr & Mrs W. J. Williams**
15 **TOUCH BACK (IRE)**, 12, b g Shantou (USA)—Back Log (IRE) **Miss L. Morgan**
16 **ULIS DE VASSY (FR)**, 10, b g Voix du Nord (FR)—Helathou (FR) **Read & Morgan**
17 **ZAKHAROVA**, 4, ch f Beat Hollow—Tcherina (IRE) **Mr & Mrs W. J. Williams**

Other Owners: Mr G. P. D. Rann, Mrs L. E. Rann, Mr P. L. Read, Mr T. Wendels, Mrs M. Williams, W. J. Williams, Mr R. F. Wright.

Assistant Trainer: Tom Morgan

Amateur: Miss A. Peck.

---

395 **MR M. F. MORRIS, Fethard**
Postal: Everardsgrange, Fethard, Co. Tipperary, Ireland
Contacts: PHONE (00353) 52 6131474 FAX (00353) 52 6131654 MOBILE (00353) 86 8543010
E-MAIL mouse@eircom.net

1 **ALPHA DES OBEAUX (FR)**, 8, b g Saddler Maker (IRE)—Omega des Obeaux (FR) **Gigginstown House Stud**
2 **ANJOU D'OR (FR)**, 6, b g East of Heaven (IRE)—Belle Adoree (FR) **B. Maloney**
3 **BAILY GORSE (IRE)**, 4, b g Milan—Lillies Bordello (IRE) **Mr R. A. Scott**
4 **BAILY MOON (IRE)**, 7, b g Milan—Givehertime (IRE) **Mr R. A. Scott**
5 **BAILY THUNDER**, 4, ch g Yorgunnabelucky (USA)—Alikat (IRE) **Mr R. A. Scott**
6 **BALAKANI (FR)**, 5, b g Khalkevi (IRE)—La Balagne (FR) **Mr R. A. Scott**
7 **BELLO CONTI (FR)**, 7, b g Coastal Path—Posterite (FR) **Gigginstown House Stud**
8 **BEYOND THE LAW (IRE)**, 6, b g Westerner—Thegoodwans Sister (IRE) **Exors of Alan & Anne Potts**
9 **CALIPTION**, 6, gr g Fair Mix (IRE)—Sheriff's Falcon (IRE) **Gigginstown House Stud**
10 **CAPTAIN ZEBO (IRE)**, 6, b g Brian Boru—Waydale Hill **Gigginstown House Stud**
11 **COMMANDANT (IRE)**, 5, br g Presenting—Miss Nomer (IRE) **Gigginstown House Stud**
12 **DESIR DU LARGE (FR)**, 5, gr g Zambezi Sun—Rapsodie Sea (FR) **Gigginstown House Stud**
13 **DESIRE DE JOIE (FR)**, 5, b g Alberto Giacometti—Promesse de Joie (FR)
14 **DOOLEY'S ROCK (IRE)**, 6, b g Let The Lion Roar—Derravarra Bay (IRE) **M. O'Flynn, J. O'Flynn**
15 **DROMNEA (IRE)**, 11, b br g Presenting—Fifth Imp (IRE) **Mrs A. Daly**
16 **EVISCERATING (IRE)**, 6, gr g Court Cave (IRE)—Titanic Quarter (IRE) **Gigginstown House Stud**

MR M. F. MORRIS - Continued

17 **FIRST CLASS RETURN (IRE)**, 5, b g Let The Lion Roar—Chitty Bang Bang (IRE) **D. O'Donohoe & P. Nelson**
18 **GROTESQUE**, 7, b g Kayf Tara—Princess Timon **Gigginstown House Stud**
19 **HICKEY'S ROCK (IRE)**, 6, b g Westerner—Golden Odyssey (IRE) **M. O'Flynn, J. O'Flynn**
20 **LAST MAN STANDING (IRE)**, 5, ch g Flemensfirth (USA)—Tricky Present (IRE) **Mr J. Magnier**
21 **NAMBOUR (GER)**, 8, b g Sholokhov (IRE)—Nanouska (GER) **Gigginstown House Stud**
22 **POTTSIE (IRE)**, 5, b g Robin des Champs (FR)—Present Gesture (IRE) **Exors of Alan & Anne Potts**
23 **ROGUE ANGEL (IRE)**, 10, b g Presenting—Carrigeen Kohleria (IRE) **Gigginstown House Stud**
24 **SETTIMO MILANESE (IRE)**, 6, b g Milan—Ad Gloria (IRE) **Lord Alfred Syndicate**
25 **SIZING JOSHUA (IRE)**, 5, b g Flemensfirth (USA)—Alleygrove Lass (IRE) **Exors of Alan & Anne Potts**
26 **SPRING WATCH (IRE)**, 6, b g Mahler—Taras Child (IRE) **J. P. McManus**
27 **THUNDER AND ROSES (IRE)**, 10, br g Presenting—Glen Empress (IRE) **Gigginstown House Stud**
28 **TOUT EST PERMIS (FR)**, 5, gr g Linda's Lad—Kadalbleue (FR) **Gigginstown House Stud**
29 **TRIANGLE ROCK (IRE)**, 5, b g Stowaway—Lucy Cooper (IRE) **M. O'Flynn & J. O'Flynn**
30 **WAR HOUSE (IRE)**, 5, br g Marienbard (IRE)—Niamhs Delight (IRE) **L. F. Curtin**
31 **WESTERN RULER (IRE)**, 6, b g Westerner—Time In Milan (IRE)
32 **WIGS ON THE GREEN (IRE)**, 6, b g Robin des Champs (FR)—Koko Rose (IRE) **J. P. McManus**
33 **WISHMOOR (IRE)**, 8, br g Winged Love (IRE)—Presentingatdawn (IRE) **Gigginstown House Stud**

---

396   **MR PATRICK MORRIS, Prescot**
Postal: **Avenue House, George Hale Avenue, Knowsley Park, Prescot, Merseyside, L34 4AJ**
Contacts: MOBILE **(07545) 425235**
E-MAIL info@patmorrisracing.co.uk WEBSITE www.patmorrisracing.co.uk

1 **ANGEL GABRIAL (IRE)**, 9, b g Hurricane Run (IRE)—Causeway Song (USA) **Dr M. B. Q. S. Koukash**
2 **BAHANGO (IRE)**, 6, b g Bahamian Bounty—Last Tango (IRE) **Mr L. P. Richards**
3 **BELL HEATHER (IRE)**, 5, b m Iffraaj—Burren Rose (USA) **Dr M. B. Q. S. Koukash**
4 **CRUISE TOTHELIMIT (IRE)**, 10, b g Le Vie Dei Colori—Kiva **Odysian Limited**
5 **ENERGIA FLAVIO (BRZ)**, 8, gr g Agnes Gold (JPN)—Lira da Guanabara (BRZ) **Dr M. B. Q. S. Koukash**
6 **GABRIAL THE TERROR (IRE)**, 8, b g Kheleyf (USA)—Simla Bibi **Dr M. B. Q. S. Koukash**
7 **GABRIAL THE THUG (FR)**, 8, b g Azamour (IRE)—Baliyna (USA) **Dr M. B. Q. S. Koukash**
8 **GABRIAL THE TIGER (IRE)**, 6, b g Kodiac—Invincible **Dr M. B. Q. S. Koukash**
9 **GABRIAL'S KAKA (IRE)**, 8, b g Jeremy (USA)—Love In May (USA) **Dr M. B. Q. S. Koukash**
10 **GABRIAL'S KING (IRE)**, 9, b g Hurricane Run (IRE)—Danella (IRE) **Dr M. B. Q. S. Koukash**
11 **GROWL**, 6, b g Oasis Dream—Desert Tigress (USA) **Dr M. B. Q. S. Koukash**
12 **LEXI'S HERO (IRE)**, 10, b g Invincible Spirit (IRE)—Christel Flame (USA) **Dr M. B. Q. S. Koukash**
13 **MAGIC CIRCLE (IRE)**, 6, b g Makfi—Minkova (IRE) **Dr M. B. Q. S. Koukash**
14 **MEHDI (IRE)**, 9, b g Holy Roman Emperor (IRE)—College Fund Girl (IRE) **Dr M. B. Q. S. Koukash**
15 **MONACO ROSE**, 5, b m Sir Percy—Pallas **Dr M. B. Q. S. Koukash**
16 **PERRAULT (IRE)**, 6, gr g Rip Van Winkle (IRE)—La Persiana **Dr M. B. Q. S. Koukash**
17 **POWERALLIED (IRE)**, 5, b g Camacho—Kaplinsky (IRE) **Dr M. B. Q. S. Koukash**
18 **PUSHKIN MUSEUM (IRE)**, 7, gr g Soviet Star (USA)—Chaste (FR) **Dr M. B. Q. S. Koukash**
19 **RESTORER**, 6, gr g Mastercraftsman (IRE)—Moon Empress (FR) **Dr M. B. Q. S. Koukash**
20 **THE HOODED CLAW (IRE)**, 7, ch g Dandy Man (IRE)—Changari (USA) **Dr M. B. Q. S. Koukash**
21 **TOP OFFER**, 9, b g Dansili—Zante **Mr M. Watkinson**
22 **VALDIZAR**, 4, b g Zamindar (USA)—Valentine Girl **Dr M. B. Q. S. Koukash**

THREE-YEAR-OLDS

23 **GOSSIP COLUMN (IRE)**, b g Arcano (IRE)—Monicalew **Dr M. B. Q. S. Koukash**
24 **TONKOLILI (IRE)**, b f Kodiac—Heart's Desire (IRE) **Mr M. Watkinson**

---

397   **MR HUGHIE MORRISON, East Ilsley**
Postal: **Summerdown, East Ilsley, Newbury, Berkshire, RG20 7LB**
Contacts: PHONE **(01635) 281678** FAX **(01635) 281746** MOBILE **(07836) 687799**
E-MAIL hughie@hughiemorrison.co.uk WEBSITE www.hughiemorrison.co.uk

1 **AFFAIR**, 4, b f Sakhee's Secret—Supatov (USA) **Mr H. Morrison**
2 **APRES LE DELUGE (FR)**, 4, gr g Stormy River (FR)—Ms Cordelia (USA) **Mr Raymond Tooth**
3 **AURORA GRAY**, 5, gr m Rip Van Winkle (IRE)—Summer's Eve **Wardley Bloodstock**
4 **BUZZ (FR)**, 4, gr g Motivator—Tiysha (IRE) **Mr M Bevan, Mr A Pickford & Mr R Angliss**
5 **CANOODLE**, 6, b m Stimulation (IRE)—Flirtatious **Mrs M. D. W. Morrison**
6 **CELTIK SECRET**, 4, ro f Sakhee's Secret—Cill Rialaig **Mr Tim Billington**

MR HUGHIE MORRISON - Continued

   7 **COLD FIRE (IRE)**, 5, ch g Frozen Power (IRE)—Eleanor Eloise (USA) **Mrs Jackie Cornwell**
   8 **COMPTON MILL**, 6, b g Compton Place—
                     Classic Millennium **Mr M Bevan, Mrs R Luard & Mrs M D W Morrison**
   9 **COUSIN KHEE**, 11, b g Sakhee (USA)—Cugina **Mrs M. D. W. Morrison**
  10 **FAR CRY**, 5, b m Sakhee's Secret—Yonder **Mrs M. D. W. Morrison**
  11 **FINALE**, 4, b f Holy Roman Emperor (IRE)—Sell Out **Mr T Rootes & Mr O Waller**
  12 **FUN MAC (GER)**, 7, ch g Shirocco (GER)—Favorite (GER) **Mrs Angela McAlpine & Partners**
  13 **HELFIRE**, 5, b m Archipenko (USA)—Relkida **Mr M Watson & Miss D Collett**
  14 **KATABATIKA**, 4, b f Shirocco (GER)—Landinium (ITY) **Lord Blyth**
  15 **MAGIC BEANS**, 4, b g Pastoral Pursuits—Jasmeno **MNC Racing**
  16 **MAJOR MAC**, 6, ch g Shirocco (GER)—Spring Fashion (IRE) **Mr Paul Brocklehurst & Partners**
  17 **MAKAARIM**, 4, b g Tamayuz—Dubawi Cheetah (IRE) **Thurloe Thoroughbred**
  18 **MARMELO**, 5, b h Duke of Marmalade (IRE)—Capriolla **The Fairy Story Partnership & Mr Aziz Kheir**
  19 **MUCH TOO MUCH**, 5, b m Stimulation (IRE)—Complication **Mr A Williams & Miss J Staughton**
  20 **MULSANNE CHASE**, 4, b g Sixties Icon—Hot Pursuits **Mrs Isabel Eavis**
  21 **NEARLY CAUGHT (IRE)**, 8, b g New Approach (IRE)—Katch Me Katie **Mr A. N. Solomons**
  22 **NOT SO SLEEPY**, 6, ch g Beat Hollow—Papillon de Bronze (IRE) **Lady Blyth**
  23 **PASTORAL PLAYER**, 11, b g Pastoral Pursuits—Copy-Cat **The Pursuits Partnership**
  24 **PLAYING GAMES**, 5, b m Pastoral Pursuits—Flirtatious **Mrs M. D. W. Morrison**
  25 **POET'S PRINCESS**, 4, ch f Poet's Voice—Palace Affair **Mr Paul Brocklehurst**
  26 **PURSUING STEED**, 4, b g Pastoral Pursuits—Emma Peel **Caveat Emptor Partnership**
  27 **QUAY POINT (IRE)**, 5, b m Royal Applause—Merle **Mrs Jackie Cornwell**
  28 **SISTER SIBYL (IRE)**, 7, br m King's Theatre (IRE)—Rose of The Erne (IRE) **The Hill Stud**
  29 **SKYLINE**, 4, b g Stimulation (IRE)—Yonder **Mrs M. D. W. Morrison**
  30 **SPECIAL RELATION (IRE)**, 4, b g Casamento (IRE)—Sindiyma (IRE) **Mr M Hankin, Mr C Fenwick & Mr C Noell**
  31 **STAR ROCK**, 4, b f Fastnet Rock (AUS)—Starfala **Ben & Sir Martyn Arbib**
  32 **TEMPLE CHURCH (IRE)**, 4, b g Lawman (FR)—All Hallows (IRE) **Mr P. C. J. Dalby & Mr R. D. Schuster**
  33 **THIRD WIND**, 4, b br g Shirocco (GER)—Act Three **Mouse Hamilton-Fairley**

THREE-YEAR-OLDS

  34 **ALL SQUARE**, ch g Equiano (FR)—Big Old Unit **Mr & Mrs R Lloyd, Mr R Wright**
  35 B c Nathaniel (IRE)—Amarullah (FR) **Trinity Park Stud**
  36 **BELATED BREATH**, ch f Bated Breath—Daffydowndilly **Lady Blyth**
  37 **BELLA RAGAZZA**, gr f Dutch Art—Sell Out **Mr Paul Brocklehurst**
  38 **BETJEMAN**, b c Poet's Voice—Respectfully **The Fairy Story Partnership**
  39 **BOSCASTLE (USA)**, ch f Sea The Stars (IRE)—Imprecation (USA) **Mr H Morrison**
  40 **BOSSINEY BAY (IRE)**, b f Camelot—Ursula Minor (IRE) **Thurloe Thoroughbreds XL**
  41 **CANDIDATE (IRE)**, b c Camelot—Miss Mariduff (USA) **Mr M. Kerr-Dineen, Mr W. Eason, Mr D. Fass**
  42 **CLIMB ABOARD**, ch g Mayson—Jump Ship **Mr M. Dixon**
  43 **CORGI**, b c So You Think (NZ)—Ermyn Express **Mr M Kerr-Dineen, M Hughes**
  44 **DAME VERA**, ch f Medicean—Some Sunny Day **Julia Scott & J. F. Dean**
  45 **DAYBREAK**, b f Dawn Approach (IRE)—Walk On Bye (IRE) **Mr & Mrs G Swire, Mr R. Callaghan & Mrs A. Scott**
  46 **DEADLY LOCATION**, br g Lethal Force (IRE)—
            Riccoche (IRE) **Mr Simon Malcolm, Mr Tony Pickford, The Hon Mary Morrison & Mr Simon de Zoete**
  47 **DORIAN GRAY (IRE)**, b g So You Think (NZ)—Flawless Beauty **Mr P. C. J. Dalby & Mr R. D. Schuster**
  48 **EARLY SUMMER (IRE)**, b f Sea The Stars (IRE)—Summer's Eve **Wardley Bloodstock**
  49 **ESCAPE THE CITY**, b f Cityscape—Jasmeno **MNC Racing**
  50 **GERANIUM**, ch f Sakhee's Secret—Kasumi **F Trenchard, Clare, Lady Margadale & The Hon Mary Morrison**
  51 **HILIGHT**, b f Archipenko (USA)—Relkida **Mr M Watson & Miss D Collett**
  52 **JEDHI**, b f Big Bad Bob (IRE)—
            Capriolla **Mr Tony Pickford, Mr Simon Malcolm, The Hon Mary Morrison & Mr Simon de Zoete**
  53 **NIKITA (IRE)**, b f Exceed And Excel (AUS)—Rosinka (IRE) **The End-R-Ways Partnership & Partners**
  54 **PAMINAH**, b f Bated Breath—
            Starry Sky **The Hon Mary Morrison & Mr Simon de Zoete, Mr Simon Malcolm, Mr Tony Pickford**
  55 **PIPPIN**, ch g Intello (GER)—Golden Delicious **Mr Nicholas Jones**
  56 **QUICKSAND (IRE)**, ch f Footstepsinthesand—Miss Bellbird (IRE) **Mrs S M Rogers & Sir Thomas Pilkington**
  57 **RACEHORSE**, b f Equiano (FR)—Lovely Dream (IRE) **TMBS Solutions Ltd**
  58 **RIPPLET**, b f Rip Van Winkle (IRE)—Seradim **The Fairy Story Partnership**
  59 **SAINT MAC**, b c Nathaniel (IRE)—Noahs Ark (IRE) **Mr Adrian McAlpine, Mrs Angela Scott**
  60 **SNATTY DANCER**, ch f Nathaniel (IRE)—Spicy Dal **Ben & Sir Martyn Arbib**
  61 **SOD'S LAW**, b g Mayson—Lawyers Choice **Mr Raymond Tooth**
  62 **STARCASTER**, b c Dansili—Shirocco Star **Castle Down Racing**
  63 **TELEKINETIC**, b f Champs Elysees—Kinetix **Helena Springfield Limited**
  64 **TOMTIT**, b g Pastoral Pursuits—Swan Queen **Sir Thomas Pilkington**

MR HUGHIE MORRISON - Continued

TWO-YEAR-OLDS

65 B c 14/4 Swiss Spirit—
   Belle des Airs (IRE) (Dr Fong (USA)) (31000) **Mr M. Kerr-Dineen, Mr D. Fass, Viscount Trenchard**
66 B c 24/3 Kodiac—Broadlands (Kheleyf (USA)) (30000) **Mr Simon Malcolm, Mr Harry & Mrs Julie Parkes**
67 B c 14/2 Cacique (IRE)—Capriolla (In The Wings) (70000) **Selwood Bloodstock & Mrs S Read**
68 Ch f 14/4 Intello (GER)—Celestial Girl (Dubai Destination (USA)) **Helena Springfield Ltd**
69 Ch c 28/2 New Approach (IRE)—Complexion (Hurricane Run (IRE)) (50000) **Brightwalton Bloodstock Ltd**
70 B c 22/2 Sea The Stars (IRE)—Coquet (Sir Percy) (85000) **Lord Margadale, Mr A. Scott, Mr M. Kerr-Dineen**
71 HENDRIX (IRE), b c 6/3 War Command (USA)—Monzza (Montjeu (IRE)) **Castle Down Racing**
72 B f 14/3 Nathaniel (IRE)—I Say (Oratorio (IRE)) **Mr Raymond Tooth**
73 B c 28/4 Havana Gold (IRE)—Jasmeno (Catcher In The Rye (IRE)) **MNC Racing**
74 B c 28/4 Requinto (IRE)—
   Joyfullness (USA) (Dixieland Band (USA)) (50000) **Mr M. Kerr-Dineen, Mr W. Eason, Mr D. Malpas**
75 KORCHO, b c 10/4 Toronado (IRE)—
   Locharia (Wolfhound (USA)) (50000) **Mr M. Kerr-Dineen, Mr M. Hughes & Mr W. Eason**
76 MUMS HOPE, gr ro f 11/3 Lethal Force (IRE)—Jadwiga (Pivotal) (23000) **Mr Martin Hughes**
77 ROBERT L'ECHELLE (IRE), b c 11/3 Big Bad Bob (IRE)—
   Damhsa Le Cheile (IRE) (Teofilo (IRE)) (9000) **Mr A. N. Solomons**
78 SANDYMAN, ch c 23/1 Footstepsinthesand—Quiz Mistress (Doyen (IRE)) **The Fairy Story Partnership**
79 SEADUCED, br gr f 15/2 Lope de Vega (IRE)—Starfala (Galileo (IRE)) **Ben & Sir Martyn Arbib**
80 B c 9/2 New Approach (IRE)—Shirocco Star (Shirocco (GER)) (180000) **Castle Down Racing**
81 Ch f 20/4 Dutch Art—
   Strictly Lambada (Red Ransom (USA)) (50000) **Sir Francis Brooke, Mr R Pilkington, Mr A Rogers**
82 B c 29/1 Cape Cross (IRE)—Talent Spotter (Exceed And Excel (AUS)) (40000) **Mr A. McAlpine**
83 B f 21/4 Champs Elysees—Tottie (Fantastic Light (USA)) **Mr Julian Richmond-Watson**
84 B f 22/4 Piccolo—Violet's Walk (Dr Fong (USA)) **Mr M. E. Wates**

Other Owners: Mr R. A. Angliss, Mr & Mrs P. Bevan, Mr T. Bevan, Mrs M. T. Bevan, Mrs P. G. Billington, Mr T. J. Billington, Mr T. M. Bird, Mr M. Brown, Mr B. Brown, Charles E. Noell ESQ, Mr J. Clitherow, Miss D. Collett, Mr Simon de Zoete, Mrs H. S. Ellingsen, Mr Charles Fenwick, Mr M. W. Goodall, Mr E. R. Goodwin, Mr J. N. Greenley, Mr M. Gregori, Mr Rupert Gregson-Williams, Mrs E. Gregson-Williams, Mr Mike Hankin, Mr T. Hester, Mr D. S. Little, Mr Rodney Lloyd, Mrs R. A. Luard, Alastair Macdonald-Buchanan, Mr Simon Malcolm, Mrs Angela McAlpine, Mr Adrian McAlpine, The Hon Miss M. A. Morrison, Mr H. Morrison, Mr Roger O'Callaghan, Mr J. W. Parker, Mr O. J. W. Pawle, A. C. Pickford, Sir Thomas Pilkington, Mr R. Pooles, Mr M. Pou, Mrs S. M. Rogers, Mr Gerald Rothwell, Mrs Angela Scott, Miss C. S. Scott-Balls, Mr Hugh Scott-Barrett, Mr J. A. B. Stafford, Mrs C. A. Swire, Mr M. Taylor, Mr K. Taylor, Viscountess Trenchard, Mr M. J. Watson, Mr G. Waylen, Mr M. Weinfeld, Mr S. Willmont.

Assistant Trainer: Mr Oliver Rix

Apprentice: Charlie Bennett, Theodore Ladd. **Amateur:** Mr Robert Pooles.

---

398 **MR MOHAMED MOUBARAK, Newmarket**
Postal: 3C Sunnyside, Park Lane, Newmarket, Suffolk, CB8 8AX
E-MAIL moubarak.mohammed17@gmail.com

1 OUT OF THE ASHES, 5, ch g Phoenix Reach (IRE)—Shrewd Decision **D. P. Fremel**
2 SHARP REPLY (IRE), 4, b g Holy Roman Emperor (IRE)—Sabindra **Champion Bloodstock Limited**
3 WARBA (IRE), 4, ch f Intense Focus (USA)—Have A Heart (IRE) **D. P. Fremel**

THREE-YEAR-OLDS

4 PAM'S ANGEL (USA), ch f Kitten's Joy (USA)—
   Summer Scene (USA) **Mrs Lyn Marshall & Mohamad Moubarak**

TWO-YEAR-OLDS

5 B f 30/4 Charm Spirit (IRE)—Dreamily (IRE) (New Approach (IRE)) (14000) **Mr M. Y. Moubarak**
6 Ch f 7/2 Sepoy (AUS)—Lilli Marlane (Sri Pekan (USA)) (17000) **Mr M. Y. Moubarak**
7 Ch c 28/1 Archipenko (USA)—Malhadinha (IRE) (New Approach (IRE)) (9000) **Mr M. Y. Moubarak**
8 B c 8/3 Foxwedge (AUS)—Midnight Fling (Groom Dancer (USA)) (18000) **Mr M. Y. Moubarak**
9 SALMON FISHING (IRE), b c 3/3 Dragon Pulse (IRE)—Lake Wanaka (IRE) (Fasliyev (USA)) (3000) **D. P. Fremel**
10 B c 24/3 Lilbourne Lad (IRE)—Santacus (IRE) (Spartacus (IRE)) (7325) **Mr S. M. Al Sabah**
11 B c 28/4 Sepoy (AUS)—Wind Surf (USA) (Lil's Lad (USA)) (13000) **Mr M. Y. Moubarak**

Other Owners: Ms L. D. Marshall.

399 MR WILLIAM MUIR, Lambourn

Postal: Linkslade, Wantage Road, Lambourn, Hungerford, Berkshire, RG17 8UG
Contacts: OFFICE (01488) 73098 HOME (01488) 73748 FAX (01488) 73490
MOBILE (07831) 457074
E-MAIL william@williammuir.com WEBSITE www.williammuir.com

1 **AMERICAN HISTORY (USA)**, 4, b br g High Chaparral (IRE)—
Spinning Time (USA) **Byrne, Devlin, Edginton, Jeffery**
2 **ANGRYWHITEPYJAMAS (IRE)**, 5, b g Manduro (GER)—Ornellaia (IRE) **O'Mulloy, Collenette, Clark**
3 **CHIEF BRODY**, 7, b g Phoenix Reach (IRE)—Cherry Plum **Miss L. J. Sandford & Mr R. B. Phillips**
4 **CODE RED**, 6, ch h Bahamian Bounty—Just Devine (IRE) **Mrs Michelle Morgan**
5 **CUTTIN' EDGE (IRE)**, 4, b g Rip Van Winkle (IRE)—How's She Cuttin' (IRE) **Purple & Lilac Racing**
6 **CYRUS DALLIN**, 4, b g Roderic O'connor (IRE)—Munaawashat (IRE) **C. L. A. Edginton**
7 **HOLLANDER**, 4, ch g Dutch Art—Thrill **Muir Racing Partnership - Ayr**
8 **LITTLE MISS DAISY**, 4, b f Arabian Gleam—Desert Liaison **Mrs J. M. Muir**
9 **MISS M (IRE)**, 4, b f Mastercraftsman (IRE)—Tintern **Brian Willis**
10 **MOONLIGHT SILVER**, 4, gr f Makfi—Moon Empress (FR) **Foursome Thoroughbreds**
11 **PASS THE CRISTAL (IRE)**, 4, b g Raven's Pass (USA)—Crystal Melody **O'Mulloy, Schwartz**
12 **PEACE AND PLENTY**, 4, ch c Exceed And Excel (AUS)—Putois Peace **Muir Racing Partnership - Doncaster**
13 **PHIJEE**, 4, gr c Sepoy (AUS)—Likeable **Mr Martin P. Graham**
14 **SECRET AGENT**, 4, b g Equiano (FR)—Varnish **Mrs Michelle Morgan**
15 **SPEEDY GONZALEZ**, 4, b g Josr Algarhoud (IRE)—Tellmethings **Mr J. M. O'Mulloy**
16 **SPIN TOP**, 4, b g Acclamation—Miss Work of Art **Mr J C Buckland & Mr N J Doyne**
17 **WHITE SHAHEEN**, 5, b g Makfi—Likeable **Mr S. P. Hussain**

THREE-YEAR-OLDS

18 **CENT FLYING**, b g Sepoy (AUS)—Sea of Leaves (USA) **Clarke, Edginton, Niven**
19 **CHARITY JOY**, b c Oasis Dream—Morzine **Mr Y. L. A. Lee**
20 B f Mount Nelson—China Beads **Mr S. Lamb**
21 **CORALIE (IRE)**, b f Born To Sea (IRE)—Tintern **Mrs J. M. Muir**
22 **DATA PROTECTION**, b g Foxwedge (AUS)—Midnight Sky **Muir Racing Partnership - Santa Anita**
23 B c Rock of Gibraltar (IRE)—Gamra (IRE) **Mr F Hope & Mr G Hope**
24 **GENERAL ZOFF**, b g Zoffany (IRE)—Aunt Julia **Purple & Lilac Racing X**
25 **GREENEYEDAFGHAN**, b g Sepoy (AUS)—Extremely Rare (IRE) **Mr J O'Mulloy & Mr K Jeffery**
26 **JAMAICAN JILL**, b f Teofilo (IRE)—Kahlua Kiss **Mr M. J. Caddy**
27 **JAVELIN**, ch f Lethal Force (IRE)—Amitola (IRE) **Mr Guy Leach**
28 **JUNEAU PEAK**, b c Kodiac—Singed **Mr M. J. Caddy**
29 **MALAGUENA**, ch f Mazameer (IRE)—Shore Light (USA) **Dulverton Equine**
30 **MILLE TANK**, b f Mastercraftsman (IRE)—Millevini (IRE) **Mr Y. L. A. Lee**
31 B c Excelebration (IRE)—Portrait **Mr S. P. Hussain**
32 **PREZZIE**, b f Major Cadeaux—Yearbook **Foursome Thoroughbreds**
33 B g Doncaster Rover (USA)—Tellmethings **Mr J. M. O'Mulloy**
34 **TONKOLILI (IRE)**, b f Kodiac—Heart's Desire (IRE) **Mr J. M. O'Mulloy**
35 Ch c Intello (GER)—Welsh Cake **M. J. Caddy**

TWO-YEAR-OLDS

36 B c 10/4 Nathaniel (IRE)—Danehill Dreamer (USA) (Danehill (USA)) (40000) **O'Mulloy, Schwartz**
37 B c 19/2 Bated Breath—Effervesce (IRE) (Galileo (IRE)) (45000)
38 Ch c 1/2 Helmet (AUS)—Island Sunset (IRE) (Trans Island) **Muir Racing Partnership - Leicester**
39 **JACK'S POINT**, b c 25/2 Slade Power (IRE)—Electra Star (Shamardal (USA)) (120000) **C. L. A. Edginton**
40 **JUST HUBERT (IRE)**, b c 25/1 Dunaden (FR)—
La Tulipe (FR) (Authorized (IRE)) (20000) **Foursome Thoroughbreds**
41 B c 5/3 Mount Nelson—London Welsh (Cape Cross (IRE)) **Mr M. P. Graham**
42 B c 20/3 Lilbourne Lad (IRE)—Ornellaia (IRE) (Mujadil (USA))
43 **SO CLAIRE**, br f 27/3 Kyllachy—If So (Iffraaj) (50000) **Foursome Thoroughbreds**

Other Owners: Mr P. Abberley, Mr J C Buckland, Mr A. A. Byrne, Mr Nick Clark, Mr D. G. Clarke, Mr J. Collenette, R. W. Devlin, Mr N J Doyne, Mr C. L. A. Edginton, Mr G. Hope, Mr F. Hope, Mr Ken Jeffery, Mr Kenny Kok, Mr Carl D. Moore, Mr W. R. Muir, Mr Alasdair Niven, Mr John O'Mulloy, Mr R. B. Phillips, Mr P. D. Quaintance, Mr D. L. Quaintance, Miss L. J. Sandford, Ms B. Schwartz, Mr Clive Washbourn.

Assistant Trainer: Richard Phillips

Jockey (flat): Martin Dwyer.

400 **MR CLIVE MULHALL, Scarcroft**
Postal: **Scarcroft Hall Farm, Thorner Lane, Scarcroft, Leeds, LS14 3AQ**
Contacts: PHONE **(0113) 2893095** FAX **(0113) 2893095** MOBILE **(07979) 527675**
E-MAIL **clive@scarcrofthallracing.co.uk** WEBSITE **www.clivemulhallracing.co.uk**

1 **ANEEDH,** 8, b g Lucky Story (USA)—Seed Al Maha (USA) **Mrs C. M. Mulhall**
2 **BEAU STRATA (IRE),** 4, b f Dandy Man (IRE)—Stratospheric **Mr C. Chapman & Mrs C. M. Mulhall**
3 **BIGBADBOY (IRE),** 5, b g Big Bad Bob (IRE)—Elegantly (IRE) **Ms Y Featherstone & Mrs M Mulhall**
4 **DUBAI MYSTERY (IRE),** 6, b g Dahjee (USA)—Precious Mystery (IRE) **Mr C. Chapman & Mrs C. M. Mulhall**

Other Owners: Mr C. Chapman, Ms Y. P. Featherstone.

Assistant Trainer: Mrs Martina Mulhall

401 **MR NEIL MULHOLLAND, Limpley Stoke**
Postal: **Conkwell Grange Stables, Conkwell, Limpley Stoke, Bath, Avon, BA2 7FD**
Contacts: MOBILE **(07739) 258607**
E-MAIL **neil@neilmulhollandracing.com** WEBSITE **www.neilmulhollandracing.com**

1 **ADMIRAL KID (IRE),** 7, b g Mythical Kid (USA)—English Clover **Equi ex Incertis Partners**
2 **AMBUSCADE,** 5, b m Dick Turpin (IRE)—Tarqua (IRE) **Earl of Carnarvon**
3 **AMERICAN PATROL (IRE),** 4, ch g Rio de La Plata (USA)—Gutter Press (IRE) **Neil Mulholland Racing Ltd**
4 **ARDEN DENIS (IRE),** 9, ch g Generous (IRE)—Christian Lady (IRE) **T. C. and A. Winter & Partners**
5 **ATTRACTIVE LIASON (IRE),** 8, b m Scorpion (IRE)—Sounds Attractive (IRE) **N Webb & P J Proudley**
6 **BACHY BABY,** 6, b g Bach (IRE)—Bathwick Annie **H. M. W. Clifford**
7 **BAIHAS,** 8, b g Nayef (USA)—Allegretto (IRE) **Turner, Webb, & Bgc Racing**
8 **BALLYANTICS (IRE),** 7, b g Marienbard (IRE)—Ballindante (IRE) **B. A. Derrick**
9 **BELLAMY,** 7, ch g Black Sam Bellamy (IRE)—Bonne Anniversaire **Mrs H. Dale-Staples**
10 **BETTER NEWS,** 7, b m Fair Mix (IRE)—Welcome News **Mrs C. L. Shaw**
11 **BISHOPS COURT,** 8, b g Helissio (FR)—Island of Memories (IRE) **Mr P. C. Tory & Mr P. S. Frampton**
12 **BOY IN A BENTLEY (IRE),** 8, b g Kayf Tara—All Our Blessings (IRE) **The Risk Takers Partnership**
13 **BUBSY BURBIDGE,** 7, b g Helissio (FR)—Twin Time **Dajam Ltd**
14 **BURNS CROSS (IRE),** 6, b g Mahler—Strokestown Queen (IRE) **Mr P. M. Simmonds**
15 **CAPE BANJO (USA),** 5, ch g Cape Blanco (IRE)—Magic of Love **A.B Partnership**
16 **CAROLE'S DESTRIER,** 10, b g Kayf Tara—Barton May **Mrs C. Skipworth**
17 **CAROLE'S VIGILANTE (IRE),** 7, ch g Flemensfirth (USA)—Gotta Goa (IRE) **Mrs C. Skipworth**
18 **CAVICIANA,** 5, b m Court Cave (IRE)—Viciana
19 **CESAR ET ROSALIE (FR),** 6, ch g Network (GER)—Regle de L'art (FR) **Mrs J. M. Abbott**
20 **CHAMPAGNE GEORGE (IRE),** 8, gr g Acambaro (GER)—Charannah (IRE) **7RUS**
21 **CHANTARA ROSE,** 9, br m Kayf Tara—Fragrant Rose **Steve & Jackie Fleetham**
22 **CHANTECLER,** 7, b g Authorized (IRE)—Snow Goose **Mr J. Hobbs**
23 **CHEEKY CHICA (IRE),** 5, bl m Stowaway—Hats And Heels (IRE) **A. R. Turnbull**
24 **CHIEF SITTINGBULL,** 5, ch g Indian Haven—Saharan Song (IRE) **Mr A. A. Byrne**
25 **CHIRICO VALLIS (FR),** 6, b g Poliglote—Quora Vallis (FR) **Mr J. P. McManus**
26 **CINTEX (FR),** 6, b g Assessor (IRE)—Precieuze (FR) **Miss J. A. Goddard**
27 **CLONDAW CRACKER (IRE),** 7, b g Court Cave (IRE)—Twelve Pence (IRE) **R. S. Brookhouse**
28 **CODE OF LAW,** 8, ch g Papal Bull—Fyvie **The Affordable (3) Partnership**
29 **COLLODI (GER),** 9, b g Konigstiger (GER)—Codera (GER) **Neil Mulholland Racing Club**
30 **COOLE CHARMER (IRE),** 9, ch g Flemensfirth (USA)—Ericas Charm **Heart Racing**
31 **CORNISH WARRIOR (IRE),** 7, b g Oscar (IRE)—Ballylooby Moss (IRE) **Strawberry Field Catering Ltd**
32 **DALAMAN (IRE),** 7, b g Duke of Marmalade (IRE)—Crimphill (IRE) **Diamond Racing Ltd**
33 **DANCE ROCK,** 5, b g Oasis Dream—Zee Zee Top **Mrs F. Houlihan**
34 **DANDOLO DU GITE (FR),** 5, b g Khalkevi (IRE)—Lavande d'eproniere (FR) **Equi ex Incertis Partners**
35 **DELANNOY,** 4, ch g Le Havre (IRE)—Raving Monsun **Mr Ashley Carr & Mr Derek Heeney**
36 **DEPUTY JONES (IRE),** 5, b m Milan—Hudson Hope (IRE) **A.**
37 **DIEG MAN (FR),** 5, ch g Kapgarde (FR)—Majestic Card (FR) **Mr J. P. McManus**
38 **DITES RIEN (IRE),** 6, b m Kalanisi (IRE)—Our Soiree (IRE) **Neil Mulholland Racing Club**
39 **DOING FINE (IRE),** 10, b g Presenting—Howaya Pet (IRE) **Mr Ashley Carr & Mr Andy Smith**
40 **DREAM MACHINE (IRE),** 4, ch g Dream Ahead (USA)—Last Cry (FR) **D. M. Bell**
41 **DUKE OF KILCORRAL (IRE),** 5, gr g Duke of Marmalade (IRE)—Miss Shaan (FR) **Mr J. Kehoe**
42 **FINGERONTHESWITCH (IRE),** 8, b g Beneficial—Houseoftherisinsun (IRE) **Cahill, Atwell & Crofts**
43 **FLORAL QUEEN,** 5, b m Emperor Fountain—Florentino **The Dickinsons,Butlin,Clegg,Finch&Lacey**
44 **FREE BOUNTY,** 5, b g Dick Turpin (IRE)—Native King (FR) **Four Winds Racing & Serafino Agodino**
45 **FULL (FR),** 6, b g Mr Sidney (USA)—Funny Feerie (FR) **Mr J. Moran**
46 **GLOBAL RHAPSODY,** 4, b g Presenting—Rhapsody In Blue (GER) **Dr J. Hon**

MR NEIL MULHOLLAND - Continued

47 **GOODGIRLTERESA (IRE)**, 8, b m Stowaway—Decheekymonkey (IRE) **Peter and Ruth Turner**
48 **GREEN OR BLACK (IRE)**, 6, gr m Zebedee—Boucheron **The Chosen Few**
49 **HADFIELD (IRE)**, 6, b g Sea The Stars (IRE)—Rezyana (AUS) **Mr T. J. Clyne**
50 **HALO MOON**, 10, br g Kayf Tara—Fragrant Rose **Level Par Racing**
51 **HAPPY ESCAPE**, 4, ch f Delegator—Saharan Song (IRE) **Mr A. A. Byrne**
52 **HARBOUR FORCE (FR)**, 4, b g Harbour Watch (IRE)—Dam Beautiful **Mr A. A. Byrne**
53 **HIGHBURY HIGH (IRE)**, 11, gr g Salford Express (IRE)—Betseale (IRE) **The Affordable Partnership**
54 **HYGROVE PERCY**, 5, ch g Sir Percy—Hygrove Welshlady (IRE) **G. P. and Miss S. J. Hayes**
55 **IM BACK (USA)**, 9, b g Don't Get Mad (USA)—I'm Gonna Shine (USA) **Mrs Capucine Mourier**
56 **IMPULSIVE STAR (IRE)**, 8, b g Busy Flight—Impulsive Ita (IRE) **Mr R. B. Waley-Cohen**
57 **INAMINNA (IRE)**, 7, b g Oscar (IRE)—Amber Trix (IRE) **Inaminna Partnership**
58 **INCH LALA (IRE)**, 6, ch m Mahler—Aboo Lala (IRE) **Clifford, Gosden & House**
59 **INDIAN STREAM (IRE)**, 8, b g Generous (IRE)—Zaffarimbi (IRE) **Mrs G. A. Davies**
60 **ISIS BLUE**, 8, b g Cockney Rebel (IRE)—Bramaputra (IRE) **High Oaks Racing**
61 **ISKRABOB**, 8, ch g Tobougg (IRE)—Honour Bolton **Mrs S. B. Bolton**
62 **JOHNS LUCK (IRE)**, 9, b g Turtle Island (IRE)—Jemima Yorke **Mr J. Hobbs**
63 **JUST FRED (IRE)**, 5, br g Excellent Art—Consignia (IRE) **Mr D. B. Harris**
64 **KALONDRA (IRE)**, 7, b g Spadoun (FR)—Mystic Vic (IRE) **Mr J. Henderson**
65 **KANSAS CITY CHIEF (IRE)**, 9, b g Westerner—Badawi Street **Mr A. G. Bloom**
66 **KNIGHT OF NOIR (IRE)**, 9, b g Winged Love (IRE)—At Dawn (IRE) **H. M. W. Clifford**
67 **KOUBBA (IRE)**, 5, b m Peintre Celebre (USA)—Elyaadi **Mr M. D. Ryan**
68 **KRISTAL HART**, 9, b m Lucky Story (USA)—Moly (FR) **The White Hart Racing Syndicate**
69 **LADY CARDUROS (IRE)**, 4, b f Byron—Saranjo (IRE) **Pray That Shes Good**
70 **LAKE BAIKAL (FR)**, 4, gr g Martaline—La Curamalal (IRE) **Mr J. P. McManus**
71 **LEE SIDE LADY (IRE)**, 8, ch m Mountain High (IRE)—Vicante (IRE) **The Affordable (2) Partnership**
72 **LIST ONE**, 6, b m Tobougg (IRE)—Minibelle **The Dickinsons,Butlin,Clegg,Finch&Lacey**
73 **LOOKS FROZEN (IRE)**, 4, ch g Frozen Fire (GER)—Miss Beverley **Kevin Corcoran Aaron Pierce Chris Weare**
74 **LOUGH RYN (IRE)**, 6, br g Court Cave (IRE)—Media View (IRE) **Level Par Racing**
75 **LUBATIC (FR)**, 5, b g Sleeping Car (FR)—Luba (FR) **The Keith Adams Racing Partnership**
76 **LUCKY ESTEEM**, 4, b f Yorgunnabelucky (USA)—Dream Esteem **R. S. Brookhouse**
77 **MAC TOTTIE**, 5, b g Midnight Legend—Tot of The Knar **Steve & Jackie Fleetham**
78 **MAGICAL THOMAS**, 6, ch g Dylan Thomas—Magical Cliche (USA) **G. P. and Miss S. J. Hayes**
79 **MASQUERADE BLING (IRE)**, 4, b f Approve (IRE)—Mataji (IRE) **Mr C. E. Weare**
80 **MASTER BURBIDGE**, 7, b g Pasternak—Silver Sequel **Dajam Ltd**
81 **MATROW'S LADY (IRE)**, 11, b m Cloudings (IRE)—I'm Maggy (NZ) **Matrow Properties Limited**
82 **MERIBEL MILLIE**, 7, b m Kayf Tara—Ede'iff **Mr A. D. Polson**
83 **MILKWOOD (IRE)**, 4, b g Dylan Thomas—Tropical Lake (IRE) **Ms J. Bridel**
84 **MIND YOUR BACK (IRE)**, 5, b g Getaway (GER)—Local Hall (IRE) **Mr & Mrs Paul & Clare Rooney**
85 **MINELLA PRESENT (IRE)**, 9, b g Presenting—Dabaya (IRE) **Mrs J. Gerard-Pearse**
86 **MINELLATILLMORNING (IRE)**, 6, gr g King's Theatre (IRE)—Line Kendie (FR) **Mr C. W. Rodgers**
87 **MISS JEANNE MOON (IRE)**, 4, b f Getaway (GER)—Moon Approach (IRE) **Mrs H. R. Cross & Mrs S. A. Keys**
88 **MISS MOLLY MAE (IRE)**, 6, b m Getaway (GER)—Miss Mary Mac (IRE) **H A Marks Ltd**
89 **MOAYADD (USA)**, 6, b g Street Cry (IRE)—Aryaamm (IRE) **Mr P & Mrs K E Malcolm**
90 **MOLLY CAREW (IRE)**, 6, b m Midnight Legend—Moyliscar **Mrs H. R. Cross & Mrs S. A. Keys**
91 **MORNING SEQUEL**, 5, b m Revoque (IRE)—Silver Sequel **Dajam & Hart**
92 **MORRIS THE MINER**, 8, b g Apple Tree (FR)—Miner Yours **Neil Mulholland Racing Ltd**
93 **MOST CELEBRATED (IRE)**, 5, b g New Approach (IRE)—Pietra Santa (FR) **Stephen & Gloria Seymour**
94 **MOUNT OLIVER (IRE)**, 8, b g Mountain High (IRE)—Little Nancy (IRE) **Mr C. Hallahan**
95 **MOVING IN STYLE (IRE)**, 7, ch g Mountain High (IRE)—Good To Travel (IRE) **B. A. Derrick**
96 **MRS BURBIDGE**, 8, b m Pasternak—Twin Time **Dajam Ltd**
97 **MY STORY (IRE)**, 6, b g Court Cave (IRE)—Holloden (IRE) **R. S. Brookhouse**
98 **NEACHELLS BRIDGE (IRE)**, 6, ch g Getaway (GER)—Strawberry Lane (IRE) **Mr M. C. Creed**
99 **NIBLAWI (IRE)**, 6, b g Vale of York (IRE)—Finnmark **Mr A. G. Bloom**
100 **NOVIS ADVENTUS (IRE)**, 6, b g New Approach (IRE)—Tiffed (USA) **The General Asphalte Company Ltd**
101 **OCHOS RIOS**, 5, b g Shirocco (GER)—Society Rose **H. M. W. Clifford**
102 **ON ALBERTS HEAD (IRE)**, 8, b g Mountain High (IRE)—Dear Money (IRE) **Peter and Ruth Turner**
103 **OSCARS BOSS**, 8, b g Norse Dancer (IRE)—Kimmeridge Bay **Mr J. Nicholson**
104 **OWNERS DAY**, 8, gr m Fair Mix (IRE)—Charmeille (FR) **The Dickinsons,Butlin,Clegg,Finch&Lacey**
105 **PARWICH LEES**, 6, ch g Pasternak—Barton Dante **Mrs J. Gerard-Pearse**
106 **PERFECT TIMING**, 10, b g Shantou (USA)—Winnetka Gal (IRE) **The Mogg Family Racing Partnership**
107 **PILGRIMS BAY (IRE)**, 8, b g Turtle Island (IRE)—Lady Ariadna (IRE) **Clifford, Gosden & House**
108 **POETIC LADY (IRE)**, 7, b m Yeats (IRE)—Apollo Lady **Mrs P. L. Bridel**
109 **PRETTYLITTLETHING (IRE)**, 8, b m Tajraasi (USA)—Cloncunny Girl (IRE) **N Webb & P J Proudley**
110 **RAINY DAY DYLAN (IRE)**, 7, br g Spadoun (FR)—Honeyed (IRE) **Burnham Plastering & Drylining Ltd**
111 **REBEL COLLINS (IRE)**, 7, gr g Jeremy (USA)—Million All Day (IRE) **Star Contractors Ltd**

MR NEIL MULHOLLAND - Continued

112 **ROSSETTI**, 10, gr g Dansili—Snowdrops **Sheikh A'Leg Racing**
113 6, B m Alflora (IRE)—Royal Squeeze (IRE) **The Dickinsons,Butlin,Clegg,Finch&Lacey**
114 **RUBHEIRA**, 6, ch m Arkadian Hero (USA)—Devon Ruby **Mr A. Marsh**
115 **RUNASIMI RIVER**, 5, ch m Generous (IRE)—Zaffaranni (IRE) **Mrs G. A. Davies**
116 **SEVEN CLANS (IRE)**, 6, b g Cape Cross (IRE)—Cherokee Rose (IRE) **The Affordable (2) Partnership**
117 **SHANTOU VILLAGE (IRE)**, 8, b g Shantou (USA)—Village Queen (IRE) **Mrs J. Gerard-Pearse**
118 **SHEE'S LUCKY**, 4, b f Yorgunnabelucky (USA)—She's The Lady **R. S. Brookhouse**
119 **SIGNED AND SEALED**, 5, b g Authorized (IRE)—Broken Peace (USA) **R. S. Brookhouse**
120 **SLEEP EASY**, 6, b g Rip Van Winkle (IRE)—Strictly Lambada **Mr A. G. Bloom**
121 **SOLIGHOSTER (FR)**, 6, ch g Loup Solitaire (USA)—Miss Martine (FR) **The Colony Stable LLC & Dajam Ltd**
122 **SOLOMN GRUNDY (IRE)**, 8, b g Westerner—Marika's King (IRE) **R. S. Brookhouse**
123 **SOUPY SOUPS (IRE)**, 7, ch g Stowaway—Near Dunleer (IRE) **Equi ex Incertis Partners**
124 **SOUTHFIELD ROYALE**, 8, b g Presenting—Chamoss Royale (FR) **Mrs A. B. Yeoman**
125 **TELL THE TALE (IRE)**, 8, b g Craigsteel—Club Member (IRE) **A. Mann**
126 **THE DETAINEE**, 5, b g Aqlaam—Jakarta Jade (IRE) **Crowd Racing Partnership**
127 **THE DRUIDS NEPHEW (IRE)**, 11, b g King's Theatre (IRE)—Gifted **The Stonehenge Druids**
128 **THE TWISLER**, 6, b g Motivator—Panna **Mrs V. J. Hodsoll**
129 **THE WAY YOU DANCE (IRE)**, 6, b g Thewayyouare (USA)—Beautiful Dancer (IRE) **BG Racing Partnership**
130 **THE WICKET CHICKEN (IRE)**, 6, b m Milan—Soniadoir (IRE) **Dajam & Colm Hearne**
131 **THE YOUNG MASTER**, 9, b g Echo of Light—Fine Frenzy (IRE) **Mike Burbidge & The Old Masters**
132 **THEATRE ROUGE (IRE)**, 8, b m King's Theatre (IRE)—Toulon Rouge (IRE) **Strictly Come Racing**
133 **TIKKANBAR (IRE)**, 7, b g Tikkanen (USA)—Fields of Barley (IRE) **Mr B. F. Mulholland**
134 **VANCOUVER**, 6, ch g Generous (IRE)—All Told (IRE) **J. J. Maguire**
135 **VERY EXTRAVAGANT (IRE)**, 9, ch m Touch of Land (FR)—Raveleen Rose (IRE) **B. A. Derrick**
136 **VEXILLUM (IRE)**, 9, br g Mujadil (USA)—Common Cause **Mr J. Heaney**
137 **WALT (IRE)**, 7, b g King's Theatre (IRE)—Allee Sarthoise (FR) **Mr P. M. Simmonds**
138 **WHATSTHATALLABOUT (IRE)**, 7, b m Milan—Peinture Francaise (FR) **Neil Mulholland Racing Ltd**
139 **WHERE'S CHERRY (IRE)**, 7, b m King's Theatre (IRE)—I'm Grand (IRE) **F&M Bloodstock Limited**
140 **WILLYEGOLASSIEGO**, 5, br m Kheleyf (USA)—Kryena **Mr J. Hobbs**

THREE-YEAR-OLDS

141 **HOLLYWOOD DREAM**, b f Delegator—Royal Obsession (IRE) **Neil Mulholland Racing Club**
142 **JUST FOR THE CRAIC (IRE)**, b g Most Improved (IRE)—Beziers (IRE) **J. J. Maguire**
143 **MOLLIANA**, b f Olden Times—The Screamer (IRE) **Dajam Ltd**
144 **MORE HARRY**, b g Aussie Rules (USA)—Native Ring (FR) **Four Winds Racing Partnership**
145 **SILVERTURNSTOGOLD**, ch c Equiano (FR)—Saharan Song (IRE) **Mr A. A. Byrne**
146 **WHERE'S MUMMY**, b f Swiss Spirit—Vitta's Touch (USA) **Mr & Mrs Paul & Clare Rooney**

Other Owners: Mr C. Adams, Mr S. Agodino, Mr J. Ashley, Mrs L. Atwell, BGC Racing, Miss R Bailey, Mr G. J. R. Barry, Mrs I. M. Beckett, Mr S. Bedworth, Mr R. Bonney, Mrs H. M. Bonney, Mr P. Bowden, Mrs S. L. Boyle, Mr P. Boyle, Sir M. F. Broughton, Mr S. W. Broughton, Mr M. S. Burbidge, Mr A. Butlin, Mr P. A. Cafferty, Mr M. G. Cahill, Mr B. Carter, Mr S. Clegg, Colony Stable Llc, K. J. Corcoran, Mrs A. C. Crofts, Mrs H. R. Cross, Mr C. G. Dando, Mrs R. L. J. Dickinson, Mr R. R. Dickinson, Mr H. G. Doubtfire, Mr F. C. Durbin, Mr J. H. W. Finch, Mr S. Fleetham, Mrs J. Fleetham, Mr P. S. Frampton, J. L. Frampton, Mr I. F. Gosden, Mr R. T. Greenhill, Mrs J. A. Hart, Mr G. P. Hayes, Miss S. J. Hayes, Mr C. Hearne, Mr D. R. Heaney, Mr P. Hill, Mr R. House, Mr D. T. Irving, Mr A. S. Keys, Mr D. L. Lacey, Mrs C. Lewis, Mr M. J. Lowry, Sir I. Magee, B. D. Makepeace, Mr W. P. L. Malcolm, Mrs K. E. Malcolm, Mrs S. J. McKenna, Mr C. McKenna, Mrs E. A. Mear, Mr R. J. Mear, Mr J. G. Mogg, Mr S. G. T. D. Mogg, R. D. Nicholas, Mr A. T. Pierce, Mr P. J. Proudley, Mrs C. Rooney, Mr P. A. Rooney, Mr M. S. Rose, Mrs G. P. Seymour, Mr S. G. Seymour, Mr A. J. Smith, Mr M. Swallow, Mrs D. J. Symes, Mr D. Tiernan, P. C. Tory, Mr Simon Trant, Mrs R. Turner, Mr P. Turner, Mr G. J. Villis, Mr R. Ward, Mrs L. Webb, Mr P. Webb, N. E. Webb, Mr E. Wilmott, Mr C. W. Winter, Mr A. L. Winter, Mr T. W. Winter, Mr J. Wright.

Assistant Trainer: Mark Quinlan

Conditional: Philip Donovan, Harry Reed. **Amateur:** Mr James King.

---

402 **MR LAWRENCE MULLANEY, Malton**
Postal: Raikes Farm, Great Habton, Malton, North Yorkshire, YO17 6RX
Contacts: PHONE (01653) 668595 MOBILE (07899) 902565
E-MAIL nicolamullaney@yahoo.co.uk

1 **ARCANE DANCER (IRE)**, 5, b m Arcano (IRE)—La Reine Mambo (USA) **Mr S. J. Rimmer**
2 **BEVERLEY BULLET**, 5, b g Makfi—Don't Tell Mary (IRE) **Mrs Jean Stapleton & Rob Wilson**
3 **DARK INTENTION (IRE)**, 5, b m High Chaparral (IRE)—Ajiaal **Ian Buckley**
4 **DIAMOND RUNNER (IRE)**, 6, b g Amadeus Wolf—Hawk Eyed Lady (IRE) **Bawtry Racing Club**

MR LAWRENCE MULLANEY - Continued

5 **FIRST SARGEANT**, 8, gr g Dutch Art—Princess Raya **L. A. Mullaney**
6 **JACK LUEY**, 11, b g Danbird (AUS)—Icenaslice (IRE)
7 **SAVED BY THE BELL (IRE)**, 8, b g Teofilo (IRE)—Eyrecourt (IRE) **Mr J Blackburn, Mr A Turton & Ptr**
8 **TATTING**, 9, ch g Street Cry (IRE)—Needlecraft (IRE) **The Usual Suspects**
9 **ZIGGY LEE**, 12, b g Lujain (USA)—Mary O'grady (USA) **L. A. Mullaney**

THREE-YEAR-OLDS

10 **GORGEOUS GENERAL**, ch c Captain Gerrard (IRE)—Gorgeous Goblin (IRE) **Mr S. Humphries**
11 **OUR LITTLE PONY**, b f Bated Breath—Cracking Lass (IRE) **Mr J. R. Swift**

Other Owners: Mrs A. Barrett, Mr B. P. Barrett, Mr J. N. Blackburn, M. J. Dyas, Mrs J. Stapleton, Mr A. Turton, Mr R. J. Wilson.

---

403 MR MICHAEL MULLINEAUX, Tarporley
Postal: **Southley Farm, Alpraham, Tarporley, Cheshire, CW6 9JD**
Contacts: PHONE (01829) 261440 FAX (01829) 261440 MOBILE (07753) 650263
E-MAIL southlearacing@btinternet.com WEBSITE www.southleyfarm.co.uk

1 **ANTON DOLIN (IRE)**, 10, ch g Danehill Dancer (IRE)—Ski For Gold **S. A. Pritchard**
2 **BIGERN**, 11, b g Firebreak—Lady Boxer
3 **CAPTAIN REVELATION**, 6, ch g Captain Rio—Agony Aunt **Cheshire Racing**
4 **DODGY BOB**, 5, b g Royal Applause—Rustam **J P Daly and S & M Ashbrooke**
5 **DOLLAR AND A DREAM (IRE)**, 9, b g Fruits of Love (USA)—Gorgeous Georgina (IRE) **Mr K. M. Bebbington**
6 **HES OUR ROBIN (IRE)**, 8, b g Robin des Pres (FR)—Poly Sandstorm (IRE) **The Hon Mrs S. Pakenham**
7 **JACKSONFIRE**, 6, ch g Firebreak—Fitolini **Mr O. D. Knight**
8 **KEEM BAY**, 4, b f Multiplex—Copsehill Girl (IRE) **Mr Denis Gallagher**
9 **LORD BUNNACURRY**, 7, ch g Black Sam Bellamy (IRE)—Lunareva (USA) **Mr M. J. Lynch**
10 **MINTY JONES**, 9, b g Primo Valentino (IRE)—Reveur **P. Clacher**
11 **ORPEN BID (IRE)**, 13, b g Orpen—Glorious Bid (IRE) **Miss L. S. Young**
12 **PEACHEY CARNEHAN**, 4, ch g Foxwedge (AUS)—Zubova **Mr K. Jones**
13 **PEADAR MIGUEL**, 11, b g Danroad (AUS)—La Corujera **Mr G. Cornes**
14 **POOR DUKE (IRE)**, 8, b g Bachelor Duke (USA)—Graze On Too (IRE) **Mr G. McCarthy**
15 **POPPYINTHEPARK**, 5, b m Bahri (USA)—Lark In The Park (IRE) **Mia Racing**
16 **POUND NOTE**, 6, b g Top Line Dancer (IRE)—Avondale Girl (IRE) **M. Mullineaux**
17 **RESPECTABILITY**, 6, b m Echo of Light—Respectfilly **We Enjoy Racing Club**
18 **ROMANN ANGEL**, 9, b m Sir Harry Lewis (USA)—Roman Gospel **Miss L. S. Young**
19 **SECRETINTHEPARK**, 8, ch g Sakhee's Secret—Lark In The Park (IRE) **Mia Racing**
20 **SOMEWHERE SECRET**, 4, ch g Sakhee's Secret—Lark In The Park (IRE) **Mia Racing**
21 **STAR OF NAMIBIA (IRE)**, 8, b g Cape Cross (IRE)—Sparkle of Stones (FR) **Mr K. Jones**
22 **TEEPEE TIME**, 5, b m Compton Place—Deora De **Mr G. Cornes**
23 **VERY FIRST BLADE**, 9, b g Needwood Blade—Dispol Verity **Mr G. Cornes**

THREE-YEAR-OLDS

24 **INVINCIBLE PURSUIT**, b f Pastoral Pursuits—Fettuccine (IRE)
25 **RED ALLURE**, ch f Mayson—Lark In The Park (IRE) **Mia Racing**

Other Owners: Mr S. Ashbrooke, Mrs M. Ashbrooke, Mr S. A. Coxon, Mr J. P. Daly, Mr S. Laffan, Mr K. R. Lawton, Mrs A. Milburn, M. A. Tickle, A. Tickle, Mrs I. M. Tickle.

Assistant Trainers: Stuart Ross, Susan Mullineaux

Amateur: Miss M. J. L. Mullineaux.

---

404 MR SEAMUS MULLINS, Amesbury
Postal: **Wilsford Stables, Wilsford-Cum-Lake, Amesbury, Salisbury, Wiltshire, SP4 7BL**
Contacts: PHONE/FAX (01980) 626344 MOBILE (07702) 559634
E-MAIL info@jwmullins.co.uk WEBSITE www.seamusmullins.co.uk

1 **AMIRR (IRE)**, 8, b g New Approach (IRE)—Dress Uniform (USA) **Mr M. Adams**
2 **ARTHINGTON**, 5, b g Haafhd—Pequenita **Mr C. J. Baldwin**
3 **BANCO DE LOGOS (FR)**, 7, b g Laverock (IRE)—Funkia (FR) **Mr & Mrs C R Whittaker**

MR SEAMUS MULLINS - Continued

    4 **BEE CROSSING**, 7, b m Fair Mix (IRE)—Indeed To Goodness (IRE) **Harriet Waight & Friends**
    5 **BLACKDOWN HILLS**, 8, b m Presenting—Lady Prunella (IRE) **Mrs P. de W. Johnson**
    6 **BONDS CONQUEST**, 9, ch g Monsieur Bond (IRE)—Another Conquest **F. G. Matthews**
    7 **BOOLA RIVER (IRE)**, 8, b m Craigsteel—Hy Kate (IRE) **S Mullins Racing Club**
    8 **BROTHER NORPHIN**, 6, b g Norse Dancer (IRE)—Orphina (IRE) **Mr J. A. Mould**
    9 **BURST YA BUBBLE (IRE)**, 6, b g Spadoun (FR)—Accordian Lady (IRE) **Mr M. Adams**
  10 **CAP HORNER (FR)**, 6, gr g Apsis—Rapsodie Sea (FR) **Mr M. Adams**
  11 **CHESTERFIELD (IRE)**, 8, ch g Pivotal—Antique (IRE) **The Rumble Racing Club**
  12 **COURT AFFAIRS (IRE)**, 6, b g Court Cave (IRE)—
                                    Rock Money (IRE) **Mark Adams, Andrew Cocks & Tara Johnson**
  13 **COURTESY CALL (IRE)**, 9, br g Manduro (GER)—Three Wrens (IRE) **First Impressions Racing Group**
  14 **DANCING CONQUEST**, 8, b m Imperial Dancer—Another Conquest **F. G. Matthews**
  15 **FENLONS COURT (IRE)**, 6, b g Court Cave (IRE)—Classic Note (IRE) **Mrs D. H. Potter**
  16 **FLUGZEUG**, 10, gr g Silver Patriarch (IRE)—Telmar Flyer **New Forest Racing Partnership**
  17 **GARDE FORESTIER (FR)**, 6, b g Forestier (FR)—Nette Rousse (FR) **Mr & Mrs C R Whittaker**
  18 **GOWELL (IRE)**, 7, b m Gold Well—Glen Supreme (IRE) **Mrs M. M. Rayner**
  19 **HARDTOROCK (IRE)**, 9, b g Mountain High (IRE)—Permissal (IRE) **Mr N. A. Eggleton**
  20 **I SEE YOU WELL (FR)**, 5, b g Air Chief Marshal (IRE)—Bonne Mere (FR) **A. A. Goodman**
  21 **INSPIREUS (IRE)**, 5, b g Scorpion (IRE)—Miniconjou (IRE) **S Mullins Racing Club**
  22 **JARLATH**, 7, b g Norse Dancer (IRE)—Blue Lullaby (IRE) **Phoenix Bloodstock & Mr A A Goodman**
  23 **JUBILYMPICS**, 6, b m Kapgarde (FR)—Pepite de Soleil (FR) **Caloona Racing**
  24 **KASTANI BEACH (IRE)**, 12, b g Alderbrook—Atomic View (IRE) **Seamus Mullins & Philippa Downing**
  25 **KENTFORD HEIRESS**, 8, b m Midnight Legend—Kentford Duchess D. I. **Bare**
  26 **KENTFORD MALLARD**, 5, b m Sulamani (IRE)—Kentford Grebe **D. I. Bare**
  27 **KENTFORD MYTH**, 8, b m Midnight Legend—Quistaquay **D. I. Bare**
  28 **LANDIN (GER)**, 5, b g Sir Percy—Lupita (GER) **Four Candles Partnership**
  29 5, B g Court Cave (IRE)—Like A Miller (IRE) **Andrew Cocks & Tara Johnson**
  30 **MAEBH (IRE)**, 4, b f Doyen (IRE)—South Queen Lady (IRE) **J. W. Mullins**
  31 **MANHATTAN SPRING**, 7, b g Central Park (IRE)—Risky May **Woodford Valley Racing**
  32 **MARATT (FR)**, 5, gr g Martaline—Lavi (FR) **Dr & Mrs John Millar**
  33 **MIDNIGHT GLEN**, 6, b m Midnight Legend—Kali **The Up The Glens Partnership**
  34 **MOGESTIC (IRE)**, 9, b g Morozov (USA)—Crosschild (IRE) **Mrs J. C. Scorgie**
  35 **NELSON'S TOUCH**, 5, gr g Mount Nelson—Lady Friend **Mrs P de W Johnson & Mr John M Cole**
  36 **NORPHIN**, 8, b g Norse Dancer (IRE)—Orphina (IRE) **Mr J. A. Mould**
  37 **NUCLEAR (IRE)**, 5, b g Elusive Pimpernel (USA)—Heroine **S Mullins Racing Club**
  38 **OBORNE LADY (IRE)**, 5, b m Watar (IRE)—Lady Shackleton (IRE) **Simon & Christine Prout**
  39 **ORMSKIRK**, 5, gr g Hellvelyn—River Song (USA) **Mrs G. Morgan**
  40 **PLANTAGENET**, 6, b g Midnight Legend—Marsh Court **Mrs P. de W. Johnson**
  41 **PRESENT DESTINY (IRE)**, 6, b g Dubai Destination (USA)—Anns Present (IRE) **The Friday Night Club**
  42 **ROBINDENEST (IRE)**, 6, br g Robin des Pres (FR)—Baby Harriet (IRE) **Seamus Mullins & Friends**
  43 **ROBINROYALE (IRE)**, 7, b g Robin des Champs (FR)—Rosafi (IRE) **Mrs G. Morgan**
  44 **ROMANOR**, 4, b g Holy Roman Emperor (IRE)—Salinia (IRE) **The Rumble Racing Club**
  45 **SHE'S GINA (GER)**, 5, b m It's Gino (GER)—Song of Night (GER) **Four Candles Partnership**
  46 **SOMCHINE**, 10, b g Volochine (IRE)—Seem of Gold **Mr Clive Dunning & Mr Seamus Mullins**
  47 **SUNDIAL STORM**, 5, ch m Shantou (USA)—Shadow Line (FR) **The Up The Glens Partnership & D J Erwin**
  48 **TAKE A DROP (IRE)**, 5, b m Bushranger (IRE)—Brogan's Well (IRE) **J. W. Mullins**
  49 **THE RAVEN'S RETURN**, 5, b g Scorpion (IRE)—Mimis Bonnet (FR) **The Rumble Racing Club**
  50 **TRICKY ISSUE (IRE)**, 6, b m Manduro (GER)—Tricky Situation **Caloona Racing**
  51 **WESTERBEE (IRE)**, 7, b m Westerner—Pass The Honey (IRE) **Roger & Rachel Jowett**
  52 **WESTERBERRY (IRE)**, 6, b m Westerner—Casiana (GER) **Roger & Rachel Jowett**

THREE-YEAR-OLDS

  53 Ch f Sakhee's Secret—Blase Chevalier (IRE) **Andrew Cocks & Tara Johnson**
  54 **HAPPY ENDING (IRE)**, b f Big Bad Bob (IRE)—Heroic Performer (IRE) **J. W. Mullins**

Other Owners: P. R. Attwater, Mr L. D. Clarke, Mr A. P. Cocks, Mr J. M. Cole, Miss P. M. Downing, Mr C. R. Dunning, Mr D. J. Erwin, Mr P. R. Greeves, R. Hatchard, Mrs V. F. Hewett, Mr A. K. Horsman, Miss T. Johnson, Mrs R. A. Jowett, Dr R. Jowett, Dr J. W. Millar, Mrs J. D. Millar, J. D. Oakey, Mrs C. A. Prout, Mr S. P. Prout, Mr J. Pyatt, Mr S. Reid, Mr J. C. Saunders, Mr R. J. Stammers, D. Sutherland, Miss R. Toppin, Mrs H. Waight, C. R. Whittaker, Mrs H. E. Whittaker, Mr C. Wilson.

Assistant Trainer: Paul Attwater

Jockey (NH): Kevin Jones, Andrew Thornton. **Conditional:** Jeremiah McGrath. **Amateur:** Mr Daniel Sansom.

405 MR WILLIAM P. MULLINS, Carlow

Postal: Closutton, Bagenalstown, Co. Carlow, Ireland
Contacts: PHONE (00353) 5997 21786 FAX (00353) 5997 22709 MOBILE (00353) 8725 64940
E-MAIL wpmullins@eircom.net WEBSITE www.wpmullins.com

1 **ABBYSSIAL (IRE)**, 8, ch g Beneficial—Mega d'estruval (FR) **Mrs Violet O'Leary**
2 **ACAPELLA BOURGEOIS (FR)**, 8, ch g Network (GER)—Jasmine (FR) **Slaneyville Syndicate**
3 **AINSI VA LA VIE (FR)**, 8, gr m Lavirco (GER)—Joie de La Vie (FR) **Supreme Horse Racing Club**
4 **AL BOUM PHOTO (FR)**, 6, b g Buck's Boum (FR)—Al Gane (FR) **Mrs M. Donnelly**
5 **ALELCHI INOIS (FR)**, 10, b g Night Tango (GER)—Witness Gama (FR) **Mrs M. McMahon**
6 **ALLBLAK DES PLACES (FR)**, 6, b br g Full of Gold (FR)—Amiraute (FR) **George Creighton**
7 **AMERICAN TOM (FR)**, 7, b g American Post—Kirkla (FR) **Mrs S. Ricci**
8 **ANTEY (GER)**, 5, b g Lord of England (GER)—Achinora **Mrs S. Ricci**
9 **ARBRE DE VIE (FR)**, 8, b g Antarctique (IRE)—Nouvelle Recrue (FR) **Mrs S. Ricci**
10 **ASTHURIA (FR)**, 7, b m Sagacity (FR)—Baturia (FR) **George Creighton**
11 **AUGUSTA KATE (FR)**, 7, b m Yeats (IRE)—Feathard Lady (IRE) **The Masters Syndicate**
12 **AUGUSTIN (FR)**, 8, gr g Martaline—Lili Bleue (FR) **Mrs M. McMahon**
13 **BACARDYS (FR)**, 7, b br g Coastal Path—Oasice (FR) **Shanakiel Racing Syndicate**
14 **BACHASSON (FR)**, 7, gr g Voix du Nord (FR)—Belledonne (FR) **Edward O'Connell**
15 **BALLYCASEY (IRE)**, 11, gr g Presenting—Pink Mist (IRE) **Mrs S. Ricci**
16 **BALLYWARD (IRE)**, 6, b g Flemensfirth (USA)—Ifyoucouldseemenow (IRE) **Andrea & Graham Wylie**
17 **BAMAKO MORIVIERE (FR)**, 7, b g Califet (FR)—Halladine (FR) **Mrs S. Ricci**
18 **BANG BANG ROSIE (IRE)**, 6, b m Stowaway—Restless Dreams (IRE) **John A. Coleman**
19 **BAPAUME (FR)**, 5, b g Turtle Bowl (IRE)—Brouhaha (FR) **Mrs S. Ricci**
20 **BARGY LADY (IRE)**, 6, b m Yeats (IRE)—Jolivia (FR) **Oakroom Racing Club**
21 **BELLOW MOME (FR)**, 7, b g Honolulu (IRE)—Oll Mighty Fellow (FR) **Mrs Audrey Turley**
22 **BELLSHILL (IRE)**, 8, b g King's Theatre (IRE)—Fairy Native (IRE) **Andrea & Graham Wylie**
23 **BEN BUTTON (IRE)**, 8, b g Double Eclipse (IRE)—Lady Coldunell **Martin McHale**
24 **BENIE DES DIEUX (FR)**, 7, b m Great Pretender (FR)—Cana (FR) **Mrs S. Ricci**
25 **BLACK HERCULES (IRE)**, 9, b g Heron Island (IRE)—Annalecky (IRE) **Andrea Wylie**
26 **BLACKBOW (IRE)**, 5, b g Stowaway—Rinnce Moll (IRE) **Roaringwater Syndicate**
27 **BLAZER (FR)**, 7, ch g Network (GER)—Juppelongue (FR) **J. P. McManus**
28 **BLEU BERRY (FR)**, 7, b g Special Kaldoun (FR)—Somosierra (FR) **Mrs M. McMahon**
29 **BLEU ET ROUGE (FR)**, 7, gr g Charming Groom (FR)—Lady du Renom (FR) **J. P. McManus**
30 **BON PAPA (FR)**, 7, br g Network (GER)—Gibelotte (FR) **J. P. McManus**
31 **BONBON AU MIEL (FR)**, 7, b g Khalkevi (IRE)—Friandise II (FR) **Andrea & Graham Wylie**
32 **BRAHMA BULL (IRE)**, 7, ch g Presenting—Oligarch Society (IRE) **Mrs S. Ricci**
33 **BRAVISSIMO (FR)**, 7, gr g Al Namix (FR)—Mimi Valley (FR) **Mrs S. Ricci**
34 **BUNK OFF EARLY (IRE)**, 6, ro g Zebedee—Ctesiphon (USA) **Supreme Horse Racing Club**
35 **BURROWS SAINT (FR)**, 5, b g Saint des Saints (FR)—La Bombonera (FR) **Mrs S. Ricci**
36 **C'EST JERSEY (FR)**, 6, b g Protektor (GER)—Myrtille Jersey (FR) **Simon Munir & Isaac Souede**
37 **CADMIUM (FR)**, 6, b g Early March—Mirquille (FR) **Supreme Horse Racing Club**
38 **CAMELIA DE COTTE (FR)**, 6, br m Laveron—Traviata Valtat (FR) **Mrs S. Ricci**
39 **CAP D'AUBOIS (FR)**, 6, b g Snow Cap (FR)—Caline Grace (FR) **Mrs S. Ricci**
40 **CAREFULLY SELECTED (IRE)**, 6, b g Well Chosen—Knockamullen Girl (IRE) **Miss M. A. Masterson**
41 **CARO DES FLOS (FR)**, 6, b g Tiger Groom—Royale Marie (FR) **Highclere Thoroughbred Racing**
42 **CARTER MCKAY (FR)**, 7, gr g Martaline—Saxona (FR) **Pearl Bloodstock**
43 **CASTELLO SFORZA (IRE)**, 7, b g Milan—Young Elodie (FR) **J. P. McManus**
44 **CHAMBORD DU LYS (FR)**, 6, b m Great Pretender (IRE)—
                                        Pot Jolie (FR) **Supreme Horse Racing Club/Brett T.Graham**
45 **CHATEAU CONTI (FR)**, 6, b g Vendangeur (IRE)—Regina Conti (FR) **E. O'Connell**
46 **CHILDRENS LIST (IRE)**, 8, b g Presenting—Snipe Hunt (IRE) **Mrs S. Ricci**
47 **CILAOS EMERY (FR)**, 6, b g Califet (FR)—Queissa (FR) **Luke McMahon**
48 **CLINTON HILL (IRE)**, 7, b g Flemensfirth (USA)—Smooching (IRE) **Andrea Wylie**
49 **CLITANDRE (FR)**, 6, b g Zambezi Sun—Where Is My Gold (FR) **Supreme Horse Racing Club & Kenneth Sharp**
50 **COLREEVY (IRE)**, 5, b m Flemensfirth (USA)—Poetics Girl (IRE) **Mrs N. Flynn**
51 **COME TO ME (FR)**, 6, b g Spanish Moon (USA)—Hasta Manana (FR) **Mrs M. Masterson**
52 **CONTINGENCY**, 5, b m Champs Elysees—Cyclone Connie **Bowes Lodge Stables Partnership**
53 **COQUIN MANS (FR)**, 6, b br g Fragrant Mix (IRE)—Quissisia Mans (FR) **George Creighton**
54 **COURT ARTIST (IRE)**, 7, b m Court Cave (IRE)—Native Artist (IRE) **Blue Dotal Racing Club**
55 **CRACK MOME (FR)**, 6, ch g Spanish Moon (USA)—Peche Mome (FR) **Andrea Wylie**
56 **CRACK TIEPY (FR)**, 6, gr m Voix du Nord (FR)—Naltiepy (FR) **Mrs S. Ricci**
57 **CUT THE MUSTARD (FR)**, 6, br m Al Namix (FR)—Tadorna (FR) **Sullivan Bloodstock Limited**
58 **DANDY MAG (FR)**, 5, br g Special Kaldoun (IRE)—Naiade Mag (FR) **G Mercer/D Mercer/Mrs Caren Walsh**
59 **DEAL D'ESTRUVAL (FR)**, 5, b g Balko (FR)—Option d'estruval (FR) **Mrs S. Ricci**
60 **DEFY DE MEE (FR)**, 5, b g Country Reel (USA)—Koeur de Mee (FR) **Mrs J. Donnelly**

MR WILLIAM P. MULLINS - Continued

61 **DEMI SANG (FR)**, 5, b g Gris de Gris (IRE)—Morvandelle (FR) **J. P. McManus**
62 **DIDERO VALLIS (FR)**, 5, b g Poliglote—Oreade Vallis (FR) **Mrs S. Ricci**
63 **DJAKADAM (FR)**, 9, b g Saint des Saints (FR)—Rainbow Crest (FR) **Mrs S. Ricci**
64 **DOLCIANO DICI (FR)**, 5, b g Assessor—Louve Rina (FR) **Slaneyville Syndicate**
65 **DOUVAN (FR)**, 8, b g Walk In The Park (IRE)—Star Face (FR) **Mrs S. Ricci**
66 **DRACONIEN (FR)**, 5, br g Linda's Lad—Holding (FR) **Clipper Logistics Group Limited**
67 **DUC DES GENIEVRES (FR)**, 5, gr g Buck's Boum (FR)—Lobelie (FR) **Sullivan Bloodstock Limited**
68 **EPICURIS**, 6, b g Rail Link—Argumentative **Mrs S. Ricci**
69 **EXCHANGE RATE (GER)**, 6, b g Monsun (GER)—Erytheis (USA) **Mrs A. F. Mee**
70 **FAUGHEEN (IRE)**, 10, b g Germany (USA)—Miss Pickering (IRE) **Mrs S. Ricci**
71 **FOOTPAD (FR)**, 6, b g Creachadoir (IRE)—Willamina (IRE) **Mr Simon Munir**
72 **FRANCIN (FR)**, 5, b g Air Chief Marshal (IRE)—Fulgence (FR) **Mrs S. Ricci**
73 **GETABIRD (IRE)**, 6, b g Getaway (GER)—Fern Bird (IRE) **Mrs S. Ricci**
74 **GIANT SPIRIT (USA)**, 6, ch g Giant's Causeway (USA)—Saintlike (USA) **Ms Michelle Doyle & Sean Barton**
75 **GLENS HARMONY (IRE)**, 6, b m King's Theatre (IRE)—Glens Music (IRE) **Ms Fiona McStay**
76 **GLORIOUS LEGEND (IRE)**, 5, b g Pour Moi (IRE)—Endearing **Supreme Horse Racing Club & Kenneth Sharp**
77 **GOOD THYNE TARA**, 8, b br m Kayf Tara—Good Thyne Mary (IRE) **N. G. King**
78 **GREAT FIELD (FR)**, 7, b g Great Pretender (IRE)—Eaton Lass (IRE) **John P. McManus**
79 **HAYMOUNT (IRE)**, 9, ch g Presenting—Ali's Dipper (IRE) **Mrs C. M. Hurley**
80 **HEY LITTLE BOY (GER)**, 5, b g Adlerflug (GER)—Homing Instinct **Le Nom Pas Nous Syndicate**
81 **HOLLOWGRAPHIC (IRE)**, 5, ch g Beat Hollow—Corskeagh Shadow (IRE) **Ballylinch Stud**
82 **HOT BEAT (IRE)**, 6, b g Dylan Thomas (IRE)—Hungry Heart **C. V. Wentworth**
83 **IFYOUCATCHMENOW (IRE)**, 5, b m Westerner—Ifyoucouldseemenow (IRE) **Coldunell Limited**
84 **INVITATION ONLY (IRE)**, 7, b g Flemensfirth (USA)—Norabelle (FR) **Andrea Wylie**
85 **IRISH LASS (IRE)**, 5, b m Getaway (GER)—Screaming Witness (IRE) **Bowes Lodge Stables Partnership**
86 **ISLEOFHOPENDREAMS**, 11, b g Flemensfirth (USA)—Cool Island (IRE) **Sean Sweeney**
87 **ITSONLYROCKNROLL (IRE)**, 6, ch g Shantou (USA)—Compelled (IRE) **BGC Racing**
88 **JARRY D'HONNEUR (FR)**, 9, b br g Baroud d'honneur (FR)—True Lovely (FR) **J. P. McManus**
89 **KARALEE (FR)**, 7, gr m Martaline—Change Partner (FR) **Mrs S. Ricci**
90 **KATE APPLEBY SHOES (IRE)**, 9, b m Flemensfirth (USA)—Gotta Goa (IRE) **Leo McArdle**
91 **KATIE CONNELL (IRE)**, 5, b m Doyen (IRE)—Sylverlune (FR) **Mrs Caren Walsh**
92 **KEMBOY (FR)**, 6, b g Voix du Nord (FR)—Vitora (FR) **Supreme Horse Racing Club**
93 **KILLULTAGH VIC (IRE)**, 9, b g Old Vic—Killultagh Dawn (IRE) **Mrs Rose Boyd**
94 **KOLUMBUS (IRE)**, 7, b g Robin des Champs (FR)—Saabga (USA) **Sean Sweeney**
95 **KOSHARI (FR)**, 6, br g Walk In The Park (IRE)—Honor May (FR) **Mrs S. Ricci**
96 **LAGOSTOVEGAS (IRE)**, 6, b m Footstepsinthesand—Reine de Coeur (USA) **Mr J. Donohue**
97 **LAURINA (FR)**, 5, b m Spanish Moon (USA)—Lamboghina (GER) **Sullivan Bloodstock Limited**
98 **LAW GIRL (IRE)**, 5, b m Lawman (FR)—Lamarsa (FR) **Mrs S. Ricci**
99 **LAWS OF SPIN (IRE)**, 5, b h Lawman (FR)—Spinning Well (IRE) **B. Hourihane**
100 **LET'S DANCE (FR)**, 6, b m Poliglote—Baraka du Berlais (FR) **Mrs S. Ricci**
101 **LIMINI (IRE)**, 7, ch m Peintre Celebre (USA)—Her Grace (IRE) **Mrs S. Ricci**
102 **LISTEN DEAR (IRE)**, 8, b m Robin des Champs (FR)—Crescendor (FR) **Supreme Horse Racing Club**
103 **LIVELOVELAUGH (IRE)**, 8, b g Beneficial—Another Evening (IRE) **Mrs S. Ricci**
104 **LOW SUN**, 5, b g Champs Elysees—Winter Solstice **Mrs S. Ricci**
105 **MAKITORIX (FR)**, 5, gr g Makfi—Goldamix (IRE) **Twenty Seven Black Partnership**
106 **MARY SUN**, 5, b m Soldier Hollow—Mary James **J. R. Brennan**
107 **MAX DYNAMITE (FR)**, 8, b h Great Journey (JPN)—Mascara (GER) **Mrs S. Ricci**
108 **MELON**, 6, ch g Medicean—Night Teeny **Mrs J. Donnelly**
109 **MERI DEVIE (FR)**, 5, ch m Spirit One (FR)—Folle Biche (FR) **Andrea & Graham Wylie**
110 **MIN (FR)**, 7, b g Walk In The Park (IRE)—Phemyka (FR) **Mrs S. Ricci**
111 **MINELLA BEAU (IRE)**, 7, br g King's Theatre (IRE)—Ney Will (FR) **Mrs A. F. Mee Partnership**
112 **MINELLA ENCORE (IRE)**, 6, b g King's Theatre (IRE)—Stashedaway (IRE) **David Bobbett**
113 **MONTALBANO**, 6, ch g Monsieur Bond (IRE)—Alpen Glen **Mrs S. Ricci**
114 **MR ADJUDICATOR**, 4, b g Camacho—Attlongglast **David Bobbett**
115 **MSASSA (FR)**, 4, b g Sholokhov (IRE)—Ramina (GER) **Sullivan Bloodstock Limited**
116 **NESSUN DORMA (IRE)**, 5, b g Canford Cliffs (IRE)—Idle Chatter (IRE) **N. D. Kennelly Partnership**
117 **NEXT DESTINATION (IRE)**, 6, b g Dubai Destination (USA)—Liss Alainn (IRE) **Malcolm C. Denmark**
118 **OPEN EAGLE (IRE)**, 9, b g Montjeu (IRE)—Princesse de Viane (FR) **Supreme Horse Racing Club**
119 **ORATORIANO (FR)**, 7, b g East of Heaven (IRE)—Oratoriane (FR) **Paul Connell**
120 **ORION D'AUBRELLE (FR)**, 5, b g Saint des Saints (FR)—Erbalunga (FR) **Mr J. A. Coleman**
121 **PAUSE AND PONDER (IRE)**, 9, b g Oscar (IRE)—Hazel Grove (IRE) **GGGE Syndicate**
122 **PENCREEK (FR)**, 5, ch g Konig Shuffle (GER)—Couture Fleurs (FR) **Mr M. G. Worcester**
123 **PENHILL**, 7, b g Mount Nelson—Serrenia (IRE) **Anthony Bloom**
124 **PIETRALUNGA (FR)**, 5, b m Soldier of Fortune (IRE)—Ascot One (FR) **Pietralunga Syndicate**
125 **PLEASANT COMPANY (IRE)**, 10, b g Presenting—Katie Flame (IRE) **Malcolm C. Denmark**

MR WILLIAM P. MULLINS - Continued

126 **POLIDAM (FR)**, 9, b g Trempolino (USA)—Eladame (FR) **Mr Simon Munir/Mr Isaac Souede**
127 **POLY ROCK (FR)**, 7, b g Policy Maker (IRE)—Gastinaise (FR) **Supreme House Racing Club**
128 **PRAIRIENATIVE (IRE)**, 6, b g Robin des Champs (FR)—Lost Prairie (IRE) **Andrea & Graham Wylie**
129 **PRAVALAGUNA (FR)**, 6, b m Great Pretender (IRE)—Arnette (FR) **Bruton Street IV Partnership**
130 **PRINCE D'AUBRELLE (FR)**, 8, ch g Malinas (GER)—La Star (FR) **Allan McLuckie**
131 **PYLONTHEPRESSURE (IRE)**, 8, b g Darsi (FR)—Minnie O'grady (IRE) **Mrs S. Ricci**
132 **QUICK GRABIM (IRE)**, 6, b g Oscar (IRE)—Top Her Up (IRE) **Mr M. G. Worcester**
133 **RACING PULSE (IRE)**, 9, b g Garuda (IRE)—
                                       Jacks Sister (IRE) **Paul Byrne/Dominic Ryan/A. J. Horan/P. W. Mullins**
134 **RATHVINDEN (IRE)**, 10, b g Heron Island (IRE)—Peggy Cullen (IRE) **R. A. Bartlett**
135 **REAL STEEL (FR)**, 5, gr g Loup Breton (IRE)—Kalimina (FR) **Sullivan Bloodstock Limited**
136 **REDHOTFILLYPEPPERS (IRE)**, 6, ch m Robin des Champs (FR)—Mhuire Na Gale (IRE) **Coldunell Limited**
137 **RELEGATE (IRE)**, 5, b m Flemensfirth (USA)—Last of The Bunch **Paul McKeon**
138 **RENNETI (FR)**, 9, b g Irish Wells (FR)—Caprice Meill (FR) **Mrs S. Ricci**
139 **RETOUR EN FRANCE (IRE)**, 8, b m Robin des Champs (FR)—Rayane (FR) **Mrs S. Ricci**
140 **RIA D'ETEL (FR)**, 6, b m Martaline—Angesse (FR) **Simon Munir**
141 **RIO VIVAS (FR)**, 6, b g Voix du Nord (FR)—Rio Amata (GER) **Sullivan Bloodstock Limited**
142 **RIVEN LIGHT (IRE)**, 6, b g Raven's Pass (USA)—Vivacity **Mrs S. Ricci**
143 **ROBIN DES FORET (IRE)**, 8, br g Robin des Pres (FR)—Omyn Supreme (IRE) **Byerley Racing Syndicate**
144 **SANDSEND (IRE)**, 5, gr g Turgeon (USA)—Sans Rien (IRE) **Sullivan Bloodstock Limited**
145 **SATURNAS (FR)**, 7, b g Davidoff (GER)—Sayuri (GER) **Wicklow Bloodstock (Ireland) Ltd**
146 **SAYAR (IRE)**, 5, b g Azamour (IRE)—Seraya (FR) **Mrs Audrey Turley**
147 **SCARPETA (FR)**, 5, b g Soldier of Fortune (IRE)—Sanada (IRE) **Thurloe Thoroughbreds Ireland Limited**
148 **SCREAMING ROSE (IRE)**, 7, b m Darsi (FR)—Screaming Witness (IRE) **N. G. King**
149 **SHANESHILL (IRE)**, 9, b g King's Theatre (IRE)—Darabaka (IRE) **Andrea & Graham Wylie**
150 **SHANNING (FR)**, 5, b m Spanish Moon (USA)—Idaho Falls (FR) **Supreme Horse Racing Club/Brett T. Graham**
151 **SHARJAH (FR)**, 5, b g Doctor Dino (FR)—Saaryeh **Mrs S. Ricci**
152 **SHARPS CHOICE (IRE)**, 7, ch g Montmartre (FR)—Behra (IRE) **Supreme Horse Racing Club**
153 **SHOULDA LIED (IRE)**, 4, b g Henrythenavigator (USA)—
                                       Pray (IRE) **Supreme Horse Racing Club & Courtney L. Barr**
154 **SMALL FARM (IRE)**, 6, b g Westerner—Eastertide (IRE) **Sullivan Bloodstock Limited**
155 **SOME NECK (FR)**, 7, gr g Yeats (IRE)—Maternelle (FR) **Mrs S. Ricci**
156 **SQUADRON COMMANDER (IRE)**, 5, b g Oscar (IRE)—
                                       Glor Na Gaoithe (IRE) **Regulatory Finance Solutions Limited**
157 **STEEL WAVE (IRE)**, 8, br g Craigsteel—Musical Waves (IRE) **Here For A Good Time Syndicate**
158 **STORMY IRELAND (FR)**, 4, b f Motivator—Like A Storm (IRE) **Sullivan Bloodstock Limited**
159 **SUPER BOWL (FR)**, 5, b h Turtle Bowl (IRE)—Ekadzati (FR) **Supreme Horse Racing Club**
160 **SWEET FLIGHT (GER)**, 5, b g Adlerflug (GER)—Sworn Pro (GER) **Supreme Horse Racing Club**
161 **THE CRAFTY BUTCHER (IRE)**, 11, b g Vinnie Roe (IRE)—
                                       Ivy Queen (IRE) **Paul Byrne/ P.W. Mullins/ Dominic Ryan/ Ian Madigan (Partnership)**
162 **THOMAS HOBSON**, 8, b g Halling (USA)—La Spezia (IRE) **Mrs S. Ricci**
163 **TIMI ROLI (FR)**, 6, b g Roli Abi (FR)—Tiana (FR) **George Creighton**
164 **TOTAL RECALL (IRE)**, 9, b g Westerner—Augest Weekend (IRE) **Slaneyville Syndicate**
165 **TOWNSHEND (GER)**, 7, b g Lord of England (GER)—Trikolore (GER) **Mrs S. Ricci**
166 **TRUE SELF (IRE)**, 5, b m Oscar (IRE)—Good Thought (IRE) **Three Mile House Partnership**
167 **TURCAGUA (FR)**, 8, gr g Turgeon (USA)—Acancagua (FR) **Mrs S. Ricci**
168 **UN DE SCEAUX (FR)**, 10, b g Denham Red (FR)—Hotesse de Sceaux (FR) **E. O'Connell**
169 **UP FOR REVIEW (IRE)**, 9, br g Presenting—Coolsilver (IRE) **Andrea & Graham Wylie**
170 **URADEL (GER)**, 7, b g Kallisto (GER)—Unavita (GER) **Mrs M. McMahon**
171 **URANO (FR)**, 10, b g Enrique—Neiland (FR) **Mrs M. Mahon**
172 **VOIX DES TIEP (FR)**, 6, b br g Voix du Nord (FR)—Tiepataxe (FR) **OMG II Partnership**
173 **VOIX DU REVE (FR)**, 6, br g Voix du Nord (FR)—Pommbelle (FR) **Andrea & Graham Wylie**
174 **VROUM VROUM MAG (FR)**, 9, b m Voix du Nord (FR)—Naiade Mag (FR) **Mrs S. Ricci**
175 **WHISKEY SOUR (FR)**, 5, b h Jeremy (USA)—Swizzle Stick (IRE) **Luke McMahon**
176 **WICKLOW BRAVE**, 9, b g Beat Hollow—Moraine **Wicklow Bloodstock Limited**
177 **YORKHILL (IRE)**, 8, ch g Presenting—Lightning Breeze (IRE) **Andrea Wylie**

THREE-YEAR-OLDS

178 **BRONAGH'S BELLE (IRE)**, b f High Chaparral (IRE)—South Atlantic (USA) **Sean Sweeney**
179 **MAZE RUNNER (IRE)**, b g Authorized (IRE)—Alice Rose (IRE) **Mrs J. M. Mullins**

406 MISS AMY MURPHY, Newmarket

Postal: **The Looking Glass Cottage, Hamilton Stables, Hamilton Road, Newmarket, Suffolk, CB8 7JQ**
Contacts: PHONE **(01638) 429033** MOBILE **(07711) 992500**
E-MAIL **info@amymurphyracing.com** WEBSITE **www.amymurphyracing.com**

1 **CARNIVAL KING (IRE)**, 6, b g Arcano (IRE)—Validate **Miss A. L. Murphy**
2 **ENOLA (IRE)**, 4, b f Lawman (FR)—Kelowna (IRE) **Essex Racing Club 2**
3 **ENTERTAINING BEN**, 5, b g Equiano (FR)—Fatal Attraction **Amy Murphy Racing Club**
4 **HAWTHORN COTTAGE (IRE)**, 5, b m Gold Well—Miss Kilkeel (IRE) **Melbourne 10 Racing**
5 **KALASHNIKOV (IRE)**, 5, br g Kalanisi (IRE)—Fairy Lane (IRE) **Mr P. Murphy**
6 **KING'S RESTE (IRE)**, 6, b m King's Theatre (IRE)—J'y Reste (FR) **Mr P. Murphy**
7 **LAZARUS (IRE)**, 4, b g Zoffany (IRE)—Knysna (IRE) **Amy Murphy Racing Club**
8 **MARIAH'S LEGEND**, 6, b m Flying Legend (USA)—Mariah Rollins (IRE) **Mr P. Murphy**
9 **MERCIAN KING (IRE)**, 7, b g Robin des Pres (FR)—Mariah Rollins (IRE) **The Thoroughbred Club II**
10 **MERCIAN PRINCE (IRE)**, 7, b g Midnight Legend—Bongo Fury (FR) **Mr P. Murphy**
11 **REALLY SUPER**, 4, b f Cacique (IRE)—Sensationally **White Diamond Racing Partnership 1**
12 **SHAN DUN NA NGALL (IRE)**, 7, b g Shantou (USA)—Omanah (USA) **Prosecco Club**
13 **STRAWBERRY SPIRIT (IRE)**, 5, b m Saint des Saints (FR)—Strawberry (IRE) **Mr P. Murphy**
14 **THAQAFFA (IRE)**, 5, b g Kodiac—Incense **Prosecco Club**
15 **TUPOLEV (IRE)**, 5, b g Black Sam Bellamy (IRE)—Mariah Rollins (IRE) **Mr P. Murphy**

THREE-YEAR-OLDS

16 **ADDICUS (IRE)**, b f Lord Shanakill (USA)—Ballyquirke Lake (IRE) **Mr S. M. Al Sabah**
17 **APPROACHING MENACE**, b f Cityscape—Candle **Gwyn & Samantha Powell**
18 **AVLOS**, b g Arcano (IRE)—Royal Blush **Charles Auld & Partner**
19 **BLESSED TO EMPRESS (IRE)**, b f Holy Roman Emperor (IRE)—
Blessing Box **White Diamond Racing Partnership 1**
20 B f Makfi—Cursory **Miss A. L. Murphy**
21 **GIVEN LEADER**, ch g Nathaniel (IRE)—Chieftess (IRE) **Miss A. L. Murphy**
22 **MARBLE STATUE**, b f Makfi—Czarna Roza **R S Hoskins & Partners**
23 **SANDKISSED (IRE)**, b f Sir Prancealot (IRE)—Hapipi **Mr S. P. King**
24 **THE ACCOUNTANT**, ch g Dylan Thomas (IRE)—Glorybe (GER) **The Rann Family**
25 **THE WIRE FLYER**, b g Champs Elysees—Good Morning Star (IRE) **Corbsinger Thoroughbreds**

TWO-YEAR-OLDS

26 Ch c 18/3 Equiano (FR)—Conversational (IRE) (Thousand Words) (30000) **Miss A. L. Murphy**
27 B f 3/2 Kodiac—Of Course Darling (Dalakhani (IRE)) (20000) **Miss A. L. Murphy**
28 Ch c 16/2 Showcasing—Pivotal Bride (Dubawi (IRE)) (7500) **Nina Rajani & Partner**
29 **UPONASTAR (IRE)**, b f 8/1 Zebedee—Eponastone (IRE) (Footstepsinthesand) (15238) **Mr S. P. King**
30 **WHINNIE**, b f 28/3 Garswood—Sakhya (IRE) (Barathea (IRE)) **Saxtead Livestock Ltd**

Other Owners: Mr C. C. Auld, Mr I. J. Barratt, Mrs C. J. Barratt, Mr T. Castle, Essex Racing Club, Miss R. Grensinger, Mr R. S. Hoskins, Miss T. R. Lewis, G. E. Powell, Mrs S. Powell, Miss N. K. Rajani, Mr G. P. D. Rann, Mrs L. E. Rann, Mr D. Redvers, Mr R. B. Root, Mrs J. P. Root, Mr J. P. Ryan, White Diamond Racing Partnership.

408 MR MIKE MURPHY, Westoning

Postal: **Broadlands, Manor Park Stud, Westoning, Bedfordshire, MK45 5LA**
Contacts: PHONE **(01525) 717305** FAX **(01525) 717305** MOBILE **(07770) 496103**
E-MAIL **mmurphy@globalnet.co.uk** WEBSITE **www.mikemurphyracing.co.uk**

1 **ANNA MEDICI**, 4, b f Sir Percy—Florentia **Victoria Taylor & Family**
2 **BAMO MC**, 4, gr g Hellvelyn—Soft Touch (IRE) **M&O Construction & Civil Engineering Ltd**
3 **DESERT FOX**, 4, b g Foxwedge (AUS)—Snow Moccasin (IRE) **Rogerson, Lemon, Cooper & Arlotte**
4 **JUST MAYBE**, 4, b c Mayson—Phantasmagoria **The Maysonettes**
5 **LADY PRIMA**, 4, b f Sir Percy—Alla Prima (IRE) **J L Rowsell & F Mooney**
6 **LILY ASH (IRE)**, 5, b m Lilbourne Lad (IRE)—Ashdali (IRE) **Ms A. D. Tibbett**
7 **MAGICINTHEMAKING (USA)**, 4, br f Wildcat Heir (USA)—Love in Bloom (USA) **Victoria Taylor & Family**
8 **MAID OF ROCK (IRE)**, 4, b f Rock of Gibraltar (IRE)—Embark **Lemon, Papworth, Hazelwood & Sullivan**
9 **MULZIM**, 4, b c Exceed And Excel (AUS)—Samaah (IRE) **Hamdan bin Rashid Al Maktoum**
10 **MUSICAL COMEDY**, 7, b g Royal Applause—Spinning Top **Ms A. D. Tibbett**
11 **PREMIER CURRENCY (IRE)**, 5, b g Elusive Pimpernel (USA)—Zeena **Llewelyn Yardley Runeckles**
12 **RIO RONALDO (IRE)**, 6, b g Footstepsinthesand—Flanders (IRE) **The Castaways**
13 **STREET ART (IRE)**, 6, ch g Excellent Art—Via Aurelia (IRE) **Ms A. D. Tibbett**
14 **TITAN GODDESS**, 6, b m Equiano (FR)—Phoebe Woodstock (IRE) **Phoebe's Friends**

MR MIKE MURPHY - Continued

15 **WHISPERED KISS**, 5, b m Medicean—Desert Kiss **D.Ellison - B.Olkowicz - P.Speller**
16 **YOUNG JOHN (IRE)**, 5, b g Acclamation—Carpet Lady (IRE) **Mr M. Murphy**
17 **ZAMPERINI (IRE)**, 6, ch g Fast Company (IRE)—Lucky Date (IRE) **Mr R. E. Tillett**

THREE-YEAR-OLDS

18 B br f Kitten's Joy (USA)—Keeping Watch (IRE)
19 **KODIAC EXPRESS (IRE)**, b f Kodiac—Excel Yourself (IRE) **The Kodi Bunch**
20 **OVERTRUMPED**, b f Champs Elysees—Perfect Hand **Mr Borgatti & Mr Moir**
21 Ch f Equiano (FR)—Zia (GER)

TWO-YEAR-OLDS

22 Ch f 11/5 Toronado (IRE)—Dusty Answer (Zafonic (USA)) (30000)
23 B c 28/2 Dansili—Much Promise (Invincible Spirit (IRE))
24 B c 22/3 Havana Gold (IRE)—Sunset Kitty (USA) (Gone West (USA)) (24000)

Other Owners: Mr M. Borgatti, Mrs D. Ellison, G. I. D. Llewelyn, Mr S. Moir, Mr F. Mooney, Mr B. Olkowicz, Mr B. Rogerson, J. L. Rowsell, Mr J. F. Runeckles, Mrs P.S. Speller.

Assistant Trainer: Michael Keady

---

409 | **MR OLLY MURPHY, Wilmcote**
Postal: **Warren Chase Stables, Wilmcote, Stratford-Upon-Avon, Warwickshire, CV37 9XG**
Contacts: **PHONE (01789) 613347**
E-MAIL office@ollymurphyracing.com WEBSITE www.ollymurphyracing.com

1 **AFTER ASPEN (IRE)**, 8, b g Mountain High (IRE)—None The Wiser (IRE)
2 **ATAMAN (IRE)**, 6, b g Sholokhov (IRE)—Diora (IRE) **Olly Murphy Racing Club**
3 **AVOCET (USA)**, 5, b m Artie Schiller (USA)—Striking Example (USA) **Mr P. Foster**
4 **BALLINSLEA BRIDGE (IRE)**, 6, b g Pierre—Feelin' Looser (IRE) **Ashley, Carr, Duncan, Ives**
5 **BANFF (IRE)**, 5, b g Papal Bull—Hugs 'n Kisses (IRE) **Mary Shalvey & Aiden Murphy**
6 **BISOUBISOU**, 5, b m Champs Elysees—Marathea (FR) **Wells House Racing**
7 **BREWIN'UPASTORM (IRE)**, 5, b g Milan—Daraheen Diamond (IRE) **Ms B. J. Abt**
8 **CALIPSO COLLONGES (FR)**, 6, b g Crossharbour—Ivresse Collonges (FR) **The Black Horse Hotel Bridgnorth**
9 **CAPTIVA ISLAND (IRE)**, 5, b g Scorpion (IRE)—Sapphire Eile **Still Scoobyless**
10 **CARRAIGIN AONAIR (IRE)**, 6, b m Fastnet Rock (AUS)—Omanah (USA) **Mr O. J. Murphy**
11 **COSTA GALERA (IRE)**, 4, b g Rock of Gibraltar (IRE)—Albany Rose (IRE) **Ready Steady Go**
12 **CRUMPLEDANDCREASED (IRE)**, 6, br m Big Bad Bob (IRE)—Sunset Queen (IRE) **Mr M. Fennessy**
13 **EOLIAN**, 4, b g Poet's Voice—Charlecote (IRE) **Premier Thoroughbred Racing**
14 **FLOW WITH EVE**, 9, b m With The Flow (USA)—Vercheny **Michael & Will Potter**
15 **FLYNNVINCIBLE**, 7, b g Tobougg (IRE)—Shiny Thing (USA) **Murphy's Law Partnership**
16 **FOXTROT JULIET**, 5, b m Shirocco (GER)—Miami Explorer **Foxtrot Racing: Foxtrot Juliet**
17 **FRESH NEW DAWN (IRE)**, 6, ch g Flemensfirth (USA)—Star Shuil (IRE) **Not For Friends Partnership**
18 **GARRETTSTOWN (IRE)**, 5, b g Doyen (IRE)—Azur (IRE) **The Phillies Partnership**
19 **GENERAL BUX**, 7, b g Lucarno (USA)—Cadoutene (FR) **The Scoobyless Partnership**
20 **GENERAL CUSTARD (IRE)**, 5, b g Shirocco (GER)—Diamant Noir **Syder, Whateley, Murphy, Burke**
21 **HUNTERS CALL (IRE)**, 8, b g Medaaly—Accordiontogelica (IRE) **Holloway,Clarke,Black**
22 **HURRICANE RITA (FR)**, 4, gr m Sagamix (FR)—Madonna da Rossi **From the Front Racing, Twopoundpunt2**
23 **IMPERIAL KNIGHT (IRE)**, 6, b g Mahler—And Whatever Else (IRE) **Nicholas Piper & Claire E. Piper**
24 **IT'S O KAY**, 5, b m Shirocco (GER)—Presenting Copper (IRE) **Aiden Murphy & Alan Peterson**
25 **KNIGHT COMMANDER**, 5, br g Sir Percy—Jardin **The Rebelle Boys**
26 **KNOCKGRAFFON (IRE)**, 8, b g Flemensfirth (USA)—Gleaming Spire **Ms B. J. Abt**
27 **KOLOSS D'AGROSTIS (FR)**, 4, b br g Cima de Triomphe (IRE)—Maeva Candas (FR)
28 **MILES TO MILAN (IRE)**, 8, b g Milan—Princesse Rooney (FR) **Mrs L. H. Field**
29 **MORE THAN LUCK (IRE)**, 7, br g Gothland (FR)—Pretty Impressive (IRE) **Elphick's Hardy Hubbard Banks**
30 **MULLAGHBOY (IRE)**, 7, b g Beneficial—Mellowthemoonlight (IRE) **Ready Steady Go**
31 **NO ALARM (IRE)**, 6, b g Getaway (GER)—Chapanga (IRE) **Touchwood Racing**
32 **OXFORD BLU**, 4, b g Aqlaam—Blue Zealot (IRE) **geegeez.co.uk OM**
33 **PIRI MASSINI (IRE)**, 7, b g Pierre—Lady Doctor (IRE) **Mr C. J. Haughey**
34 **RIO QUINTO (FR)**, 5, b g Loup Breton (FR)—Seal of Cause (IRE) **Mrs D. L. Whateley**
35 **SABLE ISLAND (IRE)**, 4, b g New Approach (IRE)—Ratukidul (FR) **Mr R. Treacy**
36 **SANGHA RIVER (IRE)**, 5, br g Arcadio (GER)—Hidden Reserve (IRE) **Ms B. J. Abt**
37 **SAUCYSIOUX**, 8, b m Tobougg (IRE)—Mohican Pass **Olly Murphy Racing Club**
38 **SEVILLA**, 5, b m Duke of Marmalade (IRE)—Glittering Prize (UAE) **Olly Murphy Racing Club**
39 **SIMAFAR (IRE)**, 4, b g Makfi—Simawa (IRE) **Darkhorse Racing 30 Syndicate**

MR OLLY MURPHY - Continued

40 **SKILLED**, 7, b g Mastercraftsman (IRE)—Treacle (USA) **Olly Murphy Racing Club/K Lowe/A Murphy**
41 **SWAFFHAM BULBECK (IRE)**, 4, b g Jeremy (USA)—Ballygologue (IRE) **geegeez.co.uk OM**
42 **TELEGRAPH PLACE (IRE)**, 5, br g Yeats (IRE)—Sea Skate (USA)
43 **THE GEEGEEZ GEEGEE (IRE)**, 9, b g Beneficial—Shanann Lady (IRE) **En Famille**
44 **UNDEFINED BEAUTY (IRE)**, 9, gr m Kayf Tara—Lorna (IRE) **Mrs E. Murphy**
45 **WEEBILL**, 6, b g Schiaparelli (GER)—Wee Dinns (IRE) **Mrs C. Skan**
46 **WHISKEY IN THE JAR (IRE)**, 6, b g Oscar (IRE)—Baie Barbara (IRE) **Ms B. J. Abt**
47 **WISHFULL DREAMING**, 7, ch g Alflora (IRE)—Poussetiere Deux (FR) **Mrs D. L. Whateley**
48 **WOOD PIGEON (IRE)**, 9, b g Presenting—Come In Moscow (IRE) **Mr C. J. Haughey**
49 **YENSIR**, 5, ch g Sir Percy—Yensi **Mr O. J. Murphy**
50 **ZAMALIGHT**, 4, ch g Zamindar (USA)—Mountain Chain (USA) **Mr O. J. Murphy**

Other Owners: Mr D. Abraham, Mrs J. Abraham, Mr S. A. Ashley, Mr N. W. Bailey, Mr M. Bisogno, Mr S. T. Black, Mrs V. F. Burke, A. Carr, Miss E. J. Clarke, P. W. Clement, Mr W. Downs, Mr M. Duncan, Mr T. Elphick, Mr D. M. Forrester, Mr S. Franks, From the Front Racing, Twopoundpunt, Mr A. N. Gargan, Mr J. R. Holloway, Mrs C. M. Hopkirk, Mr P. J. Hopkirk, Mr D. L. Ives, Mr B. Kelleher, Mrs J. I. S. King, Mr K. Lowe, Ms M. Machin-Jefferies, Mr P. McBride, Mr J. McMahon, Mr B. H. Mellon, Mr M. Muldoon, H. A. Murphy, Mrs A. L. M. Murphy, Mr A. E. Peterson, Miss C. E. Piper, Mr N. Piper, Mr C. D. Platel, Mr W. E. Potter, M. Potter, Mr A. R. Purvis, Ms M. Shalvey, Mrs S. Stanley, Mr T. D. J. Syder, Mrs C. J. Walsh.

Assistant Trainer: Ed Telfer

Jockey (NH): David England, Richard Johnson, Ian Popham, Charlie Poste. **Conditional:** Fergus Gregory. **Amateur:** Mr Lewis Stones.

---

410 **MR PAT MURPHY, Hungerford**
Postal: **Glebe House Stables, School Lane, East Garston, Nr Hungerford, Berkshire, RG17 7HR**
Contacts: OFFICE **(01488) 648473** MOBILE **(07831) 410409**
E-MAIL **patmurphy13@gmail.com** WEBSITE **www.patmurphyracing.com**

1 **NESSFIELD BLUE**, 4, b g Kayf Tara—Bella Medici **Murphy & Chantler**

Other Owners: Mrs B. I. Chantler, P. G. Murphy.

Jockey (NH): Leighton Aspell.

---

411 **MR BARRY MURTAGH, Carlisle**
Postal: **Hurst Farm, Ivegill, Carlisle, Cumbria, CA4 0NL**
Contacts: PHONE **(01768) 484649** FAX **(01768) 484744** MOBILE **(07714) 026741**
E-MAIL **suemurtagh7@gmail.com**

1 4, B g Josr Algarhoud (IRE)—Animal Cracker **Mrs Sue Murtagh**
2 **BARABOY**, 8, b g Barathea (IRE)—Irina (IRE) **A. R. White**
3 **BORDER VICTOR**, 6, b g Beat All (USA)—Sambara (IRE) **Mrs A. Stamper**
4 **CLONDAW BANKER (IRE)**, 9, b g Court Cave (IRE)—Freya Alex **A. R. White**
5 **JUSTATENNER**, 7, b g Northern Legend—Shelavly (IRE) **Raymond, Eddie & Joyce Wharton**
6 **PAPAGAYO (IRE)**, 6, b g Shirocco (GER)—Jomana (IRE) **M. A. Proudfoot**
7 **RECOGNITION (IRE)**, 5, gr g Rip Van Winkle (IRE)—Bali Breeze (IRE) **Mrs Sue Murtagh**
8 **ROBIN DE PLAN (IRE)**, 7, b m Robin des Pres (FR)—Nice Resemblance (IRE) **Hurst Farm Racing**
9 **STANS BLACK FIVE**, 5, b g Multiplex—Globe Dream (IRE) **Mr Eric Chapman**
10 **STARSHELL (IRE)**, 4, b g Sea The Stars (IRE)—Aquarelle Bleue **Mr G Fell & Don't Tell Henry**
11 **SWANTYKAY (IRE)**, 9, b g Darsi (FR)—Glamorous Leader (IRE) **Murtagh, Trinder & Trinder**
12 **SYMBOLIC STAR (IRE)**, 6, b g New Approach (IRE)—Epitome (IRE) **Murtagh, O'Rourke & Trinders**
13 **WHATSTHESTORYMAN (IRE)**, 10, b g Alderbrook—Express Way Lady (IRE) **Miss Emma Dunkley**

Other Owners: Mr James Callow, Mr G. Fell, Mr F. P. Murtagh, Mrs Sue Murtagh, Mr Rory O'Rourke, Mr A. Trinder, Mrs A. Trinder, Mr Eddie Wharton, Mrs Joyce Wharton, Mr T. Wharton, Mr Derek Wilson.

Assistant Trainer: S A Murtagh

Conditional: Lorcan Murtagh. **Apprentice:** Connor Murtagh.

412 DR JEREMY NAYLOR, Shrewton
Postal: **The Cleeve Stables, Elston, Shrewton, Salisbury, Wiltshire, SP3 4HL**
Contacts: **PHONE (01980) 620804 MOBILE (07771) 740126**
E-MAIL **info@jeremynaylor.com** WEBSITE **www.jeremynaylor.com**

1 **CROUCHING HARRY (IRE)**, 9, b g Tiger Hill (IRE)—Catwalk Dreamer (IRE) **Mrs S. P. Elphick**
2 **FEARSOME FRED**, 9, b g Emperor Fountain—Ryewater Dream **Mrs S. P. Elphick**
3 **JUST ARCHIE (USA)**, 10, b g Arch (USA)—Copper Rose (USA) **Mrs S. P. Elphick**
4 **LADY CARDINAL (IRE)**, 7, ch m Papal Bull—St Finan's Bay (IRE) **Mrs S. P. Elphick**
5 **PADOVA**, 12, b g Shahrastani (USA)—My Song of Songs **Dr J. R. J. Naylor**
6 **SANCHES**, 4, b g Delegator—Flamenco Dancer **Mrs R. R. Swift**
7 **WHAT LARKS (IRE)**, 10, b g Pierre—Bint Rosie **Mrs H. A. Heal**

413 MR JOHN NEEDHAM, Ludlow
Postal: **Gorsty Farm, Mary Knoll, Ludlow, Shropshire, SY8 2HD**
Contacts: **PHONE (01584) 872112/874826 FAX (01584) 873256 MOBILE (07811) 451137**
E-MAIL **johnlneedham@btconnect.com**

1 **DOWNTON FOX**, 10, b g Oscar (IRE)—Leinthall Fox **Miss J. C. L. Needham**
2 **MAIN REASON (IRE)**, 10, b m Golan (IRE)—Regents Dream
3 6, Br m Sagamix (FR)—Marlbrook Fox **Miss J. C. L. Needham**
4 **RIGHT ROYALS DAY**, 9, b m Beneficial—Just For A Laugh **Miss J. C. L. Needham**

Assistant Trainer: P. Hanly

Jockey (NH): Richard Johnson. **Amateur:** Mr R Jarrett.

414 MRS HELEN NELMES, Dorchester
Postal: **Warmwell Stables, 2 Church Cottages, Warmwell, Dorchester, Dorset, DT2 8HQ**
Contacts: **PHONE/FAX (01305) 852254 MOBILE (07977) 510318**
E-MAIL **warmwellstud@tiscali.co.uk** WEBSITE **www.warmwellstables.co.uk**

1 **GARRYDUFF CROSS (IRE)**, 8, b g Stowaway—Cooleycall (IRE) **K. A. Nelmes**
2 **ITSABOUTTIME (IRE)**, 8, gr g Whitmore's Conn (USA)—Blazing Love (IRE) **K. A. Nelmes**
3 **KALMBEFORETHESTORM**, 10, ch g Storming Home—Miss Honeypenny (IRE) **Warmwellcome Partnership**
4 **KEEPYOURHEADUP**, 7, b g Sir Percy—Sweet Lemon (IRE) **Mr K. Tyre**
5 **MENAPIAN (IRE)**, 7, b br g Touch of Land (FR)—Mannequin (IRE) **Warmwellcome Partnership**
6 **MYLITTLEMOUSE (IRE)**, 10, b m Turtle Island (IRE)—Ballybeg Rose (IRE) **K. A. Nelmes**
7 **NORSE DA**, 8, b g Norse Dancer (IRE)—End of An Error **T M W Partnership**
8 **SERVEONTIME (IRE)**, 7, b g Echo of Light—Little Lovely (IRE) **K. A. Nelmes**
9 **THE CLYDA ROVER (IRE)**, 14, ch g Moonax (IRE)—Pampered Molly (IRE) **K. A. Nelmes**
10 **THE FINGER POST (IRE)**, 11, b g Zagreb (USA)—Mystic Madam (IRE) **K. A. Nelmes**

Other Owners: Miss V. O. Kardas, Ms A. M. Neville, Mr D. Price.

Assistant Trainer: K Nelmes

Conditional: Conor Ring.

415 MR TONY NEWCOMBE, Barnstaple
Postal: **Lower Delworthy, Yarnscombe, Barnstaple, Devon, EX31 3LT**
Contacts: **PHONE/FAX (01271) 858554 MOBILE (07785) 297210**
E-MAIL **huntshawequineforest@talktalk.net**

1 **ANGELITO**, 9, ch g Primo Valentino (IRE)—Supreme Angel **Mr M. Wilson**
2 **BUSHEL (USA)**, 8, b g Street Cry (IRE)—Melhor Ainda (USA) **Mr N. P. Hardy**
3 **DANA'S PRESENT**, 9, ch g Osorio (GER)—Euro Empire **9.36 from Paddington**
4 **DAYDREAM (IRE)**, 5, b m Dream Ahead (USA)—Intricate Dance (USA) **Mr I. R. Newman**
5 **DUBAI WAVES**, 4, b f Poet's Voice—Pencarrow **Joli Racing**
6 **HOUSE OF FRAUDS (IRE)**, 10, b g Storming Home—Bogus Penny (IRE) **Joli Racing**
7 **KAY SERA**, 10, b g Kayf Tara—Inflation **Mr N. P. Hardy**
8 **KODIAC PEARL (IRE)**, 4, b f Kodiac—Valmirez (USA) **A. G. Newcombe**

MR TONY NEWCOMBE - Continued

9 **NUZHA**, 4, ch f Mayson—Always On My Mind **A. G. Newcombe**
10 **SIGN OF THE KODIAC (IRE)**, 5, b h Kodiac—Summer Magic (IRE) **Dr S. P. Hargreaves**
11 **SPELLMAKER**, 9, b g Kheleyf (USA)—Midnight Spell **Joli Racing**
12 **SURENESS (IRE)**, 8, ch m Hurricane Run (IRE)—Silk Dress (IRE) **Mr P. T. Mott**
13 **TUOLUMNE MEADOWS**, 5, b m High Chaparral (IRE)—Seren Devious **Mr N. P. Hardy**
14 **TURAATHY (IRE)**, 5, b m Lilbourne Lad (IRE)—Key Girl (IRE) **David Freeman & Tony Newcombe**
15 **WAR OF SUCCESSION**, 4, b g Casamento (IRE)—Rohlindi **Dr S. P. Hargreaves**

THREE-YEAR-OLDS

16 **SOVEREIGN STATE**, b g Compton Place—One Night In May (IRE) **A. G. Newcombe**

Other Owners: Mr A. G. Craig, R. Eagle, Mr D. R. J. Freeman, Mr D. A. Klein.

Assistant Trainer: John Lovejoy

Jockey (flat): Fergus Sweeney, Dane O'Neill. **Jockey (NH):** Andrew Thornton.

416
DR RICHARD NEWLAND, Claines
Postal: **Linacres Farm, Egg Lane, Claines, Worcester, WR3 7SB**
Contacts: **PHONE (07956) 196535**
E-MAIL **richard.newland1@btopenworld.com**

1 **AARON LAD (IRE)**, 7, b g Daylami (IRE)—Borntobepampered **Off The Clock Partners & Dr RDP Newland**
2 **ABOLITIONIST (IRE)**, 10, b g Flemensfirth (USA)—All The Roses (IRE) **M Albon, J A Provan & C E Stedman**
3 **AUDACIOUS PLAN (IRE)**, 9, b g Old Vic—North Star Poly (IRE) **ValueRacingClub.co.uk**
4 **BAND OF BLOOD (IRE)**, 10, b g King's Theatre (IRE)—Cherry Falls (IRE) **J A Provan & C E Stedman**
5 **BEAU BAY (FR)**, 7, b g Bernebeau (FR)—Slew Bay (FR) **Dr R. D. P. Newland**
6 **BLAGAPAR (FR)**, 7, b g Al Namix (FR)—Samarkand Bleue (FR) **Foxtrot Racing: Blagapar**
7 **BOB FORD (IRE)**, 11, b g Vinnie Roe (IRE)—Polar Lamb (IRE) **Dr R. D. P. Newland**
8 **CAID DU LIN (FR)**, 6, b g Della Francesca (USA)—Asia du Lin (FR) **Foxtrot Racing**
9 **CAPITOUL (FR)**, 6, b g Enrique—Ranavalo (FR) **Mr Paull Drinkwater/Dr R.D.P. Newland**
10 **CATAMARAN DU SEUIL (FR)**, 6, b g Network (GER)—Fleur du Tennis (FR) **Mr M. P. Tudor**
11 **DASHING PERK**, 7, b g Kayf Tara—Dashing Executive (IRE) **Mr P. Jenkins**
12 **DESERT SENSATION (IRE)**, 6, b g Authorized (IRE)—Awwal Malika (USA) **Doom Bar Beach Club**
13 **DESTINY'S GOLD (IRE)**, 8, b g Millenary—Knockhouse Rose (IRE) **Brewers Racing Club**
14 **GETTYSBURG ADDRESS (IRE)**, 7, b g Milan—Cat Burglar (IRE) **Mr M. P. Tudor**
15 **GREYED A (IRE)**, 7, gr g Daylami (IRE)—Broadcast **Plan B**
16 **LE PATRIOTE (FR)**, 6, b g Poliglote—Sentosa (FR) **Canard Vert Racing Club**
17 **LOVATO (GER)**, 6, br g Lauro (GER)—Larella (GER) **Plan B**
18 **MASTEROFDECEPTION (IRE)**, 10, b g Darsi (FR)—Sherberry (IRE) **The Berrow Hill Partnership**
19 **MAURICIO (IRE)**, 4, ch g Helmet (AUS)—Essexford (IRE) **J A Provan & Partner**
20 **MCGROARTY (IRE)**, 7, b g Brian Boru—Uffizi (IRE) **Chris Stedman & Mark Albon**
21 **ROCK GONE (IRE)**, 10, b g Winged Love (IRE)—Guillem (USA) **Chris Stedman & Mark Albon**
22 **SLIM PICKENS (IRE)**, 10, b g Craigsteel—Couleurs D'automne (FR) **Mr P. C. W. Green**
23 **SUDDEN DESTINATION (IRE)**, 6, ch g Dubai Destination (USA)—
Sudden Approach (USA) **Foxtrot Nh Racing Syndicate**
24 **SUPREME STEEL (IRE)**, 7, b g Craigsteel—Tubber Gael Holly (IRE) **Foxtrot Racing: Supreme Steel**
25 **THEO (IRE)**, 8, b g Westerner—Jemima Jay (IRE) **P Jenkins & Partner**
26 **TIGER TREK (IRE)**, 9, b g Tiger Hill (IRE)—Zayana (IRE) **Mr M Davies & Dr RDP Newland**
27 **TRIGGER NICHOL (IRE)**, 6, b g Dubai Destination (USA)—Run For Cover (IRE) **ValueRacingClub.co.uk**
28 **VOSNE ROMANEE**, 7, ch g Arakan (USA)—Vento Del Oreno (FR) **Foxtrot NH Racing Partnership VI**
29 **WEST OF THE EDGE (IRE)**, 10, b g Westerner—Bermuda Bay (IRE) **ValueRacingClub.co.uk**
30 **WHOSHOTWHO (IRE)**, 7, br g Beneficial—Inishbeg House (IRE) **Foxtrot Racing: Whoshotwho**

Other Owners: Mrs J. Abraham, Mr D. Abraham, Mr M. L. Albon, Mr M. Ansell, Mr P.D. Couldwell, Mr J. R. Couldwell, Mr M. S. Davies, Mr A. S. P. Drake, Mr P. Drinkwater, Mr J. M. O. Evans, Foxtrot Racing Management Ltd, Mr L. A. Goodfellow, Mr A. W. Hinton, Mr T. N. Lewis, Mrs L. J. Newland, Mr R. J. L. Newland, Off The Clock Partners, Mr J. A. Provan, Mr R. B. Stanley, Mr C. E. Stedman.

Assistant Trainer: Rod Trow

Amateur: Mr T. Weston.

417 MISS ANNA NEWTON-SMITH, Jevington
Postal: Bull Pen Cottage, Jevington, Polegate, East Sussex, BN26 5QB
Contacts: PHONE (01323) 488354 FAX (01323) 488354 MOBILE (07970) 914124
E-MAIL annanewtonsmith@gmail.com WEBSITE www.annanewtonsmith.co.uk

1 ALBATROS DE GUYE (FR), 8, ch g Maille Pistol (FR)—Balibirds (FR) **Mr G. E. Goring**
2 BURGESS DREAM (IRE), 9, b g Spadoun (FR)—Ennel Lady (IRE) **The Beano Partnership**
3 GORING ONE (IRE), 13, b g Broadway Flyer (USA)—Brigette's Secret **Mr G. E. Goring**
4 WALK OF GLEAMS, 9, b m Gleaming (IRE)—Harlequin Walk (IRE) **Mrs J. Brightling**

Other Owners: Mr R. W. Brooker, Mr P. C. Worley.

Assistant Trainer: Nicola Worley

Jockey (NH): Jeremiah McGrath, Andrew Thornton, Adam Wedge. **Conditional:** Charlie Deutsch.

418 MR ADRIAN NICHOLLS, Sessay
Postal: The Ranch, Sessay, Thirsk, North Yorkshire, YO7 3ND
Contacts: PHONE (01845) 597428

1 CALLOMANIA (USA), 4, b f Medaglia d'oro (USA)—Bellasimo (USA) **Mr H. Sultan Saeed**
2 RACING ANGEL (IRE), 6, b m Dark Angel (IRE)—Roclette (USA) **Mr A. Nicholls**
3 RIAL (IRE), 5, b m Dark Angel (IRE)—Coin Box **Mr A. Nicholls**
4 SIR LANCELOTT, 6, b g Piccolo—Selkirk Rose (IRE) **The Golden Horse Racing Club**

THREE-YEAR-OLDS
5 PRINCESS NOORA, ch f Farhh—Finnmark **Mr H. Sultan Saeed**

TWO-YEAR-OLDS
6 B f 14/2 Kyllachy—Equitissa (IRE) (Chevalier (IRE)) (17000) **Malih L. Al Basti**
7 B f 8/5 Milk It Mick—Formidable Girl (USA) (Roman Ruler (USA)) **Mr M. D. McGeever**

Other Owners: Mr B. Tait, Mr C. J. Woods.

419 MR PAUL NICHOLLS, Ditcheat
Postal: Manor Farm Stables, Ditcheat, Shepton Mallet, Somerset, BA4 6RD
Contacts: PHONE (01749) 860656 MOBILE (07977) 270706
E-MAIL info@paulnichollsracing.com WEBSITE www.paulnichollsracing.com

1 ACT OF VALOUR, 4, b g Harbour Watch (IRE)—B Berry Brandy (USA) **McNeill Family Ltd**
2 ADRIEN DU PONT (FR), 6, b g Califet (FR)—Santariyka (FR) **Mrs S. De La Hey**
3 AMOUR DE NUIT (IRE), 6, b g Azamour (IRE)—Umthoulah (IRE) **Mr A. N. V. Williams**
4 ANTARTICA DE THAIX (FR), 8, gr m Dom Alco (FR)—
   Nouca de Thaix (FR) **D.Macdonald, C.Barber, I.Fogg & C.Giles**
5 ART MAURESQUE (FR), 8, b g Policy Maker (IRE)—Modeva (FR) **Mrs S. De La Hey**
6 AS DE MEE (FR), 8, b br g Kapgarde (FR)—Koeur de Mee (FR) **The Stewart Family & Judi Dench**
7 ATAGUISEAMIX (FR), 5, b g Al Namix (FR)—Olafane (FR) **McNeill Family Ltd**
8 BILL AND BARN (IRE), 7, br g Presenting—Forgotten Star (IRE) **Mr D Coles & Mr M Adams**
9 BINGE DRINKER (IRE), 9, b g Spadoun (FR)—Our Honey (IRE) **Corsellis & Seyfried**
10 BIRDS OF PREY (IRE), 6, b g Sir Prancealot (IRE)—Cute **Mrs K. A. Stuart**
11 BLACK CORTON (FR), 7, br g Laverock (FR)—Pour Le Meilleur (FR) **The Brooks, Stewart Families & J. Kyle**
12 BLACK VALENTINE (IRE), 7, b g Stowaway—Kavolan (IRE) **Sparkes & Gibson I**
13 BLACKJACK KENTUCKY (IRE), 5, b g Oscar (IRE)—My Name's Not Bin (IRE)
14 BLU CAVALIER, 8, b g Kayf Tara—Blue Ride (IRE) **Mrs Angela Tincknell & Mr W. Tincknell**
15 BOUVREUIL (FR), 7, b g Saddler Maker (IRE)—Madame Lys (FR) **Mr J. P. McManus**
16 BRAHMS DE CLERMONT (FR), 7, b g Epalo (GER)—Colline de Clermon (FR) **Donlon & Doyle**
17 BRAQUEUR D'OR (FR), 7, b g Epalo (FR)—Hot d'or (FR) **Corsellis & Seyfried**
18 BRAZTIME, 4, b f Canford Cliffs (IRE)—Briery (IRE) **Mr C. M. Giles**
19 BRELAN D'AS (FR), 7, b g Crillon (FR)—Las de La Croix (FR) **Mr J. P. McManus**
20 BRIO CONTI (FR), 7, gr g Dom Alco (FR)—Cadoulie Wood (FR) **The Gi Gi Syndicate**

MR PAUL NICHOLLS - Continued

21 **BUBBLE O'CLOCK (IRE)**, 5, ch g Robin des Champs (FR)—
Flaithiuil (IRE) **Executors & Trustees of C G Roach Estate**
22 **CAP ST VINCENT (FR)**, 5, b g Muhtathir—Criquetot (FR) **Grech & Parkin**
23 **CAPELAND (FR)**, 6, b b g Poliglote—Neiland (FR) **Mrs K. A. Stuart**
24 **CAPITAINE (FR)**, 6, gr g Montmartre (FR)—Patte de Velour (FR) **Martin Broughton & Friends 2**
25 **CAPTAIN BUCK'S (FR)**, 6, b g Buck's Boum (FR)—Ombre Jaune (FR) **Donlon & Doyle**
26 **CAPTAIN CATTISTOCK**, 5, b g Black Sam Bellamy (IRE)—Pearl Buttons **P. L. Hart**
27 **CASKO D'AIRY (FR)**, 6, b g Voix du Nord (FR)—Quaska d'airy (FR) **G Mason, Sir A Ferguson & J Kyle**
28 **CEREAL KILLER (FR)**, 6, b g Buck's Boum (FR)—Dombrelle (FR) **Mr C. A. Donlon**
29 **CHAMERON (FR)**, 5, b g Laveron—Chamanka (FR) **Done, Ferguson, Fogg & Mason**
30 **CHIEF CRAFTSMAN**, 4, gr ro g Mastercraftsman (IRE)—Eurolink Raindance (IRE) **Mr & Mrs J. D. Cotton**
31 **CHOIX DES ARMES (FR)**, 6, b g Saint des Saints (FR)—Kicka **Mrs S. De La Hey**
32 **CLAN DES OBEAUX (FR)**, 6, b g Kapgarde (FR)—
Nausicaa des Obeaux (FR) **Mr&Mrs P.K.Barber,G.Mason,Sir A Ferguson**
33 **CLIFFS OF DOVER**, 5, b g Canford Cliffs (IRE)—Basanti (USA) **Mr & Mrs J. D. Cotton**
34 **COASTAL TIEP (FR)**, 6, b g Coastal Path—Jaltiepy (FR) **Ditcheat Thoroughbreds Coastal Tiep**
35 **COILLTE LASS (FR)**, 7, b m Beneficial—Black Mariah (IRE) **Ditcheat Thoroughbreds Coillte Lass**
36 **CONNETABLE (FR)**, 6, b g Saint des Saints (FR)—Montbresia (FR) **Mr Chris Giles & Mr Dan Macdonald**
37 **COPAIN DE CLASSE (FR)**, 6, b g Enrique—Toque Rouge (FR) **Kyle, Stewart, Vogt & Wylie**
38 **COUP DE PINCEAU (FR)**, 6, b g Buck's Boum (FR)—Castagnette III (FR) **Mr C. A. Donlon**
39 **CYRNAME (FR)**, 6, b g Nickname (FR)—Narquille (FR) **Mrs S. De La Hey**
40 **DAN MCGRUE (FR)**, 6, b g Dansant—Aahsaypasty (IRE) **Mr&Mrs P.K.Barber, D. Bennett, D. Martin**
41 **DANNY KIRWAN (IRE)**, 5, b g Scorpion (IRE)—Sainte Baronne (FR) **Mrs S. De La Hey**
42 **DARLING MALTAIX (FR)**, 5, b g Voix du Nord (FR)—Rosalie Malta (FR) **Mrs S. De La Hey**
43 **DEMI D'OUVERTURE (FR)**, 5, b g Great Pretender (IRE)—La Pelodette (FR) **Martin Broughton & Friends 4**
44 **DENSFIRTH (IRE)**, 5, b g Flemensfirth (USA)—Denwoman (IRE) **G Mason,Sir A Ferguson,Mr&Mrs P K Barber**
45 **DIAMOND GUY (FR)**, 5, b g Konig Turf (GER)—Unique Chance (FR) **Executors & Trustees of C G Roach Estate**
46 **DIEGO DU CHARMIL (FR)**, 6, b g Ballingarry (IRE)—Daramour (FR) **Mrs S. De La Hey**
47 **DIVIN BERE (FR)**, 5, b g Della Francesca (USA)—Mofa Bere (FR) **Mr C. M. Giles**
48 **DJINGLE (FR)**, 5, b g Voix du Nord (FR)—Jourie (FR) **McNeill Family Ltd**
49 **DOLOS (FR)**, 5, b g Kapgarde (FR)—Redowa (FR) **Mrs S. De La Hey**
50 **DR RHYTHM (IRE)**, 5, b g Kalanisi (IRE)—Muscova Rose (IRE) **MCWS Racing Club Ltd**
51 **DYNAMITE DOLLARS (FR)**, 5, b br g Buck's Boum (FR)—Macadoun (FR) **Mr M. F. Geoghegan**
52 **EARTH LEADER (IRE)**, 5, br g Presenting—Full of Spirit (IRE) **R. M. Penny**
53 **EARTH PRINCE (FR)**, 4, gr ro g Al Namix (FR)—Quarline de L'ecu (FR) **R. M. Penny**
54 **EASON (FR)**, 4, b g Coastal Path—Maitresse de Maison (FR) **Mr A. N. V. Williams**
55 **EL BANDIT (IRE)**, 7, b br g Milan—Bonnie Parker (IRE) **Barry Fulton, Colm Donlon & Chris Giles**
56 **EMERGING TALENT (IRE)**, 9, b g Golan (IRE)—Elviria (IRE) **Mr & Mrs Paul Barber**
57 **ENRILO (FR)**, 4, bl g Buck's Boum (FR)—Rock Treasure (FR) **Martin Broughton & Friends 4**
58 **FAVORITO BUCK'S (FR)**, 6, b g Buck's Boum (FR)—Sangrilla (FR) **Mrs S. De La Hey**
59 4, B g Gold Well—Five Star Present (IRE)
60 **FLIC OU VOYOU (FR)**, 4, b g Kapgarde (FR)—Hillflower (FR) **Mr C. A. Donlon**
61 **FRODON (FR)**, 6, b g Nickname (FR)—Miss Country (FR) **Mr P. J. Vogt**
62 **GARO DE JUILLEY (FR)**, 6, b g Ungaro (GER)—Lucy de Juilley (FR) **Ditcheat Thoroughbreds Garo de Juilley**
63 **GET OUT THE GATE (IRE)**, 5, b g Mahler—Chartani (IRE) **MCWS Racing Club Ltd**
64 **GETAWAY TRUMP (IRE)**, 5, b g Getaway (GER)—Acinorev (IRE)
65 **GIBBES BAY (FR)**, 6, gr g Al Namix (FR)—Nouvelle Donne (FR) **The Gi Gi Syndicate**
66 **GIVE ME A COPPER (IRE)**, 8, ch g Presenting—Copper Supreme (IRE) **Done, Ferguson, Kyle, Mason & Wood**
67 **GRAND SANCY (FR)**, 4, b g Diamond Boy (FR)—La Courtille (FR) **Martin Broughton Racing Partners**
68 **GREANETEEN (FR)**, 4, b g Great Pretender (IRE)—Manson Teene (FR) **Mr C. M. Giles**
69 **HIGH SECRET (IRE)**, 7, b g High Chaparral (IRE)—Secret Question (USA) **Axom LXV**
70 **HUGOS OTHER HORSE**, 4, b g Gold Well—Wicked Crack (IRE) **The Stewart Family**
71 **IBIS DU RHEU (FR)**, 7, b g Blue Bresil (FR)—Dona du Rheu (FR) **Mr J. Hales**
72 **IF YOU SAY RUN (IRE)**, 6, b m Mahler—De Lissa (IRE) **Highclere T'Bred Racing If You Say Run**
73 **IRISH SAINT (FR)**, 9, b br g Saint des Saints (FR)—Minirose (FR) **Mrs S. De La Hey**
74 **IRVING**, 10, b g Singspiel (IRE)—Indigo Girl (GER) **Axom XLIX**
75 **JESSBER'S DREAM (IRE)**, 8, b m Milan—Maddy's Supreme (IRE) **Ditcheat Thoroughbreds Jessber's Dream**
76 **JUDGE JOHN DEED (IRE)**, 7, ch g Robin des Champs (FR)—
Milogan (IRE) **Mrs Angela Tincknell & Mr W. Tincknell**
77 **KAPCORSE (FR)**, 5, br g Kapgarde—Angesse (FR) **Mr J. P. McManus**
78 **KINGS INN (IRE)**, 4, b g Mawatheeq (USA)—Afnoon (USA) **Owners Group 021**
79 **LE PREZIEN (FR)**, 7, br g Blue Bresil (FR)—Abu Dhabi (FR) **Mr J. P. McManus**
80 **LOU VERT (FR)**, 5, b g Vertigineux (FR)—Lourinha (FR) **The Brooks & Stewart Families**
81 **MAGOO (IRE)**, 6, gr g Martaline—Noche (IRE) **Brooks, Fulton, Stewart & Vogt**
82 **MALAYA (FR)**, 4, b f Martaline—Clarte d'or (FR) **Mrs S. De La Hey**

MR PAUL NICHOLLS - Continued

83 **MARRACUDJA (FR)**, 7, b g Martaline—Memorial (FR) **Ditcheat Thoroughbreds Marracudja**
84 **MASTER TOMMYTUCKER**, 7, b g Kayf Tara—No Need For Alarm **A. G. Fear**
85 **MOABIT (GER)**, 6, b g Azamour (IRE)—Moonlight Danceuse (IRE) **Owners Group 014**
86 **MODUS**, 8, ch g Motivator—Alessandra **Mr J. P. McManus**
87 **MONSIEUR CO (FR)**, 5, b g Turgeon (USA)—Cayras Style (FR) **Ditcheat Thoroughbreds Monsieur Co**
88 **MONT DES AVALOIRS (FR)**, 5, b g Blue Bresil (FR)—Abu Dhabi (FR) **Mrs S. De La Hey**
89 **MORE BUCK'S (IRE)**, 8, ch g Presenting—Buck's Gale (FR) **The Stewart Family**
90 **MR MIX (FR)**, 7, gr g Al Namix (FR)—Royale Surabaya (FR) **Mr Ian Fogg & Mr Dan Macdonald**
91 **NEW GUARD**, 4, b f Kayf Tara—Easibrook Jane **The Brooks, Stewart Families & J. Kyle**
92 **OLD GUARD**, 7, b g Notnowcato—Dolma (FR) **The Brooks, Stewart Families & J. Kyle**
93 **ONE NIGHT IN MILAN (IRE)**, 5, b g Milan—Native Mo (IRE) **Ditcheat Thoroughbreds One Night In Milan**
94 **ORBASA (FR)**, 7, b g Full of Gold (FR)—Ierbasa de Kerpaul (FR) **Ditcheat Thoroughbreds Orbasa**
95 **OSTUNI (FR)**, 5, b g Great Pretender (IRE)—Mamassita (FR) **B. N. Fulton**
96 **OVERLAND FLYER (IRE)**, 7, b g Westerner—Love Train (IRE) **Mr C. A. Donlon**
97 **PACHA DU POLDER (FR)**, 11, b g Muhtathir—Ambri Piotta (FR) **The Stewart Family**
98 **PARODY**, 4, br f Presenting—Arctic Actress **Owners Group 019**
99 **PERSIAN DELIGHT**, 8, b g Lucarno (USA)—Persian Walk (FR) **Hypnotised**
100 **PETER THE MAYO MAN (IRE)**, 8, ch g Dylan Thomas (IRE)—Mommkin **Million in Mind Partnership**
101 **PILANSBERG**, 6, b g Rail Link—Posteritas (USA) **Martin Broughton & Friends 3**
102 **POLITOLOGUE (FR)**, 7, gr g Poliglote—Scarlet Row (FR) **Mr J. Hales**
103 **PORT MELON (IRE)**, 10, br g Presenting—Omyn Supreme (IRE) **David Maxwell Racing Limited**
104 **POSH TRISH (IRE)**, 5, b m Stowaway—Moscow Demon (IRE) **Highclere T'Bred Racing - Posh Trish**
105 **PRESENT MAN (IRE)**, 8, b g Presenting—Glen's Gale (IRE) **Woodhouse & Sutton**
106 **PTIT ZIG (FR)**, 9, b g Great Pretender (IRE)—Red Rym (FR) **Mr Barry Fulton & Mr Chris Giles**
107 **RHYTHM IS A DANCER**, 5, b g Norse Dancer (IRE)—Fascinatin Rhythm **Mr W. A. Harrison-Allan**
108 **RIDGEWAY FLYER**, 7, b g Tobougg (IRE)—Running For Annie **A. J. Norman**
109 **RINGA DING DING**, 5, b g Shirocco (GER)—Blue Dante (IRE) **Mrs Angela Tincknell & Mr W. Tincknell**
110 **RISK AND ROLL (FR)**, 4, b g No Risk At All (FR)—Rolie de Vindecy (FR) **Mrs S. De La Hey**
111 **ROCK ON OSCAR (IRE)**, 8, b g Oscar (IRE)—Brogeen Lady (IRE) **I Fogg,C Barber,D Bennett & D Macdonald**
112 **ROMAIN DE SENAM (FR)**, 6, b g Saint des Saints (FR)—Salvatrixe (FR) **Mr Chris Giles & Mr Dan Macdonald**
113 4, B g Milan—Rossavon (IRE)
114 **SAINT DE REVE (FR)**, 4, b g Saint des Saints (FR)—Ty Mat (FR) **Mrs S. De La Hey**
115 **SAMETEGAL (FR)**, 9, b g Saint des Saints (FR)—Loya Lescribaa (FR) **Mr & Mrs J. D. Cotton**
116 **SAN BENEDETO (FR)**, 7, ch g Layman (USA)—Cinco Baidy (FR) **Mr P. J. Vogt**
117 **SAN SATIRO (IRE)**, 7, b g Milan—Longueville Quest (IRE) **The Manor Syndicate**
118 **SAO (FR)**, 4, b br g Great Pretender (IRE)—Miss Country (FR) **Mrs S. De La Hey**
119 **SAPHIR DU RHEU (FR)**, 9, gr g Al Namix (FR)—Dona du Rheu (FR) **The Stewart Family**
120 **SECRET INVESTOR**, 6, b g Kayf Tara—Silver Charmer **Hills of Ledbury Ltd**
121 **SELFCONTROL (FR)**, 7, b br g Al Namix (FR)—L'ascension (FR) **The Brooks, Stewart Families & J. Kyle**
122 **SILENT STEPS (IRE)**, 7, b m Milan—Taking Silk (IRE) **Mr C. M. Giles**
123 **SILSOL (GER)**, 9, b g Soldier Hollow—Silveria (GER) **Michelle And Dan Macdonald**
124 **SOME MAN (IRE)**, 5, b g Beat Hollow—Miss Denman (IRE) **Grech & Parkin**
125 **SOUTHFIELD STONE**, 5, gr g Fair Mix (IRE)—Laureldean Belle (IRE) **Mrs Angela Hart & Mrs Angela Yeoman**
126 **SOUTHFIELD THEATRE (IRE)**, 10, b g King's Theatre (IRE)—Chamois Royale (IRE) **Mrs A. B. Yeoman**
127 **SOUTHFIELD TORR**, 5, gr ro g Fair Mix (IRE)—Chamoss Royale (FR) **Mrs Angela Hart & Mrs Angela Yeoman**
128 4, B f Milan—Sparky May
129 **STARSKY (IRE)**, 4, b g Shantou (USA)—Lunar Star (IRE) **Miss Rachael Evans & Mr Matt Booth**
130 **STRADIVARIUS DAVIS (FR)**, 5, b g Turgeon (USA)—
                                   Trumpet Davis (FR) **D & M Macdonald & M & M McPherson**
131 **THE DELLERCHECKOUT (IRE)**, 5, b g Getaway (GER)—Loreley (IRE) **Mr J. Hales**
132 **THE EAGLEHASLANDED (IRE)**, 8, b g Milan—Vallee Doree (FR) **Mrs Angela Tincknell & Mr W. Tincknell**
133 **THE LAST BUT ONE (IRE)**, 6, b g Kutub (IRE)—Last Hope (IRE) **Jockey Club Ownership (SW 2016) Limited**
134 **TOMMY HALLINAN (IRE)**, 4, b g Intense Focus (USA)—Bowstring (IRE) **Mr P. J. Vogt**
135 **TOMMY SILVER (FR)**, 6, b g Silver Cross (FR)—Sainte Mante (FR) **Done, Ferguson, Mason & Wood**
136 **TOMORROW MYSTERY**, 4, b f Nathaniel (IRE)—Retake **Mr J. P. McManus**
137 **TOPOFTHEGAME (IRE)**, 6, ch g Flemensfirth (USA)—Derry Vale (IRE) **Mr Chris Giles & Mr&mrs P K Barber**
138 **TOUCH KICK (IRE)**, 7, b g Presenting—Bay Pearl (FR) **Mr T. J. Hemmings**
139 **TREVELYN'S CORN (IRE)**, 5, b g Oscar (IRE)—Present Venture (IRE)
140 **UNIONISTE (FR)**, 10, gr g Dom Alco (FR)—Gleep Will (FR) **David Maxwell Racing Limited**
141 **VICENTE (FR)**, 9, b g Dom Alco (FR)—Ireland (FR) **Mr T. J. Hemmings**
142 **VIRAK (FR)**, 9, b g Bernebeau (FR)—Nosika d'airy (FR) **Hills of Ledbury Ltd**
143 **VIVALDI COLLONGES (FR)**, 9, b g Dom Alco (FR)—Diane Collonges (FR) **David Maxwell Racing Limited**
144 **VOLPONE JELOIS (FR)**, 5, gr g Vol de Nuit—Jenne Jelois (FR) **Ditcheat Thoroughbreds Volpone Jelois**
145 **WARRIORS TALE**, 9, b g Midnight Legend—Samandara (FR) **Michelle And Dan Macdonald**
146 **WINNINGTRY (IRE)**, 7, br g Flemensfirth (USA)—Jeruflo (IRE) **Mr T. J. Hemmings**

MR PAUL NICHOLLS - Continued

147 **WONDERFUL CHARM (FR)**, 10, b g Poliglote—Victoria Royale (FR) **RJH Geffen, Sir J Ritblat, R Waley-Cohen**
148 **WORTHY FARM (IRE)**, 5, b g Beneficial—Muckle Flugga (IRE) **YOLO**
149 **ZARKANDAR (IRE)**, 11, b g Azamour (IRE)—Zarkasha (IRE) **Mr Chris Giles & Mr Paul Nicholls**
150 **ZUBAYR (IRE)**, 6, b g Authorized (IRE)—Zaziyra (IRE) **Mr P. J. Vogt**
151 **ZYON**, 4, gr g Martaline—Temptation (FR) **Mrs S. De La Hey**

TWO-YEAR-OLDS

152 B f 14/2 War Command (USA)—
    Attracted To You (IRE) (Hurricane Run (IRE)) (40700) **Macdonald, Gibson & Nicholls**
153 B c 11/4 Battle of Marengo (IRE)—
    Kawaha (IRE) (Danehill Dancer (IRE)) (40700) **Fogg, Nicholls, Penny & Williams**
154 **KING OF THE RING**, br c 7/4 Sepoy (AUS)—Anosti (Act One) (44761) **P. F. Nicholls**
155 Gr f 21/2 Alhebayeb (IRE)—Lilly Be (IRE) (Titus Livius (FR)) (11395)
156 **WHATAGUY**, ch c 19/2 Mayson—La Fortunata (Lucky Story (USA)) (23809) **P. F. Nicholls**

Other Owners: Mr R. J. Acock, Mr M. Adams, Mr S. R. Aston, Axom Ltd, P. Bamford, Mrs M. G. Barber, Mr C. L. Barber, P. K. Barber, Mr D. Bennett, P. H. Betts, Mr M. Booth, A. R. Bromley, Mr G. F. Brooks, Lady J. M. Broughton, Sir M. F. Broughton, Mr S. W. Broughton, Mr A. P. Brown, Mr D. J. Coles, Mrs J. C. Corsellis, J. D. Cotton, Mrs B. Cotton, Dame J. O. Dench, Ditcheat Thoroughbreds Ltd, Mr J. Diver, Mr P. E. Done, Mr D. Downie, Mr A. Doyle, Mr R. G. Eddy, Miss R. Evans, Sir A. Ferguson, Mr I. J. Fogg, Mr R. J. H. Geffen, Mrs M. J. K. Gibson, Mr A. Gibson, G. F. Goode, Mr C. M. Grech, Mrs D. M. Gregory, Mr R. Hales, Miss L. J. Hales, Mr J. R. Hales, Mr M. P. Hammond, Mrs A. R. Hart, Highclere Nominated Partner Limited, Highclere Thoroughbred Racing Ltd, Mr A. J. Hill, Mr M. B. M. Hillier, Mr M. J. Holman, Mr J. H. Jackson, Mrs N. Jones, Mr J. Kyle, Mr W. D. Macdonald, Mrs M. Macdonald, Mr P. D. Maddocks, Mrs C. Mant, Mr D. J. Martin, Marwyn Asset Management SPC, G. A. Mason, Mr B. J. McManus, Mrs M. W. McPherson, Mr M. H. McPherson, Mr W. D. C. Minton, Mrs M. E. Moody, Mrs D. C. Nicholson, Mr S. J. Parkin, Sir J. H. Ritblat, Mr E. J. N. Seyfried, Mr B. D. Smith, Mrs K. M. Sparkes, Mr D. D. Stevenson, Mr A. Stewart, Mrs J. A. Stewart, Ms C. Sutton, Mrs A. Tincknell, W. C. Tincknell, Mr D. J. Trembath, Mr R. B. Waley-Cohen, Mr R. J. Wood, Mrs T. A. Woodhouse, M. J. M. Woodhouse, Mr A. W. G. Wylie, Mrs A. Wylie.

Assistant Trainers: Andrew Doyle, Harry Derham

Jockey (NH): Sam Twiston-Davies, Sean Bowen, Harry Cobden. **Conditional:** Bryony Frost, Megan Nicholls, Stan Sheppard, Alexander Thorne. **Apprentice:** Megan Nicholls. **Amateur:** Mr Ed Bailey, Mr Will Biddick, Mr Matt Hampton, Mr Ed Henderson, Miss Harriet Tucker, Mr Lorcan Williams.

---

420   **MR PETER NIVEN, Malton**
Postal: **Clovafield, Barton-Le-Street, Malton, North Yorkshire, YO17 6PN**
Contacts: **PHONE (01653) 628176 FAX (01653) 627295 MOBILE (07860) 260999**
E-MAIL pruniven@btinternet.com WEBSITE www.peterniven.co.uk

1 **BRIAN BORANHA (IRE)**, 7, b g Brian Boru—Tapneiram (IRE) **Mrs K. J. Young**
2 **BROMANCE**, 5, b g Showcasing—Romantic Destiny **The SB Club**
3 **CLEVER COOKIE**, 10, b g Primo Valentino (IRE)—Mystic Memory **Mr P. D. Niven**
4 **HAAFAPRINCESS**, 5, b m Haafhd—Mystic Glen **Mrs J A Niven & Angus Racing Club**
5 **LOVE AT DAWN (IRE)**, 5, br m Winged Love (IRE)—Presentingatdawn (IRE) **The Dawn Risers**
6 **METRONOMIC (IRE)**, 4, b g Roderic O'connor (IRE)—Meon Mix **Keep The Faith Partnership**
7 **PATENT**, 5, b g Paco Boy (IRE)—Film Script **The SB Club**
8 **PIXIEPOT**, 8, b m Alflora (IRE)—Folly Foster **The Rumpole Partnership**
9 **SIMPLY MANI**, 6, ch g Sulamani (IRE)—Simply Mystic **Mrs J A Niven & Angus Racing Club**
10 **THE FOOZLER**, 5, ch g Haafhd—Blades Baby **Hedley, Little, Sharkey & Tomkins**
11 **ZAFAYAN (IRE)**, 7, b g Acclamation—Zafayra (IRE) **Ms J. A. French**

THREE-YEAR-OLDS

12 **WICKLOW WARRIOR**, b g Sleeping Indian—Vale of Clara (IRE) **Mr P. D. Niven**

Other Owners: Angus Racing Club, S. J. Bowett, Mr B. W. Ewart, Miss C. Foster, Mr W. E. Gill, Mr A. B. Hanna, Mr G. S. Harrison, Mr C. R. Hedley, Mr K. J. Little, Mr A. M. Murray, Mrs J. A. Niven, Mr M. W. G. Niven, M. A. Scaife, Mr W. K. D. Sharkey, J. M. Swinglehurst, Mrs G. M. Swinglehurst, Ms L. P. Tomkins.

421 MRS LUCY NORMILE, Glenfarg

Postal: Duncrievie, Glenfarg, Perthshire, PH2 9PD
Contacts: PHONE (01577) 830330 FAX (01577) 830658 MOBILE (07721) 454818
E-MAIL lucy@normileracing.co.uk WEBSITE www.normileracing.co.uk

1 **CADORE (IRE)**, 10, b g Hurricane Run (IRE)—Mansiya **Twentys Plenty**
2 **CALL ME (IRE)**, 7, b g Craigsteel—Wake Me Gently (IRE) **The Explorers**
3 **CRUACHAN (IRE)**, 9, b g Authorized (IRE)—Calico Moon (USA) **P Carnaby & B Thomson**
4 **GRANITE CITY DOC**, 5, b g Arabian Gleam—Hansomis (IRE) **Corsby Racing**
5 **KARINGO**, 11, ch g Karinga Bay—Wild Happening (GER) **Douglas Black,P A Carnaby,P J Carnaby**
6 **MALHAM COVE (IRE)**, 4, b g Lilbourne Lad (IRE)—Fordhill (IRE) **Mrs L. B. Normile**
7 **REMEMBER ROCKY**, 9, ch g Haafhd—Flower Market **Byrne Racing**
8 **RINNAGREE ROSIE**, 12, gr m Silver Patriarch (IRE)—Gretton **The Silver Tops**
9 **ROYAL DUCHESS**, 8, b m Dutch Art—Royal Citadel (IRE) **Mr S. W. Dick**
10 **ROYAL REGENT**, 6, b g Urgent Request (IRE)—Royal Citadel (IRE) **Mr S. W. Dick**
11 **SENSE OF URGENCY (IRE)**, 6, ch m Captain Rio—Itsallaracket (IRE) **Mrs F. E. Bocker**
12 **SILVERTON**, 11, gr m Silver Patriarch (IRE)—Gretton **Twentys Plenty**
13 **SON OF FEYAN (IRE)**, 7, ch g Nayef (USA)—Miss Penton **Mrs L. B. Normile**
14 **SPACE SAFARI (FR)**, 5, gr g Kapgarde (FR)—Prodiga (FR) **Mrs F. E. Bocker**
15 **STORM NELSON (IRE)**, 5, b g Gold Well—Dabiyra (IRE) **Mrs F. E. Bocker**
16 **WOLF HEART (IRE)**, 10, b g Dalakhani (IRE)—Lisieux Orchid (IRE) **Twentys Plenty**
17 **ZAMARKHAN (FR)**, 5, b g Great Journey (JPN)—Zannkiya **Mrs F. E. Bocker**

TWO-YEAR-OLDS

18 **ROYAL COUNTESS**, b f 16/4 Coach House (IRE)—Dont Tell Nan (Major Cadeaux) **Mr S. W. Dick**
19 **ROYAL FIREQUEEN**, ch f 6/2 Firebreak—Devassa (Reel Buddy) (USA) **Mr S. W. Dick**

Other Owners: Mr D. M. Black, P Byrne, Mr P. J. Carnaby, Mr P. Carnaby, Miss P. A. Carnaby, R. N. Ker-Ramsay, Mr A. C. Rodger, B. Thomson, Mrs F. M. Whitaker, J. R. Williams.

Assistant Trainer: Libby Brodie (07947) 592438

Jockey (NH): Lucy Alexander. Amateur: Mr R. Wilson.

422 MR JOHN NORTON, Barnsley

Postal: Globe Farm, High Hoyland, Barnsley, South Yorkshire, S75 4BE
Contacts: PHONE/FAX (01226) 387633 MOBILE (07970) 212707
E-MAIL johnrnorton@hotmail.com WEBSITE www.johnrnortonracehorsetrainer.co.uk

1 **ALNEEL (IRE)**, 4, ch g New Approach (IRE)—Almass (IRE) **J. R. Norton Ltd**
2 **AYE AYE ENYA**, 5, b g Sixties Icon—Ishka Baha (IRE) **Barley Racing Club 2**
3 **FIDDLER'S FLIGHT (IRE)**, 12, b g Convinced—Carole's Dove **Fellowship Of The Rose Partnership**
4 **FLYING POWER**, 10, b g Dubai Destination (USA)—Rah Wa (USA) **Jaffa Racing Syndicate**
5 **MUFTAKKER**, 4, gr g Tamayuz—Qertaas (IRE) **Mr C. Holder**
6 **MUTAMAYEL (IRE)**, 4, b g Mawatheeq (USA)—Musharakaat (IRE) **J. R. Norton Ltd**
7 **NAASIK**, 5, b g Poet's Voice—Shemriyna (IRE) **J. R. Norton Ltd**
8 **SPY FI**, 4, b f Dick Turpin—Sindarbella **J. R. Norton Ltd**
9 **THE JUNIOR MAN (IRE)**, 7, b g Darsi (FR)—Pear Tart (IRE) **Fellowship Of The Rose Partnership 2**

THREE-YEAR-OLDS

10 **EYES OF FIRE**, gr g Helmet (AUS)—Lady Xara (IRE) **Mr A. Rush**
11 **MAGIC SHIP (IRE)**, b g Kodiac—Baltic Belle (IRE) **J. R. Norton Ltd**

Other Owners: Barley Racing Club, Fellowship Of The Rose Partnership, Mr R. M. Firth, J. R. Norton Ltd, Mr P. J. Marshall, Mr P. Newman, Mr J. Norton, Mr Glen Smith, Mr P. Woodcock-Jones.

423 MR JEREMY NOSEDA, Newmarket

Postal: Shalfleet, 17 Bury Road, Newmarket, Suffolk, CB8 7BX
Contacts: PHONE (01638) 664010 FAX (01638) 664100 MOBILE (07710) 294093
E-MAIL jeremy@jeremynoseda.com WEBSITE www.jeremynoseda.com

1 **ABE LINCOLN (USA)**, 5, b h Discreet Cat (USA)—Truly Blushed (USA)

MR JEREMY NOSEDA - Continued

  2 CENOTAPH (USA), 6, b g War Front (USA)—Sanserif (IRE)
  3 INTREPIDLY (USA), 4, b g Medaglia d'oro (USA)—Trepidation (USA)
  4 JUS PIRES (USA), 4, br g Scat Daddy (USA)—Liza Lu (USA)
  5 KEYSTROKE, 6, b h Pivotal—Fondled
  6 LA FIGLIA (IRE), 4, ch f Frankel—Finsceal Beo (IRE)

THREE-YEAR-OLDS

  7 ANGEL'S WHISPER (IRE), gr f Dark Angel (IRE)—Tasheyaat
  8 BETTY F, ch f Frankel—Instance
  9 BEYOND THE FRINGE (IRE), b f Kodiac—April (IRE)
10 BOLD WARRIOR (IRE), b c Declaration of War (USA)—Rochitta (USA)
11 CONTRIVE (IRE), gr f Mastercraftsman (IRE)—Sixpenny Sweets (IRE)
12 DEJA (FR), b c Youmzain (IRE)—Atarfe (IRE)
13 DIAMONDSANDPEARLS (USA), b br f Congrats (USA)—Azalea Belle (USA)
14 GRONKOWSKI (USA), b br c Lonhro (AUS)—Four Sugars (USA)
15 I FEEL IT COMING (USA), b f More Than Ready (USA)—Music Score (USA)
16 LANSKY (IRE), b c Dark Angel (IRE)—Goldthroat (IRE)
17 LAUGHING STRANGER (USA), b c Medaglia d'oro (USA)—Laughing Lashes (USA)
18 MISSY MISCHIEF (USA), b f Into Mischief (USA)—Ring True (USA)
19 PERFECT HUSTLER (USA), ch g Jimmy Creed (USA)—Jacqui's Promise (USA)
20 PRINCE MAURICE (USA), gr c The Factor (USA)—Ramblin Rosie (USA)
21 QUARGENT (USA), b f War Front (USA)—Naples Bay (USA)
22 QUIVERY (USA), b br f Violence (USA)—Passion du Coeur (USA)
23 STAUNCH (USA), b g Union Rags (USA)—Stylish Storm (USA)
24 TAKE ME WITH YOU (USA), b f Scat Daddy (USA)—Me and Miss Jones (USA)
25 TRADE TALKS, b g Cacique (IRE)—Esteemed Lady (IRE)
26 WALK IN THE SUN (USA), b c Street Sense (USA)—Mystic Melody (USA)
27 ZAIN HANA, b f Shamardal (USA)—Lavender And Lace

TWO-YEAR-OLDS

28 B br f 18/3 Scat Daddy (USA)—Auction (IRE) (Mr Greeley (USA)) (619434)
29 B br c 4/4 Union Rags (USA)—Caragh Queen (USA) (Hard Spun (USA)) (100658)
30 DEARLY BELOVED (USA), b f 16/3 Scat Daddy (USA)—Beloveda (USA) (Ghostzapper (USA)) (774293)
31 DURESS (USA), b c 2/2 Violence (USA)—Mattieandmorgan (USA) (Smart Strike (CAN)) (162601)
32 B c 30/3 War Front (USA)—Dynamic Feature (USA) (Rahy (USA)) (851722)
33 B f 5/4 Dansili—Instance (Invincible Spirit (IRE))
34 B c 14/4 No Nay Never (USA)—Jessica Rocks (Fastnet Rock (AUS)) (390720)
35 LOST IN ALASKA (USA), b c 23/2 Discreet Cat (USA)—Truly Blushed (USA) (Yes It's True (USA)) (27100)
36 Ch c 5/3 Scat Daddy (USA)—Miss Lamour (USA) (Mr Greeley (USA)) (735578)
37 MYSTIQUESTAR (IRE), b f 9/4 Sea The Stars (IRE)—Magique (IRE) (Jeremy (USA))
38 NO TROUBLE (IRE), b c 2/3 No Nay Never (USA)—Lady Babooshka (Cape Cross (IRE)) (120000)
39 POET'S CORNER, b c 27/2 Poet's Voice—Helter Helter (USA) (Seeking The Gold (USA)) (30000)
40 B gr c 25/1 Acclamation—Queen of Power (IRE) (Medicean) (100000)
41 SETENTA (IRE), b c 28/4 Canford Cliffs (IRE)—Sentimental (IRE) (Galileo (IRE))
42 B f 11/2 Dark Angel (IRE)—Warshah (IRE) (Shamardal (USA)) (400000)
43 B c 21/2 Into Mischief (USA)—Yes Liz (USA) (Yes It's True (USA)) (387146)

Owners: Mr Al Banwan, Mr Charles Fox, Front Runner Racing, GG Thoroughbreds, Happy Valley Racing & Breeding, Mr T Hind, Miss Y Jacques, Mr Marc Keller, The Honourable Earle I Mack, Mr P Makin, Mr N O'Sullivan, Phoenix Thoroughbred Limited, Mr Charles Pigram, Mrs Susan Roy, Mrs Doreen Swinburn, Mrs D A Tabor, Mr Des Thurlby, Mr N Watts, Mr Ben Wilson.

Assistant Trainer: Dave Bradley

424

MR A. P. O'BRIEN, Ballydoyle
Postal: **Ballydoyle Stables, Cashel, Co. Tipperary, Ireland**
Contacts: **PHONE (00353) 6262615**
E-MAIL racingoffice@ballydoyle.com

  1 CAPRI (IRE), 4, gr c Galileo (IRE)—Dialafara (FR)
  2 CLIFFS OF MOHER (IRE), 4, b c Galileo (IRE)—Wave (IRE)
  3 DEAUVILLE (IRE), 5, b h Galileo (IRE)—Walklikeanegyptian (IRE)
  4 HYDRANGEA (IRE), 4, b f Galileo (IRE)—Beauty Is Truth (IRE)
  5 IDAHO (IRE), 5, b h Galileo (IRE)—Hveger (AUS)

MR A. P. O'BRIEN - Continued

  6 **INTELLIGENCE CROSS (USA)**, 4, b c War Front (USA)—Good Vibes (USA)
  7 **LANCASTER BOMBER (USA)**, 4, b c War Front (USA)—Sun Shower (IRE)
  8 **ORDER OF ST GEORGE (IRE)**, 6, b h Galileo (IRE)—Another Storm (USA)
  9 **RHODODENDRON (IRE)**, 4, b f Galileo (IRE)—Halfway To Heaven (IRE)
10 **SPIRIT OF VALOR (USA)**, 4, b c War Front (USA)—Stone Hope (USA)
11 **WAR DECREE (USA)**, 4, b c War Front (USA)—Royal Decree (USA)
12 **WAR SECRETARY (USA)**, 4, b c War Front (USA)—Upperline (USA)
13 **WASHINGTON DC (IRE)**, 5, b h Zoffany (IRE)—How's She Cuttin' (IRE)
14 **YUCATAN (IRE)**, 4, b c Galileo (IRE)—Six Perfections (FR)

THREE-YEAR-OLDS

15 **A LONG TIME AGO (IRE)**, b f Galileo (IRE)—Wave (IRE)
16 **ACTRESS (IRE)**, b f Declaration of War (USA)—Nasty Storm (USA)
17 **AIR DEFENCE (IRE)**, b br c War Front (USA)—Twirl (IRE)
18 **AIRCRAFT CARRIER (IRE)**, b c Declaration of War (USA)—Strategy
19 **AMEDEO MODIGLIANI (IRE)**, b c Galileo (IRE)—Gooseberry Fool
20 **ASTRONOMER (IRE)**, b c Galileo (IRE)—Like A Dame
21 **ATHENA (IRE)**, b f Camelot—Cherry Hinton
22 **AWAY (IRE)**, b f Galileo (IRE)—Reprise
23 **BABY PINK (IRE)**, b f Invincible Spirit (IRE)—Dress Rehearsal (IRE)
24 **BALLET SHOES (IRE)**, b f Galileo (IRE)—Emerald Ring (IRE)
25 **BATTLE OF JERICHO (USA)**, b c War Front (USA)—Together (IRE)
26 **BLACKHILLSOFDAKOTA (IRE)**, b c Galileo (IRE)—Aymara
27 **BOND STREET (IRE)**, b c Galileo (IRE)—After (IRE)
28 **BROADWAY (IRE)**, b f Galileo (IRE)—Danedrop (IRE)
29 **BUTTERSCOTCH (IRE)**, b f Galileo (IRE)—Lesson In Humility (IRE)
30 **BYE BYE BABY (IRE)**, b f Galileo (IRE)—Remember When (IRE)
31 **CHEERING (USA)**, b f War Front (USA)—Kissed (IRE)
32 **CHRISTOPHER ROBIN (IRE)**, b c Camelot—Iowa Falls
33 **CLEMMIE (IRE)**, b f Galileo (IRE)—Meow (IRE)
34 **CLIFFS OF DOONEEN (IRE)**, ch c Galileo (IRE)—Devoted To You (IRE)
35 **CONCLUSION (JPN)**, b c Deep Impact (JPN)—Cherokee (USA)
36 **CONQUEST (IRE)**, b f Galileo (IRE)—Lillie Langtry (IRE)
37 **COULD IT BE LOVE (USA)**, b f War Front (USA)—Playa Maya (USA)
38 **CURLY (IRE)**, b f Galileo (IRE)—Glass Slipper (IRE)
39 **CYPRESS CREEK (IRE)**, gr c Galileo (IRE)—Dialafara (FR)
40 **DALI (USA)**, b c Scat Daddy (USA)—Alegendinmyownmind
41 **DARKNESS FALLS (USA)**, b br f War Front (USA)—Was (IRE)
42 **DECLARATIONOFPEACE (USA)**, b br c War Front (USA)—Serena's Cat (USA)
43 **DELANO ROOSEVELT (IRE)**, b c Galileo (IRE)—Again (IRE)
44 **DIFFERENT LEAGUE (FR)**, b f Dabirsim (FR)—Danseuse Corse (IRE)
45 **DRAMATICALLY (USA)**, b f War Front (USA)—Wonder of Wonders (USA)
46 **EASTER LILY (IRE)**, ch f Galileo (IRE)—Chanting (USA)
47 **EL GRECO (IRE)**, b c Galileo (IRE)—Missvinski (USA)
48 **EMPIREOFTHEDRAGON (IRE)**, b c Galileo (IRE)—Atlantic Jewel (AUS)
49 **ERIN (IRE)**, b f Mastercraftsman (IRE)—Queen Cleopatra (IRE)
50 **FAMILY TREE**, ch c Galileo (IRE)—Sant Elena
51 **FIGHTFORTHEROSES (IRE)**, b c Galileo (IRE)—Gwynn (IRE)
52 **FIRE OPAL (USA)**, b f War Front (USA)—Good Vibes (USA)
53 **FLAG OF HONOUR (IRE)**, b c Galileo (IRE)—Hawala (IRE)
54 **FLATTERING (IRE)**, b f Galileo (IRE)—Pikaboo
55 **FLEET REVIEW (USA)**, b c War Front (USA)—A Star Is Born (IRE)
56 **FLUTTER (IRE)**, b f Galileo (IRE)—Rumplestiltskin (IRE)
57 **FOREIGN LEGION (IRE)**, ch c Declaration of War (USA)—Solar Event
58 **FOREIGN SECRETARY**, ch c Galileo (IRE)—Finsceal Beo (IRE)
59 **FOREVER TOGETHER (IRE)**, b f Galileo (IRE)—Green Room (USA)
60 **FRANKINCENSE (IRE)**, b c Galileo (IRE)—Anna Karenina (IRE)
61 **FREETOWN (IRE)**, b c Galileo (IRE)—Viz (IRE)
62 **FULL MOON (IRE)**, b c Declaration of War (USA)—Dowager
63 **GARDENS OF BABYLON (IRE)**, b c Camelot—Condition
64 **GIUSEPPE GARIBALDI (IRE)**, b c Galileo (IRE)—Queenscliff (IRE)
65 **GLORIOUSLY (IRE)**, b f Galileo (IRE)—Queen of France (USA)
66 **GUSTAV KLIMT (IRE)**, b c Galileo (IRE)—Massarra
67 **HAPPILY (IRE)**, b f Galileo (IRE)—You'resothrilling (USA)
68 **HENCE (IRE)**, ch f Galileo (IRE)—Aleagueoftheirown (IRE)

MR A. P. O'BRIEN - Continued

69 HUNTING HORN (IRE), b c Camelot—Mora Bai (IRE)
70 I CAN FLY, b f Fastnet Rock (AUS)—Madonna Dell'orto
71 INDIANAPOLIS (IRE), b c Galileo (IRE)—Adoration (USA)
72 JAMES COOK (IRE), b c Galileo (IRE)—Red Evie (IRE)
73 KENYA (IRE), b c Galileo (IRE)—Tender Morn (USA)
74 KEW GARDENS (IRE), b c Galileo (IRE)—Chelsea Rose (IRE)
75 LOST TREASURE (IRE), b c War Front (USA)—Wading (IRE)
76 LUCIUS TIBERIUS (IRE), b c Camelot—Keegsquaw (IRE)
77 MADRID (IRE), b c Galileo (IRE)—Logjam (IRE)
78 MAGIC WAND (IRE), b f Galileo (IRE)—Prudenzia (IRE)
79 MAGICAL (IRE), b f Galileo (IRE)—Halfway To Heaven (IRE)
80 MENDELSSOHN (USA), b c Scat Daddy (USA)—Leslie's Lady (USA)
81 MOST GIFTED (USA), b f War Front (USA)—Gagnoa (USA)
82 MURILLO (USA), b c Scat Daddy (USA)—Mostaqeleh (USA)
83 NELSON (IRE), b c Frankel—Moonstone
84 NORTH FACE (IRE), b c Declaration of War (USA)—Queen Titi (IRE)
85 PREPARE FOR BATTLE (USA), ch c Declaration of War (USA)—Red Carpet Miss (USA)
86 QUEEN ISEULT, b f Camelot—Rumored (USA)
87 ROSTROPOVICH (IRE), b c Frankel—Tyranny
88 ROYAL NAVY WARSHIP (USA), b c War Front (USA)—Magical Dream (IRE)
89 SARACEN KNIGHT (IRE), b c Camelot—Za'hara (IRE)
90 SARROCCHI (IRE), b f Galileo (IRE)—Thai Haku (IRE)
91 SAXON WARRIOR (JPN), b c Deep Impact (JPN)—Maybe (IRE)
92 SEAHENGE (USA), b c Scat Daddy (USA)—Fools In Love (USA)
93 SEPTEMBER (IRE), b br f Deep Impact (JPN)—Peeping Fawn (USA)
94 SIOUX NATION (USA), b c Scat Daddy (USA)—Dream The Blues (IRE)
95 SIR EREC (IRE), b c Camelot—Quiritis
96 SIZZLING (IRE), ch f Galileo (IRE)—Weekend Strike (USA)
97 SNOWFLAKES (IRE), br gr f Galileo (IRE)—Laddies Poker Two (USA)
98 SOMERSET MAUGHAM (IRE), b c Galileo (IRE)—Fire Lily (IRE)
99 SOUTHERN FRANCE (IRE), b c Galileo (IRE)—Alta Anna (FR)
100 SPANISH POINT, ch c Frankel—Peeress
101 THE PENTAGON (IRE), b c Galileo (IRE)—Vadawina (IRE)
102 THREEANDFOURPENCE (USA), b c War Front (USA)—Liscanna (IRE)
103 U S NAVY FLAG (USA), b br c War Front (USA)—Misty For Me (IRE)
104 VICTORY SALUTE (IRE), ch c Galileo (IRE)—One Moment In Time (IRE)
105 ZABRISKIE (IRE), b c Frankel—Moonlight's Box (USA)

TWO-YEAR-OLDS

106 B f 13/4 Zoffany (IRE)—Abbasharjah (GER) (Tiger Hill (IRE)) (90000)
107 B f 28/2 Galileo (IRE)—Again (IRE) (Danehill Dancer (IRE))
108 B c 7/5 Galileo (IRE)—Aleagueoftheirown (IRE) (Danehill Dancer (IRE))
109 B c 29/3 Galileo (IRE)—Atlantic Jewel (AUS) (Fastnet Rock (AUS))
110 B f 4/4 Zoffany (IRE)—Azafata (SPA) (Motivator) (81400)
111 B c 4/4 Scat Daddy (USA)—Bailzee (IRE) (Grand Slam (USA)) (232288)
112 B f 6/5 Galileo (IRE)—Beauty Is Truth (IRE) (Pivotal)
113 B c 18/3 Frankel—Belesta (Xaar) (1302400)
114 Ch c 14/2 Australia—Beyond Brilliance (IRE) (Holy Roman Emperor (IRE))
115 B f 14/2 Galileo (IRE)—Butterfly Cove (USA) (Storm Cat (USA))
116 B c 25/2 Invincible Spirit (IRE)—Cabaret (IRE) (Galileo (IRE))
117 B c 6/2 Scat Daddy (USA)—Canterbury Lace (USA) (Danehill (USA))
118 B f 19/4 Invincible Spirit (IRE)—Cassandra Go (IRE) (Indian Ridge) (1600000)
119 B br c 21/1 No Nay Never (USA)—Chaibia (IRE) (Peintre Celebre (USA)) (325600)
120 B f 27/2 Camelot—Cherry Hinton (Green Desert (USA))
121 B c 28/2 Sea The Stars (IRE)—Coolree Marj (IRE) (Marju (IRE)) (425000)
122 B c 15/5 Galileo (IRE)—Crazyforlovingyou (USA) (Arch (USA))
123 B br c 21/1 Scat Daddy (USA)—Dream The Blues (IRE) (Oasis Dream)
124 B c 23/4 Scat Daddy (USA)—Dreams of Fire (USA) (Dynaformer (USA)) (387146)
125 B c 25/1 War Front (USA)—Drifting Cube (AUS) (Encosta de Lago (AUS))
126 B c 9/3 Australia—Dundalk Dust (USA) (Military (USA)) (162800)
127 B c 8/2 Galileo (IRE)—Duntle (IRE) (Danehill Dancer (IRE))
128 Ch c 24/1 Galileo (IRE)—Famous (IRE) (Danehill Dancer (IRE)) (232288)
129 Gr ro c 1/5 Declaration of War (USA)—Goodness Gray (USA) (Pulpit (USA)) (143244)
130 Br c 22/4 Camelot—Hitra (IRE) (Langfuhr (CAN))
131 B c 14/4 Galileo (IRE)—Honour Bright (IRE) (Danehill (USA))

MR A. P. O'BRIEN - Continued

132 B f 1/2 Scat Daddy (USA)—Hopeoverexperience (USA) (Songandaprayer (USA)) (309717)
133 B c 6/5 Galileo (IRE)—Hveger (AUS) (Danehill (USA)) (240000)
134 B c 25/4 Dansili—Ideal (Galileo (IRE))
135 B br f 27/4 War Front (USA)—Imagine (IRE) (Sadler's Wells (USA))
136 B c 27/3 No Nay Never (USA)—Kawn (Cadeaux Genereux)
137 B c 10/3 War Front (USA)—Kissed (IRE) (Galileo (IRE))
138 Ch f 1/5 Galileo (IRE)—Laddies Poker Two (IRE) (Choisir (AUS))
139 B c 28/2 Dark Angel (IRE)—Last Bid (Vital Equine (IRE)) (238095)
140 B f 14/5 Scat Daddy (USA)—Lavender Baby (USA) (Rubiano (USA)) (387146)
141 Ch c 11/3 No Nay Never (USA)—Law of The Jungle (IRE) (Catcher In The Rye (IRE)) (244200)
142 B f 27/5 Galileo (IRE)—Lillie Langtry (IRE) (Danehill Dancer (IRE))
143 Ch c 18/4 Galileo (IRE)—Love Me True (USA) (Kingmambo (USA))
144 B c 24/4 Scat Daddy (USA)—Love's Blush (USA) (Not For Love (USA)) (212930)
145 B f 22/1 War Front (USA)—Marvellous (IRE) (Galileo (IRE))
146 Ch f 9/4 Galileo (IRE)—Massarra (Danehill (USA))
147 Ch c 5/3 Galileo (IRE)—Meow (IRE) (Storm Cat (USA))
148 B f 9/3 War Front (USA)—Misty For Me (IRE) (Galileo (IRE))
149 Ch c 3/3 Galileo (IRE)—Moonlight Cloud (Invincible Spirit (IRE))
150 B br c 19/2 Scat Daddy (USA)—My Sister Sandy (USA) (Montbrook (USA))
151 B c 5/2 Scat Daddy (USA)—Orchard Beach (CAN) (Tapit (USA)) (851722)
152 B c 29/2 Australia—Peeping Fawn (USA) (Danehill (USA))
153 B c 13/3 Magician (IRE)—Perfect Step (IRE) (Iffraaj) (210000)
154 B f 14/1 Kodiac—Queenofthefairies (Pivotal) (925000)
155 Br f 9/2 Camelot—Question Times (Shamardal (USA)) (309320)
156 B f 7/5 Galileo (IRE)—Red Evie (IRE) (Intikhab (USA))
157 B f 25/1 Australia—Remember You (IRE) (Invincible Spirit (IRE))
158 B f 21/2 Galileo (IRE)—Sasuela (GER) (Dashing Blade) (325600)
159 B c 28/3 No Nay Never (USA)—Seeking Solace (Exceed And Excel (AUS)) (200000)
160 B c 22/2 Galileo (IRE)—Shastye (IRE) (Danehill (USA)) (1300000)
161 B c 14/2 War Front (USA)—Shell House (IRE) (Galileo (IRE))
162 B c 14/1 No Nay Never (USA)—Shelley Beach (IRE) (Danehill Dancer (IRE)) (150000)
163 B c 21/4 Camelot—Silver Star (Zafonic (USA))
164 Ch c 28/3 Australia—Sitara (Salse (USA)) (525000)
165 B c 3/5 Galileo (IRE)—Six Perfections (FR) (Celtic Swing)
166 B c 19/1 Dubawi (IRE)—Sky Lantern (IRE) (Red Clubs (IRE)) (2000000)
167 B c 9/2 Camelot—Sparrow (IRE) (Oasis Dream)
168 B c 26/3 Galileo (IRE)—Sumora (IRE) (Danehill (USA))
169 B c 8/2 Australia—Sweepstake (IRE) (Acclamation) (150000)
170 B c 17/3 Australia—Thai Haku (IRE) (Oasis Dream) (380000)
171 B c 22/2 No Nay Never (USA)—Theann (Rock of Gibraltar (IRE)) (284900)
172 B c 2/2 Australia—Tocqueville (FR) (Numerous (USA))
173 B c 12/2 Galileo (IRE)—Tonnara (IRE) (Linamix (FR)) (814000)
174 B c 29/4 Galileo (IRE)—Turbulent Descent (USA) (Congrats (USA))
175 U S S MICHIGAN (USA), gr ro c 22/5 War Front (USA)—Photograph (USA) (Unbridled's Song (USA))
176 B f 3/2 Dansili—Wading (IRE) (Montjeu (IRE))
177 B f 30/1 War Front (USA)—Was (IRE) (Galileo (IRE))
178 Ch c 6/4 Australia—What A Treasure (IRE) (Cadeaux Genereux) (260000)

| **425** | **MR DANIEL O'BRIEN, Tonbridge**
Postal: **Knowles Bank, Capel, Tonbridge, Kent, TN11 0PU**
Contacts: **PHONE (01892) 824072** |

1 CHOCOLATE DIAMOND (IRE), 7, ch g Intense Focus (USA)—Sagemacca (IRE) **D. C. O'Brien**

Assistant Trainer: Christopher O'Bryan

Jockey (NH): Mattie Batchelor, Sam Twiston-Davies.

426 MR FERGAL O'BRIEN, Cheltenham

Postal: **Upper Yard, Grange Hill Farm, Naunton, Cheltenham, Gloucestershire, GL54 3AY**
Contacts: PHONE **(01285) 721150** MOBILE **(07771) 702829**
E-MAIL **fergaljelly@aol.com**

1 **ALVARADO (IRE)**, 13, ch g Goldmark (USA)—Mrs Jones (IRE) **Mr & Mrs William Rucker**
2 **AWEEMINIT (IRE)**, 4, b f Arcadio (GER)—Campanella (GER) **Mr F. M. O'Brien**
3 **AYE AYE CHARLIE**, 6, b g Midnight Legend—Trial Trip **All Four One**
4 **BARNEY DWAN (IRE)**, 8, b g Vinnie Roe (IRE)—Kapricia Speed (FR) **Mr & Mrs Paul & Clare Rooney**
5 **BARRAKILLA (IRE)**, 11, b g Milan—Kigali (IRE) **Mr & Mrs William Rucker**
6 **BELLE AMIS**, 5, ch m Black Sam Bellamy (IRE)—Amaretto Rose **Peter Hockenhull & Paul Rich**
7 **BELLS 'N' BANJOS (IRE)**, 8, b g Indian River (FR)—Beechill Dancer (IRE) **The Maple Hurst Partnership**
8 **BENECHENKO (IRE)**, 6, b g Beneficial—Beann Ard (IRE) **Keeping The Dream Alive**
9 **BENNY'S BRIDGE (IRE)**, 5, b g Beneficial—Wattle Bridge (IRE) **Biddestone Racing I**
10 **BLUE MERLIN**, 5, b g Fair Mix (IRE)—Mighty Merlin **Mrs J. A. Watts**
11 **CAP SOLEIL (FR)**, 5, b m Kapgarde (FR)—Move Again (FR) **Mrs S. A. Noott**
12 **CHASE THE SPUD**, 10, b g Alflora (IRE)—Trial Trip **Mrs C. J. Banks**
13 **CHELTENAM DE VAIGE (FR)**, 6, b g Forestier (FR)—Ratina de Vaige (FR) **Matt & Sally Burford**
14 **CHILLI ROMANCE (IRE)**, 7, b m Flemensfirth (USA)—Blue Romance **Mr I. Slatter**
15 **COLIN'S SISTER**, 7, b m Central Park (IRE)—Dd's Glenalla (IRE) **Mrs C. S. C. Beresford-Wylie**
16 **COOLANLY (IRE)**, 6, b g Flemensfirth (USA)—La Fisarmonica (IRE) **Five Go Racing**
17 **COSMIC KING (FR)**, 6, b g Kingsalsa (USA)—Kikinda (FR) **Mrs J. A. Watts**
18 **CREEVYTENNANT (IRE)**, 14, b g Bob's Return (IRE)—Northwood May **Mrs P. Duncan**
19 **CUDDLES MCGRAW (IRE)**, 5, b g Court Cave (IRE)—Stepfonic (IRE) **Graham & Alison Jelley**
20 **DIAMOND FORT (IRE)**, 6, ch g Gamut (IRE)—Ellie Forte **D. J. Shorey**
21 **FEEL THE PINCH**, 4, b g Librettist (USA)—Liqueur Rose **Miss S. Randell**
22 **GLOBAL STAGE**, 7, b g Multiplex—Tintera (IRE) **The Yes No Wait Sorries**
23 **GRAND INTRODUCTION (IRE)**, 8, b g Robin des Pres (FR)—What A Breeze (IRE) **Geoffrey & Donna Keeys**
24 **HERECOMESTHEBOOM (IRE)**, 6, b g Darsi (FR)—Dympnajane **Mr W. Marzouk**
25 **I SHOT THE SHERIFF (IRE)**, 11, b g Westerner—Sherin (GER) **M. C. Denmark**
26 **IMPERIAL ELIXIR (IRE)**, 5, b g Doyen (IRE)—Blond's Addition (IRE) **Imperial Racing Partnership 2016**
27 **IMPERIAL ELOQUENCE (IRE)**, 6, b g Kalanisi (IRE)—Babble On (IRE) **Imperial Racing Partnership**
28 **INDIAN REEL (IRE)**, 8, br g Indian River (FR)—Ceilidh Dancer (IRE) **Spencer, Atwell & Ikin**
29 **INFINITE SUN**, 7, b g And Beyond (IRE)—Kingussie Flower **Mrs V. J. R. Ramm**
30 **JARVEYS PLATE (IRE)**, 5, ch g Getaway (GER)—She's Got To Go (IRE) **The Yes No Wait Sorries**
31 **JENNIFER JUNIPER (IRE)**, 5, b m Kalanisi (IRE)—Assidua (IRE) **Mr Peter Elliott & Mr Stephen Skinner**
32 **JENNYS SURPRISE (IRE)**, 10, b m Hawk Wing (USA)—Winning Jenny (IRE) **Foxtrot Nh Racing Syndicate**
33 **KNOCKADERRY FLYER (IRE)**, 9, b g Aolus (GER)—Tastao (IRE) **D. J. Shorey**
34 **LIP SERVICE (IRE)**, 9, ch g Presenting—Top Her Up (IRE) **M. C. Denmark**
35 **LOVELY JOB (IRE)**, 8, ch g Touch of Land (FR)—Wyckoff Queen **Mr & Mrs Paul & Clare Rooney**
36 **LUCCOMBE DOWN (IRE)**, 8, b g Primo Valentino (IRE)—Flaming Rose (IRE) **Mr & Mrs Paul & Clare Rooney**
37 **MASTER DEE (IRE)**, 9, b g King's Theatre (IRE)—Miss Lauren Dee (IRE) **Mr & Mrs Paul & Clare Rooney**
38 **MERCY MERCY ME**, 6, b g Shirocco (GER)—Monsignorita (IRE) **M. C. Denmark**
39 **MILLIONDOLLARBILL (IRE)**, 6, b g Dubai Destination (USA)—Rapid Dawn (IRE) **Mr F. M. O'Brien**
40 **MINELLA SCAMP (IRE)**, 9, b g King's Theatre (IRE)—Forgotten Star (IRE) **M. C. Denmark**
41 **MOUNT BATUR (IRE)**, 5, ch g Mahler—Massini's Daughter (IRE) **Geoffrey & Donna Keeys**
42 **MYSTIFIABLE**, 10, gr g Kayf Tara—Royal Keel **Graham & Alison Jelley**
43 **NO DICE (IRE)**, 9, ch g Presenting—Roxbury **M. C. Denmark**
44 **OCEAN COVE (IRE)**, 6, ch g Ask—Sand Eel (IRE) **The FOB Racing Partnership**
45 **OKOTOKS (IRE)**, 8, b g Gamut (IRE)—Whats Another One (IRE) **M. C. Denmark**
46 **OSCAR ROSE (IRE)**, 6, b m Oscar (IRE)—Ben Roseler (IRE) **Mrs K.Exall/The General Asphalte Company Ltd**
47 **OUT OF STYLE (IRE)**, 7, b g Court Cave (IRE)—Portanob (IRE) **Mr & Mrs William Rucker**
48 **PAULS HILL (IRE)**, 6, b g Marienbard (IRE)—Lunar Star (IRE) **The B Lucky Partnership**
49 **PERFECT CANDIDATE (IRE)**, 11, b g Winged Love (IRE)—Dansana (IRE) **ISL Recruitment**
50 **PETITE POWER (IRE)**, 9, b g Subtle Power (IRE)—Little Serena **Mr J. J. King**
51 **POETIC RHYTHM (IRE)**, 7, ch g Flemensfirth (USA)—Sommer Sonnet (IRE) **The Yes No Wait Sorries**
52 **RATIFY**, 14, br g Rakaposhi King—Sea Sky **Mr J. J. King**
53 **RED HOT CHILLY (IRE)**, 5, b g Frozen Power (IRE)—She's Got The Look **Mr & Mrs A. J. Mutch**
54 **RGB THE ARCHITECT**, 5, b g Mount Nelson—Dialma (USA) **Mrs J. A. Watts**
55 **ROCKERY GARDEN (IRE)**, 5, b g Wareed (IRE)—Rock Garden (IRE) **Mr B. Davis**
56 **SATURDAYNIGHTFEVER**, 6, b g King's Theatre (IRE)—Get Me Home (IRE) **M. C. Denmark**
57 **SHINE'S BAR (IRE)**, 5, b g Darsi (FR)—Ninty Annie **Hudson Bay Partnership**
58 **SISSINGHURST (IRE)**, 8, b g Kalanisi (IRE)—Sissinghurst Storm (IRE) **The FOB Racing Partnership 2**
59 **SMOOTH OPERATOR**, 6, b g Azamour (IRE)—Teggiano (IRE) **M. C. Denmark**
60 **SOCKSY (IRE)**, 7, ch m Flemensfirth (USA)—Bachello (IRE) **C. B. Brookes**
61 **SOLDIER OF LOVE**, 5, b g Yeats (IRE)—Monsignorita (IRE) **M. C. Denmark**

MR FERGAL O'BRIEN - Continued

62 **SPOILT ROTTEN**, 9, b g Kayf Tara—Rosita Bay **M. C. Denmark**
63 **STRONG GLANCE**, 5, bl g Passing Glance—Strong Westerner (IRE) **Welfordgolf syndicate**
64 **TASHUNKA (IRE)**, 5, b m Flemensfirth (USA)—Las Palmias (IRE) **The FOB Racing Partnership 3**
65 **THE GROOVE**, 5, b g Azamour (IRE)—Dance East **The Groovy Gang**
66 **TIME TO MOVE ON (IRE)**, 5, ch g Flemensfirth (USA)—Kapricia Speed (FR) **Mr & Mrs Paul & Clare Rooney**
67 **TROUBLED SOUL (IRE)**, 9, ch m Definite Article—Dorrha Lass (IRE) **Neville Statham & Family**
68 **VIVA STEVE (IRE)**, 10, b g Flemensfirth (USA)—Eluna **Mr & Mrs Paul & Clare Rooney**
69 **WAR ON THE ROCKS (IRE)**, 9, b g Wareed (IRE)—Rock Garden (IRE) **Shorey Fancutt Tucker**
70 **WELLS GOLD (IRE)**, 7, b g Gold Well—Exit Baby (IRE) **Mr F. M. O'Brien**

Other Owners: Mr D. Abraham, Mr V. Askew, Mrs L. Atwell, M. A. Blackford, Mrs G. P. Bostwick, T. P. Bostwick, Mr S. W. Bowers, Mrs S. Burford, M. Burford, C. S. J. Coley, Mr M. Costello, Mr P. P. Elliott, Mr D. England, Mrs Judy England, Mrs K. G. Exall, Mr G. S. Fancutt, Foxtrot Racing Management Ltd, The General Asphalte Company Ltd, Mr A. Grewcock, P. D. Hockenhull, D. M. Hussey, Mrs C. J. Ikin, Mrs A. D. Jelley, G. S. Jelley, G. F. Keeys, Mrs C. M. Keeys, Mr J. P. Lambe, Mr J. B. Lawson, Mr A. J. Mutch, Mrs S. Mutch, Mr M. A. Nutting, Miss S. Pilkington, Mr C. H. Plumb, Mr R. J. Rainbow, P. M. Rich, Mr I. Robinson, Miss M. R. Robinson, Mrs C. Rooney, Mr P. A. Rooney, Mrs A. Rucker, W. J. Rucker, Mr S. P. Skinner, Mr P. E. Smith, Mr N. J. Statham, Mrs P. Statham, Mr G. W. A. Stone, Miss M. L. Taylor, M. Tucker, Mr M. K. Warren, Mr R. Williams.

---

427 MR JEDD O'KEEFFE, Leyburn

Postal: Highbeck, Brecongill, Coverham, Leyburn, North Yorkshire, DL8 4TJ
Contacts: **PHONE** (01969) 640330 **MOBILE** (07710) 476705
E-MAIL jedd@jeddokeefferacing.co.uk **WEBSITE** www.jeddokeefferacing.co.uk

1 **AMERICAN CRAFTSMAN (IRE)**, 4, gr g Mastercraftsman (IRE)—Quiet Mouse (USA) **The Fatalists**
2 **DESERT RULER**, 5, b g Kheleyf (USA)—Desert Royalty (IRE) **Highbeck Racing**
3 **DOCTOR THEA**, 5, b m Multiplex—Kallithea (IRE) **Mrs A. M. O'Sullivan**
4 **INJAM (IRE)**, 5, b g Pour Moi (IRE)—Sniffle (IRE) **Miss S. Long**
5 **INSTANT ATTRACTION (IRE)**, 7, b g Tagula (IRE)—Coup de Coeur (IRE) **United We Stand**
6 **JACK LAMB**, 6, gr g Sulamani (IRE)—Charlotte Lamb **Miss S. E. Hall**
7 **LORD OF THE ROCK (IRE)**, 6, b g Rock of Gibraltar (IRE)—La Sylphide **Geoff & Sandra Turnbull**
8 **LORD YEATS**, 5, b g Yeats (IRE)—Bogside Theatre (IRE) **Geoff & Sandra Turnbull**
9 4, B f Passing Glance—Lucinda Lamb **Miss S. E. Hall**
10 **MONTANNA**, 4, ch g Notnowcato—Asi (USA) **Highbeck Racing**
11 **MR SCRUMPY**, 4, b g Passing Glance—Apple Days **Mr H. Posner**
12 **REBEL STATE (IRE)**, 5, b g Zoffany (IRE)—Stately Princess **Mr Jedd O'Keeffe**
13 **SAM SPINNER**, 6, b g Black Sam Bellamy (IRE)—Dawn Spinner **Caron & Paul Chapman**
14 **SHARED EQUITY**, 7, b g Elnadim (USA)—Pelican Key (IRE) **Caron & Paul Chapman**
15 **WHITKIRK**, 5, b g Iffraaj—Bedouin Bride (USA) **Mr T. S. Ingham**

THREE-YEAR-OLDS

16 **AIR RAID**, b c Raven's Pass (USA)—Siren Sound **Caron & Paul Chapman**
17 **ARMED RESPONSE**, b c Sepoy (AUS)—Respondez **Caron & Paul Chapman**
18 **COCKTAIL (IRE)**, ch g Dream Ahead (USA)—Pina Colada **Caron & Paul Chapman**
19 **COLLINGHAM PARK (IRE)**, b g Dragon Pulse (IRE)—Curraline (IRE) **Ingham Racing Syndicate**
20 **ECHO (IRE)**, b g Zoffany (IRE)—Aweebounce (IRE) **Miss S. E. Hall & Mr Colin Platts**
21 **FRENCH RESISTANCE (IRE)**, b g Elusive Pimpernel (USA)—Ivy Batty (IRE) **Geoff & Sandra Turnbull**
22 **HIPPEIA (IRE)**, b f Lilbourne Lad (IRE)—Majestic Oasis **Geoff & Sandra Turnbull**
23 **INGENUITY**, b c Slickly (FR)—Onlyyouknowme (IRE) **Highbeck Racing**
24 **JOYSOFTEAMWORK (IRE)**, b c Intikhab (USA)—Art Work **The Lions, Foxes & Tigers Partnership**
25 **KENMARE RIVER**, gr g Kendargent (FR)—Isabella Glyn (IRE) **Mrs A. M. O'Sullivan**
26 **PRETTY MOI (IRE)**, b f Pour Moi (IRE)—Dunbrody (FR) **The Fatalists**
27 **RARE GROOVE (IRE)**, ch c Lope de Vega (IRE)—Ascot Lady (IRE) **Mr John Dance**
28 **SAISONS D'OR (IRE)**, b g Havana Gold (IRE)—Deux Saisons (IRE) **Caron & Paul Chapman**
29 **SHARED ASSET**, b g Power—On The Nile (IRE) **Caron & Paul Chapman**

TWO-YEAR-OLDS

30 **DEVIL'S ANGEL**, gr c 20/2 Dark Angel (IRE)—Rocking The Boat (IRE) (Zebedee) (47619) **Mr John Dance**
31 Ch c 12/2 Sir Percy—Famusa (Medicean) (25000) **Highbeck Racing 2**
32 Br f 24/4 Dawn Approach (IRE)—French Bid (AUS) (Anabaa (USA)) **Caron & Paul Chapman**
33 B f 3/4 War Command (USA)—Hazarista (Barathea (IRE)) **Caron & Paul Chapman**
34 B f 21/4 Sir Percy—Katy O'hara (Komaite (USA)) **Miss S. E. Hall**
35 **KODELIGHT**, b f 13/5 Kodiac—Night Delight (IRE) (Night Shift (USA)) **Mr John Dance**

MR JEDD O'KEEFFE - Continued

36 **MELLO DEE (IRE)**, b gr f 16/2 Alhebayeb (IRE)—Comes A Time (IRE) (Arcano (IRE)) (42857) **Mr John Dance**
37 B c 18/3 Coach House (IRE)—Pelican Key (IRE) (Mujadil (USA)) (50000) **Caron & Paul Chapman**
38 B f 6/3 Kyllachy—Protectress (Hector Protector (USA)) (9523) **Mr John Dance**
39 **RIPON SPA**, b c 22/1 Rock of Gibraltar (IRE)—Lady Lahar (Fraam) (80000) **Mr T. S. Ingham & Mrs L. Ingham**
40 Ch c 14/3 Stimulation (IRE)—Thicket (Wolfhound (USA)) (10000) **Mr John Dance**
41 B f 25/4 Swiss Spirit—Where's Broughton (Cadeaux Genereux) (12000) **Highbeck Racing 1**

Other Owners: Mr R. Butler, Jenny & Ray Butler, Mr P. Chapman, Mrs C. A. Chapman, Mr D. Chapman, Mr D. G. Colledge, Mrs M. E. Ingham, Mr T. S. Ingham, Mr & Mrs B. McAllister, Mr Jedd O'Keeffe, Mr R. P. Ord, Mr M. D. Parker, Mr B. Thompson, Mrs S. E. Turnbull, Mr Geoffrey Turnbull, Mr A. Walker, Mr A. C. Welch, Mr C. Welch.

Assistant Trainers: Mr Tim Hogg, Miss Leanne Kershaw

Amateur: Miss Alana Cawley.

---

428 MR DAVID O'MEARA, Upper Helmsley
Postal: **Willow Farm, Upper Helmsley, York, Yorkshire, YO41 1JX**
Contacts: PHONE (01759) 372427 MOBILE (07747) 825418
E-MAIL info@davidomeara.co.uk WEBSITE www.davidomeara.co.uk

1 **ABRAJ DUBAI (USA)**, 4, b f Street Cry (IRE)—Pulitzer (USA) **Hambleton Racing Ltd XXV**
2 **ACRUX**, 5, b g Dansili—Ikat (IRE) **Mr G. Brogan**
3 **AL QAHWA (IRE)**, 5, b g Fast Company (IRE)—Cappuccino (IRE) **Gallop Racing**
4 **ALEEF (IRE)**, 5, b h Kodiac—Okba (USA) **Nick Bradley Racing 8**
5 **ALFRED HUTCHINSON**, 10, ch g Monsieur Bond (IRE)—Chez Cherie **R. C. Bond**
6 **ALSVINDER**, 5, b h Footstepsinthesand—Notting Hill (BRZ) **Mr F. Gillespie**
7 **ANYTHINGTODAY (IRE)**, 4, b g Zoffany (IRE)—Corking (IRE) **Woodhurst Construction Ltd**
8 **AREEN HEART (FR)**, 4, b g Exceed And Excel (AUS)—Reine Zao (FR) **Sheikh Abdullah Almalek Al Sabah**
9 **BLACK ISLE BOY (IRE)**, 4, b g Elzaam (AUS)—Shadow Mountain **Mr E. M. Sutherland**
10 **BRAVERY (IRE)**, 5, b g Galileo (IRE)—Lady Icarus **Sprint Thoroughbred**
11 **BREANSKI**, 4, b g Delegator—Jubilee **Mrs P. Good**
12 **CAPTAIN BOND**, 4, b g Captain Gerrard (IRE)—Forever's Girl **Casino Royale Racing**
13 **COVIGLIA (IRE)**, 4, ro c Invincible Spirit (IRE)—Bright Snow (USA) **J. Blackburn**
14 **CUSTOM CUT (IRE)**, 9, b g Notnowcato—Polished Gem (IRE) **Frank Gillespie, Pat Breslin, Nawton Racing**
15 **DAAWY (IRE)**, 4, ch g Teofilo (IRE)—Juno Marlowe (IRE) **Hollowdean**
16 **DALSHAND (FR)**, 5, ch g New Approach (IRE)—Daltaiyma (IRE) **Middleham Park Racing**
17 **DUNDUNAH (USA)**, 4, ch f Sidney's Candy (USA)—Sealedwithapproval (USA) **Rabbah Bloodstock Ltd**
18 **EDDIEBET**, 4, ch g Monsieur Bond (IRE)—Champagne Katie **Bond Thoroughbred Corporation**
19 **EDWARD LEWIS**, 5, b g Kyllachy—Tahirah **Akela Construction Ltd**
20 **ESCOBAR (IRE)**, 4, b g Famous Name—Saying Grace (IRE) **Tiffin Sandwiches Limited**
21 **EXCHEQUER (IRE)**, 7, ch g Exceed And Excel (AUS)—Tara's Force (IRE) **A. R. Barnes**
22 **FAYEZ (IRE)**, 4, b g Zoffany (IRE)—Gems **Nawton Racing Partnership**
23 **FIRMAMENT**, 6, b g Cape Cross (IRE)—Heaven Sent **Gallop Racing**
24 **FLEETFOOT JACK**, 4, b g Kyllachy—Move **Mr F. Gillespie**
25 **HAJJAM**, 4, b g Paco Boy (IRE)—Amanda Carter **Sheikh Abdullah Almalek Al Sabah**
26 **HAMISH MCGONAGAIN**, 5, b g Kyllachy—Inya Lake **The Lawton Bamforth Partnership**
27 **HIGHLAND ACCLAIM (IRE)**, 7, b g Acclamation—Emma's Star (ITY) **Mr E. M. Sutherland**
28 **IMPART**, 4, b g Oasis Dream—Disclose **Marwan Koukash**
29 **INGLEBY ANGEL (IRE)**, 9, br g Dark Angel (IRE)—Mistress Twister **Ingleby Bloodstock Ltd**
30 **INGLEBY HOLLOW**, 6, ch g Beat Hollow—Mistress Twister **Dave Scott & The Fallen Angels**
31 **INTISAAB (IRE)**, 7, b g Elnadim (USA)—Katoom (IRE) **Mr S. M. Graham**
32 **JACBEQUICK**, 7, b g Calcutta—Toking N' Joken (IRE) **Richard Walker, Stu Graham**
33 4, B f Sir Percy—Jazan (IRE) **R. S. Cockerill (Farms) Ltd**
34 **KHARBETATION (IRE)**, 5, b g Dream Ahead (USA)—Anna's Rock (IRE) **Rabbah Bloodstock Ltd**
35 **LAMLOOM (IRE)**, 4, b g Cape Cross (IRE)—Lulua (USA) **Rabbah Bloodstock Ltd**
36 **LARCHMONT LAD (IRE)**, 4, b c Footstepsinthesand—Fotini (IRE) **Cheveley Park Stud Limited**
37 **LEOFRIC (IRE)**, 4, b g Galileo (IRE)—Ice Mint (USA) **Sue Johnson**
38 **MA FEE HEELA (FR)**, 4, b g Siyouni (FR)—Olympic Skater (IRE) **Gallop Racing**
39 **MAJOR CRISPIES**, 7, b g Pastoral Pursuits—Nellie Melba **The Roses Partnership II**
40 **MARAAKIB (IRE)**, 6, b g Dark Angel (IRE)—Mrs Cee (IRE) **Mr E. M. Sutherland**
41 **MON BEAU VISAGE (IRE)**, 5, br g Footstepsinthesand—Hurricane Lily (IRE) **Pink Pot Partnership**
42 **MUJASSAM**, 6, ch g Kyllachy—Naizak **Sprint Thoroughbred**
43 **MUSCIKA**, 4, b g Kyllachy—Miss Villefranche **Gallop Racing & Dynast Racing**
44 **MUTADAFFEQ (IRE)**, 5, b g New Approach (IRE)—Saajidah (USA) **DFS Limited**
45 **MYTHICAL MADNESS**, 7, b g Dubawi (IRE)—Miss Delila (USA) **Jimmy Chua**

MR DAVID O'MEARA - Continued

46 **OUT DO,** 9, ch g Exceed And Excel (AUS)—Ludynosa (USA) **Mr E. M. Sutherland**
47 **PIONEERING (IRE),** 4, b g Shamardal (USA)—Oregon Trail (USA) **A. Franks**
48 **PRIMERO (FR),** 5, b g Cape Cross (IRE)—Flamenba (USA) **Sheikh Abdullah Almalek Al Sabah**
49 **RAPID RANGER,** 4, b g Kyllachy—Director's Dream (IRE) **Kristen McEwen & Caroline Head**
50 **ROYAL RESERVE,** 5, b g Duke of Marmalade (IRE)—Lady Hawkfield (IRE) **Royal Guinness Reserve Partnership**
51 **SALATEEN,** 6, ch h Dutch Art—Amanda Carter **Sheikh A. H. F. M. A. Al Sabah**
52 **SARYSHAGANN (FR),** 5, gr g Iffraaj—Serasana **Middleham Park Racing IV**
53 **SHORT WORK,** 5, ch g Kyllachy—Agony Aunt **N D Crummack Ltd & Mr Arthur Rhodes**
54 **SHYMKENT,** 4, b g Pivotal—Shabyt **Hesmonds Stud**
55 **SO BELOVED,** 8, b g Dansili—Valencia **Sprint Thoroughbred**
56 **STEEL TRAIN (FR),** 7, b g Zafeen (FR)—Silent Sunday (IRE) **Rasio Cymru I, S. Taylor & D. O'Meara**
57 **STONIFIC (IRE),** 5, b g Sea The Stars (IRE)—Sapphire Pendant (IRE) **Dilwyn Pierce, Steve Jessop**
58 **SUEDOIS (FR),** 7, b br g Le Havre (IRE)—Cup Cake (IRE) **Mr George Turner & Clipper Logistics**
59 **SULTAN BAYBARS,** 4, b g Invincible Spirit (IRE)—Rock Salt **Middleham Park Racing XII**
60 **SUMMERGHAND (IRE),** 4, b g Lope de Vega (IRE)—Kate The Great **Rabbah Bloodstock Ltd**
61 **SUNGLIDER (IRE),** 5, br g High Chaparral (IRE)—Desert Ease (IRE) **Mr G. Brogan**
62 **SUNRIZE (IRE),** 4, b g Azamour (IRE)—Valmari (IRE) **Leonard Jay Ltd, Robert & Stanley Cohen**
63 **TAWDEEA,** 6, b g Intikhab (USA)—Sharedah (IRE) **Middleham Park Racing LXVI**
64 **THE AMBER FORT (USA),** 4, b g Elusive Quality (USA)—Unreachable (USA) **Marwan Koukash**
65 **TRADING POINT (IRE),** 4, b c Siyouni (FR)—Zita Blues (IRE) **Sheikh Abdullah Almalek Al Sabah**
66 **TRANSATLANTIC (IRE),** 4, b c Galileo (IRE)—Sent From Heaven (IRE) **Qatar Racing Ltd & Clipper Logistics**
67 **USTINOV,** 5, b g Exceed And Excel (AUS)—Tamzin **Mrs P. Good**
68 **WAARIF (IRE),** 5, b g Arcano (IRE)—Indian Belle (IRE) **Middleham Park Racing XLIX**
69 **WARRIOR'S SPIRIT (IRE),** 4, b g Requinto (IRE)—Sandbox Two (IRE) **Mr David Lumley**
70 **WONDERFILLO (IRE),** 4, b g Teofilo (IRE)—Wonderfilly (FR) **Burn Fencing Ltd**

THREE-YEAR-OLDS

71 **AJWAN,** gr ro g Helmet (AUS)—Rock Ace (IRE) **Sheikh Abdullah Almalek Al Sabah**
72 **AREEN FAISAL (IRE),** ch g Bahamian Bounty—Yellow Trumpet **Sheikh Abdullah Almalek Al Sabah**
73 **BAREFOOT CONTESSA (FR),** b f Dansili—Bastet (IRE) **Geoff Turnbull**
74 **BILLY DYLAN (IRE),** b g Excelebration (IRE)—It's True (IRE) **Gallop Racing**
75 **BOWLER HAT,** b g Helmet (AUS)—Fatima's Gift **Cheveley Park Stud Limited**
76 **BREAKFASTATTIFFINS (IRE),** ch f Dawn Approach (IRE)—Sassy Gal (IRE) **Tiffin Sandwiches Limited**
77 **CAT BALLOU,** ch f Equiano (FR)—Flamenco Dancer **York Thoroughbred Racing**
78 **COLD STARE (IRE),** b g Intense Focus (USA)—Ziria (IRE) **Middleham Park Racing XC**
79 **CONVERSANT (IRE),** gr g Zebedee—Tea Cup **Cheveley Park Stud Limited**
80 **DEBAWTRY (IRE),** b f Camacho—Muluk (IRE) **Cliff Stud**
81 **DOSC (IRE),** b c Dream Ahead (USA)—Flanders (IRE) **Malih L. Al Basti**
82 **GABRIAL THE DEVIL (IRE),** b g Epaulette (AUS)—Grasshoppergreen (IRE) **Marwan Koukash**
83 **GABRIALS CENTURION (IRE),** b g Society Rock (IRE)—Flamanda **Marwan Koukash**
84 **HIGHLAND BOBBY,** b g Big Bad Bob (IRE)—Eolith **Mr E. M. Sutherland**
85 **INGLEBY MOLLY (IRE),** ch f Choisir (AUS)—Mistress Twister **Ingleby Bloodstock Ltd**
86 **LAUBALI,** ch c Kyllachy—Different **Mrs F. Denniff**
87 **LINA'S STAR (IRE),** b f Lawman (FR)—Readyandaway (USA) **Sheikh Abdullah Almalek Al Sabah**
88 **ME BEFORE YOU (IRE),** b g f Clodovil (IRE)—Pinewoods Lily (IRE) **Gallop Racing & D. O'Meara**
89 **SAFRANI (IRE),** b g Lope de Vega (IRE)—Wadjeka (USA) **Sheikh A. H. F. M. A. Al Sabah**
90 **SEEK THE MOON (USA),** b f Giant's Causeway (USA)—Crescent Moon (USA) **Geoff Turnbull**
91 **STRAFFAN (IRE),** b f Clodovil (IRE)—Laureldean Spirit (IRE) **Hambleton Racing Ltd XXV**
92 **THREE SAINTS BAY (IRE),** b g Kodiac—Fiuise (IRE) **Johnny Collins**
93 **VALENTINO DANCER,** ch c Mastercraftsman (IRE)—Bertie's Best **Dreaming Victory**
94 **VENTURA ROYAL (IRE),** ch f Teofilo (IRE)—Ermine And Velvet **Middleham Park Racing CXVII**
95 **WEELLAN,** ch g Mayson—Regal Salute **Sheikh Abdullah Almalek Al Sabah**

TWO-YEAR-OLDS

96 B c 22/3 Showcasing—Ahwahnee (Compton Place) (85000) **Sheikh Abdullah Almalek Al Sabah**
97 **ANGEL CAKES (IRE),** gr f 2/4 Dark Angel (IRE)—Halouella (Halling (USA)) (13024) **The Earl of Ronaldshay**
98 Ch f 29/2 Garswood—Ardessie (Bahamian Bounty) (26666) **Cliff Stud**
99 B f 24/3 Bated Breath—Aubrietia (Dutch Art) (30476) **Sheikh Abdullah Almalek Al Sabah**
100 B f 19/2 Kyllachy—Bondesire (Misu Bond (IRE)) **Geoff Turnbull**
101 B c 3/4 Mayson—Branston Gem (So Factual (USA)) (25714) **Mr E. M. Sutherland**
102 B c 5/4 Dandy Man (IRE)—Deceptive (Red Ransom (USA)) (13023) **Willow Farm Syndicate**
103 B c 11/2 Gale Force Ten—Diminish (IRE) (Raven's Pass (USA)) (10476) **Willow Farm Syndicate**
104 **FASTMAN (IRE),** b br c 3/4 Elzaam (AUS)—
                          Manalisa (IRE) (Manduro (GER)) (23809) **Craig Miller & Mark Westbrook Racing**
105 **FIGHTING SPIRIT (IRE),** b f 17/3 War Command (USA)—Pina Colada (Sabrehill (USA)) (13023) **Trendy Ladies**

MR DAVID O'MEARA - Continued

106 B c 25/1 Le Havre (IRE)—Hestia (FR) (High Chaparral (IRE)) (14652)
107 Br f 16/4 Camacho—Jouel (FR) (Machiavellian (USA)) (17094)
108 B f 21/1 Kodiac—Kaiulani (IRE) (Danehill Dancer (IRE)) **Geoff Turnbull**
109 B f 9/5 Dandy Man (IRE)—Pinewoods Lily (IRE) (Indian Ridge) (12209) **Willow Farm Syndicate**
110 B c 10/3 Tamayuz—She's A Character (Invincible Spirit (IRE)) (37444) **Gallop Racing**
111 Gr c 19/3 Kyllachy—Silver Act (IRE) (Aqlaam) **Geoff Turnbull**
112 Br c 3/4 Swiss Spirit—Summer Spice (IRE) (Key of Luck (USA)) (48840) **Sheikh Abdullah Almalek Al Sabah**
113 B f 11/4 Dalakhani—Valmari (IRE) (Kalanisi (IRE)) **Mr D. O'Meara**
114 B f 28/3 Showcasing—Viola d'amour (IRE) (Teofilo (IRE)) (36000) **Rabbah Bloodstock Ltd**
115 B f 15/3 Dandy Man (IRE)—Violet Lashes (USA) (Badge of Silver (USA))

Other Owners: Mr S. Allison, Mrs Penelope Avison, Mr Peter Baker, Mr P. Bamford, Mr S. H. Bamforth, Mr J. M. Binns, Mr R. C. Bond, Mr C. S. Bond, Mr N. Bradley, Mr P. Breslin, Mr P. A. Burgess, Mr A. W. Clark, Clipper Group Holdings Ltd, Mr P. Coates, Mr S. J. Cohen, Mr J. W. Cox, Mr Chris Cox, Mr L. Davies, Mr M. Dunn, Dutch Rose Partnership, Dynast Racing, Mr A. W. Ellis, The Fallen Angels, Ms J. C. Finucane, S. Franks, Mr A. Franks, Mr Stuart Graham, Hambleton Racing Ltd, Mr Dermot Hanafin, Mr Paul Hancock, Mrs Caroline Head, Miss S. Holden, Hurn Racing Club, Mrs Marian Ireland, Mrs I. M. Jessop, Ms S. Johnson, Mr I. Kellett, Mr Jason Kelly, Mr M. F. Lawton, Leonard Jay Ltd, Mrs Kristen McEwen, Mr Alan McLaren, Mr Craig Miller, N D Crummack Ltd, Willow Racing Partnership, Mr K. Nicholson, Northern Hart Racing, Northern Lads Racing, Mr D. O'Meara, Mr T. S. Palin, Mr J. D. Pierce, Mr M. Prince, Qatar Racing Limited, Mrs Melinda Quirk, Rasio Cymru Racing 1, Mr Hugh T. Redhead, A. Rhodes, Mr Dave Scott, Mr P. D. Shepherd, Mr D. Solan, Mr K. B. Suntay, Mr S. M. Taylor, Mr S. R. Tennant, Mr Ken Thompson, Mr A. S. Trott, Mrs S. E. Turnbull, Mr Geoffrey Turnbull, Mr G. D. Turner, Mr S. R. H. Turner, Mrs Alice M. Walker, Mr Richard Walker, Mr Mark Westbrook.

Assistant Trainer: Jason Kelly

Jockey (flat): Daniel Tudhope. **Apprentice:** Shelley Birkett, Josh Doyle, Patrick Vaughan. **Amateur:** Miss Carly Scott.

---

429 **MISS DANIELLE O'NEILL, North Fawley**
Postal: **The Old Granary, North Fawley, Wantage, Oxfordshire, OX12 9NJ**
Contacts: **PHONE (01488) 639350 MOBILE (07931) 193790**
E-MAIL danni@fawleyhousestud.com

1 BISHOPSLOUGH (IRE), 10, b g Fruits of Love (USA)—Maid In Blue (IRE) **Mrs S. McGrath**

Assistant Trainer: Stephen O'Neill

---

430 **MR JOHN O'NEILL, Bicester**
Postal: **Hall Farm, Stratton Audley, Nr Bicester, Oxfordshire, OX27 9BT**
Contacts: **PHONE (01869) 277202 MOBILE (07785) 394128**
E-MAIL jgoneill4@gmail.com

1 BITE MY TONGUE (IRE), 5, b g Vale of York (IRE)—Near Relation **J. G. O'Neill**
2 BOLLYWOOD BOY, 7, b g Indian Danehill (IRE)—Little Miss Prim **Ms D. Keane**
3 ONURBIKE, 10, b g Exit To Nowhere (USA)—Lay It Off (IRE) **J. G. O'Neill**
4 PHOENIX SONG, 5, b g Phoenix Reach (IRE)—Temple Heather **J. G. O'Neill**
5 W S GILBERT, 4, b g Librettist (USA)—Little Miss Prim **Ms D. Keane**

---

431 **MR JONJO O'NEILL, Cheltenham**
Postal: **Jackdaws Castle, Temple Guiting, Cheltenham, Gloucestershire, GL54 5XU**
Contacts: **PHONE (01386) 584209**
E-MAIL reception@jonjooneillracing.com WEBSITE www.jonjooneillracing.com

1 ADAM DU BRETEAU (FR), 8, ch g Network (GER)—Odelie de Fric (FR) **Mrs G. K. Smith**
2 4, B g Fame And Glory—Ar Muin Na Muice (IRE) **Mrs G. K. Smith**
3 AS YOU LIKE (IRE), 7, b br g Beneficial—Rubys Shadow (IRE) **Mr J. P. McManus**
4 BAHAMA MOON (IRE), 6, b g Lope de Vega (IRE)—Bahama Bay (GER) **Eric Chapman & Douglas Pryde**
5 BEGGARS CROSS (IRE), 8, b g Presenting—Ballygill Heights (IRE) **Mr T. J. Hemmings**

MR JONJO O'NEILL - Continued

6 **BIG PENNY (IRE)**, 6, b m Oscar (IRE)—Lady Marnay (IRE) **Mrs D. Carr**
7 **BRONCO BILLY (IRE)**, 8, b g Flemensfirth (USA)—La Fisarmonica (IRE) **London Design Group Limited**
8 **CAKE DE L'ISLE (FR)**, 6, b g Fragrant Mix (IRE)—Talga de L'isle (FR) **Mr T. J. Hemmings**
9 **CAPARD KING (IRE)**, 9, b g Beneficial—Capard Lady (IRE) **Mr J B Gilruth & Eric Chapman**
10 **CAPOTE (IRE)**, 10, b g Oscar (IRE)—Kinsellas Rose (IRE) **Mr T. J. Hemmings**
11 **CATCHING ON (IRE)**, 10, b g Milan—Miracle Lady **Mrs G. K. Smith**
12 **CHAMPAGNE AT TARA**, 9, gr g Kayf Tara—Champagne Lil **Mr J. P. McManus**
13 **CLOTH CAP (IRE)**, 6, b g Beneficial—Cloth Fair (IRE) **Mr T. J. Hemmings**
14 **CLUBS ARE TRUMPS (IRE)**, 9, b g Flemensfirth (USA)—Pairtree **Mr J. P. McManus**
15 **COBOLOBO (FR)**, 6, br g Maresca Sorrento (FR)—Nanou des Brosses (FR) **Anne, Harriet & Lucinda Bond**
16 **COISA BLANCO (IRE)**, 5, b g Jeremy (USA)—Moon Legend (USA) **Mr P. Hickey**
17 **COMPADRE (IRE)**, 7, b g Yeats (IRE)—Jolivia (FR) **London Design Group Limited**
18 **CORLAY (FR)**, 6, b g Saddler Maker (IRE)—Overn (FR) **Mr J. P. McManus**
19 **DEMON D'AUNOU (FR)**, 5, b g Martaline—Jimagine II (FR) **Mr J. P. McManus**
20 **DESERT CROSS**, 5, b g Arcano (IRE)—Secret Happiness **Mr P. Hickey**
21 **DESTINY'S STAR**, 6, br g Beneficial—Lady Cad (FR) **Delancey Real Estate Asset Management Limited**
22 **DJANGO DJANGO (FR)**, 5, b br g Voix du Nord (FR)—Lady Jannina **Martin Broughton & Friends 5**
23 **DOESYOURDOGBITE (IRE)**, 6, b g Notnowcato—Gilah (IRE) **DYDB Marketing & Friends Of Jackdaws**
24 **DREAMSOFTHEATRE (IRE)**, 10, gr g King's Theatre (IRE)—Caroline Fontenail (IRE) **Mr J. P. McManus**
25 **EASTLAKE (IRE)**, 12, b g Beneficial—Guigone (FR) **Mr J. P. McManus**
26 **EBONYS ENCORE (IRE)**, 6, b m Oscar (IRE)—Ebony Queen **Mr J. P. McManus**
27 **EY UP ROCKY**, 5, b g Dylan Thomas (IRE)—Polo **Martyn & Elaine Booth**
28 4, B g Fame And Glory—Felinious **D. Smith**
29 **FESTIVE AFFAIR (IRE)**, 10, b g Presenting—Merry Batim (IRE) **Four The Fun Of It Partnership**
30 **FLEMINPORT (IRE)**, 5, b g Flemensfirth (USA)—Geek Chic (IRE) **Mr J. P. McManus**
31 **FORZA MILAN (IRE)**, 6, b g Milan—Nonnetia (FR) **Deep Sea Partnership**
32 **FOUNDATION MAN (IRE)**, 11, b g Presenting—Function Dream (FR) **Mr P. Hickey**
33 **FROZEN FLAME (IRE)**, 5, b g Frozen Fire (GER)—
       Flame Supreme (IRE) **Delancey Real Estate Asset Management Limited**
34 **GET IN THE QUEUE**, 4, b g Mount Nelson—Amarullah (FR) **Mr & Mrs Paul & Clare Rooney**
35 **GNARLY**, 6, b m Midnight Legend—Diamant Noir **Mr D. J. Burke**
36 **GO CONQUER (IRE)**, 9, b g Arcadio (GER)—Ballinamona Wish (IRE) **Mr & Mrs Paul & Clare Rooney**
37 **GOLDEN PROMISE (IRE)**, 4, b g Flemensfirth (USA)—Loadsapromise (IRE) **D & H Ashley, R Marks & D Sandon**
38 **HANDSOME PANTS (IRE)**, 4, b g Oscar (IRE)—Rose Tanner (IRE) **Mrs J. S. T. O'Neill**
39 **HEAD LAD (FR)**, 5, b br g Linda's Lad—Orabelle (FR) **Head Lad Partnership**
40 **HIDDEN OASIS (IRE)**, 7, b g Lawman (FR)—Spesialta **Mr J. P. McManus**
41 **HIS DREAM (FR)**, 5, b g Yeats (IRE)—Rosa Muscosa (USA) **Local Parking Security Limited**
42 **I CARE DES SOURCES (FR)**, 4, gr f Turgeon (USA)—Baraka du Berlais (FR) **Mrs S. Hoffmann**
43 **I KNOW U TOO WELL (IRE)**, 6, b g Stowaway—Kilbricken Leader (IRE) **Mr & Mrs Paul & Clare Rooney**
44 **IT'S A GIMME (IRE)**, 11, b g Beneficial—Sorcera (GER) **Mr J. P. McManus**
45 **JOIN THE CLAN (IRE)**, 9, b g Milan—Millicent Bridge (IRE) **Mr J. P. McManus**
46 **KELVINGROVE (IRE)**, 8, b g Hurricane Run (IRE)—Silversword (FR) **The All In Syndicate**
47 **KNIGHT DESTROYER (IRE)**, 4, b g Dark Angel (IRE)—Do The Deal (IRE) **Mrs D. Carr**
48 **LITHIC (IRE)**, 7, b g Westerner—Accoola (IRE) **Jon & Julia Aisbitt**
49 **MAD FOR ACTION (IRE)**, 5, b g Beneficial—Subtle Hint (IRE) **Mrs John Magnier,Mr D Smith & Mr M Tabor**
50 **MANNY OWENS (IRE)**, 6, b br g Manduro (GER)—Arabian Coral (IRE) **Veterinary Immunogenics Ltd**
51 **MARMALADE MIST (IRE)**, 5, ch m Stowaway—Shean Rose (IRE) **Racegoers Club Owners Group**
52 **MATORICO (IRE)**, 7, gr g Mastercraftsman (IRE)—Hashbrown (GER) **Mr J. P. McManus**
53 **MINELLA ROCCO (IRE)**, 8, b g Shirocco (GER)—Petralona (USA) **Mr J. P. McManus**
54 **MONT ROYALE**, 10, b g Hurricane Run (IRE)—Wild Academy (IRE) **Phil Tufnell Racing**
55 **MORE OF THAT (IRE)**, 10, b g Beneficial—Guigone (FR) **Mr J. P. McManus**
56 **MOUNTAIN PATH**, 5, b m Mount Nelson—Vino **Recycling Pallet Services**
57 **MR SHANTU (IRE)**, 9, b g Shantou (USA)—Close To Shore (IRE) **Local Parking Security Limited**
58 **MUSTMEETALADY (IRE)**, 8, b g Mustameet (USA)—Ladymcgrath (IRE) **Mrs D. Carr**
59 **NOBLE ROBIN (IRE)**, 7, b g Robin des Champs (FR)—Which Thistle (IRE) **Mr J. P. McManus**
60 **OI OI (IRE)**, 5, b m Oscar (IRE)—Mandys Native (IRE) **Oi Digital Limited**
61 **PALMERS HILL (IRE)**, 6, b g Gold Well—Tosca Shine (IRE) **Mr J. P. McManus**
62 **PHOENIX ROCK (IRE)**, 6, br m Winged Love (IRE)—Guillaume Rock (IRE) **Successio**
63 **POP ROCKSTAR (IRE)**, 6, b br g Flemensfirth (USA)—Special Ballot (IRE) **Vamhensid**
64 **QUARENTA (FR)**, 6, b br g Voix du Nord (FR)—Negresse de Cuta (FR) **Martin, Jocelyn & Steve Broughton**
65 **READY AND ABLE (IRE)**, 5, b g Flemensfirth (USA)—
       Gypsy Mo Chara (IRE) **Mr D Smith, Mrs J Magnier & Mr M Tabor**
66 **REINE DES MIRACLES**, 5, br m Poet's Voice—Cheerleader **The Piranha Partnership**
67 **RIVERSIDE CITY (IRE)**, 9, ch g Presenting—Blazing Sky (IRE) **Mr J. P. McManus**
68 **ROSIE MCQUEEN (IRE)**, 6, b m Milan—Royal Rosy (IRE) **Mr J. P. McManus**

MR JONJO O'NEILL - Continued

69 **SEE THE ROCK (IRE)**, 8, b g Shirocco (GER)—Samara (IRE) **Mr J. P. McManus**
70 **SERMANDO (FR)**, 4, ch g Fuisse (FR)—Josephjuliusjodie (IRE)
71 **SKY PIRATE**, 5, b g Midnight Legend—Dancingwithbubbles (IRE) **Lady Bamford & Alice Bamford**
72 **SPIRITUAL MAN (IRE)**, 6, b g Lawman (FR)—Vee Gita (IRE) **Mrs L. Jones**
73 **SPOOKYDOOKY (IRE)**, 10, b g Winged Love (IRE)—Kiora Lady (IRE) **The Piranha Partnership**
74 **STATE THE OBVIOUS (IRE)**, 6, ch g Presenting—New Vega (FR) **Mr J. P. McManus**
75 **STRONGLY SUGGESTED**, 11, b g Kayf Tara—Branston Lily **Mr J. P. McManus**
76 **TERRY THE FISH (IRE)**, 6, b g Milan—Have More **Terry The Fishers**
77 **THE FLAME (IRE)**, 5, b g Flemensfirth (USA)—Molly Round (IRE) **Sean O'Driscoll and Michael O'Flynn**
78 **THE MANUSCRIPT (IRE)**, 5, b g Mahler—Limavady (IRE) **The Valentine Partnership**
79 **THE TAILGATER (IRE)**, 7, b g Oscar (IRE)—Zaffaran Express (IRE) **Mr & Mrs Paul & Clare Rooney**
80 **TIMEFORWEST (IRE)**, 6, b m Westerner—Shang A Lang (IRE) **Jockey Club Ownership (SW 2016) Limited**
81 **TOUT POUR TOI (FR)**, 4, b g Fuisse (FR)—Malandra **Mr M. J. Tedham**
82 **TRANSPENNINE STAR**, 5, ch g Mount Nelson—Brave Mave **Transpennine Partnership**
83 **TRAVERTINE (IRE)**, 8, b g Danehill Dancer (IRE)—Mer de Corail (IRE) **Mr J. P. McManus**
84 **UTILITY (GER)**, 7, b g Yeats (IRE)—Ungarin (GER) **Team Tuff**
85 **WALTER ONEEIGHTONE (IRE)**, 6, b g Morozov (USA)—Matinee Show (IRE) **Anne, Harriet & Lucinda Bond**
86 **WASHED ASHORE (IRE)**, 7, ch g Presenting—Give It Time **Mr J. P. McManus**
87 **WESTERLY WIND (IRE)**, 4, b g Westerner—Milanella (IRE) **Mr C Taylor & Mr A Bound**
88 **YOU'RE SO RIGHT (IRE)**, 5, b g Presenting—Miss Brandywell (IRE) **Mr & Mrs Paul & Clare Rooney**
89 **YOUR WAN (IRE)**, 5, b m Galileo (IRE)—Mayasta (IRE) **Mr J. P. McManus**
90 **ZIGGY ROSE (IRE)**, 4, b f Fame And Glory—Koko Rose (IRE) **Elaine Chivers Racing**

Other Owners: Mr Jon Aisbitt, Mrs Julia Aisbitt, Mr W. P. Aitkenhead, Mr David Ashley, Mrs Hayley Ashley, Mr David Balchin, Miss A. C. Bamford, Lady Bamford, Mr G. C. V. Blakemore, Mrs N. D. Blakemore, Miss Lucinda Bond, Miss Harriet Bond, Mrs Peter Bond, Mr Martyn Booth, Mrs Elaine Booth, Mr A. C. Bound, Lady Jocelyn Broughton, Mr Stephen Broughton, Sir Martin Broughton, Mrs Bridget Byrne, Mr Eric Chapman, Chelston (Ireland), Ms Elaine Chivers, Miss Charlotte Chivers, Ms Lauren Chivers, Mr J. G. Cockcroft, DYDB Marketing Limited, Mr E. J. Dolan-Abrahams, Mrs E. J. Dolan-Abrahams, Miss Y. Edwards, Mrs Joanna Farrant, Friends Of Jackdaws, Ms C. Gilder, Mr J. B. Gilruth, Mr T. Hart, Mrs Noel Harwerth, Mr T. Jackson, Mr C. S. P. Johnson, Mr W. S. D. Lamb, Mrs John Magnier, Mr R. Marks, Mr Russell McAllister, Mr A. Miles, Mr Sean O'Driscoll, Mr Michael O'Flynn, Mr Joe O'Neill, Mr Jonjo O'Neill, Mr C. J. Pearce, Mr Stephen Perry, Mr D. G. Pryde, Mr P. A. Rooney, Mrs C. Rooney, Mr David Sandon, Mr Mervyn Smith, Mr P. J. Smith, Mr Derrick Smith, Mr R. Stanton Gleaves, Mr Mark Stone, Mr M. Tabor, Mr C Taylor, Mrs Carole Worsley, Wynatt.

Conditional: Killian Moore, Jonjo O'Neill.

---

432 **MR JOHN O'SHEA, Newnham-on-Severn**
Postal: **The Stables, Bell House, Lumbars Lane, Newnham, Gloucestershire, GL14 1LH**
Contacts: **(01452) 760835 FAX (01452) 760233 MOBILE (07917) 124717**
WEBSITE www.johnoshearacing.co.uk

1 **AGENT GIBBS**, 6, ch g Bertolini (USA)—Armada Grove **The Cross Racing Club**
2 **AMBITIOUS BOY**, 9, bl g Striking Ambition—Cherished Love (IRE) **Mr P. Smith**
3 **CAPE DIGNITY (IRE)**, 5, b g Teofilo (IRE)—Eclaircie (IRE) **K. W. Bell**
4 **CELER ET AUDAX**, 6, b m Kayf Tara—Wannaplantatree **Mr N. G. H. Ayliffe**
5 **CHAMPAGNE FREDDIE**, 5, b g Sleeping Indian—Shes Minnie **The Cross Racing Club**
6 **CLEMENT (IRE)**, 8, b g Clodovil (IRE)—Winnifred **K. W. Bell**
7 **COUGAR KID (IRE)**, 7, b g Yeats (IRE)—Western Skylark (IRE) **The Cross Racing Club**
8 **DALNESS EXPRESS**, 5, b g Firebreak—Under My Spell **Mr P. Smith**
9 **FRIDAY FEELING**, 4, b f Schiaparelli (GER)—Lac Marmot (FR) **S. P. Bloodstock**
10 **FROZEN LAKE (USA)**, 6, b g Elusive Quality (USA)—
Creative Design (USA) **N G Ayliffe & The Cross Racing Club**
11 **GENERAL BROOK (IRE)**, 8, b g Westerner—Danse Grecque (IRE) **K. W. Bell**
12 **GET UP THEM STEPS**, 4, b g Excelebration (IRE)—Flag Day **The Cross Racing Club**
13 **IMPERIAL LINK**, 6, b m Rail Link—Imperia (GER) **The Cross Racing Club**
14 **JIMMY BELL**, 7, b g Tiger Hill (IRE)—Armada Grove **K. W. Bell**
15 **KINGLAMI**, 9, b g Kingsalsa (USA)—Red Japonica **Pete Smith & Phil Hart Racing**
16 **LOUIS VEE (IRE)**, 10, b br g Captain Rio—Mrs Evans (IRE) **Quality Pipe Supports (Q.P.S.) Ltd**
17 **MAJOR VALENTINE**, 6, b g Major Cadeaux—Under My Spell **Mr P. Smith**
18 **ONE LINER**, 4, b g Delegator—Quip **The Cross Racing Club**
19 **OUTRAGEOUS ROMANA (IRE)**, 7, b m Malinas—South West Nine (IRE) **Ms S. A. Howell**
20 **PEAK STORM**, 9, b g Sleeping Indian—Jitterbug (IRE) **Pete Smith & The Cross Racing Club**

MR JOHN O'SHEA - Continued

21 SPENVIA, 7, b g Fair Mix (IRE)—Wannaplantatree **Quality Pipe Supports (Q.P.S.) Ltd**
22 SWENDAB (IRE), 10, b g Trans Island—Lavish Spirit (USA) **E&G Racing: Swendab**
23 TRIBAL DANCE (IRE), 12, br g Flemensfirth (USA)—Native Sparkle (IRE) **Quality Pipe Supports (Q.P.S.) Ltd**
24 WAROFINDEPENDENCE (USA), 6, b br g War Front (USA)—
My Dear Annie (USA) **Keith Davies & The Cross Racing Club**

Other Owners: Mr D. Abraham, Mr K. Davies, Mr R. D. J. East, Mr J. M. Gibbs, Mrs S. Guest, Mr P. G. Hart, Mrs S. Smith, Mr S. T. Wallace, Mrs P. S. Wallace.

Jockey (flat): Robert Havlin, Luke Morris, Fergus Sweeney.

433

MR HENRY OLIVER, Abberley
Postal: **Stable End, Worsley Racing Stables, Bank Lane, Abberley, Worcester,**
Worcestershire, WR6 6BQ
Contacts: **PHONE (01299) 890143 MOBILE (07701) 068759**
E-MAIL henryoliverracing@hotmail.co.uk WEBSITE www.henryoliverracing.co.uk

1 AFTER HOURS (IRE), 9, b g Milan—Supreme Singer (IRE) **R. G. Whitehead**
2 BURRENBRIDGE HOTEL (IRE), 7, b g Ivan Denisovich (IRE)—Hearthstead Dancer (USA) **Mr H. J. Oliver**
3 DARLYN, 5, b m Authorized (IRE)—Darariyna (IRE) **Best Foot Forward**
4 DESPICABLE ME (IRE), 4, b g Gold Well—Bun Buns (IRE) **Mr H. J. Oliver**
5 DIAMOND ROCK, 7, b g Kayf Tara—Crystal Princess (IRE) **R. G. Whitehead**
6 DOC CARVER (IRE), 7, ch g Lakeshore Road (USA)—Tuney Tulip (IRE) **WKD Four**
7 DR DES (IRE), 7, b g Double Eclipse (IRE)—Dans Belle (IRE) **R. G. Whitehead**
8 DRESDEN (IRE), 10, b g Diamond Green (FR)—So Precious (IRE) **Mr D. M. J. Lloyd**
9 FAIRY POL (IRE), 5, b m Milan—Culmore Lady (IRE) **R. G. Whitehead**
10 5, B g Kalanisi (IRE)—Full of Birds (FR)
11 GENEROUS DAY (IRE), 6, b g Daylami (IRE)—Our Pride **R. G. Whitehead**
12 HIJRAN (IRE), 5, ch m Mastercraftsman (IRE)—Sunny Slope **Mrs H. M. Oliver**
13 KEEL HAUL (IRE), 10, br g Classic Cliche (IRE)—Tara Hall **R. G. Whitehead**
14 LOVE LANE (IRE), 5, b m Stowaway—Inquisitive Look **D Pain & Sons**
15 MAJOR HINDRANCE (IRE), 8, ch g Kris Kin (USA)—
Ten Dollar Bill (IRE) **Catchtwentytwo,Andyfreight Holdingsltd**
16 MEGABUCKS (IRE), 7, b g Well Chosen—Clonmayo (IRE) **Mr D. M. J. Lloyd**
17 MURRAY MOUNT (IRE), 8, b g Trans Island—Ash **Mr M. S. Hitchcroft**
18 OZZY THOMAS (IRE), 8, b g Gold Well—Bramble Leader (IRE) **Ms S. A. Howell**
19 SAMARAYIA, 6, b m Black Sam Bellamy (IRE)—Samrana (FR) **Best Foot Forward**
20 SHROUGHMORE LASS (IRE), 7, b m Flemensfirth (USA)—
Smokey Bandit (IRE) **Mark Hitchcroft & Henry Oliver**
21 SPARKLING RIVER (IRE), 8, gr m Indian River (FR)—Full Deck (IRE) **Mr M. P. Dunphy**
22 STEPS AND STAIRS (IRE), 8, b g Robin des Pres (FR)—Be Mine Tonight (IRE) **Mr Mark Dunphy**
23 TEMIR KAZYK, 4, b g Oasis Dream—Tingling (USA) **Mr M. S. Hitchcroft**
24 THE CRAZED MOON (IRE), 6, b m Yeats (IRE)—Rose Gallery (FR) **Mr M. P. Dunphy**
25 THE DAWN MAN (IRE), 7, b g Milan—Calling Classy (IRE) **Mr M. P. Dunphy**
26 TODAY PLEASE (IRE), 8, b g Westerner—Casiana (GER) **Mr M. P. Dunphy**
27 TROJAN LASS (IRE), 6, b m Robin des Champs (FR)—Berties Sister (IRE) **Mr H. J. Oliver**
28 WHISPERING HARRY, 9, b g Sir Harry Lewis (USA)—Welsh Whisper **R. G. Whitehead**
29 YORGONNAHEARMEROAR (IRE), 7, b g Scorpion (IRE)—Etoile Margot (FR) **Mr M. P. Dunphy**

Other Owners: Andyfreight Holdings Limited, Catch Twenty Two, Mr G. Hibbert, Mr C. Mastoras, Mr P. R. Pain, Mr A. Pain, Mrs S. Pain, Mrs P. R. Pain, Mrs A. S. Taylor.

Assistant Trainer: Heather Oliver

434

MR JAMIE OSBORNE, Upper Lambourn
Postal: **The Old Malthouse, Upper Lambourn, Hungerford, Berkshire, RG17 8RG**
Contacts: **PHONE (01488) 73139 FAX (01488) 73084 MOBILE (07860) 533422**
E-MAIL info@jamieosborne.com WEBSITE www.jamieosborne.com

1 ARABIC CULTURE (USA), 4, b g Lonhro (AUS)—Kydd Gloves (USA) **D Reynolds & C Watkins**
2 BATTALION (IRE), 8, b g Authorized (IRE)—Zigarra **Melbourne 10 Racing**
3 BORN TO FINISH (IRE), 5, b g Dark Angel (IRE)—Music Pearl (IRE) **Crowd Racing Partnership**
4 CLIFFS OF CAPRI, 4, b g Canford Cliffs (IRE)—Shannon Spree **Melbourne 10 Racing**

MR JAMIE OSBORNE - Continued

5 **DE LITTLE ENGINE (IRE)**, 4, ch g Power—Reveuse de Jour (IRE) **Melbourne 10 Racing**
6 **DRUMOCHTER**, 4, br f Bated Breath—Dixey **Melbourne 10 Racing**
7 **ENIGMATIC (IRE)**, 4, b g Elnadim (USA)—Meanwhile (IRE) **Melbourne 10 Racing**
8 **HARAZ (IRE)**, 5, b g Acclamation—Hanakiyya (IRE) **Melbourne 10 Racing**
9 **HUNGARIAN RHAPSODY**, 4, b g Exceed And Excel (AUS)—Sharp Terms **Mr Michael Buckley**
10 **KINGOFMERROWS (IRE)**, 4, br g Kodiac—Tamara Gervasoni (IRE) **Melbourne 10 Racing**
11 **LONG JOHN SILVER (IRE)**, 4, b g Rip Van Winkle (IRE)—Tropical Lady (IRE) **Mr Michael Buckley & Mr T Hyde**
12 **MANCHEGO**, 4, b g Lope de Vega (IRE)—Gooseberry Pie **D Reynolds & C Watkins**
13 **PALAWAN**, 5, b g Mount Nelson—Apple Sauce **Melbourne 10 Racing**
14 **RAISING SAND**, 6, b g Oasis Dream—Balalaika **Nick Bradley Racing 22 & Partner**
15 **RECKLESS ENDEAVOUR (IRE)**, 5, b g Kodiac—Red Fanfare **Melbourne 10 Racing**
16 **SAM MISSILE (IRE)**, 5, b g Smart Strike (CAN)—Kitty Matcham (IRE) **Melbourne 10 Racing**
17 **SECRET SALVAGE (IRE)**, 4, b f Roderic O'connor (IRE)—Violet Flame (IRE) **The Bo Derek 10 Partnership**
18 **SKETCHING**, 4, b f Nathaniel (IRE)—Prove **Tony O'Callaghan**
19 **START SEVEN**, 6, br g Dilum (USA)—Dancinginthecloudes (IRE) **Melbourne 10 Racing**
20 **STRATEGIC HEIGHTS (IRE)**, 9, b g Strategic Prince—Shot of Redemption **Melbourne 10 Racing**
21 **TOAST OF NEW YORK (USA)**, 7, b h Thewayyouare (USA)—Claire Soleil (USA) **Al Shaqab Racing UK Limited**
22 **TOP HATTER**, 4, ch f Helmet (AUS)—Miss Marvellous (USA) **J. A. Osborne**
23 **VOLATILE**, 4, b g Poet's Voice—Neshla **Melbourne 10 Racing**
24 **VOLTURNUS**, 4, b g Azamour (IRE)—Daffydowndilly **The Hon A. A. Blyth**
25 **WAPPING (USA)**, 5, b g Smart Strike (CAN)—Exciting Times (FR) **Melbourne 10 Racing**

THREE-YEAR-OLDS

26 **ALIFAX**, gr c Mayson—Scrupulous **Melbourne 10 Racing**
27 **BOOMERANG BETTY (IRE)**, b f Havana Gold (IRE)—Arbeel **Melbourne 10 Racing**
28 **BREAKFAST (IRE)**, b c Kodiac—Pride Celebre (IRE) **Melbourne 10 Racing**
29 **CARP KID (IRE)**, b c Lope de Vega (IRE)—Homegrown (IRE) **Melbourne 10 Racing**
30 **COSMIC LANDSCAPE**, b c Lawman (FR)—Dancinginthecloudes (IRE) **Mr M. Kurt**
31 **COSMOGYRAL (IRE)**, b f Camelot—Fanditha (IRE) **Mr M. Kurt**
32 **DARKEST LIGHT**, b c Lethal Force (IRE)—Deora De **Mr M. Kurt**
33 **DUKE OF ALBA (IRE)**, b c Lope de Vega (IRE)—Royal Alchemist **Mr Michael Buckley & Ballylinch Stud**
34 **ESCAPE TO THE CITY**, ch f Cityscape—Dauphine (IRE) **The Hon A. A. Blyth**
35 **FAB (IRE)**, b f Society Rock (IRE)—Dubai Princess (IRE) **Mr N Bashir & Mr R Ridout**
36 **FORBIDDEN PLANET**, b c Pivotal—Aiming **Mr M. Kurt**
37 **GATES PASS**, b c Showcasing—Molly Mello (GER) **Mr Michael H. Watt**
38 **GENUINELY CROWDED (IRE)**, b f Zoffany—Genuinely (IRE) **Crowd Racing**
39 **GEORDIELASS**, b f Geordieland (FR)—La Verte Rue (USA) **Mr A. Taylor**
40 **GOOD KARMA (IRE)**, b c Kodiac—Turuqaat **Mr Michael Buckley & Mrs Karima Burman**
41 **GOT TRUMPED**, ch c Thewayyouare (USA)—Madam President **Michael Buckley & Chuck Esserman**
42 **JABAROUT (USA)**, b c Uncle Mo (USA)—Tell Me Twice (CAN) **Mr A. Alqallaf**
43 **KION (IRE)**, ch c Dragon Pulse (IRE)—Diamond Duchess (IRE) **Melbourne 10 Racing**
44 **LA MERNANCIA (IRE)**, b f Kodiac—Nashatara (USA) **Melbourne 10 Racing**
45 **LAYTOWN (IRE)**, ch f Footstepsinthesand—Miss Mocca (IRE) **Melbourne 10 Racing**
46 **LIVE BY NIGHT**, b c Oasis Dream—Shaleela (IRE) **Michael Buckley & Michael Watt**
47 **LUSH LIFE (IRE)**, gr f Mastercraftsman (IRE)—Break of Day (USA) **Mr Michael Buckley & Mrs Paul Shanahan**
48 **MONTAGUE (IRE)**, b c Poet's Voice—Silicon Star (IRE) **Melbourne 10 Racing**
49 **MR RECKLESS (IRE)**, gr c Reckless Abandon—Zarabaya (IRE) **The Q Party**
50 B c Zoffany (IRE)—Myrtle Beach (IRE)
51 **PREACHER MAN (IRE)**, b c Lope de Vega (IRE)—Daniysha (IRE) **Mr Michael Buckley**
52 **SARASOTA (IRE)**, b f Zoffany—Saldenaera (GER) **Mrs M V Magnier M Buckley Mrs P Shanahan**
53 **SEA ESS SEAS (IRE)**, b c Swiss Spirit—Rabshih (IRE) **Melbourne 10 Racing**
54 **SEA SERENADE**, b f Henrythenavigator (USA)—Discophilia **Miss I. Oliva Salinas**
55 **SICARIO (IRE)**, b g Thewayyouare (USA)—Blessed Beauty (USA) **Mr Michael Buckley**
56 **TEXAS RANGER (IRE)**, b c Declaration of War (USA)—Spirit of Tara (IRE) **Mr Michael Buckley**
57 **TURN OF LUCK (IRE)**, b c Pivotal—Side of Paradise (IRE) **Merriebelle Irish Farm Limited**
58 **VEGAS BOY (IRE)**, ch g Society Rock (IRE)—Consensus (IRE) **The Fabulous Fifty Boys**
59 **VOYAGER BLUE**, br c Footstepsinthesand—Bristol Fashion **Mr & Mrs I. H. Bendelow**
60 **YOU'RE NO BETTER**, b c High Chaparral (IRE)—Wiener Wald (USA) **Mr Michael Buckley & Mrs Paul Shanahan**
61 **YOUR BAND**, b g Helmet (AUS)—Kampai **Mr F. McGrath**

TWO-YEAR-OLDS

62 B f 12/3 So You Think (NZ)—Alpha Lupi (IRE) (Rahy (USA)) (58000) **Flaxman Stables Ireland Ltd and Partner**
63 B f 21/3 Toronado (IRE)—Amberley Heights (IRE) (Elnadim (USA)) (11000) **Five Grand Fillies Partnership**
64 B c 21/3 Sir Prancealot (IRE)—Balamiyda (IRE) (Ashkalani (IRE)) (10000)
65 **BRAINS**, b c 1/4 Dandy Man (IRE)—Pure Jazz (Marju (IRE)) (17094) **The Judges**

MR JAMIE OSBORNE - Continued

66 B f 23/3 Power—Break of Day (USA) (Favorite Trick (USA)) **Mrs P Shanahan**
67 Ch c 25/1 No Nay Never (IRE)—Brigids Cross (IRE) (Sadler's Wells (USA)) (61050) **Mr Michael Buckley**
68 B c 31/3 Requinto (IRE)—Cadescia (IRE) (Cadeaux Genereux) (23809)
69 Ch c 6/4 Pivotal—Carlanda (FR) (Lando (GER)) (25000) **Mr Michael Buckley**
70 B c 3/3 Dream Ahead (USA)—
  Daganya (IRE) (Danehill Dancer (IRE)) (33333) **Ian Barratt, Adam Signy, Ben Spiers**
71 B f 11/4 Camacho—Dancing Lauren (IRE) (Oratorio (IRE)) (15238) **Five Grand Fillies Partnership**
72 B f 2/2 Dream Ahead (USA)—Dartrix (Dutch Art) (17142) **Five Grand Fillies Partnership**
73 Gr c 16/3 Kendargent (FR)—Desca (GER) (Cadeaux Genereux) (26048) **Ian Barratt, Adam Signy, Ben Spiers**
74 B f 27/3 Society Rock (IRE)—Edelfa (FR) (Fasliyev (USA)) (19536) **Bashir, Deerman, Ridout**
75 B c 9/3 Sir Prancealot (IRE)—Friendly Heart (CAN) (Lion Heart (USA)) (7326)
76 Ch c 11/4 Mastercraftsman (IRE)—High Praise (USA) (Quest For Fame) **T Hyde and Partner**
77 B f 6/4 War Command (USA)—Highindi (Montjeu (IRE)) (32560) **Ian Barratt, Adam Signy, Ben Spiers**
78 C c 11/2 Pour Moi (IRE)—Laughing Water (FR) (Duke of Marmalade (IRE)) **R C Tooth Esq**
79 **LE BOULEVARDIER**, b c 9/3 Champs Elysees—Daffydowndilly (Oasis Dream) **The Hon A. A. Blyth**
80 B c 29/1 Lope de Vega (IRE)—Liberating (Iffraaj) (60000) **Airlie Stud and Partner**
81 B f 29/1 Canford Cliffs (IRE)—
  Life Is Golden (USA) (Giant's Causeway (USA)) (10476) **Five Grand Fillies Partnership**
82 B f 31/3 Camelot—Lily of Kenmare (IRE) (Exceed And Excel (AUS)) (28490)
83 Ch c 14/2 Zoffany (IRE)—Magena (USA) (Kingmambo) (40000)
84 B c 29/3 Declaration of War (USA)—
  Memories For Us (USA) (Street Cry (IRE)) (40700) **Ian Barratt, Adam Signy, Ben Spiers**
85 Ch c 14/3 Footstepsinthesand—Noble Penny (Pennekamp (USA)) (5714) **Five Grand Fillies Partnership**
86 B c 20/2 Dream Ahead (USA)—Nurture (IRE) (Bachelor Duke (USA)) (17908)
87 **ORION'S SHORE**, ch c 3/4 Sea The Stars (IRE)—Bright Snow (USA) (Gulch (USA)) **Mr R. Kinch**
88 B c 6/4 Kyllachy—Pious (Bishop of Cashel) (100000) **Mr Michael Buckley**
89 **RIVIERA CLAIRE**, b f 13/5 Showcasing—Seldemosa (Selkirk (USA)) (16000) **Mr & Mrs I Barratt**
90 Ch f 7/1 No Nay Never (IRE)—Sliabh Na Mban (IRE) (Sadler's Wells (USA))
91 Ch f 29/3 Nathaniel (IRE)—So Belle (Singspiel (IRE)) **Mr and Mrs H Shipton**
92 B c 2/4 Lope de Vega (IRE)—Sound of Guns (Acclamation) (40700) **Mr Michael Buckley**
93 B f 26/4 Australia—Teddy Bears Picnic (Oasis Dream) (48840)
94 **USANECOLT (IRE)**, b c 25/3 Olympic Glory (IRE)—
  Never Busy (USA) (Gone West (USA)) (38095) **Homecroft Wealth Racing**
95 B c 27/4 Sea The Stars (IRE)—
  Wizz Kid (IRE) (Whipper (USA)) (155000) **Mr Michael Buckley and Ballylinch Stud**

Assistant Trainer: Jimmy McCarthy

Apprentice: Jack Dinsmore, Emma Taff.

---

435 MISS EMMA OWEN, Nether Winchendon
Postal: Musk Hill Stud Farm, Nether Winchendon, Aylesbury, Buckinghamshire, HP18 0EB
Contacts: PHONE (01844) 290282 MOBILE (07718) 984799
E-MAIL emma.l.owen@hotmail.com

1 **DIVINE MESSENGER**, 4, b c Firebreak—Resentful Angel **Miss E. L. Owen**
2 **FIREGUARD**, 5, b g Firebreak—Leaping Flame (USA) **L S Olley & E L Owen**
3 **GUNNER MOYNE**, 6, b g Excellent Art—Maramkova (IRE) **L S Olley & E L Owen**
4 **HIGHER COURT (USA)**, 10, b g Shamardal (USA)—Nawalat (USA) **Miss E. L. Owen**
5 **HIGHPLAINS DRIFTER (IRE)**, 7, b g High Chaparral (IRE)—Qhazeenah **Miss E. L. Owen**
6 **JOSHLEE (IRE)**, 4, b f Dark Angel (IRE)—Kay Es Jay (FR) **Miss E. L. Owen**
7 **LEGAL MIND**, 5, ch h Firebreak—La Sorrela (IRE) **Miss E. L. Owen**
8 **LUTINE CHARLIE (IRE)**, 11, br g Kheleyf (USA)—Silvery Halo (USA) **Miss E. L. Owen**
9 **SEA THE WAVES**, 5, b g Canford Cliffs (IRE)—April (IRE) **Mr L. F. Daly**

THREE-YEAR-OLDS

10 **REIGNITE**, b c Firebreak—Resentful Angel **Miss E. L. Owen**
11 **THE ARISTOCAT (IRE)**, b f Kitten's Joy (USA)—Letters (FR) **Miss E. L. Owen**

MISS EMMA OWEN - Continued

TWO-YEAR-OLDS

12 PEDDERY, b c 28/3 Pastoral Pursuits—Resentful Angel (Danehill Dancer (IRE)) **Miss E. L. Owen**
13 B f 24/3 Dick Turpin (IRE)—Vera Lou (IRE) (Manduro (GER)) **Mr L. F. Daly**

Other Owners: Mr Leo Daly, Mr L S Olley, Miss Emma L. Owen.

---

436 **MR HUGO PALMER, Newmarket**
Postal: **Kremlin Cottage Stables, Snailwell Road, Newmarket, Suffolk, CB8 7DP**
Contacts: **PHONE (01638) 669880 FAX (01638) 666383 MOBILE (07824) 887886**
E-MAIL info@hugopalmer.com WEBSITE www.hugopalmer.com

1 ALOUJA (IRE), 4, ch f Raven's Pass (USA)—Artisti **Saleh Al Homaizi & Imad Al Sagar**
2 ARCHITECTURE (IRE), 5, b m Zoffany (IRE)—Brigayev (ITY) **Lael Stable**
3 AVENTINUS (IRE), 4, b g Zoffany (IRE)—Luminous Gold **Seventh Lap Racing**
4 FRANCIS XAVIER (IRE), 4, b g High Chaparral (IRE)—
                                    Missionary Hymn (USA) **The Missionary Hymn Partnership**
5 GIFTED MASTER (IRE), 5, b g Kodiac—Shobobb **Dr A. Ridha**
6 GULLIVER, 4, b g Sayif (IRE)—Sweet Coincidence **Saleh Al Homaizi & Imad Al Sagar**
7 HUMBERT (IRE), 4, b g Kodiac—Fee Eria (FR) **Woodhurst Construction Ltd**
8 HYPERFOCUS (IRE), 4, b br g Intense Focus (USA)—Jouel (FR) **MPH Racing - II**
9 KOHINUR, 4, b f Dubawi (IRE)—Vita Nova (IRE) **Al Asayl Bloodstock Ltd**
10 LIGHT AND BOLD (FR), 4, b c Redoute's Choice (AUS)—Thislillightofmine (USA) **Sheikh J. D. Al Maktoum**
11 MAZYOUN, 4, br g Mayson—Hypnotize **Al Shaqab Racing UK Limited**
12 PART EXCHANGE, 4, b f Champs Elysees—Market Forces **K. Abdullah**
13 SAMARMADI, 4, ch g Sepoy (AUS)—Sweet Folly (IRE) **Mr A. Menahi**
14 STAGE NAME, 4, ch f Famous Name—Striking Choice (USA) **Mr H. Palmer**
15 STAR ARCHER, 4, b g Champs Elysees—Postale **K. Abdullah**
16 TEMERAIRE (FR), 4, gr f Mount Nelson—Tadorne (FR) **Blessingdisguise Partnership**
17 TO BE WILD (IRE), 5, br g Big Bad Bob (IRE)—Fire Up **Mrs F. J. Carmichael**
18 UNFORGETABLE FILLY, 4, b f Sepoy (AUS)—Beautiful Filly **Dr A. Ridha**
19 VINTAGE FOLLY, 4, b f Makfi—Katimont (IRE) **Mr R. W. Hill-Smith**

THREE-YEAR-OLDS

20 AD LIBITUM, b g Elusive Quality (USA)—Sarmad (USA) **Mr V. I. Araci**
21 B c Cape Cross (IRE)—Almansoora (USA) **Mr H. R. Bin Ghedayer**
22 ALPINE GLOW (IRE), b f Teofilo (IRE)—Asawer (IRE) **Mr G. Schoeningh**
23 ALTERED METHOD (IRE), ch g Dawn Approach (IRE)—Swift Action (IRE) **Mr J. E. Dance**
24 ARBALET (IRE), gr c Dark Angel (IRE)—Miss Beatrix (IRE) **Mr V. I. Araci**
25 ATLAAL, b f Dansili—Igugu (AUS) **Sheikh M. B. K. Al Maktoum**
26 BALLERINA POINTE, b f Frankel—Chigun **Mr V. I. Araci**
27 BREAKING RECORDS (IRE), b c Kodiac—Querulous (IRE) **Dr A. Ridha**
28 BURFORD BROWN, br c Swiss Spirit—Sareb (FR) **Mr A. D. Gott**
29 CALIBURN (IRE), b c Camelot—Enchanted Evening (IRE) **M M Stables**
30 CENTRAL CITY (IRE), b g Kodiac—She Basic (IRE) **Mr L. L. Lee**
31 COLLIDE, b c Frankel—Scuffle **K. Abdullah**
32 CONFEDERATE, b c Teofilo (IRE)—Merry Jaunt (USA) **Highclere T'bred Racing-Kelly Holmes**
33 CONFRERIE (IRE), b c Society Rock (IRE)—Intellibet One
34 CORROSIVE (USA), b c Uncle Mo (USA)—Lovely Syn (USA) **Mr V. I. Araci**
35 CURIOSITY (IRE), b g High Chaparral (IRE)—Precautionary **H Moorhead, C Fahy & J Collins**
36 DAWN DELIGHT, b f Dawn Approach (IRE)—Al Mahmeyah **Mr H. R. Bin Ghedayer**
37 DELSHEER (FR), b c Iffraaj—Rose Et Noire (IRE) **Al Shaqab Racing UK Limited**
38 DIEULEFIT (IRE), b f Oasis Dream—Tereschenko (USA) **Al Asayl Bloodstock Ltd**
39 DRAGON MOUNTAIN, b c Sir Percy—Rouge Dancer **Fiona and Ian Carmichael-Jennings**
40 DRAGON TATTOO (IRE), b f Zoffany (IRE)—Geisha Lily (FR) **Anglia Bloodstock Syndicate XII**
41 DREAM ASCOT, b f Oasis Dream—World Class **Lady Mary Manton**
42 DUBAI EYE, ch f Pivotal—Jumeirah Palm Star **Mr H. R. Bin Ghedayer**
43 DUBAI LANDMARK (IRE), b c Helmet (AUS)—Cairncross (IRE) **Rabbah Racing**
44 DUKHAN, br c Teofilo (IRE)—Vedela (FR) **Al Shaqab Racing UK Limited**
45 EMPLOYER (IRE), b c Camelot—Close Regards (IRE) **Mr V. I. Araci**
46 ENCRYPTED, b c Showcasing—Disclose **K. Abdullah**
47 EVINCE, b f New Approach (IRE)—Prove **K. Abdullah**

MR HUGO PALMER - Continued

48 **EXPENSIVE LIAISON (IRE)**, b f Camelot—Indigo Lady **W. J. and T. C. O. Gredley**
49 **EXPROMPT (FR)**, b c Choisir (AUS)—Councilofconstance (IRE) **Mr V. I. Araci**
50 **FAJJAJ (IRE)**, ch c Dawn Approach (IRE)—Pleasantry **Al Shaqab Racing UK Limited**
51 **FORMULA ONE (IRE)**, b c Frankel—Wizz Kid (IRE) **Carmichael-Jennings / Ballylinch Stud**
52 **FORT APACHE**, b c High Chaparral (IRE)—Frivolity **Al Asayl Bloodstock Ltd**
53 **GHAYADH**, b g Kyllachy—Safe House (IRE) **Al Shaqab Racing UK Limited**
54 **GODODDIN**, b c Camelot—Spritza (IRE) **Fiona and Ian Carmichael-Jennings**
55 **GRATIFIED (IRE)**, b c Society Rock (IRE)—Generous Gesture (IRE) **Cheveley Park Stud Limited**
56 **GUELTA**, b f Oasis Dream—Canada Water **K. Abdullah**
57 **HARBOUR NIGHTS**, b g Harbour Watch (IRE)—Irtahal (USA) **Biddestone Racing XIV**
58 **HEAVENLY HOLLY (IRE)**, b f Shamardal (USA)—Happy Holly (IRE) **Hunscote Stud**
59 **HIGH SEAS (IRE)**, b f Henrythenavigator (USA)—High Days (IRE) **Al Asayl Bloodstock Ltd**
60 **HYPOTHETICALLY (IRE)**, b f Medicean—Hespera **Al Asayl Bloodstock Ltd**
61 **INTENSE PLEASURE (IRE)**, b c Sepoy (AUS)—Promesse de L'aube (FR) **Mr V. I. Araci**
62 **JOUSI**, ch f Dubawi (IRE)—Soon (IRE) **Saleh Al Homaizi & Imad Al Sagar**
63 **LA BASS (FR)**, b c Style Vendome (FR)—Feel **Mr K. M. Al Attiyah**
64 **LABREGA**, b f Cacique (IRE)—Postale **Al Shaqab Racing UK Limited**
65 **LADY IN LIGHTS (IRE)**, b f Dansili—Cabaret (IRE) **Sheikh J. D. Al Maktoum**
66 **LEFT ALONE**, b f Reckless Abandon—Akhmatova **Sheikh J. D. Al Maktoum**
67 **LEIGH'S LAW (IRE)**, b f Lawman (FR)—Delira (FR) **Cityside Electrical Co Limited**
68 **LEXINGTON FLAIR (FR)**, b c Dabirsim (FR)—Kyleam **Middleham Park Racing XXVIII**
69 **LOVELY APPROACH**, ch c New Approach (IRE)—Lovely Pass (IRE) **Dr A. Ridha**
70 **MAYASEEN (FR)**, gr f Style Vendome (FR)—Wing Stealth (IRE) **Al Shaqab Racing UK Limited**
71 **MINOVIA (SPA)**, gr f Caradak (IRE)—Private Dancer (FR) **Mr J. E. Dance**
72 **MOMENTARILY**, b f Cityscape—Firebelly **TCO Gredley, Mrs Magnier, Mrs P Shanahan**
73 **MOOTASADIR**, b c Dansili—Mahbooba (AUS) **Sheikh M. B. K. Al Maktoum**
74 **MORNING BEAUTY**, ch f Dawn Approach (IRE)—Extreme Beauty (USA) **Dr A. Ridha**
75 **MORNING SKYE (IRE)**, b c Famous Name—Agnetha (GER) **Nick Bradley Racing 44 & Partner**
76 **MYSTIC MEG**, b f Camelot—Hypnology (USA) **The Duke Of Roxburghe**
77 **NEVER BACK DOWN (IRE)**, b c Kodiac—Steer By The Stars (IRE) **M M Stables**
78 **NEW ORLEANS (IRE)**, b g Red Jazz (USA)—Agnista (IRE) **Anglia Bloodstock Syndicate X**
79 **NOVA SCOTIA (IRE)**, b c Oasis Dream—Vita Nova (IRE) **Al Asayl Bloodstock Ltd**
80 **PATHS OF GLORY**, b c Mastercraftsman (IRE)—Pacific Rim (IRE) **China Horse Club International Limited**
81 **PEPPER STREET (IRE)**, b f Born To Sea (IRE)—Mindy (IRE) **Anglia Bloodstock Syndicate XI**
82 **PHOTONICS (IRE)**, b g Power—Naval Affair (IRE) **Mr J. E. Dance**
83 **POWER TO EXCEED (IRE)**, b f Exceed And Excel (AUS)—Power of Light (IRE) **Dr A. Ridha**
84 **PRECIPITATE**, b f Dansili—Hasten (IRE) **Al Asayl Bloodstock Ltd**
85 **PULITZER**, b f Kodiac—Solola (GER) **W. J. and T. C. O. Gredley**
86 **QUEEN MAUREEN (USA)**, b f Elusive Quality (USA)—Star of Paris (USA) **Miss J. K. Allison**
87 **RAINBOW HILL**, b f Fastnet Rock (AUS)—Riot of Colour **Lady Mary Manton**
88 **RASHDAN (FR)**, b c Big Bad Bob (IRE)—On Fair Stage (IRE) **Al Shaqab Racing UK Limited**
89 **REFEREE**, b c Dansili—Zulema **K. Abdullah**
90 B c Kodiac—Refuse To Give Up (IRE) **Seventh Lap Racing**
91 **ROYSTONIA (IRE)**, b f Redoute's Choice (AUS)—Waterlilly (IRE) **Al Asayl Bloodstock Ltd**
92 **SILVER QUARTZ**, gr c Frankel—Rosamixa (FR) **Al Asayl Bloodstock Ltd**
93 **STRANGE SOCIETY (IRE)**, br c Society Rock (IRE)—Strange Magic (IRE) **M M Stables**
94 **SUDONA**, b f Zoffany (IRE)—Vickers Vimy **D. Hulse S. Saunders & Lady Cobham**
95 **TEMUR KHAN**, br c Dansili—Slink **Mr V. I. Araci**
96 **TENEDOS**, b c High Chaparral (IRE)—Garanciere (FR) **Mr V. I. Araci**
97 **THE REVENANT**, ch c Dubawi (IRE)—Hazel Lavery (IRE) **Al Asayl Bloodstock Ltd**
98 **THUNDERBOLT ROCKS**, b c Farhh—Coquette Noire (IRE) **Nick Bradley 45 & Partner**
99 **TORO (IRE)**, b g Clodovil (IRE)—Vanity's Girl (IRE) **Seventh Lap Racing**
100 **TRADE MISSION (USA)**, b c Artie Schiller (USA)—Sheba Queen (USA) **K. Abdullah**
101 **VOICE OF DUBAI**, b c Poet's Voice—Pencarrow **Rabbah Racing**
102 **WHITE MOCHA (USA)**, ch c Lope de Vega (IRE)—Lastroseofsummer (IRE) **Dr A. Ridha**

TWO-YEAR-OLDS

103 B c 1/4 Zoffany (IRE)—Ahd (USA) (Elusive Quality (USA)) (34188) **Mr L. L. Lee**
104 B f 10/2 Sepoy (AUS)—Akhmatova (Cape Cross (IRE)) (75000) **Sheikh J. D. Al Maktoum**
105 B c 30/1 Lope de Vega (IRE)—Allegation (FR) (Lawman (FR)) (22000) **Dr A. Ridha**
106 B f 26/1 Deep Impact (JPN)—Amanee (AUS) (Pivotal) **Sheikh M. B. K. Al Maktoum**
107 Ch c 27/3 New Approach (IRE)—Anayid (A P Indy (USA)) (24420) **Dr A. Ridha**
108 Ch f 7/5 Slade Power (IRE)—Beautiful Filly (Oasis Dream) (50000) **Dr A. Ridha**
109 **BIRDCAGE WALK**, b f 7/2 Sea The Moon (GER)—Baisse (High Chaparral (IRE)) **Mr G. Schoeningh**

MR HUGO PALMER - Continued

110 **BLOND WARRIOR (IRE)**, ch c 8/2 Zoffany (IRE)—
    Dame Blanche (IRE) (Be My Guest (USA)) (170940) **Mrs F. J. Carmichael**
111 B f 4/3 Lawman (FR)—Bright Sapphire (IRE) (Galileo (IRE)) (81400) **Mr A. Kheir**
112 B c 21/3 Nathaniel (IRE)—Caravan of Dreams (Anabaa (USA)) (150000) **Dr A. Ridha**
113 **CARPIO**, ch c 17/3 Lope de Vega (IRE)—Waterlilly (IRE) (Galileo (IRE)) **Al Asayl Bloodstock Ltd**
114 B c 11/1 Frankel—Chigun (Oasis Dream) **Mr V. I. Araci**
115 B f 30/4 Camelot—Close Regards (IRE) (Danehill (USA)) (56980)
116 B f 31/3 Nathaniel (IRE)—Conquete (FR) (Kyllachy) (26500) **Lady Mary Manton**
117 **CROCHET (USA)**, b br f 2/3 First Defence (USA)—Magic Motif (USA) (Giant's Causeway (USA)) **K. Abdullah**
118 **DEBBONAIR (IRE)**, b c 13/4 Slade Power (IRE)—
    Bryanstown Girl (IRE) (Kalanisi (IRE)) (25714) **Commission Air Limited**
119 **DESERT WAR (USA)**, gr c 13/4 Oasis Dream—
    Gracie Square (USA) (Awesome Again (CAN)) (38000) **Mr Martin Hughes & Lord de La Warr**
120 **DRAGON KUZA**, b c 3/4 Dragon Pulse (IRE)—Mylaporyours (IRE) (Jeremy (USA))
121 Ch c 5/3 Nathaniel (IRE)—Dudley Queen (IRE) (Excellent Art) (40000) **Mr H. Palmer**
122 **EAGLE HUNTER**, b c 23/4 Dansili—Zeva (Zamindar (USA)) **Al Asayl Bloodstock Ltd**
123 B c 18/4 Dansili—Endless (Sadler's Wells (USA)) **Sheikh M. B. K. Al Maktoum**
124 **EVERYMANANEMPROR**, br c 1/4 Gregorian (IRE)—
    Winterbourne (Cadeaux Genereux) (35238) **Mr G. M. Richardson**
125 B f 10/3 Dubawi (IRE)—Filia Regina (Galileo (IRE))
126 **GEORGE FORMBY**, ch c 10/3 Mayson—Supa Sal (King's Best (USA)) (29304)
127 B c 5/2 Toronado (IRE)—Green Tern (ITY) (Miswaki Tern (USA)) (120000) **Al Shaqab Racing UK Limited**
128 B f 26/3 Oasis Dream—Hasten (IRE) (Montjeu (IRE)) (200000) **Al Asayl Bloodstock Ltd**
129 B c 24/3 Slade Power (IRE)—Heart's Desire (IRE) (Royal Applause) (65000) **Nick Bradley Racing 23**
130 B f 13/3 Zoffany (IRE)—Height of Elegance (IRE) (Galileo (IRE)) **Lady Mary Manton**
131 Ch c 5/2 Bated Breath—I'm In Love (USA) (Zafonic (USA)) (22000) **Lady Mary Manton**
132 B f 25/1 Kingman—Intense Pink (Pivotal) (47000) **Dr A. Ridha**
133 B f 29/4 Battle of Marengo (IRE)—Letters (FR) (Raven's Pass (USA)) **Al Asayl Bloodstock Ltd**
134 Ch c 4/5 Dawn Approach (IRE)—Mamonta (Fantastic Light (USA)) (50000) **Mrs C. McStay**
135 Ch f 6/3 Pivotal—Phillipina (Medicean) (90000) **Dr A. Ridha**
136 **RACHEL ZANE (IRE)**, b f 20/3 Sea The Moon (GER)—
    Mark of An Angel (IRE) (Mark of Esteem (IRE)) (27500) **FOMO Syndicate**
137 B c 9/2 Oasis Dream—Scarborough Fair (Pivotal) (60000)
138 Ch f 28/2 Iffraaj—Sloane Square (Teofilo (IRE)) (70000) **Sheikh R. D. Al Maktoum**
139 B f 19/1 Dansili—Souviens Toi (Dalakhani (IRE)) (40000) **Nick Bradley Racing 24**
140 Gr c 14/2 Kodiac—Spinamix (Spinning World (USA)) (160000) **Al Shaqab Racing UK Limited**
141 **STARTEGO**, b c 4/5 New Approach (IRE)—Tafiya (Bahri (USA)) **Al Asayl Bloodstock Ltd**
142 **TAKE FRIGHT**, br f 19/4 Bated Breath—Tipping Over (IRE) (Aussie Rules (USA)) **Lady Mimi Manton & Partner**
143 B f 1/4 Exceed And Excel (AUS)—Unity (IRE) (Sadler's Wells (USA)) **Mr V. I. Araci**
144 B f 12/3 Dark Angel (IRE)—Vasilia (Dansili) **Mr V. I. Araci**
145 **WILLIAM MCKINLEY**, b c 13/4 Exceed And Excel (AUS)—
    Pure Song (Singspiel (IRE)) (40000) **W. J. and T. C. O. Gredley**

Other Owners: I. J. Al-Sagar, S. Ali, Mr M. Almutairi, Mr M. Almutairi, Ballylinch Stud, Mr T. Blessing, Mr P. Blessing, Ms R. H. Blessing, Mr K. Blessing, T. P. Bostwick, Mrs G. P. Bostwick, Mr N. Bradley, Mrs A. J. Brudenell, Mr J. A. Bryan, Mr I. Carmichael-Jennings, Lady N. F. Cobham, Mr A. J. A. Collins, Lord De La Warr, Mr C. J. Fahy, W. J. Gredley, T. C. O. Gredley, Mr P. Hernon, Highclere Nominated Partner Limited, Highclere Thoroughbred Racing Ltd, Mr M. P. Hills, Miss S. Holden, Saleh Al Homaizi, Mr M. B. Hughes, The Hon Mrs D. Hulse, Mr R. Jackson, Mrs G. S. Jackson, Mr R. P. Jones, Mrs E. Magnier, Miss P. E. Mains, Mr M. J. McStay, Nick Bradley Racing 44, Nick Bradley Racing 45, Mr T. O'Connor, T. S. Palin, M. Prince, Mrs S. Saunders, Mrs L. M. Shanahan, S. M. Smith, Mrs L. A. Smith.

Jockey (flat): Josephine Gordon. **Apprentice:** Noel Garbutt.

---

437 **MR MARK PATTINSON, Epsom**
Postal: **Flat 3, White House Stables, Tattenham Corner Road, Epsom, Surrey, KT18 5PP**
Contacts: **PHONE (01737) 913469**

1 **ALMANACK**, 8, b g Haatef (USA)—Openness **M I Pattinson Racing**
2 **BRIAC (FR)**, 7, b g Kapgarde (FR)—Jarwin Do (FR) **Mr O. S. Harris**
3 **CHIP OR PELLET**, 5, b g Hellvelyn—Concentration (IRE) **Mr O. Blatchford-Potten**
4 **JUST US TWO (IRE)**, 6, b g Royal Applause—Sarah's First **Mr O. S. Harris**
5 **READY (IRE)**, 8, ch g Elnadim (USA)—Fusili (IRE) **M I Pattinson Racing**

MR MARK PATTINSON - Continued

THREE-YEAR-OLDS

6 **ONE MORE DAWN**, b f Kheleyf (USA)—Jocasta Dawn **M I Pattinson Racing**

TWO-YEAR-OLDS

7 B c 17/3 Nayef (USA)—The Lady Lapwing (Mark of Esteem (IRE))

Other Owners: Mr C. R. Pattinson, Mr M. Pattinson.

438

MR BEN PAULING, Bourton-on-the-Water
Postal: **Bourton Hill Farm, Bourton-On-The-Water, Gloucestershire, GL54 2LF**
Contacts: **PHONE (01451) 821252 MOBILE (07825) 232888**
E-MAIL ben@benpaulingracing.com WEBSITE www.benpaulingracing.com

1 **A HARE BREATH (IRE)**, 10, b g Alkaadhem—Lady Willmurt (IRE) **Mrs S N J Embiricos / Mr S N J Embiricos**
2 **ALPINE SECRET (IRE)**, 6, br g Stowaway—Squaw Valley (IRE) **Off Piste Partnership**
3 **AM I APPROPRIATE**, 5, b m Kadastrof (FR)—Shuil Do (IRE) **The Kykie Allsopp Partnership**
4 **AMETHEA (IRE)**, 4, b f Yeats (IRE)—Moricana (GER) **Pump&Plant ServicesLtd&TheLateMrMartinHolder**
5 **ANIGHTINLAMBOURN (IRE)**, 4, b f Gold Well—Madgehil (IRE) **Mr & Mrs Paul & Clare Rooney**
6 **BALLY GILBERT (IRE)**, 7, ch g Stowaway—Reedsbuck (FR) **The Aldaniti Partnership**
7 **BARDISTA (IRE)**, 6, b g Marienbard (IRE)—Rapsan (IRE) **The Ben Pauling Racing Club**
8 **BARLEY HILL (IRE)**, 5, ch g Stowaway—Saysi (IRE) **Circle Of Friends**
9 **BARTERS HILL (IRE)**, 8, b g Kalanisi (IRE)—Circle The Wagons (IRE) **Circle Of Friends**
10 **BLACK KALANISI (IRE)**, 5, b g Kalanisi (IRE)—Blackthorne Winter (IRE) **The Harefield Racing Club**
11 **BOREHAM BILL (IRE)**, 6, b g Tikkanen (USA)—Crimond (IRE) **Mrs S. P. Foran**
12 **BOSS MANS LADDER (IRE)**, 6, b g Mahler—Glen Supreme (IRE) **Presumption in Favour Partnership**
13 **CADEAU GEORGE**, 9, b g Relief Pitcher—Sovereign's Gift **Genesis Racing Partnership**
14 **CANGODEMAYO**, 6, b m Lucarno (USA)—Cadoutene (FR) **The Swing Along Partnership**
15 **CARLOS DU FRUITIER (IRE)**, 6, b g Diableneyev (USA)—Odyssee Madrik (FR) **The Sandbaggers Club**
16 **CAVERNOUS (IRE)**, 5, br g Court Cave (IRE)—Willoughby Sue (IRE) **Mr C. A. Washbourn**
17 **CHAMPAGNE POPPY (IRE)**, 5, b m Scorpion (IRE)—Princess Supreme (IRE) **Mr R. P. D. T. Dineen**
18 **CHAT TO CHARLIE (IRE)**, 4, ch g Stowaway—Miss Izzy (IRE) **Mrs C. Kendrick**
19 **CHUFFY CHUFFNELL (IRE)**, 4, b g Flemensfirth (USA)—Cathy Doun (IRE) **The Megsons**
20 **CITY STAR**, 6, b m Black Sam Bellamy (IRE)—Danarama
21 **COEUR PENSIF (FR)**, 6, br g Laveron—Lady Easter (FR) **Lost In 1936 Partnership**
22 **COOLE WELL (IRE)**, 5, b g Gold Well—Bobs Lass (IRE) **Mrs C. Kendrick**
23 **CREEP DESBOIS (FR)**, 6, b g Great Pretender (IRE)—
                                        Brigade Mondaine (FR) **Slater Stockwood Nicholson Partnership**
24 **CYRIUS MORIVIERE (FR)**, 8, b g Vendangeur (IRE)—Sagesse Moriviere (FR) **The Pillar P Partnership**
25 **DAVERON (IRE)**, 10, b g Winged Love (IRE)—Double Doc (IRE) **Mr N. A. Holder**
26 **DELIRE D'ESTRUVAL (FR)**, 5, b g Youmzain (FR)—
                                        Question d'estruval (FR) **Mr Simon Munir & Mr Isaac Souede**
27 **EAST COAST (FR)**, 4, b g Day Flight—Similaresisoldofa (FR) **The Megsons**
28 **EAU TOP (FR)**, 4, b g Barastraight—Monepopee (FR)
29 **EQUUS SECRETUS (IRE)**, 6, b g Brian Boru—Bodega Bay (IRE) **The Bourtoneers**
30 **FAWSLEY SPIRIT (IRE)**, 5, b g Stowaway—Apple Trix (IRE) **Exors of the Late P. Bush**
31 **FIFTH SYMPHONY (IRE)**, 4, b g Mahler—Nicolemma (IRE) **Mr C. A. Washbourn**
32 **GLOBAL CITIZEN (IRE)**, 6, b g Alkaadhem—Lady Willmurt (IRE) **The Megsons**
33 **GOWITHTHEFLOW (IRE)**, 5, b g Westerner—Maryiver (IRE) **Bruton Street**
34 **HARGREAVES**, 5, b g Big Bad Bob—Lady Cad (FR) **Pump & Plant Services Ltd**
35 **HERO'S CREEK (IRE)**, 5, br g Kalanisi (IRE)—Iktitafs Sister (IRE) **Middleham Park Racing XXIV & C & R Poole**
36 **HIDDEN GLEN (IRE)**, 5, ch g Stowaway—Gleanntan (IRE) **J Petit,C Skinner,R Sanders & J Tuttiett**
37 **HIGH BRIDGE**, 7, b g Monsun (GER)—Ameerat **Mrs D. M. Ferguson**
38 **IFYOUCANSEEMENOW (IRE)**, 4, br g Stowaway—Sandrinechoix (FR) **Mr & Mrs Paul & Clare Rooney**
39 4, B g Kalanisi (IRE)—Iktitafs Sister (IRE)
40 **JALEO (GER)**, 6, ch g New Approach (IRE)—Jambalaya (GER) **Mrs D. M. Ferguson**
41 **KERRY'S BOY (IRE)**, 5, b g Oscar (IRE)—Kerry's Girl (IRE) **Mr M. P. Ardley**
42 **KILDISART (IRE)**, 6, br g Dubai Destination (USA)—Princess Mairead (IRE) **Mr Simon Munir & Mr Isaac Souede**
43 **LADY CHUFFNELL (IRE)**, 4, b f Jeremy (USA)—Taraval (USA) **The Megsons**
44 **LE BREUIL (FR)**, 6, ch g Anzillero (GER)—Slew Dancer **Miss E. A. Collins**
45 **LEGAL EYES (IRE)**, 5, br g Court Cave (IRE)—Grass Tips (IRE) **OAP Syndicate**
46 **LINENHALL (IRE)**, 6, ch g Stowaway—Option (IRE) **Mrs E. L. Kendall**
47 **MALACHYS GIRL (IRE)**, 5, b m Darsi (FR)—Borleagh Princess (IRE) **Mrs S. J. Lanz**
48 **MARKOV (IRE)**, 8, b g Morozov (USA)—Willoughby Sue (IRE) **Mr A. R. W. Marsh**

MR BEN PAULING - Continued

49 **MARTEN (FR)**, 6, b g Martaline—Commande Blue (FR) **Lord Vestey**
50 **MONK'S VIEW**, 5, bl g Multiplex—Evelith Abbey (IRE) **The High T Party**
51 **MY TURGEON (FR)**, 5, gr g Turgeon (USA)—My Belle (FR) **Peel Racing Club**
52 **NADAITAK**, 4, b g Teofilo (IRE)—Tanfidh **The Megsons**
53 **NESTOR PARK (FR)**, 5, b g Walk In The Park (IRE)—Cila (IRE) **Mrs S. P. Davis**
54 **NEWTON GERONIMO**, 9, b br g Brian Boru—Newton Commanche (IRE) **J H & N J Foxon Ltd**
55 **NOBUTTABOY (IRE)**, 7, b g Darsi (FR)—Buckalong (IRE) **Easy Going Racing**
56 **OISTRAKH LE NOIR (FR)**, 4, b g Kentucky Dynamite (USA)—
                                  Linares Noire (FR) **Mr Simon Munir & Mr Isaac Souede**
57 5, B g Observatory (USA)—One For Philip **S W Group Logistics Limited**
58 **ONE LUCKY LORD**, 7, b g Lucky Story (USA)—One For Philip **S W Group Logistics Limited**
59 **OSKAR DENARIUS (IRE)**, 7, b g Authorized (IRE)—Elizabethan Age (FR) **Promanco Ltd**
60 **PADDY'S FIELD (IRE)**, 8, b g Flemensfirth (USA)—Kittys Oscar (IRE) **Mr & Mrs Paul & Clare Rooney**
61 **PARLOUR GAMES**, 10, ch g Monsun (GER)—Petrushka (IRE) **Mrs D. M. Ferguson**
62 **PERFECT PIRATE**, 6, b g Black Sam Bellamy (IRE)—Supreme Gem (IRE) **MastersRacingClub**
63 **PLUS ONE (IRE)**, 6, b g Winged Love (IRE)—Balwaney (FR) **The Megsons**
64 **POWERFUL SYMBOL (IRE)**, 8, b g Robin des Champs (FR)—Be My Rainbow (IRE) **The Megsons**
65 **RAVEN'S TOWER (USA)**, 8, b g Raven's Pass (USA)—Tizdubai (USA) **Faithful Friends**
66 **RED INDIAN**, 6, b g Sulamani (IRE)—Rafiya **Preston Lodge Stud**
67 4, B g Getaway (GER)—Rosetiepy (FR)
68 5, B m Sulamani (IRE)—Royal Bride **Mrs S. N. J. Embiricos**
69 **SALIX (FR)**, 4, gr g Grey Risk (FR)—Yes Mate (FR) **Mr Simon Munir & Mr Isaac Souede**
70 **SAVANNA ROAR (IRE)**, 5, b g Let The Lion Roar—Addie's Choice (IRE) **The Jp Girls**
71 **SCRAFTON**, 7, b g Leporello (IRE)—Some Diva **Mrs P. J. Clark**
72 **SILVER HOLLOW**, 6, gr g Beat Hollow—Onemix **S W Group Logistics Limited**
73 **SKIDOOSH**, 5, b g Midnight Legend—Southern Exit **Mr L. J. Strangman**
74 **SMOKING DIXIE (IRE)**, 7, ch g Beneficial—Jacksister (IRE) **Mrs Robin Birley**
75 **STAGE SUMMIT (IRE)**, 5, gr g Tikkanen (USA)—Summittotalkabout (IRE) **Fortnum Racing**
76 **STEP YOU GAILY**, 5, b m Crosspeace (IRE)—Khadija **The Kykie Allsopp Partnership**
77 **SUPREME SOVIET (IRE)**, 4, b g Sholokhov (IRE)—Bay Pearl (FR) **El Vino Did Flow Syndicate**
78 **TAKEMEOUT FREDDIE (IRE)**, 4, ch g Doyen (IRE)—Me No Puppet **Mrs C. Kendrick**
79 **TEL'ART (FR)**, 4, b g Montmartre (FR)—Textuelle (FR)
80 **TENNEWROW (IRE)**, 6, b m Stowaway—Silent Supreme (IRE) **Mr P. C. Bickmore**
81 **THE COB (IRE)**, 4, b g Let The Lion Roar—Millenium Love (IRE)
82 **TREATY GIRL (IRE)**, 7, b m Milan—Back To Coughing (IRE) **The Bourtoneers**
83 **TWO SWALLOWS**, 8, b m Kayf Tara—One Gulp **Mrs C. A. Waters**
84 **UNCLE PERCY**, 5, b g Sir Percy—Forsythia **The Ben Pauling Racing Club**
85 **WAY BACK THEN (IRE)**, 7, b g Robin des Champs (FR)—Ashwell Lady (IRE) **Nicholas Piper & Claire E. Piper**
86 **WILLOUGHBY COURT (IRE)**, 7, br g Court Cave (IRE)—Willoughby Sue (IRE) **Mr & Mrs Paul & Clare Rooney**
87 **WORLD PREMIER (FR)**, 5, gr g Montmartre (FR)—Kelbelange (FR) **Mr J. P. McManus**

THREE-YEAR-OLDS

88 **BOKO FITTLEWORTH (IRE)**, b g Most Improved (IRE)—Sycamores (FR) **The Megsons**

Other Owners: Mr R. V. Alberto, Mr J. A. C. Ayton, Mr G. Bennett, Mr M. Booth, Mr Charles E. Noell Esq, Mrs G. Collier, Mrs P. M. Colson, Mr J. Deacon, Mr N. C. Deacon, Mr M. G. Donnellan, S. N. Embiricos, Ms A. E. Embiricos, Mr C. Fenwick, Hon S. Foster, Mr R. Foxon, Mr L. P Green, Mr D. E. Greenway, Mr M. D. Hankin, Mr W. P. Harriman, Mrs C. S. Heber-Percy, Mr B. L. Hiskey, Exors of the Late M. J. Holder, Mr W. R. Kinsey, Mrs J. E. B. Leigh-Pemberton, Mrs J. Megson, Mr A. P. Megson, Mr J. M. Melvin, S. E. Munir, J. M. Nicholson, T. S. Palin, Mrs S. Pauling, Mr B. P. Pauling, Mrs J. Pauling, Mr J. W. Petit, Mr C. M. Pickard, Miss J. Pimblett, Mr N. Piper, Miss C. E. Piper, M. Prince, Mr T. Robinson-Gamby, Mr P. A. Rooney, Mrs C. Rooney, Mr R. D. Sanders, Mr C. A. L. Skinner, Mr T. C. Smith, Mr I. Souede, Mr J. Stockwood, Mrs M. T. Stopford-Sackville, Mr D. F. Sumpter, Mr P. Taylor, Mr J. E. Tuttiett, Mrs S. F. Weatherby, Mr J. R. Weatherby, Mr W. R. B. Webb, Mr R. W. P. Weeks.

Assistant Trainer: Thomas David

Jockey (NH): David Bass, Daryl Jacob, Nico De Boinville. **Amateur:** Mr A. Ferguson, Mr A. Rid.

---

439 **MR RAY PEACOCK, Tenbury Wells**
Postal: **Elliott House Farm, Vine Lane, Kyre, Tenbury Wells, Worcestershire, WR15 8RL**
Contacts: **PHONE (01885) 410772 MOBILE (07748) 565574/ 07881440135**

1 **GIFTED HEIR (IRE)**, 14, b g Princely Heir (IRE)—Inzar Lady (IRE) **R. E. Peacock**
2 **INTERCHOICE STAR (IRE)**, 13, b g Josr Algarhoud (IRE)—Blakeshall Girl **Mr J. P. Evitt**

MR RAY PEACOCK - Continued

3 **LES GAR GAN (IRE)**, 7, b m Iffraaj—Story **Mr J. P. Evitt**
4 **MUNAAWIB**, 10, b g Haafhd—Mouwadh **R. E. Peacock**
5 **PORTRUSH STORM**, 13, ch m Observatory (USA)—Overcast (IRE) **R. E. Peacock**
6 **RICH HARVEST (USA)**, 13, b br g High Yield (USA)—Mangano (USA) **R. E. Peacock**

Assistant Trainer: Mrs C Peacock

Jockey (flat): David Probert. **Amateur:** Miss S. Peacock.

---

440 **MRS LYDIA PEARCE, Newmarket**
Postal: **Wroughton House, 37 Old Station Road, Newmarket, Suffolk, CB8 8DT**
Contacts: **PHONE (01638) 664669 MOBILE (07787) 517864**
E-MAIL lsp_8@live.co.uk

1 **AFRICAN GIRL**, 4, b f Equiano (FR)—Tychy **Killarney Glen Partnership**
2 **BARTHOLOMEW J (IRE)**, 4, ch g Fast Company (IRE)—Mana (IRE) **Mr P. J. Stephenson Partnership**
3 **CAMARADORIE (IRE)**, 4, ch f Camacho—Lady Duxyana **Mr R. G. Thurston Partnership**
4 **GENERAL PATTON**, 4, b g Intense Focus (USA)—Blandish (USA) **Audrey Lanham**
5 **KATAHDIN (IRE)**, 5, b g Kayf Tara—Keyaza (IRE) **Jay Three Racing**
6 **LUNA MAGIC**, 4, gr g Mayson—Dayia (IRE) **Lady J. Green**
7 **NOBLE PEACE**, 5, b g Kyllachy—Peace Concluded **Killarney Glen**
8 **SEXY SECRET**, 7, b g Sakhee's Secret—Orange Walk (IRE) **Personal Racehorse Owners 1**
9 **UPTOWN GIRL**, 4, b f Doncaster Rover (USA)—Mon Petit Diamant **Mr H Crothers**

Other Owners: Mr Stuart Andrews, Mr S. Bush, Mr Harry Crothers, Mr N. M. Hanger, Mr John Harrison, Mr C. S. Heaps, Mr Eric Jones, Mr A. B. Puddick, Mr P. J. Stephenson, Mr R. G. Thurston.

Assistant Trainer: Jeff Pearce

Jockey (flat): Simon Pearce.

---

441 **MR OLLIE PEARS, Malton**
Postal: **The Office, Old Farmhouse, Beverley Road, Norton, Malton, North Yorkshire, YO17 9PJ**
Contacts: **PHONE (01653) 690746 MOBILE (07760) 197103**
E-MAIL info@olliepearsracing.co.uk WEBSITE www.olliepearsracing.co.uk

1 **DANDY HIGHWAYMAN (IRE)**, 4, ch g Dandy Man (IRE)—Paradise Blue (IRE) **Ontoawinner & Ollie Pears**
2 **DYNA MIGHT**, 4, b f Foxwedge (AUS)—Dyna Bowl (USA) **Ownaracehorse Ltd & Mr Ollie Pears**
3 **JENNIES GEM**, 5, b g Mount Nelson—Kaspirit (IRE) **Mr R. S. Marshall**
4 **KROY**, 4, b g Sleeping Indian—Valley of The Moon (IRE) **Mrs S. A. Elsey**
5 **LEAN ON PETE**, 9, b g Oasis Dream—Superfonic (FR) **Keith West & Ollie Pears Racing Club**
6 **MONT ROYAL (FR)**, 4, gr g Naaqoos—Take Blood (FR) **T. Elsey**
7 **MR C (IRE)**, 4, b g Fast Company (IRE)—Vanitycase (IRE) **Mr A. Caygill**
8 **ROARING RORY**, 5, ch g Sakhee's Secret—Barbieri (IRE) **Ownaracehorse Ltd & Mr Ollie Pears**
9 **UNNOTICED**, 6, b g Observatory (USA)—Celestial Empire (USA) **Keith West & Ollie Pears Racing Club**

THREE-YEAR-OLDS

10 **AMITY ISLAND**, ch c Harbour Watch (IRE)—Mylington Light **Ollie Pears & Ownaracehorse Ltd**
11 **CHRISTMAS NIGHT**, ch g Compton Place—Night Haven **Ownaracehorse Ltd & Mr Ollie Pears**
12 **LAYDEE VICTORIA (IRE)**, b f Sir Prancealot (IRE)—Damask (IRE) **Ontoawinner, Wilson-Crane & Ollie Pears**
13 **PLACEBO EFFECT (IRE)**, b g Lilbourne Lad (IRE)—
Hawaiian Dream (IRE) **Timothy O'Gram, Keith West & Ollie Pears**
14 **POPPY WALTON (IRE)**, ch f Society Rock (IRE)—Bellacoola (GER) **Mr A. Caygill**

TWO-YEAR-OLDS

15 **LEXIKON**, b f 29/3 Mayson—Fairy Steps (Rainbow Quest (USA)) (5000) **Mrs S. D. Pearson**
16 B f 5/3 Bated Breath—Otelia (IRE) (Teofilo (IRE))
17 B c 20/2 Heeraat (IRE)—Passkey (Medicean) (4000) **Mr T O'Gram, Mrs P Moll & Mr R Marshall**
18 **PERCY DRAKE**, ch c 1/2 Sir Percy—
Stilettoesinthemud (IRE) (Footstepsinthesand) (4761) **Andrew Caygill & Ollie Pears**
19 **QUEEN OF SCHEME (IRE)**, b f 11/3 Tagula (IRE)—
Gimmick (IRE) (Siyouni (FR)) (2857) **Ownaracehorse Ltd & Mr Ollie Pears**
20 **SAPPHIRE JUBILEE**, b f 12/2 Lethal Force (IRE)—Queens Jubilee (Cayman Kai (IRE)) **Mrs S. D. Pearson**

MR OLLIE PEARS - Continued

21 Ch c 7/4 Kyllachy—Smile For Me (IRE) (Elnadim (USA)) (4285) **O. J. Pears**
22 **SWERVED (IRE)**, b f 13/3 Excelebration (IRE)—
Manoeuvre (IRE) (Galileo (IRE)) (2000) **Ownaracehorse Ltd & Mr Ollie Pears**

Other Owners: Mr S. Bridge, Mrs P. E. Moll, Mr N. J. O'Brien, T. J. O'Gram, Ollie Pears Racing Club, Ontoawinner, Wilson-Crane, Ownaracehorse Ltd, K. C. West.

Assistant Trainer: Vicky Pears

Jockey (NH): Brian Hughes.

---

442 **MR GEORGE PECKHAM, Newmarket**
Postal: **Eve Lodge Stables, Hamilton Road, Newmarket, Suffolk, CB8 0NY**
Contacts: **MOBILE (07823) 335013**
E-MAIL george@aislabie.com

1 **DIRAYAH (IRE)**, 4, b f Dark Angel (IRE)—Folga **Mr F. Nass**
2 **INSHIRAAH (FR)**, 4, b f Holy Roman Emperor (IRE)—Blessed Catch (USA) **Mr F. Nass**
3 **MAJROOH (IRE)**, 6, b g Acclamation—Neve Lieve (IRE) **Mr F. Nass**
4 **MUHAJJAL**, 4, b c Cape Cross (IRE)—Muqantara (USA) **Mr F. Nass**
5 **SANIYAAT**, 4, b f Galileo (IRE)—Starlit Sands **Mr F. Nass**
6 **WHIRL ME ROUND**, ch g Piccolo—Give Her A Whirl **Justin Byrne & Fawzi Abdulla Nass**
7 **YEMNAAK (FR)**, 4, b g Medicean—Aujiang (GER) **Mr F. Nass**
8 **ZOFFANY BAY (IRE)**, 4, b g Zoffany (IRE)—Trois Graces (USA) **Mr F. Nass**

THREE-YEAR-OLDS

9 **JANABIYA**, b f Nathaniel (IRE)—Date With Destiny (IRE) **Mr F. Nass**
10 B c Kodiac—La Petite Bleue (GER) **Mr F. Nass**
11 B g Acclamation—Muqantara (USA) **Mr F. Nass**
12 B g Epaulette (AUS)—Rayon Rouge (IRE) **Mr F. Nass**
13 B g Showcasing—Swan Wings **Mr F. Nass**
14 **TOUGH LASS (IRE)**, b f Kodiac—Sagemacca (IRE) **Mr F. Nass**
15 **TWO SEAS**, b g Sepoy (AUS)—Fifty (IRE) **Mr F. Nass**

TWO-YEAR-OLDS

16 Br c 17/2 Cape Cross (IRE)—Angel Oak (Teofilo (IRE)) (97680) **H.H. Sheikh Nasser Al Khalifa**
17 Gr ro f 28/2 Exchange Rate (USA)—Blazing Whip (USA) (Street Boss (USA)) (61943) **Mr F. Nass**
18 B c 26/3 Kyllachy—Cara Gina (Bahamian Bounty) (70000) **Mr F. Nass**
19 B c 4/5 Distorted Humor (USA)—Cherokee Jewel (USA) (Cherokee Run (USA)) (154858) **Mr F. Nass**
20 B c 16/2 Scat Daddy (USA)—Dancing Trieste (USA) (Old Trieste (USA)) (193573) **Mr F. Nass**
21 B c 6/2 Declaration of War (USA)—Escampette (USA) (Smart Strike (CAN)) (85172) **Mr F. Nass**
22 Ch c 23/2 Distorted Humor (USA)—Forbidden Gift (USA) (A P Indy (USA)) (348432) **Mr F. Nass**
23 Br f 10/3 Kyllachy—Hot Reply (Notnowcato) **Mr F. Nass**
24 B f 18/2 Poet's Voice—Jadeel (Green Desert (USA)) (10000) **Mr F. Nass**
25 Ch f 8/2 Sepoy (AUS)—Katevan (IRE) (Heliostatic (USA)) (50000) **Mr F. Nass**
26 B c 10/5 More Than Ready (USA)—Lady of Substance (IRE) (Sadler's Wells (USA)) (50000) **Mr F. Nass**
27 B c 7/3 Shanghai Bobby (USA)—Lady Pecan (USA) (Concerto (USA)) (77429) **Mr F. Nass**
28 B c 3/2 Campanologist (USA)—Limeira (Bertolini (USA)) (50000) **Mr F. Nass**
29 B c 25/1 Bernardini (USA)—No Curfew (USA) (Curlin (USA)) (309717) **H.H. Sheikh Nasser Al Khalifa**
30 B c 1/5 Rhagaas—Persian Bolt (USA) (U S Ranger (USA)) **Mr F. Nass**
31 B c 19/2 Delegator—Qanateer (IRE) (Iffraaj) (15000) **Mr F. Nass**
32 B c 9/3 Tiznow (USA)—Street Girl (USA) (Street Hero (USA)) (77429) **H.H. Sheikh Nasser Al Khalifa**
33 B f 10/2 Camelot—Tinaar (USA) (Giant's Causeway (USA)) (28000) **Mr F. Nass**
34 Ch c 21/2 Lope de Vega (IRE)—
Venus de Milo (IRE) (Duke of Marmalade (IRE)) (244200) **H.H. Sheikh Nasser Al Khalifa**

Other Owners: Mr J. A. Byrne.

Jockey (flat): Harry Bentley, Luke Morris.

443 **MISS LINDA PERRATT, East Kilbride**
Postal: **North Allerton Farm, East Kilbride, Glasgow, Lanarkshire, G75 8RR**
Contacts: **PHONE (01355) 303425 MOBILE (07931) 306147**
E-MAIL linda.perratt@btinternet.com

1 **ANITOPIA**, 13, gr g Alflora (IRE)—The Whirlie Weevil **Nil Sine Labore Partnership**
2 **DARK CRYSTAL**, 7, b m Multiplex—Glitz (IRE) **Nil Sine Labore Partnership**
3 **DAWOODI**, 4, ch g Exceed And Excel (AUS)—Anna Amalia (IRE) **Mr J. Murphy**
4 **DUTCH DREAM**, 5, ch m Dutch Art—Starry Sky **Mr B. A. Jordan**
5 **INTIWIN (IRE)**, 6, b g Intikhab (USA)—Muluk (IRE) **Mr J. Murphy**
6 **LET RIGHT BE DONE**, 6, gr g Lawman (FR)—Cheerfully **Mr Ken Mcgarrity & Linda Perratt Racing Club**
7 **LUCKY VIOLET (IRE)**, 6, b m Dandy Man (IRE)—Rashida **Mr A. R. Allan**
8 **MAGISTRAL**, 8, b g Manduro (GER)—Tamalain (USA) **Smith Friel Sawers**
9 **SCHMOOZE (IRE)**, 9, b m One Cool Cat (USA)—If Dubai (USA) **Miss L. A. Perratt**
10 **STARDRIFTER**, 6, b g Rock of Gibraltar (IRE)—Alchemilla **Miss L. A. Perratt**

THREE-YEAR-OLDS

11 **RETIREMENT BECKONS**, b g Epaulette (AUS)—Mystical Ayr (IRE) **Nil Sine Labore Partnership**

Other Owners: Mr B. Atkins, Mr M. Friel, Mr T. Hughes, Mr J. K. McGarrity, M. Sawers, Mr J. J. Sheridan.

Jockey (flat): Tom Eaves, P. J. McDonald. **Apprentice:** Leanne Ferguson.

444 **MRS AMANDA PERRETT, Pulborough**
Postal: **Coombelands Racing Stables, Pulborough, West Sussex, RH20 1BP**
Contacts: **OFFICE (01798) 873011 HOME (01798) 874894 FAX (01798) 875163**
MOBILE (07803) 088713
E-MAIL aperrett@coombelands-stables.com WEBSITE www.amandaperrett.com

1 **ANNIE ANGEL (IRE)**, 7, b m King's Theatre (IRE)—Lady Rene (IRE) **G. D. P. Materna**
2 **ARCH VILLAIN (IRE)**, 9, b g Arch (USA)—Barzah (IRE) **Mr & Mrs F Cotton,Mr & Mrs P Conway**
3 **CHAPARRACHIK (IRE)**, 4, b g High Chaparral (IRE)—Chocolat Chaud (IRE) **John Connolly & Odile Griffith**
4 **ELTEZAM (IRE)**, 5, b g Kodiac—Tymora (USA) **The Eltezam Partnership**
5 **ELYSIAN FIELDS (GR)**, 7, ch m Champs Elysees—
Second of May **Mrs Alexandra J. Chandris/Mrs Amanda Perrett**
6 **KASBAH (IRE)**, 6, b g Acclamation—Dance Hall Girl (IRE) **Coombelands Racing Syndicate**
7 **LIGHTNING DANCE**, 4, b f Nathaniel (IRE)—Dance Lively (USA) **Mrs A. J. Chandris**
8 **LIGHTNING CHARLIE**, 6, b g Myboycharlie (IRE)—Lighted Way **Lightning Charlie Partnership**
9 4, Gr g Kheleyf (USA)—Molly Mello (GER) **Mrs A. J. Perrett**
10 **MR BOSSY BOOTS (IRE)**, 7, b g Teofilo (IRE)—Zelding (IRE) **Mr Bossy Boots Partnership**
11 **OPEN WIDE (USA)**, 4, b br g Invincible Spirit (IRE)—Nunavik (IRE) **George Materna & John McInerney**
12 **PARNASSIAN (IRE)**, 4, b g Elzaam (AUS)—Adaptation **The Parnassian Partnership**
13 **PLATITUDE**, 5, b g Dansili—Modesta (IRE) **Mrs S. M. Conway**
14 **ROC ASTRALE (IRE)**, 4, ch g Teofilo (IRE)—Lumiere Astrale (FR) **John Connolly & Odile Griffith**
15 **SALUTI (IRE)**, 4, b g Acclamation—Greek Easter (IRE) **Mr J E Bodie & Partners**
16 **SENSIBLE FRIEND (GR)**, 5, b g Reel Buddy—
Senseansensibility (USA) **Winterfields Farm, Hancock & Pope**
17 **TAPDANCEALLTHEWAY**, 4, b f Nathaniel (IRE)—Tap Dance Way (IRE) **Mrs A. J. Chandris**
18 **THE WARRIOR (IRE)**, 6, b g Exceed And Excel (AUS)—Aymara **The Warrior Partnership**
19 **WORDISMYBOND**, 9, b g Monsieur Bond (IRE)—La Gessa **Bond Racing**
20 **YOU'RE HIRED**, 5, b g Dalakhani (IRE)—Heaven Sent **G. D. P. Materna**
21 **ZHUI FENG (IRE)**, 5, b h Invincible Spirit (IRE)—Es Que **John Connolly & Odile Griffith**
22 **ZZORO (IRE)**, 5, br g Manduro (GER)—Krynica (USA) **Mr & Mrs F Cotton,Mr & Mrs P Conway**

THREE-YEAR-OLDS

23 **ASTROMACHIA**, b c Sea The Stars (IRE)—Fontley **John Connolly & Odile Griffith**
24 **BIRTHDAY GIRL (IRE)**, b f Excelebration (IRE)—Street Style (IRE) **Mrs A. M. Lewis**
25 **COGITAL**, b c Invincible Spirit (IRE)—Galaxy Highflyer **John Connolly & Odile Griffith**
26 **COTTINGHAM**, b g Dalakhani (IRE)—Echelon **G. D. P. Materna**
27 **COUNT OTTO (IRE)**, b g Sir Prancealot (IRE)—Dessert Flower (IRE) **Count Otto Partnership**
28 **DAGIAN (IRE)**, ch g Dawn Approach (IRE)—Hen Night (IRE) **John Connolly & Odile Griffith**
29 **DESERT PATH**, ch g Champs Elysees—Desert Image **K. Abdullah**
30 **DOUBLE LEGEND (IRE)**, b g Finsceal Fior (IRE)—Damask Rose **Mrs A. J. Perrett**
31 **FLIRTARE (IRE)**, b f Oasis Dream—Federation **Mr & Mrs F Cotton,Mr & Mrs P Conway**

MRS AMANDA PERRETT - Continued

32 **GATHER**, b f Showcasing—Acquisition **K. Abdullah**
33 **PORT OF CALL**, b g Harbour Watch (IRE)—Valiantly **Mr Alan Spence**
34 **PROCURE**, b f Sepoy (AUS)—Silent Entrance **K. Abdullah**
35 **SING A RAINBOW (IRE)**, ch f Frankel—Beatrice Aurore (IRE) **B. Andersson**
36 **SPIRIT RIDGE**, b g Nathaniel (IRE)—Tates Creek (USA) **K. Abdullah**
37 **THRESHOLDFADREAM (IRE)**, b f Camelot—Signella **Mr D M James & Woodcote Stud**

TWO-YEAR-OLDS

38 **AEGEUS (USA)**, b br c 8/2 First Defence (USA)—Supposition (Dansili) **K. Abdullah**
39 **AZETS**, b c 10/1 Dubawi (IRE)—Nashmiah (IRE) (Elusive City (USA)) (300000) **John Connolly & Odile Griffith**
40 **BARB'S PRINCE (IRE)**, b c 11/4 Casamento (IRE)—Bibury (Royal Applause) (43000) **Mrs B. R. James**
41 **BARRENJOEY**, ch c 8/4 Australia—Heavenly Dawn (Pivotal) (45000) **Mr M Quigley & Mr D M James**
42 B c 30/4 Mayson—Kiruna (Northern Park (USA)) (45000) **Maykbelieve Partnership**
43 **MANUCCI (IRE)**, b c 12/3 Nathaniel (IRE)—
          American Spirit (IRE) (Rock of Gibraltar (IRE)) (55000) **John Connolly & Odile Griffith**
44 **SEEING RED (IRE)**, b f 29/2 Sea The Stars (IRE)—
          Red Fantasy (High Chaparral (IRE)) (200000) **Mr & Mrs F Cotton,Mr & Mrs P Conway**
45 Ch c 3/3 Dutch Art—Shamandar (FR) (Exceed And Excel (AUS)) (55000) **R. Scott**
46 **ZUBA**, b c 30/1 Dubawi (IRE)—Purr Along (Mount Nelson) (210000) **John Connolly & Odile Griffith**

Other Owners: J. E. Bodie, J. P Connolly, Mr J. F. Correale, Mr F. G. Cotton, Mrs S. H. Cotton, Mrs R. J. Doel, Ms O. L. Griffith, Guy Harwood, Mr D. M. James, Mr S. J. Jenkins, Mrs B. A. Karn-Smith, Dr J. P McInerney, Mr D. C. Perrett, Mrs S. E. Perrett, Mr M. F. Quigley, Mr R. J. Steele, Winterfields Farm Ltd, Woodcote Stud Ltd.

Assistant Trainer: Mark Perrett

---

445 | **MR PAT PHELAN, Epsom**
Postal: Ermyn Lodge, Shepherds Walk, Epsom, Surrey, KT18 6DF
Contacts: **PHONE** (01372) 229014 **FAX** (01372) 229001 **MOBILE** (07917) 762781
E-MAIL pat.phelan@ermynlodge.com **WEBSITE** www.ermynlodge.com

1 **AMANDA'S TEDDY**, 4, b g Dick Turpin (IRE)—Molly Pitcher (IRE) **Mr P. Bocking**
2 **AVANTGARDIST (GER)**, 4, ch g Campanologist (USA)—Avocette (GER) **Mr P. Bocking**
3 **DELUXE**, 6, b g Acclamation—Ainia **Mr P. J. Wheatley**
4 **DESERT SONG**, 4, b g Makfi—Lyra's Daemon **Epsom Downers**
5 **EPSOM SECRET**, 4, ch f Sakhee's Secret—My Amalie (IRE) **Epsom Racegoers No.3**
6 **ERMYN'S EMERALD**, 6, b br g Alflora (IRE)—Emerald Project (IRE) **Ermyn Lodge Stud Limited**
7 **HATSAWAY (IRE)**, 7, b g Dubawi (IRE)—Scotch Bonnet (IRE) **Mr P. J. Wheatley**
8 **KEEP TO THE BEAT**, 3, b m Beat Hollow—Cadeau Speciale **Mr Paul Cox & Mr Liam Russell**
9 **LEGEND OF FRANCE**, 5, ch m Flying Legend (USA)—Bonne Anniversaire **Ermyn Lodge Stud Limited**
10 **MAZALTO (IRE)**, 5, b m Teofilo (IRE)—Mazaaya (USA) **Maginn Hasan**
11 **PIVOTAL FLAME (IRE)**, 5, b m Pivotal—Saadiah (IRE) **Mr J. F. Lang**
12 **PRESENCE PROCESS**, 4, b g Dansili—Loulwa (IRE) **Mr P. Bocking**
13 **SETTLE PETAL**, 4, b f Peintre Celebre (USA)—Shall We Dance **I. W. Harfitt**
14 **THE PREMIER CELTIC**, 5, b g Black Sam Bellamy (IRE)—Maria Antonia (IRE) **Celtic Contractors Limited**

THREE-YEAR-OLDS

15 **DOLYDAYDREAM**, b f Equiano (FR)—Ellie In The Pink (IRE) **A. B. Pope**
16 **EDE'S A WINNER**, ch f Archipenko (USA)—Run For Ede's **Mr A. J. Smith**
17 **EPSOM BOUNTY**, ch g Bahamian Bounty—My Amalie (IRE) **Epsom Racegoers No.2**
18 **HACKBRIDGE**, br g Archipenko (USA)—Famcred **Sutton Business Centre**
19 **MAYTHEORSEBEWITHU (IRE)**, b f Shirocco (GER)—Amoya (GER) **Mr A. J. Smith**

TWO-YEAR-OLDS

20 B c 2/4 Sir Percy—My Amalie (IRE) (Galileo (IRE)) **Ermyn Lodge Stud Limited**

Other Owners: Mr P. Cox, Mr N. M. Hasan, Mrs J. K. Lukas, Mr G. Maginn, Sir D. J. Prosser, Mr L. R. Russell, Mrs L. Smith, Mr D. Stockdale, Mr T. D. J. Syder.

Jockey (flat): J. F. Egan, Shane Kelly, Kieran O'Neill. **Jockey (NH):** James Best, Niall Madden, Josh Moore. **Conditional:** Sean Houlihan. **Apprentice:** Paddy Bradley, Sophie Ralston.

446 MR ALAN PHILLIPS, Callow End
Postal: **Jennet Tree Farm, Kents Green, Callow End, Worcestershire, WR2 4UA**
Contacts: PHONE (01905) 831774 MOBILE (07870) 112235
E-MAIL alan@alanphillipsracing.com WEBSITE www.alanphillipsracing.com

1 BERLIEF ARAMIS, 8, b g Bertolini (USA)—Kaylifa Aramis **Ms I. Phipps Coltman**
2 BOHER LAD (IRE), 11, b g Gold Well—Shindeesharnick (IRE) **Miss R. L. Edwards**
3 GOLDEN ESTHER (IRE), 5, b m Scorpion (IRE)—Mascareigne (FR) **Mr M. Hollis**
4 GOLDEN MILAN (IRE), 10, b g Milan—Belle Provence (FR) **Miss R. L. Edwards**
5 LINED WITH SILVER (IRE), 9, gr g Cloudings (IRE)—Tinkers Lady **Mr M. Slingsby**
6 MR STANDFAST, 5, b g Mullionmileanhour (IRE)—Phantom Ridge (IRE) **Miss R. L. Edwards**
7 SILENT DOCTOR (IRE), 8, br g Dr Massini (IRE)—Wild Noble (IRE) **Mr A. J. Phillips**
8 TARRONA, 9, b g Kayf Tara—Lisrona (IRE) **Mr D. G. Redfern**
9 THE MODEL COUNTY (IRE), 8, b m Robin des Champs (FR)—Ware It Vic (IRE) **Mr D. G. Redfern**

447 MR RICHARD PHILLIPS, Moreton-in-Marsh
Postal: **Adlestrop Stables, Adlestrop, Moreton-in-Marsh, Gloucestershire, GL56 0YN**
Contacts: PHONE (01608) 658710 FAX (01608) 658713 MOBILE (07774) 832715
E-MAIL info@richardphillipsracing.com WEBSITE www.richardphillipsracing.com

1 ARCTIC CHIEF, 8, b g Sleeping Indian—Neiges Eternelles (FR) **Too Many Chiefs**
2 BEAUTIFUL PEOPLE (FR), 7, b br m Early March—Night Fever (FR) **Beautiful People**
3 BELLA'S VISION (FR), 5, ch m Vision d'etat (FR)—Dalina (FR) **Mr D. A. Halsall**
4 BERTIE BARNES (IRE), 7, b g Craigsteel—Mahon Rose (IRE) **The Aspirationals**
5 BIG FIDDLE, 5, b m Kayf Tara—Fiddling Again **Mrs E. C. Roberts**
6 BRAVE HELIOS, 8, b g High Chaparral (IRE)—Renowned (IRE) **Dozen Dreamers Partnership**
7 CELESTIAL MAGIC, 6, b g Black Sam Bellamy (IRE)—Mighty Merlin **Mrs J. A. Watts**
8 5, B m Kayf Tara—Giovanna **Mr R. T. Phillips**
9 4, B g Stowaway—Ilikeyou (IRE) **Mr C. Pocock**
10 IRON HORSE, 7, b g Kayf Tara—What A Vintage (IRE) **The Someday's Here Racing Partnership**
11 LAZIO (IRE), 5, b g Intikhab (USA)—La Spezia (IRE) **Mr R. T. Phillips**
12 MASTER VINTAGE, 10, b g Kayf Tara—What A Vintage (IRE) **The Adlestrop Club**
13 MIGHTY ELSA, 5, b m Schiaparelli (GER)—Tiger Moss **S. M. Smith**
14 MINELLA WHISPER, 7, b g Kayf Tara—Celtic Native (IRE) **Mrs E. A. Prowting**
15 MRS BARNES (IRE), 5, b m Ask—Jills Oscar (IRE) **Mr & Mrs R. Scott**
16 MUTHABIR (IRE), 8, b g Nayef (USA)—Northern Melody (IRE) **The Adlestrop Experience**
17 NEXT LOT, 8, b g Mountain High (IRE)—Martha Reilly (IRE) **Upthorpe Racing**
18 ORGANDI (FR), 6, br m Early March—Creme Pralinee (FR) **Beautiful People**
19 OVER STATED (IRE), 6, b g Shantou (USA)—Mrs Gordi **Mr E. J. Ware**
20 PRESENT FROM DUBAI (IRE), 5, b g Dubai Destination (USA)—Inch Promise (IRE) **Hopeful Travellers**
21 SECRET LOOK, 8, ch g Sakhee's Secret—Look Here's Carol (IRE) **Mr R. T. Phillips**
22 SHEELBEWHATSHEELBE (IRE), 8, b m Oscar (IRE)—Cheerymount (IRE) **B. J. Duckett**
23 STONEY CROSS, 6, b m Sulamani (IRE)—Stoney Path **Mrs S. C. Welch**
24 TIMETOBENEFIT (IRE), 7, b m Beneficial—Shokalocka Baby (IRE) **Mrs H. M. Nixseaman**
25 TOTTERDOWN, 7, b g Pasternak—Yeldham Lady **Fairford Goes Racing**
26 VIVA RAFA (IRE), 8, b g Scorpion (IRE)—Back To Stay (IRE) **Ms F. Baxter**
27 WESTERN STORM (IRE), 6, b g Westerner—Torduff Storm (IRE) **Ware & Fish**
28 WHAT A SCORE, 8, gr g Rail Link—Karsiyaka (IRE) **Nut Club Partnership**

THREE-YEAR-OLDS
29 GOLDEN DEAL (IRE), b f Havana Gold—Lady Rockfield (IRE) **Mr T. F. Parrett**
30 MADAME RITZ (IRE), b f Canford Cliffs (IRE)—Sky Red **The Firebirds**
31 TULANE (IRE), br g Arcano (IRE)—Jeunesse Doree (IRE) **The Tulanes**

TWO-YEAR-OLDS
32 B f 22/4 Dandy Man (IRE)—El Mirage (IRE) (Elusive Quality (USA)) **The Aspirationals**
33 B f 24/4 Canford Cliffs (IRE)—Ice Pie (Mount Nelson) (2857) **S. F. Benton**

Other Owners: Ms K. M. Anderson, J. E. Barnes, Mr M. R. Barnes, Mr J. R. Brown, Mr E. G. Brown, Mr J. E. S. Colling, Mr T. B. N. Farazmand, Mr D. T. Fish, Mrs S. H. Jones, M. T. Phillips, Mr R. B. Rowe, R. Scott, Mrs P. M. Scott, Dr E. D. Theodore, Mr M. A. W. Thompson.

Conditional: Daniel Hiskett.

448 MISS IMOGEN PICKARD, Kingsland
Postal: **The Granary, Sodgeley Farm, Kingsland, Leominster, Herefordshire, HR6 9PY**
Contacts: MOBILE **(07884) 437720**
E-MAIL **bundlepickardracing@yahoo.co.uk** WEBSITE **www.bundlepickardracing.co.uk**

1 **CONSORTIUM (IRE)**, 6, b g Teofilo (IRE)—Wish List (IRE) **Bundle Pickard Racing Club**
2 **HEATH KING (IRE)**, 8, b br g Fruits of Love (USA)—Shamaiyla (FR) **The Wonder Partnership**
3 **MISTER FIZZ**, 10, b g Sulamani (IRE)—Court Champagne **Mrs M. J. Wilson**

Other Owners: Ms S. Bather, Mr D. Fitzgerald, Miss I. H. Pickard, Mrs Margaret J. Wilson.

449 MR TIM PINFIELD, Upper Lambourn
Postal: **Flemington Stables, Upper Lambourn, Hungerford, Berkshire, RG17 8QH**
E-MAIL **timpinfieldracing@hotmail.com**

1 6, Ch m Lucarno (USA)—A Fistful of Euros
2 **BAMBAJEE (FR)**, 5, b m Rock of Gibraltar (IRE)—Heaven's Dream (IRE) **Arion Equine Limited**
3 **COULD YOU**, 6, b m Beat All (USA)—Wahiba Reason (IRE) **Mrs G. A. Pinfield**
4 **FREEDOM FIGHTER (IRE)**, 8, b g Danehill Dancer (IRE)—Rose of Petra (IRE) **Mr K. M. Pinfield**
5 **KAVASS**, 4, b g Kheleyf (USA)—Purely By Chance
6 7, B m Royal Applause—Lone Spirit (IRE)
7 4, Ch g Sir Prancealot (IRE)—Malta (USA)
8 4, B g Mayson—Milkie Way
9 4, Ch g Yorgunnabelucky (USA)—Noor El Houdah (IRE)
10 **REGGIE BLUE**, 6, b g Captain Marvelous (IRE)—Amoras (IRE)
11 **SATELLITE EXPRESS (IRE)**, 7, ch m Observatory (USA)—Composition **Mr K. M. Pinfield**
12 6, B m Multiplex—Silver Gyre (IRE)
13 **ZAYDANIDES (FR)**, 6, bl g American Post—Ouarzazate (IRE) **Ladies who Lunch Syndicate**

THREE-YEAR-OLDS
14 B c Dutch Art—Loquacity
15 **MAXIMUM POWER (FR)**, b g Power—Keisha (FR) **Bigmores Racing Partnership**

Other Owners: Mr J. Davies, Mr A. C. Nettleship.

450 MR DAVID PIPE, Wellington
Postal: **Pond House, Nicholashayne, Wellington, Somerset, TA21 9QY**
Contacts: PHONE **(01884) 840715** FAX **(01884) 841343**
E-MAIL **david@davidpipe.com** WEBSITE **www.davidpipe.com**

1 **ABRACADABRA SIVOLA (FR)**, 8, br g Le Fou (IRE)—Pierrebrune (FR) **The Arthur White Partnership**
2 **AERO MAJESTIC (IRE)**, 5, b g Arcadio (GER)—So Pretty (IRE) **Pond House Classics**
3 **ALDRIN (FR)**, 5, b g New Approach (IRE)—Trip To The Moon **ValueRacingClub.co.uk**
4 **AURILLAC (FR)**, 8, gr g Martaline—Ombrelle (FR) **D Mossop, P John & R White**
5 **BAMBI DU NOYER (FR)**, 7, b br g Sageburg (IRE)—Zouk Wood (USA) **Jimmy Hack Racing Partners**
6 **BIDOUREY (FR)**, 7, b br g Voix du Nord (FR)—Love Wisky (FR) **Brocade Racing**
7 **BROADWAY BUFFALO (IRE)**, 10, ch g Broadway Flyer (USA)—Benbradagh Vard (IRE) **Mrs Jo Tracey & Partner**
8 **BUSTER EDWARDS (IRE)**, 5, b g Kalanisi (IRE)—Hot Oscar (IRE) **Mr Jonathan Williams & Partner**
9 **CASTLEMORRIS KING**, 10, br g And Beyond (IRE)—Brookshield Baby (IRE) **Mr Stuart & Simon Mercer**
10 **CELESTIAL PATH (IRE)**, 6, b g Footstepsinthesand—Miss Kittyhawk (IRE) **Prof C. Tisdall**
11 **CHAMPERS ON ICE (IRE)**, 8, gr g Robin des Champs (FR)—
Miss Nova **Professor Caroline Tisdall & Bryan Drew**
12 **COURT OF MILAN (IRE)**, 6, b g Milan—Derrygowna Court (IRE) **Mr A. J. Ryan**
13 **DAKLONDIKE (IRE)**, 6, b g Gold Well—Strong Irish (IRE) **Prof C. Tisdall**
14 **DAUPHINE EREINE (FR)**, 6, b m Saint des Saints (FR)—Bellissima de Mai (FR) **John White & Anne Underhill**
15 **DELFACE (FR)**, 5, b g Della Francesca (USA)—Septieme Face (USA) **Pipe's Prospectors**
16 **DELL' ARCA (IRE)**, 9, b g Sholokhov (IRE)—Daisy Belle (GER) **Prof C. Tisdall**
17 **DRAMA KING (IRE)**, 7, b g King's Theatre (IRE)—Miss Arteea (IRE) **Mr M. D. Poland**
18 **DROMINEER (IRE)**, 5, br g Oscar (IRE)—Aileen Supreme (IRE) **Mr William Frewen & Partner**
19 **DUSKY HERCULES (IRE)**, 4, b g Shantou (USA)—Annalecky (IRE) **Prof C. Tisdall**
20 **EAMON AN CNOIC (IRE)**, 7, b g Westerner—Nutmeg Tune (IRE) **The Angove Family**
21 **EUR GONE WEST (IRE)**, 5, b g Westerner—Floating Euro (IRE) **Mrs J. Gerard-Pearse**

MR DAVID PIPE - Continued

22 **FRIDAY NIGHT LIGHT (FR)**, 5, b g Air Chief Marshal (IRE)—Peninsula (FR) **Prof C. Tisdall**
23 **GARRAN CITY (IRE)**, 7, ch g City Honours (USA)—Native Orchid (IRE) **Jim Humberstone & Tom Ritzema**
24 **GLEN VINE**, 4, ch g Robin des Champs (FR)—Gaspara (FR) **Mr T. J. Hemmings**
25 **GRAND RIGEL (IRE)**, 5, b g Grandera (IRE)—Nora D (IRE) **The Blue Ball Syndicate**
26 **GREAT TEMPO (FR)**, 5, b g Great Pretender (IRE)—Prima Note (FR) **The Angove Family**
27 **HONEYMOON COCKTAIL (FR)**, 7, gr g Martaline—Caipirinia (FR) **M. C. Pipe**
28 **I'M ALWAYS TRYING (IRE)**, 5, b g Westerner—Pepsi Starlet (IRE) **Mr & Mrs Paul & Clare Rooney**
29 **ILOVEMINTS**, 6, b m Kayf Tara—La Harde (FR) **ValueRacingClub.co.uk**
30 **IMPULSIVE AMERICAN**, 6, b g American Post—Impulsive Decision (IRE) **Mrs J. Tracey**
31 **INICIAR (GER)**, 8, b g Galileo—Iota (GER) **D. E. Pipe**
32 **IRISH PRINCE (IRE)**, 5, b g Presenting—Court Leader (IRE) **Professor Caroline Tisdall & Alan Kaplan**
33 **IT'S OBVIOUS**, 6, b g Tobougg (IRE)—Hiho Silver Lining **Prof C. Tisdall**
34 **JUST MIDAS (IRE)**, 5, b g Shantou (USA)—Desert Gail (IRE) **Mr David Robinson & Partner**
35 **KALIFOURCHON (FR)**, 7, gr g Martaline—Kaly Flight (FR) **CHM Partnership**
36 **KATKEAU (FR)**, 11, b g Kotky Bleu (FR)—Levine (FR) **Prof C Tisdall, Mr J A Gent, Mr R C Wilkin**
37 **KEATING (IRE)**, 6, b g King's Theatre (IRE)—Tus Nua (IRE) **Pond House Classics**
38 **KING'S SOCKS (FR)**, 6, b g King's Best (USA)—Alexandrina (GER) **Mr B. J. C. Drew**
39 **KNOW THE SCORE (IRE)**, 5, b g Flemensfirth (USA)—Prairie Bell (IRE) **The Angove Family**
40 **LADY OF LONGSTONE (IRE)**, 8, ch m Beneficial—Christdalo (IRE) **Miss S. E. Hartnell & Partner**
41 **LITTLE RED LION (IRE)**, 4, b g Sans Frontieres (IRE)—Rever Up (IRE) **Prof C. Tisdall**
42 **MARTABOT (FR)**, 7, gr g Martaline—Reine de Sabot (FR) **Mrs S. J. Ling**
43 **MAX DO BRAZIL (FR)**, 6, b g Blue Bresil (FR)—Lili Valley (FR) **Professor Caroline Tisdall & Bryan Drew**
44 **MECHELEN, (IRE)**, 4, br f Malinas (GER)—Helen Wood **Mr P. J. Green**
45 **MIDNIGHT MAGIC**, 6, b g Midnight Legend—Arctic Magic (IRE) **Midd Shire Racing**
46 **MIDNIGHT SAPPHIRE**, 8, ch m Midnight Legend—Norton Sapphire **Mr R. Harding**
47 **MISS TYNTE (IRE)**, 6, b m Mahler—Top Quality **N. Shutts**
48 **MISTER DRIFTER (IRE)**, 6, b g Stowaway—Graces Choice (IRE) **Brocade Racing**
49 **MOON RACER (IRE)**, 9, b g Saffron Walden (FR)—Angel's Folly **Professor Caroline Tisdall & Bryan Drew**
50 **MOUNT HAVEN (IRE)**, 8, b g Mountain High (USA)—Castlehaven (IRE) **D. E. Pipe**
51 **MR BIG SHOT (IRE)**, 7, br g Flemensfirth (USA)—Une Etoile (IRE) **Prof C. Tisdall**
52 **MR CLARKSON (IRE)**, 6, b g Jeremy (USA)—Wynsleydale (USA) **Pipe's Prospectors**
53 **MRS MIGGINS (IRE)**, 5, b m Presenting—Carrigeen Lunaria (IRE) **Mr Barry Wright & Mrs Rosemary White**
54 **ORCHARD THIEVES (IRE)**, 6, b g Ask—Ballycleary (IRE) **Brocade Racing**
55 **POKER PLAY (FR)**, 5, ch g Martaline—Becquarette (FR) **The Angove Family**
56 **PURPLE 'N GOLD (IRE)**, 9, b g Strategic Prince—Golden Dew (IRE) **Mrs L. Webb**
57 **QUEENS CAVE (IRE)**, 5, b m Court Cave (IRE)—Shuilan (IRE) **Mr K. Alexander**
58 **RAMSES DE TEILLEE (FR)**, 6, gr g Martaline—Princesse d'orton (FR) **John White & Anne Underhill**
59 **RATHLIN ROSE (IRE)**, 10, b g Bonbon Rose (FR)—A Plus Ma Puce (FR) **Mr F. G. Wilson**
60 **RED SQUARE REVIVAL (IRE)**, 7, b g Presenting—Alder Flower (IRE) **Halewood International Ltd**
61 **REMASTERED**, 5, ch g Network (GER)—Cathodine Cayras (FR) **Brocade Racing**
62 **RIVER DUN**, 8, br m Indian River (FR)—Sight'n Sound **The Blue Ball Syndicate**
63 **SAINT JOHN HENRY (FR)**, 8, b g Saint des Saints (FR)—Noceane (FR) **Mr B. J. C. Drew**
64 **SHAAMA GRISE (FR)**, 6, gr m Montmartre (FR)—Shaama Rose (FR) **The Angove Family**
65 **SHELL CRYSTAL**, 4, b f Schiaparelli (GER)—Solent Crystal **Mr M. D. Poland**
66 **SKINFLINT (IRE)**, 6, b g Scorpion (IRE)—Gales Hill (IRE) **Prof Caroline Tisdall & Mr John Gent**
67 **TAJ BADALANDABAD (IRE)**, 8, ch g Shantou (USA)—Last Chance Lady (IRE) **W. F. Frewen**
68 **THE DRACONIAN (IRE)**, 7, b g Kalanisi (IRE)—Lucky Hand (IRE) **Mr P. J. Green & Partner**
69 **THREE STAR GENERAL**, 5, b g Montjeu (IRE)—Honorlina (FR) **Mr The Mercer & Igoe Families**
70 **TIGGER TWO (IRE)**, 6, b g Getaway (GER)—Anne Hathaway (IRE) **Prof C. Tisdall**
71 **TIMEFORBEN (IRE)**, 6, ch m Beneficial—Shokalocka Baby (IRE) **The Bravo Partnership**
72 **TIS WHAT IT IS (IRE)**, 5, b g Gold Well—Justines Joy (IRE) **Murr & Green**
73 **TOBACCO ROAD (IRE)**, 8, b g Westerner—Virginias Best **Chris & David Stam**
74 **UN TEMPS POUR TOUT (IRE)**, 9, b g Robin des Champs (FR)— Rougedespoir (FR) **Professor Caroline Tisdall & Bryan Drew**
75 **UNIQUE DE COTTE (FR)**, 10, b g Voix du Nord (FR)—Kadalka de Cotte (FR) **Mr J. P. McManus**
76 **VANITEUX (FR)**, 9, br g Voix du Nord (FR)—Expoville (FR) **Alexander, Drew, Tracey**
77 **VIEUX LION ROUGE (FR)**, 9, ch g Sabiango (GER)—Indecise (FR) **Prof Caroline Tisdall & Mr John Gent**
78 **VIRTUEL D'OUDON (FR)**, 9, b g Network (GER)—La Belle Illusion (FR) **Ms J. Robinson**
79 **WARTHOG (FR)**, 6, gr g Martaline—Shekira (FR) **Professor Caroline Tisdall & Bryan Drew**
80 **WHAT A MOMENT (IRE)**, 8, b g Milan—Cuiloge Lady (IRE) **Bryan Drew & Steve Roper**
81 **WHITLEY NEILL (FR)**, 6, b g Shantou (USA)—Maidrin Rua (IRE) **Halewood International Ltd**
82 **YOU SAY WHAT (IRE)**, 8, b g Milan—Wave Back (IRE) **Turner Webb**

MR DAVID PIPE - Continued

Other Owners: Mr S. J. Angove, Mr D. B. Angove, Mrs A. E. M. Broom, Mr G. R. Broom, Mr S. W. Buckley, Mr S. F. Coton, Mr P. D. Couldwell, Mr J. R. Couldwell, Mrs C. Cruddace, J. S. Dale, Mrs H. Danson, Mr P. A. Deal, Mrs L. A. Farquhar, J. A. Gent, Mr P. George, S. R. Harman, Miss S. E. Hartnell, Mr J. Humberstone, Mr J. F. Igoe, Mr P. D. H. John, Mrs D. A. Johnson, Mr S. D. Johnson, Alan Kaplan, Mr S. S. Mercer, Mr S. M. Mercer, B. G. Middleton, D. Mossop, Mr I. D. Murr, Mr J. S. Nutley, Mr C. G. Paletta, Mr G. L. Phippen, D. J. Reid, Mr T. P. Ritzema, D. G. Robinson, Mr P. A. Rooney, Mrs C. Rooney, Mr S. R. Roper, A. J. Shire, Mr D. B. Stam, Dr C. Stam, Mr P. Turner, Mrs A. Underhill, J. B. Webb, Mrs R. E. White, Mr A. J. White, Mr R. C. Wilkin, Mr J. C. Williams, Mr B. Wright.

Assistant Trainer: Mr M. C. Pipe C.B.E.

Jockey (NH): David Noonan, Tom Scudamore. **Conditional:** Michael Heard. **Amateur:** Mr Rex Dingle.

---

451 **MR MARK PITMAN, Leafield**
Postal: **Fairspear Racing Stables, Fairspear Road, Leafield, Oxfordshire, OX29 9NT**
Contacts: **MOBILE (07836) 792771**
E-MAIL pitman6@icloud.com

1 CAPTAINOFINDUSTRY (IRE), 9, b g Definite Article—Talk of Rain (FR) **M. C. Denmark**
2 FACE TO FACE, 9, b g Kayf Tara—Monsignorita (IRE) **M. C. Denmark**
3 6, B g Shirocco (GER)—Ryde On **M. C. Denmark**
4 SEA SOVEREIGN (IRE), 5, b g Sea The Stars (IRE)—Lidakiya (IRE) **G. C. Stevens**

---

452 **MR CHARLES POGSON, Newark**
Postal: **Allamoor Farm, Mansfield Road, Farnsfield, Nottinghamshire, NG22 8HZ**
Contacts: **PHONE (01623) 882275 MOBILE (07977) 016155**

1 BALLYCAMP (IRE), 9, br g Kayf Tara—All Our Blessings (IRE) **Pete & Pauline Wordingham & Partner**
2 BRIDEY'S LETTUCE (IRE), 6, b g Iffraaj—Its On The Air (IRE) **Pete & Pauline Wordingham & Partner**
3 CUSHEEN BRIDGE (IRE), 10, b g Oscar (IRE)—One Hell Ofa Woman (IRE) **Pete & Pauline Wordingham**
4 MOIDORE, 9, b g Galileo (IRE)—Flash of Gold **C. T. Pogson**
5 MONDO CANE (IRE), 11, b g Beneficial—La Vita E Bella (FR) **C. T. Pogson**
6 OVERTOUJAY, 8, b br g Overbury (IRE)—Ouh Jay **Pete & Pauline Wordingham & Partner**
7 REAL KING, 6, b g Multiplex—Gertrude Webb **C. T. Pogson**
8 REAL WARRIOR (IRE), 7, b g Tikkanen (USA)—Muffin Top (IRE) **C. T. Pogson**
9 ROLLERBALL ROCCO (IRE), 6, b g Ask—Jamica Ginger (IRE) **C. T. Pogson**
10 UNZING (FR), 10, b g Voix du Nord (FR)—Magik (FR) **Pete & Pauline Wordingham & Partner**
11 WEST TO CROSSGALES (IRE), 7, b g Westerner—Mooreshill Bay (IRE) **P & P Wordingham, J Allott, C Pogson**

Other Owners: Mr J. Allott, P. L. Wordingham, Mrs P. A. Wordingham.

Assistant Trainer: Adam Pogson

Jockey (NH): Adam Pogson.

---

453 **MR KEITH POLLOCK, Carluke**
Postal: **10 Lee Meadow Road, Braidwood, Carluke, Lanarkshire, ML8 5PJ**
Contacts: **PHONE (01555) 772194 FAX (01555) 772194 MOBILE (07714) 293556**
E-MAIL info@mosko.co.uk

1 DESTINY AWAITS (IRE), 9, b g Dubai Destination (USA)—Mellow Jazz **Mr K. Pollock**
2 GLASGOW ALHAMBRA (IRE), 6, b g Dahjee (USA)—Lady Ward (IRE) **Mr K. Pollock**
3 INDIAN SAHIB (IRE), 11, b g Indian Creek—Lady Ward (IRE) **Mr K. Pollock**

Assistant Trainer: James Banks

454   MR JONATHAN PORTMAN, Upper Lambourn

Postal: Whitcoombe House Stables, Upper Lambourn, Hungerford, Berkshire, RG17 8RA
Contacts: PHONE (01488) 73894 MOBILE (07798) 824513
E-MAIL jonathan@jonathanportmanracing.com WEBSITE www.jonathanportmanracing.com

1 ASHAZURI, 4, b f Dick Turpin (IRE)—Shesha Bear **RWH Partnership**
2 BALMORAL CASTLE, 9, b g Royal Applause—Mimiteh (USA) **J. G. B. Portman**
3 BROAD APPEAL, 4, ch g Medicean—Shy Appeal (IRE) **Berkeley Racing**
4 FORESTRY, 4, b g Firebreak—Oak Leaves **Jaliza Partnership**
5 FRESH FOX, 4, ch f Sakhee's Secret—May Fox **Fillies First**
6 HEWOULDWOULDNTHE, 4, b f Sixties Icon—Gib (IRE) **J. G. B. Portman**
7 JOE PACKET, 11, ch g Joe Bear (IRE)—Costa Packet (IRE) **J. G. B. Portman**
8 LIFE HAPPENS, 4, b f Pastoral Pursuits—Halfwaytoparadise **Mascalls Stud**
9 MANCINI, 4, ch g Nathaniel (IRE)—Muscovado (USA) **Laurence Bellman**
10 MRS DANVERS, 4, gr f Hellvelyn—Rebecca de Winter **Turf Club 2016**
11 ORIN SWIFT (IRE), 4, b g Dragon Pulse (IRE)—Hollow Green (IRE) **Mr J. T. Habershon-Butcher**

THREE-YEAR-OLDS

12 ACADEMICIAN, b g Zoffany (IRE)—Eternity Ring **Phillip Afia**
13 ASPIRINGLY, b f Bated Breath—Spiralling **S McPhee & Partners**
14 CHORAL MUSIC, b f Equiano (FR)—Gospel Music **Mrs J Sinclair**
15 DAWN OF RECKONING, b f Dawn Approach (IRE)—Reckoning (IRE) **Mascalls Stud**
16 FLEETING FAME (IRE), ch g Famous Name—Twiggy's Girl (IRE) **J. G. B. Portman**
17 FOLIES BERGERES, ch f Champs Elysees—May Fox **Fillies First**
18 GAINSAY, b f Sayif (IRE)—Pesse (IRE) **Lambourne, Forbes, Losse**
19 GOLDEN IMAGE, b f Havana Gold (IRE)—Photographie (USA) **Mrs H Maitland-Jones**
20 GOLDEN IRIS, b f Havana Gold (IRE)—Sparkling Eyes **Mrs M. A. Parker**
21 GOODNIGHT GIRL (IRE), gr f Clodovil (IRE)—Leenavesta (USA) **Alex Chesterman**
22 GROUNDNUT, b g Rip Van Winkle (IRE)—Hard Walnut (IRE) **J. G. B. Portman**
23 HOMING STAR, b f Harbour Watch (IRE)—Nightunderthestars **P S & Miss R Emmet and Partners**
24 INDISCRETION (IRE), b f Big Bad Bob (IRE)—Fleeting Affair (USA) **Turf Club 2016**
25 IPSILANTE, b f Nayef (USA)—Rosacara **Mrs D. Joly & Mr David F. Powell**
26 KEVLAR, b g Helmet (AUS)—Madhaaq (IRE) **Hever Stud Farm Ltd**
27 KING OF BURGUNDY, b g Holy Roman Emperor (IRE)—Brilliant Sunshine **Tony Wechsler & Ann Plummer**
28 MADAM POMFREY, b f Sayif (IRE)—Miss Poppy
29 MANDALAYAN (IRE), b g Arakan (USA)—Danza Nera (IRE) **Simon Skinner & Partners**
30 MY BETTER HALF, b g Rip Van Winkle (IRE)—Red Intrigue (IRE) **J Gompertz**
31 NAUTICA (IRE), ch f Born To Sea (IRE)—Moynsha Lady (IRE) **Laurence Bellman & Partners**
32 NIGHT GARDEN (IRE), b f Zebedee—Kyanight (IRE) **J. G. B. Portman**
33 QUICK BREATH, b g Bated Breath—Shy Appeal (IRE) **Wood Street Syndicate**
34 SHINING GEM, ch f Monsieur Bond (IRE)—Saphire **Clipper Logistics**
35 SHOW OF FORCE, gr f Lethal Force (IRE)—Craighall **Alex Chesterman**
36 SUNDAY BEST, ch f Nathaniel (IRE)—Lacy Sunday (USA) **S McPhee & Partners**
37 TOORMAKEADY, gr f Mastercraftsman (IRE)—Liberally (IRE) **Whitcoombe Park Racing**
38 UNVEILING, b f Mayson—Silkenveil (IRE) **J. G. B. Portman**

TWO-YEAR-OLDS

39 B c 27/3 Charm Spirit (IRE)—Arch of Colours (Monsun (GER)) (5000)
40 B g 29/2 Toronado (IRE)—Byrony (IRE) (Byron) (20000)
41 B f 26/1 American Post—Casabermeja (USA) (Elusive Quality (USA)) (26000) **Lambourne, Forbes, Losse**
42 DEMERARA (IRE), b f 28/1 Kingman—Caster Sugar (USA) (Cozzene (USA)) **Mrs J. Wigan**
43 Ch c 13/2 Born To Sea (IRE)—Dew (IRE) (Whipper (USA)) (12000) **Berkeley Racing**
44 B c 5/5 Swiss Spirit—Happy Clapper (Royal Applause)
45 Ch f 10/4 Cityscape—Heartsease (Pursuit of Love) **Mrs R Pease**
46 Ch f 6/4 Assertive—Level Pegging (IRE) (Common Grounds) **Lady Whent**
47 B f 13/2 Medicean—Masque Rose (Oasis Dream) (15000) **Whitcoombe Park Racing**
48 Ch f 19/3 Nathaniel (IRE)—May Fox (Zilzal (USA)) (22000) **Mrs R Pease**
49 MRS WORTHINGTON (IRE), b f 25/2 Dark Angel (IRE)—
             Mirror Effect (Shamardal (USA)) (270000) **Tony Wechsler & Ann Plummer**
50 B c 29/2 Aussie Rules (USA)—Saffron Fox (Safawan) (20350) **M. J. Vandenberghe & Partners**
51 B f 1/2 Kodiac—Sahafh (USA) (Rock Hard Ten (USA)) (20000)
52 B f 14/3 Dutch Art—Station House (IRE) (Galileo (IRE)) **Mascalls Stud**
53 TOYBOX, ch f 5/3 Paco Boy (IRE)—Play Street (Tobougg (IRE)) (2380) **Anthony Boswood & Mrs R Pease**

MR JONATHAN PORTMAN - Continued

Other Owners: Mr R. Bailey, Mr A. N. Cheyne, Mr G. F. Clark, Mr O. Davin, Mr S. Dawes, Mr A. Edwards, Mr Barry Hearn, Mrs Susan Hearn, Mr J. Hobson, Mr J. Homan, Mrs L. J. Losse, Col Sandy Malcolm, Mr S. McDonald, Mr P. Milmo, Mr S. Parkin, Mr R. Popely, Mr R. Pritchard, Mr J. Repard, Mr G. Thomas, Mr M. Tye, Mr P. Tye, Miss S. Von Schilcher, Mr G. Wickens.

Amateur: Mr J. Harding.

455 MR BRENDAN POWELL, Upper Lambourn
Postal: **Frenchmans Lodge Stables, Upper Lambourn, Hungerford, Berkshire, RG17 8QW**
Contacts: **PHONE (01488) 73650 FAX (01488) 73650 MOBILE (07785) 390737**
E-MAIL brendan.powell@btconnect.com WEBSITE www.powell-racing.com

1 CHORAL CLAN (IRE), 7, b g Oratorio (IRE)—Campbellite **Bob Harris & Patricia Mitchell**
2 DYNAMIC GIRL (IRE), 5, b m Holy Roman Emperor (IRE)—Boca Dancer (IRE) **Miss A K Lee & Miss J A Challen**
3 FINULA (IRE), 6, b g Robin des Champs (FR)—Glens Ruby (IRE) **P. H. Betts**
4 GANNICUS, 7, b g Phoenix Reach (IRE)—Rasmani **Winterbeck Manor Stud Ltd**
5 GARTH ROCKETT, 4, b g Delegator—Leelu **P. Banfield**
6 HOLD HANDS, 7, b m Lawman (FR)—Tiponi (IRE) **B. G. Powell**
7 IN THE PIPELINE (IRE), 5, b g Oscar (IRE)—Kerriemuir Lass (IRE) **Mr J. P. McManus**
8 KASPERENKO, 4, b g Archipenko (USA)—Jardin **Mr C. F. Harrington**
9 KIRKLAND FOREVER, 4, ch f Sakhee (USA)—Maystock **Mrs M Fairbairn & Mr P Dean**
10 LE CURIEUX (FR), 6, br g Lauro (GER)—La Curieuse (FR) **Mr J. P. McManus**
11 LETTHERIVERRUNDRY (IRE), 8, br g Diamond Green (FR)—Dissitation (IRE) **Mr J. P. McManus**
12 MERE IRONMONGER, 6, ch g Galileo (IRE)—Kindling **The Arkle Bar Partnership**
13 MR ANDROS, 5, b g Phoenix Reach (IRE)—Chocolada **Winterbeck Manor Stud Ltd**
14 MR BROWNSTONE, 4, b g Sakhee (USA)—Sweet Child O'mine **Mr J. A. Byrne**
15 OAKIDOAKI, 6, b g Sulamani (IRE)—Sweet Robinia (IRE) **P. H. Betts**
16 PHOENIX DAWN, 4, b g Phoenix Reach (IRE)—Comtesse Noire (CAN) **Winterbeck Manor Stud Ltd**
17 SPIRITOFEDINBURGH (IRE), 4, br g Lilbourne Lad—Xema **M Humphreys I Mallard**
18 STOCKHILL STAR, 4, b f Aqlaam—April Stock **Mrs M. Fairbairn & E. Gadsden**
19 SWEETLITTLEMYSTERY, 7, b m Black Sam Bellamy (IRE)—Eau de Vie **Mr J Byrne & Mrs R Byrne**
20 UDOGO, 7, b g Lucky Story (USA)—Welanga **B. G. Powell**

THREE-YEAR-OLDS
21 DE BRUYNE HORSE, b c Showcasing—Right Rave (IRE) **B. G. Powell**
22 FILLY MIGNON, b f Piccolo—One Pixel **I. S. Smith**
23 JAZZY GIRL (IRE), br f Red Jazz (USA)—Intimate Secret (IRE) **Mr K. R. E. Rhatigan**
24 JONNYSIMPSON (IRE), gr f Zebedee—Applauding (IRE) **Sterling Racing**

Other Owners: Mrs R. J. Byrne, Miss J. A. Challen, P. Dean, Mrs M. Fairbairn, G. M. Flood, E. J. S. Gadsden, Mr G. R. Harris, Mr M. A. Humphreys, Mrs A. K. Lee, D. Leon, Mr I. Mallard, Mrs P. A. Mitchell, Mr A. J. Parish, Mr D. J. Pentney.

Jockey (NH): Brendan Powell, Andrew Tinkler. **Apprentice:** Matthew Lawson, Jenny Powell.

456 SIR MARK PRESCOTT BT, Newmarket
Postal: **Heath House, Moulton Road, Newmarket, Suffolk, CB8 0DZ**
Contacts: **PHONE (01638) 662117 FAX (01638) 666572**
E-MAIL sirmark@heathhousestables.com WEBSITE www.heathhousestables.com
Twitter: @HeathHouseNkt

1 ELYSEES PALACE, 4, b g Champs Elysees—Ventura Highway **J. Fishpool - Osborne House**
2 EXIT EUROPE, 6, ch g Bahamian Bounty—Depressed **Mr A. S. Reid**
3 GALILEO'S SPEAR (FR), 5, b h Galileo (IRE)—Lady Shakespeare (USA) **Mr Charles Fipke**
4 MELINOE, 4, b f Sea The Stars (IRE)—Persefona (IRE) **Mr Fergus Anstock**
5 PIEDITA (IRE), 4, b f Authorized (IRE)—Archina (IRE) **Mrs Carmen Frubeck & Denford Stud**
6 ST MICHEL, 5, b g Sea The Stars (IRE)—Miss Provence **John Pearce Racing Ltd**
7 WOLFCATCHERJACK (IRE), 3, b g Lawman (FR)—Alleluia **Ne'er Do Wells V**

THREE-YEAR-OLDS
8 ALTRA VITA, b f Animal Kingdom (USA)—Alma Mater **Miss K. Rausing**
9 BATH AND TENNIS (IRE), b f Footstepsinthesand—Goldamour (IRE) **Mr Timothy J. Rooney**
10 BOFFO (IRE), b g Intello (GER)—Claxon **Bluehills Racing Limited**

SIR MARK PRESCOTT BT - Continued

11 **BOODLEY,** b f Acclamation—Galapagar (USA) **Mrs Olivia Hoare**
12 **CODICIL,** b f Lawman (FR)—Macleya (GER) **Cheveley Park Stud**
13 **CONNOISSEUR,** gr f Mastercraftsman (IRE)—Critical Acclaim **Suffolk Bloodstock**
14 **DISTANT CHIMES (GER),** b g Campanologist (USA)—Dyveke (GER) **Phil Fry - Osborne House**
15 **DONE DEAL (IRE),** b g Azamour (IRE)—Dundel's Spirit (IRE) **Baxter, Gregson, Jenkins & Warman**
16 **DUTCH MONARCH,** b f Dutch Art—Regal Heiress **Cheveley Park Stud**
17 **FERRIER,** b f Iffraaj—Ratukidul (IRE) **Mr Fergus Anstock**
18 **FINAL ROCK,** b g Rock of Gibraltar (IRE)—Up At Last **Mr G. C. Woodall**
19 **FLEETING STEPS (IRE),** b g Footstepsinthesand—Breedj (IRE) **G. Moore - Osborne House**
20 **FROLIC,** b f Dutch Art—Jamboretta (IRE) **Cheveley Park Stud**
21 **GREY SPIRIT (IRE),** gr g Dark Angel (IRE)—Buttonhole **Philip Bamford - Osborne House**
22 **HARMONICA,** b f Pivotal—Affinity **Elite Racing Club**
23 **ISLE OF AVALON (IRE),** b f Camelot—Adeste **Mrs Perle O'Rourke**
24 **JOY STREET (IRE),** b f Street Cry (IRE)—Stupendous Miss (USA) **Sonia Rogers & Anthony Rogers**
25 **KINGOFTHESINGERS,** bc Leroidesanimaux (BRZ)—Songerie **Gregson, Fox-Andrews, Hare & Vetch**
26 **MATCHMAKING (GER),** ch g Mastercraftsman (IRE)—Monami (GER) **W. E. Sturt - Osborne House II**
27 **MIDNIGHT BLUE,** gr f Pivotal—Arabescatta **Denford Stud**
28 **PRAECEPS (IRE),** b g Canford Cliffs (IRE)—Sliding Scale **Mr John Kelsey-Fry**
29 **RUDE AWAKENING,** b g Rip Van Winkle (IRE)—First Exhibit **W. E. Sturt - Osborne House**
30 **SPECIAL MISSION,** b f Declaration of War (USA)—Soft Morning **Miss K. Rausing**
31 **TIMOSHENKO,** ch g Archipenko (USA)—Nezhenka **Middleham Park Racing XXXVI**
32 **TROUBLE AND STRIFE (IRE),** b f Declaration of War (USA)—Rare Tern (IRE) **Lady O'Reilly**
33 **TRUE NORTH (IRE),** b g Henrythenavigator (USA)—Cosmic Fire (FR) **Owners Group 018**
34 **TWISTER (IRE),** ch g Hurricane Run (IRE)—Arizona Sun (IRE) **The Green Door Partnership**
35 **WHITE GUARD,** b c Frankel—Arbella **Qatar Racing Limited**

TWO-YEAR-OLDS

36 **B c 14/3** Authorized (IRE)—Al Jasrah (IRE) (Shirocco (GER)) (40000) **Sheikh Juma Dalmook Al Maktoum**
37 **Gr f 2/3** Sea The Moon (GER)—Alba Stella (Nashwan (USA)) **Miss K. Rausing**
38 **ALL POINTS WEST,** b c 13/4 Speightstown (USA)—
    Albamara (Galileo (IRE)) (37444) **Tim Bunting - Osborne House II**
39 **B f 27/3** Holy Roman Emperor (IRE)—Alleviate (IRE) (Indian Ridge) (36630) **Mt. Brilliant Farm & Ranch, LLC**
40 **ALMA LINDA,** gr f 18/2 Invincible Spirit (IRE)—Alvarita (Selkirk (USA)) **Miss K. Rausing**
41 **ANANDITA,** b f 16/4 Showcasing—
    Joyeaux (Mark of Esteem (IRE)) (42000) **Lady Fairhaven & The Hon Melanie Broughton**
42 **B c 8/5** Sir Percy—Attainable (Kalanisi (IRE)) **Mr W Charnley, Mr C Jenkins, Mr & Mrs C Jones**
43 **AUTONOMY,** b c 21/1 Dansili—Funsie (FR) (Saumarez) (75000) **Tim Bunting - Osborne House**
44 **BE MY HEART (FR),** b c 8/3 Pastorius (GER)—
    Breezy Hawk (GER) (Hawk Wing (USA)) (65120) **Middleham Park Racing (VII)**
45 **BRASSICA (IRE),** b f 9/3 Australia—Lasilia (IRE) (Acclamation) (40700) **Denford Stud**
46 **CHANCER,** b c 14/4 Lope de Vega (IRE)—Misk (FR) (Linamix (FR)) **Denford Stud**
47 **Ch f 14/2** Poet's Voice—Classical Flair (Distant Music (USA)) **Hot to Trot Racing & Paddy Barrett**
48 **B c 9/3** Declaration of War (USA)—
    Garden of Eden (USA) (Curlin (USA)) (30971) **Charles C. Walker - Osborne House III**
49 **HEATWAVE,** b f 20/3 Leroidesanimaux (BRZ)—Here To Eternity (USA) (Stormy Atlantic (USA)) **Miss K. Rausing**
50 **Gr c 4/2** Oasis Dream—Infamous (IRE) (Galileo (IRE)) (50000) **Mt. Brilliant Farm & Ranch, LLC**
51 **LAND OF OZ,** ch c 20/3 Australia—
    Madame Defarge (IRE) (Motivator) (80000) **Mr John Brown & Mrs Megan Dennis**
52 **MILLERS CREEK,** b c 20/3 Aussie Rules (USA)—
    Miss Katmandu (IRE) (Rainbow Quest (USA)) **John Pearce Racing Ltd**
53 **MISS CELESTIAL (IRE),** b f 21/3 Exceed And Excel (AUS)—
    Liber Nauticus (IRE) (Azamour (IRE)) (180000) **John Pearce Racing Ltd**
54 **MON FRERE (IRE),** b c 22/2 Pour Moi (IRE)—Sistine (Dubai Destination (USA)) **Elite Racing Club**
55 **B f 1/2** Dawn Approach (IRE)—Newsroom (IRE) (Manduro (GER)) (28489) **Axom LXXII**
56 **B f 23/3** Galileo (IRE)—Pink Symphony (Montjeu (IRE)) **Mrs Fitri Hay**
57 **RAMATUELLE,** ch f 27/2 Champs Elysees—Florentia (Medicean) **Mr Neil Greig**
58 **ROAD TO PARIS (IRE),** b c 3/4 Champs Elysees—
    Alchemilla (Dubai Destination (USA)) (27000) **Jones, Julian, Lee, Royle & Wicks**
59 **ROYAL GUILD (IRE),** b c 5/2 Mastercraftsman (IRE)—
    Be My Queen (IRE) (Sadler's Wells (USA)) (38000) **Cheveley Park Stud**
60 **SCHEME,** b f 9/2 Pivotal—Between Us (Galileo (IRE)) **Neil Greig - Osborne House**
61 **SHINING SEA (IRE),** b f 3/5 Sea The Stars (IRE)—
    Shamwari Lodge (IRE) (Hawk Wing (USA)) (100000) **Elite Racing Club**
62 **B c 12/2** Canford Cliffs (IRE)—Sliding Scale (Sadler's Wells (USA)) **Mr John Kelsey-Fry**
63 **STARTER,** b c 11/4 Sea The Stars (IRE)—Froglet (Shaamit (IRE)) **Mr B. Haggas**

SIR MARK PRESCOTT BT - Continued

64 **THE GAME IS ON,** b c 11/3 Garswood—Paquerettza (FR) (Dr Fong (USA)) (58000) **Mr Timothy J. Rooney**
65 **TOLERANCE BRIDGE,** ch c 30/4 Helmet (AUS)—Dubai Power (Cadeaux Genereux) (6000) **Mr Malih L. Al Basti**
66 B c 5/3 Pour Moi (IRE)—Walk On Water (Exceed And Excel (AUS)) (47000) **Axom LXXIII**
67 **YVETTE,** b f 26/2 Le Havre (IRE)—Macleya (GER) (Winged Love (IRE)) **Cheveley Park Stud**

Other Owners: Mr P Bamford, Mr E A Baxter, Mrs M Baxter, Mr R Bentley, Mr G Brickwood, Mr C Burnet, Mr E Bush, Mr C Chisholm, Mr E Coughlin, Mr D Ellis, Mr & Mrs B Elton, Mrs E Fox-Andrews, Mr R Greenwood & The Hon Mrs G Greenwood, Mrs C Gregson, Lady Hare, Mr David Howard, Mr M Jeffrey, Mr C Jenkins, Mr M Julian, Mrs Kelsey-Fry, Mr L Larratt, Mr P Lee, Mr D Mann, Mr P J McSwiney, The Hon Pleydell-Bouverie, Dr J Royle, Mr M Rudd, Mrs Y Russell, Mr & Mrs B Taylor, Mr M Tracey, Sir T Troubridge, Mrs A Vetch, Mrs E Wicks, Mrs S Wicks, Mr E J Williams, Mr D Williams.

Assistant Trainer: William Butler (william@Heathhousestables.com), **Pupil Assistant:** Joshua Hamer

Jockey (flat): Luke Morris, Ryan Powell, Rosie Jessop. **Apprentice:** Gavin Ashton.

---

457 MISS KATY PRICE, Llanigon
Postal: **Willow Croft, Llanigon, Hereford, Herefordshire, HR3 5PN**
Contacts: **PHONE (07976) 820819**
E-MAIL katyprice2005@aol.com WEBSITE www.facebook.com/katypriceracing

1 **CLONDAW RIGGER (IRE),** 6, b g Stowaway—Daytona Lily (IRE) **Katy Price Racing Club**
2 **DEFINITE WINNER (IRE),** 7, b m Definite Article—Sindabezi (IRE) **Mr Oscar Singh & Miss Priya Purewal**
3 **FARM THE ROCK (IRE),** 7, b g Yeats (IRE)—Shades of Lavender (IRE) **Mr N. Elliott**
4 **FRIARY GOLD (IRE),** 6, b g Mountain High (IRE)—Platinium Ambition (IRE) **Peers Pleasure**
5 **HOLLOW PARK (IRE),** 6, b m Flemensfirth (USA)—Love And Beauty (IRE) **Mr N. Elliott**
6 **ITSAMANSLIFE (IRE),** 5, b g Mahler—Medieval Banquet (IRE) **McLeish & Elliott**
7 **JENNYS DAY (IRE),** 7, b g Daylami—Jennys Oscar (IRE) **Mr N. Elliott**
8 **JOHNNY YUMA (IRE),** 5, b g Alfred Nobel—Rossbridge Lass (IRE) **Mr A. D. McLeish**
9 **KILMOGANNY (IRE),** 6, b g Stowaway—Gowayourdat (IRE) **Katy Price Racing Club**
10 **LUCCA LADY (IRE),** 7, b m Milan—Trail Storm (IRE) **Making Hay**
11 **MINELLACELEBRATION (IRE),** 8, b g King's Theatre (IRE)—Knocktartan (IRE) **Mr N. Elliott**
12 **OUT FOR JUSTICE (IRE),** 5, b g Beneficial—Dustys Delight (IRE) **Mr A. D. McLeish**
13 **SCHINDLER'S PRINCE (IRE),** 13, ch g Oscar Schindler (IRE)—Coppeen Storm (IRE) **Mr A. D. McLeish**
14 **WOODFIELD ROBIN (IRE),** 7, ch m Robin des Champs (FR)—Ticket To Mars (IRE) **Mr A. D. McLeish**

Other Owners: Miss K. J. Price, Miss P. Purewal, Mr A. Singh.

---

458 MR RICHARD PRICE, Hereford
Postal: **Criftage Farm, Ullingswick, Hereford, Herefordshire, HR1 3JG**
Contacts: **PHONE (01432) 820263 MOBILE (07929) 200598**

1 **BELLEVARDE (IRE),** 4, b f Kodiac—Pearl Mountain (IRE) **B. Veasey**
2 **BLANDFORDS GUNNER,** 9, b g Needle Gun (IRE)—Miss Millbrook **Kevin & Anne Glastonbury**
3 **BONJOUR STEVE,** 7, b g Bahamian Bounty—Anthea **B. Veasey**
4 **CAPTAIN JACK,** 5, b g Mount Nelson—Court Princess **Mr & Mrs D. C. Holder**
5 **CHAMPAGNE BOB,** 6, gr g Big Bad Bob (IRE)—Exclusive Approval (USA) **Mr M. F. Oseman**
6 **DISTANT HIGH,** 7, b m High Chaparral (IRE)—Distant Dreamer (USA) **My Left Foot Racing Syndicate**
7 **EASTERN LADY (IND),** 5, ch m Dancing Forever (USA)—Oriental Lady (IRE) **K. Reece**
8 **KINGS WATCH (IRE),** 7, b g Rainwatch—Leavemealoneawhile (IRE) **Mrs V. J. Morse**
9 **MISS CLYRO,** 8, b m Needle Gun (IRE)—Miss Millbrook **Kevin & Anne Glastonbury**
10 **OCEAN GALE,** 5, b m Shirocco (GER)—Ocean Transit (IRE) **The Super Fruit Partnership**
11 **OLLIE VAAR,** 6, b g Sulamani (IRE)—It's A Discovery (IRE) **Kevin & Anne Glastonbury**
12 **SAMSON'S REACH,** 5, b g Phoenix Reach (IRE)—Court Wing (IRE) **Court Reclamation & Salvage Ltd**
13 **SUZIE STAPLES,** 4, ch f Black Sam Bellamy (IRE)—Dawn Breaker **Mrs V. J. Morse**
14 **WHAT'S UP RORY (IRE),** 7, b g Craigsteel—Clifton Four (USA) **Mrs V. J. Morse**
15 **ZARIA,** 7, b m Tomba—Princess Zara **Mrs K. E. Oseman**

THREE-YEAR-OLDS

16 **OUR MAN IN HAVANA,** b c Havana Gold (IRE)—Auntie Kathryn (IRE) **D. J. Oseman**

Other Owners: Mr G. E. Amey, Mr Douglas Boddy, Mr S. J. Fletcher, Mr Kevin Glastonbury, Mrs Anne Glastonbury, Mr P. J. Hoare, Mrs Cheryl Holder, Mr Derek C. Holder.

Assistant Trainer: Jane Price

459 MR PETER PRITCHARD, Shipston-on-Stour
Postal: Upper Farm Lodge, Upper Farm, Whatcote, Shipston-On-Stour, Warwickshire, CV36 5EF
Contacts: PHONE (01295) 680689

1 ANNIE'SBOYDAVE, 8, b g Passing Glance—Earcomesannie (IRE) Annie Miller,R W Stowe,David Pritchard
2 EARCOMESTHEDREAM (IRE), 15, b g Marignan (USA)—
Play It By Ear (IRE) Mrs Alison Pritchard&Woodland Generators
3 EARCOMESTOM, 6, b g Passing Glance—Earcomesannie (IRE) Mrs A. D. Pritchard
4 4, B g Dubai Destination (USA)—Shanella (IRE)

Other Owners: Mrs A. J. Miller, Mr D. Pritchard, Mr R. W. Stowe, Woodlands (Worcestershire) Ltd.

Assistant Trainer: Mrs. E. Gardner

Jockey (NH): Tom Bellamy. **Conditional:** Archie Bellamy. **Amateur:** Claire Hardwick, Jordan Nailor.

460 MR DENIS QUINN, Newmarket
Postal: Stockbridge Stables, 192 High Street, Newmarket, Suffolk, CB8 9AP
Contacts: MOBILE (07435) 340008

1 ARSENIO LUPIN, 4, b c Delegator—Tenebrae (IRE) Mr A. Dal Pos
2 GREY DIAMOND, 4, gr g Shamardal (USA)—Tiffany Diamond (IRE) Mr O. S. Harris
3 LITTLE CUPCAKE, 7, b m Myboycharlie (IRE)—Imco Cracking (IRE) Mr D. P. Quinn
4 MAD ROSE (IRE), 4, b f Royal Applause—Na Zdorovie Mr D. P. Quinn
5 NORMAN'S STAR, 7, b g Tiger Hill (IRE)—Canis Star Mr D. P. Quinn
6 PIXEL (IRE), 5, b m Rip Van Winkle (IRE)—Hadarama (IRE) Mr J. T. Mangan
7 RELIGHT THE FIRE, 7, ch g Firebreak—Alula Mr D. P. Quinn
8 SHINING ROMEO, 6, b g Royal Applause—Silver Pivotal (IRE) Mr J. T. Mangan
9 STONECOLDSOBA, 5, b g Aqlaam—Aswaaq (IRE) Mr J. T. Mangan
10 TINKER TAILOR (IRE), 5, ch m Intikhab (USA)—Luanas Pearl (IRE) John Mangan, Marco Sanna & Denis Quinn
11 UPPER LAMBOURN (IRE), 10, b g Exceed And Excel (AUS)—In The Fashion (IRE) Mr D. P. Quinn
12 WILLOW SPRING, 6, b m Compton Place—Upstream Scampi On Sea Syndicate

THREE-YEAR-OLDS

13 CALVIN'S GAL (IRE), ch f Casamento (IRE)—Spirit of Hope (IRE) Mr M. E. A. Lutfallah
14 HONEY BLOSSOM, b f Makfi—Seasonal Blossom (IRE) Mr A. Almutairi
15 B c Swiss Spirit—Nordic Theatre (IRE)
16 ROCKIES SPIRIT, br c Swiss Spirit—Red Mischief (IRE) J Mangan & D Quinn
17 SIR HAMILTON (IRE), b c Canford Cliffs (IRE)—Cawett (IRE) Mr B. Syversen

Other Owners: Mr D. Lyons, Mr M. Sanna, Mr W. Woodward.

461 MR JOHN QUINN, Malton
Postal: Bellwood Cottage Stables, Settrington, Malton, North Yorkshire, YO17 8NR
Contacts: PHONE (01944) 768370 MOBILE (07899) 873304
E-MAIL info@johnquinnracing.co.uk WEBSITE www.johnquinnracing.co.uk

1 ACADIAN ANGEL (IRE), 4, b f Dark Angel (IRE)—Bon Ton Roulet The Desperados
2 ASCOT WEEK (USA), 4, br g Lonhro (AUS)—Millenia JJ Quinn Racing Ltd
3 AURORAN LIGHTS (IRE), 4, b g Arctic Cosmos (USA)—Akarita (IRE) A. Stennett
4 BEAUDEN BARRETT, 5, b g Dick Turpin (IRE)—Riccoche (IRE) Mr S. A. T. Quinn
5 BELLANEY KNIGHT (IRE), 8, b g Marienbard (IRE)—Bellaney Jewel (IRE) Mr J. W. Rosbotham
6 BENJAMIN THOMAS (IRE), 4, b g Mayson—Strudel (IRE) Hart Inn I
7 BODACIOUS NAME (IRE), 4, b g Famous Name—Nice Wee Girl (IRE) Excelsior Racing Ltd
8 BREAKING FREE, 4, ch g Kyllachy—Hill Welcome Adams, Allen, Blades, Bruton & Ellis
9 CHEBSEY BEAU, 8, b g Multiplex—Chebsey Belle (IRE) Kent, Greaves, Dawson
10 CLEMENTO (IRE), 4, b g Canford Cliffs (IRE)—Street Style (IRE) Blackburn, Balfe, Houlton
11 COSMIC TIGRESS, 7, b m Tiger Hill (IRE)—Cosmic Case The Cosmic Cases
12 EL ASTRONAUTE (IRE), 5, ch g Approve (IRE)—Drumcliffe Dancer (IRE) Mr Ross Harmon Racing
13 4, B f Shirocco (GER)—Ellway Prospect Mrs M. L. Luck
14 HARGAM (FR), 7, gr g Sinndar (IRE)—Horasana (FR) Mr J. P. McManus
15 INDIAN PURSUIT (IRE), 5, b g Compton Place—Church Melody Mr Malcolm Walker
16 INDY (IRE), 7, b g Indian Haven—Maddie's Pearl (IRE) White Rose Racing

MR JOHN QUINN - Continued

17 **JE SUIS CHARLIE**, 4, b g High Chaparral (IRE)—Fin **The JAM Partnership**
18 **LOOK MY WAY**, 4, b g Pour Moi (IRE)—Casual Glance **Drew & Ailsa Russell**
19 **MASTER OF IRONY (IRE)**, 6, b g Makfi—Mother of Pearl (IRE) **Highfield Racing 6**
20 **MISTIROC**, 7, b g Rocamadour—Mistinguett (IRE) **Drew & Ailsa Russell**
21 **MOONLIGHTNAVIGATOR (USA)**, 6, b g Henrythenavigator (USA)—Victorica (USA) **Mr Malcolm Walker**
22 **NAPLES BAY**, 4, b g Kodiac—Trombe (FR) **Mr D. Ward Racing**
23 **PROJECT BLUEBOOK (FR)**, 5, bl g Sinndar (IRE)—Apperella **Mr J. P. McManus**
24 **RAISED ON GRAZEON**, 7, ch m Lucky Story (USA)—Graze On And On **J. R. Rowbottom**
25 **REPUTATION (IRE)**, 5, b g Royal Applause—Semaphore **Fulbeck Horse Syndicate Ltd**
26 **SAFE VOYAGE (IRE)**, 5, b g Fast Company (IRE)—Shishangaan (IRE) **Mr Ross Harmon**
27 **SHE'S ZOFF (IRE)**, 4, b f Zoffany (IRE)—Vindication People (USA) **R. Kent**
28 **SPEED COMPANY (IRE)**, 5, b g Fast Company (IRE)—Trentini (IRE) **A. Stennett**
29 **SPIRIT OF ZEBEDEE (IRE)**, 5, gr g Zebedee—Sampers (IRE) **Mr Malcolm Walker**
30 **TRED SOFTLY (IRE)**, 5, b g Yeats (IRE)—Elayoon (USA) **Mr Ben Parish**
31 **WOTABREEZE (IRE)**, 5, ch g Excellent Art—Sparkling Crystal (IRE) **The New Century Partnership**
32 **ZANETTO**, 8, b g Medicean—Play Bouzouki **Mr Malcolm Walker**

THREE-YEAR-OLDS

33 B c Epaulette (AUS)—Air Maze **Mr Ross Harmon & Partner**
34 **ALEXIS CARRINGTON (IRE)**, b f Mastercraftsman (IRE)—
Cozzene's Angel (USA) **Chelsea T'Breds - Andy Smith & Friends**
35 **BLUE HAVANA (IRE)**, b f Havana Gold (IRE)—Labyrinthine (IRE) **Fulbeck Horse Syndicate Ltd**
36 **BURNIEBOOZLE (IRE)**, b g Frozen Power (IRE)—Tea Chest (IRE) **Excelsior Racing Ltd**
37 **BUSTAM (IRE)**, b g Worthadd (IRE)—Malayan Mist (IRE) **Al Shaqab Racing**
38 **CAPTAIN JAMESON (IRE)**, b g Camacho—Cross Section (USA) **The JAM Partnership**
39 **DUBAI EMPIRE (FR)**, b c Motivator—Cable Beach (USA) **Mr Ahmad Abdulla Al Shaikh**
40 **GHOST**, gr f Footstepsinthesand—Actionplatinum (IRE) **Ryedale Racing**
41 **LADY WILLPOWER**, b f Multiplex—Gagajulu **Mr P Wilkins & Mickley Stud**
42 **LISHEEN CASTLE (IRE)**, b c Most Improved (IRE)—Mafaaza (USA) **Qatar Racing Limited**
43 **LORD RIDDIFORD (IRE)**, gr br g Zebedee—Beacon of Hope (IRE) **The JAM Partnership**
44 **MILITARY MADAME (IRE)**, b f Epaulette (AUS)—Sweet Kristeen (USA) **The Jam Partnership**
45 **MR WAGYU (IRE)**, ch g Choisir (AUS)—Lake Louise (IRE) **The New Century Partnership**
46 **NORTHERN ANGEL (IRE)**, b f Dark Angel (IRE)—Muzdaan (IRE) **Mr D. Ward**
47 **NORTHERN LAW (IRE)**, b g Lawman (FR)—Polly Perkins (IRE) **D Ward & R Harmon**
48 **SHAHEEN (IRE)**, b g Society Rock (IRE)—La Chicana (IRE) **Al Shaqab Racing**
49 **SWISS MARLIN**, b f Swiss Spirit—Piranha (IRE) **Mr R. Kent**
50 **TWEETING (IRE)**, b f Sleeping Indian—Lady Sledmere (IRE) **Ryedale Racing**

TWO-YEAR-OLDS

51 **ALKHAWANEEJ EMPIRE (FR)**, b c 22/1 Le Havre (IRE)—
Zalia (FR) (Oasis Dream) (22385) **Ahmad Abdulla Al Shaikh & Co**
52 **CAREY STREET (IRE)**, b g 29/4 Bungle Inthejungle—
Undulant Way (Hurricane Run (IRE)) (10581) **Mr P. G. Shorrock**
53 Ch c 14/3 No Nay Never (USA)—Challow Hills (USA) (Woodman (USA)) (47619) **Mr Ross Harmon**
54 B c 19/4 Camacho—Cockaleekie (USA) (Alphabet Soup (USA)) (21164)
55 **COUNTESS WELLS (IRE)**, b f 19/3 So You Think (NZ)—
Alzaroof (USA) (Kingmambo (USA)) (9523) **Excelsior Racing Ltd**
56 B f 6/2 Dark Angel (IRE)—Encore View (Oasis Dream) (32560)
57 B f 11/2 Nathaniel (IRE)—Glen Rosie (IRE) (Mujtahid (USA)) (45000) **Mr D. Ward**
58 Ch c 27/2 Archipenko (IRE)—Graze On And On (Elmaamul (USA)) **Mr J. Rowbottom**
59 B f 12/4 New Approach (IRE)—Hallowed Park (IRE) (Barathea (IRE)) (27000) **Mr D. Ward**
60 B f 17/1 Camacho—Journalist (IRE) (Night Shift (USA)) (20000)
61 B c 1/4 Planteur (IRE)—Miss Mysterious (FR) (Dubai Destination (USA)) (8140) **Traines House Enterprise**
62 **MOONLIGHT ESCAPADE**, ch c 15/4 Cityscape—Marmalade Moon (Shamardal (USA)) **Lord D. G. Crawshaw**
63 **PANDORA STAR**, b f 8/4 Epaulette (AUS)—Gracefilly (Invincible Spirit (IRE)) (2380) **Ryedale Racing**
64 B c 30/3 Zoffany (IRE)—Queen's Pudding (IRE) (Royal Applause) (16280)
65 B g 4/4 Born To Sea (IRE)—Start The Music (IRE) (King's Best (USA)) (16280) **Mr D. Ward**
66 B f 9/4 Gale Force Ten—Swift Winged (Motivator) (8140)
67 **TEASE MAID**, b f 17/1 Heeraat (IRE)—Flirtinaskirt (Avonbridge) (28571) **Mr P. Wilkins**
68 **THE GREAT STORY**, b c 9/3 Sea The Moon (GER)—Lovina (ITY) (Love The Groom (USA)) (22000) **A. Al Shaikh**

Other Owners: Mr Ahmad Abdulla Al Shaikh, Mr Abdulla Ahmad Al Shaikh, Mr R. J. Blades, Mr J. Bruton, Mr Andrew Derry, Mr J. I. Derry, Mr Ross Harmon, JJ Quinn Racing Ltd, Mr R. Kent, Mrs S. Quinn, Mr S. A. T. Quinn, Mr Martin Rapley, Mrs Ailsa Russell, Mr Drew Russell, Mr Andy J. Smith, Mr D. Ward, Mr Philip Wilkins.

MR JOHN QUINN - Continued

Assistant Trainer: Sean Quinn

Jockey (flat): Jason Hart.

462
MR MICK QUINN, Newmarket
Postal: **Southgate Barn, Hamilton Road, Newmarket, Suffolk, CB8 0WY**
Contacts: **PHONE (01638) 660017 FAX (01638) 660017 MOBILE (07973) 260054**
E-MAIL mickquinn2562@gmail.com

1 COLONEL FRANK, 4, b g Dutch Art—Loquacity **Mr K. F. C. Bruce**
2 GREAT HALL, 8, b g Halling (USA)—L'affaire Monique **Mr M. Quinn**
3 POPSILCA, 4, b f Captain Gerrard (IRE)—Silca Destination **Mr John Quorn & Mr R. Kent**
4 TAWAAFOQ, 4, b g Showcasing—Gilt Linked **Mr K. F. C. Bruce**

THREE-YEAR-OLDS

5 NO MORE COMMISERY (IRE), b f Dandy Man (IRE)—Lady Bracknell (IRE) **Mr K. F. C. Bruce**
6 PRINCESS HARLEY (IRE), gr f Dark Angel (IRE)—Tonle Sap (IRE) **Mr K. F. C. Bruce**
7 PRINCESS KEIRA (IRE), b f Acclamation—La Reine de Pearls (IRE) **Mr K. F. C. Bruce**
8 PURPLE DRAGON, b f Captain Gerrard (IRE)—Dragon Flyer (IRE) **Mr Kenny Bruce & Mr M Quinn**

TWO-YEAR-OLDS

9 GEORGE THOMAS, b c 26/3 Heeraat (IRE)—Lexington Rose (Captain Gerrard (IRE)) (23606) **Mr K. F. C. Bruce**
10 MRS DISCOMBE, b f 2/3 Garswood—Dora's Sister (IRE) (Dark Angel (IRE)) (48000) **Mr K. F. C. Bruce**

Other Owners: Mr Kenny Bruce, Mr R. Kent, Mr M. Quinn, Mr John Quorn, Mr A. Viner.

Assistant Trainer: Miss Karen Davies

463
MR ALASTAIR RALPH, Bridgnorth
Postal: **Bynd Farm, Bynd Lane, Billingsley, Bridgnorth, Shropshire, WV16 6PQ**
Contacts: **PHONE (07912) 184217**
E-MAIL alistair_ralph1@hotmail.com

1 BILLINGSLEY (IRE), 6, b g Millenary—Retain That Magic (IRE) **Mrs K. L. Maxwell**
2 BROUGHTONS ADMIRAL, 4, b g Born To Sea (IRE)—Chanter **ValueRacingClub.co.uk**
3 COMBER MILL (FR), 6, ch g Le Fou (IRE)—Kalistina (FR) **Mr F. B. Hawkins**
4 CUT THE CORNER (IRE), 10, b g Vinnie Roe (IRE)—Snipe Victory (IRE) **B. Hawkins**
5 GUSTAVE MAHLER (IRE), 8, ch g Mahler—Kloetta (IRE) **Mr R. C. Jones**
6 IT'S OSCAR (IRE), 11, b g Oscar (IRE)—Lady Bramble (IRE) **Miss S. Troughton**
7 NATIVE GAMUT (IRE), 8, b g Gamut (IRE)—Gonearethedays (IRE) **Mr S. D. Barling**
8 QUINE DES CHAMPS, 6, b m Midnight Legend—Quine de Sivola (FR) **Kerry & Richard Pool**
9 SCORE CARD (IRE), 8, b g Scorpion (IRE)—Auditing Empress (IRE) **Mrs D. J. Ralph**
10 SEYMOUR STAR, 10, b g Alflora (IRE)—Seymour Chance **Mrs C J Black & Mrs Sue Briscoe**
11 TEMPURAN, 9, b g Unbridled's Song (USA)—Tenderly (IRE) **Bind Racing Club**

Other Owners: Mrs C. J. Black, Mrs S. Briscoe, Mr J. R. Couldwell, Mr P.D. Couldwell, Mr R. D. Pool, Mrs K. E. Pool, Mr R. D. Ralph.

Assistant Trainer: Ali Galliers-Pratt

464
MR TIM REED, Hexham
Postal: **Moss Kennels, Haydon Bridge, Hexham, Northumberland, NE47 6NL**
Contacts: **PHONE (01434) 344016 MOBILE (07703) 270408**
E-MAIL timreed8@aol.com

1 AULDTHUNDER (IRE), 11, b g Oscar (IRE)—Jill's Girl (IRE) **Mr W. T. Reed**
2 BUMBLES BABE, 5, b m Paco Boy (IRE)—Brooklyn's Sky **Mr W. T. Reed**
3 CARLINGFORD PRINCE (IRE), 9, ch g Definite Article—Castle Hope (IRE) **Mr W. T. Reed**
4 CHOIX DE L'AMOUR (IRE), 6, br g Fruits of Love (USA)—Carlas Choice (IRE) **Mr W. T. Reed**
5 ELLA'S DENE, 7, ch m Millkom—Oh So Perky (IRE) **Mrs C. J. Todd**
6 FIVE BAR BRIAN (IRE), 4, br g Elusive Pimpernel (USA)—Vayenga (FR) **Mr B. Ryan-Beswick**

MR TIM REED - Continued

   7 **INDIAN TEMPLE (IRE)**, 9, b g Indian River (FR)—Ballycraggan (IRE) **Mr J. K. Huddleston**
   8 **STORM WARNING (IRE)**, 6, b g September Storm (GER)—Ceo Draiochta (IRE) **Mr W. Ryan-Beswick**

Assistant Trainer: Mrs E. J. Reed (07889) 111885

Conditional: Harry Reed.

---

465 **MR WILLIAM REED, Umberleigh**
Postal: **Stowford Farm, East Stowford, Chittlehampton, Umberleigh, Devon, EX37 9RU**
Contacts: **PHONE (01769) 540292 MOBILE (07967) 130991**

   1 **ALL DOWNHILL (IRE)**, 8, b g Indian Danehill (IRE)—Socialite Girl **W. J. Reed**
   2 **BELLE BANJO (FR)**, 7, gr m Smadoun (FR)—Calingyou (FR) **W. J. Reed**

---

466 **MR DAVID REES, Haverfordwest**
Postal: **The Grove Yard, Clarbeston Road, Haverfordwest, Pembrokeshire, SA63 4SP**
Contacts: **PHONE (01437) 731308 FAX (01437) 731551 MOBILE (07775) 662463**
E-MAIL davidreesfencing@lineone.net

   1 **BACKOFTHEROCK**, 9, b g Scorpion (IRE)—Oscars Vision (IRE) **Mr D Rees & Mr P Evans**
   2 **BUCK BRAVO (IRE)**, 6, b g Mahler—Damoiselle **D. A. Rees**
   3 **CAWDOR HOUSE BERT**, 11, b g Kayf Tara—Lady Shanan (IRE) **A. J. & Dai Rees**
   4 **DREAM BOLT (IRE)**, 10, ch g Urban Ocean (FR)—Riviera Dream (IRE) **Mr D A Rees & Mr N Adams**
   5 **GARDINERS HILL (IRE)**, 8, br g Stowaway—Mysterious Lass (IRE) **Mr D A Rees & Mr N Adams**
   6 **GONE PLATINUM (IRE)**, 9, b g Mountain High (IRE)—Miss Platinum (IRE) **D. A. Rees**
   7 **MAY'S MILAN (IRE)**, 7, b g Milan—Opera Mask (IRE) **Mr R. J. C. Lewis**
   8 **MISTY MAI (IRE)**, 8, b m Westerner—Arcanum (IRE) **Eddie & Dai**
   9 **PERSISTANTPRINCESS (IRE)**, 6, b m Scorpion (IRE)—Classy Conflict (IRE) **D. A. Rees**
10 **QALINAS (FR)**, 11, gr g Malinas (GER)—Tabletiere (FR) **D. A. Rees**
11 **STEEL NATIVE (IRE)**, 7, b g Craigsteel—Princess Gloria (IRE) **Mr R. J. C. Lewis**

Other Owners: Mr N. W. Adams, P. Evans, Mr E. W. Morris, Mr A. J. Rees.

---

467 **MRS HELEN REES, Dorchester**
Postal: **Distant Hills, Chalmington, Dorchester, Dorset, DT2 0HB**
Contacts: **PHONE (01300) 320683 MOBILE (07715) 558289**
E-MAIL helen-rees@live.co.uk

   1 **KAHDIAN (IRE)**, 8, br g Rock of Gibraltar (IRE)—Katiykha (IRE) **Mrs H. E. Rees**
   2 **RESIDENCE AND SPA (IRE)**, 10, b g Dubai Destination (USA)—Toffee Nosed **Mrs H. E. Rees**

Assistant Trainer: Mr Rupert Rees

---

468 **MR SEAN REGAN, Middleham**
Postal: **Low Beck, Coverham, Middleham, Leyburn, North Yorkshire, DL8 4TJ**
Contacts: **MOBILE (07866) 437476**
E-MAIL sean@seanreganracing.com WEBSITE www.seanreganracing.com

   1 **ROCK A DOODLE DOO (IRE)**, 11, b g Oratorio (IRE)—Nousaiyra (IRE) **Mrs C. D. Taylor**
   2 **SHE'S A PRIMADIVA**, 6, b m Primitive Academy—Petrovka (IRE) **S. Regan**
   3 **SOUTHVIEW LADY**, 6, b m Misu Bond (IRE)—Salalah **S. Regan**
   4 **TOM'S ANNA (IRE)**, 8, b m Antonius Pius (USA)—Vanilla Delight (IRE) **Mrs C. D. Taylor**

470 **MRS LYDIA RICHARDS, Chichester**
Postal: **Lynch Farm, Hares Lane, Funtington, Chichester, West Sussex, PO18 9LW**
Contacts: **YARD (01243) 574379 HOME (01243) 574882 MOBILE (07803) 199061**
E-MAIL lydia.richards@sky.com

1 FAHEEM, 7, b g Halling (USA)—White Star (IRE) **Mrs E. F. J. Seal**
2 GOLD DECREE (IRE), 6, b g Golan (IRE)—De Verdict (IRE) **Mrs Lydia Richards**
3 GOOD NEWS, 6, b g Midnight Legend—Venetian Lass **The Good News Partnership**
4 HONG KONG JOE, 8, b g Oasis Dream—Singed **The Demoiselle Bond Partnership**
5 MAIGH DARA (IRE), 9, br g Cacique (IRE)—Dara Diva (IRE) **The Inner Steel Partnership**
6 MURHIB (IRE), 6, b g Sea The Stars (IRE)—Mood Swings (IRE) **Mrs Lydia Richards**
7 SOUTHERN STATES, 5, b g Medaglia d'oro (USA)—Little Belle (USA) **The Beep Partnership**
8 SUNSET SKYE, 5, b m Sea Freedom—Money Central **Yeomanry Racing**
9 VENETIAN LAD, 13, ro g Midnight Legend—Henrietta Holmes (IRE) **The Venetian Lad Partnership**
10 4, Ch g Midnight Legend—Venetian Lass **Mrs Lydia Richards**

THREE-YEAR-OLDS

11 B g Foxwedge (AUS)—Demoiselle Bond **Mr H. B. Kinmond**

Other Owners: Mr I. W. Moss, Mr G. H. R. Musker, Mr N. J. Watts.

471 **MR NICKY RICHARDS, Greystoke**
Postal: **Rectory Farm, Greystoke, Penrith, Cumbria, CA11 0UJ**
Contacts: **OFFICE (01768) 483392 HOME (01768) 483160 FAX (01768) 483933**
MOBILE (07771) 906609
E-MAIL office@nickyrichardsracing.com WEBSITE www.nickyrichardsracing.com

1 AMBEROSE, 5, ch m Sulamani (IRE)—Miss Nellie (IRE) **Langdale Bloodstock**
2 ANOTHER BILL (IRE), 8, ch g Beneficial—Glacier Lilly (IRE) **David & Nicky Robinson**
3 BALLYBOKER BREEZE (IRE), 10, b g Gold Well—Ballyboker Lady (IRE) **Mr & Mrs Paul & Clare Rooney**
4 BAYWING (IRE), 9, br g Winged Love (IRE)—Cerise de Totes (FR) **David & Nicky Robinson**
5 BERNARDELLI (IRE), 10, b g Golan (IRE)—Beautiful Blue (IRE) **Henriques & Lloyd-Bakers**
6 BETTER GETALONG (IRE), 7, b g Gold Well—Arequipa (IRE) **D. Wesley-Yates**
7 BIG BAD BEAR (IRE), 4, b g Jeremy (USA)—Our Polly (IRE) **Tor Side Racing**
8 BLAKERIGG (IRE), 7, b g Presenting—Azalea (IRE) **David & Nicky Robinson**
9 BOOYAKASHA (IRE), 6, b g Presenting—Land of Honour **Celtic Shamrock Racing**
10 CAIUS MARCIUS (IRE), 7, b g King's Theatre (IRE)—Ain't Misbehavin (IRE) **Mr Peter Norbury**
11 CHAPEL STILE (IRE), 6, b g Scorpion (IRE)—Peggy Cullen (IRE) **Langdale Bloodstock**
12 CHIDSWELL (IRE), 9, b g Gold Well—Manacured (IRE) **David & Nicky Robinson**
13 COCKLEY BECK (IRE), 6, b m Westerner—Bobnval (IRE) **Mrs C Walsh & Bill Peacock**
14 CONQUER GOLD (IRE), 8, b m Gold Well—Ballinamona Wish (IRE) **Mr & Mrs Paul & Clare Rooney**
15 COURT DREAMING, 5, b g Court Cave (IRE)—Louis's Teffia (IRE) **Dark Horse Racing**
16 CULTRAM ABBEY, 11, br g Fair Mix (IRE)—Kansas City (FR) **Tarzan Bloodstock**
17 DERRIANA SPIRIT (IRE), 5, b m Flemensfirth (USA)—Distillery Lane (IRE) **The Spirit Partnership**
18 DUKE OF NAVAN (IRE), 10, b br g Presenting—Greenfieldflyer (IRE) **David & Nicky Robinson**
19 ECHO EXPRESS (IRE), 6, b g Echo of Light—If Dubai (USA) **Henriques, Lloyd-Baker, Westoll, Wrigley**
20 ELIOS D'OR (FR), 4, b g Puit d'or (IRE)—Naker Mome (FR) **Langdale Bloodstock**
21 GLINGER FLAME (IRE), 6, ro g Daylami (IRE)—Titian Flame (IRE) **Mr James Westoll**
22 GUITAR PETE (IRE), 8, gr g Dark Angel (IRE)—Innishmore (IRE) **Mrs Pat Sloan**
23 HELLO FELLAS (IRE), 6, b g Gold Well—Archdale Ambush (IRE) **Mr & Mrs Paul & Clare Rooney**
24 HOLME ABBEY, 5, b g Fair Mix (IRE)—Brockwell Abbey **The Roper Family**
25 IDEE DE GARDE (FR), 6, b g Kapgarde (FR)—Idee Recue (FR) **Langdale Bloodstock**
26 ILLWALKTHELINE (IRE), 6, b m Presenting—Jigs'n Reels (IRE) **Mr G Tunstall & Mrs C Walsh**
27 IMADA (IRE), 8, br g Arcadio (GER)—Anck Su Namun (IRE) **Kenny & Laura Haughey**
28 ISAACSTOWN LAD (IRE), 11, b g Milan—Friends of Friends (IRE) **M S Borders Racing Club & Partners**
29 KARAMOKO (IRE), 6, b g Manduro (GER)—Virevolte (FR) **Tarzan Bloodstock**
30 LOOKING WELL (IRE), 9, b g Gold Well—Different Level (IRE) **D. Wesley-Yates**
31 5, B g Westerner—Miss Greinton (GER) **D. Wesley-Yates**
32 MY OLD GOLD (IRE), 8, b m Gold Well—Tenbo (IRE) **Tor Side Racing**
33 NANDO (GER), 6, b g Dai Jin—Natalis (GER) **Langdale Bloodstock**
34 ON A PROMISE (IRE), 6, gr g Definite Article—Silvers Promise (FR) **Richard & Katherine Gilbert**
35 ONE FOR HARRY (IRE), 10, b g Generous (IRE)—Strawberry Fool (FR) **The Fife Boys**
36 PETERS COUSIN (IRE), 5, b m Presenting—Sunwake (GER) **Mr K. Alexander**
37 PETITE GANACHE (IRE), 6, ch g Presenting—Ain't Misbehavin (IRE) **Golden Dragon Racing**

MR NICKY RICHARDS - Continued

38 **PROGRESS DRIVE (IRE)**, 7, b g Stowaway—Dolphins View (IRE) **Mr A. Cochrane**
39 **REIVERS LAD**, 7, b g Aflora (IRE)—Reivers Moon **Mr John Stenhouse**
40 **RUBYTWO**, 6, b m Sulamani (IRE)—Miss Nellie (IRE) **Langdale Bloodstock**
41 **SIMPLY NED (IRE)**, 11, ch g Fruits of Love (USA)—Bishops Lass (IRE) **David & Nicky Robinson**
42 **STRAIT OF MAGELLAN (IRE)**, 6, ch g Captain Rio—Golden (FR) **Mrs Pat Sloan**
43 **TAKINGRISKS (IRE)**, 9, b g Golden Tornado (IRE)—Downtown Rosie (IRE) **Mr F. Bird**
44 **TEDDY TEE (IRE)**, 9, b g Mountain High (IRE)—Knocksouna Lady (IRE) **David & Nicky Robinson**
45 **THAT'S LIFE (IRE)**, 6, b g Presenting—Leader's Hall (IRE) **Eddie Melville & Kenny Haughey**
46 **TOP BILLING**, 9, br g Monsun (GER)—La Gandilie (FR) **Doreen McGawn & Stewart Tate**
47 **UN NOBLE (FR)**, 8, gr g Near Honor (GER)—Noble Gary (FR) **Mrs C. A. Torkington**
48 **UNCLE ALASTAIR**, 6, b g Midnight Legend—Cyd Charisse **Mr & Mrs Paul & Clare Rooney**
49 **WESTERN RULES (IRE)**, 8, b g Westerner—Ryehill Lady (IRE) **Bob Bennett & Jimmy Dudgeon**
50 **WICKED SPICE**, 9, b g Old Vic—Afdala (IRE) **Mrs E. E. R. Sloan**
51 **WOT A SHOT (IRE)**, 9, b g Refuse To Bend (IRE)—Ashdali (IRE) **M S Borders Racing Club & Partners**

Other Owners: Mr A. Cartledge, Mrs R. L. Elliot, Mr Guy Henriques, Mr M. Henriques, Miss Rhonda Hill, Mr P. Laverty, Mrs E. M. Lloyd, Mr H. M. A. Lloyd-Baker, Mrs Charles Lloyd-Baker, Mrs N. G. Robinson, Mr D. Robinson, Mr Ken Roper, Mrs Elinor M. Roper, Mrs Nicholas Wrigley.

Assistant Trainers: Miss Joey Richards, Mr Harry Haynes

Jockey (NH): Craig Nichol, Adam Nicol, Conor O'Farrell, Davy Russell. **Conditional:** Ryan Day. **Amateur:** Mr M. Jenkins, Mr D. McMenamin.

---

472 **MR JOHN DAVID RICHES, Pilling**
Postal: **Moss Side Farm, Off Lancaster Road, Scronkey, Pilling, Lancashire, PR3 6SR**
Contacts: **PHONE (01253) 799190**
E-MAIL jrracing@btinternet.com

1 **ABOUT GLORY**, 4, b g Nayef (USA)—Lemon Rock **J R Racing**
2 **PICKS PINTA**, 7, b g Piccolo—Past 'n' Present **J R Racing**
3 **SPOKEN WORDS**, 9, b m Fruits of Love (USA)—Jerre Jo Glanville (USA) **J R Racing**
4 **TRULOVE**, 5, b m Piccolo—Snow Dancer (IRE) **J R Racing**

THREE-YEAR-OLDS

5 **ANGEL EYES**, b f Piccolo—Miacarla **J R Racing**

Other Owners: J. D. Riches, Mrs L. Wohlers.

---

473 **MR MARK RIMELL, Witney**
Postal: **Fairspear Equestrian Centre, Fairspear Road, Leafield, Witney, Oxfordshire, OX29 9NT**
Contacts: **PHONE (01993) 878551 MOBILE (07778) 648303/(07973) 627054**
E-MAIL rimell@rimellracing.com WEBSITE www.rimellracing.com

1 **BINGO GEORGE (IRE)**, 5, b g Holy Roman Emperor (IRE)—Kalleidoscope **Mr J. R. Henley**
2 **MAGIC MIRROR**, 5, b m Dutch Art—Balatoma (IRE) **Mr W. J. Wood**
3 4, Ch f Sakhee (USA)—Royal Roxy (IRE)
4 4, B f Sulamani (IRE)—Vin Rose

Assistant Trainer: Anne Rimell

---

474 **MR DAVE ROBERTS, Kenley**
Postal: **Leasowes Farm, Kenley, Shrewsbury, Shropshire, SY5 6NY**
Contacts: **PHONE (01746) 785255**

1 **CHESHAM ROSE (IRE)**, 5, gr m Mastercraftsman (IRE)—Rose's Destination (IRE) **Mr D. Bradbury**
2 **G'DAY AUSSIE**, 5, b g Aussie Rules (USA)—Moi Aussi (USA) **Mr D. Bradbury**

MR DAVE ROBERTS - Continued

3 **MILAN OF CRYSTAL (IRE)**, 9, b m Milan—Native Crystal (IRE) **D. B. Roberts**
4 **RACING SPIRIT**, 6, ch g Sir Percy—Suertuda **D. B. Roberts**
5 **SCOGLIO**, 10, b g Monsieur Bond (IRE)—Ex Mill Lady **D. B. Roberts**
6 **SLEEPY SUNDAY**, 8, b m Revoque (IRE)—Cool Spring (IRE) **D. B. Roberts**
7 **STORYTALE**, 6, ch g Rip Van Winkle (IRE)—Night Haven **D. B. Roberts**
8 **TILIVER (FR)**, 6, b g Muhaymin (USA)—Springtale (FR) **Mr D. Bradbury**
9 **VIF ARGENT (FR)**, 9, b g Dom Alco (FR)—Formosa (FR) **D. B. Roberts**

---

475 MR MIKE ROBERTS, Hailsham
Postal: **Summertree Farm, Bodle Street Green, Hailsham, East Sussex, BN27 4QT**
Contacts: **PHONE (01435) 830231 MOBILE (07774) 208040**
E-MAIL mike@summertree-racing.com

1 **DREAM BAIE (FR)**, 5, b g Crillon (FR)—Montaraza (FR) **M. J. Roberts**
2 **ELEGANT (IRE)**, 7, b m Oscar (IRE)—Good Thought (IRE) **M. J. Roberts**
3 **LIGHTNINGBOLT**, 5, b g Black Sam Bellamy (IRE)—Migigi **M. J. Roberts**
4 **PERFECT MOMENT (IRE)**, 5, b m Milan—Faucon **M. J. Roberts**
5 **SNIPPETYDOODAH**, 10, b m King's Theatre (IRE)—Kimpour (FR) **M. J. Roberts**
6 **THEYDON PARK**, 5, b g Royal Applause—Velvet Waters **M. J. Roberts**
7 **UP THE NAVAN ROAD (IRE)**, 6, b g Stowaway—Tisiphone (IRE) **M. J. Roberts**
8 **VIA VOLUPTA**, 8, b m Kayf Tara—Via Ferrata (FR) **M. J. Roberts**

Assistant Trainer: Marie Martin

---

476 MISS SARAH ROBINSON, Bridgwater
Postal: **Newnham Farm, Shurton, Stogursey, Bridgwater, Somerset, TA5 1QG**
Contacts: **PHONE (01278) 732357 FAX (01278) 732357 MOBILE (07866) 435197 / (07518) 785291**
E-MAIL info@sarahrobinsonracing.co.uk WEBSITE www.sarahrobinsonracing.co.uk

1 **DAWN'S LITTLE LADY**, 6, b m Dr Massini (IRE)—Kopylova **Mr L. Davies**
2 **MARTHA'S DREAM**, 4, ch f Captain Gerrard (IRE)—Rose Bounty **Mr B. Robinson**
3 **OFF THE SCALE (IRE)**, 6, b g Strategic Prince—Vanilla Delight (IRE) **Mr R. J. Bailey**
4 **SPANISH OPTIMIST (IRE)**, 12, b g Indian Danehill (IRE)—La Traviata **Mr N. S. Shaw**

Assistant Trainers: Mr B. Robinson, Mr R. J. Bailey

Jockey (NH): Ian Popham, James Best. **Conditional:** Kieron Edgar. **Amateur:** Miss S. Robinson.

---

477 MISS PAULINE ROBSON, Capheaton
Postal: **Kidlaw Farm, Capheaton, Newcastle Upon Tyne, NE19 2AW**
Contacts: **PHONE (01830) 530241 MOBILE (07721) 887489 or (07814) 708725 (David)**
E-MAIL pauline@prracing.co.uk

1 **CASTLETOWN (FR)**, 6, gr g Poliglote—Message Personnel (FR) **Mr & Mrs Raymond Anderson Green**
2 **KATGARY (FR)**, 8, b g Ballingarry (IRE)—Kotkira (FR) **D&D Armstrong Limited**
3 **MARTILA (FR)**, 6, b m Martaline—Paola Pierji (FR) **Mr & Mrs Raymond Anderson Green**
4 **MARTILOO (FR)**, 8, b m Martaline—Paola Pierji (FR) **Mr & Mrs Raymond Anderson Green**
5 **MIDNITE GRACE**, 8, gr m Midnight Legend—Ardentinny **It's a Bargain Syndicate**
6 **PETAPENKO**, 7, b g Archipenko (USA)—Tricoteuse **Hale Racing Limited**
7 **SILVER BULLION**, 7, br g Three Valleys (USA)—Silver Yen (USA) **J. Wade**
8 **SPECIAL PREP (IRE)**, 6, b g Brian Boru—Schindler's Dame (IRE) **Mr E. A. Elliott**
9 **UPSILON BLEU (FR)**, 10, b g Panoramic—Glycine Bleue (FR) **Mr & Mrs Raymond Anderson Green**

Other Owners: Mrs J. E. Dodd, Mrs E. M. Fairbairn, Mrs A. Green, R. A. Green.

Assistant Trainer: David Parker

Jockey (NH): Brian Hughes, Craig Nichol.

478 MR W. M. ROPER, Curragh
Postal: **French Furze, Maddenstown, The Curragh, Co. Kildare, Ireland**
Contacts: **PHONE (00353) 45 441821 MOBILE (00353) 86 823 4279**
E-MAIL markroper1@eircom.net

1 **CLARIOR EX OBSCURO (IRE)**, 12, br g Morozov (USA)—Achates (IRE) **Mr W. M. Roper**
2 **IDYLLIC ACRYLIC**, 4, b f Art Connoisseur (IRE)—Mother's Hope (IRE) **M. H. Keogh**
3 **PLAY THE PART (IRE)**, 7, b g Kutub (IRE)—Pretty Contender (IRE) **P. E. I. Newell**
4 **ROONEY O'MARA**, 4, ch f Dragon Pulse (IRE)—Date Mate (USA) **M. H. Keogh**
5 **SAMMYJADE (IRE)**, 4, b f Zoffany (IRE)—Dama'a (IRE) **Barry & Alfie Partnership**
6 **THE MAGPIE MAN (IRE)**, 7, b g Echo of Light—Inspectors Choice (IRE) **Mr W. M. Roper**
7 **VAALWATER (IRE)**, 13, b g Danehill Dancer (IRE)—Amaranthus (USA) **Mr W. M. Roper**

THREE-YEAR-OLDS

8 B g Elusive Pimpernel (USA)—Larsen Bee (IRE) **Mr W. M. Roper**

TWO-YEAR-OLDS

9 B f 16/4 Red Jazz (USA)—Amatara (IRE) (Indian Haven) (976) **M. H. Keogh**

Assistant Trainer: Barry Heffernan

Amateur: Mr Archie Macauley.

479 MR RUSSELL ROSS, Consett
Postal: **Rock Cottage Farm, 79 Iveston Lane, Consett, Co. Durham, DH8 7TB**

1 **PENNINGTON**, 4, b g Poet's Voice—Pryka (ARG) **R. A. Ross**
2 **STETCHWORTH (IRE)**, 7, ch g New Approach (IRE)—Hallowed Park (IRE) **R. A. Ross**

480 MR BRIAN ROTHWELL, Malton
Postal: **Old Post Office, Oswaldkirk, York, North Yorkshire, YO62 5XT**
Contacts: **PHONE (01439) 788859 MOBILE (07969) 968241**
E-MAIL brian.rothwell1@googlemail.com

1 **ROSE MARMARA**, 5, ch m Exceed And Excel (AUS)—Show Rainbow **Mrs G. Sparks**
2 **SIRIUS STAR**, 9, b g Beat All (USA)—Miss Sirius **The Sirius Racing Partnership**
3 **THORNTON FRANK**, 4, b g Misu Bond (IRE)—Byton **S. P. Hudson**
4 **THORNTON MARY**, 4, b f Mawatheeq (USA)—Bezant (IRE) **Mr S. P. Hudson & Mr Brian Rothwell**
5 **TIGER TWENTY TWO**, 7, b g Authorized (IRE)—Collette's Choice **Mr A. J. Sparks**

TWO-YEAR-OLDS

6 B f 11/4 Kuroshio (AUS)—Artistic Dawn (IRE) (Excellent Art) **Brian Rothwell**
7 B f 6/2 Kuroshio (AUS)—Byton (Byron) **Mr S. P. Hudson**
8 B f 12/3 Heeraat (IRE)—Lady Azamour (IRE) (Azamour (IRE)) **Brian Rothwell**
9 B g 10/3 Burwaaz—Lady Norlela (Reset (AUS)) **Brian Rothwell**
10 **YASMIN FROM YORK**, b f 30/4 Sixties Icon—Bonnie Burnett (IRE) (Hawk Wing (USA)) **Mrs G. Sparks**

Other Owners: Mr Andrew Sparks.

481 MR J.-C. ROUGET, Pau
Postal: **Chemin de la Foret Bastard, Domaine de L'Aragnon, 64000 Pau, France**
Contacts: **PHONE (0033) 5593 32790 FAX (0033) 5593 32930 MOBILE (0033) 6102 70335**
E-MAIL ste.rouget@orange.fr

1 **ACADEMIC (IRE)**, 5, ch g Zamindar (USA)—Heliocentric (FR) **Seb. Lauray**
2 **AL MOTASIM (USA)**, 4, ch c Elusive Quality (USA)—Melody Dawn (USA) **Al Shaqab Racing**
3 **BROADWAY BOOGIE (IRE)**, 6, b g Distorted Humor (USA)—Grande Melody (IRE) **B. Belinguier**
4 **ECHAUFFOUR (FR)**, 5, b g Le Havre (IRE)—Langrune (IRE) **G. Augustin-Normand**
5 **FEELIN ALRIGHT (IRE)**, 4, b c Clodovil (IRE)—Littlepromisedland (IRE) **L. Dassault/D.-Y. Treves**

MR J.-C. ROUGET - Continued

6 **LA COCHERE (FR)**, 4, b f Le Havre (IRE)—Lady Meydan (FR) **G. Augustin-Normand**
7 **MAELIA (USA)**, 4, b f Redoute's Choice (AUS)—Mantilla (USA) **Ecurie des Charmes**
8 **MARKAZI**, 4, gr c Dark Angel (IRE)—Marasima (IRE) **H. H. Aga Khan**
9 **RONCEY (FR)**, 4, b c Pivotal—Mixed Intention (IRE) **G. Augustin-Normand**
10 **SPEED ROAD (FR)**, 7, ch g King's Best (USA)—Life On The Road (IRE) **J. C. Rouget**
11 **TAAREEF (USA)**, 5, ch g Kitten's Joy (USA)—Sacred Feather (USA) **Hamdan Al Maktoum**
12 **ZAFIRO (FR)**, 6, b g Sageburg (IRE)—La Romagne (FR) **Ecurie A. Caro**

THREE-YEAR-OLDS

13 **AJAYEB (IRE)**, b f Frankel—Harmonious (USA) **Al Shaqab Racing**
14 **AL MASHRAB**, b c Style Vendome (FR)—Candicans **Al Shaqab Racing**
15 **ALMAHA (FR)**, b f Galileo (IRE)—Zagora (FR) **Al Shaqab Racing**
16 **AROK (IRE)**, b c Exceleration (IRE)—Miss Bex (IRE) **F. Pinault**
17 **AUBEVOYE (FR)**, b c Le Havre (IRE)—Keira (FR) **G. Augustin-Normand/B. Benaych**
18 **AUNACIS (FR)**, ch c George Vancouver (USA)—Nazlia (FR) **Ecurie des Charmes/Ecurie J. L. Tepper**
19 **AUTRETOT (FR)**, b c Youmzain (IRE)—Great Queen (FR) **G. Augustin-Normand**
20 **AVEIRO (IRE)**, ch c Declaration of War (USA)—Ideal **F. McNulty**
21 **BALLET DE LA REINE (USA)**, b f War Front (USA)—All For Glory (USA) **Orpendale/Chelston**
22 **BLUE BLUE EYES (FR)**, b c Sageburg (IRE)—Blue Hollow (IRE) **A. Delaey**
23 **BOOMBOOM KISS (FR)**, ch c Kentucky Dynamite (USA)—Medical Kiss (FR) **Ecurie I.M. Fares**
24 **BOURDAINVILLE (FR)**, b f Le Havre (IRE)—Racemate **G. Augustin-Normand/Ecurie J. L. Tepper**
25 **BRIYENZA (FR)**, b f Iffraaj—Bryanka (FR) **H. H. Aga Khan**
26 **CAMEO (FR)**, b f Camelot—Reine des Plages (IRE) **Coolmore**
27 **CAPODIMONTE**, gr f Dalakhani (IRE)—Misk (FR) **Denford Stud**
28 **CHAILLOUE (FR)**, b c Le Havre (IRE)—Equity Card (FR) **G. Augustin-Normand/A. Jathiere**
29 **CHANPOUR (FR)**, b c Le Havre (IRE)—Cherana (FR) **H. H. Aga Khan**
30 **CINNAMON GIRL (FR)**, b f Canford Cliffs (IRE)—Diena (FR) **D-Y. Treves**
31 **CRISTOT (FR)**, b c Siyouni (FR)—Count The Cost (USA) **G. Augustin-Normand/Ecurie A. Caro**
32 **DANEYAN (FR)**, gr c Shamardal (USA)—Dayita (FR) **H. H. Aga Khan**
33 **DANZIG SPRING (FR)**, b f Motivator—Smyrnes (FR) **Sunderland Holding Inc.**
34 **ELDENA (FR)**, b f Elusive City (USA)—Elva (IRE) **H. H. Aga Khan**
35 **ELHABUB (IRE)**, b c Acclamation—Countess Ferrama **Hamdan Al Maktoum**
36 **ELUSIVE TRUST (FR)**, b c Elusive City (USA)—Wedge Trust (IRE) **Ecurie I. M. Fares**
37 **EMBROIDERED SILK (IRE)**, b f Galileo (IRE)—Secrete Marina (IRE) **Coolmore**
38 **EMIN (IRE)**, b c Camelot—Chocolat Chaud (IRE) **D.-Y. Treves**
39 **EPOUVILLE (FR)**, b f Footstepsinthesand—Vidiyna (FR) **G. Augustin-Normand**
40 **ESTEVE (IRE)**, gr c Mastercraftsman (IRE)—Russiana (IRE) **D.-Y. Treves**
41 **EVERGLOW (FR)**, b f Dawn Approach (IRE)—Frangy **B. Benaych/J.C. Rouget**
42 **FERALIA (FR)**, b f Pedro The Great (USA)—Centralienne (USA) **B. Belinguier**
43 **FIFTH ELEMENT (FR)**, b f Most Improved (IRE)—Miryale (FR) **F. Pinault/P. Segalot**
44 **FLEETING FANCY (IRE)**, b f Galileo (IRE)—Just Pretending (USA) **Coolmore**
45 **GIOVANNI DAL PONTE**, gr c Holy Roman Emperor (FR)—Cherisearch (USA) **C. Marzocco**
46 **GOUVILLE (FR)**, b br f Rajsaman (FR)—Sandsnow (IRE) **G. Augustin-Normand**
47 **GRATEFULLY (IRE)**, b f Dubawi (IRE)—Gracefully (IRE) **Ecurie des Monceaux**
48 **HEROINE (FR)**, b f Camelot—Elusive Galaxy (IRE) **F. Pinault/P. Segalot**
49 **INFINITE CHEERS (FR)**, b f Acclamation—Wadjet (IRE) **Sunderland Holding Inc.**
50 **INITIAL SPIRIT (IRE)**, b f Invincible Spirit (IRE)—Tanguista (FR) **Sunderland Holding Inc.**
51 **KAZORINA (FR)**, b f Footstepsinthesand—Kozaka (FR) **H. H. Aga Khan**
52 **KERENA**, b f Exceed And Excel (AUS)—Kerasha (FR) **H. H. Aga Khan**
53 **KING OF LEOGRANCE (FR)**, b c Camelot—Amourette (FR) **Coolmore**
54 **KIRIKETA (IRE)**, b f Cape Cross (IRE)—Whipped (IRE) **Ecurie J. L. Tepper/D.-Y. Treves/ F. McNulty**
55 **LA HOUBLONNIERE (FR)**, b f Le Havre (IRE)—Mixed Intention (IRE) **G. Augustin-Normand**
56 **LA PEREGRINA (FR)**, b f Exceleration (IRE)—Private Eye (FR) **P. Segalot**
57 **LABARTOLI (IRE)**, b c Intello (GER)—Blanche Dubawi (IRE) **Ecurie des Charmes/Ecurie J. L. Tepper**
58 **LADY OF THE LAKE (FR)**, b f Camelot—Roxelana (FR) **Ecurie des Charmes/Ecurie J. L. Tepper**
59 **LATITA (FR)**, b f Silver Frost (IRE)—Amazing Story (FR) **P. Van Belle/J. Bruneau de la Salle**
60 **LE RAFALE (FR)**, ch c Le Havre (IRE)—Elzebieta (FR) **L. Dassault**
61 **LIGNOU (FR)**, b c Rajsaman (FR)—Lady Meydan (FR) **G. Augustin-Normand**
62 **MANATIYA (FR)**, b f Redoute's Choice (AUS)—Makana (FR) **H. H. Aga Khan**
63 **MARIE DE MEDICIS**, b f Cape Cross (IRE)—Caterina de Medici (FR) **C. Marzocco**
64 **MAWROOTH**, b c Dubawi (IRE)—Ghaidaa (IRE) **Hamdan Al Maktoum**
65 **MIRANDA (IRE)**, b f Camelot—Great Artist (IRE) **Ecurie A. Caro/G. Augustin-Normand**
66 **MISSION IMPASSIBLE (IRE)**, ch f Galileo (IRE)—
Margot Did (IRE) **M. Lagasse/Riviera Equine/Haras d'Etreham**
67 **MISTER JO (IRE)**, br c High Chaparral (IRE)—Zanzibar Girl (USA) **Ecurie des Charmes**

MR J.-C. ROUGET - Continued

68 **MISTER PRESIDENT (FR),** b c Mastercraftsman (IRE)—Via Milano (FR) **F. Pinault**
69 **MON ETOILE (FR),** b f Thewayyouare (USA)—Uruguay (IRE) **L. Dassault**
70 **MONNAI (FR),** b c Le Havre (IRE)—Minted (USA) **G. Augustin-Normand**
71 **MONNEYPENNY'S (FR),** b f Penny's Picnic (IRE)—Princess Liu (IRE) **Mandore/J. C. Rouget**
72 **MORIENNE (FR),** b f Rajsaman (FR)—Isanous (FR) **G. Augustin-Normand**
73 **MOSKOVA (FR),** b f Invincible Spirit (IRE)—Lunashkaya **A. Jathiere**
74 **NIGHT SHERIFF,** b f Lawman (FR)—Moonlight Rhapsody (IRE) **Ecurie I. M. Fares**
75 **NOBOKHOV,** b c Iffraaj—Nantes (GER) **A. Jathiere**
76 **NOUAINVILLE (FR),** gr f Rajsaman (FR)—Jetfire **G. Augustin-Normand**
77 **NUWAIES,** b f Iffraaj—Fairly Fair (FR) **Al Shaqab Racing**
78 **OCTEVILLE (IRE),** b f Le Havre (IRE)—My Memoir (IRE) **Ecurie J.-L. Tepper/G. Augustin-Normand**
79 **OLESKA (IRE),** b f Excelebration (IRE)—Varsity **A. Jathiere**
80 **OLMEDO (FR),** b c Declaration of War (USA)—Super Pie (USA) **Ecurie A. Caro/G. Augustin-Normand**
81 **OUT OF TOWN (FR),** ch f Kentucky Dynamite (USA)—Beynotown **Ecurie I. M. Fares**
82 **PERFECT CITY (IRE),** b c Elusive City (USA)—Tall Perfection (USA) **Ecurie I. M. Fares**
83 **PHARRELL (FR),** ch c Manduro (GER)—Censure (FR) **Ecurie J.L. Tepper**
84 **PRETREVILLE (FR),** b c Acclamation—Pegase Hurry (USA) **G. Augustin-Normand**
85 **PRIMULA (FR),** b f Authorized (IRE)—Exit The Straight (FR) **J. Detre**
86 **PURE ELEGANCE (IRE),** b f Galileo (IRE)—Society Selection (USA) **Coolmore**
87 **SADARAK (FR),** b c Myboycharlie (IRE)—Sadiyna (FR) **H. H. Aga Khan**
88 **SALYAZI (USA),** gr ro c Elusive Quality (USA)—Saliyna (FR) **H. H. Aga Khan**
89 **SEAELLA (IRE),** b f Canford Cliffs (IRE)—Gems **D.-Y. Treves**
90 **SERAKALA (FR),** b f Rock of Gibraltar (IRE)—Serasana **H. H. Aga Khan**
91 **SHAMSABAD (FR),** ch c Rock of Gibraltar (IRE)—Shamsa (FR) **H. H. Aga Khan**
92 **SOUNDS GOOD (FR),** b c Falco (USA)—Darkova (FR) **Ecurie J. L. Bouchard**
93 **SPIRITINTHENIGHT,** b c So You Think (USA)—Shanghai Noon (FR) **D.-Y. Treves**
94 **SUNNY DREAM,** b f Oasis Dream—February Sun **R. Shatyudinov**
95 **THAWRY,** b c Iffraaj—Salacia (IRE) **Hamdan Al Maktoum**
96 **TOUJOURS READY,** b f More Than Ready (USA)—Split Trois (FR) **Ecurie I. M. Fares**
97 **TRANQUIL STORM (IRE),** b f Oasis Dream—Sparkle Plenty (IRE) **Qatar Racing**
98 **VIRIDORIX,** b gr c Dawn Approach (IRE)—Chill (FR) **Ecurie La Vallee Martigny/T. Olivier**
99 **WAREGA (FR),** b f Penny's Picnic (IRE)—Miss Carmie (FR) **D.-Y. Treves**
100 **WILD IMPALA (FR),** b f Monsieur Bond (IRE)—Dilag (FR) **Sheikh J. D. Al Maktoum**
101 **ZAVRINKA (FR),** b f Rajsaman (FR)—Salvation **A. Jathiere/G. Augustin-Normand**

TWO-YEAR-OLDS

102 B f 6/5 Dabirsim (FR)—Aamaal (GER) (Mamool (IRE)) (15466) **Ecurie Normandy Pur Sang**
103 **AIR DANCE (FR),** b c 1/4 So You Think (NZ)—Spring Morning (FR) (Ashkalani (IRE)) (138380) **J. L. Bouchard**
104 **ALBORAYA (FR),** ch f 18/5 Style Vendome (FR)—Tropical Mark (Mark of Esteem (IRE)) (40700) **Ecurie A. Caro**
105 B c 24/5 Siyouni (FR)—Almilea (GER) (Galileo (IRE)) (89540) **Haras de Saint Pair**
106 **ALZIRE (FR),** b f 11/2 Shamardal (USA)—Purely Priceless (IRE) (Galileo (IRE)) (325600) **Haras Voltaire**
107 **ANDUJAR (FR),** b c 11/2 Footstepsinthesand—Cannes To Capri (IRE) (Galileo (IRE)) (28490) **Ecurie A. Caro**
108 **ANN VAN KLEEF,** b c 25/2 Siyouni (FR)—How High The Sky (IRE) (Danehill Dancer (IRE)) (100000) **J. Romel**
109 **ARROW (FR),** b c 30/3 Toronado (IRE)—Jeu de Vivre (IRE) (Montjeu (IRE)) (73260) **Ecurie P. Segalot/F. Pinault**
110 **ART PREMIER (IRE),** b c 19/2 Dutch Art—Slippers Best (Mount Nelson) (20350) **D.-Y.Treves**
111 **AZORA (FR),** b f 9/3 Invincible Spirit (IRE)—Straight Lass (Machiavellian (USA)) (260480) **Haras Voltaire**
112 Gr c 24/4 Dark Angel (IRE)—Back In The Frame (Dutch Art) (150000) **Hamdan Al Maktoum**
113 B f 2/2 Australia—Barenia (FR) (Zamindar (USA)) **Al Shaqab Racing**
114 **BEAUTIFUL VISION (FR),** b c 6/2 Rajsaman (FR)—
Java Jazz (Singspiel (IRE)) (73260) **G. Augustin-Normand/Ecurie A. Caro**
115 B f 11/2 Galileo (IRE)—Beauty Bright (IRE) (Danehill (USA)) **Coolmore**
116 **BIGMOUTH (FR),** b f 20/4 Rajsaman (FR)—Little Jaw (Footstepsinthesand) (19536) **Ecurie I. M. Fares**
117 B f 21/3 Camelot—Brasileira (Dubai Destination (USA)) (61050) **G. Augustin-Normand**
118 Ch c 13/2 Showcasing—Cafetiere (Iffraaj) (170000) **Hamdan Al Maktoum**
119 **CAMPAGNOLLES (FR),** b f 14/1 Le Havre (IRE)—Vaunoise (FR) (Teofilo (IRE)) **G. Augustin-Normand**
120 **CAPE SOUNION (FR),** b f 8/2 Le Havre (IRE)—
Heliocentric (FR) (Galileo (IRE)) (101750) **Martin S. Schwartz Racing**
121 **CARTIEM (FR),** b f 30/1 Cape Cross (IRE)—Mintaka (FR) (Zamindar (USA)) (113960) **Ecurie J. L. Tepper**
122 B f 29/3 Sea The Stars (IRE)—Changing Skies (IRE) (Sadler's Wells (USA)) **Al Shaqab Racing**
123 **CHAPTAL (FR),** b c 3/4 Le Havre (IRE)—Amacali (FR) (Danehill Dancer (IRE)) (32560) **D.-Y. Treves**
124 B f 1/1 Camelot—Clarify (Zamindar (USA)) (89540) **F. Pinault**
125 B f 22/4 Iffraaj—Clarinda (FR) (Montjeu (IRE)) **H. H. Aga Khan**
126 **CLITOURPS (FR),** b f 15/3 Le Havre (IRE)—Coutances (Shamardal (USA)) **G. Augustin-Normand**
127 **COMMES (FR),** b f 15/1 Le Havre (IRE)—Leaupartie (IRE) (Stormy River (FR)) **G. Augustin-Normand**

MR J.-C. ROUGET - Continued

128 COQUAINVILLIERS (FR), b f 13/2 Le Havre (IRE)—
Mixed Intention (IRE) (Elusive City (USA)) **G. Augustin-Normand**
129 COURTESY (FR), b f 28/4 Siyouni (FR)—Totem (USA) (Mizzen Mast (USA)) (105820) **J. Romel**
130 DAN, b c 12/5 Slade Power (IRE)—Moonlit Garden (IRE) (Exceed And Excel (AUS)) (52000) **D.-Y. Treves**
131 DOLYNSKA (FR), b f 4/5 Dabirsim (FR)—Veronique (GER) (Big Shuffle (USA)) (32560) **A. Jathiere**
132 DREAM IN NORMANDY (IRE), b c 14/3 Oasis Dream—Ana Luna (Dream Well (FR)) **Ecurie La Vallee Martigny**
133 EBONY (FR), b f 1/3 Le Havre (IRE)—Ennaya (FR) (Nayef (USA)) (130240) **Faisal Salman**
134 ELLON (FR), b f 3/3 Le Havre (IRE)—Hallotiere (IRE) (Hurricane Run (IRE)) **G. Augustin-Normand**
135 B f 9/3 Siyouni (FR)—Elva (IRE) (King's Best (USA)) **H. H. Aga Khan**
136 B f 29/4 Makfi—Epatha (FR) (Highest Honor (FR)) (22792) **J. Romel**
137 ESSON (FR), b f 16/1 Le Havre (IRE)—Malegganda (FR) (Divine Light (JPN)) **G. Augustin-Normand**
138 ETOILE (FR), b f 22/1 Siyouni (FR)—Milena's Dream (IRE) (Authorized (IRE)) (130240) **Ecurie P. Segalot**
139 FALSTAFF (FR), b c 2/3 Never On Sunday (FR)—Cry of Love (FR) (Sakhee (USA)) (32560) **D.-Y. Treves**
140 FLANDERS COLORS (USA), ch f 26/2 Declaration of War (USA)—
Kate's Winnie (USA) (Distorted Humor (USA)) (89540) **J. Romel**
141 B f 1/1 Lope de Vega (IRE)—Foreign Legionary (IRE) (Galileo (IRE)) (309320) **Hamdan Al Maktoum**
142 FOXY POWER (FR), b f 16/3 Power—Foxxy Cleopatra (FR) (Slickly (FR)) (8140) **B. Benaych**
143 B c 8/6 Dabirsim (FR)—Glowing Cloud (Dylan Thomas (IRE)) **Ecurie Normandy Pur Sang**
144 B f 7/3 Style Vendome (FR)—Gointobegone (USA) (Smart Strike (CAN)) **Al Shaqab Racing**
145 HABLOVILLE (FR), b f 12/1 Rajsaman (FR)—Lady Ana (FR) (Anabaa (USA)) **G. Augustin-Normand**
146 HODENG (IRE), br c 20/4 Cape Cross (IRE)—Seasons (Dubai Destination (USA)) (75000) **G. Augustin-Normand**
147 HOUSELADY (FR), b f 9/5 Anodin (FR)—Lady Elgar (FR) (Sadler's Wells (USA)) **Ecurie I. M. Fares**
148 INCITATUS (FR), b c 17/2 Anodin (FR)—Narva (Grand Slam (USA)) (122100) **Ecurie P. Segalot**
149 JUSTFIRSTLADY (IRE), b f 12/4 Siyouni (FR)—
Just Little (FR) (Grand Slam (USA)) (122100) **Ecurie J. L. Tepper**
150 B c 22/3 Charm Spirit (IRE)—Kartica (Rainbow Quest (USA)) (407000) **Hamdan Al Maktoum**
151 B f 9/2 Dansili—Kerasona (FR) (Oasis Dream) **S. A. Aga Khan**
152 B c 4/2 Makfi—Khadima (FR) (Zamindar (USA)) **S. A. Aga Khan**
153 KHOZMA (FR), b f 11/5 Canford Cliffs (IRE)—Faustina (FR) (Antonius Pius (USA)) (30932) **A. Jathiere**
154 KING COBRA (FR), b c 24/2 Rajsaman (FR)—Kinlochrannoch (Kyllachy) (32560) **G. Augustin-Normand**
155 B f 25/1 Siyouni (FR)—Kozideh (FR) (Gold Away (IRE)) **S. A. Aga Khan**
156 LA BLOUTIERE (FR), b f 18/1 Dansili—La Hoguette (FR) (Le Havre (IRE)) **G. Augustin-Normand**
157 LA GODEFROY (FR), br b f 1/1 Le Havre (IRE)—Langrune (FR) (Fasliyev (USA)) **G. Augustin-Normand**
158 LA REGLE DU JEU (FR), b f 29/1 Pedro The Great (USA)—
Darwin's Rhea (FR) (Della Francesca (USA)) (28490) **D.-Y. Treves**
159 LADY IN POWER (FR), ch f 1/4 Evasive—Respected (IRE) (Invincible Spirit (IRE)) **J. Romel**
160 LE GRIFFONIER (FR), b c 2/2 Peer Gynt (JPN)—Centralienne (USA) (Dixie Union (USA)) (36630) **D.-Y. Treves**
161 LEGA (FR), b f 12/5 Harbour Watch (IRE)—Mansoura (IRE) (Kalanisi (IRE)) (62678) **D.-Y. Treves**
162 B f 9/5 Exceed And Excel (AUS)—Lidiyana (FR) (Motivator) **H. H. Aga Khan**
163 B f 1/4 Iffraaj—Ludiana (FR) (Dalakhani (IRE)) **H. H. Aga Khan**
164 MAJOR DUNDEE (FR), gr c 17/5 Literato—Isalou (FR) (Unfuwain (USA)) (28490) **Ecurie J. L. Tepper**
165 B c 1/4 Rock of Gibraltar (IRE)—Makana (FR) (Dalakhani (IRE)) **S. A. Aga Khan**
166 MARY DISTRICT (FR), b f 23/3 Evasive—Waseelh (IRE) (Kheleyf (USA)) **J. Romel**
167 MARYLIN (FR), b f 12/2 Motivator—Anabaa (USA) (40700) **Ecurie J. L. Tepper**
168 Ch c 25/4 Intello (GER)—Masaafat (Act One) **Hamdan Al Maktoum**
169 B f 28/1 Frankel—Mashoora (IRE) (Barathea (IRE)) **Hamdan Al Maktoum**
170 MEROPE (FR), b f 20/2 Myboycharlie (IRE)—Belle Esprit (Warning) (81400) **Haras Voltaire**
171 MIGHTY WEST (FR), b c 26/4 Kendargent (FR)—West of Saturn (USA) (Gone West (USA)) (24420) **S. Boucheron**
172 MILLESIME (IRE), ch f 29/1 Dawn Approach (IRE)—Ermine And Velvet (Nayef (USA)) (22000) **Ecurie P. Segalot**
173 MISTER CHARM (FR), b c 27/1 Wootton Bassett—Nova Luz (Divine Light (JPN)) (105820) **Ecurie des Charmes**
174 MME DE MONTESPAN, b f 19/2 Oasis Dream—Greek Goddess (IRE) (Galileo (IRE)) (40000) **J. Romel**
175 MON MYSTERE (IRE), b c 3/5 Power—Shistera (FR) (Lando (GER)) (29304) **L. Dassault**
176 MON OURAGAN (IRE), b c 1/1 Toronado (IRE)—
Lady of The House (IRE) (Holy Roman Emperor (IRE)) (30932) **L. Dassault**
177 MONTVIETTE (FR), b f 30/3 Le Havre (IRE)—Lady Meydan (FR) (American Post) **G. Augustin-Normand**
178 MOONLIGHTPAINTER (FR), b c 26/2 Invincible Spirit (IRE)—
Pilagea (IRE) (New Approach (IRE)) (146520) **Ecurie J. L. Tepper**
179 B c 15/4 Olympic Glory (IRE)—No Truth (IRE) (Galileo (IRE)) **Al Shaqab Racing**
180 NOORMANDY (FR), ch c 14/3 Le Havre (IRE)—Wedge Trust (FR) (Zamindar (USA)) (32560) **Ecurie I. M. Fares**
181 NORMANDY DELA VEGA (FR), b c 19/3 Lope de Vega (IRE)—
Hadrian's Waltz (IRE) (Holy Roman Emperor (IRE)) **Ecurie La Vallee Martigny**
182 B c 11/3 Frankel—Nuit d'amour (FR) (Azamour (IRE)) **Al Shaqab Racing**
183 OLYMPE (FR), b f 23/1 Charm Spirit (IRE)—
Naissance Royale (IRE) (Giant's Causeway (USA)) (105820) **Haras Voltaire**

MR J.-C. ROUGET - Continued

184 **OLYMPIC GAMES (FR)**, b f 20/3 Olympic Glory (IRE)—
Super Anna (FR) (Anabaa (USA)) (62678) **Martin S. Schwartz Racing**
185 **PASSION FOR LIFE (FR)**, b f 5/3 Le Havre (IRE)—Passion Blanche (Dutch Art) (48840) **G. Augustin-Normand**
186 **PEDRASEA (FR)**, b f 27/5 Pedro The Great (USA)—Candle of The Sea (IRE) (Makfi) (17094) **J.P. Vallee Lambert**
187 B f 22/1 Frankel—Peinture Abstraite (Holy Roman Emperor (IRE)) (341880) **En Attente de Propriete**
188 **PERSONA (FR)**, ch f 4/2 Kendargent (FR)—Pioneer Girl (IRE) (Anabaa (USA)) **White Birch Farm**
189 B c 4/4 Dubawi (IRE)—Puggy (IRE) (Mark of Esteem (IRE)) **Al Shaqab Racing**
190 **QUIET DIGNITY (USA)**, ch f 7/5 Kitten's Joy (USA)—
Figarie (USA) (Bernardini (USA)) (131629) **Martin S. Schwartz Racing**
191 **RIFF RAFF (FR)**, b f 24/1 Iffraaj—Delhi (High Chaparral (IRE)) (211640) **Martin S. Schwartz Racing**
192 B f 1/3 Champs Elysees—Sachet (USA) (Royal Academy (USA)) (52910) **Ecurie I. M. Fares**
193 B f 24/5 Poet's Voice—Sagalina (IRE) (Linamix (FR)) **S. A. Aga Khan**
194 **SALINA (FR)**, b f 14/3 Pedro The Great (USA)—Valibi Bere (FR) (Russian Blue (IRE)) (25234) **D.-Y. Treves**
195 **SATURDAYNIGHTFEVER (FR)**, b f 5/3 Wootton Bassett—Saturnine (IRE) (Galileo (IRE)) **Ecurie I. M. Fares**
196 **SCHOENREID (FR)**, b c 17/2 Style Vendome (FR)—
Madame Beatrice (FR) (Hold That Tiger (USA)) (17908) **D.-Y. Treves**
197 B f 1/1 Archipenko (USA)—Serasana (Red Ransom (USA)) **S. A. Aga Khan**
198 B f 28/1 Le Havre (IRE)—Shalaiyma (FR) (New Approach (IRE)) **S. A. Aga Khan**
199 B c 26/4 Casamento (IRE)—Shamsa (FR) (Selkirk (USA)) **S. A. Aga Khan**
200 B c 24/3 Include (USA)—Shediyama (FR) (Red Ransom (USA)) **S. A. Aga Khan**
201 **SHOWMETHEMOON**, b f 29/2 Le Havre (IRE)—
Pacific Queen (FR) (Sunday Break (JPN)) (146520) **Ecurie J. L. Tepper**
202 **SILVER SEAM (FR)**, b c 23/4 Dark Angel (IRE)—
Sub Rose (IRE) (Galileo (IRE)) (244200) **Haras de Saint Pair/White Birch Farm**
203 **SIYOULATER (FR)**, b f 1/2 Siyouni (FR)—Bonanza Creek (IRE) (Anabaa (USA)) **White Birch Farm**
204 **SOTTSASS (FR)**, ch c 24/3 Siyouni (FR)—Starlet's Sister (IRE) (Galileo (IRE)) (276760) **White Birch Farm**
205 **SPIRIT OF LIBERTY (IRE)**, b c 29/3 Lawman (FR)—Diva (GER) (Oasis Dream) (22000) **A. Delaey**
206 B f 3/4 Magician (IRE)—Starlight Tiara (USA) (More Than Ready (USA)) **Haras d'Etreham**
207 Gr c 15/3 Motivator—Symba's Dream (USA) (Vindication (USA)) (40700) **P. Maher**
208 B c 23/1 Dark Angel (IRE)—Tahaany (IRE) (Raven's Pass (USA)) **Hamdan Al Maktoum**
209 **TAOS (FR)**, b c 25/2 Toronado (IRE)—
Just With You (FR) (Sunday Break (JPN)) (126170) **Martin S. Schwartz Racing**
210 **THE REVENANT (FR)**, b c 11/5 Authorized (IRE)—Blazing Mary (FR) (Gone West (USA)) **J. Romel**
211 **THIAGO (FR)**, bl g 2/2 Kendargent (FR)—Lunaba (FR) (Anabaa (USA)) (48840) **Ecurie J. L. Tepper**
212 **TONNENCOURT (FR)**, b c 4/3 Pedro The Great (USA)—
Double Mix (FR) (Sagamix (FR)) (73260) **G. Augustin-Normand**
213 **TURF WAR (USA)**, b f 15/2 War Front (USA)—
Starstruck (IRE) (Galileo (IRE)) (329074) **Martin S. Schwartz Racing**
214 B f 24/3 Pour Moi (IRE)—Varega (FR) (Danehill Dancer (IRE)) (8140) **J. Seche**
215 **VAYENI (FR)**, b c 7/3 Dalakhani (IRE)—Vaderana (FR) (Monsun (GER)) **H. H. Aga Khan**
216 B f 20/1 Sea The Stars (IRE)—Visoriyna (FR) (Dansili) **H. H. Aga Khan**
217 **VIVA ZAPATA (FR)**, b c 10/3 Lope de Vega (IRE)—
Parade Militaire (IRE) (Peintre Celebre (USA)) **White Birch Farm**
218 **WAKISASHI ONE (FR)**, b c 2/4 Rajsaman (FR)—Northern Ocean (FR) (Green Tune (USA)) **J. Romel**
219 **ZAFFERANA (FR)**, b f 14/4 Pedro The Great (USA)—Realdad (ARG) (Victory Speech (USA)) (32560) **D.-Y. Treves**

Assistant Trainers: Jean Bernard Roth, Jean Rene Dubosc

Jockey (flat): Jean-Bernard Eyquem, Hugo Journiac, Christophe Soumillon. **Apprentice:** Jules Mobian.

---

482 **MR RICHARD ROWE, Pulborough**
Postal: **Ashleigh House Stables, Sullington Lane, Storrington, Pulborough, West Sussex, RH20 4AE**
Contacts: **PHONE (01903) 742871 MOBILE (07831) 345636**
E-MAIL r.rowe.racing@virgin.net WEBSITE www.richardrowe-racing.co.uk

1 **BATTLE ANTHEM (IRE)**, 7, b g Royal Anthem (USA)—Chika Boom (IRE) **The Battle Anthem Partnership**
2 **CELMA DES BOIS (FR)**, 6, b g Ballingarry (IRE)—Palafixe (FR) **Encore Partnership V**
3 **FULL OF MISCHIEF (IRE)**, 10, ch m Classic Cliche (IRE)—Drama Chick **The Chicanery Partnership**
4 **GOTHIC EMPIRE (IRE)**, 6, b g Dark Angel (IRE)—Box of Frogs (IRE) **Mr R. Crumley**
5 **LAKETOUR LEADER (IRE)**, 6, b g Publisher (USA)—Gay da Cheen (IRE) **Mr R. Crumley**
6 **LIKE SULLY (IRE)**, 10, b or g Presenting—Swing Into Action (IRE) **Winterfields Farm Ltd**
7 **OVER THE ARCH (IRE)**, 6, br g Presenting—On The Outside (IRE)
8 **QUINLANDIO (IRE)**, 8, b g Thousand Words—La Shalak (IRE) **Mr T. M. Clarke**
9 **REMEMBER FOREVER (IRE)**, 8, b g Indian River (FR)—Running Wild (IRE) **The Forever Partnership**

MR RICHARD ROWE - Continued

10 **REMEMBER ME WELL (IRE)**, 5, b m Doyen (IRE)—Creidim (IRE) **R. Rowe**
11 **SIR HUBERT**, 8, b g Multiplex—Lacounsel (FR) **Capt Adrian Pratt & Friends**
12 **SWEET'N'CHIC (IRE)**, 8, b m Midnight Legend—Sweetbitter (FR) **Richard Rowe Racing Partnership**
13 **TZAR DE L'ELFE (FR)**, 8, b g Satri (IRE)—Rue Tournefort (FR) **Lord Clinton & Captain Adrian Pratt**
14 **ZIGGER ZAGGER (IRE)**, 9, b g Mountain High (IRE)—Main Suspect (IRE) **Scott Parnell Limited**

Other Owners: Mr C. J. Baldwin, Mr D. M. Bradshaw, Mrs H. C. G. Butcher, Mr N. S. Campbell, Mrs J. Case, Lord Clinton, Mr C. S. Coombe-Tennant, Mrs J. E. Debenham, Mr C. B. Hatch, Capt A. Pratt, T. W. Wellard, Mr P. D. West, Mr P. R. Wilby.

---

483 **MISS MANDY ROWLAND, Lower Blidworth**
Postal: **Kirkfields, Calverton Road, Lower Blidworth, Nottingham, Nottinghamshire, NG21 0NW**
Contacts: **PHONE (01623) 794831 MOBILE (07768) 224666**
E-MAIL kirkfieldsriding@hotmail.co.uk

1 **CHINA EXCELS**, 11, b g Exceed And Excel (AUS)—China Beauty **Miss M. E. Rowland**
2 **DON KEYHOE TAY (IRE)**, 6, b h Danehill Dancer (IRE)—Arosa (IRE) **Miss M. E. Rowland**
3 **INSTILL**, 6, ch g Pivotal—Insijaam (USA) **Dallas Racing**
4 **JAZZ LEGEND (USA)**, 5, b g Scat Daddy (USA)—Champion Ride (USA) **Dallas Racing**
5 **PIPERS PIPING (IRE)**, 12, b g Noverre (USA)—Monarchy (IRE) **Miss M. E. Rowland**
6 **RICHARDS REJECT**, 5, b m Dutch Art—Focal
7 **STARFIELD**, 9, b g Marju (IRE)—Sister Moonshine (FR) **Dallas Racing**

Other Owners: Mr M. A. Glassett, Mr O. Robinson.

Assistant Trainer: Sarah Thomas

Jockey (flat): Rob Hornby, Adam Kirby, Jimmy Quinn. **Jockey (NH):** Adam Pogson.

---

484 **MS LUCINDA RUSSELL, Kinross**
Postal: **Arlary House Stables, Milnathort, Kinross, Tayside, KY13 9SJ**
Contacts: **PHONE (01577) 865512 FAX (01577) 861171 MOBILE (07970) 645261**
E-MAIL lucindarussellracing@outlook.com WEBSITE www.lucindarussell.com

1 **ALIZEE DE JANEIRO (FR)**, 8, b m Network (GER)—Katana (GER) **Ms D. Thomson**
2 **ARGENTIX (FR)**, 8, gr g Fragrant Mix (IRE)—Fleche Noir II (FR) **Miss A. Bramall**
3 **ASK THE TYCOON (IRE)**, 5, b g Ask—Mountainviewqueen (IRE) **Mrs S Russell & A M Russell**
4 **AURORA THUNDER**, 4, b f Malinas (GER)—Ninna Nanna (FR) **Allson Sparkle Ltd**
5 **BADGER FOOT (IRE)**, 13, br g Beneficial—Droim Alton Gale (IRE) **Mr P. J. S. Russell**
6 **BALLYCOOL (IRE)**, 11, b g Helissio (FR)—Carnoustie (USA) **Mr & Mrs T. P. Winnell**
7 **BEHINDTHELINES (IRE)**, 6, b g Milan—Sunset Leader (IRE) **London Scots for Doddie**
8 **BESCOT SPRINGS (IRE)**, 13, b g Saddlers' Hall (IRE)—Silver Glen (IRE) **Mr P. J. S. Russell**
9 **BIALCO (FR)**, 7, gr g Dom Alco (FR)—Lacanale (FR) **Mr M. Buskop**
10 **BIG MCINTOSH (IRE)**, 6, b g Bushranger (IRE)—Three Decades (IRE) **Kilco (International) Ltd**
11 **BIG RIVER (IRE)**, 8, b g Milan—Call Kate (IRE) **Two Black Labs**
12 **BLAYDON (IRE)**, 5, b g Milan—Pretty Impressive (IRE) **Mrs S Russell & A M Russell**
13 **BLUE BATON (IRE)**, 5, b m Presenting—Blu Louisiana (IRE) **The Kestrel Partnership**
14 **BOY'S ON TOUR (IRE)**, 6, b g Beneficial—Galant Tour (IRE) **Foresight Racing**
15 **CATCHTHEMOONLIGHT**, 10, b m Generous—Moon Catcher **Dig In Racing**
16 **CEEGEM (IRE)**, 6, b g Kalanisi (IRE)—Aboo Who (IRE) **Mrs E. Conetta**
17 **CELTIC FLAMES (IRE)**, 8, gr g Celtic Swing—Don't Forget Shoka (IRE) **Mr W. T. Scott**
18 **CHAMPAGNENDIAMONDS (IRE)**, 5, b g Milan—Shebeganit (IRE) **Two Black Labs**
19 **CHANCEITON (IRE)**, 7, b g Vinnie Roe (IRE)—Lissnabrucka (IRE) **Mr P. J. S. Russell**
20 **CHARLIE'S LASS**, 5, b m Getaway (GER)—Oh So Beautiful (IRE) **G. S. Brown**
21 **CHASSEUR DE TETE (FR)**, 6, b g Coastal Path—Escomptee (FR) **Skye Larks**
22 **CHOUQUETTE**, 4, b f Fame And Glory—Mille Et Une (FR) **Netherfield House Stud**
23 **CLONDAW KNIGHT (IRE)**, 10, b g Heron Island (IRE)—
Sarah Supreme (IRE) **Mr & Mrs Raymond Anderson Green**
24 **COCKLE BAY (IRE)**, 8, b g Milan—Theredandthegreen (IRE) **The Kestrel Partnership**
25 **CRUMBS**, 4, gr g Fair Mix (IRE)—Granary House **Major A. R. Trotter**
26 **DANCING AMY (IRE)**, 5, ch m Doyen (IRE)—Dew Drop **Mr J. Fyffe**
27 **DEEPSAND (IRE)**, 9, br g Footstepsinthesand—Sinamay (USA) **Mrs B. V. Evans**
28 **DEVITO'SGOLDENGIRL (IRE)**, 7, b m Gold Well—Caracool (FR) **County Set Five & Peter J S Russell**

MS LUCINDA RUSSELL - Continued

29 **DR HOOVES (IRE)**, 5, b g Yeats (IRE)—Sejour (IRE) **Mr G. R. McGladery**
30 **EMISSAIRE (FR)**, 4, b g Kap Rock (FR)—Jacee (FR) **A Nicol & L S Russell**
31 **FOREST DES AIGLES (FR)**, 7, b g Balko (FR)—Rose des Aigles (FR) **Mr & Mrs Raymond Anderson Green**
32 **GAYE FLIER (IRE)**, 7, b m Milan—Gaye Preskina (IRE) **J. R. Adam**
33 **GRAND MORNING**, 6, b g Midnight Legend—Valentines Lady (IRE) **Mr J. P. McManus**
34 **HAUL US IN (IRE)**, 6, br m Kalanisi (IRE)—Shuilan (IRE) **Mr & Mrs J. Morrison-Bell**
35 **HEY LISTEN (IRE)**, 6, b g Kutub (IRE)—Crescendor (FR) **British Racing Club**
36 **HIGHLAND HUNTER (IRE)**, 5, gr g Subtle Power (IRE)—Loughine Sparkle (IRE) **T. Barr**
37 **IMJOEKING (IRE)**, 11, b g Amilynx (FR)—Go Franky (IRE) **Mr K. Alexander**
38 **ISLAND HEIGHTS (IRE)**, 9, b g Heron Island (IRE)—La Reina (IRE) **Mr G. R. McGladery**
39 **ITSTIMEFORAPINT (IRE)**, 10, b g Portrait Gallery (IRE)—Executive Pearl (IRE) **IMEJ Racing**
40 **IZZY'S CHAMPION (IRE)**, 4, b g Gold Well—Native Crystal (IRE) **Mr & Mrs T. P. Winnell**
41 **JACK STEEL (IRE)**, 8, b g Craigsteel—Wake Me Gently (IRE) **Mr P. J. S. Russell**
42 **JUMP FOR DOUGH (IRE)**, 7, b g Milan—Collopy's Girl (IRE) **Kelso Lowflyers & Jumping For Dough**
43 **KELPIES MYTH**, 5, b g Dutch Art—Miss Respect **Bolton, McGladery & Duncan-Black**
44 **KILBRIE CHIEF (IRE)**, 10, b g Dr Massini (IRE)—Lame Excuse (IRE) **J. R. Adam**
45 **LE FRANK (IRE)**, 6, b g King's Theatre (IRE)—Dream Lass (IRE) **S. M. Smith**
46 **LOOKS LIKE MURT (IRE)**, 5, b g Well Chosen—Ninetypenceapound (IRE) **Mr P. J. S. Russell**
47 **LOST FREQUENCY**, 6, b g Yeats (IRE)—Lauderdale (GER) **The County Set Three**
48 **MAKE IT HAPPEN (IRE)**, 9, b g Saffron Walden (FR)—Kelpie (IRE) **Wright Mitchell**
49 **MARAWEH (IRE)**, 8, b g Muhtathir—Itqaan (USA) **Tay Valley Chasers Racing Club**
50 **MARCUS ANTONIUS**, 11, b g Mark of Esteem (IRE)—Star of The Course (USA) **Ms L. V. Russell**
51 **MIGHTY THUNDER**, 5, b g Malinas (GER)—Cool Island (IRE) **Allson Sparkle Ltd**
52 **MINT GOLD (IRE)**, 4, b g Gold Well—Lady Flyer (IRE) **Mrs S Russell & A M Russell**
53 **MISFITS (IRE)**, 7, b g Beneficial—Park Rose (IRE) **County Set Four & Keith Hunter**
54 **MISS JOEKING (IRE)**, 7, b m Alkaadhem—Go Franky (IRE) **Mr Michael & Lady Jane Kaplan**
55 **MISS TIGGY (IRE)**, 8, b m Milan—Rockwell College (IRE) **John R. Adam & Sons Ltd**
56 **MOORSTOWN (IRE)**, 8, b g Oscar (IRE)—Glacial Princess (IRE) **The County Set and Team Kirkton**
57 **MORITO DU BERLAIS (FR)**, 9, b g Turgeon (USA)—Chica du Berlais (FR) **Mr P. J. S. Russell**
58 **MR GRUMPY**, 5, b g Sir Percy—Panna **Mr P. J. S. Russell**
59 **MUMGOS DEBUT (IRE)**, 10, b g Royal Anthem (USA)—Black Queen (IRE) **Mrs Suzy Brown & Mr Peter R Brown**
60 **NEWTOWN LAD (IRE)**, 8, b g Craigsteel—Rocher Lady (IRE) **Mr John J Murray & Mrs Lynne MacLennan**
61 4, B f Shantou (USA)—Oh So Beautiful (IRE) **G. S. Brown**
62 **ONE FOR ARTHUR (IRE)**, 9, b g Milan—Nonnetia (FR) **Two Golf Widows**
63 **ORIONINVERNESS (IRE)**, 7, b g Brian Boru—Woodville Leader (IRE) **Tay Valley Chasers Racing Club**
64 **PARKER (IRE)**, 4, b g Cape Cross (IRE)—Mount Elbrus **Champagne Charlies Club**
65 **PINSPOT**, 4, ch g Presenting—Amber Cloud **Mr Michael & Lady Jane Kaplan**
66 **PRECIOUS CARGO**, 5, b g Yeats (IRE)—Kilbarry Classic (IRE) **T. Barr**
67 **PRESENT FLIGHT (IRE)**, 9, ch g Presenting—Grangeclare Flight (IRE) **Kilco (International) Ltd**
68 **PRESENT LODGER (IRE)**, 10, b g Presenting—Hannigan's Lodger (IRE) **Mr P. J. S. Russell**
69 **PRINCE DUNDEE (IRE)**, 5, b g Stowaway—Miss Dundee (IRE) **Jw McNeill, County Set Three & W Landels**
70 **REVOCATION**, 10, b g Revoque (IRE)—Fenella **Mr Michael & Lady Jane Kaplan**
71 **RICH COAST**, 10, b g King's Best (USA)—Costa Rica (IRE) **Mr P. J. S. Russell**
72 **RISING MARIENBARD (IRE)**, 6, b g Marienbard (IRE)—Dromkeen Wood **Mrs R. A. Stobart**
73 **RIVABODIVA (IRE)**, 8, ch m Flemensfirth (USA)—Sheebadiva (IRE) **Mrs S Russell & A M Russell**
74 **ROSSAMILAN (IRE)**, 7, b g Milan—Beautiful Blue (IRE) **Mr D. W. Ross**
75 **RUBYDOOBS (IRE)**, 5, b m Beneficial—Time In Milan (IRE) **Mr J. Fyffe**
76 **RUN ROCKY RUN (IRE)**, 5, b g Vertical Speed (FR)—Marlatara (USA) **County Set & Kendall Stewart Johnston**
77 **RYALEX (IRE)**, 7, b g Arcadio (GER)—Lady Ramona (IRE) **County Set Five & Keith Hunter**
78 **SAINT FREULE (FR)**, 5, br g Saint des Saints (FR)—Topsy Blue (FR) **Mr K. Alexander**
79 **SCALES OF JUSTICE (IRE)**, 4, b g Galileo (IRE)—Half Queen (USA) **Mrs F. H. Hay**
80 **SHANROE STREET (IRE)**, 8, b g Mustameet (USA)—Zaffran Lady (IRE) **Netherfield House Stud**
81 **SIMONE (IRE)**, 6, b m Presenting—Dusty Too **Mr K. Alexander**
82 **SKY KHAN**, 9, b g Cape Cross (IRE)—Starlit Sky **The Ormello Way**
83 **SLAINTE MHOR (IRE)**, 4, br g Milan—Founding Daughter (IRE) **Mr P. J. S. Russell**
84 **SPOILS OF WAR (IRE)**, 9, b g Craigsteel—Mooreshill Lady (IRE) **Wilde Duff Stewart Dawson**
85 **SUPERIOR COMMAND (IRE)**, 9, b g Lahib (USA)—Decent Dime (USA) **British Racing Club**
86 **TANTAMOUNT**, 9, b g Observatory (USA)—Cantanta **Mutual Friends**
87 **TAP NIGHT (USA)**, 11, ch g Pleasant Tap (USA)—Day Mate (USA) **Mr J. P. McManus**
88 **TEMPLENABOE (IRE)**, 6, b g Milan—Pretty Impressive (IRE) **Two Golf Widows**
89 **THE BANASTOIR (IRE)**, 9, b br g Presenting—Kimouna (FR) **Mrs A. L. Morshead**
90 **THE COMPELLER (IRE)**, 6, b g Lawman (FR)—Mark Too (IRE) **W M D Racing**
91 **THE ROAD HOME (IRE)**, 6, b g Oscar (IRE)—In Fact (IRE) **Mrs S Russell & A M Russell**
92 **THEPENSIONFUND (IRE)**, 6, b g Big Bad Bob (IRE)—Whizz **Mr Gerry McGladery & Mr PJS Russell**
93 **THORPE (IRE)**, 8, b g Danehill Dancer (IRE)—Minkova (IRE) **Mr Michael & Lady Jane Kaplan**

MS LUCINDA RUSSELL - Continued

94 **TIMESAWAITING (IRE)**, 5, b g Arakan (USA)—Princess Nicole (IRE) **Mr P. J. S. Russell**
95 **TOPHAM BAY (IRE)**, 6, b m Milan—Topham Gale (IRE) **BSN Racing**
96 **URBAN KODE (IRE)**, 10, b g Kodiac—Urbanize (USA) **Suzy Brown, John Baird, Tony Evans**
97 **VENGEUR DE GUYE (FR)**, 9, b g Dom Alco (FR)—Mascotte de Guye (FR) **Brahms & Liszt**
98 **VERTIGO (IRE)**, 6, b g Jeremy (USA)—Lady Coquette (SWE) **Mrs S Russell & A M Russell**
99 **VINO'S CHOICE (IRE)**, 6, b g Kalanisi (IRE)—Ard's Pet (IRE) **A Bit of GG Fun**
100 **VOYAGE A NEW YORK (FR)**, 9, b g Kapgarde (FR)—Pennsylvanie (FR) **County Set Five & Peter J S Russell**
101 **WELL ABOVE PAR (IRE)**, 6, b g Gold Well—Glynn Glory (IRE) **The Eagle Partnership**
102 **WHERE'S TIGER**, 7, b g Tiger Hill (IRE)—Where's Broughton **Mr Michael & Lady Jane Kaplan**

THREE-YEAR-OLDS

103 **FLUTTER DOWN (FR)**, b g Rob Roy (USA)—Florifere (FR) **Mr P. J. S. Russell**
104 **HETRE POURPRE (FR)**, b g Enrique—Sweet Jaune (FR) **Mr P. J. S. Russell**

Other Owners: Mr W. Agnew, Mr J. A. Aitkenhead, Mr W. M. Allan, Mr J. B. Baird, Mrs S. Brown, Mr P. R. Brown, Mr G. R. Brown, Mr E. Bruce, C. Bryce, A. Cadger, The County Set (Five), Mr N. A. Crofts, Mr A. B. Cuthill, Mr J. T. Dawson, Mr E. W. Dempster, Mr C. Dempster, Mr R. Doak, Mr I. Dobson, Mr R. J. Duff, Mr A. S. Duncan, Mr A. Evans, Mr R. J. Fowler, Mrs B. S. Fowler, Mr A. T. Galloway, Gilbert McClung (Kelso) Ltd, G. Godsman, Mrs I. M. Grant, Mrs A. Green, R. A. Green, E. D. Haggart, Mr C. D. Harrison, K. L. Hunter, J. W. McNeill & WD Landels, Mr D. R. James, Mrs P. James, Mr J. A. Johnston, Jumping For Dough, Kelso Members Lowflyers Club, Mr T. S. Kendall, Mrs M Kennedy, Mr A. Kerr, Mrs C. J. Lamb, Mr R. M. Landale, Mrs Y. M. V. Learmonth, Mr J. S. Lessells, M. W. Lightbody, Mrs J. Lightbody, Ms A. M. MacInnes, Ms F. E. MacInnes, Mr M. F. Mackay, Mrs L. Maclennan, Mr M. G. Mellor, Mr J. Mitchell, Mr J. Morrison-Bell, Mrs K. A. Morrison-Bell, Mr J. J. Murray, Mr W. E. Nicholson, Mr A. G. Nicol, Racing Club Ltd, Mrs S. C. Russell, Mr A. M. Russell, Mr L. S. Russell, A. W. Sinclair, Mr D. R. Skinner, Ms P Spours, Mrs V. M. Stewart, T Kendall VM Stewart J Johnston, Mr P. A. Taylor, Team Kirkton, Mr N. J. Turnbull, Mr L. M. Wilde, Mrs M. Winnell, Mr T. P. Winnell, Mr D. J. Gordon Wright.

Assistant Trainers: Peter Scudamore, Jamie Turnbull, Jaimie Duff

Jockey (NH): Derek Fox. **Conditional:** Blair Campbell, Stephen Mulqueen, Thomas Willmott. **Amateur:** Miss Maisie Sharp, Mr Cameron Wadge.

---

485 | MR JOHN RYAN, Newmarket
Postal: **Cadland Stables, Moulton Road, Newmarket, Suffolk, CB8 8DU**
Contacts: PHONE (01638) 664172 MOBILE (07739) 801235
E-MAIL john.ryan@jryanracing.com WEBSITE www.jryanracing.com Twitter: JohnRyanRacing

1 **BATTLE OF MARATHON (USA)**, 6, b g War Front (USA)—Sayedah (IRE) **Mr G. F. Smith-Bernal**
2 **CIAOADIOSIMDONE (IRE)**, 4, ch f Arcano (IRE)—Croque Madame (FR) **Pull It Right Back Partnership**
3 **GREY BRITAIN**, 4, gr g Arcano (IRE)—Reaching Ahead (USA) **Mr G. F. Smith-Bernal**
4 **LADY FREYJA**, 4, b f Mayson—Third Party **Mr J. A. Thompson**
5 **MAX LIEBERMANN (IRE)**, 4, b g Galileo (IRE)—Anna Karenina (IRE) **Mr G. R. McGladery**
6 **MERHOOB (IRE)**, 6, b g Cape Cross (IRE)—Lady Slippers (IRE) **Mr G. R. McGladery**
7 **NORMAL NORMAN**, 4, ch g Shamardal (USA)—Ambria (GER) **Mr G. R. McGladery**
8 **OCEAN TEMPTRESS**, 4, b f Equiano (FR)—Ipsa Loquitur **The Temptations**
9 **PLUCKY DIP**, 7, b g Nayef (USA)—Plucky **Mr J. B. Ryan**
10 **TENOR (IRE)**, 8, b g Oratorio (IRE)—Cedar Sea (IRE) **Kilco (International) Ltd**
11 **THE GAY CAVALIER**, 7, b g Henrythenavigator (USA)—Dear Daughter **The Gay Cavaliers Partnership**

THREE-YEAR-OLDS

12 **DARK SIDE JAZZ (IRE)**, ch g Red Jazz (USA)—Marianne's Dancer (IRE) **Mr M. M. Foulger**
13 B f Harbour Watch (IRE)—Enthralled
14 **MIDNIGHT WILDE**, gr g Poet's Voice—Si Belle (IRE) **Mr J. A. Thompson**
15 **QUEEN ADELAIDE**, b f Helmet (AUS)—Spunger **BB Bloodstock**
16 **ROLAND ROCKS (IRE)**, b c Red Jazz (USA)—Toy Show (IRE) **Mr G. R. McGladery**
17 **SAPHIL (IRE)**, b g Holy Roman Emperor (IRE)—Lafite **Mr J. F. Stocker**
18 **SPENNY'S LASS**, br f Bated Breath—Midnight Hush (FR) **Mr M. Firth**
19 **STAR OF ASSISI (USA)**, b f Arch (USA)—Charming Tale (USA) **Mr G. F. Smith-Bernal**
20 **THUNDERHOOVES**, ro c Raven's Pass (USA)—Regrette Rien (USA) **Kilco (International) Ltd**

TWO-YEAR-OLDS

21 B f 3/2 Gregorian (IRE)—Back On Baileys (Kyllachy)
22 **BELLA BELUGA**, b f 10/5 Nathaniel (IRE)—Move (Observatory) (20000) **Mr G. F. Smith-Bernal**
23 B f 22/4 Society Rock (IRE)—Clapperboard (Royal Applause) (3500) **Mr W. J. S. Prosser**

MR JOHN RYAN - Continued

24 **FLASH SENTRY**, b g 1/3 Dick Turpin (IRE)—Twilight Sparkle (IRE) (Rock of Gibraltar (IRE)) **Mr G. R. McGladery**
25 **HIROSHIMA**, b c 29/2 Nathaniel (IRE)—Lisiere (IRE) (Excellent Art) (28000) **Mr G. F. Smith-Bernal**
26 Ch g 28/3 Bated Breath—Likeable (Dalakhani (IRE)) (3000)
27 B f 23/3 Gregorian (IRE)—Love Quest (Pursuit of Love) **Mr W. J. S. Prosser**
28 **SHE CAME TO PASS**, ch f 7/3 Nathaniel (IRE)—
　　　　　　　　　　Sylvestris (IRE) (Arch (USA)) (11000) **Mr Graham Smith Bernal & Mr Jon Thompson**
29 B f 17/1 Zebedee—Villa Nova (IRE) (Petardia (IRE)) (14000) **Mr S. D. Russell**

Other Owners: Mr S. D. Kerr, Mrs L. M. Lambert, S & M Supplies (Aylsham) Ltd.

Apprentice: Jack Osborn.

486　**MR KEVIN RYAN, Hambleton**
Postal: Hambleton Lodge, Hambleton, Thirsk, North Yorkshire, YO7 2HA
Contacts: PHONE Office (01845) 597010 / (01845) 597622 FAX (01845) 597622
MOBILE (07768) 016930
E-MAIL kevin.hambleton@virgin.net WEBSITE www.kevinryanracing.com

1 **AL HAWRAA**, 5, b m Iffraaj—Kashoof **Mr Allan Kerr Mr Peter McGivney**
2 **AL KHAN (IRE)**, 9, b g Elnadim (USA)—Popolo (IRE) **Mr J. C. G. Chua**
3 **ANGEL'S ACCLAIM (IRE)**, 4, gr f Dark Angel (IRE)—Miss Otis **Hambleton Racing Ltd XLV**
4 **ARMANDIHAN (IRE)**, 4, b g Zoffany (IRE)—Flying Flag (IRE) **Mr T. A. Rahman**
5 **ASHADIHAN**, 5, b m Kyllachy—Miss Delila (USA) **Mr T. A. Rahman**
6 **BEYOND THE CLOUDS**, 5, ch g Peintre Celebre (USA)—Evening **Guy Reed Racing**
7 **BOGART**, 9, ch g Bahamian Bounty—Lauren Louise **Mrs Angie Bailey**
8 **BRANDO**, 6, ch g Pivotal—Argent du Bois (USA) **Mrs Angie Bailey**
9 **BRILLIANT VANGUARD (IRE)**, 5, b g Fast Company (IRE)—Alyska (IRE) **JCG Chua & CK Ong**
10 **CANNY STYLE**, 5, b m Canford Cliffs (IRE)—Stylish One (IRE) **Hambleton Racing Ltd XXXVII**
11 **CARIDADE (USA)**, 4, b f Medaglia d'oro (USA)—
　　　　　　　　　　Raffle Ticket (USA) **Hambleton Racing Ltd XVIII & CN Farm Ltd**
12 **COMPANY ASSET (IRE)**, 5, ch m Fast Company (IRE)—Changari (USA) **Hambleton Racing Ltd XVI**
13 **COUNT MONTECRISTO (FR)**, 6, b g Siyouni (FR)—Blackberry Pie (USA) **Middleham Park Racing XLVI**
14 **ERIK THE RED (FR)**, 4, b g Kendargent (FR)—Norwegian Princess (IRE) **Mr F. Gillespie**
15 **EVERYTHING FOR YOU (IRE)**, 4, b g Pivotal—Miss Delila (USA) **Mr T. A. Rahman**
16 **EYES ON ASHA (IRE)**, 4, b f Redoute's Choice (AUS)—Sunday Nectar (IRE) **Mr T. A. Rahman**
17 **FAST ACT (IRE)**, 6, ch g Fast Company (IRE)—Nullarbor **Hambleton Racing Ltd XXXII**
18 **FIKHAAR**, 4, b f Oasis Dream—Fawaayed (IRE) **Hambleton Racing Ltd XVIII & CN Farm Ltd**
19 **HEIR OF EXCITEMENT (IRE)**, 4, b g Tagula (IRE)—Gimli's Treasure (IRE) **STS Racing Limited**
20 **KAJAKI (IRE)**, 5, gr g Mastercraftsman (IRE)—No Quest (IRE) **Mr F. Gillespie**
21 **KODICAT (IRE)**, 4, b f Kodiac—Mimiteh (USA) **Reilly JDM Holdings Ltd**
22 **LANJANO**, 4, ch r Foxwedge (AUS)—Hot Property (USA) **Collier Holmes Racing**
23 **LAUGHTON**, 5, b g Acclamation—Peach Pearl **Mrs Angie Bailey**
24 **LEXINGTON ABBEY**, 7, b g Sleeping Indian—Silvereine (FR) **Middleham Park Racing XIX**
25 **LUALIWA**, 4, b g Foxwedge (AUS)—Sunpearl **Mrs Rosie Richer**
26 **MAJOR JUMBO**, 4, gr g Zebedee—Gone Sailing **Mr T. A. Rahman**
27 **MONT KIARA (FR)**, 5, b g Kendargent (FR)—Xaarienne (USA) **JCG Chua & CK Ong 1**
28 **MOUNT TAHAN (IRE)**, 6, b g Lope de Vega (IRE)—Sorpresa (USA) **Mr T. A. Rahman**
29 **NAADIRR (IRE)**, 7, b g Oasis Dream—Beach Bunny (IRE) **Middleham Park Racing XXX**
30 **NAUTICAL HAVEN**, 4, b g Harbour Watch (IRE)—Mania (IRE) **Nick Bradley Racing 38 & Partners**
31 **PENNSYLVANIA DUTCH**, 4, b g Dutch Art—Map of Heaven
32 **RUTHERFORD (IRE)**, 4, ch f Dutch Art—Carraigoona (IRE) **Mrs Angie Bailey**
33 **SAVANNAH MOON (IRE)**, 4, b f Canford Cliffs (IRE)—Tennessee Moon **Hambleton Racing Ltd XXXVI**
34 **SCRUTINY**, 7, b g Aqlaam—Aunty Mary **Miss E. J. Butterworth**
35 **TAGUR (IRE)**, 4, ch g Tagula (IRE)—Westcote (USA) **Andy Turton & John Blackburn**
36 **TERUNTUM STAR (FR)**, 6, ch g Dutch Art—Seralia (USA) **Mr T. A. Rahman**
37 **TEWAFEEDJ**, 4, b g Mawatheeq (USA)—It's The War (USA) **Mr H. M. K. Al Mehairi**
38 **TOMMY TAYLOR (USA)**, 4, b c Mizzen Mast (USA)—Sharp Apple (USA) **Mrs Angie Bailey**
39 **TROOPER'S GOLD**, 4, ch g Sepoy (AUS)—Samira Gold (FR) **Mr Saeed Jaber**

THREE-YEAR-OLDS

40 **AL EMARAT (IRE)**, b c Sea The Stars (IRE)—Ocean Talent (USA) **Mr Ahmad Abdulla Al Shaikh**
41 **ALKHAWANEEJ BOY (IRE)**, b c Elzaam (AUS)—Kaplinsky (IRE) **Mr Ahmad Abdulla Al Shaikh**
42 **AYUTTHAYA (IRE)**, ch c Lope de Vega (IRE)—Pivotal Role **JCG Chua & CK Ong 1**
43 **BAKHT KHAN (IRE)**, ch g Sepoy (AUS)—Naddwah **K&J Bloodstock Ltd & Partner**

MR KEVIN RYAN - Continued

44 **BERARDI (IRE)**, b g Sea The Stars (IRE)—Dhanyata (IRE) **Highbank Stud**
45 **BILLY RUSKIN**, b g Bahamian Bounty—Fluffy **K&J Bloodstock Ltd**
46 **BUNGEE JUMP (IRE)**, b f Canford Cliffs (IRE)—Starchy **Nick Bradley Racing 7 & Partner**
47 **COMMANDER HAN (FR)**, ch c Siyouni (FR)—Acentela (IRE) **Mr T. A. Rahman**
48 **DALAWYNA (FR)**, gr f Kendargent (FR)—Dalawysa (FR) **Mr Guy Pariente**
49 **DANDY'S BEANO (IRE)**, ch f Dandy Man (IRE)—Hear My Cry (USA) **Hambleton Racing Ltd XLVII**
50 **DEAR BELOVED (IRE)**, ch f Pivotal—Calakanga **Mr T. A. Rahman**
51 **ELNADIM STAR (IRE)**, ch f Elnadim (USA)—Fancy Feathers (IRE) **Mr Jaber Abdullah**
52 **FALABELLA (IRE)**, ch f Choisir (AUS)—Mooching Along (IRE) **K&J Bloodstock Ltd**
53 **FINISHER (USA)**, br g Street Cry (IRE)—Morena (PER) **Aquis Farm Pty Ltd**
54 **FOXY LADY**, b f Foxwedge (AUS)—Catherine Palace **K&J Bloodstock Ltd**
55 **GOLD STONE**, b f Havana Gold (IRE)—Slatey Hen (IRE) **Mr Jaber Abdullah**
56 **HAVANA STAR (IRE)**, b g Havana Gold (IRE)—Nagham (IRE) **Hambleton Racing Ltd XXXVIII**
57 **HEY JONESY (IRE)**, b c Excelebration (IRE)—Fikrah **Pallister Racing**
58 **HOW BIZARRE**, ch g Society Rock (IRE)—Amanda Carter **K&J Bloodstock Ltd**
59 **IBN AL EMARAT (IRE)**, b g Excelebration (IRE)—Grace of Dubai (FR) **Mrs J. Ryan**
60 Ch f Monsieur Bond (IRE)—Jord (IRE) **Mr A. Grice**
61 **JUNGLE ROOM (USA)**, b g Violence (USA)—Raised Right (USA) **Matt & Lauren Morgan**
62 **KINGS FULL (IRE)**, b g Galileo (IRE)—Half Queen (USA) **Aquis Farm Pty Ltd**
63 **KNIGHTED (IRE)**, b g Sir Prancealot (IRE)—Olympia Theatre **Highclere T'bred Racing- Nick Skelton**
64 **KYNANCE (IRE)**, b f Canford Cliffs (IRE)—Janoubi **Mr E Wilson & Partner**
65 **LAIT AU CHOCOLAT (USA)**, b f Sidney's Candy (USA)—Mother's Milk (USA) **Mr Fergus Galvin**
66 B g Footstepsinthesand—Lille Ida **Mr E Wilson & Partner**
67 **MONT KINABALU (IRE)**, b g Society Rock (IRE)—Startori **JCG Chua & CK Ong 1**
68 **MORNING WONDER (IRE)**, ch c Dawn Approach (IRE)—Mount Elbrus **Mr Sultan Ali**
69 **NEAREST GREEN**, b c Exceed And Excel (AUS)—Aria di Festa (IRE) **Nearest Green Partners**
70 **NEW SHOW (IRE)**, ch c New Approach (IRE)—Music Show (IRE) **Mr Jaber Abdullah**
71 **NOW THEN**, b f Duke of Marmalade (IRE)—Now And Then **Guy Reed Racing**
72 **PREDICTION (IRE)**, b g Dream Ahead (USA)—Sho Girl (IRE) **Highclere T'Bred Racing- Rio Olympics**
73 **QUEEN'S SARGENT (FR)**, gr g Kendargent (FR)—Queen's Conquer **STS Racing Limited**
74 **ROYAL PURSUIT (USA)**, br c Lonhro (AUS)—Catch the Queen (USA) **Sahara Bloodstock**
75 **SALAZAR (IRE)**, ch g Raven's Pass (USA)—Queen Padme (IRE) **Mrs Angie Bailey**
76 **SANDYTOWN (IRE)**, b g Tamayuz—Wild Ways **Quinn & Co**
77 **SAVALAS (IRE)**, gr c Zebedee—Tap The Dot (IRE) **Mrs Angie Bailey**
78 **SENTIMENTAL GENT (FR)**, b g Kendargent (FR)—Sentimental Union (USA) **Hambleton Racing Ltd XXXIV**
79 **STORMBRINGER**, b c Dutch Art—Riva Royale **Mr Charles Wentworth**
80 **VJ DAY (USA)**, b g War Front (USA)—Sassy Image (USA) **Aquis Farm Pty Ltd**
81 **WONDERING SPIRIT**, b f Invincible Spirit (IRE)—Wonder Why (GER) **Mr Jaber Abdullah**
82 **ZARJAZ (USA)**, b g First Defence (USA)—Fanzine (USA) **Mr Ahmad Abdulla Al Shaikh**

TWO-YEAR-OLDS

83 **ALHAN BIL EMARATI (IRE)**, b c 28/4 Alhebayeb (IRE)—
Tartan Blue (Kyllachy) (26047) **Mr Ahmad Abdulla Al Shaikh**
84 B f 11/5 Footstepsinthesand—Asian Lady (Kyllachy) **Mr T. A. Rahman**
85 Ch c 15/3 Dutch Art—Bertie's Best (King's Best (USA)) (40000) **Mr T. A. Rahman**
86 Ch c 23/2 Haafhd—Bigger Picture (IRE) (Raven's Pass (USA)) **Ms P. Cokerill**
87 B c 23/4 Camacho—Blessed Beauty (IRE) (Alhaarth (IRE)) (18095) **Hambleton Racing Ltd XXIX**
88 B c 17/2 Swiss Spirit—Bling Bling (Indian Ridge) (36190) **Mr T. A. Rahman**
89 B f 11/2 Helmet (AUS)—Bochafina (FR) (High Chaparral (IRE)) (13333) **Mr T. A. Rahman**
90 Ch c 10/3 Excelebration (IRE)—Dance Hall Girl (IRE) (Dansili) (21904) **Hambleton Racing Ltd XXII**
91 **EMARAATY ANA**, b c 10/5 Shamardal (USA)—
Spirit of Dubai (IRE) (Cape Cross (IRE)) **Mr Ahmad Abdulla Al Shaikh**
92 Br c 3/3 Foxwedge (AUS)—Frequent (Three Valleys (USA)) (70818) **Mrs Angie Bailey**
93 **GLASS SLIPPERS**, b f 25/3 Dream Ahead (USA)—Night Gypsy (Mind Games) **Mr T. G. & Mrs M. E. Holdcroft**
94 B f 30/3 Slade Power—Gold Hush (USA) (Seeking The Gold (USA)) (10000) **Hambleton Racing Ltd**
95 Ch c 28/2 Monsieur Bond (IRE)—Hopes N Dreams (IRE) (Elusive City (USA)) **JCG Chua & CK Ong**
96 Ch f 13/3 More Than Ready (USA)—Legs Lawlor (USA) (Unbridled (USA)) (38257)
97 Ch c 24/4 Gale Force Ten—Ma Nikitia (IRE) (Camacho) (24420) **Hambleton Racing Ltd**
98 Ch c 13/5 Sea The Moon (GER)—Majestic Roi (USA) (Street Cry (IRE)) **Mr Jaber Abdullah**
99 Br g 10/2 Camacho—Mezogiorno (IRE) (Zamindar (USA)) (17093)
100 Br c 16/4 Gregorian (IRE)—Nafa (IRE) (Shamardal (USA)) (37443)
101 Gr f 7/4 Dark Angel (IRE)—Pivotal Era (Pivotal) (72000) **Mr T. A. Rahman**
102 B f 13/2 War Command (USA)—Regatta (FR) (Layman (USA)) (29304) **Mr T. A. Rahman**
103 **ROCK PARTY (IRE)**, br f 16/2 Society Rock (IRE)—
Bacchanalia (IRE) (Blues Traveller (IRE)) (19536) **Mr Craig Buckingham**

MR KEVIN RYAN - Continued

104 B c 22/4 Kodiac—Spasha (Shamardal (USA)) **Mr Jaber Abdullah**
105 B c 5/5 No Nay Never (USA)—Special Assignment (USA) (Lemon Drop Kid (USA)) (100000) **Mr T. A. Rahman**
106 THE GREAT HEIR (FR), b c 14/2 Pedro The Great (USA)—
 Lady McKell (IRE) (Raven's Pass (USA)) (26862) **Mr Dave Stone**
107 B f 23/2 War Command (USA)—Tohaveandtohold (Pivotal) (40000) **Mr K. Alexander**
108 B f 30/4 Foxwedge (AUS)—Vive Les Rouges (Acclamation) (16000)
109 B c 17/5 Kingman—Wild Mimosa (IRE) (Dynaformer (USA)) (35000) **Hambleton Racing Ltd XXXVII**
110 YOUSINI, b c 18/2 Siyouni (FR)—War Effort (USA) (War Front (USA)) (50000) **Middleham Park Racing XXI**
111 Ch f 15/3 Iffraaj—Zayn Zen (Singspiel (IRE)) (50000) **Mr Sultan Ali**

Other Owners: Mr J. N. Blackburn, Mr N. Bradley, CN Farm Limited, Mr J. C. G. Chua, Mr B. N. Collier, Mrs Margaret Forsyth, Hambleton Racing Ltd., Hambleton Racing Ltd XVIII, Hambleton Racing Ltd XXIX, Mr A. C. Henson, Highclere Nominated Partner Limited, Highclere Thoroughbred Racing Ltd, Mrs R. G. Hillen, Miss S. Holden, Mr A. Holmes, Mr R. Jackson, Mrs G. S. Jackson, Kaniz Bloodstock Investments Ltd, Mr Allan Kerr, Mr Peter McGivney, Mrs Lauren Morgan, Mr Matthew Morgan, Nick Bradley Racing 38, Nick Bradley Racing 7, Mr A. Olesen, Mr C. K. Ong, Mr T. S. Palin, Mrs J. E. Pallister, Mrs A. H. Pallister, Mr J. G. Pallister, Mr M. Prince, Mr P. Quinn, Mrs J. Ryan, Mr S. R. H. Turner, Mr Andrew Turton, Mr M. Wainwright, Mrs I. M. Wainwright, Mr E. Wilson.

Assistant Trainers: Joe O'Gorman, Adam Ryan

Jockey (flat): Shane Gray, Kevin Stott. **Amateur:** Miss Harriet Lees.

---

487 **MR AYTACH SADIK, Kidderminster**
Postal: **Wolverley Court Coach House, Wolverley, Kidderminster, Worcestershire, DY10 3RP**
Contacts: **PHONE** (01562) 852362 **MOBILE** (07803) 040344

1 LUCA BRAZI (IRE), 6, b g Mahler—Carriacou **A. M. Sadik**
2 SUSSEX ROAD (IRE), 8, b g Mahler—Rose Island **A. M. Sadik**
3 THECORNISHBARRON (IRE), 6, b g Bushranger (IRE)—Tripudium (IRE) **A. M. Sadik**

---

488 **MR MATTHEW SALAMAN, Porth**
Postal: **Ty-Yr-Heol Farm, Tonyrefail, Porth, Mid-Glamorgan, CF39 8HX**
Contacts: **MOBILE** (07912) 039015
E-MAIL matthewsalaman@hotmail.com

1 BIRIKYNO, 7, b g Piccolo—Alvarinho Lady **Mrs D. J. Hughes**
2 BOSPHORUS PRINCE (IRE), 6, b h Hurricane Run (IRE)—Bosphorus Queen (IRE) **Mrs D. J. Hughes**
3 CALL HIM ANYTHING, 4, b g Mount Nelson—Focosa (ITY) **Mrs D. J. Hughes**
4 5, B m Mount Nelson—Focosa (ITY) **Mrs D. J. Hughes**
5 IGNIGHT, 7, ch g Compton Place—Time Clash **Mrs D. J. Hughes**
6 6, B m Piccolo—In Some Style (IRE)
7 INSPIRE, 6, gr m Hellvelyn—Time Clash **Mrs D. J. Hughes**
8 4, B br g Sayif (IRE)—Just Down The Road (IRE)
9 LOCOMMOTION, 6, gr g Proclamation (IRE)—Miss Madame (IRE) **Susannah Green, Debbie Hughes**
10 MAJOR ASSAULT, 5, b h Kyllachy—Night Premiere (IRE) **Mrs D. J. Hughes**
11 MOLLY JONES, 9, b m Three Valleys (USA)—And Toto Too **Mrs D. J. Hughes**
12 OLIVERAIE, 6, b g Dutch Art—Angie And Liz (IRE) **Mr I. Rachid**
13 PICC AND GO, 5, b m Piccolo—Just Down The Road (IRE) **Mrs D. J. Hughes**
14 SAXONY, 7, b m Bertolini (USA)—Just Down The Road (IRE) **Mrs D. J. Hughes**
15 SLUMBER PARTY, 5, gr g Hellvelyn—In Some Style (IRE) **Mrs D. J. Hughes**
16 STOP N START, 6, ch m Piccolo—Dim Ots **Mrs D. J. Hughes**

THREE-YEAR-OLDS

17 THOUGHT SO (IRE), b g So You Think (NZ)—Holder's Hill (IRE) **Mrs D. J. Hughes**

Other Owners: Ms S. Green.

Assistant Trainer: Debbie Hughes

489 **MR GARY SANDERSON, Sheriff Hutton**
Postal: Lilling Hall Farm, Moor Lane, Near Flaxton, York, North Yorkshire, YO60 6RL
Contacts: **(01904) 468200 MOBILE (07950) 622402**
E-MAIL garysanderson.lhf@gmail.com
WEBSITE http://lillinghallracing.wix.com/lilling-hall-racing

1 **DAWLISH**, 7, b g Rail Link—Pnyka (IRE) **Lilling Hall Racing**
2 **GOT MY MOJO**, 8, b g Motivator—Habla Me (IRE) **Lilling Hall Racing**
3 4, B f Champs Elysees—Leah's Pride
4 **MISS GISELLE**, 9, b m Desideratum—Pride of The Oaks **Lilling Hall Racing**
5 **MISS REBERO**, 8, b m Cockney Rebel (IRE)—One Zero (USA) **Lilling Hall Racing**
6 4, B g Native Ruler—Pride of The Oaks
7 **WHIGWHAM**, 4, ch f Sleeping Indian—Normandy Maid **Lilling Hall Racing**

TWO-YEAR-OLDS

8 B c 9/4 Passing Glance—Clipper Line (USA) (Mizzen Mast (USA))
9 **MY BOY MONTY**, b c 14/5 Passing Glance—Sudden Impulse (Silver Patriarch (IRE))

Other Owners: Peter Dodsworth, Dermot Fallon, Neil Francis, Mark Holdsworth, Richard Mansfield, Steven Nellis, Teresa Nellis, John Seymour Reed, Mr G. Sanderson, Colin Smith, Stuart Woods, Mr N. Woods, David Woods, Sallie Wrath.

Assistant Trainer: Lynne Sanderson

Jockey (flat): Cam Hardie. **Apprentice:** Jason Watson, Zak Wheatley. **Amateur:** Miss Georgia Woodcock.

490 **MRS KATHLEEN SANDERSON, Tiverton**
Postal: New Cottage, Rackenford Road, Calverleigh, Tiverton, Devon, EX16 8BE
Contacts: **PHONE (01884) 254217 MOBILE (07391) 897775**
E-MAIL h9bas@live.co.uk

1 **JABBEA (IRE)**, 6, b g Robin des Pres (FR)—Welsh Bea (IRE) **Mrs K. M. Sanderson**
Amateur: Mr Nick Lawton.

491 **MR JOSE SANTOS, Lambourn**
Postal: Sherwood Bungalow, Folly Road, Lambourn, Hungerford, Berkshire, RG17 8QE
Contacts: **MOBILE (07789) 906694**

1 **CARAMURU (IRE)**, 4, b g Casamento (IRE)—Zaynaba (IRE)
2 **LADY VALDEAN**, 4, ch f Helmet (AUS)—Symphonic Dancer (USA) **Mr R. Cooper**
3 **LORD COOPER**, 4, b g Sir Percy—Zooming (IRE) **Mr R. Cooper**

THREE-YEAR-OLDS

4 **A FEW GOOD MEN**, b g Compton Place—Slap And Tickle (IRE) **The Villains**
5 **ARROGANT (IRE)**, b g Haatef (USA)—Keep Bacckinhit (IRE) **Jose Santos Racing Ltd**
6 **DANDY FANTASIE (IRE)**, ch f Dandy Man (IRE)—First Rains **Jose Santos Racing Ltd**
7 **DRACARYS**, b c Sepoy (AUS)—Fen Guest **The Villains**
8 **FOXANGEL**, ch f Foxwedge (AUS)—Tech Zinne **Mr R. Cooper**
9 **LADY MALDIVA (IRE)**, b f Thewayyouare (USA)—Rapid Review (IRE) **Jose Santos Racing Ltd**
10 **PRECIOUS SILK (IRE)**, ch f Harbour Watch (IRE)—Fine Silk (USA) **Mr P. Moyles**

Other Owners: Mr S. A. J. Penny, L. R. Turland.

492 **MR MALCOLM SAUNDERS, Wells**
Postal: Blue Mountain Farm, Wells Hill Bottom, Haydon, Wells, Somerset, BA5 3EZ
Contacts: **OFFICE/FAX (01749) 841011 MOBILE (07771) 601035**
E-MAIL malcolm@malcolmsaunders.co.uk WEBSITE www.malcolmsaunders.co.uk

1 **AMBERINE**, 4, b f Equiano (FR)—Crimson Fern (IRE) **M. S. Saunders**
2 **BABYFACT**, 7, b m Piccolo—Pennyspider (IRE) **Mrs Ginny Nicholas & Mr M. S. Saunders**
3 **CORONATION COTTAGE**, 4, b f Pastoral Pursuits—Avrilo **Pat Hancock & Eric Jones**

MR MALCOLM SAUNDERS - Continued

4 **EASY TIGER**, 6, b g Refuse To Bend (IRE)—Extremely Rare (IRE) **Miss E. Tanner**
5 **LUCKY CLOVER**, 7, ch m Lucky Story (USA)—Willisa **Paul Nicholas / M S Saunders**
6 **NUTINI (IRE)**, 5, b g Lope de Vega (IRE)—My Eurydice **Mrs L. F. Wei**
7 **PASTFACT**, 4, br g Pastoral Pursuits—Matterofact (IRE) **Premier Conservatory Roofs**
8 **SARANGOO**, 10, b m Piccolo—Craic Sa Ceili (IRE) **M. S. Saunders**
9 **SECRETFACT**, 5, br g Sakhee's Secret—Matterofact (IRE) **Premier Conservatory Roofs**
10 **SHOWMETHEWAYAVRILO**, 5, ch g Showcasing—Avrilo **Pat Hancock & Eric Jones**
11 **SILVERRICA (IRE)**, 8, gr m Ad Valorem (USA)—Allegorica (IRE) **Mrs Ginny Nicholas & Mr M. S. Saunders**
12 **TITUS SECRET**, 6, ch g Sakhee's Secret—Crimson Fern (IRE) **M. S. Saunders**

THREE-YEAR-OLDS

13 **SCARLET RED**, b f Equiano (FR)—Crimson Fern (IRE) **M. S. Saunders**

Other Owners: D. J. Collier, Mr P. K. Hancock, Mr E. W. Jones, Mrs V. L. Nicholas, Mr P. S. G. Nicholas.

---

493 **MRS DIANNE SAYER**, Penrith
Postal: **Town End Farm, Hackthorpe, Penrith, Cumbria, CA10 2HX**
Contacts: **PHONE (01931) 712245 MOBILE (07980) 295316**

1 **BAILEYS CONCERTO (IRE)**, 12, b g Bach (IRE)—None The Wiser (IRE) **United Five Racing & Mr Andrew Sayer**
2 **ENDEAVOR**, 13, ch g Selkirk (USA)—Midnight Mambo (USA) **Mrs Margaret Coppola & Mrs Dianne Sayer**
3 **FRIGHTENED RABBIT (USA)**, 6, b g Hard Spun (USA)—Champagne Ending (USA) **Mr R. A. Harrison**
4 **GENTLEMAN JAMES**, 6, b g Sixties Icon—Cashback Rose (IRE) **Mrs M. R. Lewis**
5 **GOLD CHAIN (IRE)**, 8, b m Authorized (IRE)—
Mountain Chain (USA) **Mrs Margaret Coppola & Mrs Dianne Sayer**
6 **HONEYCHILE RYDER**, 7, ch m Black Sam Bellamy (IRE)—Dusky Dante (IRE) **Mrs H. D. Sayer**
7 **HOT GOSSIP (IRE)**, 4, b f Fast Company (IRE)—On The Make (IRE) **Mr Dennis J. Coppola & Mrs Dianne Sayer**
8 **I'LL RUN WITH YOU (IRE)**, 5, b m Darsi (FR)—Suzy Q (IRE) **Mr Dennis J. Coppola & Mrs Dianne Sayer**
9 **IN FOCUS (IRE)**, 7, ch g Intense Focus (USA)—Reine de Neige **Mr G. H. Bell**
10 **IOLANI (GER)**, 6, b g Sholokhov (IRE)—Imogen (GER) **SJD Racing & Dianne Sayer**
11 **JACKHAMMER (IRE)**, 4, b g Thewayyouare (USA)—Ask Annie (IRE) **SJD Racing & Dianne Sayer**
12 **MAIN FACT (USA)**, 5, b g Blame (USA)—Reflections **A. R. White**
13 **MILLIE THE MINX (IRE)**, 4, b f Medicean—Popocatepetl (FR) **A. R. White**
14 **MY VALENTINO (IRE)**, 5, ch g Duke of Marmalade (IRE)—
Nadwah (USA) **Mr Dennis J. Coppola & Mrs Dianne Sayer**
15 **REDARNA**, 4, ch g Aqlaam—Curtains **Graham Lund & Dianne Sayer**
16 **THE PHANTOM (FR)**, 6, b g Apsis—Idee Recue (FR) **Mr A. S. Ambler**
17 **ZARIB (IRE)**, 7, b g Azamour (IRE)—Zariziyna (IRE) **Appleby Racing & Partner**

TWO-YEAR-OLDS

18 **SIMUL AMICIS**, b f 29/2 Hurricane Run (IRE)—Xaphania (Sakhee (USA)) (4500) **Graham Lund & Dianne Sayer**
19 **VITA VIVET**, ch f 24/2 Bated Breath—Cresta Gold (Halling (USA)) (10000) **Graham Lund & Dianne Sayer**

Other Owners: Mr K. J. Burrow, Mr A. J. Burrow, Mr I. T. Conroy, Mrs M. Coppola, Mr D. J. Coppola, Mr T. W. Ewbank, Mr D. Hunter, Mr G. Lund, Mrs J. Macrae, Mr P. Moorby, Mr S. Nicholson, S J D Racing, J. A. Sayer.

Assistant Trainer: Miss Joanna Sayer

Amateur: Miss Liz Butterworth, Miss Emma Sayer.

---

494 **DR JON SCARGILL**, Newmarket
Postal: **Red House Stables, Hamilton Road, Newmarket, Suffolk, CB8 0TE**
Contacts: **PHONE (01638) 667767 MOBILE (07785) 350705**
E-MAIL jdscargill@gmail.com WEBSITE www.jonscargill.co.uk

1 **CHERBOURG (FR)**, 6, b g Dunkerque (FR)—Seduisante (FR) **Mr S. J. Howard**
2 **GABRIELLE**, 5, b m Paco Boy (IRE)—Bounty Box **JPT Partnership**
3 **MISSISSIPPI MISS**, 4, ch f Equiano (FR)—Junket **Silent Partners**
4 **THE GINGER BERRY**, 8, ch g First Trump—Dolly Coughdrop (IRE) **Silent Partners**
5 4, B g Showcasing—Torver **Mrs S. M. Scargill**

DR JON SCARGILL - Continued

THREE-YEAR-OLDS

6 BILLIE BEANE, b f Sir Percy—Torver **Silent Partners**

TWO-YEAR-OLDS

7 Ch f 23/4 Dragon Pulse (IRE)—Miss Otis (Danetime (IRE)) (21000) **Theme Tune Partnership**
8 B f 16/1 Lawman (FR)—Well Focused (IRE) (Intense Focus (USA)) **GB Horseracing Services**

Other Owners: R. A. Dalton, P. J. Darlington, J. Dutton, P. J. Edwards, P. Lewsey, D. Meilton, Mr G. F. L. Robinson, Dr E. Robson, Mrs Susan Scargill, A. Shevas, D. Tunmore, B. Watson, R. Watson.

495
MR DERRICK SCOTT, Minehead
Postal: **East Lynch, Minehead, Somerset, TA24 8SS**
Contacts: **PHONE (01643) 702430 FAX (01643) 702430**

1 ACTONETAKETWO, 8, b m Act One—Temple Dancer **Mrs R. Scott**
2 ROYBUOY, 11, b g Royal Applause—Wavy Up (IRE) **Mrs R. Scott**

496
MR GEORGE SCOTT, Newmarket
Postal: **Saffron Stables, Hamilton Road, Newmarket, Suffolk, CB8 0NY**
Contacts: **MOBILE (07833) 461294**
E-MAIL george@georgescottracing.com WEBSITE www.georgescottracing.com

1 GILGAMESH, 4, b g Foxwedge (AUS)—Flaming Cliffs (USA) **Niarchos Family**
2 JAARIH (IRE), 6, ch g Starspangledbanner (AUS)—Bridge Note (USA) **Mr G. O. Scott**
3 JACK THE TRUTH (IRE), 4, ch g Dandy Man (IRE)—Friendly Heart (CAN) **Mr J. Stephenson**
4 KEIR HARDIE (IRE), 4, gr c Dark Angel (IRE)—Penicuik **W. J. Gredley**
5 PHOSPHORESCENCE (IRE), 8, b g Sakhee (USA)—Eccentricity (USA) **Mr G. O. Scott**
6 ROAD TO DUBAI (IRE), 4, ch c Aqlaam—Fragrancy (IRE) **M. Al Nabouda**

THREE-YEAR-OLDS

7 ADVANCED VIRGO (IRE), b c Holy Roman Emperor (IRE)—Amaraja (GER) **Niarchos Family**
8 ANOTHER BATT (IRE), ch g Windsor Knot (IRE)—Mrs Batt (IRE) **Excel Racing (Another Batt)**
9 ARTHUR DALEY (IRE), b c Camelot—Nasanice (IRE) **Chelsea Thoroughbreds - Minder**
10 BASTIDE BLANCHE (FR), ch f Champs Elysees—Starlit Sky **The Harnage Partnership II**
11 BELLA FERRARI, b f Bated Breath—Massarossa **Biddestone Racing XV**
12 BRIGHT SAFFRON, ch f Champs Elysees—Mercy Pecksniff **W. J. and T. C. O. Gredley**
13 CATHERINE TRAMELL (IRE), b f Zoffany (IRE)—Aine (IRE) **Chelsea TB's & Kings Bloodstock**
14 CRASH HELMET, b g Helmet (AUS)—Hot Secret **Ontoawinner & Saffron Racing II**
15 GAJA (IRE), b f High Chaparral (IRE)—Subtle Charm **Mrs S. Spencer**
16 GRAFFITISTA (IRE), b f Kodiac—Noble Galileo (IRE) **Bartram, Slade, Bolingbroke & Law**
17 HOLY TIBER (IRE), b f Holy Roman Emperor (IRE)—Quiet Waters (USA) **Mr M. Bartram**
18 JAMES GARFIELD (IRE), b c Exceed And Excel (AUS)—Whazzat **W. J. and T. C. O. Gredley**
19 MAGIC APPLAUSE (IRE), b f Zebedee—Last Hooray **Redman, Philipps & Hodge**
20 MAGNETIC BOUNDARY (USA), ch c Union Rags (USA)—Enthused (USA) **Flaxman Stables Ireland Ltd**
21 MANKIND (FR), b g Dabirsim (FR)—Pastiches **Mrs S. Spencer**
22 MARILYN M (IRE), b f Red Jazz (USA)—Jilly Choo **W. J. and T. C. O. Gredley**
23 MEWTOW, b c Helmet (AUS)—White Spirit (IRE) **Al Rabban Racing**
24 OLYMPIC ODYSSEY, b c Camelot—Field of Hope (IRE) **W. J. and T. C. O. Gredley**
25 SIGRID NANSEN, b f Cityscape—Hail Shower (IRE) **Hunscote Stud**
26 SLIPSTREAM (IRE), b g Invincible Spirit (IRE)—Kiltumber (IRE) **Mrs Michael Spencer & Ballylinch Stud**
27 STARBOY (IRE), br g Camacho—New Magic (IRE) **Excel Racing & Keith Breen**
28 ZIZUM, ch c Showcasing—Proud Duchess (IRE) **Al Rabban Racing**

TWO-YEAR-OLDS

29 ALBANDERI, b f 25/4 Kingman—Hazel Lavery (IRE) (Excellent Art) (195360) **Al Rabban Racing**
30 BARDO (IRE), b c 16/1 Galileo (IRE)—
   Gilt Edge Girl (Monsieur Bond (IRE)) (150000) **W J & T C O Gredley & Flaxman Stables Ire Ltd**
31 BELLUM, b c 23/2 Battle of Marengo (IRE)—
   Quail Landing (Mark of Esteem (IRE)) (61904) **Orbis Bloodstock (UK) Limited**
32 B f 20/2 Gregorian (IRE)—Big Moza (Pastoral Pursuits) **Mr A Watson, Mr B Malyon, Mr M Shenfield**

MR GEORGE SCOTT - Continued

33 **BYRD (IRE)**, b c 18/4 Kodiac—Precious Gem (IRE) (Sadler's Wells (USA)) (61049) **W. J. and T. C. O. Gredley**
34 **CLEM A**, b c 7/3 Helmet (AUS)—Mondovi (Kyllachy) (70000) **W. J. and T. C. O. Gredley**
35 **CRANTOCK BAY**, b c 7/2 Havana Gold (IRE)—Orton Park (IRE) (Moss Vale) (47619) **Mr K. J. Breen**
36 Ch f 16/2 Universal (IRE)—Dance For Georgie (Motivator) **Mr A. Al Mansoori**
37 **EARTH AND SKY (USA)**, b f 24/3 Noble Mission—
Youre So Sweet (USA) (Storm Cat (USA)) **Flaxman Stables Ireland Ltd**
38 B c 29/3 Casamento (IRE)—Emerald Peace (IRE) (Green Desert (USA)) (18722) **Blue Starr Racing**
39 Ch c 13/3 Shamardal (USA)—Fragrancy (IRE) (Singspiel (IRE)) **M. Al Nabouda**
40 **GEORGE GERSHWIN**, b c 5/3 Bated Breath—
Sharp Relief (IRE) (Galileo (IRE)) (65120) **Chelsea Thoroughbreds Ltd**
41 **LAHESSAR**, b c 29/2 Exceed And Excel (AUS)—
Burlesque Star (IRE) (Thousand Words) (120000) **Al Rabban Racing**
42 **LYNDON B (IRE)**, b c 31/1 Charm Spirit (IRE)—Kelsey Rose (Most Welcome) (56980) **W. J. and T. C. O. Gredley**
43 **MERGE (IRE)**, b c 25/2 Dandy Man (IRE)—Interlacing (Oasis Dream) (104761) **Orbis Bloodstock (UK) Limited**
44 **MY EXCELSA (IRE)**, b f 27/2 Exceed And Excel (AUS)—
Emirates Joy (USA) (Street Cry (IRE)) (66666) **Mr A Boyd Rochfort & Mr S Leslie**
45 **NARAK**, ch f 29/5 Dubawi (IRE)—Chachamaidee (IRE) (Footstepsinthesand) **Mr R. A. H. Evans**
46 Ch f 29/1 Sepoy (AUS)—Portland River (FR) (Stormy River (FR)) (8000) **Mr A. Al Mansoori**
47 B c 11/2 Dutch Art—Sea Meets Sky (FR) (Dansili) (36190) **The Rum Babas**
48 Ch f 20/2 Sir Prancealot (IRE)—Shiftin Bobbins (Selkirk (USA))
49 **SLEEPER QUEEN**, ch f 16/4 Holy Roman Emperor (IRE)—Rainbows Guest (IRE) (Indian Lodge (IRE))
50 **STRAWBERRY JACK**, b c 1/4 Foxwedge (AUS)—Strawberry Leaf (Unfuwain (USA)) (5500) **Mr J. Stephenson**
51 B c 23/5 Dawn Approach (IRE)—Surrealism (Pivotal) (32000) **A. Saeed**
52 Gr f 13/3 Foxwedge (AUS)—Sweet Alabama (Johannesburg (USA)) **Biddestone Racing Club**
53 B f 2/3 Sir Percy—Sweet Cando (IRE) (Royal Applause) (105820) **Breen, Elliott & Ware**
54 B br c 20/2 Artie Schiller (USA)—Sweet Temper (USA) (Stormy Atlantic (USA)) (38714) **Excel Racing**
55 B c 20/4 Society Rock (IRE)—Warm Welcome (Motivator) (57142) **Bartram,Kilburn & Ware**
56 B f 25/1 Dawn Approach (IRE)—Winner's Wish (Clodovil (IRE)) (2000) **Mr A. Al Mansoori**
57 **ZIGELLO (IRE)**, b f 30/1 Intello (GER)—Zigarra (Halling (USA)) (162800) **Orbis Bloodstock (UK) Limited**

Other Owners: Mr H. A. Al Jehani, Mr A. K. M. K. Al-Rabban, Mr C. Austin, Mr L. A. Bolingbroke, T. P. Bostwick, Mrs G. P. Bostwick, Mr A. R. Boyd-Rochfort, Chelsea TB's & Kings Bloodstock 1, Chelsea Thoroughbreds Ltd, Mr P. Fisher, Flaxman Stables Ireland Ltd, T. C. O. Gredley, D. Kilburn, Lady C. Law, Mr S. Leslie, Mrs S. Magnier, Mrs E. Magnier, Mrs P. N. D. McClean, Mr N. J. O'Brien, P. A. Philipps, Mr T. J. Ramsden, Mr T. S. Redman, Saffron Racing II, Mrs J. A. Scott, Mrs L. M. Shanahan, Mr J. H. Slade, S. M. Smith, Mrs L. A. Smith, Mr E. J. Ware.

Apprentice: Fletcher Yarham.

---

497 **MR JEREMY SCOTT, Dulverton**
Postal: **Higher Holworthy Farm, Brompton Regis, Dulverton, Somerset, TA22 9NY**
Contacts: **PHONE (01398) 371414 MOBILE (07709) 279483**
E-MAIL holworthyfarm@yahoo.com

1 **BANG ON (IRE)**, 5, ch g Fracas (IRE)—Carramanagh Lady (IRE) **Cash For Honours**
2 **BEAU PHIL (FR)**, 7, ch g Cachet Noir (USA)—Neyrianne (FR) **The Beau Phil Partnership**
3 **BLUE APRIL (FR)**, 7, b g Blue Bresil (FR)—Royale Little (FR) **Mr J P Carrington & Partner**
4 **BONZA GIRL**, 5, b m Midnight Legend—Purple Patch **Mr G. T. Lever**
5 **BUILDING FUTURES (IRE)**, 5, b g Kalanisi (IRE)—Lady of The Mill (IRE) **Mrs C. C. Scott**
6 **COLMERS HILL**, 8, b g Crosspeace (IRE)—My Dancing Kin **Gale Force Four**
7 **COMRAGH (IRE)**, 8, br m Desert King (IRE)—Akica (IRE) **London Erratics Racing Club**
8 **DASHEL DRASHER**, 5, b g Passing Glance—So Long **Mrs B Tully & Mr R Lock**
9 **ELLENS WAY**, 6, b m Black Sam Bellamy (IRE)—Function Dreamer **Bet The Farm Partners**
10 **GARRANE (IRE)**, 6, b g Tikkanen (USA)—Ballooley (IRE) **Friends From Insurance**
11 **GONNABEGOOD (IRE)**, 7, b g Kutub (IRE)—Angels Flame (IRE) **The Free Spirits Partnership**
12 **HEY BUD**, 5, b g Fair Mix (IRE)—Azione **Mr M. Brend**
13 **JACK SNIPE**, 9, b g Kirkwall—Sea Snipe **Pillhead House Partners**
14 **KILMURVY (IRE)**, 10, b g Shantou (USA)—Spagna (IRE) **I. R. Murray**
15 **L'AUBERGE DU BOIS (IRE)**, 6, br g Olden Times—Midway (IRE) **George & Glenda Giles**
16 **LADY LONGSHOT**, 7, b m Needle Gun (IRE)—So Long **Mr R Lock, Mrs B Tully & Mrs C Scott**
17 **MISS MINUTY**, 6, gr m Verglas (IRE)—Miss Provence **Miss J. S. Dorey**
18 **MOONLIGHT FLYER (IRE)**, 6, b g Broadway Flyer (USA)—Monteleena (USA) **Wot No Coz**
19 **MOORLANDS JACK**, 13, b g Cloudings (IRE)—Sandford Springs (USA) **Mr C. H. Vicary**
20 **NATIVE ROBIN (IRE)**, 8, br g Robin des Pres (FR)—Homebird (IRE) **The Punchestown Syndicate**
21 **NIFTY AT FIFTY (IRE)**, 5, b g Gold Well—Tropical Sunset (IRE) **Mrs H. L. Stoneman**

MR JEREMY SCOTT - Continued

22 **NOTARFBAD (IRE)**, 12, b g Alderbrook—Angels Flame (IRE) **Govier & Brown**
23 **SHOOFLY MILLY (IRE)**, 9, b m Milan—Jacksister (IRE) **Gale Force One**
24 **SPEEDALONG (IRE)**, 7, b g Vertical Speed (FR)—Emily's Bracelet (IRE) **Mrs S. J. Lanz**
25 **THAT'S GONNA STING (IRE)**, 7, b g Scorpion (IRE)—Creme d'arblay (IRE) **Mr C. J. James**
26 **TIKKINTHEBOX (IRE)**, 6, b g Tikkanen (USA)—Surfing France (FR) **On A Mission**
27 **TWO HOOTS (IRE)**, 7, gr g Tikkanen (USA)—Supreme Beneficial (IRE) **CCM Partnership**
28 **UNISON (IRE)**, 8, b g Jeremy—Easter Song (USA) **Mr J. P. Carrington**
29 **URTHEONETHATIWANT (IRE)**, 5, ch g Shantou (USA)—Roberta Supreme (IRE) **The Barmy Men 4**
30 **ZULU OSCAR**, 9, b g Oscar (IRE)—Loxhill Lady **The Barmy Men 2**

Other Owners: Mr Mark Ansell, Mr John Purefoy, Mr Glynn Berrington-Evans, Mr M. Bower-Dyke, Mr A. P. Brown, Mr G. Brown, Mr J. P. Carrington, Mr G. Carstairs, Mr Phillip Cartwright, Mrs S. Cliff, Mrs S. Cole, Mr Clive Cole, Mr D. J. Coles, Miss A. Delve, Mr J. M. O. Evans, Mr Richard Flood, Mr Tony Gale, Mrs Glenda Giles, Mr George Giles, Mr I. F. Gosden, Mr P. T. Govier, Mr P. F. Govier, Mr C. F. Hayes, Mr M. Holman, Mr James Illingworth, Mr Chris Keey, Mr G. T. Lever, Mr R. J. Lock, Mr S. Loosemore, Mr Christopher Lyles, Mr Richard Marker, Mr Brendan McManus, Mr P. Moore, Mrs S. M. Ragg, Mr A. Rennison, Mrs Camilla Scott, Mr B. D. Smith, Mr M. J. Swallow, Mrs Bridget Tully, Mr P. J. Upton.

Assistant Trainer: Camilla Scott

Jockey (NH): Matt Griffiths, Nick Scholfield. **Conditional:** Rob Hawker. **Amateur:** Miss V. Wade.

498

MISS KATIE SCOTT, Galashiels
Postal: **Stables Cottage, Millhaugh, Lindean, Galashiels, Scottish Borders**
Contacts: **MOBILE (07826) 344577**

1 **CHAIN OF BEACONS**, 9, b g Midnight Legend—Millennium Girl **Simon & Angela Gillie**
2 **HERECOMESNELSON (IRE)**, 9, b g Morozov (USA)—Undesperado View (IRE) **Millhaugh Racing**
3 **KALASTAR (IRE)**, 9, b g Kalanisi (IRE)—Katsura **Mr K. J. Telfer**
4 **KNOCKLAYDE (IRE)**, 6, b g Mountain High (IRE)—Foret Noire (IRE) **The Jackson Partnership**
5 4, B g Getaway (GER)—Loch Dhu (IRE) **Mr W. M. Scott**
6 **NICE VINTAGE (IRE)**, 6, b br m Big Bad Bob (IRE)—High Vintage (IRE) **The Vintage Flyers**
7 **RORY'S VALENTINE (IRE)**, 7, br m Windsor Knot (IRE)—Housekeeping **Mrs S. Scott**
8 4, B f Westerner—Supreme Nova **Mr E. Cassie**
9 **THE DAWN BANDIT (IRE)**, 5, gr m Daylami (IRE)—Queen of The Dawn (IRE) **The Bandits**
10 **WESTERN LASS (IRE)**, 5, br m Westerner—Lady Roania (IRE) **Edward Cassie & Katie Scott**
11 **WHATSTHESTORYMAN (IRE)**, 10, b g Alderbrook—Express Way Lady (IRE) **Miss E. Dunkley**

Other Owners: Mr Edward Cassie, Mrs Angela Gillie, Mr Simon Gillie, Dr Dianne McGuiness, Miss K. Scott, Mr Kenny Telfer.

499

MR MICHAEL SCUDAMORE, Bromsash
Postal: **Eccleswall Court, Bromsash, Nr. Ross-on-Wye, Herefordshire, HR9 7PP**
Contacts: **PHONE (01989) 750844 FAX (01989) 750281 MOBILE (07901) 853520**
E-MAIL michael.scu@btconnect.com WEBSITE www.michaelscudamoreracing.co.uk

1 **AMARANTH (IRE)**, 5, b g New Approach (IRE)—Kitty Kiernan **Mr C. G. J. Chua**
2 **BELMONT JEWEL (IRE)**, 6, b m Westerner—Maddy's Supreme (IRE) **Having A Mare & Mr W J Fenn**
3 **CADEYRN (IRE)**, 6, b g Flemensfirth (USA)—Kapricia Speed (FR) **Mr John J Murray & Mrs Lynne MacLennan**
4 **COBAJAYISLAND (IRE)**, 10, b g Heron Island (IRE)—Shinora (IRE) **Mrs L. Maclennan**
5 **COPPER COIN**, 5, ch g Sulamani (IRE)—Silken Pearls **Mr P. E. Truscott**
6 **CORNER CREEK (IRE)**, 8, b g Presenting—No Moore Bills **Mr M. R. Blandford**
7 **COTTONWOOL BABY (IRE)**, 7, b m Gold Well—Golden Steppes **Mr M. Scudamore**
8 **COURT MASTER (IRE)**, 5, b g Court Cave (IRE)—Lusos Wonder (IRE) **Mrs L. Maclennan**
9 **DAN EMMETT (USA)**, 8, ch g Flower Alley (USA)—Singing Dixie (USA) **Mrs L. Maclennan**
10 **DANCING HEARTS**, 5, b m Makfi—Danceabout **Mr Mark Savidge Mr Richard Green**
11 **DAWNIERIVER (IRE)**, 8, br m Indian River (FR)—In Sin (IRE) **Don't Tell Ken**
12 **DINSDALE**, 5, b g Cape Cross (IRE)—Emmy Award (IRE) **Mr M. Jones**
13 **GAELIC ANGEL (IRE)**, 5, b m Pour Moi (IRE)—Missionary Hymn (USA) **Mrs L. Maclennan**
14 **GRACE TARA**, 9, b m Kayf Tara—Fenney Spring **Having A Mare I**
15 **HEAD HUNTER (IRE)**, 5, b g Rip Van Winkle (IRE)—Superfonic (FR) **Mrs B. V. Evans**
16 **HELIS (FR)**, 5, b g Footstepsinthesand—Xaara (SWE) **S. M. Smith**

MR MICHAEL SCUDAMORE - Continued

17 **JUPITER CUSTOS (FR)**, 6, b g Le Havre (IRE)—Angel Rose (IRE) **Mr C. G. J. Chua**
18 **JUSTICE KNIGHT (IRE)**, 6, b g Raven's Pass (USA)—New Story (USA) **Mr Mark Savidge & Mr H Bennett**
19 **KINGSWELL THEATRE**, 9, b g King's Theatre (IRE)—Cresswell Native (IRE) **Mr J. J. Murray**
20 **KRAFTY ONE**, 6, ch m Mastercraftsman (IRE)—Wonderful Desert **Simpson-Daniel & Scudamore Racing**
21 **LADY MARWAH (IRE)**, 5, b m Iffraaj—Eyrecourt (IRE) **K Hanson W Fenn Having A Mare D Lee**
22 **LICKETY SPLIT (FR)**, 5, b m Buck's Boum (FR)—Sninfia (IRE) **Mark & Jane Frieze**
23 **MISSISSIPPI MOON (IRE)**, 8, g Dansili—Funny Girl (IRE) **Mr Martin Jones & Mr Michael Scudamore**
24 **MONBEG AQUADUDE (IRE)**, 7, b g Flemensfirth (USA)—Mite Dash (IRE) **Mr M. R. Blandford**
25 **MYSTEREE (IRE)**, 10, b g Gold Well—Hillside Native (IRE) **Mrs L. Maclennan**
26 **NO THROUGH ROAD**, 11, b g Grape Tree Road—Pendil's Delight **Mr A. P. Barwell**
27 **NOBEL DUKE (IRE)**, 5, ch g Duke of Marmalade (IRE)—Dowager **Roberts Green Whittal-Williams Savidge**
28 **NORTHERN BEAU (IRE)**, 5, b m Canford Cliffs (IRE)—View (IRE) **Lynne & Angus Maclennan**
29 **ORIENTAL FIXER (IRE)**, 9, b g Vertical Speed (FR)—Hannah Rose (IRE) **JCG Chua & CK Ong**
30 **PLENTY OF BUTTY (IRE)**, 5, b g Germany (USA)—Jump For Joy (IRE) **Mr M. R. Blandford**
31 **SHENEEDEDTHERUN (IRE)**, 8, b m Kayf Tara—Lady Moon (IRE) **Mr M. Jones**
32 **SKINT**, 12, b g King's Theatre (IRE)—No More Money **Mrs B. V. Evans**
33 **SOUNDS OF ITALY (IRE)**, 9, b g Milan—Sound Hill (FR) **The Whippetears**
34 **STATE SOVEREIGNTY**, 6, b m Authorized (IRE)—Sovereign's Honour (USA) **Mr C. G. J. Chua**
35 **STREETS OF PROMISE (IRE)**, 9, b m Westerner—Miracle Lady **Gempro**
36 **TURBOTIM (IRE)**, 5, b g Arakan (USA)—Katy McKay (IRE) **Gempro**
37 **TWENTY EIGHT GUNS**, 8, b m Black Sam Bellamy (IRE)—Glory Be **Mason Scudamore Racing**
38 **TWO SMOKIN BARRELS**, 9, b m Kayf Tara—Coldabri (IRE) **Mr M. Jones**
39 **VOILA ERIC**, 6, b g Bollin Eric—Et Voila **Wink N' A Drink**
40 **WIMPOLE**, 5, b g Zamindar (USA)—Proportional **Mr John J Murray & Mrs Lynne MacLennan**
41 **ZAYFIRE ARAMIS**, 9, ch g Zafeen (FR)—Kaylifa Aramis **Aramis Racing**

THREE-YEAR-OLDS

42 **ISAAC WONDER (IRE)**, b g Born To Sea (IRE)—Najaaba (USA) **Mrs L. Maclennan**
43 **SHE'S BLORENCE**, ch f Arvico (FR)—Lefty's Dollbaby (USA) **Mark & Jane Frieze**

Other Owners: Mr D. I. Alexander, Mr H. Bennett, Mr C. Breeze, Mr D. E. Coltman, Mr S. J. Daws, Mr W. J. Fenn, Mrs J. Frieze, Mr M. A. Frieze, Mr R. R. Green, F. M. Green, Mr K. Hanson, Mrs J. Hanson, Having A Mare, Mr T. S. Hopkins, Mr D. J. Lee, Mr A. Maclennan, Mr A. Mason, Mr N. McGawley, Mrs J. M. Murray, Mr F. Ong, Ms I. Phipps Coltman, G. A. Roberts, Mr N. J. Robinson, Mr S. Robson, Mr M. G. Savidge, Mrs M. L. Scudamore, Mrs L. J. Sluman, Ms N. Walls, Mr E. B. Whittall-Williams, Mr S. Williams.

Assistant Trainer: Miss Kate Hanson

---

500 | **MR DEREK SHAW**, Sproxton
Postal: **The Sidings, Saltby Road, Sproxton, Melton Mowbray, Leicestershire, LE14 4RA**
Contacts: PHONE (01476) 860578 FAX (01476) 860578 MOBILE (07721) 039645
E-MAIL mail@derekshawracing.com WEBSITE www.derekshawracing.com

1 **BAZ (FR)**, 8, b g Mount Nelson—Zelah (IRE) **P. E. Barrett**
2 **BOKETTO (IRE)**, 4, b f Canford Cliffs (IRE)—Olimpic Girl (IRE) **Mr D. Shaw**
3 **BOROUGH BOY (IRE)**, 8, b g Jeremy (USA)—Ostrusa (AUT) **Mr B. Johnson**
4 **CAPTAIN LARS (SAF)**, 4, b g Captain Al (SAF)—Polar Charge **Mr C. B. Hamilton**
5 **DYNAMO WALT (IRE)**, 7, b g Acclamation—Cambara **Mr B. Johnson**
6 **EMIGRATED (IRE)**, 5, b g Fastnet Rock (AUS)—Ecoutila (USA) **Mr D. Shaw**
7 **FOXY FEELIN**, 4, b g Foxwedge (AUS)—Strawberry Dale (IRE) **Shawthing Racing Partnership**
8 **HAMMER GUN (USA)**, 5, b g Smart Strike (CAN)—Caraboss **Mr A. Flint**
9 **LAQAB (IRE)**, 5, b g Teofilo (IRE)—Ghaidaa (IRE) **Mr A. H. Malik**
10 **LE MANEGE ENCHANTE (IRE)**, 5, gr g Zebedee—Beth **Mr N. P. Franklin**
11 **LOYALTY**, 11, b g Medicean—Ecoutila (USA) **The Whiteman Partnership**
12 **MUTAWAARY (IRE)**, 4, b g Shamardal—Shuhra (IRE) **Mr A. H. Malik**
13 **NARALSAIF (IRE)**, 4, b f Arcano (IRE)—Mejala (IRE) **Shawthing Racing Partnership**
14 **PETRUCCI (IRE)**, 6, b g Azamour (IRE)—Spring Symphony (IRE) **Mr B. Johnson**
15 **POLARBROOK (IRE)**, 11, br g Alderbrook—Frozen Cello (IRE) **Mr J. R. Saville**
16 **RUN WITH PRIDE (IRE)**, 8, b g Invincible Spirit (IRE)—Zibilene **The Whiteman Partnership**
17 **SAMPHIRE COAST**, 5, b g Fastnet Rock (AUS)—Faslen (USA) **P. E. Barrett**
18 **SAVANNAH BEAU**, 6, b m Major Cadeaux—Mancunian Way **Market Avenue Racing Club Ltd**
19 **SOCKS AND SHARES (IRE)**, 5, b g Elnadim (USA)—Al Andalyya (USA) **Mr D. Shaw**

MR DEREK SHAW - Continued

20 **TINA TEASPOON**, 4, b f Kheleyf (USA)—Button Moon (IRE) **P. E. Barrett**
21 **TOP BOY**, 8, b g Exceed And Excel (AUS)—Injaaz **Mr B. Johnson**
22 **TREATY OF ROME (USA)**, 6, b br g War Front (USA)—Blading Gold Ring (USA) **Mr J. R. Saville**
23 **ULTIMATE CLIMAX (IRE)**, 4, ch g Casamento (IRE)—Intricate Design **Tony Flint & Bryn Ilsley**
24 **WELLIESINTHEWATER (IRE)**, 8, b g Footstepsinthesand—Shadow Ash (IRE) **Shawthing Racing Partnership**

THREE-YEAR-OLDS

25 **AMAZING AMAYA**, b f New Approach (IRE)—Faslen (USA) **P. E. Barrett**
26 **BOMAD**, b g Kheleyf (USA)—Fenella Fudge **Mr B. Johnson**
27 **BORN FOR PROSECCO (IRE)**, ch f Red Jazz (USA)—Kelso Magic (USA) **Mr D. Shaw**
28 **CRIKEYITSWHYKIE**, b g Piccolo—Kitty Kitty Cancan **Mrs L. J. Shaw**
29 **ELLIOT THE DRAGON (IRE)**, b g Raven's Pass (USA)—Somerset Falls (UAE) **Mr D. Shaw**
30 **PEAS ON EARTH**, ch f Showcasing—Meditation **P. E. Barrett**
31 **POLITICAL SLOT**, ch f Helmet (AUS)—Lady Elalmadol (IRE) **Mr B. Johnson**
32 **POPPY LINE**, b f Equiano (FR)—Ming Meng (IRE) **P. E. Barrett**

Yard Sponsor : Grosvenor Contracts Leasing Ltd

Apprentice: Charlotte McFarland.

501

MRS FIONA SHAW, Dorchester
Postal: **Skippet Cottage, Bradford Peverell, Dorchester, Dorset, DT2 9SE**
Contacts: **PHONE (01305) 889350 MOBILE (07970) 370444**
E-MAIL fiona.shaw05@gmail.com

1 **ACT CASUAL**, 8, b m Act One—Eatons **P. B. Shaw**
2 **DARWINS THEORY (IRE)**, 10, b g Montjeu (IRE)—Thrift (IRE) **Mrs F. M. Shaw**
3 **HALLY'S KITCHEN**, 6, b m Getaway (GER)—Crystal Ballerina (IRE) **Mr P. J. Legg**
4 **HYMN AND A PRAYER**, 5, br g Eastern Anthem (IRE)—Kryssa **Mrs F. M. Shaw**
5 **KIWI MYTH**, 6, b m Midnight Legend—Kiwi Katie **John & Heather Snook**
6 **THE MIGHTY ASH (IRE)**, 8, b g Arcadio (GER)—She's Got To Go (IRE) **Mrs A. Hollier**
7 **TIMES OF TROUBLE**, 8, b g Tobougg (IRE)—Let It Be **Mrs F. M. Shaw**

Other Owners: Mrs H. A. Snook, J. W. Snook.

502

MR MARK SHEARS, Newton Abbot
Postal: **Lower Nattadon, Chagford, Newton Abbot, Devon, TQ13 8ER**
Contacts: **PHONE (01647) 432356 FAX (01647) 432356 MOBILE (07881) 745314**
E-MAIL markshearsracing@gmail.com

1 **HOW'S VIENNA (IRE)**, 8, b g Westerner—Plant A Smacker (IRE) **Mr M. B. Shears**
2 **MICKEYSMATEDUSTY**, 6, b g Revoque (IRE)—Dusty Anne (IRE) **Mr M. B. Shears**
3 **NICE THOUGHTS (IRE)**, 6, b g Shamardal (USA)—Zacheta **Mr M. B. Shears**
4 **SCENIC STAR (IRE)**, 8, b g Erewhon (USA)—African Scene (IRE) **Mr M. B. Shears**
5 **TUFFSTUFF**, 10, b g Generous (IRE)—Life Line **J. B. Shears**

Assistant Trainer: Miss K. Reynolds

503

MR MATT SHEPPARD, Ledbury
Postal: **Home Farm Cottage, Eastnor, Ledbury, Herefordshire, HR8 1RD**
Contacts: **FAX (01531) 634846 MOBILE (07770) 625061**
E-MAIL matthew.sheppard@cmail.co.uk

1 **GO ON HENRY (IRE)**, 10, b g Golan (IRE)—The Millers Tale (IRE) **P J & S E Bailey**
2 **HANDSOME SAM**, 7, ch g Black Sam Bellamy (IRE)—Rose Marine **P J & S E Bailey**
3 **HILL FORT**, 8, ch g Pivotal—Cairns (UAE) **Mr A. J. Scrivin**
4 **INVINCIBLE WISH (IRE)**, 6, b g Vale of York (USA)—Moonlight Wish (IRE) **Michael & Lesley Wilkes**
5 **KESTREL VALLEY**, 4, b f Dr Massini (IRE)—Lady Karinga **Mrs N. Sheppard**
6 **MODELIGO (IRE)**, 9, b g Indian Danehill (IRE)—Glens Lady (IRE) **S. J. D. Gegg**
7 **PHANGIO (USA)**, 9, ch g Invasor (ARG)—Muneera (USA) **S. J. D. Gegg**

MR MATT SHEPPARD - Continued

8 **ROCK ON ROCKY**, 10, b g Overbury (IRE)—Tachometer (IRE) **Jan Johnson & Terry Harman**
9 **TAMAYEF (IRE)**, 4, b g Sir Prancealot (IRE)—Miss Glitters (IRE) **Michael & Lesley Wilkes**
10 **TB BROKE HER (IRE)**, 8, br m Indian River (FR)—Catch Ball **W. R. Gaskins**
11 **THE BAY BIRCH (IRE)**, 7, b m Beneficial—Tournant Vic (IRE) **Mr A. J. Scrivin**

Other Owners: Mr P. J. Bailey, Mrs S. E. Bailey, Mr T. A. Harman, Mrs J. M. Johnson, Mrs L. Wilkes, Mr M. H. A. Wilkes.

Conditional: Stan Sheppard. **Amateur:** Mr Ed Bailey.

---

504 **MR OLIVER SHERWOOD, Upper Lambourn**
Postal: **Rhonehurst House, Upper Lambourn, Hungerford, Berkshire, RG17 8RG**
Contacts: PHONE (01488) 71411 FAX (01488) 72786 MOBILE (07979) 591867
E-MAIL oliver.sherwood@virgin.net WEBSITE www.oliversherwood.co.uk

1 **BLAMEITALONMYROOTS (IRE)**, 8, b m Turtle Island (IRE)—Makingyourmindup (IRE) **Mr T. D. J. Syder**
2 **BOOK OF GOLD (IRE)**, 6, b g Flemensfirth (USA)—Ballerina Queen (IRE) **Mr A Lousada & Mr A Kaplan**
3 **BORN LEGEND (IRE)**, 4, b g Born To Sea (IRE)—Hallowed Park (IRE) **British Racing Club**
4 **BRIERY BUNNY**, 6, b m Lucarno (USA)—Blackbriery Thyne (IRE) **Mrs H. Plumbly**
5 **BROUGHTONS RHYTHM**, 9, b g Araafa (IRE)—Broughton Singer (IRE) **Broughton Thermal Insulations**
6 **CAPTAIN PEACOCK**, 5, b g Champs Elysees—Blast Furnace (IRE) **Joule, Apiafi & Black**
7 **DOMINATEUR (FR)**, 5, b g Desir d'un Soir (FR)—Sourya d'airy (FR) **Mr A. L. Brooks**
8 **DUNCOMPLAINING (IRE)**, 9, b g Milan—Notcomplainingbut (IRE) **Mrs J Kinsey & Mrs J Greenway**
9 **EASTER DAY (FR)**, 10, b g Malinas (GER)—Sainte Lea (FR) **Broughton Thermal Insulations**
10 **ENJOY RESPONSIBLY (IRE)**, 9, b g Flemensfirth (USA)—Spice Patrol (IRE) **Mr J. Beswick**
11 **EUXTON LANE (IRE)**, 6, b g Getaway (GER)—Local Hall (IRE) **Mr T. J. Hemmings**
12 **FELIX D'AUTRY (FR)**, 4, b g Khalkevi (IRE)—Hassaya (FR)
13 **FIGHT COMMANDER (IRE)**, 9, b g Oscar (IRE)—Creidim (IRE) **Mrs J. M. Rathbone**
14 **FORT SMITH (IRE)**, 9, b g Presenting—Land of Honour **Mr J. Beswick**
15 **GEORDIELAD**, 4, ch g Geordieland (FR)—Adees Dancer **Mr A. Taylor**
16 **GOT AWAY (FR)**, 5, b m American Post—Hideaway Girl **B McDonald & B Mellon**
17 **HITHERJACQUES LADY (IRE)**, 6, br m Robin des Champs (FR)—Crackin' Liss (IRE) **Mr A. F. Lousada**
18 **ICING ON THE CAKE (IRE)**, 8, b g Spadoun (FR)—
          Honeyed (IRE) **Palmer-Brown Worcester Lousada Shrubsall**
19 **ITS A STING (IRE)**, 9, b g Scorpion (IRE)—Wyndham Sweetmarie (IRE) **Mr M. A. Burton**
20 4, Br g Westerner—Jemima Jay (IRE)
21 **JERSEY BEAN (IRE)**, 5, b g Court Cave (IRE)—Jennifers Diary (IRE) **Mr A. Taylor**
22 **JURBY**, 8, b g Motivator—Darariyna (IRE) **Mr T. J. Hemmings**
23 **LAURIE COME ON (IRE)**, 4, br g Robin des Champs (FR)—Seekayclaire (IRE) **Mr P. Mellett**
24 **LEGEND LADY**, 7, b m Midnight Legend—Aoninch **Legend Lady Partnership**
25 **MANNING ESTATE (IRE)**, 4, b g Stowaway—Specifiedrisk (IRE) **Mr & Mrs Norman**
26 **MIGHT STING (IRE)**, 6, b g Scorpion (IRE)—One Cool Kate (IRE) **F. R. Jarvey**
27 **MINELLA ON LINE (IRE)**, 9, b g King's Theatre (IRE)—Bally Bolshoi (IRE) **AHB Racing Partnership**
28 **MORNING REGGIE**, 9, gr g Turgeon (USA)—Nile Cristale (FR) **Mr T. D. J. Syder**
29 **MR DORRELL SAGE (FR)**, 5, b gr g Sageburg (IRE)—Miss Breezy (FR) **The Three Fields**
30 **NO NO JOLIE (FR)**, 6, gr m Martaline—Virgata (FR) **R. Jenner & J. Green**
31 **NO NO JULIET (IRE)**, 5, br m Scorpion (IRE)—Full Imperatrice (FR) **Don Sebastiao Partnership**
32 **OURVILLE'S MILLION (FR)**, 5, b g Sageburg (IRE)—Madeka (FR) **The Ivy Syndicate**
33 **PAPAGANA**, 5, b m Martaline—New Destiny (FR) **Mr D. J. Burke**
34 **PEUR DE RIEN (FR)**, 5, b g Kapgarde (FR)—Tango Princess (FR) **Mr T. D. J. Syder**
35 **PITON PETE (FR)**, 7, b g Westerner—Glenair Lucy (IRE) **Mr P. Mellett**
36 **PONTRESINA (IRE)**, 5, b g Milan—Gilt Benefit (IRE) **Winterfields Farm Ltd, M Burton & H Cox**
37 **PUFFIN BILLY**, 10, b g Heron Island (IRE)—Downtown Train (IRE) **Mr T. D. J. Syder**
38 **QUERRY HORSE (FR)**, 6, b g Equerry (USA)—La Richelandiere (FR) **Luksonwood Partnership**
39 **RAYVIN BLACK**, 9, b g Halling (USA)—Optimistic **Mr R. White & Mr V. J. Walsh**
40 **ROAD TO ROME (IRE)**, 8, b g Choisir (AUS)—Tibbie **Peel Racing Club**
41 **ROBINSSON (IRE)**, 8, b g Robin des Champs (FR)—Silver Proverb **Mr A. Taylor**
42 **ROUGE ET BLANC (FR)**, 13, ch g Mansonnien (FR)—Fidelety (FR) **Mr O. M. C. Sherwood**
43 **ROYALRAISE (IRE)**, 9, b g Royal Anthem (USA)—
          Raise The Issue (IRE) **Ian Barratt, Stephen Short & Adam Signy**
44 **SAFE HARBOUR (IRE)**, 6, b g Stowaway—Beharista (FR) **Jeremy Dougall & Will Watt**
45 **SAINT JUDE (IRE)**, 5, b g Presenting—Native Monk (FR) **Mr T. J. Hemmings**
46 **SEASTON SPIRIT**, 5, b g Kayf Tara—Aphrodisias (FR) **Mr M. Fiddy**
47 **SEVARANO (IRE)**, 5, b g Shantou (USA)—Eva La Diva (IRE) **Mr T. D. J. Syder**
48 **SHAUGHNESSY**, 5, b g Shantou (USA)—Sudden Beat **Mr T. D. J. Syder**

MR OLIVER SHERWOOD - Continued

49 **SURTEE DU BERLAIS (IRE)**, 8, b m High Chaparral (IRE)—Marina du Berlais (FR) **Mrs S. Griffiths**
50 **THE FRESH PRINCE (IRE)**, 8, b g Robin des Pres (FR)—Hayley Cometh (IRE) **Mr T. J. Hemmings**
51 **THE GROOVY HOOVY**, 6, b g Sulamani (IRE)—Kingennie **The Groovy Hoovy Partnership**
52 **THE ORGANIST (IRE)**, 7, b m Alkaadhem—Go On Eileen (IRE) **Mr J. P. McManus**
53 **TOVIERE (IRE)**, 7, ch g Presenting—Aventia (IRE) **Mr T. D. J. Syder**
54 **VALDAS PRINCESS**, 6, b m King's Theatre (IRE)—Valdas Queen (GER) **A. P. Racing**
55 **VALJAN**, 4, b f Shirocco (GER)—Miracle **David Bellamy & Dominic Burke**
56 **VERSIFIER**, 6, b m Yeats (IRE)—Daprika (FR) **Personal Racehorse Owners 4**
57 **WHAT'S OCCURRING (IRE)**, 5, b g Rail Link—Lovely Origny (FR) **Mr Andrew Cohen & Mr Alan Kaplan**
58 **WORKING CLASS**, 4, b g Bahri (USA)—Louise d'arzens **Mr B. Ryan-Beswick**

Other Owners: Mr J. Allison, Mr J. Apiafi, Mr I. J. Barratt, D. Bellamy, A. W. Black, Mr A. L. Cohen, Mr H. W. Cox, Mr J. M. Dougall, Mr B. Etchells, Mr R. J. Fowler, Mrs B. S. Fowler, Mrs A. J. Green, Mrs J. Greenway, Mr C. S. Heaps, Mr J. C. I. Heilbron, Mrs S. A. Hodgkiss, D. M. W. Hodgkiss, Ms R. A. Jenner, Mr T. S. L. Joule, Alan Kaplan, Mrs J. Kinsey, Mr W. R. Kinsey, Mrs A. T. Lambert, G. J. Larby, Mrs J. K. Lukas, B. T. McDonald, Mr B. H. Mellon, Mr R. R. Norman, Mrs S. D. Norman, Mr P. J. O'Neill, Mr J. Palmer-Brown, Racing Club Ltd, Mr M. A. Sherwood, The Hon Mrs L. J. Sherwood, Mr B. T. E. Shrubsall, Mr A. Signy, Mr P. J. Smith, Lady Thompson, V. J. Walsh, Mr W. S. Watt, Mr R. White, Winterfields Farm Ltd, Mr M. G. Worcester.

Assistant Trainer: Andy Llewellyn **Head Lad:** Stefan Namesansky **Secretary:** Emma Chugg

Jockey (NH): Leighton Aspell, Thomas Garner. **Conditional:** Harrison Beswick.

MR RAYMOND SHIELS, Jedburgh
Postal: **Thickside Farm, Jedburgh, Roxburghshire, TD8 6QY**
Contacts: **PHONE (01835) 864060 MOBILE (07790) 295645**

1 **LUCARNO DANCER**, 8, b m Lucarno (USA)—Sing And Dance **R. Shiels**
2 **TIKKANDEMICKEY (IRE)**, 12, gr g Tikkanen (USA)—Miss Vikki (IRE) **R. Shiels**

MISS LYNN SIDDALL, Tadcaster
Postal: **Stonebridge Farm, Colton, Tadcaster, North Yorkshire, LS24 8EP**
Contacts: **PHONE (01904) 744291 FAX (01904) 744291 MOBILE (07778) 216692/4**

1 **ALFIE'S BOW**, 11, ch g Alflora (IRE)—Long Shot **Mr G. Kennington**
2 **ASTROPHYSICS**, 6, ch g Paco Boy (IRE)—Jodrell Bank (IRE) **Mr J. A. Kay**
3 **BLUE COVE**, 13, ch g Karinga Bay—Meadow Blue **Mr J. A. Kay**
4 **CADGERS HOLE**, 11, b g Helissio (FR)—Not So Prim **Jan Slater & Partners**
5 **ENCODED (IRE)**, 5, ch m Sakhee's Secret—Confidentiality (IRE) **Mr J. A. Kay**
6 **FIRST OF NEVER (IRE)**, 12, b g Systematic—Never Promise (FR) **Lynn Siddall Racing II**
7 **I KNOW THE CODE (IRE)**, 13, b g Viking Ruler (AUS)—Gentle Papoose **Lynn Siddall Racing II**
8 **IN VINO VERITAS (IRE)**, 7, b g Art Connoisseur (IRE)—Robin **Mr J. A. Kay**
9 **LA HAVRESE (FR)**, 7, ch m Le Havre (IRE)—La Buena (IRE) **Mr J. A. Kay**
10 **LISDONAGH HOUSE (IRE)**, 16, b g Little Bighorn—Lifinsa Barina (IRE) **J. P. G. Cooke**
11 **LITTLE MISS LOLA**, 4, ch f Dandy Man (IRE)—Purepleasureseeker (IRE) **Lynn Siddall Racing II**
12 **MR CONUNDRUM**, 5, b g Paco Boy (IRE)—Folly Drove **Mr J. A. Kay**
13 **PADDY'S ROCK (IRE)**, 7, b g Whipper (USA)—Hedera (USA) **Mr J. A. Kay**
14 **PERFECT AIM**, 6, b m Kalanisi (IRE)—Long Shot **Mr G. Kennington**
15 **SERVO (IRE)**, 4, b g Power—Parade Scene (USA) **Mr J. A. Kay**
16 **YORKSHIREMAN (IRE)**, 8, b g Red Clubs (IRE)—Ossiana (IRE) **Jan Slater & Partners**

THREE-YEAR-OLDS

17 **JAZZ MAGIC (IRE)**, ch g Red Jazz (USA)—Caerella (IRE) **Mr J. A. Kay**

Other Owners: Miss L. C. Siddall, Miss J. M. Slater.

Assistant Trainer: Stephen Hackney

507 MR DAVID SIMCOCK, Newmarket

Postal: **The Office, Trillium Place, Birdcage Walk, Newmarket, Suffolk, CB8 0NE**
Contacts: **PHONE (01638) 662968 FAX (01638) 663888**
MOBILE (07808) 954109 (David) (07702) 851561 (Jennie)
E-MAIL david@davidsimcock.co.uk WEBSITE www.davidsimcock.co.uk

1 **ALGOMETER**, 5, gr h Archipenko (USA)—Albanova
2 **ANOTHER ECLIPSE (IRE)**, 4, b g Lope de Vega (IRE)—Black Dahlia
3 **AROD (IRE)**, 7, b h Teofilo (IRE)—My Personal Space (USA)
4 **ASCOT DAY (IRE)**, 4, b g Kheleyf (USA)—My Lucky Liz (IRE)
5 **BLESS HIM (IRE)**, 4, b c Sea The Stars (IRE)—Happy Land (IRE)
6 **BRETON ROCK (IRE)**, 8, b g Bahamian Bounty—Anna's Rock (IRE)
7 **BRITTANIC (IRE)**, 4, ch c Excelebration (IRE)—Fountain of Peace (USA)
8 **CALLING OUT (FR)**, 7, b g Martaline—Exit The Straight (IRE)
9 **CURBYOURENTHUSIASM (IRE)**, 7, gr g Mastercraftsman (IRE)—Mohican Princess
10 **DESERT ENCOUNTER (IRE)**, 6, b g Halling (USA)—La Chicana (IRE)
11 **DOCTOR SARDONICUS**, 7, ch g Medicean—Never A Doubt
12 **DRAGON MALL**, 5, b g Blame (USA)—Petition the Lady (USA)
13 **GHALIB (IRE)**, 6, ch g Lope de Vega (IRE)—Gorband (USA)
14 **GLORY AWAITS (IRE)**, 8, ch g Choisir (AUS)—Sandbox Two (IRE)
15 **INTERN (IRE)**, 4, b g Rip Van Winkle (IRE)—Uliana (USA)
16 **INVERROCHE (IRE)**, 4, gr f Dark Angel (IRE)—Mia Madonna
17 **LIGHTNING SPEAR**, 7, ch h Pivotal—Atlantic Destiny (IRE)
18 **MAJEED**, 8, b g Mount Nelson—Clever Millie (USA)
19 **MARINE ONE**, 4, b g Frankel—Marine Bleue (FR)
20 **MR OWEN (USA)**, 6, b h Invincible Spirit (USA)—Mrs Lindsay (USA)
21 **NEW WORLD POWER (JPN)**, 5, b h Deep Impact (JPN)—Listen (IRE)
22 **NONIOS (IRE)**, 6, b g Oasis Dream—Young and Daring (USA)
23 **POLYBIUS**, 7, b g Oasis Dream—Freedonia
24 **RUBENSIAN**, 5, ch g Medicean—Hymnsheet
25 **SHEIKHZAYEDROAD**, 9, b g Dubawi (IRE)—Royal Secrets (IRE)
26 **SINGYOURSONG (IRE)**, 5, b m Aqlaam—Dhan Dhana (IRE)
27 **SUMBAL (IRE)**, 6, gr h Danehill Dancer (IRE)—Alix Road (FR)
28 **WHITE CHOCOLATE (IRE)**, 4, br f Mastercraftsman (IRE)—Coco Demure (IRE)

THREE-YEAR-OLDS

29 **ALACRITAS**, gr f Leroidesanimaux (BRZ)—Albaraka
30 **ALCINA (IRE)**, b f Leroidesanimaux (BRZ)—Allannah Abu
31 **ASIAN SKY**, ch f Universal (IRE)—My Order
32 **AZEZATI (IRE)**, ch f Dream Ahead (USA)—Sweet Nicole
33 **BIRCH GROVE (IRE)**, b f Galileo (IRE)—Danehurst
34 **BOB'S GIRL**, b f Big Bad Bob (IRE)—Linda (FR)
35 **COME ON TIER (IRE)**, b c Kendargent (FR)—Milwaukee (FR)
36 **COURT OF JUSTICE (FR)**, b c Dabirsim (FR)—Great News (FR)
37 **COURTSIDE (FR)**, ch g Siyouni (FR)—Memoire (FR)
38 **EJTYAH**, b f Frankel—Darysina (USA)
39 **ENCRYPTION (IRE)**, b g High Chaparral (IRE)—Challow Hills (USA)
40 **EXEC CHEF (IRE)**, ch g Excelebration (IRE)—Donnelly's Hollow (IRE)
41 **FORWARD THINKER**, ch f Dream Ahead (USA)—Avodale (USA)
42 Ch f Teofilo (IRE)—Funday
43 **HIGHBROW**, b c Intello (GER)—Wild Gardenia
44 **HIGHLAND SKY (IRE)**, br g Camelot—Healing Music (FR)
45 **IMPERIAL COURT (IRE)**, b g Zoffany (IRE)—La Vita Bella
46 **KEHAL (IRE)**, b f High Chaparral (IRE)—Tamazug
47 **KILLER QUEEN**, b f Havana Gold (IRE)—Radio Gaga
48 **KWANZA**, b f Exchange Rate (USA)—Kiswahili
49 **LADY OF SHALOTT**, b f Camelot—Silent Act (USA)
50 **LATE CHANGE**, b f Exceed And Excel (AUS)—Khione
51 **LOLLYS DREAM**, b f Declaration of War (USA)—Bunood (IRE)
52 **MAVERICK OFFICER**, b g Exceed And Excel (AUS)—Gradara
53 B f Dubawi (IRE)—Meeznah (USA)
54 **MISS LATIN (IRE)**, b f Galileo (IRE)—Breeze Hill (IRE)
55 **MOBHAM (IRE)**, b c Teofilo (IRE)—Elegant Beauty
56 **MOSS LANDING (JPN)**, b c Lord Kanaloa (JPN)—Monterey Street (USA)

MR DAVID SIMCOCK - Continued

57 **MRS SIPPY (USA)**, b f Blame (USA)—Qushchi
58 **MULTICURRENCY (USA)**, b c Exchange Rate (USA)—Istamara
59 **NEVER WAIT (GER)**, b c Cacique (IRE)—Notre Dame (GER)
60 **NICE SHOT (IRE)**, b c Kodiac—Emma Dora (IRE)
61 **QAYED (CAN)**, b c Blame (USA)—Endless Journey (USA)
62 **RAID (IRE)**, b c Havana Gold (IRE)—Remarkable Story
63 **SARSHAMPLA (IRE)**, b f Elzaam (AUS)—Red Riddle (IRE)
64 **SEAT OF POWER (IRE)**, b c Sea The Stars (IRE)—Ice Mint (USA)
65 **SILCHESTER (USA)**, ch c Bellamy Road (USA)—Looks Like Rain
66 **SOLID MAN (JPN)**, b g Lord Kanaloa (JPN)—Maruka Sawayaka (JPN)
67 B f Camelot—Splendid (IRE)
68 **STIRLING VALUE**, b c Pour Moi (IRE)—Celebre Vadala (FR)
69 **STONE OF DESTINY**, b c Acclamation—Irishstone (IRE)
70 **SUPERNOVA**, b c Intello (GER)—Carding (USA)
71 **TEPPAL (FR)**, b f Camacho—Jummana (FR)
72 **THAT'S SO COOL (IRE)**, b g Born To Sea (IRE)—Bibury
73 **WALK ON WALTER (IRE)**, b g Footstepsinthesand—Hajmah (IRE)
74 Ch g Galileo (IRE)—Walklikeanegyptian (IRE)
75 **WORSHIP (IRE)**, b f Havana Gold (IRE)—Up In Time
76 B f Dark Angel (IRE)—Zallerina

TWO-YEAR-OLDS

77 Ch f 28/2 New Approach (IRE)—Alasha (IRE) (Barathea (IRE)) (70000)
78 **ALEMAGNA**, b f 25/2 Sea The Moon (GER)—Alta Moda (Sadler's Wells (USA))
79 B c 5/5 Pomellato (GER)—Anne Boleyn (Rainbow Quest (USA)) (13024)
80 Ch c 19/3 Dutch Art—Baileys Jubilee (Bahamian Bounty) (80000)
81 B f 25/2 Dunaden (FR)—Belle Blonde (IRE) (Lawman (FR))
82 **BLAST OFF**, b c 19/2 Sea The Moon (GER)—Having A Blast (USA) (Exchange Rate (USA)) (113960)
83 Gr c 26/4 Mastercraftsman (IRE)—Bunood (IRE) (Sadler's Wells (USA)) (110000)
84 B f 10/2 Nathaniel (IRE)—Carmens Fate (Cape Cross (IRE)) (42000)
85 **CONFECTOR (IRE)**, ch c 9/1 Mastercraftsman (IRE)—Uliana (USA) (Darshaan) (252340)
86 **DALMORE**, gr f 7/3 Dalakhani (IRE)—Get Happy (IRE) (Zamindar (USA))
87 Ch c 4/4 No Nay Never (USA)—Enharmonic (USA) (E Dubai (USA)) (110000)
88 B c 17/5 Universal (IRE)—Fly Free (Halling (USA))
89 B c 25/2 Camacho—Fork Handles (Doyen (IRE)) (52000)
90 B c 1/3 Intello (GER)—Galipette (Green Desert (USA)) (52910)
91 Ch f 13/3 Dawn Approach (IRE)—Galley (Zamindar (USA)) (50000)
92 B c 14/2 Charm Spirit (IRE)—Kite Mark (Mark of Esteem (IRE)) (115000)
93 B c 1/4 Kodiac—La Chicana (IRE) (Invincible Spirit (IRE)) (150000)
94 B f 29/2 Shamardal (USA)—Lady Liberty (IRE) (Shirocco (GER)) (120000)
95 B f 20/2 Lawman (FR)—Leopard Creek (Weldnaas (USA)) (72000)
96 Ch c 25/1 Universal (IRE)—My Order (Raven's Pass (USA)) (21000)
97 Ch c 8/3 Iffraaj—Ninja Lady (Nayef (USA)) (56980)
98 **PADURA**, b c 15/3 Havana Gold (IRE)—Indian Story (IRE) (Indian Ridge) (47619)
99 Br f 1/3 Speightstown (USA)—Qushchi (Encosta de Lago (AUS))
100 **RANGALI ISLAND (IRE)**, b c 1/3 Camacho—Tender Surprise (Doyen (IRE)) (37142)
101 B f 2/2 Universal (IRE)—Ras Shaikh (USA) (Sheikh Albaddou) (11000)
102 B f 25/2 Rip Van Winkle (IRE)—Red Avis (Exceed And Excel (AUS)) (27675)
103 **SALTITO**, bl c 8/1 Harbour Watch (IRE)—Hispanic Dancer (IRE) (Jeremy (USA)) (40000)
104 B c 29/3 Zoffany (IRE)—Sanadaat (Green Desert (USA)) (34187)
105 B f 25/1 Poet's Voice—Secret Era (Cape Cross (IRE)) (42000)
106 Gr c 13/5 Dark Angel (IRE)—Secret Key (IRE) (Key of Luck (USA)) (162800)
107 **SIBYLLINE**, ch f 31/3 Leroidesanimaux (BRZ)—Selenography (Selkirk (USA))
108 B c 3/2 Scat Daddy (USA)—Similu (Danehill Dancer (IRE)) (350000)
109 B c 5/2 Lope de Vega (IRE)—Sorella Bella (IRE) (Clodovil (USA))
110 **STARCZEWSKI (USA)**, b c 19/4 Magician (IRE)—Lucifer's Stone (USA) (Horse Chestnut (SAF)) (28000)
111 B c 5/2 Kingman—Starlet (IRE) (Sea The Stars (IRE)) (113960)
112 **UPPER SCHOOL**, b f 11/1 Oasis Dream—Upper Street (IRE) (Dansili)
113 B f 15/5 Galileo (IRE)—Walklikeanegyptian (IRE) (Danehill (USA))
114 B c 6/2 Charm Spirit (IRE)—Ysper (FR) (Orpen (USA))

MR DAVID SIMCOCK - Continued

Owners: Sheikh Juma Dalmook Al Maktoum, Sheikh Hamad Dalmook Al Maktoum, Sheikh Rashid Dalmook Al Maktoum, Abdullah Al Mansoori, Abdullah Saeed Al Naboodah, Mohammed Al Nabouda, Saeed Al Qassimi, Sheikh Mohammed Bin Kalifa Al Thani, Sultan Ali, Mr Saif Ali, Roger & Yvonne Allsop, Saeed H Altayer, Amo Racing Limited, Mrs J. M. Annable, Mr William Baker, Mr James Barnett, Mr Stephen W Barrow, Mr A. S. Belhab, Mr R. G. W. Brown, Marcella Burns, Mr Malcolm Caine, Chola Dynasty, Mr John Cook, Mr Khalifa Dasmal, Dunchurch Lodge Stud Co, Equine Racing Ltd, Genting Casino's UK Ltd, Mrs Fitri Hay, Mrs R. G. Hillen, Mr S. R. Hope, Mr Andrew Howells, Sara Humber, Ahmed Jaber, Mohammed Jaber, Saeed Jaber, Ms Sue Johnson, Mr Kin Hung Kei, Mrs John Magnier, Saeed Manana, Millingbrook Racing, Never Say Die Partnership, Mr Anders Olesen, Orbis Bloodstock Ltd, Mr Daniel Pittack, Qatar Racing Limited, Miss Kirsten Rausing, Jos & Jane Rodosthenous, Rumble Racing Club, Sahara Bloodstock, Mr Philip V Simpson, Dr Arujuna Sivananthan, St Albans Bloodstock Ltd, Mrs Doreen Tabor, Tick Tock Partnership, Mr Charles Wentworth, Major M Wyatt.

Assistant Trainers: Camille Valette, Alex French, Sam Goldsmith

Jockey (flat): Jamie Spencer. **Apprentice:** George Bass.

508
MR DAN SKELTON, Alcester
Postal: **Lodge Hill, Shelfield Green, Shelfield, Alcester, Warwickshire, B49 6JR**
Contacts: **PHONE (01789) 336339**
E-MAIL office@danskeltonracing.com WEBSITE www.danskeltonracing.com

1 **AINTREE MY DREAM (FR)**, 8, b br g Saint des Saints (FR)—Pretty Melodie (FR) **Mr M. Olden**
2 **AL SHAHIR (IRE)**, 6, b g Robin des Champs (FR)—Sarah Massini (IRE) **N. W. Lake**
3 **ALLONOK**, 5, b g Kalanisi (IRE)—Isabello (IRE) **The Can't Say No Partnership**
4 **AMOOLA GOLD (GER)**, 5, b g Mamool (IRE)—Aughamore Beauty (IRE) **Mr & Mrs Gordon Pink**
5 **AMORE ALATO**, 9, b g Winged Love (IRE)—Sardagna (FR) **Mrs S. J. Faulks**
6 **ANTUNES**, 4, b c Nathaniel (IRE)—Aigrette Garzette (IRE) **Mr M. Adams**
7 **ANYTIME WILL DO (IRE)**, 5, b g Scorpion (IRE)—Pellerossa (IRE) **Miss F. Nimmo**
8 **APPLESANDPIERRES (IRE)**, 10, b g Pierre—Cluain Chaoin (IRE) **Mr M. J. Rozenbroek**
9 **ASHKOUL (FR)**, 5, b g Tamayuz—Asharna (IRE) **Mr C. Buckingham**
10 **ATLANTIC STORM (IRE)**, 6, b g September Storm (GER)—Double Dream (IRE) **Mr D. N. Skelton**
11 **AWAY FOR SLATES (IRE)**, 8, b g Arcadio (GER)—Rumi **Belbroughton Racing Club**
12 **AZZURI**, 6, b g Azamour (IRE)—Folly Lodge **The Blind Squirrels**
13 **BANDSMAN**, 7, b g Bandmaster (USA)—Soleil Sauvage **Mrs S. J. Faulks**
14 **BARON VON CHILL**, 6, b g Sulamani (IRE)—Kings Maiden (IRE) **Rio Gold Racing Club Ltd**
15 **BEAKSTOWN (IRE)**, 5, b g Stowaway—Midnight Reel (IRE) **Mr B. J. C. Drew**
16 **BEKKENSFIRTH (FR)**, 8, b g Flemensfirth (USA)—Bekkaria (FR) **Mrs P. M. Scott**
17 **BERTIMONT (FR)**, 8, gr g Slickly (FR)—Bocanegra (FR) **Mr D. N. Skelton**
18 **BETAMECHE (FR)**, 7, gr g Kapgarde (FR)—Kaldona (FR) **Miss J. Craymer**
19 **BLAIRS COVE**, 6, b g Presenting—Raitera (FR) **Simon & Lisa Hobson**
20 **BORN SURVIVOR (IRE)**, 7, b g King's Theatre (IRE)—
    Bob's Flame (IRE) **Mrs G. Widdowson & Mrs R. Kelvin-Hughes**
21 **BUCKY BOY**, 5, br g Shirocco (GER)—Fair View (GER) **Mrs Gill Duckworth & Mrs Pat Dry**
22 **CABARET QUEEN**, 6, b m King's Theatre (IRE)—La Dame Brune (FR) **Highclere T'Bred Racing - Cabaret Queen**
23 **CAFE AU LAIT (GER)**, 8, b g Nicaron (GER)—Cariera (GER) **Faithful Followers**
24 **CAPTAIN CHAOS (IRE)**, 7, ch g Golan (IRE)—Times Have Changed (IRE) **Mike and Eileen Newbould**
25 **CAPTAIN SIMON (IRE)**, 6, b g Dubai Destination (USA)—Gayephar **Axom LXX**
26 **CAUSE TOUJOURS (FR)**, 6, b g Khalkevi (IRE)—Viana (FR) **Mr C. S. Hinchy**
27 **CH'TIBELLO (FR)**, 7, b g Sageburg (IRE)—Neicha (FR) **The Can't Say No Partnership**
28 **CITADEL (FR)**, 6, b g Al Namix (FR)—Oreli (FR) **Rio Gold Racing Club Ltd**
29 **CKALCO DES LOGES (FR)**, 6, b g Balko (FR)—Olla des Loges (FR) **Miss J. Craymer**
30 **CLASSICO DAIS (FR)**, 6, br g Al Namix (FR)—Fabema (FR) **Bob Whitby & Dan Skelton**
31 **CLONDAW ANCHOR (IRE)**, 5, gr g Stowaway—Masiana (IRE)
32 **COBRA DE MAI (FR)**, 6, b g Great Pretender (FR)—Miria Galanda (FR) **Norman Lake & Susan Carsberg**
33 **COMRADE CONRAD (IRE)**, 4, br c Canford Cliffs (IRE)—View (IRE) **Mr J. Lane**
34 **CONISTONE**, 4, ch f Poet's Voice—Protectress **Rio Gold Racing Club Ltd**
35 **COSY CLUB (IRE)**, 4, br g So You Think (NZ)—Bali Breeze (IRE) **BGC Racing**
36 **DESTRIER (FR)**, 5, b g Voix du Nord (FR)—Razia (FR) **Three Celts**
37 **DOES IT IN STYLE (FR)**, 5, b g Balko (FR)—Malta de Ronceray (FR) **The Can't Say No Partnership**
38 **EARLSHILL (IRE)**, 7, b g Milan—Mrs Marples (IRE) **The Horwoods Partnership**
39 **ELTON DES MOTTES (FR)**, 4, b g Maresca Sorrento (FR)—Ouhetu des Mottes (FR) **Mr D. N. Skelton**
40 **EMBOLE (FR)**, 4, b g Buck's Boum (FR)—Urielle Collonges (FR) **Mr C. A. Donlon**
41 **ETAMINE DU COCHET (FR)**, 4, gr f Martaline—Nuance du Cochet (FR) **Mrs S. L. Edwards**
42 **EXCELLENT TEAM**, 6, b g Teofilo (IRE)—Seradim **Mr M. Olden**

MR DAN SKELTON - Continued

43 **EZANAK (IRE)**, 5, b g Sea The Stars (IRE)—Ebaza (IRE) **Mr D. N. Skelton**
44 **FALCON SUN (FR)**, 4, b g Falco (USA)—Pray For Sun (IRE) **Mezzone Family**
45 **FLASH THE STEEL (IRE)**, 6, b br g Craigsteel—Anna's Melody (IRE) **Mr J. J. Reilly**
46 **FOCACCIA (IRE)**, 7, b g Milan—Dantes Term (IRE) **Mr T. Spraggett**
47 **FRANKIE RAPPER (IRE)**, 6, b g Milan—Parkdota (IRE) **Miss J. Craymer**
48 **FREE RANGE (IRE)**, 8, b g Subtle Power (IRE)—Tullyspark Rose (IRE) **Mr C. Buckingham**
49 **FREE STONE HILL (IRE)**, 8, b g Beneficial—Claramanda (IRE) **Mr D. N. Skelton**
50 **FUTURE SECURITY (IRE)**, 9, ch g Dalakhani (IRE)—Schust Madame (IRE) **Faithful Followers**
51 **GEORGE GENTLY (FR)**, 5, b g Gentlewave (IRE)—Sindibad (USA) **Holt,Macnabb,Taylor,Clark,Nugent,Peters**
52 **GET ON THE YAGER**, 8, b g Tamure (IRE)—Florentino **Dick and Mandy Higgins**
53 **GET READY FREDDY**, 8, b g Sixties Icon—Summer Shades **Carbon Racing**
54 **GI JAYNE (IRE)**, 7, b m Millenary—Lady of Appeal (IRE) **Mr D. N. Skelton**
55 **GIBENO (IRE)**, 4, b g Fastnet Rock (AUS)—Dance To The Top **CNC Routing Limited**
56 **GOFORTHECRAIC (IRE)**, 5, b g Arcadio (GER)—
Valin Thyne (IRE) **Holt, Macnabb, Clark, Jeffrey, Milton, Robinson**
57 **GOLDEN VISION (FR)**, 6, bl m Vision d'etat (FR)—My Gold du Fanil (FR) **Mr C. Buckingham**
58 **GORTROE JOE (IRE)**, 6, b g Beneficial—Rowlands Star (IRE) **J. T. Warner**
59 **GRAN PARADISO (IRE)**, 6, ch g Galileo (IRE)—Looking Lovely (IRE) **Mike and Eileen Newbould**
60 **HATCHER (IRE)**, 5, b g Doyen (IRE)—African Keys (IRE) **P. H. Betts**
61 **HEAR NO EVIL (IRE)**, 6, b g Getaway (GER)—Listening (IRE) **Mrs S. Magnier**
62 **HOLRYALE (IRE)**, 6, b g Trans Island—Lady Ramona (IRE) **The Holryale Partnership**
63 **HURRICANE HOLLOW**, 8, b g Beat Hollow—Veenwouden **Mr M. J. Rozenbroek**
64 **INDIROCCO (IRE)**, 5, ch g Shirocco (GER)—Indigo Girl (GER) **Mr & Mrs J. D. Cotton**
65 **INTIFADAH (IRE)**, 6, b g Intikhab (USA)—Cuilaphuca (IRE) **Rio Gold Racing Club Ltd**
66 **ISTIMRAAR (IRE)**, 7, b g Dansili—Manayer (IRE) **Rio Gold Racing Club Ltd**
67 **ITSNONOFURBUSINESS (IRE)**, 6, b g Flemensfirth (USA)—Moon Storm (IRE) **Mr D. Johnston**
68 **JANE LAMB**, 5, b m Haafhd—Lucinda Lamb **Foxtrot Racing: Jane Lamb**
69 **JUST A FEELING**, 8, ch m Flemensfirth (USA)—Precious Lady **Mr D. N. Skelton**
70 **JUST ROCKY**, 5, b g Yeats (IRE)—High Benefit (IRE) **Halmurritt Racing**
71 **KEREMAN (IRE)**, 4, b g Azamour (IRE)—Kerania (IRE) **Miss H. Watson**
72 **KNIGHT IN DUBAI (IRE)**, 5, b g Dubai Destination (USA)—Bobbies Storm (IRE) **Mr & Mrs Ben Houghton**
73 **LADY MALEFICENT**, 4, b f Malinas (GER)—Lush Lady (IRE) **Lodge Hill Syndicate**
74 **LATE NIGHT LILY**, 7, b m Midnight Legend—Ready To Crown (USA) **Braybrooke Lodge Partnership**
75 **LISTEN TO THE MAN (IRE)**, 8, b m Court Cave—Badia Dream (IRE) **Mrs S. Carsberg**
76 **LONG HOUSE HALL (IRE)**, 10, b g Saddlers' Hall (IRE)—Brackenvale (IRE) **Mr C. S. Hinchy**
77 **LOVERBOY (FR)**, 7, b g Winged Love (FR)—Tartan Belle **Susan Page & Dan Skelton**
78 **MABELA**, 4, b f Oscar (IRE)—Histoire de Moeurs (FR) **S Smith & S Campion**
79 **MAIRE BANRIGH**, 6, b m King's Theatre (IRE)—La Marianne **Mr J Hales & Mr J Diver**
80 **MARLEY FIRTH (IRE)**, 6, b g Flemensfirth (USA)—Merrill Gaye (IRE) **Surrey Racing (mf)**
81 **MISS BENEFITZ (IRE)**, 7, ch m Beneficial—African Keys (IRE) **Rio Gold Racing Club Ltd**
82 **MISTER MIYAGI (IRE)**, 9, b g Zagreb (USA)—Muckle Flugga (IRE) **Ben Turner & Jay Tabb**
83 **MISTER UNIVERSUM (GER)**, 6, b g Cape Cross (IRE)—Miss Europa (IRE) **Notalotterry**
84 **MOHAAYED**, 6, b g Intikhab (USA)—Reyaada **Mrs J. A. Watts**
85 **MOLLY THE DOLLY (IRE)**, 7, b m Flemensfirth (USA)—Pistol Flash (IRE) **Mr D. Hanafin**
86 **MOMELLA (IRE)**, 6, ch m Sholokhov (IRE)—Missing Link (USA) **Holt, Clark, Macnabb, Nugent & Robinson**
87 **MOONLIGHT DANCER**, 5, gr m Kayf Tara—Dissolve **Mrs J. A. Watts**
88 **MUST HAVEA FLUTTER (IRE)**, 6, b g Mustameet (USA)—Secret Flutter (IRE) **Winter Gold Racing**
89 **NEW QUAY (IRE)**, 5, b g Mahler—Beg La Eile (IRE) **Norman Lake & Susan Carsberg**
90 **NIMBY (IRE)**, 4, ch g Doyen (IRE)—Ain't Misbehavin (IRE) **Mr & Mrs Paul & Clare Rooney**
91 **NO GETAWAY (IRE)**, 5, ch g Getaway (GER)—Nonnetia (IRE) **Dick, Keenan, Sawer, Stevenson**
92 **NO HASSLE HOFF (IRE)**, 6, b br g Craigsteel—Endless Patience (IRE) **Exors of the Late Mrs J. S. Allen**
93 **NORTH HILL HARVEY**, 7, b g Kayf Tara—Ellina **Mrs G. Widdowson & Mrs R. Kelvin-Hughes**
94 **NOT THAT FUISSE (FR)**, 5, b g Fuisse (FR)—Edelmira (FR) **Mr C. A. Donlon**
95 **NUBE NEGRA (SPA)**, 4, b g Dink (FR)—Manly Dream (FR) **Mr T. Spraggett**
96 **OLDGRANGEWOOD**, 7, b g Central Park (IRE)—Top of The Class (IRE) **Chris Giles & Sandra Giles**
97 **ONE FOR BILLY**, 6, b g Midnight Legend—Saxona (IRE) **Mr & Mrs Paul & Clare Rooney**
98 **OPTIMUS PRIME (FR)**, 6, b g Deportivo—Diluvienne (FR) **Masterson Holdings Limited**
99 **OR DE VASSY (FR)**, 6, b g Assessor (IRE)—Mona Vassy (FR) **Andy Jansons & Keith Wetton**
100 **PARTHENIUS (GER)**, 5, b g Soldier Hollow—Princess Li (GER) **Pegasus Bloodstock Limited**
101 **PETROU (IRE)**, 5, b g Mountain High (IRE)—Evnelu (IRE) **Rio Gold Racing Club Ltd**
102 **POKORA DU LYS (FR)**, 7, b g Saint des Saints (FR)—Shailann (FR) **Mr C. Buckingham**
103 **POTTERS APPROACH (IRE)**, 7, b g Scorpion (IRE)—Moon Approach (IRE) **Surrey Racing (PA)**
104 **PREMIER ROSE (IRE)**, 9, b m Westerner—Alltoplayfor (IRE) **Rio Gold Racing Club Ltd**
105 **PRESENT RANGER (IRE)**, 5, b g Presenting—Papoose (IRE) **Dick and Mandy Higgins**

MR DAN SKELTON - Continued

106 **PRETTY RECKLESS (IRE)**, 5, b m Scorpion (IRE)—
Deep Supreme (IRE) **Royale Racing Syndicate & Dan Skelton**
107 **QAVIY CASH**, 4, b g Oasis Dream—Neartica (FR) **The Warriors**
108 **REBEL ROYAL (IRE)**, 5, b g Getaway (GER)—Molly Duffy (IRE) **Jerry Wright,Martin Walker & Tony Hughes**
109 **RED RISING (IRE)**, 7, ch g Flemensfirth (USA)—Fugal Maid (IRE) **Mr & Mrs Paul & Clare Rooney**
110 **RED TORNADO (IRE)**, 6, ch g Dr Fong (USA)—Encircle (USA) **Notalotterry**
111 **RENE'S GIRL (IRE)**, 8, b m Presenting—Brogella (IRE) **Andy & Sharon Measham**
112 **RENWICK (IRE)**, 5, b g Milan—Come In Moscow (IRE) **Mrs D. L. Whateley**
113 **RESILIENCY (IRE)**, 7, ch g Mastercraftsman (IRE)—Euroceleb (IRE) **Mr Frank McAleavy & Mr Ian McAleavy**
114 **RIGHT OF REPLY (IRE)**, 7, b g Presenting—Baliya (IRE) **W. J. and T. C. O. Gredley**
115 **ROBIN WATERS (FR)**, 5, b g Irish Wells (FR)—Skandia (FR) **Mr C. A. Donlon**
116 **ROCKU**, 8, b g Great Palm (USA)—Suetsu (IRE) **Carbon Racing**
117 **RODEO DODO (IRE)**, 8, b g Milan—Laney Mary (IRE) **Mr B. G. Acheson**
118 **ROKSANA (IRE)**, 6, b m Dubai Destination (USA)—Talktothetail (IRE) **Mrs S. J. Faulks**
119 **SAM RED (FR)**, 7, b g Denham Red (FR)—Call Me Nana (FR) **BGC Racing**
120 **SAUVIGNON**, 7, b m Yeats (IRE)—Dalriath **Mrs C. M. Graves**
121 **SAVELLO (IRE)**, 12, ch g Anshan—Fontaine Frances (IRE) **S Smith & S Campion**
122 **SEA OF MYSTERY (IRE)**, 5, b g Sea The Stars (IRE)—Sassenach (IRE) **Mr Frank McAleavy & Mr Ian McAleavy**
123 **SET LIST (IRE)**, 9, b g Heron Island (IRE)—Copper Magic (IRE) **Rio Gold Racing Club Ltd**
124 **SHANNON BRIDGE (IRE)**, 5, ch g Flemensfirth (USA)—
Bridgequarter Lady (IRE) **M Boothright G Lovett P Deffains**
125 **SHANTOU ROCK (IRE)**, 6, b g Shantou (USA)—Cool Cool (IRE) **Mr & Mrs Gordon Pink**
126 **SHELFORD (IRE)**, 9, b g Galileo (IRE)—Lyrical **Mr C. Hodgson**
127 **SHRUBLAND**, 5, b g High Chaparral (IRE)—Ratukidul (FR) **Mr D. N. Skelton**
128 **SIGNIFICANT OTHER (IRE)**, 4, b f Fame And Glory—Etoile Margot (FR) **Mr D. N. Skelton**
129 **SIMPLY LUCKY (IRE)**, 9, b g Flemensfirth (USA)—Derrygowna Court (IRE) **Rio Gold Racing Club Ltd**
130 **SIR MANGAN (IRE)**, 10, b g Darsi (FR)—Lady Pep (IRE) **Mr Frank McAleavy & Mr Ian McAleavy**
131 **SKANDIBURG (FR)**, 4, b g Sageburg (IRE)—Skandia (FR)
132 **SOLO SAXOPHONE (IRE)**, 4, b c Frankel—Society Hostess (USA) **BGC Racing**
133 **SOLOMON GREY (FR)**, 6, gr g Sulamani (IRE)—Sardagna (FR) **Mrs S. J. Faulks**
134 **SPADER (IRE)**, 5, b g Jeremy (USA)—Poulkovo (IRE) **Mr M. Olden**
135 **SPIRITOFTHEGAMES (IRE)**, 6, b g Darsi (FR)—Lucy Walters (IRE) **N. W. Lake**
136 **STARCROSSED**, 6, b g Cape Cross (IRE)—Gretna **R. C. Tooth**
137 **STICK TO THE PLAN (IRE)**, 6, b g Gold Well—Chloes Choice (IRE) **Mr T. P. Radford**
138 **SUPERB STORY (IRE)**, 7, b g Duke of Marmalade (IRE)—
Yes My Love (FR) **A Holt, J Robinson, A Taylor & S Miller**
139 **SUPREMELY LUCKY (IRE)**, 6, b g Milan—Lucky Supreme (IRE) **Mr M. Olden**
140 **THAT'STHESCOOP**, 5, ch g Dabbers Ridge (IRE)—Artemise (FR) **Mr D. N. Skelton**
141 **THE LAST BAR**, 8, b m Kayf Tara—Ardenbar **Mrs C. A. Wyatt**
142 **THE MISTRESS (IRE)**, 7, b m Kalanisi (IRE)—Sonnerschien (IRE) **Emdells Limited**
143 **THE PINE MARTIN (IRE)**, 8, br g Kalanisi (IRE)—Regal Holly **Mr D. N. Skelton**
144 **THE RAVEN MASTER (IRE)**, 4, b g Raven's Pass (USA)—
Rainbow Desert (USA) **M Boothright G Lovett P Deffains**
145 **THISONETIME (IRE)**, 7, b g Kalanisi (IRE)—Dizzy's Whisper (IRE) **Mr J. J. Reilly**
146 **THREE MUSKETEERS (IRE)**, 8, b g Flemensfirth (USA)—
Friendly Craic (IRE) **Mr Frank McAleavy & Mr Ian McAleavy**
147 **TOBY LERONE (IRE)**, 11, b g Old Vic—Dawn's Double (IRE) **Mrs Gill Duckworth & Mrs Pat Dry**
148 **TOKAY DOKEY (IRE)**, 4, b g Gold Well—Charming Present (IRE) **Mr C. A. Donlon**
149 **TUMMY RAPPER (IRE)**, 7, b g Milan—Supreme Evening (IRE) **Judy Craymer & Nick Skelton**
150 **TOO MANY DIAMONDS (IRE)**, 7, br g Diamond Green (FR)—Too Much Color (IRE) **Mr D. N. Skelton**
151 **TWO TAFFS (IRE)**, 8, b g Flemensfirth (USA)—Richs Mermaid (IRE) **Walters Plant Hire & James & Jean Potter**
152 **VALUE AT RISK (IRE)**, 9, b g Kayf Tara—Miss Orchestra (IRE) **D. M. Huglin**
153 **WEST TO THE BRIDGE (IRE)**, 5, b g Flemensfirth (USA)—Godlylady (IRE) **Mr P. J. Tierney**
154 **WESTERN BREEZE (IRE)**, 9, b m Westerner—Winsome Breeze (IRE) **Mr D. N. Skelton**
155 **WHATDUHAVTOGET (IRE)**, 6, b m Presenting—
Smooching (IRE) **Highclere Thoroughbred Racing - Presenting**
156 **WHATZDJAZZ (IRE)**, 6, b m Yeats (IRE)—What A Mewsment (IRE) **Mr M. Fennessy**
157 **WINGS ATTRACT (IRE)**, 9, b g Winged Love (IRE)—Huncheon Siss (IRE) **The Rann Family**
158 **WORK IN PROGRESS (IRE)**, 8, b g Westerner—Parsons Term (IRE) **Donlon & Doyle**
159 **WORKBENCH (FR)**, 10, b g Network (GER)—Danhelis (FR) **N. W. Lake**
160 **ZAMPARELLI (IRE)**, 6, b g Mahler—Goulburn Bridge (IRE) **Mrs S. C. Welch**
161 **ZEBI BOY**, 7, b g Multiplex—Atlantic Jane **Mrs M. J. Hughes**

THREE-YEAR-OLDS

162 **GEORGE VALENTINE (FR)**, b g George Vancouver (USA)—Yes My Love (FR) **A Holt, J Robinson, A Taylor**

MR DAN SKELTON - Continued

Other Owners: Mr D. Abraham, Axom Ltd, Mr D. Balchin, M. A. Bates, M. Boothright, Mr H. F. Bowley, Mr N. J. Brown, Mrs S. E. Brown, Mr M. J. Brown, Ms J. S. Campion, Mr C. N. Clark, Mr J. C. Cleary, Mrs B. Cotton, J. D. Cotton, Dr J. D. Dalton, Mr P. Deffains, Mrs D. Dewbery, Mr A. D. Dick, Mr J. Diver, Mr D. Downie, Mr A. Doyle, Mrs P. Dry, Mrs G. Duckworth, Mr A. C. Elliott, Mr A. Fellowes, Mrs L. Fellows, Foxtrot Racing Management Ltd, Mr C. M. Giles, Mrs A. E. Giles, Mr J. B. Gilruth, T. C. O. Gredley, W. J. Gredley, Mr S. Grubb, Mr C. R. Hadingham, Mr J. R. Hales, Mr R. S. Higgins, Mrs A. J. Higgins, Highclere Nominated Partner Limited, Highclere Thoroughbred Racing Ltd, Mr A. J. Hill, Mr S. E. Hobson, Mrs L. C. Hobson, Mr A. Holt, Mr P. B. R. Houghton, Mrs V. K. Houghton, Mr A. P Hughes, James & Jean Potter, Mr A. Jansons, Miss A. Jeffrey, Mr N. R. Jennings, Mr K. D. Jones, R. G. Kelvin-Hughes, Mrs E. A. Kelvin-Hughes, Mr G. P. A. Lovett, Mr I. Macnabb, Mr I. Marmion, Mr I. McAleavy, Mr F. McAleavy, Mr A. R. Measham, Mrs S. M. Measham, Mr G. G. Mezzone, Mrs S. M. Mezzone, Mr L. M. Mezzone, Mr S. R. Miller, Mr C. J. Milton, Mrs K. J. Morgan, Mr J. M. Newbould, Mrs E. E. Newbould, T. H. Northwood, Mr J. O. Nugent, Mr J. S. S. Page, Mr D. G. Peters, Mr G. K. G. Pink, Mrs K. M. Pink, Mrs M. J. Potter, J. E. Potter, Mr A. J. Ramsden, Mr A. Randle, Mr G. P. D. Rann, Mrs L. E. Rann, Mr J. D. Robinson, Mrs C. Rooney, Mr P. A. Rooney, Royale Racing Syndicate, A. G. Sim, Mr N. Skelton, Mrs S. Smith, Mr D. M. Standring, Mr J. M. Stevenson, Surrey Racing Limited, Mr J. A. Tabb, Mr A. Taylor, Mr B. H. Turner, Mr M. S. Walker, Walters Plant Hire Ltd, Mr R. Ward, Mr K. Wetton, Mr R. M. Whitby, Mrs B. A. Widdowson, J. Wright.

Assistant Trainer: Tom Messenger

Jockey (NH): Harry Skelton. **Amateur:** Miss Bridget Andrews.

---

509 MR KENNETH SLACK, Appleby-In-Westmorland
Postal: Heather Bank, Brackenber, Appleby-In-Westmorland, Cumbria, CA16 6LP
Contacts: PHONE (01768) 351354 MOBILE (07931) 137413

1 ADHERENCE, 5, b g Sir Percy—Straight Laced **More Fools Than Horses**
2 BEENO (IRE), 9, b g Exit To Nowhere (USA)—Kay Theatre (IRE) **A. Slack**
3 BELL WEIR, 10, gr g Tobougg (IRE)—Belly Dancer (IRE) **A. Slack**
4 DISCOVERIE, 10, b g Runyon (IRE)—Sri (IRE) **Mr Dennis Coppola & Mr Arthur Slack**
5 FAST AND FRIENDLY (IRE), 4, b g September Storm (GER)—Merewood Lodge (IRE) **Ar White Racing**
6 ITALIAN RIVIERA, 9, b g Galileo (IRE)—Miss Corniche **More Fools Than Horses**
7 JOKERS AND ROGUES (IRE), 10, b g Beneficial—Ashfield Girl (IRE) **A. Slack**
8 KURAGINA (IRE), 4, b f Raven's Pass (USA)—Russian Society **Paul Cairns Racing Limited**
9 LEGALIZED, 4, br f Authorized (IRE)—Laurena (GER) **Boom Racing**
10 MYDOR (FR), 8, ch g Stormy River (FR)—Fabulousday (USA) **Mr D. L. Hogg**
11 ONWITHTHEPARTY, 9, b g Sir Harry Lewis (USA)—Kentford Fern **Boom Racing**
12 PORT SOIF, 4, b f Foxwedge (AUS)—Positivity **A. Slack**
13 RAVENSWOOD, 5, b g Lawman (FR)—Whatami **Boom Racing**
14 SUMMER LIGHTENING, 4, gr f Fair Mix (IRE)—Kristineau **Messrs A & R Lyle**
15 TAB HOGARTH (IRE), 5, b g Westerner—Vintage Vic (IRE) **A. Slack**
16 TONTO'S SPIRIT, 6, b g Authorized (IRE)—Desert Royalty (IRE) **A. Slack**

THREE-YEAR-OLDS

17 MY SHIROCCO, ch f Shirocco (GER)—Auberge (IRE) **Mrs D. E. Slack**
18 SILVERLIGHT (IRE), gr f Fast Company (IRE)—Rangooned **Mrs D. E. Slack**

Other Owners: Mr K. Buckle, Mr D. J. Coppola, Mr T. W. Ewbank, Mrs M. Gleeson, Mr R. G. Huschka, Mr J. R. Lyle, R. Lyle, Mrs A. Lyle, A. R. White.

---

510 MRS PAM SLY, Peterborough
Postal: Singlecote, Thorney, Peterborough, Cambridgeshire, PE6 0PB
Contacts: PHONE (01733) 270212 MOBILE (07850) 511267
E-MAIL pamslyracing@btconnect.com

1 ACERTAIN CIRCUS, 8, ch g Definite Article—Circus Rose **G. Libson, D. Bayliss, T. Davies & P. Sly**
2 ACTINPIECES, 7, gr m Act One—Bonnet's Pieces **Mrs P. M. Sly**
3 ALL MY LOVE (IRE), 6, b m Lord Shanakill (USA)—Afilla **D. L. Bayliss**
4 BONNET'S VINO, 10, b m Grape Tree Road—Bonnet's Pieces **Mrs P. M. Sly**
5 ESKENDASH (USA), 5, ch g Eskendereya (USA)—Daffaash (USA) **Boyle Racing**
6 FRANSHAM, 4, b g Sulamani (IRE)—Circus Rose **Mrs P. M. Sly**
7 GAYTON, 4, ch f Haafhd—Wistow **Mrs P. M. Sly**
8 GHINIA (IRE), 7, b m Mastercraftsman (IRE)—Jorghinia (FR) **D. L. Bayliss**
9 HAAFAPIECE, 5, ch g Haafhd—Bonnet's Pieces **Mrs I. A. Coles**

MRS PAM SLY - Continued

10 **KEEPUP KEVIN**, 4, b g Haafhd—Black Salix (USA) **Mrs P. M. Sly**
11 **MORTENS LEAM**, 6, b g Sulamani (IRE)—Bonnet's Pieces **G Libson & P M Sly**
12 **PACIFIC SALT (IRE)**, 5, gr g Zebedee—Villa Nova (IRE) **D.L. Bayliss & G.A. Libson**
13 **POPELYS GULL (IRE)**, 6, ch g Recharge (IRE)—Circus Rose **Mrs V. M. Edmonson & Mrs P. M. Sly**
14 **RUSTY FOX (FR)**, 5, ch g Excellent Art—Damoiselle (USA) **Mrs P. M. Sly**
15 **SHIFT ON SHEILA**, 5, b m Aussie Rules (USA)—Black Salix (USA) **Mrs P. M. Sly**
16 **SPINART**, 5, ch g Dutch Art—Spinneret **Mr D. J. Bourne**
17 **VERNATTI**, 5, b m Teofilo (IRE)—Speciosa (IRE) **M. H. Sly, Dr T. Davies & Mrs P. Sly**
18 **WALSINGHAM GRANGE (USA)**, 5, b g Paddy O'prado (USA)—Mambo Queen (USA) **Pam's People**
19 **WELLAND**, 5, ch g Beat Hollow—Circus Rose **Mrs P. M. Sly**
20 **ZAFARANAH (USA)**, 4, ch f Raven's Pass (USA)—Jiwen (CAN) **Pam's People**

THREE-YEAR-OLDS

21 **DARK SPEC**, b c Dark Angel (IRE)—Speciosa (IRE) **M. H. Sly, Dr T. Davies & Mrs P. Sly**

TWO-YEAR-OLDS

22 **JOHN CLARE (IRE)**, b c 7/3 Poet's Voice—Specialty (IRE) (Oasis Dream) **M. H. Sly, Mrs P. M. Sly**
23 B c 1/4 Monsieur Bond (IRE)—Kaloni (IRE) (Kalanisi (IRE)) **Mrs P. M. Sly**

Other Owners: Mr David L. Bayliss, Mr P. J. J. Boyle, Mr S. Boyle, Dr T. J. W. Davies, Mrs V. M. Edmonson, Mr G. A. Libson, Mrs P. M. Sly, Mr Michael H. Sly.

Assistant Trainer: Chris Scudder

Jockey (NH): Kielan Woods. **Amateur:** Miss Gina Andrews.

---

511 **MR DAVID SMAGA, Lamorlaye**
Postal: 17 Voie de la Grange des Pres, 60260 Lamorlaye, France
Contacts: PHONE (0033) 3442 15005 FAX (0033) 3442 15356 MOBILE (0033) 6078 37287
E-MAIL david-smaga@wanadoo.fr

1 **COUNTY FAIR**, 4, b c Nayef (USA)—Village Fete **Prince Khalid Abdullah**
2 **DJIGUITE (FR)**, 6, b h Makfi—Envoutement (FR) **Mr A. Louis-Dreyfus**
3 **DON TOMMASINO (IRE)**, 5, b h Fastnet Rock (AUS)—M'oubliez Pas (USA) **Mr A. M. Haddad**
4 **FLYING DESIRE**, 5, b g Rail Link—Arrow of Desire **Mr R. Nahas**
5 **GAETANO DONIZETTI (IRE)**, 5, b h Makfi—Galipette **Mr M. Lagasse**
6 **JEITOSO BAYER (BRZ)**, 6, b h Peintre Celebre (USA)—Kyanite (BRZ) **Benjamin Steinbruch**
7 **KIT KAT JET (BRZ)**, 5, gr h T H Approval (USA)—Yiddish Mama (ARG) **Benjamin Steinbruch**
8 **KIWI GREEN SUITE (BRZ)**, 5, b h T H Approval (USA)—Hypnose (BRZ) **Benjamin Steinbruch**
9 **LA POUTANESCA (IRE)**, 4, ch f Falco (USA)—Victoria College (FR) **Mr A. M. Haddad**
10 **MATE STORY (IRE)**, 4, b c Makfi—Tierra Luna (IRE) **Aleyrion Bloodstock**
11 **MILLFIELD (FR)**, 5, b h Whipper (USA)—Victoria College (FR) **Mr A. M. Haddad**
12 **PERFECTO RAGAZZO (IRE)**, 4, b c Nayef (USA)—Ibizane (USA) **Mr A. M. Haddad**
13 **PRIMUS INCITATUS (IRE)**, 7, ch h Mastercraftsman (IRE)—Chaibia (IRE) **Mr A. M. Haddad**
14 **PRIVATE SCHOOL (IRE)**, 5, ch m Mastercraftsman (IRE)—Poltava (IRE) **Mr D. Smaga**
15 **RIP THE TOP (IRE)**, 4, b c Rip Van Winkle (IRE)—Stefer (USA) **Mr R. Nahas**
16 **SAPHIRSIDE (IRE)**, 9, b g Elusive City (USA)—Silirisa (FR) **Mr G. Augustin-Normand**
17 **SHAMS BRAZILERO (IRE)**, 4, b c Shamardal (USA)—Lumiere du Soir (FR) **Mr R. Nahas**
18 **TAMARAMA (FR)**, 4, b f Vale of York (IRE)—Happy Way (FR) **Mme J.-E. Dubois**
19 **VICTORIOUS CHAMP (FR)**, 7, b g New Approach (USA)—Sasanuma (USA) **Mr R. Nahas**
20 **VILARO (FR)**, 5, b h Whipper (USA)—Envoutement (FR) **Mr A. Louis-Dreyfus**

THREE-YEAR-OLDS

21 **AIR FROST**, br c Iffraaj—Winter Silence **Prince Khalid Abdullah**
22 **COMFORTING (USA)**, b br f First Defence (USA)—Treat Gently **Prince Khalid Abdullah**
23 **DUQUE**, b c Elusive City (USA)—Dariena (FR) **Mr M. Lagasse**
24 **EL MANIFICO**, b c High Chaparral (IRE)—Envoutement (FR) **Mr A. Louis-Dreyfus**
25 **FIVE ICE CUBES**, b c Rip Van Winkle (IRE)—Victoria College (FR) **Mr A. M. Haddad**
26 **FLYING DESIRE**, b c Intello (GER)—Arrow Of Desire **Mr R. Nahas**
27 **GALOUSKA (FR)**, b f Kentucky Dynamite (USA)—Calia (FR) **Mr A. Louis-Dreyfus**
28 **JULIAN ROCK**, b c Invincible Spirit (IRE)—Soneva (USA) **Aleyrion Bloodstock**
29 **LUMINOSA (FR)**, b f Makfi—Katchagua (FR) **Mr A. Louis-Dreyfus**
30 **MAKTAVA (FR)**, b c Makfi—Poltava (FR) **Ecurie Haras du Cadran**
31 **ON MY MIND (IRE)**, b f High Chaparral (IRE)—Onereuse **Mr J. Kalmanson**

MR DAVID SMAGA - Continued

32 **PRESTO**, b c Cacique (IRE)—Allegro Viva (USA) **Prince Khalid Abdullah**
33 **PRINCIPIA**, b f High Chaparral (IRE)—Zero Gravity **Prince Khalid Abdullah**
34 **SIGNATURE PIECE (USA)**, b f Lemon Drop Kid (USA)—Aviate **Prince Khalid Abdullah**
35 **TALK POSH (IRE)**, b f So You Think (NZ)—Refined (IRE) **Mr J. Kalmanson**
36 **TERRAVISTA (FR)**, b f Teofilo (IRE)—Tierra Luna (IRE) **Aleyrion Bloodstock**
37 **THE RIGGER**, b c Mizzen Mast (USA)—Tolerance (USA) **Prince Khalid Abdullah**
38 **VOIX DU SOIR**, b c Rip Van Winkle (IRE)—Lumiere du Soir (FR) **Mr R. Nahas**
39 **WESTFIELD**, b c Nathaniel (IRE)—Ossun (FR) **Mr J. E. Dubois**

TWO-YEAR-OLDS

40 **AGUANA (FR)**, b f 2/3 Motivator—Katchagua (FR) (Anabaa (USA)) **Alain Louis-Dreyfus**
41 Ch c 10/2 Kendargent (FR)—Envoutement (FR) (Vettori (IRE)) **A. Louis-Dreyfus, N. Nahas**
42 Ch f 21/2 Champs Elysees—Intricate Design (Zafonic (USA)) (28489) **John Kalmanson**
43 Ch f 27/3 Makfi—Loutka (FR) (Trempolino (USA)) **Malcolm Parish, D. Smaga**
44 **NELITA (FR)**, b f 23/4 Makfi—Calia (FR) (Orpen (USA)) **A. Louis-Dreyfus**
45 **PIKES PEAK (FR)**, b f 21/3 Sepoy (AUS)—
           Pietra Santa (FR) (Acclamation) (17908) **Aleyrion Bloodstock Ltd, David Smaga**
46 Ch f 5/4 Mastercraftsman (IRE)—Renowned (IRE) (Darshaan) (61863) **John Kalmanson**
47 **SWINGY (FR)**, b c 5/3 Anodin (IRE)—La Fee de Breizh (FR) (Verglas (IRE)) **A. Louis-Dreyfus**

Jockey (flat): Thibault Speicher. **Apprentice:** Michaelle Michel.

---

512   MR BRYAN SMART, Hambleton

Postal: Hambleton House, Sutton Bank, Thirsk, North Yorkshire, YO7 2HA
Contacts: **PHONE** (01845) 597481 **FAX** (01845) 597480 **MOBILE** (07748) 634797
E-MAIL office@bryansmart.plus.com **WEBSITE** www.bryansmart-racing.com

1 **ALPHA DELPHINI**, 7, b g Captain Gerrard (IRE)—Easy To Imagine (USA) **The Alpha Delphini Partnership**
2 **BLACK HAMBLETON**, 5, b g Dick Turpin (IRE)—Duena **The Smart Duena Partnership**
3 **COMPTON RIVER**, 6, b g Compton Place—Inagh River **The Smart Inagh River Partnership**
4 **FENDALE**, 6, b g Exceed And Excel (AUS)—Adorn **Mr S. E. Chappell**
5 **GERRARD'S SLIP**, 6, b g Captain Gerrard (IRE)—Park's Girl **Mr B. Smart**
6 **GINGER LOVE**, 4, ch g Kheleyf (USA)—La Peinture (GER) **Mr B. Smart**
7 **HELOVAPLAN (IRE)**, 4, b g Helmet (AUS)—Watsdaplan (IRE) **The Smart Set**
8 **JAMEERAH**, 5, b m Dansili—Jira **Mr S. E. Chappell**
9 **KENTUCKYCONNECTION (USA)**, 5, b g Include (USA)—Youcanringmybell (USA) **Woodcock Electrical Limited**
10 **KI KI**, 6, ch m Kheleyf (USA)—Peryllys **Mr B. Smart**
11 **KING ROBERT**, 5, b g Royal Applause—Generously Gifted **Ceffyl Racing**
12 **KYLLACH ME (IRE)**, 6, b g Kyllachy—Good For Her **Mr B. Smart**
13 **MELROSE GIRL**, 4, b f Monsieur Bond (IRE)—Keyaki (IRE) **The Barber Girls**
14 **MYTHMAKER**, 6, b g Major Cadeaux—Mythicism **Crossfields Racing**
15 **NAMEITWHATYOULIKE**, 9, b g Trade Fair—Emma Peel **Mr S. E. Chappell**
16 **OUTFOX**, 4, b f Foxwedge (AUS)—Spontaneity (IRE) **Crossfields Racing**
17 **PEPYS**, 4, b g Aqlaam—Generously Gifted **Mr G. Lowe & Mr P. Darling**
18 **RED PIKE (IRE)**, 7, ch g Kheleyf (USA)—Fancy Feathers (IRE) **Mr Michael Moses & Mr Terry Moses**
19 **SIYAHAMBA (IRE)**, 4, ch g Helmet (AUS)—Kalabunga (IRE) **Mr B. Smart**
20 **SNOW EXCUSE**, 4, gr g Hellvelyn—Satin Doll **Mrs A. D. Bourne**
21 **STRAIGHTOTHEPOINT**, 6, b g Kyllachy—Choisette **Crossfields Racing**
22 **TIVRA (IRE)**, 4, b f Kodiac—Bokhara Silk (IRE) **Mr S. E. Chappell**

THREE-YEAR-OLDS

23 **ALFA MCGUIRE (IRE)**, b c Lord Shanakill (USA)—Watsdaplan (IRE) **Alfa Site Services Ltd**
24 **BEN MY CHREE**, gr f Lethal Force (IRE)—Steal The Curtain **Middleham Park Racing (XCIV) & Partner**
25 **BONANZA BOWLS**, b g Zebedee—Twilight Belle (IRE) **Mr J A Milburn & Partner**
26 **DEJAN**, b g Nathaniel (IRE)—Blue Azure (USA) **D. Blake, A. Welch, C. Dinsdale**
27 **DYSON'S GIRL**, ch f Equiano (FR)—Choisette **Crossfields Racing**
28 **EXCELLENTLY POISED**, b g Sepoy (AUS)—Excelette (IRE) **Sir A Ferguson Mr G Lowe Mr H Agustsson**
29 **GAMESTERS ICON**, b f Sixties Icon—Gamesters Lady **Gamesters Partnership**
30 **HOT ROCK (IRE)**, ch g Society Rock—Red Roar (IRE) **Bagtoon Villas**
31 **LADY SOPHIEBELLA**, b f Monsieur Bond (IRE)—Lady Paris (IRE) **R. C. Bond**
32 **LEADEROFTHEPACK**, gr g Lethal Force (IRE)—Spontaneity (IRE) **Crossfields Racing**
33 **MAFDET**, b f Rip Van Winkle (IRE)—Fabulous Speed (USA) **Northmore Stud**
34 **MONTANA DAWN (USA)**, b f Jimmy Creed (USA)—Page Dancer (USA) **Ms D. Aldridge**

MR BRYAN SMART - Continued

35 **PORT LINCOLN (USA)**, b g Data Link (USA)—Waverly Place (USA) **Middleham Park Racing (ix) & Partner**
36 **SHE'S ROYAL**, b f Delegator—Sukuma (IRE) **Davis, Moody, Hogan, Styles**
37 **SITSI**, ch f Captain Gerrard (IRE)—Ayasha **Crossfields Racing**
38 **SPIRITOFNINETYSIX**, br f Swiss Spirit—Equinox **Crossfields Racing**
39 **TIGERSHARK (IRE)**, gr g Lethal Force (IRE)—Fearless Flyer (IRE) **L C & A E Sigsworth**
40 **TREVITHICK**, b c Champs Elysees—New Choice (IRE) **Mrs P. A. Clark**
41 **WHERERAINBOWSEND (IRE)**, br f Roderic O'connor (IRE)—Mikes Baby (IRE) **Miss C. R. Holmes**
42 **WRENTHORPE**, ch c Hellvelyn—Milly-M **Mr Dan Maltby & Mr B. Smart**

TWO-YEAR-OLDS

43 B c 27/2 Camacho—A Childs Dream (IRE) (Intense Focus (USA)) (15465) **M. Barber**
44 **AEROSPHERE**, b f 26/1 Gregorian (IRE)—Rhal (IRE) (Rahy (USA)) (10000) **Crossfields Racing**
45 **ANTAGONIZE**, b c 21/2 Epaulette (AUS)—Hakuraa (IRE) (Elnadim (USA)) (15000) **Crossfields Racing**
46 **ARMAGEDDON**, b f 31/1 War Command (USA)—Nizhoni (USA) (Mineshaft (USA)) (33000) **Crossfields Racing**
47 Ch f 7/5 Farhh—Dhan Dhana (IRE) (Dubawi (IRE)) (13000) **Ms D. Aldridge**
48 B c 17/4 Havana Gold (IRE)—Eleventh Hour (IRE) (Invincible Spirit (IRE)) (15238) **The Smart Set**
49 Ch f 1/5 Exceed And Excel (AUS)—Fashionable (Nashwan (USA)) (48000)
50 B f 21/2 Kodiac—Kerfuffle (IRE) (Kheleyf (USA)) (16190)
51 **NEIGH DRAMAS**, ch c 1/4 Equiano (FR)—Silvee (Avonbridge) (5714) **Mr L. S. Olley & Partner**
52 **NORTHERNPOWERHOUSE**, b c 18/4 Harbour Watch (IRE)—
                                    Mortitia (Dansili) (15000) **Mr Michael Moses & Mr Terry Moses**
53 B c 25/3 Moohaajim (IRE)—Omanome (IRE) (Acclamation) (28571) **Alfa Site Services Ltd & Mrs C Cashman**
54 Br c 11/3 Harbour Watch (IRE)—
                                    Rock Ace (IRE) (Verglas (IRE)) (19047) **Middleham Park Racing (XCIV) & Partner**
55 B c 2/2 Swiss Spirit—Sofonisba (Rock of Gibraltar (IRE)) (50000)
56 **STRONSAY (IRE)**, b c 23/2 Gale Force Ten—
                                    Perfect Blossom (One Cool Cat (USA)) (16280) **The Unscrupulous Judges**
57 **TICK TOCK CROC (IRE)**, b c 20/3 Requinto (IRE)—Quinine (Dark Angel (IRE)) (16190) **Ceffyl Racing**

Other Owners: Mr H. Agustsson, Mr D. S. Blake, Mr M. Bullock, Mrs T. Bullock, Mrs Catherine Cashman, Mr P. A. Darling, Mr I. F. Davis, Mr J. C. Dinsdale, D. B. Elders, Sir A. Ferguson, Mr K. J. Hogan, Mrs A. C. Hudson, Mr T. D. Jones, G. A. Lowe, Mr D. L. Maltby, Mrs B. A. Matthews, Middleham Park Racing IX, Middleham Park Racing XCIV, J. A. Milburn, Mrs F. B. Moody, Mr T. J. Moses, Mr M. Moses, Mr L. Olley, R. A. Page, T. S. Palin, M. Prince, Mr G. M. Sheldon, L. C. Sigsworth, Mrs A. E. Sigsworth, Mrs V. R. Smart, Mrs E. K. Styles, Mrs S. E. Trivass, Mr D. B. Watroba, Mr A. Welch, Mr D. V. Williams.

Assistant Trainers: Mrs V. R. Smart, Mr K. Edmunds **Pupil Assistant:** Miss Beth Smart

Apprentice: Harry Russell.

---

513 **MR CHARLES SMITH, Temple Bruer**
Postal: 6-7 Thompsons Bottom, Temple Bruer, Lincoln, Lincolnshire, LN5 0DE
Contacts: **PHONE/FAX (01526) 833245 MOBILE (07778) 149188**

1 **ALPHA TAURI (USA)**, 12, b g Aldebaran (USA)—Seven Moons (JPN) **Mr J. R. Theaker**
2 **EJABAH (IRE)**, 4, b f Iffraaj—Relinquished **Mr N. J. Baines**
3 **GENERAL TUFTO**, 13, b g Fantastic Light—Miss Pinkerton **Mr J. R. Theaker**
4 **RED SHANGHAI (IRE)**, 4, ch f Tamayuz—Rouge Noir (USA) **Mr M. J. Smeed**
5 **ROBBIAN**, 7, b g Bertolini (USA)—Crathes **R. J. Lewin**

---

514 **MR JULIAN SMITH, Tirley**
Postal: Tirley Court, Tirley, Gloucester
Contacts: **PHONE (01452) 780461 FAX (01452) 780461 MOBILE (07748) 901175**
E-MAIL nicola.smith9156@o2.co.uk

1 **DIAMOND ROSE**, 6, b m Sagamix (FR)—Swiss Rose **Grand Jury Partnership**
2 **EMERALD ROSE**, 11, b m Sir Harry Lewis (USA)—Swiss Rose **Grand Jury Partnership**
3 **HARRIET'S ARK**, 11, ch m Sir Harry Lewis (USA)—Brush The Ark **Exors of the Late Mr D. E. S. Smith**
4 **IONA DAYS (IRE)**, 13, bg g Epistolaire (IRE)—Miss Best (FR) **Mrs J.A. Benson & Miss S.N. Benson**
5 6, Gr m Proclamation (IRE)—Midnight Ocean **Exors of the Late Mr D. E. S. Smith**
6 **NO PRINCIPLES**, 15, b g Overbury (IRE)—Selective Rose **Exors of the Late Mr D. E. S. Smith**
7 **PENNIES AND POUNDS**, 11, b m Sir Harry Lewis (USA)—Sense of Value **Exors of the Late Mr D. E. S. Smith**

MR JULIAN SMITH - Continued

Other Owners: Mrs J. A. Benson, Miss S. N. Benson, Mr A. W. Brookes, R. Brookes.

Assistant Trainer: Mrs Nicky Smith

Jockey (NH): Mark Grant, Sam Twiston-Davies. **Amateur:** Mr J. M. Ridley.

---

515 MR MARTIN SMITH, Newmarket
Postal: **Stable Cottage, Calder Park, Hamilton Road, Newmarket, Suffolk, CB8 0NY**
Contacts: **MOBILE (07712) 493589**
WEBSITE www.martinsmithracing.com

1 **ARCH MY BOY,** 4, b g Archipenko (USA)—Fairy Slipper **Mr Robert P Clarke & Mr Martin Smith**
2 **BRAVE TART,** 4, b f Pastoral Pursuits—Poyle Kiera **Four To One Partnership**
3 **IFWECAN,** 7, b g Exceed And Excel (AUS)—Kirk **Henry & Jade Syndicate**
4 **IN THE RED (IRE),** 5, b g Elusive Pimpernel (USA)—Roses From Ridey (IRE) **Sunville Rail Limited**
5 **MAJORETTE,** 4, ch f Major Cadeaux—So Discreet **M & M Bloodstock**
6 **NO REFUND (IRE),** 7, b g Invincible Spirit (IRE)—Evangeline **Mrs M Smith, Mrs R Rennie & Mrs M Smyth**
7 **OSSIE'S DANCER,** 9, ch g Osorio (GER)—Nina Ballerina **Mrs V. Garner**
8 **PANDINUS IMPERATOR (IRE),** 5, b g Scorpion (IRE)—Casiana (GER) **R Clarke, M Smith, Sunville Rail Ltd**
9 **RIVERS OF ASIA,** 5, ch g Medicean—Aliena (IRE) **Mr Robert P Clarke & Mr Martin Smith**

THREE-YEAR-OLDS

10 **AFFLUENCE (IRE),** b c Thewayyouare (USA)—Castalian Spring (IRE) **M & M Bloodstock**
11 **ROMAN RIVER,** b c Holy Roman Emperor (IRE)—Inagh River **M B S Racing**
12 **THE EMPEROR WITHIN (FR),** b c Holy Roman Emperor (IRE)—Watchful (IRE) **M B S Racing**

TWO-YEAR-OLDS

13 B c 11/3 Dylan Thomas (IRE)—Castalian Spring (IRE) (Oasis Dream)
14 Ch c 8/2 Helmet (AUS)—Lady Pitrizza (IRE) (Night Shift (USA)) (11000) **M & M Bloodstock**

Other Owners: H.H. Sheikh S. B. M. Al Khalifa, Sheikh Mohammed Bin Isa Al Khalifa, Mr R. P. Clarke, Mrs R. T. Rennie, Mr M. P. B. Smith, Mrs M. E. Smith, Mrs M. Smyth, Mrs A. Yorke, Mr P. Yorke.

---

516 MR R. MIKE SMITH, Galston
Postal: **West Loudoun Farm, Galston, Ayrshire, KA4 8PB**
Contacts: **PHONE (01563) 822062 MOBILE (07711) 692122**
E-MAIL mike@mikesmithracing.co.uk WEBSITE www.mikesmithracing.co.uk

1 5, Br m Westerner—Afairs (IRE) **West Loudoun Racing Club**
2 **AKAMANTO (IRE),** 4, b g Cape Cross (IRE)—Allofus (IRE) **Reid Ross Smith**
3 **ALPHABETICAL ORDER,** 10, b g Alflora (IRE)—Lady Turk (FR) **Great Northern Partnership**
4 **AN FEAR CIUIN (IRE),** 7, b g Galileo (IRE)—Potion **P. Tsim**
5 **ARCHIBELLE,** 4, b f Archipenko (USA)—Cloud Hill **Belstane Racing Partnership**
6 **CHINESE SPIRIT (IRE),** 4, gr g Clodovil—In The Ribbons **Mr Y. C. Luk**
7 **CIARABELLA (IRE),** 5, b m Gold Well—Fancy Fashion (IRE) **Miss J. Girasoli**
8 **COOPER'S FRIEND (IRE),** 9, b g Kayf Tara—Graphic Lady (IRE) **Smith & Russell**
9 **FIRSTYMINI (FR),** 7, gr g Slickly (FR)—Jolie Lola (FR) **Mr R. M. Smith**
10 **GLENNA (IRE),** 7, br g Scorpion (IRE)—Scoop Thirty Nine **West Loudoun Racing Club**
11 **GLINGERSIDE (IRE),** 7, b g Milan—Kettle 'n Cran (IRE) **A L Gregg & B H McFadzean**
12 **GWORN,** 8, b g Aussie Rules (USA)—Crochet (IRE) **Mr R. Gibson**
13 **HAYMARKET,** 9, b g Singspiel (IRE)—Quickstyx **Mr A. M. Ross**
14 **IRVINE LADY (IRE),** 5, ch m Footstepsinthesand—Ascot Lady (IRE) **Mr G. Kerr**
15 **J AND M GREENGAIRS,** 10, b g Flemensfirth (USA)—Smooth Technology (IRE) **Mr J. C. Higgins**
16 **LAS TUNAS (FR),** 6, b br g Country Reel (USA)—Grey Winner (FR) **Spittal Family**
17 **MISS MACKIE (IRE),** 7, b m Mr Combustible (IRE)—Grannys Kitchen (IRE) **Smith Millar Hynd Russell**
18 **MR SANDGATE (IRE),** 5, b g Sandmason—Ballybeg Princess (IRE) **Mrs Smith & Matheson**
19 **NAKADAM (FR),** 8, b g Nickname (FR)—Cadoudame (FR) **Smith & Spittal**
20 **OUR LUCAS (IRE),** 6, b br g Jeremy (USA)—Alassio (USA) **M. Sawers**
21 **PETERS GREY (IRE),** 8, gr g Aussie Rules (USA)—Aliyshan (IRE) **P. Tsim**
22 **READ'EM AND WEEP (IRE),** 8, b g Kutub (IRE)—Amalita (IRE) **Gregg Russell & Smith**
23 **ROOSTER SPIRIT (IRE),** 5, gr g Craigsteel—Turlututu (FR) **M. Sawers**
24 **SPES NOSTRA,** 10, b g Ad Valorem (USA)—Millagros (IRE) **J. A. Cringan**

MR R. MIKE SMITH - Continued

25 **STRONG ECONOMY (IRE)**, 6, ch g Sandmason—Odd Decision (IRE) **M. Sawers**
26 **TRONGATE (IRE)**, 6, b g Dansant—Val Eile (IRE) **M. Sawers**
27 **U NAME IT (IRE)**, 10, b g Gold Well—Bypharthebest (IRE) **Smith & Spittal**
28 **URIAH HEEP (FR)**, 9, b g Danehill Dancer (IRE)—Canasita **Mrs P. McLeish**

Other Owners: W. Brand, Mr A. L. Gregg, Mr J. Hampson, Ms M. Hynd, Mrs A. D. Matheson, Mr B. McFadzean, Mrs L. M. Millar, Mr G. P. O'Shea, Mr G. Reid, Mr M. J. Russell, Mr A. H. Spittal, Miss B. Spittal.

517 **MR RALPH J. SMITH, Epsom**
Postal: **1 Christopher Court, High Street, Tadworth, Surrey, KT20 5QX**
Contacts: **PHONE (01372) 273870 FAX (01737) 201693 MOBILE (07795) 327003**
E-MAIL rjsmith.racing@hotmail.com WEBSITE www.rjsmithracing.com

1 **AKUNA MATTATTA (IRE)**, 4, b g Approve (IRE)—Akuna Magic (IRE) **Partnership Terminated**
2 **DUHR (IRE)**, 4, b g Mawatheeq (USA)—Dijlah **Mrs J. C. Smith**
3 **INNSTIGATOR**, 4, b g Delegator—Page **Clear Racing With SMD Investments**
4 **L'AMI DE ROUGE**, 5, b m Excellent Art—Coup de Torchon (FR) **Homecroft Wealth Racing**
5 **LONDON GRAMMAR (IRE)**, 4, b f Sir Prancealot (IRE)—Emmas Princess (IRE) **Mr K. Old**
6 **MAGIC PASS**, 4, ch g Raven's Pass (USA)—Magic America (USA) **G. Strawbridge**
7 **ST JAMES'S PARK (IRE)**, 5, br g Invincible Spirit (IRE)—Rakiza (IRE) **Mr K. Old**
8 **TOPTEMPO**, 9, ch m Halling (USA)—Topatoo **Mrs J. C. Smith**
9 **VICTOR'S BET (SPA)**, 9, b g Leadership—Marmaria (SPA) **Homecroft Wealth Racing & Mr Kevin Old**

Other Owners: Mr B. J. Greening, Mrs M. M. Greening, Mr B. Pettis, Mr S. J. Piper, SMD Investments Ltd.

Assistant Trainer: Jayne Smith

Amateur: Miss Ella Smith.

518 **MRS SUE SMITH, Bingley**
Postal: **Craiglands Farm, High Eldwick, Bingley, West Yorkshire, BD16 3BE**
Contacts: **PHONE (01274) 564930 FAX (01274) 560626**
E-MAIL craiglandsracing@yahoo.co.uk

1 **ABSOLUTELY DYLAN (IRE)**, 5, b g Scorpion (IRE)—Cash Customer (IRE) **Mrs S. J. Smith**
2 **ALFIBOY**, 8, b g Alflora (IRE)—Cloudy Pearl **Mrs S. J. Smith**
3 **ALPHIE**, 6, b g Alflora (IRE)—Clever Liz **Mrs S. J. Smith**
4 **BLACK ART**, 6, ch g Black Sam Bellamy (IRE)—Art Series **Jacqueline & John Conroy**
5 **BLAKEMOUNT (IRE)**, 10, br g Presenting—Smashing Leader (IRE) **Mrs J. Conroy**
6 **BLOTTOS (IRE)**, 6, b g Westerner—Autumn Beauty (IRE) **Mr T. J. Hemmings**
7 **BOBNDAVE (IRE)**, 6, b g Brian Boru—Sidblack (IRE) **Mrs S. J. Smith**
8 **CAPTAIN MOIRETTE (FR)**, 6, gr g Kap Rock (FR)—Rahana Moirette (FR) **Mrs A. Clarke**
9 **CLOUDY TOO (IRE)**, 12, b g Cloudings (IRE)—Curra Citizen (IRE) **Formulated Polymer Products Ltd**
10 **CRACKING FIND (IRE)**, 7, b g Robin des Pres (FR)—Crack The Kicker (IRE) **Mrs A. Ellis**
11 **DARTFORD WARBLER (IRE)**, 11, b g Overbury (IRE)—Stony View (IRE) **Mrs S. J. Smith**
12 **DE VOUS A MOI (FR)**, 10, b g Sinndar (IRE)—Dzinigane (FR) **Mrs J. Morgan**
13 **DELUSIONOFGRANDEUR (IRE)**, 8, b g Mahler—Olivia Rose (IRE) **McGoldrick Racing 3**
14 **DICK DARSIE (IRE)**, 8, br g Darsi (FR)—Hurricane Jane (IRE) **Mrs S. J. Smith**
15 **FLEMERINA (IRE)**, 9, b m Flemensfirth (USA)—Ballerina Laura (IRE) **Mrs S. J. Smith**
16 **GETAWAY BAY (IRE)**, 6, b g Getaway (GER)—Wayward Star (IRE) **Mrs S. J. Smith**
17 **GRATE FELLA (IRE)**, 10, b g King's Best (USA)—Moonlight Paradise (USA) **Mrs M. Ashby**
18 **HAINAN (FR)**, 7, gr g Laveron—Honor Smytzer **Mrs J. Morgan & Mrs Lindsey J. Shaw**
19 **HOOVES THE DADDY (IRE)**, 5, b g Robin des Pres (FR)—Countessdee (IRE) **Mrs A. Ellis**
20 **I JUST KNOW (IRE)**, 8, b g Robin des Pres (FR)—Desperado Queen (IRE) **M. B. Scholey & R. H. Scholey**
21 **INFORMATEUR (FR)**, 5, b g Maresca Sorrento (FR)—Isarella (GER) **Mrs J M Gray & Mr G R Orchard**
22 **ISKABEG LANE (IRE)**, 7, b g Westerner—Nosey Oscar (IRE) **Mr D. Sutherland**
23 **IT'S BUSTER (IRE)**, 7, b g Stowaway—Late Guest (IRE) **Mrs S. J. Smith**
24 **JOKE DANCER**, 5, ch g Authorized (IRE)—Missy Dancer **Mrs A. Clarke**
25 **JUST GEORGIE**, 8, b g Kayf Tara—Just Kate **M. B. Scholey & R. H. Scholey**
26 **JUST MINDED (IRE)**, 7, b g Kayf Tara—Georgia On My Mind (IRE) **Mr T. J. Hemmings**
27 **KLARE CASTLE (IRE)**, 6, b g Black Sam Bellamy (IRE)—Always Forgiving **Mr D. Sutherland**
28 **LAVELLA WELLS (IRE)**, 10, b m Alflora (IRE)—Jazzy Refrain (IRE) **Mrs S. J. Smith**
29 **LE DRAPEAU (FR)**, 6, ch g Satri (IRE)—La Bandera (FR) **A. D. Hollinrake**

MRS SUE SMITH - Continued

30 LOUGH LEGEND (IRE), 4, b g Watar (IRE)—Gibboghstown (IRE) Broadway Racing Club 15
31 LUCKY LUCARNO, 6, b g Lucarno (USA)—Sari Rose (FR) Mrs S. J. Smith
32 MAXED OUT KING (IRE), 10, ch g Desert King (IRE)—Lady Max (IRE) Mrs S. J. Smith
33 MIDNIGHT SHADOW, 5, b g Midnight Legend—Holy Smoke Mrs A. Clarke
34 MINELLA FIVEO (IRE), 10, b g Westerner—Autumn Sky (IRE) Mrs S. J. Smith
35 MUTAWAASEL, 6, b g Teofilo (IRE)—Muwakleh Mrs S. J. Smith
36 NEVER UP (GER), 7, b g Danehill Dancer (IRE)—Never Green (IRE) Mr & Mrs G. Turnbull
37 NO PLANNING, 4, b g Kayf Tara—Poor Celt Mrs J. Conroy
38 NOMOREBLACKJACK (IRE), 7, b g Robin des Pres (FR)—Hardabout (IRE) Mr John Wade & Mrs S. Smith
39 PERSEID (IRE), 8, br g Robin des Pres (FR)—Cowanstown Miss (IRE) Mrs S. J. Smith
40 QUIETLY (IRE), 7, b g Oscar (IRE)—Gimme Peace Mr T. J. Hemmings
41 RED DANAHER (IRE), 11, ch g Shantou (USA)—Red Rover Mrs S. J. Smith
42 SHARP RESPONSE (IRE), 7, b g Oscar (IRE)—Lambourne Lace (IRE) Formulated Polymer Products Ltd
43 SHINE AWAY (IRE), 8, b m Robin des Pres (FR)—Bramble Bree (IRE) Mrs S. J. Smith
44 SILVA ECLIPSE, 5, gr g Multiplex—Linen Line Mr & Mrs G. Turnbull
45 SMOOTH STEPPER, 9, b g Alflora (IRE)—Jazzy Refrain (IRE) Mrs A. Clarke
46 STRAIDNAHANNA (IRE), 9, gr g Medaaly—Sue's Song M. B. Scholey & R. H. Scholey
47 SWING HARD (IRE), 10, gr g Zagreb (USA)—Hurricane Jane (IRE) D P Van Der Hoeven & D G Pryde
48 TRESHNISH (IRE), 5, ch g Gold Away (IRE)—Didn't I Tell You (IRE) D G Pryde & D Van Der Hoeven
49 TROOBLUE, 6, gr m Great Palm (USA)—Touch of Ivory (IRE) Mrs S. J. Smith
50 VINTAGE CLOUDS (IRE), 8, gr g Cloudings (IRE)—Rare Vintage (IRE) Mr T. J. Hemmings
51 WAKANDA (IRE), 9, b g Westerner—Chanson Indienne (FR) M. B. Scholey & R. H. Scholey
52 WOLF SWORD (IRE), 9, b g Flemensfirth (USA)—Dame O'neill (IRE) Mr G. R. Orchard & Mrs J. M. Gray
53 YOUNG TOM, 5, b g Sir Percy—Enford Princess Formulated Polymer Products Ltd

Other Owners: Mrs Jacqueline Conroy, Mr J. Conroy, Mrs J. M. Gray, Mr Richard Longley, Mr Charles MacMillan, Mr P. J. Martin, McGoldrick Racing, Mrs J. Morgan, Mr G. R. Orchard, Mr D. G. Pryde, Mrs M. B. Scholey, Mr R. H. Scholey, Mrs Lindsey J. Shaw, Mrs S. Smith, Mr Geoffrey Turnbull, Mrs S. E. Turnbull, Mr David van der Hoeven.

Assistant Trainer: Ryan Clavin

Jockey (NH): Danny Cook, Nathan Moscrop, Sean Quinlan. Conditional: Sam Coltherd.

---

519 MISS SUZY SMITH, Lewes
Postal: County Stables, The Old Racecourse, Lewes, East Sussex, BN7 1UR
Contacts: PHONE (01273) 477173 FAX (01273) 477173 MOBILE (07970) 550828
E-MAIL suzy@suzysmithracing.co.uk WEBSITE www.suzysmithracing.co.uk

1 BOLD IMAGE (IRE), 7, b m Milan—Golden Bay Mrs S. A. Addington-Smith
2 CLONDAW BISTO (IRE), 7, b g September Storm (GER)—
Solo Venture (IRE) Mr J.Gordon-Watson & Suzy Smith
3 CLONDAW CIAN (IRE), 8, br g Gold Well—Cocktail Bar (IRE) Wolf Allisat & Chris Ames
4 CRACKER JAK (IRE), 4, b g September Storm (GER)—Princess Jaffa (IRE) Mrs V. Palmer
5 DUBAI DIRHAM, 5, ch m Dubai Destination (USA)—Rolline (IRE) Mrs C. L. Dennis
6 HOOK LANE ROOBEE, 5, b g Spendent—Sharp Action Mrs J. Reece
7 HUNTRESS (IRE), 6, b m Flemensfirth (USA)—Madgehil (IRE) Crawford-Smith Family
8 INVICTA LAKE (IRE), 11, b g Dr Massini (IRE)—Classic Material The Invicta Partnership
9 KING CHARLIE (IRE), 8, b g Chevalier (IRE)—Desert Treat (IRE) Graham Jones, Trevor Loftus & Suzy Smith
10 LITTLE BOY BORU (IRE), 10, b g Brian Boru—How Is Things (IRE) J Logan, D Harrison, T Loftus & S Smith
11 MIGHTY VIC (IRE), 10, b g Old Vic—Mighty Marble (IRE) S. Gordon-Watson
12 MOODY MAGGIE (IRE), 5, b m Milan—Golden Bay Mrs S. A. Addington-Smith
13 4, B f Champs Elysees—Plaisterer David Andrews Plastering
14 RED DEVIL STAR (IRE), 8, b g Beneficial—Gortbofearna (IRE) Mrs V. Palmer
15 5, B m Multiplex—Roslin Mr & Mrs R. Allsop
16 ROSY WORLD, 5, b m Shirocco (GER)—Material World Kate Allisat & Hilary Ames
17 SO SHE SAYS (IRE), 6, b m Kalanisi (IRE)—Accordingtoherself (IRE) John Logan & Suzy Smith
18 STORM PATROL, 7, b m Shirocco (GER)—Material World Southern Bloodstock (GB)
19 STRIKE THE FLINT, 4, b f Shirocco (GER)—Material World Table For Six
20 THE GINGER NINJER, 5, ch m Malinas (GER)—Atabaas Allure (FR) Smarden Thoroughbreds

Other Owners: Mrs K. H. Allisat, Mr W. Allisat, Mr R. Allsop, Mrs Y. E. Allsop, Mr C. B. Ames, Mrs H. J. Ames, Mr S. D. Bradley, Mr C. J. Crawford-Smith, Mr N. L. Crawford-Smith, Mrs N. J. Crawford-Smith, Mrs H. J. Fitzsimons, Mr J. M. F. Gordon-Watson, Mr D. J. Harrison, Mr G. R. Jones, Mr T. H. Loftus, J. A. A. S. Logan, Mr J. Rimmer, Mrs C. A. Smith, Miss S. Smith, Mr C. P. Thompkins, Vogue Development Company (Kent) Ltd, D. P. Walsh, Mrs H. M. T. Woods.

MISS SUZY SMITH - Continued

Assistant Trainer: Mr S E Gordon-Watson

Jockey (flat): Luke Morris. **Jockey (NH):** Gavin Sheehan. **Conditional:** Jack Sherwood.

520
MR GILES SMYLY, Broadway
Postal: **Garden Cottage, Wormington Grange, Broadway, Worcestershire, WR12 7NJ**
Contacts: **PHONE (01386) 584085 FAX (01386) 584085 MOBILE (07747) 035169**
E-MAIL gilessmiler@aol.com WEBSITE www.smylyracing.co.uk

1 BRICE CANYON (FR), 7, b g Kapgarde (FR)—Fille Formidable (USA) **David Maxwell Racing Limited**
2 DESCARO (USA), 12, gr g Dr Fong (USA)—Miarixa (FR) **Miss N. L. Slack**
3 GALICE DU CIEL, 7, br g Septieme Ciel (USA)—Galice Du Soleil (FR) **Ms Gillian Metherell**
4 HENRY OLIVER (IRE), 10, b g Hasten To Add (USA)—Lisnabrin (IRE) **Miss N. L. Slack**
5 HIT THE HIGHWAY (IRE), 9, b g Pierre—Highway Belle (IRE) **A. C. Ward-Thomas**

Assistant Trainer: Kim Smyly

Jockey (NH): David England. **Conditional:** Ed Cookson.

521
MR JAMIE SNOWDEN, Lambourn
Postal: **Folly House, Upper Lambourn Road, Lambourn, Hungerford, Berkshire, RG17 8QG**
Contacts: **PHONE (01488) 72800 (office) MOBILE (07779) 497563**
E-MAIL info@jamiesnowdenracing.co.uk
WEBSITE www.jamiesnowdenracing.co.uk Twitter: @jamiesnowden

1 ADRRASTOS (IRE), 6, b g Areion (GER)—Laren (GER) **Mrs K. B. Gunn**
2 ALRIGHTJACK (IRE), 4, b g Stowaway—Brogella (IRE) **The GD Partnership**
3 BETWEEN THE WATERS (IRE), 7, ch g Indian River (FR)—Catch Ball **The Folly Partnership**
4 BLUE BULLET (FR), 5, b g Le Fou (IRE)—Jiletta (FR) **Me, Myself & I**
5 CAPSY DE MEE (FR), 6, b g Apsis—Koeur de Mee (FR) **Wiggin Robinson Wainwright Hill Davidson**
6 CARNTOP, 5, b g Dansili—Milford Sound **The Duchess Of Cornwall & Chips Keswick**
7 CAUTORILLO, 6, ch m Black Sam Bellamy (IRE)—Cent Prime **Fawley House Stud**
8 CHAMPAGNE JAMES (IRE), 10, b g Stowaway—
Champagne Lady (IRE) **Ian Barratt, Stephen Short & Adam Signy**
9 COURT OUT (IRE), 5, b g Court Cave (IRE)—Madame Martine (IRE) **Mr A Signy & Mr P Jacobs**
10 DANS LE VENT (FR), 5, b g Skins Game—Boreade (FR) **Marek Gumienny & Adam Signy**
11 DOUBLE TREASURE, 7, b g King's Theatre—Double Red (IRE) **Sir Chippendale Keswick**
12 DR WALUIGI (IRE), 8, b g Shirocco (GER)—Daruliyya (IRE) **The Galloping Grannies**
13 ETAT MAJOR AULMES (FR), 4, b g Della Francesca (USA)—River Gold Aulmes (FR) **Mr A. Signy**
14 FACT OF THE MATTER (IRE), 8, b g Brian Boru—Womanofthemountain (IRE) **The Sandylini Racing Partnership**
15 FATIMA BLUSH, 5, b m Black Sam Bellamy (IRE)—Samar Qand **Fawley House Stud**
16 FILEMON, 6, gr g Kayf Tara—L'ultima (FR) **E. Penser**
17 FLORAL BOUQUET, 5, bl m Fair Mix (IRE)—Florarossa **The Picnic Party**
18 FLOW FROM DEVON, 5, b m With The Flow (USA)—Sally Army **Miss R. J. Dobson**
19 FOOTLOOSE, 4, b g Sulamani (IRE)—Altesse de Sou (FR) **Wiggin Robinson Wainwright Hill Davison**
20 GRANGE RANGER (IRE), 6, b g Kalanisi (IRE)—
Grangeclare Flight (IRE) **Wiggin Robinson Wainwright Hill Davison**
21 HAVISHAM, 6, b g Mount Nelson—Ile Deserte **Mr D. E. Brownlow**
22 HOGAN'S HEIGHT (IRE), 7, b g Indian River (FR)—Electre du Berlais (FR) **Foxtrot Racing: Hogan's Height**
23 INSTANT KARMA (IRE), 7, b g Peintre Celebre (USA)—Kotdiji **Melbourne 10 Racing**
24 KALAHARI QUEEN, 5, br m Kalanisi (IRE)—Queen's Leader **Sir Chippendale Keswick**
25 KING VINCE, 5, gr g Mawatheeq (USA)—Tussah **P Fox, S Beccle, D Scott Et Al**
26 LORD TOPPER, 5, b g Sir Percy—Fugnina **Best Of Worlds**
27 LOSTNFOUND (IRE), 5, b m Midnight Legend—La Cerisaie **Turf Club, Mayoh & Callan**
28 LUNAR FLOW, 7, b g With The Flow (USA)—Misty Move (IRE) **L G Partnership**
29 MARLOW MOSS (IRE), 4, b f Fame And Glory—Moss Artiste (IRE) **Duckworth, Jordan & Wright**
30 MIDNIGHT CHILL, 6, b g Midnight Legend—Chilla Cilla **League Of Nations**
31 MIDNIGHT MONTY, 8, ch g Midnight Legend—Marello **The Cherry Pickers**
32 MONBEG THEATRE (IRE), 9, b g King's Theatre (IRE)—Amberina (IRE) **Tim Dykes & Lynda Lovell**
33 NARANJA, 6, ch m Black Sam Bellamy (IRE)—Full of Fruit (FR) **Mrs J. A. Thomas & Ms K. J. Austin**
34 OSCAR STAR (IRE), 5, b m Oscar (IRE)—Tucacas (FR) **Lambourne, Forbes, Losse, Beese & Fiddes**
35 OUR REWARD (IRE), 8, b g Morozov (USA)—Paddyeoin (IRE) **EPDS Racing Partnership**
36 OUR THREE SONS (IRE), 7, b g Shantou (USA)—Ballyquinn (IRE) **Mr A. J. & Mrs J. Ward**

MR JAMIE SNOWDEN - Continued

37 **PRESENTING PEARL (IRE)**, 5, b m Presenting—Asigh Pearl (IRE) **Chalke Valley Racing Partnership**
38 **PRIDE OF PEMBERLEY (IRE)**, 6, ch g Flemensfirth (USA)—On Galley Head (IRE) **EPDS Racing Partnership 19**
39 **SCORPION SID (IRE)**, 6, b g Scorpion (IRE)—Gaye Lady (IRE) **Apache Star Racing**
40 **SHANTEWE (IRE)**, 4, b f Shantou (USA)—Step On My Soul (IRE) **Sheep As A Lamb Syndicate**
41 **SHOCKINGTIMES (IRE)**, 11, b g Wareed (IRE)—Jolly Lady (IRE) **S Beccle,Lady Hart,Boscobel Estates Ltd**
42 **SOME DAY SOON (IRE)**, 5, b g Robin des Champs (FR)—Creative Approach (IRE)
43 **THEBANNERKINGREBEL (IRE)**, 5, b g Arakan (USA)—One Love (IRE) **Jamie Snowden Racing Club**
44 **THISTLE DO NICELY (IRE)**, 4, b g Arcadio (GER)—
April Thistle (IRE) **Apple Tree Stud, M. Gumienny & A. Signy**
45 **THREE WAYS**, 7, b g Flemensfirth (USA)—Serenique **Mr D. E. Brownlow**

Other Owners: Mrs J. Abraham, Mr D. Abraham, Ms K. J. Austin, Mrs C. Barratt, Mr Ian Barratt, Mr Tony Bath, Mr S. Beccle, Mr J. Beese, Boscobel Estates Limited, Mr Ian Callan, Mr A. N. Cheyne, Mrs Robert Cooper, Duchess of Cornwall, Mr A. Courtine, Mrs Camilla Flach, Mr Chris Craig-Wood, Mr G. B. Davison, Mrs C. A. M. Dunlop, Mr Tim Dykes, Mr S. J. Fiddes, Col P. Flach, Mrs Camilla Flach, Mr M. I. Forbes, Mr Philip Fox, Foxtrot Racing Management Ltd, Mr N. S. Freeland, Mrs R. Fuller, Mr R. H. F. Fuller, The Galloping Grannies, Mrs Jane Glyn-Davies, Mr H. M. Glyn-Davies, Lady Hart, Mr Marek Gumienny, Lady Hart, Mr Michael D. Hill, Mr Paul G. Jacobs, Mr R. J. Kilford, Mr C. R. Lambourne, Mr D. R. Losse, Mrs L. J. Losse, Mrs L. R. Lovell, Mrs I. M. J. Matthews, Mr R. Matthews, Dr Bryan Mayoh, Mrs S. D. McGrath, Mr R. H. Mcgrath, Dr M. M. Ogilvy, Mr J. R. Powell, Mr M. J. Pryce, Mr Nick R. Robinson, S Beccle D Scott et al, Mr D. Scott, Mr Adam Signy, Miss T. Sloan, Mrs L. Snowden, Mr J. E. Snowden, Mr J. R. Sykes, Mrs J. A. Thomas, Mr Graham P. Triefus, Turf Club 2016, Mr Michael Wainwright, Mr William Wallace, Mr A. J. Ward, Mrs J. Ward, Mr David Wiggin, Mr Jordan Wylie.

Assistant Trainer: Oliver Signy **Head Girl:** Kate Robinson

Jockey (NH): Daryl Jacob, Micheal Nolan, Nick Scholfield, Gavin Sheehan. **Amateur:** Miss Page Fuller.

---

522 **MR MIKE SOWERSBY, York**
Postal: **Southwold Farm, Goodmanham Wold, Market Weighton, York, East Yorkshire, YO43 3NA**
Contacts: **PHONE (01430) 810534 MOBILE (07855) 551056**

1 **AGENT LOUISE**, 10, b m Alflora (IRE)—Oso Special **Mr M.E.Sowersby/Mrs Carrie Zetter-Wells**
2 **ARBORETUM**, 10, b g Kayf Tara—Step Lively **A. Lyons**
3 **BEAUTIFUL BEN (IRE)**, 8, b g Beneficial—Almnadia (IRE) **A. Lyons**
4 **ENCOURAGING (IRE)**, 9, ch g Rock of Gibraltar (IRE)—Unreachable Star **M. E. Sowersby**
5 **FOIBLE**, 5, b g Fastnet Rock (AUS)—Nyarhini **M. E. Sowersby**
6 **FROSTY DAWN**, 10, b m Desideratum—Frosty Petal **Mrs J. M. Plummer**
7 **GASOLINE (IRE)**, 8, b g Mahler—Judelle de Thou (FR) **Mrs Janet Cooper & Mr M. E. Sowersby**
8 **GLORIOUS DANCER**, 6, br g Royal Applause—Provence **The Southwold Set**
9 **HARMONIC LADY**, 8, ch m Trade Fair—First Harmony **M. E. Sowersby**
10 **INDULGENT**, 5, b g Makfi—Santa Agata (FR) **M. E. Sowersby**
11 **KIWAYU**, 9, b g Medicean—Kibara **Mounted Gamess Assoc Syndicate**
12 **KLEITOMACHOS (IRE)**, 10, b g Barathea (IRE)—Theben (GER) **M. E. Sowersby**
13 **LARKHALL**, 11, b g Saddlers' Hall (IRE)—Larkbarrow **T. J. Stubbins**
14 **LILY LITTLE LEGS (IRE)**, 9, gr m Westerner—Silvers Promise (IRE) **Mrs Janet Cooper & Mr M. E. Sowersby**
15 **MELODYA (IRE)**, 5, b m Arcano (IRE)—Fall Habit (IRE) **Mounted Gamess Assoc Syndicate**
16 **MONARCH'S GLORY (IRE)**, 8, br g Royal Anthem (USA)—Hazel's Glory (IRE) **A. Nicholls**
17 **RIDGEWAY PEARL**, 5, b m Malinas (GER)—Sparkling Jewel **R. D. Seldon**
18 **RIP VAN GO**, 4, b g Rip Van Winkle (IRE)—Thousandkissesdeep (IRE) **Mr B. Valentine**
19 **SILVER DRAGON**, 10, gr g Silver Patriarch (IRE)—Gotogeton **J. Payne**
20 **TENNESSEE BIRD**, 10, b g Danbird (AUS)—Tennessee Star **Queens Head Racing Club**
21 **THAT MAN OF MINE (IRE)**, 6, ch g Thewayyouare (USA)—
Do the Deal (IRE) **Mr Brian Valentine & Mr M. E. Sowersby**
22 **TURTLE CASK (IRE)**, 9, b g Turtle Island (IRE)—Sayce (IRE) **T. J. Stubbins**

Other Owners: Mr P. W. Clifton, Mrs J. H. Cooper, Mr J. Heslop, Mr J. E. Scott, Mrs J. Wiltschinsky, Mrs C. J. Zetter-Wells.

Assistant Trainer: Mary Sowersby

Jockey (flat): Tom Eaves, James Sullivan. **Jockey (NH):** Brian Hughes. **Conditional:** Adam Nichol, Gavin Sheehan. **Amateur:** Mr Russell Lindsay.

523 **MR JOHN SPEARING, Kinnersley**
Postal: **Kinnersley Racing Limited, Kinnersley Racing Stables, Kinnersley, Severn Stoke, Worcestershire, WR8 9JR**
Contacts: **PHONE** (01905) 371054 **FAX** (01905) 371054 **MOBILE** (07801) 552922
E-MAIL jlspearing@aol.com

1 A SURE WELCOME, 4, b g Pastoral Pursuits—Creoso Bach **Kinnersley Partnership 3**
2 BARTON GIFT, 11, b g Alflora (IRE)—Marina Bird **Miss C. J. Ive**
3 CAPTAIN SEDGWICK (IRE), 4, b f Approve (IRE)—Alinda (IRE) **Personal Racehorse Owners 3**
4 CLEAR SPRING (IRE), 10, b g Chineur (FR)—Holly Springs **Mr H. James**
5 GLORIOUS POET, 5, ch g Poet's Voice—Sky Wonder **Sohi & Sohi**
6 IT'S HOW WE ROLL (IRE), 4, b g Fastnet Rock (AUS)—Clodora (FR) **Kinnersley Partnership**
7 KEY TO THE WEST (IRE), 11, b g Westerner—Monte Solaro (IRE) **Miss R S Newell & Mr T P Morrissey**
8 LADY GWHINNYVERE (IRE), 4, b f Sir Prancealot (IRE)—Johar Jamal (IRE) **Personal Racehorse Owners 3**
9 LOST HISTORY (IRE), 5, b g Strategic Prince—Prelude **Mr J. J. Reilly**
10 4, B g Milan—Miss Conduct **Miss C. J. Ive**
11 PEARLS LEGEND, 11, b g Midnight Legend—Pearl's Choice (IRE) **The Corsairs**
12 ROCKALATER, 4, b f Delegator—Rock Candy (IRE) **Mr T. M. Hayes**
13 SWEEPING ROCK (IRE), 8, b g Rock of Gibraltar (IRE)—Sweeping Story (USA) **Kinnersley Partnership II**
14 WHITECREST, 10, ch m Ishiguru (USA)—Risky Valentine **G. M. Eales**

Other Owners: Mr C. S. Heaps, Mrs S. R. Keable, Mr T. P. Morrissey, Miss R. S. Newell, Mr H. C. M. Porter, Mr J. Sohi, Mr K. Sohi, Mr J. L. Spearing, Mrs C. J. Welch.

Assistant Trainer: Miss C Ive

524 **MR RICHARD SPENCER, Newmarket**
Postal: **The Flat, Albert House Stables, Moulton Road, Newmarket, Suffolk, CB8 8DU**
Contacts: **PHONE** (01638) 675780

1 APTLY PUT (IRE), 6, b br g Yeats (IRE)—Versatile Approach (IRE) **Mr G. M. Spencer**
2 BERNARDO O'REILLY (IRE), 4, b c Intikhab (USA)—Baldovina **Rebel Racing (2)**
3 BO SELECTA (IRE), 4, b c Dream Ahead (USA)—Chicane **Rebel Racing (2)**
4 DRAGSTONE ROCK (IRE), 4, ch g Dragon Pulse (IRE)—Rock Exhibition **Fathers & Sons**
5 EXCELLENT RESULT (IRE), 8, b c Shamardal (USA)—Line Ahead (IRE) **Rebel Racing**
6 GUSTAVO FRING (IRE), 4, b g Kodiac—Maleha (IRE) **Rebel Racing (2)**
7 ITS'AFREEBEE (IRE), 8, br g Danroad (AUS)—Aphra Benn (IRE) **Rebel Jumping**
8 KEYSER SOZE (IRE), 4, ch g Arcano (IRE)—Causeway Queen (IRE) **Rebel Racing (2)**
9 LA ISLA BONITA, 4, b f Foxwedge (AUS)—Excello **Rebel Racing (2)**
10 MOVIE SET (USA), 6, b br g Dubawi (IRE)—Short Skirt **Fathers & Sons**
11 REBEL CAUSE, 5, ch g Cockney Rebel—Happy Go Lily **Rebel Racing III**
12 REBEL SURGE (IRE), 5, b m Kodiac—Face The Storm (IRE) **Rebel Racing III**
13 SEA OF FLAMES, 5, ch g Aqlaam—Hidden Fire **Rebel Racing & Rebel Racing III**
14 SIR JACK YEATS (IRE), 7, b g Yeats (IRE)—Quadrennial (IRE) **Gowing's Eleven**
15 THISTIMENEXTYEAR, 4, gr g New Approach (IRE)—Scarlet Empire (IRE) **Rebel Racing (2)**

THREE-YEAR-OLDS

16 CLUB TROPICANA, ch f Helmet (AUS)—Twenty Seven (IRE) **Rebel Racing**
17 FLUX CAPACITOR (IRE), b c Society Rock (IRE)—Maleha (IRE) **Rebel Racing**
18 GOWING GOWING GONE (IRE), ch f Society Rock (IRE)—Face The Storm (IRE) **Rebel Racing**
19 HANDSOME SAMSON, b c Nathaniel (IRE)—Factice (USA) **Rebel Racing**
20 LITTLELORDCONFORD (IRE), b g Intikhab (USA)—Anna Law (IRE) **Rebel Racing**
21 PATTY PATCH, b f Big Bad Bob (IRE)—Cockney Dancer **Rebel Racing**
22 PESKY WABBITT, b g Compton Place—Good Girl **Rebel Racing**
23 PHILAMUNDO (IRE), b g Sir Prancealot (IRE)—Rublevka Star (USA) **Rebel Racing**
24 RAJASINGHE (IRE), b c Choisir (AUS)—Bunditten (IRE) **Rebel Racing**

TWO-YEAR-OLDS

25 ALFIE SOLOMONS (IRE), b c 25/3 Acclamation—
Vastitas (IRE) (Green Desert (USA)) (80952) **Rebel Racing Premier**
26 CALIFORNIA LOVE, ch f 6/3 Power—La Pantera (Captain Rio) (17142) **Mr A. Cunningham**
27 COBWEB CATCHER, b c 25/4 Swiss Spirit—Sugar Beet (Beat Hollow) (10000) **T. H. Chadney**

MR RICHARD SPENCER - Continued

28 **COOKUPASTORM (IRE)**, b f 23/4 Camacho—
    No Clubs (IRE) (Red Clubs (IRE)) (8953) **Balasuriya,CookCunningham,Gowing,Spencer**
29 B c 3/4 Sir Prancealot (IRE)—
    Dream Applause (IRE) (Royal Applause) (10476) **Balasuriya,CookCunningham,Gowing,Spencer**
30 **JEAN VALJEAN**, b c 10/2 Bated Breath—Waitingonacloud (In The Wings) (28571) **Mr P. M. Cunningham**
31 B c 15/4 Requinto (IRE)—Kathleen Rafferty (IRE) (Marju (IRE)) (27675)
32 **LOUIS TREIZE (IRE)**, ch c 27/2 Slade Power (IRE)—
    Black Rodded (Bahamian Bounty) (114285) **Rebel Racing Premier**
33 **MATERIAL GIRL**, b f 19/2 Pivotal—Apace (IRE) (Oasis Dream) (49523) **Miss L. Cunningham**
34 **NO DIGGITY (IRE)**, b c 2/4 Sir Prancealot (IRE)—
    Monarchy (IRE) (Common Grounds) (3809) **Balasuriya,CookCunningham,Gowing,Spencer**
35 **NOSTROVIA (IRE)**, gr f 6/3 Alhebayeb (IRE)—
    Na Zdorovie (Cockney Rebel (IRE)) (28571) **Bland, Cunningham, Hall, Cliff Stud.**
36 **RUMBLE INTHEJUNGLE (IRE)**, ch c 18/4 Bungle Inthejungle—
    Guana (IRE) (Dark Angel (IRE)) (66666) **Rebel Racing Premier**
37 **SPAGHETTI WESTERN (IRE)**, b c 30/3 Pastoral Pursuits—
    Western Tune (IRE) (Piccolo) (6918) **Balasuriya,CookCunningham,Gowing,Spencer**
38 **SPENCERS SON (IRE)**, br c 29/4 Arcano (IRE)—
    Zalama (FR) (Red Ransom (USA)) (7619) **Balasuriya,CookCunningham,Gowing,Spencer**
39 **STALLONE (IRE)**, b c 29/3 Dandy Man (IRE)—Titian Queen (Tobougg (IRE)) (95238) **Rebel Racing Premier**
40 **STAY CLASSY (IRE)**, ch f 24/3 Camacho—
    Hollow Green (IRE) (Beat Hollow) (8546) **Balasuriya,CookCunningham,Gowing,Spencer**
41 **SUSSUDIO**, b f 19/3 Compton Place—
    Glen Molly (IRE) (Danetime (IRE)) (11000) **Balasuriya,CookCunningham,Gowing,Spencer**
42 **THRILLA IN MANILA**, b c 29/3 Iffraaj—Tesary (Danehill (USA)) (76190) **Rebel Racing Premier**
43 **YOU NEVER CAN TELL (IRE)**, b c 25/3 Elzaam (USA)—
    Zanida (IRE) (Mujadil (USA)) (28571) **Mr P. M. Cunningham**

Other Owners: Mr P. Cunningham, Mr M.R Gowing.

525
MR SEB SPENCER, Malton
Postal: **Highfield Farm Stables, Beverley Road, Norton, Malton, YO17 9PJ**
Contacts: **MOBILE (07790) 060050**
E-MAIL **sebspencerracing@gmail.com**

1 **EIUM MAC**, 9, b g Presidium—Efipetite **Derek & Elizabeth Hughes**
2 **GENEVA TRUMPET**, 7, b g Virtual—Quotation **Mr G. R. Oldroyd**
3 **MISU MAC**, 8, b m Misu Bond (IRE)—Umbrian Gold (IRE) **Mr J. D. Martin & Mr N. Bycroft**
4 **MUIRSHEEN DURKIN**, 4, b g Fastnet Rock (AUS)—As My Queen (IRE) **Mr R. Postlethwaite**
5 **ORSINO (IRE)**, 4, b g Galileo (IRE)—Birmanie (USA) **Mr R. Postlethwaite**
6 **SHUDBEME**, 5, ch g Monsieur Bond (IRE)—Oomph **Mr N. Bycroft**
7 **SUNNYSIDE BOB (IRE)**, 5, b g Big Bad Bob (IRE)—Jinxy Jill **Mr G. R. Oldroyd**

THREE-YEAR-OLDS

8 Ch f Equiano (FR)—Golden Valley **Mr N. Bycroft**
9 Ch g Monsieur Bond (IRE)—Julie's Gift **Mr N. Bycroft**

Assistant Trainer: Geoff Oldroyd

526
MR HENRY SPILLER, Newmarket
Postal: **Henry Spiller Racing Ltd, Saville House, St Mary's Square, Newmarket, Suffolk, CB8 0HZ**
Contacts: **PHONE (01638) 662899 MOBILE (07786) 263997**
E-MAIL **office@henryspillerracing.com** WEBSITE **www.henryspillerracing.com**

1 **ARGANTE (FR)**, 9, b br g Singspiel (IRE)—Abyaan (IRE) **Dethrone Racing**
2 **CAPTAIN PUGWASH (IRE)**, 4, b g Sir Prancealot (IRE)—Liscoa (IRE) **Miss Alison Jones**
3 **GOOD BUSINESS (IRE)**, 4, ch f Dutch Art—Parakopi (IRE) **Front Runner Racing II**
4 **INDIA JANE (FR)**, 4, b f Zoffany (IRE)—Irisijana (GER) **Charles & Fiona Spiller**

MR HENRY SPILLER - Continued

5 **IRISH SKY (IRE)**, 4, b f Elnadim (USA)—Royal Aly (USA) **Dethrone Racing**
6 **KING OF ROOKS**, 5, b g Acclamation—Slap Shot (IRE) **Saville House Racing Club**
7 **KYOTO STAR (FR)**, 4, b c Oasis Dream—Hanami **G. B. Partnership**
8 **LAWMAKING**, 5, b g Zamindar (USA)—Canada Water **Marchwood Aggregates**
9 **LEADER WRITER (FR)**, 6, b h Pivotal—Miss Emma May (IRE) **G. B. Partnership**
10 **NATALIE EXPRESS (FR)**, 4, b f Excebration (IRE)—Miss Emma May (IRE) **G. B. Partnership**
11 **ROYAL MEZYAN (IRE)**, 7, b g Royal Applause—Rice Mother (IRE) **Mrs D. Vaughan**
12 **STAFF COLLEGE (FR)**, 4, b g Slickly (FR)—School of Music (FR) **Mr R. P. A. Spiller**
13 **STAR GLIMMER (IRE)**, 5, b m Kodiac—Skyscape **Dethrone Racing**
14 **STRADA DI CARSOLI**, 5, br g Showcasing—Carsulae (IRE) **Saville House Racing Club**
15 **THE THIRD MAN**, 7, gr g Dalakhani (IRE)—Spinning Queen **Mrs D. Spiller**
16 **VAN DIEST**, 6, b g Hurricane Run (IRE)—Miracle **Mr R. P. A. Spiller**
17 **VISCOUNT BARFIELD**, 5, b g Raven's Pass (USA)—Madonna Dell'orto **Mr H. C. Spiller**

THREE-YEAR-OLDS

18 **AERODROME**, b f Nathaniel (IRE)—Westerly Air (USA) **P. Charalambous**
19 **ARNOUL OF METZ**, b g Kyllachy—Appointee (IRE) **Mr R. P. A. Spiller**
20 **BROUGHTON EXCELS**, b c Kyllachy—Excello **Broughton Thermal Insulations**
21 **CATCH THE TIDE (FR)**, ch f Kendargent (FR)—Coiffure **Mr R. P. A. Spiller**
22 **DILLIE DALLIE (IRE)**, b f Zoffany (IRE)—Dalliefour (IRE) **Dethrone Racing**
23 **FOLIE DOUZE**, b g Foxwedge (AUS)—Chicklade **Dethrone Racing**
24 **HERRINGSWELL (FR)**, b f Pour Moi (IRE)—Sovereign's Honour (USA) **Mr B. Boyle**
25 **INITIATIVE (IRE)**, b c Excebration (IRE)—Viking Fair **Saville House Racing Club**
26 **IRISH TIMES**, b c Swiss Spirit—Amouage Royale (IRE) **Saville House Racing Club**
27 **LAUNCESTON PLACE (FR)**, br c Le Havre (IRE)—Last Song **Mr R. P. A. Spiller**
28 **LIBERTIE BELLE (IRE)**, b f Canford Cliffs (IRE)—Belle Watling (IRE)
29 **MOUNT WELLINGTON (IRE)**, b g Invincible Spirit (IRE)—Marvada (IRE) **Dethrone Racing**
30 **STREETS OF JOY**, b f Champs Elysees—Nellie Gwyn **G. B. Partnership**
31 **THEYDON BOXER**, b g Piccolo—Angel of Fashion **Eamonn O'Riordan Peter Charalambous**
32 **THEYDON SPIRIT**, ch g Piccolo—Ela Gorrie Mou **Eamonn O'Riordan Peter Charalambous**

TWO-YEAR-OLDS

33 Ch c 3/2 Compton Place—Corryvreckan (IRE) (Night Shift (USA)) **Saville House Racing Club**
34 Ch f 22/5 Dragon Pulse (IRE)—Lara Celeb (IRE) (Peintre Celebre (USA)) **Saville House Racing Club**
35 **LAST TO BID (FR)**, ch c 1/2 Makfi—Last Song (Singspiel (IRE)) **Mr R. P. A. Spiller**
36 Br f 8/2 Mukhadram—Patuca (Teofilo (IRE)) (8000) **Saville House Racing Club**
37 B f 13/4 Paco Boy (IRE)—Seduct (IRE) (Intense Focus (USA)) **Charles & Fiona Spiller**
38 B f 7/5 Lawman (FR)—Sensational Samba (IRE) (Exceed And Excel (AUS)) (30000) **Saville House Racing Club**
39 Ch c 4/4 Makfi—Soho Rocks (Rock of Gibraltar (IRE)) **Saville House Racing Club**

Other Owners: Miss J. S. Gill, Mr G. Gill, M. G. H. Heald, Mr A. M. H. Heald, Mr E. O'Riordan, Mrs F. J. D. Spiller, Mr C. R. G. Spiller.

---

527 MR FOZZY STACK, Cashel
Postal: **Thomastown Castle Stud, Golden, Cashel, Co. Tipperary, Ireland**
Contacts: PHONE **(00353) 62 54129**
E-MAIL **tommystackracing@gmail.com**

1 **ALEXIOS KOMNENOS (IRE)**, 4, b c Choisir (AUS)—Alexiade (IRE)
2 **ANGEL ISLAND (IRE)**, 4, b f So You Think (NZ)—Dombeya (IRE)
3 **BAMBARI (IRE)**, 5, b g Arcano (IRE)—Blue Dahlia (IRE)
4 **COURT QUEEN (IRE)**, 4, b f Choisir (AUS)—Blue Dahlia (IRE)
5 **DUKE OF WASPINGTON (IRE)**, 5, b g Duke of Marmalade (IRE)—Queen Wasp (IRE)
6 **ONENIGHTIDREAMED (IRE)**, 7, ch g Footstepsinthesand—Pivotalia (IRE)
7 **SHORT STACKED**, 5, b g Dutch Art—Rotunda
8 **SON OF REST**, 4, b c Pivotal—Hightime Heroine (IRE)
9 **THUNDER SPEED**, 4, b c Dylan Thomas (IRE)—Insoumise (IRE)

THREE-YEAR-OLDS

10 **ACRUX CASS (IRE)**, b c Footstepsinthesand—Golden Mask (USA)
11 **ASTROSPEED (IRE)**, ch c Choisir (AUS)—Angel Stevens (IRE)
12 **CALIFORNIA JUMBO (USA)**, ch g Scat Daddy (USA)—Nafisah (IRE)

MR FOZZY STACK - Continued

13 CALIFORNIA YOOHOO (USA), b g Scat Daddy (USA)—That Voodoo Youdo (USA)
14 CARLO BIRAGHI (IRE), ch c Galileo (IRE)—Kirinda (IRE)
15 B f Approve (IRE)—Diavolezza
16 GOTTARDO (IRE), b g Choisir (AUS)—Chantarella (IRE)
17 HARVESTFORTHEWORLD (IRE), b br f So You Think (NZ)—Israar
18 HIGHLAND STAR (USA), b g Gio Ponti (USA)—Marieval (USA)
19 IIEX EXCELSA (IRE), ch f Excelebration (IRE)—Holly Blue
20 Ch f Mastercraftsman (IRE)—Insight (FR)
21 LADY HEART, ch f Kyllachy—Hightime Heroine (IRE)
22 LIR (IRE), b f Declaration of War (USA)—Sandglass
23 MISS MARGARITA, b br f Scat Daddy (USA)—Royal Empress (IRE)
24 OTTAVA (IRE), b g Shamardal (USA)—Musical Note
25 PEACE PROCESS (IRE), b f Declaration of War (USA)—Front House (IRE)
26 QUEEN RABAB (IRE), b br f Fastnet Rock (AUS)—Dame Blanche (IRE)
27 SHIFTED STRATEGY (IRE), b c Choisir (AUS)—Pure Greed (IRE)
28 TAHILLA (IRE), b f Holy Roman Emperor (IRE)—Tarascon (IRE)
29 TOOREEN KATIE (IRE), b f Intello (GER)—Ultra Appeal (IRE)
30 B f Fastnet Rock (AUS)—Vintage Tipple (IRE)
31 WISHING STAR (IRE), b f Galileo (IRE)—Crazyforlovingyou (USA)
32 ZIHBA (IRE), b c Choisir (AUS)—Fancy Vivid (IRE)

TWO-YEAR-OLDS

33 B f 24/4 Morpheus—Addictedtoprogress (IRE) (Holy Roman Emperor (IRE))
34 B c 3/4 Dark Angel (IRE)—Ashtown Girl (IRE) (Exceed And Excel (AUS)) (65120)
35 B f 3/3 Zoffany (IRE)—Belle Isle (Pastoral Pursuits) (146520)
36 B c 8/3 Gale Force Ten—Blue Dahlia (IRE) (Shamardal (USA))
37 B f 8/2 Zoffany (IRE)—Dacio (USA) (Harlan's Holiday (USA)) (41904)
38 B f 8/4 Power—Diavolezza (Iceman)
39 B f 18/4 No Nay Never (USA)—Dowager (Groom Dancer (USA)) (65120)
40 B f 1/2 No Nay Never (USA)—Falling Rain (IRE) (Danehill Dancer (IRE)) (47619)
41 B f 7/4 Camelot—Flamingo Sea (USA) (Woodman (USA)) (56980)
42 B c 25/1 Zoffany (IRE)—Foolish Act (IRE) (Sadler's Wells (USA)) (44769)
43 Ch c 25/1 Dream Ahead (USA)—Gentle Breeze (IRE) (Dubawi (IRE))
44 B c 22/4 Camelot—Israar (Machiavellian (USA)) (39071)
45 Ch c 28/1 Ruler of The World (IRE)—Lady Miletrian (IRE) (Barathea (IRE)) (40700)
46 B f 8/2 Holy Roman Emperor (IRE)—Mango Groove (IRE) (Unfuwain (USA)) (29304)
47 B c 30/4 Holy Roman Emperor (IRE)—Many Hearts (USA) (Distorted Humor (USA))
48 B f 2/4 War Command (USA)—Medicean Star (IRE) (Galileo (IRE))
49 B br c 5/5 Footstepsinthesand—Neds Bypass (IRE) (High Chaparral (IRE)) (50000)
50 Ch f 26/4 Galileo (IRE)—Nell Gwyn (IRE) (Danehill (USA))
51 NICARO (IRE), b c 17/4 No Nay Never (USA)—Mironica (IRE) (Excellent Art)
52 B c 23/3 Declaration of War (USA)—Pan Dulce (USA) (Candy Ride (ARG)) (48006)
53 B f 12/3 Ruler of The World (IRE)—Pectin (IRE) (Duke of Marmalade (IRE))
54 B f 29/2 Requinto (IRE)—Pillars of Society (IRE) (Caerleon (USA)) (16280)
55 Ch f 30/1 Australia—San Sicharia (IRE) (Daggers Drawn (USA))
56 B c 11/3 Galileo (IRE)—Scream Blue Murder (IRE) (Oratorio (IRE))
57 Ch f 31/3 Australia—Silver Rain (FR) (Rainbow Quest (USA))
58 Ch c 8/2 Tamayuz—Sunbula (USA) (Singspiel (IRE)) (26048)
59 B f 7/5 Holy Roman Emperor (IRE)—Tarascon (IRE) (Tirol)
60 Ch f 19/2 Zoffany (IRE)—Umniya (IRE) (Bluebird (USA)) (36190)
61 B f 4/3 Australia—Waltzing Matilda (IRE) (Danehill Dancer (IRE))

Owners: Mr Rick Barnes, Mr Michael Begley, Peter Chiu, Mr Arunas Cicenas, Iman Hartono, Mr T. Hyde Jnr, JSC Kasandros Grupe, Mr D. Keoghan, Mrs J. Magnier, Mr Casey McLiney, The New Pension Fund Syndicate, Mr B. Parker, The Pension Fund II Syndicate, Mr P. Piller, Mrs Jane Rowlinson, G. A. Rupert, Mary Slack, Mr M L Slevin, Mr Michael Tabor, Sir Peter Vela, Mr Neil Werrett.

Jockey (flat): Chris Hayes, W. J. Lee. **Apprentice:** Killian K. Hennessy, Michael J. O'Connor.

528 MR EUGENE STANFORD, Newmarket
Postal: **Flat 4, Macdonald Buchanan House, Howard De Walden Way, Newmarket, Suffolk, CB8 7JQ**
Contacts: **PHONE (01638) 665507 MOBILE (07761) 223096**
E-MAIL e.stanford077@btinternet.com WEBSITE www.eugenestanfordracing.com

1 BELLA BLUR, 6, ch m Showcasing—Ellablue **Miss C. R. Williams**
2 ISLAND AUTHORITY, 6, b m Authorized (IRE)—Island Odyssey **Mr E. V. Stanford**
3 Q CEE, 5, b g Denounce—Gibraltar Lass (USA) **Mr M. W. Goodridge**
4 UNTIL MIDNIGHT (IRE), 8, b g Moss Vale (IRE)—Emma's Star (ITY) **Newmarketracingclub.co.uk**

THREE-YEAR-OLDS
5 SHOW THE MONEY, ch c Showcasing—Rio Belle (IRE) **Mr M. W. Goodridge**
6 TOMTIT, b g Pastoral Pursuits—Swan Queen **Sir Thomas Pilkington**

TWO-YEAR-OLDS
7 B f 16/2 Zoffany (IRE)—Firecrest (IRE) (Darshaan) **Sir Thomas Pilkington**
8 Br c 31/3 Gregorian (IRE)—Swan Queen (In The Wings) **Sir Thomas Pilkington**

Other Owners: New Sports Media Ltd, C. Woof.

Jockey (flat): Jimmy Quinn, Robert Tart. **Jockey (NH):** Jack Quinlan.

529 MR DANIEL STEELE, Hassocks
Postal: **New Barn Farm, Clayton Hill, Clayton, Hassocks, West Sussex, BN6 9PG**
Contacts: **MOBILE (07500) 556398**
E-MAIL danielsteele14@hotmail.co.uk

1 BENNELONG, 12, b g Bahamian Bounty—Bundle Up (USA) **Mr J. J. Smith**
2 CASSIVELLAUNUS (IRE), 6, b g Danehill Dancer (IRE)—Celtic Heroine (IRE) **Vectis Racing**
3 CHIVERS (IRE), 7, b g Duke of Marmalade (IRE)—Thara (USA) **Mr D. R. Steele**
4 FALSE ID, 5, b g Aqlaam—Miss Dutee **Mr K. A. Percy**
5 FOOTSTEPSINTHERAIN (IRE), 8, b g Footstepsinthesand—Champagne Toni (IRE) **Mr J. J. Smith**
6 GLENALMOND (IRE), 6, b g Iffraaj—Balladonia **Mr D. R. Steele**
7 HOLD THE BUCKS (USA), 12, b g Hold That Tiger (USA)—Buck's Lady (USA) **Mr D. R. Steele**
8 LANDSCAPE (FR), 10, b g Lando (GER)—Universelle (USA) **Mr D. R. Steele**
9 SEEK THE FAIR LAND, 12, b g Noverre (USA)—Duchcov **Mr J. J. Smith**
10 STRINGYBARK CREEK, 4, b g Bushranger (IRE)—Money Note **Mr K. A. Percy**
11 TABLA, 6, b m Rail Link—Questa Nova **Mr J. J. Smith**
12 TEE IT UP TOMMO (IRE), 9, gr g Clodovil (IRE)—Lamh Eile (IRE) **Mr D. R. Steele**
13 THE YELLOW BUS, 5, b m Zoffany (IRE)—Caribbean Queen (IRE) **Mr K. A. Percy**
14 WILLIAM B (IRE), 7, b br g Yeats (IRE)—Gallic Approach (IRE) **Mr K. A. Percy**

Other Owners: Mrs S. L. Morley, Mr G. Morley.

Jockey (NH): Conor Shoemark. **Amateur:** Miss Megan Spencer.

530 MRS JACKIE STEPHEN, Inverurie
Postal: **Conglass Farmhouse, Inverurie, Aberdeenshire, AB51 5DN**
Contacts: **PHONE (01467) 621267 FAX (01467) 620511 MOBILE (07980) 785924**
E-MAIL jackiestephen123@hotmail.com WEBSITE www.jackiestephenracing.com

1 AMILLIONTIMES (IRE), 10, b g Olden Times—Miss Million (IRE) **Mr P. G. Stephen**
2 BALLINVEGGA (IRE), 8, gr g Royal Anthem (USA)—
Gill's Honey (IRE) **Mrs Mrs P Clark, Mrs J Stephen & Mrs PM Stephen**
3 BRIGHT PROSPECT (IRE), 9, b g Kutub (IRE)—Bright Future (IRE) **Lessells, Pirie, Ritchie & Stephen**
4 HIGHLAND PEAK, 6, b g Distant Peak (IRE)—Flower Appeal **Mr P. G. Stephen**
5 LOVELY SCHTUFF (IRE), 6, b g Court Cave (IRE)—The Long Bill (IRE) **Mrs J. S. Stephen**
6 MICK'S WISH (IRE), 6, b br g Westerner—Bells Chance (IRE) **Northern Lights Racing**
7 MIDNIGHT KATE (IRE), 4, gr f Midnight Legend—Primrose Time **Mr C. T. Reid**
8 MO ROUGE (IRE), 10, b g Croco Rouge (IRE)—Just A Mo (IRE) **Mrs J. S. Stephen**
9 MOTION TO STRIKE (IRE), 8, b g Beneficial—Comeragh Girl (IRE) **Jackie Stephen Racing Club**
10 WELCOME BEN (IRE), 9, b g High Roller (IRE)—Bramble Cottage (IRE) **Northern Lights Racing**

MRS JACKIE STEPHEN - Continued

Other Owners: Mr J. Anderson, Mr M. C. Barron, Mrs P K. Clark, Mr J. A. Dickson, Mr J. S. Lessells, Mr N. Patience, Mr A. C. Pirie, Mr G. G. Ritchie.

Assistant Trainer: Patrick Stephen

---

531   **MRS KATIE STEPHENS, Shaldon**
Postal: **Trainer did not wish details of her string to appear**

---

532   **MR ROBERT STEPHENS, Caldicot**
Postal: **The Knoll, St. Brides Netherwent, Caldicot, Gwent, NP26 3AT**
Contacts: **MOBILE (07717) 477177**
E-MAIL robertdavidstephens@btinternet.com WEBSITE www.robertstephensracing.com

1 ALL FOR THE BEST (IRE), 6, b g Rip Van Winkle (IRE)—Alleluia **Mr E. A. Elliott**
2 AWAYWITHTHEBLUES (IRE), 6, b g Stowaway—Rhythm 'n' Blues (IRE) **Mrs B Ayres, Mr E & Mrs K Neville**
3 BALKINSTOWN (IRE), 8, b g Westerner—Graffogue (IRE) **Mrs C. Ford-Ellis**
4 BEL ESPRIT (IRE), 9, b m Presenting—D Judge (IRE) **Ms J. Ludlam**
5 CADIRA BEECHES, 8, b m Lucarno (USA)—Gipsy Girl **Mr D. O. Stephens**
6 CASTLELYONS (IRE), 6, br g Papal Bull—Summercove (IRE) **The Warriors**
7 DAY IN PARADISE, 7, b m Tobougg (IRE)—Sunnyland **Mr R. D. Stephens**
8 ESPRESSO FREDDO (IRE), 4, b g Fast Company (IRE)—Spring Bouquet (IRE) **Threes Company**
9 INDIANA DAWN, 5, b m Sleeping Indian—Street Diva (USA) **Mr R. D. Stephens**
10 MASSINI'S VISION, 6, b m Dr Massini—Cathy's Dream (IRE) **Mr R. D. Stephens**
11 MUSKETEER, 6, ch g Schiaparelli (GER)—Suave Shot **Mr R. D. Stephens**
12 NOBLE BEHEST, 4, b g Sir Percy—Lady Hestia (USA) **Mr A. C. Elliott**
13 PERSONAL COACH (FR), 5, b g Motivator—Castellina (USA) **D. J. Deer**
14 RULER OF THE NILE, 6, b g Exceed And Excel (AUS)—Dinka Raja (USA) **Threes Company**
15 SECONDO (FR), 8, b g Sakhee's Secret—Royal Jade **D. J. Deer**
16 SENIERGUES, 6, ch g Midnight Legend—Lady Samantha **Mr E. A. Elliott**
17 SIMPLY LOVELEH, 5, b m Beneficial—Pippedatthepost
18 THREE COLOURS RED (IRE), 6, b g Camacho—Colour's Red (IRE) **The Red Partnership**
19 TIR DUBH (IRE), 9, br m Sandmason—Turbine Hill (IRE) **Threes Company**
20 TUDORS TREASURE, 7, b g Dr Massini—Rude Health **Four Seasons Partnership**
21 WINTOUR LEAP, 7, b m Nayef (USA)—Mountain Leap (IRE) **Mr P. M. Cooper**

Other Owners: Mrs B. M. Ayres, Mr I. Croker, Mr A. C. Elliott, Colleen Ford-Ellis, Mr Eddie Neville, Mrs Kathleen Neville, Mr Hugh Scale, Mrs Jennette Scale, Mr David Shorthouse, Mr Kevin Slade, Mr Gareth Winstone.

Assistant Trainer: Rosie Stephens

Jockey (NH): Micheal Nolan, Tom O'Brien. **Conditional:** Ciaran Gethings. **Amateur:** Mr Craig Dowson, Mr Morgan Winstone.

---

533   **MR WILLIAM STONE, West Wickham**
Postal: **The Meadow, Streetly End, West Wickham, Cambridge, Cambridgeshire, CB21 4RP**
Contacts: **MOBILE (07788) 971094**
E-MAIL williamstone1@hotmail.co.uk

1 DIAMOND LADY, 7, b m Multiplex—Ellen Mooney **The Going Great Guns Partnership**
2 EAST COAST LADY (IRE), 6, b m Kodiac—Alexander Anapolis (IRE) **Miss C. M. Scott**
3 EVENING ATTIRE, 7, b g Pastoral Pursuits—Markova's Dance **Miss C. M. Scott**
4 HIDDEN STASH, 4, b g Sakhee's Secret—Marajuana **Miss C. M. Scott**
5 KIMENE, 4, b f Aqlaam—Aditi **Miss C. M. Scott**
6 TIGERFISH (IRE), 4, b f Lilbourne Lad (IRE)—Nisriyna (IRE) **Miss C. M. Scott**
7 TOUCH THE CLOUDS, 7, b g Sleeping Indian—Aptina (USA) **Miss C. M. Scott**

THREE-YEAR-OLDS

8 INVISIBLE STORM, b f Multiplex—Dawn Lightning **C. M. Scott & A. J. Wittering**
9 RED SNAPPER, b f Kheleyf (USA)—Amistress **Miss C. M. Scott**

MR WILLIAM STONE - Continued

TWO-YEAR-OLDS

10 B f 3/3 Dick Turpin (IRE)—Clock Opera (IRE) (Excellent Art) **Miss C. M. Scott & Shane Fairweather**

Other Owners: Mr S. Fairweather, Going Great Guns Partnership, Mr J. A. Ross, Mr Caroline Scott, Mr A. J. Wittering.

---

534 | **MR WILF STOREY, Consett**
Postal: **Grange Farm & Stud, Mugglesswick, Consett, Co. Durham, DH8 9DW**
Contacts: **PHONE (01207) 255259 FAX (01207) 255259 MOBILE (07860) 510441**
E-MAIL wlstorey@metronet.co.uk WEBSITE www.wilfstorey.com

1 ADRAKHAN (FR), 7, b g Martaline—Annee de La Femme (IRE) **Mr W. L. Storey**
2 BETTY GRABLE (IRE), 4, b f Delegator—Danella (IRE) **R. C. Tooth**
3 CARD HIGH (IRE), 8, b g Red Clubs (IRE)—Think (FR) **Gremlin Racing**
4 CIRCUIT, 4, br f Foxwedge (AUS)—Lady Circe (USA) **Mr W. L. Storey**
5 CLIMAX, 4, b f Acclamation—Blue Rocket (IRE) **R. C. Tooth**
6 HIGHWAY ROBBER, 5, b g Dick Turpin (IRE)—Lawyers Choice **Gremlin Racing**
7 JAN SMUTS (IRE), 10, b g Johannesburg (USA)—Choice House (USA) **H. S. Hutchinson & W. Storey**
8 MR SUNDOWNER (USA), 6, b br g Scat Daddy (USA)—Bold Answer **Wilf Storey & Ray Glendinning**
9 NEARLY THERE, 5, br g Virtual—Nicoise (IRE) **Mr W. L. Storey**
10 NELSON'S BAY, 9, b g Needwood Blade—In Good Faith (USA) **The Durham Company & W Storey**
11 TABLE MANNERS, 6, b m Dutch Art—Nine Red **Geegeez.co.uk 1**

THREE-YEAR-OLDS

12 EQUO, b g Equiano (FR)—Catfish (IRE) **Mr W. L. Storey**
13 FRENCH KISS (IRE), b c French Fifteen (FR)—Ms Cordelia (USA) **R. C. Tooth**
14 MAY GREEN, ch f Mayson—Grass Green **Mr W. L. Storey**
15 NELSON RIVER, b g Mount Nelson—I Say (IRE) **R. C. Tooth**

TWO-YEAR-OLDS

16 B g 4/2 Mount Nelson—Nine Red (Royal Applause) **Mr W. L. Storey**

Other Owners: Mr M. Bisogno, M. Burton, The Durham Company, Mr D. D. Gillies, Ray Glendinning, Mr H. S. Hutchinson, P. McVey, S. Meikle, A. Morrison, A. Rugg, Mr W. Storey, D. Westerman.

Assistant Trainer: Miss S. Storey

Amateur: Miss S. M. Doolan.

---

535 | **SIR MICHAEL STOUTE, Newmarket**
Postal: **Freemason Lodge, Bury Road, Newmarket, Suffolk, CB8 7BY**
Contacts: **PHONE (01638) 663801 FAX (01638) 667276**

1 ADAMANT (GER), 4, gr g Dalakhani (IRE)—Attima
2 AUTOCRATIC, 5, b h Dubawi (IRE)—Canda (USA)
3 CONVEY, 6, b g Dansili—Insinuate (USA)
4 CRYSTAL OCEAN, 4, b c Sea The Stars (IRE)—Crystal Star
5 DREAM OF DREAMS (IRE), 4, ch c Dream Ahead (USA)—Vasilia
6 FRONTISPIECE, 4, b c Shamardal (USA)—Free Verse
7 KARAWAAN (IRE), 4, b g Sea The Stars (USA)—Magic Sister
8 MELTING DEW, 4, b g Cacique (IRE)—Winter Sunrise
9 MIRAGE DANCER, 4, b c Frankel—Heat Haze
10 MORI, 4, b f Frankel—Midday
11 MUSTASHRY, 5, b br h Tamayuz—Safwa (IRE)
12 POET'S WORD (IRE), 5, b h Poet's Voice—Whirly Bird
13 PRECISION, 4, b g Galileo (IRE)—Pearl Earrine (FR)
14 SMART CALL (SAF), 7, b m Ideal World (USA)—Good Judgement (USA)

THREE-YEAR-OLDS

15 ADMIRED, gr f Oasis Dream—Souviens Toi
16 ALLANTE (IRE), b f Pivotal—Have Faith (IRE)
17 ALLIED, ch c Dawn Approach (IRE)—Mambo Halo (USA)
18 BARITONE (IRE), b c Camelot—Star Ruby (IRE)

SIR MICHAEL STOUTE - Continued

19 **BEACHWALK,** b g Showcasing—Esplanade
20 **BEDWYYAH (IRE),** b f Invincible Spirit (IRE)—Shirley A Star (USA)
21 **BHODI (IRE),** b c Dark Angel (IRE)—Modesty's Way (USA)
22 **BRAEMAR,** b c Oasis Dream—Spectacle
23 **COLLEGIATE (IRE),** b f Declaration of War (USA)—Cochabamba (IRE)
24 **COMMENDED,** ch c Frankel—Laurelei (IRE)
25 **COMRADE IN ARMS (USA),** b g War Front (USA)—Maryinsky (IRE)
26 **CRYSTAL HOPE,** ch f Nathaniel (IRE)—Crystal Etoile
27 **CRYSTAL KING,** ch c Frankel—Crystal Star
28 **CRYSTAL MOONLIGHT,** ch f New Approach (IRE)—Crystal Capella
29 **DESERT BREEZE,** b f Dubawi (IRE)—Galatee (FR)
30 **DESERT DIAMOND,** b f Dubawi (IRE)—Arizona Jewel
31 **DESERT SON,** ch c Dubawi (IRE)—Russelliana
32 **DRIFTING STAR (IRE),** b c Sea The Stars (IRE)—Drifting (IRE)
33 **EHMAJ (JPN),** b c Empire Maker (USA)—Upward Spiral
34 **ELECTOR,** b c Dansili—Enticement
35 **ELEDEED,** b g Al Kazeem—Resort
36 **EQTIDAAR (IRE),** b c Invincible Spirit (IRE)—Madany (IRE)
37 **EXPERT EYE,** b c Acclamation—Exemplify
38 **FINAL SET (IRE),** b f Dark Angel (IRE)—Two Sets To Love (IRE)
39 **GABR,** ch c Intello (GER)—Spacious
40 **GARDEN OASIS,** b c Excelebration (IRE)—Queen Arabella
41 **GATESOFTHEARCTIC (IRE),** br c Dansili—Rajaratna (IRE)
42 **GEORGIAN MANOR (IRE),** br g Iffraaj—Southern House (IRE)
43 **GLITTERDUST,** b f Intello (GER)—Glitterball (IRE)
44 **HAMLUL (FR),** gr c Frankel—Alix Road (FR)
45 **HARAWI,** b c Camelot—Nigh (IRE)
46 **HAREEQ,** b c New Approach (IRE)—Fallen Star
47 **HAZARFIYA,** b f Fastnet Rock (AUS)—Hazariya (IRE)
48 **HAZM (IRE),** br c Shamardal (USA)—Hikari (IRE)
49 **HEAVENLY SECRET (IRE),** b c Sea The Stars (IRE)—Prime Run
50 **HERDWICK,** b c Makfi—Bellwether
51 **HIDDEN DEPTHS (IRE),** b c Dark Angel (IRE)—Liber Nauticus (IRE)
52 **HOMEOPATHIC,** b f Dark Angel (IRE)—Holistic
53 **IHTITHAR (IRE),** b c Lope de Vega (IRE)—Kapria (FR)
54 **LEDHAM (IRE),** b c Shamardal (USA)—Pioneer Bride (USA)
55 **LUNAR CORONA,** br f Dansili—Starscope
56 **MAHAARAT,** ch f Dubawi (IRE)—Ashaaqah (IRE)
57 **MAYFAIR SECRET (IRE),** b f Galileo (IRE)—Secrete (FR)
58 **MEKONG,** b g Frankel—Ship's Biscuit
59 **MIDI,** b c Frankel—Midday
60 **MOOJIB (IRE),** b c Dubawi (IRE)—Safwa (IRE)
61 **MOQARRAR (USA),** b br c Exchange Rate (USA)—Time to Enjoy (USA)
62 **MOTTAHAM (FR),** b c Siyouni (FR)—Moune (IRE)
63 **MUKTASIB,** bl g Lethal Force (IRE)—Ha'penny Beacon
64 **NASEE,** b c Intello (GER)—Mischief Making (USA)
65 **ONE DOLLAR MORE,** b f New Approach (IRE)—Cape Dollar (IRE)
66 **PHANTASMIC,** b f Frankel—Diary (IRE)
67 **PRIVATE VIEW,** b f Exceed And Excel (AUS)—Confidential Lady
68 **PROCEDURE,** gr f Invincible Spirit (IRE)—Clinical
69 **PROSERPINE (USA),** b f Hat Trick (JPN)—Shiva (JPN)
70 **QAROUN,** b c Dark Angel (IRE)—Exotic Isle
71 **RADIO SOURCE (IRE),** ch c Raven's Pass (USA)—Roshanak (IRE)
72 **RAPIER (USA),** ch g Animal Kingdom (USA)—Shadow Cast (USA)
73 **RARE (IRE),** b f Galileo (IRE)—Miarixa (FR)
74 **RAWDAA,** b f Teofilo (IRE)—Lady Laman
75 **RED STRIKER (IRE),** b c Sea The Stars (IRE)—Coolree Marj (IRE)
76 **REFRAIN (IRE),** b c Dubawi (IRE)—Folk Opera (IRE)
77 **REGAL REALITY,** b c Intello (GER)—Regal Realm
78 **REKINDLE,** ch f Frankel—Hot Snap
79 **REVELEON,** ch g Exceed And Excel (AUS)—Rosika
80 **SCANDALEUSE (USA),** b f War Front (USA)—Aruna (USA)
81 **SEPTIMER (IRE),** br c Maxios—Freedonia
82 **SEXTANT,** b c Sea The Stars (IRE)—Hypoteneuse (IRE)
83 **SHAREEF STAR,** b c Sea The Stars (IRE)—Gotlandia (FR)

SIR MICHAEL STOUTE - Continued

84 **SHARP PRACTICE**, b f Redoute's Choice (AUS)—Momentary
85 **SHARROW BAY (IRE)**, br f Intikhab (USA)—Mid Mon Lady (IRE)
86 **SUN MAIDEN**, b f Frankel—Midsummer
87 **TAHREEK**, b c Dansili—Rifqah (USA)
88 **TRULY HONOURED**, ch f Frankel—Honorine (IRE)
89 **UJOOR (IRE)**, ch f Dutch Art—Samaah (IRE)
90 **URBINO**, b c Dansili—Novellara
91 **VERACIOUS**, b f Frankel—Infallible
92 **WAJIH**, b g Kodiac—Spangle
93 **WEEKDAY**, b f Dansili—Timepiece
94 **WHITEHALL**, b g Dansili—Majestic Roi (USA)
95 **WILD WEST HERO**, b c Exceed And Excel (AUS)—Hi Calypso (IRE)
96 **ZAAKI**, b c Leroidesanimaux (BRZ)—Kesara

TWO-YEAR-OLDS

97 B c 20/3 War Front (USA)—Agreeable Miss (USA) (Speightstown (USA))
98 B c 5/4 Kodiac—Al Manaal (Echo of Light) (60000)
99 **ALIGNED (IRE)**, b c 2/5 Dubawi (IRE)—Ikat (IRE) (Pivotal)
100 B c 26/3 Pour Moi (IRE)—Amathusia (Selkirk (USA))
101 **ANNA OF LORRAINE**, b f 1/4 Dutch Art—Ladyship (Oasis Dream)
102 B c 1/2 Oasis Dream—Ashaaqah (IRE) (Dansili)
103 B c 15/4 Cape Cross (IRE)—Asheerah (Shamardal (USA))
104 B f 1/2 Intello (GER)—Bristol Fashion (Dansili)
105 **BUTTERFLY KISS (USA)**, b f 20/4 Medaglia d'oro (USA)—Laughing Lashes (USA) (Mr Greeley (USA)) (271002)
106 **CALCULATION**, br c 4/2 Dubawi (IRE)—Estimate (IRE) (Monsun (GER))
107 B c 16/2 Frankel—Cape Dollar (IRE) (Cape Cross (IRE))
108 B f 19/1 Siyouni (FR)—Carnoustie (FR) (Acclamation)
109 Ch c 5/4 Australia—Circle of Life (USA) (Belong To Me (USA))
110 **CLERISY**, b f 7/2 Kingman—Exemplify (Dansili)
111 **CRYSTAL DREAM**, b f 14/3 Oasis Dream—Crystal Etoile (Dansili)
112 Ch c 15/2 Galileo (IRE)—Daivika (USA) (Dynaformer (USA)) (150000)
113 B f 30/1 Kingman—Damaniyat Girl (USA) (Elusive Quality (USA))
114 **DAVYDENKO**, ch c 9/3 Intello (GER)—Safina (Pivotal)
115 **DEREVO**, b c 23/2 Dansili—Pavlosk (Arch (USA))
116 **DETECTIVE**, b c 22/5 Kingman—Promising Lead (Danehill (USA))
117 **DITTISHAM**, b f 4/4 Shamardal (USA)—Havant (Halling (USA))
118 B f 1/3 Frankel—Dubian To (IRE) (Sea The Stars (IRE))
119 **EL PICADOR (IRE)**, b c 15/2 Dansili—West of Venus (USA) (Street Cry (IRE))
120 B c 5/2 Sea The Stars (IRE)—Elegant Shadow (GER) (Shamardal (USA)) (1000000)
121 B c 8/4 Acclamation—Ellen (IRE) (Machiavellian (USA)) (200000)
122 **FIERY MISSION (USA)**, b c 12/2 Noble Mission—Quickfire (Dubai Millennium)
123 **GHADBBAAN**, ch c 3/2 Intello (GER)—Rock Choir (Pivotal) (425000)
124 **GIVE ME BREATH**, b f 15/2 Bated Breath—Watchoverme (Haafhd)
125 **GOLD AT MIDNIGHT**, b f 18/3 Havana Gold (IRE)—Midnight Ransom (Red Ransom (USA))
126 Ch c 19/2 Exceed And Excel (AUS)—Great Hope (IRE) (Halling (USA)) (230000)
127 **HAWTHORN ROSE**, ch f 30/1 Nathaniel (IRE)—Russelliana (Medicean)
128 B f 2/4 Dansili—Hazariya (IRE) (Xaar)
129 **HEAVENLY BLISS**, ch f 22/2 Intello (GER)—Heaven Sent (Pivotal)
130 **HOOYAM (USA)**, ch f 19/1 Kitten's Joy (USA)—Double Ante (USA) (Purim (USA)) (60000)
131 B f 29/2 Camelot—Hurricane Emma (USA) (Mr Greeley (USA)) (130000)
132 **INVICTUS SPIRIT**, b c 8/2 Frankel—Daring Aim (Daylami (IRE))
133 **JEWELLER**, ch c 31/3 Mastercraftsman (IRE)—Allegretto (IRE) (Galileo (IRE))
134 **JOYFUL MISSION (USA)**, b c 2/2 Noble Mission—Hint of Joy (USA) (Empire Maker (USA))
135 **JUBILOSO**, b f 20/1 Shamardal (USA)—Joyeuse (Oasis Dream)
136 Br c 12/2 Shamardal (USA)—Landmark (USA) (Arch (USA)) (360000)
137 B f 11/3 Acclamation—Malaspina (IRE) (Whipper (USA)) (350000)
138 Ch f 4/3 Australia—Mango Mischief (IRE) (Desert King (IRE))
139 B c 25/2 Noble Mission—Miner's Secret (USA) (Mineshaft (USA)) (116144)
140 B c 3/2 Acclamation—Missisipi Star (IRE) (Mujahid (USA)) (130000)
141 **MOKAMMAL**, b c 1/3 Mukhadram—My Inspiration (IRE) (Invincible Spirit (IRE))
142 B f 21/3 Le Havre (IRE)—Mumayeza (Indian Ridge)
143 **NANTUCKET (IRE)**, b f 30/4 Sea The Stars (IRE)—Lucy Cavendish (USA) (Elusive Quality (USA)) (125000)
144 B f 9/1 Sea The Stars (IRE)—Nectar de Rose (FR) (Shamardal (USA)) (130000)
145 **NEFERTITI (IRE)**, b f 12/2 Galileo (IRE)—Divine Proportions (USA) (Kingmambo (USA))
146 B f 23/3 Kingman—Platonic (Zafonic (USA)) (244200)

SIR MICHAEL STOUTE - Continued

147 PRODIGIOUS, ch f 30/3 Intello (GER)—Spacious (Nayef (USA))
148 B br c 21/3 Dubawi (IRE)—Qareenah (USA) (Arch (USA))
149 QUEEN'S SCEPTRE, b f 7/4 Pivotal—Queen's Best (King's Best (USA))
150 Gr ro c 26/1 Speightstown (USA)—Ready to Act (USA) (More Than Ready (USA)) (387146)
151 B c 14/4 Australia—Rock Kristale (IRE) (Fastnet Rock (AUS)) (135000)
152 ROMOLA, b f 1/2 Pivotal—Dianora (New Approach (IRE))
153 B f 22/4 Frankel—Sayyedati Storm (USA) (Storm Cat (USA))
154 B c 3/4 Australia—Sent From Heaven (IRE) (Footstepsinthesand) (500000)
155 B c 7/2 Cape Cross (IRE)—Shama's Song (IRE) (Teofilo (IRE))
156 B br f 24/4 Declaration of War (USA)—Shawara (IRE) (Barathea (IRE)) (407000)
157 SOVEREIGN GRANT, b c 16/1 Kingman—Momentary (Nayef (USA))
158 B c 24/3 Kingman—Split Trois (FR) (Dubawi (IRE))
159 B c 11/3 Frankel—This Time (FR) (Zafeen (FR)) (244200)
160 B f 18/4 Intello (GER)—Ventura Highway (Machiavellian (USA)) (130000)
161 VIVIONN, ch f 9/2 Dubawi (IRE)—Giants Play (USA) (Giant's Causeway (USA)) (500000)
162 WEMYSS WARE (IRE), b c 11/2 Dubawi (IRE)—White Moonstone (USA) (Dynaformer (USA))
163 Gr f 12/3 Pivotal—Yanabeeaa (USA) (Street Cry (IRE))

Owners: HM The Queen, Mr Khalid Abdullah, Mr Mohammed Al Attiya, Mr Hamdan Al Maktoum, Mr Abdullah Saeed Al Naboodah, Mr Ahmad Alotaibi, Mr Ahmad Abdulla Al Shaikh, Al Shaqab Racing, Cheveley Park Stud, Mr Athos Christodoulou, Mr Peter Done, Sir Alex Ferguson, Flaxman Stables Ireland Ltd, Mrs Denis Haynes, Highclere Thoroughbred Racing, Mr Kin Hung Kei, Mrs John Magnier, Mr Ged Mason, Mr Mike Morris, Newsells Park Stud, Mr Philip Newton, Mr Robert Ng, Niarchos Family, Mr Mohamed Obaida, Phoenix Thoroughbred Limited, Qatar Racing Ltd, RDF Digital, Sir Evelyn de Rothschild, Miss Jessica Slack, Mr Derrick Smith, Mr Gay Smith, Mr Saeed Suhail, Mrs Doreen Tabor, Mr Michael Tabor, Mrs Anita Wigan, Mr James Wigan.

---

536 MRS ALI STRONGE, Eastbury
Postal: **Castle Piece Racing Stables, Eastbury, Hungerford, Berkshire, RG17 7JR**
Contacts: **PHONE (01488) 72818 FAX (01488) 670378 MOBILE (07779) 285205**
E-MAIL office@castlepiecestables.com WEBSITE www.castlepiecestables.com

1 AMANTO (GER), 8, b g Medicean—Amore (GER) **Shaw Racing Partnership 2**
2 ARDMAYLE (IRE), 6, ch g Whitmore's Conn (USA)—Welsh Connection (IRE) **The Wishful Thinkers**
3 BALGEMMOIS (FR), 5, ch g Balko—Venise Doree (FR) **Marlborough Racing-(Balgemmois)**
4 BOOBOROWIE (IRE), 5, b br g Big Bad Bob (IRE)—Rejuvenation (IRE) **The Jury's Out Partnership**
5 CAMAKASI (IRE), 7, b g Camacho—Innocence **Shaw Racing 2 & Friends Of Castle Piece**
6 CHEZ CASTEL MAIL (FR), 6, ch g My Risk (FR)—Queenly Mail (FR) **The One and Only Partnership**
7 DREWMAIN LEGEND, 6, b m Midnight Legend—Ryders Hill **Mrs J. Andrews**
8 HEPBURN, 5, b m Sixties Icon—Mighty Splash **ROA Racing Partnership V**
9 HERESMYNUMBER (IRE), 8, b g Kalanisi (IRE)—Broken Rein (IRE) **Pieces Of Eight Racing**
10 JALINGO (IRE), 7, b g Cape Cross (IRE)—Just Special **Paul Whitehead & Clare Spencer-Herbert**
11 LET'S BE HAPPY (IRE), 4, gr f Mastercraftsman (IRE)—Corrozal (GER) **The Test Valley Partnership**
12 MEETINGS MAN (IRE), 11, gr g Footstepsinthesand—Missella **Mrs B. V. Evans**
13 NAVAJO WAR DANCE, 5, b br g Makfi—Navajo Rainbow **Mr G. S. Bishop**
14 PROSECUTE (FR), 5, b g Lawman (FR)—Dissitation (IRE) **The Jury's Out Partnership**
15 PROUD TIMES (USA), 12, b br g Proud Citizen (USA)—Laura's Pistolette (USA) **Mrs A. J. Stronge**
16 SCORPION HAZE (IRE), 5, b g Scorpion (IRE)—Sea Maiden (IRE) **Shaw Racing Partnership 2**
17 SUM FUN NOW (IRE), 4, b g Jeremy (USA)—Blond's Addition (USA) **Mrs M. Kidger**
18 THE SPECIAL ONE (IRE), 5, br m Cape Cross (IRE)—Capote West (USA) **BGC Racing IX**
19 THOMAS BLOSSOM (IRE), 8, b g Dylan Thomas (IRE)—Woman Secret (IRE) **Kings Of The Castle**
20 WAR AT SEA (IRE), 4, gr g Mastercraftsman (IRE)—Swirling (IRE) **Mr M. G. St Quinton**

THREE-YEAR-OLDS

21 DON'T CRY ABOUT IT (IRE), ch g Casamento (IRE)—Back At de Front (IRE) **Pms Oxford & Mrs Ali Stronge**
22 GOOD IMPRESSION, b g Showcasing—Daintily Done **Mrs A. J. Stronge**
23 HE'S OUR STAR (IRE), b g Lord Shanakill (USA)—Afilla (IRE) **MrsJayneFrench & MrsJacquelinePilling**
24 STAR OF ATHENA (IRE), b f Champs Elysees—Aswaaq (IRE) **Tim Dykes & Hugh Doubtfire**
25 WINDSOR WHIRLYBIRD (IRE), ch f Harbour Watch (IRE)—Charaig **Mrs A. J. Stronge**

TWO-YEAR-OLDS

26 B c 17/3 Poet's Voice—Amber Heights (Kyllachy) (12000) **BGC Racing**
27 GRANDAD'S LEGACY, b c 25/3 Harbour Watch (IRE)—
Vodka Shot (USA) (Holy Bull (USA)) (12000) **Mrs A. J. Stronge**

MRS ALI STRONGE - Continued

28 B c 21/4 Foxwedge (AUS)—La Cucina (IRE) (Last Tycoon) (10000) **BGC Racing**
29 Ch c 17/3 Casamento (IRE)—Reem Star (Green Tune) (5000) **Mrs A. J. Stronge**
30 B c 16/1 Olympic Glory (IRE)—Tunkwa (FR) (Gold Away (IRE)) (10000) **BGC Racing**

Other Owners: Mr N. G. Charlton, Mr H. G. Doubtfire, Mr T. J. Dykes, Mrs S. Evans, Mr J. Fairrie, Mrs J. French, Friends Of Castle Piece, Mr I. Kidger, Mr J. J. King, Mr I. P Mason, Mrs J. M. Pilling, Project Management Services Oxford Ltd, Ms C. L. Spencer-Herbert, Mr F. W. Tulloch, Dr P. G. Walker, Mr R. Ward, Mr P. Whitehead, Mr T. Williams.

Assistant Trainer: Sam Stronge

---

537 **MISS KRISTIN STUBBS, Malton**
Postal: **4 Evergreen Way, Norton, Malton, North Yorkshire, YO17 8BY**
Contacts: **PHONE (01653) 698731**

1 BRONZE BEAU, 11, ch g Compton Place—Bella Cantata **Miss K. Stubbs**
2 CLOWANCE ONE, 6, b g Oasis Dream—Clowance **Mr C. R. Stirling**
3 COOKIE RING (IRE), 7, b g Moss Vale (IRE)—Talah **Mrs A. M. Stirling**
4 LAGENDA, 5, b g Dick Turpin (IRE)—Whirly Dancer **Oakfield Racing**

Other Owners: Miss M. A. Stirling, Mr R. J. Stirling.

---

538 **MR ROB SUMMERS, Solihull**
Postal: **Summerhill Cottage, Danzey Green, Tanworth-in-Arden, Solihull**
Contacts: **PHONE (01564) 742667 MOBILE (07775) 898327**

1 RED WHISPER, 14, ch g Midnight Legend—Secret Whisper **Mrs G. M. Summers**
2 4, Ch f Schiaparelli (GER)—Secret Whisper **Mrs G. M. Summers**
3 ST MERRYN (IRE), 7, b g Oscar (IRE)—Kigali (IRE) **Mrs G. M. Summers**

Assistant Trainer: Mrs G. M. Summers

---

539 **MR ALEX SWINSWOOD, Lambourn**
Postal: **4 Walkers Lane, Lambourn, Hungerford, Berkshire, RG17 8YE**

1 FIFTY PEACH WAY, 6, b m Black Sam Bellamy (IRE)—Aphrodisia **Mr M. Swinswood**

---

540 **MR TOM SYMONDS, Hentland**
Postal: **Dason Cottage, Hentland, Ross-On-Wye, Herefordshire, HR9 6LW**
Contacts: **PHONE (01989) 730869 MOBILE (07823) 324649**
E-MAIL dasoncourt@gmail.com WEBSITE www.thomassymonds.co.uk

1 ALBERTO'S DREAM, 9, b g Fantastic Spain (USA)—Molly's Folly **Wallys Dream Syndicate**
2 ASK CATKIN (IRE), 6, b m Ask—Simple Reason (IRE) **Mrs C. M. Antcliff**
3 BOBO MAC (IRE), 7, gr g Whitmore's Conn (USA)—Blazing Love (IRE) **C & M Baker, K Ibberson, H Pearman**
4 BRUSHED UP, 5, b m Doyen (IRE)—Definite Artist (IRE) **The Mumbo Jumbos**
5 COLD SHOULDER, 4, b g Passing Glance—Averami **Mr T. R. Symonds**
6 DON BERSY (FR), 5, b g Califet (FR)—Tropulka God (FR) **Sir Peter & Lady Gibbings**
7 DRAMATIC PAUSE (IRE), 5, b g Oscar (IRE)—Night Heron (IRE) **The Dramatic Partners**
8 EATON MILLER (IRE), 6, b g Milan—Four Fields (IRE) **Mr K. J. Price**
9 EVERYTHING NOW (IRE), 4, b g Gold Well—Givehertime (IRE)
10 FALCONS FALL (IRE), 7, ch g Vertical Speed (FR)—Ellie Park (IRE) **The Eventful Partnership**
11 FISCAL SPACE (IRE), 6, b g Court Cave (IRE)—Honeyed (IRE) **Celia & Michael Baker**
12 FRANKLY SPEAKING, 8, ch g Flemensfirth (USA)—No More Money **David Jenks & Celia & Michael Baker**
13 JANES BOUTIQUE (IRE), 7, b m Presenting—Supreme Touch (IRE) **Mr S. Davies**

MR TOM SYMONDS - Continued

14 **KAKI DE LA PREE (FR)**, 11, b g Kapgarde (FR)—Kica (FR) **Sir Peter & Lady Gibbings**
15 **LLANTARA**, 7, b m Kayf Tara—Lady Llancillo (IRE) **Bailey-Carvill Equine**
16 **LOUD AS LIONS (IRE)**, 5, b g Flemensfirth (USA)—Misspublican (IRE) **C & M Baker, K Ibberson, H Pearman**
17 **LUGG RIVER**, 4, b f Kayf Tara—Supreme Gem (IRE) **F. M. Green**
18 **MIRZAM (IRE)**, 4, gr f Mastercraftsman (IRE)—Luxie (IRE) **Mr S. Davies**
19 **POLITICAL QUIZ**, 8, b g Lucarno (USA)—Quiz Night **I. A. Low**
20 **PRESENTEDWITHWINGS (IRE)**, 4, br g Presenting—Rosa Rugosa (IRE) **Mr S. Davies**
21 **RIVER ARROW**, 7, b m Kayf Tara—Supreme Gem (IRE) **Frank Green & Mike Roberts**
22 **ROYAL CLARET**, 6, b m Yeats (IRE)—Kerada (FR) **The Nigel Jones & Roy Ovel Syndicate**
23 **ROYALE ZANZIBAR (FR)**, 4, gr g Blue Bresil (FR)—Royale Punta Cana (FR) **Sir Peter & Lady Gibbings**
24 **TOOSEY**, 7, b g Lucarno (USA)—Quiz Night **I. A. Low**
25 **VICTORIAN TEO (FR)**, 8, b br g Teofilo (IRE)—Chalouchi (USA) **Mr M. R. Lennon**

Other Owners: Mrs Peter Andrews, Mr Philip Andrews, Mr R. F. Bailey, Mrs Celia Baker, Mr Michael Baker, Mrs P. J. Buckler, Mr R. K. Carvill, Sir Peter Gibbings, The Hon Lady Gibbings, Mr F. M. Green, Miss K. J. Ibberson, Mr David Jenks, Mr Nigel Jones, Mr Roy Ovel, Mr H. J. Pearman, Mr Michael Roberts, Mr Thomas R. Symonds, Mrs Jane Symonds.

---

541 **MR JAMES TATE, Newmarket**
Postal: **Jamesfield Place, Hamilton Road, Newmarket, Suffolk, CB8 7JQ**
Contacts: **PHONE (01638) 669861 FAX (01638) 676634 MOBILE (07703) 601283**
E-MAIL james@jamestateracing.com WEBSITE www.jamestateracing.com

1 **KYLLANG ROCK (IRE)**, 4, b g Kyllachy—Megec Blis (IRE) **Sheikh Juma Dalmook Al Maktoum**
2 **VIA VIA (IRE)**, 6, b h Lope de Vega (IRE)—Atalina (FR) **Saeed Manana**

THREE-YEAR-OLDS

3 **ARCTIC HAZE (IRE)**, b f Kodiac—Hazium (IRE) **Saeed Manana**
4 **ASTONISHED (IRE)**, ch f Sea The Stars (IRE)—An Saincheann (IRE) **Saeed Manana**
5 **BATTLE LINES**, ch c Sepoy (AUS)—Goslar **Saeed Manana**
6 **BIDDING WAR**, ch f Champs Elysees—Locharia **Saeed Manana**
7 B f Kyllachy—Bit By Bit **Sheikh Rashid Dalmook Al Maktoum**
8 **BLIND SPOT (IRE)**, b c Invincible Spirit (IRE)—Najam **Saeed Manana**
9 **COMPLIANCE (IRE)**, b c Exceed And Excel (AUS)—Saadiah (IRE) **Saeed Manana**
10 **CROSS SWORDS**, b c Invincible Spirit (IRE)—Alaia (IRE) **Saeed Manana**
11 **CULTIVATE (IRE)**, gr f Clodovil (IRE)—Fork Handles **Saeed Manana**
12 **DELTA RIVER**, b c Kodiac—Waterways (IRE) **Saeed Manana**
13 **EFFERVESCENCE (IRE)**, b f Epaulette (AUS)—Miss Rosie **Saeed Manana**
14 **EQUIDAE**, ch c Equiano (FR)—Dularame (IRE) **Saeed Manana**
15 B br f Street Cry (IRE)—Fashion's Flight (USA) **Sheikh Juma Dalmook Al Maktoum**
16 **FORESEEABLE FUTURE (FR)**, b c Harbour Watch (IRE)—Russian Spirit **Saeed Manana**
17 **GRECIAN SPIRIT**, b c Teofilo (IRE)—Ghar Shoop (IRE) **Saeed Manana**
18 **HADDAF (IRE)**, b g Dawn Approach (IRE)—Deveron (USA) **Saif Ali**
19 **HAVANA SUNRISE**, b f Havana Gold (IRE)—Sweet Lemon (IRE) **Saeed Manana**
20 **HEY GAMAN**, b c New Approach (IRE)—Arsaadi (IRE) **Sultan Ali**
21 **HOUSE OF CARDS**, b f Mayson—Neyraan **Saeed Manana**
22 **ICONIC SUNSET**, ch c Farhh—Manila Bay (IRE) **Saeed Manana**
23 **IMMINENT APPROACH**, b f New Approach (IRE)—Nashmiah (IRE) **Saeed Manana**
24 **INVINCIBLE ARMY (IRE)**, b c Invincible Spirit (IRE)—Rajeem **Saeed Manana**
25 **KINGS HIGHWAY (IRE)**, b c Shamardal (USA)—Bimini **Saeed Manana**
26 **LAST REQUEST**, b f Foxwedge (AUS)—Royal Pardon **Saeed Manana**
27 **LIGHT RELIEF**, b f Medicean—Tickle Me (GER) **Saeed Manana**
28 **LITIGATION**, b f Foxwedge (AUS)—Torcross **Saeed Manana**
29 **MATHEMATICAL (IRE)**, b f Acclamation—Doctrine **Saeed Manana**
30 **NEW GRADUATE (IRE)**, b f New Approach—Srda (USA) **Saeed Manana**
31 B c Kodiac—Operissimo **Sheikh Juma Dalmook Al Maktoum**
32 **REAL ESTATE (IRE)**, b c Dansili—Maskunah (IRE) **Saeed Manana**
33 **REASSURANCE**, b f Champs Elysees—Timely Words **Saeed Manana**
34 **RESOLUTION**, b f Swiss Spirit—Kummel Excess (IRE) **Saeed Manana**
35 **ROYAL PARKS**, b f Bated Breath—Kensington Gardens **Saeed Manana**
36 **ROYAL RESIDENCE**, b c Epaulette (AUS)—Jubilant Queen **Saeed Manana**
37 **RUNWAY**, ch f Sepoy (AUS)—Doors To Manual (USA) **Saeed Manana**
38 **SHARP REMINDER**, b f Kyllachy—Sharp Relief (IRE) **Saeed Manana**

MR JAMES TATE - Continued

39 Ch c Teofilo (IRE)—Sospira **Sheikh Juma Dalmook Al Maktoum**
40 **TAKE SHELTER**, b f Harbour Watch (IRE)—Secret Night **Saeed Manana**
41 **TRIBAL WARRIOR**, b c New Approach (IRE)—Lunda (IRE) **Saeed Manana**
42 **TURN OF EVENTS (IRE)**, b f Pivotal—Wahylah (IRE) **Saeed Manana**
43 **UNDER OFFER (IRE)**, ch f Bated Breath—Bailonguera (ARG) **Saeed Manana**
44 **VOICEMAIL**, b f Poet's Voice—Dame Helen **Saeed Manana**
45 **WIDE ACCLAIM (IRE)**, b f Acclamation—Riynaaz (IRE) **Saeed Manana**
46 **YAMUNA RIVER**, b f Foxwedge (AUS)—Harryana To **Saeed Manana**
47 **ZIARAH (IRE)**, b f Iffraaj—Ashtown Girl (IRE) **Sheikh Juma Dalmook Al Maktoum**

TWO-YEAR-OLDS

48 Ch f 5/4 Speightstown (USA)—Aerocat (USA) (Tale of The Cat (USA)) (166473) **Sultan Ali**
49 B f 29/2 Kodiac—Alioonagh (USA) (Giant's Causeway (USA)) (50000) **Saeed Manana**
50 B f 26/1 Dubawi (IRE)—Alsindi (IRE) (Acclamation) **Saeed Manana**
51 B c 10/2 Shamardal (USA)—Aqlaam Vision (Aqlaam) (70000) **Saeed Manana**
52 B c 24/4 Moohaajim (IRE)—Barracade (IRE) (Barathea (IRE)) (55000) **Saeed Manana**
53 B br c 6/4 Gregorian (IRE)—Beautiful Lady (IRE) (Peintre Celebre (USA)) (36000) **Saeed Manana**
54 B c 17/5 Dawn Approach (IRE)—Cape Alex (Cape Cross (IRE)) (10000) **Saeed Manana**
55 B f 1/2 Dawn Approach (IRE)—Cape Good Hope (Cape Cross (IRE)) (26000) **Saeed Manana**
56 B f 13/2 Camelot—Carioca (IRE) (Rakti) (80000) **Saif Ali**
57 B c 7/5 Dark Angel (IRE)—Countess Ferrama (Authorized (IRE)) (26000) **Saeed Manana**
58 B f 9/4 Lope de Vega (IRE)—Dazzle Dancer (IRE) (Montjeu (IRE)) (69190) **Sheikh Juma Dalmook Al Maktoum**
59 B f 21/4 Kingman—Deveron (USA) (Cozzene (USA)) **Saif Ali**
60 B f 18/4 Authorized (IRE)—Dinaria (IRE) (Holy Roman Emperor (IRE)) (20000) **Saeed Manana**
61 B f 30/3 Oasis Dream—Eleanora Duse (IRE) (Azamour (IRE)) (65000) **Saeed Manana**
62 B f 25/1 New Approach (IRE)—
        Excel's Beauty (Exceed And Excel (AUS)) (320000) **Sheikh Juma Dalmook Al Maktoum**
63 **FIELDS OF ATHENRY (USA)**, b br c 12/3 Candy Ride (ARG)—Purple (IRE) (Galileo (IRE)) (87619) **Saeed Manana**
64 B f 11/2 War Command (USA)—Foreplay (Lujain (USA)) (87619) **Saeed Manana**
65 Ch c 22/3 Shamardal (USA)—Guarantia (Selkirk (USA)) **Saeed Manana**
66 B c 28/2 Dandy Man (IRE)—Harvest Joy (IRE) (Daggers Drawn (USA)) (49523) **Saeed Manana**
67 B c 28/2 Poet's Voice—International Love (IRE) (Manduro (GER)) (7000) **Saeed Manana**
68 B c 21/2 Ruler of The World (IRE)—Just Wondering (IRE) (Danehill Dancer (IRE)) (30000) **Saeed Manana**
69 B c 9/2 Gregorian (IRE)—Kasalla (IRE) (Footstepsinthesand) (20000) **Saeed Manana**
70 Ch f 22/2 Dandy Man (IRE)—Kitty Softpaws (IRE) (Royal Applause) (16000) **Saeed Manana**
71 B f 22/1 Morpheus—Lilium (Nashwan (USA)) (62000) **Saeed Manana**
72 B f 27/2 Sepoy (AUS)—Local Fancy (Bahamian Bounty) (8000) **Saeed Manana**
73 B c 11/5 Lawman (FR)—Maidin Maith (IRE) (Montjeu (IRE)) (22000) **Saeed Manana**
74 Ch f 1/4 Australia—Mona Lisa (Giant's Causeway (USA)) (81400) **Saeed Manana**
75 Ch f 22/3 Iffraaj—Nantyglo (Mark of Esteem (IRE)) (50000) **Saeed Manana**
76 B f 18/2 Lemon Drop Kid (USA)—Night Song (Oasis Dream) (45000) **Saeed Manana**
77 B f 9/2 Toronado (IRE)—Oasis Jade (Oasis Dream) (28000) **Saeed Manana**
78 B f 1/4 Dandy Man (IRE)—Park Haven (IRE) (Marju (IRE)) (30476) **Saeed Manana**
79 B c 23/2 Sea The Stars (IRE)—Path Wind (FR) (Anabaa (USA)) (85000) **Saeed Manana**
80 B c 14/5 Lawman (FR)—Polygon (USA) (Dynaformer (USA)) **Saeed Manana**
81 B c 23/4 Harbour Watch (IRE)—Princess Luna (GER) (Grand Lodge (USA)) (26000) **Saeed Manana**
82 Ch c 26/3 Iffraaj—Regal Hawk (Singspiel (IRE)) (42000) **Saeed Manana**
83 Ch f 13/2 Iffraaj—Remember (Selkirk (USA)) (29000) **Saeed Manana**
84 **SECOND GENERATION**, b f 8/3 Dawn Approach (IRE)—
        El Manati (IRE) (Iffraaj) (22000) **Sheikh Rashid Dalmook Al Maktoum**
85 B f 3/2 Slade Power (IRE)—Shamardal Phantom (IRE) (Shamardal (USA)) (65000) **Saif Ali**
86 Ch f 7/3 Showcasing—Sinduda (Anabaa (USA)) (45000) **Saeed Manana**
87 B f 13/4 Cape Cross (IRE)—Solar Moon (Pivotal) (69189) **Saeed Manana**
88 B c 11/4 Footstepsinthesand—Sommer Queen (IRE) (Thousand Words) (10000) **Saeed Manana**
89 B g 30/3 New Approach (IRE)—Sooraah (Dubawi (IRE)) (16000) **Saeed Manana**
90 Ch f 12/2 Sea The Stars (IRE)—Table Bay (IRE) (Nayef (USA)) (101749) **Saeed Manana**
91 B f 25/1 Kingman—The Miniver Rose (IRE) (High Chaparral (IRE)) (45000) **Saeed Manana**
92 Ch f 28/3 Toronado (IRE)—Under The Rainbow (Fantastic Light (USA)) (21000) **Saeed Manana**
93 Ch c 6/3 Exceed And Excel (AUS)—Wahylah (IRE) (Shamardal (USA)) **Saeed Manana**
94 B f 4/3 Australia—Who Is Camille (USA) (Dixie Union (USA)) (26000) **Saeed Manana**

Assistant Trainer: Mrs Lucinda Tate

542 **MR TOM TATE, Tadcaster**
Postal: **Castle Farm, Hazelwood, Tadcaster, North Yorkshire, LS24 9NJ**
Contacts: **PHONE (01937) 836036 FAX (01937) 530011 MOBILE (07970) 122818**
E-MAIL tomptate@zen.co.uk WEBSITE www.tomtate.co.uk

1 **AWAKE MY SOUL (IRE)**, 9, ch g Teofilo (IRE)—Field of Hope (IRE) **T T Racing**
2 **DESTROYER**, 5, b g Royal Applause—Good Girl (IRE) **T T Racing**
3 **EQUIANO SPRINGS**, 4, b g Equiano (FR)—Spring Clean (FR) **T T Racing**
4 **GROUPIE**, 4, b f Requinto (IRE)—Amour Fou (IRE) **T T Racing**
5 **LEODIS (IRE)**, 6, ch g Shirocco (GER)—Leonica **T T Racing**
6 **LUCY'S LAW (IRE)**, 4, b f Lawman (FR)—Lucy Limelites **Ms Fionnuala Cassidy & Mr T. P. Tate**
7 **MULTITALENTED**, 5, b g Multiplex—Star Welcome **T T Racing**
8 **RODDY (IRE)**, 4, ch g Roderic O'connor (IRE)—Sweet Chilli (IRE) **T T Racing**
9 **WAITING FOR RICHIE**, 5, b g Rail Link—Heart of Hearts **The Ivy Syndicate**
10 **YOUNG TIGER**, 5, b g Captain Gerrard (IRE)—Blades Princess **T T Racing**

THREE-YEAR-OLDS

11 **GLACIER FOX**, ch g Foxwedge (AUS)—Beat Seven **T T Racing**

TWO-YEAR-OLDS

12 B c 27/4 Heeraat (IRE)—Baymist (Mind Games) (9523)

Other Owners: James Campbell, Nuala Cassidy, Ivy Syndicate, Mr T. P. Tate, Mrs Hazel Tate.

Assistant Trainer: Hazel Tate

Jockey (flat): James Sullivan.

543 **MR COLIN TEAGUE, Wingate**
Postal: **Bridgefield Farm, Trimdon Lane, Station Town, Wingate, Co. Durham, TS28 5NE**
Contacts: **PHONE (01429) 837087 MOBILE (07967) 330929**
E-MAIL colin.teague@btopenworld.com

1 **DIAL A LOG**, 5, b g Mullionmileanhour (IRE)—Angelic Kitten (IRE) **Mr J. Hamilton**
2 **GRANDAD CHUNK (IRE)**, 7, gr g Acclamation—
Silverdreammachine (IRE) **Collins Chauffeur Driven Executive Cars**
3 **INGLEBY GEORGE**, 4, b c Rail Link—Ingleby Princess **Ingleby Bloodstock Limited**
4 **IVY MATILDA**, 5, b m Monsieur Bond (IRE)—Ingleby Princess **Ingleby Bloodstock Ltd & The Ivy League**
5 5, B m Prime Defender—Lady Rock
6 **LEES ANTHEM**, 11, b g Mujahid (USA)—Lady Rock **Collins Chauffeur Driven Executive Cars**
7 **ON THE HIGH TOPS (IRE)**, 10, b g Kheleyf (USA)—Diplomats Daughter **Mr A. Rice**
8 **RISE UP SINGING**, 5, b m Showcasing—Sambarina (IRE) **Mr J. Hamilton**
9 **SILHUETTE (IRE)**, 5, b m Canford Cliffs (IRE)—Lisfannon **Mr Peter Baker & Partner**
10 **THORNABY PRINCESS**, 7, b m Camacho—Ingleby Princess **Mr D. Scott**
11 **YORKSHIRE ROVER**, 4, b g Doncaster Rover (USA)—Mother Jones **Mr A. Rice**

Other Owners: Mr P. I. Baker, Mr C. M. Hills, The Ivy League.

544 **MR ROGER TEAL, Hungerford**
Postal: **Shefford Valley Stables, East Shefford Farm, Hungerford, Berkshire, RG17 7EF**
Contacts: **PHONE (01488) 649869 MOBILE (07710) 325521**
E-MAIL info@rogertealracing.com WEBSITE www.rogertealracing.co.uk

1 **AGINCOURT REEF (IRE)**, 9, b g Gold Well—Hillside Native (IRE) **Mr R. A. Teal**
2 **BERKELEY VALE**, 7, b g Three Valleys (USA)—Intriguing Glimpse **Mrs Muriel Forward & Dr G C Forward**
3 **CAPTAIN COCKLE**, 5, b g Indian Haven—Demand **Withyslade**
4 **FIVE AGAIN**, 6, b m Schiaparelli (GER)—Tabulate **Calne Engineering Ltd**
5 **HIGH ACCLAIM (USA)**, 4, b g Elusive Quality (USA)—La Reine Lionne (USA) **Excel Racing**
6 **HOWABOUTNEVER (IRE)**, 10, b g Shantou (USA)—
Sarah's Cottage (IRE) **Mr Barry Kitcherside & Mr Roger Teal**
7 **JACK BEAR**, 7, b g Joe Bear (IRE)—Colins Lady (FR) **Joe Bear Racing**
8 **JACK OF DIAMONDS (IRE)**, 9, b g Red Clubs (IRE)—Sakkara Star (IRE) **Inside Track Racing Club**
9 **JASANI**, 10, b g Gentleman's Deal (IRE)—Bred For Pleasure **M. F. Waghorn**

MR ROGER TEAL - Continued

10 **JUST CALL ME BLUE (IRE)**, 6, b g Blueprint (IRE)—Island-Bay (IRE) **Mrs S. M. Teal**
11 **KYLLACHYS TALE (IRE)**, 4, b f Kyllachy—Betray **B. Kitcherside**
12 **LANGLEY VALE**, 9, b g Piccolo—Running Glimpse (IRE) **Mrs Muriel Forward & Dr G C Forward**
13 **LITTLE MISS TANGO**, 4, ch f Steele Tango (USA)—Many Welcomes **Mr D. G. Waterer**
14 **LOOK SURPRISED**, 5, ch m Kier Park (IRE)—Cloridja **Withyslade**
15 **LUCKY LOUIE**, 5, ch g Dutch Art—Ardessie **Great Shefford Racing**
16 **MASTER BILLIE (IRE)**, 4, ro g Mastercraftsman (IRE)—Billie Jean **Mrs S. M. Teal**
17 **ROSIE ROYALE (IRE)**, 6, gr m Verglas (IRE)—Fearn Royal (IRE) **The Idle B's**
18 **STONEMADFORSPEED (IRE)**, 10, b g Fruits of Love (USA)—Diamond Forever **Mr R. A. Teal**
19 **SWOT**, 6, b g Exceed And Excel (AUS)—House Point **The Big Cat Partnership**

THREE-YEAR-OLDS

20 **DIAMOND EXPRESS (IRE)**, b f Fast Company (IRE)—South Ring (IRE) **Idle B's 2 & Roger Teal**
21 **TIP TWO WIN**, gr c Dark Angel (IRE)—Freddie's Girl (USA) **Mrs A. Cowley**

Other Owners: Mr C. Austin, Mr David Bond, A. J. Chambers, Mrs E. Curley, Mr P. Fisher, Dr G. C. Forward, Mrs M. E. Forward, The Idle B's 2, Mrs H. I. Jinks, Mr R. B. Kolien, Mr P. O. Mooney, Miss H. Pease, Mrs R. Pott, Mr S. M. Ransom, Mr M. A. Ransom, Mr E. Sames, Mr M. S. Wynn.

Conditional: Harry Teal.

545
MR HENRY TETT, Lambourn
Postal: **Wormstall, Wickham, Newbury, Berkshire, RG20 8HB**
Contacts: MOBILE (07796) 098220
WEBSITE www.henrytettracing.co.uk

1 **ALANJOU (FR)**, 8, b g Maresca Sorrento (FR)—Partie Time (FR) **The Cap All Partnership**
2 **CEASE TO SURRENDER**, 7, b g Refuse To Bend (IRE)—Bel **Mr H. G. M. Tett**
3 **GENERAL ALLENBY**, 4, b g Medicean—Cat Hunter **D. Cohen**
4 **GYPSY RIDER**, 9, b g Ishiguru (USA)—Spaniola (IRE) **The Racing 4 Fun Partnership**
5 **HOLY TIGER**, 7, b g Tiger Hill (IRE)—Divina Mia **Mr H. G. M. Tett**
6 **LIGHT GUNNER (IRE)**, 4, b g Lawman (FR)—Neve Lieve (IRE) **Mr C. C. Tett**
7 **MR RED CLUBS (IRE)**, 9, b g Red Clubs (IRE)—Queen Cobra (IRE) **Mrs Victoria Tett**
8 **SUIT OF LIGHTS (IRE)**, 4, b g Approve (IRE)—Lindoras Grace **Mr C. C. Tett**
9 **VICTORY RICH (IRE)**, 7, b g Kheleyf (USA)—Imperial Graf (USA) **Mrs Victoria Tett**

THREE-YEAR-OLDS

10 B c Arcano (IRE)—Kylemore (IRE)
11 **PEVERIL POINT (IRE)**, b c Canford Cliffs (IRE)—Galeaza **Mr H. G. M. Tett**

Other Owners: Mr A. Crichton, Mrs D. S. Gibbs, Mr P. D. Hensher.

Amateur: Mr C. A. Jones, Mr F. Tett.

546
MR SAM THOMAS, Upper Lambourn
Postal: **Saxon House Stables, Upper Lambourn, Hungerford, Berkshire, RG17 8QH**
Contacts: PHONE (01488) 73969 MOBILE (07929) 101751
E-MAIL samthomasracing@outlook.com / emma@samthomasracing.com
WEBSITE www.samthomasracing.com

1 **AMALFI DOUG (FR)**, 8, gr g Network (GER)—Queissa (FR) **Mr B. Ryan-Beswick**
2 **BREEZE ALONG**, 8, ch g Denounce—Briery Breeze (IRE) **Mr S. J. Thomas**
3 **DANCING DOUG (IRE)**, 5, br g Kalanisi (IRE)—Drumcay Polly (IRE) **Mr W. Ryan-Beswick**
4 **GLENTROOL**, 5, b g Passing Glance—Killala Bay (IRE) **Mr S. J. Thomas**
5 **GOLDEN FRIDAY (IRE)**, 5, b g Gold Well—Azulada (FR) **Mr A. N. Brooke Rankin**
6 4, B g Mawatheeq (USA)—Island Odyssey
7 **IWILLDOIT**, 5, b g Flying Legend (USA)—Lyricist's Dream **Diamond Racing Ltd**
8 **KALA NOIRE (IRE)**, 4, b g Kalanisi (IRE)—Lady Taipan (IRE) **Mr & Mrs Capper, Mr Trolan & Mr Stovin**
9 **LITTLE ALLSTAR (IRE)**, 5, b g Morozov (USA)—Little Twinkle (IRE) **Diamond Racing Ltd**
10 **LOVELY TOUCH (IRE)**, 9, b g Humbel (USA)—My Touch (IRE) **Third Match Officials**
11 **MEGA MIND**, 5, ch g Captain Rio—Final Leave (IRE) **Mr S. J. Thomas**
12 **MUSICAL STARDUST**, 5, b m Passing Glance—Royal Musical **Mrs J. Way**
13 **NOT A ROLE MODEL (IRE)**, 6, b g Helissio (FR)—Mille Et Une Nuits (FR) **St Mamadasado**

MR SAM THOMAS - Continued

14 **OSCARS LITTLE ROSE (IRE)**, 5, b m Oscar (IRE)—One Swoop (IRE) **Sam Thomas Racing Club**
15 **POWERSTOWN PARK (IRE)**, 5, b g Craigsteel—Smiths Lady (IRE) **The Ipsden Invincibles**
16 **ROYAL MAGIC (IRE)**, 6, b g Whitmore's Conn (USA)—Room To Room Magic (IRE) **Luke Harvey Racing Club**
17 **SIROBBIE (IRE)**, 4, br g Arakan (USA)—Presentbreeze (IRE) **Mr R. J. Gurr**
18 **SPARKLEANDSHINE (IRE)**, 5, b g Olden Times—Little Flower (IRE) **Mr R. J. Gurr**
19 4, Ch f Windsor Knot (IRE)—Tara Tara (IRE)
20 **THE CANNISTER MAN (IRE)**, 6, b g Arakan (USA)—Ladyrosaro (IRE) **Keith Ali & Eamon Murchan**
21 **TORHOUSEMUIR**, 7, b g Sagamix (FR)—Royal Musical **Honourable Scoundrels**
22 **WONGA SWINGER**, 8, b g Lucky Story (USA)—Chippewa (FR) **Mr S. J. Thomas**

TWO-YEAR-OLDS

23 B c 16/4 Pour Moi (IRE)—Preach (IRE) (Danehill Dancer (IRE)) (13023)

Other Owners: Mr K. Ali, Mrs P. L. Capper, Mr T. G. Fillery, Mrs S. C. Fillery, Mr L. J. Harvey, Mr C. Haslam, Mr A. P. G. Holmes, Mr S. Howell, Mr T. L. Llewellyn, Mr E. Murchan, Mrs J. C. Noel, Mr M. Saunders, Mr W. D. Stovin, Mr J. Trolan.

Jockey (NH): James Davies, Adrian Heskin, Adam Nicol. **Conditional:** Harry Beswick, Charlie Deutsch.

---

547 **MR DAVID THOMPSON, Darlington**
Postal: **South View Racing, Ashley Cottage, South View, Bolam, Darlington, Co. Durham, DL2 2UP**
Contacts: **PHONE (01388) 835806 (01388) 832658 FAX (01325) 835806 MOBILE (07795) 161657**
E-MAIL dwthompson61@hotmail.co.uk WEBSITE www.dwthompson.co.uk

1 **BALLYTHOMAS**, 11, b g Kayf Tara—Gregale **Mr Alan Moore & Mr Tony Livingston**
2 **CAMINO LADY (IRE)**, 8, br m Robin des Pres (FR)—Andromeda (IRE) **Mrs J. Snailum**
3 **CATCHING SHADOWS (IRE)**, 9, b g Catcher In The Rye (IRE)—Castletown Girl **HorsingAround**
4 **CONHALT**, 6, b g Rainbow High—Girl of Pleasure (IRE) **J. A. Moore**
5 **HIGHWAYMAN**, 5, b g Dick Turpin (IRE)—Right Rave (IRE) **Mr N. Park**
6 **LONDON GLORY**, 5, b g Archipenko (USA)—Reflected Image (IRE) **Mr W. Fleming**
7 **LORD ROB**, 7, b g Rob Roy (USA)—First Grey **A. Suddes**
8 **LUKOUTOLDMAKEZEBAK**, 5, b g Arabian Gleam—Angelofthenorth **Mr P. J. McMahon**
9 **RAJAPUR**, 5, gr ro g Dalakhani (IRE)—A Beautiful Mind (GER) **Mr B. Lapham**
10 **RED CARAVEL (IRE)**, 4, b g Henrythenavigator (USA)—Red Fantasy (IRE) **Mr T. J. A. Thompson**
11 **ROCK N RHYTHM (IRE)**, 8, b g Rock of Gibraltar (IRE)—Dark Rosaleen (IRE) **The Cartmel Syndicate**
12 **ROMAN COIN**, 7, b g I Was Framed (USA)—Classic Quartet **J. A. Moore**
13 **ROMAN NUMERAL (IRE)**, 10, b g King's Best (USA)—Trespass **Mr S. Murray**
14 **SHAIYZAR (IRE)**, 9, b g Azamour (IRE)—Shaiyzima (IRE) **J. A. Moore**
15 **SOMEONE EXCITING**, 5, b m Notnowcato—Quite Something **Mr W. Fleming**
16 **SPLASH OF VERVE (IRE)**, 6, b g Fast Company (IRE)—Ellistown Lady (IRE) **B.L.U.E. Racing Syndicate**
17 **TAWAAFEEJ (IRE)**, 4, gr g Zebedee—Absolutely Cool (IRE) **Mr Stuart Murray**
18 **VISITANT**, 5, ch g Pivotal—Invitee **Mr N. Park**
19 **WOLFSLAIR (IRE)**, 7, b g Yeats (IRE)—Hidden Reserve (IRE) **J. A. Moore**

THREE-YEAR-OLDS

20 **LITTLE POEM**, b f Holy Roman Emperor (IRE)—Gerika (FR) **Mr B. Lapham & Mr J Souster**
21 **NO CIVIL JUSTICE**, b g Milk It Mick—Flashing Floozie **Mrs A. Kenny**

Other Owners: Mr A. J. Livingston, D. Musgrave, Mr D. R. Platt, Mrs J. B. Pye, Mr J. Souster.

Assistant Trainer: J. A. Moore.

Jockey (flat): Tony Hamilton.

---

548 **MR RONALD THOMPSON, Doncaster**
Postal: **No 2 Bungalow, Haggswood Racing Stable, Stainforth, Doncaster, South Yorkshire, DN7 5PS**
Contacts: **PHONE (01302) 845904 FAX (01302) 845904 MOBILE (07713) 251141**
E-MAIL ronracing@gmail.com

1 **GREAT ROAR (USA)**, 10, b g Thunder Gulch (USA)—Boasting (USA) **Ronald Thompson**
2 **JOHNNY CAVAGIN**, 9, b g Superior Premium—Beyond The Rainbow **A. Bell**
3 **JON H THE LAWMAN (IRE)**, 5, b g Lawman (FR)—Lan Pham Ti (IRE) **Partnership Terminated**
4 **MAJESTIC MAN (IRE)**, 5, b g Majestic Missile (IRE)—Windomen (IRE) **Ronald Thompson**

MR RONALD THOMPSON - Continued

5 **MALLY COLLIER**, 5, ch g Flying Legend (USA)—Isaflo **Ronald Thompson**
6 **MR STRUTTER (IRE)**, 4, ch g Sir Prancealot (IRE)—Khajool (IRE) **Mrs A. Harrison**
7 **PRECIOUS SKYE (IRE)**, 4, b f Born To Sea (IRE)—Secret Flame **Ronald Thompson**

THREE-YEAR-OLDS

8 **DEBBI'S DREAM**, b f Foxwedge (AUS)—Let's Dance (IRE) **Ronald Thompson**
9 **FURNI FACTORS**, b g Captain Gerrard (IRE)—Calgary **B. Bruce & R. Thompson**
10 B f Libranno—Scented Garden
11 **WESTFIELD WONDER**, b c Captain Gerrard (IRE)—Flying Highest **R Thompson & W A Robinson**

Other Owners: Mr B. Bruce, Mr W. A. Robinson.

549
MR VICTOR THOMPSON, Alnwick
Postal: **Link House Farm, Newton By The Sea, Embleton, Alnwick, Northumberland, NE66 3ED**
Contacts: **PHONE (01665) 576272 MOBILE (07739) 626248**

1 **ATLAS PEAK (IRE)**, 13, b g Namid—My Delilah (IRE) **V. Thompson**
2 **CHANCEOFA LIFETIME (IRE)**, 11, ch g Beneficial—Bounty Queen (IRE) **V. Thompson**
3 **COURT PAINTER (IRE)**, 8, b g Court Cave (IRE)—Comings (IRE) **V. Thompson**
4 **DOLLY'S DOT (IRE)**, 7, b m Vertical Speed (FR)—Our Dot (IRE) **V. Thompson**
5 **DUHALLOWCOUNTRY (IRE)**, 12, b g Beneficial—Milltown Lass (IRE) **V. Thompson**
6 **GIN COBBLER**, 12, b g Beneficial—Cassia **V. Thompson**
7 **MILLROSE BELL (IRE)**, 6, b m Flemensfirth (USA)—Laboc **V. Thompson**
8 **MR SHAHADY (IRE)**, 13, b g Xaar—Shunaire (USA) **V. Thompson**
9 **NELLY LA RUE (IRE)**, 11, b m Flemensfirth (USA)—Desperately Hoping (IRE) **V. Thompson**
10 **PC DIXON**, 5, ch g Sixties Icon—Lakaam **V. Thompson**
11 **RAPID FRITZ (IRE)**, 9, ch g Kutub (IRE)—Another Pet (IRE) **V. Thompson**
12 **SCORPO (IRE)**, 7, b g Scorpion (IRE)—Maltesse (IRE) **V. Thompson**
13 **TRUST ME I'M A DR (IRE)**, 9, b g Dr Massini (IRE)—Friendly Flick (IRE) **V. Thompson**

Assistant Trainer: M Thompson

550
MR SANDY THOMSON, Greenlaw
Postal: **Lambden, Greenlaw, Duns, Berwickshire, TD10 6UN**
Contacts: **PHONE (01361) 810211 MOBILE (07876) 142787**
E-MAIL sandy@lambdenfarm.co.uk WEBSITE www.sandythomsonracing.co.uk

1 **ARTHURS SECRET**, 8, ch g Sakhee's Secret—Angry Bark (USA) **Mr J. K. McGarrity**
2 **BALLYCRYSTAL COURT (IRE)**, 6, b g Court Cave (IRE)—Monavale (IRE) **PMPro31 Ltd**
3 **BERKSHIRE DOWNS**, 8, b m Tiger Hill (IRE)—Cut Corn **Miss S. McQueen**
4 **BLUE KASCADE (IRE)**, 11, ch g Kaieteur (USA)—Lydia Blue **Mr J. K. McGarrity**
5 **BUCKLED**, 8, b g Midnight Legend—Mulberry Wine **Miss S. McQueen**
6 **CAVENTARA**, 6, b g Kayf Tara—L'aventure (FR) **Mr C. J. Harriman**
7 **CHEENYS VENTURE**, 6, b m King's Theatre (IRE)—Daisies Adventure (IRE) **Mr A. M. Thomson**
8 **DONNA'S DELIGHT (IRE)**, 7, b g Portrait Gallery (IRE)—Hot Lips (IRE) **D&D Armstrong Limited**
9 **FULL JACK (FR)**, 11, b g Kahyasi—Full Contact (FR) **Mr & Mrs Raymond Anderson Green**
10 **FULLY BOOKED**, 5, b g Beat Hollow—Friendly Craic (IRE)
11 **GLENLORA**, 5, ch m Supreme Sound—Rainha
12 **HARRY THE VIKING**, 13, ch g Sir Harry Lewis (USA)—Viking Flame **Jim Beaumont & Quona Thomson**
13 **JOHN WILLIAMS (IRE)**, 9, b g Presenting—Duhallow Park (IRE) **Mrs C. S. Stephenson**
14 **JOHNNY PEDLAR**, 7, b g Revoque (IRE)—Festival Fancy **Midnight Racing Club**
15 **KING'S WHARF (IRE)**, 9, gr g Clodovil (IRE)—Global Tour (USA) **Ken McGarrity & the Western Chasers**
16 6, B g Multiplex—Life Is Life (FR) **R. A. Green**
17 **MCGOWAN'S PASS**, 7, b g Central Park (IRE)—Function Dreamer **Mrs A. E. Lee**
18 **NENDRUM (IRE)**, 9, br g Westerner—Westgrove Berry (IRE) **Mrs M. Coppola**
19 **ROBINTHEAULAD (IRE)**, 7, b g Robin des Champs (FR)—Brotenstown (IRE) **Quona Thomson & Ken McGarrity**
20 **ROWDY ROCHER (IRE)**, 12, br g Winged Love (IRE)—Madam Rocher (IRE) **Michelle And Dan Macdonald**
21 **SEEMORELIGHTS (IRE)**, 6, b g Echo of Light—Star Lodge **Watson & Lawrence**
22 **SEEYOUATMIDNIGHT (IRE)**, 10, b g Midnight Legend—Morsky Baloo **Mrs Q. R. Thomson**
23 **SELDOM INN**, 10, ch g Double Trigger (IRE)—Portland Row (IRE) **Seldom Inn Partnership**
24 **SIRWILLIAMWALLACE (IRE)**, 5, b g Getaway (GER)—Mrs Milan (IRE) **Mr Ken McGarrity**
25 **THE SHRIMP (IRE)**, 11, gr g Indian Danehill (IRE)—Rheban Lass (IRE) **Mrs Q. R. Thomson**

MR SANDY THOMSON - Continued

26 7, Ch h Kadastrof (FR)—Triggers Ginger
27 **WIDE AWAKE,** 9, b m And Beyond (IRE)—Quonarose **Midnight Racing Club**

Other Owners: Mr Jim Beaumont, Mr Neil Boyle, Mrs Anita Green, Mr Raymond Anderson Green, Mr David Lawrence, Mr Duncan Lawrence, Mr Dan Macdonald, Mrs Michelle Macdonald, Mr Ken McGarrity, Mr Derek McIntyre, The Western Chasers, Mrs A. M. Thomson, Mr A. M. Thomson, Mr Varlien Vyner-Brooks.

Assistant Trainer: Mrs A. M. Thomson

Conditional: Rachael McDonald. **Amateur:** Mr Alex Chadwick.

---

551 **MR NIGEL TINKLER, Malton**
Postal: **Trainer did not wish details of his string to appear**

---

552 **MR COLIN TIZZARD, Sherborne**
Postal: **Venn Farm, Milborne Port, Sherborne, Dorset, DT9 5RA**
Contacts: **PHONE** (01963) 250598 **FAX** (01963) 250598 **MOBILE** (07976) 778656
E-MAIL info@colintizzard.co.uk **WEBSITE** www.colintizzard.co.uk

1 **AINCHEA (IRE),** 5, b g Flemensfirth (USA)—Lady Petit (IRE) **Ann & Alan Potts Limited**
2 **ALLCHILLEDOUT,** 9, b g Alflora (IRE)—Miss Chinchilla **Gale Force Six**
3 **ANNIVERSARY GIFT,** 5, b g Sulamani (IRE)—Methodical **Miss Juliet E Reed & Mr Michael Truan**
4 4, bl g Scorpion (IRE)—Ariesanne (IRE)
5 **BALLY LONGFORD (IRE),** 10, b g Gold Well—Stay On Line (IRE) **Ann & Alan Potts Limited**
6 **BARCALONA,** 6, gr m Sulamani (IRE)—Ruby Isabel (IRE) **Ms J. Abrahams**
7 **BATTLE OF IDEAS (IRE),** 5, ch g Fracas (IRE)—Haven't A Notion **Coral Champions Club**
8 **BEARS RAILS,** 8, b g Flemensfirth (USA)—Clandestine **Mr P. M. Warren**
9 **BRAMBLE BROOK,** 8, b g Kayf Tara—Briery Ann **Brocade Racing**
10 **BRYNMAWR,** 8, b g Double Trigger (IRE)—Little Feat **Mr G. Nicholas**
11 **BUCKHORN TIMOTHY,** 9, b g Tamure (IRE)—Waimea Bay **The Buckhorn Racing Team**
12 **BURN VALLEY,** 5, ch m With The Flow (USA)—Countess Point **Mr D. S. Purdie**
13 **CARRICK ROADS (IRE),** 4, ch g Robin des Champs (FR)—Jay Lo (IRE) **Brocade Racing**
14 **COASTAL DRIFT,** 4, b g Black Sam Bellamy (IRE)—Absalom's Girl **Brocade Racing**
15 **COPPERHEAD,** 4, ch g Sulamani (IRE)—How's Business **Mrs G. C. Pritchard**
16 **CUCKLINGTON,** 7, b g Kayf Tara—Ardrom **Mrs C. M. Hinks**
17 **CUE CARD,** 12, b g King's Theatre (IRE)—Wicked Crack (IRE) **Mrs J. R. Bishop**
18 **DARLAC (FR),** 5, b br g Lucarno (USA)—Pail Mel (FR)
19 **DARLING ALKO (FR),** 5, b g Al Namix (FR)—Padalko Tatou (FR)
20 **DRINKS INTERVAL,** 6, b m King's Theatre (IRE)—Dame Fonteyn **The Land Value Partnership**
21 **DUC KAUTO (FR),** 5, b g Ballingarry (IRE)—Kauto Lorette (FR) **Ann & Alan Potts Limited**
22 **ELEGANT ESCAPE (IRE),** 6, b g Dubai Destination (USA)—Graineuaile (IRE) **Mr J. P. Romans**
23 **EMPREINTE RECONCE (FR),** 4, b f Voix du Nord (FR)—Petite Fille (FR) **Mr J. P. McManus**
24 **EXXARO (IRE),** 8, b g Presenting—Mandys Gold (IRE) **Ann & Alan Potts Limited**
25 **FERGAL MAEL DUIN,** 10, gr g Tikkanen (USA)—Fad Amach (IRE) **James Messenger Jean-Marie Buob-Aldorf**
26 **FINIAN'S OSCAR (IRE),** 6, b g Oscar (IRE)—Trinity Alley (IRE) **Ann & Alan Potts Limited**
27 **FLAMING CHARMER (IRE),** 10, ch g Flemensfirth (USA)—Kates Charm (IRE) **Tom Chadney & Peter Green**
28 **FLO'SBOY SAM,** 5, b g Tobougg (IRE)—Madam Flora **Wendy Pope & Tim Swaffield**
29 **FOURTH ACT (IRE),** 9, b g King's Theatre (IRE)—Erintante (IRE) **Wendy & Malcolm Hezel**
30 **FOX NORTON (FR),** 8, b g Lando (GER)—Natt Musik (FR) **Ann & Alan Potts Limited**
31 **GENTLEMAN JON,** 10, b g Beat All (USA)—Sudden Spirit (FR) **Mr J. P. Romans**
32 **GOLDEN SUNRISE (IRE),** 5, ch g Stowaway—Fairy Dawn **Brocade Racing**
33 **GRAND VISION (IRE),** 12, gr g Old Vic—West Hill Rose (IRE) **J K Farms**
34 **HELFORD RIVER,** 4, b g Presenting—Lovely Origny (FR) **Brocade Racing**
35 **IVOR'S QUEEN (IRE),** 9, b m King's Theatre (IRE)—Sonnerschien (IRE) **Ivor Perry & Ashton Selway**
36 **JAYTRACK PARKHOMES,** 4, b g Multiplex—Sudden Beat **DT Hoyland JS Hoyland JP Romans**
37 **JOG ON (IRE),** 5, b g Definite Article—Azabu Juban (IRE) **Bradley Partnership**
38 **KALARIKA (IRE),** 5, b m Kalanisi (IRE)—Katariya (IRE) **Gale Force Three**
39 **KAUTO THE KING (FR),** 4, b g Ballingarry (IRE)—Kauto Luisa (FR) **Jenny Perry & Celia Goaman**
40 **KILBRICKEN STORM (IRE),** 7, b g Oscar (IRE)—Kilbricken Leader (IRE) **A. G. Selway**
41 **KINGS LAD (IRE),** 11, b g King's Theatre (IRE)—Festival Leader (IRE) **G. F. Gingell**
42 **KINGS WALK (IRE),** 7, b g King's Theatre (IRE)—Shuil Sionnach (IRE) **Mrs J. R. Bishop**

MR COLIN TIZZARD - Continued

43 **LEG LOCK LUKE (IRE)**, 8, b g Indian River (FR)—Delirious Tantrum (IRE) **J. T. Warner**
44 **LILLINGTON (IRE)**, 6, br g Westerner—Kind Word (IRE) **The Colin Tizzard Racing Club**
45 **LITTLE VERN (IRE)**, 4, b g Oscar (IRE)—Silver Valley (IRE) **Nightingale Syndicate**
46 **LOSTINTRANSLATION (IRE)**, 6, b g Flemensfirth (USA)—Falika (FR) **Taylor & O'Dwyer**
47 **MICK THONIC (FR)**, 8, gr g Maresca Sorrento (FR)—Mick Madona (FR) **Ann & Alan Potts Limited**
48 **MILANO'S MELODY (IRE)**, 4, br f Milan—Tizzy Frizzy **Gale Force Seven**
49 **MISTER MALARKY**, 5, ch g Malinas (GER)—Priscilla **Wendy & Malcolm Hezel**
50 **MOLINEAUX (IRE)**, 7, b g King's Theatre (IRE)—Steel Grey Lady (IRE) **John & Heather Snook**
51 **MOUNT RUSHMOORE (IRE)**, 6, b g Shantou (USA)—Knock On The Door (IRE) **Jenny Perry & Celia Goaman**
52 **MUFFINS FOR TEA**, 8, ch g With The Flow (USA)—Countess Point **Mr D. S. Purdie**
53 **MY LADY GREY**, 4, gr f Presenting—Wassailing Queen **The Alyasan Partnership**
54 **NATIVE RIVER (IRE)**, 8, ch g Indian River (FR)—Native Mo (IRE) **Brocade Racing**
55 **NEVER LEARN (IRE)**, 7, b g King's Theatre (IRE)—
　　　　　　　　　　　　　　　　　　　　　　　Hamari Gold (IRE) **Brocade Racing J P Romans Terry Warner**
56 **NEW TO THIS TOWN (IRE)**, 7, b g Milan—Jade River (FR) **Ann & Alan Potts Limited**
57 **NORSE LEGEND**, 7, b g Norse Dancer (IRE)—Methodical **Woodhaven Racing Syndicate**
58 4, B g Presenting—Oilily (IRE) **Mr & Mrs R. Tizzard**
59 **ON DEMAND**, 7, ch m Teofilo (IRE)—Mimisel **Ms Christine Thomas & Mr Jim Hoyland**
60 **PADLEYOUROWNCANOE**, 4, b g Nayef (USA)—
　　　　　　　　　　　　　　　　　　Pooka's Daughter (IRE) **Kevin Corcoran Aaron Pierce Chris Weare**
61 **PINGSHOU (IRE)**, 8, b g Definite Article—Quest of Passion (FR) **Ann & Alan Potts Limited**
62 **QUEEN OF THE WIND**, 5, b m Shirocco (GER)—Kaydee Queen (IRE) **Chasing Gold Limited**
63 **QUITE BY CHANCE**, 9, b g Midnight Legend—Hop Fair **T Hamlin,J M Dare,J W Snook,J T Warner**
64 **QUIZ MASTER (IRE)**, 6, b g Ask—Good Bye Dolly (IRE) **Brocade Racing**
65 **ROBINSFIRTH (IRE)**, 9, b g Flemensfirth (USA)—Phardester (IRE) **Christine Knowles & Wendy Carter**
66 **ROCKPOINT**, 5, b g Shirocco (GER)—Tinagoodnight (FR) **John & Heather Snook**
67 **ROYAL VACATION (IRE)**, 8, b g King's Theatre (IRE)—Summer Break (IRE) **Mrs J. R. Bishop**
68 **RUBY RUSSET**, 6, b m Apple Tree (FR)—Fair Coppelia **Mrs G. C. Pritchard**
69 **SANDY BEACH**, 8, b g Notnowcato—Picacho (IRE) **Brocade Racing**
70 **SARTORIAL ELEGANCE**, 7, b g Kayf Tara—Blue Ride (IRE) **R. G. Tizzard**
71 **SHANAHAN'S TURN (IRE)**, 10, b g Indian Danehill (US)—Chanson Indienne (FR) **Ann & Alan Potts Limited**
72 **SHILLINGSWORTH (IRE)**, 5, b g Presenting—Miss Bobs Worth (IRE) **J. M. Dare, T. Hamlin, J. W. Snook**
73 **SHOAL BAY (IRE)**, 5, b g Gold Well—Ring Hill **Mrs C. Skan**
74 **SILVERHOW (IRE)**, 7, br g Yeats (IRE)—Monte Solaro (IRE) **Swallowfield Racing**
75 **SIZING CODELCO (IRE)**, 9, b g Flemensfirth (USA)—La Zingarella (IRE) **Ann & Alan Potts Limited**
76 **SIZING CUSIMANO**, 5, b g Midnight Legend—Combe Florey **Ann & Alan Potts Limited**
77 **SIZING GRANITE (IRE)**, 10, b g Milan—Hazel's Tisrara (IRE) **Ann & Alan Potts Limited**
78 **SIZING PLATINUM (IRE)**, 10, b g Definite Article—Quest of Passion (FR) **Ann & Alan Potts Limited**
79 **SIZING SCORPION (IRE)**, 9, b g Scorpion (IRE)—Fair Present (IRE) **Ann & Alan Potts Limited**
80 **SIZING TARA**, 5, b g Kayf Tara—As Was **Ann & Alan Potts Limited**
81 **SIZING TENNESSEE (IRE)**, 10, ch g Robin des Champs (FR)—Jolivia (FR) **Ann & Alan Potts Limited**
82 **SLATE HOUSE (IRE)**, 6, b g Presenting—Bay Pearl (FR) **Eric Jones, Geoff Nicholas, John Romans**
83 **SOLATENTIF (FR)**, 8, b g Solon (GER)—Indian Mist (FR) **Ann & Alan Potts Limited**
84 **SPARKY'S SPIRIT (IRE)**, 9, ch g Flemensfirth (USA)—Pretty In Pink (IRE) **Richard & Ruth Dimond**
85 **STORM HOME (IRE)**, 6, br g King's Theatre (IRE)—Miss Mayberry (IRE) **Mr J. P. Romans**
86 4, Ch g Flemensfirth (USA)—Tap The Beat (IRE) **C. L. Tizzard**
87 **THE BROTHERS (IRE)**, 5, b g Flemensfirth (USA)—Laboc **DT Hoyland JS Hoyland JP Romans**
88 **THE CIDER MAKER**, 8, b g Kayf Tara—Dame Fonteyn **Mrs C Djivanovic, Joanna Tizzard, KSB**
89 **THE DUTCHMAN (IRE)**, 8, b g King's Theatre (IRE)—Shivermetimber (IRE) **SprayClad UK**
90 **THE RUSSIAN DOYEN (IRE)**, 5, b g Doyen (IRE)—Namloc (IRE) **The Gosden Mob**
91 **THEATRE GUIDE (IRE)**, 11, b g King's Theatre (IRE)—Erintante (IRE) **Mrs J. R. Bishop**
92 **THEATRICAL STAR**, 12, b g King's Theatre (IRE)—Lucy Glitters **Brocade Racing**
93 **THIRD ACT (IRE)**, 9, b g King's Theatre (IRE)—Starry Lady (IRE) **Blackmore Vale Syndicate**
94 **THIRD INTENTION (IRE)**, 11, b g Azamour (IRE)—Third Dimension (FR) **Mr & Mrs R. Tizzard**
95 **THISTLECRACK**, 10, b g Kayf Tara—Ardstown **John & Heather Snook**
96 **TIKKAPICK (IRE)**, 8, b g Tikkanen (USA)—Takeanotherpick (IRE) **The Con Club**
97 **ULTRAGOLD (FR)**, 10, b br g Kapgarde (FR)—Hot d'or (FR) **Brocade Racing J P Romans Terry Warner**
98 **UNSAFE CONDUCT**, 5, ch g Pasternak—Symbiosis **The Alyasan Partnership**
99 **VALHALLA (IRE)**, 8, b g Scorpion (IRE)—Fox Theatre (IRE) **J P Romans & Terry Warner**
100 **VICONTE DU NOYER (IRE)**, 9, gr g Martaline—Zouk Wood (USA) **Ann & Alan Potts Limited**
101 **VISION DES FLOS (FR)**, 5, b g Balko (FR)—Marie Royale (FR) **Ann & Alan Potts Limited**
102 **WATERLOO WARRIOR (IRE)**, 6, b g Kalanisi (IRE)—Vindonissa (IRE) **Brocade Racing**
103 **WEST APPROACH**, 8, b g Westerner—Ardstown **John & Heather Snook**
104 **WHITE MOON (GER)**, 6, gr g Sholokhov (USA)—Westalin (GER) **Brocade Racing**

MR COLIN TIZZARD - Continued

105 **WIZARDS BRIDGE,** 9, b g Alflora (IRE)—Island Hopper **The Butterwick Syndicate**
106 **ZANSTRA (IRE),** 8, b g Morozov (USA)—Enistar (IRE) **Moonrakers**

Other Owners: Mr L. G. Aldsworth, Mr G. S. Bennet, Mr J. G. Bennet, Mrs S. J. Biggins, Mrs A. E. M. Broom, Mr G. R. Broom, Mr J. P. R. Buob-Aldorf, Mrs W. Carter, T. H. Chadney, S. J. Clare, Mr C. Cole, Mrs S. S. Cole, Mr C. E. G. Collier, K. J. Corcoran, Mr J. M. Dare, R. E. Dimond, Mrs R. Dimond, Mrs C. J. Djivanovic, Mr A. L. Ellison, Mr A. P. Gale, Mr P. Gibbs, Mr S. Gillett, Mrs C. J. Goaman, Mr R. Goodfellow, Mr I. F. Gosden, Mr P. C. W. Green, T. Hamlin, Mr T. Hanrahan, Mrs W. M. Hezel, Mr M. W. Hezel, Mrs J. Honeybun, Mr K. F. Honeybun, M. M. Hooker, Mr J. S. Hoyland, Mr D. T. Hoyland, Mr R. Jones, Mr E. Jones, Mrs C. Knowles, Mr G. J. Le Prevost, C. A. Leafe, Mr D. A. Makins, Miss N. Martin, Mr D. A. Mayes, Mr D. R. Mayes, Mrs S. A. Mayes, J. M. Messenger, Mr R. O'Dwyer, Mrs J. M. Perry, W. I. M. Perry, Mr A. T. Pierce, Mrs W. M. Pope, Miss J. E. Reed, Mr D. J. Rushbrook, Mr M. L. Sharp, Mr J. Simpson, Mrs H. A. Snook, J. W. Snook, Mrs M. R. Spearing, Mr D. J. Stevens, Mr T. J. Swaffield, Mr R. L. Tappin, Ms C. Thomas, Mrs S. L. Tizzard, Miss J. Tizzard, Mr M. R. Truan, Mr E. R. Vickery, Mr C. E. Weare.

Assistant Trainers: Mrs Kim Gingell, Joe Tizzard

Jockey (NH): Paddy Brennan, Harry Cobden, Tom O'Brien, Tom Scudamore. **Amateur:** Mr Jamie Thomas.

---

553 **MR MARTIN TODHUNTER,** Penrith
Postal: **The Park, Orton, Penrith, Cumbria, CA10 3SD**
Contacts: **PHONE** (01539) 624314 **FAX** (01539) 624314 **MOBILE** (07976) 440082
WEBSITE www.martintodhunter.co.uk

1 **ADELPHI PRINCE,** 5, b g Schiaparelli (GER)—Cailin Na Ri (IRE) **Mr B. Brown**
2 **BELLE OF YORK (IRE),** 5, b m Vale of York (IRE)—Belle Rebelle (IRE) **Mr & Mrs Ian Hall**
3 **BOCASIEN DESBOIS (FR),** 7, gr g Smadoun (FR)—Quocasienne (FR) **J. D. Gordon**
4 **BULLS HEAD (IRE),** 6, b g Darsi (FR)—Mrs Jenks **Murphy's Law Partnership**
5 **CHOCOLAT NOIR (IRE),** 5, b m Yeats (IRE)—Valrhona (IRE) **Javas Charvers**
6 **DARRY DESBOIS (FR),** 5, ch g Ballingarry (IRE)—Tiwa (FR) **Mr & Mrs Ian Hall**
7 **EARTH LADY,** 6, b m Presenting—Simply Divine (IRE) **Park Farms Racing Syndicate 1**
8 **MISS BARBOSSA (IRE),** 7, b m Gold Well—Queens Quay **Mr & Mrs Ian Hall**
9 **MONBEG CAVE (IRE),** 6, b g Court Cave (IRE)—Reynella Cross (IRE) **Mrs Mrs Matthews & Mr B Hazeldean**
10 **MONBEG RIVER (IRE),** 9, b g Indian River (IRE)—So Pretty (IRE) **V Vyner-Brookes & Bill Hazeldean**
11 **ONCE AN ANGEL (IRE),** 6, br m Robin des Pres (FR)—Easter Day (IRE) **Mr W. & Mrs J. Garnett**
12 **PRESENTING JUNIOR (IRE),** 11, b g Presenting—Dr Alice (IRE) **Mr W. & Mrs J. Garnett**
13 **PRETTY MISS MAHLER (IRE),** 7, b m Mahler—So Pretty (IRE) **Murphy's Law Partnership**
14 **PRETTY PASSE,** 4, b f Exceed And Excel (AUS)—Passe Passe (USA) **J. D. Gordon**
15 **QUESTION OF FAITH,** 7, b m Yeats (IRE)—Anastasia Storm **Mr K. Fitzsimons & Mr G. Fell**
16 **SOPHIE OLIVIA (IRE),** 6, b m Ask—Gill's Honey (IRE) **Mr A. Bell**
17 **TALKOFGOLD (IRE),** 6, gr m Gold Well—Talk of Rain (IRE) **Leeds Plywood & Doors Ltd**
18 **WHAT ABOUT BOB (IRE),** 4, br g Big Bad Bob (IRE)—Hymn of Love (IRE) **Mr G. Fell**
19 **WISTY (IRE),** 9, gr g Cloudings (IRE)—Alpine Message **Murphy's Law Partnership**

Other Owners: Mr P. G. Airey, P. W. Clement, Mr W. Downs, K. Fitzsimons, Mr J. W. Fryer-Spedding, Mrs J. M. Garnett, Exors of the Late W. W. Garnett, J. W. Hazeldean, Mrs S. J. Matthews, Mr J. I. A. Spedding, Mr D. M. Todhunter, Mr V. R. Vyner-Brookes.

Jockey (flat): David Nolan. **Jockey (NH):** Danny Cook. **Conditional:** Ross Chapman.

---

554 **MR MARK TOMPKINS,** Newmarket
Postal: **Frankland Lodge, Hamilton Road, Newmarket, Suffolk, CB8 7JQ**
Contacts: **PHONE** (01638) 661434 **FAX** (01638) 668107 **MOBILE** (07799) 663339
E-MAIL mht@marktompkins.co.uk **WEBSITE** www.marktompkins.co.uk

1 **BRACKEN BRAE,** 6, b m Champs Elysees—Azure Mist **Mr David P. Noblett & Mr M. H. Tompkins**
2 **CLEARANCE,** 4, b g Authorized (IRE)—Four Miracles **Mr Richard W Farleigh & Partner**
3 **GEE SIXTY SIX,** 4, b g Mount Nelson—Azure Mist **Mr David P. Noblett & Mr M. H. Tompkins**
4 **GINGER LADY (IRE),** 4, ch f Helmet (AUS)—Theola (IRE) **Graham and Yolanda King**
5 **INDIAN RED,** 4, ch g Sir Percy—Missouri **AEDOS, Sexton & Tompkins**
6 **LOST THE MOON,** 5, b m Authorized (IRE)—Missouri **AEDOS, Milligan & Tompkins**
7 **TOPALOVA,** 5, ch m Champs Elysees—Topatori (IRE) **Mr M. P. Bowring & Partner**
8 **VELVET VOICE,** 4, b f Azamour (IRE)—Battery Power **Sarabex**

MR MARK TOMPKINS - Continued

THREE-YEAR-OLDS

9 **ASTROBLAZE**, ch f Havana Gold (IRE)—Astrodonna **Mystic Meg Limited**
10 **ASTROBREEZE**, b f Lawman (FR)—Astromagick **Mystic Meg Limited**
11 **ASTROFIRE**, b f Kheleyf (USA)—Astromancer (USA) **Mystic Meg Limited**
12 **ASTROJEWEL**, b f Havana Gold (IRE)—Astrolibra **Mystic Meg Limited**
13 **FOUR FIFTY THREE**, b g Kheleyf (USA)—Velvet Waters **Sarabex**
14 **NESS OF BRODGAR**, b f Harbour Watch (IRE)—Missouri **Tompkins, Harvey, King & Tompkins**
15 **ROOF GARDEN**, ch c Cityscape—Celebrity **Sarabex**
16 **RUM RATION**, b g Mount Nelson—Myriades d'etoiles (IRE) **Sarabex**
17 **SAINT ANTHONY**, ch g Pastoral Pursuits—Mega (IRE) **Raceworld**
18 **TOPAPINION**, b c So You Think (NZ)—Topatoo **Bowring, Guest & Tompkins**
19 **TRUE CALLING**, ch f Pastoral Pursuits—Trew Class **Raceworld**
20 **TTMAB**, b c Mawatheeq (USA)—Astrodiva **Judi Dench & Bryan Agar**
21 **VELVET VISION**, b f Nathaniel (IRE)—Battery Power **Sarabex**

TWO-YEAR-OLDS

22 **ASTROMERRY**, br f 7/4 Farhh—Astrodonna (Carnival Dancer) **Mystic Meg Limited**
23 **ASTROSPARKLE**, b f 8/3 Dunaden (FR)—
                                 Astrodiva (Where Or When (IRE)) **Mystic Meg Limited & Mr M. H. Tompkins**
24 **FARNE ODYSSEY**, b f 9/2 Farhh—Diverting (Nayef (USA)) **J. A. Reed**
25 **GARREL GLEN**, ch f 23/1 Mount Nelson—
                                 Azure Mist (Bahamian Bounty) **Mr David P. Noblett & Mr M. H. Tompkins**
26 **GARRISON LAW**, b c 15/2 Garswood—Cushat Law (IRE) (Montjeu (IRE)) **Mr M. Franklin**
27 **ISAAC MURPHY (USA)**, b c 10/3 Medaglia d'oro (USA)—Marietta (USA) (Machiavellian (USA)) (20000) **Sarabex**
28 **MELO PEARL**, ch f 29/4 Paco Boy (IRE)—Jewelled (Fantastic Light (USA)) **Mr M. Franklin**
29 **PAGEANT MASTER (IRE)**, ch c 18/3 Casamento (IRE)—Skiphall (Halling (USA)) (13023) **Dullingham Park**
30 **QUANAH (IRE)**, ch c 18/2 Dandy Man (IRE)—Boucheron (Galileo (IRE)) (28000) **Killarney Glen & Sarabex**
31 B f 3/3 Epaulette (AUS)—Trew Class (Inchinor) **Dullingham Park**
32 **VELVET VISTA**, b f 8/4 Sea The Moon (GER)—Battery Power (Royal Applause) **Sarabex**

Other Owners: B. R. Agar, S. Andrews, M. P. Bowring, Dame J. O. Dench, Mr R. W. Farleigh, Mrs S. R. Goddard, Mr R. H. Guest, N. M. Hanger, Mr M. D. Harvey, Mr E. Jones, Killarney Glen, Mr G. R. King, Mrs Y. L. King, Mr O. P. C. Magnus, Mrs W. L. Marriott, Mr R. D. E. Marriott, Mr D. P. Noblett, D. G. Tompkins, Mr M. H. Tompkins, Mrs A. M. Tompkins.

Assistant Trainer: Tim Bryce

MR MARCUS TREGONING, Whitsbury

Postal: **Whitsbury Manor Racing Stables, Whitsbury, Fordingbridge, Hampshire, SP6 3QQ**
Contacts: PHONE (01725) 518889 FAX (01725) 518042 MOBILE (07767) 888100
E-MAIL info@marcustregoningracing.co.uk WEBSITE www.marcustregoningracing.co.uk

1 **BRONZE ANGEL (IRE)**, 9, b g Dark Angel (IRE)—Rihana (IRE) **Lady Tennant & Mr M P N Tregoning**
2 **CLOVELLY BAY (IRE)**, 7, b g Bushranger (IRE)—Crystalline Stream (FR) **Mr M. P. Tregoning**
3 **DANCE THE DREAM**, 5, b m Sir Percy—Shadow Dancing **Mrs M. A. Dalgety**
4 **HAVANA BREEZE (IRE)**, 4, b f Teofilo (IRE)—Cala (FR) **Mr G. C. B. Brook**
5 **HAWKERLAND (IRE)**, 5, b g Sea The Stars (IRE)—Zarara (USA) **Mr G. C. B. Brook**
6 **IMPHAL**, 4, b g Nathaniel (IRE)—Navajo Rainbow **Mrs H. I. Slade**
7 **MISS BLONDELL**, 5, ch m Compton Place—Where's Broughton **Miss S. M. Sharp**
8 **MONAADHIL (IRE)**, 4, b g Dark Angel (IRE)—Urban Daydream (IRE) **Hamdan Bin Rashid Al Maktoum**
9 **MUKALAL**, 4, b g Mawatheeq (USA)—Misdaqeya **Hamdan Bin Rashid Al Maktoum**
10 **NEVALYASHKA**, 4, b f Sir Percy—Ninotchka (USA) **Miss K. Rausing**
11 **PORT ISAAC (IRE)**, 5, b g Sakhee's Secret—Dombeya (IRE) **M. Tregoning & It's Better Than Fishing**
12 **SEAFARER (IRE)**, 4, br g Henrythenavigator (USA)—Rose of Petra (IRE) **Green, Hoare, Raw & Tregoning**
13 **SIR TITAN**, 4, b g Aqlaam—Femme de Fer **Wedgewood Estates**
14 **STAR STREAM**, 4, b g Acclamation—Ellen (IRE) **R. C. C. Villers**
15 **WAQT (IRE)**, 4, b g Acclamation—Needles And Pins (IRE) **FTP Equine Holdings Ltd**

THREE-YEAR-OLDS

16 **ALRAHAAL (IRE)**, ch c Raven's Pass (USA)—Loose Julie (IRE) **Hamdan Bin Rashid Al Maktoum**
17 **BARNAY**, b g Nayef (USA)—Barnezet (GR) **Mr Robin Blunt & Mr M P N Tregoning**
18 **BLODWYN**, ch f Medicean—Rotunda **Mr J. A. Tabet**
19 **BOLERO (IRE)**, b f Power—Nancy Spain (IRE) **Lady Tennant**
20 **BOSTON T PARTY**, b c Declaration of War (USA)—Sri Kandi **Mr R. C. C. Villers & Mr J. P. Cavanagh**

MR MARCUS TREGONING - Continued

21 **CHAMPS DE REVES**, b c Champs Elysees—Joyeaux **Park Walk Racing**
22 **DIBLAH**, b f Kyllachy—Canukeepasecret **Hamdan Bin Rashid Al Maktoum**
23 **DIVA STAR**, ch f Siyouni (FR)—Kissin Sign **FTP Equine Holdings Ltd**
24 **EXCEEDINGLY DIVA**, b f Exceed And Excel (AUS)—Anqooda (USA) **FTP Equine Holdings Ltd**
25 **FIELDEN FROLIC**, br f Pastoral Pursuits—Full Bloom **Boanas, Raw & Tregoning**
26 **FRECKLES**, ch f Arakan (USA)—Tarneem (USA) **John & Heather Raw**
27 **HONOURBOUND (IRE)**, b g Thewayyouare (USA)—Lavender List (IRE) **Park Walk Racing**
28 **KHAZAF**, b c Dawn Approach (IRE)—Winds of Time (IRE) **Hamdan Bin Rashid Al Maktoum**
29 **LANDUE**, b c Champs Elysees—Time of Gold (USA) **Mr M. P. Tregoning**
30 **MARGUB**, ch c Bated Breath—Bahamian Babe **Hamdan Bin Rashid Al Maktoum**
31 **MARQUISETTE**, b f Archipenko (USA)—Maria di Scozia **Miss K. Rausing**
32 **POWER OF DARKNESS**, b c Power—Summers Lease **R. C. C. Villers**
33 **SCOTS SNAP (IRE)**, b f Kyllachy—Sensational Samba (IRE) **Owenstown Stud & Mr M. P. N. Tregoning**
34 **SERJEANT PAINTER**, b g Royal Applause—Szabo's Art **Park Walk Racing**
35 **SMILES A LOT**, b g Motivator—Azariane (FR) **Mrs C. J. Wates**
36 **STRATHSPEY STRETTO (IRE)**, ch f Kyllachy—
Rhythm And Rhyme (IRE) **Owenstown Stud & Mr M. P. N. Tregoning**
37 **TASHEERA**, b f New Approach (IRE)—Thakafaat (IRE) **Hamdan Bin Rashid Al Maktoum**
38 **WATHEER**, ch g Leroidesanimaux (BRZ)—Sunset Shore **Hamdan Bin Rashid Al Maktoum**

TWO-YEAR-OLDS

39 **ALAMINTA**, b f 29/3 Archipenko (USA)—Alamamia (Hernando (FR)) **Miss K. Rausing**
40 B f 15/3 Champs Elysees—Craighall (Dubawi (IRE)) (18000)
41 **DENIS THE DIVA**, b c 7/2 Aussie Rules (USA)—Lunarian (Bahamian Bounty) **FTP Equine Holdings Ltd**
42 **DIVA BELLA**, ch f 8/2 Helmet (AUS)—Dame Helen (Royal Applause) (18000) **FTP Equine Holdings Ltd**
43 B c 22/2 Raven's Pass (USA)—Namely (IRE) (Rock of Gibraltar (IRE)) (24420)
44 B f 17/2 Alhebayeb (IRE)—Red Blossom (Green Desert (USA)) (8140) **Hamdan Bin Rashid Al Maktoum**
45 B c 26/4 Showcasing—Roodeye (Inchinor) (110000) **Hamdan Bin Rashid Al Maktoum**
46 **SADLERS BEACH (IRE)**, b f 19/2 Pour Moi (IRE)—Dusty Boots (IRE) (Footstepsinthesand) (10476) **Roy Kingston**
47 B br f 10/4 Cape Cross (IRE)—Salhooda (IRE) (Nayef (USA)) **Hamdan Bin Rashid Al Maktoum**
48 B c 31/3 Cape Cross (IRE)—Sharedah (IRE) (Pivotal) **Hamdan Bin Rashid Al Maktoum**
49 B f 30/3 Dandy Man (IRE)—Silvertine (IRE) (Alzao (USA)) (15238)
50 B c 28/1 Dark Angel (IRE)—Spirit of Cuba (IRE) (Invincible Spirit (IRE)) (28489) **Owenstown Stud**
51 B f 3/5 Mukhadram—Sulaalah (IRE) (Darshaan) **Hamdan Bin Rashid Al Maktoum**
52 B c 14/4 Sea The Moon (GER)—Summer Night (Nashwan (USA)) (35000)
53 **SUMMER SKIES**, b f 15/1 Leroidesanimaux (BRZ)—Sunset Shore (Oasis Dream) **Miss K. Rausing**
54 B c 21/1 Invincible Spirit (IRE)—Swiss Kiss (Dansili) (60000) **R. C. C. Villers**

Other Owners: Mr Robin Blunt, Mrs Ann Boanas, Mr Nicholas Brown, Mr J. Cavanagh, Mr R. F. U. Gaskell, Sir Thomas Pilkington, Mr John Raw, Mrs H. Raw, Mrs Sonia Rogers, Lady Tennant, Mr M. P. N. Tregoning, Mr J. Tuthill, Mr R. C. C. Villers, Mr J. R. Wallis.

Assistant Trainer: Angie Kennedy

Jockey (flat): Martin Dwyer. **Apprentice:** Tyler Saunders. **Amateur:** Mr George Tregoning.

---

556 MR GRANT TUER, Northallerton
Postal: **Home Farm, Great Smeaton, Northallerton, North Yorkshire, DL6 2EP**
Contacts: **PHONE (01609) 881094 FAX (01609) 881094 MOBILE (07879) 698869**
E-MAIL grant_tuer@btinternet.com

1 **BULAS BELLE**, 8, b m Rob Roy (USA)—Bula Rose (IRE) **E. Tuer**
2 **CANFORD BELLE**, 5, b m Canford Cliffs (IRE)—Ballyea (IRE) **ARC Racing Yorkshire X**
3 **ESCAPE CLAUSE (IRE)**, 4, b g Lawman (FR)—Discophilia **Mr G. F. Tuer**
4 **ETIKAAL**, 4, ch g Sepoy (AUS)—Hezmah **Mr G. F. Tuer**
5 **FYRECRACKER (IRE)**, 7, ch g Kheleyf (USA)—Spirit of Hope (IRE) **Allerton Racing**
6 **IBERICA ROAD (USA)**, 5, b br g Quality Road (USA)—Field of Clover (CAN) **Mr G. F. Tuer**
7 **MYWAYISTHEONLYWAY (IRE)**, 5, b g Tamayuz—Soul Custody (CAN) **ARC Racing Yorkshire X**
8 **PALENVILLE (IRE)**, 5, ch m Rip Van Winkle (IRE)—Faithful Duchess (IRE) **ARC Racing Yorkshire X**
9 **THE BLUE BANANA (IRE)**, 9, b g Red Clubs (IRE)—Rinneen (IRE) **ARC Racing Yorkshire X**

THREE-YEAR-OLDS

10 **CHAMPARISI**, b f Champs Elysees—Parisi **Allerton Racing & G Tuer**
11 **LADY ISLE**, b f Monsieur Bond (IRE)—Ailsa Craig (IRE) **Mr G. F. Tuer**

MR GRANT TUER - Continued

TWO-YEAR-OLDS

12 Ch c 14/4 Monsieur Bond (IRE)—Ailsa Craig (IRE) (Chevalier (IRE)) **Mr G. F. Tuer**
13 B f 2/4 Coach House (IRE)—Bookiesindexdonter (Piccolo) (3500)
14 B f 24/4 Helmet (AUS)—Cry Pearl (USA) (Street Cry (IRE)) (4000) **Mr G. F. Tuer**
15 Ch c 20/4 Monsieur Bond (IRE)—Easy Terms (Trade Fair) (3333) **Mr E. Tuer**
16 B f 28/1 Poet's Voice—Juncea (Elnadim (USA)) (8000) **Moment Of Madness**
17 B c 7/2 Epaulette (AUS)—Point Perfect (Dansili) (20000) **Hornby Hornets**
18 B f 22/3 Garswood—Rise (Polar Falcon (USA)) (4952)

Other Owners: Mr J. Black, Mr A. G. Leggott, Mr M. Marsh, Mrs V. Thompson.

---

557 **MR JOSEPH TUITE, Lambourn**
Postal: **Felstead Stables, Folly Road, Lambourn, Hungerford, Berkshire, RG17 8QE**
Contacts: **MOBILE (07769) 977351**
E-MAIL **joe.tuite@tuiteracing.com** WEBSITE **www.tuiteracing.co.uk**

1 CINCUENTA PASOS (IRE), 7, ch g Footstepsinthesand—Sweet Nicole **Mr M. J. Wellbelove**
2 CONKERING HERO (IRE), 4, ch g Arakan (USA)—Brioney (IRE) **C.R. Lambourne, M. Forbes, D. Losse**
3 FAST DANCER (IRE), 6, b g Fast Company (IRE)—Tereed Elhawa **Alan & Christine Bright**
4 FORTUNE AND GLORY (USA), 5, b g War Front (USA)—Spain (USA) **Mr R. J. Gurr**
5 GRECIAN DIVINE (IRE), 4, b f Kodiac—Grecian Glory (IRE) **Just Back The Boreen**
6 INTERMODAL, 4, b g Rail Link—Rule of Nature **Mr R. J. Gurr**
7 LADY MOREL (IRE), 4, b f Arcano (USA)—Heart's Desire (IRE) **Felstead Court Flyers**
8 LAST WORD, 4, b f Bated Breath—Intermission (IRE) **Miss K. J. Keir**
9 MACHINE LEARNER, 5, b g Sir Percy—My First Romance **Mr M. F. Geoghegan**
10 REBEL WOODS (FR), 5, br g Cockney Rebel (IRE)—In The Woods **Mr A. R. Pittman**
11 SHABBAH (IRE), 5, br g Sea The Stars (IRE)—Alizaya (IRE) **Mr M. F. Geoghegan**
12 SURREY HOPE (USA), 4, b c Lemon Drop Kid (USA)—She Be Classy (USA) **Surrey Racing (SH)**
13 TOPOLOGY, 5, br g Passing Glance—Bold Byzantium **The Singleton Park Partnership 2**
14 WHO TOLD JO JO (IRE), 4, b g Bushranger (IRE)—Shenkara (IRE) **Mr J. M. Tuite**
15 ZIPEDEEDODAH (IRE), 6, gr g Zebedee—Beverley Macca **D.M Synergy & Mark Wellbelove**

THREE-YEAR-OLDS

16 AVON GREEN, b f Avonbridge—Greenery (IRE) **I & K Prince**
17 DREAM MALFUNCTION (IRE), ch f Mastercraftsman (IRE)—Limetree Lady **Mr T. Geary**
18 DREAMDANCER (IRE), b f Rip Van Winkle (IRE)—Silver Samba **BA Racing & R G Levin**
19 FELSTEAD KNIGHT (IRE), b g Tough As Nails (IRE)—Fine Day **Felstead Court Flyers II**
20 GOZO GIRL, b f Nayef (USA)—Trust The Wind **Penny/Adrian Burton, Bob/Angela Lampard**
21 KIMIFIVE (IRE), ch c Born To Sea (IRE)—Appletreemagic (IRE) **Mr R. J. Gurr**
22 LOOKS A MILLION, b f Kyllachy—Look Busy (IRE) **P. J. Gleeson**
23 OUR KARISMA (IRE), gr f Zebedee—Ruacana Falls (USA) **Alfred Walls & Barry Strickland**
24 Ch g Equiano (FR)—Oystermouth **Mrs C. Martin**
25 PENWOOD (FR), b f Orpen (USA)—In The Woods **Mr A. R. Pittman**
26 RIVENDICATO, b f Showcasing—Carsulae (IRE) **Mrs Olivia Hoare & Mrs Paola Hewins**
27 SURREY BLAZE (IRE), b g Thewayyouare (USA)—Catadalya (IRE) **Surrey Racing Limited**

Other Owners: BA Racing, Mr D. Barrett, Mrs D. M. Barrett, Mr P. Blaydon, Mr A. D. Bright, Mrs C. Bright, Mrs P. C. Burton, Mr M. Chesney, M. I. Forbes, Mr S. Grubb, Mr C. R. Hadingham, Mr S. J. Harding, Mrs P. Hewins, Mrs O. Hoare, Mr C. R. Lambourne, Mr R. J. Lampard, Mr R. G. Levin, Mr D. R. Losse, Mrs L. J. Losse, Mr D. Marsh, Mr C. McGarrity, Mrs E. McGarrity, Mr I. D. Prince, Mrs K. Prince, Mr B. Strickland, A. F. Walls.

---

558 **MR BILL TURNER, Sherborne**
Postal: **Sigwells Farm, Sigwells, Corton Denham, Sherborne, Dorset, DT9 4LN**
Contacts: **PHONE (01963) 220523 FAX (01963) 220046 MOBILE (07932) 100173**
E-MAIL **billturnerracing@gmail.com**

1 CASSIS DE REINE, 4, ch f Quatre Saisons—Reine de Violette **Mrs P. A. Turner**
2 CRUCIAL MOMENT, 4, b g Pivotal—Moonglow **E. A. Brook**
3 IL SICARIO (IRE), 4, b g Zebedee—Starring (FR) **Mrs H. A. Heal**
4 MARETTIMO (IRE), 4, b g Harbour Watch (IRE)—Renowned (IRE) **R. A. Bracken**
5 MIDNIGHT CALAMITY, 4, ch f Malinas (GER)—Miss Calamity **The Floral Farmers**
6 REBEL HEART, 4, b f Kyllachy—Just Like A Woman **Mascalls Stud**

MR BILL TURNER - Continued

  7 **RIGHTEOUS RIVER**, 4, b f Bahri (USA)—Marie Louise **Mrs P. A. Turner**
  8 **SPRINGCOMBE JOE**, 6, b g Kayf Tara—Dissolve **D. Coombes**
  9 **TAKE THIS WALTZ**, 4, b f Royal Applause—Constant Craving **Mascalls Stud**

THREE-YEAR-OLDS

10 **BORN AT MIDNIGHT**, b g Midnight Legend—Wavet **Mr B. Goldsmith**
11 **LITTLE BOY BLUE**, gr g Hellvelyn—Dusty Dazzler (IRE) **Mrs P. A. Turner**

TWO-YEAR-OLDS

12 Ch f 30/4 Coach House (IRE)—Frontline In Focus (IRE) (Daggers Drawn (USA)) (1142) **E. A. Brook**
13 **HELLOVASINGER**, b g 10/4 Hellvelyn—Sing Alana Sing (Singspiel (IRE)) **Mr F. Horsington**
14 B c 24/3 Swiss Spirit—High Class Girl (Royal Applause) (5000) **Mr E. A. Brook**
15 **JOHN BETJEMAN**, b c 8/2 Poet's Voice—A Great Beauty (Acclamation) (4285) **Mr Ronald Rivers**
16 B f 29/3 Havana Gold—Laminka (Intikhab (USA)) (3000) **Mrs P. A. Turner**
17 Ch f 18/2 Zebedee—Two Smart (IRE) (Cape Cross (IRE)) (2380) **Mr George Woollatt**
18 Ch c 4/5 Haafhd—Valley of The Moon (Monashee Mountain (USA)) (4285) **E. A. Brook**
19 B g 12/6 Midnight Legend—Wavet (Pursuit of Love) **Mr Barry Goldsmith**
20 **WHAT A DAZZLER**, ch f 21/3 Coach House (IRE)—Dusty Dazzler (IRE) (Titus Livius (FR)) **Tracy Turner**

Other Owners: Mr Barry Hearn, Mrs Susan Hearn.

---

559   **MRS KAREN TUTTY, Northallerton**
Postal: Trenholme House Farm, Osmotherley, Northallerton, North Yorkshire, DL6 3QA
Contacts: **PHONE** (01609) 883624 **FAX** 01609 883624 **MOBILE** (07967) 837406
E-MAIL karentutty@btinternet.com **WEBSITE** www.karentuttyracing.co.uk

  1 **BROUGHTONS FANCY**, 5, b m Pastoral Pursuits—Lifetime Romance (IRE) **Thoroughbred Homes Ltd**
  2 **COOL STRUTTER (IRE)**, 6, b g Kodiac—Cassava (IRE) **Mrs Mary Winetroube & Thoroughbred Homes**
  3 **DASHEEN**, 5, b g Bahamian Bounty—Caribbean Dancer (USA) **Mr H. C. Hart**
  4 **GAELIC WIZARD (IRE)**, 10, b g Fasliyev (USA)—Fife (IRE) **Thoroughbred Homes Ltd**
  5 **JORVIK PRINCE**, 4, br g Kheleyf (USA)—Wotatomboy **Thoroughbred Homes Ltd**
  6 **NOVABRIDGE**, 10, ch g Avonbridge—Petrovna (IRE) **Thoroughbred Homes Ltd**
  7 **TALENT SCOUT (IRE)**, 12, b g Exceed And Excel (AUS)—Taalluf (USA) **Thoroughbred Homes Ltd**
  8 **THORNABY NASH**, 7, br g Kheleyf (USA)—Mistress Twister **Mr Dave Scott**
  9 **WILLSY**, 5, b g Sakhee's Secret—Blakeshall Rose **Max Europe Limited**

THREE-YEAR-OLDS

10 **IDEAL CANDY (IRE)**, b f Canford Cliffs (IRE)—Forever More (IRE) **Mr D. A. Robinson**
11 **IDEAL SPIRIT**, b f Swiss Spirit—Silver Sail **Mr D. A. Robinson**

TWO-YEAR-OLDS

12 B f 19/4 Dawn Approach (IRE)—Early Morning Rain (IRE) (Rock of Gibraltar (IRE)) (5000) **Mr D. A. Robinson**

Other Owners: Mrs M. T. Winetroube.

Apprentice: Gemma Tutty.

---

560   **MR NIGEL TWISTON-DAVIES, Cheltenham**
Postal: T/a Grange Hill Farm Limited, Grange Hill Farm, Naunton, Cheltenham,
Gloucestershire, GL54 3AY
Contacts: **PHONE** (01451) 850278 **MOBILE** (07836) 664440
E-MAIL nigel@nigeltwistondavies.co.uk **WEBSITE** www.nigeltwistondavies.co.uk

  1 **ALLTHEGEAR NO IDEA (IRE)**, 11, b g Sayarshan (FR)—All The Gear (IRE) **The Yes No Wait Sorries**
  2 **ANGELS ANTICS**, 5, b m Schiaparelli (GER)—Safari Run (IRE) **Walters Plant Hire & Spiers & Hartwell**
  3 **ANOTHER FRONTIER (IRE)**, 7, b g Darsi (FR)—Scent With Love (IRE) **Jump For Fun Racing**
  4 **ARCTIC GOLD (IRE)**, 7, b g Gold Well—Arctic Warrior (IRE) **Geoffrey & Donna Keeys**
  5 **ARTHUR MC BRIDE (IRE)**, 9, b br g Royal Anthem (USA)—Lucky Diverse (IRE) **John Gaughan & Rob Rexton**
  6 **ARTHUR'S GIFT (IRE)**, 7, b g Presenting—Uncertain Affair (IRE) **Arthur's Gift Partnership**
  7 **ASTRACAD (FR)**, 12, br g Cadoudal (FR)—Astre Eria (FR) **Mr M. Barlow**
  8 **ATLANTIC GREY (IRE)**, 5, gr g Acambaro (GER)—Clooney Eile (IRE) **Milltown Racing**

MR NIGEL TWISTON-DAVIES - Continued

9 BABY TED, 5, ch g Pasternak—Dd's Glenalla (IRE) **Mr N. A. Twiston-Davies**
10 BALLYANDREW (IRE), 7, b g Westerner—Royale Acadou (FR) **Mr N. A. Twiston-Davies**
11 BALLYANDY, 7, b g Kayf Tara—Megalex **Options O Syndicate**
12 BALLYARTHUR (IRE), 8, b g Kayf Tara—Ariels Serenade (IRE) **Graham & Alison Jelley**
13 BALLYBOLLEY (IRE), 9, b g Kayf Tara—Gales Hill (IRE) **Mr Simon Munir & Mr Isaac Souede**
14 BALLYCROSS, 7, b g King's Theatre (IRE)—Ninna Nanna (FR) **The Autism Rockers**
15 BALLYHILL (FR), 7, b br g Al Namix (FR)—Laly Light (FR) **S Such & CG Paletta**
16 BALLYKAN, 8, b g Presenting—La Marianne **Mr Simon Munir & Mr Isaac Souede**
17 BALLYMALIN (IRE), 8, b g Presenting—Mururrundi (IRE) **Mills & Mason Partnership**
18 BALLYMOY (IRE), 8, b g Flemensfirth (USA)—John's Eliza (IRE) **Mr Simon Munir & Mr Isaac Souede**
19 BALLYOPTIC (IRE), 8, b g Old Vic—Lambourne Lace (IRE) **Mills & Mason Partnership**
20 BALLYRATH (IRE), 8, b g Flemensfirth (USA)—Rose Wee (IRE) **The Stirling Partnership**
21 BELMOUNT (IRE), 9, b g Westerner—Artist's Jewel **Mrs S. Jones**
22 BENBENS (IRE), 13, ch g Beneficial—Millicent Bridge (IRE) **S Such & CG Paletta**
23 BENDOMINGO (IRE), 7, b g Beneficial—Bobbies Storm (IRE) **DG Partners**
24 BETTER DAYS (IRE), 7, gr g Daylami (IRE)—Miss Edgehill (IRE) **Mrs L. M. Berryman**
25 BIGBADJOHN (IRE), 9, br g Vinnie Roe (IRE)—Celtic Serenade (IRE) **Mr N. D. Morris**
26 BISHOPSWOOD FLYER (IRE), 4, br g Arcadio (GER)—Catch The Class (IRE) **Mr N. A. Twiston-Davies**
27 BLAKLION, 9, b g Kayf Tara—Franciscaine (FR) **S Such & CG Paletta**
28 BLUE FLIGHT (FR), 5, b g Blue Bresil (FR)—Lover Flight (FR) **Mr N. A. Twiston-Davies**
29 BOMBER'S MOON, 7, b g Erhaab (USA)—Flaviola (IRE) **Charlie Walker & Jim Old**
30 BRING BACK CHARLIE, 8, b g Green Card (USA)—Nafertiti (IRE) **Mr D. D. Genner**
31 BRISTOL DE MAI (FR), 7, gr g Saddler Maker (IRE)—La Bole Night (FR) **Mr Simon Munir & Mr Isaac Souede**
32 BROWNVILLE, 9, b g Kayf Tara—Cool Spice **Mrs F. E. Griffin**
33 CALETT MAD (FR), 6, b br g Axxos (GER)—Omelia (FR) **Mr Simon Munir & Mr Isaac Souede**
34 COGRY, 9, b g King's Theatre (IRE)—Wyldello **Graham & Alison Jelley**
35 COLIN'S BROTHER, 8, b g Overbury (IRE)—Dd's Glenalla (IRE) **Mrs C. S. C. Beresford-Wylie**
36 CORZEAM (IRE), 6, gr g Early March—Night Fever (FR) **The Four Musketeers**
37 COSTANTE VIA (IRE), 7, b m Milan—Spirit Rock (IRE) **Miss K. J. Holland**
38 COUNT GUIDO DEIRO (IRE), 11, b g Accordion—Ivy Lane (IRE) **R. Bevis**
39 COUNT MERIBEL, 6, ch g Three Valleys (USA)—Bakhtawar (IRE) **C. C. Walker**
40 CRIEVEHILL (IRE), 6, b g Arcadio (GER)—Ma Douce (IRE) **Highclere T'Bred Racing- Crievehill**
41 CYDERCOURT (IRE), 5, b g Court Cave (IRE)—Lavender Track (IRE) **Mr N. A. Twiston-Davies**
42 DAWN MISSILE, 6, b g Nayef (USA)—Ommadawn (IRE) **Options O Syndicate**
43 DOUBLE COURT (IRE), 7, b g Court Cave (IRE)—Miss Top (IRE) **Synergy Racing**
44 DOUBLE ROSS (IRE), 12, ch g Double Eclipse (IRE)—Kinross **Options O Syndicate**
45 EARLOFTHECOTSWOLDS (FR), 4, bl g Axxos (GER)—Sissi Land (FR) **Mr N. A. Twiston-Davies**
46 EL TERREMOTO (FR), 6, b g Spirit One (FR)—By Decree (FR) **Mr Simon Munir & Mr Isaac Souede**
47 EQUUS MILLAR (IRE), 5, b g Masterofthehorse (IRE)—Lets Get Busy (IRE) **James & Jean Potter**
48 EVERYBODY'S TALKIN (IRE), 5, ch g Robin des Champs (FR)—
         Miss Otis Regrets (IRE) **Mr Simon Munir & Mr Isaac Souede**
49 FLORRIE BOY (IRE), 7, b g Milan—Second Best (IRE) **Options O Syndicate**
50 FLYING ANGEL (IRE), 7, b g Arcadio (GER)—Gypsy Kelly (IRE) **Mr R. J. Rexton**
51 FOXTAIL HILL (IRE), 9, b g Dr Massini (IRE)—Flynn's Girl (IRE) **Options O Syndicate**
52 FRONTIER VIC, 11, b g Old Vic—Right On Target (IRE) **Mr N. A. Twiston-Davies**
53 GAUCHO, 5, b g Shirocco (GER)—Gulshan **Mrs J. K. Powell**
54 GENERAL MALARKEY (IRE), 6, b g Scorpion (IRE)—Andreas Benefit (IRE) **Baker, Dodd, Cooke & Heler**
55 GINGE DE SOPHIA (IRE), 5, b m Presenting—Me Grannys Endoors (IRE) **Mr J. Neild**
56 GOOD BOY BOBBY (IRE), 5, b g Flemensfirth (USA)—Princess Gaia (IRE) **Mr & Mrs Paul & Clare Rooney**
57 GOODBYE DANCER (IRE), 7, b g Dragon Dancer—Maribia Bella (FR) **The Yes No Wait Sorries**
58 GRANARD (IRE), 6, b g Getaway—Yes Darling (IRE) **Mr Simon Munir & Mr Isaac Souede**
59 HILLARY C, 6, b m Kayf Tara—Dd's Glenalla (IRE) **Mr N. A. Twiston-Davies**
60 HORSEGUARDSPARADE, 7, b g Montjeu (IRE)—Honorlina (FR) **Mr N. A. Twiston-Davies**
61 IMPERIAL NEMESIS (IRE), 5, b g Stowaway—Liss Alainn (IRE) **Imperial Racing Partnership 2016**
62 JABULANI (FR), 5, gr g Martaline—Incorrigible (FR) **Walters Plant Hire Ltd**
63 JAMESON, 6, br g Midnight Legend—Shatabdi (IRE) **Walters Plant Hire Ltd**
64 KALARIYA (IRE), 6, b m Kalanisi (IRE)—Katariya (IRE) **R. Bevis**
65 KERISPER (FR), 8, b g Robin des Champs (FR)—Tina Rederie (FR) **The Autism Rockers**
66 KINGOFTHECOTSWOLDS (IRE), 4, b g Arcadio (GER)—Damoiselle **Mr N. A. Twiston-Davies**
67 KINGSPLACE (IRE), 6, b g Ask—Winsome Breeze (IRE) **Mr N. A. Twiston-Davies**
68 LAGAVARA (IRE), 6, b m Exit To Nowhere (USA)—Knockalyde Rose (IRE) **Mr C. Roberts**
69 5, B m Kayf Tara—Late For Class (IRE) **Mr N. A. Twiston-Davies**
70 LIGHT BREAKS (IRE), 6, b g Dylan Thomas (IRE)—Anywaysmile (IRE) **Mr N. A. Twiston-Davies**
71 LITTLE JON, 10, b g Pasternak—Jowoody **Mr R. N. Frosell**
72 LITTLE POP, 10, b g Pasternak—Flagship Daisy May (IRE) **S Such & CG Paletta**

MR NIGEL TWISTON-DAVIES - Continued

73 **LUCKOFTHEDRAW (FR)**, 5, gr g Martaline—La Perspective (FR) **Walters Plant Hire Ltd**
74 **MARGARET'S ROSE (IRE)**, 8, b m Millenary—Alannah Rose (IRE) **Miss K. J. Holland**
75 **MIDNIGHT TROUBLE**, 6, b g Midnight Legend—Friendly Request **Mrs J. Organ**
76 **MILANSTORM (IRE)**, 5, b g Milan—Deise Rose (IRE) **Mr N. A. Twiston-Davies**
77 **MILLICENT SILVER**, 9, gr m Overbury (IRE)—Common Girl (IRE) **Mr J. Goodman**
78 **MR ANTOLINI (IRE)**, 8, b g Catcher In The Rye (IRE)—Victory Run (IRE) **Alan & Sally Coney**
79 **MUCKLE ROE (IRE)**, 9, b g Westerner—Island Crest **Mrs V. J. Lane**
80 **NATTER JACK CROAK (IRE)**, 6, b g Gold Well—Native Euro (IRE) **Mr N. D. Morris**
81 **NOBODYDOESITBETTER**, 6, b g Apple Tree (FR)—Elfailwen **Mr N. A. Twiston-Davies**
82 **OH MICHELLE**, 7, br m Kayf Tara—Grenfell (IRE) **The True Acre Partnership**
83 **ONE FOR ROSIE**, 5, gr g Getaway (GER)—Whisky Rose (IRE) **Mr & Mrs Paul & Clare Rooney**
84 **ONE FORTY SEVEN (IRE)**, 6, b g Beneficial—Still Bubbly (IRE) **Graham & Alison Jelley**
85 **PINK GIN**, 10, ch g Alflora (IRE)—Miss Mailmit **Mrs J Fowler & Mr C Jenkins**
86 **QUIMBA (SPA)**, 4, b f Dink (FR)—Die Beste (SPA) **Mr N. A. Twiston-Davies**
87 **RAVENSDALE (IRE)**, 6, ch g Flemensfirth (USA)—Thunder Belle (IRE) **Mr Simon Munir & Mr Isaac Souede**
88 **RED RIVERMAN**, 10, b g Haafhd—Mocca (IRE) **Mr N. A. Twiston-Davies**
89 **RIZZARDO**, 6, gr g Tikkanen (USA)—Last Spruce (USA) **Mr N. A. Twiston-Davies**
90 **ROBINSHILL (IRE)**, 7, ch g Robin des Champs (FR)—I Remember It Well (IRE) **Mr R. J. Rexton**
91 **ROCCO (IRE)**, 5, b g Shantou (USA)—Navaro (IRE) **Grech & Parkin**
92 **SARTENE'S SON (FR)**, 5, ch g Linda's Lad—Sartene (FR) **Walters Plant Hire Ltd**
93 **SAVER**, 9, b g Darnay—Lifeguard (IRE) **Mr N. A. Twiston-Davies**
94 **SCOTCHTOWN (IRE)**, 6, ch g Beneficial—Always Present (IRE) **Valda Burke & Bryan Burrough**
95 **SIR GEORGE SOMERS (USA)**, 5, ch g Cape Blanco (IRE)—Sense of Class (USA) **Mr N. A. Twiston-Davies**
96 **SNOBBERY (IRE)**, 5, b g Duke of Marmalade (IRE)—Boast **Options O Syndicate**
97 **SOUTHERLY BUSTER**, 6, b g Shirocco (GER)—Appleby **Mrs J Fowler & Mr A Britten**
98 **SOUTHPORT**, 6, b g Robin des Pres (FR)—First Katoune (FR) **Mr I. F. Guest**
99 **SPLASH OF GINGE**, 10, b g Oscar (IRE)—Land of Honour **Mr J. Neild**
100 **SUMMIT LIKE HERBIE**, 6, ch g Sulamani (IRE)—Colline de Fleurs **Friends Of Herbie**
101 **SUPAKALANISTIC (IRE)**, 5, b g Kalanisi (IRE)—Keys Hope (IRE) **Jump For Fun Racing**
102 **TARA MUCK**, 11, b m Kayf Tara—Madam Muck **Mr N. A. Twiston-Davies**
103 **TEMPLEHILLS (IRE)**, 7, b br g Kalanisi (IRE)—Sissinghurst Storm (IRE) **Oi Digital Limited**
104 **TEMPLEPOINT**, 7, b g Fair Mix (IRE)—Flamebird (IRE) **Mr N. A. Twiston-Davies**
105 **TEMPLEROSS (IRE)**, 7, b g Presenting—Dame O'neill (IRE) **Mr A. G. Bloom**
106 **THE HOLLOW GINGE (IRE)**, 5, b g Oscar (IRE)—Some Gem (IRE) **The Ginge Army**
107 **THE NEW ONE (IRE)**, 10, b g King's Theatre (IRE)—Thuringe (FR) **S Such & CG Paletta**
108 **THUNDER SHEIK (IRE)**, 10, b g Green Tune (USA)—Realy Queen (USA) **Mr R. J. Rexton**
109 **TINTERN THEATRE (IRE)**, 8, b g King's Theatre (IRE)—Rith Ar Aghaidh (IRE) **Jimmy & Susie Wenman**
110 **TOPOFTHECOTSWOLDS (IRE)**, 4, b g Arcadio (GER)—Bambootcha (IRE) **Mr N. A. Twiston-Davies**
111 **TURNING GOLD**, 4, ch g Pivotal—Illusion **Turning Gold**
112 **TWIST ON GINGE (IRE)**, 6, b g Craigsteel—Miss Top (IRE) **J D Neild, A Bridges & N Twiston-Davies**
113 **UNBLINKING**, 5, b g Cacique (IRE)—Deliberate **R. Bevis**
114 **VERYGOODVERYGOOD (FR)**, 7, b g Yeats (IRE)—Rose d'or (IRE) **Spiers & Hartwell and N A Twiston-Davies**
115 **WEST TORR (IRE)**, 7, br g Scorpion (IRE)—Native Craft (IRE) **Mr N. A. Twiston-Davies**
116 **WHISKEY MOON**, 6, b g Erhaab (USA)—Flaviola (IRE) **J. A. B. Old**
117 **WHOLESTONE (IRE)**, 7, br g Craigsteel—Last Theatre (IRE) **Mr Simon Munir & Mr Isaac Souede**
118 **WICKED WILLY (IRE)**, 7, br g Arcadio (GER)—How Provincial (IRE) **Mr C. Roberts**
119 **WOOD YER (IRE)**, 12, ch g Anshan—Glenasheen (IRE) **Miss K. J. Holland**
120 **WOODFORT**, 6, gr g Dalakhani (IRE)—Akdara (IRE) **Million in Mind Partnership**
121 **YANMARE (IRE)**, 8, b g Soapy Danger—Bell Walks Caroll (IRE) **Bryan & Philippa Burrough**

Other Owners: Mr J. B. Baker, Mr A. P. Bridges, Mr A. J. Britten, A. R. Bromley, Mrs V. F. Burke, Mrs P. J. Burrough, B. R. H. Burrough, C. S. J. Coley, Mr A. R. Coney, Mrs S. Coney, Mr P. G. Cooke, Mr C. G. Dando, Mr A. N. Dixon, Mr P. A. Docker, Mr G. T. G. Dodd, Mr H. G. Doubtfire, Mr J. Flannery, Mrs J. A. Fowler, Mr J. Gaughan, G. F. Goode, Mr C. M. Grech, Mr A. B. Greenfield, Mr J. H. Gumbley, Mr T. M. Hailstone, Mr M. J. Heler, Mr P. R. Henderson, Highclere Nominated Partner Limited, Highclere Thoroughbred Racing Ltd, D. M. Hussey, G. S. Jelley, Mrs A. D. Jelley, Mr C. J. Jenkins, Mr J. Jessemey, G. F. Keeys, Mrs C. M. Keeys, Mr H. J. Kelly, Mr D. M. Mason, Miss S. McDonnell, Mrs L. Merson, W. R. Mills, F. J. Mills, Mr W. D. C. Minton, S. E. Munir, Mrs D. C. Nicholson, Mr T. H. Ounsley, Mr C. G. Paletta, Mr S. J. Parkin, Mr N. L. Payne, J. E. Potter, Mrs M. J. Potter, Mr P. Preston, Mr I. Robinson, Mr P. A. Rooney, Mrs C. Rooney, Mr S. Shah, Mr H. B. Shouler, Mr I. Souede, Spiers & Hartwell Ltd, Mr M. A. Stratford, Mrs S. E. Such, Miss M. L. Taylor, J. Wenman, Mrs S. Wenman, Mr S. G. Wignall.

Jockey (NH): Sam Twiston-Davies. **Conditional:** Jamie Bargary, Ryan Hatch.

561 MR JAMES UNETT, Wolverhampton
Postal: **1 Dunstall Mews, Gorsebrook Road, Wolverhampton, West Midlands, WV6 0PE**
Contacts: **PHONE** (01691) 610001 **FAX** (01691) 610001 **MOBILE** (07887) 534753
E-MAIL jamesunett1327@yahoo.co.uk **WEBSITE** www.jamesunettracing.com

1 **ALMUTAMARRED (USA)**, 6, ch g Street Cry (IRE)—Sortita (GER) **Mr J. R. Salter**
2 **CLARATY**, 8, b m Firebreak—Claradotnet **Mr G. D. Kendrick**
3 **EBQAA (IRE)**, 4, b f Cape Cross (IRE)—Estedaama (IRE) **J. W. Unett**
4 **HEAT STORM (IRE)**, 7, b g Lawman (FR)—Coconut Show **J. W. Unett**
5 **KING OSWALD (USA)**, 5, b g Street Cry (IRE)—Northern Melody (IRE) **M. Watkinson & Mr P. Steadman**
6 **MARCRET (ITY)**, 11, b g Martino Alonso (IRE)—Love Secret (USA) **Northern Line Racing Ltd**
7 **NONEEDTOTELLME (IRE)**, 5, gr m Fast Company (IRE)—Gemma's Delight (IRE) **Mr M. B. Hall**
8 **SMOKETHATTHUNDERS (IRE)**, 8, gr g Elusive City (USA)—Zinstar (IRE) **Mrs S. A. Downes**

THREE-YEAR-OLDS

9 **CITTA D'ORO**, b g Cityscape—Corsa All Oro (USA) **P. S. Burke**
10 **STORM DORIS (IRE)**, br f Lilbourne Lad (IRE)—Big Sylv (IRE) **Mr M. Watkinson**

Other Owners: Mr D. P. Steadman.

Assistant Trainer: Miss C. H. Jones

562 MR MARK USHER, Lambourn
Postal: **Rowdown House Stables, Upper Lambourn, Hungerford, Berkshire, RG17 8QP**
Contacts: **PHONE** (01488) 72598 (01488) 73630 **MOBILE** (07831) 873531
E-MAIL markusher.racing@btconnect.com **WEBSITE** www.markusherracing.co.uk

1 **ALL ABOUT THE PACE**, 4, ch f Sixties Icon—Phoebe Woodstock (IRE) **Ushers Court**
2 **ARLECCHINO'S LEAP**, 6, br g Kheleyf (USA)—Donna Giovanna **Mr K. Senior**
3 **BAY FORTUNA**, 9, b g Old Vic—East Rose **Ridgeway Partnership**
4 **BAYSTON HILL**, 4, br g Big Bad Bob (IRE)—Jessica Ennis (USA) **High Five Racing and Partners**
5 **BIRD FOR LIFE**, 4, b f Delegator—Birdolini **The Mark Usher Racing Club**
6 **BLACK TRUFFLE (FR)**, 8, b g Kyllachy—Some Diva **The Mark Usher Racing Club**
7 **BORN TO PLEASE**, 4, b f Stimulation (IRE)—Heart Felt **The Mark Usher Racing Club**
8 **MAKHFAR (IRE)**, 7, b g Bushranger (IRE)—Let Me Shine (USA) **Roemex Ltd**
9 **MARSHALL AID (IRE)**, 5, b g Lawman (FR)—Dievotchkina (IRE) **Mr B. C. Rogan**
10 **METTE**, 5, b m Virtual—Regal Gallery (IRE) **Mrs B. Sumner**
11 **MEZMAAR**, 9, b g Teofilo (IRE)—Bay Tree (IRE) **Roemex Ltd**
12 **MIRACLE OF MEDINAH**, 7, ch g Milk It Mick—Smart Ass (IRE) **High Jinks**
13 **MISTRY**, 5, b m Mullionmileanhour (IRE)—Smart Ass (IRE) **Ushers Court**
14 **MISU PETE**, 6, b g Misu Bond (IRE)—Smart Ass (IRE) **The Mark Usher Racing Club**
15 **SHAMONIX (IRE)**, 4, b f Elusive Pimpernel (USA)—Shamora (FR) **Mrs J. F. Pellett**
16 **SHUFOOG**, 5, b m Mawatheeq (USA)—Hamloola **Champagne And Shambles**
17 **THREEDIAMONDRINGS**, 5, ch g Geordieland (FR)—Five Gold Rings (IRE) **Miss L. A. Harbord**

THREE-YEAR-OLDS

18 **ARLECCHINO'S ARC (IRE)**, ch g Arcano (IRE)—Sir Cecil's Girl (IRE) **Mr K. Senior**
19 **BULLSEYE BULLET**, ch g Kheleyf (USA)—Satin Doll **Mr Clark Fortune & Mrs A D Bourne**
20 **DREAMBOAT ANNIE**, b f Piccolo—Bold Rose **Ushers Court**
21 **LITTLE AUB**, b g Milk It Mick—Makindi **Ushers Court**
22 **POINT IN TIME (IRE)**, b f Champs Elysees—Creme Anglaise **GAF Racing**
23 **Q TWENTY BOY (IRE)**, ch g Dandy Man (IRE)—Judies Child (IRE) **Saxon House Racing**
24 **RAINBOW JAZZ (IRE)**, b g Red Jazz (USA)—Let's Pretend **Goodracing Partnership**
25 **ROCUS (IRE)**, br g Rock of Gibraltar (IRE)—Mythologie (FR) **Ushers Court**
26 **ROODEPARIS**, ch g Champs Elysees—Roodeye **GAF Racing**
27 **TIN FANDANGO**, b g Steele Tango (USA)—Littlemoor Lass **Mike Humphreys**

TWO-YEAR-OLDS

28 B f 1/2 Palavicini (USA)—Alpine Mysteries (IRE) (Elusive City (USA)) (813) **Mark Usher**
29 B f 21/2 Havana Gold (IRE)—Audaz (Oasis Dream) (11500) **Saxon House Racing**
30 B f 2/2 Footstepsinthesand—Sveva (IRE) (Danehill Dancer (IRE)) (10500) **The Ridgeway Partnership**

MR MARK USHER - Continued

Other Owners: Mrs A. D. Bourne, Mr R. H. Brookes, Mrs T. J. Channing-Williams, Mr D. P. Duffy, Paul Duffy, David Semmens, Viv Williams, Mr A. C. Fortune, Mr P. Hobbs, Ms D. M. Ray, Mr D. M. Semmens, Mr J. A. Stansfield, Mr M. D. I. Usher.

Assistant Trainer: Michael Usher

Jockey (flat): Liam Keniry.

---

563 MR ROGER VARIAN, Newmarket
Postal: **Carlburg Stables, 49 Bury Road, Newmarket, Suffolk, CB8 7BY**
Contacts: **PHONE** (01638) 661702 **FAX** (01638) 667018
E-MAIL office@varianstable.com **WEBSITE** www.varianstable.com

1 **AJMAN KING (IRE)**, 4, ch c Lope de Vega (IRE)—Third Dimension (FR) **Sheikh Mohammed Obaid Al Maktoum**
2 **APPEARED**, 6, b g Dubawi (IRE)—Appearance **Sheikh Mohammed Obaid Al Maktoum**
3 **ATLETICO (IRE)**, 6, b g Kodiac—Queenofthefairies **Mr Alan Spence**
4 **BARSANTI (IRE)**, 6, b g Champs Elysees—Silver Star **Sheikh Mohammed Obaid Al Maktoum**
5 **BATTERSEA**, 7, b g Galileo (IRE)—Gino's Spirits **H.R.H. Sultan Ahmad Shah**
6 **BOWERMAN**, 4, b c Dutch Art—Jamboretta (IRE) **Mr P. D. Smith**
7 **CALL ME GRUMPY (IRE)**, 4, b g Holy Roman Emperor (IRE)—Miss Rochester (IRE) **Mr W. Y. C. Leung**
8 **CAPE BYRON**, 4, ch c Shamardal (USA)—Reem Three **Sheikh Mohammed Obaid Al Maktoum**
9 **COMMANDER**, 4, b c Frankel—Model Queen (USA) **China Horse Club International Limited**
10 **DAIRA PRINCE (IRE)**, 4, b g Dubawi (IRE)—Chiang Mai (IRE) **Sheikh Mohammed Obaid Al Maktoum**
11 **DEALER'S CHOICE (IRE)**, 4, gr f Exchange Rate (USA)—Micaela's Moon (USA) **Mr J. Shack & Mr G. Barnard**
12 **DEFOE (IRE)**, 4, gr c Dalakhani (IRE)—Dulkashe (IRE) **Sheikh Mohammed Obaid Al Maktoum**
13 **DHAJEEJ (IRE)**, 4, b g Cape Cross (IRE)—Nimboo (USA) **Mr Hamdan Al Maktoum**
14 **DOUBLE UP**, 7, b g Exceed And Excel (AUS)—My Love Thomas (IRE) **Mr A D Spence & Mr M B Spence**
15 **DUBAWI PRINCE**, 4, b c Dubawi (IRE)—Flawly **Sheikh Mohammed Obaid Al Maktoum**
16 **EKHTIYAAR**, 4, b c Bated Breath—Bayja (IRE) **Mr Hamdan Al Maktoum**
17 **EMMAUS (IRE)**, 4, b c Invincible Spirit (IRE)—Prima Luce (IRE) **China Horse Club International Limited**
18 **EQUITATION**, 4, b g Equiano (FR)—Sakhee's Song (IRE) **The Equitation Partnership**
19 **FUJAIRA PRINCE (IRE)**, 4, gr ro g Pivotal—Zam Zoom (IRE) **Sheikh Mohammed Obaid Al Maktoum**
20 **GAKKU**, 4, ch f Pivotal—Gakalina (IRE) **Mr Nurlan Bizakov**
21 **GIBBS HILL (GER)**, 5, gr g Mastercraftsman (IRE)—Gold Charm (GER) **Mr P. D. Smith**
22 **GOLDEN SLAM**, 4, ch g Pastoral Pursuits—Strawberry Leaf
23 **GREAT COURT (IRE)**, 4, gr f Mastercraftsman (IRE)—Neat Shilling (IRE) **Qatar Racing Limited**
24 **JUMIRA PRINCE (IRE)**, 4, ch g Exceed And Excel (AUS)—
Aoife Alainn (IRE) **Sheikh Mohammed Obaid Al Maktoum**
25 **MINDUROWNBUSINESS (IRE)**, 7, b g Cape Cross (IRE)—Whos Mindin Who (IRE) **Mr Alan Spence**
26 **MOUNT LOGAN (IRE)**, 7, ch g New Approach (IRE)—Vistaria (USA) **Sheikh Mohammed Obaid Al Maktoum**
27 **MOUNTAIN ANGEL (IRE)**, 4, b g Dark Angel (IRE)—Fanciful Dancer **Z. A. Galadari**
28 **SCREAMING GEMINI (IRE)**, 4, b g Shamardal (USA)—Littlefeather (IRE) **Mr W. Y. C. Leung**
29 **SHABEEB (USA)**, 5, b g Smart Strike (CAN)—Sortita (GER) **Mr Hamdan Al Maktoum**
30 **SHARGIAH (IRE)**, 5, ch g New Approach (IRE)—Zacheta **S. Ali**
31 **SHARJA BRIDGE**, 4, b c Oasis Dream—Quetena (GER) **Sheikh Mohammed Obaid Al Maktoum**
32 **SHENANIGANS (IRE)**, 4, b f Arcano (IRE)—Ladylishandra (IRE) **Ann Black,M Al Qatami & K M Al Mudhaf**
33 **SPANISH CITY**, 4, ch g Exceed And Excel (AUS)—Annabelle's Charm (IRE) **Merry Fox Stud Limited**
34 **TO DIBBA**, 4, gr c Dubawi (IRE)—Rose Diamond (IRE) **Sheikh Ahmed Al Maktoum**
35 **TOMYRIS**, 4, b f Invincible Spirit (IRE)—Totally Devoted (USA) **Mr Nurlan Bizakov**
36 **UAE KING**, 4, b c Frankel—Zomaradah **Sheikh Mohammed Obaid Al Maktoum**
37 **UAE PRINCE (IRE)**, 5, b g Sea The Stars (IRE)—By Request **Sheikh Mohammed Obaid Al Maktoum**
38 **VICTORY ANGEL**, 4, b c Acclamation—Golden Shadow (IRE) **Z. A. Galadari**
39 **WATCHMAN (IRE)**, 4, b g Oasis Dream—Caphene **Sheikh Mohammed Obaid Al Maktoum**
40 **WHITE LAKE**, 6, b g Pivotal—White Palace **Sheikh Mohammed Obaid Al Maktoum**
41 **ZABEEL PRINCE (IRE)**, 5, ch g Lope de Vega (IRE)—
Princess Serena (USA) **Sheikh Mohammed Obaid Al Maktoum**
42 **ZEELANDER**, 4, b c Dubawi (IRE)—Zeeba (IRE) **Sheikh Mohammed Obaid Al Maktoum**

THREE-YEAR-OLDS

43 **ACE VENTURA**, b c Mayson—Ventura Highway **Sheikh Mohammed Obaid Al Maktoum**
44 **ACT OF BRAVERY**, b c Invincible Spirit (IRE)—Mama Quilla (USA) **Mr & Mrs G. Middlebrook**
45 **ADAMS PARK**, b g Mastercraftsman (IRE)—Ile Deserte **Mr P. D. Smith**
46 **ALTYN ORDA (IRE)**, ch f Kyllachy—Albanka (USA) **Mr Nurlan Bizakov**
47 **ANGEL'S GLORY**, b f Invincible Spirit (IRE)—Dutch Diamond **Sheikh Mohammed Obaid Al Maktoum**

MR ROGER VARIAN - Continued

48 **AUGENBLICK (IRE)**, b f Epaulette (AUS)—Freezing Love (USA) **Mr Ajay Anne & Partner**
49 **BALAAWY**, b f Bated Breath—Cartoon **Mr M. Al-Qatami & Mr K. M. Al-Mudhaf**
50 **CANVASSED (IRE)**, b c Shamardal (USA)—Painter's Pride (FR) **Sheikh Mohammed Obaid Al Maktoum**
51 **CAVALRY**, b c Exceed And Excel (AUS)—Queen's Best **Cheveley Park Stud Limited**
52 **CHARACTER WITNESS (IRE)**, b g Casamento (IRE)—She's A Character **Biddestone Racing XII**
53 **COMPULSIVE (IRE)**, ch c Lope de Vega (IRE)—Fand (USA) **Cheveley Park Stud Limited**
54 B f Iffraaj—Dashing (IRE) **Saleh Al Homaizi & Imad Al Sagar**
55 **EKANSE (IRE)**, b c Society Rock (IRE)—Esterlina (IRE) **Sheikh Mohammed Obaid Al Maktoum**
56 **ELASIA**, b f Nathaniel (IRE)—Elas Diamond **Sheikh Mohammed Obaid Al Maktoum**
57 **ELATION (IRE)**, b f Invincible Spirit (IRE)—Hallowed Park (IRE) **Highclere T'Bred Racing - Hallowed Park**
58 **FAADHEL (GER)**, b c Maxios—Firedance (GER) **Sheikh Ahmed Al Maktoum**
59 **FANTASY IN RED**, b f Pivotal—Fantasy In Blue **Cheveley Park Stud Limited**
60 **FLAVIUS TITUS**, ch c Lethal Force (IRE)—Furbelow **Sheikh Mohammed Obaid Al Maktoum**
61 **FROLOVA**, ch f Dutch Art—Zykina **Cheveley Park Stud Limited**
62 **GAGAGAI (FR)**, ch f Dutch Art—Gakalina (IRE) **Mr Nurlan Bizakov**
63 **GAME PLAYER (IRE)**, gr c Dark Angel (IRE)—Lucky Clio (IRE) **Sheikh Mohammed Obaid Al Maktoum**
64 **GIFT OF RAAJ (IRE)**, b c Iffraaj—Gift of Spring (USA) **Sheikh Mohammed Obaid Al Maktoum**
65 **GILDED HEAVEN**, ch f Medicean—Heavenly **Cheveley Park Stud Limited**
66 **HERMOSITA**, b f Exceed And Excel (AUS)—Honorlina (FR) **Newsells Park Stud Limited**
67 **HOWMAN (IRE)**, b c Sea The Stars (IRE)—Hoity Toity **Sheikh Mohammed Obaid Al Maktoum**
68 **IBRAZ**, br c Farhh—Wadaa (USA) **Mr Hamdan Al Maktoum**
69 **IMAGINATIVE (IRE)**, b c Camelot—Just Wondering (IRE) **Mr Alan Spence**
70 **INPROMPTU (IRE)**, br f Cacique (IRE)—Flowers of Spring (IRE) **Miss Y. M. G. Jacques**
71 **JAMIL (IRE)**, b c Dansili—Havant **Mr A. A. Al-Abdulrazzaq**
72 **JURZ (IRE)**, ch c Exceed And Excel (AUS)—Bahja (USA) **Mr Hamdan Al Maktoum**
73 **KAANOON**, b c Bated Breath—Going For Gold **Sheikh Ahmed Al Maktoum**
74 **KAWASIR (USA)**, ch c Speightstown (USA)—Bashful Bertie (USA) **Mr Hamdan Al Maktoum**
75 B c Mastercraftsman (IRE)—Keep Dancing (IRE) **Saleh Al Homaizi & Imad Al Sagar**
76 **KINDRED (IRE)**, ch g Champs Elysees—Kogershin (USA) **Nurlan Bizakov Jon Collins Michael Hill**
77 **KNIGHTLY SPIRIT**, b c Dalakhani (IRE)—Elysian **Sheikh Mohammed Obaid Al Maktoum**
78 **LADY MOMOKA (IRE)**, b f Shamardal (USA)—Juno Marlowe (IRE) **Sheikh Mohammed Obaid Al Maktoum**
79 **LASHABEEH (IRE)**, gr c Acclamation—Do The Honours (IRE) **Mr Hamdan Al Maktoum**
80 **LAUGH A MINUTE**, b c Mayson—Funny Enough **Sheikh Mohammed Obaid Al Maktoum**
81 Ch f Sepoy (AUS)—Loulou (USA) **Saleh Al Homaizi & Imad Al Sagar**
82 **LOVEISILI**, b c Dansili—Loveisallyouneed (IRE) **Sheikh Mohammed Obaid Al Maktoum**
83 **MADELINE (IRE)**, b br f Kodiac—Madhulika (FR) **Sheikh Mohammed Obaid Al Maktoum**
84 **MASAARR (USA)**, ch c Distorted Humor (USA)—Aryaamm (IRE) **Sheikh Ahmed Al Maktoum**
85 **MASKED IDENTITY**, b c Intello (GER)—Red Bloom **Sheikh Mohammed Obaid Al Maktoum**
86 **MAZBOON (IRE)**, ch c Sea The Stars (IRE)—Fresnay **Mr Hamdan Al Maktoum**
87 **MOJIKA**, b f Redoute's Choice (AUS)—Blaugrana (IRE) **Mrs H. Varian**
88 **MONADEE**, b g Showcasing—Messelina **Sheikh Ahmed Al Maktoum**
89 **MUBHIJ (IRE)**, b c Dark Angel (IRE)—Diva (GER) **Mr Hamdan Al Maktoum**
90 **MYSTIC FLIGHT (IRE)**, b g Kendargent (FR)—Mystic Spirit (IRE) **Cheveley Park Stud Limited**
91 **NARELLA (IRE)**, gr f Reliable Man—Naomia (GER) **T. Yoshida**
92 **NARYNKOL**, ch c Declaration of War (USA)—Nazym (IRE) **Mr Nurlan Bizakov**
93 **NEERAAN (USA)**, gr c Mizzen Mast (USA)—Ishraak (USA) **Mr Hamdan Al Maktoum**
94 **NOBLE EXPRESSION**, b c Sir Percy—Disposition **Sheikh Mohammed Obaid Al Maktoum**
95 **NORTH ANGEL (IRE)**, gr f Dark Angel (IRE)—Woodcock Moon **Fishlake Commercial Motors Ltd**
96 **PILASTER**, b f Nathaniel (IRE)—Portal **Cheveley Park Stud Limited**
97 **PIVOTAL MAN**, b c Pivotal—Privacy Order **Mr Arjun Waney / Mr Jai Waney**
98 **PLAYER'S LUCK (IRE)**, b c Speightstown (USA)—Arkadina (IRE) **Merry Fox Stud Limited**
99 **PROCEED (IRE)**, ch f Mastercraftsman (IRE)—Roanne (USA) **Mr J Shack & Mr S Roden**
100 **QALLAAB (IRE)**, ch c Dawn Approach (IRE)—Gazebo **Mr Hamdan Al Maktoum**
101 **QAZYNA (IRE)**, b f Frankel—First **Mr Nurlan Bizakov**
102 **QUEEN OF DESIRE (IRE)**, b f Dubawi (IRE)—Beyond Desire **Clipper Group Holdings Ltd**
103 **RAAQYAH (USA)**, b f Elusive Quality (USA)—My Dubai (IRE) **Sheikh Ahmed Al Maktoum**
104 **RASIMA**, gr f Iffraaj—Raushan (IRE) **Mr Nurlan Bizakov**
105 **RICH IDENTITY**, gr c Dubawi (IRE)—Rose Diamond (IRE) **Sheikh Mohammed Obaid Al Maktoum**
106 **SAM GOLD**, b c Iffraaj—Samdaniya **Sheikh Mohammed Obaid Al Maktoum**
107 **SARY ARQA**, ch f Dubawi (IRE)—Rock Salt **Mr Nurlan Bizakov**
108 **SHARJA SILK**, b c Dubawi (IRE)—So Silk **Sheikh Mohammed Obaid Al Maktoum**
109 **SHEIKHA REIKA (FR)**, b f Shamardal (USA)—Screen Star (IRE) **Sheikh Mohammed Obaid Al Maktoum**
110 **SPARKLING SURF**, ch f Frankel—Shimmering Surf (IRE) **P. L. Winkworth**
111 **STAR SHIELD**, ch c Helmet (AUS)—Perfect Star **Sheikh Mohammed Obaid Al Maktoum**
112 **TA ALLAK**, ch c New Approach (IRE)—Nahrain **Sheikh Ahmed Al Maktoum**

MR ROGER VARIAN - Continued

113 **TALAS (IRE)**, b g Dansili—Tamarind (IRE) **Mr Nurlan Bizakov**
114 **TAMAARA (IRE)**, b f Sepoy (AUS)—Alwarga (USA) **Sheikh Ahmed Al Maktoum**
115 **TAWHEED (IRE)**, ch c Dawn Approach (IRE)—Dhelaal **Mr Hamdan Al Maktoum**
116 **THE CHEMIST**, ch f Dutch Art—Prescription **Cheveley Park Stud Limited**
117 **TO WAFIJ (IRE)**, b c Kodiac—Rajmahal (UAE) **Sheikh Ahmed Al Maktoum**
118 **TOLKYN (FR)**, b f Intello (GER)—Totally Devoted (USA) **Mr Nurlan Bizakov**
119 **TURAYA**, ch f Teofilo (IRE)—Tingling (USA) **Mr Nurlan Bizakov**
120 **UAE SOLDIER (USA)**, b g Dansili—Time On **Sheikh Mohammed Obaid Al Maktoum**
121 **UPFRONT LADY**, b f War Front (USA)—Maid To Master (IRE) **Sheikh Mohammed Obaid Al Maktoum**
122 **WATHEEQA (USA)**, b f More Than Ready (USA)—Tafaneen (USA) **Mr Hamdan Al Maktoum**
123 **WILBURY TWIST**, b f Pivotal—Dylanesque **Helena Springfield Ltd**
124 **WILLIE JOHN**, b c Dansili—Izzi Top **Sheikh Mohammed Obaid Al Maktoum**
125 **ZAMANDAS (IRE)**, b c Pivotal—Zimira (IRE) **Mr Nurlan Bizakov**

TWO-YEAR-OLDS

126 Ch c 24/4 Kitten's Joy (USA)—Afraah (USA) (Hard Spun (USA)) **Mr Hamdan Al Maktoum**
127 Ch c 8/2 Raven's Pass (USA)—Almashooqa (USA) (Dubawi (IRE)) **Mr Hamdan Al Matoum**
128 B c 9/4 Dubawi (IRE)—Appearance (Galileo (IRE)) **Sheikh Mohammed Obaid Al Maktoum**
129 B gr c 22/2 Dark Angel (IRE)—Ballet Move (Oasis Dream) (68000) **Sheikh Mohammed Obaid Al Maktoum**
130 B br f 10/2 Sepoy (AUS)—Bashasha (USA) (Kingmambo (USA)) **Mr Hamdan Al Maktoum**
131 **BAYROOT (IRE)**, b c 1/4 Exceed And Excel (AUS)—
　　　　　　　　Alwarga (USA) (Street Sense (USA)) **Sheikh Ahmed Al Maktoum**
132 B c 25/2 Lope de Vega (IRE)—
　　　　　　　　Boston Rocker (IRE) (Acclamation) (500000) **Sheikh Mohammed Obaid Al Maktoum**
133 B c 13/5 Kitten's Joy (USA)—
　　　　　　　　Cat On A Tin Roof (USA) (Catienus (USA)) (220000) **Sheikh Mohammed Obaid Al Maktoum**
134 Ch c 29/2 Mastercraftsman (IRE)—Cochabamba (IRE) (Hurricane Run (IRE)) (150000) **Mr P. D. Smith**
135 **DASHED**, b f 8/4 Pivotal—Shatter (IRE) (Mr Greeley (USA)) **Cheveley Park Stud Limited**
136 B c 4/3 Exceed And Excel (AUS)—Deglet Noor (New Approach (IRE)) **Mr Hamdan Al Maktoum**
137 B c 20/1 Intello (GER)—Dream Girl (Oasis Dream) (146520) **Sheikh Mohammed Obaid Al Maktoum**
138 Ch f 6/1 Teofilo (IRE)—Ejadah (IRE) (Clodovil (IRE)) **Mr Hamdan Al Maktoum**
139 **ELAMIR (IRE)**, b c 29/2 Exceed And Excel (AUS)—Ameerat (Mark of Esteem (IRE)) **Sheikh Ahmed Al Maktoum**
140 B c 5/3 Kingman—Elshaadin (Dalakhani (IRE)) **Mr Hamdan Al Maktoum**
141 B f 7/4 Scat Daddy (USA)—Entwine (USA) (Empire Maker (USA)) **H.H. Sheikh Mohammed bin Khalifa Al-Thani**
142 **FABRIANO (GER)**, b br c 14/2 Sinndar (IRE)—
　　　　　　　　Four Roses (IRE) (Darshaan) (300000) **Sheikh Mohammed Obaid Al Maktoum**
143 Ch c 23/5 Dubawi (IRE)—
　　　　　　　　Finsceal Beo (IRE) (Mr Greeley (USA)) (650000) **Sheikh Mohammed Obaid Al Maktoum**
144 **FLEURSALS**, b f 6/4 Poet's Voice—Entitlement (Authorized (IRE)) (32000) **The Happy Go Lucky Partnership**
145 B c 14/4 Coach House (USA)—Funny Enough (Dansili) (125000) **Sheikh Mohammed Obaid Al Maktoum**
146 B c 2/4 Dubawi (IRE)—Gemstone (IRE) (Galileo (IRE)) (400000) **Sheikh Mohammed Obaid Al Maktoum**
147 **GLEEFUL**, b f 19/1 Pivotal—Merletta (Raven's Pass (USA)) **Cheveley Park Stud Limited**
148 B f 7/3 Dabirsim (FR)—Glorious Adventure (IRE) (Galileo (IRE)) (154660) **Sheikh Juma Dalmook Al Maktoum**
149 B c 14/4 Kingman—Go Lovely Rose (IRE) (Pivotal) (529100) **Sheikh Mohammed Obaid Al Maktoum**
150 B c 17/2 Swiss Spirit—Hot Secret (Sakhee's Secret) (114285) **Mr Hamdan Al Maktoum**
151 **IDEOLOGICAL (IRE)**, b f 9/4 Dawn Approach (IRE)—
　　　　　　　　Micaela's Moon (Malibu Moon (USA)) (12000) **J. Shack**
152 **INCITEMENT**, b c 15/4 Intello (GER)—Hooray (Invincible Spirit (IRE)) (100000) **Cheveley Park Stud Limited**
153 **INTUIT (IRE)**, b f 29/4 Intello (GER)—Sindirana (IRE) (Kalanisi (IRE)) (75000) **Cheveley Park Stud Limited**
154 Ch c 11/3 Dubawi (IRE)—Izzi Top (Pivotal) (2600000) **Sheikh Mohammed Obaid Al Maktoum**
155 **JALEEL**, b c 3/2 Iffraaj—Precariously Good (Oasis Dream) (80000) **Mr A. Al-Abdulrazzaq**
156 B c 25/1 Lope de Vega (IRE)—
　　　　　　　　Jillnextdoor (IRE) (Henrythenavigator (USA)) (89540) **Sheikh Mohammed Obaid Al Maktoum**
157 B f 8/4 Motivator—Jomana (IRE) (Darshaan) (146520) **S. Ali**
158 **KENZOHOPE (FR)**, gr c 11/5 Kendargent (FR)—Bedford Hope (GER) (Chato (USA))
159 **KHABEERAH**, b f 19/2 Dubawi (IRE)—Hadaatha (IRE) (Sea The Stars (IRE)) **Mr Hamdan Al Maktoum**
160 Ch c 15/1 Frankel—Khor Sheed (Dubawi (IRE)) **Sheikh Mohammed Obaid Al Maktoum**
161 B c 23/3 Sea The Stars (IRE)—
　　　　　　　　Lady Heidi (High Chaparral (IRE)) (150000) **Sheikh Mohammed Obaid Al Maktoum**
162 **LEHOOGG**, ch c 11/4 Bated Breath—Button Moon (IRE) (Compton Place) (85000) **Sheikh Ahmed Al Maktoum**
163 B c 30/1 Kodiac—Loch Ma Naire (IRE) (Galileo (IRE)) (280000) **Sheikh Mohammed Obaid Al Maktoum**
164 Br f 26/3 Kodiac—Lucrece (Pivotal) (146520) **Sheikh Mohammed Obaid Al Maktoum**
165 **MACKAAR (IRE)**, b c 1/2 Cape Cross (IRE)—Albemarle (King's Best (USA)) (80000) **Sheikh Ahmed Al Maktoum**
166 B f 28/3 Charm Spirit (IRE)—
　　　　　　　　Maid For Winning (USA) (Gone West (USA)) (120000) **Sheikh Mohammed Obaid Al Maktoum**

MR ROGER VARIAN - Continued

167 **MANORAH (IRE),** b f 8/4 The Factor (USA)—
　　　　Fifth Avenue Doll (USA) (Marquetry (USA)) (82000) **Mr A. Al-Abdulrazzaq**
168 **MAWAKIB,** b c 22/4 Havana Gold (IRE)—
　　　　Keladora (USA) (Crafty Prospector (USA)) (190000) **Sheikh Ahmed Al Maktoum**
169 B f 28/3 Dalakhani (IRE)—Mid Mon Lady (IRE) (Danetime (IRE)) (34187) **S. Ali**
170 B c 16/3 Dawn Approach (IRE)—Min Banat Alreeh (IRE) (Oasis Dream) **Mr Hamdan Al Maktoum**
171 **MOTAWAJ,** b c 15/3 Dubawi (IRE)—Tantshi (IRE) (Invincible Spirit (IRE)) **Sheikh Ahmed Al Maktoum**
172 **MUNAAZIL (IRE),** br c 28/3 Dubawi (IRE)—Aljaaziah (Medaglia d'oro (USA)) **Mr Hamdan Al Maktoum**
173 B f 16/4 Dawn Approach (IRE)—Mundana (IRE) (King's Best (USA)) **Sheikh Mohammed Obaid Al Maktoum**
174 **MUTAMAASIK,** ch c 4/3 Dubawi (IRE)—Muhawalah (IRE) (Nayef (USA)) **Mr Hamdan Al Maktoum**
175 **MUTASAAMY (IRE),** b c 24/3 Oasis Dream—Eswarah (Unfuwain (USA)) **Mr Hamdan Al Maktoum**
176 **NAAEELL (IRE),** b c 21/2 New Approach (IRE)—Sajjhaa (King's Best (USA)) **Sheikh Ahmed Al Maktoum**
177 **NABEYLA,** b br f 22/3 New Approach (IRE)—Feedyah (USA) (Street Cry (IRE)) **Sheikh Ahmed Al Maktoum**
178 **NAFITHAA,** b f 4/2 Shamardal (USA)—Lanansaak (IRE) (Zamindar (USA)) **Mr Hamdan Al Maktoum**
179 B c 3/2 Invincible Spirit (IRE)—Nancy O (IRE) (Pivotal) (90000) **Z. A. Galadari**
180 B f 2/3 New Approach (IRE)—Nargys (IRE) (Lawman (FR)) **Sheikh Mohammed Obaid Al Maktoum**
181 **NEAROOZ,** b f 17/3 New Approach (IRE)—Modeyra (Shamardal (USA)) **Sheikh Ahmed Al Maktoum**
182 B c 9/2 Mastercraftsman (IRE)—
　　　　Nebraas (Green Desert (USA)) (187220) **China Horse Club International Limited**
183 B c 20/2 Shamardal (USA)—Night Frolic (Night Shift (USA)) (500000) **Sheikh Mohammed Obaid Al Maktoum**
184 B f 7/3 Teofilo (IRE)—Qawaafy (USA) (Street Cry (IRE)) **Mr Hamdan Al Maktoum**
185 Ch c 15/4 Dubawi (IRE)—
　　　　Rainbow Dancing (Rainbow Quest (USA)) (187220) **Sheikh Mohammed Obaid Al Maktoum**
186 B gr f 20/4 Dansili—Rose Diamond (IRE) (Daylami (IRE)) **Sheikh Mohammed Obaid Al Maktoum**
187 **SEZIM,** b c 28/2 Dansili—Serres (IRE) (Daylami (IRE)) **Mr Nurlan Bizakov**
188 Ch f 10/4 Lope de Vega (IRE)—Solar Event (Galileo (IRE)) (350000) **Sheikh Mohammed Obaid Al Maktoum**
189 **SPOKESMAN (IRE),** b c 21/2 Alhebayeb (IRE)—
　　　　Xema (Danehill) (50000) **H Moorhead, C Fahy & J Collins**
190 B f 17/4 Cape Cross (IRE)—Suba (USA) (Seeking The Gold (USA)) **Sheikh Mohammed Obaid Al Maktoum**
191 **SURFMAN,** b c 7/2 Kingman—Shimmering Surf (IRE) (Danehill Dancer (IRE)) (140000) **P. L. Winkworth**
192 Ch f 4/3 Iffraaj—Sweet Cecily (IRE) (Kodiac) (105820) **Sheikh Mohammed Obaid Al Maktoum**
193 **TAMMOOZ,** b c 13/2 Lawman (FR)—
　　　　La Concorde (FR) (Sadler's Wells (USA)) (35000) **Sheikh Ahmed Al Maktoum**
194 **TAUTEKE,** b f 15/3 Sea The Stars (IRE)—Tamarind (IRE) (Sadler's Wells (USA)) **Mr Nurlan Bizakov**
195 **THRIVING,** b f 8/4 Kodiac—Najam (Singspiel (IRE)) (30000) **J Barnett, J Shack & G Barnard**
196 **TICKLE THE MOON (GER),** b c 14/2 Sea The Moon (GER)—
　　　　Tickle Me Pink (Groom Dancer (USA)) (525000) **Sheikh Mohammed Obaid Al Maktoum**
197 **VOICEOFTHEEMIRATES,** b c 2/5 Showcasing—Makaaseb (Pulpit (USA)) (69189) **A. Al Shaikh**
198 B f 7/2 Shamardal (USA)—Whazzis (Desert Prince (IRE)) (525000) **Sheikh Mohammed Obaid Al Maktoum**
199 Ch f 19/3 Mastercraftsman (IRE)—White Cay (Dalakhani (USA)) (40000) **Sheikh Juma Dalmook Al Maktoum**
200 **ZAULA,** gr f 26/2 Dark Angel (IRE)—Zimira (IRE) (Invincible Spirit (IRE)) **Mr Nurlan Bizakov**

Other Owners: K. M. Al-Mudhaf, Mohammed Jasem Al-Qatami, I. J. Al-Sagar, Mrs J. A. Allen, Mr K. Allen, Mr A. Anne, G. M. Barnard, Mr J. Barnett, Mrs A. C. Black, Mrs G. P. Bostwick, T. P. Bostwick, Mr J. A. Collins, Jon Collins & Michael Hill, Mr C. J. Fahy, Dowager Countess of Harrington, Highclere Nominated Partner Limited, Highclere Thoroughbred Racing Ltd, Michael Hill, Saleh Al Homaizi, Mrs G. A. S. Jarvis, Mr S. Marchant, Mr R. P. Marchant, Mrs L. A. Middlebrook, Mr G. Middlebrook, Mr G. Moss, Mrs S. J. Piper, Mr S. G. Roden, Mr S. Rubin, Mr M. B. Spence, Mr A. C. Waney, Mr J. S. Waney.

Assistant Trainer: T J Kent

Jockey (flat): Andrea Atzeni. **Apprentice:** David Egan.

---

564 | **MR ED VAUGHAN, Newmarket**
Postal: **Machell Place Cottage, Old Station Road, Newmarket, Suffolk, CB8 8DW**
Contacts: **PHONE (01638) 667411 FAX (01638) 667452 MOBILE (07799) 144901**
E-MAIL ed@efvaughan.com WEBSITE www.efvaughan.com

1 **CAPTAIN COURAGEOUS (IRE),** 5, b g Canford Cliffs (IRE)—Annacloy Pearl (IRE)
2 **EXCELLENT SUNSET (IRE),** 4, b f Exceed And Excel (AUS)—Sunset Avenue (USA)
3 **PROST (GER),** 4, b g Tin Horse (IRE)—Plebeya (IRE)

MR ED VAUGHAN - Continued

THREE-YEAR-OLDS

 4 **CHOCO BOX**, b f Harbour Watch (IRE)—Bible Box (IRE)
 5 **COLOURFIELD (IRE)**, b f Makfi—Rainbow Desert (USA)
 6 **DANCING BRAVE BEAR (USA)**, b f Street Cry (IRE)—Baghdaria (USA)
 7 **DESERT WIND (IRE)**, b c Worthadd (IRE)—Matula (IRE)
 8 **HEAVEN UP HERE (IRE)**, b f Holy Roman Emperor (IRE)—High Fun (FR)
 9 **HIKMAA (IRE)**, b f Roderic O'connor (IRE)—Alice Liddel (IRE)
10 **LOVE TO BREEZE**, b f Azamour (IRE)—Burn The Breeze (IRE)
11 **MISS MILLA B**, b f Sepoy (AUS)—Dreamily (IRE)
12 **NORTH BAY SUNRISE (IRE)**, b f Kodiac—Cat Fire (IRE)
13 **PRIME MINISTER (IRE)**, b c Dream Ahead (USA)—Logica (IRE)
14 **ROSEDALE TOPPING (IRE)**, b f Zebedee—Callmeakhab (IRE)
15 **TAKE IT DOWN UNDER**, b c Oasis Dream—Roz
16 **TRAILBOSS (IRE)**, b g High Chaparral (IRE)—Seeking Solace

TWO-YEAR-OLDS

17 B f 27/3 Champs Elysees—Acquainted (Shamardal (USA)) (34000)
18 B c 28/3 Dream Ahead (USA)—Avodale (IRE) (Lawman (FR))
19 Ch c 29/1 Poet's Voice—Caldy Dancer (IRE) (Soviet Star (USA)) (14000)
20 Gr f 4/2 Mastercraftsman (IRE)—Easy Lover (Pivotal) (42000)
21 Br c 8/4 Holy Roman Emperor (IRE)—Eleanor Roosevelt (IRE) (Dalakhani (IRE)) (38095)
22 B c 1/3 Camacho—Foxtrot Pearl (IRE) (Bahamian Bounty) (38095)
23 B c 14/1 Aussie Rules (USA)—Gala Rose (Selkirk (USA)) (23000)
24 Ch c 27/2 Ruler of The World (IRE)—Independent Girl (IRE) (Bachelor Duke (USA)) (25000)
25 Ch c 23/4 Sepoy (AUS)—Junket (Medicean) (22000)
26 B c 19/4 Alpha (USA)—Palestrina (USA) (Medaglia d'oro (USA)) (13837)

Owners: Sheikh Juma Dalmook Al Maktoum, Sheikh Hamed Dalmook Al Maktoum, Ballymore Sterling Syndicate, Mr H R Bin Ghadeyer, Bloomsbury Stud, Mr C Bryce, Mr K A Dasmal, Elite Racing Equine Limited, Front Runner Racing-1, GG Thoroughbreds, Sir Owen Glen, Mr E W Lee, Mr P A Moroney, Mr A E Oppenheimer, Mr A M Pickering, Mr S Rashid, Mr G Sharp, Mr G Van Ameyden, Mr E Ware.

---

565 MR TIM VAUGHAN, Cowbridge

Postal: Pant Wilkin Stables, Llanquian Road, Aberthin, Cowbridge, South Glamorgan, CF71 7HE
Contacts: PHONE (01446) 771626 FAX (01446) 774371 MOBILE (07841) 800081
E-MAIL tim@timvaughanracing.com WEBSITE www.timvaughanracing.com

 1 **AKKAPENKO (FR)**, 4, b g Archipenko (USA)—Akka **T. E. Vaughan**
 2 **ALLTIMEGOLD (IRE)**, 5, b g Gold Well—Carryonharriet (IRE) **Mrs B. N. Ead**
 3 **ASKPHILMOR (IRE)**, 5, b m Ask—Barchetta (IRE) **The Bill & Ben Partnership**
 4 **BALLYROCK (IRE)**, 12, b g Milan—Ardent Love (IRE) **Pearn's Pharmacies Ltd**
 5 **BASSARABAD (FR)**, 7, b g Astarabad (USA)—Grivette (FR) **Pearn's Pharmacies Ltd**
 6 **BELIZE**, 7, b g Rail Link—Costa Rica (IRE) **Mr D. R. Passant**
 7 **BELLS OF AILSWORTH (IRE)**, 8, b g Kayf Tara—Volverta (FR) **Mr S. Grys & Mr M. O'Boyle**
 8 **BELLS OF WANSFORD (IRE)**, 4, b g Multiplex—Et Voila **Mr S. Grys & Mr M. O'Boyle**
 9 **BENABILITY (IRE)**, 8, b g Beneficial—Whataliability (IRE) **Mrs L. Bowtell**
10 **BENNACHIE (IRE)**, 9, b g Milan—Stormy Lady (IRE) **Oceans Racing**
11 **BERGHOLT (IRE)**, 5, b g Sir Percy—Sularina (IRE) **Mr B Jones & Son**
12 **BLEU ET NOIR**, 7, b g Enrique—Gastina (FR) **Mr A. E. Peterson**
13 **BOLTON BOY (IRE)**, 4, br g Arcadio (GER)—Peggy Maddock (IRE) **JRFB Ltd**
14 **BUCKING THE TREND**, 10, b g Kayf Tara—Macklette (IRE) **The Marinades**
15 **C'EST DU GATEAU (FR)**, 6, b g Laveron—Programmee (FR) **Pearn's Pharmacies Ltd**
16 **CALARULES**, 5, gr g Aussie Rules (USA)—Ailincala (IRE) **Oceans Racing**
17 **CANTON PRINCE (IRE)**, 7, b g Shantou (USA)—Hasainm (IRE) **Tertia Racing**
18 **CAPPIELOW PARK**, 9, b g Exceed And Excel (AUS)—Barakat **T. E. Vaughan**
19 **CATCHAROSE (IRE)**, 8, b m Catcher In The Rye (IRE)—Persian Flower **T. E. Vaughan**
20 **CHAMPAGNE CHASER**, 8, b g Tobougg (IRE)—Champagne Lil **Mrs M. A. O'Sullivan**
21 **CHOZEN (IRE)**, 6, b g Well Chosen—Kneeland Lass (IRE) **Pearn's Pharmacies Ltd**
22 **CONCEALED AMBITION (IRE)**, 6, br g Stowaway—Clairefontaine **The Pant Wilkin Partnership**
23 **COPPER GONE WEST (IRE)**, 5, b m Westerner—Copper Dusht (IRE) **Paul & Louise Bowtell**
24 **DADSINLUCK**, 5, b g Presenting—Gemini Lucy (IRE) **Paul & Louise Bowtell**
25 **DADSINTROUBLE (IRE)**, 8, b g Presenting—Gemini Lucy (IRE) **Mr J. P. M. Bowtell**
26 **DANCE AND ROMANCE**, 6, b m Kayf Tara—Sweetheart **T. E. Vaughan**

MR TIM VAUGHAN - Continued

27 **DEBECE,** 7, b g Kayf Tara—Dalamine (FR) **R. M. Kirkland**
28 **DESHAN (GER),** 7, b g Soldier Hollow—Desimona (GER) **S. Clarke & and the Late Mr M. S. Clarke**
29 **DOVILS DATE,** 9, gr g Clodovil (IRE)—Lucky Date (IRE) **Itsfuninit**
30 **DRUMSHEIL (GER),** 6, b m Sholokhov (IRE)—Damascena (GER) **T. E. Vaughan**
31 **DUSKY RAIDER (IRE),** 5, gr g Clodovil (IRE)—Rahila (IRE) **Vernaschi & Edgell**
32 **EMELL,** 8, ch g Medicean—Londonnetdotcom (IRE) **Mr & Mrs D. D. Clee**
33 **ESPALION (FR),** 4, b g Khalkevi (IRE)—Somosierra (FR) **Mr J. H. Frost**
34 **FIELDS OF GLORY (FR),** 8, b g King's Best (USA)—Lavandou **Pearn's Pharmacies Ltd**
35 **FRASER CANYON,** 6, b g Halling (USA)—Valley of Gold (FR) **Bovian Racing**
36 **GAELIC POET (IRE),** 4, b g Yeats (IRE)—Hasainm (IRE) **G & L Handley & M & C Hardcastle**
37 **GLENTEENEASAIGH (IRE),** 10, gr g Vinnie Roe (IRE)—Edward Street (IRE) **T. E. Vaughan**
38 **GLIMPSE OF GOLD,** 7, b g Passing Glance—Tizzy Blue (IRE) **The Craftsmen**
39 **IT'S ALL AN ACT (IRE),** 10, br g Presenting—Royal Lucy (IRE) **Mr J. H. Frost**
40 **JAUNTY FLYER,** 6, b g Sulamani (IRE)—Jaunty June **PP Control & Automation Limited**
41 **JEMBUG DRUMMER (IRE),** 4, b g Jeremy (USA)—Drumbug (IRE) **Paul & Louise Bowtell**
42 **KING'S TEMPLE (IRE),** 5, b g Kalanisi (IRE)—I Don't Know (IRE) **R. M. Kirkland**
43 4, b g Martaline—Knock Down (IRE) **Pearn's Pharmacies Ltd**
44 **LAUGHARNE,** 7, b g Authorized (IRE)—Corsican Sunset (USA) **Oceans Racing**
45 **LOOKSNOWTLIKEBRIAN (IRE),** 7, b g Brian Boru—Sheebadiva (IRE) **SC Botham & RG Botham**
46 **LORD FENDALE (IRE),** 9, ch g Erewhon (USA)—Upton Lady (IRE) **Mr B Jones & Son**
47 **MARONETTE,** 5, b m Milan—Wyldello **Pearn's Pharmacies Ltd**
48 **MASTER DANCER (IRE),** 7, gr g Mastercraftsman (IRE)—Isabella Glyn (IRE) **select-racing-club.co.uk & Mr C Davies**
49 **MATTS LEGACY (IRE),** 6, b g Arcadio (GER)—How Provincial (IRE) **S. Clarke & and the Late Mr M. S. Clarke**
50 **MIDNIGHT QUEEN,** 8, b m Rainbow High—Questionit (IRE) **T. E. Vaughan**
51 **MISTER BUDDY (IRE),** 5, gr g Fairly Ransom (USA)—Hasainm (IRE) **T. E. Vaughan**
52 **MONSIEUR ARKADIN (FR),** 7, b g Dream Well (FR)—Quenta des Bordes (FR) **Passant & Butt**
53 4, B g Jeremy (USA)—Mrs Masters (IRE) **T. E. Vaughan**
54 **NATHANS PRIDE (IRE),** 10, ch g Definite Article—Tricias Pride (IRE) **Mr J. P. M. Bowtell**
55 **NORMANDY KING (IRE),** 7, b g King's Theatre (IRE)—Clairefontaine **The 600 Club**
56 **OFFICER HOOLIHAN,** 8, b g Kayf Tara—Major Hoolihan **R. M. Kirkland**
57 **ONE LEADER (IRE),** 7, b g Oscar (IRE)—Be My Leader (IRE) **Tertia Racing**
58 **ORIENTAL CROSS (IRE),** 5, b m Cape Cross (IRE)—Orion Girl (GER) **T. E. Vaughan**
59 **PANIS ANGELICUS (FR),** 9, b g Panis (USA)—Pyu (GER) **Oceans Racing**
60 **POINT OF PRINCIPLE (IRE),** 5, b g Rip Van Winkle (IRE)—L'ancresse (IRE) **Oceans Racing**
61 **PRESENTING BERKLEY (IRE),** 8, br g Presenting—Tynelucy (IRE) **optimumracing.co.uk**
62 **QUASI (IRE),** 6, ch g Presenting—Pink Mist (IRE) **Mr D. R. Passant**
63 **RASASEE (IRE),** 5, gr g Rip Van Winkle (IRE)—Gleaming Silver (IRE) **R. M. Kirkland**
64 **REDDINGTON (IRE),** 6, b g Getaway (GER)—Nikkis Alstar (IRE) **Mrs B. N. Ead**
65 **RONNIE LAWSON (IRE),** 9, b g King's Theatre (IRE)—Sarahs Quay (IRE) **Double Trouble Partnership**
66 **ROYALE DJANGO (IRE),** 9, b g Kayf Tara—Royale Boja (FR) **Mr J Durston & Mr N Harris**
67 **RUACANA,** 9, b g Cape Cross (IRE)—Farrfesheena (USA) **The 600 Club**
68 6, B g Kayf Tara—Salamarie (FR) **T. E. Vaughan**
69 4, Gr g Shirocco (GER)—Sardagna (FR) **R. J. Prince**
70 **SATELLITE (IRE),** 7, b g Danehill Dancer (IRE)—Perihelion (IRE) **Paul & Louise Bowtell**
71 **SCRUTINISE,** 6, b g Intense Focus—Tetravella (IRE) **Paul & Louise Bowtell**
72 **SEABORN (IRE),** 4, b g Born To Sea (IRE)—Next To The Top **Barnett & Beach**
73 **SERGIO (IRE),** 6, b g Flemensfirth (USA)—Aventia (IRE) **Mr J. P. M. Bowtell**
74 **SHOW'S OVER (IRE),** 7, b g Curtain Time (IRE)—Sailors Run (IRE) **Mr B Jones & Son**
75 **SPECTATOR,** 7, br g Passing Glance—Averami **Pearn's Pharmacies Ltd**
76 **STAUNTON,** 7, b m Kayf Tara—Aranga (IRE) **T. E. Vaughan**
77 **TAKE EM OUT (IRE),** 6, b g Amadeus Wolf—Toorah Laura La (USA) **The Bill & Ben Partnership**
78 **TANACANDO (FR),** 6, b g Ballingarry—Tamaziya (IRE) **Flat Out Shinton Racing**
79 **TANIT RIVER (IRE),** 8, br g Indian River (FR)—Tanit Lady (IRE) **Brian Ead & Martin Moore**
80 **TARA MAC,** 9, b m Kayf Tara—Macklette (IRE) **Mr B Jones & Son**
81 **TERMSNCONDITIONS (IRE),** 4, b g Kodiac—Sweet'n Sassy (IRE) **A L Gregg & Partner**
82 **THELIGNY (FR),** 7, gr g Martaline—Romilly (FR) **Pearn's Pharmacies Ltd**
83 **TIDESTREAM,** 8, b g Galileo (IRE)—Sweet Stream (ITY) **Delamere Cottage Racing Partners (1996)**
84 **TIME AND AGAIN (FR),** 8, b g Sassanian (USA)—Petillante Royale (FR) **The Junction Partnership**
85 **TIMELY GIFT,** 5, b g Presenting—Give It Time **Carl, JJ, Chris, Mike, John & Hugh**
86 **TRIXSTER (IRE),** 5, b g Beneficial—Our Trick (IRE) **The Pant Wilkin Partnership**
87 **WINGS OF SMOKE (IRE),** 13, gr g King's Theatre (IRE)—Grey Mo (IRE) **Pearn's Pharmacies Ltd**
88 **WINIDO,** 6, b g Sulamani (IRE)—Princess Claudia (IRE) **JRFB Ltd**
89 **WISTARI ROCKS (IRE),** 9, b g Heron Island (IRE)—Hi Honey (IRE) **Four Leaf Clover Partnership**
90 **WITHOUT FRONTIER (IRE),** 6, b g Stowaway—Hollygrove Samba (IRE) **Mr J Durston & Mr N Harris**
91 **WITHOUTDEFAVOURITE (IRE),** 10, b g Oscar (IRE)—Camden Confusion (IRE) **Kendari Racing**

MR TIM VAUGHAN - Continued

THREE-YEAR-OLDS

92 **POWERFUL SOCIETY (IRE)**, b f Power—Society Gal (IRE) **Mr S. Hosie**

Other Owners: Mr P. G. Amos, Dr C. A. Barnett, Mr I. Beach, Mr P. Beach, S. C. Botham, Mr T. G. Brooks, Mr G. W. T. Butt, S. J. Clare, Exors of the Late Mr M. S. Clarke, Mr S. A. Clarke, Mrs J. P. Clee, D. D. Clee, Mr M. J. Curtis, Mr C. Davies, Mr H. G. Doubtfire, Mr J. Durston, Mr B. Ead, Mr T. E. A. Edgell, Mr P. C. Etty, Mr M. Gear, Mr A. L. Gregg, Mr S. Grys, Mr G. Handley, Mr M. J. Hardcastle, Mr N. Harris, Mr S. R. Hartley, Mr D. L. Hill, Mrs K. E. Hollingworth, Mr I. C. Jenkins, Mr B. M. Jones, Mr W. Jones, Mr T. E. Kerfoot, Mr G. T. Lever, Mrs D. J. Lowrie, A. D. Lowrie, Dr C. H. Mason, Mr M. E. Moore, Mr J. M. Mordecai, Mr M. O'Boyle, Miss D. E. Pettle, Mr J. T. Phillips, Mr R. G. Price, Mr N. S. C. Proctor, A. Robinson, The Select Racing Club Limited, Mr J. Shinton, Mr D. A. Shinton, Mr A. Smallman, Mr M. A. Stratford, Mr R. G. V. Vernaschi, D. J. Wallis, Mr N. D. Whitham, Mrs C. S. Wilson.

Jockey (flat): David Probert. **Jockey (NH):** Richard Johnson, Alan Johns. **Amateur:** Mr Evan David, Mr Charlie Price.

---

566 **MR CHRISTIAN VON DER RECKE, Weilerswist**
Postal: **Rennstall Recke GmbH, Hovener Hof 1, D-53919, Weilerswist, Germany**
Contacts: **PHONE (0049) 2254 84 53 14 FAX (0049) 2254 845315 MOBILE (0049) 171 542 50 50**
E-MAIL recke@t-online.de WEBSITE www.rennstall-recke.de

1 **ADMIRAL (GER)**, 5, b g Electric Beat—Adela (GER) **Rennstall Saarbrucken e.V.**
2 **AIRFIELD BEAUTY**, 4, b f Delegator—Anthea **M-B-A Racing**
3 **ALL TALK N NO DO (IRE)**, 7, b g Kodiac—Woodren (USA) **Busch**
4 **AMUN (GER)**, 4, b c Soldier Hollow—Albula (GER) **Stall Nizza**
5 **ARIOST (GER)**, 4, b c Nicaron (GER)—Antique Rose (GER) **Imm GbR**
6 **ATHOU DU NORD (FR)**, 8, b g Voix du Nord (FR)—Orathou du Plaid (FR) **Himmelsbach**
7 **AUTHORIZED CADEAUX**, 6, b g Authorized (IRE)—Nord's Cadeaux **Schwager**
8 **BALDUCCI**, 11, b g Dansili—Miss Meltemi (IRE) **Rennstall Recke GmbH**
9 **BEQUIA (IRE)**, 4, ch f Helmet (AUS)—Bunditten (IRE) **Joe Hernon**
10 **BEST TRIP (IRE)**, 11, b g Whipper (USA)—Tereed Elhawa **Rennstall Recke GmbH**
11 **BURANO (IRE)**, 9, ch g Dalakhani (IRE)—Kalimanta (IRE) **Rennstall Recke GmbH**
12 **CADMIUM**, 7, b m Major Cadeaux—Miss Mirasol **Stall Walcheren**
13 **CANTON DELIGHT (IRE)**, 4, ch c Rio de La Plata (USA)—Portella (GER) **Jen**
14 **CIRCUMCANES (IRE)**, 4, ch f Dragon Pulse (IRE)—Et Dona Ferentes **Veeck**
15 **CLASSIC BRIGHT (FR)**, 5, b m Volfonic (IRE)—Classic Night (GER) **van der Hulst**
16 **COMMISSARIO (GER)**, 4, br c Wiener Walzer (GER)—Chandos Rose (IRE) **Brand**
17 **COMPARATIVE**, 6, b g Oasis Dream—Indication **Stall M-B-A**
18 **CUMBRIANO (GER)**, 5, b h Wiener Walzer (GER)—Carrie Anne **Dieter Brand**
19 **DABADIYAN (IRE)**, 8, b g Zamindar (USA)—Dabista (USA) **Wahler Eugen-Andreas**
20 **DAULYS ANTHEM (IRE)**, 10, br g Royal Anthem (USA)—Over Dubai **Rennstall Recke GmbH**
21 **DELAIRE**, 6, b g Sakhee's Secret—Moody Margaret **Bach**
22 **DELLA GRATZIA (IRE)**, 5, b m Holy Roman Emperor (IRE)—Easter Heroine (IRE) **Stall Karlshorst**
23 **DIVISIONIST**, 5, b h Oasis Dream—Exemplify **von Hodenberg Marquardt**
24 **DREAMSPEED (IRE)**, 11, b g Barathea (IRE)—Kapria (FR) **Keller**
25 **EASTSITE ONE (GER)**, 6, b h Mamool (IRE)—Ericarrow (IRE) **Gaul**
26 **ERIC (GER)**, 7, ch h Tertullian (USA)—Ericarrow (IRE) **Gaul**
27 **ERICA (GER)**, 5, b m Mamool (USA)—Ericarrow (IRE) **Gaul**
28 **EXCEED MY BUDGET**, 5, ch m Exceed And Excel (AUS)—Best Side (IRE) **Stall M-B-A**
29 **FAIR MOUNTAIN (GER)**, 6, b h Tiger Hill (IRE)—Fair Breeze (GER) **Stall Margarethe**
30 **FISHERMAN'S BLUES (IRE)**, 5, b g Zebedee—Southern Barfly (USA) **Stall esto87**
31 **FIT FOR THE JOB (IRE)**, 6, b g Lawman (FR)—Spesialta **Rennstall Recke GmbH**
32 **FROM FROST**, 7, b g Nayef (USA)—Salutare (IRE) **Schmeer**
33 **FUTURE SECURITY (IRE)**, 9, ch g Dalakhani (IRE)—Schust Madame (IRE) **Dewberry**
34 **GUIDING PASSION (FR)**, 4, b f Iffraaj—Right Ted (IRE) **Rennstall Recke GmbH**
35 **HIT THE JACKPOT (IRE)**, 9, ch g Pivotal—Token Gesture (IRE) **Renstall Recke GmbH**
36 **IBIZA EMPRESS (IRE)**, 5, b m Tertullian (USA)—Ibiza Dream **Stall M-B-A**
37 **INTERIOR MINISTER**, 8, b g Nayef (USA)—Sister Maria (USA) **Wahler Eugen-Andreas**
38 **JUNGLEBOOGIE (GER)**, 6, b h Nicaron (GER)—Jive (GER) **Imm GbR**
39 **KAKS ROOSID (FR)**, 5, b h Youmzain (IRE)—Danidh Dubai (IRE) **Rennstall Recke GmbH**
40 **KOLONEL KIRKUP**, 8, b g Dr Fong (USA)—Strawberry Lolly **Stall Rettstadt**
41 **L C SALOON**, 5, ch g Equiano (FR)—Aberdovey **Rennstall Recke GmbH**
42 **LA SUPERBA (IRE)**, 6, ch m Medicean—La Spezia (IRE) **Mount Coote Stud**
43 **LADY SMYTHE (IRE)**, 5, gr m Getaway (GER)—Courting Shinney **Smith**
44 **LINCOLN COUNTY**, 7, b g Authorized (IRE)—Lane County (USA) **Kage**
45 **LYNX (GER)**, 6, b br g Medicean—La Martina (GER) **Stall M-B-A**

MR CHRISTIAN VON DER RECKE - Continued

46 **MADURAI (GER)**, 7, b g Marju (IRE)—Moonlight Danceuse (IRE) **Gestut Am Schlossgarten**
47 **MARILLION (GER)**, 4, br g Lawman (FR)—Macara (GER) **Sauren Eckerhardt**
48 **MESARIA (IRE)**, 6, b m Montjeu (IRE)—Parakopi (IRE) **Lady O'Reilly**
49 **MODESTE (FR)**, 4, b c Equiano (FR)—Amarinda (GER) **Manfred Hofer**
50 **NORTH GERMANY**, 9, b g Monsun (GER)—North America (GER) **Himmelsbach**
51 **NOVALIS (GER)**, 6, b g Soldier Hollow—Naomia (GER) **Sauren**
52 **PARDELS (GER)**, 4, br f Jukebox Jury (IRE)—Paradise Search (IRE) **Stall Klosters-Serneus**
53 **PARIGINO (FR)**, 10, b g Panis (USA)—Loretta Gianni (FR) **Stall M-B-A**
54 **PERFECT SWING (IRE)**, 7, b g Milan—Lakil Princess (IRE) **Stall Winterhude**
55 **PHANTOM RIVER**, 6, b m Observatory (USA)—Madam'x **B. J. Friesdorf**
56 **POWER GAME**, 6, ch g Shamardal (USA)—Counterclaim **Rennstall Recke GmbH**
57 **QUICK STEP (GER)**, 5, ch h Distant Music (USA)—Quadraga (GER) **Marquardt von Hodenberg**
58 **RAVENS HILL (IRE)**, 5, ch g Raven's Pass (USA)—Sister Red (IRE) **Wahler Eugen-Andreas**
59 **RAZOR WIND (IRE)**, 7, b g Dubawi (IRE)—Tender Is Thenight (IRE) **Stall M-B-A**
60 **RENNY STORM (CZE)**, 8, b g Stormy Jail (IRE)—Renaissance (CZE) **Stall Chevalex**
61 **RIVO ALTO (USA)**, 4, b br g Lonhro (AUS)—Venetian Causeway (USA) **Rennstall Recke GmbH**
62 **ROCK CHARM**, 7, b g Araafa (IRE)—Evening Charm (IRE) **Schwager**
63 **ROYAL FLAG (GER)**, 4, ch c Jukebox Jury (IRE)—Royal Lomita (GER) **Frau R.u.A. Hacker**
64 **RUSSIAN FLAMENCO (GER)**, 5, b h Tertullian (USA)—Russian Samba (IRE) **Rennstall Darboven**
65 **SAINT POIS (FR)**, 7, b g Le Havre (FR)—Our Dream Queen **Rennstall Recke GmbH**
66 **SANG DASHER (GER)**, 6, b g Dashing Blade—Sang Sun (GER) **Staub Martin Silvio**
67 **SARITA (GER)**, 4, ch f Tertullian (USA)—Sybella
68 **SHADOW SADNESS (GER)**, 6, b h Soldier Hollow—Shadow Queen (GER) **Stall Weiss-Blau**
69 **SHOJA (GER)**, 5, ch m Dylan Thomas (IRE)—Serenata (GER) **Stall Burg Muggenhausen**
70 **TARA MARA (GER)**, 5, b m Mamool (IRE)—Templemore (USA) **Gestut Romerhof**
71 **THEODOSIA (IRE)**, 4, b c Teofilo (IRE)—Tiz The Whiz (USA) **M-B-A Racing**
72 **TICONDEROGA (IRE)**, 7, b g Robin des Champs (FR)—Wayward Star (IRE) **Rennstall Recke GmbH**
73 **TOP PRIORITY (IRE)**, 7, b g Solon (GER)—Firstote (FR) **Rennstall Recke GmbH**
74 **VARTAN (IRE)**, 4, br g Rock of Gibraltar (IRE)—Vestavia (IRE) **Imm GbR**
75 **ZADARA (GER)**, 4, b f Teofilo (IRE)—Zavaala (GER) **Veeck Martin Ernst**

THREE-YEAR-OLDS

76 **ABBAFRIDA (IRE)**, b f Most Improved (IRE)—Abbasharjah (GER) **M-B-A Racing**
77 **ALLONGE (IRE)**, ch f Dansant—Paix Royale **BMK Racing**
78 **AMERICAN OXYGEN**, b f Bahamian Bounty—Amalfi (IRE) **Schmidt-Pauli u.a. G.v.**
79 **ARONIUS (GER)**, b c Pastorius (GER)—Aronia (IRE) **Stall Nizza**
80 **BASILLUS**, ch c Kendargent (FR)—Bambara **Cabkhat s.r.o.**
81 **BENTELE (IRE)**, b f Rock of Gibraltar (IRE)—Divisme (USA) **Rennstall Recke GmbH**
82 **DREAM OF FUTURE (IRE)**, b c Dream Ahead (USA)—Deportment **Stall Schildhorst**
83 **EARL (GER)**, b c Tertullian (USA)—Ericarrow (IRE) **Frau G. Gaul**
84 **FLAMINGO LOVE (GER)**, b f Areion (GER)—Flamingo Island (GER) **Stall Nizza**
85 **JACAMAR (GER)**, b c Maxios—Juvena (GER) **Imm GbR**
86 **JANUS (IRE)**, b c Rock of Gibraltar (IRE)—Jardina (GER) **Stall Nizza**
87 **KITTEN'S MUSIC (USA)**, b c Kitten's Joy (USA)—Melody Dawn (USA) **Cabkhat s.r.o.**
88 **KONIG POLDI (GER)**, b c Soldier Hollow—Konigin Platina (GER) **Gestut Elsetal**
89 **MARRACASH (GER)**, gr c Reliable Man—Magic Love (GER) **M-B-A Racing**
90 **NOBLE LORD**, b c Pastorius (GER)—Noble Lady (GER) **Hofer**
91 **ROSINANTE (IRE)**, b f Maxios—Russian Samba (IRE) **Gestut IDEE GmbH & Co. KG**
92 **SCHESAPLANA (GER)**, b f Dabirsim (FR)—See Me Well (IRE) **Stall Klosters-Serneus**
93 **SHILO (IRE)**, b f Most Improved (IRE)—Sacre Fleur (GER) **Stall Sternental**
94 **STONE THE CROWS (HOL)**, ch c Wiesenpfad (FR)—Classic Night (GER) **Van Der Hulst**
95 **TWIST AND SHOUT (HOL)**, ch c Xl (USA)—Second D **Mulder**
96 **URSUS (GER)**, b c Most Improved (IRE)—Ulieska (GER) **Imm GbR**

TWO-YEAR-OLDS

97 **ALFONSO (GER)**, b c 28/4 Maxios—Artemisia (IRE) (Peintre Celebre (USA)) **Stall Nizza**
98 B f 10/1 Makfi—Bambara (High Chaparral (IRE)) **Cabkhat s.r.o.**
99 **CANTERBURY (GER)**, b c 4/3 Mamool (IRE)—Carrie Anne (Piccolo) **Dieter Brand**
100 **DYNAMITE GOLD (GER)**, b c 20/2 Lord of England (GER)—
                    Dynamite Cat (GER) (One Cool Cat (USA)) (19536) **Rennstall Saarbrucken e.V.**
101 B f 7/3 Denon (USA)—Fantastic Fire (GER) (Platini (GER)) (6512) **Rennstall Recke GmbH**
102 **FORSTER**, ch c 21/3 Sepoy (AUS)—Fleeting Image (Sir Percy) **Andreas & R. Hacker**
103 **JASON (GER)**, b c 18/4 Lawman (FR)—Jardina (GER) (Shirocco (GER)) **Stall Nizza**
104 B f 23/3 So You Think (NZ)—Knightsbridge (BRZ) (Yagli (USA)) **Cabkhat s.r.o.**

MR CHRISTIAN VON DER RECKE - Continued

105 **KODRAT (FR)**, b c 1/1 Kodiac—Empreinte (FR) (Russian Blue (IRE)) **Cabkhat s.r.o.**
106 **RICHELIEU (GER)**, b c 10/2 Lilbourne Lad (IRE)—Right Key (IRE) (Key of Luck (USA)) **Stall Nizza**

Jockey (flat): Alexander Pietsch. **Jockey (NH):** Paul Johnson. **Conditional:** Sonja Daroszewski.
Apprentice: Alexandra Liebert, Kristin Weidemann. **Amateur:** Miss Laura Giesgen.

---

567 | **MRS LUCY WADHAM, Newmarket**
Postal: **The Trainer's House, Moulton Paddocks, Newmarket, Suffolk, CB8 7PJ**
Contacts: **PHONE (01638) 662411 FAX (01638) 668821 MOBILE (07980) 545776**
E-MAIL lucy@wadhamracing.com WEBSITE www.lucywadhamracing.co.uk

1 **A BOY NAMED SUZI**, 10, b g Medecis—Classic Coral (USA) **ABS Partnership**
2 **AGATHE ROSALIE (IRE)**, 5, b m Presenting—Agathe du Berlais (FR) **Suiter Developments Ltd & JJW Wadham**
3 **ALIZEE JAVILEX (FR)**, 8, b m Le Fou (IRE)—Etoile du Lion (FR) **A F Lousada & J J W Wadham**
4 **AMBERJAM (IRE)**, 8, b g Duke of Marmalade (IRE)—Makarova (IRE) **Amblyn Racing**
5 **ARTIFICE SIVOLA (FR)**, 8, gr g Dom Alco (FR)—Kerrana (FR) **R. B. Holt**
6 **BANJO GIRL (IRE)**, 6, ch m Presenting—Oh Susannah (FR) **Living In Hope Partnership**
7 **BROADWATER**, 4, ch g Malinas (GER)—Sweet Robinia (IRE) **P. H. Betts**
8 **EASTER GOLD (FR)**, 4, b f Kapgarde (FR)—Une Dame d'or (FR) **Mr J. Summers**
9 **ECHNATON (GER)**, 5, b g Lord of England (GER)—Easy Sunshine (IRE) **Suiter Developments Limited**
10 **ECLAIR DE GUYE (FR)**, 4, gr g Lord du Sud (FR)—Jouvence de Guye (FR) **R. B. Holt**
11 **GAME ON (IRE)**, 6, b g Gamut (IRE)—Dar Dar Supreme **Personal Racehorse Owners 5**
12 **GREGARIOUS (IRE)**, 5, gr g Big Bad Bob (IRE)—Sense of Greeting (IRE) **Mr J. Summers**
13 **ICONIC SKY**, 5, gr m Sixties Icon—Kentucky Sky **Mr T. R. Wood**
14 4, B f Authorized (IRE)—Julatten (IRE) **Mr J. D. Abell**
15 **LE REVE (IRE)**, 10, br g Milan—Open Cry (IRE) **P. H. Betts**
16 **MASTER OF FINANCE (IRE)**, 7, ch g Mastercraftsman (IRE)—Cheal Rose (IRE) **Mr J. D. Abell**
17 4, Br f Stowaway—Maxwells Demon (IRE) **Ms E. L. Banks**
18 **MOVIE LEGEND**, 8, b g Midnight Legend—Cyd Charisse **The Movie Legend Partnership**
19 **MR LOVE (IRE)**, 6, b g Winged Love (IRE)—Bonny Rathlin (IRE) **Ms E. L. Banks**
20 **MYSTIC SKY**, 7, b m Midnight Legend—Kentucky Sky **Mr Tim Wood**
21 **NEWTOWN CRAIG (IRE)**, 6, b g Craigsteel—Form A Circle (IRE) **P.A.Philipps,T.S.Redman & Mrs L. Redman**
22 **PEACEFUL VALLEY (FR)**, 4, b f No Risk At All (FR)—Si Parfaite (FR) **Suiter Developments Ltd & JJW Wadham**
23 **PHOENICIANA**, 7, b m Phoenix Reach (IRE)—Viciana **Mr G. W. Paul**
24 **PINE MOSS**, 5, br m Shirocco (GER)—Pochard **Mrs J J Shaw**
25 **POTTERS HEDGER**, 6, b g Midnight Legend—Loose Morals (IRE) **Mrs J. May**
26 **POTTERS LADY JANE**, 6, b m Sir Percy—Arabescato (UAE) **Mrs J. May**
27 **POTTERS LEGEND**, 8, b g Midnight Legend—Loose Morals (IRE) **Mrs J. May**
28 **POTTERS MIDNIGHT**, 8, b m Midnight Legend—Craughwell Suas (IRE) **Mrs J. May**
29 **POTTERS SAPPHIRE**, 5, gr m Aussie Rules (USA)—Arabescato (UAE) **Mrs J. May**
30 **RUBY RAMBLER**, 8, b m Notnowcato—Arruhan (IRE) **Sara Dennis,J J W Wadham & J C S Wilson**
31 **RUTH RENDELL (IRE)**, 4, b f Flemensfirth (USA)—May's June (IRE) **Suiter Developments Ltd & JJW Wadham**
32 **SHAMBRA (IRE)**, 4, b f Clodovil (IRE)—Shambodia (IRE) **Pali Pali Syndicate**
33 **SHANROE SANTOS (IRE)**, 9, b g Definite Article—Jane Hall (IRE) **Mr J. Summers**
34 **SHANTUNG (IRE)**, 5, ch m Shantou (USA)—Sarah's Cottage (IRE) **P A Philipps & Mrs G J Redman**
35 **SHOCK TACTICS**, 4, b g Schiaparelli (GER)—Fashionable Gal (IRE) **Dr & Mrs Clive Layton**
36 **SOMEKINDOFSTAR (IRE)**, 5, ch g Getaway (GER)—Katty Barry (IRE) **G. J. Pascoe**
37 **TALK OF MONTY**, 5, b g Fair Mix (IRE)—Talk The Talk **Mrs J. E. Micklethwait**
38 **TENSION TIME (IRE)**, 4, b g Dubai Destination (USA)—Leader's Hall (IRE) **Suiter Developments Ltd**
39 **TRINCOMALEE**, 5, b g Malinas (GER)—Royal Tango **Mrs E. Gordon Lennox**

THREE-YEAR-OLDS

40 **ANNA JAMMEELA**, b f Big Bad Bob (IRE)—All Annalena (IRE) **Mr & Mrs A. E. Pakenham**
41 **BELLADONNA**, b f Medicean—Nicola Bella (IRE) **Mr & Mrs A. E. Pakenham**
42 **DANCE TO PARIS**, b f Champs Elysees—Riabouchinska **The Calculated Speculators**
43 **GALMARLEY**, b f Sir Percy—Crystal Gal (IRE) **Chasemore Farm LLP**
44 **HARBOUR BREEZE (IRE)**, b c Le Havre (IRE)—Retiens La Nuit (USA) **Mr B. J. Painter**
45 **MISS BOLIVAR**, b f Sir Percy—Bolivia (GER) **The FOPS**
46 **SORBET**, b f Passing Glance—Fireburst **Mrs P. J. Toye**

MRS LUCY WADHAM - Continued

TWO-YEAR-OLDS

47 Ch f 19/2 Farhh—First Embrace (IRE) (Dubawi (IRE)) **Abdullah Saeed Al Naboodah**
48 SCARLET SILK, ch f 4/5 Sir Percy—Tussah (Daylami (IRE)) **The FOPS**
49 B f 2/3 Bated Breath—Temple of Thebes (IRE) (Bahri (USA)) **Mr & Mrs A. E. Pakenham**

Other Owners: The A. T. Partnership, Mrs J. E. Black, A. W. Black, Mrs A. L. Dash, Mrs S. Dennis, Mr C. S. Heaps, Ms L. K. Heaton-Jacques, Mr S. J. High, D. J. Hing, Miss N. J. Langstaff, Mrs H. M. Layton, Dr C. A. Layton, Mr K. Little, Mr A. F. Lousada, Mrs V. H. Pakenham, Mr A. E. Pakenham, Mr M. Pendlebury, P. A. Philipps, Mrs L. E. Redman, Mr T. S. Redman, Mrs G. J. Redman, Mr C. D. Smith, Mrs L. A. M. Wadham, J. J. W. Wadham, Mr E. R. Wakelin, J. C. S. Wilson.

Jockey (NH): Leighton Aspell, Maxime Tissier.

MISS TRACY WAGGOTT, Spennymoor
Postal: **Awakening Stables, Merrington Road, Spennymoor, Co. Durham, DL16 7HD**
Contacts: **PHONE (01388) 819012 MOBILE (07979) 434498**
E-MAIL tracywaggott@hotmail.com

1 BARRISTER, 4, b f Lawman (FR)—Ella **David Tate & Tracy Waggott**
2 CAYMUS, 5, b m Compton Place—Midnight Sky **Mr D. Tate**
3 ECHO BEAT (IRE), 5, b m Beat Hollow—Calendula **Mr W. J. Laws**
4 HADLEY, 5, b g Royal Applause—Brush Strokes **Mr D. Tate**
5 HENLEY, 6, b g Royal Applause—Making Waves (IRE) **Mr D. Tate**
6 HIGHFIELD LASS, 7, b m Cayman Kai (IRE)—Jendorcet **Mrs P. J. Taylor-Garthwaite**
7 LITTLE KINGDOM (IRE), 4, b f Royal Applause—Hadba (IRE) **Miss T. Waggott**
8 MARKET CHOICE (IRE), 5, b g Majestic Missile (IRE)—
Ron's Secret **Wensleydale Bacon Ltd and Mr Rod Rider**
9 PATHWAY TO FREEDOM, 4, b g Cape Cross (IRE)—Emancipation **David Tate & Tracy Waggott**
10 PERCY VERENCE, 5, b g Sir Percy—Bermondsey Girl **Mr D. Tate**
11 RASELASAD (IRE), 4, b g Acclamation—Wajaha (IRE) **Mr D. Tate**
12 SPECIAL YOU, 4, b f Arabian Gleam—Mighty Flyer (IRE) **Mr D. Tate**
13 SUPREME POWER (IRE), 4, b g Power—Supreme Spirit (IRE) **Mr D. Tate**
14 WINDFORPOWER (IRE), 8, b g Red Clubs (IRE)—Dubai Princess (IRE) **Mr D. Tate**

THREE-YEAR-OLDS

15 LAST GLANCE (IRE), b g Shamardal (USA)—Linda Radlett (IRE) **Mr D. Tate**

Other Owners: Mr R. Rider, Wensleydale Bacon Limited.

MR JOHN WAINWRIGHT, Malton
Postal: **Granary House, Beverley Road, Norton, Malton, North Yorkshire, YO17 9PJ**
Contacts: **PHONE (01653) 692993 MOBILE (07798) 778070**
E-MAIL jswainwright@googlemail.com

1 CLAYTON HALL (IRE), 5, b g Lilbourne Lad (IRE)—Hawk Dance (IRE) **I. J. Barran**
2 EXIT TO FREEDOM, 12, ch g Exit To Nowhere (USA)—Bobanvi **I. J. Barran**
3 HENRIETTA'S DREAM, 4, b f Henrythenavigator (USA)—Timeless Dream **Chatterbox Racing Partnership**
4 ITALIAN BEAUTY (IRE), 6, b m Thewayyouare (USA)—Edelfa (IRE) **Mr T. G. Davies**
5 JUST HEATHER (IRE), 4, gr f Zebedee—Miss Sundance (IRE) **Mr T. G. Davies**
6 KNOCKAMANY BENDS (IRE), 8, b g Majestic Missile (IRE)—Sweet Compliance **D. R. & E. E. Brown**
7 LOTS OV (IRE), 4, b f Rock of Gibraltar (IRE)—Bright Enough **I. J. Barran**
8 QUASHA, 5, b m Black Sam Bellamy (IRE)—Gloriana **Miss P. M. Smith**
9 ROSIE HALL (IRE), 8, ch m Lion Heart (USA)—Baltic Dip (IRE) **R & E Hall & Son**
10 ROSSINGTON, 9, b g Gentleman's Deal (IRE)—Ettrbee **Brian Robb. David Hoyes. Mark Phillips.**
11 ROUGH JUSTICE (IRE), 10, b g Beneficial—Ringzar (IRE) **Mr D. J. Sturdy**
12 TICKS THE BOXES (IRE), 6, ch g Fast Company (IRE)—Swan Sea (USA) **Caballo Racing**
13 ZARKAVON, 4, b f Avonbridge—Zarkavean **J. S. Wainwright & Peter Clarke**
14 ZILLA, 4, ch f Zamindar (USA)—Caesarea (GER) **Mr W Bavill & Mr D. Bavill**

THREE-YEAR-OLDS

15 ANGIE B (IRE), b f Acclamation—Musical Peace (IRE) **Mr W Bavill & Mr D. Bavill**
16 MR WING (IRE), b br c Dandy Man (IRE)—Siesta Time **Gareth Davis & John Wainwright**

MR JOHN WAINWRIGHT - Continued

Other Owners: Mr W. C. Bavill, Mr D. Bavill, D. R. Brown, Mrs E. E. Brown, Mr P. R. Clarke, Mr R. Hall, Mr R. C. Hall, Mr D. N. Hoyes, Mr M. D. Phillips, Mr B. W. Robb, J. S. Wainwright, Mr B. J. P. Walker.

Assistant Trainer: Mrs Fiona Wainwright

Jockey (flat): Tom Eaves, Paddy Aspell.

---

570 **MR ROBERT WALEY-COHEN, Banbury**
Postal: Upton Viva, Banbury, Oxfordshire, OX15 6HT
Contacts: PHONE (02072) 446022 MOBILE (07831) 888778
E-MAIL rwc@uptonviva.co.uk WEBSITE www.uptonestate.co.uk

1 FACILE BIEN (IRE), 7, b g Beneficial—Up A Dee (IRE) **Mr R. B. Waley-Cohen**
2 LUCARNO EXPRESS, 7, b g Lucarno (USA)—Tay Jay Vay (IRE) **Mr R. B. Waley-Cohen**
3 THE JAFFNA QUEEN, 5, b m Black Sam Bellamy (IRE)—Shatabdi (IRE) **Mr R. B. Waley-Cohen**

Assistant Trainer: Kate Mawle

Amateur: Mr S. Waley-Cohen.

---

571 **MR MARK WALFORD, Sheriff Hutton**
Postal: Trainer did not wish details of his string to appear

---

572 **MR ROBERT WALFORD, Blandford**
Postal: Heart of Oak Stables, Okeford Fitzpane, Blandford, Dorset, DT11 0LW
Contacts: MOBILE (07815) 116209
E-MAIL robertwalford1@gmail.com

1 ACARO (FR), 4, b g Sinndar (IRE)—Accusation (IRE) **Alvin Trowbridge & Christine Hinks**
2 BACT TO BLACK, 6, b g Black Sam Bellamy (IRE)—Linagram **Cole, Gale, Levy & Mortimer**
3 BOMBAY RASCAL, 5, ch m Indian Haven—Kohiba (IRE) **Withyslade**
4 CASTARNIE, 10, b g Alflora (IRE)—Just Jenny (IRE) **Sue & Clive Cole & Ann & Tony Gale**
5 CHLOE'S COURT (IRE), 5, br m Court Cave (IRE)—Howaya Pet (IRE) **Cole, Gale, Levy & Mortimer**
6 DRUID'S FOLLY (IRE), 8, b g Beneficial—Sweet Vale (IRE) **R. H. Alner**
7 DUSKY LARK, 8, b g Nayef (USA)—Snow Goose **Mrs Sara Biggins & Mrs Celia Djivanovic**
8 JEFFREY, 5, ch g Apple Tree (FR)—Jambles **Tony & Susan Brimble**
9 KOHUMA, 8, ch m Halling (USA)—Kohiba (IRE) **Withyslade**
10 LE BOIZELO (FR), 7, b g Irish Wells (FR)—Bois Tendre (FR) **Dr & Mrs John Millar**
11 LLANCILLO LORD (IRE), 8, b g Beneficial—Llancillo Lady (IRE) **Mr R. J. Brown**
12 MR MEDIC, 7, b g Dr Massini (IRE)—Danse Slave (FR) **The White Hart Company**
13 OUR MERLIN, 6, b g Pasternak—Lorgnette **A. J. M. Trowbridge**
14 SMAOINEAMH ALAINN (IRE), 6, b m Shantou (USA)—Dathuil (IRE) **Yeo Racing Partnership**
15 SYDNEY DE BAUNE (FR), 7, b g Califet (FR)—Perle De Baune (FR) **Mrs S. De Wilde**
16 TIKKEN AWAY (IRE), 7, gr g Tikkanen (USA)—Lady Goldilocks (IRE) **The Keightley Lambert Partnership**
17 TOM NEARY (IRE), 11, b g Atraf—La Fandango (IRE) **Mrs C. A. Lewis-Jones**
18 UMBERTO D'OLIVATE (FR), 10, b g Alberto Giacometti (FR)—Komunion (FR) **Mrs S. De Wilde**
19 VAZIANI (FR), 4, b g Sinndar (IRE)—Visinova (FR) **C. C. Pugsley**
20 WALK IN THE MILL (FR), 8, b g Walk In The Park (IRE)—Libre Amour (FR) **Baroness D. M. Harding**

Other Owners: Mrs S. J. Biggins, Mr David Bond, Mrs S. L. Brimble, Mr A. F. G. Brimble, Mr C. Cole, Mrs S. S. Cole, Mrs C. J. Djivanovic, Mr A. P. Gale, Mrs A. G. Gale, Mr A. G. Ham, Mrs C. M. Hinks, Mrs C. Keightley, Mr T. P. Lambert, Mr A. R. Levy, Dr J. W. Millar, Mrs J. D. Millar, Mr B. Mortimer, K. B. W. Parkhouse, Miss H. Pease, Mr E. W. White, Mrs K. D. Yeo.

Jockey (NH): James Best.

573 MR ED WALKER, Upper Lambourn

Postal: **Kingsdown Stables, Upper Lambourn, Hungerford, Berkshire, RG17 8QX**
Contacts: PHONE **(01488) 674148** MOBILE **(07787) 534145**
E-MAIL **ed@edwalkerracing.com** WEBSITE **www.edwalkerracing.com**

1 **ABEL TASMAN,** 4, b g Mount Nelson—Helena Molony (IRE) **Laurence Bellman & David Ward**
2 **AEOLUS,** 7, b g Araafa (IRE)—Bright Moll **Mr A. R. F. Buxton**
3 **BIG BAD LOL (IRE),** 4, b g Big Bad Bob (IRE)—Indienne (IRE) **Mr L. A. Bellman**
4 **BOLD PREDICTION,** 8, b g Kodiac—Alexander Eliott (IRE) **John Nicholls (Trading) & Matthew Cottis**
5 **BOYCHICK (IRE),** 5, b g Holy Roman Emperor (IRE)—Al Saqiya (USA) **Mr L. A. Bellman**
6 **BURRUMBEET (IRE),** 4, b g Fastnet Rock (AUS)—Bright Bank (IRE) **O.T.I. Racing**
7 **CORKED (IRE),** 5, b m Mastercraftsman (IRE)—Dama'a (IRE) **Benatom Racing**
8 **DARK PEARL (IRE),** 4, b g Born To Sea (IRE)—Luanas Pearl (IRE) **O.T.I. Racing & Mr Chi Un Fred Ma**
9 **DI ALTA (IRE),** 4, b f High Chaparral (IRE)—Dibiya (IRE) **Mr R. Ng**
10 **DREAM FARR (IRE),** 5, b g Dream Ahead (USA)—French Lady (NZ) **Kingsdown Racing Club**
11 **GARBANZO (IRE),** 4, gr g Mastercraftsman (IRE)—Noble Fantasy (GER) **Mr C. E. Stedman**
12 **INDIAN BLESSING,** 4, ch f Sepoy (AUS)—Alpen Glen **Mr P. K. Siu**
13 **INLAWED,** 4, b g Bahamian Bounty—Regent's Park **Mr L. A. Bellman**
14 **KNOW YOUR LIMIT (IRE),** 4, ch g Tamayuz—Rapid Ransom (USA) **Mr B. T. C. Liu**
15 **MADAME BOUNTY (IRE),** 4, b f Bahamian Bounty—Madame Boulangere **Paola Hewins Olivia Hoare**
16 **PARADISE LAKE (IRE),** 4, b g Siyouni (FR)—Kalandara (IRE) **Laurence Bellman & Partner**
17 **RECKLESS WAVE (IRE),** 5, b m Cape Cross (IRE)—Fairybook (USA) **Mrs G. Walker**
18 **SABADOR (FR),** 4, gr g Kendargent (FR)—Sabadora (FR) **Mr P. K. Siu**
19 **SAYEM,** 4, b f Sayif (IRE)—Usem **B Greenwood, I Dodds-Smith & R Hatter**
20 **SKY EAGLE (IRE),** 4, ch c Lope de Vega (IRE)—Penelope Star (GER) **Mr M. Betamar**
21 **SKY MARSHAL (IRE),** 4, b g Lawman (FR)—Evensong (GER) **Dubai Thoroughbred Racing**
22 **SMILEY BAGEL (IRE),** 5, b g Kyllachy—Epistoliere (IRE) **Mr L. A. Bellman**
23 **STORMY ANTARCTIC,** 5, ch g Stormy Atlantic (USA)—Bea Remembered **Mr P. K. Siu**
24 **TINOS (GER),** 4, b g Soldier Hollow—Ticinella (GER) **H.H. Sheikh Mohammed bin Khalifa Al-Thani**
25 **TUFF ROCK (USA),** 4, b g Fastnet Rock (USA)—
            Wonder of Wonders (USA) **H.H. Sheikh Mohammed bin Khalifa Al-Thani**
26 **ULTIMATE AVENUE (IRE),** 4, b g Excelebration (IRE)—Dance Avenue (IRE) **Mr P. K. Siu**
27 **WOLOWITZ (IRE),** 5, b g Intense Focus (USA)—Tranquil Sky **Mr P. K. Siu**

THREE-YEAR-OLDS

28 **AGROTERA (IRE),** ch f Mastercraftsman (IRE)—Lombatina (FR) **B. E. Nielsen**
29 **AKBAR SHAH (IRE),** b g Oasis Dream—Priceless Jewel **B. E. Nielsen**
30 **ARENDELLE,** b f Camelot—Ape Attack **Chasemore Farm LLP**
31 **ARMED (IRE),** b c Invincible Spirit (IRE)—Ange Bleu (USA) **B. E. Nielsen**
32 **ASSASSINATOR,** b c Hurricane Run (IRE)—Saphira's Fire (USA) **Mr Bjorn Nielsen & Eastwind Racing Ltd**
33 **ASTOLAT,** b f Camelot—Sablonne **Mr C. E. Stedman**
34 **BLACKHEATH,** b g Excelebration (IRE)—Da's Wish (IRE) **Mr M. J. Cottis**
35 **BRIGHAM YOUNG,** b r c Street Cry (IRE)—Bible Belt (IRE) **B. E. Nielsen**
36 **CARADOC (IRE),** b c Camelot—Applause (FR) **Mr P. K. Siu**
37 **CATOCA (USA),** b f Lemon Drop Kid (USA)—Catrageous (USA) **B. E. Nielsen**
38 **DESERT DOCTOR (IRE),** ch g Society Rock (IRE)—Dorn Hill **Mrs F. H. Hay**
39 **ENZO (IRE),** b g Exceed And Excel (AUS)—Zamhrear **Mr P. K. Siu**
40 **FILLE DE REVE,** b f Iffraaj—Danehill Dreamer (USA) **Mr Bjorn Nielsen & Lord Lloyd Webber**
41 **GLOBAL EXCEL,** b c Exceed And Excel (AUS)—Seta **KIR (HK) Ltd & Dr Johnny Hon**
42 **GLOBAL MELODY,** b g Hellvelyn—Dash of Lime **Dr J. Hon**
43 **GLOBAL PASS,** b g Exceed And Excel (AUS)—Mary Boleyn (IRE) **KIR (HK) Ltd & Dr Johnny Hon**
44 **GLORIOUS ARMY,** ch c Declaration of War (USA)—Shibina (IRE) **Kangyu Int. Racing (HK) Ltd & Mr F Ma**
45 **GOLDEN FOOTSTEPS (IRE),** b f Footstepsinthesand—Contemplate **Fly Like An Eagle Syndicate**
46 **GRACE'S SECRET,** ro f Mastercraftsman (IRE)—Silent Music (IRE) **Mr C. E. Stedman**
47 **GREAVES,** b g Paco Boy (IRE)—Noble Plum (IRE) **South Wind Racing 3**
48 **GUNNAR JULIUS (USA),** b c Lonhro (AUS)—Peinture Ancienne (USA) **Mr P. K. Siu**
49 **HOMBRE CASADO (FR),** b c Siyouni (FR)—Storma (FR) **Mr P. K. Siu**
50 **ICONIC KNIGHT (IRE),** b g Sir Prancealot (IRE)—Teutonic (IRE) **J Nicholls, J Moorhouse & J Kinning**
51 **ISOLETTA,** b f Oasis Dream—Miss Cap Estel **John Pearce Racing Limited**
52 B f New Approach (IRE)—Kelly Nicole (IRE) **Lord A. Lloyd-Webber**
53 **LEGAL HISTORY (IRE),** b c Lawman (FR)—Nina Celebre (USA) **Mr P. K. Siu**
54 **MAYGOLD,** b f Mayson—Spanish Gold **Farleigh Racing**
55 **MIRACLE WORKS,** gr g Kyllachy—Eastern Destiny **Mr P. K. Siu**
56 **MOLLS MEMORY,** ch f Helmet (AUS)—Bright Moll **Mr A. R. F. Buxton**
57 **MOM SAID (IRE),** b g Lawman (FR)—Istishaara (USA) **Mrs D. A. LaRoche**

MR ED WALKER - Continued

58 **MOOD FOR MISCHIEF,** b c Nathaniel (IRE)—Tina's Spirit (IRE) **Dubai Thoroughbred Racing**
59 **MOUNTAIN PEAK,** b g Swiss Spirit—Nolas Lolly (IRE) **Ebury Racing**
60 **PETRUCHIO (IRE),** b c New Approach (IRE)—The Shrew **OTI Racing & Anglo Australian Racing**
61 **QUALITY SEEKER (USA),** b c Quality Road (USA)—Arravale (USA) **Mr P. K. Siu**
62 **SIMPSON (IRE),** ch g Dragon Pulse (IRE)—Salydora (FR) **Mr R. A. Pegum**
63 **SINGING SHERIFF,** b g Lawman (FR)—La Felicita **Mr R. Ng**
64 **STEPHENSONS ROCKET (IRE),** gr c Teofilo (IRE)—Tipperary Honor (FR) **B. E. Nielsen**
65 **TOSHIMA (IRE),** b g Sea The Stars (IRE)—Sabreon **Mr P. K. Siu**
66 **TREVENA,** b f Camelot—Santolina (USA) **Mr Bjorn Nielsen & Eastwind Racing Ltd**
67 **U S S MISSOURI (USA),** b g War Front (USA)—
         I'm So Excited (USA) **H.H. Sheikh Mohammed bin Khalifa Al-Thani**
68 **VELVET BROCADE,** b f Cacique (IRE)—Venteuse **Marchwood Aggregates**
69 **WAR NO MORE (USA),** br f War Front (USA)—Moth (IRE) **H.H. Sheikh Mohammed bin Khalifa Al-Thani**

TWO-YEAR-OLDS

70 B f 21/3 Kodiac—Audacia (IRE) (Sixties Icon) (40000) **Mr L. A. Bellman**
71 **BEGUILING CHARM (IRE),** b f 18/5 Charm Spirit (IRE)—Bryanstown (IRE) (Galileo (IRE)) (6000) **Mr M. J. Cottis**
72 **CAP FRANCAIS,** b c 19/2 Frankel—Miss Cap Ferrat (Darshaan) **John Pearce Racing Limited**
73 **GLOBAL ARMY,** gr c 6/3 Lethal Force (IRE)—
         Path of Peace (Rock of Gibraltar (IRE)) (115000) **Dr Johnny Hon & KIR (HK) Ltd**
74 **GLORIOUS CHARMER,** b c 27/1 Charm Spirit (IRE)—
         Fantacise (Pivotal) (52000) **Kangyu International Racing (HK) Limited**
75 **GLORIOUS GALAXY,** b c 18/3 Garswood—
         Celeste (Green Desert (USA)) (55000) **Kangyu International Racing (HK) Limited**
76 **GLORIOUS LOVER (IRE),** b c 2/2 Tamayuz—
         Love Match (Danehill Dancer (IRE)) (100000) **KIR (HK) Ltd & Dr Johnny Hon**
77 B c 10/3 Frankel—Guaranda (Acatenango (GER)) (475000) **Mr Bjorn Nielsen & Eastwind Racing Ltd**
78 Br f 1/5 New Approach (IRE)—Hoity Toity (Darshaan) (280000) **B. E. Nielsen**
79 B br c 15/4 Raven's Pass (USA)—Inchberry (Barathea (IRE)) (15000) **Ebury Racing 2**
80 B c 6/4 Mastercraftsman (IRE)—Livia's Dream (IRE) (Teofilo (IRE))
81 B f 3/2 Sea The Stars (IRE)—Lombatina (FR) (King's Best (USA)) **B. E. Nielsen**
82 B c 23/4 Helmet (AUS)—
         Loose Julie (IRE) (Cape Cross (IRE)) (42000) **Highclere Thoroughbred Racing -SyonHouse**
83 Ch f 15/4 Fast Company (IRE)—Melpomene (Peintre Celebre (USA)) (6000) **Mr E. C. D. Walker**
84 B f 13/4 Iffraaj—Morning Frost (IRE) (Duke of Marmalade (IRE)) (150000) **B. E. Nielsen**
85 **NARYSHKINA,** ch f 14/3 Leroidesanimaux (BRZ)—Nadeszhda (Nashwan (USA)) **Miss K. Rausing**
86 B f 3/2 New Approach (IRE)—Padmini (Tiger Hill (IRE))
87 B c 26/1 Xtension (IRE)—Park Glen (IRE) (Tagula (IRE)) (109523) **Mr S. F. Hui**
88 Ch c 20/2 Slade Power (IRE)—Pivotal's Princess (IRE) (Pivotal) (89540) **Mr P. K. Siu**
89 B c 9/3 Invincible Spirit (IRE)—Priceless Jewel (Selkirk (USA)) (105000) **B. E. Nielsen**
90 **QUICKSILVER,** b f 5/4 Coach House (IRE)—
         Poulaine Bleue (Bertolini (USA)) (12000) **Mr B Greenwood & Mr Hatter**
91 Br gr c 10/3 Dark Angel (IRE)—Silver Shoon (IRE) (Fasliyev (USA)) (480000) **Mr P. K. Siu**
92 B f 21/1 Casamento (IRE)—Siphon Melody (USA) (Siphon (BRZ)) **Mr D. Ward**
93 B f 6/4 Swiss Spirit—Spotlight (Dr Fong (USA)) (19047) **Lordship Stud**
94 **SUNDAY STAR,** b f 24/1 Kodiac—Northern Star (IRE) (Montjeu (IRE)) **Mr D. Ward**
95 B c 2/4 Dansili—Super Sleuth (IRE) (Selkirk (USA)) (46000)
96 B c 25/4 Dandy Man (IRE)—Surreal (IRE) (Shamardal (USA)) (40700) **Mr C. U. F. Ma**
97 Ch c 17/3 Mastercraftsman (IRE)—Tara Moon (Pivotal) (120000) **Mr Bjorn Nielsen & Eastwind Racing Ltd**
98 B c 4/2 Dandy Man (IRE)—Triggers Broom (IRE) (Arcano (IRE)) (195360) **Mr P. K. Siu**
99 Gr ro c 6/2 Gio Ponti (USA)—Vapour Musing (Manduro (GER))

Other Owners: Mr P. Afia, Anglo Australian Racing, Mr A. M. Basing, A. W. Black, Mrs J. E. Black, Mr H. Branch, Mr J. Clark, Mr L. Cowan, Mr I. Dodds-Smith, Mr A. Donald, East Wind Racing Ltd, B. J. R. Greenwood, Mrs E. A. Harris, T. F. Harris, Mr R. M. Hatter, Mr T. Henderson, Mrs P Hewins, Highclere Thoroughbred Racing Ltd, Mrs O. Hoare, Sir C. J. S. Hobhouse, Lady A. Hobhouse, Mr J. Hobson, John Nicholls (Trading) Ltd, Mr J. Kinning, Mr D. A. MacCarthy, Mr J. H. Moorhouse, Mrs L. Mulcahy, Mr S. O'Donnell, Mr R. Pritchard, Mr S. Straker, Mr I. R. Twigden, T. J. D. Walker, Mrs O. J. Wilmott, Mr E. Wilmott.

Assistant Trainer: Jack Steels

574 MR CHRIS WALL, Newmarket
Postal: **Induna Stables, Fordham Road, Newmarket, Suffolk, CB8 7AQ**
Contacts: **OFFICE (01638) 661999 HOME (01638) 668896 FAX (01638) 667279**
MOBILE (07764) 940255
E-MAIL christianwall@btconnect.com WEBSITE www.chriswallracing.co.uk

1 **ATLANTA BELLE (IRE)**, 4, ch f Zebedee—Tara Too (IRE) **The Leap Year Partnership**
2 **CALM CHARM (IRE)**, 4, ch f Teofilo (IRE)—Mango Lady **Ms A. Fustoq**
3 **DECIDING VOTE**, 4, b f Pivotal—Clincher Club **Mrs Barry Green & Partners**
4 **FIRST SITTING**, 7, b g Dansili—Aspiring Diva (USA) **Bringloe & Clarke**
5 **FLOOD DEFENCE (IRE)**, 4, b f Harbour Watch (IRE)—Krynica (USA) **Horsetrader One**
6 **HI HO SILVER**, 4, gr g Camacho—Silver Spell **Mrs P. J. Toye**
7 **ICE LORD (IRE)**, 6, gr g Verglas (IRE)—Special Lady (FR) **Hintlesham Racing Ltd**
8 **MARILYN**, 4, ch f Sixties Icon—Donatia **Lady Juliet Tadgell, D Swinburn & C Wall**
9 **MOUNTAIN RESCUE (IRE)**, 6, b g High Chaparral (IRE)—Amber Queen (IRE) **ValueRacingClub.co.uk**
10 **OH IT'S SAUCEPOT**, 4, b f Sir Percy—Oh So Saucy **The Eight of Diamonds**
11 **OH SO SASSY**, 8, b m Pastoral Pursuits—Almasi (IRE) **The Eight of Diamonds**
12 **SEYASAH (IRE)**, 4, b f Casamento (IRE)—Defensive Boast (USA) **Archangels 2**
13 **SYRIAN PEARL**, 7, gr m Clodovil (IRE)—Syrian Queen **The Clodhoppers**
14 **ZEYZOUN (FR)**, 4, b g Excelebration (IRE)—Zayanida (IRE) **Mr M. J. Bringloe**

THREE-YEAR-OLDS
15 **BLACK LOTUS**, b f Declaration of War (USA)—Ravensburg **Ms A. Fustoq**
16 **FOLLOW INTELLO (IRE)**, b g Intello (GER)—Sauvage (FR) **Ms A. Fustoq**
17 **HAN SOLO BERGER (IRE)**, b g Lord Shanakill (USA)—Dreamaway (IRE) **Mrs B. J. Berresford**
18 **JUMPING CATS**, ch g Champs Elysees—Pivotal Drive (IRE) **Mr D. M. Thurlby**
19 **LADY TULIP**, b f Lord Shanakill (USA)—Red Tulip **The Red Heads Partnership**
20 **PARISIAN AFFAIR**, b f Champs Elysees—Trinkila (USA) **Mr D. S. Lee**
21 **PENTLAND HILLS (IRE)**, b g Motivator—Elle Galante (GER) **Mr D. M. Thurlby**
22 B g Swiss Spirit—Snow Angel (IRE) **Mr D. S. Lee**
23 **SPRITZIG**, ch f Exceed And Excel (AUS)—Generous Lady **Ms A. Fustoq**
24 **THE FIDDLER**, b g Big Bad Bob (IRE)—Strings **The Equema Partnership**
25 **VANTASY**, b g Rip Van Winkle (IRE)—Tesary **Botham & Tilbrook**
26 **WILD MIX**, ch f Mastercraftsman (IRE)—Mango Lady **Ms A. Fustoq**

TWO-YEAR-OLDS
27 B c 4/2 Intello (GER)—Brazilian Bride (IRE) (Pivotal) (24000) **Induna Racing**
28 B c 23/4 Sepoy (AUS)—Generous Lady (Generous (IRE)) **Ms A. Fustoq**
29 B f 23/3 Charm Spirit (IRE)—
Lalectra (King Charlemagne (USA)) (35000) **Valueracingclub.co.uk & Bickmarsh Stud**
30 **LUCKY CHARM**, b f 22/2 Charm Spirit (IRE)—Drift And Dream (Exceed And Excel (AUS)) **Lady Juliet Tadgell**
31 **PURGATORY**, b c 15/2 Dark Angel (IRE)—Meet Me Halfway (Exceed And Excel (AUS)) (50000) **Mr D. M. Thurlby**
32 B f 3/5 Kingman—World Class (Galileo (IRE)) **Ms A. Fustoq**

Other Owners: Mr S. Atkin, Mrs C. & Mr D. Atkinson, Mr T. J. Bater, Mr J. Beighton, Mr H. Bethell, Mr Peter Botham, Mr Michael Bringloe, Mr R. A. Clarke, Mr N. Collins, Mr James Couldwell, Mr Paul Couldwell, Mrs J. E. Dobie, Mr Stuart Feast, Mr R. Fraiser, Mr E. Fronteddu, Mr G. Gibbs, Mr H. Hurst, Mr & Mrs H. Hurst, Mrs Jill Kerr-Smiley, Mr R. Machin, Mr Roger Nash, Mr G. Nutting, Mr P. Proctor, Mr S. Sin, Mrs Jill Smith, Mrs Emma Stamper, Mr M. Stevens, Mr R. Sutton, Mrs Doreen M. Swinburn, Mr Michael Swinburn, Lady Juliet Tadgell, Mr M. Tilbrook, Mrs C. J. Walker, Mrs C. A. Wall, Mr R. J. Wayman, Mr B. Westley, Mrs J. Westley.

Assistant Trainer: Michael Fenton

Jockey (flat): Ted Durcan.

575 MR TREVOR WALL, Craven Arms
Postal: **Hope Farm Stables, Twitchen, Clunbury, Craven Arms, Shropshire, SY7 0HN**
Contacts: **PHONE (01588) 660219 MOBILE (07972) 732080**
E-MAIL trevorwall56@outlook.com

1 **MAXI MAC (IRE)**, 8, ch g Thousand Words—Crimada (IRE) **D. Pugh**
2 **MAY MIST**, 6, b m Nayef (USA)—Midnight Mist (IRE) **A. H. Bennett**
3 **TARA'S RAINBOW**, 8, b m Kayf Tara—Nile Cristale (FR) **C. G. Johnson**

MR TREVOR WALL - Continued

THREE-YEAR-OLDS

4 B f Mawatheeq (USA)—Curtains

Assistant Trainer: Mrs J. A. Wall

Conditional: Josh Wall.

---

576 | MR CHARLIE WALLIS, Ardleigh
Postal: **Benson Stud, Harts Lane, Ardleigh, Colchester, Essex, CO7 7QE**
Contacts: **PHONE (01206) 230779 MOBILE (07725) 059355**
E-MAIL cwallis86@hotmail.com

1 AFRICAN BLESSING, 5, ch g Mount Nelson—Bella Beguine **Mr J. O. C. Tomkins**
2 BILLYOAKES (IRE), 6, b g Kodiac—Reality Check (IRE) **Roalco Ltd**
3 CHETAN, 6, b g Alfred Nobel (IRE)—Island Music (IRE) **Roger & Val Miles, Tony Stamp**
4 COORG (IRE), 6, ch g Teofilo (IRE)—Creese **Exors of the Late Mrs I. L. Sneath**
5 COULD BE GOLD (IRE), 4, b g Delegator—Outshine
6 DIVINE CALL, 11, b g Pivotal—Pious **Roalco Ltd**
7 FAREEQ, 4, gr g Dark Angel (IRE)—Spate (IRE) **P. E. Axon**
8 FAVORITE STORY, 4, b g Equiano (FR)—Primavera
9 GEORGE DRYDEN (IRE), 6, gr g Zebedee—Key To Fortune (GER) **Dab Hand Racing**
10 LA FORTUNA, 5, b m Zamindar (USA)—Hyperspace **P. E. Axon**
11 SHARP OPERATOR, 5, ch g Medicean—Helen Sharp **Mr L. Brooks**
12 TIME TO REASON (IRE), 5, b g Kyllachy—Danehurst **J.E.Titley & J.Goddard**
13 ZAC BROWN (IRE), 7, b g Kodiac—Mildmay (USA) **Porterhouse Ltd. J Goddard**

THREE-YEAR-OLDS

14 SIR HECTOR (IRE), ch g Sir Prancealot (IRE)—Awwal Malika (USA) **Roalco Ltd**

Other Owners: Mr J. W. Goddard, Mrs V. Miles, Mr K. R. Miles, D. Pearson, A. D. Pirie, Porterhouse Building Services Ltd, Mr A. P Stamp, J. E. Titley.

Assistant Trainer: Hayley Wallis

---

577 | MRS JANE WALTON, Otterburn
Postal: **Dunns Houses, Otterburn, Newcastle Upon Tyne, Tyne and Wear, NE19 1LB**
Contacts: **PHONE (01830) 520677 FAX (01830) 520677 MOBILE (07808) 592701**
E-MAIL dunnshouses@hotmail.com WEBSITE www.janewaltonhorseracing.co.uk

1 DEVILS WATER, 7, b g Overbury (IRE)—Reel Charmer **Mrs J. M. Walton**
2 REAL ARMANI, 6, ch g Sulamani (IRE)—Reel Charmer **Mrs J. M. Walton**
3 REVERSE THE CHARGE (IRE), 11, b g Bishop of Cashel—Academy Jane (IRE) **Fresh Start Partnership**
4 THEDFACTOR (IRE), 9, b g Kalanisi (IRE)—Insan Magic (IRE) **Fresh Start Partnership**
5 WESTEND THEATRE (IRE), 9, b g Darsi (FR)—Ballyvelig Lady (IRE) **Mrs J. M. Walton**

Other Owners: Mrs M. Ridley, Mrs J. M. Walton.

Assistant Trainer: Mrs Patricia Robson (07947)152350

Conditional: Callum Bewley, Tommy Dowson, Dale Irving. **Amateur:** Miss Amy Waugh.

---

578 | MR JASON WALTON, Morpeth
Postal: **Flotterton Hall, Thropton, Morpeth, Northumberland, NE65 7LF**
Contacts: **PHONE (01669) 640253 FAX (01669) 640288 MOBILE (07808) 592701**

1 CATCHAMAT, 9, b m Overbury (IRE)—More Flair **Messrs F. T. Walton**
2 CENTRAL FLAME, 10, ch g Central Park (IRE)—More Flair **Messrs F. T. Walton**
3 DUN FAW GOOD, 11, b g Grape Tree Road—Dun Rose **Messrs F. T. Walton**
4 FRENCH TICKET, 7, b g Bollin Eric—Merry Tina **Messrs F. T. Walton**
5 MATTHEW MAN, 7, b g Bollin Eric—Garden Feature **Messrs F. T. Walton**
6 PLAY PRACTICE, 8, b m Josr Algarhoud (IRE)—More Flair **Messrs F. T. Walton**
7 5, B g Sulamani (IRE)—Posh Stick

MR JASON WALTON - Continued

   8 RIPSTICK, 7, b g Lucarno (USA)—Posh Stick **Messrs F. T. Walton**
   9 ROLL OF THUNDER, 9, b g Antonius Pius (USA)—Ischia **Messrs F. T. Walton**
10 5, B m Flying Legend (USA)—Watch The Wind

Other Owners: F. A. Walton, J. B. Walton.

---

579   **MRS SHEENA WALTON, Hexham**
Postal: **Linacres, Wark, Hexham, Northumberland, NE48 3DP**
Contacts: **PHONE (01434) 230656 MOBILE (07752) 755184**
E-MAIL **linacres@btconnect.com**

1 ALL MY FRIENDS SAY (IRE), 7, b g Scorpion (IRE)—Sounds Attractive (IRE) **R. H. & S. C. Walton**
2 DAYDREAM ISLAND (IRE), 8, b g Trans Island—Ring Hill **Mr J. A. Ogle**
3 5, Ch m Stowaway—Drama Chick **R. H. & S. C. Walton**
4 NATIVE OPTIMIST (IRE), 11, b g Broadway Flyer (USA)—Native Orchid (IRE) **R. H. & S. C. Walton**
5 THE CONN (IRE), 8, b g Milan—Grandy Invader (IRE) **R. H. & S. C. Walton**
6 WARKSBURN BOY, 8, b g Kayf Tara—Bonchester Bridge **Rede Tyne Racing**

Other Owners: Mr S. Hutton, Mrs M. Rogerson, Mrs S. Walton, R. H. Walton.

Assistant Trainer: Mr R. H. Walton

Amateur: Miss C. Walton.

---

580   **MR JASON WARD, Middleham**
Postal: **The Dante Yard, Manor House Stables, Middleham, Leyburn, North Yorkshire, DL8 4QL**
Contacts: **PHONE (01969) 622730 MOBILE (07967) 357595**
E-MAIL **info@jasonwardracing.co.uk WEBSITE www.jasonwardracing.co.uk**

1 BITTERSWEET (IRE), 4, ch f Power—Jessie Jane (IRE) **Mrs Teresa Ward**
2 KING'S PAVILION (IRE), 5, b g King's Best (USA)—Embassy **Mr Peter Ward**
3 MAIFALKI (FR), 5, b g Falco (USA)—Makila (IRE) **Lamont Racing**
4 MONTE CINQ (IRE), 4, b g Bushranger (IRE)—Invincible Me (IRE) **John Sutton, Ian Cope, Dante Yard Racing**
5 ROLL ON RORY, 5, b g Mullionmileanhour (IRE)—Fangfoss Girls **P Adams, J Sutton, T Wickins, J Hetherington**
6 YPRES, 9, b g Byron—Esligier (IRE) **Dante Yard Racing Club**

THREE-YEAR-OLDS

7 MEERPAT, br f Kyllachy—Fluttering Rose **Lamont Racing**

TWO-YEAR-OLDS

   8 Gr f 1/1 Toronado (IRE)—Alabastrine (Green Desert (USA)) (16280) **Mr Oscar Ortmans**
   9 B f 24/1 Hurricane Run (IRE)—Driven Snow (FR) (Linamix (FR)) (5698) **Mr Oscar Ortmans**
10 MY GIRL (IRE), gr f 15/5 Kendargent (FR)—Zewara (FR) (Alhaarth (IRE)) (8954) **Mr Oscar Ortmans**
11 WEE JIM (IRE), b c 31/3 Canford Cliffs (IRE)—Marydale (Aqlaam) **Lamont Racing**

Other Owners: Dante Yard Racing Club, Mrs W. Hutchinson, Mr S. Jack, Mr G. Rowe, Mr J. Teal.

Assistant Trainer: James Roberts

---

581   **MISS TRACEY WATKINS, Kington**
Postal: **Rose Villa, Holmes Marsh, Lyonshall, Kington, Herefordshire, HR5 3JS**
Contacts: **MOBILE (07812) 804758**
E-MAIL **traceyswatkins@googlemail.com**

1 GOAL (IRE), 10, b g Mujadil (USA)—Classic Lin (FR) **K. M. Parry**
2 ONE COOL BOY (IRE), 9, b br g One Cool Cat (USA)—Pipewell (IRE) **K. M. Parry**

Assistant Trainer: Kevin Parry

Jockey (NH): Ben Poste. **Amateur:** Miss Brodie Hampson.

582 **MR ARCHIE WATSON, Upper Lambourn**
Postal: **Saxon Gate, Upper Lambourn, Hungerford, Berkshire, RG17 8QH**
Contacts: **PHONE (01488) 491247**
E-MAIL office@archiewatsonracing.com WEBSITE www.archiewatsonracing.com

1 **ABSOLUTE BLAST (IRE),** 6, b m Kodiac—Perfect Fun **Apple Tree Stud**
2 **ATTAIN,** 9, b g Dansili—Achieve **Boadicea Bloodstock**
3 **CAPTOR,** 4, b g Frankel—Hasten (IRE) **Al Asayl Bloodstock Ltd**
4 **CHEVALLIER,** 6, b g Invincible Spirit (IRE)—Magical Romance (IRE) **The Chevallier Partnership II**
5 **DUTCH UNCLE,** 6, b g Dutch Art—Evasive Quality (FR) **Mrs Fiona Shaw**
6 **ERINYES (IRE),** 4, gr f Dalakhani (IRE)—Endearing **Al Asayl Bloodstock Ltd**
7 **GENERAL HAZARD (IRE),** 5, gr g Cacique—In The Soup (USA) **Boadicea Bloodstock**
8 **KARIJINI (GER),** 4, b f Siyouni (FR)—Kalahari Dancer **Greenfield Racing**
9 **MACH ONE,** 4, b g Makfi—Perfect Spirit (IRE) **Dr Bridget Drew & Partners**
10 **PETITE JACK,** 5, ch g Champs Elysees—Pilcomayo (IRE) **Mr W. Burn**
11 **PRINCESS DE LUNE (IRE),** 4, gr f Shamardal (USA)—Princess Serena (USA) **Kaniz Bloodstock Investments Ltd**
12 **PULSATING,** 4, b f Dragon Pulse—Safqa **Dream Racing Club**
13 **SNOWY WINTER (USA),** 4, b f Elusive Quality (USA)—Pamona Ball (USA) **Boadicea Bloodstock**
14 **ZENOVIA (IRE),** 4, b f Invincible Spirit (IRE)—Zallerina **Boadicea Bloodstock**

THREE-YEAR-OLDS

15 **ARDEN PEARL (IRE),** b f Swiss Spirit—Music Pearl (IRE) **Jack & Freya Cork**
16 **AXE CAP (IRE),** b f Zebedee—Clouded Leopard (USA) **Mr K. Sohi**
17 **BE THANKFUL,** ch f Helmet (AUS)—Be Joyful (IRE) **Mrs S. L. Richardson**
18 **BLACK SAILS,** br f Lope de Vega (IRE)—Missouri Belle **Mr A. M. B. Watson**
19 **COME ON BEAR (IRE),** b f Dandy Man (IRE)—Blusienka (IRE) **M7 Come On Bear LLP**
20 **CORINTHIA KNIGHT (IRE),** ch c Society Rock (IRE)—Victoria Lodge (IRE) **Ontoawinner & Partner**
21 **DE MEDICI (IRE),** ch g Makfi—Bride Unbridled (IRE) **Al Asayl Bloodstock Ltd**
22 **DEADLY REEL (IRE),** b f Pour Moi (IRE)—Lady Ederle (USA) **Chasemore Farm LLP**
23 **DUBSTEP,** b g Footstepsinthesand—Double Star **Mr K. Sohi**
24 **GHOST SERGE (IRE),** gr c Zebedee—Cornakill (USA) **Champagne Charlies Club & Partners**
25 **HERECOMESTHESUN (IRE),** b f Invincible Spirit (IRE)—Intimacy (IRE) **Carmel Stud**
26 **MERCER'S TROOP (IRE),** b c Canford Cliffs (IRE)—Meek Appeal (USA) **Mr G. P. M. Morland**
27 **MRS CLAYPOOL (IRE),** b f Myboycharlie (IRE)—Melandia (IRE) **Mr W. J. A. Nash**
28 **MRS TEASDALE,** ch f Harbour Watch (IRE)—Ardessie **Mr W. J. A. Nash**
29 **PACIFIC FLEET (IRE),** ch c Elusive Quality (USA)—Coronado Rose (USA) **Apple Tree Stud**
30 **RIO FESTIVAL (USA),** b f First Defence (USA)—Rio Carnival (USA) **Kaniz Bloodstock Investments Ltd**
31 **WE ARE THE WORLD,** b g Sir Percy—Emerald Sea **Mr C. R. Hirst**
32 **YABASS (IRE),** ch c Lope de Vega (IRE)—Fresh Mint (IRE) **The Ride The Lightning Partnership**

TWO-YEAR-OLDS

33 **ALICE'S LEGACY (IRE),** b f 24/2 Society Rock (IRE)—Poetry Aloud (Kheleyf (USA)) (61904) **Mr C. R. Hirst**
34 **ARDEN WARRIOR (IRE),** gr c 27/3 War Command (USA)—
Glowing Star (IRE) (Clodovil (IRE)) (32000) **Jack & Freya Cork**
35 **CLOUD SEEDING (IRE),** ch f 25/2 Gale Force Ten—Indian Angel (Indian Ridge) (29523) **Mr A. M. B. Watson**
36 **FREDDIE'S SPIRIT,** b c 29/3 Swiss Spirit—
Loughtownlady (IRE) (Statue of Liberty (USA)) (24761) **Ontoawinner & Partner**
37 **GALLOVIE,** b f 2/2 Kyllachy—Rowan Brae (Haafhd) (28571) **Marlborough Racing- Gallovie**
38 **GIFTED GEISHA,** b f 6/4 Epaulette (AUS)—Generously Gifted (Sakhee (USA)) (20000) **Mr A. M. B. Watson**
39 **IN TRUTINA,** ch f 28/1 Firebreak—Yearbook (Byron) (8500) **Mrs S. E. A. Sloan**
40 **ISAAN QUEEN (IRE),** b f 6/2 War Command (USA)—
Dundel's Spirit (IRE) (Invincible Spirit (IRE)) (34188) **Mr C. R. Hirst**
41 **JULIUS LIMBANI (IRE),** b c 20/3 Anodin (IRE)—Kshanti (USA) (Diesis) (54538) **Mr W. J. A. Nash**
42 **KHEROS,** b c 17/3 Harbour Watch (IRE)—Almunia (IRE) (Mujadil (USA)) (19536)
43 B c 11/4 Zoffany (IRE)—Loquacity (Diktat) (15000) **Seventh Lap Racing**
44 **LUCHADOR,** b f 30/4 Holy Roman Emperor (IRE)—
Bride Unbridled (IRE) (Hurricane Run (IRE)) **Al Asayl Bloodstock Ltd**
45 **MERINGUE (IRE),** b f 8/2 Battle of Marengo (IRE)—Passaggio (Pivotal) (16280) **Mrs E. Capon**
46 **NATE THE GREAT,** b c 2/2 Nathaniel (IRE)—
Theladyinquestion (Dubawi (IRE)) (30000) **Mildmay Racing & D. H. Caslon**
47 **NINA PETROVNA,** ch f 1/3 Havana Gold (IRE)—
Naizak (Medicean) (30476) **Mr Justin Dowley & Mr Michael Pescod**
48 **SECRET ACE,** ch f 20/1 Compton Place—Secret Romance (Sakhee's Secret) (29304) **Mr C. Brammer**

MR ARCHIE WATSON - Continued

49 B c 25/2 Data Link (USA)—Spring Heather (IRE) (Montjeu (IRE)) (40000) **Mr A. M. B. Watson**
50 Gr c 12/3 Dalakhani (IRE)—St Roch (IRE) (Danehill (USA)) (40700) **The Ride The Lightning Partnership**
51 SURREY BREEZE (IRE), b c 6/2 Footstepsinthesand—
Breezeway (IRE) (Grand Lodge (USA)) (28490) **Surrey Racing Limited**

Other Owners: Mrs J. E. Black, A. W. Black, D. H. Caslon, Champagne Charlies Club, The Chevallier Partnership, Mr J. F. P. Cork, Mrs F. H. B. Cork, Mr R. M. H. Croft-Sharland, Mr L. J. Dowley, Miss P. B. Drew, N. R. R. Drew, Dr S. B. Drew, Mrs D. Dunkley, P. J. Dunkley, Mr J. Fairrie, Mr C. D. Harrison, Mr N. Hassan, Mr P. Hernon, Mr S. Hill, Mr R. P. Jones, Mildmay Racing, Mrs M. E. Morgan, P. H. Morgan, Mr N. J. O'Brien, Mr T. Pearman, M. Pescod, Saxon Thoroughbreds II, Miss C. E. Short, Mr G. E. C. Sloan, Mr P. A. Taylor, Mr T. Williams.

Jockey (flat): E. Greatrex, L. Morris, O. Murphy. **Apprentice:** O. Box-Pook, P. L. Jamin.

---

583 MR FREDERICK WATSON, Sedgefield
Postal: **Beacon Hill, Sedgefield, Stockton-On-Tees, Cleveland, TS21 3HN**
Contacts: PHONE **(01740) 620582** MOBILE **(07773) 321472**
E-MAIL **fredwatson@talktalk.net**

1 BRETON BLUES, 8, b g Street Cry (IRE)—Many Colours **F. Watson**
2 DESTINATION AIM, 11, b g Dubai Destination (USA)—Tessa Reef (IRE) **F. Watson**
3 GLEAMING ARCH, 4, b g Arabian Gleam—Mrs Quince **F. Watson**
4 JOYFUL STAR, 8, b g Teofilo (IRE)—Extreme Beauty (USA) **F. Watson**
5 NEWSPEAK (IRE), 6, b g New Approach (IRE)—Horatia (IRE) **F. Watson**
6 SPOKESPERSON (USA), 10, b g Henny Hughes (USA)—Verbal (USA) **F. Watson**
7 STAR CITIZEN, 6, b g New Approach (IRE)—Faslen (USA) **F. Watson**
8 STRIKE AGAIN, 7, b g Misu Bond (IRE)—Mrs Quince **F. Watson**

---

584 MRS SHARON WATT, Richmond
Postal: **Rosey Hill Farm, Scorton Road, Brompton on Swale, Richmond, North Yorkshire, DL10 7EQ**
Contacts: PHONE **(01748) 812064** FAX **(01748) 812064** MOBILE **(07970) 826046**
E-MAIL **wattfences@aol.com**

1 ARCTIC VODKA, 6, gr g Black Sam Bellamy (IRE)—Auntie Kathleen **Rosey Hill Partnership**
2 CHAMPAGNE RULES, 7, gr g Aussie Rules (USA)—Garabelle (IRE) **Rosey Hill Partnership**
3 KEEPINUPWITDJONES, 6, b g Multiplex—Ceoperk (IRE) **Major E. J. Watt**
4 MADAM LILIBET (IRE), 9, b m Authorized (IRE)—Foxilla (IRE) **Mr D H & E Montgomerie**
5 MYSTERIAL, 8, b g Invincible Spirit (IRE)—Diamond Dilemma (IRE) **Major E. J. Watt**
6 TOO MANY CHIEFS (IRE), 7, br g Indian River (FR)—Wahiba Hall (IRE) **Major E. J. Watt**

THREE-YEAR-OLDS

7 SHAKIAH (IRE), b f Farhh—Dubai Sea (USA) **Mr D H & E Montgomerie**

Other Owners: Mr D. H. Montgomerie, Mrs Elizabeth Montgomerie, Mr F. Previtali, Major E. J. Watt.

---

585 MR SIMON WAUGH, Morpeth
Postal: **A G Waugh & Sons Limited, Molesden House, Molesden, Morpeth, Northumberland, NE61 3QF**
Contacts: MOBILE **(07860) 561445**
E-MAIL **swaugh@dircon.co.uk**

1 BORDER BREAKER (IRE), 9, br g Indian Danehill (IRE)—Flying Answer (IRE) **Jimmy Hack Racing Partners**
2 BORIC, 10, b g Grape Tree Road—Petrea **Mrs S. A. York**
3 CORINDA, 7, b m Midnight Legend—Conchita **Miss R. G. Brewis**
4 DARK AND DANGEROUS (IRE), 10, b g Cacique (IRE)—Gilah (IRE) **Yacht London Racing Ltd**
5 IMPERIAL FOCUS (IRE), 5, b g Intense Focus (USA)—Mrs Cee (IRE) **Yacht London Racing Ltd**
6 KARAT OF GOLD, 7, ch m Lucarno (USA)—Coole Presence (IRE) **S. G. Waugh**
7 LONGMORE (GER), 7, br g Mamool (IRE)—Linara (GER) **Mrs S. A. York**
8 7, B m Multiplex—Mays Delight (IRE)
9 MY ESCAPADE (IRE), 7, ch m Tamayuz—Highly Respected (IRE) **Northumberland Racing Club**
10 NICKI'S NIPPER, 10, b m Denounce—Mistress Star **Northumberland Racing Club**

MR SIMON WAUGH - Continued

11 **NO BOUNDARIES (IRE)**, 6, ch g Spadoun (FR)—Dawn Princess (IRE) **Northumberland Racing Club**
12 **NOTEBOOK**, 7, b g Invincible Spirit (IRE)—Love Everlasting **S. G. Waugh**
13 **ROYAL FLUSH**, 7, b g Multiplex—Mystical Feelings (BEL) **S. G. Waugh**
14 **SINGLE ESTATE**, 4, b g Tamayuz—Duo de Choc (IRE) **S. G. Waugh**
15 **SKYE CHIEF**, 6, b g Sulamani (IRE)—Isle of Skye **Mrs S. A. Sutton**
16 **TOTAL ASSETS**, 10, b m Alflora (IRE)—Maid Equal **Northumberland Racing Club**

Other Owners: Mr S. W. Buckley, Mr S. F. Coton, Mrs V. A. Y. Knox.

---

586 **MR PAUL WEBBER**, Banbury
Postal: Cropredy Lawn, Mollington, Banbury, Oxfordshire, OX17 1DR
Contacts: PHONE (01295) 750226 FAX (01295) 758482 MOBILE (07836) 232465
E-MAIL paul@paulwebberracing.com WEBSITE www.paulwebberracing.com

1 **ALL CHANGE**, 5, b m Motivator—Polly Flinders **Big Bucks Racing**
2 5, B g Jeremy (USA)—Aweebounce (IRE) **Mr J. P. McManus**
3 **BLENHEIM WARRIOR**, 6, gr g Galileo (IRE)—Crystal Swan (IRE) **Saleh Al Homaizi & Imad Al Sagar**
4 **BOUGHTBEFORELUNCH (IRE)**, 5, b g Dubai Destination (USA)—Anie (IRE) **The Let's Do Lunch Partnership**
5 **BREATH OF BLIGHTY (FR)**, 7, b br g Policy Maker (IRE)—Nosika d'airy (FR) **John Nicholls (Trading) Ltd**
6 **CIRCUIT COURT (IRE)**, 7, br g Court Cave (IRE)—Norwich Breeze (IRE) **Mr I. R. Watters**
7 **COPPERFACEJACK (IRE)**, 8, b g Robin des Pres (FR)—Leone Des Pres (FR) **R. W. Barnett**
8 **COSMIC DIAMOND**, 8, b m Multiplex—Lucy Glitters **Economic Security 1**
9 **DASSETT GOLD (FR)**, 5, b g Full of Gold (FR)—Marsavrile (FR) **R. P. Rocher**
10 **ELITE GARDE (FR)**, 4, b g Kapgarde (FR)—Queyrann (FR) **R. P. Rocher**
11 **EURKASH (FR)**, 4, b g Irish Wells (FR)—Meralda (FR) **Paul Webber & Partner**
12 **FINGERS CROSSED (IRE)**, 8, b g Bach (IRE)—Awesome Miracle (IRE) **Cropredy Lawn Racing 2**
13 **GWAFA (IRE)**, 7, gr g Tamayuz—Atalina (FR) **Saleh Al Homaizi & Imad Al Sagar**
14 **KERRERA**, 5, ch m Champs Elysees—Questa Nova **Mrs G. Thomas**
15 **LORD MARMADUKE**, 5, ch g Duke of Marmalade (IRE)—Maid To Treasure (IRE) **The Good Lord Partnership**
16 **MISS TONGABEZI**, 9, b m Overbury (IRE)—Shiwa **Mrs D. J. Webber**
17 **MR BANKS (IRE)**, 7, br g Kalanisi (IRE)—She's Supersonic (IRE) **Cropredy Lawn Racing**
18 **NEW AGENDA**, 6, b g New Approach (IRE)—Prove **Bowden C Magee**
19 4, Br g Oscar (IRE)—Nolagh Supreme (IRE) **Mrs L. M. Shanahan**
20 **ROBIN DEUZ POIS (IRE)**, 6, ch m Robin des Champs (FR)—Native Wood (IRE) **Equi ex Incertis Partners**
21 **ROYAL DEBUTANTE (IRE)**, 7, b m Presenting—Chinatownqueen (IRE) **The Ping Partnership**
22 **SPECIAL ACCEPTANCE**, 5, b g Malinas (GER)—Doubly Guest **The Syndicators 2**
23 **STARJAC (FR)**, 4, gr g Linda's Lad—Star's Mixa (FR) **The Starjac Partnership**
24 **THE HIKING VIKING**, 5, b g Beat Hollow—Swaythe (USA) **Higgy, Mette & Friends 2**
25 **THE VENERABLE BEDE (IRE)**, 7, b g Kalanisi (IRE)—Feedthegoodmare (IRE) **Sir W. J. A. Timpson**
26 **TINDARO (FR)**, 11, gr g Kingsalsa (USA)—Star's Mixa (FR) **Mrs C. L. Smith**
27 **VERY LIVE (FR)**, 9, b g Secret Singer (FR)—Iona Will (FR) **Miss Sheena Pilkington & Partner**
28 **VIKING QUEEN**, 7, b m Presenting—Swaythe (USA) **Higgy, Mette & Friends 1**
29 **WINGS OF DARKNESS (IRE)**, 4, b g Winged Love (IRE)—Night Therapy (IRE) **Bailey Chapman Partnership**
30 **YOUKNOWELL (IRE)**, 5, b m Gold Well—Islands Sister (IRE) **Mr J. P. McManus**

TWO-YEAR-OLDS

31 B c 27/4 Pour Moi (IRE)—Aqua Aura (USA) (Distorted Humor (USA)) **Pour Moi Partnership**
32 B f 19/1 Planteur (IRE)—Belle Chasse (Kyllachy)
33 **DARK MIRACLE (IRE)**, b c 4/3 Mukhadram—Eolith (Pastoral Pursuits) (4500) **Hunor Szebo**

Other Owners: Mr Imad Al-Sagar, Mr R. K. Aston, Mr Bill Bailey, Mr Peter Bell, Mr Nigel Birch, Mr P. Bowden, Mr D. G. Carrington, Mr Peter Charter, Mr D. W. Higgins, Higgy, Mette & Friends, Mr Saleh Al Homaizi, Mr R. S. Jago, Mr Charlie Longsdon, Sir I. Magee, Mr J. Neville, Mr J. G. O'Neill, Mr Martin Pepper, Miss S. Pilkington, Mr Paul Webber.

Jockey (NH): Richie McLernon. **Amateur:** Miss Sophie Smith.

587 **MR D. K. WELD, The Curragh**
Postal: **Rosewell House, Curragh, Co. Kildare, Ireland**
Contacts: **PHONE (00353) 4544 1273 FAX (00353) 4544 1119**
E-MAIL dkweld@rosewellracing.ie

1 **BELLA ESTRELLA (IRE)**, 4, b f High Chaparral (IRE)—Uncharted Haven **Ballylinch Stud**
2 **ESPOIR D'SOLEIL (IRE)**, 4, ch f Galileo (IRE)—Lady Luck (IRE) **Moyglare Stud Farm**
3 **EZIYRA (IRE)**, 4, ch f Teofilo (IRE)—Eytarna (IRE) **H. H. Aga Khan**
4 **KNOWING YOU (IRE)**, 4, ch f Pivotal—She's Our Mark **Moyglare Stud Farm**
5 **MAKING LIGHT (IRE)**, 4, b f Tamayuz—Instant Sparkle (IRE) **Moyglare Stud Farm**
6 **SORELLE DELLE ROSE (IRE)**, 4, gr f Dark Angel (IRE)—Kelsey Rose **Moyglare Stud Farm**
7 **TOCCO D'AMORE (IRE)**, 4, b f Raven's Pass (USA)—Spirit of Tara (IRE) **Moyglare Stud Farm**

THREE-YEAR-OLDS

8 **ALANANNDA (IRE)**, b f Invincible Spirit (IRE)—Alanza (IRE) **H. H. Aga Khan**
9 **ALESSANDRO ALLORI (IRE)**, ch c Dawn Approach (IRE)—Truly Mine (IRE) **Mrs C. C. Regalado-Gonzalez**
10 **BALIYAD (IRE)**, ch c Sea The Stars (IRE)—Baliyana (IRE) **H. H. Aga Khan**
11 **BANDUA (USA)**, gr c The Factor (USA)—If Angels Sang (USA) **Calumet Farm**
12 **BETSEY TROTTER (IRE)**, b f Camacho—Inourthoughts **Mr Frank Gillespie**
13 **BONA FIDE**, ch f Frankel—Honest Quality (USA) **Mr K. Abdullah**
14 **BRIGHT EYED (IRE)**, b f Galileo (IRE)—Christmas Kid (USA) **Mrs J. Magnier**
15 **BROAD STREET**, b c Sea The Stars (IRE)—Bracing Breeze **Mr K. Abdullah**
16 **BURGUNDY BOY (IRE)**, gr c Red Jazz (USA)—Zibaline (FR) **Mr Y. Zhang**
17 **CENTROID**, b c Dansili—Concentric **Mr K. Abdullah**
18 **CHATEAU LA FLEUR (IRE)**, b f Frankel—Cassydora **Moyglare Stud Farm**
19 **CHIARA LUNA (USA)**, b br f War Front (USA)—Princess Highway (USA) **Moyglare Stud Farm**
20 **CHILLED WHITE (IRE)**, b f Dawn Approach (IRE)—Miss Corinne **Moyglare Stud Farm**
21 **CLIQUE**, ch f Bated Breath—Insinuate (USA) **Mr K. Abdullah**
22 **CONTINGENT**, b f Frankel—Proportional **Mr K. Abdullah**
23 **CRECERELLE (IRE)**, b g Redoute's Choice (AUS)—Sense of Purpose (IRE) **Moyglare Stud Farm**
24 **CRIMSON MYSTERY (IRE)**, b c Shamardal (USA)—Moving Heart (IRE) **Moyglare Stud Farm**
25 **EBADALI (IRE)**, b c Cape Cross (IRE)—Ebalista (IRE) **H. H. Aga Khan**
26 **ELEANOR RIGBY**, b f Vinnie Roe (IRE)—Scarlet O'hara (IRE) **Mr Kris Weld**
27 **FALCON EIGHT (IRE)**, b c Galileo (IRE)—Polished Gem (IRE) **Moyglare Stud Farm**
28 **FLAVIUS (USA)**, b c War Front (USA)—Starformer (USA) **Mr K. Abdullah**
29 **GLOW IN THE DARK (IRE)**, b f Shamardal (USA)—Campfire Glow (IRE) **Newtown Anner Stud**
30 **HASANABAD (IRE)**, b c Nathaniel (IRE)—Hasanka (IRE) **H. H. Aga Khan**
31 **HASIMIYYA (IRE)**, ch f Shamardal (USA)—Haziyna (IRE) **H. H. Aga Khan**
32 **HAZAPOUR (IRE)**, ch c Shamardal (USA)—Hazarafa (IRE) **H. H. Aga Khan**
33 **HAZEL BAY (IRE)**, b f Iffraaj—Sadima (IRE) **Moyglare Stud Farm**
34 **HIGHDIVE (IRE)**, b f Big Bad Bob (IRE)—Hawaiian Heat (IRE) **Lady Chryss O'Reilly**
35 **IMAGING (IRE)**, b c Oasis Dream—Mirror Lake **Mr K. Abdullah**
36 **JASSAAR**, b c Dansili—Rasmeyaa (IRE) **Sheikh Hamdan Al Maktoum**
37 **JEWEL MAKER (IRE)**, b c Invincible Spirit (IRE)—Sapphire (IRE) **Moyglare Stud Farm**
38 **KASHIKA (IRE)**, b f Rock of Gibraltar (IRE)—Kastovia (USA) **H. H. Aga Khan**
39 **KISANGA (IRE)**, b f Redoute's Choice (AUS)—Kasanka (IRE) **H. H. Aga Khan**
40 **KITHARA (IRE)**, b f Iffraaj—Katiola (IRE) **H. H. Aga Khan**
41 **LAAJIDAAL (IRE)**, ch f Teofilo (IRE)—Louve Imperiale (USA) **Sheikh Hamdan Al Maktoum**
42 **LUZUM (IRE)**, b g Epaulette (AUS)—Empress Ella (IRE) **Sheikh Hamdan Al Maktoum**
43 **MAKE THE SWITCH (IRE)**, b c Dansili—Switch (USA) **Moyglare Stud Farm**
44 **MANZIL (IRE)**, ch g Bated Breath—Pointed Arch (IRE) **Sheikh Hamdan Al Maktoum**
45 **MAYAADEEN (IRE)**, b c Invincible Spirit (IRE)—Rose de France (IRE) **Sheikh Hamdan Al Maktoum**
46 **MILLION SMILES (IRE)**, ch f Galileo (IRE)—Es Que **Moyglare Stud Farm**
47 **MUJID (IRE)**, b f Frankel—Bethrah (IRE) **Sheikh Hamdan Al Maktoum**
48 **MUTAABEQ (IRE)**, ch c Teofilo (IRE)—Khulood (USA) **Sheikh Hamdan Al Maktoum**
49 **RAMBLING**, b f Kyllachy—Marching West (USA) **Mr K. Abdullah**
50 **RAYDA (IRE)**, b f Mastercraftsman (IRE)—Raydiya (IRE) **H. H. Aga Khan**
51 **RAYNAMA (IRE)**, b f Siyouni (FR)—Rayka (IRE) **H. H. Aga Khan**
52 **ROCK SOUND (IRE)**, ch c Lope de Vega (IRE)—Thoughtless Moment (IRE) **Moyglare Stud Farm**
53 **SAPIENS (IRE)**, b c Frankel—Etoile Montante (USA) **Mr K. Abdullah**
54 **SHAREVA (IRE)**, b f Rip Van Winkle (IRE)—Shareen (IRE) **H. H. Aga Khan**
55 **SHEBERGHAN (IRE)**, b c Sea The Stars (IRE)—Shebella (IRE) **H. H. Aga Khan**
56 **SMILE AHEAD (IRE)**, b f Dream Ahead (USA)—Instant Sparkle (IRE) **Moyglare Stud Farm**
57 **SPIORAD (IRE)**, b c Invincible Spirit (IRE)—Gift From Heaven (IRE) **H. E. The President of Ireland**
58 **TAAKHY (IRE)**, b f Dawn Approach (IRE)—Qaadira (USA) **Sheikh Hamdan Al Maktoum**

MR D. K. WELD - Continued

59 **TARASILA (IRE),** ch f Shamardal (USA)—Tarakala (IRE) **H. H. Aga Khan**
60 **TIMINIYA (IRE),** b f Footstepsinthesand—Timabiyra (IRE) **H. H. Aga Khan**
61 **YULONG GOLD FAIRY,** b f Mount Nelson—Quite A Thing **Mr Y. Zhang**
62 **ZAMROUDPOUR (USA),** ch c Stormy Atlantic (USA)—Zaralanta (IRE) **H. H. Aga Khan**
63 **ZANA (IRE),** b f Raven's Pass (USA)—Zanara (IRE) **H. H. Aga Khan**
64 **ZARENA (IRE),** b f Rock of Gibraltar (IRE)—Zarebiya (IRE) **H. H. Aga Khan**
65 **ZAYRIYAN (IRE),** ch g Shamardal (USA)—Zariyna (IRE) **H. H. Aga Khan**

TWO-YEAR-OLDS

66 **ACAPELLA BLU (IRE),** b f 29/2 Dubawi (IRE)—Galvaun (IRE) (Galileo (IRE)) (420000) **Moyglare Stud Farm**
67 **ACCOMPANIED (USA),** b c 3/3 Distorted Humor (USA)—
      Unaccompanied (IRE) (Danehill Dancer (IRE)) **Moyglare Stud Farm**
68 **ALEZIA (IRE),** b f 5/2 Dansili—Alanza (IRE) (Dubai Destination (USA)) **H. H. Aga Khan**
69 **ALL OUR TOMORROWS (IRE),** b f 3/3 Kingman—
      Justlookdontouch (IRE) (Galileo (IRE)) (1700000) **Moyglare Stud Farm**
70 **ANYA YLINA (IRE),** b f 2/5 Oasis Dream—Es Que (Inchinor) **Moyglare Stud Farm**
71 **ANYONE SPECIAL (IRE),** b f 23/3 Invincible Spirit (IRE)—Just Special (Cadeaux Genereux) **Mr J. Higgins**
72 **B f 26/1 Pivotal**—Askeria (IRE) (Sadler's Wells (USA)) **H. H. Aga Khan**
73 **Ch c 9/3 Australia**—Attire (IRE) (Danehill Dancer (IRE)) (20350) **Mr Y. Zhang**
74 **AZWAH,** b f 14/4 Invincible Spirit (IRE)—Bethrah (IRE) (Marju (IRE)) **Sheikh Hamdan Al Maktoum**
75 **Ch f 10/2 Pivotal**—Balansiya (IRE) (Shamardal (USA)) **H. H. Aga Khan**
76 **B c 7/3 Invincible Spirit (IRE)**—Baliyana (IRE) (Dalakhani (IRE)) **H. H. Aga Khan**
77 **B c 19/3 Elzaam (AUS)**—Bloomsday Babe (USA) (Cherokee Run (USA)) (42327) **Mr Y. Zhang**
78 **B c 8/5 Mastercraftsman**—Brazilian Samba (IRE) (Sadler's Wells (USA)) (24420) **Mr Y. Zhang**
79 **COCO BLANCO (IRE),** gr f 9/2 Dark Angel (IRE)—I'm Yours (Invincible Spirit (IRE)) **Moyglare Stud Farm**
80 **COEUR D'OR (IRE),** b c 2/3 Dubawi (IRE)—Irresistible Jewel (IRE) (Danehill (USA)) **Moyglare Stud Farm**
81 **B c 11/4 Shamardal (USA)**—Danelissima (IRE) (Danehill (USA)) (81400) **Mr Y. Zhang**
82 **B c 10/3 Dutch Art**—Danseuse de Reve (IRE) (Invincible Spirit (IRE)) **Sheikh Hamdan Al Maktoum**
83 **DEE SPRINTER (IRE),** b c 1/5 Clodovil (IRE)—Inourthoughts (IRE) (Desert Style (IRE)) (40700) **Mr G. Davies**
84 **B f 4/5 Casamento (IRE)**—Desert Lily (IRE) (Redoute's Choice (AUS)) (5697) **Mr Y. Zhang**
85 **Ch c 5/4 Lope de Vega (IRE)**—Edelmira (IRE) (Peintre Celebre (USA)) **H. H. Aga Khan**
86 **B f 21/4 Distorted Humor (USA)**—Emiyna (USA) (Maria's Mon (USA)) **H. H. Aga Khan**
87 **FIREY FLOWER (IRE),** ch f 20/4 Lemon Drop Kid (USA)—Firey Red (IRE) (Pivotal) **Moyglare Stud Farm**
88 **FROSTY BEACH (IRE),** b f 2/2 Footstepsinthesand—
      Scarlet O'hara (IRE) (Sadler's Wells (USA)) (16280) **Mr G. Davies**
89 **GREY HILL (IRE),** b c 11/3 Grey Swallow (IRE)—
      Sharp Crisp Air (IRE) (Danehill Dancer (IRE)) **Moyglare Stud Farm**
90 **HASANKEY (IRE),** gr c 4/3 Mastercraftsman—Haziyna (IRE) (Halling (USA)) **H. H. Aga Khan**
91 **INSAAN (IRE),** b c 17/5 Cape Cross (IRE)—Khulood (USA) (Storm Cat (USA)) **Sheikh Hamdan Al Maktoum**
92 **B f 19/2 Siyouni (FR)**—Karamaya (IRE) (Invincible Spirit (IRE)) **H. H. Aga Khan**
93 **Ch c 16/4 Poet's Voice**—Karasiyra (IRE) (Alhaarth (IRE)) **H. H. Aga Khan**
94 **B f 11/3 Rock of Gibraltar (IRE)**—Kasanka (IRE) (Galileo (IRE)) **H. H. Aga Khan**
95 **B c 22/2 Tamayuz**—Katiola (IRE) (Oratorio (IRE)) **H. H. Aga Khan**
96 **KISS FOR A JEWEL (IRE),** b f 2/3 Kingman—Sapphire (IRE) (Medicean) **Moyglare Stud Farm**
97 **LIGHTNING AMBER (IRE),** ch f 4/4 Dutch Art—Amber Romance (IRE) (Bahamian Bounty) **Moyglare Stud Farm**
98 **B f 8/3 Morpheus**—Lipsia (IRE) (Dubai Destination (USA)) (13837) **Mr Y. Zhang**
99 **MANQOOSH (IRE),** b c 17/3 Dubawi (IRE)—Qaadira (USA) (Mr Greeley (USA)) **Sheikh Hamdan Al Maktoum**
100 **MARIA CHRISTINA (IRE),** b f 4/3 Kodiac—Suitably Discreet (Mr Prospector (USA)) **Moyglare Stud Farm**
101 **Ch c 13/4 Raven's Pass (USA)**—Masiyma (IRE) (Dalakhani (IRE)) **H. H. Aga Khan**
102 **B c 25/4 Showcasing**—May Day Queen (IRE) (Danetime (IRE)) (125000) **Sheikh Hamdan Al Maktoum**
103 **MIA MARIA (IRE),** gr f 13/2 Dansili—Majestic Silver (IRE) (Linamix (FR)) **Moyglare Stud Farm**
104 **MIDNIGHT SUNSHINE (USA),** b f 20/3 Medaglia d'oro (USA)—
      Princess Highway (USA) (Street Cry (IRE)) **Moyglare Stud Farm**
105 **B c 27/4 City Zip**—Mouraniya (USA) (Azamour (IRE)) **H. H. Aga Khan**
106 **MUFARREJ,** ch c 30/3 Dubawi (IRE)—Rasmeyaa (IRE) (New Approach (IRE)) **Sheikh Hamdan Al Maktoum**
107 **B f 30/4 Australia**—Muneefa (USA) (Storm Cat (USA)) (50467) **Mr Y. Zhang**
108 **MUSALSAL (IRE),** b c 20/5 Shamardal (USA)—
      Sundus (USA) (Sadler's Wells (USA)) **Sheikh Hamdan Al Maktoum**
109 **B f 21/4 Zoffany (IRE)**—Nightime (IRE) (Galileo (IRE)) (195360) **Mrs C. C. Regalado Gonzalez**
110 **NOSTRA CASA (IRE),** b c 15/2 Dubawi (IRE)—Utterly Heaven (IRE) (Danehill (USA)) **Moyglare Stud Farm**
111 **B c 28/2 Siyouni (FR)**—Oriental Magic (GER) (Doyen (IRE)) (146520) **Sheikh Hamdan Al Maktoum**
112 **PEPPER'N SALT (IRE),** gr c 12/3 Mastercraftsman—
      Hidden Charm (IRE) (Big Shuffle (USA)) **Moyglare Stud Farm**
113 **QUEEN MIA (IRE),** ch f 25/4 Famous Name—Agnetha (GER) (Big Shuffle (USA)) **Mr J. Higgins**
114 **RAKAN,** b c 27/2 Sea The Stars (IRE)—Tarfasha (IRE) (Teofilo (IRE)) **Sheikh Hamdan Al Maktoum**

MR D. K. WELD - Continued

115 B c 21/2 Lope de Vega (IRE)—Rawaaq (Invincible Spirit (IRE)) **Sheikh Hamdan Al Maktoum**
116 **RHOSGOBEL (IRE),** b f 19/2 Dandy Man (IRE)—Hunting Goddess (Galileo (IRE)) (11395) **Deus Bros Syndicate**
117 B c 28/3 Dark Angel (IRE)—Rhythm And Rhyme (IRE) (Elnadim (USA)) (140000) **Sheikh Hamdan Al Maktoum**
118 **SEARCH FOR A SONG (IRE),** ch f 30/3 Galileo (IRE)—Polished Gem (Danehill (USA)) **Moyglare Stud Farm**
119 B c 5/2 Siyouni (FR)—Sharleez (IRE) (Marju (IRE)) **H. H. Aga Khan**
120 Gr c 4/4 Dark Angel (IRE)—Shelina (IRE) (Dalakhani (IRE)) **H. H. Aga Khan**
121 **SWITCH AROUND (IRE),** b f 11/4 Galileo (IRE)—Switch (USA) (Quiet American (USA)) **Moyglare Stud Farm**
122 Gr c 19/4 Mastercraftsman (IRE)—Tanami Kitten (One Cool Cat (USA)) (20349) **Mr Y. Zhang**
123 Ch f 9/2 Shamardal (USA)—Tarana (IRE) (Cape Cross (IRE)) **H. H. Aga Khan**
124 **THIRD WORLD (IRE),** b c 27/4 Dansili—Sense of Purpose (IRE) (Galileo (IRE)) **Moyglare Stud Farm**
125 B c 4/3 Oasis Dream—Timarwa (IRE) (Daylami (IRE)) **H. H. Aga Khan**
126 **TITANIUM SKY (IRE),** gr f 23/2 Dark Angel (IRE)—She's Our Mark (Ishiguru (USA)) **Moyglare Stud Farm**
127 **TRANCHEE (IRE),** b c 6/4 War Front (USA)—Terrific (IRE) (Galileo (IRE)) **Moyglare Stud Farm**
128 **TUO SOGNO (IRE),** b c 24/2 Kendargent (FR)—Pirita (IRE) (Invincible Spirit (IRE)) **Moyglare Stud Farm**
129 **ZARANDI (IRE),** b c 14/3 Scat Daddy (USA)—Zaralanta (Danehill Dancer (IRE)) **H. H. Aga Khan**
130 B c 17/3 Zoffany (IRE)—Zarebiya (IRE) (Galileo (IRE)) **H. H. Aga Khan**
131 B c 27/3 Shamardal (USA)—Zarshana (IRE) (Sea The Stars (IRE)) **H. H. Aga Khan**
132 Gr c 24/2 Havana Gold (IRE)—Zindana (IRE) (Dalakhani (IRE)) **H. H. Aga Khan**

Jockey (flat): P. J. Smullen, L. F. Roche.

---

588 **MR ADAM WEST, Epsom**
Postal: **Thirty Acre Barn, Shepherds Walk, Epsom, Surrey, KT18 6BX**
Contacts: **MOBILE (07939) 030046**
E-MAIL westracing@outlook.com

1 ASHFORD ISLAND, 5, b g Munnings (USA)—Falling Angel **Mr R. C. P. Deacon**
2 EMERALD CROSS (IRE), 5, b g Cape Cross (IRE)—Yaqootah (USA) **Steve & Jolene De'Lemos & Mr P O'Neill**
3 HIT THE LIGHTS (IRE), 8, b g Lawman (FR)—Dawn Chorus (IRE) **The Oliver Twins & Lenny Mayhew-lewis**
4 INTREPID (IRE), 8, b g Invincible Spirit (IRE)—Imiloa (USA) **Mr D. Phelan**
5 STORM TROOPER (IRE), 7, b g Acclamation—Maid To Order (IRE) **Mr M. Furnass**
6 TRUST THE MAN (IRE), 5, br g Manduro (GER)—Saree **Mr A. J. Morton**
7 ULYSSES OF TROY, 6, ch g Rock of Gibraltar (IRE)—Takegawa **Mr Peter Hagger & Mrs Roseanne Hagger**

THREE-YEAR-OLDS

8 AVENGING RED (IRE), b g Red Jazz (USA)—Lorena (IRE) **Mr S. K. Francis**
9 BAMBINO LOLA, b f Helmet (AUS)—Lifetime Romance (IRE) **Mr J. M. Freeze**
10 B g Dick Turpin (IRE)—Chrissycross (IRE) **Mr A. J. Morton**
11 COULDN'T COULD SHE, b f Sixties Icon—Emperatriz **Ross Deacon & Partners**
12 LEGAL ENTITLEMENT, gr c Lethal Force (IRE)—Entitled **Nick Pike & John Freeze**
13 ONE HANDSOME DUDE (IRE), b g Canford Cliffs (IRE)—Allegrina (IRE) **Steve & Jolene de'Lemos**
14 PEGGIE SUE, b f Captain Gerrard (IRE)—Aunt Minnie **West Racing Partnership**
15 REGULAR INCOME (IRE), b g Fast Company (IRE)—
                                          Max Almabrouka (USA) **Ian & Amanda Maybrey John Freeze J West**
16 TORNEQUETA MAY, b f Style Vendome (FR)—Alabastrine **Mrs Neila Wohanka & Mrs Janice West**
17 VODKA PIGEON, ch f Sepoy (AUS)—Hanging On **Mr A. J. Morton**

TWO-YEAR-OLDS

18 B c 28/4 Heeraat (IRE)—Aunt Minnie (Night Shift (USA))
19 B g 8/2 Morpheus—Fingal Nights (IRE) (Night Shift (USA)) (7619) **Mr J. M. Freeze**
20 B c 16/2 Swiss Spirit—Jezebel (Owington) (8571) **Ross Deacon & Oliver Blatchford**
21 B f 17/4 Zebedee—Jillolini (Bertolini (USA)) **D. R. Botterill**
22 B c 13/3 Canford Cliffs (IRE)—Kaylee (Selkirk (USA)) **Mr D. Phelan**
23 Ch c 23/2 Helmet (AUS)—Little Italy (IRE) (Proud Citizen (USA)) (15000) **Mr J. M. Freeze**
24 Ch c 20/4 Roderic O'connor (IRE)—Ms Cromby (IRE) (Arakan (USA)) (5500) **Nick Pike & John Morton**
25 B f 20/4 Epaulette (AUS)—
                                          Oriental Romance (IRE) (Elusive City (USA)) (7619) **S &j De'lemos K Allen T Goodwin L Eggar**
26 B c 10/3 Gale Force Ten—Robin Alexandra (IRE) (Danehill Dancer (IRE)) **S &j De'lemos K Allen T Goodwin L Eggar**
27 B f 20/4 Monsieur Bond (IRE)—
                                          Someone's Angel (USA) (Runaway Groom (CAN)) (6666) **S &j De'lemos K Allen T Goodwin L Eggar**
28 B f 21/4 Epaulette (AUS)—Tattling (Warning) (6666) **Mr Peter Hagger & Mrs Roseanne Hagger**

MR ADAM WEST - Continued

Other Owners: Miss K. Allen, Mr O. Blatchford-Potten, Mr E. Boumans, Mr S. De'Lemos-Pratt, Mr L. Eggar, Mr T. J. Goodwin, Mr P. Hagger, Mrs R. Hagger, Mrs A. J. Maybrey, Mr I. N. Maybrey, Mr L. Mayhew-Lewis, Mr P. O'Neill, Ms L. A. C. Oliver, Ms J. A. Oliver, Mr N. B. Pike, Mr J. Webb, Mrs J. M. West, Mrs N. Wohanka, Mrs J. de'Lemos.

589

MISS SHEENA WEST, Lewes
Postal: **5 Balmer Farm Cottages, Brighton Road, Lewes, East Sussex, BN7 3JN**
Contacts: **PHONE (01273) 621303 FAX (01273) 622189 MOBILE (07748) 181804**
E-MAIL sheenawest11@aol.com WEBSITE www.sheenawest.com

1 BRESLIN, 5, ch g Atlantic Sport (USA)—Aries (GER) **Mr M. Moriarty**
2 DING DING, 7, ch m Winker Watson—Five Bells (IRE) **Mr I. E. Poysden**
3 ELOCUTION, 5, b m Paco Boy (IRE)—Speech **B&W Racing Club**
4 FEB THIRTYFIRST, 9, ch g Shirocco (GER)—My Mariam **Mr M. Moriarty**
5 GOLDEN CANNON, 7, b m Winker Watson—Kalmina (USA) **Mr M. Moriarty**
6 HARMONISE, 4, b f Sakhee's Secret—Composing (IRE) **Mr I. E. Poysden**
7 JUSTANOTHER MUDDLE, 9, gr g Kayf Tara—Spatham Rose **Saloop**
8 SIXTIES IDOL, 5, b m Sixties Icon—Fading Away **Mr M. Moriarty**
9 SIXTIES SHEILA, 4, ch f Sixties Icon—Quinzey's Best (IRE) **Miss S. West**

Other Owners: Mr P. C. Hopkins, Mrs C. S. Muddle, Mrs P. L. C. L. Sarzi-Braga.

Jockey (NH): M. Goldstein.

590

MR SIMON WEST, Middleham
Postal: **14A St Alkeldas Road, Middleham, Leyburn, North Yorkshire, DL8 4PW**
Contacts: **MOBILE (07855) 924529**
E-MAIL simonwest21@hotmail.co.uk WEBSITE www.mkmracing.co.uk

1 BANDOL (IRE), 10, b g Zagreb (USA)—Formal Affair **Mr P. Hothersall**
2 BOSS DES MALBERAUX (FR), 7, b g Antarctique (IRE)—Scavenger (FR) **Mr S. G. West**
3 CAPTAIN CLAYTON (IRE), 11, b g Subtle Power (IRE)—Dont Hurry (IRE) **Wild West Racing**
4 5, B g Tikkanen (USA)—Dusty Road (IRE) **Mr S. G. West**
5 ERUDIT (FR), 4, b g Maresca Sorrento (FR)—Miss d'anjou (FR) **Mr P. Hothersall**
6 INSHAA, 5, b g Dansili—Hidden Brief **Mrs B. Hothersall**
7 JESSE JUDE (IRE), 5, ch g Doyen (IRE)—La Belle Bleu (IRE) **J. D. Gordon**
8 JIMINY CRICKET (IRE), 7, ch g Golden Lariat (USA)—Lady Smurfette (IRE) **J. D. Gordon**
9 MADAKHEEL (USA), 7, b m Mr Greeley (USA)—Manaal (USA) **Miss K Milligan & Mr P Fowlie**
10 MAXIMISER (IRE), 10, gr g Helissio (FR)—Clydeside (IRE) **J. D. Gordon**
11 NELLIE DEEN (IRE), 5, b m Dream Ahead (USA)—Dorothy Dene **Mr S. G. West**
12 NEWS FOR PASCAL (IRE), 10, b g Kutub (IRE)—Direction **Mr P. Hothersall**
13 OVERTHEEDGE (IRE), 9, b g Morozov (USA)—Ballyroe Hill (IRE) **Mr P. Hothersall**
14 SLIPPER SATIN (IRE), 8, b m Excellent Art—In The Ribbons **Mrs J. M. L. Milligan**
15 WILLBEME, 10, b m Kyllachy—Befriend (USA) **Wild West Racing**

Other Owners: Mr P. Fowlie, Mr D. Howarth, Miss M. K. Milligan.

591

MR DAVID WESTON, West Overton
Postal: **c/o Flintstone Stud, West Overton, Marlborough, Wiltshire, SN8 4ER**
Contacts: **MOBILE (07966) 641001**
E-MAIL flintstone007@icloud.com

1 ADMIRAL'S SUNSET, 5, b m Mount Nelson—Early Evening **Miss E. Tanner**
2 AT FIRST LIGHT, 9, b m Echo of Light—Bisaat (USA) **Miss E. Tanner**
3 BEDROCK FRED, 12, ch g Monsieur Bond (IRE)—Sea Mist (IRE) **Miss E. Tanner**
4 PAC IT IN, 4, b f Paco Boy (IRE)—Bisaat (USA) **Miss E. Tanner**
5 SOLSTALLA, 6, b m Halling (USA)—Solstice **Miss E. Tanner**

592 **MR TOM WESTON, Hindlip**
Postal: **Offerton Farm, Offerton Lane, Hindlip, Worcester, Worcestershire, WR3 8SX**
Contacts: **MOBILE (07752) 313698**

1 **AUTUM RAIN (IRE)**, 6, b m Arcadio (GER)—Liberty Miss (IRE) **Mr T. H. Weston**
2 **COOPERS SQUARE (IRE)**, 7, b g Mahler—Jessaway (IRE) **Mr T. H. Weston**
3 **DINA MAKER (FR)**, 5, b m Policy Maker (IRE)—Kalinca de Thaix (FR) **Mr T. H. Weston**
4 **FREE RETURN (IRE)**, 7, b g Mr Combustible (IRE)—Marisha (IRE) **Int-Ex Contracting Limited**
5 **IWASTHEFUTUREONCE (IRE)**, 5, b g Fruits of Love (USA)—Ruthy Lukey (IRE) **Mr T. H. Weston**
6 **POUGNE HELIO (FR)**, 5, b g Heliostatic (IRE)—Amicus **Mr T. H. Weston**
7 **SILENT MAN (IRE)**, 8, br g Morozov (USA)—Outdoor Heather (IRE) **Mr D. M. J. Lloyd**
8 **SUNDAY CENTRAL**, 7, ch g Central Park (IRE)—Sunday News'n'echo (USA) **Int-Ex Contracting Limited**
9 **TAKEN BY FORCE (IRE)**, 5, b g Millenary—Along Came Polly (IRE) **Mr T. H. Weston**
10 **THOONAVOLLA (IRE)**, 10, ch g Beneficial—Another Partner **The Troubled Pink Partnership**
11 **WESTERN CLIMATE (IRE)**, 9, b g Westerner—Jo Peeks (IRE) **Mr D. M. J. Lloyd**
12 **YPSILANTI (IRE)**, 9, ch g Beneficial—Glacialjoy (IRE) **The First Equus Syndicate**

Other Owners: Mr A. Allan, Mr J. Bruce, Mrs D. Grove, M. H. Weston.

593 **MISS JESSICA WESTWOOD, Chulmleigh**
Postal: **Molland Ridge Farm, Chulmleigh, Devon, EX18 7EF**
Contacts: **MOBILE (07536) 021449**
E-MAIL **Jesswestwoodracing@gmail.com** WEBSITE **www.jesswestwoodracing.com**

1 **WILLIES DREAM**, 5, b g Dream Eater (IRE)—Willies Witch **Miss J. J. Westwood**

THREE-YEAR-OLDS
2 B f Tiger Groom—Some Secret **Miss J. J. Westwood**

594 **MR JOHN WEYMES, Middleham Moor**
Postal: **Trainer did not wish details of his string to appear**

595 **MR ALISTAIR WHILLANS, Hawick**
Postal: **Esker House, Newmill-On-Slitrig, Hawick, Roxburghshire, TD9 9UQ**
Contacts: **PHONE (01450) 376642 FAX (01450) 376082 MOBILE (07771) 550555**
E-MAIL **acwracing@hotmail.com**

1 **AJMAN PRINCE (IRE)**, 5, b g Manduro (GER)—Jumaireyah **Mr J. D. Wright & Mrs S. Wright**
2 **ALEXANDRAKOLLONTAI (IRE)**, 8, b m Amadeus Wolf—Story **Chris Spark & William Orr**
3 **APACHEE PRINCE (IRE)**, 9, b g Indian Danehill (IRE)—
Wheredidthemoneygo (IRE) **Mr J. D. Wright & Mrs S. Wright**
4 4, B c Aqlaam—Blazing Field **Mr W. Orr**
5 **CHU CHU PERCY**, 7, b g Tobougg (IRE)—First Katoune (FR) **Mr & Mrs Paul & Clare Rooney**
6 **CLAUDE CARTER**, 14, b g Elmaamul (USA)—Cruz Santa **Mrs L. M. Whillans**
7 **COURT BALOO (IRE)**, 7, b g Court Cave (IRE)—Tremplin (IRE) **A. C. Whillans**
8 **DONNACHIES GIRL (IRE)**, 5, b m Manduro (GER)—Russian Society **Mrs K. Spark**
9 **DUBAI SHEN (IRE)**, 7, b g Dubai Destination (USA)—Graineuaile (IRE) **A. C. Whillans**
10 **FLY VINNIE (IRE)**, 9, b g Vinnie Roe (IRE)—Great Days (IRE) **MPACT**
11 **GALILEE CHAPEL (IRE)**, 9, b g Baltic King—Triple Zero (IRE) **A. C. Whillans**
12 **GRIFFIN STREET**, 5, gr g Zebedee—Twilight Belle (IRE) **Miss D. Auld**
13 **GUN CASE**, 6, b g Showcasing—Bassinet (USA) **A. C. Whillans**
14 **HELLAVASHOCK**, 5, gr g Hellvelyn—Surprise Statement **Mrs H. Greggan**
15 **HENPECKED**, 8, b m Footstepsinthesand—Poule de Luxe (IRE) **Eildon Hill Racing**
16 **HIDDEN REBEL**, 6, b m Cockney Rebel (IRE)—Medicea Sidera **Mr J. D. Wright & Mrs L. M. Whillans**
17 4, Ch g Assertive—Jozafeen
18 **KALAHARRY (IRE)**, 6, b g Kalanisi (IRE)—Full Imperatrice (FR) **Charlie Baxter Bloodstock**
19 **LEOSTAR**, 4, ch g Nathaniel (IRE)—Gaditana **Mrs E. B. Ferguson**
20 **MAYZE BELL**, 9, br m And Beyond (IRE)—Eleanor May **A. C. Whillans**

MR ALISTAIR WHILLANS - Continued

21 **MEADOWCROFT BOY,** 9, b g Kayf Tara—Blackbriery Thyne (IRE) **Mr W J E Scott & Mrs M A Scott**
22 **OLIVIA JOAN,** 7, ch m Grape Tree Road—Thorterdykes Lass (IRE) **John & Liz Elliot**
23 **ROYAL SHAHEEN (FR),** 5, b g Myboycharlie (IRE)—Viola Royale (IRE) **Mr F. Lowe**
24 **SAMSTOWN,** 11, b g Kingsalsa (USA)—Red Peony **Mrs E. B. Ferguson**
25 **SCRAPPER SMITH (IRE),** 12, b g Choisir (AUS)—Lady Ounavarra (IRE) **A. C. Whillans**
26 **SHTAN ON (IRE),** 7, b g Generous (IRE)—Lady Oakwell (IRE) **Mr M. Wright**
27 **WEE BOGUS,** 5, b g Multiplex—Silver Gyre (IRE) **Mrs L. M. Whillans**
28 **WIND OF HOPE (IRE),** 9, b g September Storm (GER)—Ciara's Run (IRE) **A. J. Brown**
29 **WISE COCO,** 5, b m Shirocco (GER)—Sensible **Mclafferty & Pacheco**
30 **WYFIELD ROSE,** 9, b m Kayf Tara—Miniature Rose **John & Liz Elliot**

THREE-YEAR-OLDS

31 **ANNIE BROWN,** b f And Beyond (IRE)—Nevsky Bridge **Mr J. R. L. Wilson**
32 **NEW RHYTHM,** b f Monsieur Bond (IRE)—Social Rhythm
33 **SIENNA DREAM,** b f Swiss Spirit—Angry Bark (USA) **A. C. Whillans**

Other Owners: J. D. Baxter, Mr N. Dalgarno, Mr J. J. Elliot, Mrs E. J. Elliot, Mr M. McLafferty, Mr W. J. Muir, Mrs C. Rooney, Mr P. A. Rooney, W. J. E. Scott, Mrs M. A. Scott, Mr C. Spark, Mr S. A. Taylor, J. D. Wright, Mrs S. L. Wright, Mr P. D. Wringe.

---

596 | MR DONALD WHILLANS, Hawick
Postal: **Dodlands Steading, Hawick, Roxburghshire, TD9 8LG**
Contacts: BUSINESS **(01450) 373128** HOME **(01450) 379810** FAX **(01450) 376082**
MOBILE **(07840) 997570**
E-MAIL helenwhillans24@gmail.com WEBSITE www.donaldwhillansracing.com

1 **BABY TICKER,** 9, ch m Endoli (USA)—Baby Gee **C. N. Whillans**
2 **BIG BAD DREAM (IRE),** 6, b g Mountain High (IRE)—Stay At Home (IRE) **D. W. Whillans**
3 6, B g Spadoun (FR)—Blue Dragon (IRE)
4 **BLUEFORTYTWO,** 5, gr g Overbury (IRE)—Celine Message **J. R. Bewley**
5 **DALI MAIL (FR),** 5, gr g Satri (IRE)—Queenly Mail (FR) **The Zidane Partnership**
6 **DANCED EVERY DANCE (IRE),** 5, b m Oscar (IRE)—Kinnegads Pride (IRE) **D. W. Whillans**
7 **EGON SPENGLAR,** 10, b g River Falls—Wee Willow **D. W. Whillans**
8 **ETERNALLY YOURS,** 5, b m Sulamani (IRE)—Well Disguised (IRE) **Mr A. J. M. Duncan**
9 **HARTFORTH,** 10, ch g Haafhd—St Edith (IRE) **The Brave Lads Partnership**
10 5, B g Scorpion (IRE)—High Court Action (IRE)
11 **KEYBOARD GANGSTER (IRE),** 7, b g Gamut (IRE)—Vic O'tully (IRE) **The Buyers Club**
12 **NIGHT COMES IN (IRE),** 6, b g Definite Article—Couture Daisy (IRE) **Denholm Park Racing**
13 **PAPER PROMISE (IRE),** 6, ch m Gamut (IRE)—Rose Vic (IRE) **Mrs E. Smith**
14 **PAPER ROSES (IRE),** 7, b m Gamut (IRE)—Rose Vic (IRE) **Mrs E. Smith**
15 **SIDE OF THE ROAD (IRE),** 6, b m Beneficial—Roses And Wine (IRE) **Mr A. J. M. Duncan**
16 **SNAPPING TURTLE (IRE),** 13, b g Turtle Island (IRE)—Rachael's Dawn **D. W. Whillans**
17 **TOMAHAWK WOOD,** 9, ch g Courteous—Meda's Song **The Enduria Partnership**
18 **WOR LASS,** 10, br m And Beyond (IRE)—Patience Please **Mr L. J. Dodds**

THREE-YEAR-OLDS

19 **BORDERS DREAM,** b c Dream Ahead (USA)—Songseeker (IRE) **Onwards & Upwards Partnership**

Other Owners: Mr S. G. Adams, Mr G. Aitken, Mr N. Bannerman, Mr C. Murphy, Mrs H. M. Whillans.

Assistant Trainer: Garry Whillans.

Jockey (flat): Garry Whillans. **Jockey (NH):** Callum Whillans. **Amateur:** Mr Ryan Nichol.

---

597 | MR RICHARD WHITAKER, Scarcroft
Postal: Hellwood Racing Stables, Hellwood Lane, Scarcroft, Leeds, West Yorkshire, LS14 3BP
Contacts: PHONE **(01132) 892265** MOBILE **(07831) 870454**
E-MAIL rmwhitaker@btconnect.com WEBSITE www.richardwhitaker.org

1 **COSMIC DUST,** 5, b m Equiano (FR)—Cosmic Song **Mr R. M. Whitaker**
2 **ORIENTELLE,** 4, ch f Compton Place—Oriental Girl **Nice Day Out Partnership**
3 **PENNY POT LANE,** 5, b m Misu Bond (IRE)—Velvet Band **Mr A. Melville**
4 **PONTECARLO BOY,** 4, ch g Piccolo—Dahshah **Mr A. Lumb**

MR RICHARD WHITAKER - Continued

5 **ROUND THE ISLAND**, 5, b g Royal Applause—Luanshya **Nice Day Out Partnership**
6 **SILK MILL BLUE**, 4, b g Piccolo—Marysienka **Mr R. M. Whitaker**
7 **TOTALLY MAGIC (IRE)**, 6, b m Captain Rio—Hypocrisy **Mr James Marshall & Mr Chris Marshall**
8 **ZAKATAL**, 12, gr g Kalanisi (IRE)—Zankara (FR) **David Furman & John Sugarman**

THREE-YEAR-OLDS

9 **DAWN BREAKING**, b g Firebreak—Jubilee Dawn **D Gration, G Sutcliffe, N Farman, Jeaton**
10 **DICKTATION**, b g Dick Turpin (IRE)—Curly Come Home **Mr Michael Sinclair & Mr R.M. Whitaker**
11 **SILK MILL TWO**, b g Mayson—Spin A Wish **Country Lane Partnership**
12 Ch g Equiano (FR)—Wotatomboy

TWO-YEAR-OLDS

13 Ch g 24/3 Coach House (IRE)—Cocabana (Captain Rio) (12380)
14 **HIGHWAY BLOSSOM**, b f 17/2 Dick Turpin (IRE)—Mey Blossom (Captain Rio) **Waz Developments Ltd**
15 **JILL ROSE**, ch f 8/4 Coach House (IRE)—Wotatomboy (Captain Rio)
16 B c 15/3 Harbour Watch (IRE)—Pigeon Pie (Bahamian Bounty) (5714)
17 **SWEET SONG**, b f 3/2 Dick Turpin (IRE)—Cosmic Song (Cosmonaut)

Other Owners: Mr N. Farman, Mr D. E. Furman, Mr D. Gration, Jeaton Ltd, J. R. Marshall, Mr C. R. Marshall, M. Sinclair, Mr J. B. Sugarman, Mr G. Sutcliffe, Mr B. Thompson, Mrs R. M. Whitaker, Mr S. R. Whitaker.

Assistant Trainer: Simon R Whitaker (07771) 821955

598
MR ARTHUR WHITEHEAD, Craven Arms
Postal: **Lawn Farm, Beambridge, Aston on Clun, Craven Arms, Shropshire, SY7 0HA**
Contacts: **PHONE (01588) 660424**
E-MAIL ajwhitehead@farming.co.uk

1 **DELLA SUN (FR)**, 12, b g Della Francesca (USA)—Algarve Sunrise (IRE) **A. J. Whitehead**
2 **MARLAIS**, 6, b g Dylan Thomas (IRE)—Super Motiva **A. J. Whitehead**
3 **MODERATOR (CZE)**, 8, b g Security Risk (USA)—Modrenka (CZE) **A. J. Whitehead**
4 **ZALGARRY (FR)**, 11, b g Ballingarry (IRE)—Spleen (FR) **A. J. Whitehead**

Conditional: Josh Wall.

599
MR ARTHUR WHITING, Dursley
Postal: **38 Barrs Lane, North Nibley, Dursley, Gloucestershire, GL11 6DT**
Contacts: **PHONE (01453) 546375 MOBILE (07786) 152539**

1 **BONNIE BLACK ROSE**, 8, b m Black Sam Bellamy (IRE)—Fragrant Rose **A. J. Whiting**
2 **DECK OF CARDS (IRE)**, 6, br g Daylami (IRE)—Miss Edgehill (IRE) **A. J. Whiting**

600
MR CHARLES WHITTAKER, Frome
Postal: Trainer did not wish details of his string to appear

601
MR HARRY WHITTINGTON, Sparsholt
Postal: **Hill Barn, Sparsholt, Wantage, Oxfordshire, OX12 9XB**
Contacts: **PHONE (01235) 751869 MOBILE (07734) 388357**
E-MAIL info@harrywhittington.co.uk WEBSITE www.harrywhittington.co.uk

1 **AFFAIRE D'HONNEUR (FR)**, 7, ch g Shirocco (GER)—
Affaire de Moeurs (FR) **Holt Robinson Kronbauer Macnabb O'Connor**
2 **ANEMOI (FR)**, 4, b g Manduro (GER)—Recambe (IRE) **Kate & Andrew Brooks**
3 4, B g Court Cave (IRE)—Bespoke Baby (IRE) **J. H. Henderson**
4 **BIGMARTRE (FR)**, 7, b g Montmartre (FR)—Oh La Miss (FR) **Mr P. J. Dixon**
5 **BLEU DES TAILLONS (FR)**, 4, gr g Gris de Gris (IRE)—Bleue Et Bleue (FR)

MR HARRY WHITTINGTON - Continued

6 **BLUE VALENTINE (FR)**, 7, b m Born King (JPN)—Pompom Girl (FR) **A Holt J Robinson I Macnabb & C Clark**
7 **BRIDGE OF CALLY (IRE)**, 5, b g September Storm (GER)—Cathy's Pal (IRE) **The Racing Demon Partnership**
8 **CHARLEMAR (FR)**, 6, b g Ballingarry (IRE)—Passemare (FR) **The Hennessy Six**
9 **CHARLIE PAPA LIMA (IRE)**, 7, b g Winged Love (IRE)—Fairylodge Scarlet (IRE) **Lead The Way Syndicate**
10 4, B g Arcadio (GER)—Chloes Choice (IRE) **Holt,Macnabb,Robinson,Taylor,Tucker**
11 **COLD MARCH (FR)**, 8, b br g Early March—Tumultueuse (FR) **Mr A. L. Brooks**
12 **COURT LIABILITY (IRE)**, 5, b g Court Cave (IRE)—
Whataliability (IRE) **Nashwebbpavervandenberghe&10percenters**
13 **DANCING DRAGON (IRE)**, 4, b f Dragon Pulse (IRE)—Abbeyleix Lady (IRE) **Robinson S P Ltd**
14 **DETTE DE JEU (FR)**, 5, b g Desir d'un Soir (FR)—Queltalent (FR) **Mr A. L. Brooks**
15 **DJIN CONTI (FR)**, 5, b g Lucarno (USA)—Regina Conti (FR) **Mr A. L. Brooks**
16 **EMERGING FORCE (IRE)**, 8, b g Milan—Danette (GER) **Webb Holt Carpenter Tucker**
17 **HOKE COLBURN (IRE)**, 6, br g Beneficial—Ravaleen (IRE) **Aylett Batcheler McCarthy & Pearson**
18 **KASDAR (FR)**, 4, b g Sinndar (IRE)—Kayza (GER) **Janet Bromet & Andrew Brooks**
19 **KLEOS (IRE)**, 4, b f Fame And Glory—Ginandit (IRE) **Holt,Atkin,Macnabb,O'Connor, Milton**
20 **LET'S GET AT IT (IRE)**, 5, b g Mustameet (USA)—Last Hope (IRE) **Kate & Andrew Brooks**
21 4, Ch g Salutino (GER)—Luas Luso (IRE)
22 **MEDALLA DE ORO**, 4, b g Teofilo (IRE)—Nyarhini **The Rogues Gallery Two**
23 **OCTAGON**, 8, b g Overbury (IRE)—Dusky Dante (IRE) **A. Carr**
24 **PASAKA BOY**, 8, ch g Haafhd—Shesha Bear **RWH Partnership**
25 **PERFECT MOMENTS**, 4, b f Midnight Legend—Perfect Silence **Richard Vines & David Nott**
26 6, Gr g Beneficial—Rosealainn (IRE) **Brooks & Owles Families**
27 **ROUGE VIF (FR)**, 4, b g Sageburg (IRE)—Rouge Amour (FR)
28 **RUBY YEATS**, 7, b m Yeats (IRE)—Newbay Lady **The Sawgrass Survivors**
29 **SAINT CALVADOS (FR)**, 5, b g Saint des Saints (FR)—Lamorrese (FR) **Mr A. L. Brooks**
30 **SALTO CHISCO (IRE)**, 10, b g Presenting—Dato Fairy (IRE) **British Racing Club**
31 4, B g Milan—Senora Snoopy (IRE)
32 **SIMPLY THE BETTS (IRE)**, 5, b g Arcadio (GER)—Crimson Flower (IRE) **Kate & Andrew Brooks**
33 **SPIRIT OF ROME (IRE)**, 4, ch f Mastercraftsman (IRE)—Zagreb Flyer **Harry Whittington Racing Club**
34 **TANGOED (IRE)**, 5, ch m Papal Bull—Dainty Steps (IRE) **Harry Whittington Racing Club**
35 **TARAS DAY**, 5, b m Kayf Tara—One of Those Days **Mrs H. M. Harvey**
36 **THE DUBAI WAY**, 6, b g Dubai Destination (USA)—Britway Lady (IRE) **A. Carr**
37 **THE GO TOU MAN (IRE)**, 5, b g Shantou (USA)—Golan Lady (IRE) **A Lady & The Tramps Partnership**
38 **TIERRA VERDE**, 7, b m Josr Algarhoud (IRE)—La Corujera **Greenlands Racing Syndicate**
39 **VBADGE TREAT (FR)**, 5, b m My Risk (FR)—Peutiot (FR) **The Cothill Racing Club**
40 **VINNIE LEWIS (IRE)**, 7, b g Vinnie Roe (IRE)—Ballyann Lewis (IRE) **The Racing Demon Partnership**
41 **ZEPHYROS BLEU (IRE)**, 8, b g Westerner—Quel Bleu (IRE) **Atkin, Bellman, Chamberlain, Murray**

Other Owners: 10 Percenters, Mrs C. J. Atkin, Mr T. Aylett, Mr S. Batcheler, Mr L. A. Bellman, Mrs J. E. Bromet, Mrs K. L. Brooks, Mr B. D. Carpenter, Mrs K. Casini, Mr C. N. Clark, Mr P. D. Dennis, Mr A. R. Elliott, Mrs A. M. Fitzgerald O'Connor, Mr R. J. Fowler, Mrs B. S. Fowler, Mr D. Hanafin, Mr A. W. Harding, Mr A. Holt, Mr J. Homan, Ms M. Kronbauer, Mr I. Macnabb, Mr K. P McCarthy, Mr C. J. Milton, I. R. Murray, Mr C. T. Nash, Mr D. F. Nott, Mr G. Owles, Mr G. J. Paver, Mr M. J. Pearson, Mr A. Penfold, Racing Club Ltd, Mr J. D. Robinson, Miss E. Scott, Mrs J. M. M. Scott, Mr A. Taylor, Mr A. J. Tucker, Mr J. Vandenberghe, R. J. Vines, Mrs I. M. Webb, Exors of the late Mr H. J. M. Webb, C. H. O. Whittington, Mr G. C. Wickens.

Assistant Trainer: Joe Quintin

Conditional: James Nixon.

---

602 MR MICHAEL WIGHAM, Newmarket
Postal: Hamilton Stables, Hamilton Road, Newmarket, Suffolk, CB8 7JQ
Contacts: PHONE (01638) 668806 MOBILE (07831) 456426
E-MAIL michaelwigham@hotmail.co.uk WEBSITE www.michaelwighamracing.co.uk

1 **CLEAR WATER (IRE)**, 5, b m Hard Spun (USA)—Storm Lily (USA)
2 **DEEDS NOT WORDS (IRE)**, 7, b g Royal Applause—Wars (IRE)
3 **EXECUTIVE FORCE**, 4, b g Sepoy (AUS)—Mazuna (IRE)
4 **FOXY FOREVER (IRE)**, 8, b g Kodiac—Northern Tara (IRE)
5 **GIN AND TONIC**, 8, ch g Phoenix Reach (IRE)—Arctic Queen
6 **GLENAMOY LAD**, 4, b g Royal Applause—Suzy Alexander
7 **JAI HANUMAN (IRE)**, 4, b g Requinto (IRE)—Almost Blue (USA)
8 **MANSFIELD**, 5, b g Exceed And Excel (AUS)—Jane Austen (IRE)
9 **MY TARGET (IRE)**, 7, b g Cape Cross (IRE)—Chercheuse (USA)
10 **NICK VEDDER**, 4, b g Rip Van Winkle (IRE)—Devotion (IRE)

MR MICHAEL WIGHAM - Continued

11 **SANAADH,** 5, ch h Exceed And Excel (AUS)—Queen's Logic (IRE)
12 **VERNE CASTLE,** 5, ch g Sakhee's Secret—Lochangel

THREE-YEAR-OLDS

13 **AWSAAF,** b g Swiss Spirit—Atheera (IRE)

TWO-YEAR-OLDS

14 B f 18/2 Champs Elysees—King's Guest (IRE) (King's Best (USA)) (12000)

Owners: Mr Tugay Akman, Mr Carl Appleton, J. Cullinan, Mr A. Dearden, Mr A. Dearden, Mr P. J. Edwards, Mr D. Hassan, Ms I. D. Heerowa, G. D. J. Linder, Mr G. Linder, Mr Tim McIntosh, Miss M. A. Quinlan, Mr D. T. Spratt, Mrs Ali Tait, Mr Michael Wigham, Mr J Williams, Mr J. B. Williams.

Assistant Trainer: Sharon Kenyon

---

603 **MR MARTIN WILESMITH, Dymock**
Postal: Bellamys Farm, Dymock, Gloucestershire, GL18 2DX
Contacts: PHONE (01531) 890410 (01684) 561238 FAX (01684) 893428 MOBILE (07970) 411638
E-MAIL martin@mswilesmith.co.uk

1 **BELLAMYS BELLE,** 8, b m Black Sam Bellamy (IRE)—Mrs White (IRE) **M. S. Wilesmith**
2 **FAIR ALICE,** 9, gr m Fair Mix (IRE)—Mrs White (IRE) **M. S. Wilesmith**
3 **LOOKSLIKERAINTED (IRE),** 11, b g Milan—Kilcrea Gale (IRE) **M. S. Wilesmith**
4 **MIDNIGHT FRENSI,** 9, b g Midnight Legend—Flame O'frensi **M. S. Wilesmith**
5 **SILK PATH,** 11, b g Grape Tree Road—Silk Oats **M. S. Wilesmith**

Assistant Trainer: Ms E. C. Wilesmith (07976 926906)

---

604 **MR CHRISTIAN WILLIAMS, Bridgend**
Postal: Ogmore Farm, Ogmore Road, Ogmore-by-Sea, Glamorgan, CF32 0QP
Contacts: MOBILE (07702) 896759

1 **CAP DU NORD (FR),** 5, br g Voix du Nord (FR)—Qualite Controlee (FR) **The Unnamed Favourites**
2 **CAVIAR D'ALLEN (FR),** 6, b g Laveron—Quadanse (FR) **All Stars Sports Racing 5**
3 **COURT FRONTIER (IRE),** 10, b g Court Cave (IRE)—Dame En Rouge (IRE) **The Unnamed Favourites**
4 **FIFTY SHADES (IRE),** 5, gr g Tajraasi (USA)—Baylough Mist (IRE) **Mr C. R. P. Williams**
5 **HEDGEINATOR (IRE),** 8, ch g Beneficial—Annalecky (IRE) **All Stars Sports Racing 5**
6 **LIMITED RESERVE (IRE),** 6, b g Court Cave (IRE)—Lady Blackie (IRE) **All Stars Sports Racing 3**
7 **SAINTMONT (FR),** 4, b g Monitor Closely (IRE)—Saintheze (FR) **The Unnamed Favourites**

Assistant Trainer: Nicky Williams

---

605 **MR DAI WILLIAMS, Broad Hinton**
Postal: Flat Ashley House, Hodson, Swindon, Wiltshire, SN4 0QG
Contacts: HOME (01488) 638636 FAX (01488) 638121 MOBILE (07879) 403160 (07879) 403595

1 **BABYTAGGLE (IRE),** 7, b g Brian Boru—Ardnataggle (IRE) **Mr F. Michael**
2 **BENNYS GIRL (IRE),** 10, b m Beneficial—Be My Flower (IRE) **We Must Be Barmy**
3 **BOBONYX,** 8, b g Phoenix Reach (IRE)—Twist The Facts (IRE) **Caldonia Racing Club**
4 **HAVE A GO HERO (IRE),** 10, b g Flemensfirth (USA)—Blue Bank (IRE) **We Must Be Barmy**
5 **INDIAN RUPEE (IRE),** 9, b g Indian Danehill (IRE)—Get A Few Bob Back (IRE) **Mr F. Michael**
6 **IRISH THISTLE (IRE),** 11, b g Luso—Which Thistle (IRE) **Mr F. Michael**
7 **LORD BEN (IRE),** 13, b g Beneficial—Lady Bluebell (IRE) **Mr F. Michael**
8 **MILK KING (IRE),** 5, gr g Cloudings (IRE)—Snow Keeper **Mr G. T. Sainsbury**
9 **MINELLA STYLE (IRE),** 8, b g King's Theatre (IRE)—Rose of The Erne (IRE) **Mr G. T. Sainsbury**

MR DAI WILLIAMS - Continued

10 **MISTER MISTER (IRE)**, 7, b g September Storm (GER)—The Long Bill (IRE) **Mr A. M. Rennison**
11 **NORUKI (IRE)**, 8, b g Flemensfirth (USA)—Classic Material **Mr F. Michael**
12 **PETIT ECUYER (FR)**, 12, b g Equerry (USA)—Petite Majeste (FR) **Mr G. C. Farr**
13 **PONIEL**, 6, b g Bahri (USA)—Rafta (IRE) **Mr S. R. Williams**
14 **POSITIVE TOUCH (IRE)**, 7, b g Misternando—Independant Flora **Mr S. R. Williams**
15 **RAKAIA ROSA (IRE)**, 9, b m Balakheri (IRE)—Ashanti's Dream (IRE) **Mrs P. Williams**
16 **STOLBERG (IRE)**, 10, br g Vinnie Roe (IRE)—Giveherthewhistle (IRE) **Mr A. M. Rennison**

Other Owners: Mr G. Bell.

Assistant Trainer: Miss Lucy Horner

Amateur: Miss L. Horner.

---

606 **MR EVAN WILLIAMS, Llancarfan**
Postal: **Aberogwrn Farm, Llancarfan, Nr Barry, Vale of Glamorgan**
Contacts: **PHONE (01446) 754069 FAX (01446) 754069 MOBILE (07950) 381227**
E-MAIL cath@evanwilliams.co.uk WEBSITE www.evanwilliamsracing.co.uk

1 **ABBEYGREY (IRE)**, 9, b g Generous (IRE)—Garw Valley **R. E. R. Williams**
2 **AMERTON LANE**, 6, b g Multiplex—Sunisa (IRE) **Mr G Greaves & Mickley Stud**
3 **APOLLO CREED (IRE)**, 6, b g Vinnie Roe (IRE)—Just Cassandra (IRE) **Mr & Mrs William Rucker**
4 **BACH DE CLERMONT (FR)**, 7, b g Della Francesca (USA)—Fleur de Princesse (FR) **Mr & Mrs William Rucker**
5 **BILLY BRONCO**, 7, ch g Central Park (IRE)—Nan **Mr & Mrs William Rucker**
6 **BUYWISE (IRE)**, 11, b g Tikkanen (USA)—Greenogue Princess (IRE) **Mr T. Hywel Jones**
7 **CANICALLYOUBACK**, 10, b g Auction House (USA)—Island Colony (USA) **Mrs D. E. Cheshire**
8 **CAPE CASTER (IRE)**, 7, br g Cape Cross (IRE)—Playboy Mansion (IRE) **D P Barrie & D Redhead**
9 **CAPPAWAY (IRE)**, 5, b g Getaway (GER)—Cappa Or (IRE) **R. E. R. Williams**
10 **CATCHER ON THE GO (IRE)**, 8, b g Catcher In The Rye (IRE)—Suspicious Minds **T Hywel Jones Racing**
11 **CESAR COLLONGES (FR)**, 6, ch g Fragrant Mix (IRE)—Prouesse Collonges (FR) **Mr & Mrs William Rucker**
12 **CHOOSEYOURWEAPON (IRE)**, 5, br g Flemensfirth (USA)—Definite Love (IRE) **Mr & Mrs William Rucker**
13 **CLASSIC JEWEL (IRE)**, 11, b g Classic Cliche (IRE)—Be My Libby (IRE) **Feilim O'Muiri & Brendan White**
14 **CLYNE**, 8, b g Hernando (FR)—Lauderdale (GER) **Mr D. M. Williams**
15 **COURT MINSTREL (IRE)**, 11, b g Court Cave (IRE)—Theatral **Mrs J. Davies**
16 **COURT ROYALE (IRE)**, 5, b g Court Cave (IRE)—Windsor Dancer (IRE) **Mrs Janet Davies**
17 **DARK INVADER (FR)**, 6, b g Saint des Saints (FR)—Minirose (FR) **Walters Plant Hire Ltd**
18 **DE DOLLAR MAN (IRE)**, 7, ch g Vinnie Roe (IRE)—Dollar Bay (IRE) **Mr & Mrs William Rucker**
19 **DE FAOITHESDREAM (IRE)**, 12, br g Balakheri (IRE)—Cutteen Lass (IRE) **Mr R Abbott & Mr M Stavrou**
20 **EVENING HUSH (IRE)**, 5, b m Excellent Art—Applause (IRE) **Mr M. J. Haines**
21 **FILLE DES CHAMPS (IRE)**, 7, b m Robin des Champs (FR)—South Queen Lady (IRE) **Mrs Janet Davies**
22 **FIREBIRD FLYER (IRE)**, 11, b g Winged Love (IRE)—Kiora Lady (IRE) **R. E. R. Williams**
23 **FLIGHT TO MILAN (IRE)**, 5, b g Milan—Kigali (IRE) **R. E. R. Williams**
24 **GAYEBURY**, 8, b g Overbury (IRE)—Gaye Sophie **Mr R Abbott & Mr M Stavrou**
25 **GO LONG (IRE)**, 8, b g Hurricane Run (IRE)—Monumental Gesture **Mr & Mrs William Rucker**
26 **GOLDEN WHISKY (IRE)**, 5, ch g Flemensfirth (USA)—Derry Vale (IRE) **Mr & Mrs William Rucker**
27 **GRANIA O'MALLEY (IRE)**, 5, ch m Beat Hollow—Oh Susannah (FR) **Ms S. Howell**
28 **GWALIA**, 5, b g Beat Hollow—Payphone **Mr D. M. Williams**
29 **HANDS OF STONE (IRE)**, 6, b g Shantou (USA)—Hayabusa **R. E. R. Williams**
30 **HOLDBACKTHERIVER (IRE)**, 6, b g Presenting—Fairy Lane (IRE) **W J Evans Racing**
31 **JOHN CONSTABLE (IRE)**, 7, b g Montjeu (IRE)—Dance Parade (USA) **Walters Plant Hire Ltd**
32 **KING'S ODYSSEY (IRE)**, 9, b g King's Theatre (IRE)—Ma Furie (FR) **Mr & Mrs William Rucker**
33 **MAC BELLA**, 6, ch m Black Sam Bellamy (IRE)—Macnance (IRE) **Keith & Sue Lowry**
34 **MARBLE MOON (IRE)**, 6, b g Millenary—Royal Marble (IRE) **Mr Emrys Jones & Partner**
35 **MARKET ROAD (IRE)**, 8, gr g Tikkanen (USA)—Clydeside (IRE) **W J Evans Racing**
36 **MONBEG OSCAR (IRE)**, 6, b g Oscar (IRE)—Simply Joyful **Mr & Mrs William Rucker**
37 **MORIANOUR (FR)**, 7, b g Valanour (IRE)—Moriane (FR) **Mr T. Hywel Jones**
38 **MR KIT CAT (IRE)**, 8, ch g Lucarno (USA)—Makeabreak (IRE) **Mr & Mrs William Rucker**
39 **NANSAROY**, 8, br g Indian River (FR)—Jurado Park (IRE) **Mr T. Hywel Jones**
40 **NEWQUAY CARDS (IRE)**, 6, gr g Tikkanen (USA)—Sanadja (IRE) **Mr T. Hywel Jones**
41 **NORTH WEST WIND**, 5, b g Shirocco (GER)—Crystal Ballerina (IRE) **R. E. R. Williams**
42 **OLD SALT (IRE)**, 6, b g Craigsteel—Andrea Gale (IRE) **Mr W. P. Bates**
43 **ON THE ROAD (IRE)**, 8, b g Stowaway—B Greenhill **Mrs C. A. Williams**
44 **ON TOUR (IRE)**, 10, b g Croco Rouge (IRE)—Galant Tour (IRE) **Mr T. Hywel Jones**
45 **OXWICH BAY (IRE)**, 6, b g Westerner—Rose de Beaufai (FR) **Mr David M. Williams**

MR EVAN WILLIAMS - Continued

46 **PADGE (IRE)**, 9, b g Flemensfirth (USA)—Mona Vic (IRE) **Mr & Mrs William Rucker**
47 **PETERBOROUGH (FR)**, 5, b g Fuisse (FR)—Peony Girl (FR) **Norwester Racing Club & Partner**
48 **POBBLES BAY (IRE)**, 8, b g Oscar (IRE)—Rose de Beaufai (FR) **Mr D. M. Williams**
49 **PODILI ROAD (IRE)**, 6, b g Darsi (FR)—Geray Lady (IRE) **R. E. R. Williams**
50 **POSITIVELY DYLAN**, 7, b g Multiplex—Wou Oodd **Mrs Janet Davies**
51 **PRESENT TIMES (IRE)**, 7, b g Kalanisi (IRE)—Beguiling (IRE) **Mrs C. A. Waters**
52 **PRIME VENTURE (IRE)**, 7, br g Primary (USA)—Next Venture (IRE) **Mrs Janet Davies**
53 **PRUSSIAN EAGLE (IRE)**, 7, br g Jeremy (USA)—Absolutely Cool (IRE) **Mrs Janet Davies**
54 **RADICAL ARCHIE**, 7, ch g Prince Arch (USA)—Radical Gunner **Mrs Janet Davies**
55 **RAILROAD JUNKIE (IRE)**, 5, b g Thousand Words—Eckbeag (USA) **Mrs J. Davies**
56 **REPORT TO BASE (IRE)**, 6, b g Westerner—Marina du Berlais (FR) **Mr & Mrs William Rucker**
57 **ROCK AND ROLL KING (IRE)**, 6, b g King's Theatre (IRE)—Lunar Path (IRE) **Ms S. Howell**
58 **RUSSIAN SPY (IRE)**, 5, b g Sholokhov (IRE)—Elle Desert (GER) **R. E. R. Williams**
59 **SILVER STREAK (IRE)**, 5, gr g Dark Angel (IRE)—Happy Talk (IRE) **Mr T. L. Fell**
60 **SKEWIFF**, 6, b m Doyen (IRE)—Skew **Mrs Janet Davies**
61 **ST JOHN'S**, 5, b g Aqlaam—Diam Queen (GER) **Simone & Yasmin Cuddy**
62 **STILL BELIEVING (IRE)**, 10, ch m Blueprint (IRE)—Im A Believer (IRE) **R. E. R. Williams**
63 **SUTTER'S MILL (IRE)**, 7, b g Gold Well—Shamriyna (IRE) **R. E. R. Williams**
64 **SWIFT CRUSADOR**, 7, b g Kayf Tara—Goldenswift (IRE) **Mr & Mrs William Rucker**
65 **TANGO DU ROY (IRE)**, 5, b g Court Cave—Hamari Gold (IRE) **Mr & Mrs William Rucker**
66 **THE GIPPER (IRE)**, 8, b g King's Theatre (IRE)—Merrill Gaye (IRE) **POS Partnership**
67 **THE LAST DAY (IRE)**, 6, b g Oscar (IRE)—The Last Bank (IRE) **Mr & Mrs William Rucker**
68 **THEATRE STAGE (IRE)**, 6, b g Gamut (IRE)—Castletown Girl **Morse, Footman & Williams**
69 **TORNADO IN MILAN (IRE)**, 12, b g Milan—Julika (IRE) **Mrs C. A. Williams**
70 **TOSSAPENNY (IRE)**, 5, b g Presenting—Blueanna (IRE) **Mr & Mrs William Rucker**
71 **UNDER THE WOODS**, 6, b g Kayf Tara—Palmito (IRE) **Mrs C. A. Williams**
72 **VIRGINIA CHICK (FR)**, 6, b g Nickname (FR)—Sweet Jaune (FR) **Mrs C. A. Williams**
73 **VOODOO DOLL (IRE)**, 5, b g Getaway (GER)—Voodoo Magic (GER) **R. E. R. Williams**
74 **WYLDE MAGIC (IRE)**, 7, b g Oscar (IRE)—Voodoo Magic (GER) **Mr & Mrs William Rucker**
75 **YELLOW KANGAROO (IRE)**, 6, b g Aussie Rules (USA)—Sue N Win (IRE) **R. E. R. Williams**

Other Owners: Mr Richard Abbott, Mr D. P. Barrie, Mrs D. E. Cheshire, Mrs S. Cuddy, Miss Yasmin Cuddy, Mrs Janet Davies, Mr Mike Dawson, Mr W. J. Evans, Mr Charles Footman, Mr G. A. Greaves, Mr M. J. Haines, Ms S. Howell, Mr T. Hywel Jones, Mr Emrys Jones, Mr R. Kent, Mr D. G. Long, Mrs Keith Lowry, Mr Keith Lowry, Mr Gareth Morse, Norwester Racing Club, Mr F. T. O'Muiri, Mr D. Redhead, Mrs A. Rucker, Mr William Rucker, Mr M. Stavrou, Mr C. Trigg, Mr P. B. White, Mrs C. Williams, Mr David M. Williams, Mr R. E. R. Williams.

Assistant Trainer: Cath Williams

Jockey (NH): Adam Wedge. **Conditional:** Conor Ring.
Amateur: Miss Isabel Williams.

 607

MR IAN WILLIAMS, Alvechurch
Postal: **Dominion Racing Stables, Seafield Lane, Alvechurch, Birmingham, B48 7HL**
Contacts: **PHONE (01564) 822392 FAX (01564) 829475 MOBILE (07976) 645384**
E-MAIL info@ianwilliamsracing.com WEBSITE www.ianwilliamsracing.com

1 **ACES (IRE)**, 6, b g Dark Angel (IRE)—Cute Ass (IRE) **M. H. Watt**
2 **ADMAN SAM (IRE)**, 7, b g Black Sam Bellamy (IRE)—Koral Bay (FR) **Mr P. A. Downing**
3 **ALMOST GOLD (IRE)**, 5, b g Gold Well—Shining Lights (IRE) **Mr S. Cox**
4 **AMBER GAMBLER (GER)**, 8, b g Doyen (IRE)—Auenglocke (GER) **P. Kelly**
5 **BABETTE (IRE)**, 4, b f Cape Cross (IRE)—Crinoline (USA) **Mr K. Sohi**
6 **BALLYALTON (IRE)**, 11, b g Pierre—Almllto (IRE) **Mr J. Westwood**
7 **BALLYNAGOUR (IRE)**, 12, b g Shantou (USA)—Simply Deep (IRE) **A. Stennett**
8 **BAMAKO DU CHATELET (FR)**, 7, gr g Voix du Nord—Royale du Chatelet (FR) **Macable Partnership**
9 **BANDITRY (IRE)**, 6, b g Ilfraaj—Badalona **Buxted Partnership**
10 **BARON DU PLESSIS (FR)**, 7, b g Network (GER)—Larme A L'oeil (FR) **Mrs J. Hitchings**
11 **BAYDAR**, 5, b g Rock of Gibraltar (IRE)—Splashdown **Mr K. Sohi**
12 **BELLE BELLA (IRE)**, 6, b m Kalanisi (IRE)—Reseda (GER) **I. P. Williams**
13 **BLUE RAMBLER**, 8, b g Monsun (GER)—La Nuit Rose (FR) **Mr P. A. Downing**
14 **BOBCATBILLY (IRE)**, 12, b g Overbury (IRE)—Cush Jewel (IRE) **The Ferandlin Peaches**
15 **BODEGA**, 10, b g Grape Tree Road—Gurleigh (IRE) **Mr P. R. Williams**
16 **BOY IN THE BAR**, 7, ch g Dutch Art—Lipsia (IRE) **Sovereign Racing**
17 **BYRON FLYER**, 7, b g Byron—Nursling (IRE) **Anchor Men**

MR IAN WILLIAMS - Continued

18 5, B m Haafhd—Callitwhatyalike **The Ferandlin Peaches**
19 **CAPTAIN SUE (IRE)**, 4, ch f Tamayuz—Correct **I. P. Williams**
20 **CASEMATES SQUARE (IRE)**, 4, b g Casamento (IRE)—Marhaba **The Ferandlin Peaches**
21 **COOL SKY**, 9, b g Millkom—Intersky High (USA) **Norte Sur Partnership**
22 **DIAKTOROS (IRE)**, 8, b g Red Clubs (IRE)—Rinneen (IRE) **Mr S. Coomes**
23 **DON'T ACT UP**, 7, gr g Act One—Lucky Arrow **Ian Williams Racing Club**
24 **DR DORO (IRE)**, 5, b m Holy Roman Emperor (IRE)—Stellarina (IRE) **Mr S. Rudolf**
25 **EAT MY DIRT (IRE)**, 6, b g Mahler—Aos Dana (IRE) **I. P. Williams**
26 **FIRE AHEAD (IRE)**, 5, b g Yeats (IRE)—Ring of Fire (USA) **P. Kelly**
27 **FIRST ASSIGNMENT (IRE)**, 5, b g Vinnie Roe (IRE)—Rebel Dream (IRE) **The DTTW Partnership**
28 **FREUD (FR)**, 8, b g Dalakhani (IRE)—Ailette **A & P Skips Limited**
29 **GALA CELEBRATION (IRE)**, 4, b g Excelebration (IRE)—Elusive Galaxy (IRE) **Caveat Emptor Partnership**
30 **GAS LINE BOY (IRE)**, 12, b g Blueprint (IRE)—Jervia **The Three Graces**
31 **GETAWAY MISSION (IRE)**, 4, b g Getaway (GER)—Emeranna (IRE)
32 **GHOST OF A SMILE (IRE)**, 10, b g Oscar (IRE)—Dix Huit Brumaire (FR) **Mr S. Cox**
33 **GLENGRA (IRE)**, 9, gr g Beneficial—Zaraza (IRE) **The Ferandlin Peaches**
34 **GRAND INQUISITOR**, 6, b g Dansili—Dusty Answer **Sir Alex Ferguson & Mr Peter Done**
35 **HERNANDES (FR)**, 4, gr g Clodovil (IRE)—Gontcharova (IRE) **John Moorhouse & John Nicholls (Trading)**
36 **INDIAN CASTLE (IRE)**, 10, b g Dr Massini (IRE)—Indian Legend (IRE) **Askew Dick Hernon Reynard**
37 5, B m Oscar (IRE)—Iona Flyer (IRE)
38 **JAM SESSION (IRE)**, 6, ch g Duke of Marmalade (IRE)—Night Dhu **Mr A. L. R. Morton**
39 **JUMPING AROUND (IRE)**, 4, b f Dark Angel (IRE)—Box of Frogs (IRE) **Mr K. Sohi**
40 **KAPSTADT (IRE)**, 8, b br g Country Reel (USA)—King's Parody (IRE) **Anchor Men**
41 **KING OF REALMS (IRE)**, 6, b g King's Theatre (IRE)—Sunny South East (IRE) **Chandler Ferguson Hanafin Kelly**
42 **KREB'S CYCLE (IRE)**, 4, ch g Helmet (AUS)—La Noe **Ontoawinner Upton Group Tredwell**
43 **MICHAEL'S MOUNT**, 5, ch g Mount Nelson—Dumnoni **Andrew Dick & Mark Dennis**
44 **MIDTECH STAR (IRE)**, 6, b g Kodiac—Royal Rival (IRE) **Midtech**
45 **MIDTECH VALENTINE**, 7, b m Act One—Eveon (IRE) **Midtech 1**
46 **MIRACLE GARDEN**, 6, ch g Exceed And Excel (AUS)—Sharp Terms **Mr M. A. Geobey**
47 **MODERNISM**, 9, b g Monsun (GER)—La Nuit Rose (FR) **Dr M. B. Q. S. Koukash**
48 **MONJENI**, 5, b g Montjeu (IRE)—Polly's Mark (IRE) **I. P. Williams**
49 **MY FANTASEA (IRE)**, 5, b g Sea The Stars (IRE)—Speed Song **Mrs A. M. O'Sullivan**
50 **NO CEILING (IRE)**, 8, b g Turtle Island (IRE)—Pyrexie (FR) **The Ferandlin Peaches**
51 **NOMINATION GAME (IRE)**, 7, b g Oscar (IRE)—Tiarella (IRE) **John Nicholls (Trading) Ltd**
52 **NORTH HILL (IRE)**, 7, b g Westerner—Hill Fairy **Exors of the Late Mrs J. S. Allen**
53 **OK BY ME (IRE)**, 4, ch f Arcano (IRE)—Kindest **Mike Nolan, John Abbey and Chris Heron**
54 **OSCAR HOOF (IRE)**, 10, b g Oscar (IRE)—New Legislation (IRE)
55 **OUR IDIC BOY (IRE)**, 4, b g Royal Anthem (USA)—Next Best Thing (IRE) **Mr K. McKenna**
56 **PADDY A (IRE)**, 4, b g Holy Roman Emperor (IRE)—Lilting (USA) **DBAC Syndicate**
57 **PERFECT SUMMER (IRE)**, 8, b m High Chaparral (IRE)—Power of Future (GER) **The Ferandlin Peaches**
58 **POKER SCHOOL (IRE)**, 8, b g Gold Well—Broken Pockets (IRE) **M Aniol A Chandler J Medcroft S Turner**
59 **PORTWAY FLYER (IRE)**, 10, br g King's Theatre (IRE)—Next Best Thing (IRE) **P. Kelly**
60 **PREDICT A RIOT (IRE)**, 7, ch g Flemensfirth (USA)—Ballerina Laura (IRE) **Mr P. R. Williams**
61 **PRINCE JAI**, 5, ch g Showcasing—Play Around (IRE) **Mr & Mrs H. Parmar**
62 **PSYCHEDELIC ROCK**, 7, b g Yeats (IRE)—Gemini Lucy (IRE) **John Nicholls (Trading) Ltd**
63 **PSYCHOCANDY (IRE)**, 6, b m Oscar (IRE)—Derrigra Sublime (IRE) **Mr S. Cox**
64 **PURE AFFECTION (IRE)**, 7, b m Beneficial—Regents Dancer (IRE) **Ian Williams Racing Club**
65 **PURE SHORES (IRE)**, 4, b f Dubawi (IRE)—Polly's Mark (IRE) **Fergus Anstock**
66 **REBEL BEAT**, 7, b g Lucarno (USA)—Callitwhatyalike **The Ferandlin Peaches**
67 **RED INFANTRY (IRE)**, 8, ch g Indian River (FR)—Red Rover **Mr R. Little**
68 **RESHOUN (FR)**, 4, b g Shamardal (USA)—Radiyya (IRE) **Michael Watt & Roy David**
69 **RICHIE MCCAW**, 5, b g Zamindar (USA)—Cochin (USA) **Michael Watt & Billy Slater (aus)**
70 **ROCKNROLLRAMBO (IRE)**, 11, b g Winged Love (IRE)—Lady Padivor (IRE) **Ian Williams Racing Club**
71 **SAILORS WARN (IRE)**, 11, b g Redback—Coral Dawn (IRE) **Ian Williams Racing Club**
72 **SAUNTER (FR)**, 5, gr g Myboycharlie (IRE)—Marie des Fleurs (FR) **Michael Watt & Billy Slater (aus)**
73 **SECRET LEGACY (IRE)**, 7, b g Flemensfirth (USA)—Wingfield Lady (IRE) **Andrew Dick & Mike Askew**
74 **SHADY MCCOY (USA)**, 8, b g English Channel (USA)—Raw Gold (USA) **Allwins Stables**
75 **SIR MAXIMILIAN (IRE)**, 9, b g Royal Applause—Nebraska Lady (IRE) **Mr P. E. Wildes**
76 **SLIDING DOORS (IRE)**, 5, b g Ask—Reseda (GER) **The Three Graces**
77 **SO CELEBRE (GER)**, 5, ch g Peintre Celebre (USA)—Saldenname (GER) **Miss J. Melnika**
78 **SPEEDO BOY (FR)**, 4, ch g Vision d'etat (FR)—Shamardanse (USA) **Mr P. R. Williams**
79 **SPIN POINT (IRE)**, 6, b g Pivotal—Daneleta (IRE) **Mr J. O'Shea**
80 **STELLARISTA (IRE)**, 4, b f Mastercraftsman (IRE)—Stellarina (IRE) **Mr S. Rudolf**
81 **SUNNYTAHLIATEIGAN (IRE)**, 6, b g Robin des Pres (FR)—Wavering Bee (IRE) **Mr P. Hernon**
82 **TAKING A CHANCE (IRE)**, 5, b m Flemensfirth (USA)—Northern Mill (IRE) **I. P. Williams**

MR IAN WILLIAMS - Continued

83 **TEAK (IRE)**, 11, b g Barathea (IRE)—Szabo (IRE) **Macable Partnership**
84 **TIKK TOCK BOOM (IRE)**, 6, gr m Tikkanen (USA)—Henrietta (IRE) **The Ferandlin Peaches**
85 **TOMAHAWK KID**, 5, b g Major Cadeaux—Say A Prayer **Mr P. L. Mousley**
86 **TURANGA LEELA**, 4, ch f Paco Boy (IRE)—Sunday Bess (JPN) **Eventmasters Racing**
87 **TWOJAYSLAD**, 9, b g Kayf Tara—Fulwell Hill **J. Tredwell**
88 **WAR BRIGADE (FR)**, 4, b g Manduro (GER)—Adjudicate
89 **WART BRODERICK (IRE)**, 9, ch g Hawk Wing (USA)—Kingsridge (IRE) **P. Kelly**
90 **WOLFCATCHER (IRE)**, 6, b g King's Best (USA)—Miss Particular (IRE) **Buxted Partnership**
91 **XHALE (FR)**, 6, br g Halling (USA)—Xanadu Bliss (FR) **The Blue Harlequin Racing Club**
92 **ZERACHIEL (IRE)**, 8, b g Winged Love (IRE)—At Dawn (IRE) **John Nicholls (Trading) Ltd**

THREE-YEAR-OLDS

93 **BORN TO SPEND (IRE)**, ch f Born To Sea (IRE)—Banco Suivi (IRE) **Farranamanagh**
94 B c Jeremy (USA)—Coill Cri (IRE)
95 **JACK REGAN**, b g Rock of Gibraltar (IRE)—Chelsey Jayne (IRE) **Sohi & Sohi**
96 **LADY JAYNE (IRE)**, b f Henrythenavigator (USA)—Stellavera (FR) **Mr S. Rudolf**
97 **MATEWAN (IRE)**, b g Epaulette (AUS)—Cochin (USA) **Michael Watt & Billy Slater (aus)**
98 **MISS MUMTAZ (IRE)**, ch f Lope de Vega (IRE)—Ispanka **Sohi & Sohi**
99 Gr c Zebedee—Munaasaba (IRE)
100 **OI THE CLUBB OI'S**, gr g Champs Elysees—Red Boots (IRE) **The Albatross Club**
101 **PADDY THE CHEF (IRE)**, b g Dandy Man (IRE)—The Reek **Mr & Mrs H. Parmar**
102 **RUNTHATBYMEAGAIN (IRE)**, b ro f Sir Prancealot (IRE)—Romanylei **Mike Nolan & John Abbey**
103 **SHANIA SAYS (IRE)**, b f Red Jazz (USA)—Vexatious (IRE) **Sohi & Sohi**
104 **SHUHOOD (IRE)**, b g Tamayuz—Walayef (USA) **Sohi & Sohi**
105 **SWORDBILL**, ch g Champs Elysees—Dream Wild **Sohi & Sohi**
106 **TOMMY BOY**, ch c Camacho—Jacaranda Ridge **Sohi & Sohi**

TWO-YEAR-OLDS

107 **THE EASTER GIFT (FR)**, b c 27/3 Zanzibari (USA)—King's Parody (IRE) (King's Best (USA)) (24420)

Other Owners: J. E. Abbey, Mr S. M. P. Adcock, Mr G. Anderson, Mr A. Aniol, Mr M. R. Askew, Mr A. Chandler, Mr A. Cocum, Mr R. David, Mr M. N. Dennis, Mr A. D. Dick, Mr P. E. Done, Dr P. A. I. Doro, Sir A. Ferguson, Mr N. D. Ford, Mrs M. Forsyth, Mr M. W. Goodall, Mr J. N. Greenley, Mr D. Hanafin, J. P Hanifin, Ms R. J. Harris, Mr J. C. Heron, Mrs D. Hopkins, Mr D. P. G. Jones, Mr P. J. Legros, Mr F. W. Mackintosh, Mr S. Mackintosh, Mr C. R. Mander, Mr G. Marshall, Mr J. McConkey, Mr J. R. Medcroft, Mr J. H. Moorhouse, Mrs A. Morrissey, Mr M. Morrissey, M. F. Nolan, Mr N. J. O'Brien, Palatinate Thoroughbred Racing Limited, Mrs K. Parmar, Mr H. Parmar, Mr P. Ratcliffe, Mr A. M. Reason, Mr J. A. Reynard, Mrs J. Ruthven, Mr E. J. N. Sheasby, Mrs D. Sheasby, Mr A. Shreeve, Mr W. N. Slater, Mr J. Sohi, Mr P. Thwaites, Mr S. W. Turner.

Assistant Trainer: Richard Ryan

Jockey (NH): Will Kennedy, Tom O'Brien. **Apprentice:** Luke Catton.

---

 608 **MR NICK WILLIAMS, South Molton**
Postal: Culverhill Farm, George Nympton, South Molton, Devon, EX36 4JE
Contacts: PHONE (01769) 574174 MOBILE (07855) 450379
E-MAIL nandjwilliams@live.co.uk

1 **ADMIRAL BARRATRY (FR)**, 5, b g Soldier of Fortune (IRE)—Haskilclara (FR) **Mr R. Forster**
2 **AGRAPART (FR)**, 7, b br g Martaline—Afragha (IRE) **The Gascoigne Brookes Partnership III**
3 **AIMEE DE SIVOLA (FR)**, 4, ch f Network (GER)—Neva de Sivola (FR) **Larkhills Racing Partnership IV**
4 **AUBUSSON (FR)**, 9, b g Ballingarry (IRE)—Katioucha (FR) **Mrs J. R. Williams**
5 **CABERNET D'ALENE (FR)**, 6, b g Day Flight—Haifa du Noyer (FR) **Larkhills Racing Partnership**
6 **COO STAR SIVOLA (FR)**, 6, b g Assessor (IRE)—Santorine (FR) **Babbit Racing**
7 **CULTURE DE SIVOLA (FR)**, 6, b m Assessor (IRE)—Neva de Sivola (FR) **Larkhills Racing Partnership II**
8 **DAIM PIERJI (FR)**, 5, b g Coastal Path—Keensland (FR) **Mrs J. R. Williams**
9 **DAISY DE SIVOLA (FR)**, 5, b m Assessor (IRE)—Kerrana (FR) **Mr K. Alexander**
10 **DENTLEY DE MEE (FR)**, 5, b g Lauro (GER)—Natty Twigy (FR) **Babbit Racing**
11 **DIABLE DE SIVOLA (FR)**, 5, b g Noroit (GER)—Grande Route (IRE) **Mr R. Forster**
12 **DIAMANT BLEU (FR)**, 5, b g Montmartre (FR)—Cate Bleue (FR) **Jane Williams,Len Jakeman & Martin Booth**
13 **ERICK LE ROUGE (FR)**, 4, ch g Gentlewave (IRE)—Imperia II (FR) **The Culverhill Racing Club**
14 **ESPRIT DE SOMOZA (FR)**, 4, b g Irish Wells (FR)—Topaze de Somoza (FR) **Mr R. Forster**

MR NICK WILLIAMS - Continued

15 **FLYING TIGER (IRE)**, 5, bl g Soldier of Fortune (IRE)—Ma Preference (FR) **The Macaroni Beach Society**
16 **GAMAIN (IRE)**, 9, b g Gamut (IRE)—Glass Curtain (IRE) **Mrs J. R. Williams**
17 **HORATIO HORNBLOWER (IRE)**, 10, b br g Presenting—Countess Camilla **Chasing Gold Limited**
18 **JEU DE MOTS (FR)**, 5, b g Saint des Saints (FR)—Nanouska (GER) **Mrs J. R. Williams**
19 **LE ROCHER (FR)**, 8, b g Saint des Saints (FR)—Belle du Roi (FR) **John White & Anne Underhill**
20 **MERCENAIRE (FR)**, 4, gr g Soldier of Fortune (IRE)—Southwold **K Alexander/ R Watts**
21 **MONSIEUR LECOQ (FR)**, 4, b g Diamond Boy (FR)—Draga (FR) **Mrs J. R. Williams**
22 **MOONLIGHTER**, 5, b g Midnight Legend—Countess Camilla **Mrs Jane Williams, Huw & Richard Davies**
23 **NIGHT OF SIN (FR)**, 5, gr g Sinndar (IRE)—Natt Musik (FR) **Simon Brown & Ron Watts**
24 **ONE FOR THE TEAM**, 4, b g Shirocco (GER)—One Gulp **Forty Winks Syndicate 2**
25 **ONE OF US**, 6, b g Presenting—One Gulp **Forty Winks Syndicate**
26 **PERUVIEN BLEU (FR)**, 6, b br g Fuisse (FR)—Edelmira (FR) **Mrs J. R. Williams**
27 **ROCOCO RIVER**, 4, b g Shirocco (GER)—Noun de La Thinte (FR) **Mrs J Williams & Mr R Stark**
28 **ROMEO BROWN**, 4, br g Yeats (IRE)—Santia **Mrs J. R. Williams**
29 **SIRUH DU LAC (FR)**, 5, b g Turgeon (USA)—Margerie (FR) **John White & Anne Underhill**
30 **TEA FOR TWO**, 9, b g Kayf Tara—One For Me **Mrs Jane Williams & Mr Len Jakeman**
31 **WILLOW MAY**, 4, b f Sakhee (USA)—Cerise Bleue (FR) **Mrs J. R. Williams**
32 **ZEPHYR**, 7, ch g Shirocco (GER)—Pelagia (IRE) **Mrs J. R. Williams**

THREE-YEAR-OLDS

33 B g Montmartre (FR)—Cate Bleue (FR) **Mrs J Williams & Mr R Stark**
34 **FAIRE PART SIVOLA (FR)**, b g Noroit (GER)—Lettre d'estruval (FR) **K Alexander/ R Watts**
35 **FAVORI DE SIVOLA (FR)**, b g Noroit (GER)—Suave de Sivola (FR) **John White & Anne Underhill**
36 **FELICIDAD (FR)**, b f Racinger (FR)—Sacade (FR) **Mr K. Alexander**
37 **FOX PRO (FR)**, b g Coastal Path—Devise II (FR) **Mrs J. R. Williams**
38 **IN REM (FR)**, b g Kapgarde (FR)—Etoile des Iles (FR) **Mr R. Forster**
39 **LE CAMELEON**, b br g Great Pretender (IRE)—Countess Camilla **The Pretenders**
40 **MONTESTREL (FR)**, b g Montmartre (FR)—La Estrella (GER) **Mrs J. R. Williams**
41 Ch g Martaline—Panzella (FR) **The Gascoigne Brookes Partnership III**
42 **SPARKY VALENTINE (FR)**, b f Kapgarde (FR)—Qualite Controlee (FR) **Mrs J. R. Williams**

TWO-YEAR-OLDS

43 **GALAHAD QUEST (FR)**, b g 12/3 American Post—Atacames (FR) (Dom Alco (FR))
44 **KAPACHE (FR)**, b g 11/5 Kapgarde (FR)—Playact (IRE) (Hernando (FR)) (56980)
45 B f 15/2 Fame And Glory—Laetitia (IRE) (Priolo (USA)) (7619) **Mrs J. R. Williams**
46 Ch f 6/1 Sea The Stars (IRE)—Lockup (IRE) (Inchinor) (17908) **Miss E. Morgan**
47 B g 23/3 Le Havre (IRE)—Lune Orientale (IRE) (Dalakhani (IRE)) (44770) **The Macaroni Beach Society**
48 **SAINT DU ROI (FR)**, b g 16/3 Saint des Saints (FR)—
                                Belle du Roi (Adieu Au Roi (IRE)) (89540) **John White & Anne Underhill**
49 B g 10/2 Le Havre (IRE)—Salvation (Montjeu (IRE)) (36630) **The Macaroni Beach Society**

Other Owners: K. Barker, Dr M. Booth, J. N. W. Brookes, Mr S. J. Brown, Mr K. Conlan, Mr R. L. Davies, Mr H. G. Davies, Huw & Richard Davies, Mr G. Devlin, Mr M. J. Freer, Mr S. D. Garner, Mr C. J. Garner, D. A. Gascoigne, Mr A. Holt, Mr L. J. Jakeman, Mr J. E. Lawrence, D. Morgan, Mr I. Paye, M. L. Pepper, G. C. Pratt, Mr J. D. Robinson, Mrs K. Salters, Ms A. M. Simmons, Mr R. Stark, Mr J. Summers, Mrs A. Underhill, Mr R. C. Watts, Mr A. J. White, Mr N. S. L. Williams.

Assistant Trainer: Mrs Jane Williams

Conditional: Lizzie Kelly. **Amateur:** Mr C. Williams.

---

609 | **MR NOEL WILLIAMS, Blewbury**
Postal: **Churn Stables, Churn Estate, Blewbury, Didcot, Oxfordshire, OX11 9HG**
Contacts: **PHONE (01235) 850806 MOBILE (07887) 718678**
E-MAIL info@noelwilliamsracing.co.uk **WEBSITE** www.noelwilliamsracing.co.uk

1 **ANOTHER CRICK**, 5, b g Arcadio (GER)—Suetsu (IRE) **Mr D. J. S. Sewell**
2 **AUTHORIZED TOO**, 7, b g Authorized (IRE)—Audaz **Stonepoint Racing Club**
3 **BALLI MARTINE (FR)**, 5, b g Ballingarry (IRE)—Miss Martine (FR) **Alma Vale Racing**
4 **BREAKING WAVES**, 4, b g Yeats (IRE)—Acoola (IRE) **Mr C. Peake**
5 **BRIERY EXPRESS**, 5, b m Rail Link—Blackbriery Thyne (IRE) **Helen Plumbly & Kathryn Leadbeater**

MR NOEL WILLIAMS - Continued

6 **BRIERY QUEEN**, 9, b m King's Theatre (IRE)—Briery Gale **Helen Plumbly & Kathryn Leadbeater**
7 **CECILATOR**, 4, b f Delegator—Cecily Parsley **EPDS Racing Partnership 20**
8 **DALIANCE (IRE)**, 9, ch g Dalakhani (IRE)—Everlasting Love **EPDS Racing Partnership 15**
9 **DIVA DU MAQUIS (FR)**, 5, b m Buck's Boum (FR)—
                                             Qualine du Maquis (FR) **Mr Stuart Campbell & Non League Racing**
10 **DRIFT**, 5, b m With The Flow (USA)—Lady Exe **Mr N. Williams**
11 **DRUNKEN PIRATE**, 5, b g Black Sam Bellamy (IRE)—Peel Me A Grape **Mrs E. A. Prowting**
12 **FRIENDLY SOCIETY (IRE)**, 13, ch g Moscow Society (USA)—Friendly Breeze **Whiteshoot Racing**
13 **HOT WHISKEY N ICE (IRE)**, 9, b g Milan—Fair Gina (IRE) **Whitehorsemen**
14 **KINCORA FORT (IRE)**, 9, b g Brian Boru—Glenview Rose (IRE) **EPDS Racing Partnership 8**
15 **MIDNIGHT MERLOT**, 6, b g Midnight Legend—Peel Me A Grape **Mrs E. A. Prowting**
16 **MINELLA TREASURE (IRE)**, 8, b g King's Theatre (IRE)—Ringzar (IRE) **Mr D. J. S. Sewell**
17 **PASSING SHADOW**, 4, b g Passing Glance—Peel Me A Grape **Mrs E. A. Prowting**
18 **PRIMO BLUE**, 8, b g Primo Valentino (IRE)—Flintwood **Mr R. Skillen**
19 **SAMSON THE MAN**, 5, b g Black Sam Bellamy (IRE)—Princess Cara **Ms S. Flook**
20 **SENSULANO (IRE)**, 5, b m Milan—Espresso Lady (IRE) **Allison, Allison, Williams**
21 **THEATRE GOER**, 9, b m King's Theatre (IRE)—Clover Green (IRE) **Noel Williams Bloodstock**
22 **UNDISPUTED (IRE)**, 7, b m King's Theatre (IRE)—Gleanntan (IRE) **Mr E. T. D. Leadbeater**
23 4, B g Kalanisi (IRE)—Valamareha (IRE) **Allison, Allison, Williams**
24 **WILD MURPHY (IRE)**, 7, b g Winged Love (IRE)—Yolande (IRE) **Stonepoint Racing 2**

THREE-YEAR-OLDS

25 **PERCY PROSECCO**, b c Sir Percy—Grapes Hill **Didntt Partnership**
26 **SANTIAGO ROCK (IRE)**, b g Rock of Gibraltar (IRE)—Snowpalm **Mr David Bellamy & Mr Peter Harding**

Other Owners: Mr Austin Allison, Mr Jonny Allison, Mr David Bellamy, Mr D. C. Bellamy, Mr Stuart Campbell, Mr Peter Harding, Mrs Kathryn Leadbeater, Mr L. Martin, Non League Racing, Mrs Helen Plumbly, Mr David Pollitt, Mr John Powell, Mrs L. L. Skillen, Miss T. Sloan, Mr G. Spurway, Mrs C. Williams.

Assistant Trainer: Jeremy Mahot

Jockey (NH): Leighton Aspell, Thomas Garner, Wayne Hutchinson.

MR OLLY WILLIAMS, Market Rasen
Postal: **Stone Stables, Nettleton Top, Market Rasen, Lincolnshire, LN7 6SY**
Contacts: **MOBILE (07793) 111600**
E-MAIL williams.olly@yahoo.co.uk WEBSITE www.ollywilliamsracing.co.uk

1 **CAN CAN DREAM**, 4, b f Stimulation (IRE)—Can Can Dancer **I. Robinson**
2 **NEW TALE**, 4, b g Harbour Watch (IRE)—Perfect Story (IRE) **D. L. Bayliss**
3 **TRICKY DICKY**, 5, b g Holy Roman Emperor (IRE)—Tricky Situation **Eight Gents & A Lady**
4 **VIGEE LE BRUN (IRE)**, 4, gr f Dark Angel (IRE)—Wonderful Town (USA) **Chessy Millers Partnership**

THREE-YEAR-OLDS

5 **DARK HEDGES**, b f Zebedee—Bella Chica (IRE) **Olly Williams Rhys Williams James Hanna**
6 **GOING NATIVE**, ch f Speightstown (USA)—Latin Love (IRE) **D. L. Bayliss**
7 **VIKING WAY (IRE)**, ch g Society Rock (IRE)—Patrimony **Folk From The Shire**

TWO-YEAR-OLDS

8 **EMILANDRA (IRE)**, b f 26/3 Slade Power (IRE)—
                                 Soul Mountain (IRE) (Rock of Gibraltar (IRE)) (57142) **Mr G. J. Douglas**
9 **LINCOLN RED**, ch c 7/4 Monsieur Bond (IRE)—Roxy Hart (Halling (USA)) (3333) **Top Of The Wolds Racing**
10 **MATTYMILLER**, bc c 12/4 Garswood—Marigot Bay (Paco Boy (IRE)) (5714) **Mr G. J. Douglas**

Other Owners: Mr Danny Ablott, Mr N. Baker, Mr Gary Douglas, Dynast Racing, Mr Andy Farrell, Mr Stuart Graham, Mr James Hanna, Mr Mark Pearson, Mr T. A. Pocklington, Mrs L. E. Rann, Mr Philip Rann, Mr Ralph Roberts, Mr Trevor Smithson, Mr Mark Spicer, Mr A. S. Trott, Mr Evan Williams, Mr Rhys Williams, Mr Olly Williams, Mr N. S. Wood.

Assistant Trainer: Lynsey Williams

Jockey (flat): Sam James. **Jockey (NH):** Tom Cannon.

611 **MR STUART WILLIAMS, Newmarket**
Postal: **Diomed Stables, Hamilton Road, Newmarket, Suffolk, CB8 0PD**
Contacts: **STABLES/OFFICE** (01638) 663984 **HOME** (01638) 560143 **MOBILE** (07730) 314102
E-MAIL **stuart@stuartwilliamsracing.co.uk WEBSITE www.stuartwilliamsracing.co.uk Twitter:@-
Williamsstuart**

1 **ABLE JACK**, 5, b g Iffraaj—Solva **Happy Valley Racing & Breeding Limited**
2 **ALAADEL**, 5, ch g Dubawi (IRE)—Infallible **Mr T. W. Morley**
3 **BURGUILLOS**, 5, ch g Lope de Vega (IRE)—Hazy Dancer
4 **COMPAS SCOOBIE**, 5, br g Kheleyf (USA)—Fantastic Santanyi **Mrs M. J. Morley**
5 **DASCHAS**, 4, b g Oasis Dream—Canada Water **Mr T. W. Morley**
6 **DEREK DUVAL (USA)**, 4, b g Lope de Vega (IRE)—Lady Raj (USA) **GJ Racing**
7 **EXAMINER (IRE)**, 7, ch g Excellent Art—Therry Girl (IRE) **DJM Racing**
8 **EXCELLENT GEORGE**, 6, b g Exceed And Excel (AUS)—
Princess Georgina **D.A.Shekells, J.W.Parry, Stuart C. Williams**
9 **GLENN COCO**, 4, gr g Aussie Rules (USA)—Las Hilanderas (USA) **Miss Emily Stevens Partnership**
10 **HART STOPPER**, 4, b g Compton Place—Angel Song **Mr T. W. Morley**
11 **HUMAN NATURE (IRE)**, 5, b g Kodiac—Sundown **Enticknap, Reynolds & Watkins**
12 **INTRUDE**, 6, b g Intikhab (USA)—Don't Tell Mum (IRE) **Happy Valley Racing & Breeding Limited**
13 **LUNAR DEITY**, 9, b g Medicean—Luminda (IRE) **Mr W E Enticknap & Partner**
14 **MARATHA (IRE)**, 4, gr g Cape Cross (IRE)—Middle Persia **Happy Valley Racing & Breeding Limited**
15 **ME TOO NAGASAKI (IRE)**, 4, b g Iffraaj—Distinguish (IRE) **Mrs M. J. Morley**
16 **PACTOLUS (IRE)**, 7, b g Footstepsinthesand—Gold Marie (IRE) **T W Morley & Mrs J Morley**
17 **PINNATA (IRE)**, 4, b g Shamardal (USA)—Lavande Violet (GER) **Mr David N Reynolds & Mr C D Watkins**
18 **RELEVANT (IRE)**, 4, b f So You Think (NZ)—Germane **Graf Stauffenberg**
19 **ROYAL BIRTH**, 7, b g Exceed And Excel (AUS)—Princess Georgina **The Morley Family**
20 **SHAMSHON (IRE)**, 7, b g Invincible Spirit (IRE)—Greenisland (IRE) **T W Morley & Regents Racing**
21 **STELLAR SURPRISE**, 4, b f Notnowcato—Crystal Etoile **Mr J. W. Parry & Mr Robert Levitt**
22 **SUZI'S CONNOISSEUR**, 7, b g Art Connoisseur (IRE)—Suzi Spends (IRE) **The Connoisseurs**
23 **SWIFT APPROVAL (IRE)**, 6, ch g Approve (IRE)—Tiltili (IRE) **JLM Racing**
24 **UPAVON**, 8, b g Avonbridge—Blaina **Morley, Reynolds & Watkins**
25 **VIA SERENDIPITY**, 4, b g Invincible Spirit (IRE)—Mambo Light (USA) **Happy Valley Racing & Breeding Limited**
26 **YORKEE MO SABEE (IRE)**, 5, ch g Teofilo (IRE)—Pivotal's Princess (IRE) **Mrs M. J. Morley**

THREE-YEAR-OLDS

27 **AHFAD**, br g Dick Turpin (IRE)—Big Moza **Mr A Watson, Mr B Malyon, Mr M Shenfield**
28 **BAJAN GOLD (IRE)**, ch c Lope de Vega (IRE)—Charmgoer (USA) **Patrick B Doyle (Construction) Ltd**
29 **BREATHTAKING LOOK**, b f Bated Breath—Love Your Looks **J. W. Parry**
30 **CAPE CYCLONE (IRE)**, b f Cape Cross (IRE)—Dubai Cyclone (USA) **Mr A. A. Lyons**
31 **CAROLYN'S VOICE**, br f Poet's Voice—Two Days In Paris (FR) **Mr B Piper & Mr D Cobill**
32 **DICHATO (USA)**, b g Scat Daddy (USA)—Dolce Lemone (CAN) **Mr T. W. Morley**
33 **EPISCIA (IRE)**, b f Arcano (IRE)—Violet Flame (IRE) **Mr T. W. Morley**
34 **I'M A STAR (IRE)**, b g High Chaparral (IRE)—Etoile de Lune **Happy Valley Racing & Breeding Limited**
35 **JAMPOWER**, b g Equiano (FR)—Wiki Tiki **J. W. Parry**
36 **JAN'S JOY**, br f Kheleyf (USA)—Overwing (IRE) **Mr K. R. Robinson**
37 **LALANIA**, br f Kheleyf (USA)—George's Gift **Mrs M. Shone**
38 **LETHAL ANGEL**, gr f Lethal Force (IRE)—Heliograph **The Secretly Hopeful Partnership**
39 **LUCIFUGOUS (IRE)**, gr f Footstepsinthesand—Krasotka (IRE) **Nick Bradley Racing 11 & Partner**
40 **MY BOY SEPOY**, ch c Sepoy (AUS)—Emily Carr (IRE) **Mr & Mrs G. Bhatti**
41 **OAKLEY MIMOSA**, br f Cape Cross (IRE)—Upskittled **J. W. Parry**
42 **RESTLESS ROSE**, ch f Power—Albany Rose (IRE) **Happy Valley Racing & Breeding Limited**
43 **RIVER RULE**, b f Bated Breath—Ocean Countess (IRE) **Mr W. McLuskey**
44 **SPINNERETT**, b f Sir Percy—Las Hilanderas (USA) **Mr D A Shekells & Partner**
45 **WHAT ABOUT BARB**, ch f Excelebration (IRE)—Annie's Fortune (IRE) **Mr G Johnson & Mr J W Parry**
46 **WIFF WAFF**, b g Poet's Voice—Eraadaat (IRE) **Mr J W Parry & Partner**

TWO-YEAR-OLDS

47 Ch c 26/2 Lope de Vega (IRE)—A Huge Dream (IRE) (Refuse To Bend (IRE)) (30000) **Mr B Piper**
48 B f 12/3 Lope de Vega (IRE)—Anna Sophia (USA) (Oasis Dream) (26000) **J. W. Parry**
49 B f 5/3 Acclamation—Church Melody (Oasis Dream) (16000) **Mr & Mrs George Bhatti**
50 B f 4/2 Footstepsinthesand—Cincinnati Kit (Cape Cross (IRE)) **J. W. Parry**
51 **DIAMOND CARA**, ch f 27/4 Equiano (FR)—Tychy (Suave Dancer (USA)) **Mr & Mrs George Bhatti**
52 Ch f 30/3 Le Havre (IRE)—Happy Wedding (IRE) (Green Tune (USA)) (47000) **J. W. Parry**
53 Ch c 26/3 Lope de Vega (IRE)—
Kerry Gal (IRE) (Galileo (IRE)) (150000) **Happy Valley Racing & Breeding Limited**

MR STUART WILLIAMS - Continued

54 **MARRONNIER (IRE)**, ch c 16/2 Lope de Vega (IRE)—
        Beach Bunny (High Chaparral (IRE)) (17908) **GG Thoroughbred Racing**
55 B f 8/3 Oasis Dream—Miss Corniche (Hernando (FR)) (15000) **Mr & Mrs George Bhatti**
56 Gr c 5/3 Mukhadram—Si Belle (IRE) (Dalakhani (IRE)) (14000) **GG Thoroughbred Racing**
57 Gr c 2/4 Lawman (FR)—Silver Samba (Dalakhani (IRE)) (12500) **Mr & Mrs George Bhatti**

Other Owners: Mrs C. J. Bhatti, Mr G. Bhatti, Mr D. L. Cobill, W. E. Enticknap, Mr G. M. C. Johnson, Mr R. M. Levitt, Mrs H. J. Lewis, Mr B. Malyon, Mr T. W. Morley, Mrs J. Morley, Mr J. W. Parry, Mr B. V. Piper, Mr G. R. Pooley, Regents Racing, Mr D. N. Reynolds, Mr D. A. Shekells, P. W. Stevens, Miss E. V. Stevens, Mr C. D. Watkins, Mr A. Watson, Mr S. C. Williams.

Assistant Trainer: Mr J W Parry

Apprentice: Aaron Jones, Milly Naseb.

---

612 | **MISS VENETIA WILLIAMS, Hereford**
Postal: **Aramstone, Kings Caple, Hereford, Herefordshire, HR1 4TU**
Contacts: **PHONE (01432) 840646 MOBILE (07770) 627108**
E-MAIL office@venetiawilliams.com WEBSITE www.venetiawilliams.com

1 **ACHILLE (FR)**, 8, gr g Dom Alco (FR)—Hase (FR) **Mrs V. A. Bingham**
2 **AIR DE ROCK (FR)**, 6, b g High Rock (IRE)—Onciale (FR) **Lady Bolton**
3 **ASO (FR)**, 8, b br g Goldneyev (USA)—Odyssee du Cellier (FR) **The Bellamy Partnership**
4 **BECAUSESHESAIDSO (IRE)**, 10, b g Winged Love (IRE)—Huit de Coeur (FR) **Lady M. A. Bolton**
5 **BELAMI DES PICTONS (FR)**, 7, b g Khalkevi (IRE)—Nina des Pictons (FR) **Hills of Ledbury (AGA)**
6 **BELLE'S THEATRE**, 5, b m Black Sam Bellamy (IRE)—Falcons Theatre (IRE) **Falcon's Line Ltd**
7 **BONNE QUESTION (FR)**, 9, gr g Tagula (IRE)—Amonita (GER) **Falcon's Line Ltd**
8 **BRIGHT NEW DAWN (IRE)**, 11, br g Presenting—Shuil Dorcha (IRE) **Boultbee Brooks Ltd**
9 **CALIPTO (FR)**, 8, b g Califet (FR)—Peutiot (FR) **Mr A. L. Brooks**
10 **CENTURIUS**, 8, ch g New Approach—Questina (FR) **Venetia Williams Racehorse Syndicate III**
11 **CEPAGE (FR)**, 6, b g Saddler Maker (IRE)—Sience Fiction (FR) **The Bellamy Partnership**
12 **CHAMBARD (FR)**, 6, b g Gris de Gris (IRE)—Regina Park (FR) **David & Carol Shaw**
13 **CLOUDY BEACH (IRE)**, 11, gr g Cloudings (IRE)—Niki Beach (IRE) **The Beachcombers**
14 **CLOUDY GLEN (IRE)**, 5, b g Cloudings (IRE)—Ribble (IRE) **Mr T. J. Hemmings**
15 **COLD AS ICE (FR)**, 6, gr g Montmartre (FR)—Turiama (FR) **Kate & Andrew Brooks**
16 **COMMIS D'OFFICE (FR)**, 6, b g Califet (FR)—Pas de Bal (FR) **Mrs Julian Blackwell**
17 **COMMODORE (FR)**, 6, gr g Fragrant Mix (FR)—Morvandelle (FR) **Mrs C Watson & Mrs S Graham**
18 **COUDEFOUDRE (FR)**, 6, gr g Martaline—Chamoss World (FR) **Venetia Williams Racehorse Syndicate 1**
19 **CUBAN PETE (IRE)**, 6, b g Flemensfirth (USA)—Gee Whizz (FR) **Mrs J. Jones**
20 **D'ARCY'S SOUND (IRE)**, 8, b g Kalanisi (IRE)—Semillina (IRE) **David & Carol Shaw**
21 **DARK FORCE (FR)**, 5, gr g Gris de Gris (IRE)—Maciga (FR) **Janet Bromet & Andrew Brooks**
22 **DESQUE DE L'ISLE (FR)**, 5, b g Special Kaldoun (IRE)—Naiade de Lisle (FR) **The Hon Lady M. J. Heber-Percy**
23 **DESSINATEUR (FR)**, 5, b g Alberto Giacometti (IRE)—Castagnette III (FR) **Mr A. L. Brooks**
24 **DON HERBAGER (FR)**, 4, b g Saddler Maker (IRE)—Marie d'altoria (FR) **M. Willcocks & V. Williams**
25 **DRUMVIREDY (IRE)**, 9, b m Flemensfirth (USA)—Leitrim Bridge (IRE) **The M. Shones**
26 **DU SOLEIL (FR)**, 6, ch g Zambezi Sun—Cykapri (FR) **Mr A. L. Brooks**
27 **ECEPARTI (FR)**, 4, b g Enrique—La Pommeraie (FR) **Mrs Sandra Champ**
28 **EMINENT POET**, 3, b g Montjeu (IRE)—Contare **B. C. Dice**
29 **EMPEROR'S CHOICE (IRE)**, 11, b g Flemensfirth (USA)—House-of-Hearts (IRE) **The Bellamy Partnership**
30 **ENOLA GAY (FR)**, 5, b g Fuisse (FR)—Enolaland (FR) **Calvados Racing**
31 **GARDEFORT (FR)**, 9, b br g Agent Bleu (FR)—La Fresnaie (FR) **Mr A. L. Brooks**
32 **GEORDIE B**, 5, br g Geordieland (FR)—Sari Rose (FR) **Boultbee Brooks Ltd**
33 **GRAND TURINA**, 7, b m Kayf Tara—Cesana (FR) **Mr A. J. Taylor**
34 **HOUBLON DES OBEAUX (FR)**, 11, b g Panoramic—Harkosa (FR) **Mrs J. Blackwell**
35 **IFANDABUT (IRE)**, 6, b g Scorpion (IRE)—Native Wonder (IRE) **The Gambling Cousins**
36 **INHERITANCE THIEF**, 6, b g Black Sam Bellamy (IRE)—Red And White (IRE) **F. M. P. Mahon**
37 **JURYS OUT (IRE)**, 5, b g Witness Box (USA)—
        No Complaints But (IRE) **Venetia Williams Racehorse Syndicate III**
38 **KAP JAZZ (FR)**, 8, b g Kapgarde (FR)—Jazz And Liquer (FR) **Charles Barlow & Fiona Neill**
39 **KAPGA DE LILY (FR)**, 5, ch m Kapgarde (FR)—Louvisy (FR) **Kate & Andrew Brooks**
40 **KHAIRAGASH (IRE)**, 5, b g Sinndar (IRE)—Khazina (FR) **Venetia Williams**
41 **LADY CHARTREUSE (IRE)**, 5, ch m Flemensfirth (USA)—Verde Goodwood **Old Carthusian Racing Society (I)**
42 **LADY KARINA**, 7, b m Kayf Tara—Lady Rebecca **Kinnersley Optimists**

MISS VENETIA WILLIAMS - Continued

43 **LAKE WASHINGTON (FR)**, 5, ch g Muhtathir—La Curamalal (IRE) **Boultbee Brooks Ltd**
44 **LAST SHOT (FR)**, 11, b g Le Fou (IRE)—Lucky Shot (FR) **Lady M. A. Bolton**
45 **LITTLE GINGE (FR)**, 5, ch g Kapgarde (FR)—Aconit (FR) **Boultbee Brooks Ltd**
46 **LONGHOUSESIGNORA (IRE)**, 6, b m Milan—Moscow Madame (IRE) **Nora's Playmates**
47 **LOWER HOPE DANDY**, 11, gr g Karinga Bay—Cheeky Mare **Miss V. M. Williams**
48 **LUCKIME (IRE)**, 6, gr g Oscar (IRE)—Blossom Rose (IRE) **Mr T. J. Hemmings**
49 **MARCILHAC (FR)**, 9, b g Smadoun (FR)—One Way (FR) **Mr A. L. Brooks**
50 **MASTER OF VERSE (IRE)**, 9, b g Milan—Bacchonthebottle (IRE) **C Barlow, A Beaumont & S Trowbridge**
51 **MIXCHIEVOUS (FR)**, 6, gr g Fair Mix (IRE)—Cheeky Mare **Tolostley Partnership**
52 **NESTERENKO (GER)**, 9, b g Doyen (IRE)—Nordwahl (GER) **Mrs V. A. Bingham**
53 **OTAGO TRAIL (IRE)**, 10, b g Heron Island (IRE)—Cool Chic (IRE) **Mrs Marie Shone**
54 **PINK LEGEND**, 4, b f Midnight Legend—Red And White (IRE) **F. M. P. Mahon**
55 **PINK TARA**, 7, b m Kayf Tara—Red And White (IRE) **Frank Mahon**
56 **PLAISIR D'AMOUR (FR)**, 6, b m Linngari (IRE)—Analfabeta (FR) **Calvados Racing**
57 **PRESSURIZE (IRE)**, 12, b g Witness Box (USA)—Cockpit Rose (IRE) **Mrs S. A. Williams**
58 **QUICK WAVE (FR)**, 5, b m Gentlewave (IRE)—Magicaldoun (FR) **Ms Sharon Kinsella**
59 **RIGADIN DE BEAUCHENE (FR)**, 13, b br g Visionary (FR)—Chipie d'angron (FR) **Mr A. O. Wiles**
60 **ROC MERLE (IRE)**, 6, b g Milan—Me Grannys Endoors (IRE) **The Bellamy Partnership**
61 **ROUERGATE (FR)**, 5, b m Sageburg (IRE)—Rouge des Champs (FR) **Calvados Racing**
62 **ROYAL PALLADIUM (FR)**, 10, gr g King's Theatre (IRE)—Dent Sucree (FR) **Sir W. J. A. Timpson**
63 **ROYAL TARA (IRE)**, 9, b g Kayf Tara—The Irish Whip **Boultbee Brooks Ltd**
64 **RUSSBOROUGH (FR)**, 9, b g Turgeon (USA)—Heritage River (FR) **Lady M. A. Bolton**
65 **SAROQUE (IRE)**, 11, b g Revoque (IRE)—Sarakin (IRE) **Charles Nugent & Caroline Wilson**
66 **SHALAKAR (FR)**, 5, b g Cape Cross (IRE)—Shalanaya (IRE) **Sheila Schwartz & Lady Eliza Mays-Smith**
67 **SHIVERMETIMBERS (IRE)**, 6, br g Black Sam Bellamy (IRE)—Kimouna (FR) **Old Carthusian Racing Society**
68 **SNUFF BOX (IRE)**, 7, b g Witness Box (USA)—Dara Supreme (IRE) **Mr & Mrs Peter Nathan & Mrs Julia Young**
69 **STORM WIZARD (IRE)**, 6, b g Milan—Tempest Belle (IRE) **Taylor,Coe,Vaughan & Lambert**
70 **SUBCONTINENT (IRE)**, 6, b g Dubawi (IRE)—Saree **Shire Birds**
71 **TARA FLOW**, 8, b m Kayf Tara—Poppet **Kate & Andrew Brooks**
72 **TENOR NIVERNAIS (FR)**, 11, b g Shaanmer (IRE)—Hosanna II (FR) **Boultbee Brooks Ltd**
73 **UHLAN BUTE (FR)**, 10, ch g Brier Creek (USA)—Jonquiere (FR) **The Autumn Partnership**
74 **UN PROPHETE (FR)**, 7, gr g Carlotamix (FR)—Pollita (FR) **Sir W. J. A. Timpson**
75 **VIC DE TOUZAINE (FR)**, 9, gr g Dom Alco (FR)—Diana de Vonnas (FR) **A Brooks & G Moore**
76 **VIVACCIO (FR)**, 9, b g Antarctique (FR)—Cybelle (FR) **Boultbee Brooks Ltd**
77 **WALDORF SALAD**, 10, b g Millenary—Ismene (FR) **Mr A. G. Parker**
78 **WILLIE BOY (IRE)**, 7, b g Tikkanen (USA)—Pandora's Moon (IRE) **Mr A. L. Brooks**
79 **YALA ENKI (FR)**, 8, b br g Nickname (FR)—Cadiane (FR) **Hills of Ledbury Ltd**
80 **YALLTARI**, 7, gr g Kayf Tara—Lily Grey (FR) **Venetia Williams Racehorse Syndicates II**
81 **ZAMDY MAN**, 9, b g Authorized (IRE)—Lauderdale (GER) **Mr J. P. McManus**

Other Owners: Mr C. J. M. Barlow, Mr Edward Beckley, Mrs C. Boultbee-Brooks, Mrs Kate Brazier, Mrs Janet Bromet, Mrs K. L. Brooks, Mr M. Checketts, Mr Bob Clarke, Lady Coe, Mr J. S. Dale, Mr P. Davies, Mr Michael J. Davies, Mr R. J. Elliott, Mrs P. A. H. Hartley, Mr P. A. H. Hartley, Mrs D. M. Hill, Mr T. B. James, Mrs Michael Lambert, Mr B. H. Lenaghan, Mrs Peter Nathan, Mr P. G. Nathan, Mrs C. F. Neill, Cr. R. Nugent, Mr Basil Richards, Mr Jeremy Schwartz, Mr Michael Shone, Ms Melissa Shone, Mr Ian Stirling Tagg, Mr James Richard Terry, Mr Julian Tolhurst, Mr Charlie Vaughan, Mrs C. S. Wilson.

Conditional: Charlie Deutsch. **Amateur:** Mr Hugh Nugent, Miss Lucy Turner.

---

613 MRS LISA WILLIAMSON, Tarporley

Postal: **5 Ridley Wood Court, Ridley Wood, Wrexham, Clwyd, LL13 9UW**
Contacts: **PHONE (07970) 437679**
E-MAIL info@lisawilliamson.co.uk WEBSITE www.lisawilliamson.co.uk

1 **BERTIE BLU BOY**, 10, b g Central Park (IRE)—Shaymee's Girl **A V Wilding (Chester) Ltd**
2 **BLUE ROCKS**, 4, b g Indesatchel (IRE)—Mabinia (IRE) **E. H. Jones (Paints) Ltd**
3 **CELERITY (IRE)**, 4, ch f Casamento (IRE)—Shinko Dancer (IRE) **Heath House Racing**
4 **FIRESNAKE (IRE)**, 5, b g Dandy Man (IRE)—La Bataille (USA) **Pritchard & Woodward**
5 **GO CHARLIE**, 7, b g Myboycharlie (IRE)—Branston Gem **Miss H. J. Roberts**
6 **LAMBRINI LEGACY**, 4, b f Captain Gerrard (IRE)—Lambrini Lace (IRE) **Halewood International Ltd**
7 **MAKES YOU STRONGER**, 6, ch g Major Cadeaux—Verus Decorus (IRE) **Mr J. Deaves**
8 **MIGHTY ZIP (USA)**, 6, ch g City Zip (USA)—Incredulous (FR) **Mr A. T Sykes**
9 **RED STRIPES (USA)**, 6, b g Leroidesanimaux (BRZ)—Kaleidoscopic (USA) **E. H. Jones (Paints) Ltd**

MRS LISA WILLIAMSON - Continued

10 **SASHEEDA**, 4, br f Putra Sas (IRE)—Majeeda (IRE) **Mrs A. J. Swadling**
11 **SECRET ASSET (IRE)**, 13, gr g Clodovil (IRE)—Skerray **Simon & Jeanette Pierpoint**
12 **SERAPHIMA**, 8, b m Fusaichi Pegasus (USA)—Millestan (IRE) **Heath House Racing**
13 **YALLA HABIBTI**, 5, b m Kayf Tara—Majeeda (IRE) **Mrs A. J. Swadling**
14 **YOUR GIFTED (IRE)**, 11, b m Trans Island—Dame Laura (IRE) **Mr A. T Sykes**

THREE-YEAR-OLDS

15 **AONEDAMPROOFING**, b g Westlake—Pinball (IRE) **Mrs L. V. Williamson**
16 **GO SANDY**, ch f Captain Gerrard (IRE)—Lily Jicaro (IRE) **Miss Hazel Roberts**
17 **ISABELLA RUBY**, b f Power—Scarlet Rocks (IRE) **Mr D. Woods**
18 B f Captain Gerrard (IRE)—Lambrini Lace (IRE)
19 **MARIAH'S MELODY (IRE)**, gr f Graydar (USA)—In Seconds (USA) **E. H. Jones (Paints) Ltd**
20 **MATILDA GRACE (IRE)**, gr f Lilbourne Lad (IRE)—New Deal **Mr D. Woods**

TWO-YEAR-OLDS

21 Ch g 27/3 Leroidesanimaux (BRZ)—Apparatchika (Archipenko (USA)) (4000) **E H Jones (Paints) Ltd**

Other Owners: Exors of the Late Mr M. S. Heath, Miss C. Howard, Mrs W. E. Hughes, Mr D. R. Hughes, Mr S. W. Pierpoint, Mrs J. T. Pierpoint, Mr Andrew Pritchard, Mr Jeremy Woodward.

---

614 | ## MR ANDREW WILSON, Greystoke
Postal: **Silver Howe, Orton, Penrith, Cumbria, CA10 3RQ**
Contacts: PHONE **(01539) 624071** MOBILE **(07813) 846768**
E-MAIL **andywilsonorton@gmail.com**

1 **CULLY MAC (IRE)**, 7, b g Coroner (IRE)—Catch Those Kisses **Mr A. C. Wilson**
2 **FRIENDS IN HEAVEN (IRE)**, 6, br g Asian Heights—Native Bev (IRE) **Mr A. C. Wilson**
3 **KINGS ECLIPSE (IRE)**, 8, b g Double Eclipse (IRE)—Good Times Ahead (IRE) **Mr A. C. Wilson**
4 **SENDIYM (FR)**, 11, b g Rainbow Quest (USA)—Seraya (FR) **Mr A. C. Wilson**

---

615 | ## MR CHRISTOPHER WILSON, Darlington
Postal: **Manor Farm, Manfield, Darlington, Co. Durham, DL2 2RW**
Contacts: PHONE **(01325) 374595** FAX **(01325) 374595** MOBILE **(07815) 952306/(07721) 379277**
E-MAIL **wilsonracing@aol.com**

1 5, B m Josr Algarhoud (IRE)—Celtic Flow **Mrs J. Wilson**
2 **LATEST FASHION (IRE)**, 12, ch m Ashkalani (IRE)—Musical Bramble (IRE) **Mrs J. Wilson**
3 **NO TIME TO CRY**, 9, b m Josr Algarhoud (IRE)—Autumn Bloom (IRE) **Mrs J. Wilson**

Assistant Trainer: Julie Wilson

Jockey (NH): Colm McCormack.

---

616 | ## MR JIM WILSON, Cheltenham
Postal: **Glenfall Stables, Ham, Charlton Kings, Cheltenham, Gloucestershire, GL52 6NH**
Contacts: PHONE **(01242) 244713** MOBILE **(07932) 157243**
E-MAIL **ajwglenfall@aol.com**

1 **MAX DYNAMO**, 8, b g Midnight Legend—Vivante (IRE) **Mrs M. J. Wilson**
2 **SEYMOUR LEGEND**, 12, b g Midnight Legend—Rosehall **Mrs M. J. Wilson**
3 **VITARRA**, 9, b m Kayf Tara—Vivante (IRE) **Mrs M. J. Wilson**

617 **MISS MAIRI WILSON, Bawtry**
Postal: **Martin Common Farm, Bawtry, Doncaster, South Yorkshire, DN10 6DB**

1 BRANDBERG (IRE), 5, b g Cape Cross (IRE)—Eaton Street **Mrs M. F. and Miss M. C. Wilson**
2 COFFEE KING (IRE), 9, b g King's Best (USA)—Passarelle (USA) **Mrs M. F. and Miss M. C. Wilson**
3 PLAYMAKER (IRE), 6, b g Dubawi (IRE)—Playful Act (IRE) **Mrs M. F. and Miss M. C. Wilson**

Other Owners: Miss M. C. Wilson, Mrs M. F. Wilson.

Assistant Trainer: Mrs M. Wilson

618 **MR NOEL WILSON, Barnard Castle**
Postal: **Mount Pleasant, Coal Road, Marwood, Barnard Castle, Co. Durham, DL12 8RP**
Contacts: **MOBILE (07939) 905477**
E-MAIL nlwilson69@live.com

1 BILLY FLIGHT (FR), 6, b g Walk In The Park (IRE)—Moon Flight (FR) **Marwood, Alderson, Ridgway & Murphy**
2 DISCREET HERO (IRE), 5, ch g Siyouni (FR)—Alfaguara (USA) **Slaters Arms Racing Club**
3 GHOSTLY ARC (IRE), 6, b g Arcano (IRE)—Cheyenne's Spirit (IRE) **Mr G. J. Paver**
4 HAYWARD FIELD (IRE), 5, b g Cape Blanco (IRE)—Keepers Hill (IRE) **Marwood Racing**
5 KICKING THE CAN (IRE), 7, gr g Aussie Rules (IRE)—Silk Meadow (IRE) **Mr D Mawer**
6 KINLOCH PRIDE, 6, ch m Kyllachy—Pride of Kinloch **Mr G. Paver**
7 LONGROOM, 6, b g Oasis Dream—Phantom Wind (USA) **Marwood Racing & Trevor Alderson**
8 MAJDOOL (IRE), 5, b g Acclamation—Maany (USA) **Marwood Racing**
9 OUR PLACE IN LOULE, 5, ch g Compton Place—Show Off **Mr Paver & Marwood Racing**
10 PAVERS PRIDE, 4, ch g Bahamian Bounty—Pride of Kinloch **Mr Paver**
11 VINTAGE DREAM (IRE), 4, b g Dream Ahead (USA)—Stella Del Mattino (USA) **Pow Partnership**

THREE-YEAR-OLDS

12 BARNEY BULLET (IRE), b g Havana Gold (IRE)—Lalinde **Marwood Racing**
13 CATHIE'S DREAM (USA), b f More Than Ready (USA)—Mantilla (USA) **The Pavers**
14 LAHARNA (IRE), b f Epaulette (AUS)—Maughami **Marwood Racing & Savva Roberts**
15 PAVARELLA SHOES, ch f Lethal Force (IRE)—Shena's Dream (IRE) **Pavarella Shoes Partnership**
16 THE MEKON, ch g Red Jazz (USA)—Date Mate **Marwood Racing**

Other Owners: Mr T. Alderson, Mr M. R. Baker, Mr J. M. Barker, Mr N. R. Hutchinson, Mr D. J. Murphy, Mr J. R. Owen, Mr I. K. Paver, Prof K. Ridgway, Mr S. Roberts, P. M. Watson.

Assistant Trainer: Miss Alex Porritt

Jockey (flat): Phil Dennis, Joe Fanning, Barry McHugh.

619 **MR KEN WINGROVE, Bridgnorth**
Postal: **6 Netherton Farm Barns, Netherton Lane, Highley, Bridgnorth, Shropshire, WV16 6NJ**
Contacts: **HOME (01746) 861534 MOBILE (07974) 411267**
E-MAIL kenwingrove@btinternet.com

1 EDE'S THE BUSINESS, 7, ch m Halling (USA)—My Amalie (IRE) **Mr D. G. Wingrove**
2 5, B h Mount Nelson—Ellcon (IRE) **Mr D. G. Wingrove**
3 ERICUS ERICI, 8, b g Include (USA)—Eze (USA) **Mr D. G. Wingrove**
4 FALLING LEAF (IRE), 8, ch m Sandmason—Turbine Hill (IRE) **Mr D. G. Wingrove**
5 HEAVEN SCENT, 5, ch m Phoenix Reach (IRE)—Hel's Angel (IRE) **Mr D. G. Wingrove**
6 LYME PARK, 7, gr m Multiplex—So Cloudy **Mr D. G. Wingrove**
7 PIVOTAL DREAM (IRE), 5, br m Excellent Art—Oasis Fire (IRE) **Mr D. G. Wingrove**
8 TRENDY NURSE (IRE), 10, b m Gold Well—Rotoruasprings (IRE) **Mr D. G. Wingrove**
9 WILLIE'S ANNE (IRE), 4, b f Lilbourne Lad (IRE)—Cape Sydney (IRE) **Mr D. G. Wingrove**

Assistant Trainer: Isobel Willer

620 **MR PETER WINKS, Barnsley**
Postal: **Homefield, Rotherham Road, Little Houghton, Barnsley, South Yorkshire, S72 0HA**
Contacts: **MOBILE (07846) 899993**
E-MAIL **lynnpwracing@outlook.com**

1 **BACK TO BALLOO (IRE)**, 12, gr g Jimble (FR)—Fleur Du Chenet (FR) **Mr P. Winks**
2 **BALLYFARSOON (IRE)**, 7, ch g Medicean—Amzara (IRE) **Mr P. Winks**
3 **GRAN MAESTRO (USA)**, 9, ch g Medicean—Red Slippers (USA) **P W O'Mara & Peter Winks**
4 **GROW NASA GROW (IRE)**, 7, ch g Mahler—Dereenavurrig (IRE) **Nature and Science Agriculture Limited**
5 **HARTSIDE (GER)**, 9, b g Montjeu (IRE)—Helvellyn (USA) **Mr P. Winks**
6 **MODULUS**, 9, b g Motivator—Wild Academy (IRE) **Mr P. Winks**
7 **NEW KID IN TOWN (IRE)**, 9, b g Gamut (IRE)—Echo Queen (IRE) **Severnwinks**
8 **SOLSTICE DAWN**, 10, b m Lyphento (USA)—Ryders Hill **Mr P. Winks**
9 **WEST CLASS (IRE)**, 7, b g Westerner—Catch The Class (IRE) **Mr P. Winks**

Other Owners: Mr P. W. O'Mara, Mr P. Rowbottom, Mr R. Taberner.

Assistant Trainer: Ryan Winks

Amateur: Mr Ryan Winks.

621 **MR ADRIAN WINTLE, Westbury-On-Severn**
Postal: **Yew Tree Stables, Rodley, Westbury-On-Severn, Gloucestershire, GL14 1QZ**
Contacts: **MOBILE (07767) 351144**

1 **ALEX THE LION (IRE)**, 5, b g Let The Lion Roar—Belle Dame (IRE) **Mr A. J. Rhead**
2 **AMLOVI (IRE)**, 5, b m Court Cave (IRE)—Portanob (IRE) **Mr S. R. Whistance**
3 **BOYFROMNOWHERE (IRE)**, 11, br g Old Vic—Eist Do Gale (IRE) **Mr R. G. Owens**
4 **CAIUS COLLEGE GIRL (IRE)**, 6, b m Royal Applause—Galeaza **A. A. Wintle**
5 **DISTANT SOUND (IRE)**, 11, b g Luso—Distant Dreams (IRE) **A. A. Wintle**
6 **EXOTIC FRIEND (IRE)**, 10, ch g Croco Rouge (IRE)—Prima Nox **Mr S. R. Whistance**
7 **FREIGHT TRAIN (IRE)**, 6, b g Manduro (GER)—Sigonella (IRE) **A. A. Wintle**
8 **GOLD HUNTER (IRE)**, 8, b g Invincible Spirit (IRE)—Goldthroat (IRE) **G. Byard**
9 **IS LOVE ALIVE**, 9, ch g Presenting—Lovely Origny (FR) **Mr S R Whistance & Mr A J Williams**
10 **KENSTONE (FR)**, 5, gr g Kendargent (FR)—Little Stone (FR) **G. Byard**
11 **MARJU'S QUEST (IRE)**, 8, b g Marju (IRE)—Queen's Quest **Terry Warren & Adrian Wintle**
12 **MISTER RAINMAN (IRE)**, 6, b g Westerner—Khimki (IRE) **Mr A J Rhead & Mr G B Williams**
13 **MR FRANKIE**, 7, b g Sleeping Indian—Shes Minnie **A. A. Wintle**
14 **PEAK HILL**, 5, ch g Bahamian Bounty—River Naiad **Mr C. J. Williams**
15 **ROCK'N GOLD**, 5, b g Fastnet Rock (AUS)—La Concorde (FR) **Mr E. Wilson**
16 **ROCKY ELSOM (USA)**, 11, b g Rock of Gibraltar (IRE)—Bowstring (IRE) **Search For Stars**
17 **SALLEE**, 4, b f Sakhee's Secret—Rabshih (IRE) **A. A. Wintle**
18 **SECRET GLANCE**, 6, b g Sakhee's Secret—Look Here's Dee **Mr E. Wilson**
19 **THREE C'S (IRE)**, 4, b g Kodiac—Ms Mary C (IRE) **A. A. Wintle**
20 **TWISTSANDTURNS (IRE)**, 5, b g Acclamation—Shesthebiscuit **A. A. Wintle**
21 **WHISKEY BARON (IRE)**, 6, b g Darsi (FR)—Roupolino (IRE) **Mr A. J. Rhead**

Other Owners: Mr T. G. Warren, Mr G. B. Williams, A. J. Williams.

622 **MISS REBECCA WOODMAN, Chichester**
Postal: **Souters Cottage, 21 East Lavant, Chichester, West Sussex, PO18 0AG**
Contacts: **PHONE (01243) 527260 MOBILE (07821) 603063**
E-MAIL **rebeccawoodman@msn.com**

1 **BIT SPICY (IRE)**, 7, gr m Tikkanen (USA)—Like A Bolt (IRE) **Miss R. Woodman**
2 **HONEY P (IRE)**, 7, b m Winged Love (IRE)—Luck's A Lady (IRE) **Miss R. Woodman**
3 **MAJANALMA (IRE)**, 8, b m Robin des Pres (FR)—Evangelica (USA) **Miss R. Woodman**

623 **MR STEVE WOODMAN, Chichester**
Postal: **Parkers Barn Stables, 8 Pook Lane, East Lavant, Chichester, West Sussex, PO18 0AU**
Contacts: **OFFICE** (01243) 527136 **FAX** (01243) 527136 **MOBILE** (07889) 188519
E-MAIL stevewoodman83@msn.com

1 **GOING TWICE**, 13, b g Josr Algarhoud (IRE)—Its Your Bid **Mrs S. B. Woodman**
2 **HIGHLY LIKELY (IRE)**, 9, b g Elnadim (USA)—Height of Fantasy (IRE) **Miss R. Woodman**
3 **LORD ALDERVALE (IRE)**, 11, br g Alderbrook—Monavale (IRE) **Mr D. N. Boxall**
4 **SOLVEIG'S SONG**, 6, b m Norse Dancer (IRE)—Ivory Lace **Sally Woodman & D. Mortimer**

THREE-YEAR-OLDS
5 **BLACK LACE**, b f Showcasing—Ivory Lace **The Lacemakers**

Other Owners: Mrs P. A. Miles, Mr D. Mortimer, Mrs P. M. Tyler.

624 **MRS KAYLEY WOOLLACOTT, South Molton**
Postal: **Nethercott Manor, Rose Ash, South Molton, Devon, EX36 4RE**
Contacts: **PHONE** (01769) 550483
E-MAIL info@richardwoollacottracing.co.uk WEBSITE www.richardwoollacottracing.co.uk

1 **BORN TO SIZE (GER)**, 6, b g Sholokhov (IRE)—Beyonce (GER) **Nethercott Manor Racing**
2 **BRERETON (IRE)**, 7, b g Kalanisi (IRE)—Westgrove Berry (IRE) **Rose Farm Developments & Eight Ball**
3 **DIABLERETS (FR)**, 5, ch g Vendangeur (IRE)—Lavande (FR) **West Country Partners**
4 **DINOS BENEFIT (IRE)**, 6, ch m Mr Dinos (IRE)—Beneficial Lady (IRE) **Mr A. P. Maddox**
5 **DORRANA (IRE)**, 4, br f Darsi (FR)—Arts Theater (IRE) **Gale Force Five**
6 **FLORESCO (GER)**, 8, ch g Santiago (GER)—Fiori (GER) **D. G. Staddon**
7 **JEPECK (IRE)**, 9, b g Westerner—Jenny's Jewel (IRE) **Mr J. M. Pike**
8 **LALOR (GER)**, 6, b g It's Gino (GER)—Laviola (GER) **D. G. Staddon**
9 **MANVERS HOUSE**, 5, b g Schiaparelli (GER)—Freydis (GER) **K S B, Mr M Doughty & Mrs Sarah Tizzard**
10 **MILLANISI BOY**, 9, b g Kalanisi (IRE)—Millennium Rose (IRE) **Mr D Stevens & Mrs S Stevens**
11 **PRINCE MAHLER (IRE)**, 8, b g Mahler—Strokestown Queen (IRE) **Taunton Racecourse Owners Club**
12 **SCRUMPY BOY**, 6, b g Apple Tree (IRE)—Presuming **SMLC Racing**
13 **SHEER POETRY (IRE)**, 7, b m Yeats (IRE)—Sassari (IRE) **R. J. Weeks**
14 **THE KINGS WRIT (IRE)**, 7, b g Brian Boru—Letterwoman (IRE) **Mr D Stevens & Mrs S Stevens**
15 **THE MAJOR**, 5, b g Major Cadeaux—Ballerina Suprema (IRE) **Mr D Stevens & Mrs S Stevens**

Other Owners: M. J. Bevan, Mrs S. J. Biggins, Mr M. Doughty, Eight Ball Partnership, Mr G. J. Evans, Mr A. P. Gale, Mrs A. G. Gale, Mr J. Heal, Mr M. N. Higgs, K S B Bloodstock, Mr D. Lockwood, Miss N. Martin, Mr M. R. Rhoades, Mr D. J. Rogers, Rose Farm Developments (UK) Ltd, Mr J. Simpson, Mr S. C. C. Stacey, Mr D. J. Stevens, Mrs S. E. Stevens, Mrs S. L. Tizzard.

625 **MR PHILLIP YORK, Effingham Common**
Postal: **Mornshill Farm, Banks Lane, Effingham, Leatherhead, Surrey, KT24 5JB**
Contacts: **PHONE** (01372) 457102

1 **ALL THE COLOURS**, 7, b g Rainbow High—Stephanie **Exors of the Late Mr R. H. York**
2 **BROUGHTONS BANDIT**, 11, b g Kyllachy—Broughton Bounty **Exors of the Late Mr R. H. York**
3 **CARRIED AWAY**, 6, b m Trans Island—Carry Me (IRE) **Mrs K. H. York**
4 **CLIVE CLIFTON (IRE)**, 5, b g Wootton Bassett—Dearest Daisy **J. L. Collins**
5 **GERSJOEYCASEY (IRE)**, 9, b m Milan—Derrigra Sublime (IRE) **Exors of the Late Mr R. H. York**
6 **OVERSHOT**, 6, b m Overbury (IRE)—Aya **P. York**
7 **SPIRITOFCHARTWELL**, 10, ch g Clerkenwell (USA)—Rollin Rock **Mrs K. H. York**

626 MRS LAURA YOUNG, Bridgwater

Postal: **Rooks Castle Stables, Broomfield, Bridgwater, Somerset, TA5 2EW**
Contacts: **PHONE (01278) 664595 FAX (01278) 661555 MOBILE (07766) 514414**
E-MAIL ljyracing@hotmail.com WEBSITE www.laurayoungracing.com

1 ADMIRAL BLAKE, 11, b g Witness Box (USA)—Brenda Bella (FR) **Soul Galore**
2 AUENWIRBEL (GER), 7, b g Sholokhov (IRE)—Auentime (GER) **Mr T. J. Moynihan**
3 BUCKBORU (IRE), 10, b m Brian Boru—Buckland Filleigh (IRE) **Mrs L. J. Young**
4 EGGESFORD, 4, b g Foxwedge (AUS)—Elegant Pride **Mrs L. J. Young**
5 GOODNIGHTIRENE (IRE), 8, ch m Indian River (FR)—Markskeepingfaith (IRE) **Mr T. J. Moynihan**
6 HITCHHIKER (IRE), 7, b g Milan—No Easy Way (IRE) **Mrs L. J. Young**
7 MOYNIHANS GIRL (IRE), 4, ch f Frammassone (IRE)—Catch Ball **Mr T. J. Moynihan**
8 MY DIAMOND (IRE), 7, b g Brian Boru—Our Idol (IRE) **The Isle Of Frogs Partnership**
9 SUFFICE (IRE), 9, b g Iffraaj—Shallat (IRE) **Mrs L. J. Young**
10 THE GREENVET (IRE), 8, b g Acrobat (IRE)—Glacial Air (IRE) **The Isle Of Frogs Partnership**
11 VALSHAN TIME (IRE), 6, b br g Atraf—Valshan (IRE) **Mrs L. J. Young**
12 WHISKEY JOHN, 8, b g Westerner—Cherry Lane **The Isle Of Frogs Partnership**
13 WHITE NILE (IRE), 9, b h Galileo (IRE)—Super Gift (IRE) **Mrs L. J. Young**

Other Owners: Mr K. Quant, Mr M. J. Rees, Mr G. C. Vining, Mr C. V. Vining.

Assistant Trainer: James Young

Jockey (NH): Robert Dunne.

627 MR WILLIAM YOUNG, Carluke

Postal: **Watchknowe Lodge, Crossford, Carluke, Lanarkshire, ML8 5QT**
Contacts: **PHONE (01555) 860856 (01555) 860226 FAX (01555) 860137 MOBILE (07900) 408210**
E-MAIL watchknowe@talktalk.net

1 FORMIDABLEOPPONENT (IRE), 11, b g Arakan (USA)—Sliding **W. G. Young**
2 HERE COMES LOVE (IRE), 8, b g Winged Love (IRE)—Heres McGoogan (IRE) **W. G. Young**
3 MILANS WELL (IRE), 12, b g Milan—Panoora Queen (IRE) **W. G. Young**
4 RAIFTEIRI (IRE), 11, b g Galileo (IRE)—Naziriya (FR) **W. G. Young**
5 WHY BUT WHY (USA), 10, b g Whywhywhy (USA)—Miss Orah **W. G. Young**

Assistant Trainer: William G Young Snr

INDEX TO HORSES

The Figure before the name of the horse refers to the number of the team in which it appears and **The Figure after** the horse supplies a ready reference to each animal. Horses are indexed strictly alphabetically, e.g. THE BOTTOM BAR appears in the T's, MR MONOCHROME In the MR's, ST ERNEY in the ST'S etc.

166 **APHAEA** (GB) 62
606 **APOLLO CREED** (IRE) 3
613 **APPARATCHIKA** (GB) G 21
261 **APPAREL** (FR) F 123
563 **APPEARANCE** (GB) C 127
563 **APPEARED** (GB) 2
295 **APPENZELLER** (USA) 19
254 **APPLAUS** (GER) 5
97 **APPLE ANNI** (IRE) 28
235 **APPLE BLOSSOM TIME** (IRE) F 10
175 **APPLE SAUCE** (GB) C 9
174 **APPLE'S JADE** (GB) 8
274 **APPLE'S SHAKIRA** (IRE) 3
7 **APPLEBERRY** (IRE) 4
508 **APPLESANDPIERRES** (GB) 8
387 **APPLESOLUTELY** (GB) 1
239 **APPLETREE LANE** (GB) 1
49 **APPLY HEAT** (IRE) 57
167 **APPOINTED** (GB) 3
406 **APPROACHING MENACE** (GB) 17
75 **APPROACHING STAR** (FR) 1
371 **APRES LE DELUGE** (FR) 2
146 **APRICOT SKY** (GB) 1
176 **APROVADO** (IRE) 4
176 **APTERIX** (FR) 5
524 **APTLY PUT** (IRE) 1
335 **APURA** (IRE) 6
6 **AQABAH** (USA) 47
541 **AQLAAM VISION** (GB) C 51
281 **AQSAAM** (USA) F 92
586 **AQUA AURA** (USA) C 31
85 **AQUA LIBRE** (GB) 3
318 **AQUARIUM** (GB) 34
281 **AQUASULIS** (IRE) C 93
185 **AQUITAINE BOY** (IRE) 39
392 **AR MAD** (FR) 9
392 **AR MEST** (FR) 10
431 **AR MUIN NA MUICE** (IRE) G 2
331 **ARAB MOON** (GB) 5
41 **ARABIAN BEAUTY** (IRE) C 113
114 **ARABIAN FAIRYTALE** (GB) 23
6 **ARABIAN GIFT** (IRE) 48
261 **ARABIAN HIDEAWAY** (IRE) F 5
41 **ARABIAN HOPE** (USA) 1
29 **ARABIAN JAZZ** (IRE) 13
434 **ARABIC CULTURE** (USA) 1
271 **ARAMIST** (IRE) 2
383 **ARAQEEL** (GB) 1
41 **ARAQELLA** (IRE) F 114
436 **ARBALET** (IRE) 24
522 **ARBORETUM** (GB) 2
405 **ARBRE DE VIE** (FR) 9
354 **ARBUCKLE** (GB) 12
28 **ARCADIAN CAT** (USA) 21
308 **ARCADIAN SEA** (IRE) 1
28 **ARCADIENNE** (GB) 73
131 **ARCANADA** (IRE) 1
402 **ARCANE DANCER** (IRE) 1
249 **ARCANEARS** (IRE) 32
376 **ARCANGELA** (GB) F 34
163 **ARCANISTA** (IRE) 2
146 **ARCAVALLO** (IRE) 20
318 **ARCH GOLD** (USA) 35
515 **ARCH MY BOY** (GB) 1
454 **ARCH OF COLOURS** (GB) C 39
377 **ARCH STANTON** (IRE) 4
444 **ARCH VILLAIN** (IRE) 2
302 **ARCHDEACON** (GB) 44

41 **ARCHER'S ARROW** (USA) 2
118 **ARCHETYPE** (FR) 2
146 **ARCHI'S AFFAIRE** (GB) 2
516 **ARCHIBELLE** (GB) 5
104 **ARCHIE** (IRE) 1
211 **ARCHIE RICE** (USA) 1
173 **ARCHIE STEVENS** (GB) 2
240 **ARCHIMEDES** (IRE) 2
278 **ARCHIMENTO** (GB) 1
258 **ARCHINA** (IRE) C 138
307 **ARCHIPELIGO** (IRE) 2
173 **ARCHIPENTURA** (GB) 4
328 **ARCHIPPOS** (GB) 3
436 **ARCHITECTURE** (IRE) 2
176 **ARCHIVE** (FR) 6
334 **ARCMANIA** (IRE) 35
447 **ARCTIC CHIEF** (GB) 1
368 **ARCTIC DESTINATION** (IRE) 2
61 **ARCTIC FLOWER** (IRE) 2
560 **ARCTIC GOLD** (IRE) 4
541 **ARCTIC HAZE** (IRE) 3
71 **ARCTIC ROLL** (GB) 8
106 **ARCTIC SEA** (GB) 1
187 **ARCTIC TREASURE** (IRE) 63
584 **ARCTIC VODKA** (GB) 1
390 **ARDAMIR** (FR) 2
50 **ARDEATINA** (GB) 10
401 **ARDEN DENIS** (IRE) 4
582 **ARDEN PEARL** (IRE) 1
582 **ARDEN WARRIOR** (IRE) 34
428 **ARDESSIE** (GB) F 98
536 **ARDMAYLE** (IRE) 2
334 **ARECIBO** (FR) 8
258 **AREEDA** (IRE) F 139
428 **AREEN FAISAL** (GB) 72
428 **AREEN HEART** (FR) 8
573 **ARENDELLE** (GB) 30
526 **ARGANTE** (FR) 1
275 **ARGEM** (GB) 4
301 **ARGENT BLEU** (FR) 10
376 **ARGENT DU BOIS** (USA) C 35
322 **ARGENT KNIGHT** (GB) 2
232 **ARGENTELLO** (IRE) 25
484 **ARGENTIX** (FR) 1
160 **ARGUS** (IRE) 1
392 **ARGYLE** (IRE) 11
8 **ARIA ROSE** (GB) 12
199 **ARIAN** (IRE) 3
552 **ARIESANNE** (IRE) G 4
308 **ARIGATO** (GB) 12
261 **ARION SKY** (IRE) 6
566 **ARIOST** (GER) 5
376 **ARIS** (FR) F 36
185 **ARISTO DU PLESSIS** (FR) 2
184 **ARISTOCLES** (IRE) 4
227 **ARIZONA BOUND** (IRE) 2
263 **ARIZONA SNOW** (GB) 1
303 **ARIZONA SUNRISE** (GB) 1
562 **ARLECCHINO'S ARC** (IRE) 18
562 **ARLECCHINO'S LEAP** (IRE) 4
274 **ARMAANS WISH** (IRE) 4
512 **ARMAGEDDON** (GB) 46
486 **ARMANDIHAN** (IRE) 4
573 **ARMED** (IRE) 31
427 **ARMED RESPONSE** (GB) 17
239 **ARMEDANDBEAUTIFUL** (GB) 2
207 **ARMOROUS** (GB) 1
158 **ARMUM** (IRE) 23

158 **ARNARSON** (GB) 5
154 **ARNOLD** (GB) 1
526 **ARNOUL OF METZ** (GB) 19
507 **AROD** (IRE) 3
41 **AROK** (IRE) 16
281 **AROMATHERAPY** (GB) C 94
566 **ARONIUS** (GER) 79
376 **AROSA** (IRE) C 37
42 **ARQUEBUSIER** (FR) 1
138 **ARQUUS** (IRE) 2
266 **ARRAY OF STARS** (IRE) C 28
334 **ARRIATE** (FR) 9
491 **ARROGANT** (IRE) 5
481 **ARROW** (FR) 109
166 **ARROWTOWN** (GB) 5
212 **ARROWZONE** (GB) 2
161 **ARRYZONA** (GB) 1
460 **ARSENIO LUPIN** (USA) 1
352 **ART ECHO** (GB) 1
239 **ART LOOKER** (IRE) 3
419 **ART MAURESQUE** (FR) 5
383 **ART OBSESSION** (IRE) 2
377 **ART OF AMERICA** (GB) 110
214 **ART OF PAYROLL** (GER) 7
377 **ART OF SECURITY** (IRE) 5
254 **ART OF SUPREMACY** (IRE) 6
392 **ART OF SWING** (IRE) 12
377 **ART OF SYNERGY** (IRE) 6
377 **ART OF UNITY** (GB) 111
481 **ART PREMIER** (IRE) 110
29 **ARTAIR** (IRE) 49
29 **ARTARMON** (IRE) 14
127 **ARTFUL ROGUE** (IRE) 3
281 **ARTHENIA** (IRE) 18
404 **ARTHINGTON** (GB) 2
153 **ARTHUR BURRELL** (GB) 1
496 **ARTHUR DALEY** (GB) 9
131 **ARTHUR KITT** (GB) 54
283 **ARTHUR MAC** (IRE) 4
560 **ARTHUR MC BRIDE** (IRE) 5
560 **ARTHUR'S GIFT** (IRE) 6
236 **ARTHUR'S QUEEN** (FR) 1
85 **ARTHUR'S REUBEN** (GB) 4
550 **ARTHURS SECRET** (GB) 1
229 **ARTIC MILAN** (IRE) 1
32 **ARTIC QUEST** (IRE) 2
237 **ARTICLE FIFTY** (IRE) 4
52 **ARTIESHOW** (USA) 24
567 **ARTIFICE SIVOLA** (FR) 5
33 **ARTISTIC BELLE** (IRE) C 1
480 **ARTISTIC DAWN** (IRE) F 6
47 **ARTISTIC LICENSE** (IRE) C 13
131 **ARTISTIC STREAK** (GB) 55
238 **ARTY BUT POOR** (GB) 30
344 **ARTY CAMPBELL** (IRE) 1
261 **ARTY CRAFTY** (USA) F 124
134 **ARVICO'S LIGHT** (GB) 4
79 **ARWAAH** (IRE) F 68
92 **ARYA STARK** (GB) 5
163 **ARZAAK** (IRE) 3
419 **AS DE MEE** (FR) 6
119 **AS DE PIQUE** (IRE) 2
214 **AS I SEE IT** (GB) 8
431 **AS YOU LIKE** (IRE) 3
114 **ASAATIER** (USA) 81
79 **ASBAAB** (USA) 4
190 **ASCENDANT** (GB) 6
507 **ASCOT DAY** (IRE) 4

586 **BLENHEIM WARRIOR** (GB) 3
507 **BLESS HIM** (IRE) 5
174 **BLESS THE WINGS** (IRE) 19
486 **BLESSED BEAUTY** (IRE) C 87
406 **BLESSED TO EMPRESS** (IRE) 19
89 **BLETCHLEY** (FR) 6
405 **BLEU BERRY** (FR) 28
601 **BLEU DES TAILLONS** (FR) 5
565 **BLEU ET NOIR** (GB) 12
405 **BLEU ET ROUGE** (FR) 29
541 **BLIND SPOT** (IRE) 8
486 **BLING BLING** (IRE) C 88
259 **BLING KING** (GB) 1
122 **BLISTERING BARNEY** (IRE) 9
336 **BLISTERING BOB** (GB) 69
92 **BLISTERING DANCER** (IRE) 11
555 **BLODWYN** (GB) 18
97 **BLOND BEAUTY** (USA) C 75
436 **BLOND WARRIOR** (IRE) 110
17 **BLOOD EAGLE** (FR) 112
331 **BLOODSWEATANDTEARS** (GB) 4
58 **BLOODY NOSE** (IRE) 3
587 **BLOOMSDAY BABE** (USA) C 77
518 **BLOTTOS** (IRE) 4
174 **BLOW BY BLOW** (IRE) 20
102 **BLOWING DIXIE** (GB) 70
419 **BLU CAVALIER** (GB) 14
497 **BLUE APRIL** (FR) 3
484 **BLUE BATON** (IRE) 13
217 **BLUE BATTALION** (GB) 21
389 **BLUE BEACON** (GB) C 19
481 **BLUE BLUE EYES** (FR) 22
521 **BLUE BULLET** (FR) 4
41 **BLUE BUNTING** (USA) C 118
304 **BLUE CANNON** (IRE) 1
506 **BLUE COVE** (GB) 3
527 **BLUE DAHLIA** (IRE) C 36
112 **BLUE DE VEGA** (GER) 3
596 **BLUE DRAGON** (GB) G 3
560 **BLUE FLIGHT** (FR) 28
77 **BLUE HARMONY** (GB) 28
461 **BLUE HAVANA** (IRE) 35
254 **BLUE HUSSAR** (IRE) 10
550 **BLUE KASCADE** (GB) 4
143 **BLUE LYRIC** (GB) F 40
197 **BLUE MEDICI** (FR) 3
426 **BLUE MERLIN** (GB) 10
102 **BLUE MIST** (GB) 21
106 **BLUE MOTION** (GB) 16
190 **BLUE N YELLOW** (IRE) 12
6 **BLUE POINT** (IRE) 6
607 **BLUE RAMBLER** (GB) 13
189 **BLUE REFLECTION** (GB) 27
613 **BLUE ROCKS** (GB) 2
267 **BLUE SIRE** (FR) 4
75 **BLUE TOP** (GB) 2
601 **BLUE VALENTINE** (FR) 6
271 **BLUE VISION** (FR) 5
180 **BLUE WHISPER** (GB) 20
235 **BLUEBERRY GAL** (IRE) F 12
318 **BLUEFIRE** (GB) C 135
596 **BLUEFORTYTWO** (GB) 4
355 **BLUEGRASS BLUES** (IRE) 2
7 **BLUELLA** (GB) 79
367 **BLUFF CRAG** (GB) 1
234 **BLUNDER BUSS** (IRE) 4
244 **BLUSH'S GIFT** (GB) F 21
336 **BLUSHING RED** (FR) 7

322 **BLYTHE PRINCE** (GB) 3
226 **BLYTON LASS** (GB) 9
524 **BO SELECTA** (IRE) 3
388 **BOA ISLAND** (IRE) 3
318 **BOADICEE** (GB) C 136
223 **BOAGRIUS** (IRE) 11
326 **BOARD OF TRADE** (GB) 8
25 **BOARDMAN** (GB) 41
73 **BOARDWALK EMPIRE** (IRE) 1
29 **BOASTFUL** (IRE) F 52
416 **BOB FORD** (IRE) 7
237 **BOB MAHLER** (IRE) 7
24 **BOB MAXWELL** (IRE) 5
56 **BOB THE BUTCHER** (GB) 2
348 **BOB TUCKER** (IRE) 8
507 **BOB'S GIRL** (GB) 34
319 **BOBBITS WAY** (GB) 1
321 **BOBBLE EMERALD** (IRE) 4
148 **BOBBY BISCUIT** (USA) 16
90 **BOBBY JOE LEG** (GB) 4
118 **BOBBY K** (IRE) 23
302 **BOBBY VEE** (GB) 3
114 **BOBBY WHEELER** (IRE) 1
112 **BOBBY'S CHARM** (USA) 23
607 **BOBCATBILLY** (IRE) 14
518 **BOBNDAVE** (IRE) 7
540 **BOBO MAC** (IRE) 3
605 **BOBONYX** (GB) 3
553 **BOCASIEN DESBOIS** (FR) 3
486 **BOCHAFINA** (FR) F 89
461 **BODACIOUS NAME** (IRE) 7
607 **BODEGA** (GB) 15
361 **BODEKIN POINT** (IRE) 3
237 **BODES WELL** (IRE) 81
25 **BODY AND SOUL** (IRE) C 42
247 **BOERHAN** (GB) 114
456 **BOFFO** (IRE) 10
291 **BOGARDUS** (IRE) 5
486 **BOGART** (IRE) 7
211 **BOGOSS DU PERRET** (FR) 4
29 **BOHEMIAN DANCE** (IRE) F 53
22 **BOHEMIAN RHAPSODY** (IRE) 4
446 **BOHER LAD** (IRE) 2
328 **BOHERNAGORE** (IRE) 8
261 **BOHO** (IRE) 92
258 **BOING** (IRE) 47
237 **BOITE** (IRE) 8
258 **BOITRON** (FR) 146
500 **BOKETTO** (IRE) 2
438 **BOKO FITTLEWORTH** (IRE) 88
230 **BOL D'AIR** (FR) 6
49 **BOLD APPROACH** (IRE) 59
376 **BOLD ASSUMPTION** (GB) F 38
97 **BOLD BIDDER** (GB) G 32
519 **BOLD IMAGE** (IRE) 1
345 **BOLD LOVE** (GB) F 6
573 **BOLD PREDICTION** (IRE) 4
178 **BOLD PRINCE RUPERT** (IRE) 1
232 **BOLD REASON** (GER) 29
91 **BOLD SPIRIT** (GB) 1
423 **BOLD WARRIOR** (IRE) 10
375 **BOLDMERE** (IRE) 6
555 **BOLERO** (IRE) 19
392 **BOLISTER** (FR) 23
245 **BOLLIHOPE** (GB) 3
167 **BOLLIN ACE** (GB) 8
167 **BOLLIN ANNABEL** (GB) F 79
167 **BOLLIN JOAN** (GB) 80

172 **BOLLIN LINE** (GB) 2
167 **BOLLIN TED** (GB) 9
430 **BOLLYWOOD BOY** (GB) 2
334 **BOLSHINA** (GB) 12
565 **BOLTON BOY** (IRE) 13
130 **BOLVING** (IRE) 4
500 **BOMAD** (GB) 26
138 **BOMBASTIC** (IRE) 29
572 **BOMBAY RASCAL** (GB) 3
560 **BOMBER'S MOON** (GB) 29
138 **BOMBERO** (FR) 3
258 **BOMBSHELL BAY** (IRE) 48
189 **BOMBYX** (GB) 28
388 **BON CHIC** (GB) 4
237 **BON ENFANT** (FR) 9
405 **BON PAPA** (FR) 30
258 **BON SCOTTE** (IRE) 49
587 **BONA FIDE** (GB) 13
512 **BONANZA BOWLS** (GB) 25
405 **BONBON AU MIEL** (FR) 31
101 **BONCHESTER** (GB) 3
181 **BOND ANGEL** (GB) 22
329 **BOND DO TIGRAO** (GB) 13
424 **BOND STREET** (IRE) 27
367 **BOND STREET BEAU** (GB) 2
428 **BONDESIRE** (GB) F 100
65 **BONDI BEACH BOY** (GB) 2
221 **BONDI MIST** (IRE) 2
404 **BONDS CONQUEST** (GB) 6
10 **BONGO BEAT** (GB) 3
169 **BONIFACE** (IRE) 11
458 **BONJOUR STEVE** (GB) 3
612 **BONNE QUESTION** (FR) 7
510 **BONNET'S VINO** (GB) 4
599 **BONNIE BLACK ROSE** (GB) 1
384 **BONNIE GREY** (GB) F 32
377 **BONNY KATE** (IRE) 14
497 **BONZA GIRL** (GB) 4
526 **BOOBOROWIE** (IRE) 4
456 **BOODLEY** (GB) 11
143 **BOOGEY WONDERLAND** (GB) 3
227 **BOOGIE LIFE** (GB) 3
283 **BOOK DIRECT** (IRE) 12
318 **BOOK OF DREAMS** (IRE) 43
504 **BOOK OF GOLD** (IRE) 2
556 **BOOKIESINDEXDOTNET** (GB) F 13
61 **BOOKMAKER** (GB) 4
404 **BOONA RIVER** (IRE) 7
92 **BOOM THE GROOM** (IRE) 12
336 **BOOMARANG** (GB) 8
481 **BOOMBOOM KISS** (GB) 23
434 **BOOMERANG BETTY** (IRE) 27
174 **BOOT CAMP** (IRE) 21
143 **BOOTS AND SPURS** (GB) 4
471 **BOOYAKASHA** (IRE) 9
166 **BOP IT** (GB) 9
176 **BORDEAUX BILL** (IRE) 13
585 **BORDER BREAKER** (IRE) 1
411 **BORDER VICTOR** (GB) 3
596 **BORDERS DREAM** (GB) 19
138 **BOREAGH LASS** (IRE) 30
438 **BOREHAM BILL** (IRE) 11
585 **BORIC** (GB) 2
394 **BORN A SAINT** (GB) 1
558 **BORN AT MIDNIGHT** (GB) 10
500 **BORN FOR PROSECCO** (GB) 27
223 **BORN FOR WAR** (IRE) 12
216 **BORN IN THORNE** (GB) 4

181 **BROCKEY RISE** (IRE) 23	249 **BUFFALO BERRY** (IRE) F 64	4 **BUSH BEAUTY** (IRE) 2
83 **BROCKHOLES** (GB) 2	102 **BUFFER ZONE** (GB) 23	415 **BUSHEL** (USA) 2
255 **BROCKTON GANDT** (GB) 1	295 **BUGIE D'AMORE** (GB) C 49	180 **BUSKIN RIVER** (IRE) 4
48 **BROCTUNE RED** (GB) 22	25 **BUGLE MAJOR** (USA) 8	79 **BUSTAAN** (USA) 72
6 **BRODERIE** (GB) 53	230 **BUGSIE MALONE** (IRE) 7	461 **BUSTAM** (IRE) 37
148 **BROGANS BAY** (IRE) 17	377 **BUGSY SIEGEL** (IRE) 14	334 **BUSTER** (FR) 13
160 **BROKE AWAY** (IRE) 3	497 **BUILDING FUTURES** (IRE) 5	450 **BUSTER EDWARDS** (IRE) 3
77 **BROKEN FORCE** (USA) 29	9 **BUILDMEUPBUTTERCUP** (GB) 2	336 **BUSTER THOMAS** (IRE) 9
140 **BROKEN QUEST** (IRE) 4	556 **BULAS BELLE** (GB) 1	113 **BUSY BARO** (IRE) 1
77 **BROKEN TIME** (IRE) 30	326 **BULFIN ISLAND** (IRE) 10	231 **BUSY BUSH** (IRE) 2
127 **BROKEN WINGS** (IRE) 78	31 **BULGE BRACKET** (GB) 2	271 **BUSY STREET** (GB) 6
420 **BROMANCE** (GB) 2	254 **BULKOV** (FR) 11	176 **BUTHELEZI** (USA) 14
405 **BRONAGH'S BELLE** (IRE) 178	159 **BULLETIN** (IRE) 10	320 **BUTLERSBRIDGE** (IRE) 2
377 **BRONCO BILL** (IRE) 17	122 **BULLETPROOF** (IRE) 3	385 **BUTNEY ISLAND** (IRE) 1
431 **BRONCO BILLY** (IRE) 7	392 **BULLFROG** (IRE) 25	127 **BUTOOLAT** (GB) 4
118 **BRONWEN** (IRE) F 81	258 **BULLINGDON** (GB) 52	278 **BUTTERFIELD** (IRE) 4
238 **BRONZALLURE** (IRE) 4	99 **BULLINGTON BEAR** (FR) 1	424 **BUTTERFLY COVE** (USA) F 115
555 **BRONZE ANGEL** (IRE) 1	99 **BULLINGTON BOY** (FR) 19	535 **BUTTERFLY KISS** (USA) 105
97 **BRONZE BABY** (USA) F 79	185 **BULLION** (FR) 8	10 **BUTTERFLY SPIRIT** (GB) 19
537 **BRONZE BEAU** (GB) 1	214 **BULLIONAIRE** (IRE) 13	424 **BUTTERSCOTCH** (IRE) 29
159 **BROOKLYN BOY** (GB) 34	553 **BULLS HEAD** (IRE) 4	274 **BUVEUR D'AIR** (FR) 20
223 **BROOM TIP** (IRE) 16	562 **BULLSEYE BULLET** (GB) 19	380 **BUXLOW BELLE** (FR) 10
17 **BROROCCO** (GB) 6	464 **BUMBLES BABE** (GB) 2	121 **BUXTED DREAM** (USA) 3
261 **BROTHER BEAR** (IRE) 94	223 **BUN DORAN** (IRE) 17	291 **BUYER BEWARE** (IRE) 6
136 **BROTHER BENNETT** (FR) 2	486 **BUNGEE JUMP** (IRE) 46	606 **BUYWISE** (IRE) 6
92 **BROTHER IN ARMS** (IRE) 14	118 **BUNIANN** (IRE) 82	397 **BUZZ** (FR) 4
167 **BROTHER MCGONAGALL** (GB) 12	405 **BURN OFF EARLY** (IRE) 34	278 **BUZZ LIGHTYERE** (GB) 5
404 **BROTHER NORPHIN** (GB) 8	507 **BUNOOD** (GB) C 83	343 **BY RAIL** (GB) 1
82 **BROTHER SCOTT** (GB) 2	118 **BUNTINGFORD** (IRE) C 83	7 **BY ROYAL APPROVAL** (IRE) 80
240 **BROTHER TIGER** (GB) 3	339 **BUONAROTTI BOY** (IRE) 3	14 **BY THE BOARDWALK** (IRE) 12
207 **BROTHERLY COMPANY** (IRE) 2	91 **BUONARROTI** (IRE) 2	424 **BYE BYE BABY** (IRE) 30
526 **BROUGHTON EXCELS** (GB) 20	566 **BURANO** (IRE) 11	316 **BYGONES FOR COINS** (IRE) 2
463 **BROUGHTONS ADMIRAL** (GB) 2	57 **BURAUQ** (GB) 2	496 **BYRD** (IRE) 33
625 **BROUGHTONS BANDIT** (GB) 2	274 **BURBANK** (IRE) 18	61 **BYRD IN HAND** (IRE) 5
559 **BROUGHTONS FANCY** (GB) 1	52 **BURCAN** (FR) 5	22 **BYRON BLUE** (IRE) 5
55 **BROUGHTONS KNIGHT** (GB) 3	436 **BURFORD BROWN** (GB) 28	607 **BYRON FLYER** (GB) 17
504 **BROUGHTONS RHYTHM** (GB) 5	377 **BURGAS** (FR) 19	146 **BYRON'S CHOICE** (GB) 21
367 **BROUGHTONS STORY** (GB) 2	417 **BURGESS DREAM** (IRE) 2	355 **BYRONESS** (GB) F 20
224 **BROWN BEAR** (IRE) 4	255 **BURGESS VIEW** (IRE) 2	454 **BYRONY** (IRE) G 40
201 **BROWN REVEL** (GB) 3	318 **BURGONET** (GB) 45	480 **BYTON** (GB) F 7
179 **BROWN TRIX** (IRE) 3	611 **BURGUILLOS** (GB) 3	355 **C NOTE** (IRE) 1
169 **BROWNVILLE** (GB) 32	102 **BURGUNDY** (IRE) 24	167 **C'EST DEJA CA** (FR) 13
307 **BRUICHLADDICH** (GB) 9	587 **BURGUNDY BOY** (IRE) 16	565 **C'EST DU GATEAU** (FR) 15
6 **BRUNDTLAND** (IRE) 54	258 **BURIDAN** (FR) 53	405 **C'EST JERSEY** (FR) 36
258 **BRUNO MARIS** (FR) F 51	28 **BURIRAM** (IRE) 75	273 **C'EST NO MOUR** (GER) 2
540 **BRUSHED UP** (GB) 4	249 **BURKE'S ROCK** (GB) C 65	259 **CABAL** (GB) 2
85 **BRYDEN BOY** (IRE) 9	372 **BURLINGTON BERT** (FR) 1	424 **CABARET** (IRE) C 116
41 **BRYNICA** (FR) F 120	176 **BURN SOME DUST** (IRE) 83	89 **CABARET DANCER** (FR) 7
552 **BRYNMAWR** (GB) 10	41 **BURN THE BREEZE** (IRE) C 121	508 **CABARET QUEEN** (GB) 22
53 **BUACHAILL ALAINN** (IRE) 5	552 **BURN VALLEY** (GB) 12	2 **CABARITA** (GB) 70
419 **BUBBLE O'CLOCK** (IRE) 21	248 **BURNER** (IRE) 2	608 **CABERNET D'ALENE** (FR) 5
194 **BUBBLY** (GB) 16	461 **BURNIEBOOZLE** (IRE) 36	41 **CABLEKNIT** (USA) F 122
310 **BUBBLY BAILEY** (GB) 6	281 **BURNING LAKE** (IRE) 95	380 **CACOPHONOUS** (GB) 11
62 **BUBLE** (IRE) 4	335 **BURNING SUNSET** (GB) F 25	438 **CADEAU GEORGE** (GB) 13
401 **BUBSY BURBIDGE** (GB) 13	177 **BURNING THREAD** (IRE) 8	94 **CADEAUX BOXER** (GB) 2
383 **BUCCANEERS VAULT** (IRE) 3	401 **BURNS CROSS** (IRE) 14	348 **CADEAUX'S FIRE** (GB) 10
466 **BUCK BRAVO** (IRE) 2	185 **BURNS SUPPER** (IRE) 41	414 **CADESCIA** (GB) C 68
274 **BUCK'S BLUE** (FR) F 17	51 **BURNT CREAM** (GB) 1	499 **CADEYRN** (IRE) 3
626 **BUCKBORU** (IRE) 3	193 **BURNT SUGAR** (IRE) 2	506 **CADGERS HOLE** (GB) 4
508 **BUCKBY BOY** (GB) 21	174 **BURREN LIFE** (IRE) 23	532 **CADIRA BEECHES** (GB) 5
552 **BUCKHORN TIMOTHY** (GB) 11	433 **BURRENBRIDGE HOTEL** (IRE) 2	230 **CADMAR** (GB) 8
565 **BUCKING THE TREND** (GB) 14	274 **BURROWS EDGE** (FR) 19	405 **CADMIUM** (FR) 37
194 **BUCKLAND BEAU** (GB) 2	405 **BURROWS SAINT** (FR) 35	566 **CADMIUM** (GB) 12
194 **BUCKLAND BOY** (IRE) 17	214 **BURROWS TREAT** (FR) 91	421 **CADORE** (IRE) 1
321 **BUCKLE STREET** (GB) 6	573 **BURRUMBEET** (IRE) 6	77 **CAERELLA** (IRE) C 82
108 **BUCKLED** (GB) 5	404 **BURST YA BUBBLE** (IRE) 9	17 **CAERLONORE** (IRE) C 113
108 **BUDARRI** (GB) 3	131 **BURSTINGDALAK** (IRE) C 60	383 **CAESAR'S COMET** (IRE) 4
1 **BUFFALO BALLET** (GB) 6	83 **BURTONWOOD** (GB) 3	508 **CAFE AU LAIT** (GER) 23

395 **CAPTAIN ZEBO** (IRE) 10
25 **CAPTAIN'S GIRL** (FR) 9
451 **CAPTAINOFINDUSTRY** (IRE) 1
409 **CAPTIVA ISLAND** (IRE) 9
86 **CAPTON** (GB) 1
582 **CAPTOR** (GB) 3
442 **CARA GINA** (GB) C 18
174 **CARA'S WAY** (IRE) 26
573 **CARADOC** (FR) 36
423 **CARAGH QUEEN** (USA) C 29
254 **CARALINE** (FR) 14
41 **CARAMEL SNAP** (USA) F 124
491 **CARAMURU** (IRE) 1
65 **CARANBOLA** (GB) F 18
436 **CARAVAN OF DREAMS** (IRE) C 112
97 **CARAVELA** (IRE) 3
534 **CARD HIGH** (GB) 3
9 **CARDAW LILY** (FR) 41
348 **CARDIGAN BAY** (FR) 12
318 **CARDSHARP** (GB) 46
405 **CAREFULLY SELECTED** (IRE) 40
461 **CAREY STREET** (IRE) 52
27 **CAREYANNE** (GB) 1
318 **CARIBBEAN DANCER** (USA) C 140
359 **CARIBBEAN SPRING** (IRE) 1
214 **CARIBERT** (FR) 16
486 **CARIDADE** (USA) 11
9 **CARING TOUCH** (USA) 79
541 **CARIOCA** (IRE) F 56
434 **CARLANDA** (FR) C 69
13 **CARLI KING** (IRE) 1
464 **CARLINGFORD PRINCE** (IRE) 3
285 **CARLITA MORIVIERE** (FR) 2
527 **CARLO BIRAGHI** (IRE) 14
438 **CARLOS DU FRUITIER** (FR) 15
322 **CARLOW BOY** (IRE) 10
166 **CARLTON FRANKIE** (GB) 13
166 **CARLTON RYAN** (IRE) 14
166 **CARLTON THOMAS** (GB) 37
507 **CARMENS FATE** (GB) F 84
245 **CARNAGE** (GB) 20
187 **CARNAGEO** (FR) 6
406 **CARNIVAL KING** (IRE) 1
189 **CARNIVAL ROSE** (GB) 64
535 **CARNOUSTIE** (FR) F 108
237 **CARNSPINDLE** (FR) 12
521 **CARNTOP** (GB) 6
194 **CARNWENNAN** (IRE) 18
405 **CARO DES FLOS** (FR) 41
401 **CAROLE'S DESTRIER** (GB) 16
401 **CAROLE'S VIGILANTE** (IRE) 17
194 **CAROLINAE** (GB) 3
611 **CAROLYN'S VOICE** (GB) 31
17 **CAROUSE** (IRE) 49
434 **CARP KID** (FR) 29
24 **CARPET TIME** (IRE) 33
436 **CARPIO** (GB) 113
14 **CARQALIN** (FR) 13
409 **CARRAIGIN AONAIR** (IRE) 10
356 **CARRERA** (FR) 2
552 **CARRICK ROADS** (IRE) 13
307 **CARRICKCROSS BOYE** (IRE) 10
295 **CARRICKLANE** (GB) 21
244 **CARRIE ON DUBAI** (GB) 7
625 **CARRIED AWAY** (GB) 3
174 **CARRIG CATHAL** (GB) 27
21 **CARRIGDHOUN** (IRE) 4
293 **CARRIGEEN QUEEN** (IRE) F 41

6 **CARRIWITCHET** (IRE) 57
281 **CARRY ME HOME** (GB) 6
41 **CARRY ON DERYCK** (GB) 9
5 **CARTA BLANCA** (IRE) 2
405 **CARTER MCKAY** (GB) 42
176 **CARTHAGE** (FR) 5
481 **CARTIEM** (FR) 121
376 **CARTOGRAPHER** (GB) 1
174 **CARTWRIGHT** (GB) 28
34 **CASA COMIGO** (IRE) 17
454 **CASABERMEJA** (USA) F 41
274 **CASABLANCA MIX** (FR) 22
163 **CASARUBINA** (IRE) 17
121 **CASCATA** (IRE) C 45
14 **CASCAYE** (FR) 14
376 **CASCOVA** (IRE) 11
7 **CASE KEY** (GB) 13
607 **CASEMATES SQUARE** (IRE) 20
102 **CASEMENT** (FR) 4
192 **CASEY BANTER** (GB) 18
232 **CASEY JONES** (IRE) 31
266 **CASH AGAIN** (FR) 2
224 **CASHANOVA** (IRE) 6
131 **CASHEL** (IRE) 21
114 **CASIMA** (GB) 29
108 **CASIMIR DU CLOS** (FR) 6
52 **CASINA DI NOTTE** (IRE) 6
155 **CASINA VALADIER** (IRE) C 17
336 **CASINO MARKETS** (IRE) 10
377 **CASK MATE** (IRE) 21
419 **CASKO D'AIRY** (FR) 27
326 **CASPAR THE CUB** (FR) 137
283 **CASPER KING** (IRE) 14
115 **CASPIAN PRINCE** (IRE) 3
424 **CASSANDRA GO** (IRE) F 118
392 **CASSE TETE** (FR) 26
232 **CASSINI** (FR) 32
558 **CASSIS DE REINE** (GB) 1
529 **CASSIVELLAUNUS** (IRE) 2
348 **CASTAFIORE** (USA) 13
515 **CASTALIAN SPRING** (IRE) C 13
263 **CASTANEA** (GB) 4
572 **CASTARNIE** (GB) 4
334 **CASTELLAR** (FR) 14
405 **CASTELLO SFORZA** (IRE) 43
290 **CASTER SEMENYA** (GB) 19
4 **CASTERBRIDGE** (GB) 3
283 **CASTERLY ROCK** (IRE) 15
258 **CASTING** (FR) 150
249 **CASTLE GUEST** (IRE) 3
266 **CASTLE HILL CASSIE** (IRE) 3
234 **CASTLE ON A CLOUD** (IRE) 6
104 **CASTLE TALBOT** (FR) 1
357 **CASTLEBROOK** (IRE) 2
532 **CASTLELYONS** (IRE) 6
450 **CASTLEMORRIS KING** (GB) 3
289 **CASTLEREA TESS** (GB) 1
477 **CASTLETOWN** (FR) 1
178 **CASTLEY LANE** (GB) 2
38 **CASUAL CAVALIER** (IRE) 1
17 **CASUAL GLANCE** (GB) F 114
376 **CASUAL LOOK** (USA) C 39
102 **CASUAL REPLY** (GB) 71
428 **CAT BALLOU** (GB) 77
563 **CAT ON A TIN ROOF** (USA) C 132
80 **CAT ROYALE** (IRE) 2
298 **CATACLYSM** (GB) 1
416 **CATAMARAN DU SEUIL** (FR) 10

342 **CATAPULT** (GB) 4
32 **CATCH MY DRIFT** (IRE) 3
261 **CATCH THE EYE** (IRE) F 127
138 **CATCH THE PIGEON** (GB) 31
526 **CATCH THE TIDE** (FR) 21
578 **CATCHAMAT** (GB) 1
565 **CATCHAROSE** (IRE) 19
606 **CATCHER ON THE GO** (IRE) 10
299 **CATCHIN TIME** (IRE) 2
431 **CATCHING ON** (IRE) 11
547 **CATCHING SHADOWS** (IRE) 3
484 **CATCHTHEMOONLIGHT** (GB) 15
608 **CATE BLEUE** (FR) G 33
309 **CATHAL'S STAR** (GB) 7
51 **CATHEADANS FURY** (GB) 3
496 **CATHERINE TRAMELL** (IRE) 13
208 **CATHERINETHEGRACE** (IRE) 3
618 **CATHIE'S DREAM** (USA) 13
106 **CATHOLIC POETRY** (IRE) 30
347 **CATIVO RAGAZZO** (GB) 4
215 **CATMYGIRL** (GB) 1
573 **CATOCA** (USA) 37
174 **CAUSE OF CAUSES** (USA) 29
508 **CAUSE TOUJOURS** (FR) 26
349 **CAUSEWAY QUEEN** (FR) F 44
236 **CAUTIOUS KATE** (IRE) 4
521 **CAUTORILLO** (GB) 7
563 **CAVALRY** (GB) 51
247 **CAVATINA** (GB) 39
238 **CAVE TOP** (IRE) 5
71 **CAVENDISH PLACE** (GB) 10
550 **CAVENTARA** (GB) 6
438 **CAVERNOUS** (IRE) 16
604 **CAVIAR D'ALLEN** (FR) 4
184 **CAVIAR ROYALE** (GB) 19
401 **CAVICIANA** (GB) 18
466 **CAWDOR HOUSE BERT** (GB) 3
98 **CAYAMBE** (IRE) G 1
162 **CAYIRLI** (FR) 3
328 **CAYMAN SOUND** (GB) F 52
568 **CAYMUS** (GB) 2
314 **CAYUGA** (GB) 1
284 **CAZZA CAZAM** (GB) 3
383 **CE DE NULLIS** (IRE) 38
127 **CE LA VIE** (GB) 5
237 **CEANN SIBHEAL** (IRE) 13
248 **CEARA BE** (IRE) 3
545 **CEASE TO SURRENDER** (GB) 2
28 **CECCHINI** (IRE) 26
174 **CECIL CORBETT** (GB) 30
609 **CECILATOR** (GB) 7
268 **CECILE DE VOLANGES** (GB) 2
283 **CEDAR VALLEY** (IRE) 16
484 **CEEGEM** (IRE) 16
28 **CEILIDHS DREAM** (GB) 27
49 **CEISTIU** (IRE) 60
118 **CELEBRATION DAY** (IRE) 3
89 **CELEBRE D'ALLEN** (FR) 8
432 **CELER ET AUDAX** (GB) 4
613 **CELERITY** (FR) 3
141 **CELESTIAL CHIMES** (IRE) 7
131 **CELESTIAL FORCE** (IRE) 22
397 **CELESTIAL GIRL** (GB) F 68
447 **CELESTIAL MAGIC** (GB) 7
450 **CELESTIAL PATH** (IRE) 10
6 **CELESTIAL SPHERES** (IRE) 10
185 **CELLAR VIE** (GB) 11
482 **CELMA DES BOIS** (FR) 2

261 **CHICAS AMIGAS** (IRE) 128
329 **CHICKLADE** (GB) F 38
29 **CHICKPEA** (GB) 17
132 **CHICORIA** (IRE) 2
471 **CHIDSWELL** (GB) 12
399 **CHIEF BRODY** (GB) 3
419 **CHIEF CRAFTSMAN** (GB) 30
308 **CHIEF IRONSIDE** (GB) 14
187 **CHIEF JUSTICE** (GB) 67
401 **CHIEF SITTINGBULL** (GB) 24
232 **CHIEFDOM** (USA) 34
194 **CHIEFOFCHIEFS** (GB) 4
212 **CHIEFTAIN'S CHOICE** (IRE) 4
436 **CHIGUN** (GB) C 114
97 **CHIKOKO TRAIL** (GB) 36
1 **CHIL CHIL** (GB) 115
355 **CHILDE HAROLD** (GB) 13
405 **CHILDRENS LIST** (IRE) 46
376 **CHILEAN** (GB) 12
293 **CHILL FACTOR** (IRE) 4
195 **CHILL IN THE WOOD** (GB) 2
159 **CHILLALA** (IRE) 11
587 **CHILLED WHITE** (IRE) 20
426 **CHILLI ROMANCE** (IRE) 14
7 **CHILLILILLI** (GB) 15
309 **CHILLY MISS** (GB) 8
373 **CHIMES OF DYLAN** (IRE) 3
399 **CHINA BEADS** (GB) F 20
90 **CHINA CHERUB** (GB) F 42
483 **CHINA EXCELS** (GB) 1
331 **CHINESE ALPHABET** (GB) 34
516 **CHINESE SPIRIT** (IRE) 6
318 **CHINESE WHITE** (GB) C 141
187 **CHINGACHGOOK** (GB) 68
247 **CHIOSINA** (GB) C 118
437 **CHIP OR PELLET** (GB) 3
32 **CHIP SHOT** (IRE) 4
102 **CHIPPIE HILL** (GB) 25
401 **CHIRICO VALLIS** (FR) 25
189 **CHIRKOVA** (USA) C 65
155 **CHIRPY** (IRE) 12
111 **CHISWICK BEY** (IRE) 1
529 **CHIVERS** (IRE) 3
332 **CHIZZ DE BIZ** (IRE) 12
572 **CHLOE'S COURT** (IRE) 5
310 **CHLOELLIE** (GB) 36
601 **CHLOES CHOICE** (GB) G 10
232 **CHLORIS** (GB) 35
564 **CHOCO BOX** (GB) 4
553 **CHOCOLAT NOIR** (IRE) 5
349 **CHOCOLATE BOX** (IRE) 7
425 **CHOCOLATE DIAMOND** (IRE) 1
29 **CHOICE ENCOUNTER** (GB) 18
359 **CHOISETTE** (GB) C 16
464 **CHOIX DE L'AMOUR** (IRE) 4
419 **CHOIX DES ARMES** (FR) 31
258 **CHONBURI** (GB) 152
179 **CHOOCHOOBUGALOO** (GB) 4
127 **CHOOKIE DUNEDIN** (GB) 84
127 **CHOOKIE ROYALE** (GB) 7
86 **CHOOSEY** (IRE) 23
606 **CHOOSEYOURWEAPON** (IRE) 12
311 **CHORAL BEE** (GB) 2
455 **CHORAL CLAN** (IRE) 1
454 **CHORAL MUSIC** (GB) 14
160 **CHORUS OF LIES** (GB) 5
131 **CHOSEN CHARACTER** (IRE) 6
326 **CHOSEN PATH** (IRE) 15

176 **CHOSEN THEATRE** (IRE) 17
326 **CHOSEN WELL** (IRE) 16
83 **CHOSEN WORLD** (GB) 5
484 **CHOUQUETTE** (GB) 22
565 **CHOZEN** (IRE) 21
392 **CHRIS PEA GREEN** (IRE) 29
281 **CHRISELLAINE** (IRE) 25
588 **CHRISSYCROSS** (IRE) G 10
274 **CHRISTMAS IN APRIL** (IRE) 28
1 **CHRISTMAS IN USA** (FR) 8
441 **CHRISTMAS NIGHT** (GB) 11
254 **CHRISTMAS TWENTY** (IRE) 16
238 **CHRISTO** (GB) 2
424 **CHRISTOPHER ROBIN** (IRE) 32
29 **CHRISTOPHER WOOD** (IRE) 19
368 **CHTI BALKO** (FR) 13
595 **CHU CHU PERCY** (GB) 5
281 **CHUCK WILLIS** (IRE) 99
438 **CHUFFY CHUFFNELL** (IRE) 19
42 **CHURCH HALL** (IRE) 6
96 **CHURCH LEAP** (IRE) 2
611 **CHURCH MELODY** (GB) F 49
485 **CIAOADIOSIMDONE** (IRE) 2
516 **CIARABELLA** (IRE) 7
324 **CIBOIR** (FR) 3
89 **CIEL DE PARIS** (GB) 9
405 **CILAOS EMERY** (FR) 47
392 **CILAOS GLACE** (FR) 30
41 **CILEOPATRA** (IRE) 80
199 **CILLIAN'S WELL** (IRE) 7
49 **CIMEARA** (IRE) 11
611 **CINCINNATI KIT** (GB) F 50
557 **CINCUENTA PASOS** (IRE) 1
338 **CINDERFELLA** (GB) 6
50 **CINDERS' PRIZE** (GB) C 18
38 **CINDY'S FANCY** (IRE) G 2
481 **CINNAMON GIRL** (FR) 30
62 **CINTA** (GB) G 40
401 **CINTEX** (FR) 26
247 **CINTRA** (GB) 40
535 **CIRCLE OF LIFE** (USA) C 109
249 **CIRCLING MOON** (IRE) 4
534 **CIRCUIT** (GB) 4
586 **CIRCUIT COURT** (IRE) 6
276 **CIRCUIT JUDGE** (GB) 1
566 **CIRCUMCANES** (IRE) 14
77 **CIRRUS MINOR** (FR) 32
508 **CITADEL** (FR) 28
561 **CITTA D'ORO** (GB) 9
315 **CITY DAZZLER** (IRE) C 48
326 **CITY DREAMER** (IRE) 17
28 **CITY GIRL** (IRE) C 77
359 **CITY GUEST** (IRE) 8
118 **CITY LIGHTS** (GB) 25
438 **CITY STAR** (GB) 20
293 **CITY SUPREME** (IRE) 5
104 **CITY VAULTS GIRL** (IRE) C 17
97 **CITY WANDERER** (IRE) 81
185 **CIVIL UNREST** (IRE) 13
22 **CIVITESSES** (FR) 7
508 **CKALCO DES LOGES** (FR) 29
274 **CLAIMANTAKINFORGAN** (FR) 29
49 **CLAIOMH GEAL** (GB) 12
367 **CLAIRE'S SECRET** (GB) 3
102 **CLAIRETTE** (IRE) 26
419 **CLAN DES OBEAUX** (FR) 32
1 **CLAN LEGEND** (GB) 9
162 **CLAN MCGREGOR** (IRE) 15

158 **CLAND DI SAN JORE** (IRE) C 67
314 **CLANDON** (GB) 2
485 **CLAPPERBOARD** (GB) F 23
392 **CLARA PEETERS** (GB) 143
318 **CLARAMARA** (IRE) 47
561 **CLARATY** (GB) 2
174 **CLARCAM** (FR) 33
249 **CLAREGATE STREET** (IRE) 5
481 **CLARIFY** (GB) F 124
481 **CLARINDA** (FR) F 125
478 **CLARIOR EX OBSCURO** (IRE) 1
237 **CLASH OF D TITANS** (IRE) 15
170 **CLASSIC BEN** (IRE) 5
566 **CLASSIC BRIGHT** (GB) F 15
302 **CLASSIC CHARM** (GB) 30
174 **CLASSIC ESCAPE** (IRE) 34
161 **CLASSIC FLYER** (GB) 3
368 **CLASSIC IMPACT** (IRE) 14
606 **CLASSIC JEWEL** (IRE) 13
302 **CLASSIC LASS** (GB) C 45
7 **CLASSIC PURSUIT** (GB) 16
197 **CLASSIC SENIORITY** (GB) 5
164 **CLASSIC TUNE** (GB) 4
97 **CLASSICAL DANCER** (GB) F 82
456 **CLASSICAL FLAIR** (GB) F 47
38 **CLASSICAL MILANO** (IRE) 3
119 **CLASSICAL ROSE** (GB) 7
145 **CLASSICAL SOUND** (IRE) 1
508 **CLASSICO DAIS** (FR) 30
138 **CLASSIFIED** (IRE) 6
164 **CLASSULA** (GB) 5
595 **CLAUDE CARTER** (GB) 6
86 **CLAUDINE** (IRE) 24
392 **CLAYTON** (GB) 31
569 **CLAYTON HALL** (GB) 5
131 **CLEAR IMPRESSION** (IRE) C 61
523 **CLEAR SPRING** (IRE) 4
602 **CLEAR WATER** (IRE) 1
554 **CLEARANCE** (GB) 2
22 **CLEARLY CAPABLE** (IRE) 8
496 **CLEM A** (GB) 3
281 **CLEMATIS** (USA) 100
155 **CLEMENCIA** (IRE) 18
432 **CLEMENT** (IRE) 6
461 **CLEMENTO** (IRE) 10
424 **CLEMMIE** (IRE) 33
280 **CLENI WELLS** (FR) 3
381 **CLEOFE** (GB) 11
17 **CLEONTE** (IRE) 7
26 **CLERGYMAN** (GB) 3
535 **CLERISY** (GB) 110
420 **CLEVER COOKIE** (GB) 3
310 **CLEVER DIVYA** (GB) 7
284 **CLEVER LIZ** (GB) G 4
86 **CLEVERLEY** (IRE) 25
127 **CLIFF BAY** (IRE) 8
248 **CLIFFMEENA** (IRE) 4
434 **CLIFFS OF CAPRI** (GB) 4
424 **CLIFFS OF DOONEEN** (IRE) 34
419 **CLIFFS OF DOVER** (GB) 33
424 **CLIFFS OF MOHER** (IRE) 2
222 **CLIFTON DANCER** (GB) F 8
534 **CLIMAX** (GB) 5
397 **CLIMB ABOARD** (GB) 42
405 **CLINTON HILL** (GB) 48
489 **CLIPPER LINE** (USA) C 8
587 **CLIQUE** (GB) 21
405 **CLITANDRE** (FR) 49

399 **CYRUS DALLIN** (GB) 6
309 **CYRUS DARIUS** (GB) 10
309 **CYRUS KEEP** (IRE) 11
612 **D'ARCY'S SOUND** (IRE) 20
6 **D'BAI** (IRE) 13
237 **D'GENTLE REFLEXION** (FR) 17
190 **D'PINESFLYER** (IRE) 15
350 **D'WATERSIDE** (GB) 5
428 **DAAWY** (IRE) 15
566 **DABADIYAN** (IRE) 19
102 **DABBLE** (GB) 28
95 **DABIYRA** (IRE) F 6
527 **DACIO** (USA) F 37
384 **DADDIES GIRL** (IRE) 20
393 **DADDY TYRRELL** (USA) 7
302 **DADDY'S DAUGHTER** (CAN) 31
565 **DADSINLUCK** (GB) 24
565 **DADSINTROUBLE** (IRE) 25
166 **DAFFY GREY** (GB) 68
434 **DAGANYA** (GB) C 70
52 **DAGHASHAH** (GB) C 75
444 **DAGIAN** (IRE) 28
158 **DAGUENEAU** (IRE) 31
166 **DAHIK** (IRE) 69
375 **DAHILLS HILL** (IRE) 10
181 **DAILY TRADER** (GB) 5
608 **DAIM PIERJI** (FR) 8
563 **DAIRA PRINCE** (IRE) 10
77 **DAISY BERE** (FR) 7
258 **DAISY CHAIN** (IRE) 56
608 **DAISY DE SIVOLA** (FR) 9
535 **DAIVIKA** (USA) C 112
95 **DAKKAR COLLONGES** (FR) 7
450 **DAKLONDIKE** (IRE) 13
146 **DAKOTA GOLD** (GB) 3
254 **DAKOTA GREY** (GB) 19
247 **DAL HARRAILD** (GB) 6
247 **DALAALAAT** (IRE) 123
401 **DALAMAN** (IRE) 32
190 **DALASIRI** (IRE) 16
294 **DALAVIDA** (FR) 4
486 **DALAWYNA** (FR) 48
99 **DALGARNO** (FR) 2
424 **DALI** (USA) 40
596 **DALI MAIL** (FR) 5
29 **DALIANA** (GB) F 56
609 **DALIANCE** (IRE) 8
310 **DALILEO** (IRE) 49
310 **DALKADAM** (FR) 10
507 **DALMORE** (GB) 86
432 **DALNESS EXPRESS** (GB) 8
428 **DALSHAND** (FR) 16
247 **DALVINA** (GB) C 124
377 **DALY TIGER** (IRE) 28
535 **DAMANIYAT GIRL** (USA) F 113
127 **DAME D'HONNEUR** (IRE) C 123
274 **DAME DE COMPAGNIE** (FR) 38
62 **DAME DU SOIR** (FR) 9
318 **DAME FREYA STARK** (GB) 142
244 **DAME NELLIE** (GB) 11
285 **DAME ROSE** (FR) 5
397 **DAME VERA** (GB) 44
119 **DAMUT I'M OUT** (IRE) 10
481 **DAN** (GB) 130
499 **DAN EMMETT** (USA) 9
419 **DAN MCGRUE** (GB) 40
97 **DAN'S DREAM** (GB) 37
141 **DAN'S QUEST** (GB) 9

415 **DANA'S PRESENT** (GB) 3
77 **DANAT AL ATHEER** (GB) C 85
565 **DANCE AND ROMANCE** (GB) 26
112 **DANCE BID** (GB) F 47
166 **DANCE EAST** (GB) C 86
261 **DANCE EMPEROR** (GB) 96
385 **DANCE FLOOR KING** (GB) 2
496 **DANCE FOR GEORGIE** (GB) F 36
486 **DANCE HALL GIRL** (GB) C 90
167 **DANCE KING** (GB) 16
244 **DANCE LEGEND** (GB) 12
329 **DANCE ME** (USA) 14
1 **DANCE OF FIRE** (GB) 1
332 **DANCE OF LIGHT** (USA) F 13
131 **DANCE ON THE DAY** (IRE) 25
247 **DANCE PEARL** (GB) F 125
401 **DANCE ROCK** (GB) 33
177 **DANCE TEACHER** (IRE) 5
555 **DANCE THE DREAM** (GB) 3
567 **DANCE TO PARIS** (GB) 42
41 **DANCEALOT** (GB) F 127
392 **DANCECRAFT** (GB) 34
596 **DANCED EVERY DANCE** (IRE) 6
368 **DANCEINTOTHELIGHT** (GB) 21
355 **DANCER'S LEAP** (IRE) F 22
380 **DANCETERIA** (FR) 14
271 **DANCIN ALPHA** (GB) 8
146 **DANCIN BOY** (GB) 40
484 **DANCING AMY** (IRE) 26
564 **DANCING BRAVE BEAR** (USA) 6
404 **DANCING CONQUEST** (GB) 14
546 **DANCING DOUG** (IRE) 3
601 **DANCING DRAGON** (GB) 13
319 **DANCING EMILY** (IRE) G 13
272 **DANCING GREY** (GB) 3
499 **DANCING HEARTS** (GB) 10
434 **DANCING LAUREN** (FR) F 71
318 **DANCING ON A DREAM** (IRE) 143
6 **DANCING RAIN** (GB) C 130
130 **DANCING SHADOW** (IRE) 5
17 **DANCING STAR** (GB) 5
442 **DANCING TRIESTE** (USA) C 20
28 **DANCING VEGA** (IRE) 79
331 **DANCING WARRIOR** (GB) 35
158 **DANCINGWITHWOLVES** (IRE) 68
177 **DANDHU** (GB) 29
258 **DANDIESQUE** (IRE) 57
248 **DANDILION** (IRE) 7
401 **DANDOLO DU GITE** (FR) 34
391 **DANDRIDGE** (GB) 5
83 **DANDY BIRD** (GB) 6
14 **DANDY DAN** (IRE) 20
223 **DANDY DUKE** (GB) 24
491 **DANDY FANTASIE** (IRE) 6
441 **DANDY HIGHWAYMAN** (IRE) 1
295 **DANDY LAD** (IRE) 51
405 **DANDY MAG** (FR) 58
486 **DANDY'S BEANO** (IRE) 49
176 **DANDYS DENOUEMENT** (GB) 21
140 **DANECASE** (GB) 7
187 **DANEHILL DESERT** (IRE) 72
399 **DANEHILL DREAMER** (USA) C 36
258 **DANEHILL KODIAC** (IRE) 7
251 **DANEHILLS WELL** (IRE) 2
587 **DANELISSIMA** (IRE) C 81
481 **DANEYAN** (FR) 32
314 **DANGEROUS ENDS** (GB) 4
5 **DANGEROUS GROUND** (IRE) 3

167 **DANGEROUS LADY** (GB) 84
8 **DANGLYDONTASK** (GB) 3
4 **DANI RIDGE** (IRE) C 11
175 **DANICA ASHTON** (GB) 2
24 **DANIELSFLYER** (IRE) 7
90 **DANISH DUKE** (IRE) 9
419 **DANNY KIRWAN** (IRE) 41
521 **DANS LE VENT** (FR) 10
28 **DANSETTE** (GB) F 80
587 **DANSEUSE DE REVE** (IRE) C 82
17 **DANZAN** (IRE) 54
318 **DANZAY** (IRE) 50
188 **DANZELLA** (GB) 2
7 **DANZENO** (GB) 21
481 **DANZIG SPRING** (FR) 33
161 **DANZOE** (IRE) 5
274 **DAPHNE DU CLOS** (FR) 39
193 **DAPPER MAN** (IRE) 4
109 **DARCEY'S PENNY** (GB) 4
19 **DARCY WARD** (FR) 8
118 **DARE TO DREAM** (GB) C 28
392 **DAREBIN** (GER) 35
328 **DARES TO DREAM** (IRE) 12
8 **DARING DEPLOY** (IRE) 4
359 **DARING GUEST** (IRE) 2
274 **DARIUS DES BOIS** (FR) 40
334 **DARIYA** (USA) 17
52 **DARK ACCLAIM** (IRE) 32
349 **DARK ALLIANCE** (IRE) 9
585 **DARK AND DANGEROUS** (IRE) 4
387 **DARK ASTER** (GB) 2
97 **DARK BLUE** (IRE) 38
368 **DARK CONFIDANT** (IRE) 22
162 **DARK CROCODILE** (IRE) 16
443 **DARK CRYSTAL** (GB) 2
127 **DARK DEFENDER** (GB) 13
187 **DARK DEVIL** (IRE) 7
283 **DARK EPISODE** (IRE) 24
612 **DARK FORCE** (FR) 21
197 **DARK FOREST** (GB) 7
77 **DARK HAVANA** (IRE) 86
610 **DARK HEDGES** (GB) 5
318 **DARK HONEY** (IRE) 51
61 **DARK IMPULSE** (IRE) 26
402 **DARK INTENTION** (IRE) 3
606 **DARK INVADER** (FR) 17
118 **DARK LIBERTY** (IRE) 29
302 **DARK MAGIC** (GB) 5
336 **DARK MAHLER** (IRE) 15
586 **DARK MIRACLE** (GB) 33
41 **DARK ORCHID** (USA) F 128
573 **DARK PEARL** (IRE) 8
414 **DARK POWER** (IRE) 4
127 **DARK PROFIT** (IRE) 14
17 **DARK RECKONING** (GB) F 118
118 **DARK ROSE ANGEL** (IRE) 30
271 **DARK RULER** (IRE) 9
281 **DARK SERAPHIM** (IRE) 26
143 **DARK SHOT** (GB) 9
163 **DARK SIDE DREAM** (GB) 5
485 **DARK SIDE JAZZ** (IRE) 12
510 **DARK SPEC** (GB) 21
368 **DARK SUNSET** (IRE) 23
131 **DARK THUNDER** (IRE) 64
254 **DARK VALLEY** (IRE) 20
377 **DARKEST FLYER** (IRE) 29
434 **DARKEST LIGHT** (GB) 32

232 **ELHAFEI** (USA) 44
97 **ELIDOR** (GB) 6
362 **ELIDORE** (GB) F 8
471 **ELIOS D'OR** (FR) 20
586 **ELITE GARDE** (FR) 10
323 **ELITE SHADOW** (GB) 20
323 **ELITE TREATY** (GB) 2
323 **ELITE WARRIOR** (GB) 21
283 **ELIXIR DE NUTZ** (FR) 30
193 **ELIXSOFT** (IRE) 31
66 **ELIZA DOALOTT** (IRE) G 4
281 **ELIZABETH BENNET** (IRE) 30
302 **ELJADDAAF** (IRE) 7
13 **ELKSTONE** (GB) 8
97 **ELLA FITZGERALD** (IRE) F 43
393 **ELLA ROSIE** (GB) G 21
464 **ELLA'S DENE** (GB) 5
159 **ELLARY** (FR) C 36
25 **ELLASHA** (GB) F 43
619 **ELLCON** (IRE) C 2
535 **ELLEN** (IRE) C 121
295 **ELLEN GATES** (GB) 22
497 **ELLENS WAY** (GB) 9
500 **ELLIOT THE DRAGON** (IRE) 29
481 **ELLON** (FR) 134
77 **ELLTHEA** (IRE) 38
461 **ELLWAY PROSPECT** (GB) F 13
486 **ELNADIM STAR** (IRE) 51
589 **ELOCUTION** (GB) 3
318 **ELOPA** (GER) C 148
64 **ELOPE** (GER) F 17
34 **ELOUNTA** (GB) F 2
258 **ELSAABLQAAT** (GB) 161
114 **ELSE APPROACH** (GB) 37
563 **ELSHAADIN** (GB) C 139
169 **ELSIE VIOLET** (IRE) 16
444 **ELTEZAM** (IRE) 4
508 **ELTON DES MOTTES** (FR) 39
389 **ELUDING** (GB) F 21
52 **ELUSIF** (IRE) 37
81 **ELUSIVE COWBOY** (USA) 3
50 **ELUSIVE FLAME** (GB) F 19
331 **ELUSIVE GOLD** (IRE) F 36
193 **ELUSIVE HEIGHTS** (IRE) 5
119 **ELUSIVE IVY** (IRE) 13
80 **ELUSIVE SHOW** (USA) 40
481 **ELUSIVE TRUST** (IRE) 36
481 **ELVA** (FR) F 135
1 **ELVIS MAIL** (FR) 13
92 **ELVIZ** (GB) 22
79 **ELWAZIR** (GB) 26
266 **ELYSEE STAR** (GB) 20
326 **ELYSEES** (IRE) 139
456 **ELYSEES PALACE** (GB) 1
444 **ELYSIAN FIELDS** (IRE) 5
383 **ELYSIAN FLYER** (IRE) 9
327 **ELYSIAN PRINCE** (GB) 7
258 **ELYSIUM DREAM** (GB) 64
381 **ELZAWAY** (IRE) 13
232 **EMARAATY** (GB) 45
486 **EMARAATY ANA** (GB) 91
10 **EMBANKMENT** (FR) 7
318 **EMBASSY** (GB) F 149
370 **EMBER'S GLOW** (GB) 7
232 **EMBLAZONED** (IRE) 46
508 **EMBOLE** (FR) 40
481 **EMBROIDERED SILK** (IRE) 37
565 **EMELL** (GB) 32

148 **EMENEM** (GB) 2
588 **EMERALD CROSS** (IRE) 2
496 **EMERALD PEACE** (IRE) C 38
77 **EMERALD ROCKET** (IRE) 39
514 **EMERALD ROSE** (GB) 2
146 **EMERALDS SPIRIT** (IRE) C 41
601 **EMERGING FORCE** (IRE) 16
419 **EMERGING TALENT** (IRE) 56
500 **EMIGRATED** (IRE) 6
610 **EMILANDRA** (GB) 8
63 **EMILENE** (GB) 2
318 **EMILIA JAMES** (GB) 58
41 **EMILY BRONTE** (IRE) F 131
261 **EMILY MOON** (IRE) 17
481 **EMIN** (IRE) 38
376 **EMINENT** (FR) 4
612 **EMINENT POET** (GB) 28
318 **EMIRATES EMPIRE** (IRE) 150
41 **EMIRATES FLYER** (GB) 23
484 **EMISSAIRE** (FR) 30
237 **EMITOM** (IRE) 25
587 **EMIYNA** (USA) F 86
96 **EMJAYEM** (GB) 4
66 **EMMA BEAG** (GB) 5
563 **EMMAUS** (IRE) 17
283 **EMMPARA** (GB) 31
6 **EMOTIONLESS** (IRE) 14
364 **EMPEROR COMMODOS** (GB) 2
374 **EMPEROR SAKHEE** (GB) 4
612 **EMPEROR'S CHOICE** (IRE) 29
112 **EMPHATIC** (IRE) 31
174 **EMPIRE BURLEQUE** (IRE) 61
185 **EMPIRE DE MAULDE** (FR) 17
174 **EMPIRE OF DIRT** (IRE) 62
424 **EMPIREOFTHEDRAGON** (IRE) 48
436 **EMPLOYER** (IRE) 45
120 **EMPORTEPARLAFOULE** (FR) 10
552 **EMPREINTE RECONCE** (FR) 23
28 **EMPRESS OF FRANCE** (USA) C 82
392 **EMPTY MARMALADES** (FR) 44
214 **ENA BAIE** (FR) 24
232 **ENABLE** (GB) 4
232 **ENBIHAAR** (IRE) 47
301 **ENCAPSULATED** (GB) 6
290 **ENCHANTING ENYA** (IRE) 12
506 **ENCODED** (IRE) 5
112 **ENCORE D'OR** (GB) 5
140 **ENCORE DU CRISTAL** (USA) G 33
293 **ENCORE DU CRISTAL** (USA) F 13
295 **ENCORE ENCORE** (FR) C 53
461 **ENCORE VIEW** (GB) F 56
522 **ENCOURAGING** (IRE) 4
436 **ENCRYPTED** (GB) 44
507 **ENCRYPTION** (IRE) 39
493 **ENDEAVOR** (GB) 2
177 **ENDEAVOURING** (IRE) 30
436 **ENDLESS** (GB) C 123
6 **ENDLESS GOLD** (GB) 15
326 **ENDLESS RIVER** (GB) 33
131 **ENDLESS TANGENT** (IRE) 28
376 **ENDLESSLY** (IRE) 14
127 **ENEKO** (FR) 22
396 **ENERGIA FLAVIO** (BRZ) 5
79 **ENFIJAAR** (IRE) F 74
321 **ENFORCEMENT** (IRE) 33
77 **ENGLAND EXPECTS** (GB) 8
352 **ENGLISH HERO** (GB) 7
331 **ENGLISH HEROINE** (GB) 37

199 **ENGLISH PALE** (IRE) 12
57 **ENGLISHMAN** (GB) 4
507 **ENHARMONIC** (USA) C 87
226 **ENIDOFTHEAMAZON** (IRE) 19
434 **ENIGMATIC** (IRE) 7
79 **ENJAZAAT** (GB) 27
504 **ENJOY RESPONSIBLY** (IRE) 10
166 **ENLIGHTEN** (GB) 22
359 **ENLIVEN** (GB) C 17
160 **ENMESHING** (GB) 9
336 **ENNISCOFFEY OSCAR** (IRE) 19
293 **ENNISTOWN** (GB) 14
41 **ENNJAAZ** (IRE) 24
406 **ENOLA** (FR) 2
612 **ENOLA GAY** (FR) 30
62 **ENRICHISSANT** (FR) 15
41 **ENRICHMENT** (USA) C 132
419 **ENRILO** (FR) 57
187 **ENROLMENT** (GB) 77
17 **ENSIGN EWART** (GB) 61
258 **ENTERTAINING** (IRE) 162
406 **ENTERTAINING BEN** (GB) 3
118 **ENTHAAR** (GB) 31
485 **ENTHRALLED** (GB) F 13
376 **ENTRE NOUS** (IRE) C 41
189 **ENTRUSTING** (GB) 69
563 **ENTWINE** (USA) F 140
189 **ENVISAGING** (IRE) 3
511 **ENVOUTEMENT** (FR) C 41
180 **ENVOY** (GB) 9
174 **ENZANI** (IRE) 63
177 **ENZEMBLE** (IRE) 17
573 **ENZO** (FR) 39
27 **ENZO'S LAD** (IRE) 40
409 **EOLIAN** (GB) 13
49 **EPANEEMA** (IRE) 19
481 **EPATHA** (IRE) F 136
131 **EPAULEMENT** (IRE) 29
266 **EPEIUS** (IRE) 5
281 **EPIC FANTASY** (GB) 31
41 **EPIC SIMILIE** (GB) C 133
328 **EPICUREAN** (GB) G 53
405 **EPICURIS** (GB) 68
611 **EPISCIA** (IRE) 33
7 **EPITAPH** (IRE) 25
266 **EPONINA** (IRE) 6
481 **EPOUVILLE** (FR) 39
445 **EPSOM BOUNTY** (GB) 17
390 **EPSOM DAY** (GB) 3
445 **EPSOM SECRET** (GB) 5
535 **EQTIDAAR** (IRE) 36
258 **EQUAL SUM** (GB) 163
277 **EQUALLY FAST** (GB) 3
542 **EQUIANO SPRINGS** (GB) 3
541 **EQUIDAE** (GB) 14
281 **EQUILATERAL** (GB) 32
216 **EQUILIBRIUM** (GB) 31
169 **EQUIMOU** (GB) 3
97 **EQUIPPED** (GB) 87
563 **EQUITATION** (GB) 18
418 **EQUITISSA** (IRE) F 6
534 **EQUO** (GB) 12
333 **EQUUS AMADEUS** (IRE) 5
53 **EQUUS FLIGHT** (IRE) 14
560 **EQUUS MILLAR** (IRE) 47
438 **EQUUS SECRETUS** (IRE) 29
281 **ERAAD** (IRE) 33
392 **ERAGON DE CHANAY** (FR) 45

101 **FAIRLEE PEARL** (GB) 5
48 **FAIRLIE** (GB) G 4
121 **FAIRLIGHT** (IRE) 22
323 **FAIRMONT** (IRE) C 33
321 **FAIRMOUNT** (GB) 11
224 **FAIRWAY FREDDY** (IRE) 10
94 **FAIRWAY TO HEAVEN** (IRE) 3
174 **FAIRY FLUTE** (IRE) 4
24 **FAIRY LOCK** (IRE) 10
61 **FAIRY MIST** (GB) 9
433 **FAIRY POL** (IRE) 9
323 **FAIRY TALE** (IRE) 23
167 **FAIRY WINGS** (USA) G 87
318 **FAITHFUL PROMISE** (GB) 59
127 **FAITHFULBOND** (IRE) C 125
436 **FAJJAJ** (IRE) 50
24 **FAKE NEWS** (GB) 34
79 **FAKHOOR** (IRE) 29
486 **FALABELLE** (IRE) 52
174 **FALAK** (IRE) 62
80 **FALCAO** (IRE) 8
587 **FALCON EIGHT** (IRE) 27
508 **FALCON SUN** (FR) 44
127 **FALCON'S FIRE** (IRE) 26
41 **FALCON'S VIEW** (GB) 26
540 **FALCONS FALL** (IRE) 10
25 **FALCONY** (FR) 14
381 **FALCOS** (FR) 15
166 **FALDAL** (GB) G 90
367 **FALLING ANGEL** (GB) F 12
619 **FALLING LEAF** (IRE) 4
527 **FALLING RAIN** (IRE) F 40
52 **FALLING WOOD** (IRE) 39
9 **FALLS OF LORA** (IRE) C 73
307 **FALMOUTH LIGHT** (IRE) 49
529 **FALSE ID** (GB) 4
481 **FALSTAFF** (FR) 139
329 **FAMILY FORTUNES** (GB) 3
424 **FAMILY TREE** (GB) 50
424 **FAMOUS** (IRE) C 128
47 **FAMOUS DYNASTY** (IRE) 4
119 **FAMOUS MILLY** (IRE) 15
49 **FAMOUS VOICE** (IRE) 74
427 **FAMUSA** (GB) C 31
247 **FANAAR** (IRE) 134
118 **FANAN** (GB) 33
131 **FANCIFUL MISS** (GB) 30
258 **FANDITHA** (IRE) C 164
331 **FANFARE LADY** (IRE) 18
308 **FANG** (GB) 3
97 **FANNIE BY GASLIGHT** (GB) 45
105 **FANNY MAY** (GB) F 20
10 **FANOULPIFER** (GB) 5
114 **FANROUGE** (IRE) C 87
566 **FANTASTIC FIRE** (GER) F 101
302 **FANTASTIC FLYER** (GB) 34
7 **FANTASY GLADIATOR** (GB) 26
563 **FANTASY IN RED** (GB) 59
263 **FANTASY JUSTIFIER** (IRE) 8
388 **FANTASY KING** (GB) 7
397 **FAR CRY** (GB) 10
50 **FARADIBA** (FR) 5
281 **FARAWAY FIELDS** (USA) 34
174 **FARCLAS** (FR) 69
118 **FARD** (GB) 34
297 **FARE THEE WELL** (IRE) 3
576 **FAREEQ** (GB) 7
121 **FAREWELL TO YOU** (GB) 23

146 **FARHH AWAY** (GB) 23
21 **FARLAM KING** 6
457 **FARM THE ROCK** (IRE) 3
267 **FARMER BOY** (IRE) 11
554 **FARNE ODYSSEY** (GB) 24
21 **FAROCCO** (GER) 7
226 **FAROL** (GB) 20
393 **FAS LE FIOS** (IRE) 9
79 **FASCINATING** (USA) C 76
154 **FASCINATOR** (GB) 17
80 **FASHAAK** (IRE) 9
118 **FASHION LINE** (IRE) C 89
167 **FASHION THEORY** (GB) 23
102 **FASHION WORLD** (GB) 31
541 **FASHION'S FLIGHT** (USA) F 15
512 **FASHIONABLE** (GB) F 49
486 **FAST ACT** (IRE) 17
509 **FAST AND FRIENDLY** (IRE) 5
37 **FAST AND FURIOUS** (IRE) 5
258 **FAST AND HOT** (IRE) 9
557 **FAST DANCER** (IRE) 3
29 **FAST ENDEAVOUR** (GB) 62
41 **FAST LANDING** (GB) 27
24 **FAST TRACK** (GB) 11
167 **FASTALONG** (IRE) 88
428 **FASTMAN** (GB) 104
392 **FAT SAM** (GB) 47
161 **FATA MORGANA** (GB) 19
80 **FATHER AILBE** (IRE) 41
167 **FATHER BERTIE** (GB) 24
180 **FATHER MCKENZIE** (GB) 10
521 **FATIMA BLUSH** (GB) 15
405 **FAUGHEEN** (IRE) 70
261 **FAUGHILL** (IRE) 100
377 **FAUGUERNON** (FR) 35
608 **FAVORI DE SIVOLA** (FR) 35
576 **FAVORITE GIRL** (GER) 27
576 **FAVORITE STORY** (GB) 8
419 **FAVORITO BUCK'S** (FR) 58
315 **FAVOURITE ROYAL** (IRE) 7
41 **FAWAAYED** (IRE) C 135
438 **FAWSLEY SPIRIT** (IRE) 30
428 **FAYEZ** (IRE) 22
247 **FAYLAQ** (GB) 135
127 **FAYREWAY** (IRE) F 126
295 **FAYROUZ ROSE** (IRE) 23
153 **FEAR GLIC** (IRE) 5
34 **FEARLESS LAD** (IRE) 5
189 **FEARN'S PIPPIN** (GB) 36
343 **FEARSOME** (GB) 3
412 **FEARSOME FRED** (IRE) 2
194 **FEATHERY** (GB) 6
589 **FEB THIRTYFIRST** (GB) 4
368 **FEDERICI** (GB) 29
188 **FEEBI** (GB) 15
166 **FEEBS** (GB) 70
244 **FEEL THE NOIZE** (GB) 24
426 **FEEL THE PINCH** (GB) 21
47 **FEEL THE VIBES** (GB) 5
216 **FEEL THE WRATH** (IRE) 32
481 **FEELIN ALRIGHT** (IRE) 5
98 **FEELING PECKISH** (IRE) 3
185 **FEETRONIE DE KERVI** (FR) 42
155 **FEISTY KATERINA** (GB) 4
28 **FELICIANA DE VEGA** (GB) 83
608 **FELICIDAD** (FR) 36
247 **FELINE GROOVY** (USA) 49
431 **FELINIOUS** (GB) G 28

181 **FELISA** (GB) 26
121 **FELIX** (GB) 48
504 **FELIX D'AUTRY** (FR) 12
174 **FELIX DESJY** (FR) 70
108 **FELIX MENDELSSOHN** (IRE) 8
25 **FELLBECK** (GB) 15
557 **FELSTEAD KNIGHT** (IRE) 19
309 **FENCOTE BELLE** (IRE) 14
512 **FENDALE** (GB) 4
237 **FENISA'S HOOK** (GB) 82
394 **FENJACK** (IRE) 2
404 **FENLONS COURT** (IRE) 15
232 **FENNAAN** (IRE) 48
52 **FERAGUST** (GB) 40
481 **FERALIA** (FR) 42
247 **FERDOOS** (GB) F 136
102 **FEREVIA** (IRE) C 77
552 **FERGAL MAEL DUIN** (GB) 25
315 **FERIK** (IRE) 22
109 **FERNGROVE** (USA) 6
456 **FERRIER** (GB) 17
49 **FERRUM** (GB) 75
6 **FESTIVAL OF AGES** (USA) 17
431 **FESTIVE AFFAIR** (IRE) 29
349 **FETHIYE BOY** (GB) 13
326 **FEVER FEVER** (USA) C 140
327 **FFORBIDDEN LOVE** (GB) 8
258 **FIANCEE** (IRE) F 165
49 **FIANNAIOCHT** (IRE) 20
52 **FICANAS** (GB) 41
422 **FIDDLER'S FLIGHT** (IRE) 3
221 **FIDELITY** (GB) 4
271 **FIDRA BAY** (IRE) 14
326 **FIDUX** (FR) 34
247 **FIELD GUN** (USA) 50
336 **FIELD MASTER** (IRE) 20
199 **FIELD OF VISION** (IRE) 13
555 **FIELDEN FROLIC** (GB) 25
541 **FIELDS OF ATHENRY** (USA) 63
326 **FIELDS OF FORTUNE** (GB) 35
565 **FIELDS OF GLORY** (FR) 34
114 **FIELDS OF PLAY** (GB) 39
240 **FIELDSMAN** (USA) 6
169 **FIERY BREATH** (GB) 12
535 **FIERY MISSION** (USA) 122
261 **FIESTA LADY** (ARG) C 101
481 **FIFTH ELEMENT** (FR) 43
438 **FIFTH SYMPHONY** (IRE) 31
539 **FIFTY PEACH WAY** (GB) 1
604 **FIFTY SHADES** (IRE) 6
16 **FIFTYSHADESOFGREY** (IRE) 6
175 **FIFTYSHADESOFNEIGH** (IRE) 7
114 **FIG ROLL** (GB) C 88
1 **FIG'S PRIDE** (IRE) 15
343 **FIGEAC** (FR) 4
1 **FIGHT AWAY BOYS** (IRE) 16
504 **FIGHT COMMANDER** (FR) 13
390 **FIGHT FOR LOVE** (FR) 4
424 **FIGHTFORTHEROSES** (FR) 51
288 **FIGHTING BACK** (GB) 4
329 **FIGHTING FINISH** (GB) 40
159 **FIGHTING IRISH** (IRE) 13
428 **FIGHTING SPIRIT** (IRE) 105
302 **FIGHTING TEMERAIRE** (IRE) 8
486 **FIKHAAR** (GB) 18
68 **FILAMENT OF GOLD** (USA) 2
344 **FILATORE** (IRE) 5
216 **FILBERT STREET** (GB) 33

484 FLUTTER DOWN (FR) 103
356 FLUTTERBEE (GB) 4
524 FLUX CAPACITOR (IRE) 17
274 FLY AGAIN (GB) 50
6 FLY AT DAWN (USA) 19
274 FLY CAMP (IRE) 51
237 FLY DU CHARMIL (FR) 28
507 FLY FREE (GB) C 88
348 FLY HOME HARRY (GB) 18
1 FLY RORY FLY (IRE) 18
209 FLY TRUE (GB) 2
595 FLY VINNIE (IRE) 10
560 FLYING ANGEL (IRE) 50
232 FLYING DEMON (GB) 50
511 FLYING DESIRE 26
511 FLYING DESIRE (GB) 4
53 FLYING EAGLE (IRE) 16
21 FLYING JACK (GB) 3
159 FLYING MOON (GER) 37
422 FLYING POWER (GB) 4
167 FLYING PURSUIT (GB) 25
61 FLYING SAKHEE (GB) 11
336 FLYING SHADOW (GER) 22
29 FLYING SPARKLE (IRE) 22
608 FLYING TIGER (IRE) 15
140 FLYING VERSE (GB) 12
127 FLYLOWFLYLONG (IRE) G 93
166 FLYMETOTHESTARS (GB) 23
409 FLYNNVINCIBLE (GB) 15
393 FLYWHEEL (FR) 23
508 FOCACCIA (IRE) 46
488 FOCOSA (ITY) F 4
522 FOIBLE (GB) 5
163 FOIE GRAS (GB) 8
526 FOLIE DOUZE (GB) 23
454 FOLIES BERGERES (FR) 17
6 FOLK TALE (GB) 74
6 FOLKSWOOD (GB) 20
574 FOLLOW INTELLO (IRE) 16
94 FOLLOW ME (IRE) 5
274 FOLLOW THE BEAR (IRE) 52
375 FOLLOW THE SWALLOW (IRE) 13
55 FOLLOWING BREEZE (IRE) 18
216 FOLLOWTHESTEPS (IRE) 34
180 FOLLY BERGERE (IRE) 11
174 FOLSOM BLUE (IRE) 75
261 FONDA (USA) C 131
189 FONDEST (GB) 37
181 FONDLED (GB) C 130
281 FONSECA (IRE) F 107
28 FONT VERT (FR) 35
336 FONTSANTA (IRE) 23
187 FOOL FOR YOU (IRE) 78
190 FOOL TO CRY (IRE) 19
54 FOOLAAD (GB) 7
527 FOOLISH ACT (IRE) C 42
174 FOOLS AND KINGS (GB) 76
521 FOOTLOOSE (GB) 19
405 FOOTPAD (FR) 17
131 FOOTSTEPSINTHEMIST (IRE) 68
529 FOOTSTEPSINTHERAIN (IRE) 5
275 FOR CARMEL (IRE) 7
283 FOR GOOD MEASURE (IRE) 32
85 FOR JIM (IRE) 15
232 FOR NOW (IRE) 51
261 FOR YOUR EYES (IRE) 132
442 FORBIDDEN GIFT (USA) C 22
434 FORBIDDEN PLANET (GB) 36

101 FORBIDDING (USA) 6
28 FORCE MAJEURE (IRE) 36
148 FORCEFUL APPEAL (USA) 3
166 FORCES OF DARKNESS (IRE) G 92
424 FOREIGN LEGION (IRE) 57
481 FOREIGN LEGIONARY (IRE) F 141
424 FOREIGN SECRETARY (GB) 58
334 FOREIGN STAR (GB) 59
541 FOREPLAY (IRE) F 64
92 FORESEE (GER) 25
541 FORESEEABLE FUTURE (FR) 16
176 FOREST BIHAN (FR) 28
484 FOREST DES AIGLES (FR) 31
121 FOREST EXPRESS (AUS) F 49
167 FOREST FUSION (IRE) 26
214 FOREST GENERAL (GB) 28
187 FOREST RANGER (IRE) 10
454 FORESTRY (IRE) 8
127 FORE VER A LADY (IRE) 27
274 FOREVER FIELD (IRE) 53
112 FOREVER IN LOVE (GB) 33
28 FOREVER LOVED (GB) F 84
424 FOREVER TOGETHER (IRE) 59
302 FOREVER YOURS (IRE) 9
376 FOREWARNED (IRE) G 16
109 FOREWARNING (GB) 7
261 FORGE MEADOW (IRE) 20
336 FORGET ME KNOT (IRE) 24
326 FORGETTHESMALLTALK (FR) 37
223 FORGOT TO ASK (IRE) 31
507 FORK HANDLES (GB) C 89
247 FORK LIGHTNING (USA) F 140
169 FORMALLY (IRE) 19
418 FORMIDABLE GIRL (USA) F 7
131 FORMIDABLE KITT (GB) 33
627 FORMIDABLEOPPONENT (IRE) 1
436 FORMULA ONE (IRE) 51
331 FORRICHERFORPOORER (IRE) 19
17 FORSETI (GB) 125
566 FORSTER (GB) 102
436 FORT APACHE (GB) 52
62 FORT GABRIEL (FR) 17
238 FORT JEFFERSON (GB) 9
504 FORT SMITH (IRE) 14
348 FORTH BRIDGE (GB) 19
169 FORTHWITH (GB) 20
18 FORTINBRASS (IRE) 1
336 FORTUNATE GEORGE (IRE) 25
71 FORTUNATE VISION (GB) 13
557 FORTUNE AND GLORY (USA) 4
17 FORTUNE'S PEARL (IRE) 65
17 FORTUNES HIDING (IRE) 17
38 FORTY CROWN (IRE) 6
507 FORWARD THINKER (GB) 41
431 FORZA MILAN (IRE) 31
63 FOSSA (GB) 3
431 FOUNDATION MAN (IRE) 32
84 FOUNDING DAUGHTER (IRE) F 2
6 FOUNTAIN OF TIME (GB) 75
131 FOUR CHAMPS (GB) 34
86 FOUR FEET (IRE) 62
554 FOUR FIFTY THREE (GB) 13
77 FOUR KINGDOMS (IRE) 9
309 FOUR MILE BEACH (GB) 16
281 FOUR MILE BRIDGE (IRE) 108
121 FOUR WHITE SOCKS (GB) 25
356 FOURNI (GB) 3
552 FOURTH ACT (IRE) 29

118 FOUZ (GB) 35
336 FOX APPEAL (IRE) 26
17 FOX CHAIRMAN (IRE) 126
28 FOX FEARLESS (GB) 85
258 FOX HAPPY (IRE) 167
258 FOX KASPER (IRE) 168
17 FOX LEICESTER (IRE) 127
17 FOX MAFIA (IRE) 66
552 FOX NORTON (FR) 30
258 FOX POWER (IRE) 169
17 FOX PREMIER (IRE) 128
608 FOX PRO (FR) 37
17 FOX SHINJI (IRE) 129
17 FOX TAL (GB) 130
376 FOX VARDY (USA) 42
17 FOX WIN WIN (IRE) 131
491 FOXANGEL (GB) 8
185 FOXEY (GB) 43
96 FOXFORD (GB) 5
245 FOXRUSH TAKE TIME (FR) 22
560 FOXTAIL HILL (IRE) 51
409 FOXTROT JULIET (GB) 16
90 FOXTROT KNIGHT (GB) 12
17 FOXTROT LADY (GB) 67
564 FOXTROT PEARL (IRE) C 22
149 FOXY ACT (GB) 5
26 FOXY BOY (GB) 7
500 FOXY FEELIN (GB) 11
217 FOXY FEMME (GB) 22
602 FOXY FOREVER (IRE) 4
486 FOXY LADY (GB) 54
481 FOXY POWER (FR) 142
90 FOXY REBEL (GB) 13
167 FOXY'S SPIRIT (GB) 90
103 FOYLESIDEVIEW (IRE) 3
496 FRAGRANCY (IRE) C 39
28 FRAGRANT BELLE (GB) 86
281 FRAGRANT DAWN (GB) 109
291 FRAMLEY GARTH (IRE) 11
153 FRANCE DU LUKKA (FR) 6
405 FRANCIN (FR) 72
3 FRANCIS OF ASSISI (IRE) 21
436 FRANCIS XAVIER (IRE) 4
92 FRANCISCO (GB) 26
53 FRANCKY DU BERLAIS (FR) 18
273 FRANCO'S SECRET (GB) 4
318 FRANCOPHILIA (GB) 61
12 FRANGARRY (IRE) 2
315 FRANK BRIDGE (GB) 8
136 FRANK N FAIR (GB) 5
290 FRANK THE BARBER (IRE) 5
254 FRANK THE SLINK (GB) 22
216 FRANK'S LEGACY (GB) 6
25 FRANKELIO (FR) 17
247 FRANKELLINA (GB) 141
208 FRANKIE (GB) 4
207 FRANKIE BALLOU (IRE) 4
508 FRANKIE RAPPER (IRE) 47
377 FRANKIEFIVEANGELS (FR) 38
424 FRANKINCENSE (IRE) 60
540 FRANKLY SPEAKING (GB) 12
318 FRANKUUS (IRE) 8
510 FRANSHAM (GB) 6
92 FRANTICAL (GB) 27
565 FRASER CANYON (GB) 35
555 FRECKLES (GB) 26
385 FRED'S FILLY (GB) 4
582 FREDDIE'S SPIRIT (GB) 36

535 **GARDEN OASIS** (GB) 40
456 **GARDEN OF EDEN** (USA) C 48
424 **GARDENS OF BABYLON** (IRE) 63
466 **GARDINERS HILL** (IRE) 5
227 **GARGOYLE GIRL** (GB) C 36
419 **GARO DE JUILLEY** (FR) 62
450 **GARRAN CITY** (IRE) 23
497 **GARRANE** (IRE) 10
295 **GARRAUN** (IRE) C 54
554 **GARREL GLEN** (GB) 25
409 **GARRETTSTOWN** (IRE) 18
232 **GARRICK** (GB) 5
315 **GARRISON COMMANDER** (IRE) 55
554 **GARRISON LAW** (GB) 26
414 **GARRYDUFF CROSS** (IRE) 1
194 **GARRYOWEN** (GB) 36
226 **GARSBAY** (GB) 21
158 **GARSINGTON** (GB) 36
455 **GARTH ROCKETT** (GB) 5
607 **GAS LINE BOY** (GB) 30
192 **GAS MONKEY** (GB) 3
244 **GASELEE** (USA) C 25
189 **GASLIGHT** (GB) 71
522 **GASOLINE** (IRE) 7
338 **GASSIN GOLF** (GB) 12
434 **GATES PASS** (GB) 37
535 **GATESOFTHEARCTIC** (IRE) 41
444 **GATHER** (GB) 32
192 **GATILLO** (GB) 4
28 **GATTAIA** (USA) 38
560 **GAUCHO** (GB) 53
283 **GAUCHO GIL** (IRE) 37
232 **GAUDI** (IRE) 52
326 **GAVI DI GAVI** (IRE) 141
331 **GAVLAR** (GB) 6
102 **GAVOTA** (GB) 34
329 **GAWDAWPALIN** (IRE) 4
484 **GAYE FLIER** (IRE) 32
606 **GAYEBURY** (GB) 154
510 **GAYTON** (GB) 7
318 **GAZE** (GB) C 154
25 **GAZELLE** (FR) 45
289 **GEALACH GHORM** (IRE) 5
554 **GEE SIXTY SIX** (GB) 3
29 **GEETANJALI** (IRE) 24
216 **GEMBARI** (GB) 35
281 **GEMINI** (GB) 35
21 **GEMMATTYMOLL** (IRE) 21
318 **GEMOLOGIST** (GB) 63
563 **GEMSTONE** (IRE) C 145
258 **GENDARME** (GB) 67
545 **GENERAL ALLENBY** (GB) 3
432 **GENERAL BROOK** (GB) 11
409 **GENERAL BUX** (GB) 19
152 **GENERAL CONSENSUS** (GB) 6
409 **GENERAL CUSTARD** (GB) 20
354 **GENERAL GERRARD** (GB) 1
214 **GENERAL GINGER** (GB) 29
287 **GENERAL GIRLING** (GB) 6
582 **GENERAL HAZARD** (IRE) 7
315 **GENERAL JACK** (IRE) 28
176 **GENERAL MAHLER** (IRE) 29
560 **GENERAL MALARKEY** (IRE) 54
440 **GENERAL PATTON** (GB) 2
174 **GENERAL PRINCIPLE** (IRE) 78
513 **GENERAL TUFTO** (GB) 3
399 **GENERAL ZOFF** (GB) 24
375 **GENEROUS CHIEF** (IRE) 15

433 **GENEROUS DAY** (IRE) 11
574 **GENEROUS LADY** (GB) F 28
17 **GENETICS** (FR) 14
525 **GENEVA TRUMPET** (GB) 2
160 **GENI JOHNSON** (IRE) 12
381 **GENRES** (GB) 16
527 **GENTLE BREEZE** (IRE) C 43
391 **GENTLEMAN DUKE** (IRE) 6
269 **GENTLEMAN FARMER** (IRE) 4
179 **GENTLEMAN JACK** (GB) 5
493 **GENTLEMAN JAMES** (GB) 4
552 **GENTLEMAN JON** (GB) 31
392 **GENTLEMAN'S DREAM** (IRE) 49
370 **GENTLEMEN** (GB) 3
80 **GENUINE APPROVAL** (IRE) 10
434 **GENUINELY CROWDED** (IRE) 38
187 **GEOFF POTTS** (IRE) 14
49 **GEOLAI** (IRE) 79
612 **GEORDIE B** (GB) 32
123 **GEORDIE DES CHAMPS** (IRE) 3
381 **GEORDIE GEORGE** (IRE) 17
504 **GEORDIELAD** (GB) 15
434 **GEORDIELASS** (GB) 39
329 **GEORGE** (IRE) 18
209 **GEORGE BAILEY** (IRE) 5
16 **GEORGE BAKER** (IRE) 7
187 **GEORGE BOWEN** (IRE) 15
576 **GEORGE DRYDEN** (IRE) 9
436 **GEORGE FORMBY** (GB) 126
508 **GEORGE GENTLY** (FR) 51
496 **GEORGE GERSHWIN** (GB) 40
77 **GEORGE HASTINGS** (GB) 91
295 **GEORGE OF HEARTS** (FR) 24
166 **GEORGE RIDSDALE** (GB) 93
462 **GEORGE THOMAS** (GB) 9
508 **GEORGE VALENTINE** (FR) 162
232 **GEORGE VILLIERS** (GB) 53
258 **GEORGE WILLIAM** (GB) 10
77 **GEORGIAN BAY** (IRE) 11
337 **GEORGIAN FIREBIRD** (GB) 4
535 **GEORGIAN MANOR** (IRE) 42
136 **GEORGIESHORE** (IRE) 6
205 **GEORGIEZAR** (GB) 5
267 **GEORGINA JOY** (GB) 12
174 **GER's LAD** (IRE) 79
397 **GERANIUM** (GB) 50
355 **GERARDINA** (GB) C 15
258 **GERIKA** (FR) C 171
127 **GERMAN BIGHT** (IRE) 94
392 **GERMAN WHIP** (GB) 50
512 **GERRARD'S SLIP** (GB) 5
94 **GERRY THE GLOVER** (IRE) 6
625 **GERSJOEYCASEY** (IRE) 5
114 **GET BACK GET BACK** (IRE) 40
294 **GET EVEN** (GB) 17
431 **GET IN THE QUEUE** (GB) 34
146 **GET KNOTTED** (IRE) 6
508 **GET ON THE YAGER** (IRE) 52
419 **GET OUT THE GATE** (IRE) 63
508 **GET READY FREDDY** (GB) 53
223 **GET RHYTHM** (IRE) 32
432 **GET UP THEM STEPS** (GB) 12
130 **GET WISHING** (GB) 8
405 **GETABIRD** (IRE) 73
119 **GETAFLYER** (IRE) 17
518 **GETAWAY BAY** (IRE) 16
174 **GETAWAY JOHN** (IRE) 80
377 **GETAWAY KID** (GB) 40

607 **GETAWAY MISSION** (IRE) 31
419 **GETAWAY TRUMP** (GB) 64
295 **GETBACK IN PARIS** (IRE) 7
114 **GETCHAGETCHAGETCHA** (GB) 89
270 **GETONSAM** (GB) 5
18 **GETTIN' LUCKY** (IRE) 2
416 **GETTYSBURG ADDRESS** (IRE) 14
535 **GHADBBAAN** (GB) 123
6 **GHAIYYATH** (IRE) 76
507 **GHALIB** (IRE) 13
232 **GHALYOON** (GB) 54
79 **GHANDOORAH** (USA) F 77
41 **GHARABH** (GB) F 138
436 **GHAYADH** (GB) 53
167 **GHAYYAR** (IRE) 28
114 **GHAZAN** (IRE) 41
258 **GHEPARDO** (GB) 68
510 **GHINIA** (IRE) 8
461 **GHOST** (GB) 40
377 **GHOST OF A GIRL** (IRE) F 115
607 **GHOST OF A SMILE** (IRE) 32
582 **GHOST SERGE** (IRE) 24
318 **GHOSTFLOWER** (IRE) C 155
618 **GHOSTLY ARC** (IRE) 3
6 **GHOSTWATCH** (IRE) 7
508 **GI JAYNE** (GB) 54
258 **GIANT BREAK** (FR) 172
266 **GIANT REDWOOD** (IRE) 9
383 **GIANT SPARK** (GB) 12
405 **GIANT SPIRIT** (USA) 74
74 **GIBB HILL** (GB) 3
419 **GIBBES BAY** (FR) 65
563 **GIBBS HILL** (GER) 21
508 **GIBENO** (IRE) 55
213 **GIFT FROM GOD** (GB) 2
226 **GIFT IN TIME** (GB) 13
329 **GIFT OF HERA** (GB) 19
177 **GIFT OF MUSIC** (IRE) C 31
563 **GIFT OF RAAJ** (GB) 64
582 **GIFTED GEISHA** (GB) 38
439 **GIFTED HEIR** (IRE) 1
436 **GIFTED MASTER** (IRE) 5
563 **GILDED HEAVEN** (GB) 65
28 **GILDED HOUR** (GB) 39
247 **GILDED VANITY** (IRE) C 142
496 **GILGAMESH** (GB) 1
211 **GILLY GRACE** (GB) 7
185 **GILMER** (IRE) 19
335 **GILTED PRINCESS** (IRE) 10
602 **GIN AND TONIC** (GB) 5
549 **GIN COBBLER** (GB) 6
187 **GIN IN THE INN** (IRE) 16
315 **GIN PALACE** (GB) 56
131 **GINBAR** (GB) 35
560 **GINGE DE SOPHIA** (IRE) 55
95 **GINGER FIZZ** (GB) 11
258 **GINGER FOX** (GB) 173
554 **GINGER LADY** (GB) 4
512 **GINGER LOVE** (GB) 6
258 **GINGER NUT** (GB) 174
190 **GINGILI** (GB) 20
265 **GINNY BRIG** (GB) 1
338 **GINO TRAIL** (GB) 13
447 **GIOVANNA** (GB) F 8
64 **GIOVANNI** (GB) 9
102 **GIOVANNI ACUTO** (FR) 35
481 **GIOVANNI DAL PONTE** (GB) 45
162 **GIOVANNI MEDICI** (GB) 17

29 **JOE'S SPIRIT** (IRE) 33
181 **JOEGOGO** (IRE) 29
231 **JOELY** (IRE) 6
212 **JOEY'S DESTINY** (IRE) 7
552 **JOG ON** (IRE) 37
267 **JOHANOS** (FR) 16
558 **JOHN BETJEMAN** (GB) 15
135 **JOHN BISCUIT** (GB) 7
26 **JOHN CAESAR** (IRE) 15
510 **JOHN CLARE** (IRE) 22
606 **JOHN CONSTABLE** (IRE) 31
87 **JOHN DANIELL** (GB) 5
146 **JOHN KIRKUP** (GB) 28
374 **JOHN MILTON** (IRE) 9
550 **JOHN WILLIAMS** (IRE) 13
323 **JOHNI BOXIT** (GB) 28
548 **JOHNNY CAVAGIN** (GB) 2
17 **JOHNNY KIDD** (GB) 139
14 **JOHNNY OCEAN** (IRE) 36
550 **JOHNNY PEDLAR** (GB) 14
457 **JOHNNY YUMA** (IRE) 8
401 **JOHNS LUCK** (IRE) 62
431 **JOIN THE CLAN** (IRE) 45
73 **JOIN THE NAVY** (GB) 2
83 **JOINT DESTINY** (IRE) G 23
518 **JOKE DANCER** (GB) 24
509 **JOKERS AND ROGUES** (IRE) 7
1 **JOLIE CRICKETTE** (FR) 21
348 **JOLIE FRANCINE** (IRE) 25
77 **JOLIE LAIDE** (IRE) F 95
313 **JOLLY JET** (IRE) 11
214 **JOLLY'S CRACKED IT** (FR) 39
563 **JOMANA** (FR) F 156
548 **JON H THE LAWMAN** (IRE) 3
294 **JONA'S ECLIPSE** (GB) 18
161 **JONATHANS GIRL** (GB) 21
24 **JONBOY** (GB) 38
340 **JONJOELA** (IRE) 3
145 **JONNIESOFA** (IRE) 12
455 **JONNYSIMPSON** (IRE) 24
486 **JORD** (IRE) F 60
559 **JORVIK PRINCE** (GB) 5
435 **JOSHLEE** (IRE) 6
274 **JOSSES HILL** (IRE) 67
62 **JOT'EM DOWN** (IRE) 19
428 **JOUEL** (FR) F 107
123 **JOUEUR BRESILIEN** (FR) 8
461 **JOURNALIST** (IRE) F 60
436 **JOUSI** (GB) 62
349 **JOUST** (IRE) 33
21 **JOVIAL JOEY** (IRE) 11
456 **JOY STREET** (IRE) 24
343 **JOYCETICK** (FR) 7
80 **JOYFUL DREAM** (IRE) 11
535 **JOYFUL MISSION** (USA) 134
583 **JOYFUL STAR** (GB) 4
397 **JOYFULLNESS** (USA) C 74
336 **JOYRIDER** (GB) 37
349 **JOYS DELIGHT** (GB) 16
119 **JOYS OF SPRING** (IRE) C 94
427 **JOYSOFTEAMWORK** (IRE) 24
595 **JOZAFEEN** (GB) G 17
176 **JUALS SPIRIT** (IRE) 94
258 **JUAN HORSEPOWER** (IRE) 12
308 **JUANITO CHICO** (IRE) 5
535 **JUBILOSO** (GB) 135
404 **JUBILYMPICS** (GB) 23
187 **JUDGE EARLE** (IRE) 22

419 **JUDGE JOHN DEED** (IRE) 76
279 **JUDGE JUDY** (IRE) 2
83 **JUDICIAL** (IRE) 10
261 **JUDY'S OSCAR** (IRE) 33
293 **JUKEBOX JIVE** (FR) 19
567 **JULATTEN** (IRE) F 14
332 **JULES** (IRE) C 24
511 **JULIAN ROCK** 28
525 **JULIE'S GIFT** (GB) G 9
261 **JULIESPADDOCKWALK** (IRE) 34
232 **JULIET CAPULET** (IRE) 67
281 **JULIET FOXTROT** (GB) 46
582 **JULIUS LIMBANI** (IRE) 41
385 **JULLY LES BUXY** (GB) 5
53 **JUMBO'S BOY** (GB) 25
315 **JUMEIRAH** (IRE) 59
41 **JUMEIRAH JOY** (IRE) 87
41 **JUMEIRAH ONE** (GB) 150
318 **JUMEIRAH PALM STAR** (GB) C 166
112 **JUMIRA BRIDGE** (GB) 10
563 **JUMIRA PRINCE** (IRE) 24
190 **JUMP AND JUMP** (IRE) 21
484 **JUMP FOR DOUGH** (IRE) 42
607 **JUMPING AROUND** (IRE) 39
574 **JUMPING CATS** (GB) 18
230 **JUMPING JACK** (IRE) 15
556 **JUNCEA** (GB) F 16
336 **JUNCTION FOURTEEN** (IRE) 38
318 **JUNEAU** (IRE) 67
399 **JUNEAU PEAK** (GB) 28
6 **JUNGLE CAT** (IRE) 26
97 **JUNGLE INTHEBUNGLE** (IRE) 95
315 **JUNGLE QUEEN** (IRE) 32
486 **JUNGLE ROOM** (IRE) 43
566 **JUNGLEBOOGIE** (GER) 38
97 **JUNIA TEPZIA** (IRE) C 96
564 **JUNKET** (GB) C 25
217 **JUNOESQUE** (GB) 6
86 **JUPITER** (GB) 34
499 **JUPITER CUSTOS** (FR) 17
504 **JURBY** (GB) 22
247 **JURRAN** (GB) 61
174 **JURY DUTY** (IRE) 98
612 **JURYS OUT** (IRE) 37
563 **JURZ** (IRE) 72
423 **JUS PIRES** (USA) 4
508 **JUST A FEELING** (GB) 69
214 **JUST A STING** (IRE) 40
123 **JUST A THOUGHT** (IRE) 9
159 **JUST AN IDEA** (IRE) 5
159 **JUST ANOTHER IDEA** (IRE) 17
361 **JUST ANOTHER VODKA** (GB) 8
412 **JUST ARCHIE** (USA) 3
254 **JUST BOBBY** (IRE) 26
1 **JUST BROOKE** (GB) 22
544 **JUST CALL ME BLUE** (IRE) 10
120 **JUST CALL ME JENNI** (GB) 13
254 **JUST CAMERON** (GB) 27
199 **JUST CHAMPION** (GB) 30
348 **JUST DON'T ASK** (IRE) 26
488 **JUST DOWN THE ROAD** (IRE) G 8
94 **JUST FAB** (IRE) 9
349 **JUST FOR FEE** (IRE) 17
401 **JUST FOR THE CRAIC** (IRE) 142
401 **JUST FRED** (IRE) 63
518 **JUST GEORGIE** (GB) 25
263 **JUST GLAMOROUS** (IRE) 10
569 **JUST HEATHER** (IRE) 5

167 **JUST HISS** (GB) 36
399 **JUST HUBERT** (IRE) 40
326 **JUST IN TIME** (GB) 51
226 **JUST JOSEPHINE** (IRE) 23
29 **JUST LIKE A WOMAN** (GB) C 66
196 **JUST LIKE BETH** (GB) 1
408 **JUST MAYBE** (GB) 4
450 **JUST MIDAS** (IRE) 34
352 **JUST MILLY** (GB) 12
518 **JUST MINDED** (IRE) 26
16 **JUST PERFECT** (GB) 26
199 **JUST RIGHT** (GB) 28
508 **JUST ROCKY** (GB) 70
260 **JUST SKITTLES** (GB) 1
140 **JUST SO COOL** (IRE) 16
43 **JUST SPOT** (GB) 4
10 **JUST THAT LORD** (GB) 7
437 **JUST US TWO** (IRE) 4
318 **JUST WAIT** (IRE) 68
541 **JUST WONDERING** (IRE) C 68
348 **JUST YOUR TYPE** (IRE) 27
233 **JUSTADREAMYEKEN** (GB) 4
392 **JUSTANOTHER MUDDLE** (GB) 68
589 **JUSTANOTHER MUDDLE** (GB) 7
91 **JUSTANOTHERBOTTLE** (IRE) 4
214 **JUSTAPUZZLE** (GB) 41
411 **JUSTATENNER** (GB) 5
481 **JUSTFIRSTLADY** (IRE) 149
254 **JUSTFORJAMES** (IRE) 28
499 **JUSTICE KNIGHT** (IRE) 1
177 **JUSTICE LADY** (IRE) 7
193 **JUSTICE PLEASING** (GB) 11
370 **JUSTICE ROCK** (GB) 4
190 **JUSTICE SUPER** (IRE) 22
392 **JUSTIFICATION** (GB) 69
220 **JUSTTHEGREY** (IRE) 5
247 **JUTHOOR** (IRE) 62
120 **K O KENNY** (GB) 14
46 **KAABER** (USA) 9
273 **KAAFEL** (IRE) 71
563 **KAANOON** (GB) 73
17 **KABRIT** (IRE) 71
350 **KACHESS** (GB) 7
244 **KACHUMBA** (GB) 8
131 **KACHY** (GB) 8
141 **KADDYS DREAM** (GB) 13
295 **KADIZ** (GB) 57
302 **KADRIZZI** (IRE) 14
392 **KAFEEL** (USA) 70
7 **KAFOO** (GB) 35
377 **KAGNEY** (IRE) 53
467 **KAHDIAN** (IRE) 1
428 **KAIULANI** (IRE) F 108
486 **KAJAKI** (IRE) 20
540 **KAKI DE LA PREE** (FR) 14
566 **KAKS ROOSID** (FR) 39
220 **KALA LORD** (IRE) 6
546 **KALA NOIRE** (GB) 8
41 **KALAATAH** (USA) C 151
318 **KALAGIA** (IRE) 69
521 **KALAHARI QUEEN** (GB) 24
595 **KALAHARRY** (IRE) 18
234 **KALANITI** (IRE) 13
552 **KALARIKA** (IRE) 38
560 **KALARIYA** (IRE) 64
406 **KALASHNIKOV** (IRE) 5
190 **KALASKADESEMILLEY** (GB) 23
498 **KALASTAR** (IRE) 3

158 KHANMURJAN (USA) 85
428 KHARBETATION (IRE) 34
281 KHAWAATEM (USA) 48
555 KHAZAF (GB) 28
247 KHAZEENA (GB) F 151
181 KHELEYF'S GIRL (GB) 30
187 KHELMAN (IRE) 23
582 KHEROS (GB) 42
98 KHESKIANTO (IRE) 5
258 KHIBRAH (GB) 187
281 KHILWAFY 123
199 KHISMET (GB) 15
303 KHITAAMY (IRE) 5
24 KHOBARAA (GB) F 50
563 KHOR SHEED (GB) C 159
481 KHOZMA (FR) 153
512 KI KI (GB) 10
90 KIBAAR (GB) 15
166 KIBINI (GB) G 97
309 KICK ON DOTTIE (IRE) 19
114 KICK ON KICK ON (GB) 50
7 KICKBOXER (IRE) 17
618 KICKING THE CAN (IRE) 5
6 KIDMENEVER (IRE) 28
238 KIKIMORA (GB) 13
127 KIKINI BAMALAAM (IRE) 102
318 KILBARCHAN (GER) 168
484 KILBREE CHIEF (GB) 44
223 KILBREE KID (IRE) 36
95 KILBREW BOY (IRE) 15
552 KILBRICKEN STORM (IRE) 40
220 KILCASCAN (GB) 7
274 KILCREA VALE (IRE) 71
328 KILCULLEN FLEM (IRE) 24
288 KILCULLEN LADY (IRE) 9
438 KILDISART (IRE) 42
14 KILFILUM CROSS (IRE) 38
136 KILINAKIN (IRE) 8
348 KILLALA QUAY (GB) 29
119 KILLASSER BOY (GB) 21
231 KILLDUNNE (IRE) 7
383 KILLER CLASS (GB) C 49
1 KILLER CROW (IRE) 23
180 KILLER PUNCH (GB) 22
507 KILLER QUEEN (GB) 47
251 KILLONE (IRE) 3
405 KILLULTAGH VIC (IRE) 93
14 KILMAC PRINCESS (IRE) G 39
318 KILMAH (GB) 12
447 KILMOGANNY (IRE) 9
497 KILMURVY (IRE) 14
368 KILRONAN CASTLE (GB) 51
368 KILTORMER (IRE) 52
280 KIM'S LEGEND (GB) 12
187 KIMBERELLA (GB) 24
166 KIMBERLEY BOY (GB) 32
166 KIMBERLEY GIRL (GB) 98
326 KIMBERLEY POINT (GB) 55
333 KIMBERLITE CANDY (IRE) 10
533 KIMENE (GB) 5
557 KIMIFIVE (IRE) 21
28 KINAESTHESIA (GB) 44
53 KINARI (IRE) 26
609 KINCORA FORT (IRE) 14
6 KIND ACT (USA) 86
10 KINDIA (IRE) C 29
185 KINDLER (GB) 26
563 KINDRED (IRE) 76

104 KINETICA (GB) C 21
17 KING AND EMPIRE (IRE) 72
34 KING ATHELSTAN (IRE) 20
19 KING CALVIN (IRE) 15
519 KING CHARLIE (IRE) 9
230 KING CNUT (FR) 16
481 KING COBRA (GB) 154
392 KING COOL (GB) 73
80 KING CRIMSON (GB) 14
316 KING GOLAN (IRE) 4
338 KING KAYF (GB) 18
158 KING KEVIN (GB) 9
17 KING LUD (GB) 73
235 KING OF ARAN (IRE) 1
454 KING OF BURGUNDY (GB) 27
31 KING OF CASTILLA (GB) 6
481 KING OF LEOGRANCE (FR) 53
86 KING OF NEPAL (GB) 6
607 KING OF REALMS (IRE) 41
526 KING OF ROOKS (GB) 6
167 KING OF THE CELTS (IRE) 38
419 KING OF THE RING (GB) 154
392 KING OF THE SAND (IRE) 135
561 KING OSWALD (USA) 5
17 KING POWER (GB) 140
512 KING ROBERT (GB) 11
333 KING SPIRIT (IRE) 11
102 KING TUT (USA) 41
230 KING UTHER (GB) 17
521 KING VINCE (IRE) 25
90 KING'S COINAGE (IRE) 16
602 KING'S GUEST (IRE) F 14
606 KING'S ODYSSEY (IRE) 32
580 KING'S PAVILION (IRE) 2
318 KING'S PROCTOR (IRE) 70
303 KING'S REALM (IRE) 6
406 KING'S RESTE (IRE) 6
329 KING'S SIREN (IRE) C 44
114 KING'S SLIPPER (GB) 51
450 KING'S SOCKS (FR) 38
565 KING'S TEMPLE (IRE) 42
550 KING'S WHARF (GB) 15
149 KINGARA (GB) F 8
140 KINGFAST (IRE) 35
7 KINGFISHER GIRL (GB) 38
432 KINGLAMI (GB) 15
434 KINGOFMERROWS (IRE) 10
560 KINGOFTHECOTSWOLDS (GB) 66
456 KINGOFTHESINGERS (GB) 25
352 KINGS ACADEMY (GB) 13
92 KINGS CROSS (FR) 36
614 KINGS ECLIPSE (IRE) 3
486 KINGS FULL (IRE) 62
146 KINGS GOLD (IRE) 9
541 KINGS HIGHWAY (IRE) 25
419 KINGS INN (IRE) 78
552 KINGS LAD (IRE) 41
338 KINGS MONARCH (GB) 19
353 KINGS OWN (GB) 1
258 KINGS ROYAL HUSSAR (FR) 188
274 KINGS RYDE (GB) 72
232 KINGS SHIELD (USA) 69
95 KINGS TEMPTATION (GB) 16
552 KINGS WALK (IRE) 42
458 KINGS WATCH (IRE) 8
80 KINGSLEY KLARION (IRE) 15
560 KINGSPLACE (IRE) 67
92 KINGSTON (GER) 37

215 KINGSTON COLLEGE (IRE) 4
331 KINGSTON KURRAJONG (GB) 8
225 KINGSTON MIMOSA (GB) 7
90 KINGSTREET LADY (GB) 17
499 KINGSWELL THEATRE (IRE) 19
618 KINLOCH PRIDE (GB) 6
173 KINTYRELYUPTOYOU (GB) 7
434 KION (IRE) 43
127 KIRBEC (GB) 103
481 KIRIKETA (IRE) 54
249 KIRK'S DANCER (USA) 9
83 KIRKHAM (GB) 11
315 KIRKLAND FOREVER (GB) 13
455 KIRKLAND FOREVER (GB) 9
332 KIRKSTALL SPIRIT (IRE) 18
444 KIRUNA (GB) C 42
587 KISANGA (GB) 39
326 KISMAT (GB) 144
587 KISS FOR A JEWEL (IRE) 96
333 KISS JOLIE (GB) G 12
37 KISS ME GOODBYE (GB) C 29
174 KISS ME KAYF (IRE) 100
376 KISSABLE (FR) F 45
424 KISSED (IRE) C 137
120 KISSES FOR ME (IRE) F 23
335 KISSIN PARTY (USA) F 34
511 KIT KAT JET (BRZ) 7
37 KIT MARLOWE (GB) 71
79 KITAABAAT (GB) 38
507 KITE MARK (GB) C 92
232 KITE WING (GB) 70
587 KITHARA (IRE) 40
258 KITHONIA (FR) F 189
566 KITTEN'S MUSIC (USA) 87
318 KITTILEO (IRE) 72
541 KITTY SOFTPAWS (IRE) F 70
121 KITTY WELLS (GB) F 27
522 KIWAYU (GB) 11
146 KIWI BAY (GB) 10
511 KIWI GREEN SUITE (BRZ) 8
501 KIWI MYTH (GB) 5
223 KK LEXION (IRE) 37
518 KLARE CASTLE (GB) 27
247 KLASSIQUE (GB) 63
522 KLEITOMACHOS (IRE) 12
601 KLEOS (IRE) 19
392 KLOUD GATE (GB) 74
304 KNICK KNACK (IRE) 2
409 KNIGHT COMMANDER (GB) 25
431 KNIGHT DESTROYER (IRE) 47
308 KNIGHT ERRANT (IRE) 15
318 KNIGHT IN ARMOUR (IRE) 73
508 KNIGHT IN DUBAI (IRE) 72
401 KNIGHT OF NOIR (IRE) 66
189 KNIGHT OWL (GB) 7
159 KNIGHT TO BEHOLD (IRE) 18
297 KNIGHT'S PARADE (IRE) 6
486 KNIGHTED (GB) 63
274 KNIGHTHOOD (GB) 73
563 KNIGHTLY SPIRIT (GB) 77
167 KNIGHTS TABLE (GB) 39
566 KNIGHTSBRIDGE (BRZ) F 104
565 KNOCK DOWN (IRE) G 43
368 KNOCK HOUSE (IRE) 53
127 KNOCK STARS (IRE) C 104
426 KNOCKADERRY FLYER (IRE) 33
195 KNOCKALONGI (GB) 4
569 KNOCKAMANY BENDS (IRE) 6

192 **LIMERICK LORD** (IRE) 6
405 **LIMINI** (IRE) 101
604 **LIMITED RESERVE** (IRE) 10
428 **LINA'S STAR** (GB) 87
97 **LINCOLN** (IRE) 15
566 **LINCOLN COUNTY** (GB) 44
238 **LINCOLN COUNTY** (GB) 15
610 **LINCOLN RED** (GB) 9
138 **LINDA** (FR) C 39
323 **LINDA DORIS** (IRE) 3
246 **LINDEMAN** (GB) G 4
77 **LINE HOUSE** (GB) 52
383 **LINE OF REASON** (IRE) 15
446 **LINED WITH SILVER** (IRE) 5
324 **LINEN LINE** (GB) F 17
58 **LINEN LINE** (GB) G 12
438 **LINENHALL** (IRE) 46
162 **LINGUINE** (FR) 6
49 **LINGUISTIC STYLE** (IRE) 87
227 **LINNET** (GER) F 14
336 **LINNET** (GB) G 41
426 **LIP SERVICE** (IRE) 34
587 **LIPSIA** (FR) F 98
334 **LIPSTICK** (GB) 24
24 **LIQUID** (IRE) 18
187 **LIQUID GOLD** (GB) 27
527 **LIR** (IRE) 22
97 **LISCOA** (IRE) F 99
506 **LISDONAGH HOUSE** (IRE) 10
348 **LISDOONVARNA LAD** (IRE) 36
77 **LISFANNON** (GB) F 96
461 **LISHEEN CASTLE** (IRE) 42
120 **LISKEARD** (GB) 16
326 **LISP** (IRE) 60
206 **LISS RUA** (IRE) F 4
318 **LISSELAN DIVA** (IRE) F 172
341 **LISSYCASEY** (IRE) 2
401 **LIST ONE** (GB) 77
508 **LISTEN DEAR** (IRE) 102
508 **LISTEN TO THE MAN** (IRE) 75
49 **LISTENING MODE** (IRE) 88
431 **LITHIC** (GB) 48
541 **LITIGATION** (GB) 28
214 **LITTERALE CI** (FR) 47
546 **LITTLE ALLSTAR** (IRE) 9
167 **LITTLE ANNIE** (GB) C 134
562 **LITTLE AUB** (GB) 21
29 **LITTLE AUDIO** (IRE) F 70
253 **LITTLE BAVINGTON** (GB) 1
558 **LITTLE BOY BLUE** (GB) 11
519 **LITTLE BOY BORU** (IRE) 10
328 **LITTLE BRUCE** (IRE) 27
54 **LITTLE CHOOSEY** (GB) 8
460 **LITTLE CUPCAKE** (GB) 3
196 **LITTLE DOTTY** (GB) 2
612 **LITTLE GINGE** (GB) 45
310 **LITTLE INDIAN** (GB) 19
588 **LITTLE ITALY** (USA) C 23
239 **LITTLE JIMMY** (GB) 11
176 **LITTLE JO** (GB) 36
560 **LITTLE JON** (GB) 71
568 **LITTLE KINGDOM** (IRE) 7
176 **LITTLE LEGS** (GB) 96
327 **LITTLE MILLIE** (IRE) 13
399 **LITTLE MISS DAISY** (GB) 8
349 **LITTLE MISS KODI** (IRE) 18
114 **LITTLE MISS LILLY** (GB) 57
506 **LITTLE MISS LOLA** (GB) 11

283 **LITTLE MISS POET** (GB) 55
544 **LITTLE MISS TANGO** (GB) 13
155 **LITTLE MISS WILLOW** (IRE) 5
31 **LITTLE NOSEGAY** (IRE) 7
114 **LITTLE PALAVER** (GB) 12
115 **LITTLE PIPPIN** (GB) 8
547 **LITTLE POEM** (GB) 20
560 **LITTLE POP** (GB) 72
261 **LITTLE PRINCESS** (GER) 38
450 **LITTLE RED LION** (IRE) 41
368 **LITTLE STEVIE** (GB) 5
552 **LITTLE VERN** (IRE) 45
327 **LITTLE WINDMILL** (IRE) 14
524 **LITTLELORDCONFORD** (IRE) 20
281 **LITTLEPROMISEDLAND** (IRE) F 124
434 **LIVE BY NIGHT** (GB) 46
61 **LIVE DANGEROUSLY** (GB) 12
43 **LIVE FOR TODAY** (IRE) 6
405 **LIVELOVELAUGH** (IRE) 103
278 **LIVELY SPRITE** (IRE) F 14
235 **LIVIA GALILEI** (IRE) C 13
573 **LIVIA'S DREAM** (IRE) C 80
262 **LIVING LEADER** (GB) 7
318 **LIVING LEGEND** (IRE) 173
384 **LIVINGSTONES QUEST** (IRE) 22
281 **LIVVYS DREAM** (IRE) 52
315 **LIZZY'S TOWNSHIP** (USA) C 60
294 **LLAMREI** (GB) 19
572 **LLANCILLO LORD** (IRE) 11
540 **LLANTARA** (GB) 15
261 **LOAD UP TIME** (IRE) 39
541 **LOCAL FANCY** (GB) F 72
297 **LOCAL SHOW** (IRE) 8
118 **LOCAL SPIRIT** (USA) F 96
498 **LOCH DHU** (IRE) G 5
257 **LOCH GARMAN ARIS** (IRE) 6
563 **LOCH MA NAIRE** (IRE) C 162
156 **LOCHNELL** (IRE) 7
123 **LOCKER ROOM TALK** (IRE) 11
608 **LOCKUP** (IRE) F 46
488 **LOCOMMOTION** (GB) 9
368 **LOFGREN** (GB) 58
222 **LOG OFF** (IRE) 3
145 **LOG ON** (IRE) 15
102 **LOGAN'S CHOICE** (GB) 44
26 **LOGI** (IRE) 16
29 **LOGIE BAIRD** (IRE) 71
52 **LOLLINA PAULINA** (GB) C 50
507 **LOLLYS DREAM** (IRE) 51
573 **LOMBATINA** (FR) F 81
109 **LOMHARA** (GB) 11
127 **LOMU** (IRE) 39
370 **LONDON** (FR) 5
547 **LONDON GLORY** (GB) 6
517 **LONDON GRAMMAR** (IRE) 5
77 **LONDON PROTOCOL** (FR) 14
399 **LONDON WELSH** (GB) C 41
375 **LONDONIA** (GB) 21
449 **LONE SPIRIT** (IRE) F 6
508 **LONG HOUSE HALL** (IRE) 76
434 **LONG JOHN SILVER** (IRE) 11
326 **LONG SOCKS** (GB) 61
612 **LONGHOUSESIGNORA** (IRE) 46
585 **LONGMORE** (GB) 7
618 **LONGROOM** (GB) 7
180 **LONGSIDE** (GB) 14
283 **LONGTOWN** (GB) 56

86 **LONICERA** (GB) 65
195 **LOOE BAY** (GB) 5
461 **LOOK MY WAY** (GB) 18
544 **LOOK SURPRISED** (GB) 14
115 **LOOKER** (GB) C 28
289 **LOOKFORARAINBOW** (GB) 9
159 **LOOKING FOR CARL** (GB) 19
471 **LOOKING WELL** (IRE) 30
557 **LOOKS A MILLION** (GB) 22
359 **LOOKS ALL RIGHT** (IRE) F 18
401 **LOOKS FROZEN** (IRE) 73
484 **LOOKS LIKE MURT** (IRE) 46
250 **LOOKS LIKE POWER** (IRE) 6
114 **LOOKS LIKE RAIN** (GB) C 125
114 **LOOKSLIKEANANGEL** (GB) C 96
603 **LOOKSLIKERAINTED** (IRE) 3
565 **LOOKSNOWTLIKEBRIAN** (IRE) 45
249 **LOOMING** (IRE) 45
348 **LOOSE CHIPS** (GB) 37
573 **LOOSE JULIE** (IRE) C 82
28 **LOPE ATHENA** (GB) 95
181 **LOPE DE LOOP** (IRE) 32
52 **LOPE SCHOLAR** (IRE) 96
271 **LOPES DANCER** (IRE) 19
17 **LOPITO** (GB) 74
449 **LOQUACITY** (GB) C 14
582 **LOQUACITY** (GB) C 43
623 **LORCAN** (GB) 72
623 **LORD ALDERVALE** (IRE) 3
267 **LORD BALLIM** (FR) 20
605 **LORD BEN** (IRE) 7
53 **LORD BRYAN** (IRE) 29
403 **LORD BUNNACURRY** (GB) 9
266 **LORD CAPRIO** (IRE) 23
392 **LORD CLENAGHCASTLE** (IRE) 82
321 **LORD CONDI** (IRE) 15
491 **LORD COOPER** (GB) 3
238 **LORD COUNTY** (FR) 16
283 **LORD DUVEEN** (IRE) 57
565 **LORD FENDALE** (IRE) 46
120 **LORD FRANKLIN** (GB) 17
189 **LORD GEORGE** (IRE) 9
182 **LORD GETAWAY** (IRE) 6
359 **LORD GUEST** (IRE) 10
326 **LORD HUNTINGDON** (GB) 62
377 **LORD IN RED** (GB) 60
586 **LORD MARMADUKE** (GB) 15
349 **LORD MURPHY** (IRE) 19
53 **LORD NAPIER** (IRE) 30
77 **LORD OBERON** (GB) 53
227 **LORD OF THE GLEN** (GB) 32
427 **LORD OF THE ROCK** (IRE) 7
10 **LORD OF THE STORM** (GB) 8
80 **LORD REASON** (IRE) 17
461 **LORD RIDDIFORD** (IRE) 43
547 **LORD ROB** (GB) 7
174 **LORD SCOUNDREL** (IRE) 106
521 **LORD TOPPER** (GB) 26
17 **LORD VETINARI** (GB) 75
326 **LORD WALSINGHAM** (GB) 63
185 **LORD WISHES** (IRE) 27
427 **LORD YEATS** (GB) 8
17 **LORELINA** (GB) 24
41 **LORETO** (IRE) C 156
105 **LORETO ROSE** (GB) C 21
83 **LORETTA** (IRE) 30
83 **LORTON** (GB) 31
181 **LOS CAMACHOS** (IRE) 33

187 **MABO** (GB) 89
606 **MAC BELLA** (GB) 33
254 **MAC CENNETIG** (IRE) 31
127 **MAC N CHEESE** (IRE) 40
131 **MAC O'POLO** (IRE) 9
401 **MAC TOTTIE** (GB) 77
17 **MACAQUE** (GB) 77
194 **MACGREGOR'S PAL** (GB) 27
582 **MACH ONE** (GB) 9
22 **MACHIATO** (IRE) 13
386 **MACHIAVELIAN STORM** (IRE) 2
557 **MACHINE LEARNER** (GB) 9
359 **MACHO GUEST** (IRE) 11
97 **MACHO MOVER** (IRE) 52
91 **MACHREE** (IRE) 20
563 **MACKAAR** (IRE) 164
155 **MACKEN** (IRE) 20
180 **MACKSVILLE** (IRE) 15
377 **MAD CAREW** (IRE) 61
330 **MAD ENDEAVOUR** (GB) 7
431 **MAD FOR ACTION** (IRE) 49
460 **MAD ROSE** (IRE) 4
590 **MADAKHEEL** (USA) 9
313 **MADAM ANNA** (IRE) 14
112 **MADAM DEVIOUS** (GB) 37
302 **MADAM DRAGONFLY** (IRE) 36
237 **MADAM JOLIE** (IRE) F 41
584 **MADAM LILIBET** (IRE) 4
454 **MADAM POMFREY** (GB) 28
95 **MADAME BLEUE** (GB) G 36
112 **MADAME BOULANGERE** (GB) F 54
573 **MADAME BOUNTY** (GB) 15
225 **MADAME CLAUD** (GB) 9
321 **MADAME FIONA** (GB) 16
97 **MADAME HOI** (IRE) F 100
289 **MADAME JO JO** (GB) 19
345 **MADAME MIME ARTIST** (GB) 4
165 **MADAME MOZAIK** (USA) G 3
447 **MADAME RITZ** (GB) 30
79 **MADANY** (IRE) C 80
261 **MADDA'S FORCE** (ITY) F 137
77 **MADE OF HONOUR** (IRE) 16
77 **MADEENH** (IRE) C 97
86 **MADELEINE BOND** (GB) 7
563 **MADELINE** (IRE) 83
48 **MADINAT** (GB) 8
83 **MADISON** (GB) 25
261 **MADISON TO MONROE** (IRE) 42
17 **MADONNA DELL'ORTO** (GB) C 147
424 **MADRID** (IRE) 77
80 **MADRINHO** (IRE) 18
566 **MADURAI** (GER) 46
404 **MAEBH** (IRE) 30
481 **MAELIA** (USA) 7
104 **MAESTRO MAC** (IRE) 4
274 **MAESTRO ROYAL** (GB) 86
79 **MAFAAHEEM** (IRE) 11
512 **MAFDET** (GB) 33
102 **MAGELLAN** (GB) 9
434 **MAGENA** (USA) C 83
7 **MAGGIE PINK** (GB) 39
56 **MAGGIE'S DAWN** (GB) 16
187 **MAGGIES ANGEL** (IRE) 90
248 **MAGGIES LEGEND** (GB) 14
258 **MAGHAWEER** (IRE) 75
4 **MAGHFOOR** (GB) 7
158 **MAGHROOM** (IRE) 51
258 **MAGHZAA** (IRE) F 198

496 **MAGIC APPLAUSE** (IRE) 19
295 **MAGIC ART** (IRE) F 60
397 **MAGIC BEANS** (GB) 15
310 **MAGIC BUDDY** (GB) 37
396 **MAGIC CIRCLE** (IRE) 13
166 **MAGIC CITY** (IRE) 34
338 **MAGIC DANCER** (GB) 22
6 **MAGIC LILY** (GB) 90
77 **MAGIC MARK** (GB) 55
473 **MAGIC MIRROR** (GB) 2
102 **MAGIC NYMPH** (IRE) F 86
261 **MAGIC OF LIGHT** (IRE) 43
179 **MAGIC OF MILAN** (IRE) 7
517 **MAGIC PASS** (GB) 6
240 **MAGIC PULSE** (IRE) 19
422 **MAGIC SHIP** (IRE) 11
424 **MAGIC WAND** (IRE) 78
424 **MAGICAL** (GB) 79
193 **MAGICAL BUPERS** (IRE) C 38
349 **MAGICAL BUPERS** (IRE) C 35
6 **MAGICAL CROWN** (USA) F 143
189 **MAGICAL DREAMER** (IRE) 10
90 **MAGICAL EFFECT** (IRE) 21
250 **MAGICAL MAN** (GB) 7
281 **MAGICAL MEMORY** (IRE) 9
247 **MAGICAL SIGHT** (GB) 66
401 **MAGICAL THOMAS** (GB) 78
186 **MAGICHULL** (GB) 18
408 **MAGICINTHEMAKING** (USA) 7
52 **MAGIKA** (GB) C 84
281 **MAGILLEN** (IRE) 10
443 **MAGISTRAL** (GB) 8
189 **MAGISTRATE** (IRE) 47
308 **MAGLIETTA FINA** (IRE) F 27
25 **MAGNET** (FR) 22
393 **MAGNETIC** (IRE) 25
496 **MAGNETIC BOUNDARY** (USA) 20
247 **MAGNETIC CHARM** (IRE) 154
258 **MAGNIFICENT** (GB) 76
315 **MAGNOLIA SPRINGS** (IRE) 37
109 **MAGNUM** (IRE) 13
64 **MAGNUS MAXIMUS** (GB) 2
190 **MAGNUS ROMEO** (GB) 28
91 **MAGOJIRO** (USA) 21
419 **MAGOO** (IRE) 81
139 **MAGS WELL** (IRE) 7
262 **MAGUIRE'S GLEN** (IRE) 8
535 **MAHAARAT** (GB) 56
79 **MAHAATHEER** (IRE) C 81
338 **MAHARI** (IRE) 23
118 **MAHFOODH** (GB) 43
189 **MAHIMA** (IRE) F 76
316 **MAHLER BAY** (IRE) 5
368 **MAHLER LAD** (IRE) 60
130 **MAHLER'S FIRST** (IRE) 11
176 **MAHLERDRAMATIC** (IRE) 37
326 **MAHLERMADE** (IRE) 64
237 **MAHLERVOUS** (IRE) 42
151 **MAHNA MAHNA** (IRE) 4
217 **MAHUIKA** (IRE) 23
563 **MAID FOR WINNING** (USA) F 165
217 **MAID FROM THE MIST** (GB) 24
358 **MAID OF MILAN** (IRE) 8
408 **MAID OF ROCK** (IRE) 8
114 **MAID OF SPIRIT** (IRE) 58
41 **MAID TO DREAM** (GB) F 158
115 **MAID TO ORDER** (IRE) C 29
17 **MAID UP** (GB) 78

86 **MAIDEN CASTLE** (GB) 66
348 **MAIDEN VOYAGE** (GB) F 39
541 **MAIDIN MAITH** (IRE) C 73
249 **MAIDS CAUSEWAY** (GB) F 75
261 **MAIEPOMAI** (IRE) C 138
580 **MAIFALKI** (IRE) 3
470 **MAIGH DARA** (IRE) 5
29 **MAIN DESIRE** (IRE) 34
493 **MAIN FACT** (USA) 12
413 **MAIN REASON** (IRE) 2
232 **MAIN STREET** (GB) 75
318 **MAINE LOBSTER** (USA) F 176
189 **MAINSAIL ATLANTIC** (USA) 48
508 **MAIRE BANRIGH** (GB) 79
150 **MAISON BRILLET** (IRE) 1
301 **MAISON WIX** (GB) 13
622 **MAJANALMA** (IRE) 3
195 **MAJBOOR** (IRE) 6
618 **MAJDOOL** (IRE) 8
507 **MAJEED** (GB) 18
26 **MAJESTE** (GB) 17
131 **MAJESTIC ALEXANDER** (IRE) C 78
106 **MAJESTIC DAWN** (IRE) 36
263 **MAJESTIC HERO** (IRE) 13
548 **MAJESTIC MAN** (IRE) 4
336 **MAJESTIC MOLL** (IRE) 42
192 **MAJESTIC MOON** (IRE) 8
486 **MAJESTIC ROI** (USA) F 98
83 **MAJESTIC STONE** (IRE) 12
283 **MAJESTIC TOUCH** (IRE) 59
237 **MAJINGILANE** (IRE) 43
488 **MAJOR ASSAULT** (GB) 10
428 **MAJOR CRISPIES** (GB) 39
237 **MAJOR DAVIS** (FR) 44
377 **MAJOR DESTINATION** (IRE) 62
481 **MAJOR DUNDEE** (FR) 164
433 **MAJOR HINDRANCE** (IRE) 15
486 **MAJOR JUMBO** (GB) 26
397 **MAJOR MAC** (IRE) 3
167 **MAJOR MINUS** (GB) 40
174 **MAJOR MITCHELL** (IRE) 107
294 **MAJOR PEIRSON** (IRE) 20
217 **MAJOR PUSEY** (GB) 5
323 **MAJOR REACHER** (GB) 30
254 **MAJOR RIDGE** (IRE) 32
133 **MAJOR ROWAN** (GB) 4
166 **MAJOR SNUGFIT** (GB) 99
432 **MAJOR VALENTINE** (IRE) 17
515 **MAJORETTE** (GB) 5
442 **MAJROOH** (IRE) 3
397 **MAKAARIM** (GB) 17
89 **MAKAMBA PASSION** (FR) 19
281 **MAKAMBE** (IRE) 53
481 **MAKANA** (FR) C 165
83 **MAKANAH** (GB) 26
71 **MAKE GOOD** (IRE) 18
177 **MAKE HASTE SLOWLY** (GB) 21
484 **MAKE IT HAPPEN** (IRE) 48
261 **MAKE IT HURRAH** (GB) 44
197 **MAKE IT SIMPLE** (GB) 20
41 **MAKE IT UP** (GB) 43
229 **MAKE ME A FORTUNE** (IRE) 5
49 **MAKE ME SWAY** (IRE) 89
17 **MAKE MUSIC** (GB) 25
186 **MAKE ON MADAM** (IRE) 10
587 **MAKE THE SWITCH** (IRE) 43
613 **MAKES YOU STRONGER** (GB) 7
562 **MAKHFAR** (IRE) 8

405 **MINELLA BEAU** (IRE) 111
326 **MINELLA CHARMER** (IRE) 73
53 **MINELLA DADDY** (IRE) 31
405 **MINELLA ENCORE** (IRE) 112
377 **MINELLA FAIR** (IRE) 63
518 **MINELLA FIVEO** (IRE) 34
223 **MINELLA FOR ME** (IRE) 42
275 **MINELLA GATHERING** (IRE) 10
504 **MINELLA ON LINE** (IRE) 27
401 **MINELLA PRESENT** (IRE) 85
431 **MINELLA ROCCO** (IRE) 53
426 **MINELLA SCAMP** (IRE) 40
605 **MINELLA STYLE** (IRE) 9
145 **MINELLA SUITE** (IRE) 16
174 **MINELLA TILL DAWN** (IRE) 114
609 **MINELLA TREASURE** (IRE) 16
275 **MINELLA TWEET** (IRE) 11
160 **MINELLA VOUCHER** (GB) 21
447 **MINELLA WHISPER** (IRE) 14
457 **MINELLACELEBRATION** (IRE) 11
248 **MINELLAFORLEISURE** (IRE) 17
401 **MINELLATILLMORNING** (IRE) 86
535 **MINER'S SECRET** (USA) C 139
52 **MING DYNASTY** (FR) 12
9 **MINI DREAMS** (GB) 2
292 **MINI'S DESTINATION** (GB) 6
41 **MINIDRESS** (GB) F 161
233 **MINIMUM** (GB) 2
146 **MININGGOLD** (GB) 12
147 **MININGROCKS** (FR) 3
130 **MINNIE ESCAPE** (GB) 12
261 **MINNIE HAHA** (FR) 109
82 **MINNIE MILAN** (FR) 5
326 **MINNIE'S MYSTERY** (FR) C 146
104 **MINNOLA** (GB) C 22
1 **MINORA** (IRE) F 29
436 **MINOVIA** (SPA) 71
328 **MINSTREL ROYAL** (GB) 30
484 **MINT GOLD** (IRE) 52
334 **MINTED** (USA) F 42
403 **MINTY JONES** (GB) 10
17 **MINUTE MILE** (GB) 81
224 **MINUTESTOMIDNIGHT** (IRE) 16
131 **MINWAH** (IRE) C 80
607 **MIRACLE GARDEN** (GB) 46
174 **MIRACLE IN MEDINAH** (GB) 115
562 **MIRACLE OF MEDINAH** (GB) 12
573 **MIRACLE WORKS** (GB) 55
49 **MIRACULUM** (IRE) 25
535 **MIRAGE DANCER** (GB) 9
481 **MIRANDA** (IRE) 65
154 **MIRANDASSISTER** (IRE) C 29
281 **MIRBAT** (GB) 57
275 **MIRIAM VIOLET** (GB) 12
174 **MIRO** (IRE) 116
139 **MIRROR MAGIC** (GB) 13
127 **MIRSAALE** (GB) 42
244 **MIRZA** (GB) 5
540 **MIRZAM** (GB) 18
167 **MISCHIEF MANAGED** (IRE) 45
7 **MISCHIEVOUS ROCK** (GB) 85
484 **MISFITS** (GB) 53
276 **MISHAAL** (IRE) 8
127 **MISREPRESENT** (USA) C 136
382 **MISS ADVENTURE** (IRE) 4
16 **MISS ALABAMA** (FR) C 39
127 **MISS BAR BEACH** (IRE) 106
553 **MISS BARBOSSA** (IRE) 8

154 **MISS BATES** (GB) 6
508 **MISS BENEFITZ** (IRE) 81
555 **MISS BLONDELL** (GB) 7
567 **MISS BOLIVAR** (GB) 45
295 **MISS BOND** (IRE) C 62
456 **MISS CELESTIAL** (IRE) 53
368 **MISS CILLA** (IRE) F 126
458 **MISS CLYRO** (GB) 9
523 **MISS CONDUCT** (GB) 13
611 **MISS CORNICHE** (GB) F 55
326 **MISS CRICK** (GB) 74
318 **MISS DANBY** (IRE) 17
307 **MISS DD** (IRE) 55
151 **MISS DUSKY DIVA** (IRE) 5
258 **MISS ELENA** (GB) C 202
223 **MISS FLEMING** (GB) 43
14 **MISS GARBO** (IRE) G 46
122 **MISS GERONIMO** (GB) 8
489 **MISS GISELLE** (GB) 4
77 **MISS GLITTERS** (GB) C 102
411 **MISS GREINTON** (GER) G 31
177 **MISS HERITAGE** (IRE) 10
237 **MISS HONEY RYDER** (IRE) 46
295 **MISS HYGROVE** (GB) C 63
315 **MISS INGA SOCK** (IRE) 54
401 **MISS JEANNE MOON** (IRE) 87
484 **MISS JOEKING** (GB) 54
97 **MISS LAHAR** (GB) C 101
423 **MISS LAMOUR** (USA) C 36
507 **MISS LATIN** (GB) 54
399 **MISS M** (GB) 9
516 **MISS MACKIE** (IRE) 17
313 **MISS MALARKY** (IRE) 15
527 **MISS MARGARITA** (GB) 23
279 **MISS MAYFAIR** (IRE) 4
564 **MISS MILLA B** (GB) 11
497 **MISS MINUTY** (GB) 17
175 **MISS MISCHIEF** (GB) 11
258 **MISS MO BROWN BEAR** (IRE) 80
226 **MISS MOLLIE** (GB) 14
401 **MISS MOLLY MAE** (IRE) 88
607 **MISS MUMTAZ** (IRE) 98
461 **MISS MYSTERIOUS** (FR) C 61
223 **MISS NIGHT OWL** (GB) 44
494 **MISS OTIS** (GB) F 7
281 **MISS PARIS** (GB) 58
258 **MISS PLIMSOLL** (USA) C 203
92 **MISS POPPY** (GB) F 66
247 **MISS QUEEN** (USA) F 161
206 **MISS QUEST** (GB) 6
233 **MISS QUICKLY** (IRE) C 10
176 **MISS RANGER** (IRE) 40
489 **MISS REBERO** (GB) 5
354 **MISS RECYCLED** (GB) 9
154 **MISS SABINA** (GB) 30
166 **MISS SHERIDAN** (IRE) 38
114 **MISS SMILLA** (GB) C 101
249 **MISS SNOSSYBOOTS** (IRE) 14
307 **MISS T STAR** (IRE) 56
99 **MISS TENACITY** (GB) 4
484 **MISS TIGGY** (GB) 55
586 **MISS TONGABEZI** (GB) 16
307 **MISS TRISH** (IRE) F 66
450 **MISS TYNTE** (IRE) 47
216 **MISS UPPITY** (GB) 14
318 **MISS VAN WINKLE** (GB) 83
166 **MISS WOLVERINE** (GB) 77
390 **MISS YEATS** (IRE) 10

271 **MISSCARLETT** (IRE) 22
237 **MISSED APPROACH** (IRE) 47
256 **MISSESGEEJAY** (GB) 6
127 **MISSION HILLS** (GB) G 43
481 **MISSION IMPASSIBLE** (IRE) 66
291 **MISSION TRIO** (IRE) 14
535 **MISSISIPI STAR** (IRE) C 140
494 **MISSISSIPPI MISS** (GB) 3
499 **MISSISSIPPI MOON** (GB) 23
319 **MISSMEBUTLETMEGO** (GB) 7
329 **MISSTRAL** 45
29 **MISSUNITED** (IRE) C 76
423 **MISSY HOCK** (USA) 18
52 **MISSY O' GWAUN** (IRE) F 54
174 **MISSY TATA** (FR) 117
232 **MISTER AMBASSADOR** (USA) 79
146 **MISTER BELVEDERE** (GB) 13
37 **MISTER BOB** (GER) 8
565 **MISTER BUDDY** (GB) 51
481 **MISTER CHARM** (FR) 173
392 **MISTER CHOW** (GB) 90
145 **MISTER DON** (GB) 17
450 **MISTER DRIFTER** (IRE) 48
274 **MISTER FISHER** (GB) 93
448 **MISTER FIZZ** (GB) 3
96 **MISTER FREEZE** (FR) 8
481 **MISTER JO** (IRE) 8
178 **MISTER KALANISI** (IRE) 6
234 **MISTER KIT** (GB) 16
552 **MISTER MALARKY** (GB) 49
176 **MISTER MANDURO** (FR) 41
13 **MISTER MCCOY** (GB) 17
102 **MISTER MERLIN** (GB) 89
605 **MISTER MISTER** (IRE) 10
508 **MISTER MIYAGI** (GB) 82
92 **MISTER MUSIC** (GB) 39
287 **MISTER MUSICMASTER** (GB) 10
481 **MISTER PRESIDENT** (FR) 68
621 **MISTER RAINMAN** (IRE) 12
127 **MISTER SHOWMAN** (GB) 44
508 **MISTER UNIVERSUM** (GER) 83
321 **MISTER VALENTINE** (GB) 17
97 **MISTER WHITAKER** (IRE) 16
214 **MISTERTON** (GB) 12
461 **MISTIROC** (GB) 20
118 **MISTRESS OF ROME** (GB) C 102
226 **MISTRESS OF VENICE** (GB) 15
28 **MISTRESS QUICKLY** (IRE) 10
289 **MISTRESS VIZ** (IRE) 10
562 **MISTRY** (GB) 13
28 **MISTY** (GB) 101
336 **MISTY BLOOM** (GB) 43
125 **MISTY BREESE** (GB) 16
424 **MISTY FOR ME** (IRE) F 148
466 **MISTY MAI** (IRE) 8
214 **MISTY WHISKY** (GB) 52
525 **MISU MAC** (GB) 3
562 **MISU PETE** (GB) 14
174 **MITCHOUKA** (FR) 118
2 **MITCHUM** (GB) 5
28 **MITCHUM SWAGGER** (GB) 11
318 **MITHMAAR** (IRE) 179
127 **MIXBOY** (FR) 45
612 **MIXCHIEVOUS** (GB) 51
258 **MIXED BLESSING** (GB) C 204
481 **MME DE MONTESPAN** (GB) 174
368 **MO CHAILIN** (IRE) 64
530 **MO ROUGE** (IRE) 8

174 **MORGAN** (IRE) 127
390 **MORGAN'S BAY** (GB) 11
535 **MORI** (GB) 10
606 **MORIANOUR** (FR) 37
481 **MORIENNE** (FR) 72
484 **MORITO DU BERLAIS** (FR) 57
6 **MORLOCK** (IRE) 93
358 **MORNEY WING** (IRE) 9
249 **MORNING AFTER** (GB) C 78
436 **MORNING BEAUTY** (GB) 74
49 **MORNING BELL** (GB) F 90
573 **MORNING FROST** (IRE) F 84
177 **MORNING HAS BROKEN** (IRE) 23
321 **MORNING HERALD** (GB) 18
504 **MORNING REGGIE** (GB) 28
388 **MORNING ROYALTY** (IRE) 15
401 **MORNING SEQUEL** (GB) 91
436 **MORNING SKYE** (IRE) 75
274 **MORNING VICAR** (IRE) 96
109 **MORNING WITH IVAN** (IRE) 15
486 **MORNING WONDER** (IRE) 68
401 **MORRIS THE MINER** (GB) 92
510 **MORTENS LEAM** (GB) 11
41 **MOSEEB** (IRE) 92
258 **MOSHARAKKA** (IRE) 208
481 **MOSKOVA** (FR) 73
37 **MOSS GILL** (IRE) 31
507 **MOSS LANDING** (JPN) 56
223 **MOSS ON THE MILL** (GB) 45
174 **MOSSBACK** (IRE) 128
247 **MOSSEYB** (IRE) 69
34 **MOSSGO** (IRE) 10
182 **MOSSING** 8
34 **MOSSKETEER** (GB) 21
336 **MOSSPARK** (IRE) 44
93 **MOSSY'S LODGE** (GB) 6
401 **MOST CELEBRATED** (IRE) 93
424 **MOST GIFTED** (USA) 81
57 **MOSTASHREQAH** (GB) 8
258 **MOSTAWAA** (GB) 209
339 **MOSTLY BOB** (IRE) 10
330 **MOSTLY GREEN** (IRE) 20
258 **MOTAFAAWIT** (IRE) 210
91 **MOTAHASSEN** (IRE) 7
79 **MOTAJAASID** (IRE) 44
79 **MOTARAABET** (GB) 45
563 **MOTAWAJ** (IRE) 170
79 **MOTFAEL** (IRE) 83
370 **MOTHER OF DRAGONS** (IRE) 14
49 **MOTHER VINCENT** (IRE) 91
131 **MOTION LASS** (GB) C 84
530 **MOTION TO STRIKE** (IRE) 9
258 **MOTOWN MICK** (IRE) 82
535 **MOTTAHAM** (FR) 62
149 **MOTTS CROSS** (IRE) 11
283 **MOTUEKA** (IRE) 65
181 **MOUCHEE** (IRE) 34
258 **MOUILLE POINT** (GB) 15
377 **MOULIN A VENT** (GB) 67
77 **MOUNT ARARAT** (GB) 60
426 **MOUNT BATUR** (IRE) 41
256 **MOUNT CHEIRON** (USA) 8
131 **MOUNT CRYSTAL** (IRE) C 85
450 **MOUNT HAVEN** (IRE) 50
383 **MOUNT HELLVELYN** (GB) 40
121 **MOUNT LAVINIA** (IRE) F 55
563 **MOUNT LOGAN** (IRE) 26
309 **MOUNT MEWS** (IRE) 21

28 **MOUNT MORIAH** (GB) 13
401 **MOUNT OLIVER** (IRE) 94
25 **MOUNT POPA** (IRE) 24
552 **MOUNT RUSHMOORE** (IRE) 51
486 **MOUNT TAHAN** (IRE) 28
275 **MOUNT VESUVIUS** (IRE) 14
226 **MOUNT VICTORIA** (IRE) 16
526 **MOUNT WELLINGTON** (IRE) 29
563 **MOUNTAIN ANGEL** (IRE) 27
28 **MOUNTAIN BELL** (GB) 14
188 **MOUNTAIN BREATH** (GB) 13
244 **MOUNTAIN DOG** (GB) 26
309 **MOUNTAIN HAWK** (IRE) 22
41 **MOUNTAIN HUNTER** (USA) 47
183 **MOUNTAIN OF ANGELS** (GB) 2
44 **MOUNTAIN OF MOURNE** (IRE) 6
209 **MOUNTAIN OF STARS** (GB) 7
431 **MOUNTAIN PATH** (GB) 56
573 **MOUNTAIN PEAK** (GB) 59
574 **MOUNTAIN RESCUE** (IRE) 9
318 **MOUNTAIN RULER** (GB) 184
155 **MOUNTMELLICK GIRL** (IRE) 6
587 **MOURANIYA** (IRE) C 105
380 **MOUSQUETAIRE** (FR) 26
17 **MOUSSE AU CHOCOLAT** (USA) C 150
383 **MOVE IN TIME** (GB) 18
127 **MOVE IT MOVE IT** (GB) 108
247 **MOVE SWIFTLY** (GB) 70
368 **MOVE TO THE GROOVE** (IRE) 65
41 **MOVE UP** (GB) 48
118 **MOVED** (IRE) 45
567 **MOVIE LEGEND** (GB) 18
282 **MOVIE MAGIC** (GB) 3
524 **MOVIE SET** (USA) 10
19 **MOVIE THEATRE** (GB) 17
41 **MOVIN' OUT** (AUS) F 163
401 **MOVING IN STYLE** (IRE) 95
194 **MOVING SEA** (IRE) C 37
22 **MOWHOOB** (GB) 15
349 **MOXY MARES** (GB) 36
258 **MOYASSAR** (IRE) 211
626 **MOYNIHANS GIRL** (IRE) 7
377 **MOYROSS** (GB) 68
65 **MOZAYADA** (USA) C 23
293 **MOZO** (GB) 23
405 **MR ADJUDICATOR** (GB) 114
455 **MR ANDROS** (GB) 48
560 **MR ANTOLINI** (IRE) 78
338 **MR BACHSTER** (IRE) 24
586 **MR BANKS** (IRE) 17
450 **MR BIG SHOT** (IRE) 51
444 **MR BOSSY BOOTS** (IRE) 10
392 **MR BOYCIE QUEST** (GB) 91
14 **MR BRINKLEY** (IRE) 48
455 **MR BROWNSTONE** (GB) 14
441 **MR C** (IRE) 7
328 **MR CARBONATOR** (GB) 56
131 **MR CHRISTOPHER** (IRE) 11
450 **MR CLARKSON** (IRE) 52
24 **MR COCO BEAN** (USA) 21
506 **MR CONUNDRUM** (GB) 12
245 **MR COOL CASH** (GB) 11
504 **MR DORRELL SAGE** (FR) 29
336 **MR FENTON** (GB) 45
392 **MR FICKLE** (IRE) 92
135 **MR FITZROY** (IRE) 10
621 **MR FRANKIE** (GB) 13

158 **MR GENT** (IRE) 54
167 **MR GREENLIGHT** (GB) 101
14 **MR GREY SKY** (IRE) 49
484 **MR GRUMPY** (GB) 58
313 **MR JACK** (IRE) 17
92 **MR JIM** (GB) 40
606 **MR KIT CAT** (GB) 38
109 **MR KITE** (GB) 16
190 **MR LANDO** (GB) 31
174 **MR LINGO** (IRE) 129
567 **MR LOVE** (IRE) 19
273 **MR MAC** (GB) 6
14 **MR MACHO** (IRE) 50
321 **MR MAFIA** (IRE) 19
385 **MR MAGILL** (FR) 7
232 **MR MARRAKECH** (GB) 81
368 **MR MCGO** (GB) 66
220 **MR MCGUINESS** (IRE) 8
572 **MR MEDIC** (GB) 12
295 **MR MINERALS** (GB) 11
419 **MR MIX** (FR) 90
309 **MR MONOCHROME** (GB) 23
392 **MR MUDDLE** (GB) 93
275 **MR MULLINER** (IRE) 15
329 **MR NICE GUY** (IRE) 46
214 **MR ONE MORE** (IRE) 53
383 **MR ORANGE** (IRE) 19
507 **MR OWEN** (USA) 20
106 **MR POCKET** (IRE) 7
245 **MR POTTER** (GB) 12
326 **MR PUMBLECHOOK** (GB) 75
434 **MR RECKLESS** (IRE) 49
545 **MR RED CLUBS** (IRE) 7
516 **MR SANDGATE** (IRE) 18
275 **MR SCAFF** (IRE) 16
148 **MR SCARAMANGA** (GB) 9
427 **MR SCRUMPY** (GB) 11
261 **MR SECRETARY** (IRE) 141
549 **MR SHAHADY** (IRE) 8
431 **MR SHANTU** (IRE) 57
150 **MR SNIPS** (GB) 3
446 **MR STANDFAST** (GB) 6
7 **MR STORYTELLER** (IRE) 41
548 **MR STRUTTER** (IRE) 6
534 **MR SUNDOWNER** (USA) 8
181 **MR TOP HAT** (GB) 35
258 **MR TYRRELL** (IRE) 16
461 **MR WAGYU** (IRE) 45
140 **MR WASHINGTON** (IRE) 19
214 **MR WEST COAST** (IRE) 54
274 **MR WHIPPED** (IRE) 97
569 **MR WING** (IRE) 16
316 **MR WITMORE** (IRE) 6
274 **MR WOODY** (IRE) 98
238 **MR YOUNG** (FR) 18
350 **MRS ANGEL** (IRE) 9
447 **MRS BARNES** (IRE) 15
47 **MRS BENSON** (IRE) 11
401 **MRS BURBIDGE** (GB) 96
582 **MRS CLAYPOOL** (IRE) 27
454 **MRS DANVERS** (GB) 10
462 **MRS DISCOMBE** (GB) 10
308 **MRS GALLAGHER** (GB) 16
28 **MRS IVY** (GB) 102
565 **MRS MASTERS** (IRE) G 53
450 **MRS MIGGINS** (IRE) 53
507 **MRS SIPPY** (USA) 57
582 **MRS TEASDALE** (GB) 28

41 PETRUSHKA (IRE) C 165
249 PETTICOAT (GB) 16
237 PETTICOAT TAILS (GB) 59
61 PETTOCHSIDE (GB) 15
504 PEUR DE RIEN (FR) 34
95 PEVERIL POINT (IRE) 11
503 PHANGIO (USA) 7
535 PHANTASMIC (GB) 66
234 PHANTOM ISLE (GB) 19
566 PHANTOM RIVER (GB) 55
278 PHANTOM WARRIOR (GB) 15
140 PHANTOM WATERS (GB) G 37
62 PHARAWAY VIEW (GB) 26
95 PHARE ISLE (GB) 23
61 PHAROH JAKE (GB) 16
481 PHARRELL (FR) 83
104 PHEIDIPPIDES (GB) 13
399 PHIJEE (GB) 13
249 PHILAE (USA) C 83
524 PHILAMUNDO (IRE) 23
436 PHILLIPINA (GB) F 135
97 PHILLIPPA (IRE) F 106
28 PHILONIKIA (GB) 108
361 PHOBIAPHILIAC (IRE) 12
167 PHOEBELLAS ANGEL (GB) 104
567 PHOENICIANA (GB) 23
389 PHOENIX CITY (USA) C 26
455 PHOENIX DAWN (GB) 16
267 PHOENIX FIREBIRD (GB) 30
381 PHOENIX LIGHTNING (IRE) 47
281 PHOENIX OF SPAIN (IRE) 137
140 PHOENIX PARK (GB) 24
431 PHOENIX ROCK (IRE) 62
430 PHOENIX SONG (GB) 4
496 PHOSPHORESCENCE (IRE) 5
28 PHOTO FLASH (IRE) F 109
232 PHOTOGRAPHER (GB) 92
436 PHOTONICS (IRE) 82
258 PHYSICAL POWER (IRE) 90
80 PIAZON (GB) 21
136 PIAZZA SAN PIETRO (GB) 9
488 PICC AND GO (GB) 13
6 PICK A LITTLE (GB) 10
358 PICKAMIX (GB) 13
139 PICKET LINE (GB) 8
176 PICKETT'S CHARGE (GB) 50
324 PICKNICK PARK (GB) 10
472 PICKS PINTA (GB) 2
318 PICTURE HAT (USA) C 193
167 PICTURE OF LILY (GB) C 144
127 PICTURE PAINTER (GB) 50
41 PIECE OF HISTORY (IRE) 95
166 PIECE OF MAGIC (GB) G 105
456 PIEDITA (IRE) 5
330 PIEL CASTLE (GB) 22
249 PIENTA (USA) 48
405 PIETRALUNGA (FR) 124
597 PIGEON PIE (GB) C 16
138 PIKE CORNER CROSS (IRE) 16
511 PIKES PEAK (FR) 45
234 PIKES PEAK (IRE) 20
419 PILANSBERG (GB) 101
563 PILASTER (GB) 96
17 PILGRIM SOUL (GB) 89
401 PILGRIMS BAY (IRE) 107
527 PILLARS OF SOCIETY (IRE) F 54
102 PILOT WINGS (IRE) 52
258 PIMLICO PLEASER (IRE) 220

368 PINCH OF GINGER (IRE) 74
261 PINCHECK (IRE) 55
346 PINDARIC (GB) 3
567 PINE MOSS (GB) 24
170 PINE WARBLER (GB) 17
328 PINEAPPLE CRUSH (IRE) 35
283 PINEAPPLE RUSH (GB) 74
428 PINEWOODS LILY (IRE) F 109
552 PINGSHOU (IRE) 61
17 PINK DAMSEL (IRE) C 161
56 PINK EYED PEDRO (GB) 18
17 PINK FLAMES (IRE) F 162
560 PINK GIN (GB) 84
612 PINK LEGEND (GB) 54
131 PINK MOON (IRE) C 87
106 PINK PHANTOM (GB) 21
329 PINK RIBBON (IRE) 8
323 PINK SUPREME (GB) C 36
456 PINK SYMPHONY (GB) F 56
612 PINK TARA (GB) 55
190 PINKIE BROWN (FR) 33
121 PINKSTER (GB) 22
611 PINNATA (IRE) 17
484 PINSPOT (GB) 65
428 PIONEERING (IRE) 47
434 PIOUS (GB) C 88
90 PIPERS NOTE (GB) 28
483 PIPERS PIPING (IRE) F 5
162 PIPES OF PEACE (IRE) 10
226 PIPOCA (IRE) 26
397 PIPPIN (GB) 55
159 PIRATE KING (GB) 22
409 PIRI MASSINI (IRE) 33
267 PIROLO (IRE) 31
142 PISTOL (IRE) 1
176 PISTOL PAIR (FR) 51
361 PISTOL SHOOT (IRE) 13
192 PITCH HIGH (IRE) 12
504 PITON PETE (IRE) 35
104 PIVELLO (GB) 14
17 PIVOINE (IRE) 32
406 PIVOTAL BRIDE (GB) F 28
619 PIVOTAL DREAM (IRE) 7
486 PIVOTAL ERA (GB) F 101
445 PIVOTAL FLAME (IRE) 11
563 PIVOTAL MAN (GB) 97
573 PIVOTAL'S PRINCESS (IRE) C 88
460 PIXEL (IRE) 6
420 PIXIEPOT (GB) 8
380 PLACE DES VOSGES (IRE) 7
114 PLACE IN MY HEART (GB) F 105
441 PLACEBO EFFECT (IRE) 13
21 PLACEDELA CONCORDE (GB) 18
612 PLAISIR D'AMOUR (FR) 56
519 PLAISTERER (GB) F 13
77 PLAN AHEAD (GB) 62
69 PLAN TO BE (GB) 6
145 PLANET NINE (GB) 20
261 PLANET VENUS (IRE) 148
83 PLANETARIA (IRE) 16
35 PLANETOID (IRE) 12
193 PLANSINA (IRE) 34
295 PLANT POT POWER (IRE) 13
34 PLANTADREAM (GB) 23
404 PLANTAGENET (GB) 40
31 PLASTIKI (GB) 9
334 PLATANE (GB) 46
249 PLATINUM WARRIOR (IRE) 49

444 PLATITUDE (GB) 13
535 PLATONIC (GB) F 146
307 PLAY IT BY EAR (IRE) 69
578 PLAY PRACTICE (GB) 6
53 PLAY THE ACE (IRE) 34
478 PLAY THE PART (IRE) 3
127 PLAY WITH ME (GB) 51
249 PLAYAMONGTHESTARS (AUS) C 84
563 PLAYER'S LUCK (IRE) 98
232 PLAYFULL SPIRIT (GB) 93
397 PLAYING GAMES (GB) 24
617 PLAYMAKER (IRE) 3
405 PLEASANT COMPANY (IRE) 125
121 PLEASANT SURPRISE (IRE) 10
49 PLEISIUR (IRE) 31
121 PLENTIFUL (GB) 33
138 PLENTY IN THE TANK (IRE) 34
499 PLENTY OF BUTTY (IRE) 30
4 PLOUGHLAND (IRE) 98
485 PLUCKY DIP (GB) 9
106 PLUNGER (GB) 22
307 PLUS JAMAIS (FR) 28
438 PLUS ONE (GB) 63
281 PLUTONIAN (IRE) 12
318 PLYING (USA) C 194
344 PLYMOUTH SOUND (GB) 16
606 POBBLES BAY (GB) 48
185 POCAHONTAS (GB) G 13
261 POCKET DIAL (IRE) 56
112 POCKET DYNAMO (USA) 56
261 POCOTALIGO (GB) 149
6 PODEMOS (GER) 53
606 PODILI ROAD (IRE) 49
280 POET'S CHARM (IRE) 5
423 POET'S CORNER (GB) 39
167 POET'S DAWN (GB) 105
24 POET'S PRIDE (GB) 42
318 POET'S PRINCE (GB) 88
397 POET'S PRINCESS (GB) 25
7 POET'S QUEST (GB) 50
24 POET'S REWARD (GB) 22
318 POET'S SOCIETY (GB) 18
17 POET'S VANITY (GB) 33
535 POET'S WORD (IRE) 12
318 POETIC AFFAIR (GB) 89
6 POETIC CHARM (GB) 103
114 POETIC DANCER (GB) C 106
92 POETIC FORCE (IRE) 45
401 POETIC LADY (GB) 108
108 POETIC PRESENCE (IRE) 11
393 POETIC PRINCIPLE (IRE) 2
426 POETIC RHYTHM (IRE) 51
318 POETIC STEPS (FR) 90
258 POINT HOPE (IRE) 91
562 POINT IN TIME (IRE) 22
267 POINT N SHOOT (IRE) 32
18 POINT NORTH (IRE) 6
257 POINT OF DEPARTURE (IRE) 10
118 POINT OF HONOUR (IRE) 53
565 POINT OF PRINCIPLE (IRE) 60
303 POINT OF WOODS (GB) 7
556 POINT PERFECT (GB) C 17
176 POINT THE WAY (IRE) 52
283 POINTED AND SHARP (IRE) 75
189 POINTEL (FR) 15
49 POISED FOR CHANGE (IRE) 99
361 POISON ARROW (IRE) 14

295 **PRETTY EYES** (IRE) 69
138 **PRETTY LETHAL** (GB) 35
553 **PRETTY MISS MAHLER** (IRE) 13
427 **PRETTY MOI** (IRE) 26
553 **PRETTY PASSE** (GB) 14
169 **PRETTY PEARL** (GB) 13
29 **PRETTY POLLYANNA** (GB) 78
508 **PRETTY RECKLESS** (IRE) 106
96 **PRETTY RISKY** (GB) 17
401 **PRETTYLITTLETHING** (IRE) 109
28 **PREVENT** (GB) 55
399 **PREZZIE** (GB) 32
25 **PRICE RANGE** (USA) 60
573 **PRICELESS JEWEL** (GB) C 89
392 **PRIDE OF ANGELS** (GB) 101
521 **PRIDE OF PEMBERLEY** (IRE) 38
489 **PRIDE OF THE OAKS** (GB) G 6
118 **PRIDE'S GOLD** (USA) 54
49 **PRIMA LUX** (IRE) 100
564 **PRIME MINISTER** (IRE) 13
118 **PRIME RUN** (GB) F 107
606 **PRIME VENTURE** (IRE) 52
428 **PRIMERO** (FR) 48
609 **PRIMO BLUE** (GB) 18
77 **PRIMO LADY** (GB) F 112
239 **PRIMO ROSSI** (GB) 12
227 **PRIMO'S COMET** (GB) 35
481 **PRIMULA** (FR) 85
511 **PRIMUS INCITATUS** (IRE) 13
114 **PRINCE AHWAHNEE** (GB) 64
201 **PRINCE CARN** (GB) 10
405 **PRINCE D'AUBRELLE** (FR) 130
484 **PRINCE DUNDEE** (IRE) 69
21 **PRINCE FLORBURY** (GB) 19
607 **PRINCE JAI** (GB) 61
50 **PRINCE KERALI** (FR) 24
368 **PRINCE KHURRAM** (GB) 75
299 **PRINCE KUP** (IRE) 3
14 **PRINCE LLYWELYN** (GB) 53
624 **PRINCE MAHLER** (IRE) 12
423 **PRINCE MAURICE** (USA) 20
194 **PRINCE OF ARRAN** (GB) 13
221 **PRINCE OF CARDAMOM** (IRE) 8
174 **PRINCE OF SCARS** (IRE) 148
182 **PRINCE OF STEAL** (IRE) 12
114 **PRINCE OF THE DARK** (GB) 65
256 **PRINCE OF TIME** (GB) 10
148 **PRINCE ROCK** (IRE) 23
582 **PRINCESS DE LUNE** (IRE) 11
462 **PRINCESS HARLEY** (IRE) 6
462 **PRINCESS KEIRA** (IRE) 7
356 **PRINCESS KODIA** (IRE) 13
541 **PRINCESS LUNA** (GER) C 81
313 **PRINCESS MATTHEWS** (GB) C 23
368 **PRINCESS MONONOKE** (IRE) 76
291 **PRINCESS NEARCO** (IRE) 17
235 **PRINCESS NICOLE** (GB) G 7
418 **PRINCESS NOORA** (GB) 5
53 **PRINCESS ROANIA** (IRE) 37
95 **PRINCESS ROXY** (GB) 24
28 **PRINCESS SALAMAH** (IRE) 110
261 **PRINCESS SUSAN** (IRE) G 60
309 **PRINCESS TARA** (IRE) 27
181 **PRINCESS WAY** (IRE) 13
16 **PRINCESSE BASSETT** (FR) 41
327 **PRINCETON ROYALE** (IRE) 21
511 **PRINCIPIA** (GB) 33
167 **PRINGLE** (GB) 149

367 **PRISCILLA'S DREAM** (GB) 10
318 **PRIVACY ORDER** (GB) C 197
17 **PRIVATE CASHIER** (GB) 90
23 **PRIVATE DANCER** (IRE) 3
17 **PRIVATE EQUITY** (IRE) C 164
391 **PRIVATE LEDGER** (IRE) 17
336 **PRIVATE MALONE** (IRE) 53
187 **PRIVATE MATTER** (GB) 36
511 **PRIVATE SCHOOL** (IRE) 14
535 **PRIVATE VIEW** (GB) 67
249 **PRIVET** (GB) C 85
79 **PRIZE CATCH** (USA) C 90
41 **PRIZE MONEY** (GB) 55
41 **PRIZERING** (IRE) 96
535 **PROCEDURE** (GB) 68
563 **PROCEED** (GB) 99
176 **PROCESSION** (GB) C 102
127 **PROCESSION** (GB) C 110
392 **PROCRASTINATING** (IRE) 102
444 **PROCURE** (GB) 34
535 **PRODIGIOUS** (GB) 147
331 **PROFESSOR** (GB) 10
10 **PROFESSOR** (GB) 13
145 **PROFESSOR PLUM** (IRE) 21
471 **PROGRESS DRIVE** (IRE) 38
331 **PROGRESSIVE DAWN** (GB) 24
77 **PROGRESSIVE JAZZ** (IRE) 63
461 **PROJECT BLUEBOOK** (FR) 23
224 **PROJECT MARS** (IRE) 21
102 **PROJECTION** (GB) 12
92 **PROMINNA** (GB) 49
258 **PROMISING** (IRE) 21
41 **PROMISING RUN** (USA) 56
167 **PRONTO TONTO** (IRE) 58
336 **PROPHETS PRAYER** (IRE) 54
131 **PROSCHEMA** (IRE) 43
536 **PROSECUTE** (FR) 14
535 **PROSERPINE** (USA) 69
119 **PROSPECTUS** (GB) 26
564 **PROST** (GER) 3
359 **PROTECTED GUEST** (GB) 13
427 **PROTECTRESS** (GB) F 38
274 **PROTEK DES FLOS** (FR) 111
146 **PROUD ARCHI** (IRE) 18
161 **PROUD KATE** (GB) 12
536 **PROUD TIMES** (USA) 15
224 **PROUTS PUB** (IRE) 22
183 **PRU** (GB) 3
41 **PRUSSIAN** (GB) C 168
606 **PRUSSIAN EAGLE** (IRE) 53
187 **PRYING PANDORA** (FR) 37
607 **PSYCHEDELIC ROCK** (GB) 62
607 **PSYCHOCANDY** (IRE) 63
316 **PSYCHOLOGY** (GB) 9
318 **PSYCHOMETRY** (FR) C 198
380 **PSYCHOTIC** (GB) 2
106 **PTARMIGAN** (GB) 41
189 **PTARMIGAN RIDGE** (IRE) 16
419 **PTIT ZIG** (FR) 106
65 **PUCHITA** (IRE) 17
187 **PUDDING CHARE** (IRE) 38
281 **PUDS** (GB) 67
504 **PUFFIN BILLY** (IRE) 37
481 **PUGGY** (IRE) C 189
436 **PULITZER** (GB) 85
170 **PULL TOGETHER** (IRE) 18
95 **PULP FICTION** (IRE) 25
582 **PULSATING** (IRE) 12

328 **PUMAFLOR** (IRE) 36
155 **PUNCH BAG** (IRE) 8
131 **PUNKAWALLAH** (GB) 12
224 **PUPPET WARRIOR** (GB) 23
294 **PURAMENTE** (GB) 22
145 **PURCELL'S BRIDGE** (FR) 22
607 **PURE AFFECTION** (IRE) 64
481 **PURE ELEGANCE** (IRE) 86
258 **PURE EXCELLENCE** (GB) C 221
607 **PURE SHORES** (GB) 65
293 **PURE VISION** (IRE) 29
361 **PURE VODKA** (GB) 15
331 **PUREST** (GB) F 41
574 **PURGATORY** (GB) 31
450 **PURPLE 'N GOLD** (IRE) 56
462 **PURPLE DRAGON** (GB) 8
303 **PURPLE HARRY** (GB) 8
16 **PURPLE JAZZ** (IRE) 30
166 **PURPLE ROCK** (GB) 41
167 **PURPLE SILK** (GB) C 150
310 **PURPLE SPECTRUM** (GB) 22
335 **PURPLEST** (GB) 17
232 **PURSER** (USA) 96
397 **PURSUING STEED** (GB) 26
261 **PURSUIT OF MAGIC** (IRE) 150
396 **PUSHKIN MUSEUM** (IRE) 18
99 **PUSHMI PULLYU** (IRE) 21
114 **PUTTO** (IRE) 17
295 **PUZZLE** (GB) 70
280 **PUZZLE CACHE** (GB) 6
405 **PYLONTHEPRESSURE** (IRE) 131
274 **PYM** (GB) 112
283 **PYRIOS** (FR) 77
121 **PYRMONT** (GB) 34
528 **Q CEE** (GB) 3
562 **Q TWENTY BOY** (IRE) 23
158 **QAARAAT** (GB) 57
166 **QAFFAAL** (USA) 42
281 **QAFILAH** (IRE) 68
466 **QALINAS** (FR) 10
563 **QALLAAB** (IRE) 100
442 **QANATEER** (IRE) C 31
824 **QAREENAH** (USA) C 148
535 **QAROUN** (GB) 70
127 **QASR** (GB) 12
158 **QASWARAH** (IRE) 58
52 **QATAR GLORY** (IRE) 13
508 **QAVIY CASH** (GB) 107
563 **QAWAAFY** (USA) F 183
158 **QAWAMEES** (IRE) 59
507 **QAYED** (CAN) 61
258 **QAYSAR** (FR) 93
563 **QAZYNA** (IRE) 101
234 **QUADRIGA** (IRE) 21
283 **QUADRILLER** (FR) 78
319 **QUALANDO** (FR) 9
573 **QUALITY SEEKER** (USA) 61
554 **QUANAH** (IRE) 30
131 **QUANTATMENTAL** (IRE) 44
138 **QUANTUM DOT** (IRE) 15
431 **QUARENTA** (FR) 64
423 **QUARGENT** (USA) 21
86 **QUARRY BEACH** (GB) 71
248 **QUARRY LEADER** (IRE) 19
569 **QUASHA** (GB) 8
565 **QUASI** (IRE) 62
397 **QUAY POINT** (IRE) 27
301 **QUEBEC** (GB) 7

295 **RATTLE ALONG** (IRE) 72
55 **RATTLE ON** (GB) 11
112 **RAUCOUS** (GB) 15
216 **RAVEN BANNER** (IRE) 17
354 **RAVEN'S GIRL** (GB) 11
52 **RAVEN'S LADY** (GB) 4
7 **RAVEN'S RAFT** (IRE) 88
159 **RAVEN'S SONG** (IRE) 23
438 **RAVEN'S TOWER** (USA) 65
174 **RAVENHILL** (IRE) 151
174 **RAVENHILL ROAD** (IRE) 54
318 **RAVENHOE** (IRE) 20
216 **RAVENOUS** (GB) 2
566 **RAVENS HILL** (IRE) 58
560 **RAVENSDALE** (IRE) 86
509 **RAVENSWOOD** (GB) 13
321 **RAVING BONKERS** (GB) 23
348 **RAVISHED** (GB) 55
249 **RAW SILK** (USA) F 86
232 **RAWAAF** (IRE) 97
587 **RAWAAQ** (GB) C 115
535 **RAWDAA** (GB) 74
158 **RAWOOF** (IRE) C 95
232 **RAY OF SUNSHINE** (GB) 98
127 **RAY PURCHASE** (GB) 111
358 **RAY'S THE MONEY** (IRE) 14
587 **RAYDA** (IRE) 12
358 **RAYDANIYA** (IRE) C 200
77 **RAYDIANCE** (GB) 65
376 **RAYITA** (IRE) 21
258 **RAYMOND TUSK** (IRE) 96
377 **RAYNA JAYMES** (IRE) 75
328 **RAYNA'S WORLD** (IRE) 57
587 **RAYNAMA** (IRE) 51
442 **RAYON ROUGE** (IRE) G 12
91 **RAYPETEAFTERME** (GB) 28
504 **RAYVIN BLACK** (GB) 39
119 **RAZ DE MAREE** (FR) 27
1 **RAZIN' HELL** (GB) 7
566 **RAZOR WIND** (IRE) 59
429 **RAZOUL** (IRE) 52
376 **RAZZMATAZZ** (GB) 5
41 **REACH HIGH** (GB) 59
226 **REACTIVE** (GB) 17
516 **READ'EM AND WEEP** (IRE) 22
437 **READY** (GB) 5
431 **READY AND ABLE** (IRE) 65
535 **READY TO ACT** (USA) C 150
318 **READY TO IMPRESS** (USA) 94
348 **READY TOKEN** (IRE) 56
384 **REAF** (GB) C 39
577 **REAL ARMANI** (GB) 2
541 **REAL ESTATE** (IRE) 32
452 **REAL KING** (GB) 7
405 **REAL STEEL** (FR) 135
452 **REAL WARRIOR** (IRE) 8
214 **REALITY BITES** (IRE) 60
264 **REALITY SHOW** (IRE) 11
406 **REALLY SUPER** (GB) 11
89 **REALM KEEPER** (USA) 23
326 **REALMS OF FIRE** (GB) 92
49 **REALT MOR** (IRE) 152
49 **REALTIN GEAL** (USA) 32
234 **REAPLEE** (GB) 22
166 **REAR ADMIRAL** (IRE) 46
224 **REAR GUARD** (IRE) 24
62 **REASON TO BELIEVE** (FR) 27
180 **REASONED** (IRE) 27

541 **REASSURANCE** (GB) 33
86 **REBECCA ROCKS** (GB) 13
318 **REBEL ASSAULT** (IRE) 95
607 **REBEL BEAT** (GB) 66
524 **REBEL CAUSE** (IRE) 11
401 **REBEL COLLINS** (IRE) 111
274 **REBEL COMMANDER** (IRE) 115
558 **REBEL HEART** (GB) 6
508 **REBEL ROYAL** (IRE) 108
310 **REBEL SKY** (GB) 23
427 **REBEL STATE** (IRE) 12
17 **REBEL STREAK** (GB) 91
524 **REBEL SURGE** (IRE) 12
557 **REBEL WOODS** (IRE) 10
261 **REBELION BOY** (IRE) 62
293 **REBOUND** (IRE) 30
13 **RECKLESS BEHAVIOR** (IRE) 18
114 **RECKLESS DREAM** (IRE) 66
434 **RECKLESS ENDEAVOUR** (IRE) 15
573 **RECKLESS WAVE** (IRE) 17
411 **RECOGNITION** (IRE) 7
334 **RECOLETOS** (FR) 7
121 **RECOLLECT** (GB) 35
118 **RECONCILE** (IRE) 56
41 **RECORDMAN** (GB) 98
17 **RECULVER** (IRE) 92
375 **RED ADMIRABLE** (IRE) 27
92 **RED ALERT** (GB) 50
403 **RED ALLURE** (GB) 25
507 **RED AVIS** (GB) F 102
555 **RED BLOSSOM** (GB) F 44
547 **RED CARAVEL** (IRE) 10
154 **RED CHARMER** (IRE) 8
160 **RED ON ONE** (IRE) 23
247 **RED CYMBAL** (GB) 78
518 **RED DANAHER** (IRE) 41
519 **RED DEVIL STAR** (IRE) 14
143 **RED DOUGLAS** (GB) 21
131 **RED DRAGONESS** (IRE) 88
134 **RED EMPEROR** (IRE) 18
118 **RED ENSIGN** (IRE) 11
424 **RED EVIE** (IRE) F 156
7 **RED FLUTE** (IRE) 53
131 **RED FORCE ONE** (GB) 45
124 **RED FOREVER** (GB) 1
134 **RED FOUR** (GB) 19
41 **RED GALILEO** (GB) 60
85 **RED GIANT** (IRE) 28
97 **RED HANDED** (IRE) 107
426 **RED HOT CHILLY** (IRE) 53
247 **RED HUT RED** (IRE) 172
102 **RED IMPRESSION** (GB) 92
438 **RED INDIAN** (GB) 66
607 **RED INFANTRY** (IRE) 67
80 **RED INVADER** (IRE) 22
377 **RED JACK** (IRE) 76
52 **RED LABEL** (IRE) 15
359 **RED LARKSPUR** (IRE) F 20
384 **RED MIRACLE** (GB) 25
118 **RED MIST** (GB) 57
370 **RED MOHICAN** (GB) 8
234 **RED OCHRE** (GB) 23
211 **RED PENNY** (IRE) 14
512 **RED PIKE** (IRE) 18
258 **RED PLANET** (GB) C 223
508 **RED RISING** (IRE) 109
12 **RED RIVAL** (FR) 13
14 **RED RIVER** (IRE) 54

560 **RED RIVERMAN** (GB) 87
281 **RED ROMAN** (GB) 69
120 **RED SEEKER** (GB) 24
513 **RED SHANGHAI** (IRE) 4
533 **RED SNAPPER** (GB) 9
64 **RED SNIPER** (IRE) 6
450 **RED SQUARE REVIVAL** (IRE) 60
258 **RED STARLIGHT** (GB) 97
535 **RED STRIKER** (IRE) 75
613 **RED STRIPES** (USA) 9
277 **RED TEA** (GB) 9
508 **RED TORNADO** (FR) 110
85 **RED TORTUE** (IRE) 29
7 **RED TOUCH** (USA) 9
122 **RED TYCOON** (IRE) 9
158 **RED VERDON** (USA) 13
538 **RED WHISPER** (GB) 1
493 **REDARNA** (GB) 15
565 **REDDINGTON** (IRE) 64
212 **REDEMPTION SONG** (IRE) 10
405 **REDHOTFILLYPEPPERS** (IRE) 136
326 **REDICEAN** (GB) 93
393 **REDINHA** (GB) F 27
19 **REDMOND** (IRE) 19
176 **REDONA** (IRE) F 104
114 **REDOUTABLE** (IRE) C 109
4 **REDROSEZORRO** (GB) 9
4 **REDTEDD** (GB) 12
361 **REDWOOD LADY** (IRE) F 16
323 **REEDANJAS** (IRE) 6
390 **REEDWAY** (IRE) 16
536 **REEM STAR** (GB) C 29
118 **REEM THREE** (GB) F 108
112 **REEVES** (GB) 58
436 **REFEREE** (GB) 89
291 **REFLATION** (GB) 18
131 **REFLEKTOR** (IRE) 13
535 **REFRAIN** (IRE) 76
436 **REFUSE TO GIVE UP** (IRE) C 90
43 **REFUSED A NAME** (GB) 7
258 **REFUSETOLISTEN** (IRE) C 224
114 **REGAL AMBITION** (IRE) 110
118 **REGAL DIRECTOR** (IRE) 58
293 **REGAL ENCORE** (IRE) 31
74 **REGAL FLOW** (GB) 6
148 **REGAL GAIT** (IRE) 11
541 **REGAL HAWK** (GB) C 82
167 **REGAL MIRAGE** (IRE) 61
96 **REGAL MISS** (GB) 10
535 **REGAL REALITY** (GB) 77
359 **REGAL SULTANA** (GB) C 21
21 **REGARDE MOI** (GB) 21
486 **REGATTA** (FR) F 102
258 **REGENT** (GB) 225
449 **REGGIE BLUE** (GB) 10
189 **REGICIDE** (IRE) 17
258 **REGIMENTED** (IRE) 98
247 **REGINA NOSTRA** (GB) 79
102 **REGINA PACIS** (IRE) 54
101 **REGISTAN** (IRE) 10
29 **REGULAR** (GB) 80
588 **REGULAR INCOME** (IRE) 15
327 **REGULATION** (IRE) 22
187 **REGULATOR** (IRE) 99
249 **REHANA** (IRE) 17
41 **REHN'S NEST** (IRE) C 171
247 **REIFFA** (IRE) 80
274 **REIGNING SUPREME** (IRE) 116

274 **RIVER WYLDE** (IRE) 117
256 **RIVERBANK RAINBOW** (GB) G 11
390 **RIVERMOUTH** (GB) 17
515 **RIVERS OF ASIA** (IRE) 9
176 **RIVERSIDE BRIDGE** (IRE) 55
431 **RIVERSIDE CITY** (IRE) 67
127 **RIVERSIDE WALK** (GB) 112
434 **RIVIERA CLAIRE** 89
77 **RIVIERE ARGENTEE** (FR) 20
566 **RIVO ALTO** (USA) 61
249 **RIYABA** (IRE) F 87
249 **RIYAZAN** (IRE) 53
97 **RIYMAISA** (IRE) F 109
560 **RIZZARDO** (GB) 88
77 **RIZZLE DIZZLE** (GB) 67
496 **ROAD TO DUBAI** (IRE) 6
1 **ROAD TO GOLD** (IRE) 34
456 **ROAD TO PARIS** (IRE) 58
377 **ROAD TO RESPECT** (IRE) 77
377 **ROAD TO RICHES** (IRE) 78
504 **ROAD TO ROME** (IRE) 40
102 **ROAR** (IRE) 13
174 **ROARING BULL** (IRE) 156
26 **ROARING FORTIES** (IRE) 19
232 **ROARING LION** (USA) 100
441 **ROARING RORY** (GB) 8
230 **ROB ROBIN** (IRE) 26
256 **ROB ROYAL** (IRE) 12
264 **ROB'S LEGACY** (GB) 12
24 **ROBBEN RAINBOW** (GB) 24
513 **ROBBIAN** (GB) 5
218 **ROBBIE ROO ROO** (GB) 2
283 **ROBBIN'HANNON** (IRE) 80
309 **ROBBING THE PREY** (IRE) 19
318 **ROBE CHINOISE** (GB) C 201
166 **ROBERO** (GB) 47
368 **ROBERT DE BRUCE** (IRE) 77
29 **ROBERT FITZROY** (IRE) 81
397 **ROBERT L'ECHELLE** (IRE) 77
58 **ROBERT'S STAR** (IRE) 14
120 **ROBERTTOWN ROSE** (IRE) 19
588 **ROBIN ALEXANDRA** (IRE) C 26
22 **ROBIN DE BROOME** (IRE) 17
411 **ROBIN DE PLAN** (IRE) 8
328 **ROBIN DES CHAPP** (GB) 58
405 **ROBIN DES FORET** (IRE) 143
174 **ROBIN DES MANA** (IRE) 157
56 **ROBIN DES PEOPLE** (IRE) 19
586 **ROBIN DEUZ POIS** (IRE) 20
13 **ROBIN OF LOCKSLEY** (IRE) 19
159 **ROBIN OF NAVAN** (FR) 7
14 **ROBIN THE RAVEN** (IRE) 56
508 **ROBIN WATERS** (IRE) 115
404 **ROBINDENEST** (IRE) 42
404 **ROBINROYALE** (IRE) 43
234 **ROBINS LEGEND** (IRE) 24
552 **ROBINSFIRTH** (IRE) 65
560 **ROBINSHILL** (IRE) 89
258 **ROBINSON CRUSOE** (IRE) 100
504 **ROBINSSON** (IRE) 41
550 **ROBINTHEAULAD** (IRE) 19
24 **ROBOT BOY** (IRE) 25
323 **ROBSDELIGHT** (IRE) 32
444 **ROC ASTRALE** (IRE) 14
612 **ROC MERLE** (IRE) 60
560 **ROCCO** (IRE) 90
328 **ROCCOCO** (FR) 59
318 **ROCHESTER HOUSE** (IRE) 202

468 **ROCK A DOODLE DOO** (IRE) 1
512 **ROCK ACE** (IRE) C 54
606 **ROCK AND ROLL KING** (IRE) 57
349 **ROCK BOY GREY** (IRE) 39
240 **ROCK CANDY** (IRE) F 25
566 **ROCK CHARM** (GB) 62
28 **ROCK EAGLE** (GB) 58
131 **ROCK FORCE** (IRE) 46
416 **ROCK GONE** (IRE) 21
383 **ROCK HILL** (IRE) 45
294 **ROCK ICON** (GB) 9
535 **ROCK KRISTAL** (IRE) C 151
237 **ROCK MY STYLE** (IRE) 63
547 **ROCK N RHYTHM** (IRE) 11
127 **ROCK N ROLLA** (IRE) 57
48 **ROCK N'STONES** (IRE) 12
281 **ROCK OF ESTONIA** (IRE) 74
328 **ROCK OF LEON** (GB) 38
163 **ROCK ON BAILEYS** (GB) 15
419 **ROCK ON OSCAR** (IRE) 111
503 **ROCK ON ROCKY** (GB) 8
41 **ROCK OPERA** (SAF) C 173
486 **ROCK PARTY** (IRE) 103
352 **ROCK SONG** (GB) 22
587 **ROCK SOUND** (IRE) 57
283 **ROCK THE KASBAH** (IRE) 81
261 **ROCK THE WORLD** (IRE) 64
238 **ROCK WARBLER** (IRE) 22
621 **ROCK'N GOLD** (GB) 15
523 **ROCKALATER** (GB) 12
368 **ROCKALZARO** (FR) 78
426 **ROCKERY GARDEN** (IRE) 55
177 **ROCKET ACTION** (IRE) 37
233 **ROCKET MAN RODNEY** (IRE) 7
22 **ROCKET RONNIE** (IRE) 18
460 **ROCKIES SPIRIT** (GB) 16
361 **ROCKIN ON THE MOOR** (IRE) 17
145 **ROCKING BLUES** (IRE) 23
112 **ROCKING RUDOLPH** (USA) 16
223 **ROCKLANDER** (IRE) 57
254 **ROCKLIFFE** (GB) 40
607 **ROCKNROLLRAMBO** (IRE) 70
552 **ROCKPOINT** (GB) 66
237 **ROCKPORTIAN** (IRE) 64
278 **ROCKSETTE** (GB) 11
105 **ROCKSTAR MAX** (GER) 23
508 **ROCKU** (GB) 116
374 **ROCKWOOD** (GB) 10
621 **ROCKY ELSOM** (USA) 16
101 **ROCKY ONE** (GB) 11
97 **ROCKY SHORES** (GB) 58
14 **ROCKY'S TREASURE** (IRE) 57
232 **ROCOCO** (GB) 101
608 **ROCOCO RIVER** (GB) 27
229 **ROCOCO STYLE** (GB) 8
562 **ROCUS** (IRE) 25
354 **ROD OF IRON** (GB) 7
118 **RODAINI** (USA) 12
542 **RODDY** (IRE) 8
508 **RODEO DODO** (IRE) 117
258 **ROGUE** (GB) 101
395 **ROGUE ANGEL** (IRE) 23
106 **ROGUE HERO** (IRE) 23
174 **ROI DES FRANCS** (FR) 158
329 **ROKA** (GB) 48
508 **ROKSANA** (IRE) 118
485 **ROLAND ROCKS** (IRE) 16
392 **ROLL OF THE DICE** (IRE) 108

578 **ROLL OF THUNDER** (GB) 9
580 **ROLL ON RORY** (GB) 5
283 **ROLL THE DOUGH** (IRE) 82
166 **ROLLADICE** (GB) 79
166 **ROLLER** (GB) 48
452 **ROLLERBALL ROCCO** (IRE) 9
195 **ROLLING DICE** (GB) 10
283 **ROLLING DYLAN** (IRE) 83
53 **ROLLING MAUL** (GB) 38
118 **ROMAANA** (GB) 60
419 **ROMAIN DE SENAM** (FR) 112
547 **ROMAN COIN** (GB) 12
216 **ROMAN DE BRUT** (IRE) 18
140 **ROMAN FLIGHT** (IRE) 25
547 **ROMAN NUMERAL** (IRE) 13
515 **ROMAN RIVER** (GB) 11
244 **ROMAN SPINNER** (GB) 17
31 **ROMAN TIMES** (IRE) 10
159 **ROMAN WARRIOR** (IRE) 24
403 **ROMANN ANGEL** (GB) 18
404 **ROMANOR** (GB) 44
112 **ROMANTIC STORY** (GB) 17
6 **ROMANTIC TALK** (IRE) 105
608 **ROMEO BROWN** (GB) 28
41 **ROMIE'S KASTETT** (GER) C 174
535 **ROMOLA** (GB) 152
145 **ROMULUS DU DONJON** (IRE) 24
72 **RON WAVERLY** (IRE) 1
481 **RONCEY** (FR) 9
381 **RONN THE CONN** (IRE) 30
565 **RONNIE LAWSON** (IRE) 65
186 **RONNIE THE ROOSTER** (IRE) 13
53 **RONS DREAM** (GB) 39
307 **ROO ROO** (IRE) 32
562 **ROODEPARIS** (GB) 26
555 **ROODEYE** (GB) C 45
315 **ROODLE** (GB) F 73
554 **ROOF GARDEN** (GB) 15
478 **ROONEY O'MARA** (GB) 4
258 **ROONG ROONG** (IRE) 229
336 **ROOSTER COGBURN** (IRE) 55
516 **ROOSTER SPIRIT** (IRE) 23
230 **ROPARTA AVENUE** (GB) 27
498 **RORY'S VALENTINE** (IRE) 9
326 **ROSA DAMASCENA** (IRE) 95
102 **ROSA MUSCOSA** (USA) C 93
167 **ROSABEE** (GB) C 153
281 **ROSARNO** (IRE) 13
6 **ROSBY WAVES** (USA) F 154
163 **ROSE BERRY** (GB) 11
256 **ROSE BOUNTY** (GB) F 13
97 **ROSE CHEVAL** (USA) F 110
97 **ROSE CROWN** (GB) 22
261 **ROSE DE FRANCE** (IRE) C 153
563 **ROSE DIAMOND** (IRE) F 185
86 **ROSE HIP** (GB) 46
204 **ROSE ISLAND** (GB) C 7
480 **ROSE MARMARA** (GB) 1
237 **ROSE OF CIMARRON** (IRE) 65
59 **ROSE OF DUBAI** (GB) 6
318 **ROSE OF MOONCOIN** (IRE) F 203
393 **ROSE OF SHIRAZ** (GB) 13
162 **ROSE RANSOM** (IRE) F 19
118 **ROSE SAPPHIRE** (USA) 61
28 **ROSE TINTED SPIRIT** (GB) 59
14 **ROSE TO FAME** (GB) 58
109 **ROSE TREE** (IRE) 20
601 **ROSEALAINN** (IRE) G 26

86 **SEASCAPE** (IRE) 73
17 **SEASEARCH** (GB) 94
159 **SEASONAL CROSS** (GB) F 44
504 **SEASTON SPIRIT** (GB) 46
507 **SEAT OF POWER** (IRE) 64
71 **SEAVIEW** (GB) 4
127 **SEBASTIAN'S WISH** (IRE) 60
282 **SEBS SENSEI** (IRE) 6
541 **SECOND GENERATION** (GB) 84
25 **SECOND HAPPINESS** (USA) C 63
258 **SECOND PAGE** (GB) 23
102 **SECOND STEP** (IRE) 14
247 **SECOND THOUGHT** (IRE) 19
326 **SECOND TIME AROUND** (GB) 101
532 **SECONDO** (FR) 15
295 **SECRATARIO** (FR) 41
582 **SECRET ACE** (GB) 48
399 **SECRET AGENT** (GB) 14
331 **SECRET ART** (IRE) 12
613 **SECRET ASSET** (IRE) 11
214 **SECRET DOOR** (IRE) 68
507 **SECRET ERA** (GB) F 105
368 **SECRET ESCAPE** (IRE) 83
106 **SECRET EYE** (IRE) 24
77 **SECRET FRIEND** (IRE) C 113
28 **SECRET GAZE** (GB) 60
621 **SECRET GLANCE** (GB) 18
332 **SECRET HAPPINESS** (GB) F 25
419 **SECRET INVESTOR** (GB) 120
41 **SECRET KEEPER** (GB) C 179
507 **SECRET KEY** (IRE) C 106
50 **SECRET LADY** (GB) 9
607 **SECRET LEGACY** (IRE) 73
7 **SECRET LIGHTNING** (FR) 57
447 **SECRET LOOK** (GB) 21
167 **SECRET MELODY** (GB) 63
41 **SECRET NUMBER** (GB) 62
272 **SECRET PALACE** (GB) 9
176 **SECRET PASSENGER** (IRE) 59
263 **SECRET POTION** (GB) 19
222 **SECRET RETURN** (IRE) 6
434 **SECRET SALVAGE** (IRE) 17
192 **SECRET STRATEGY** (IRE) 13
122 **SECRET STRIKER** (GB) 10
538 **SECRET WHISPER** (GB) F 2
309 **SECRETE STREAM** (IRE) 34
492 **SECRETFACT** (GB) 9
403 **SECRETINTHEPARK** (GB) 18
114 **SECRETS AWAY** (IRE) C 113
85 **SECRETSISTA** (GB) 30
97 **SECTION ONESIXSIX** (IRE) 59
223 **SEDDON** (IRE) 59
77 **SEDUCE ME** (GB) 21
526 **SEDUCT** (IRE) F 37
52 **SEE EMILY PLAY** (IRE) F 89
295 **SEE OF ROME** (GB) 14
180 **SEE THE CITY** (IRE) 17
431 **SEE THE ROCK** (IRE) 69
258 **SEE THE SEA** (IRE) 24
26 **SEE VERMONT** (GB) 21
176 **SEEBRING** (IRE) 60
368 **SEEDLESS** (GB) F 84
52 **SEEFAAT** (GB) 57
444 **SEEING RED** (IRE) 44
232 **SEEING STARS** (USA) 105
529 **SEEK THE FAIR LAND** (GB) 9
428 **SEEK THE MOON** (USA) 90
114 **SEEKING MAGIC** (GB) 18

424 **SEEKING SOLACE** (GB) C 159
550 **SEEMORELIGHTS** (IRE) 21
17 **SEEUSOON** (IRE) 170
550 **SEEYOUATMIDNIGHT** (GB) 22
377 **SEEYOUINVINNYS** (IRE) 83
326 **SEGO SUCCESS** (IRE) 102
25 **SEGRA** (USA) 4
331 **SEINESIALAND** (GB) 28
25 **SEIZIEME** (GB) 29
334 **SEJO** (IRE) 28
550 **SELDOM INN** (GB) 23
166 **SELECTION** (FR) 52
263 **SELENA ROSE** (GB) 20
77 **SELF ASSESSMENT** (IRE) 114
16 **SELF CENTRED** (GB) F 44
419 **SELFCONTROL** (FR) 121
106 **SELOUS** (IRE) 43
24 **SEMANA SANTA** (GB) 27
187 **SEMPRE PRESTO** (IRE) 102
374 **SENATUS** (FR) 11
614 **SENDIYM** (FR) 4
332 **SENECA CHIEF** (GB) 10
532 **SENIERGUES** (GB) 16
326 **SENIOR CITIZEN** (GB) 103
247 **SENIORITY** (GB) 20
127 **SENOR LOMBARDY** (IRE) 61
601 **SENORA SNOOPY** (IRE) G 31
526 **SENSATIONAL SAMBA** (IRE) F 38
52 **SENSAZIONE BOY** (GB) 90
121 **SENSE OF STYLE** (USA) F 59
421 **SENSE OF URGENCY** (IRE) 11
444 **SENSIBLE FRIEND** (GR) 16
112 **SENSORY** (IRE) 41
609 **SENSULANO** (IRE) 20
535 **SENT FROM HEAVEN** (IRE) C 154
247 **SENTARIL** (GB) F 175
486 **SENTIMENTAL GENT** (FR) 78
247 **SENZA LIMITI** (IRE) 176
52 **SEPRANI** (GB) 16
424 **SEPTEMBER** (GB) 93
323 **SEPTEMBER ISSUE** (GB) 8
535 **SEPTIMER** (IRE) 81
134 **SEQUINSATDAWN** (GB) 22
481 **SERAKALA** (FR) 90
613 **SERAPHIMA** (GB) 12
481 **SERASANA** (GB) F 197
158 **SERENGETI DAY** (USA) F 98
176 **SERENITY NOW** (IRE) 61
92 **SERENITY SPA** (GB) C 67
152 **SERGEANT BRODY** (IRE) 17
565 **SERGIO** (IRE) 73
258 **SERGIO LEONE** (GB) 106
555 **SERJEANT PAINTER** (GB) 34
431 **SERMANDO** (GB) 70
214 **SEROSEVSKY** (IRE) 69
375 **SERPICO** (IRE) 32
414 **SERVEONTIME** (IRE) 8
281 **SERVILIA** (GB) 77
506 **SERVO** (IRE) 15
131 **SESAME** (IRE) 89
28 **SET DREAMS** (FR) C 116
508 **SET LIST** (IRE) 123
423 **SETENTA** (IRE) 41
274 **SETTIE HILL** (IRE) 121
395 **SETTIMO MILANESE** (IRE) 24
6 **SETTING SAIL** (GB) 108
258 **SETTING SUN** (IRE) 107
445 **SETTLE PETAL** (GB) 13

504 **SEVARANO** (IRE) 47
401 **SEVEN CLANS** (IRE) 116
140 **SEVEN KINGDOMS** (IRE) 28
160 **SEVEN NATION ARMY** (IRE) 26
38 **SEVENBALLS OF FIRE** (IRE) 19
232 **SEVENNA STAR** (IRE) 106
169 **SEVENTII** (GB) 7
409 **SEVILLA** (GB) 38
535 **SEXTANT** (GB) 82
138 **SEXY BEAST** (GB) 37
318 **SEXY LADY** (GER) C 207
440 **SEXY SECRET** (GB) 8
133 **SEXYFISH** (FR) 13
574 **SEYASAH** (IRE) 12
616 **SEYMOUR LEGEND** (GB) 2
463 **SEYMOUR STAR** (GB) 10
563 **SEZIM** (GB) 186
307 **SFUMATO** (GB) 34
283 **SGROPPINO** (IRE) 86
353 **SGT BULL BERRY** (GB) 2
131 **SHA LA LA LA LEE** (GB) 47
450 **SHAAMA GRISE** (FR) 64
79 **SHABAABY** (GB) 55
557 **SHABBAH** (IRE) 11
563 **SHABEEB** (USA) 29
273 **SHACKLED N DRAWN** (USA) 8
249 **SHADAGANN** (IRE) 21
115 **SHADES OF MIST** (GB) 21
138 **SHADES OF SILVER** (IRE) 19
144 **SHADOW BLUE** (IRE) 2
174 **SHADOW CATCHER** (GB) 165
79 **SHADOW DANCING** (GB) F 97
61 **SHADOW FORCE** (GB) 28
566 **SHADOW SADNESS** (GER) 68
125 **SHADOW WARRIOR** (GB) 3
375 **SHADY GLEN** (IRE) 33
607 **SHADY MCCOY** (USA) 74
389 **SHAFAANI** (GB) F 29
461 **SHAHEEN** (IRE) 48
114 **SHAHEREZADA** (IRE) 68
17 **SHAILENE** (IRE) 95
547 **SHAIYZAR** (IRE) 14
254 **SHAKE IT UP** (IRE) 44
106 **SHAKERATTLENROLL** (IRE) 10
584 **SHAKIAH** (IRE) 7
481 **SHALAIYMA** (FR) F 198
612 **SHALAKAR** (FR) 66
254 **SHALAMZAR** (FR) 45
214 **SHALL WE GO NOW** (GB) 70
41 **SHALLOW LAKE** (USA) F 180
52 **SHALWA** (GB) F 91
118 **SHAMA'S CROWN** (IRE) F 111
535 **SHAMA'S SONG** (IRE) C 155
259 **SHAMAHEART** (IRE) 10
334 **SHAMAN** (IRE) 47
444 **SHAMANDAR** (FR) C 45
541 **SHAMARDAL PHANTOM** (IRE) F 85
258 **SHAMARDYH** (IRE) F 234
567 **SHAMBRA** (IRE) 32
118 **SHAMLAHAR** (GB) 63
212 **SHAMLAN** (IRE) 11
562 **SHAMONIX** (IRE) 15
249 **SHAMOODA** (GB) C 89
155 **SHAMORA** (FR) F 21
34 **SHAMROCK EMMA** (IRE) 26
24 **SHAMROCK LADY** (IRE) F 55
7 **SHAMROKH** (IRE) 58
511 **SHAMS BRAZILERO** (IRE) 17

562 **SHUFOOG** (GB) 16
607 **SHUHOOD** (IRE) 104
214 **SHUIL ROYALE** (IRE) 71
271 **SHULAMMITE MAN** (IRE) 24
318 **SHUMOOS** (USA) C 208
79 **SHUROOQ** (GB) 56
230 **SHUT THE BOX** (IRE) 30
130 **SHUTSCOMBE HILL** (GB) 16
161 **SHYARCH** (GB) 5
359 **SHYJACK** (GB) 14
428 **SHYMKENT** (GB) 54
359 **SHYRON** (GB) 5
611 **SI BELLE** (FR) C 56
176 **SIANNES STAR** (IRE) 63
507 **SIBYLLINE** (GB) 107
434 **SICARIO** (GB) 55
358 **SID HOODIE** (IRE) 16
596 **SIDE OF THE ROAD** (IRE) 15
243 **SIDSTEEL** (IRE) 10
240 **SIEGE OF BOSTON** (IRE) 13
296 **SIEGE OF CORINTH** (FR) 4
119 **SIEMPRE AMIGOS** (IRE) 28
52 **SIENNA** (GB) 93
77 **SIENNA BELLA** (GB) F 116
595 **SIENNA DREAM** (GB) 33
258 **SIENNA MAY** (USA) F 236
267 **SIENNA ROYALE** (IRE) 36
193 **SIENNA SAYS** (GB) 36
372 **SIERRA OSCAR** (IRE) 3
274 **SIGN OF A VICTORY** (IRE) 123
415 **SIGN OF THE KODIAC** (IRE) 10
511 **SIGNATURE PIECE** (USA) 34
401 **SIGNED AND SEALED** (GB) 119
508 **SIGNSEALEDELIVERED** (GB) 2
120 **SIGNIFY** (FR) 20
258 **SIGNORA LINA** (IRE) C 237
350 **SIGNORE PICCOLO** (GB) 13
342 **SIGRID NANSEN** (GB) 25
496 **SIGRID NANSEN** (GB) 25
207 **SIGURD** (GER) 10
323 **SILCA BOO** (GB) C 37
114 **SILCA MISTRESS** (GB) 69
507 **SILCHESTER** (USA) 65
41 **SILENT ATTACK** (GB) 63
446 **SILENT DOCTOR** (IRE) 7
273 **SILENT ECHO** (GB) 9
95 **SILENT ENCORE** (IRE) 29
592 **SILENT MAN** (IRE) 7
419 **SILENT STEPS** (IRE) 122
332 **SILENTLY** (GB) 11
543 **SILHUETTE** (GB) 9
114 **SILK FAN** (IRE) C 114
597 **SILK MILL BLUE** (GB) 6
597 **SILK MILL TWO** (GB) 11
1 **SILK OR SCARLET** (IRE) 36
603 **SILK PATH** (GB) 5
333 **SILK RUN** (IRE) 15
143 **SILKEN MOONLIGHT** (GB) 24
318 **SILKWOOD** (GB) C 209
154 **SILS MARIA** (GB) 31
419 **SILSOL** (GER) 123
518 **SILVA ECLIPSE** (GB) 44
199 **SILVA FLINT** (GB) F 25
375 **SILVA SAMOURAI** (GB) 34
383 **SILVANUS** (IRE) 30
428 **SILVER ACT** (IRE) C 113
477 **SILVER BULLION** (GB) 7
127 **SILVER CACHE** (USA) F 141

131 **SILVER CHARACTER** (IRE) 48
127 **SILVER CONCORDE** (GB) 62
28 **SILVER CRESCENT** (GB) 61
522 **SILVER DRAGON** (GB) 19
188 **SILVER GLEAM** (IRE) 6
449 **SILVER GYRE** (IRE) F 12
438 **SILVER HOLLOW** (GB) 72
14 **SILVER KAYF** (GB) 15
297 **SILVER LILY** (IRE) G 14
41 **SILVER LINE** (GB) 64
294 **SILVER MAN** (GB) 3
301 **SILVER MARIZAH** (IRE) F 14
310 **SILVER MOUNTAIN** (GB) 26
55 **SILVER PENNY** (GB) 13
436 **SILVER QUARTZ** (GB) 92
211 **SILVER QUAY** (IRE) 16
527 **SILVER RAIN** (FR) F 57
41 **SILVER RIVER** (GB) 65
611 **SILVER SAMBA** (GB) C 57
481 **SILVER SEAM** (FR) 202
573 **SILVER SHOON** (IRE) C 91
301 **SILVER SPRINGS** (IRE) 8
424 **SILVER STAR** (GB) C 163
167 **SILVER STARLIGHT** (GB) 112
606 **SILVER STREAK** (IRE) 59
17 **SILVER SWIFT** (GB) 96
254 **SILVER TASSIE** (IRE) 46
390 **SILVER TICKET** (IRE) 21
56 **SILVER TOKEN** (GB) 20
6 **SILVERBOOK** (GB) 109
552 **SILVERHOW** (IRE) 74
509 **SILVERLIGHT** (IRE) 18
492 **SILVERRICA** (IRE) 11
555 **SILVERTINE** (IRE) F 49
421 **SILVERTON** (GB) 12
401 **SILVERTURNSTOGOLD** (GB) 145
167 **SILVERY MOON** (IRE) 65
25 **SILVERY PRINCE** (FR) 64
349 **SILVINGTON** (IRE) 41
235 **SILVRETTA SCHWARZ** (IRE) 8
409 **SIMAFAR** (IRE) 39
102 **SIMBIRSK** (GB) 59
603 **SIMILU** (GB) C 108
259 **SIMMO'S PARTYTRICK** (IRE) 11
484 **SIMONE** (IRE) 81
274 **SIMONIA** (IRE) 124
118 **SIMPLE THOUGHT** (IRE) 68
114 **SIMPLY BREATHLESS** (GB) 70
179 **SIMPLY BUSINESS** (IRE) 14
71 **SIMPLY CLEVER** (GB) 5
532 **SIMPLY LOVELEH** (GB) 17
508 **SIMPLY LUCKY** (IRE) 129
420 **SIMPLY MANI** (GB) 9
131 **SIMPLY ME** (GB) 14
471 **SIMPLY NED** (IRE) 41
601 **SIMPLY THE BETTS** (IRE) 32
348 **SIMPLY THE WEST** (IRE) 60
573 **SIMPSON** (IRE) 62
493 **SIMSALA AMICIS** (GB) 18
267 **SIN SIN** (IRE) 37
292 **SINA** (GER) F 11
338 **SINAKAR** (IRE) 30
249 **SINANIYA** (USA) F 91
328 **SINCERELY RESDEV** (GB) 60
189 **SINCERITY** (GB) 79
541 **SINDUDA** (GB) F 86
380 **SINFONIETTA** (FR) 4
444 **SING A RAINBOW** (IRE) 35

392 **SING OUT LOUD** (IRE) 138
26 **SINGEUR** (IRE) 22
28 **SINGING BIRD** (IRE) C 62
573 **SINGING SHERIFF** (GB) 63
585 **SINGLE ESTATE** (GB) 14
223 **SINGLEFARMPAYMENT** (GB) 60
26 **SINGMAN** (IRE) 29
50 **SINGSTREET** (FR) 26
507 **SINGYOURSONG** (IRE) 26
158 **SINJAARI** (IRE) 101
181 **SIONA'S BOY** (IRE) 51
187 **SIOUX FRONTIER** (IRE) 104
424 **SIOUX NATION** (USA) 94
573 **SIPHON MELODY** (USA) F 92
326 **SIR ANTONY BROWNE** (GB) 104
174 **SIR CARNO** (FR) 168
227 **SIR CHAUVELIN** (GB) 20
177 **SIR DANCEALOT** (IRE) 12
167 **SIR DERRICK** (GB) 113
291 **SIR DOMINO** (IRE) 19
246 **SIR DYLAN** (GB) 7
333 **SIR EGBERT** (GB) 16
424 **SIR EREC** (GB) 95
192 **SIR FRED** (IRE) 21
143 **SIR GEOFFREY** (IRE) 25
560 **SIR GEORGE SOMERS** (USA) 94
158 **SIR GNET** (IRE) 15
460 **SIR HAMILTON** (IRE) 17
7 **SIR HARRY COLLINS** (IRE) 59
576 **SIR HECTOR** (IRE) 14
482 **SIR HUBERT** (GB) 11
214 **SIR IVAN** (GB) 72
524 **SIR JACK YEATS** (IRE) 14
92 **SIR JAMIE** (GB) 54
418 **SIR LANCELOTT** (GB) 4
322 **SIR LUKE ARNO** (GB) 7
508 **SIR MANGAN** (IRE) 130
607 **SIR MAXIMILIAN** (IRE) 75
267 **SIR MIX** (GB) 38
216 **SIR OTTOMAN** (FR) 22
17 **SIR PASS I AM** (GB) 35
384 **SIR PLATO** (IRE) 12
302 **SIR PRIZE** (GB) 40
187 **SIR REGINALD BROWN** (GB) 49
112 **SIR ROBERT CHEVAL** (GB) 18
384 **SIR RODERIC** (IRE) 13
318 **SIR RON PRIESTLEY** (GB) 210
555 **SIR TITAN** (GB) 13
21 **SIR TOMMY** (GB) 23
4 **SIR WALTER** (IRE) 13
338 **SIR WILL** (GB) 31
174 **SIRE DU BERLAIS** (FR) 169
91 **SIRENUSE** (IRE) C 29
258 **SIRINAPHA** (IRE) 238
226 **SIRIUS SLEW** (GB) 29
480 **SIRIUS STAR** (GB) 2
546 **SIROBBIE** (IRE) 17
608 **SIRUH DU LAC** (FR) 29
550 **SIRWILLIAMWALLACE** (IRE) 24
392 **SISANIA** (IRE) 115
426 **SISSINGHURST** (IRE) 58
102 **SISTER CELINE** (IRE) 60
226 **SISTER OF THE SIGN** (IRE) 30
397 **SISTER SIBYL** (IRE) 28
273 **SISTER'S ACT** (GB) 12
189 **SITAR** (GB) 19
424 **SITARA** (GB) C 164
512 **SITSI** (GB) 37

563 **SOLAR EVENT** (GB) F 187
331 **SOLAR FLAIR** (GB) 13
224 **SOLAR GLORY** (IRE) 26
322 **SOLAR IMPULSE** (FR) 8
541 **SOLAR MOON** (GB) F 87
283 **SOLAR QUEST** (IRE) G 89
49 **SOLAR WAVE** (GB) 37
49 **SOLAR WIND** (GB) 105
552 **SOLATENTIF** (FR) 83
176 **SOLDIER BLUE** (FR) 66
318 **SOLDIER IN ACTION** (FR) 22
426 **SOLDIER OF LOVE** (GB) 61
17 **SOLDIER TO FOLLOW** (GB) 87
197 **SOLDIER'S FORTUNE** (IRE) 17
127 **SOLDIER'S MINUTE** (GB) 114
86 **SOLDIER'S SON** (GB) 74
334 **SOLESILI** (GB) 29
507 **SOLID MAN** (JPN) 66
107 **SOLID STRIKE** (GB) 4
401 **SOLIGHOSTER** (FR) 121
6 **SOLILOQUY** (GB) 110
33 **SOLITARY SISTER** (IRE) 11
376 **SOLO HUNTER** (GB) 6
508 **SOLO SAXOPHONE** (IRE) 132
401 **SOLOMN GRUNDY** (GB) 122
508 **SOLOMON GREY** (FR) 133
591 **SOLSTALLA** (GB) 5
620 **SOLSTICE DAWN** (GB) 8
293 **SOLSTICE SON** (GB) 36
321 **SOLSTICE STAR** (GB) 24
293 **SOLSTICE TWILIGHT** (GB) 37
623 **SOLVEIG'S SONG** (GB) 4
265 **SOLWAY BERRY** (GB) 8
265 **SOLWAY DANDY** (GB) 9
265 **SOLWAY LARK** (GB) 10
265 **SOLWAY LIZZIE** (GB) 11
265 **SOLWAY PALM** (GB) 12
265 **SOLWAY STORM** (IRE) 13
265 **SOLWAY SUNNY** (GB) 14
265 **SOLWAY TRIGGER** (GB) 15
404 **SOMCHINE** (GB) 46
348 **SOME AMBITION** (IRE) 61
223 **SOME ARE LUCKY** (IRE) 62
521 **SOME DAY SOON** (IRE) 42
141 **SOME FINISH** (IRE) 19
358 **SOME KINDA LAMA** (IRE) 17
419 **SOME MAN** (IRE) 124
405 **SOME NECK** (FR) 155
145 **SOME REIGN** (GB) 27
593 **SOME SECRET** (GB) F 2
261 **SOMEDAY** (GB) 70
567 **SOMEKINDOFSTAR** (IRE) 36
547 **SOMEONE EXCITING** (GB) 15
381 **SOMEONE NEW** (IRE) 37
588 **SOMEONE'S ANGEL** (USA) F 27
349 **SOMEPINK** (IRE) 25
180 **SOMERSAULT** (FR) F 28
43 **SOMERSET JEM** (GB) 8
424 **SOMERSET MAUGHAM** (IRE) 98
307 **SOMETHING BREWING** (FR) 37
7 **SOMETHING LUCKY** (IRE) 60
41 **SOMETHING MON** (USA) C 185
168 **SOMETHINGABOUTMARY** (IRE) G 5
174 **SOMETIME SOON** (IRE) 170
174 **SOMETIMES A FOX** (GB) 171
49 **SOMETIMESADIAMOND** (IRE) 38
403 **SOMEWHERE SECRET** (GB) 20

321 **SOMEWHERE TO BE** (IRE) 25
541 **SOMMER QUEEN** (IRE) C 88
348 **SOMMERVIEU** (FR) 62
127 **SOMNAMBULIST** (GB) 63
86 **SON OF AFRICA** (GB) 14
49 **SON OF BEAUTY** (IRE) 106
421 **SON OF FEYAN** (IRE) 13
527 **SON OF REST** (GB) 8
261 **SONG OF DUNES** (GB) 113
264 **SONG OF LOVE** (IRE) 16
307 **SONG OF SUMMER** (GB) 57
355 **SONG OF THE ISLES** (IRE) 23
223 **SONG SAA** (GB) 63
318 **SONGERIE** (GB) C 211
177 **SONGKRAN** (IRE) 40
10 **SONGSEEKER** (IRE) F 33
368 **SONIC** (GB) 87
281 **SONNELLINO** (GB) F 148
105 **SONNETINA** (GB) 24
181 **SONNETIST** (GB) 18
361 **SONOFTHEKING** (IRE) 18
65 **SOOQAAN** (GB) 14
541 **SOORAAH** (GB) G 89
37 **SOPHIA MARIA** (GB) 32
232 **SOPHIE GRAY** (GB) 107
553 **SOPHIE OLIVIA** (IRE) 16
181 **SOPHIE'JO** (GB) F 52
212 **SOPHISTICATED HEIR** (IRE) 13
258 **SOPRANOS ROCK** (IRE) 110
567 **SORBET** (GB) 46
24 **SORCELLERIE** (GB) C 57
507 **SORELLA BELLA** (FR) C 109
587 **SORELLE DELLE ROSE** (IRE) 6
303 **SORY** (GB) 10
118 **SORYAH** (IRE) C 112
187 **SOSIAN** (GB) 105
541 **SOSPIRA** (GB) C 39
331 **SOTO SIZZLER** (GB) 29
258 **SOTOMAYOR** (GB) 111
481 **SOTTSASS** (FR) 204
274 **SOUL EMOTION** (FR) 125
174 **SOUL KALIBER** (IRE) 172
293 **SOULSAVER** (GB) 38
127 **SOUND ADVICE** (GB) 64
6 **SOUND AND SILENCE** (GB) 111
336 **SOUND INVESTMENT** (FR) 59
434 **SOUND OF GUNS** (GB) C 92
86 **SOUND OF LIFE** (IRE) C 75
25 **SOUND OF VICTORY** (GB) 65
481 **SOUNDS GOOD** (FR) 92
499 **SOUNDS OF ITALY** (GB) 33
401 **SOUPY SOUPS** (IRE) 123
53 **SOURIYAN** (FR) 41
334 **SOUSTRACTION** (IRE) 30
49 **SOUTH EAST** (IRE) 39
17 **SOUTH SEAS** (IRE) 36
560 **SOUTHERLY BUSTER** (GB) 96
112 **SOUTHERN BELLE** (IRE) 19
424 **SOUTHERN FRANCE** (IRE) 99
97 **SOUTHERN SONG** (IRE) 115
470 **SOUTHERN STATES** (GB) 7
401 **SOUTHFIELD ROYALE** (GB) 124
419 **SOUTHFIELD STONE** (GB) 125
419 **SOUTHFIELD THEATRE** (IRE) 126
419 **SOUTHFIELD TORR** (GB) 127
560 **SOUTHPORT** (GB) 97
252 **SOUTHSEA ISLAND** (IRE) 2
468 **SOUTHVIEW LADY** (GB) 3

436 **SOUVIENS TOI** (GB) F 139
90 **SOVEREIGN DEBT** (IRE) 33
86 **SOVEREIGN DUKE** (GER) 49
535 **SOVEREIGN GRANT** (GB) 157
415 **SOVEREIGN STATE** (GB) 16
381 **SOVIET CASTLE** (IRE) 38
17 **SOVRANO** (GB) 98
28 **SOXY DOXY** (IRE) F 118
29 **SPACE BANDIT** (GB) 43
174 **SPACE CADET** (GB) 173
214 **SPACE ODDITY** (FR) 73
421 **SPACE SAFARI** (FR) 14
159 **SPACE TALK** (GB) 26
247 **SPACE WALK** (GB) 178
166 **SPACE WAR** (GB) 53
334 **SPADAY** (FR) 31
508 **SPADER** (IRE) 134
119 **SPADES ARE TRUMPS** (IRE) 29
524 **SPAGHETTI WESTERN** (IRE) 37
189 **SPANISH ARCHER** (FR) 56
356 **SPANISH BOUNTY** (GB) 15
563 **SPANISH CITY** (GB) 33
162 **SPANISH HISTORY** (USA) 12
187 **SPANISH MANE** (IRE) 106
476 **SPANISH OPTIMIST** (IRE) 106
424 **SPANISH POINT** (GB) 100
96 **SPANISH STAR** (IRE) 18
370 **SPARE PARTS** (IRE) 9
127 **SPARK OF WAR** (GB) 115
148 **SPARKALOT** (GB) 14
261 **SPARKLE'N'JOY** (IRE) 157
546 **SPARKLEANDSHINE** (IRE) 18
328 **SPARKLING CLEAR** (GB) F 63
190 **SPARKLING DAWN** (GB) 37
376 **SPARKLING EYES** (GB) C 52
433 **SPARKLING RIVER** (IRE) 21
295 **SPARKLING ROCK** (IRE) F 76
389 **SPARKLING SMILE** (IRE) C 30
563 **SPARKLING SURF** (GB) 110
419 **SPARKY MAY** (GB) F 128
608 **SPARKY VALENTINE** (FR) 42
552 **SPARKY'S SPIRIT** (GB) F 84
424 **SPARROW** (FR) C 167
137 **SPARTACULOUS** (GB) F 5
158 **SPARTE QUERCUS** (IRE) 16
486 **SPASHA** (GB) C 104
52 **SPEAK IN COLOURS** (GB) 58
486 **SPECIAL ACCEPTANCE** (GB) 22
586 **SPECIAL ASSIGNMENT** (USA) C 105
309 **SPECIAL CATCH** (IRE) 36
79 **SPECIAL ME** (USA) F 99
456 **SPECIAL MISSION** (GB) 30
477 **SPECIAL PREP** (IRE) 8
397 **SPECIAL RELATION** (IRE) 30
568 **SPECIAL YOU** (GB) 12
41 **SPECKLED** (USA) F 186
565 **SPECTATOR** (GB) 75
177 **SPECULATIVE BID** (IRE) 13
80 **SPECULATOR** (GB) 25
461 **SPEED COMPANY** (IRE) 28
50 **SPEED LIMIT** (FR) 9
481 **SPEED ROAD** (FR) 10
497 **SPEEDALONG** (IRE) 24
607 **SPEEDO BOY** (FR) 78
399 **SPEEDY GONZALEZ** (GB) 15
96 **SPEEDY LOST SOCK** (GB) 19
258 **SPELL** (GB) 241

49 SWING TILL DAWN (IRE) 42	258 TAJAANUS (IRE) 117	601 TANGOED (IRE) 34
174 SWINGBRIDGE (IRE) 180	158 TAJARROB (IRE) 62	302 TANGRAMM (GB) 23
511 SWINGY (FR) 47	318 TAJDEED (IRE) 106	565 TANIT RIVER (IRE) 79
258 SWIPER (IRE) 246	184 TAKBEER (IRE) 15	327 TANKERTON BOY (IRE) 25
187 SWISS BELLE (GB) 109	267 TAKE A BREAK (FR) 41	97 TANOJIN (IRE) C 121
114 SWISS CHILL (GB) 73	404 TAKE A DROP (IRE) 48	79 TANQEEB (GB) 102
258 SWISS CHIME (GB) 247	335 TAKE A TURN (IRE) 4	247 TANSEEQ (GB) 95
555 SWISS KISS (GB) C 54	565 TAKE EM OUT (IRE) 77	484 TANTAMOUNT (GB) 86
6 SWISS KNIGHT (GB) 117	32 TAKE FIVE (GB) 8	249 TANZANIA (IRE) F 93
247 SWISS LAKE (USA) F 182	436 TAKE FRIGHT (GB) 142	390 TANZINA (GB) 22
461 SWISS MARLIN (GB) 49	564 TAKE IT DOWN UNDER (GB) 15	86 TAOISEACH (GB) 50
217 SWISS MISS (GB) 26	423 TAKE ME WITH YOU (USA) 24	374 TAOPIX (GB) 12
370 SWISS VINNARE (GB) 10	541 TAKE SHELTER (GB) 40	481 TAOS (FR) 209
140 SWISSAL (IRE) 38	127 TAKE THE HIGH ROAD (GB) 67	52 TAP DANCING (IRE) 17
216 SWISSIE (GB) 41	558 TAKE THIS WALTZ (GB) 9	484 TAP NIGHT (USA) 87
587 SWITCH AROUND (IRE) 121	274 TAKE TO HEART (GB) 131	552 TAP THE BEAT (IRE) G 86
216 SWORD EXCEED (GER) 24	248 TAKE TWO (GB) 26	444 TAPDANCEALLTHEWAY (GB) 17
333 SWORD OF FATE (IRE) 18	174 TAKEITTOTHELIMITS (IRE) 183	174 TAPENADE (IRE) 184
184 SWORD OF THE LORD (GB) 14	438 TAKEMEOUT FREDDIE (IRE) 78	111 TAPIS LIBRE (GB) 4
6 SWORD OF TRUTH (IRE) 118	592 TAKEN BY FORCE (IRE) 9	247 TAPISSERIE (GB) 183
607 SWORDBILL (GB) 105	349 TAKEONEFORTHETEAM (GB) 43	232 TAQDEER (IRE) 17
52 SWORDCRAFT (IRE) 63	277 TAKIAH (GB) 11	394 TAQWAA (IRE) 11
544 SWOT (GB) 19	607 TAKING A CHANCE (IRE) 82	230 TARA BRIDGE (GB) 31
572 SYDNEY DE BAUNE (FR) 15	234 TAKING AIM (IRE) 25	612 TARA FLOW (GB) 71
361 SYKES (IRE) 20	471 TAKINGRISKS (IRE) 43	167 TARA FORCE (GB) 70
481 SYMBA'S DREAM (USA) C 207	247 TALAAQY (IRE) 93	22 TARA GALE (GB) G 21
411 SYMBOLIC STAR (IRE) 12	563 TALAS (IRE) 113	565 TARA MAC (GB) 80
6 SYMBOLIZATION (IRE) 119	176 TALE OF TAILS (IRE) 89	566 TARA MARA (GER) 26
154 SYMPHONIC (GB) 25	559 TALENT SCOUT (IRE) 7	573 TARA MOON (GB) C 97
375 SYMPHONY OF ANGELS (GB) 37	397 TALENT SPOTTER (GB) C 82	560 TARA MUCK (GB) 101
167 SYMPOSING (IRE) 117	567 TALK OF MONTY (GB) 37	22 TARA RIVER (FR) 22
190 SYNDEX (IRE) 39	275 TALK OF THE SOUTH (IRE) 21	546 TARA TARA (IRE) F 19
389 SYNERGY (FR) F 33	511 TALK POSH (IRE) 35	116 TARA TIARA (GB) 6
174 SYNOPSIS (IRE) 181	249 TALKATIVE (GB) C 92	326 TARA VIEW (GB) 114
573 SYRIAN PEARL (GB) 13	326 TALKISCHEAP (IRE) 113	141 TARA WELL (IRE) 20
320 TA ALLAK (GB) 112	553 TALKOFGOLD (IRE) 17	575 TARA'S RAINBOW (GB) 3
320 TA HA (IRE) 3	58 TALKSALOT (IRE) 16	247 TARAAYEF (IRE) 96
587 TAAKHY (GB) 58	114 TALLASSEE (GB) F 118	587 TARANA (IRE) F 123
481 TAAREEF (USA) 11	393 TALLAWALLA (IRE) F 33	601 TARAS DAY (GB) 35
509 TAB HOGARTH (IRE) 15	176 TALLINSKI (IRE) 69	527 TARASCON (IRE) F 59
281 TABASSOR (IRE) 149	247 TALLOW (IRE) 94	587 TARASILA (IRE) 59
79 TABDEED (GB) 58	192 TALLULAH'S QUEST (IRE) 16	281 TARBEYAH (IRE) 83
529 TABLA (GB) 11	262 TALLY'S SONG (GB) 12	383 TARBOOSH (GB) 33
541 TABLE BAY (IRE) F 90	16 TALON BLEU (FR) C 45	115 TARNEEM (USA) F 32
151 TABLE BLUFF (IRE) 6	563 TAMAARA (IRE) 114	446 TARRONA (GB) 8
534 TABLE MANNERS (GB) 11	232 TAMADDON (GB) 115	230 TARSEEKH (GB) 32
118 TABREED (GB) F 113	315 TAMALAIN (USA) F 77	318 TARTAN BUTE (GB) 24
293 TACENDA (IRE) 39	511 TAMARAMA (FR) 18	34 TARTARIA (GB) 15
160 TACTICAL MANOEUVRE (IRE) 31	339 TAMARILLO GROVE (IRE) 20	176 TARTE TROPEZIENNE (IRE) 22
281 TADAABEER 150	503 TAMAYEF (IRE) 9	176 TARZIYMA (IRE) C 90
90 TADAANY (IRE) 36	127 TAMAZUG (GB) F 143	249 TARZIYNA (IRE) F 94
193 TADAAWOL (GB) 22	366 TAMBURA (GB) 3	370 TASAABOQ (GB) 11
158 TADLEEL (GB) 61	114 TAMERLANE (GB) 74	79 TASHAABOH (IRE) 50
172 TAEL O' GOLD (GB) 8	79 TAMKEEN (GB) 59	555 TASHEERA (GB) 37
281 TAFAWOQ (GB) 81	41 TAMLEEK (USA) 67	426 TASHUNKA (IRE) 64
386 TAGINE (GB) 4	563 TAMMOOZ (GB) 192	247 TASLEET (GB) 23
174 TAGLIETELLE (GB) 182	29 TAMOCK (IRE) 84	41 TASNEEM (GB) 101
486 TAGUR (IRE) 35	281 TAMREER (GB) 210	127 TASTE OF PARADISE (IRE) 116
61 TAGUS (IRE) 25	115 TAN (GB) 13	344 TASTE THE WINE (IRE) 17
481 TAHAANY (IRE) C 208	7 TAN ARABIQ (GB) 65	310 TASTY GINGER (IRE) 29
527 TAHILLA (IRE) 28	318 TANAAWOL (GB) 214	258 TATHMEEN (IRE) 119
158 TAHIRAH (GB) F 104	565 TANACANDO (FR) 78	392 TATHRA 148
535 TAHREEK (GB) 87	587 TANAMI KITTEN (IRE) C 122	187 TATLISU (IRE) 55
258 TAI HANG DRAGON (IRE) 26	85 TANARPINO (GB) 36	102 TATSIA (GB) 100
281 TAI SING YEH (IRE) 16	383 TANASOQ (IRE) 32	402 TATTING (GB) 8
318 TAIFBALADY (IRE) 105	258 TANGLED (IRE) 118	588 TATTLING (GB) F 28
368 TAILOR TOM (IRE) 93	214 TANGLEY (GB) 76	29 TAUREAN DANCER (IRE) 44
450 TAJ BADALANDABAD (IRE) 67	606 TANGO DU ROY (IRE) 65	61 TAUREAN GOLD (GB) 21

541 **WAHYLAH** (IRE) C 93
283 **WAIHEKE** (GB) 105
392 **WAIKIKI WAVES** (FR) 127
283 **WAIT FOR ME** (FR) 106
542 **WAITING FOR RICHIE** (GB) 9
309 **WAITING PATIENTLY** (IRE) 40
46 **WAITINONASUNNYDAY** (IRE) 11
41 **WAJAAHA** (IRE) 104
70 **WAJDY** (IRE) 5
535 **WAJIH** (GB) 92
518 **WAKANDA** (IRE) 51
481 **WAKISASHI ONE** (FR) 218
339 **WALDEN PRINCE** (IRE) 24
612 **WALDORF SALAD** (GB) 77
572 **WALK IN THE MILL** (FR) 20
423 **WALK IN THE SUN** (USA) 26
417 **WALK OF GLEAMS** (GB) 4
318 **WALK ON BYE** (IRE) F 218
507 **WALK ON WALTER** (IRE) 73
456 **WALK ON WATER** (GB) C 66
507 **WALKLIKEANEGYPTIAN** (IRE) G 74
507 **WALKLIKEANEGYPTIAN** (IRE) F 113
106 **WALKMAN** (IRE) 47
131 **WALL OF SOUND** (GB) F 95
118 **WALLAA** (GB) 117
274 **WALLACE SPIRIT** (FR) 146
244 **WALLFLOWER** (IRE) 19
310 **WALLY'S WISDOM** (GB) 32
510 **WALSINGHAM GRANGE** (USA) 18
401 **WALT** (IRE) 137
431 **WALTER ONEEIGHTONE** (IRE) 86
16 **WALTER SICKERT** (IRE) 16
6 **WALTON STREET** (GB) 39
48 **WALTZ DARLING** (IRE) 21
527 **WALTZING MATILDA** (IRE) F 61
378 **WANDAOVER** (GB) 4
14 **WANDRIN STAR** (IRE) 75
80 **WANEEN** (IRE) 35
131 **WANSDYKE LASS** (GB) C 96
434 **WAPPING** (USA) 25
281 **WAQAAS** (GB) 17
555 **WAQT** (IRE) 15
536 **WAR AT SEA** (IRE) 20
607 **WAR BRIGADE** (FR) 88
326 **WAR CHIEF** (GB) 125
274 **WAR CREATION** (IRE) 147
424 **WAR DECREE** (USA) 11
127 **WAR DEPARTMENT** (IRE) 72
258 **WAR GLORY** (IRE) 32
395 **WAR HOUSE** (IRE) 30
253 **WAR JOEY** (IRE) 6
573 **WAR NO MORE** (USA) 69
415 **WAR OF SUCCESSION** (GB) 15
426 **WAR ON THE ROCKS** (IRE) 69
424 **WAR SECRETARY** (USA) 12
283 **WAR SOUND** (GB) 107
383 **WAR WHISPER** (GB) 36
398 **WARBA** (IRE) 3
6 **WARBURTON** (IRE) 121
127 **WARDADDY** (IRE) 119
222 **WARDEN ROSE** (GB) F 12
481 **WAREGA** (FR) 99
198 **WARFARE** (GB) 3
579 **WARKSBURN BOY** (GB) 6
174 **WARLIKE INTENT** (IRE) 204
189 **WARM OASIS** (GB) 23
496 **WARM WELCOME** (GB) C 55

432 **WAROFINDEPENDENCE** (USA) 24
10 **WARRANTED** (GB) 18
112 **WARRIOR GODDESS** (GB) 44
158 **WARRIOR PRINCE** (GB) 18
428 **WARRIOR'S SPIRIT** (IRE) 69
240 **WARRIOR'S VALLEY** (GB) 22
419 **WARRIORS TALE** (GB) 145
79 **WARSAAN** (IRE) 13
121 **WARSAW ROAD** (IRE) 13
423 **WARSHAH** (IRE) F 42
450 **WARTHOG** (FR) 79
424 **WAS** (IRE) C 177
122 **WASEEM FARIS** (IRE) 13
431 **WASHED ASHORE** (IRE) 87
424 **WASHINGTON DC** (IRE) 13
90 **WASM** (GB) 38
138 **WASSAIL** (GB) 24
33 **WASTED SUNSETS** (FR) 13
313 **WATAR DAY** (GB) 21
16 **WATCH TAN** (GB) 32
578 **WATCH THE WIND** (FR) F 10
7 **WATCHING SPIRITS** (GB) 92
563 **WATCHMAN** (FR) 39
280 **WATCOMBE HEIGHTS** (IRE) 10
258 **WATER DIVINER** (IRE) 255
318 **WATER FOUNTAIN** (GB) F 219
165 **WATER RAIL** (GB) 4
369 **WATER THIEF** (USA) 3
336 **WATER WAGTAIL** (GB) 67
552 **WATERLOO WARRIOR** (IRE) 102
368 **WATERLORD** (GB) 112
318 **WATERSMEET** (GB) 28
563 **WATHEEQA** (USA) 122
555 **WATHEER** (GB) 38
607 **WATT BRODERICK** (FR) 89
258 **WAVEBAND** (GB) F 256
119 **WAVEPOINT** (GB) 33
41 **WAVERING** (IRE) C 195
558 **WAVET** (GB) G 19
77 **WAX AND WANE** (GB) 75
377 **WAXIES DARGLE** (GB) 105
438 **WAY BACK THEN** (IRE) 85
341 **WAY OF THE WORLD** (FR) 7
348 **WAY OUT WEST** (IRE) 69
251 **WAYUPINTHESKY** (IRE) 10
118 **WAZIN** (GB) 72
368 **WAZOWSKI** (GB) 113
582 **WE ARE THE WORLD** (GB) 31
274 **WE HAVE A DREAM** (FR) 148
118 **WE KNOW** (IRE) 73
310 **WE WIN** (GB) 33
330 **WE'LL BE THERE** (GB) 14
176 **WEAKFIELD** (IRE) 78
66 **WEAPON OF CHOICE** (IRE) 16
86 **WEAR IT WELL** (GB) 54
374 **WEATHER FRONT** (USA) 14
256 **WEDDING BREAKFAST** (IRE) 14
114 **WEDDING PARTY** (GB) F 120
92 **WEDGEWOOD ESTATES** (GB) 59
92 **WEDGEWOOD WONDER** (GB) 60
245 **WEDIDDODONTWE** (GB) 18
595 **WEE BOGUS** (GB) 27
580 **WEE JIM** (GB) 11
130 **WEE SAXON** (GB) 19
409 **WEEBILL** (GB) 45
535 **WEEKDAY** (GB) 93
232 **WEEKENDER** (GB) 20
351 **WEEKLY GOSSIP** (IRE) 13

428 **WEELLAN** (GB) 95
530 **WELCOME BEN** (IRE) 10
358 **WELCOME POLLY** (IRE) 21
52 **WELCOME SPRING** (IRE) C 96
166 **WELD AL EMARAT** (GB) 60
29 **WELD ALDAR** (GB) 87
484 **WELL ABOVE PAR** (IRE) 101
258 **WELL DONE FOX** (GB) 257
494 **WELL FOCUSED** (IRE) F 8
289 **WELL OWD MON** (GB) 15
237 **WELL SMITTEN** (FR) 79
118 **WELL SUITED** (IRE) 74
232 **WELL YES** (IRE) 123
510 **WELLAND** (GB) 19
500 **WELLIESINTHEWATER** (IRE) 24
167 **WELLS FARHH GO** (IRE) 122
426 **WELLS GOLD** (IRE) 70
8 **WELLUPTOSCRATCH** (FR) 10
80 **WELOOF** (FR) 36
274 **WELSBY** (FR) 149
332 **WELSH ANGEL** (GB) F 26
114 **WELSH ANTHEM** (GB) C 121
368 **WELSH BARD** (FR) 114
399 **WELSH CAKE** (GB) C 35
131 **WELSH CAKE** (GB) C 97
255 **WELSH DESIGNE** (GB) 7
61 **WELSH INLET** (IRE) 22
41 **WELSH LORD** (GB) 105
172 **WELSH RAREBIT** (GB) 18
328 **WEMYSS POINT** (GB) 49
535 **WEMYSS WARE** (IRE) 162
62 **WENCESLAUS** (GER) 35
136 **WENDEN BELLE** (IRE) G 16
26 **WENSLEY** (GB) 27
259 **WENTWORTH FALLS** (GB) 12
274 **WENYERREADYFREDDIE** (IRE) 160
552 **WEST APPROACH** (GB) 103
620 **WEST CLASS** (IRE) 9
102 **WEST NEWTON** (GB) 104
416 **WEST OF THE EDGE** (IRE) 29
452 **WEST TO CROSSGALES** (IRE) 11
508 **WEST TO THE BRIDGE** (IRE) 153
560 **WEST TORR** (IRE) 114
318 **WEST WIND** (GB) F 220
339 **WEST WIZARD** (FR) 25
97 **WESTBROOK BERTIE** (GB) 68
283 **WESTEND STORY** (IRE) 108
577 **WESTEND THEATRE** (IRE) 5
404 **WESTERBEE** (IRE) 51
404 **WESTERBERRY** (IRE) 52
431 **WESTERLY WIND** (GB) 88
508 **WESTERN BREEZE** (IRE) 154
592 **WESTERN CLIMATE** (IRE) 11
174 **WESTERN COMMAND** (IRE) 205
49 **WESTERN DAWN** (IRE) 118
28 **WESTERN DUKE** (GB) 18
388 **WESTERN HONOUR** (IRE) 23
498 **WESTERN LASS** (IRE) 10
348 **WESTERN MILLER** (IRE) 70
238 **WESTERN MORNING** (IRE) 28
395 **WESTERN RULER** (GB) 31
471 **WESTERN RULES** (IRE) 49
237 **WESTERN RYDER** (GB) 80
447 **WESTERN STORM** (IRE) 27
190 **WESTERN SUNRISE** (IRE) 41
223 **WESTERN WAVE** (FR) 76
88 **WESTERN WAY** (IRE) 5
160 **WESTERNER OCEAN** (IRE) 38

LATE ENTRIES

MR RICHARD BRABAZON, Curragh
Postal: **Rangers Lodge, The Curragh, Co. Kildare, Ireland**
Contacts: **MOBILE 00353 (0) 87 2515626**
E-MAIL **richardbrabazon@eircom.net** WEBSITE **www.richardbrabazon.ie**

1 **ARCHER'S UP**, 5, ch g Archipenko (USA)—Nadeszhda **Richard Brabazon**
2 **KORBOUS (IRE)**, 9, ch g Choisir (AUS)—Puppet Play (IRE) **Mrs F. D. McAuley**
3 **PATH OF SILVER (IRE)**, 5, b m Strategic Prince—Silver Tide (USA) **Cafe du Journal Syndicate**
4 **WATERBOY (IRE)**, 4, gr g Stormy River (FR)—Happy (JPN) **David Moran / Richard Brabazon**

THREE-YEAR-OLDS

5 **FIGURE IT OUT (IRE)**, ch f Arcano (IRE)—Doubt (IRE) **Richard Brabazon**

Assistant Trainer: Ms Anna Paoletti

STOP PRESS

422 **MR JOHN NORTON, Barnsley**

1 **ALJUNOOD (IRE)**, 4, br g Bated Breath—Ataraxy **Jaffa Racing Syndicate**

RACING POST
MEMBERS' CLUB

RACE REPLAYS*

*Remember no matter how many times you watch the race the result won't change.

Take your form study to the next level. Subscribe to Members' Club Ultimate and you can watch unlimited video replays of every race from all 86 courses in Britain and Ireland.

Visit **racingpost.com/replays**

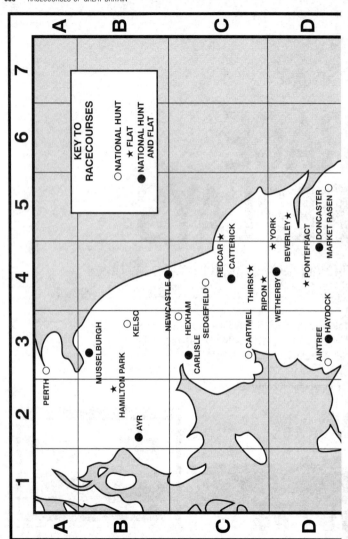

KEY TO RACECOURSES

○ NATIONAL HUNT
★ FLAT
● NATIONAL HUNT AND FLAT

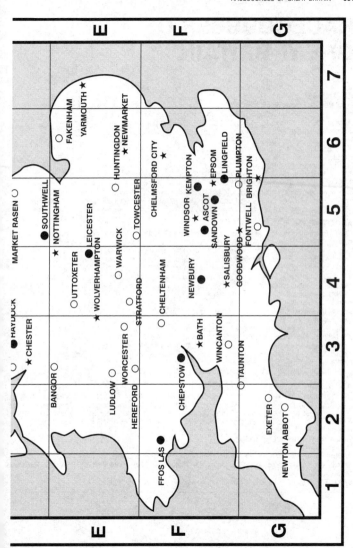

RACECOURSES OF GREAT BRITAIN

AINTREE (L.H)
Grand National Course: Triangular, 2m2f (16 fences) 494y run-in with elbow. Perfectly flat. A severe test for both horse and rider, putting a premium on jumping ability, fitness and courage.
Mildmay Course: Rectangular, 1m4f (8) 260y run-in. A very fast, flat course with sharp bends.
Address: Aintree Racecourse, Ormskirk Road, Aintree, Liverpool, L9 5AS
Tel: 0151 523 2600
Fax: 0151 522 2920
Website: www.aintree.co.uk
Regional Director: John Baker
Clerk of the Course: Andrew Tulloch 07831 315104
By Road: North of the City, near the junction of the M57 and M58 with the A59 (Preston).
By Rail: Aintree Station is adjacent to the Stands, from Liverpool Central.
By Air: Liverpool (John Lennon) Airport is 10 miles. Helicopter landing facility by prior arrangement.

ASCOT (R.H)
Flat: Right-handed triangular track just under 1m6f in length. The Round course descends from the 1m4f start into Swinley Bottom, the lowest part of the track. It then turns right-handed and joins the Old Mile Course, which starts on a separate chute. The course then rises to the right-handed home turn over an underpass to join the straight mile course. The run-in is about 3f, rising slightly to the winning post. The whole course is of a galloping nature with easy turns.
N.H. Triangular, 1m6f (10), 240y run-in mostly uphill. A galloping course with an uphill finish, Ascot provides a real test of stamina. The fences are stiff and sound jumping is essential, especially for novices.
Address: Ascot Racecourse, Ascot, Berkshire SL5 7JX Tel: 08707 271234 Fax: 08704 601250
Website: www.ascot.co.uk
Clerk of the Course: Chris Stickels 01344 878502 / 07970 621440
Chief Executive: Guy Henderson
By Road: West of the town on the A329. Easy access from the M3 (Junction 3) and the M4 (Junction 6). Car parking adjoining the course and Ascot Heath.
By Rail: Regular service from Waterloo to Ascot (500y from the racecourse).
By Air: Helicopter landing facility at the course. London (Heathrow) Airport 15 miles, White Waltham Airfield 12 miles (01427) 718800.

AYR (L.H)
Flat: A left-handed, galloping, flat oval track of 1m4f with a 4f run-in. The straight 6f is essentially flat.
N.H. Oval, 1m4f (9), 210y run-in. Relatively flat and one of the fastest tracks in Great Britain. It is a well-drained course and the ground rarely becomes testing. The track suits the long-striding galloper.
Address: Ayr Racecourse, Whitletts Road, Ayr, KA8 0JE Tel: 01292 264179 Fax: 01292 610140
Website: www.ayr-racecourse.co.uk
Clerk of the Course: Graeme Anderson
Managing Director: David Brown
By Road: East of the town on the A758. Free parking for buses and cars.
By Rail: Ayr Station (trains on the half hour from Glasgow Central). Journey time 55 minutes. Buses and taxis also to the course.
By Air: Prestwick International Airport (10 minutes), Glasgow Airport (1 hour).

BANGOR-ON-DEE (L.H)

N.H. Circular, 1m4f (9), 325y run-in. Apart from some 'ridge and furrow', this is a flat course notable for three sharp bends, especially the paddock turn. Suits handy, speedy sorts.

Address: Bangor-On-Dee Racecourse, Overton Road, Bangor-On-Dee, Wrexham, LL13 0DA

Tel: 01978 782081 Fax: 01978 780985

Website: www.bangorondeeraces.co.uk

Racecourse Manager and Clerk of the Course: Andrew Morris

Chief Executive: Richard Thomas

General Manager: Jeannie Chantler

By Road: 5 miles south-east of Wrexham, off the B5069.

By Rail: Wrexham Station (bus or taxi to the course).

By Air: Helicopters may land by prior arrangement with Clerk of the Course at entirely their own risk.

BATH (L.H)

Flat: Galloping, left-handed, level oval of 1m4f, with long, stiff run-in of about 4f which bends to the left. An extended chute provides for sprint races.

Address: The Racecourse, Lansdown, Bath, BA1 9BU Tel: 01225 424609 Fax: 01225 444415.

Website: www.bath-racecourse.co.uk

Clerk of the Course: Katie Stephens

Executive Director: Jo Hall

By Road: 2 miles northwest of the City (M4 Junction 18) at Lansdown. Unlimited free car and coach parking space immediately behind the stands. Special bus services operate from Bath to the racecourse.

By Rail: Bath Station (from Paddington).

By Air: Bristol or Colerne Airports. Helicopter landing facilities available by prior arrangement.

BEVERLEY (R.H)

Flat: A right-handed oval of 1m3f, generally galloping, with an uphill run-in of two and a half furlongs. The 5f course is very stiff.

Address: Beverley Race Co. Ltd., York Road, Beverley, Yorkshire HU17 9QZ Tel: 01482 867418 / 882645

Website: www.beverley-racecourse.co.uk

General Manager and Clerk of the Course: Sally Iggulden 07850 458605

By Road: 7 miles from the M62 (Junction 38) off the A1035. Free car parking opposite the course. Owners and trainers use a separate enclosure.

By Rail: Beverley Station (Hull-Scarborough line). Occasional bus service to the course (1 mile).

BRIGHTON (L.H)

Flat: Left-handed, 1m4f horseshoe with easy turns and a run-in of three and a half furlongs. Undulating and sharp, the track suits handy types.

Address: Brighton Racecourse, Brighton, East Sussex BN2 2XZ Tel: 01273 603580 Fax: 01273 673267

Website: www.brighton-racecourse.co.uk

Clerk of the Course: To be announced

General Manager: Sam Windridge

By Road: East of the city on the A27 (Lewes Road). Car park adjoins the course.

By Rail: Brighton Station (from Victoria on the hour, London Bridge or Portsmouth). Special bus service to the course from the station (approx 2 miles).

By Air: Helicopters may land by prior arrangement.

CARLISLE (R.H)
Flat: Right-handed, 1m4f pear-shaped track. Galloping and undulating with easy turns and a stiff uphill run-in of three and a half furlongs. The 6f course begins on an extended chute.
N.H. Pear-shaped, 1m5f (9), 300y run-in uphill. Undulating and a stiff test of stamina, ideally suited to the long-striding thorough stayer.
Address: Carlisle Racecourse, Durdar Road, Carlisle CA2 4TS Tel: 01228 554700 Fax: 01228 554747
Website: www.carlisle-races.co.uk
Regional Director: John Baker
Clerk of the Course: Andrew Tulloch
General Manager: Geraldine McKay
By Road: 2 miles south of the city (Durdar Road). Easy access from the M6 (Junction 42). The car park is free (adjacent to the course).
By Rail: Carlisle Station (2 miles from the course).
By Air: Helicopter landing facility by prior arrangement.

CARTMEL (L.H)
N.H. Oval, 1m1f (6), 800y run-in. Almost perfectly flat but very sharp, with the longest run-in in the country, approximately half a mile. The fences are stiff but fair.
Address: Cartmel Racecourse, Cartmel, nr Grange-Over-Sands, Cumbria LA11 6QF Tel: 01539 536340
Out of season: 01539 533335 Fax: 01539 536004
Website: www.cartmel-racecourse.co.uk
Managing Director: Stephen Cooper
Clerk of the Course: Anthea Morshead 07837 559861
By Road: 1 mile west of the town, 2 miles off the B5277 (Grange-Haverthwaite road). M6 (Junction 36).
By Rail: Cark-in-Cartmel Station (2 miles) (Carnforth-Barrow line). Raceday bus service.
By Air: Light aircraft facilities available at Cark Airport (4 miles from the course). Helicopter landing facility at the course, by prior arrangement only.

CATTERICK (L.H)
Flat: A sharp, left-handed, undulating oval of 1m180y with a downhill run-in of 3f.
N.H. Oval, 1m1f (9), 240y run-in. Undulating, sharp track that favours the handy, front-running sort, rather than the long-striding galloper.
Address: The Racecourse, Catterick Bridge, Richmond, North Yorkshire DL10 7PE Tel: 01748 811478
Fax: 01748 811082
Website: www.catterickbridge.co.uk
General Manager and Clerk of the Course: Fiona Needham 07831 688625
By Road: The course is adjacent to the A1, 1 mile northwest of the town on the A6136. There is a free car park.
By Rail: Darlington Station (special buses to course - 14-mile journey).
By Air: Helicopters can land by prior arrangement. Fixed wing planes contact RAF Leeming
Tel: 01677 423041

CHELMSFORD CITY (L.H)
Flat: A left-handed, Polytrack oval of 1m with sweeping bends and a 2f home straight. Races over 7f and 1m start from separate chutes. A turf track is scheduled to open in 2019.
Address: Chelmsford City Racecourse, Great Leighs, Essex, CM3 1QP Tel: 01245 362412
Fax: 01245 361850
Website: www.chelmsfordcityracecourse.com
Manager: Fraser Garritty
Clerk of the Course: Andy Waitt
By Road: At Great Leighs, five miles north of Chelmsford on the A31
By Rail: Chelmsford station (from Liverpool Street)
By Air: Stansted Airport (17 miles)

CHELTENHAM (L.H)

Old Course: Oval, 1m4f, (9) 350y run-in. A testing, undulating track with stiff fences. The ability to stay is essential.
New Course: Oval, 1m5f (10), 220y run-in. Undulating, stiff fences, testing course, uphill for the final half-mile.
Address: Cheltenham Racecourse, Prestbury Park, Cheltenham, Gloucestershire GL50 4SH
Tel: 01242 513014 Fax: 01242 224227
Website: www.cheltenham.co.uk
Regional Director: Ian Renton
Director of Racing and Clerk of the Course: Simon Claisse 07785 293966
By Road: 1.5 miles north of the town on the A435. M5 (Junction 10 or 11).
By Rail: Cheltenham Spa Station. Buses and taxis to course.
By Air: Helicopter landing site to the northeast of the stands.

CHEPSTOW (L.H)

Flat: A left-handed, undulating oval of about 2m, with easy turns, and a straight run-in of 5f. There is a straight track of 1m14y.
N.H. Oval, 2m (11), 240y run-in. Many changing gradients, five fences in the home straight. Favours the long-striding front-runner, but stamina is important.
Address: Chepstow Racecourse, Chepstow, Monmouthshire NP16 6BE
Tel: 01291 622260 Fax: 01291 627061
Website: www.chepstow-racecourse.co.uk
Clerk of the Course: Keith Ottesen 07813 043453
Executive Director: Phil Bell
By Road: 1 mile north-west of the town on the A466. (1 mile from Junction 22 of the M4 (Severn Bridge) or M48 Junction 2. There is a free public car park opposite the entrance.
By Rail: Chepstow Station (from Paddington, change at Gloucester or Newport). The course is a mile from the station.
By Air: Helicopter landing facility in the centre of the course.

CHESTER (L.H)

Flat: A level, sharp, left-handed, circular course of 1m73y, with a short run-in of 230y.
Chester is a specialists' track which generally suits the sharp-actioned horse.
Address: The Racecourse, Chester CH1 2LY Tel: 01244 304600 Fax: 01244 304648
Website: www.chester-races.co.uk
Racecourse Manager and Clerk of the Course: Andrew Morris
Chief Executive: Richard Thomas
By Road: The course is near the centre of the city on the A548 (Queensferry Road). The Owners' and Trainers' car park is adjacent to the Leverhulme Stand. There is a public car park in the centre of the course.
By Rail: Chester Station (¾ mile from the course). Services from Euston, Paddington and Northgate.
By Air: Hawarden Airport (2 miles). Helicopters are allowed to land on the racecourse by prior arrangement only.

DONCASTER (L.H)

Flat: A left-handed, flat, galloping course of 1m7f 110y, with a long run-in which extends to a straight mile.
N.H. Conical, 2m (11), 247y run-in. A very fair, flat track ideally suited to the long-striding galloper.
Address: Doncaster Racecourse, Leger Way, Doncaster, DN2 6BB Tel: 01302 304200 Fax: 01302 323271
Email: info@doncaster-racecourse.co.uk
Website: www.doncaster-racecourse.co.uk
Clerk of the Course: Roderick Duncan 07772 958685
Executive Director: Tim Banfield
By Road: East of the town, off the A638 (M18 Junctions 3 and 4). Club members' car park reserved. Large public car park free and adjacent to the course.
By Rail: Doncaster Central Station (from King's Cross). Special bus service from the station (1 mile).
By Air: Helicopter landing facility by prior arrangement only. Doncaster Robin Hood Airport is 15 minutes from the racecourse.

EPSOM (L.H)

Flat: Left-handed and undulating with easy turns, and a run-in of just under 4f. The straight 5f course is also undulating and downhill all the way, making it the fastest 5f in the world.
Address: The Racecourse, Epsom Downs, Surrey KT18 5LQ Tel: 01372 726311 Fax: 01372 748253
Website: www.epsomderby.co.uk
Regional Director: Phil White
Clerk of the Course: Andrew Cooper Tel: 01372 726311 Mobile: 07774 230850
General Manager: Simon Durrant
By Road: Two miles south of the town on the B290 (M25 Junctions 8 and 9). For full car park particulars apply to: The Club Secretary, Epsom Grandstand, Epsom Downs, Surrey KT18 5LQ. Tel: 01372 726311.
By Rail: Epsom, Epsom Downs or Tattenham Corner Stations (trains from London Bridge, Waterloo, Victoria). Regular bus services run to the course from Epsom and Morden Underground Station.
By Air: London (Heathrow) and London (Gatwick) are both within 30 miles of the course. Heliport (Derby Meeting only) - apply to Hascombe Aviation. Tel: 01279 680291.

EXETER (R.H)

N.H. Oval, 2m (11), 300y run-in uphill. Undulating with a home straight of half a mile. A good test of stamina, suiting the handy, well-balanced sort.
Address: Exeter Racecourse, Kennford, Exeter, Devon EX6 7XS Tel: 01392 832599 Fax: 01392 833454
Email: Exeter@thejockeyclub.co.uk
Website: www.exeter-racecourse.co.uk
Regional Director: Ian Renton
Clerk of the Course: Barry Johnson 07976 791578
General Manager: Jack Parkinson
By Road: The course is at Haldon, 5 miles south-west of Exeter on the A38 (Plymouth) road, 2 miles east of Chudleigh.
By Rail: Exeter (St Davids) Station. Free bus service to course.
By Air: Helicopters can land by prior arrangement.

FAKENHAM (L.H)

N.H. Square, 1m (6), 200y run-in. On the turn almost throughout and undulating, suiting the handy front-runner. The going rarely becomes heavy.
Address: The Racecourse, Fakenham, Norfolk NR21 7NY Tel: 01328 862388 Fax: 01328 855908
email: info@fakenhamracecourse.co.uk
Website: www.fakenhamracecourse.co.uk
Clerk of the Course and Chief Executive: David Hunter Tel: 01328 862388 Mobile: 07767 802206
By Road: A mile south of the town on the B1146 (East Dereham) road.
By Rail: Norwich Station (26 miles) (Liverpool Street line), King's Lynn (22 miles) (Liverpool Street/Kings Cross).
By Air: Helicopter landing facility in the centre of the course by prior arrangement only.

FFOS LAS (L.H)

Flat The track is a 60m wide, basically flat, 1m4f oval with sweeping bends. Races over 5f and 6f start on a chute.
N.H. A flat, 1m4f oval (9). The going is often testing which places the emphasis on stamina.
Address: Ffos Las Racecourse, Trimsaran, Carmarthenshire SA17 4DE Tel: 01554 811092
Fax: 01554 811037
Website: www.ffoslasracecourse.com
Racing Director: Mark Kershaw
Clerk of the Course: Keith Ottesen 07813 043453
By Road: From the east take J48 from the M4 and join the A4138 to Llanelli, then follow the brown tourist signs to the racecourse. From the west take the A48 to Carmarthen then the A484 to Kidwelly before following the brown signs.
By Air: The course has the facilities to land helicopters on race days.

FONTWELL PARK (Fig. 8)
N.H. 2m (7), 230y run-in with left-hand bend close home. The figure-of-eight chase course suits handy types and is something of a specialists' track. The left-handed hurdle course is oval and one mile round. The bottom bend, which is shared, has been converted to Fibresand.
Address: Fontwell Park Racecourse, nr Arundel, West Sussex BN18 0SX Tel: 01243 543335
Fax: 01243 543904
Website: www.fontwellpark.co.uk
Clerk of the Course: Tracey O'Meara
Executive Director: Jonathan Acott
By Road: South of village at the junction of the A29 (Bognor) and A27 (Brighton-Chichester) roads.
By Rail: Barnham Station (2 miles). Brighton-Portsmouth line (access via London Victoria).
By Air: Helicopter landing facility by prior arrangement with the Clerk of the Course.

GOODWOOD (R.H)
Flat: A sharp, undulating, essentially right-handed track with a long run-in. There is also a straight 6f course.
Address: Goodwood Racecourse Ltd., Goodwood, Chichester, West Sussex PO18 0PX
Tel: 01243 755022 Fax: 01243 755025
Website: www.goodwood.co.uk
Managing Director: Adam Waterworth
General Manager: Alex Eade
Clerk of the Course: Ed Arkell
By Road: 6 miles north of Chichester between the A286 and A285. There is a car park adjacent to the course. Ample free car and coach parking.
By Rail: Chichester Station (from Victoria or London Bridge). Regular bus service to the course (6 miles).
By Air: Helicopter landing facility by prior arrangement 01243 755030. Goodwood Airport 2 miles (taxi to the course).

HAMILTON PARK (R.H)
Flat: A sharp, undulating, right-handed course of 1m5f with a five and a half-furlong, uphill run-in. There is a straight track of 6f.
Address: Hamilton Park Racecourse, Bothwell Road, Hamilton, Lanarkshire ML3 0DW Tel: 01698 283806
Fax: 01698 286621
Website: www.hamilton-park.co.uk
Racing Manager and Clerk of the Course: Sulekha Varma
Chief Executive: Vivien Currie 01698 283806
By Road: Off the A72 on the B7071 (Hamilton-Bothwell road). (M74 Junction 5). Free parking for cars and buses.
By Rail: Hamilton West Station (1 mile).
By Air: Glasgow Airport (20 miles).

HAYDOCK PARK (L.H)
Flat: A galloping, almost flat, oval track, 1m5f round, with a run-in of four and a half furlongs and a straight six-furlong course.
N.H. Oval, 1m5f (10), 440y run-in. A flat, galloping chase course using portable fences. The hurdles track, which is sharp, is inside the chase course and has some tight bends.
Address: Haydock Park Racecourse, Newton-le-Willows, Merseyside WA12 0HQ Tel: 01942 402609
Fax: 01942 270879
Website: www.haydock-park.co.uk
Regional Director: John Baker
General Manager: Jason Fildes
Clerk of the Course: Kirkland Tellwright 01942 725963 or 07748 181595
By Road: The course is on the A49 near Junction 23 of the M6.
By Rail: Newton-le-Willows Station (Manchester-Liverpool line) is 2.5 miles from the course. Earlstown 3 miles from the course. Warrington Bank Quay and Wigan are on the London to Carlisle/Glasgow line.
By Air: Landing facilities in the centre of the course for helicopters and planes not exceeding 10,000lbs laden weight.

HEREFORD (R.H)

N.H. Square, 1m4f (9), 300y run-in. The turns, apart from the final one that is on falling ground, are easily negotiated, placing the emphasis on speed rather than stamina. A handy position round the home turn is vital, as winners rarely come from behind. The hurdle track is on the outside of the chase course.

Address: Hereford Racecourse, Roman Road, Holmer, Hereford, HR4 9QU Tel: (01432) 273560
Fax: (01432) 352807
Website: www.hereford-racecourse.co.uk
Executive Director: Rebecca Davies
Clerk of the Course: Libby O'Flaherty
By Road: 1 mile north-west of the City Centre off the A49 (Leominster) road.
By Rail: Hereford Station (1 mile from the course).

HEXHAM (L.H)

N.H. Oval, 1m4f (10), 220y run-in. An undulating course that becomes very testing when the ground is soft, it has easy fences and a stiff climb to the finishing straight, which is on a separate spur.

Address: Hexham Racecourse, The Riding, Hexham, Northumberland NE46 2JP Tel: 01434 606881
Fax: 01434 605814 Racedays: 01434 603738 Email: admin@hexham-racecourse.co.uk
Website: www.hexham-racecourse.co.uk
Chief Executive: Robert Whitelock
Clerk of the Course: James Armstrong 01434 606881 or 07801 166820
By Road: 1.5 miles south-west of the town off the B6305.
By Rail: Hexham Station (Newcastle-Carlisle line). Free bus to the course. `
By Air: Helicopter landing facility in centre of course (by special arrangement only).

HUNTINGDON (R.H)

N.H. Oval, 1m4f (9), 200y run-in. Perfectly flat, galloping track with a tricky open ditch in front of the stands. The two fences in the home straight can cause problems for novice chasers. Suits front-runners.

Address: The Racecourse, Brampton, Huntingdon, Cambridgeshire PE28 4NL Tel: 01480 453373
Fax: 01480 455275
Website: www.huntingdon-racecourse.co.uk
Regional Director: Amy Starkey
Clerk of the Course: Jack Pryor
General Manager: Liam Johnson
By Road: The course is situated at Brampton, 2 miles west of Huntingdon on the A14. Easy access from the A1 (½ mile from the course).
By Rail: Huntingdon Station. Buses and taxis to course.
By Air: Helicopter landing facility by prior arrangement.

KELSO (L.H)

N.H. Oval, 1m3f (8), uphill run-in of just over a furlong. Rather undulating with two downhill fences opposite the stands, it suits the nippy, front-running sort, though the uphill finish helps the true stayer. The hurdle course is smaller and very sharp with a tight turn away from the stands.

Address: Kelso Racecourse, Kelso, Roxburghshire TD5 7SX Tel: 01668 280800
Website: www.kelso-races.co.uk
Clerk of the Course: Anthea Morshead
Managing Director: Jonathan Garratt
By Road: 1 mile north of the town, off the B6461.
By Rail: Berwick-upon-Tweed Station. 23-mile bus journey to Kelso.
By Air: Helicopters can land at course by arrangement, fixed wing aircraft Winfield, regular aircraft Edinburgh.

KEMPTON PARK (R.H)

Flat: A floodlit Polytrack circuit. A 1m2f outer track accommodates races over 6f, 7f, 1m, 1m3f, 1m4f and 2m. The 1m inner track caters for races over 5f and 1m2f.

N.H. Triangular, 1m5f (10), 175y run-in. A practically flat, sharp course where the long run between the last obstacle on the far side and the first in the home straight switches the emphasis from jumping to speed. The hurdles track is on the outside of the chase track. The course crosses the Polytrack at two points on each circuit.

Address: Kempton Park Racecourse, Sunbury-on-Thames, Middlesex TW16 5AQ Tel: 01932 782292 Fax: 01932 782044 Raceday Fax: 01932 779525

Website: www.kempton.co.uk

Regional Director: Phil White

Clerk of the Course and Director of Racing: Brian Clifford 07880 784484

General Manager: Steve Parlett

By Road: On the A308 near Junction 1 of the M3.

By Rail: Kempton Park Station (from Waterloo).

By Air: London (Heathrow) Airport 6 miles.

LEICESTER (R.H)

Flat: Stiff, galloping, right-handed oval of 1m5f, with a 5f run-in. There is a straight course of seven furlongs.

N.H. Rectangular, 1m6f (10), 250y run-in. An undulating course with an elbow 150y from the finish, it can demand a high degree of stamina, as the going can become extremely testing and the last three furlongs are uphill.

Address: Leicester Racecourse, Oadby, Leicester, LE2 4AL Tel: 01162 716515 Fax: 01162 711746

Website: www.leicester-racecourse.co.uk

Clerk of the Course: Jimmy Stevenson 01162 712115 or 07774 497281

General Manager: Rob Bracken

By Road: The course is 2.5 miles south-east of the city on the A6 (M1, Junction 21). The car park is free.

By Rail: Leicester Station (from St Pancras) is 2.5 miles.

By Air: Helicopter landing facility in the centre of the course.

LINGFIELD PARK (L.H)

Flat, Turf: A sharp, undulating left-handed circuit, with a 7f 140y straight course.

Flat, Polytrack: The left-handed Polytrack is 1m2f round, with an extended chute to provide a 1m5f start. It is a sharp, level track with a short run-in.

N.H. Conical, 1m5f (10), 200y run-in. Severely undulating with a tight downhill turn into the straight, the chase course suits front-runners and those of doubtful resolution.

Address: Lingfield Park Racecourse, Lingfield, Surrey RH7 6PQ Tel: 01342 834800 Fax: 01342 832833

Website: www.lingfield-racecourse.co.uk

Clerk of the Course: George Hill

Executive Director: David Toulson-Burke

By Road: South-east of the town off the A22; M25 (Junction 6). Ample free parking.

By Rail: Lingfield Station (regular services from London Bridge and Victoria). Half-mile walk to the course.

By Air: London (Gatwick) Airport 10 miles. Helicopter landing facility south of wind-sock.

LUDLOW (R.H)

N.H. Oval, 1m4f (9), 185y run-in. The chase course is flat and has quite sharp bends into and out of the home straight, although long-striding horses never seem to have any difficulties. The hurdle course is on the outside of the chase track and is not so sharp.

Address: Ludlow Race Club Ltd, The Racecourse, Bromfield, Ludlow, Shropshire SY8 2BT

Tel: 01584 856221 (Racedays) or see below.

Website: www.ludlowracecourse.co.uk

Clerk of the Course: Simon Sherwood

General Manager: Bob Davies **Tel:** 01584 856221 **Mobile** 07970 861533 **Fax:** 01584 856217 **Email:** bobdavies@ludlowracecourse.co.uk

By Road: The course is situated at Bromfield, 2 miles north of Ludlow on the A49.

By Rail: Ludlow Station (Hereford-Shrewsbury line) 2 miles.

By Air: Helicopter landing facility in the centre of the course by arrangement with the Clerk of the Course and entirely at own risk.

MARKET RASEN (R.H)

N.H. Oval, 1m2f (8), 250y run-in. A sharp, undulating course with a long run to the straight, it favours the handy, front-running type.

Address: Market Rasen Racecourse, Legsby Road, Market Rasen, Lincolnshire LN8 3EA

Tel: 01673 843434 **Fax:** 01673 844532

Website: www.marketrasenraces.co.uk

Regional Director: Amy Starkey

Clerk of the Course: Jack Pryor

General Manager: Nadia Powell

By Road: The town is just off the A46, and the racecourse is one mile east of the town on the A631. Free car parks.

By Rail: Market Rasen Station 1 mile (King's Cross - Cleethorpes line).

By Air: Helicopter landing facility by prior arrangement only.

MUSSELBURGH (R.H)

Flat: A sharp, level, right-handed oval of 1m2f, with a run-in of 4f. There is an additional 5f straight course.

N.H. Rectangular, 1m3f (8), 150y run-in (variable). A virtually flat track with sharp turns, suiting the handy, front-running sort. Drains well. There is a section of Polytrack going away from the stands.

Address: Musselburgh Racecourse, Linkfield Road, Musselburgh, East Lothian EH21 7RG

Tel: 01316 652859 (Racecourse) **Fax:** 01316 532083

Website: www.musselburgh-racecourse.co.uk

Clerk of the Course: Harriet Graham 07843 380401

General Manager: Bill Farnsworth 07710 536134

By Road: The course is situated at Musselburgh, 5 miles east of Edinburgh on the A1. Car park, adjoining course, free for buses and cars.

By Rail: Waverley Station (Edinburgh). Local Rail service to Musselburgh.

By Air: Edinburgh (Turnhouse) Airport 30 minutes.

NEWBURY (L.H)

Flat: Left-handed, oval track of about 1m7f, with a slightly undulating straight mile. The round course is level and galloping with a four and a half-furlong straight. Races over the round mile start on the adjoining chute.

N.H. Oval, 1m6f (11), 255y run-in. Slightly undulating, wide and galloping in nature. The fences are stiff and sound jumping is essential. One of the fairest tracks in the country.

Address: Newbury Racecourse, Newbury, Berkshire RG14 7NZ **Tel:** 01635 40015 **Fax:** 01635 528354

Website: www.newbury-racecourse.co.uk

Chief Executive: Julian Thick

Raceday Clerk: Richard Osgood 07977 426947

By Road: East of the town off the A34 (M4, Junction 12 or 13). Car park, adjoining enclosures, free.

By Rail: Newbury Racecourse Station adjoins the course.

By Air: Light Aircraft landing strip East/West. 830 metres by 30 metres wide. Helicopter landing facilities.

NEWCASTLE (L.H)
Flat: Flat racing on turf discontinued, replaced in 2016 by a Tapeta track outside the jumps course. The straight mile is floodlit.
N.H. Oval, 1m6f (11), 220y run-in. A gradually rising home straight of four furlongs makes this galloping track a true test of stamina, especially as the ground can become very heavy.
Address: High Gosforth Park, Newcastle-Upon-Tyne, NE3 5HP Tel: 01912 362020 Fax: 01912 367761
Website: www.newcastle-racecourses.co.uk
Clerk of the Course: James Armstrong 07801 166820
Executive Director: David Williamson
By Road: 4 miles north of the city on the A6125 (near the A1). Car and coach park free.
By Rail: Newcastle Central Station (from King's Cross). A free bus service operates from South Gosforth and Regent Centre Metro Station.
By Air: Helicopter landing facility by prior arrangement. The Airport is 4 miles from the course.

NEWMARKET (R.H)
Rowley Mile Course: There is a straight ten-furlong course, which is wide and galloping. Races over 1m4f or more are right-handed. The Rowley Mile course has a long run-in and a stiff finish.
July Course: Races up to a mile are run on the Bunbury course, which is straight. Races over 1m2f or more are right-handed, with a 7f run-in. Like the Rowley Mile course, the July Course track is stiff.
Address: Newmarket Racecourse, Newmarket, Suffolk CB8 0TG Tel: 01638 663482 (Main Office) 01638 663762 (Rowley Mile) 01638 675416 (July) Fax: Rowley 01638 675340 Fax: July 01638 675410
Website: www.newmarketracecourses.co.uk
Clerk of the Course: Michael Prosser, Westfield House, The Links, Newmarket Tel: 01638 675504 or 07802 844578
Regional Director: Amy Starkey
By Road: South-west of the town on the A1304 London Road (M11 Junction 9). Free car parking at the rear of the enclosure. Annual Badge Holders' car park free all days. Free courtesy bus service from Newmarket Station, Bus Station and High Street, commencing 90 minutes prior to the first race, and return trips up to 60 minutes after the last race.
By Rail: Infrequent rail service to Newmarket Station from Cambridge (Liverpool Street) or direct bus service from Cambridge (13-mile journey).
By Air: Landing facilities for light aircraft and helicopters on racedays at both racecourses. See Flight Guide. Cambridge Airport 11 miles.

NEWTON ABBOT (L.H)
N.H. Oval, 1m2f (7), 300y run-in. Flat with two tight bends. The nippy, agile sort is favoured. The run-in can be very short on the hurdle course.
Address: Newton Abbot Races Ltd., Kingsteignton Road, Newton Abbot, Devon TQ12 3AF
Tel: 01626 353235 Fax: 01626 336972
Website: www.newtonabbotracing.com
Clerk of the Course: Jason Loosemore 07766 228109
Managing Director: Pat Masterson Tel: 01626 353235 Fax: 01626 336972 Mobile: 07917 830144
By Road: North of the town on the A380. Torquay 6 miles, Exeter 17 miles.
By Rail: Newton Abbot Station (from Paddington) ¾ mile. Buses and taxis operate to and from the course.
By Air: Helicopter landing pad in the centre of the course.

NOTTINGHAM (L.H)
Flat: Left-handed, galloping, oval of about 1m4f, and a straight of four and a half furlongs. Flat with easy turns.
Address: Nottingham Racecourse, Colwick Park, Nottingham, NG2 4BE Tel: 0870 8507634
Fax: 01159 584515
Website: www.nottinghamracecourse.co.uk
Regional Director: Amy Starkey
Clerk of the Course: Jane Hedley
Managing Director: James Knox
By Road: 2 miles east of the city centre on the B686.
By Rail: Nottingham (Midland) Station. Regular bus service to course (2 miles).
By Air: Helicopter landing facility in the centre of the course.

PERTH (R.H)

N.H. Rectangular, 1m2f (8), 283y run-in. A flat, easy track with sweeping turns. Not a course for the long-striding galloper. An efficient watering system ensures that the ground rarely gets hard.
Address: Perth Racecourse, Scone Palace Park, Perth, PH2 6BB Tel: 01738 551597 Fax: 01738 553021
Website: www.perth-races.co.uk
Clerk of the Course: Harriet Graham 07843 380401
General Manager: Hazel Peplinski
By Road: 4 miles north of the town off the A93.
By Rail: Perth Station (from Dundee) 4 miles. There are buses to the course.
By Air: Scone Airport (3.75 miles). Edinburgh Airport 45 minutes.

PLUMPTON (L.H)

N.H. Oval, 1m1f (7), 200y run-in uphill. A tight, undulating circuit with an uphill finish, Plumpton favours the handy, fast jumper. The ground often gets heavy, as the course is based on clay soil.
Address: Plumpton Racecourse, Plumpton, East Sussex BN7 3AL Tel: 01273 890383 Fax: 01273 891557
Website: www.plumptonracecourse.co.uk
Clerk of the Course: Mark Cornford 07759 151617
Chief Executive: Daniel Thompson
By Road: 2 miles north of the village off the B2116.
By Rail: Plumpton Station (from Victoria) adjoins course.
By Air: Helicopter landing facility by prior arrangement with the Clerk of the Course.

PONTEFRACT (L.H)

Flat: Left-handed oval, undulating course of 2m133y, with a short run-in of 2f. It is a particularly stiff track with the last 3f uphill.
Address: Pontefract Park Race Co. Ltd., The Park, Pontefract, West Yorkshire Tel: 01977 781307 (Racedays) Fax: 01977 781850
Website: www.pontefract-races.co.uk
Managing Director and Clerk of the Course: Norman Gundill 01977 781307
Assistant Manager and Clerk of the Course: Richard Hamill
By Road: 1 mile north of the town on the A639. Junction 32 of M62. Free car park adjacent to the course.
By Rail: Pontefract Station (Tanshelf, every hour to Wakefield), 1½ miles from the course. Regular bus service from Leeds.
By Air: Helicopters by arrangement only. (Nearest Airfields: Robin Hood (Doncaster), Sherburn-in-Elmet, Yeadon (Leeds Bradford).

REDCAR (L.H)

Flat: Left-handed, level, galloping, oval course of 1m6f with a straight run-in of 5f. There is also a straight mile.
Address: Redcar Racecourse, Redcar, Cleveland TS10 2BY Tel: 01642 484068 Fax: 01642 488272
Website: www.redcarracing.com
Clerk of the Course: Jonjo Sanderson Tel: 01642 484068 Mobile: 07766 022893
General Manager: Amy Fair
By Road: In town off the A1085. Free parking adjoining the course for buses and cars.
By Rail: Redcar Station (¼ mile from the course).
By Air: Landing facilities at Turners Arms Farm (600yds runway) Yearby, Cleveland. Two miles south of the racecourse - transport available. Durham Tees Valley airport (18 miles west of Redcar).

RIPON (R.H)

Flat: A sharp, undulating, right-handed oval of 1m5f, with a 5f run-in. There is also a 6f straight course.
Address: Ripon Racecourse, Boroughbridge Road, Ripon, North Yorkshire HG4 1UG Tel: 01765 530530
Fax: 01765 698900 E-mail: info@ripon-races.co.uk
Website: www.ripon-races.co.uk
Clerk of the Course and Managing Director: James Hutchinson
By Road: The course is situated 2 miles south-east of the city, on the B6265. There is ample free parking
for cars and coaches. For reservations apply to the Secretary.
By Rail: Harrogate Station (11 miles) or Thirsk (15 miles). Bus services to Ripon.
By Air: Helicopters only on the course. Otherwise Leeds/Bradford airport.

SALISBURY (R.H)

Flat: Right-handed and level, with a run-in of 4f. There is a straight mile track. The last half-mile is uphill,
providing a stiff test of stamina.
Address: Salisbury Racecourse, Netherhampton, Salisbury, Wiltshire SP2 8PN Tel: 01722 326461
Fax: 01722 412710
Website: www.salisburyracecourse.co.uk
Clerk of the Course and General Manager: Jeremy Martin 07880 744999
By Road: 3 miles south-west of the city on the A3094 at Netherhampton. Free car park adjoins the course.
By Rail: Salisbury Station is 3.5 miles (from London Waterloo). Bus service to the course.
By Air: Helicopter landing facility near the 1m2f start.

SANDOWN PARK (R.H)

Flat: An easy right-handed oval course of 1m5f with a stiff, straight uphill run-in of 4f. Separate straight 5f
track is also uphill. Galloping.
N.H. Oval, 1m5f (11), 220y run-in uphill. Features seven fences on the back straight; the last three (the
Railway Fences) are very close together and can often decide the outcome of races. The stiff climb to the
finish puts the emphasis very much on stamina, but accurate-jumping, free-running sorts are also
favoured. Hurdle races are run on the Flat course.
Address: Sandown Park Racecourse, Esher, Surrey KT10 9AJ Tel: 01372 464348 Fax: 01372 470427
Website: www.sandown.co.uk
Regional Director: Phil White
Clerk of the Course: Andrew Cooper, Sandown Park, Esher, Surrey Tel: 01372 461213
Mobile: 07774 230850
By Road: Four miles south-west of Kingston-on-Thames, on the A307 (M25 Junction 10).
By Rail: Esher Station (from Waterloo) adjoins the course.
By Air: London (Heathrow) Airport 12 miles.

SEDGEFIELD (L.H)

N.H. Oval, 1m2f (8), 220y run-in. Undulating with fairly tight turns, it doesn't suit big, long-striding horses.
Address: Sedgefield Racecourse, Sedgefield, Stockton-on-Tees, Cleveland TS21 2HW Tel: 01740 621925
Office Fax: 01740 620663
Website: www.sedgefield-racecourse.co.uk
Clerk of the Course: Paul Barker
General Manager: Jill Williamson
By Road: ¾ mile south-west of the town, near the junction of the A689 (Bishop Auckland) and the A177
(Durham) roads. The car park is free.
By Rail: Darlington Station (9 miles). Durham Station (12 miles).
By Air: Helicopter landing facility in car park area by prior arrangement only.

SOUTHWELL (L.H)

Flat, Fibresand: Left-handed oval, Fibresand course of 1m2f with a 3f run-in. There is a straight 5f. Sharp and level, Southwell suits front-runners.

N.H. Oval, 1m 1f (7), 220y run-in. A tight, flat track with a short run-in, it suits front-runners.

Address: Southwell Racecourse, Rolleston, Newark, Nottinghamshire NG25 0TS Tel: 01636 814481
Fax: 01636 812271

Website: www.southwell-racecourse.co.uk

Managing Director: Mark Clayton

Clerk of the Course: Roderick Duncan 07772 958685

By Road: The course is situated at Rolleston, 3 miles south of Southwell, 5 miles from Newark.

By Rail: Rolleston Station (Nottingham-Newark line) adjoins the course.

By Air: Helicopters can land by prior arrangement.

STRATFORD-ON-AVON (L.H)

N.H. Triangular, 1m2f (8), 200y run-in. Virtually flat with two tight bends, and quite a short home straight. A sharp and turning course, it suits the well-balanced, handy sort.

Address: Stratford Racecourse, Luddington Road, Stratford-upon-Avon, Warwickshire CV37 9SE
Tel: 01789 267949 Fax: 01789 415850

Website: www.stratfordracecourse.net

Managing Director: Ilona Barnett

Clerk of the Course: Nessie Lambert

By Road: A mile from the town centre, off the A429 (Evesham road).

By Rail: Stratford-on-Avon Station (from Birmingham New Street or Leamington Spa) 1 mile.

By Air: Helicopter landing facility by prior arrangement.

TAUNTON (R.H)

N.H. Elongated oval, 1m2f (8), 150y run-in uphill. Sharp turns, especially after the winning post, with a steady climb from the home bend. Suits the handy sort.

Address: Taunton Racecourse, Orchard Portman, Taunton, Somerset TA3 7BL Tel: 01823 337172
Office Fax: 01823 325881

Website: www.tauntonracecourse.co.uk

Clerk of the Course: Jason Loosemore

General Manager: Bob Young

By Road: Two miles south of the town on the B3170 (Honiton) road (M5 Junction 25).

By Rail: Taunton Station 2 miles. There are buses and taxis to course.

By Air: Helicopter landing facility by prior arrangement.

THIRSK (L.H)

Flat: Left-handed oval of 1m2f with sharp turns and an undulating run-in of 4f. There is a straight 6f track.

Address: The Racecourse, Station Road, Thirsk, North Yorkshire YO7 1QL Tel: 01845 522276
Fax: 01845 525353

Website: www.thirskracecourse.net

Clerk of the Course and Managing Director: James Sanderson

By Road: West of the town on the A61. Free car park adjacent to the course for buses and cars.

By Rail: Thirsk Station (from King's Cross), ½ mile from the course.

By Air: Helicopters can land by prior arrangement. Tel: Racecourse 01845 522276. Fixed wing aircraft can land at RAF Leeming. Tel: 01677 423041. Light aircraft at Bagby. Tel: 01845 597385 or 01845 537555.

TOWCESTER (R.H)

N.H. Square, 1m6f (10), 200y run-in uphill. The final six furlongs are uphill. One of the most testing tracks in the country with the emphasis purely on stamina.

Address: The Racecourse, London Road, Towcester, Northants NN12 6LB Tel: 01327 353414

Fax: 01327 358534

Website: www.towcester-racecourse.co.uk

Clerk of the Course: Robert Bellamy 07836 241458

Chief Executive: Kevin Ackerman

By Road: 1 mile south-east of the town on the A5 (Milton Keynes road). M1 (Junction 15a).

By Rail: Northampton Station (Euston) 9 miles, buses to Towcester; or Milton Keynes (Euston) 12 miles, taxis available.

By Air: Helicopters can land by prior arrangement with the Racecourse Manager.

UTTOXETER (L.H)

N.H. Oval, 1m2f (8), 170y run-in. A few undulations, easy bends and fences and a flat home straight of over half a mile. Suits front-runners, especially on the 2m hurdle course.

Address: The Racecourse, Wood Lane, Uttoxeter, Staffordshire ST14 8BD Tel: 01889 562561

Fax: 01889 562786

Website: www.uttoxeter-racecourse.co.uk

Clerk of the Course: Charlie Moore 07764 255500

General Manager: David MacDonald

By Road: South-east of the town off the B5017 (Marchington Road).

By Rail: Uttoxeter Station (Crewe-Derby line) adjoins the course.

By Air: Helicopters can land by prior arrangement with the raceday office.

WARWICK (L.H)

N.H. Circular, 1m6f (10), 240y run-in. Undulating with tight bends, five quick fences in the back straight and a short home straight, Warwick favours handiness and speed rather than stamina.

Address: Warwick Racecourse, Hampton Street, Warwick, CV34 6HN Tel: 01926 491553

Fax: 01926 403223

Website: www.warwickracecourse.co.uk

Regional Director: Ian Renton

Clerk of the Course: Jane Hedley

Managing Director: Andre Klein

By Road: West of the town on the B4095 adjacent to Junction 15 of the M40.

By Rail: Warwick or Warwick Parkway Stations.

By Air: Helicopters can land by prior arrangement with the Clerk of the Course.

WETHERBY (L.H)

Flat: First used in 2015, the Flat course is left-handed with a 1m4f circuit.

N.H. Oval, 1m4f (9), 200y run-in slightly uphill. A flat, very fair course which suits the long-striding galloper.

Address: The Racecourse, York Road, Wetherby, LS22 5EJ Tel: 01937 582035 Fax: 01937 588021

Website: www.wetherbyracing.co.uk

Clerk of the Course and Chief Executive: Jonjo Sanderson 07831 437453

By Road: East of the town off the B1224 (York Road). Adjacent to the A1. Excellent bus and coach facilities. Car park free.

By Rail: Leeds Station 12 miles. Buses to Wetherby.

By Air: Helicopters can land by prior arrangement

WINCANTON (R.H)
N.H. Rectangular, 1m3f (9), 200y run-in. Good galloping course where the going rarely becomes heavy. The home straight is mainly downhill.
Address: Wincanton Racecourse, Wincanton, Somerset BA9 8BJ Tel: 01963 435840
Website: www.wincantonracecourse.co.uk
Regional Director: Ian Renton
Clerk of the Course: Barry Johnson 07976 791578
General Manager: Huw Williams
By Road: 1 mile north of the town on the B3081.
By Rail: Gillingham Station (from Waterloo) or Castle Cary Station (from Paddington). Buses and taxis to the course.
By Air: Helicopter landing area is situated in the centre of the course.

WINDSOR (Fig. 8)
Flat: Figure of eight track of 1m4f 110y. The course is level and sharp with a long run-in. The 6f course is essentially straight.
Address: Royal Windsor Racecourse, Maidenhead Road, Windsor, Berkshire SL4 5JJ Tel: 01753 498400 Fax: 01753 830156
Website: www.windsor-racecourse.co.uk
Clerk of the Course: To be announced
Executive Director: Simon Williams
By Road: North of the town on the A308 (M4 Junction 6).
By Rail: Windsor Central Station (from Paddington) or Windsor and Eton Riverside Station (from Waterloo).
By Air: London (Heathrow) Airport 15 minutes. Also White Waltham Airport (West London Aero Club) 15 minutes.
River Bus: Seven minutes from Barry Avenue promenade at Windsor.

WOLVERHAMPTON (L.H)
Flat: Left-handed oval Tapeta track of 1m, with a run-in of 380y. A level track with sharp bends.
Address: Wolverhampton Racecourse, Dunstall Park, Gorsebrook Road, Wolverhampton, WV6 0PE Tel: 01902 390000 Fax: 01902 421621
Website: www.wolverhampton-racecourse.co.uk
Clerk of the Course: Fergus Cameron 07971 531162
General Manager: Dave Roberts
By Road: 1 mile north of the city centre on the A449 (M54 Junction 2 or M6 Junction 12). Car parking free.
By Rail: Wolverhampton Station (from Euston) 1 mile.
By Air: Halfpenny Green Airport 8 miles.

WORCESTER (L.H)
N.H. Elongated oval, 1m5f (9), 220y run-in. Flat with easy turns, it is a very fair, galloping track.
Address: Worcester Racecourse, Pitchcroft, Worcester, WR1 3EJ Tel: 01905 25364 Fax: 01905 617563
Website: www.worcester-racecourse.co.uk
Clerk of the Course: Libby O'Flaherty
Executive Director: Jenny Cheshire
By Road: West of the city centre off the A449 (Kidderminster road) (M5 Junction 8).
By Rail: Foregate Street Station, Worcester (from Paddington) ¾ mile.
By Air: Helicopter landing facility in the centre of the course, by prior arrangement only.

YARMOUTH (L.H)

Flat: Left-handed, level circuit of 1m4f, with a run-in of 5f. The straight course is 1m long.
Address: The Racecourse, Jellicoe Road, Great Yarmouth, Norfolk NR30 4AU Tel: 01493 842527
Fax: 01493 843254
Website: www.greatyarmouth-racecourse.co.uk
Clerk of the Course: Richard Aldous 07738 507643
Executive Director: Glenn Tubby
By Road: 1 mile east of town centre (well signposted from A47 and A12).
By Rail: Great Yarmouth Station (1 mile). Bus service to the course.
By Air: Helicopter landing available by prior arrangement with Racecourse Office

YORK (L.H)

Flat: Left-handed, level, galloping track, with a straight 6f. There is also an adjoining course of 6f 214y.
Address: The Racecourse, York, YO23 1EX Tel: 01904 683932 Fax: 01904 611071
Website: www.yorkracecourse.co.uk
Clerk of the Course and Chief Executive: William Derby 07812 961176
Assistant Clerk of the Course: Anthea Morshead
By Road: 1 mile south-east of the city on the A1036.
By Rail: 1½ miles York Station (from King's Cross). Special bus service from station to the course.
By Air: Light aircraft and helicopter landing facilities available at Rufforth aerodrome (5,000ft tarmac runway). £20 landing fee - transport arranged to course. Leeds Bradford airport (25 miles).

THE INVESTEC DERBY STAKES (GROUP 1)
EPSOM DOWNS ON SATURDAY 2ND JUNE 2018

SECOND ENTRIES BY NOON APRIL 3RD; SUPPLEMENTARY ENTRIES BY NOON MAY 28TH.

HORSE	TRAINER	HORSE	TRAINER
ADELPHI (IRE)	Aidan O'Brien	CANDIDATE (IRE)	Hughie Morrison
ADVANCED VIRGO (IRE)	George Scott	CAPE SUNRISE	C. J. M. Wolters
AIRCRAFT CARRIER (IRE)	Aidan O'Brien	CARADOC (IRE)	Ed Walker
AIRMAX (GER)	Ralph Beckett	CASCADIAN	Andre Fabre
AL AMIR	Simon Crisford	CELESTIAL FORCE (IRE)	Tom Dascombe
AL EMARAT (IRE)	Kevin Ryan	CENTAURIAN (IRE)	Joseph Patrick O'Brien
ALFURSAAN (IRE)	Jean-Claude Rouget	CENTROID	D. K. Weld
ALHAJRAS (USA)	Jean-Claude Rouget	CHANGE OF VELOCITY (IRE)	J. S. Bolger
ALIYM (IRE)	D. K. Weld	CHANPOUR (FR)	Jean-Claude Rouget
AL KHERB	Roger Charlton	CHARLES KINGSLEY	Charlie Appleby
ALLIED	Sir Michael Stoute	CHRISTOPHER ROBIN (IRE)	Aidan O'Brien
ALMOGHARED (IRE)	John Gosden	CLIFFS OF DOONEEN (IRE)	Aidan O'Brien
AL MUFFRIH (IRE)	William Haggas	COAT OF ARMS (IRE)	Aidan O'Brien
ALMUSHREF (USA)	F. Head	COGITAL	Amanda Perrett
ALPINE PEAK (USA)	Roger Varian	COLENSO	
ALTERNATIVE FACT	Ed Dunlop	COMMONWEALTH (IRE)	Martyn Meade
AMEDEO MODIGLIANI (IRE)	Aidan O'Brien	CONCLUSION (JPN)	Aidan O'Brien
ANTAGONIST	Roger Charlton	CONFEDERATE	Hugo Palmer
ANTONIAN	John Gosden	CONSTRUCT	Ralph Beckett
ARGENTELLO (IRE)	John Gosden	COOLONGOLOOK	Luca Cumani
ARTARMON (IRE)	Michael Bell	CORELLI (USA)	John Gosden
ARTHUR DALEY (IRE)	George Scott	CORGI	Hughie Morrison
ASHQAR (IRE)	D. K. Weld	COSMO IN THE HEART (JPN)	M. Nishizono
ASHTIYR (USA)	A. de Royer Dupre	CRIMSON MYSTERY (IRE)	D. K. Weld
ASPETAR (FR)	Roger Charlton	CROSSED BATON	John Gosden
ASSASSINATOR	Ed Walker	CROSSING POINT (USA)	F. Head
ASTROLOGIST (IRE)	Clive Cox	CRYSTAL KING	Sir Michael Stoute
ASTROMACHIA	Amanda Perrett	CYPRESS CREEK (IRE)	Aidan O'Brien
ASTRONOMER (IRE)	Aidan O'Brien	DALILEO (IRE)	Mark Johnston
ATTICUS BOY (IRE)	David Lanigan	DALVINI (FR)	A. de Royer Dupre
AUSTIN TEXAS (IRE)	Aidan O'Brien	DEE EX BEE	Mark Johnston
AUSTRIAN SCHOOL (IRE)	Mark Johnston	DEFINITION	Charles Hills
BALIYAD (IRE)	D. K. Weld	DELANO ROOSEVELT (IRE)	Aidan O'Brien
BARITONE (IRE)	Sir Michael Stoute	DEYAARNA (USA)	Saeed bin Suroor
BARTHOLOMEU DIAS	Charles Hills	DIOCLETIAN (IRE)	Andrew Balding
BATTLE OF ISSUS (IRE)	David Menuisier	DISCOVER DUBAI (IRE)	Saeed bin Suroor
BEAUVAIS (IRE)	Saeed bin Suroor	DOMESTIC WAY (QA)	Marco Botti
BEER WITH THE BOYS	Mick Channon	DOWNDRAFT (IRE)	Joseph Patrick O'Brien
BEING THERE (FR)	Charlie Appleby	DRAPERS GUILD	Joseph Patrick O'Brien
BERKELEY SQUARE (IRE)	Aidan O'Brien	DREAM WARRIOR	Charlie Appleby
BERKSHIRE BLUE (IRE)	Andrew Balding	DRESS COAT	Saeed bin Suroor
BERKSHIRE SPIRIT	Andrew Balding	DRIFTING STAR (IRE)	Sir Michael Stoute
BERMUDA TRIANGLE (IRE)	William Haggas	DRUMMER	
BEST BLUE	Michael Bell	DUBAI FRAME	Ed Dunlop
BILLY RAY	Mick Channon	DUBHE	Charlie Appleby
BISCAY BAY	Andre Fabre	DUKHAN	Hugo Palmer
BLACKHILLSOFDAKOTA (IRE)	Aidan O'Brien	EBADALI (IRE)	D. K. Weld
BLAZING SADDLES	Ralph Beckett	ELARQAM	Mark Johnston
BOMBYX	James Fanshawe	ELECTOR	Sir Michael Stoute
BOND STREET (IRE)	Aidan O'Brien	EL GRECO (IRE)	Aidan O'Brien
BRAEMAR	Sir Michael Stoute	ELIPHAS	Andre Fabre
BRIDPORT (IRE)	Joseph Patrick O'Brien	ELWAZIR	Owen Burrows
BRIGHAM YOUNG	Ed Walker	EMARAATY	John Gosden
BROADCAST (USA)	Andre Fabre	EMPIREOFTHEDRAGON (IRE)	Aidan O'Brien
BROAD STREET	D. K. Weld	EMPLOYER (IRE)	Hugo Palmer
BRUNDTLAND (IRE)	Charlie Appleby	FAIRLIGHT (IRE)	Luca Cumani
CACOPHONOUS	David Menuisier	FALCON EIGHT (IRE)	D. K. Weld
CAINTEACH (IRE)	J. S. Bolger	FAMILY TREE	Aidan O'Brien
CALIBURN (IRE)	Hugo Palmer	FIGHTFORTHEROSES (IRE)	Aidan O'Brien

HORSE	TRAINER
FIRST ELEVEN	John Gosden
FLAG OF HONOUR (IRE)	Aidan O'Brien
FLINTROCK (GER)	Andrew Balding
FLYING DEMON	John Gosden
FOREIGN LEGION (IRE)	Aidan O'Brien
FORGOTTEN PROMISES	
FORT APACHE	Hugo Palmer
FORTUNE TELLER (IRE)	Aidan O'Brien
FRANKINCENSE (IRE)	Aidan O'Brien
FREETOWN (IRE)	Aidan O'Brien
FULL MOON (IRE)	Aidan O'Brien
GABR	Sir Michael Stoute
GARDENS OF BABYLON (IRE)	Aidan O'Brien
GARSINGTON	Ed Dunlop
GHAIYYATH (IRE)	Charlie Appleby
GHOSTWATCH	Charlie Appleby
GIUSEPPE GARIBALDI (IRE)	Aidan O'Brien
GLASSES UP (USA)	Joseph Patrick O'Brien
GLENCADAM MASTER	John Gosden
GLOBAL GIANT	Ed Dunlop
GLOBAL STYLE (IRE)	Ed Dunlop
GLORIOUS JOURNEY	Charlie Appleby
GONZAGA	
GRANDFATHER TOM	Robert Cowell
GRANDSCAPE	Ed Dunlop
GRATOT (FR)	John Gosden
GUILD	Roger Charlton
GUSTAV KLIMT (IRE)	Aidan O'Brien
HAINAUT	
HAMLUL (FR)	Sir Michael Stoute
HANDSOME SAMSON	Richard Spencer
HARAWI	Sir Michael Stoute
HARBOUR VIEW (FR)	Luca Cumani
HAREEQ	Sir Michael Stoute
HASANABAD (IRE)	D. K. Weld Ireland
HAWTHORN (IRE)	Aidan O'Brien
HAYMAKER (IRE)	Saeed bin Suroor
HAZAPOUR (IRE)	D. K. Weld
HAZARFAN	Ed Dunlop
HAZM (IRE)	Sir Michael Stoute
HEAVENLY SECRET (IRE)	Sir Michael Stoute
HIDDEN DEPTHS (IRE)	Sir Michael Stoute
HIDDEN DRAGON (IRE)	Aidan O'Brien
HIGH MOUNTE (IRE)	Joseph Patrick O'Brien
HIGH PRIEST	John Gosden
HORIZON (IRE)	Aidan O'Brien
HOUSE EDGE	Michael Bell
HOWMAN (IRE)	Roger Varian
HUNTING HORN (IRE)	Aidan O'Brien
IBRAZ	Roger Varian
IN DEMAND (IRE)	Charlie Fellowes
INDIANAPOLIS (IRE)	Aidan O'Brien
INTANGIBLE STAR	William Haggas
INVOLVED	Daniel Kubler
ISPOLINI	Charlie Appleby
JAMES COOK (IRE)	Aidan O'Brien
JAMIH	John Gosden
JARIK (USA)	D. K. Weld
JASSAAR	D. K. Weld
JETSTREAM (IRE)	Charles Hills
JOSHUA FARADAY (IRE)	Joseph Patrick O'Brien
KAPOW (IRE)	Charles Hills
KASBAAN	Owen Burrows
KENYA (IRE)	Aidan O'Brien
KEW GARDENS (IRE)	Aidan O'Brien
KING AND EMPIRE (IRE)	Andrew Balding
KING OF CAMELOT (FR)	Aidan O'Brien

HORSE	TRAINER
KING OF LEOGRANCE (FR)	Aidan O'Brien
KINGOFTHESINGERS	Sir Mark Prescott Bt
KITE WING	John Gosden
KITTILEO (IRE)	Mark Johnston
KNIGHT TO BEHOLD (IRE)	Harry Dunlop
LARADEEF (IRE)	John Gosden
LAST VICEROY	Brian Meehan
LATROBE (IRE)	Joseph Patrick O'Brien
LAUGHING STRANGER (USA)	Jeremy Noseda
LENNOX (GER)	P. Bary
LISCANNOR BAY (IRE)	Aidan O'Brien
LOVEISILI	Roger Varian
LOYAL PROMISE (IRE)	Martyn Meade
LUCIUS TIBERIUS (IRE)	Aidan O'Brien
MADRID (IRE)	Aidan O'Brien
MANDHARI (FR)	A. de Royer Dupre
MARECHAL NEY	John Gosden
MASAR (IRE)	Charlie Appleby
MAWROOTH	Jean-Claude Rouget
MAZBOON (IRE)	Roger Varian
MEDIA CITY (IRE)	J. S. Bolger
MEKONG	Sir Michael Stoute
MERCURY RISING	Andrew Balding
MERWEB (IRE)	John Gosden
MIDI	Sir Michael Stoute
MILITARY LAW	John Gosden
MOMENT IN HISTORY (IRE)	Aidan O'Brien
MONOXIDE	Martyn Meade
MOON OF BARODA	Charles Hills
MOTARAABET	Owen Burrows
MOUNT ARARAT (IRE)	K. R. Burke
MOUNT POPA (IRE)	P. Bary
MSAYYAN (IRE)	John Gosden
MUFEED	F. Head
MUJID (IRE)	D. K. Weld
MUSAAHIB (IRE)	K. Prendergast
MUTAABEQ (IRE)	D. K. Weld
MUZAAWEL	Saeed bin Suroor
MY LORD AND MASTER (IRE)	William Haggas
MYTHOLOGICAL (IRE)	Peter Chapple-Hyam
NARYNKOL	Roger Varian
NASEE	Sir Michael Stoute
NATIONAL SECURITY (IRE)	J. S. Bolger
NEAR GOLD	F. Head
NEEDS TO BE SEEN (FR)	Joseph Patrick O'Brien
NELSON (IRE)	Aidan O'Brien
NOBLEMAN'S NEST	Simon Crisford
NORTH FACE (IRE)	Aidan O'Brien
OCCUPY (USA)	Ralph Beckett
OCEAN DEEP (IRE)	Aidan O'Brien
OLYMPIC ODYSSEY	George Scott
ON THE WARPATH	Charlie Appleby
OSCAR'S RIDGE (IRE)	John Gosden
OSTILIO	Simon Crisford
OXFORD THESPIAN (IRE)	Szabolcs Szuna
PERFECT BLUE (IRE)	
PERFECT ILLUSION	Andrew Balding
PERPETRATOR (IRE)	Roger Charlton
PERSIAN LION (IRE)	Mrs J. Harrington
PHILOTIMO (IRE)	John M. Oxx
PHOTOGRAPHER	John Gosden
PIRATE'S GOLD (IRE)	Aidan O'Brien
PREPARE FOR BATTLE (USA)	Aidan O'Brien
PRIZERING (IRE)	Saeed bin Suroor
PROSCHEMA (IRE)	Tom Dascombe
QUANTATMENTAL (IRE)	Tom Dascombe
RAKHAA	J. Hammond

HORSE	TRAINER
RAMAAS (IRE)	
RASHDAN (FR)	Hugo Palmer
REACTIVE	James Given
RECORDMAN	Saeed bin Suroor
RED MIST	Simon Crisford
RED STRIKER (IRE)	Sir Michael Stoute
REFRAIN (IRE)	Sir Michael Stoute
REGAL DIRECTOR (IRE)	Simon Crisford
RESTIVE SPIRIT	William Haggas
RHODE ISLAND (IRE)	John Gosden
RHOSNEIGR (IRE)	Charles Hills
ROARING LION (USA)	John Gosden
ROCK FORCE (IRE)	Tom Dascombe
ROSTROPOVICH (IRE)	Aidan O'Brien
ROUDRAPOUR (FR)	A. de Royer Dupre
RULE OF HONOUR	Ismail Mohammed
SAINT MAC	Hughie Morrison
SANSKRIT (IRE)	P. Bary
SARACEN KNIGHT (IRE)	Aidan O'Brien
SARIM (IRE)	
SAVITAR (IRE)	J. S. Bolger
SAWWAAH	Owen Burrows
SAXON WARRIOR (JPN)	Aidan O'Brien
SEAT OF POWER (IRE)	David Simcock
SEPTIMER (IRE)	Sir Michael Stoute
SEVENNA STAR (IRE)	John Gosden
SEXTANT	Sir Michael Stoute
SHARASTI (IRE)	A. de Royer Dupre
SHAREEF STAR	Sir Michael Stoute
SHARJA SILK	Roger Varian
SHARP SUITED	Simon Crisford
SHAUQAT (FR)	A. de Royer Dupre
SHAWAAF AL NIJOOM (IRE)	Simon Crisford
SHOWROOM (FR)	Mark Johnston
SILVER CHARACTER (IRE)	Tom Dascombe
SILVER QUARTZ	Hugo Palmer
SIR EREC (IRE)	Aidan O'Brien
SLEEPING LION (USA)	James Fanshawe
SMART CHAMPION	Simon Crisford
SMART LIVING (IRE)	J. S. Bolger
SOMERSET MAUGHAM (IRE)	Aidan O'Brien
SOUTHERN FRANCE (IRE)	Aidan O'Brien
SOVEREIGN DUKE (GER)	Henry Candy
SPACE BANDIT	Michael Bell
SPANISH POINT	Aidan O'Brien
STAGE OF BEING	P. Bary
STARCASTER	Hughie Morrison
STELLA D'ORO (USA)	Joseph Patrick O'Brien
STEPHENSONS ROCKET (IRE)	Ed Walker
STUDY OF MAN (IRE)	P. Bary
SUBJUDICE (IRE)	Joseph Patrick O'Brien
SURYA	John Gosden
SWANSON (IRE)	Joseph Patrick O'Brien
TAHREEK	Sir Michael Stoute
TAJDEED (IRE)	Mark Johnston
TANINO FRANKEL (IRE)	Katsuhiko Sumii
TASNEEM	Saeed bin Suroor
TEATRO (IRE)	James Given
TENEDOS	Hugo Palmer
THE KING (IRE)	Mrs J. Harrington
THEOBALD (IRE)	J. S. Bolger
THEOTONIUS (IRE)	J. S. Bolger
THE PENTAGON (IRE)	Aidan O'Brien
THE REVENANT	Hugo Palmer
THRAVE	Henry Candy
THUNDERHOOVES	John Ryan
THUNDER NORTH (IRE)	David Lanigan

HORSE	TRAINER
TURKMEN	
ULSTER (IRE)	Saeed bin Suroor
URBINO	Sir Michael Stoute
VADAVAR (FR)	A. de Royer Dupre
VADIYANN (FR)	Jean-Claude Rouget
VALYRIAN	Luca Cumani
VERBITUDE (IRE)	J. S. Bolger
VICTORY SALUTE (IRE)	Aidan O'Brien
VOICE OF THE NORTH	
VOLCANIC SKY	Saeed bin Suroor
VOYAGER BLUE	Jamie Osborne
WADILSAFA	Owen Burrows
WAFY (IRE)	Charles Hills
WAJAAHA (IRE)	Saeed bin Suroor
WAX AND WANE	K. R. Burke
WAX SEAL (IRE)	D. K. Weld
WE KNOW (IRE)	Simon Crisford
WHIRLING DERVISH	Mrs J. Harrington
WHITE GUARD	Sir Mark Prescott Bt
WILLIAM OF WYKEHAM (IRE)	
WILLIE JOHN	William Haggas
YAALAIL (IRE)	J. Hammond
YOU'RE NO BETTER	Jamie Osborne
YOUNG RASCAL (FR)	William Haggas
ZAAJER	Owen Burrows
ZABRISKIE (IRE)	Aidan O'Brien
ZUCCHINI	Andre Fabre
EX ASHALANDA (FR)	A. de Royer Dupre
EX BRIGID (USA)	Martyn Meade
EX CRYSTAL MOUNTAIN (USA)	
EX LAWLESS LADY (IRE)	N. Clement
EX LIDANSKI (IRE)	A. P. Keatley
EX LOLLINA PAULINA	Marco Botti
EX MARY FRITH	Marco Botti
EX PARA SIEMPRE	
EX PRAISE (USA)	John Gosden
EX RIDAFA (IRE)	
EX RIDASIYNA (FR)	M. Delzangles
EX TEDDY BEARS PICNIC	John Gosden
EX WASMI (IRE)	
EX BLUE BLUE SEA	Henri-Francois Devin
EX SPLENDEUR (FR)	Marco Botti
EX YOUDA (IRE)	Marco Botti

THE bet365
EUROPEAN FREE HANDICAP
NEWMARKET CRAVEN MEETING 2018
(ON THE ROWLEY MILE COURSE)
WEDNESDAY APRIL 18TH

The bet365 European Free Handicap (Class 1) (Listed race) with total prize fund of £50,000 for two-year-olds only of 2017 which are included in the European 2-y-o Thoroughbred Rankings or which, in 2017, either ran in Great Britain or ran for a trainer who at the time was licensed by the British Horseracing Authority, and are Rated 100 or above; lowest weight 8st; highest weight 9st 7lb.

Penalty for a winner after December 31st 2017, 5lb. Seven furlongs.

Rating		st	lb	Rating		st	lb
122	U S NAVY FLAG (USA)	9	7	109	CAPLA TEMPTRESS (IRE)	8	8
119	SAXON WARRIOR (JPN)	9	4	109	EMARAATY (GB)	8	8
118	ROARING LION (USA)	9	3	108	ALPHA CENTAURI (IRE)	8	7
117	EXPERT EYE (GB)	9	2	108	GABR (GB)	8	7
117	VERBAL DEXTERITY (IRE)	9	2	108	NEBO (IRE)	8	7
116	MENDELSSOHN (USA)	9	1	108	THREADING (IRE)	8	7
116	SANDS OF MALI (FR)	9	1	108	WELLS FARHH GO (IRE)	8	7
116	UNFORTUNATELY (IRE)	9	1	107	DANZAN (IRE)	8	6
115	CLEMMIE (IRE)	9	0	107	DECLARATIONOFPEACE (USA)	8	6
115	FLEET REVIEW (USA)	9	0	107	DREAM TODAY (IRE)	8	6
115	SIOUX NATION (USA)	9	0	107	ELLTHEA (IRE)	8	6
114	WILD ILLUSION (GB)	8	13	107	FROZEN ANGEL (IRE)	8	6
113	BECKFORD (GB)	8	12	107	GLORIOUS JOURNEY (GB)	8	6
113	HAPPILY (IRE)	8	12	107	MILDENBERGER (GB)	8	6
113	HAVANA GREY (GB)	8	12	107	MURILLO (USA)	8	6
113	LAURENS (FR)	8	12	107	RAJASINGHE (IRE)	8	6
113	OLMEDO (FR)	8	12	107	ROMANISED (IRE)	8	6
113	THE PENTAGON (IRE)	8	12	107	SHABAABY (GB)	8	6
112	ELARQAM (GB)	8	11	107	SOUND AND SILENCE (GB)	8	6
112	ERASMUS (GER)	8	11	107	TIP TWO WIN (GB)	8	6
112	HEARTACHE (GB)	8	11	107	ZAMAN (IRE)	8	6
112	JAMES GARFIELD (IRE)	8	11	106	ACTRESS (IRE)	8	5
112	MASAR (IRE)	8	11	106	CHILEAN (GB)	8	5
112	NELSON (IRE)	8	11	106	GREAT PROSPECTOR (IRE)	8	5
112	SACRED LIFE (FR)	8	11	106	HAPPY LIKE A FOOL (USA)	8	5
112	SEAHENGE (USA)	8	11	106	HEADWAY (GB)	8	5
112	SEPTEMBER (IRE)	8	11	106	JULIET CAPULET (IRE)	8	5
112	WOOTTON (FR)	8	11	106	MADELINE (IRE)	8	5
111	BARRAQUERO (IRE)	8	10	106	NOW YOU'RE TALKING (IRE)	8	5
111	CARDSHARP (GB)	8	10	106	STAGE MAGIC (GB)	8	5
111	GHAIYYATH (IRE)	8	10	106	TANGLED (IRE)	8	5
111	GUSTAV KLIMT (IRE)	8	10	105	ABEL HANDY (IRE)	8	4
111	HEY GAMAN (GB)	8	10	105	ALTYN ORDA (IRE)	8	4
111	MAGICAL (IRE)	8	10	105	BYE BYE BABY (IRE)	8	4
111	MAGIC LILY (GB)	8	10	105	CORINTHIA KNIGHT (IRE)	8	4
111	MISSION IMPASSIBLE (IRE)	8	10	105	ZYZZYVA (FR)	8	4
111	POLYDREAM (IRE)	8	10	104	BEATBOX RHYTHM (IRE)	8	3
111	THREEANDFOURPENCE (USA)	8	10	104	DARK ROSE ANGEL (IRE)	8	3
110	DIFFERENT LEAGUE (FR)	8	9	104	DARKANNA (IRE)	8	3
110	HEY JONESY (IRE)	8	9	104	FIGHTING IRISH (IRE)	8	3
110	INVINCIBLE ARMY (IRE)	8	9	104	GAVOTA (GB)	8	3
110	KEW GARDENS (IRE)	8	9	104	RED MIST (GB)	8	3
110	LUMINATE (IRE)	8	9	104	SPEAK IN COLOURS (GB)	8	3
110	MYTHICAL MAGIC (IRE)	8	9	103	AL HAJAR (IRE)	8	2
110	NYALETI (IRE)	8	9	103	ARCHIE MCKELLAR (GB)	8	2

Rating		st	lb
103	BENGALI BOYS (IRE)	8	2
103	DEE EX BEE (GB)	8	2
103	EFAADAH (IRE)	8	2
103	ENJAZAAT (GB)	8	2
103	RUFUS KING (GB)	8	2
103	TO WAFIJ (IRE)	8	2
102	AQABAH (USA)	8	1
102	BROTHER BEAR (IRE)	8	1
102	DEMONS ROCK (IRE)	8	1
102	FAJJAJ (IRE)	8	1
102	FLAG OF HONOUR (IRE)	8	1
102	GRAFFITI MASTER (GB)	8	1
102	I CAN FLY (GB)	8	1
102	LANSKY (IRE)	8	1
102	LOXLEY (IRE)	8	1
102	MOKAATIL (GB)	8	1
102	MUTAAQEB (GB)	8	1
102	PRINCE OF THE DARK (GB)	8	1
102	PURSER (USA)	8	1
102	RAYDIANCE (GB)	8	1
102	ROUSSEL (IRE)	8	1
102	SIZZLING (IRE)	8	1
102	TAJAANUS (IRE)	8	1
102	TIGRE DU TERRE (FR)	8	1
101	ALTERNATIVE FACT (GB)	8	0
101	ANOTHER BATT (IRE)	8	0

Rating		st	lb
101	ARBALET (IRE)	8	0
101	CONNECT (GB)	8	0
101	ELIZABETH DARCY (IRE)	8	0
101	FINNISTON FARM (GB)	8	0
101	FOLK TALE (IRE)	8	0
101	HIKMAA (IRE)	8	0
101	LAUGH A MINUTE (GB)	8	0
101	MAMBA NOIRE (FR)	8	0
101	OUT OF THE FLAMES (GB)	8	0
101	PETRUS (IRE)	8	0
101	STAXTON (GB)	8	0
101	THEOBALD (IRE)	8	0
100	ALBA POWER (IRE)	7	13
100	ANNA NERIUM (GB)	7	13
100	BATTLE OF JERICHO (USA)	7	13
100	BUTTERSCOTCH (IRE)	7	13
100	EIRENE (GB)	7	13
100	FORTUNE'S PEARL (IRE)	7	13
100	LUBINKA (IRE)	7	13
100	MUIRIN (IRE)	7	13
100	SEAELLA (IRE)	7	13
100	SNAZZY JAZZY (IRE)	7	13
100	SPOOF (GB)	7	13
100	TAKE ME WITH YOU (USA)	7	13
100	TRUE BLUE MOON (IRE)	7	13
100	ZAAKI (GB)	7	13

LONGINES WORLD'S BEST RACEHORSE RANKINGS AND EUROPEAN THOROUGHBRED RANKINGS 2017

for three-year-olds rated 115 or greater by the IFHA World's Best Racehorse Rankings Conference. Horses rated 114-110 by the European Thoroughbred Rankings Conference do not constitute a part of the World's Best Racehorse Rankings. Those ratings were compiled on behalf of the European Pattern Committee.

Rating		Trained
130	CRACKSMAN (GB)	GB
128	ENABLE (GB)	GB
125	HARRY ANGEL (IRE)	GB
123	BATTAASH (IRE)	GB
123	CHURCHILL (IRE)	IRE
122	LADY AURELIA (USA)	USA
122	WEST COAST (USA)	USA
121	BARNEY ROY (GB)	GB
121	BRAMETOT (IRE)	FR
121	OSCAR PERFORMANCE (USA)	USA
121	REY DE ORO (JPN)	JPN
120	ALWAYS DREAMING (USA)	USA
120	BATTLE OF MIDWAY (USA)	USA
120	CAPRI (IRE)	IRE
120	CARAVAGGIO (USA)	IRE
120	LE BRIVIDO (FR)	FR
119	AL WUKAIR (IRE)	FR
119	HYDRANGEA (IRE)	IRE
119	REKINDLING (GB)	IRE
119	WINGS OF EAGLES (FR)	IRE
119	WINTER (IRE)	IRE
118	ABEL TASMAN (USA)	USA
118	AL AIN (JPN)	JPN
118	BEAT THE BANK (GB)	GB
118	CLOUD COMPUTING (USA)	USA
118	CRYSTAL OCEAN (GB)	GB
118	ELATE (USA)	USA
118	INNS OF COURT (IRE)	FR
118	KISEKI (JPN)	JPN
118	MASTERY (USA)	USA
118	PERSIAN KNIGHT (JPN)	JPN
118	SHARP SAMURAI (USA)	USA
118	STRADIVARIUS (IRE)	GB
118	SUAVE RICHARD (JPN)	JPN
118	THUNDER SNOW (IRE)	GB
118	TRAPEZE ARTIST (AUS)	AUS
117	CLASSIC EMPIRE (USA)	USA
117	CLIFFS OF MOHER (IRE)	IRE
117	GUNNEVERA (USA)	USA
117	ICE BREEZE (GB)	FR
117	LANCASTER BOMBER (USA)	IRE
117	MERCHANT NAVY (AUS)	AUS
117	ROLY POLY (USA)	IRE
117	TAPWRIT (USA)	USA
117	WALDGEIST (GB)	FR
117	WINDSTOSS (GER)	GER
117	WUHEIDA (GB)	GB
116	ADMIRABLE (JPN)	JPN
116	BLUE POINT (IRE)	GB
116	CASH DO JAGUARETE (BRZ)	BRZ

Rating		Trained
116	DANBURITE (JPN)	JPN
116	EMINENT (IRE)	GB
116	PARADISE WOODS (USA)	USA
116	PAVEL (USA)	USA
116	RHODODENDRON (IRE)	IRE
116	ROBERT BRUCE (CHI)	CHI
116	SHAKEEL (FR)	FR
116	SUNGRAZER (JPN)	JPN
116	ACE HIGH (AUS)	AUS
115	ALOISIA (NZ)	AUS
115	AMERICAN GAL (USA)	USA
115	BEST SOLUTION (IRE)	GB
115	CLINCHER (JPN)	JPN
115	GIRVIN (USA)	USA
115	GOOD SAMARITAN (USA)	USA
115	IRAP (USA)	USA
115	IRISH WAR CRY (USA)	USA
115	IT TIZ WELL (USA)	USA
115	LEGION DE HONOR (ARG)	ARG
115	LOOKIN AT LEE (USA)	USA
115	MENARI (AUS)	AUS
115	MIGHTY BOSS (AUS)	AUS
115	MONARCHS GLEN (GB)	GB
115	MY STYLE (JPN)	JPN
115	PERMIAN (GB)	GB
115	POPOCATEPETL (JPN)	JPN
115	PRACTICAL JOKE (USA)	USA
115	RECOLETOS (FR)	FR
115	ROMAN ROSSO (ARG)	ARG
115	SOUL STIRRING (JPN)	JPN
115	SPIRIT OF VALOR (USA)	IRE
115	TAJ MAHAL (IRE)	AUS
115	TAKAFUL (USA)	USA
115	TRAIS FLUORS (GB)	FR
115	UNIQUE BELLA (USA)	USA
115	VILLAGE KING (ARG)	ARG
115	WOW CAT (CHI)	CHI
114	AVILIUS (GB)	FR
114	COLOMANO (GER)	GER
114	DRAGON LIPS (GER)	GER
114	KHALIDI (GB)	GB
114	LACAZAR (GER)	GER
114	MAC MAHON (ITY)	ITY
114	RAHEEN HOUSE (IRE)	GB
114	RIVET (IRE)	GB
113	SOBETSU (GB)	GB
113	BENBATL (GB)	GB
113	BUTHELA (FR)	FR
113	CORONET (GB)	GB
113	DEFOE (IRE)	GB

Rating	Trained
113 **DOUGLAS MACARTHUR** (IRE)	IRE
113 **FINCHE** (GB)	FR
113 **LADY FRANKEL** (GB)	FR
113 **PRECIEUSE** (IRE)	FR
113 **SENGA** (USA)	FR
113 **VENICE BEACH** (IRE)	IRE
112 **ANDA MUCHACHO** (IRE)	ITY
112 **CALLED TO THE BAR** (IRE)	FR
112 **COX BAZAR** (FR)	FR
112 **DESERT SKYLINE** (IRE)	GB
112 **ENJOY VIJAY** (GER)	GER
112 **MEGERA** (FR)	GER
112 **MOUNT MORIAH** (GB)	GB
112 **ORDEROFTHEGARTER** (IRE)	IRE
112 **PLUMATIC** (GB)	FR
112 **POETIC DREAM** (IRE)	GER
112 **SISTERCHARLIE** (IRE)	FR
112 **VIA RAVENNA** (IRE)	FR
112 **WAR DECREE** (USA)	IRE
111 **AKIHIRO** (JPN)	FR
111 **COUNT OCTAVE** (GB)	GB
111 **DABAN** (IRE)	GB
111 **DREAM CASTLE** (GB)	GB
111 **FRANKUUS** (IRE)	GB
111 **HOMESMAN** (USA)	IRE
111 **KHAN** (GER)	GER
111 **LA SARDANE** (FR)	FR

Rating	Trained
111 **ROSENPURPUR** (GER)	GER
111 **TERRAKOVA** (IRE)	FR
110 **AFANDEM** (FR)	FR
110 **ARABIAN HOPE** (USA)	GB
110 **BAY OF POETS** (IRE)	GB
110 **D'BAI** (IRE)	GB
110 **DABYAH** (IRE)	GB
110 **DELECTATION** (GER)	GER
110 **EMPIRE OF THE STAR** (FR)	GER
110 **FALCON WINGS** (GB)	FR
110 **FAS** (IRE)	FR
110 **FOREST RANGER** (IRE)	GB
110 **GLENCADAM GLORY** (GB)	GB
110 **GOLDEN LEGEND** (FR)	FR
110 **INSTIGATOR** (GER)	GER
110 **INTELLIGENCE CROSS** (USA)	IRE
110 **IRISHCORRESPONDENT** (IRE)	IRE
110 **LOCKHEED** (GB)	GB
110 **MIRAGE DANCER** (GB)	GB
110 **SALOUEN** (IRE)	GB
110 **SHUTTER SPEED** (GB)	GB
110 **SIR DANCEALOT** (IRE)	GB
110 **SIR JOHN LAVERY** (IRE)	IRE
110 **SOLEIL D'OCTOBRE** (FR)	FR
110 **SPANISH STEPS** (IRE)	IRE
110 **TALAAYEB** (GB)	GB
110 **YUCATAN** (IRE)	IRE

OLDER HORSES 2017

for four-year-olds and up rated 115 or greater by the IFHA World's Best Racehorse Rankings Conference. Horses rated 114-110 by the European Thoroughbred Rankings Conference do not constitute a part of the World's Best Racehorse Rankings. Those ratings were compiled on behalf of the European Pattern Committee.

Rating	Age	Trained	Rating	Age	Trained
134 ARROGATE (USA)	4	USA	119 OUR IVANHOWE (GER)	7	AUS
132 WINX (AUS)	6	AUS	119 PENIAPHOBIA (IRE)	6	HK
130 GUN RUNNER (USA)	4	USA	119 POET'S WORD (GB)	4	GB
126 ULYSSES (IRE)	4	GB	119 RAPPER DRAGON (AUS)	5	HK
125 CLOTH OF STARS (IRE)	4	FR	119 SHAMAN GHOST (CAN)	5	USA
124 COLLECTED (USA)	4	USA	119 SIXTIES SONG (ARG)	4	ARG
124 KITASAN BLACK (JPN)	5	JPN	119 THEWIZARDOFOZ (AUS)	6	HK
124 RIBCHESTER (IRE)	4	GB	119 TIME WARP (GB)	4	HK
123 CHEVAL GRAND (JPN)	5	JPN	119 WAR STORY (USA)	5	USA
123 HIGHLAND REEL (IRE)	5	IRE	119 WERTHER (NZ)	6	HK
123 MOR SPIRIT (USA)	4	USA	118 ADMIRE DEUS (JPN)	6	JPN
123 ORDER OF ST GEORGE (IRE)	5	IRE	118 AMAZING KIDS (NZ)	6	HK
123 SHARP AZTECA (USA)	4	USA	118 BALLET CONCERTO (GB)	4	GB
123 WORLD APPROVAL (USA)	5	USA	118 BEAUTY GENERATION (NZ)	5	HK
122 CHAUTAUQUA (AUS)	7	AUS	118 CAPTAIN AMERICA (SAF)	7	SAF
122 HUMIDOR (NZ)	5	AUS	118 CONTENTMENT (USA)	7	HK
122 JACK HOBBS (GB)	5	GB	118 COPANO RICKEY (JPN)	7	JPN
122 ROY H (USA)	5	USA	118 EDICT OF NANTES (SAF)	4	SAF
122 SATONO CROWN (JPN)	5	JPN	118 ERTIJAAL (IRE)	6	UAE
122 TAAREEF (FR)	4	FR	118 GINGERNUTS (NZ)	4	NZ
122 TALISMANIC (GB)	4	FR	118 HAWKBILL (USA)	4	GB
121 BEACH PATROL (USA)	4	USA	118 IQUITOS (GER)	5	GER
121 DREFONG (USA)	4	USA	118 NOT LISTENIN'TOME (AUS)	7	HK
121 HAPPY CLAPPER (AUS)	7	AUS	118 PAKISTAN STAR (GER)	4	HK
121 HARTNELL (GB)	6	AUS	118 PERSUASIVE (IRE)	4	GB
121 JAMEKA (AUS)	5	AUS	118 RAINBOW LINE (JPN)	4	JPN
121 MR STUNNING (AUS)	5	HK	118 REDKIRK (GB)	6	AUS
121 REDZEL (AUS)	5	AUS	118 SATONO ALADDIN (JPN)	6	JPN
120 BIG ORANGE (GB)	6	GB	118 SONGBIRD (USA)	4	USA
120 DECORATED KNIGHT (GB)	5	GB	118 STAPHANOS (JPN)	6	JPN
120 DSCHINGIS SECRET (GER)	4	GER	118 TERRAVISTA (AUS)	8	AUS
120 GOLD ACTOR (JPN)	6	JPN	118 TOSEN STARDOM (JPN)	6	AUS
120 HESHEM (IRE)	5	FR	118 TRIP TO HEAVEN (SAF)	6	SAF
120 LE ROMAIN (AUS)	5	AUS	118 WHISKY BARON (AUS)	5	SAF
120 LEGAL EAGLE (SAF)	6	SAF	117 AIR SPINEL (JPN)	4	JPN
120 MARINARESCO (SAF)	5	SAF	117 ALMANDIN (GER)	7	AUS
120 MIND YOUR BISCUITS (USA)	4	USA	117 BIGGER PICTURE (USA)	6	USA
120 MINDING (IRE)	4	IRE	117 BLACKJACKCAT (USA)	4	USA
120 MUTAKAYYEF (GB)	6	GB	117 BLAZING SPEED (GB)	8	HK
120 PUERTO ESCONDIDO (ARG)	4	ARG	117 BRAVE SMASH (AUS)	4	AUS
120 SATONO DIAMOND (JPN)	4	JPN	117 BULLARDS ALLEY (USA)	5	USA
120 VEGA MAGIC (AUS)	5	AUS	117 CHAMPIONSHIP (IRE)	6	UAE
119 BATEEL (IRE)	5	FR	117 CLEARLY INNOCENT (AUS)	6	AUS
119 BEAUTY ONLY (IRE)	6	HK	117 DEPLOY (AUS)	5	AUS
119 BLACK HEART BART (AUS)	7	AUS	117 EXTREME CHOICE (AUS)	4	AUS
119 D B PIN (NZ)	5	HK	117 FRONTIERSMAN (GB)	4	GB
119 DEAUVILLE (IRE)	4	IRE	117 GAILO CHOP (FR)	6	AUS
119 DIVERSIFY (USA)	4	USA	117 GOLD DREAM (JPN)	4	JPN
119 FOREVER UNBRIDLED (USA)	5	USA	117 HEY DOC (AUS)	4	AUS
119 GUIGNOL (GER)	5	GER	117 HOPPERTUNITY (USA)	6	USA
119 HELENE PARAGON (FR)	5	HK	117 ISLA BONITA (JPN)	6	JPN
119 IDAHO (IRE)	4	IRE	117 JIMMY TWO TIMES (FR)	4	FR
119 IMPERIAL HINT (USA)	4	USA	117 JON SNOW (NZ)	4	NZ
119 LIBRISA BREEZE (GB)	5	GB	117 JOYFUL TRINITY (IRE)	5	HK
119 LIMATO (IRE)	5	GB	117 KEEN ICE (USA)	5	USA
119 LUCKY BUBBLES (AUS)	6	HK	117 LADY ELI (USA)	5	USA
119 MARSHA (IRE)	4	GB	117 LOGOTYPE (JPN)	7	JPN
119 NEOREALISM (JPN)	6	JPN	117 LUCKY HUSSLER (AUS)	8	AUS

Rating	Age	Trained
117 **MAKAHIKI** (JPN)	4	JPN
117 **MALAGUERRA** (AUS)	6	AUS
117 **MASSAAT** (IRE)	4	GB
117 **MIDNIGHT STORM** (USA)	6	USA
117 **PALENTINO** (AUS)	5	AUS
117 **RAFEEF** (AUS)	5	SAF
117 **REAL STEEL** (JPN)	5	JPN
117 **RUSSIAN REVOLUTION** (AUS)	4	AUS
117 **SADLER'S JOY** (USA)	4	USA
117 **SEVENTH HEAVEN** (IRE)	4	IRE
117 **SIGNS OF BLESSING** (IRE)	6	FR
117 **SOUND TRUE** (JPN)	7	JPN
117 **TAVAGO** (NZ)	5	AUS
117 **THE TIN MAN** (GB)	5	GB
117 **VAZIRABAD** (FR)	5	FR
117 **VIVLOS** (JPN)	4	JPN
117 **VOADOR MAGEE** (BRZ)	4	BRZ
117 **YAMAKATSU ACE** (JPN)	5	JPN
117 **ZARAK** (FR)	4	FR
116 **ABLE FRIEND** (AUS)	8	HK
116 **ACLAIM** (IRE)	4	GB
116 **APOLLO KENTUCKY** (USA)	5	JPN
116 **BRANDO** (GB)	5	GB
116 **BULL VALLEY** (SAF)	5	SAF
116 **CLOSE UP** (NZ)	8	NZ
116 **CONNECT** (USA)	4	USA
116 **CRAZY ICON** (ARG)	4	ARG
116 **CUPID** (USA)	4	USA
116 **DEO JUVENTE** (SAF)	6	SAF
116 **DIVISIDERO** (USA)	5	USA
116 **EL BENICIO** (ARG)	4	ARG
116 **FELL SWOOP** (AUS)	6	AUS
116 **FLAMBERGE** (AUS)	8	AUS
116 **GIANT EXPECTATIONS** (USA)	4	USA
116 **GREATER LONDON** (JPN)	5	JPN
116 **HARDHAM** (AUS)	4	AUS
116 **HARPER'S CHOICE** (AUS)	4	AUS
116 **HAT PUNTANO** (ARG)	4	SAF
116 **HERE COMES WHEN** (IRE)	7	GB
116 **IMPENDING** (AUS)	4	AUS
116 **JOHANNES VERMEER** (IRE)	4	IRE
116 **K T BRAVE** (JPN)	4	JPN
116 **KAWI** (NZ)	7	NZ
116 **MUBTAAHIJ** (IRE)	5	USA
116 **NEOLITHIC** (USA)	4	USA
116 **RED FALX** (JPN)	6	JPN
116 **RISING RED** (NZ)	4	AUS
116 **SECRET WEAPON** (GB)	7	HK
116 **SEIUN KOSEI** (JPN)	4	JPN
116 **SENSE OF OCCASION** (AUS)	7	AUS
116 **SOMEWHAT** (AUS)	6	AUS
116 **SPIETH** (NZ)	5	AUS
116 **STAR TURN** (AUS)	4	AUS
116 **STELLAR WIND** (USA)	5	USA
116 **STRATUM STAR** (AUS)	6	AUS
116 **SUEDOIS** (FR)	6	GB
116 **T M JINSOKU** (JPN)	5	JPN
116 **TALKTOTHESTARS** (SAF)	6	SAF
116 **TASLEET** (GB)	4	GB
116 **THE RIGHT MAN** (GB)	5	FR
116 **TURN ME LOOSE** (NZ)	6	NZ
116 **WESTERN EXPRESS** (AUS)	5	HK
115 **ABILITY** (AUS)	5	AUS
115 **ACCELERATE** (USA)	4	USA
115 **ALBERT** (JPN)	6	JPN
115 **AMERICAN PATRIOT** (USA)	4	USA
115 **BAL A BALI** (BRZ)	7	USA
115 **BARBON** (PER)	4	PER
115 **BARSANTI** (IRE)	5	GB
115 **BEST WARRIOR** (USA)	7	JPN
115 **BLIZZARD** (AUS)	6	HK
115 **BLOND ME** (IRE)	5	GB
115 **BONNEVAL** (NZ)	4	NZ
115 **CHEMICAL CHARGE** (IRE)	5	GB
115 **COUNTERATTACK** (AUS)	5	AUS
115 **DACITA** (CHI)	6	USA
115 **DESTIN** (USA)	4	USA
115 **DICKINSON** (USA)	5	USA
115 **DIXIE WAVE** (ARG)	5	PER
115 **ECUADOR** (NZ)	8	AUS
115 **EL MARGOT** (ARG)	6	ARG
115 **EMPEROR RODERIC** (BRZ)	4	BRZ
115 **ENGLISH** (USA)	5	AUS
115 **ERUPT** (IRE)	5	FR
115 **EXOSPHERIC** (GB)	5	AUS
115 **FAME GAME** (JPN)	7	JPN
115 **FORTY ONE** (ARG)	4	ARG
115 **FULL DRAGO** (ITY)	4	ITY
115 **HEART TO HEART** (CAN)	6	USA
115 **INFERENCE** (AUS)	4	AUS
115 **ITSINTHEPOST** (FR)	5	USA
115 **JOURNEY** (GB)	5	GB
115 **KRIS FIVE** (BRZ)	4	BRZ
115 **KURILOV** (CHI)	4	CHI
115 **LIGHTNING SPEAR** (GB)	6	GB
115 **LONG ON VALUE** (USA)	6	USA
115 **MEKHTAAL** (GB)	4	FR
115 **MOONLIGHT MAGIC** (GB)	4	IRE
115 **NEZWAAH** (GB)	4	GB
115 **OFF LIMITS** (IRE)	5	USA
115 **PALACE PRINCE** (GER)	5	GER
115 **PAULASSILVERLINING** (USA)	5	USA
115 **PERBENE** (BRZ)	5	BRZ
115 **POSTPONED** (IRE)	6	GB
115 **PRIZE MONEY** (GB)	4	UAE
115 **PRIZED ICON** (AUS)	4	AUS
115 **PROFITABLE** (GB)	5	GB
115 **QUEEN'S TRUST** (GB)	4	GB
115 **QUEENS RING** (JPN)	5	JPN
115 **QUIET REFLECTION** (GB)	4	GB
115 **RANSOM THE MOON** (CAN)	5	USA
115 **RED CARDINAL** (IRE)	5	GER
115 **RED RAY** (SAF)	7	SAF
115 **RUTHVEN** (AUS)	4	AUS
115 **SAIL SOUTH** (SAF)	7	SAF
115 **SCOTTISH** (IRE)	5	GB
115 **SEASONS BLOOM** (AUS)	5	HK
115 **SHEIKHZAYEDROAD** (GB)	8	GB
115 **SILVERWAVE** (FR)	5	FR
115 **THE UNITED STATES** (IRE)	7	AUS
115 **TIME TEST** (GB)	5	GB
115 **TIVACI** (AUS)	5	AUS
115 **TORCEDOR** (IRE)	5	IRE
115 **TOSEN BASIL** (JPN)	5	JPN
115 **VALE DORI** (ARG)	5	USA
115 **VOLKSTOK'N'BARRELL** (NZ)	6	NZ
115 **WAIT A SEC** (NZ)	7	NZ
115 **WHITMORE** (USA)	4	USA
115 **WHO SHOT THEBARMAN** (NZ)	9	AUS
115 **ZELZAL** (FR)	4	FR
115 **ZHUKOVA** (IRE)	5	IRE
114 **AIR PILOT** (GB)	8	GB
114 **CASPIAN PRINCE** (IRE)	8	GB
114 **DESERT ENCOUNTER** (IRE)	5	GB

Rating	Age	Trained
114 DONJUAN TRIUMPHANT (IRE)	4	GB
114 HARBOUR LAW (GB)	4	GB
114 HOME OF THE BRAVE (IRE)	5	GB
114 KARAR (GB)	5	FR
114 MARMELO (GB)	4	GB
114 PAS DE DEUX (GER)	7	GER
114 QEMAH (IRE)	4	FR
114 ROBIN OF NAVAN (FR)	4	GB
114 SECRET NUMBER (GB)	7	GB
114 SOMEHOW (IRE)	4	IRE
114 SOVEREIGN DEBT (IRE)	8	GB
114 SPECTRE (FR)	4	FR
114 SUCCESS DAYS (IRE)	5	IRE
114 TIBERIAN (FR)	5	FR
113 AJMAN PRINCESS (IRE)	4	GB
113 BRETON ROCK (IRE)	7	GB
113 DARTMOUTH (GB)	5	GB
113 DOHA DREAM (FR)	4	FR
113 FANCIFUL ANGEL (IRE)	5	GB
113 FIRST SITTING (GB)	6	GB
113 FOLKSWOOD (GB)	4	GB
113 GARLINGARI (FR)	6	FR
113 HOLDTHASIGREEN (FR)	5	FR
113 KASPERSKY (IRE)	6	GB
113 MAX DYNAMITE (FR)	7	IRE
113 MONDIALISTE (IRE)	7	GB
113 MUNTAHAA (IRE)	4	GB
113 MUTHMIR (IRE)	7	GB
113 MY DREAM BOAT (IRE)	5	GB
113 NATHRA (IRE)	4	GB
113 STEEL OF MADRID (IRE)	4	GB
113 WICKLOW BRAVE (GB)	8	IRE
112 ALGOMETER (GB)	4	GB
112 ALJAZZI (GB)	4	GB
112 ARAB SPRING (IRE)	7	GB
112 AUTOCRATIC (GB)	4	GB
112 DANEHILL KODIAC (IRE)	4	GB
112 ENNAADD (GB)	4	GB
112 FABRICATE (GB)	5	GB
112 GIFTED MASTER (GB)	4	GB
112 GORDON LORD BYRON (IRE)	9	IRE
112 JUNGLE CAT (IRE)	5	GB
112 LEFT HAND (GB)	4	FR
112 MANIACO (GB)	4	FR
112 MATCHWINNER (GER)	6	GER
112 MILLOWITSCH (GER)	4	GER
112 MORANDO (FR)	4	GB
112 MUSTASHRY (GB)	4	GB
112 RACING HISTORY (IRE)	5	GB
112 SIYOUSHAKE (IRE)	5	FR
112 SO BELOVED (GB)	7	GB
112 SUBWAY DANCER (IRE)	5	FR
112 TAKE COVER (GB)	10	GB
112 TOSCANINI (IRE)	5	GB
112 WONNEMOND (GER)	4	GER
112 ZONDERLAND (GB)	4	GB
11 DAL HARRAILD (GB)	4	GB
11 DUTCH CONNECTION (GB)	5	GB
11 FINAL VENTURE (GB)	5	GB
11 HATHAL (USA)	5	GB
111 MILLE ET MILLE (GB)	7	FR
111 MONTALY (GB)	6	GB
111 NOOR AL HAWA (FR)	4	GER
111 ONE FOOT IN HEAVEN (IRE)	5	FR
111 POTEMKIN (GER)	6	GER
111 SIMPLE VERSE (GB)	5	GB
111 SON CESIO (FR)	6	FR
111 STORMY ANTARCTIC (GB)	4	GB
111 USHERETTE (IRE)	5	FR
111 WAY TO PARIS (GB)	4	ITY
111 WILD CHIEF (GER)	6	GER
111 WINGS OF DESIRE (GB)	4	GB
110 ARMANDE (IRE)	4	GB
110 ATTENDU (FR)	4	FR
110 BRENDAN BRACKAN (IRE)	8	IRE
110 CARRY ON DERYCK (GB)	5	GB
110 CHAIN OF DAISIES (GB)	5	GB
110 CONVEY (GB)	5	GB
110 COTAI GLORY (GB)	5	GB
110 DARING MATCH (GER)	6	GER
110 DAWN OF HOPE (IRE)	4	GB
110 DIPLOMAT (GER)	6	GER
110 DYLAN MOUTH (IRE)	6	GB
110 GABRIAL (IRE)	8	GB
110 HAGGLE (GB)	4	FR
110 HIGH JINX (IRE)	9	GB
110 HIGHER POWER (GB)	5	GB
110 JALLOTA (GB)	6	GB
110 KOOL KOMPANY (IRE)	5	GB
110 LAUGH ALOUD (GB)	4	GB
110 MIDTERM (GB)	4	GB
110 MIX AND MINGLE (IRE)	4	GB
110 MOUNT LOGAN (IRE)	6	GB
110 NEARLY CAUGHT (IRE)	7	GB
110 OPAL TIARA (IRE)	4	GB
110 PROJECTION (GB)	4	GB
110 QEWY (IRE)	7	GB
110 RARE RHYTHM (GB)	5	GB
110 REMARKABLE (GB)	4	GB
110 ROSA IMPERIAL (IRE)	4	FR
110 ROSS (IRE)	5	GER
110 SAVOIR VIVRE (IRE)	4	GER
110 SECOND STEP (IRE)	6	GB
110 SHAMREEN (IRE)	4	IRE
110 SHE IS NO LADY (GB)	5	GB
110 SMART CALL (SAF)	6	GB
110 SMART WHIP (FR)	6	FR
110 SO MI DAR (GB)	4	GB
110 ST MICHEL (GB)	4	GB
110 TABARRAK (IRE)	4	GB
110 THE BLACK PRINCESS (FR)	4	GB
110 THOMAS HOBSON (GB)	7	IRE
110 TIME TO CHOOSE (GB)	4	ITY
110 TRAFFIC JAM (IRE)	4	FR
110 TUPI (IRE)	5	GB
110 ULTRA (GB)	4	FR
110 VICTORY IS OURS (TUR)	4	TUR
110 WALL OF FIRE (IRE)	4	GB
110 WASHINGTON DC (IRE)	4	IRE
110 ZALAMEA (IRE)	4	FR

RACEFORM CHAMPIONS 2017

ONLY HORSES WHICH HAVE RUN IN EUROPE ARE INCLUDED

FOUR-YEAR-OLDS AND UP

ULYSSES	127	HIGHLAND REEL	123
CLOTH OF STARS	126	JACK HOBBS	123
RIBCHESTER	126	SIGNS OF BLESSING	123
ORDER OF ST GEORGE	125	MINDING	122

THREE-YEAR-OLD COLT

CRACKSMAN	131	CHURCHILL	125
BATTAASH	128	CARAVAGGIO	124
HARRY ANGEL	128	BARNEY ROY	124

THREE-YEAR-OLD FILLY

ENABLE	129	WINTER	119
LADY AURELIA	124	RHODODENDRON	116
HYDRANGEA	119	ROLY POLY	116

SPRINTER

BATTAAASH	128	SIGNS OF BLESSING	123
HARRY ANGEL	128	MARSHA	122
LADY AURELIA	124		

STAYER

ORDER OF ST GEORGE	125	BIG ORANGE	119
CAPRI	121	STRADIVARIUS	119
REKINDLING	121	VAZIRABAD	119
CRYSTAL OCEAN	120		

TWO-YEAR-OLD COLT

U S NAVY FLAG	122	FLEET REVIEW	116
SAXON WARRIOR	119	MENDELSSOHN	116
VERBAL DEXTERITY	119	SIOUX NATION	116
ROARING LION	118	SANDS OF MALI	116
EXPERT EYE	116	UNFORTUNATELY	116

TWO-YEAR-OLD FILLY

CLEMMIE	114	HAPPILY	112
WILD ILLUSION	114	MAGICAL	112
LAURENS	113		
SEPTEMBER	113		

MEDIAN TIMES 2018

The following Raceform median times are used in the calculation of the Split Second speed figures. They represent a true average time for the distance, which has been arrived at after looking at the winning times for all races over each distance within the past five years, except for those restricted to two or three-year-olds.

Some current race distances have been omitted as they have not yet had a sufficient number of races run over them to produce a reliable average time.

ASCOT

5f.................................... 1m 0.50	1m Straight 1m 40.80	1m 7f 209y 3m 29.00
6f.................................... 1m 14.50	1m 1f 212y 2m 7.40	2m 3f 210y 4m 24.80
7f.................................... 1m 27.60	1m 3f 211y 2m 32.50	2m 5f 143y 4m 49.40
7f 213y Round.................. 1m 40.70	1m 5f 211y 3m 1.00	

AYR

5f.................................... 59.40	1m.................................. 1m 43.80	1m 5f 26y 2m 54.00
6f.................................... 1m 12.40	1m 1f 20y 1m 57.50	1m 7f 3m 20.40
7f 50y............................. 1m 33.40	1m 2f.............................. 2m 12.00	2m 1f 105y 3m 55.00

BATH

5f 10y............................. 1m 2.50	1m 5y.............................. 1m 40.80	1m 5f 11y 2m 52.00
5f 160y........................... 1m 11.20	1m 2f 37y 2m 11.00	1m 6f 3m 3.80
1m.................................. 1m 40.80	1m 3f 137y 2m 30.60	2m 1f 24y 3m 51.90

BEVERLEY

5f.................................... 1m 3.50	1m 100y.......................... 1m 47.60	1m 4f 23y 2m 39.80
7f 96y............................. 1m 33.80	1m 1f 207y 2m 7.00	2m 32y............................ 3m 39.80

BRIGHTON

5f 60y............................. 1m 2.30	6f 210y............................ 1m 23.10	1m 1f 207y 2m 3.60
5f 215y........................... 1m 10.20	7f 211y............................ 1m 36.00	1m 3f 198y 2m 32.70

CARLISLE

5f.................................... 1m 0.80	7f 173y............................ 1m 40.00	1m 6f 32y 3m 7.50
5f 193y........................... 1m 13.70	1m 1f............................... 1m 57.60	2m 1f 47y 3m 53.00
6f 195y........................... 1m 27.10	1m 3f 39y 2m 23.10	

CATTERICK

5f.................................... 59.80	7f 6y................................ 1m 27.00	1m 5f 192y 3m 3.60
5f 212y........................... 1m 13.60	1m 4f 13y 2m 38.90	1m 7f 189y 3m 32.00

CHELMSFORD (A.W)

5f.................................... 1m 0.20	1m.................................. 1m 39.90	1m 6f 3m 3.20
6f.................................... 1m 13.70	1m 2f.............................. 2m 8.60	2m.................................. 3m 30.00
7f.................................... 1m 27.20	1m 5f 66y 2m 53.60	

CHEPSTOW

5f 16y............................. 59.30	1m 14y............................ 1m 36.20	2m.................................. 3m 38.90
6f 16y............................. 1m 12.00	1m 2f.............................. 2m 10.60	2m 2f 4m 3.60
7f 16y............................. 1m 23.20	1m 4f.............................. 2m 39.00	

CHESTER

5f 15y............................. 1m 1.00	7f 127y............................ 1m 33.80	1m 5f 84y 2m 52.70
5f 110y........................... 1m 6.20	1m 2f 70y 2m 11.20	1m 6f 87y 3m 7.00
6f 17y............................. 1m 13.80	1m 3f 75y 2m 24.80	1m 7f 196y 3m 28.00
7f 1y............................... 1m 26.50	1m 4f 63y 2m 38.50	2m 2f 140y 4m 4.80

DONCASTER

5f 3y.................................. 1m 0.50	7f 6y.................................. 1m 26.30	1m 3f 197y...................... 2m 34.90
5f 143y.............................. 1m 8.80	7f 213y Round................... 1m 39.70	1m 6f 115y....................... 3m 7.40
6f 2y................................ 1m 13.60	1m Straight....................... 1m 39.30	2m 109y........................... 3m 40.40
6f 111y............................ 1m 19.90	1m 2f 43y.......................... 2m 9.40	2m 1f 197y...................... 3m 55.00

EPSOM

5f.. 55.70	7f 3y................................ 1m 23.30	1m 2f 17y........................ 2m 9.70
6f 3y................................ 1m 9.40	1m 113y........................... 1m 46.10	1m 4f 6y.......................... 2m 38.90

FFOS LAS

5f.. 58.30	1m...................................... 1m 41.00	1m 6f............................... 3m 3.80
6f..................................... 1m 10.00	1m 2f................................ 2m 9.40	2m...................................... 3m 30.00
7f 80y.............................. 1m 33.60	1m 3f 209y...................... 2m 37.40	

GOODWOOD

5f..................................... 1m 0.20	1m 1f 11y......................... 1m 56.30	1m 6f............................... 3m 3.60
6f..................................... 1m 12.20	1m 1f 197y....................... 2m 8.10	2m...................................... 3m 29.00
7f..................................... 1m 27.00	1m 3f 44y......................... 2m 26.50	2m 4f 134y...................... 4m 31.00
1m.................................... 1m 39.90	1m 3f 218y...................... 2m 38.40	

HAMILTON

5f 7y................................ 1m 0.00	1m 1f 35y......................... 1m 59.70	1m 4f 15y........................ 2m 38.60
6f 6y................................ 1m 12.20	1m 3f 15y......................... 2m 25.60	1m 5f 16y........................ 2m 53.90
1m 68y............................ 1m 48.40		

HAYDOCK

5f..................................... 1m 0.80	7f 37y.............................. 1m 32.70	1m 3f 140y Inner 2m 33.00
5f Inner........................... 1m 0.80	7f 212y Inner................... 1m 43.70	1m 3f 175y...................... 2m 33.80
6f..................................... 1m 13.80	1m 37y............................ 1m 44.70	1m 6f............................... 3m 2.00
6f Inner........................... 1m 13.80	1m 2f 42y Inner............... 2m 12.70	2m 45y............................. 3m 34.30
6f 212y Inner.................. 1m 30.70	1m 2f 100y...................... 2m 15.50	

KEMPTON (A.W)

5f..................................... 1m 0.50	1m...................................... 1m 39.80	1m 3f 219y...................... 2m 34.50
6f..................................... 1m 13.10	1m 1f 219y....................... 2m 8.00	1m 7f 218y...................... 3m 30.10
7f..................................... 1m 26.00	1m 2f 219y...................... 2m 21.90	

LEICESTER

5f..................................... 1m 0.00	1m 53y............................ 1m 45.10	1m 2f................................ 2m 7.90
6f..................................... 1m 13.00	1m 1f 216y....................... 2m 7.90	1m 3f 179y...................... 2m 33.90
7f..................................... 1m 26.20		

LINGFIELD

4f 217y.............................. 58.20	7f 135y............................ 1m 32.30	1m 3f 133y...................... 2m 31.50
6f..................................... 1m 11.20	1m 1f................................ 1m 56.60	1m 6f............................... 3m 10.00
7f..................................... 1m 23.30	1m 2f................................ 2m 10.50	2m 68y............................. 3m 34.80

LINGFIELD (A.W)

5f 6y.................................. 58.80	1m 1y.............................. 1m 38.20	1m 5f............................... 2m 46.00
6f 1y................................ 1m 11.90	1m 2f................................ 2m 6.60	1m 7f 169y...................... 3m 25.70
7f 1y................................ 1m 24.80	1m 4f................................ 2m 33.00	

MUSSELBURGH

5f 1y	1m 0.40	1m 208y	1m 53.90	1m 5f 216y	3m 5.30
7f 33y	1m 29.00	1m 4f 104y	2m 42.00	1m 7f 217y	3m 33.50
1m 2y	1m 41.20	1m 5f	2m 52.00		

NEWBURY

5f 34y	1m 1.40	1m Straight	1m 39.70	1m 3f	2m 21.20
6f	1m 13.00	1m Round	1m 38.70	1m 4f	2m 35.50
6f 110y	1m 19.30	1m 1f	1m 55.50	1m 5f 61y	2m 52.00
7f Straight	1m 25.70	1m 2f	2m 8.80	2m	3m 32.00

NEWCASTLE (A.W)

5f	59.50	1m 5y	1m 38.60	1m 4f 98y	2m 41.10
6f	1m 12.50	1m 2f 42y	2m 10.40	2m 56y	3m 35.20
7f 14y	1m 26.20				

NEWMARKET (ROWLEY MILE)

5f	59.10	1m 1f	1m 51.70	1m 6f	2m 57.00
6f	1m 12.20	1m 2f	2m 5.80	2m	3m 30.50
7f	1m 25.40	1m 4f	2m 32.00	2m 2f	3m 52.00
1m	1m 38.60				

NEWMARKET (JULY)

5f	59.10	1m	1m 40.00	1m 5f	2m 44.00
6f	1m 12.50	1m 2f	2m 5.50	1m 6f	2m 57.70
7f	1m 25.70	1m 4f	2m 32.90	2m	3m 27.00

NOTTINGHAM

5f 8y Inner	1m 1.50	1m 75y Inner	1m 49.00	1m 6f Inner	3m 7.00
5f 8y	1m 1.50	1m 1f	1m 57.60	1m 6f	3m 7.00
6f 18y	1m 14.70	1m 2f 50y	2m 14.30	2m	3m 34.50
1m 72y Inner	1m 49.00	1m 2f 50y Inner	2m 14.30		
1m 75y	1m 49.00				

PONTEFRACT

5f 3y	1m 3.30	1m 2f 5y	2m 13.70	2m 2f 2y	3m 56.20
6f	1m 16.90	1m 4f 5y	2m 40.80	2m 5f 139y	4m 51.00
1m 6y	1m 45.90	2m 1f 27y	3m 44.60		

REDCAR

5f	58.60	7f 219y	1m 36.60	1m 5f 218y	3m 4.70
5f 217y	1m 11.80	1m 1f	1m 53.00	1m 7f 217y	3m 31.40
7f	1m 24.50	1m 2f 1y	2m 7.10		

RIPON

5f	1m 0.00	1m 1f	1m 54.70	1m 4f 10y	2m 36.70
6f	1m 13.00	1m 1f 170y	2m 5.40	2m	3m 31.80
1m	1m 41.40				

SALISBURY

5f	1m 1.00	1m	1m 43.50	1m 4f 5y	2m 38.00
6f	1m 14.80	1m 1f 198yZ	2m 9.90	1m 6f 44y	3m 7.40
6f 213y	1m 28.60	1m 1f 201y	2m 9.90		

SANDOWN

5f 10y...................................... 1m 1.60	1m 1f.................................... 1m 55.70	1m 6f..................................... 3m 4.50
7f.. 1m 29.50	1m 1f 209y........................... 2m 10.50	2m 50y................................. 3m 38.70
1m.. 1m 43.30		

SOUTHWELL (A.W)

4f 214y................................... 59.70	1m 13y................................. 1m 43.70	1m 6f 21y............................. 3m 8.30
6f 16y................................... 1m 16.50	1m 3f 23y............................. 2m 28.00	2m 102y............................... 3m 45.50
7f 14y................................... 1m 30.30	1m 4f 14y............................. 2m 41.00	

THIRSK

5f.. 59.60	7f.. 1m 27.20	1m 4f 8y............................... 2m 36.20
6f.. 1m 12.70	7f 218y................................. 1m 40.10	2m 13y................................. 3m 28.30

WETHERBY

5f 110y.................................. 1m 6.00	1m.. 1m 41.00	1m 6f..................................... 3m 5.00
7f.. 1m 27.00	1m 2f.................................... 2m 9.00	

WINDSOR

5f 21y................................... 1m 0.30	1m 31y................................. 1m 44.70	1m 2f.................................... 2m 8.70
6f 12y................................... 1m 13.00	1m 1f 194y........................... 2m 8.70	1m 3f 99y............................. 2m 29.50

WOLVERHAMPTON (A.W)

5f 21y................................... 1m 1.90	1m 142y............................... 1m 50.10	1m 5f 219y........................... 3m 8.00
6f 20y................................... 1m 14.50	1m 1f 104y........................... 2m 0.80	2m 120y............................... 3m 43.70
7f 36y................................... 1m 28.80	1m 4f 51y............................. 2m 40.80	

YARMOUTH

5f 42y................................... 1m 2.70	1m 3y................................... 1m 40.60	1m 3f 104y........................... 2m 28.70
6f 3y..................................... 1m 14.40	1m 1f 21y............................. 1m 55.80	1m 6f 17y............................. 3m 7.60
7f 3y..................................... 1m 26.60	1m 2f 23y............................. 2m 10.50	

YORK

5f.. 59.30	7f 192y................................. 1m 39.00	1m 3f 188y........................... 2m 33.20
5f 89y................................... 1m 4.10	1m 177y............................... 1m 52.00	1m 5f 188y........................... 3m 0.20
6f.. 1m 11.90	1m 2f 56y............................. 2m 12.50	2m 56y................................. 3m 34.50
7f.. 1m 25.30		

RACEFORM RECORD TIMES (FLAT)

ASCOT

DISTANCE	TIME	AGE	WEIGHT	GOING	HORSE	DATE
5f	58.80	2	9-1	Good To Firm	NO NAY NEVER	Jun 20 2013
5f	57.44	6	9-1	Good To Firm	MISS ANDRETTI	Jun 19 2007
6f	1m 12.39	2	9-1	Good To Firm	RAJASINGHE	Jun 20 2017
6f	1m 11.05	3	9-1	Good To Firm	BLUE POINT	May 3 2017
7f	1m 26.55	2	9-0	Good To Firm	MALABAR	Jul 25 2014
7f	1m 24.28	4	8-11	Good To Firm	GALICIAN	Jul 27 2013
7f 213y (Rnd)	1m 39.55	2	8-12	Good	JOSHUA TREE	Sep 26 2009
7f 213y (Rnd)	1m 37.22	3	9-0	Good To Firm	BARNEY ROY	Jun 20 2017
1m (Str)	1m 36.60	4	9-0	Good To Firm	RIBCHESTER	Jun 20 2017
1m 1f 212y	2m 1.90	5	8-11	Good To Firm	THE FUGUE	Jun 18 2014
1m 3f 211y	2m 24.60	4	9-7	Good To Firm	NOVELLIST	Jul 27 2013
1m 7f 209y	3m 24.12	4	8-12	Good To Firm	MIZZOU	Apr 29 2015
2m 3f 210y	4m 16.92	6	9-2	Good To Firm	RITE OF PASSAGE	Jun 17 2010
2m 5f 143y	4m 45.67	7	9-2	Good To Firm	ORIENTAL FOX	Jun 20 2015

AYR

DISTANCE	TIME	AGE	WEIGHT	GOING	HORSE	DATE
5f	56.98	2	8-11	Good	BOOGIE STREET	Sep 18 2003
5f	55.68	3	8-11	Good To Firm	LOOK BUSY	Jun 21 2008
6f	1m 9.73	2	7-10	Good	SIR BERT	Sep 17 1969
6f	1m 8.37	5	8-6	Good To Firm	MAISON DIEU	Jun 21 2008
7f 50y	1m 28.99	2	9-0	Good	TAFAAHUM	Sep 19 2003
7f 50y	1m 26.54	3	9-3	Good	SABADOR	May 31 2017
1m	1m 39.18	2	9-7	Good	MOONLIGHTNAVIGATOR	Sep 18 2014
1m	1m 36.00	4	7-13	Firm	SUFI	Sep 16 1959
1m 1f 20y	1m 50.30	4	9-3	Good	RETIREMENT	Sep 19 2003
1m 2f	2m 4.02	4	9-9	Good To Firm	ENDLESS HALL	Jul 17 2000
1m 5f 26y	2m 45.81	4	9-7	Good To Firm	EDEN'S CLOSE	Sep 18 1993
1m 7f	3m 13.16	3	9-4	Good	ROMANY RYE	Sep 19 1991
2m 1f 105y	3m 45.20	4	6-13	Firm	CURRY	Sep 16 1955

BATH

DISTANCE	TIME	AGE	WEIGHT	GOING	HORSE	DATE
5f 10y	59.50	2	9-2	Firm	AMOUR PROPRE	Jul 24 2008
5f 10y	58.75	3	8-12	Firm	ENTICING	May 1 2007
5f 160y	1m 8.70	2	8-12	Firm	QALAHARI	Jul 24 2008
5f 160y	1m 8.10	6	9-0	Firm	MADRACO	May 22 1989
1m 5y	1m 39.51	2	9-2	Firm	NATURAL CHARM	Sep 14 2014
1m 5y	1m 37.20	5	8-12	Good To Firm	ADOBE	Jun 17 2000
1m 5y	1m 37.20	3	8-7	Firm	ALASHA	Aug 18 2002
1m 2f 37y	2m 5.80	3	9-0	Good To Firm	CONNOISSEUR BAY	May 29 1998
1m 3f 137y	2m 25.74	3	9-0	Hard	TOP THE CHARTS	Sep 8 2005
1m 5f 11y	2m 47.20	4	10-0	Firm	FLOWN	Aug 13 1991
2m 1f 24y	3m 43.41	6	7-9	Firm	YAHESKA	Jun 14 2003

BEVERLEY

DISTANCE	TIME	AGE	WEIGHT	GOING	HORSE	DATE
5f	1m 0.89	2	8-12	Good To Firm	LANGAVAT	Jun 8 2013
5f	59.77	5	9-3	Good To Firm	JUDICIAL	Jun 20 2017
7f 96y	1m 31.10	2	9-7	Good To Firm	CHAMPAGNE PRINCE	Aug 10 1995
7f 96y	1m 31.10	2	9-0	Firm	MAJAL	Jul 30 1991
7f 96y	1m 29.50	3	7-8	Firm	WHO'S TEF	Jul 30 1991
1m 100y	1m 43.30	2	9-0	Firm	ARDEN	Sep 24 1986
1m 100y	1m 42.20	3	8-4	Firm	LEGAL CASE	Jun 14 1989
1m 1f 207y	2m 1.00	3	9-7	Good To Firm	EASTERN ARIA	Aug 29 2009
1m 4f 23y	2m 33.35	5	9-2	Good To Firm	TWO JABS	Apr 23 2015
2m 32y	3m 28.62	4	9-11	Good To Firm	CORPUS CHORISTER	Jul 18 2017

BRIGHTON

DISTANCE	TIME	AGE	WEIGHT	GOING	HORSE	DATE
5f 60y	1m 0.10	2	9-0	Firm	BID FOR BLUE	May 6 1993
5f 60y	59.30	3	8-9	Firm	PLAY HEVER GOLF	May 26 1993
5f 215y	1m 8.10	2	8-9	Firm	SONG MIST	Jul 16 1996
5f 215y	1m 7.30	3	9-1	Good To Firm	BLUNDELL LANE	May 4 2000
5f 215y	1m 7.30	3	8-9	Firm	THIRD PARTY	Jun 3 1997
7f 211y	1m 32.80	2	9-7	Firm	ASIAN PETE	Oct 3 1989
7f 211y	1m 30.50	5	8-11	Firm	MYSTIC RIDGE	May 27 1999
1m 1f 207y	2m 4.70	2	9-0	Good To Soft	ESTEEMED MASTER	Nov 2 2001
1m 1f 207y	1m 57.20	3	9-0	Firm	GET THE MESSAGE	Apr 30 1984
1m 3f 198y	2m 25.80	4	8-2	Firm	NEW ZEALAND	Jul 4 1985

CARLISLE

DISTANCE	TIME	AGE	WEIGHT	GOING	HORSE	DATE
5f	1m 0.10	2	8-5	Firm	LA TORTUGA	Aug 2 1999
5f	58.80	3	9-8	Good To Firm	ESATTO	Aug 21 2002
5f 193y	1m 12.30	2	9-2	Good To Firm	BURRISHOOLE ABBEY	Jun 22 2016
5f 193y	1m 10.83	4	9-0	Good To Firm	BO MCGINTY	Sep 11 2005
6f 195y	1m 24.30	3	8-9	Good To Firm	MARJURITA	Aug 21 2002
7f 173y	1m 37.02	4	9-5	Good To Firm	EDGAR BALTHAZAR	Jun 22 2016
1m 1f	1m 53.84	3	9-0	Firm	LITTLE JIMBOB	Jun 14 2004
1m 3f 39y	2m 20.83	5	9-10	Good To Firm	SINDARBAN	Jun 22 2016
1m 3f 206y	2m 29.13	5	9-8	Good To Firm	TEMPSFORD	Sep 19 2005
1m 6f 32y	3m 2.20	6	8-10	Firm	EXPLOSIVE SPEED	May 26 1994

CATTERICK

DISTANCE	TIME	AGE	WEIGHT	GOING	HORSE	DATE
5f	57.60	2	9-0	Firm	H HARRISON	Oct 8 2002
5f	57.10	4	8-7	Firm	KABCAST	Jul 6 1989
5f 212y	1m 11.40	2	9-4	Firm	CAPTAIN NICK	Jul 11 1978
5f 212y	1m 9.86	9	8-13	Good To Firm	SHARP HAT	May 30 2003
7f 6y	1m 24.10	2	8-11	Firm	LINDA'S FANTASY	Sep 18 1982
7f 6y	1m 22.56	6	8-7	Firm	DIFFERENTIAL	May 31 2003
1m 4f 13y	2m 30.50	3	8-8	Good To Firm	RAHAF	May 30 2003
1m 5f 192y	2m 54.80	3	8-5	Firm	GERYON	May 31 1984
1m 7f 189y	3m 20.80	4	7-11	Firm	BEAN BOY	Jul 8 1982

CHELMSFORD (AW)

DISTANCE	TIME	AGE	WEIGHT	GOING	HORSE	DATE
5f	58.72	2	9-7	Standard	SUN'AQ	Nov 19 2015
5f	57.30	7	8-13	Standard	BROTHER TIGER	Feb 7 2016
6f	1m 11.19	2	8-13	Standard	FLORENCIO	Oct 15 2015
6f	1m 10.00	4	9-2	Standard	RAUCOUS	Apr 27 2017
7f	1m 23.23	4	9-0	Standard	VOLUNTEER POINT	Jan 16 2016
1m	1m 37.15	2	9-3	Standard	DRAGON MALL	Sep 26 2015
1m	1m 35.46	4	9-7	Standard	MINDUROWNBUSINESS	Nov 23 2015
1m 2f	2m 2.33	8	9-7	Standard	BANCNUANAHEIREANN	Nov 5 2015
1m 5f 66y	2m 47.00	4	8-7	Standard	COORG	Jan 6 2016
1m 6f	2m 55.65	4	10-0	Standard	CASTLE COMBE	Sep 3 2015
2m	3m 55.65	3	9-8	Standard	DUCHESS OF MARMITE	Nov 23 2015
2m	3m 22.37	5	9-3	Standard	NOTARISED	Mar 3 2016

CHEPSTOW

DISTANCE	TIME	AGE	WEIGHT	GOING	HORSE	DATE
5f 16y	57.60	2	8-11	Firm	MICRO LOVE	Jul 8 1986
5f 16y	56.80	3	8-4	Firm	TORBAY EXPRESS	Sep 15 1979
6f 16y	1m 8.50	2	9-2	Firm	NINJAGO	Jul 27 2012
6f 16y	1m 8.10	3	9-7	Firm	AMERICA CALLING	Sep 18 2001
7f 16y	1m 20.80	2	9-0	Good To Firm	ROYAL AMARETTO	Sep 12 1996
7f 16y	1m 19.30	3	9-0	Firm	TARANAKI	Sep 18 2001
1m 14y	1m 33.10	2	8-11	Good To Firm	SKI ACADEMY	Aug 28 1995
1m 14y	1m 31.60	3	8-13	Firm	STOLI	Sep 18 2001
1m 2f 36y	2m 4.10	3	8-5	Good To Firm	ELA ATHENA	Jul 23 1999
1m 2f 36y	2m 4.10	5	8-9	Hard	LEONIDAS	Jul 5 1983
1m 2f 36y	2m 4.10	5	7-8	Good To Firm	IT'S VARADAN	Sep 9 1989
1m 4f 23y	2m 31.00	5	8-11	Hard	THE FRIEND	Aug 29 1983
1m 4f 23y	2m 31.00	3	8-9	Good To Firm	SPRITSAIL	Jul 13 1989
2m 49y	3m 27.70	4	9-0	Good To Firm	WIZZARD ARTIST	Jul 1 1989
2m 2f	3m 56.40	5	8-7	Good To Firm	LAFFAH	Jul 8 2000

CHESTER

DISTANCE	TIME	AGE	WEIGHT	GOING	HORSE	DATE
5f 15y	59.94	2	9-2	Good To Firm	LEIBA LEIBA	Jun 26 2010
5f 15y	58.88	3	8-7	Good To Firm	PETERKIN	Jul 11 2014
5f 110y	1m 6.39	2	8-7	Good To Soft	KINEMATIC	Sep 27 2014
5f 110y	1m 5.02	6	8-9	Good	BALLESTEROS	Aug 22 2015
6f 17y	1m 12.85	2	8-10	Good To Firm	FLYING EXPRESS	Aug 31 2002
6f 17y	1m 12.02	5	9-5	Good To Firm	DEAUVILLE PRINCE	Jun 13 2015
7f 1y	1m 25.29	2	9-0	Good To Firm	DUE RESPECT	Sep 25 2002
7f 1y	1m 23.75	5	8-13	Good To Firm	THREE GRACES	Jul 9 2005
7f 127y	1m 32.29	2	9-0	Good To Firm	BIG BAD BOB	Sep 25 2002
7f 127y	1m 30.91	3	8-12	Good To Firm	CUPID'S GLORY	Aug 18 2005
1m 2f 70y	2m 7.15	3	8-8	Good To Firm	STOTSFOLD	Sep 23 2006
1m 3f 75y	2m 22.17	3	8-12	Good To Firm	PERFECT TRUTH	May 6 2009
1m 4f 63y	2m 33.70	3	8-10	Good To Firm	FIGHT YOUR CORNER	May 7 2002
1m 5f 84y	2m 45.43	5	8-11	Firm	RAKAPOSHI KING	May 7 1987
1m 7f 196y	3m 20.33	4	9-0	Good To Firm	GRAND FROMAGE	Jul 13 2002
2m 2f 140y	3m 58.89	7	9-2	Good To Firm	GREENWICH MEANTIME	May 9 2007

DONCASTER

DISTANCE	TIME	AGE	WEIGHT	GOING	HORSE	DATE
5f 3y	58.04	2	9-1	Good	GUTAIFAN	Sep 11 2015
5f 3y	57.31	7	9-10	Good	TABARET	Aug 14 2010
5f 143y	1m 5.38	4	9-7	Good	MUTHMIR	Sep 13 2014
6f 2y	1m 10.65	2	9-7	Good To Firm	BLOSSOMTIME	Jul 16 2015
6f 2y	1m 9.56	3	8-10	Good To Firm	PROCLAIM	May 30 2009
6f 111y	1m 17.19	2	8-9	Good	MR LUPTON	Sep 10 2015
7f 6y	1m 22.78	2	9-5	Good	BASATEEN	Jul 24 2014
7f 6y	1m 21.81	6	8-7	Good To Firm	SIGNOR PELTRO	May 30 2009
7f 213y (Rnd)	1m 38.37	2	8-6	Good To Soft	ANTONIOLA	Oct 23 2009
7f 213y (Rnd)	1m 34.46	4	8-12	Good To Firm	STAYING ON	Apr 18 2009
1m (Str)	1m 36.72	2	8-12	Good	DANCE OF FIRE	Sep 13 2014
1m (Str)	1m 34.95	6	8-9	Firm	QUICK WIT	Jul 18 2013
1m 2f 43y	2m 4.81	4	8-13	Good To Firm	RED GALA	Sep 12 2007
1m 3f 197y	2m 27.48	3	8-4	Good To Firm	SWIFT ALHAARTH	Sep 10 2011
1m 6f 115y	3m 0.44	3	9-0	Good To Firm	MASKED MARVEL	Sep 10 2011
2m 109y	3m 34.52	7	9-0	Good To Firm	INCHNADAMPH	Nov 10 2007
2m 1f 197y	3m 48.41	4	9-4	Good To Firm	SEPTIMUS	Sep 14 2007

EPSOM

DISTANCE	TIME	AGE	WEIGHT	GOING	HORSE	DATE
5f	55.02	2	8-9	Good To Firm	PRINCE ASLIA	Jun 9 1995
5f	53.60	4	9-5	Firm	INDIGENOUS	Jun 2 1960
6f 3y	1m 7.85	2	8-11	Good To Firm	SHOWBROOK	Jun 5 1991
6f 3y	1m 7.21	5	9-13	Good To Firm	MAC GILLE EOIN	Jul 2 2009
7f 3y	1m 21.30	2	8-9	Good To Firm	RED PEONY	Jul 29 2004
7f 3y	1m 20.15	4	8-7	Firm	CAPISTRANO	Jun 7 1972
1m 113y	1m 42.80	2	8-5	Good To Firm	NIGHTSTALKER	Aug 30 1988
1m 113y	1m 40.75	3	8-6	Good To Firm	SYLVA HONDA	Jun 5 1991
1m 2f 17y	2m 3.50	5	7-11	Firm	CROSSBOW	Jun 7 1967
1m 4f 6y	2m 31.33	3	9-0	Good To Firm	WORKFORCE	Jun 5 2010

FFOS LAS

DISTANCE	TIME	AGE	WEIGHT	GOING	HORSE	DATE
5f	57.06	2	9-3	Good To Firm	MR MAJEIKA	May 5 2011
5f	56.35	5	8-8	Good	HAAJES	Sep 12 2009
6f	1m 9.00	2	9-5	Good To Firm	WONDER OF QATAR	Sep 14 2014
6f	1m 7.80	8	8-4	Good To Firm	THE JAILER	May 5 2011
1m	1m 39.36	2	9-2	Good To Firm	HALA HALA	Sep 2 2013
1m	1m 37.12	5	9-0	Good To Firm	ZEBRANO	May 5 2011
1m 2f	2m 4.85	8	8-12	Good To Firm	PELHAM CRESCENT	May 5 2011
1m 3f 209y	2m 31.58	4	8-9	Good To Firm	MEN DON'T CRY	Jul 23 2013
1m 6f	2m 58.61	4	9-7	Good To Firm	LADY ECLAIR	Jul 12 2010
2m	3m 29.58	4	8-9	Good To Firm	ANNALUNA	Jul 1 2013

GOODWOOD

DISTANCE	TIME	AGE	WEIGHT	GOING	HORSE	DATE
5f	57.14	2	9-1	Good	YALTA	Jul 27 2016
5f	56.01	5	9-0	Good To Firm	RUDI'S PET	Jul 27 1999
6f	1m 9.81	2	8-11	Good To Firm	BACHIR	Jul 28 1999
6f	1m 9.10	6	9-0	Good To Firm	TAMAGIN	Sep 12 2009
7f	1m 24.99	2	8-11	Good To Firm	EKRAAR	Jul 29 1999
7f	1m 23.88	3	8-7	Firm	BRIEF GLIMPSE	Jul 25 1995
1m	1m 37.21	2	9-0	Good	CALDRA	Sep 9 2006
1m	1m 35.61	4	8-9	Good To Firm	SPECTAIT	Aug 4 2006
1m 1f 11y	1m 56.27	2	9-3	Good To Firm	DORDOGNE	Sep 22 2010
1m 1f 11y	1m 52.81	3	9-6	Good	VENA	Jul 27 1995
1m 1f 197y	2m 2.81	3	9-3	Good To Firm	ROAD TO LOVE	Aug 3 2006
1m 3f 44y	2m 22.77	3	9-3	Good	KHALIDI	May 26 2017
1m 3f 218y	2m 31.57	3	8-10	Firm	PRESENTING	Jul 25 1995
1m 6f	2m 57.61	4	9-6	Good To Firm	MEEZNAH	Jul 28 2011
2m	3m 21.55	5	9-10	Good To Firm	YEATS	Aug 3 2006
2m 4f	4m 11.75	3	7-10	Firm	LUCKY MOON	Aug 2 1990

HAMILTON

DISTANCE	TIME	AGE	WEIGHT	GOING	HORSE	DATE
5f 7y	57.95	2	8-8	Good To Firm	ROSE BLOSSOM	May 29 2009
6f 6y	1m 10.00	2	8-12	Good To Firm	BREAK THE CODE	Aug 24 1999
6f 6y	1m 9.30	4	8-7	Firm	MARCUS GAME	Jul 11 1974
1m 68y	1m 45.46	2	9-5	Good To Firm	LAAFIRAAQ	Sep 20 2015
1m 68y	1m 42.70	6	7-7	Firm	CRANLEY	Sep 25 1972
1m 1f 35y	1m 53.60	5	9-6	Good To Firm	REGENT'S SECRET	Aug 10 2005
1m 3f 15y	2m 18.66	3	9-3	Good	POSTPONED	Jul 18 2014
1m 4f 15y	2m 30.52	5	9-10	Good To Firm	RECORD BREAKER	Jun 10 2009
1m 5f 16y	2m 45.10	6	9-6	Firm	MENTALASANYTHIN	Jun 14 1995

HAYDOCK

DISTANCE	TIME	AGE	WEIGHT	GOING	HORSE	DATE
5f	58.56	2	8-2	Good To Firm	BARRACUDA BOY	Aug 11 2012
5f	56.39	5	9-4	Firm	BATED BREATH	May 26 2012
5f (Inner)	58.51	2	9-1	Good	FOUR DRAGONS	Oct 14 2016
5f (Inner)	57.38	7	9-12	Good To Firm	FOXY FOREVER	Jul 21 2017
6f	1m 8.56	3	9-0	Firm	HARRY ANGEL	May 27 2017
6f	1m 10.98	4	9-9	Good To Firm	WOLFHOUND	Sep 4 1993
6f (Inner)	1m 9.40	7	9-3	Good To Firm	MARKAB	Sep 4 2010
6f (Inner)	1m 10.58	2	9-2	Good To Firm	PRESTBURY PARK	Jul 21 2017
6f 212y (Inner)	1m 27.51	2	9-0	Good To Firm	ROYAL PARKS	Jul 6 2017
6f 212y (Inner)	1m 25.86	5	9-9	Good	JUNGLE CAT	Jul 22 2017
7f 37y	1m 27.57	2	9-2	Good To Firm	CONTRAST	Aug 5 2016
7f 37y	1m 25.50	3	8-11	Good	FORGE	Sep 1 2016
7f 212y (Inner)	1m 37.80	3	9-4	Good To Firm	SIDEWINDER	May 26 2017
1m 37y	1m 38.50	4	8-11	Good To Firm	EXPRESS HIMSELF	Jun 10 2015
1m 2f 42y (Inner)	2m 7.25	3	8-9	Good To Firm	LARAAIB	May 26 2017
1m 2f 100y	2m 7.71	3	8-8	Good To Firm	ROYAL ARTILLERY	Aug 6 2016
1m 3f 140y (Inner)	2m 30.37	4	9-12	Good	LUGANO	Jun 15 2017
1m 3f 175y	2m 25.53	4	8-12	Good To Firm	NUMBER THEORY	May 24 2012
1m 6f	2m 55.20	5	9-9	Good To Firm	HUFF AND PUFF	Sep 7 2012
2m 45y	3m 26.98	5	8-13	Good To Firm	DE RIGUEUR	Jun 8 2013

KEMPTON (AW)

DISTANCE	TIME	AGE	WEIGHT	GOING	HORSE	DATE
5f	58.96	2	8-6	Standard	GLAMOROUS SPIRIT	Nov 28 2008
5f	58.26	7	9-5	Standard To Slow	FOXY FOREVER	Oct 17 2017
6f	1m 11.02	2	9-1	Standard To Slow	INVINCIBLE ARMY	Sep 9 2017
6f	1m 9.79	4	8-11	Standard	TRINITYELITEDOTCOM	Mar 29 2014
7f	1m 23.79	2	8-0	Standard	ELSAAKB	Nov 8 2017
7f	1m 23.10	6	9-9	Standard	SIRIUS PROSPECT	Nov 20 2014
1m	1m 37.26	2	9-0	Standard	CECCHINI	Nov 8 2017
1m	1m 35.73	3	8-9	Standard	WESTERN ARISTOCRAT	Sep 15 2011
1m 1f 219y	2m 2.93	3	8-11	Standard To Slow	PLY	Sep 25 2017
1m 2f 219y	2m 16.09	4	8-7	Standard	SALUTATION	Mar 29 2014
1m 3f 219y	2m 28.99	6	9-3	Standard	SPRING OF FAME	Nov 7 2012
1m 7f 218y	3m 21.50	4	8-12	Standard	COLOUR VISION	May 2 2012

LEICESTER

DISTANCE	TIME	AGE	WEIGHT	GOING	HORSE	DATE
5f 2y	58.40	2	9-0	Firm	CUTTING BLADE	Jun 9 1986
5f 2y	57.85	5	9-5	Good To Firm	THE JOBBER	Sep 18 2006
5f 218y	1m 9.99	2	9-0	Good	EL MANATI	Aug 1 2012
5f 218y	1m 9.12	6	8-12	Good To Firm	PETER ISLAND	Apr 25 2009
7f 9y	1m 22.60	2	9-0	Good To Firm	MARIE DE MEDICI	Oct 6 2009
7f 9y	1m 20.80	3	8-7	Firm	FLOWER BOWL	Jun 9 1986
1m 53y	1m 44.05	2	8-11	Good To Firm	CONGRESSIONAL	Sep 6 2005
1m 53y	1m 41.89	5	9-7	Good To Firm	VAINGLORY	Jun 18 2009
1m 1f 216y	2m 5.30	2	9-1	Good To Firm	WINDSOR CASTLE	Oct 14 1996
1m 1f 216y	2m 2.40	3	8-11	Firm	EFFIGY	Nov 4 1985
1m 1f 216y	2m 2.40	4	9-6	Good To Firm	LADY ANGHARAD	Jun 18 2000
1m 3f 179y	2m 27.10	5	8-12	Good To Firm	MURGHEM	Jun 18 2000

LINGFIELD (TURF)

DISTANCE	TIME	AGE	WEIGHT	GOING	HORSE	DATE
4f 217y	57.07	2	9-0	Good To Firm	QUITE A THING	Jun 11 2011
4f 217y	56.09	3	9-4	Good To Firm	WHITECREST	Sep 16 2011
6f	1m 8.36	2	8-12	Good To Firm	FOLLY BRIDGE	Sep 8 2009
6f	1m 8.13	6	9-8	Firm	CLEAR PRAISE	Aug 10 2013
7f	1m 20.55	2	8-11	Good To Firm	HIKING	Aug 17 2013
7f	1m 20.05	3	8-5	Good To Firm	PERFECT TRIBUTE	May 7 2011
7f 135y	1m 29.32	2	9-3	Good To Firm	DUNDONNELL	Aug 4 2012
7f 135y	1m 26.73	3	8-6	Good To Firm	HIAAM	Jul 11 1987
1m 1f	1m 52.40	4	9-2	Good To Firm	QUANDARY	Jul 15 1995
1m 2f	2m 4.61	3	9-3	Firm	USRAN	Jul 15 1989
1m 3f 133y	2m 23.95	3	8-5	Firm	NIGHT-SHIRT	Jul 14 1990
1m 6f	2m 59.10	5	9-5	Firm	IBN BEY	Jul 1 1989
2m 68y	3m 23.71	3	9-5	Good To Firm	LAURIES CRUSADOR	Aug 13 1988

LINGFIELD (AW)

DISTANCE	TIME	AGE	WEIGHT	GOING	HORSE	DATE
5f 6y	58.11	2	9-5	Standard	IVORS REBEL	Sep 23 2014
5f 6y	56.67	5	8-12	Standard	LADIES ARE FOREVER	Mar 16 2013
6f 1y	1m 9.99	2	8-12	Standard	SWISS DIVA	Nov 19 2008
6f 1y	1m 8.75	7	9-2	Standard	TAROOQ	Dec 18 2013
7f 1y	1m 22.67	2	9-3	Standard	COMPLICIT	Nov 23 2013
7f 1y	1m 21.92	5	9-6	Standard	GREY MIRAGE	Feb 22 2014
1m 1y	1m 35.84	2	9-5	Standard	BRAVE HERO	Nov 25 2015
1m 1y	1m 34.34	5	8-13	Standard	MY TARGET	Dec 31 2016
1m 2f	2m 0.99	4	9-0	Standard	FARRAAJ	Mar 16 2013
1m 4f	2m 26.99	6	9-11	Standard	PINZOLO	Jan 21 2017
1m 5f	2m 39.70	3	8-10	Standard	HIDDEN GOLD	Oct 30 2014
1m 7f 169y	3m 15.18	4	9-1	Standard	WINNING STORY	Apr 14 2017

MUSSELBURGH

DISTANCE	TIME	AGE	WEIGHT	GOING	HORSE	DATE
5f 1y	57.66	2	9-2	Good To Firm	IT DONT COME EASY	Jun 3 2017
5f 1y	57.10	6	8-6	Good To Firm	RED BARON	Jun 13 2015
7f 33y	1m 27.46	2	8-8	Good	DURHAM REFLECTION	Sep 14 2009
7f 33y	1m 25.00	9	8-8	Good To Firm	KALK BAY	Jun 4 2016
1m 2y	1m 40.34	2	8-12	Good To Firm	SUCCESSION	Sep 26 2004
1m 2y	1m 36.83	3	9-5	Good To Firm	GINGER JACK	Jul 13 2010
1m 208y	1m 50.42	8	8-11	Good To Firm	DHAULAR DHAR	Sep 3 2010
1m 4f 104y	2m 36.80	3	8-3	Good To Firm	HARRIS TWEED	Jun 5 2010
1m 5f	2m 46.41	3	9-5	Good To Firm	ALCAEUS	Sep 29 2013
1m 5f 216y	2m 57.98	7	8-5	Good To Firm	JONNY DELTA	Apr 18 2014
1m 7f 217y	3m 25.62	4	8-3	Good To Firm	ALDRETH	Jun 13 2015

NEWBURY

DISTANCE	TIME	AGE	WEIGHT	GOING	HORSE	DATE
5f 34y	59.19	2	8-6	Good To Firm	SUPERSTAR LEO	Jul 22 2000
5f 34y	58.44	5	9-1	Good To Firm	ROBOT BOY	Apr 17 2015
6f 8y	1m 11.07	2	8-4	Good To Firm	BAHATI	May 30 2009
6f 8y	1m 9.42	3	8-11	Good To Firm	NOTA BENE	May 13 2005
6f 110y	1m 18.06	2	9-5	Good To Firm	TWIN SAILS	Jun 11 2015
7f (Str)	1m 23.04	2	8-11	Good To Firm	HAAFHD	Aug 15 2003
7f (Str)	1m 20.80	3	9-0	Good To Firm	MUHAARAR	Apr 18 2015
1m	1m 37.50	2	9-1	Good To Firm	WINGED CUPID	Sep 16 2005
1m	1m 33.59	6	9-0	Firm	RAKTI	May 14 2005
1m 1f	1m 49.65	3	8-0	Good To Firm	HOLTYE	May 21 1995
1m 2f	2m 1.29	3	8-7	Good To Firm	WALL STREET	Jul 20 1996
1m 3f 5y	2m 16.54	3	8-9	Good To Firm	GRANDERA	Sep 22 2001
1m 4f 5y	2m 28.26	4	9-7	Good To Firm	AZAMOUR	Jul 23 2005
1m 5f 61y	2m 44.90	5	10-0	Good To Firm	MYSTIC HILL	Jul 20 1996

NEWCASTLE (AW)

Distance	Time	Age	Weight	Going	HORSE	Date
5f	57.83	3	9-4	Standard	FIRST BOMBARDMENT	Oct 7 2016
6f	1m 9.86	3	9-2	Standard	UNABATED	Mar 22 2017
7f 14y	1m 24.48	4	9-7	Standard	ALICE THORNTON	Oct 14 2016
1m 5y	1m 36.28	5	9-10	Standard	AUSPICION	Sep 12 2017
1m 2f 42y	2m 4.88	3	8-6	Standard	PALISADE	Oct 16 2016
1m 4f 98y	2m 36.76	3	8-7	Standard	AJMAN PRINCE	Oct 14 2016
2m 56y	3m 29.87	4	9-8	Standard	DANNYDAY	Jun 25 2016

NEWMARKET (ROWLEY MILE)

DISTANCE	TIME	AGE	WEIGHT	GOING	HORSE	DATE
5f	58.69	2	8-12	Good To Firm	MRS DANVERS	Oct 7 2016
5f	56.81	6	9-2	Good To Firm	LOCHSONG	Apr 30 1994
6f	1m 9.56	2	8-12	Good To Firm	BUSHRANGER	Oct 3 2008
6f	1m 9.55	3	9-1	Good To Firm	CAPTAIN COLBY	May 16 2015
7f	1m 22.37	2	9-1	Good	U S NAVY FLAG	Oct 14 2017
7f	1m 21.98	3	9-0	Good To Firm	TUPI	May 16 2015
1m	1m 35.67	2	8-12	Good	STEELER	Sep 29 2012
1m	1m 34.07	4	9-0	Good To Firm	EAGLE MOUNTAIN	Oct 3 2008
1m 1f	1m 47.26	5	8-12	Good To Firm	MANDURO	Apr 19 2007
1m 2f	2m 2.76	2	9-2	Good	KEW GARDENS	Oct 14 2017
1m 2f	2m 0.13	3	8-12	Good	NEW APPROACH	Oct 18 2008
1m 4f	2m 26.07	3	8-9	Good To Firm	MOHEDIAN LADY	Sep 22 2011
1m 6f	2m 51.59	3	8-7	Good	ART EYES	Sep 29 2005
2m	3m 18.64	5	9-6	Good To Firm	TIMES UP	Sep 22 2011
2m 2f	3m 45.59	4	8-8	Good	WITHHOLD	Oct 14 2017

NEWMARKET (JULY COURSE)

DISTANCE	TIME	AGE	WEIGHT	GOING	HORSE	DATE
5f	58.52	2	8-10	Good	SEDUCTRESS	Jul 10 1990
5f	56.09	6	9-11	Good	BORDERLESCOTT	Aug 22 2008
6f	1m 10.35	2	8-11	Good	ELNAWIN	Aug 22 2008
6f	1m 9.11	4	9-5	Good To Firm	LETHAL FORCE	Jul 13 2013
7f	1m 23.33	2	9-1	Good To Firm	BIRCHWOOD	Jul 11 2015
7f	1m 22.59	3	9-7	Firm	HO LENG	Jul 9 1998
1m	1m 37.47	2	8-13	Good	WHIPPERS LOVE	Aug 28 2009
1m	1m 34.42	3	8-12	Good To Firm	ALICE SPRINGS	Jul 8 2016
1m 110y	1m 44.10	3	8-11	Good	GOLDEN SNAKE	Apr 15 1999
1m 2f	2m 0.91	3	9-5	Good To Firm	MAPUTO	Jul 11 2013
1m 4f	2m 25.11	3	8-11	Good	LUSH LASHES	Aug 22 2008
1m 5f	2m 40.75	5	9-10	Good	WADI AL HATTAWI	Aug 29 2015
1m 6f 175y	3m 4.27	3	8-5	Good	ARRIVE	Jul 11 2001
2m 24y	3m 20.28	7	9-10	Good	YORKSHIRE	Jul 11 2001

NOTTINGHAM

DISTANCE	TIME	AGE	WEIGHT	GOING	HORSE	DATE
5f 8y (Inner)	59.05	2	9-0	Good To Firm	MAIN DESIRE	May 2 2017
5f 8y (Inner)	57.40	3	9-6	Good To Firm	CARLTON FRANKIE	May 2 2017
5f 8y	57.90	2	8-9	Firm	HOH MAGIC	May 13 1994
5f 8y	57.58	5	7-11	Good To Firm	PENNY DREADFUL	Jun 19 2017
6f 18y	1m 11.40	2	8-11	Firm	JAMEELAPI	Aug 8 1983
6f 18y	1m 10.00	4	9-2	Firm	AJANAC	Aug 8 1988
1m 72y (Inner)	1m 45.14	2	9-6	Good	RASHFORD'S DOUBLE	Nov 2 2016
1m 72y (Inner)	1m 43.22	4	9-7	Good To Firm	REAVER	Apr 22 2017
1m 2f 50y	2m 7.13	5	9-8	Good To Firm	VASILY	Jul 19 2013
1m 2f 52y (Inner)	2m 16.66	2	9-3	Soft	LETHAL GLAZE	Oct 1 2008
1m 2f 52y (Inner)	2m 9.40	3	9-5	Good	CENTURIUS	Apr 20 2013
1m 6f	2m 57.80	3	8-10	Firm	BUSTER JO	Oct 1 1985
1m 7f 219y (Inner)	3m 34.39	3	8-0	Good	BENOZZO GOZZOLI	Oct 28 2009
2m	3m 25.25	3	9-5	Good	BULWARK	Sep 27 2005

PONTEFRACT

DISTANCE	TIME	AGE	WEIGHT	GOING	HORSE	DATE
5f 3y	1m 1.10	2	9-0	Firm	GOLDEN BOUNTY	Sep 20 2001
5f 3y	1m 0.49	5	9-5	Good To Firm	JUDICIAL	Apr 24 2017
6f	1m 14.00	2	9-3	Firm	FAWZI	Sep 6 1983
6f	1m 12.60	3	7-13	Firm	MERRY ONE	Aug 29 1970
1m 6y	1m 42.80	2	9-13	Firm	STAR SPRAY	Sep 6 1983
1m 6y	1m 42.80	2	9-0	Firm	ALASIL	Sep 26 2002
1m 6y	1m 40.60	4	9-10	Good To Firm	ISLAND LIGHT	Apr 13 2002
1m 2f 5y	2m 10.10	2	9-0	Firm	SHANTY STAR	Oct 7 2002
1m 2f 5y	2m 8.20	4	7-8	Hard	HAPPY HECTOR	Jul 9 1979
1m 2f 5y	2m 8.20	3	7-13	Hard	TOM NODDY	Aug 21 1972
1m 4f 5y	2m 33.72	3	8-7	Firm	AJAAN	Aug 8 2007
2m 1f 27y	3m 40.67	4	8-7	Good To Firm	PARADISE FLIGHT	Jun 6 2005
2m 2f 2y	3m 51.10	3	8-8	Good To Firm	KUDZ	Sep 9 1986
2m 5f 139y	4m 47.80	4	8-4	Firm	PHYSICAL	May 14 1984

REDCAR

DISTANCE	TIME	AGE	WEIGHT	GOING	HORSE	DATE
5f	56.88	2	9-7	Good To Soft	WOLFOFWALLSTREET	Oct 27 2014
5f	56.01	10	9-3	Firm	HENRY HALL	Sep 20 2006
5f 217y	1m 8.84	2	8-3	Good To Firm	OBE GOLD	Oct 2 2004
5f 217y	1m 8.60	3	9-2	Good To Firm	SIZZLING SAGA	Jun 21 1991
7f	1m 21.28	2	9-3	Firm	KAROO BLUE	Sep 20 2006
7f	1m 21.00	3	9-1	Firm	EMPTY QUARTER	Oct 3 1995
7f 219y	1m 34.37	2	9-0	Firm	MASTERSHIP	Sep 20 2006
7f 219y	1m 32.42	4	10-0	Firm	NANTON	Sep 20 2006
1m 1f	1m 52.44	2	9-0	Firm	SPEAR	Sep 13 2004
1m 1f	1m 48.50	5	8-12	Firm	MELLOTTIE	Jul 25 1990
1m 2f 1y	2m 10.10	2	8-11	Good	ADDING	Nov 10 1989
1m 2f 1y	2m 1.40	5	9-2	Firm	ERADICATE	May 28 1990
1m 3f	2m 17.20	3	8-9	Firm	PHOTO CALL	Aug 7 1990
1m 5f 135y	2m 54.70	6	9-10	Firm	BRODESSA	Jun 20 1992
1m 5f 218y	2m 59.81	4	9-1	Good To Firm	ESPRIT DE CORPS	Sep 11 2006
1m 7f 217y	3m 24.90	3	9-3	Good To Firm	SUBSONIC	Oct 8 1991

RIPON

DISTANCE	TIME	AGE	WEIGHT	GOING	HORSE	DATE
5f	57.80	2	8-8	Firm	SUPER ROCKY	Aug 5 1991
5f	57.28	5	8-12	Good	DESERT ACE	Sep 24 2016
6f	1m 10.40	2	9-2	Good	CUMBRIAN VENTURE	Aug 17 2002
6f	1m 9.43	6	9-10	Good	KIMBERELLA	Aug 24 2016
1m	1m 38.77	2	9-4	Good	GREED IS GOOD	Sep 28 2013
1m	1m 36.62	4	8-11	Good To Firm	GRANSTON	Aug 29 2005
1m 1f	1m 49.97	6	9-3	Good To Firm	GINGER JACK	Jun 20 2013
1m 2f	2m 2.60	3	9-4	Firm	SWIFT SWORD	Jul 20 1991
1m 4f 10y	2m 31.40	4	8-8	Good To Firm	DANDINO	Apr 16 2011
2m	3m 27.07	5	9-12	Good To Firm	GREENWICH MEANTIME	Aug 30 2005

SALISBURY

DISTANCE	TIME	AGE	WEIGHT	GOING	HORSE	DATE
5f	59.30	2	9-0	Good To Firm	AJIGOLO	May 12 2005
5f	59.18	7	8-10	Good To Firm	EDGED OUT	Jun 18 2017
6f	1m 12.10	2	8-0	Good To Firm	PARISIAN LADY	Jun 10 1997
6f	1m 11.09	3	9-0	Firm	L'AMI LOUIS	May 1 2011
6f 213y	1m 25.97	2	9-0	Firm	MORE ROYAL	Jun 29 1995
6f 213y	1m 24.91	3	9-4	Firm	CHILWORTH LAD	May 1 2011
1m	1m 40.48	2	8-13	Firm	CHOIR MASTER	Sep 17 2002
1m	1m 38.29	3	8-7	Good To Firm	LAYMAN	Aug 11 2005
1m 1f 198y	2m 4.00	4	9-2	Good To Firm	CHAIN OF DAISIES	Aug 10 2016
1m 4f 5y	2m 31.69	3	9-5	Good To Firm	ARRIVE	Jun 27 2001
1m 6f 44y	3m 0.48	7	9-2	Good To Firm	HIGHLAND CASTLE	May 23 2015

SANDOWN

DISTANCE	TIME	AGE	WEIGHT	GOING	HORSE	DATE
5f 10y	59.48	2	9-3	Firm	TIMES TIME	Jul 22 1982
5f 10y	58.57	3	8-12	Good To Firm	BATTAASH	Jul 8 2017
7f	1m 26.56	2	9-0	Good To Firm	RAVEN'S PASS	Sep 1 2007
7f	1m 26.36	3	9-0	Firm	MAWSUFF	Jun 14 1986
1m 14y	1m 41.14	2	8-11	Good To Firm	REFERENCE POINT	Sep 23 1986
1m 14y	1m 38.87	7	9-10	Good To Firm	PRINCE OF JOHANNE	Jul 6 2013
1m 1f	1m 54.63	2	8-8	Good To Firm	FRENCH PRETENDER	Sep 20 1988
1m 1f	1m 52.40	7	9-3	Good To Firm	BOURGAINVILLE	Aug 11 2005
1m 1f 209y	2m 2.14	4	8-11	Good	KALAGLOW	May 31 1982
1m 6f	2m 56.90	4	8-7	Good To Firm	LADY ROSANNA	Jul 19 1989
2m 50y	3m 29.38	6	9-0	Good To Firm	CAUCUS	Jul 6 2013

SOUTHWELL (AW)

DISTANCE	TIME	AGE	WEIGHT	GOING	HORSE	DATE
4f 214y	57.85	2	9-3	Standard	ARCTIC FEELING	Mar 31 2010
4f 214y	56.80	5	9-7	Standard	GHOSTWING	Jan 3 2012
6f 16y	1m 14.00	2	8-5	Standard	PANALO	Nov 8 1989
6f 16y	1m 13.50	4	10-0	Standard	SALADAN KNIGHT	Dec 30 1989
7f 14y	1m 26.82	2	8-12	Standard	WINGED ICARUS	Aug 28 2012
7f 14y	1m 26.38	4	8-6	Standard	MOON RIVER	Mar 30 2016
1m 13y	1m 38.00	2	8-9	Standard	ALPHA RASCAL	Nov 13 1990
1m 13y	1m 38.00	4	8-10	Standard	ANDREW'S FIRST	Dec 30 1989
1m 13y	1m 37.25	3	8-6	Standard	VALIRA	Nov 3 1990
1m 3f 23y	2m 21.50	4	9-7	Standard	TEMPERING	Dec 5 1990
1m 4f 14y	2m 33.90	4	9-12	Standard	FAST CHICK	Nov 8 1989
1m 6f 21y	3m 1.60	3	7-8	Standard	EREVNON	Dec 29 1990
2m 102y	3m 37.60	9	8-12	Standard	OLD HUBERT	Dec 5 1990

THIRSK

DISTANCE	TIME	AGE	WEIGHT	GOING	HORSE	DATE
5f	57.20	2	9-7	Good To Firm	PROUD BOAST	Aug 5 2000
5f	56.92	5	9-6	Firm	CHARLIE PARKES	Apr 11 2003
6f	1m 9.20	2	9-6	Good To Firm	WESTCOURT MAGIC	Aug 25 1995
6f	1m 8.80	6	9-4	Firm	JOHAYRO	Jul 23 1999
7f	1m 23.70	2	8-9	Firm	COURTING	Jul 23 1999
7f	1m 22.80	4	8-5	Firm	SILVER HAZE	May 21 1988
7f 218y	1m 37.97	2	9-0	Firm	SUNDAY SYMPHONY	Sep 4 2004
7f 218y	1m 34.80	4	8-13	Firm	YEARSLEY	May 5 1990
1m 4f 8y	2m 29.90	5	9-12	Firm	GALLERY GOD	Jun 4 2001
2m 13y	3m 22.30	3	9-0	Firm	TOMASCHEK	Jul 17 1981

WETHERBY

DISTANCE	TIME	AGE	WEIGHT	GOING	HORSE	DATE
5f 110y	1m 4.25	3	9-1	Good To Firm	DAPPER MAN	Jun 19 2017
7f	1m 24.72	4	9-2	Good	SLEMY	Jul 21 2015
1m	1m 38.82	5	8-13	Good To Firm	AL NAFOORAH	Jun 19 2017
1m 2f	2m 5.13	5	9-5	Good	FIRST SARGEANT	Jul 21 2015
1m 6f	3m 0.41	3	9-7	Good To Firm	DAVY'S DILEMMA	Jun 19 2017

WINDSOR

DISTANCE	TIME	AGE	WEIGHT	GOING	HORSE	DATE
5f 21y	58.69	2	9-0	Good To Firm	CHARLES THE GREAT	May 23 2011
5f 21y	58.08	5	8-13	Good To Firm	TAURUS TWINS	Apr 4 2011
6f 12y	1m 10.50	2	9-5	Good To Firm	CUBISM	Aug 17 1998
6f 12y	1m 9.58	7	9-0	Good To Firm	TROPICS	Jun 1 2015
1m 31y	1m 41.73	2	9-5	Good To Firm	SALOUEN	Aug 7 2016
1m 31y	1m 39.81	5	9-7	Good	FRENCH NAVY	Jun 29 2013
1m 1f 194y	2m 1.62	6	9-1	Good	AL KAZEEM	Aug 23 2014
1m 3f 99y	2m 21.50	3	9-2	Firm	DOUBLE FLORIN	May 19 1980

WOLVERHAMPTON (AW)

DISTANCE	TIME	AGE	WEIGHT	GOING	HORSE	DATE
5f 21y	59.75	2	9-6	Standard	QUATRIEME AMI	Nov 13 2015
5f 21y	59.39	5	9-8	Standard	BOOM THE GROOM	Feb 22 2016
6f 20y	1m 12.67	2	9-6	Standard	PARKOUR	Nov 14 2015
6f 20y	1m 11.84	3	8-6	Standard	PRETEND	Dec 19 2014
7f 36y	1m 27.53	2	9-5	Standard	ALWAYS WELCOME	Dec 22 2015
7f 36y	1m 25.35	4	9-3	Standard	MISTER UNIVERSE	Mar 12 2016
1m 142y	1m 47.38	2	9-5	Standard	JACK HOBBS	Dec 27 2014
1m 142y	1m 45.43	4	9-4	Standard	KEYSTROKE	Nov 26 2016
1m 1f 104y	1m 56.64	8	8-13	Standard	PERFECT CRACKER	Mar 19 2016
1m 4f 51y	2m 33.92	3	8-13	Standard	NATURAL SCENERY	Oct 21 2016
1m 5f 194y	2m 57.55	6	9-7	Standard	ENTIHAA	Dec 6 2014
2m 120y	3m 31.92	7	9-3	Standard	WATERSMEET	Jan 15 2018

YARMOUTH

DISTANCE	TIME	AGE	WEIGHT	GOING	HORSE	DATE
5f 42y	1m 0.40	2	8-6	Good To Firm	EBBA	Jul 26 1999
5f 42y	59.80	4	8-13	Good To Firm	ROXANNE MILL	Aug 25 2002
6f 3y	1m 10.40	2	9-0	Firm	LANCHESTER	Sep 15 1988
6f 3y	1m 9.14	3	9-0	Good To Firm	CARTOGRAPHER	May 24 2017
7f 3y	1m 22.20	2	9-0	Good To Firm	WARRSHAN	Sep 14 1988
7f 3y	1m 22.12	4	9-4	Good To Firm	GLENBUCK	Apr 26 2007
1m 3y	1m 36.30	2	8-2	Firm	OUT RUN	Sep 15 1988
1m 3y	1m 33.90	3	8-8	Firm	BONNE ETOILE	Jun 27 1995
1m 1f 21y	1m 52.00	3	9-5	Good To Firm	TOUCH GOLD	Jul 5 2012
1m 2f 23y	2m 2.83	3	8-8	Firm	REUNITE	Jul 18 2006
1m 3f 104y	2m 23.10	3	8-9	Firm	RAHIL	Jul 1 1993
1m 6f 17y	2m 57.80	3	8-2	Good To Firm	BARAKAT	Jul 24 1990
2m	3m 26.70	4	8-2	Good To Firm	ALHESN	Jul 26 1999

YORK

DISTANCE	TIME	AGE	WEIGHT	GOING	HORSE	DATE
5f	57.11	2	9-0	Good To Firm	BIG TIME BABY	Aug 20 2016
5f	56.16	3	9-9	Good To Firm	DAYJUR	Aug 23 1990
5f 89y	1m 3.20	2	9-3	Good To Firm	THE ART OF RACING	Sep 9 2012
5f 89y	1m 1.72	4	9-7	Good To Firm	BOGART	Aug 21 2013
6f	1m 8.90	2	9-0	Good	TIGGY WIGGY	Aug 21 2014
6f	1m 8.23	3	8-11	Good To Firm	MINCE	Sep 9 2012
7f	1m 22.32	2	9-1	Good To Firm	DUTCH CONNECTION	Aug 20 2014
7f	1m 21.83	4	9-8	Good To Firm	DIMENSION	Jul 28 2012
7f 192y	1m 36.92	2	9-5	Good	AWESOMETANK	Oct 14 2017
7f 192y	1m 35.10	4	8-12	Good	HOME CUMMINS	Jul 9 2016
1m 177y	1m 46.76	5	9-8	Good To Firm	ECHO OF LIGHT	Sep 5 2007
1m 2f 56y	2m 5.29	3	8-11	Good To Firm	SEA THE STARS	Aug 18 2009
1m 3f 188y	2m 36.28	3	8-9	Good To Firm	BANDARI	Jun 18 2005
1m 5f 188y	2m 54.96	4	9-0	Good To Firm	TACTIC	May 22 2010
2m 56y	3m 28.97	5	9-5	Good To Firm	GABRIAL'S KING	Jul 12 2014

TOP FLAT JOCKEYS IN BRITAIN 2017

(JANUARY 1st -DECEMBER 31st)

WINS-RUNS	%	JOCKEY	2ND	3RD	TOTAL PRIZE	WIN PRIZE
206-1081	19%	SILVESTRE DE SOUSA	157	148	2,318,940	1,635,387
177-1510	12%	LUKE MORRIS	157	192	1,752,680	1,019,189
161-855	19%	JIM CROWLEY	119	83	5,243,361	3,174,200
146-905	16%	ADAM KIRBY	128	102	2,107,292	1,386,885
140-849	16%	JOE FANNING	112	100	1,429,390	1,010,036
137-152	24%	RYAN MOORE	82	48	8,147,097	5,746,724
128-887	14%	P J MCDONALD	119	100	1,853,510	1,414,386
127-854	15%	OISIN MURPHY	121	112	2,555,292	1,270,921
122-735	17%	DANNY TUDHOPE	103	89	1,612,101	1,062,423
110-501	22%	JAMES DOYLE	69	72	3,337,313	1,848,921
106-914	12%	JOSEPHINE GORDON	121	99	1,288,710	772,432
100-682	15%	RICHARD KINGSCOTE	82	71	1,094,807	694,901
95-504	19%	ANDREA ATZENI	70	79	3,177,648	1,866,595
94-855	11%	DAVID PROBERT	85	89	1,009,241	566,413
92-711	13%	PAUL HANAGAN	91	95	1,520,528	890,308
89-566	16%	JAMIE SPENCER	81	88	1,310,788	785,981
86-759	11%	PAUL MULRENNAN	70	86	786,752	447,601
86-829	10%	TOM MARQUAND	89	84	879,709	548,834
83-683	12%	FRANNY NORTON	80	79	1,068,023	693,138
81-368	22%	WILLIAM BUICK	56	39	3,008,220	1,829,630
80-756	11%	GRAHAM LEE	52	80	737,454	452,597
79-685	12%	BEN CURTIS	79	73	583,182	375,037
75-598	13%	PHILLIP MAKIN	68	79	716,472	449,981
73-568	13%	SEAN LEVEY	63	68	1,202,033	712,943
71-565	13%	MARTIN HARLEY	79	66	916,742	436,539
71-705	10%	TONY HAMILTON	78	79	757,084	436,604
68-806	8%	ANDREW MULLEN	66	94	556,370	299,300
68-852	8%	TOM EAVES	94	87	791,755	451,059
67-471	14%	PAT COSGRAVE	83	65	900,701	445,578
67-585	11%	ROBERT WINSTON	71	63	1,122,126	829,489
66-708	9%	FRAN BERRY	75	84	836,752	456,004
66-750	9%	SHANE KELLY	87	78	299,696	520,365
65-530	12%	KIERAN SHOEMARK	56	70	708,806	454,619
63-257	25%	FRANKIE DETTORI	38	36	4,872,579	3,727,924
63-528	12%	DAVID ALLAN	59	51	908,907	616,600
61-388	16%	DANE O'NEILL	63	45	634,668	430,501
61-420	15%	KEVIN STOTT	45	55	621,642	392,234
61-512	12%	DAVID EGAN	68	73	617,934	317,689
61-559	11%	JASON HART	67	58	477,143	293,378
60-403	15%	HARRY BENTLEY	58	36	1,026,769	582,707
60-552	11%	J F EGAN	53	57	567,391	336,970
59-516	11%	HOLLIE DOYLE	62	57	541,298	311,670
58-650	9%	STEVIE DONOHOE	74	60	616,268	390,171
57-650	9%	DOUGIE COSTELLO	52	63	407,477	239,922
55-628	9%	JAMES SULLIVAN	62	70	849,110	602,181
54-716	8%	LIAM KENIRY	58	82	331,362	195,437
51-370	14%	LEWIS EDMUNDS	42	48	356,182	240,026
51-550	9%	CONNOR BEASLEY	55	66	453,443	254,475
49-395	12%	GEORGE WOOD	44	59	597,301	400,533
46-332	14%	MARTIN LANE	39	30	356,953	242,843

TOP FLAT TRAINERS IN BRITAIN 2017

TRAINER	LEADING HORSE	W-R	2ND	3RD	4TH	WIN PRIZE	TOTAL PRIZE
A P O'BRIEN	Wings Of Eagles	32-165	24	14	17	5,563,605	8,335,027
JOHN GOSDEN	Enable	138-690	91	102	87	4,558,363	6,185,144
RICHARD FAHEY	Ribchester	200-1749	220	219	197	2,467,394	4,239,127
SIR MICHAEL STOUTE	Ulysses	82-438	68	47	49	2,370,248	3,855,061
MARK JOHNSTON	Permian	215-1379	187	166	157	2,409,999	3,555,120
RICHARD HANNON	Barney Roy	194-1354	177	165	157	1,850,403	3,000,248
WILLIAM HAGGAS	Tasleet	158-590	78	77	75	1,591,288	2,702,577
ANDREW BALDING	Here Comes When	92-677	100	73	85	1,702,065	2,565,904
CHARLIE APPLEBY	Frontiersman	106-378	63	48	34	1,274,324	2,161,034
ROGER VARIAN	Laugh A Minute	109-558	113	90	52	1,217,847	1,913,490
DAVID O'MEARA	Lord Glitters	109-1078	125	132	113	1,010,206	1,692,653
DAVID SIMCOCK	Lightning Spear	64-515	63	82	69	798,073	1,544,346
CLIVE COX	Harry Angel	60-380	54	53	40	943,050	1,496,548
ROGER CHARLTON	Decorated Knight	65-321	38	28	41	747,920	1,246,912
TIM EASTERBY	Golden Apollo	86-930	91	88	91	800,912	1,232,494
SAEED BIN SUROOR	Benbatl	65-280	51	36	29	683,146	1,230,927
CHARLES HILLS	Battaash	70-590	69	67	62	719,128	1,206,220
KEVIN RYAN	Brando	76-661	94	73	75	647,994	1,146,220
RALPH BECKETT	Chemical Charge	66-464	60	69	58	581,519	1,089,251
HUGO PALMER	Home Of The Brave	77-493	69	51	57	573,733	1,066,184
K R BURKE	Laurens	74-617	63	83	76	784,106	1,053,096
MICHAEL BELL	Big Orange	53-346	61	39	43	617,456	998,597
JAMES FANSHAWE	The Tin Man	34-273	49	42	33	656,266	958,713
DEAN IVORY	Librisa Breeze	38-387	39	34	53	696,795	903,291
KEITH DALGLEISH	Taxmeifyoucan	86-815	99	89	91	504,279	799,401
MICHAEL APPLEBY	Big Country	91-853	84	102	85	482,720	740,430
SIR MARK PRESCOTT BT	Marsha	48-282	31	38	21	422,676	687,484
EVE JOHNSON HOUGHTON	Accidental Agent	53-375	47	46	60	430,350	667,031
MARCO BOTTI	Aljazzi	40-325	43	48	36	407,785	649,804
IAIN JARDINE	Nakeeta	52-430	49	46	44	502,566	639,019
DAVID EVANS	Gracious John	81-883	114	105	106	357,597	629,911
IAN WILLIAMS	London Prize	51-388	47	38	33	389,351	617,338
HENRY CANDY	Limato	31-201	34	21	23	265,893	586,573
TOM DASCOMBE	Eartha Kitt	59-506	59	51	52	371,214	576,549
RUTH CARR	Sovereign Debt	49-480	48	51	55	394,809	567,021
DAVID ELSWORTH	Desert Skyline	24-184	20	24	18	323,282	559,958
ROBERT COWELL	Visionary	43-294	33	37	27	317,658	549,431
BRIAN MEEHAN	Barraquero	28-247	27	29	24	364,154	532,144
MICHAEL DODS	Intense Romance	62-432	51	52	48	328,162	527,518
DAVID BARRON	Above The Rest	50-430	60	53	43	349,850	525,886
MICK CHANNON	Neola	59-588	49	74	72	296,770	510,387
OWEN BURROWS	Talaayeb	27-151	27	23	25	319,587	490,537
PAUL MIDGLEY	Line Of Reason	34-363	27	32	43	347,553	485,194
HUGHIE MORRISON	Star Rock	43-331	39	35	41	288,458	482,643
JAMES TATE	Invincible Army	34-241	39	36	30	221,064	472,714
JOHN QUINN	El Astronaute	55-451	64	55	49	281,733	471,701
ED DUNLOP	Dark Red	52-478	58	54	59	250,302	470,160
ARCHIE WATSON	Absolute Blast	56-275	31	39	26	268,871	458,985
MARTYN MEADE	Eminent	13-81	9	9	9	277,292	452,493
RICHARD HUGHES	Getback In Paris	63-519	91	59	68	230,597	442,065

TOP FLAT OWNERS IN BRITAIN IN 2017

OWNER	LEADING HORSE	W-R	2ND	3RD	4TH	WIN PRIZE	TOTAL PRIZE
GODOLPHIN	RIBCHESTER	192-768	133	100	71	3,548,435	6,282,118
DERRICK SMITH & MRS JOHN MAGNIER & MICHAEL TABOR	WINGS OF EAGLES	10-42	5	7	6	2,944,100	3,576,241
HAMDAN AL MAKTOUM	TASLEET	138-734	112	87	104	1,738,291	2,813,835
K ABDULLAH	ENABLE	58-287	37	34	29	1,745,391	2,086,639
MICHAEL TABOR & DERRICK SMITH & MRS JOHN MAGNIER	CHURCHILL	11-36	3	3	4	1,009,225	1,800,136
MRS JOHN MAGNIER & MICHAEL TABOR & DERRICK SMITH	WINTER	6-49	10	3	4	1,185,239	1,774,529
CHEVELEY PARK STUD	PERSUASIVE	55-325	58	32	33	1,105,500	1,570,916
SHEIKH HAMDAN BIN MOHAMMED AL MAKTOUM	PERMIAN	60-363	41	44	37	1,039,979	1,397,666
FLAXMAN STABLES IRELAND LTD	ULYSSES	7-44	10	6	4	910,018	1,252,827
A E OPPENHEIMER	CRACKSMAN	10-39	6	4	3	907,358	1,098,492
AL SHAQAB RACING	QEMAH	56-306	42	41	49	611,704	1,081,619
QATAR RACING LIMITED	LIGHTNING SPEAR	37-252	44	43	25	484,106	1,078,450
SHEIKH MOHAMMED OBAID AL MAKTOUM	LAUGH A MINUTE	40-170	40	25	12	526,991	861,446
MRS FITRI HAY	HERE COMES WHEN	11-154	11	20	21	651,027	780,548
SAEED SUHAIL	POET'S WORD	14-62	6	5	8	434,416	772,687
TONY BLOOM	LIBRISA BREEZE	7-34	2	2	2	603,052	676,156
SALEH AL HOMAIZI & IMAD AL SAGAR	DECORATED KNIGHT	25-165	22	18	16	239,778	571,783
W J AND T C O GREDLEY	BIG ORANGE	11-67	7	13	5	358,632	564,634
B E NIELSEN	STRADIVARIUS	7-31	6	4	4	409,574	548,058
JOHN DANCE	LAURENS	17-162	25	22	25	436,514	529,234
ELITE RACING CLUB	MARSHA	13-49	10	5	5	317,139	452,479
ABDULLA AL MANSOORI	DESERT ENCOUNTER	25-134	15	14	20	264,983	450,407
THE QUEEN	DARTMOUTH	21-110	15	15	15	299,783	449,793
THE COOL SILK PARTNERSHIP	SANDS OF MALI	20-143	19	14	17	319,096	425,628
MRS MAGNIER/M TABOR/D SMITH/ M JOOSTE	CLIFFS OF MOHER	0-3	1	0	1	0	402,975
FRED ARCHER RACING - ORMONDE	THE TIN MAN	1-5	0	1	0	340,260	387,738
ABDULLAH SAEED AL NABOODAH	NATHRA	15-96	11	9	15	127,621	385,406
M TABOR/D SMITH/MRS MAGNIER/ L J WILLIAMS	ORDER OF ST GEORGE	1-2	1	0	0	263,417	349,417
SAEED MANANA	INVINCIBLE ARMY	25-212	34	27	26	145,825	346,381
SIR EVELYN DE ROTHSCHILD	CRYSTAL OCEAN	6-32	4	3	2	101,993	344,597
GEOFF & SANDRA TURNBULL	LORD GLITTERS	10-80	9	7	15	239,495	343,278
A D SPENCE	SOLDIER IN ACTION	17-79	9	8	5	262,333	338,984
DENFORD STUD	CORONET	7-30	3	5	1	146,670	333,612
TAYLOR'S BLOODSTOCK LTD	LINE OF REASON	17-120	11	9	13	239,237	315,652
ROBERT NG	CONVEY	9-54	6	9	3	281,784	308,492
SHEIKH JUMA DALMOOK AL MAKTOUM	MUFFRI'HA	25-138	18	16	14	180,399	303,254
DR MARWAN KOUKASH	GABRIAL	24-312	29	40	34	101,241	292,357
PAUL G JACOBS	LIMATO	4-17	5	1	1	84,224	291,288
KING POWER RACING CO LTD	BEAT THE BANK	8-48	4	6	7	231,951	281,933
PAUL & CLARE ROONEY	TITI MAKFI	25-154	23	16	16	159,162	266,484
AL ASAYL BLOODSTOCK LTD	BATEEL	6-63	8	8	7	91,424	252,999
SHEIKH AHMED AL MAKTOUM	NEZWAAH	17-72	11	12	7	145,463	240,644
JOHN COOK	BRETON ROCK	17-130	1	4	1	170,130	233,050
STONESTREET STABLES/G BOLTON/P LEIDEL	LADY AURELIA	1-1	0	0	0	226,840	226,840
MARTIN HUGHES & NICK ROBINSON	TANGLED	2-8	2	1	1	197,288	220,658
MICHAEL & HEATHER YARROW	LANCELOT DU LAC	3-26	1	4	6	193,435	214,582
FARLEIGH RACING	MONTALY	4-18	3	3	1	193,150	207,759
T A RAHMAN	TERUNTUM STAR	13-79	12	10	10	140,870	206,381
M J MACLEOD	SNOANO	8-67	9	7	6	136,425	203,330
KINGSCLERE RACING CLUB	BROROCCO	12-88	16	9	7	131,612	203,050

TOP FLAT HORSES IN BRITAIN 2017

HORSE (AGE)	WIN & PLACE £	W-R	TRAINER	OWNER	BREEDER
ULYSSES (4)	1,215,461	3-5	Sir Michael Stoute	Flaxman Stables & Cheveley Park Stud	Flaxman Stables Ireland Ltd
ENABLE (3)	1,169,717	4-5	John Gosden	K Abdullah	Juddmonte Farms Ltd
CRACKSMAN (3)	1,039,612	3-4	John Gosden	A E Oppenheimer	Hascombe And Valiant Studs
RIBCHESTER (4)	1,036,748	2-4	Richard Fahey	Godolphin	A Thompson & M O'Brien
WINGS OF EAGLES (3)	937,662	1-2	A P O'Brien	Derrick Smith & Mrs John Magnier & Michael Tabor	Mme Aliette Forien & Mr Gilles Forien
WINTER (3)	867,663	3-3	A P O'Brien	Magnier/Tabor/Smith	Laddies Poker Two Syndicate
HIGHLAND REEL (5)	865,027	2-4	A P O'Brien	Smith/Magnier/Tabor	Hveger Syndicate
PERSUASIVE (4)	677,560	1-2	John Gosden	Cheveley Park Stud	J F Tuthill
CHURCHILL (3)	638,350	1-4	A P O'Brien	Tabor/Smith/Magnier	Liberty Bloodstock
HARRY ANGEL (3)	617,395	3-6	Clive Cox	Godolphin	Cbs Bloodstock
HERE COMES WHEN (7)	592,536	2-4	Andrew Balding	Mrs Fitri Hay	Old Carhue & Graeng Bloodstock
BARNEY ROY (3)	583,466	2-6	Richard Hannon	Godolphin	Eliza Park International Pty Ltd
STRADIVARIUS (3)	521,361	3-6	John Gosden	B E Nielsen	Bjorn Nielsen
CLIFFS OF MOHER (3)	472,307	1-5	A P O'Brien	Magnier/Tabor/Smith/ M Jooste	Wave Syndicate
HYDRANGEA (3)	434,283	1-4	A P O'Brien	Smith/Magnier/Tabor	Beauty Is Truth Syndicate
U S NAVY FLAG (2)	421,825	2-4	A P O'Brien	Smith/Magnier/Tabor	Misty For Me Syndicate
CAPRI (3)	418,907	1-2	A P O'Brien	Smith/Magnier/Tabor	Lynch Bages Ltd & Camas Park Stud
LIBRISA BREEZE (5)	404,670	1-4	Dean Ivory	Tony Bloom	Newsells Park Stud
TASLEET (4)	395,537	1-6	William Haggas	Hamdan Al Maktoum	Whitsbury Manor Stud
THE TIN MAN (5)	387,738	1-5	James Fanshawe	Fred Archer Racing - Ormonde	Mrs Elizabeth Grundy
POET'S WORD (4)	381,445	2-4	Sir Michael Stoute	Saeed Suhail	Woodcote Stud Ltd
BIG ORANGE (6)	376,146	2-4	Michael Bell	W J and T C O Gredley	Stetchworth & Middle Park Studs
LAURENS (2)	364,431	3-3	K R Burke	John Dance	Bloodstock Agency Ltd
ORDER OF ST GEORGE (5)	349,417	1-2	A P O'Brien	Tabor/Smith/Magnier/ L J Williams	Paget Bloodstock
ROLY POLY (3)	347,645	2-4	A P O'Brien	Smith/Magnier/Tabor	Misty For Me Syndicate
CARAVAGGIO (3)	318,200	1-3	A P O'Brien	Magnier/Tabor/Smith	Windmill Manor Farms Inc Et Al
MARSHA (3)	309,132	2-4	Sir Mark Prescott Bt	Elite Racing Club	Elite Racing Club
LADY AURELIA (3)	302,090	1-2	Wesley A Ward	Stonestreet Stables Llc & Peter Leidel	Stonestreet Thoroughbred Holdings LLC
CORONET (3)	296,975	1-5	John Gosden	Denford Stud	Denford Stud Ltd
PERMIAN (3)	270,503	3-6	Mark Johnston	Godolphin	Darley
LIGHTNING SPEAR (6)	258,940	1-6	David Simcock	Qatar Racing Limited	Newsells Park Stud
IDAHO (4)	257,007	1-3	A P O'Brien	Tabor/Smith/Magnier	Hveger Syndicate
LIMATO (5)	256,192	1-4	Henry Candy	Paul G Jacobs	Seamus Phelan
CRYSTAL OCEAN (3)	254,635	2-5	Sir Michael Stoute	Sir Evelyn De Rothschild	Southcourt Stud
BATTAASH (3)	253,596	3-4	Charles Hills	Hamdan Al Maktoum	Ballyphilip Stud
BALLET CONCERTO (4)	241,037	4-7	Sir Michael Stoute	Saeed Suhail	Meon Valley Stud
BRETON ROCK (7)	226,670	1-7	David Simcock	John Cook	George Kent
MUTAKAYYEF (6)	220,998	1-2	William Haggas	Hamdan Al Maktoum	Cheveley Park Stud Ltd
TANGLED (2)	220,658	2-8	Richard Hannon	Martin Hughes & Nick Robinson	Tally-Ho Stud
DECORATED KNIGHT (5)	220,419	1-4	Roger Charlton	Saleh Al Homaizi & Imad Al Sagar	Saleh Al Homaizi & Imad Al Sagar
SOVEREIGN DEBT (8)	216,384	3-9	Ruth Carr	Lady O'Reilly, J P Hames & T Dorman	Yeomanstown Stud
RHODODENDRON (3)	215,000	0-2	A P O'Brien	Magnier/Tabor/Smith	Orpendale, Chelston & Wynatt

TOP NH JOCKEYS IN BRITAIN 2016/17

W-R	%	JOCKEY	2ND	3RD	TOTAL PRIZE	WIN PRIZE
189-1026	18%	RICHARD JOHNSON	192	139	2,334,380	1,539,130
144-866	17%	BRIAN HUGHES	164	129	1,431,074	857,238
137-673	20%	SAM TWISTON-DAVIES	103	91	1,707,545	1,122,396
122-761	17%	AIDAN COLEMAN	97	90	1,723,257	1,027,740
118-547	22%	NOEL FEHILY	93	60	2,188,954	1,433,079
101-531	19%	HARRY SKELTON	103	75	1,106,938	697,771
100-754	13%	TOM SCUDAMORE	100	86	1,302,740	859,915
95-454	21%	PADDY BRENNAN	66	62	1,282,654	899,764
88-407	22%	DARYL JACOB	63	53	1,290,541	759,630
81-583	14%	TOM O'BRIEN	65	65	966,388	659,041
79-432	18%	SEAN BOWEN	75	42	958,532	677,841
74-385	19%	WAYNE HUTCHINSON	72	68	778,860	452,560
63-326	19%	HARRY COBDEN	44	37	762,307	579,788
63-463	14%	WILL KENNEDY	61	69	471,600	302,849
59-299	20%	NICO DE BOINVILLE	40	37	855,364	653,213
56-372	15%	GAVIN SHEEHAN	49	42	461,493	275,100
54-297	18%	A P HESKIN	39	43	813,905	494,745
51-279	18%	DANNY COOK	47	35	473,081	301,615
48-388	12%	HENRY BROOKE	48	46	411,933	261,825
47-429	11%	JAMIE MOORE	62	52	627,419	357,114
45-301	15%	ALAN JOHNS	40	28	343,146	219,712
45-324	14%	DAVID BASS	46	40	469,269	293,846
44-397	11%	NICK SCHOLFIELD	45	51	574,103	378,695
43-2678	16%	JEREMIAH MCGRATH	40	30	495,546	258,447
41-153	27%	BARRY GERAGHTY	19	15	1,063,396	859,266
40-382	10%	LEIGHTON ASPELL	58	58	495,540	306,099
38-3436	11%	SEAN QUINLAN	32	36	301,443	199,155
36-344	10%	TOM CANNON	34	50	301,746	178,016
36-378	10%	DAVID NOONAN	37	44	340,856	225,004
34-252	13%	BRAIN HARDING	34	27	239,657	138,450
34-319	11%	PAUL MOLONEY	27	44	332,591	153,821
31-161	19%	HARRY BANNISTER	26	18	249,830	167,299
30-307	10%	CRAIG NICHOL	25	30	246,224	163,864
29-182	16%	STAN SHEPPARD	15	19	211,028	152,498
29-275	11%	JAMIE BARGARY	33	36	419,533	234,008
29-317	9%	BRENDAN POWELL	33	31	223,277	129,950
28-327	9%	TREVOR WHELAN	32	26	320,710	141,629
29-424	7%	RICHIE MCLERNON	39	41	260,352	150,113
27-243	11%	JAKE GREENALL	23	26	210,096	120,936
27-247	11%	KIELAN WOODS	37	33	239,479	117,867
27-303	9%	ADAM WEDGE	37	39	389,376	170,264
26-154	17%	JONATHAN MOORE	10	23	326,728	249,584
25-154	16%	CHARLIE DEUTSCH	22	15	362,858	185,418
25-212	12%	TOM BELLAMY	19	30	247,087	178,003
25-239	10%	ROBERT DUNNE	18	31	302,317	173,766
24-364	7%	JAMES BEST	30	28	308,176	208,659
23-209	11	ADAM NICOL	19	21	139,631	92,695
23-217	11%	JACK QUINLAN	16	29	191,289	140,983
22-178	12%	LIAM TREADWELL	16	19	286,203	213,078
22-206	11%	THOMAS DOWSON	27	20	142,100	90,650

TOP NH TRAINERS IN BRITAIN 2016/17

TRAINER	LEADING HORSE	W-R	2ND	3RD	4TH	WIN PRIZE	TOTAL PRIZE
NICKY HENDERSON	BUVEUR D'AIR	153-614	98	70	56	1,881,085	2,843,507
PAUL NICHOLLS	SAN BENEDETO	171-673	92	80	65	1,733,593	2,529,250
COLIN TIZZARD	NATIVE RIVER	57-407	64	56	39	1,449,147	2,041,054
NIGEL TWISTON-DAVIES	THE NEW ONE	95-587	97	84	56	950,479	1,582,656
PHILIP HOBBS	DEFI DU SEUIL	111-593	93	66	65	1,004,400	1,502,991
ALAN KING	YANWORTH	103-488	90	79	41	935,815	1,371,252
DAN SKELTON	CH'TIBELLO	118-697	134	100	65	789,125	1,328,839
TOM GEORGE	SAINT ARE	71-342	50	53	28	600,294	1,095,737
JONJO O'NEILL	MINELLA ROCCO	78-689	84	76	74	533,688	1,013,158
W P MULLINS	UN DE SCEAUX	9-52	2	4	4	754,757	941,892
LUCINDA RUSSELL	ONE FOR ARTHUR	43-411	41	53	50	800,213	926,414
GORDON ELLIOTT	CAUSE OF CAUSES	30-170	38	26	19	454,053	901,405
HARRY FRY	UNOWHATIMEANHARRY	67-284	42	33	32	648,881	886,294
NEIL MULHOLLAND	PILGRIMS BAY	107-555	76	59	54	600,848	847,884
DAVID PIPE	VIEUX LION ROUGE	59-487	47	42	71	538,974	778,982
VENETIA WILLIAMS	ASO	46-312	39	34	42	449,363	764,603
CHARLIE LONGSDON	PETE THE FEAT	51-412	66	53	40	493,577	723,414
FERGAL O'BRIEN	CHASE THE SPUD	60-325	36	48	40	433,221	611,365
EVAN WILLIAMS	CLYNE	51-460	57	55	70	279,447	598,388
DONALD MCCAIN	DESERT CRY	80-573	89	96	66	351,310	578,934
GARY MOORE	SIRE DE GRUGY	40-338	47	42	35	334,052	577,361
HENRY DE BROMHEAD	SPECIAL TIARA	3-34	6	4	1	267,967	523,387
WARREN GREATREX	MAGIC MONEY	58-318	48	52	29	298,120	518,129
MALCOLM JEFFERSON	CLOUDY DREAM	40-202	42	33	22	313,170	504,645
TIM VAUGHAN	THELIGNY	71-536	49	53	58	319,098	478,013
MRS JOHN HARRINGTON	SIZING JOHN	3-14	1	0	3	441,362	477,947
PETER BOWEN	HENLLAN HARRI	40-300	51	25	34	319,606	476,682
IAN WILLIAMS	GAS LINE BOY	45-251	28	23	31	319,228	448,838
BRIAN ELLISON	DEFINITLY RED	45-230	33	34	30	274,837	432,336
REBECCA CURTIS	SHANTOU FLYER	30-212	16	29	22	301,181	428,331
KIM BAILEY	CHARBEL	42-324	58	43	34	205,637	409,799
SUE SMITH	WOLF SWORD	41-280	33	36	41	222,258	373,880
EMMA LAVELLE	CASINO MARKETS	34-183	25	25	18	209,524	371,796
NICK WILLIAMS	TEA FOR TWO	19-147	18	20	23	241,073	369,928
NICKY RICHARDS	LOOKING WELL	45-238	34	12	27	231,052	350,229
KERRY LEE	TOP GAMBLE	22-160	31	19	20	124,390	307,343
BEN PAULING	WILLOUGHBY COURT	32-201	20	23	17	224,682	294,863
OLIVER SHERWOOD	MANY CLOUDS	22-196	28	27	19	195,476	294,187
DR RICHARD NEWLAND	HASSLE	35-167	23	21	15	181,179	291,056
ANTHONY HONEYBALL	REGAL ENCORE	32-143	19	23	16	213,711	289,483
SEAMUS MULLINS	CHESTERFIELD	17-238	27	35	35	165,506	284,483
NEIL KING	LIL ROCKERFELLER	17-179	34	17	22	78,961	276,393
NIGEL HAWKE	DEAUVILLE CRYSTAL	28-227	24	27	19	201,705	252,735
MICHAEL SCUDAMORE	MYSTEREE	26-131	12	14	15	188,745	249,055
DAVID DENNIS	ROMAN FLIGHT	20-268	38	37	32	133,327	233,757
CHRIS GORDON	REMILUC	24-174	20	27	21	133,244	206,138
JEREMY SCOTT	UNISON	24-193	24	19	18	114,144	196,632
GRAEME MCPHERSON	AMI DESBOIS	28-176	24	28	23	113,192	194,603
JENNIE CANDLISH	THEFLYINGPORTRAIT	23-175	22	17	17	129,870	190,411
JAMIE SNOWDEN	FACT OF THE MATTER	25-207	37	22	31	107,713	188,782

TOP NH OWNERS IN BRITAIN IN 2016/17

OWNER	LEADING HORSE	W-R	2ND	3RD	4TH	WIN PRIZE	TOTAL PRIZE
JOHN P MCMANUS	Buveur D'Air	94-538	74	52	52	1,534,283	2,538,065
SIMON MUNIR & ISAAC SOUEDE	Top Notch	34-116	24	17	10	485,355	834,500
PAUL & CLARE ROONEY	Willoughby Court	67-315	55	42	24	470,242	701,851
TWO GOLF WIDOWS	One For Arthur	3-5	0	0	0	606,516	610,226
TREVOR HEMMINGS	Vicente	29-172	31	18	18	404,350	576,661
ANN & ALAN POTTS	Fox Norton	11-54	8	3	6	400,462	541,601
GIGGINSTOWN HOUSE STUD	Sub Lieutenant	4-47	5	3	3	234,310	489,098
MRS JEAN R BISHOP	Cue Card	8-31	5	5	1	304,474	434,713
ANN & ALAN POTTS PARTNERSHIP	Sizing John	2-9	1	0	0	381,565	414,984
BROCADE RACING	Native River	6-67	16	9	10	252,886	380,863
S SUCH & CG PALETTA	The New One	6-30	2	5	7	135,184	311,120
EDWARD O'CONNELL	Un De Sceaux	3-3	0	0	0	295,307	295,307
MRS S ROWLEY-WILLIAMS	Special Tiara	2-5	1	1	0	255,281	292,082
ANDREA & GRAHAM WYLIE	Nichols Canyon	2-9	0	1	0	260,124	279,174
MRS PATRICIA PUGH	Altior	9-15	1	1	0	269,402	271,229
P J MARTIN	Definitly Red	19-93	14	14	8	161,017	241,202
MRS DIANA L WHATELEY	Menorah	11-56	10	8	9	124,423	227,435
MICHAEL BUCKLEY	Brain Power	8-26	2	6	2	205,785	223,643
OPTIONS O SYNDICATE	Ballyandy	7-25	3	4	1	168,964	220,568
JOHN AND HEATHER SNOOK	Thistlecrack	7-24	3	3	3	179,657	216,082
CARL HINCHY	Shantou Flyer	12-64	4	7	6	133,218	181,481
P J VOGT	San Benedeto	6-18	2	3	2	128,108	177,976
THE KNOT AGAIN PARTNERSHIP	Might Bite	4-6	1	0	0	166,458	167,984
RODDY OWEN & PAUL FULLAGAR	Minella Daddy	14-69	14	8	9	101,011	167,468
MRS S RICCI	Vroum Vroum Mag	2-14	1	2	2	74,035	162,376
GRECH & PARKIN	River Wylde	16-52	5	5	8	99,669	158,532
WALTERS PLANT HIRE LTD	Whisper	9-54	17	7	4	62,126	157,270
CROSSED FINGERS PARTNERSHIP	Double Shuffle	7-30	5	4	1	56,346	153,533
MASTERSON HOLDINGS LIMITED	Neon Wolf	10-49	10	7	6	85,955	145,314
MCNEILL FAMILY	The Worlds End	10-30	5	4	1	121,518	143,293
PROF CAROLINE TISDALL & JOHN GENT	Vieux Lion Rouge	2-3	0	0	0	121,294	134,494
PROFESSOR CAROLINE TISDALL & BRYAN DREW	Un Temps Pour Tout	6-17	2	1	0	110,889	129,985
MARTIN BROUGHTON & FRIENDS 1	Taquin Du Seuil	1-5	1	0	2	91,120	128,047
MRS JOHNNY DE LA HEY	Diego Du Charmil	6-42	4	5	2	90,228	127,491
P J VOGT & IAN FOGG	Frodon	6-9	0	0	0	124,412	127,062
MRS JANE WILLIAMS & LEN JAKEMAN	Tea For Two	2-7	1	0	1	98,263	126,218
THE STEWART FAMILY	Saphir Du Rheu	6-21	3	4	3	67,181	125,703
MR & MRS R KELVIN-HUGHES	Vaniteux	7-21	3	3	2	69,959	124,412
N T GRIFFITH & H M HADDOCK	Max Ward	10-45	4	8	7	75,891	122,880
J HALES	Politologue	4-24	6	3	2	57,109	122,483
BRADLEY PARTNERSHIP	According To Harry	14-85	12	11	9	78,477	118,523
D W FOX	Saint Are	0-8	1	2	0	0	114,509
DOONE HULSE SUSIE SAUNDERS & LADY COBHAM	Sir Valentino	2-7	1	1	1	51,233	113,847
DAVIES SMITH GOVIER & BROWN	Lil Rockerfeller	0-5	3	1	1	0	113,476
A D SPENCE	Josses Hill	6-21	2	2	1	80,337	112,468
FAVOURITES RACING LTD	Roman Flight	7-57	10	9	9	73,262	109,920
THE BELLAMY PARTNERSHIP	Aso	2-17	1	3	3	29,868	109,182
TONY BLOOM	Penhill	4-21	2	3	4	86,132	103,980
THE CAN'T SAY NO PARTNERSHIP	Ch'Tibello	2-19	1	4	4	67,748	102,766
MME LYNNE MACLENNAN	Mysteree	3-12	2	1	1	72,549	102,493

TOP NH HORSES IN BRITAIN 2016/17

HORSE (AGE)	WIN & PLACE £	W-R	TRAINER	OWNER	BREEDER
ONE FOR ARTHUR (8)	610,226	3-4	Lucinda Russell	Two Golf Widows	J P Dwan
BUVEUR D'AIR (6)	371,069	5-5	Nicky Henderson	John P McManus	Gerard Ferte
SIZING JOHN (7)	327,462	1-1	Mrs John Harrington	Ann & Alan Potts Partnership	Bryan & Sandra Mayoh, Eskdale Stud
NATIVE RIVER (7)	297,980	3-5	Colin Tizzard	Brocade Racing	Fred Mackey
UN DE SCEAUX (9)	295,307	3-3	W P Mullins	Edward O'Connell	Haras De La Rousseliere Et Al
CUE CARD (11)	292,312	2-6	Colin Tizzard	Mrs Jean R Bishop	R T Crellin
SPECIAL TIARA (10)	292,082	2-5	Henry De Bromhead	Mrs S Rowley-Williams	D E M Young
FOX NORTON (7)	275,150	3-5	Colin Tizzard	Ann & Alan Potts	S A Scuderia Del Bargelo
ALTIOR (7)	252,281	6-6	Nicky Henderson	Mrs Patricia Pugh	Paddy Behan
CAUSE OF CAUSES (9)	251,912	1-3	Gordon Elliott	John P McManus	Flaxman Holdings Limited
YANWORTH (7)	232,321	4-5	Alan King	John P McManus	Wood Farm Stud
DEFI DU SEUIL (4)	205,205	7-7	Philip Hobbs	John P McManus	Mme Catherine Boudot
THISTLECRACK (9)	184,653	4-5	Colin Tizzard	John and Heather Snook	R F And S D Knipe
THE NEW ONE (9)	173,105	2-6	Nigel Twiston-Davies	S Such & CG Paletta	R Brown & Ballylinch Stud
NICHOLS CANYON (7)	170,850	1-1	W P Mullins	Andrea & Graham Wylie	Rabbah Bloodstock Limited
MY TENT OR YOURS (10)	170,001	0-5	Nicky Henderson	John P McManus	F Dunne
MIGHT BITE (8)	167,984	4-6	Nicky Henderson	The Knot Again Partnership	John O'Brien
SAN BENEDETO (6)	152,430	6-12	Paul Nicholls	P J Vogt	E A R L Ecurie Haras Du Cadran Et Al
UNOWHATIMEANHARRY (9)	151,695	3-4	Harry Fry	John P McManus	R J Smith
VIEUX LION ROUGE (8)	134,494	2-3	David Pipe	Prof Caroline Tisdall & John Gent	F M Cottin
MINELLA ROCCO (7)	128,227	0-3	Jonjo O'Neill	John P McManus	Eclipse Bloodstock & C & G Hadden
TAQUIN DU SEUIL (10)	128,047	1-5	Jonjo O'Neill	Martin Broughton & Friends 1	Marc Boudot
FRODON (5)	127,062	6-9	Paul Nicholls	P J Vogt & Ian Fogg	Philippe Gasdoue
TEA FOR TWO (8)	125,973	2-6	Nick Williams	Mrs Jane Williams & Len Jakeman	Mrs P G Lewin
VICENTE (8)	125,524	1-6	Paul Nicholls	Trevor Hemmings	Thierry Cypres & Jean-Francois Naudin
BRAIN POWER (6)	119,187	2-4	Nicky Henderson	Michael Buckley	David Harvey
SAINT ARE (11)	114,509	0-5	Tom George	D W Fox	Jacques Cypres
SIR VALENTINO (8)	113,847	2-7	Tom George	Doone Hulse Susie Saunders & Lady Cobham	Mlle Camille Serveau & Mr Roger Simon
LIL ROCKERFELLER (6)	113,476	0-5	Neil King	Davies Smith Govier & Brown	Brushwood Stable
CLOUDY DREAM (7)	113,205	3-7	Malcolm Jefferson	Trevor Hemmings	Eimear Purcell
SUB LIEUTENANT (8)	106,380	0-2	Henry De Bromhead	Gigginstown House Stud	Edmond Coleman
BALLYANDY (6)	105,510	1-5	Nigel Twiston-Davies	Options O Syndicate	Pleasure Palace Racing
TOP NOTCH (6)	105,432	4-7	Nicky Henderson	Simon Munir & Isaac Souede	Haras Des Sablonnets & Dr Vet B Gabeur
ASO (7)	100,723	1-7	Venetia Williams	The Bellamy Partnership	I Pacault, A Pacault & M Pacault
HENLLAN HARRI (9)	98,928	2-12	Peter Bowen	Einsley Harries	Paul Ryan
FINIAN'S OSCAR (5)	98,230	4-4	Colin Tizzard	Ann & Alan Potts	Richard & Martin O'Keeffe
WILLOUGHBY COURT (6)	95,361	3-4	Ben Pauling	Paul & Clare Rooney	J H Kidd
SIRE DE GRUGY (11)	94,789	1-4	Gary Moore	The Preston Family & Friends Ltd	La Grugerie
CHESTERFIELD (7)	94,443	2-5	Seamus Mullins	The Rumble Racing Club	Darley
CH'TIBELLO (6)	93,450	1-5	Dan Skelton	The Can't Say No Partnership	Mme Elisabeth Cucheval
MYSTEREE (9)	92,793	2-4	Michael Scudamore	Mme Lynne Maclennan	Lar & Fiona Cloke
WHISPER (9)	92,429	2-4	Nicky Henderson	Walters Plant Hire Ltd	Hubert & Sandra Hosselet
ULTRAGOLD (9)	91,507	2-8	Colin Tizzard	Brocade Racing J P Romans Terry Warner	Gilles Chaignon
UN TEMPS POUR TOUT (8)	90,531	2-5	David Pipe	Professor Caroline Tisdall & Bryan Drew	Felix Talbot

LEADING SIRES OF 2017 IN GREAT BRITAIN AND IRELAND

STALLION	BREEDING	RNRS	WNRS	WINS	WIN MONEY	PLACES	PLACE MONEY	TOTAL
GALILEO (IRE)	by Sadler's Wells (USA)	216	88	134	8108469	417	3590377	11698846
DARK ANGEL (IRE)	by Acclamation (GB)	240	99	149	2665136	542	1154856	3819992
DUBAWI (IRE)	by Dubai Millennium (GB)	175	96	136	1885035	280	1444928	3329964
FRANKEL (GB)	by Galileo (IRE)	77	40	59	1651863	134	1104819	2756682
KODIAC (GB)	by Danehill (USA)	267	126	192	1507446	568	1031732	2539178
ACCLAMATION (GB)	by Royal Applause (GB)	203	87	123	1318082	476	854354	2172435
IFFRAAJ (GB)	by Zafonic (USA)	140	49	82	1174984	265	974052	2149036
SEA THE STARS (IRE)	by Cape Cross (IRE)	85	40	61	1085303	157	919619	2004922
NATHANIEL (IRE)	by Galileo (IRE)	93	33	51	1689965	144	241004	1930969
INVINCIBLE SPIRIT (IRE)	by Green Desert (USA)	187	80	111	971110	405	859877	1830987
EXCEED AND EXCEL (AUS)	by Danehill (USA)	201	90	130	1134255	417	611249	1745503
TEOFILO (IRE)	by Galileo (IRE)	136	60	95	1083917	248	616084	1700001
FASTNET ROCK (AUS)	by Danehill (USA)	121	47	73	905908	238	743920	1649827
PIVOTAL (GB)	by Polar Falcon (USA)	112	58	95	927694	255	714414	1642108
WAR FRONT (USA)	by Danzig (USA)	59	30	43	1106340	101	532056	1638396
SCAT DADDY (USA)	by Johannesburg (USA)	28	17	28	1035088	32	400859	1435947
DANSILI (GB)	by Danehill (USA)	107	40	59	948314	190	406904	1355218
POUR MOI (IRE)	by Montjeu (IRE)	41	16	20	1090618	61	239739	1330356
SHAMARDAL (USA)	by Giant's Causeway (USA)	133	54	84	847764	231	478172	1325936
KYLLACHY (GB)	by Pivotal (GB)	157	72	126	807780	359	368470	1176250
NEW APPROACH (IRE)	by Galileo (IRE)	134	49	76	755631	195	415049	1170680
LAWMAN (FR)	by Invincible Spirit (IRE)	154	49	77	617717	302	536208	1153925
POET'S VOICE (GB)	by Dubawi (IRE)	135	53	73	424486	241	729061	1153547
MOUNT NELSON (GB)	by Rock of Gibraltar (IRE)	76	23	29	640496	160	457960	1098456
EQUIANO (FR)	by Acclamation (GB)	156	51	76	726723	298	356361	1083084

LEADING SIRES OF 2017
(GREAT BRITAIN, IRELAND AND OVERSEAS)

STALLION	BREEDING	DOMESTIC WNRS	WINS	WIN MONEY	OVERSEAS WNRS	WINS	WIN MONEY	TOTAL
GALILEO (IRE)	by Sadler's Wells (USA)	88	134	8108469	55	84	3186870	11295339
DUBAWI (IRE)	by Dubai Millennium (GB)	96	136	1885035	63	96	3617393	5502428
EXCEED AND EXCEL (AUS)	by Danehill (USA)	90	130	1134255	45	78	3806986	4941240
NATHANIEL (IRE)	by Galileo (IRE)	33	51	1689965	19	30	2663678	4353643
DARK ANGEL (IRE)	by Acclamation (GB)	99	149	2665136	55	82	1623930	4289066
HIGH CHAPARRAL (IRE)	by Sadler's Wells (USA)	34	53	507634	44	67	3099064	3606697
FASTNET ROCK (AUS)	by Danehill (USA)	47	73	905908	48	88	2623387	3529295
FRANKEL (GB)	by Galileo (IRE)	40	59	1651863	16	24	1804733	3456596
HALLING (USA)	by Diesis	16	22	245154	19	31	3121627	3366781
DEEP IMPACT (JPN)	by Sunday Silence (USA)	5	8	264495	4	4	2964642	3229137
INVINCIBLE SPIRIT (IRE)	by Green Desert (USA)	80	111	971110	61	100	2181753	3152863
SEA THE STARS (IRE)	by Cape Cross (IRE)	40	61	1085303	37	57	1290637	2375941
HOLY ROMAN EMPEROR (IRE)	by Danehill (USA)	55	82	551729	78	134	1784895	2336624
TEOFILO (IRE)	by Galileo (IRE)	60	95	1083917	41	59	1215925	2299842
IFFRAAJ (GB)	by Zafonic (USA)	49	82	1174984	46	75	1038241	2213225
LOPE DE VEGA (IRE)	by Shamardal (USA)	53	79	640836	47	71	1558120	2198956
SHAMARDAL (USA)	by Giant's Causeway (USA)	54	84	847764	58	83	1305819	2153583
ARCHIPENKO (USA)	by Kingmambo (USA)	24	34	141118	16	35	2007248	2148366
ACCLAMATION (GB)	by Royal Applause (GB)	87	123	1318082	46	66	828597	2146679
MASTERCRAFTSMAN (IRE)	by Danehill Dancer (IRE)	60	82	656209	47	86	1475606	2131815
SIYOUNI (FR)	by Pivotal (GB)	15	24	525169	65	101	1500670	2025839
DANSILI (GB)	by Danehill (USA)	40	59	948314	43	70	1057096	2005410
PIVOTAL (GB)	by Polar Falcon (USA)	58	95	927694	52	93	1000852	1928546
KODIAC (GB)	by Danehill (USA)	126	192	1507446	36	57	408996	1916442
HELMET (AUS)	by Exceed And Excel (AUS)	32	39	220728	12	26	1617742	1838469

LEADING TWO-YEAR-OLD SIRES OF 2017 IN GREAT BRITAIN AND IRELAND

STALLION	BREEDING	RNRS	WNRS	WINS	WIN MONEY	PLACES	PLACE MONEY	TOTAL
GALILEO (IRE)	by Sadler's Wells (USA)	54	21	33	837224	72	355659	1192883
KODIAC (GB)	by Danehill (USA)	106	54	68	427205	183	388403	815609
WAR FRONT (USA)	by Danzig (USA)	24	10	15	540970	36	141506	682476
DARK ANGEL (IRE)	by Acclamation (GB)	74	29	36	317102	132	244363	561465
SCAT DADDY (USA)	by Johannesburg (USA)	20	10	15	292483	23	229874	522357
SOCIETY ROCK (IRE)	by Rock of Gibraltar (IRE)	70	25	36	316142	116	156235	472377
EXCEED AND EXCEL (AUS)	by Danehill (USA)	48	18	24	359866	55	87389	447255
DEEP IMPACT (JPN)	by Sunday Silence (USA)	4	2	5	246518	4	155724	402242
SIYOUNI (FR)	by Pivotal (GB)	10	3	7	386755	11	14824	401579
MAYSON (GB)	by Invincible Spirit (IRE)	35	15	21	268323	74	128901	397224
VOCALISED (USA)	by Vindication (USA)	23	9	14	293789	35	85448	379237
BATED BREATH (GB)	by Dansili (GB)	45	18	22	175666	65	195723	371389
ACCLAMATION (GB)	by Royal Applause (GB)	49	20	28	268787	83	93896	362683
FRANKEL (GB)	by Galileo (IRE)	28	15	19	259022	29	103104	362126
HAVANA GOLD (IRE)	by Teofilo (IRE)	58	18	25	206643	75	130532	337175
CHOISIR (AUS)	by Danehill Dancer (IRE)	32	13	19	229959	49	61354	291313
RED JAZZ (USA)	by Johannesburg (USA)	45	15	22	223241	60	47590	270831
DUBAWI (IRE)	by Dubai Millennium (GB)	52	28	33	221523	47	46334	267857
KYLLACHY (GB)	by Pivotal (GB)	34	10	15	213160	45	52083	265243
IFFRAAJ (GB)	by Zafonic (USA)	50	14	20	170799	58	86848	257647
ZEBEDEE (GB)	by Invincible Spirit (IRE)	43	19	22	196626	66	53928	250554
ARCANO (IRE)	by Oasis Dream (GB)	44	10	18	148532	63	101982	250514
INVINCIBLE SPIRIT (IRE)	by Green Desert (USA)	41	15	16	99504	56	149966	249471
LETHAL FORCE (IRE)	by Dark Angel (IRE)	55	21	24	121158	89	109069	230227
DECLARATION OF WAR (USA)	by War Front (USA)	34	8	11	93762	36	134215	227977

LEADING FIRST CROP SIRES OF 2017 IN GREAT BRITAIN AND IRELAND

STALLION	BREEDING	RNRS	WNRS	WINS	WIN MONEY	PLACES	PLACE MONEY	TOTAL
SOCIETY ROCK (IRE)	by Rock of Gibraltar (IRE)	70	25	36	316142	116	156235	472377
HAVANA GOLD (IRE)	by Teofilo (IRE)	58	18	25	206643	75	130532	337175
RED JAZZ (USA)	by Johannesburg (USA)	45	15	22	223241	60	47590	270831
LETHAL FORCE (IRE)	by Dark Angel (IRE)	55	21	24	121158	89	109069	230227
DECLARATION OF WAR (USA)	by War Front (USA)	34	8	11	93762	36	134215	227977
EPAULETTE (AUS)	by Commands (AUS)	55	17	22	111383	57	70506	181890
SWISS SPIRIT (GB)	by Invincible Spirit (IRE)	38	13	18	65563	51	62066	127629
FARHH (GB)	by Pivotal (GB)	18	6	8	107219	13	19742	126961
DAWN APPROACH (IRE)	by New Approach (IRE)	39	8	10	57807	49	69024	126631
CAMELOT (GB)	by Montjeu (IRE)	51	9	10	64051	51	51410	115461
DABIRSIM (FR)	by Hat Trick (JPN)	8	1	1	45368	6	49752	95120
CITYSCAPE (GB)	by Selkirk (USA)	20	7	7	37809	28	43855	81664
MOST IMPROVED (IRE)	by Lawman (FR)	25	7	8	36195	21	22125	58320
RECKLESS ABANDON (GB)	by Exchange Rate (USA)	9	3	4	27627	14	30602	58229
AL KAZEEM (GB)	by Dubawi (IRE)	7	2	3	29561	10	20130	49691
INTELLO (GER)	by Galileo (IRE)	21	5	5	18760	15	30859	49619
MAZAMEER (IRE)	by Green Desert (USA)	9	2	5	24694	11	8766	33461
TOUGH AS NAILS (IRE)	by Dark Angel (IRE)	5	1	1	9214	18	18212	27425
FINJAAN (GB)	by Royal Applause (GB)	14	1	1	3881	25	16629	20510
MAXIOS (GB)	by Monsun (GER)	9	1	2	12938	8	5731	18669
VIOLENCE (USA)	by Medaglia d'Oro (USA)	2	1	2	7763	2	2433	10195
PENNY'S PICNIC (IRE)	by Kheleyf (USA)	2	1	1	7116	4	2839	9954
LIBRANNO (GB)	by Librettist (USA)	2	1	1	2588	5	2646	5234
POINT OF ENTRY (USA)	by Dynaformer (USA)	2			4528	0	0	4528
JIMMY CREED (USA)	by Distorted Humor (USA)	2	1	1	3235	1	963	4197

LEADING MATERNAL GRANDSIRES OF 2017 IN GREAT BRITAIN AND IRELAND

STALLION	BREEDING	RNRS	WNRS	WINS	WIN MONEY	PLACES	PLACE MONEY	TOTAL
PIVOTAL (GB)	by Polar Falcon (USA)	280	118	175	2887473	608	1806806	4694279
SADLER'S WELLS (USA)	by Northern Dancer	330	109	166	2874030	591	1252697	4126727
GALILEO (IRE)	by Sadler's Wells (USA)	261	116	170	2685281	479	1354612	4039893
DANEHILL (USA)	by Danzig (USA)	194	72	112	1982305	402	1468595	3450899
STORM CAT (USA)	by Storm Bird (CAN)	51	22	40	1824574	91	750541	2575115
KINGMAMBO (USA)	by Mr Prospector (USA)	102	46	75	1495428	181	849031	2344459
CHOISIR (AUS)	by Danehill Dancer (IRE)	43	16	27	1838188	72	275247	2113435
DANSILI (GB)	by Danehill (USA)	177	71	107	1122503	359	954209	2076712
CADEAUX GENEREUX	by Young Generation	133	48	70	1197892	276	845691	2043583
MARJU (IRE)	by Last Tycoon	96	38	63	1205186	180	803804	2008990
DANEHILL DANCER (IRE)	by Danehill (USA)	207	75	98	933632	383	894731	1828362
CAPE CROSS (IRE)	by Green Desert (USA)	142	69	109	1223253	288	561961	1785213
OASIS DREAM (GB)	by Green Desert (USA)	185	80	124	1056434	376	554470	1610904
ANABAA (USA)	by Danzig (USA)	64	19	24	1299077	110	262385	1561461
SINGSPIEL (IRE)	by In The Wings	139	53	85	694049	266	601989	1296038
MARK OF ESTEEM (IRE)	by Darshaan	96	41	68	722200	175	517275	1239475
INDIAN RIDGE	by Ahonoora	149	63	92	551131	277	582067	1133198
DARSHAAN	by Shirley Heights	108	36	50	555128	197	534794	1089922
MONTJEU (IRE)	by Sadler's Wells (USA)	144	53	79	547043	289	530307	1077350
SELKIRK (USA)	by Sharpen Up	149	58	78	545674	284	529117	1074791
GREEN DESERT (USA)	by Danzig (USA)	203	69	106	685221	324	375746	1060966
KENDOR (FR)	by Kenmare (FR)	9	2	2	924772	8	134757	1059529
ROYAL APPLAUSE (GB)	by Waajib	152	53	76	508755	296	526455	1035210
DIKTAT (GB)	by Warning	82	41	68	696524	150	281029	977554
GONE WEST (USA)	by Mr Prospector (USA)	66	20	44	762983	128	211309	974291

FLAT STALLIONS' EARNINGS FOR 2017

(includes every stallion who sired a winner on the Flat in Great Britain and Ireland in 2017)

STALLIONS	RNRS	STARTS	WNRS	WINS	PLACES	TOTAL (£)
ACCLAMATION (GB)	203	1252	87	123	476	2172435.49
ACT ONE (GB)	2	16	1	3	10	15207.33
AD VALOREM (USA)	12	87	3	3	27	38207.51
AFLEET ALEX (USA)	1	11	1	4	4	66307.80
AGNES GOLD (JPN)	2	15	1	2	7	14849.15
AIR CHIEF MARSHAL (IRE)	4	14	1	3	3	25223.11
ALDEBARAN (USA)	1	10	1	2	2	7912.50
ALFRED NOBEL (IRE)	20	109	4	7	27	49454.04
ALGORITHMS (USA)	3	14	1	1	6	12662.76
ALHAARTH (IRE)	7	31	1	1	10	10937.26
AL KAZEEM (GB)	7	19	2	3	10	49690.88
AMADEUS WOLF (GB)	19	145	10	18	31	136208.89
AMERICAN POST (GB)	6	46	3	10	20	93163.61
ANTONIUS PIUS (USA)	11	59	1	1	21	26894.63
APPROVE (IRE)	62	444	21	37	130	309967.16
AQLAAM (GB)	57	403	29	48	141	348278.60
ARABIAN GLEAM (GB)	16	95	5	7	34	64973.67
ARAKAN (USA)	29	137	9	14	43	121679.93
ARCANO (IRE)	127	720	50	77	274	975177.54
ARCH (USA)	15	65	3	4	25	173706.10
ARCHIPENKO (USA)	58	352	24	34	123	295605.52
AREION (GER)	4	31	2	5	9	57373.35
ART CONNOISSEUR (IRE)	30	174	7	9	48	104488.19
ASHKALANI (IRE)	1	10	1	1	2	5538.46
ASK (GB)	7	46	4	10	15	89269.36
ASSERTIVE (GB)	33	231	15	22	65	161238.34
ASTRONOMER ROYAL (USA)	4	13	1	2	6	17530.06
AUSSIE RULES (USA)	48	321	19	33	125	257869.92
AUTHORIZED (IRE)	55	254	17	26	103	302276.83
AVONBRIDGE (GB)	23	165	7	11	50	128248.32
AZAMOUR (IRE)	41	198	15	22	69	278123.73
BACHELOR DUKE (USA)	7	46	3	6	10	47356.55
BAHAMIAN BOUNTY (GB)	102	641	40	62	225	723100.03
BAHRI (USA)	12	63	6	9	20	48925.15
BALTIC KING (GB)	17	107	6	10	29	118596.39
BATED BREATH (GB)	102	462	40	58	183	774804.28
BEAT HOLLOW (GB)	14	70	7	12	27	233213.01
BERNARDINI (USA)	13	51	4	4	19	37417.33
BERTOLINI (USA)	22	138	7	13	43	72996.60
BIENAMADO (USA)	1	17	1	2	6	15082.06
BIG BAD BOB (IRE)	111	592	34	55	193	543395.39
BLACK SAM BELLAMY (IRE)	6	25	2	2	5	9757.45
BLAME (USA)	8	20	1	1	9	10643.82
BOB AND JOHN (USA)	1	10	1	1	2	10413.86
BOLLIN ERIC (GB)	2	11	1	2	2	9967.45
BORN TO SEA (IRE)	65	345	26	35	133	396902.86
BUSHRANGER (IRE)	94	653	33	52	219	480509.98
BYRON (GB)	22	181	9	11	75	238598.34
CACIQUE (IRE)	38	166	13	20	63	185920.42
CADEAUX GENEREUX	3	29	1	1	14	25982.80
CALCUTTA (GB)	1	16	1	1	7	17187.20
CAMACHO (GB)	78	486	33	48	169	378957.81
CAMELOT (GB)	51	119	9	10	51	115461.09
CAMPANOLOGIST (USA)	3	14	1	2	5	20662.85
CANDY RIDE (ARG)	3	14	1	1	5	9120.80
CANFORD CLIFFS (IRE)	110	595	42	60	214	626018.24
CAPE BLANCO (IRE)	13	53	4	5	18	29345.64
CAPE CROSS (IRE)	127	593	55	86	230	1041542.00

STALLIONS	RNRS	STARTS	WNRS	WINS	PLACES	TOTAL (£)
CAPTAIN AL (SAF)	1	18	1	3	3	17448.87
CAPTAIN GERRARD (IRE)	68	409	14	20	112	193106.87
CAPTAIN MARVELOUS (IRE)	6	28	1	1	5	13094.88
CAPTAIN RIO (GB)	30	268	12	22	79	215686.98
THE CARBON UNIT (USA)	9	65	5	8	26	173851.75
CARLOTAMIX (FR)	1	12	1	1	8	11193.78
CASAMENTO (IRE)	88	425	26	38	152	412487.21
CATCHER IN THE RYE (IRE)	5	18	3	3	4	17767.84
CHAMPS ELYSEES (GB)	109	457	37	58	177	985408.33
CHEVALIER (IRE)	2	13	1	1	7	12234.04
CHINEUR (FR)	5	30	1	1	11	18218.33
CHOISIR (AUS)	71	345	23	36	137	577565.56
CITYSCAPE (GB)	20	73	7	7	28	81664.41
CITY ZIP (USA)	4	23	2	5	6	22734.52
CLODOVIL (IRE)	72	404	26	39	124	466605.92
COMPTON PLACE (GB)	72	440	21	40	127	223277.07
COUNTRY REEL (USA)	4	21	2	2	10	51418.54
CREACHADOIR (IRE)	2	16	1	1	9	43579.15
DAAHER (CAN)	1	10	1	2	2	5525.15
DABIRSIM (FR)	8	19	1	1	6	95119.87
DALAKHANI (IRE)	42	207	18	33	80	483543.54
DANDY MAN (IRE)	131	714	40	59	239	586745.32
DANEHILL (USA)	1	5	1	1	0	2264.15
DANEHILL DANCER (IRE)	45	216	14	17	71	922416.37
DANSILI (GB)	107	472	40	59	190	1355217.80
DAPPER (GB)	3	21	2	5	4	20710.69
DARK ANGEL (IRE)	240	1379	99	149	542	3819991.73
DASHING BLADE	1	8	1	1	5	12198.30
DAWN APPROACH (IRE)	39	107	8	10	49	126831.01
DECLARATION OF WAR (USA)	34	100	8	11	36	227977.37
DEEP IMPACT (JPN)	11	51	5	8	25	454201.72
DELEGATOR (GB)	53	286	18	24	90	298746.75
DELTA DANCER (GB)	2	17	1	2	7	8673.86
DENOUNCE (GB)	6	32	3	3	9	93632.55
DESERT KING (IRE)	2	10	1	1	2	5322.85
DESERT STYLE (IRE)	3	8	1	1	1	5038.75
DESIDERATUM (GB)	4	31	1	3	8	13225.47
DIAMOND GREEN (FR)	9	48	2	3	15	23632.46
DICK TURPIN (IRE)	40	195	12	16	71	168544.40
DILUM (USA)	1	11	1	3	4	12693.55
DISCREET CAT (USA)	3	22	1	2	7	14036.69
DISTORTED HUMOR (USA)	28	90	13	16	40	205803.60
DOMINUS (USA)	1	6	1	1	3	8868.37
DONCASTER ROVER (USA)	7	32	2	3	8	13759.28
DOYEN (IRE)	9	41	3	4	12	21981.12
DRAGON PULSE (IRE)	61	362	26	36	155	400148.04
DREAM AHEAD (USA)	98	472	33	57	187	928002.27
DREAM EATER (IRE)	1	15	1	1	8	5114.43
DR FONG (USA)	8	30	1	1	5	7550.38
DROSSELMEYER (USA)	1	4	1	1	3	4416.25
DUBAI DESTINATION (USA)	11	60	3	6	25	42563.42
DUBAWI (IRE)	175	657	96	136	280	3329963.71
DUKE OF MARMALADE (IRE)	50	222	15	21	73	630765.24
DUNKIRK (USA)	2	11	1	1	1	6773.51
DUTCH ART (GB)	159	796	63	93	325	1046466.18
DYLAN THOMAS (IRE)	39	255	18	32	95	469645.57
DYNAFORMER (USA)	5	33	1	1	5	4812.92
ECHO OF LIGHT (GB)	15	70	8	12	23	105064.95
ELNADIM (USA)	38	252	15	24	91	295097.03
ELUSIVE CITY (USA)	33	222	14	24	66	201229.38
ELUSIVE PIMPERNEL (USA)	28	119	7	12	32	160007.52
ELUSIVE QUALITY (USA)	34	152	9	15	51	107019.40
ELZAAM (AUS)	56	288	21	31	109	417047.84

STALLIONS	RNRS	STARTS	WNRS	WINS	PLACES	TOTAL (£)
ENGLISH CHANNEL (USA)	6	37	1	2	10	29066.67
ENRIQUE (GB)	2	9	1	1	1	4100.75
EPAULETTE (AUS)	55	173	17	22	57	181889.90
EQUIANO (FR)	156	846	51	76	298	1083084.16
ESKENDEREYA (USA)	3	11	2	2	4	12832.02
EXCEED AND EXCEL (AUS)	201	1095	90	130	417	1745503.06
EXCELEBRATION (IRE)	78	351	30	47	147	1058610.34
EXCELLENT ART (GB)	62	374	20	32	119	361401.33
EXCHANGE RATE (USA)	20	96	9	13	37	181863.43
THE FACTOR (USA)	8	28	2	3	14	44928.68
FALCO (USA)	7	41	3	5	16	33172.42
FAMOUS NAME (GB)	28	153	8	12	53	100625.02
FARHH (GB)	18	48	6	8	13	126961.30
FASLIYEV (USA)	6	51	1	1	14	8249.02
FAST COMPANY (IRE)	110	638	46	69	212	880773.96
FASTNET ROCK (AUS)	121	596	47	73	238	1649827.33
FATH (USA)	1	11	1	1	6	6434.53
FINJAAN (GB)	14	51	1	1	25	20510.33
FINSCEAL FIOR (IRE)	9	37	1	1	12	8992.21
FIREBREAK (GB)	36	228	11	20	69	171140.88
FIRST DEFENCE (USA)	11	55	4	5	19	44685.90
FIRST SAMURAI (USA)	2	12	1	2	3	5982.50
FIRST TRUMP (GB)	3	21	2	4	4	11050.65
FLEMENSFIRTH (USA)	2	4	1	1	1	6458.98
FOOTSTEPSINTHESAND (GB)	106	573	36	62	226	831091.98
FOXWEDGE (AUS)	68	380	24	40	143	430697.17
FRAGRANT MIX (IRE)	2	5	2	3	1	18885.48
FRANKEL (GB)	77	261	40	59	134	2756682.08
FROZEN POWER (IRE)	43	263	11	19	91	296872.57
FRUITS OF LOVE (USA)	6	19	2	2	4	13611.54
GALILEO (IRE)	216	857	88	134	417	11698846.11
GENTLEWAVE (IRE)	3	15	1	1	8	22556.89
GETAWAY (GER)	4	22	1	1	8	13425.30
GIANT'S CAUSEWAY (USA)	12	65	3	4	35	95897.33
GIO PONTI (USA)	7	25	2	4	7	22553.51
GLORY OF DANCER (GB)	2	13	1	2	5	110056.23
GOLD AWAY (IRE)	3	24	1	1	10	63124.20
GREAT JOURNEY (JPN)	1	1	1	1	0	7107.69
GREEN DESERT (USA)	1	4	1	1	3	33413.85
HAAFHD (GB)	36	196	9	12	50	99603.72
HAATEF (USA)	19	127	12	14	49	160300.84
HALLING (USA)	39	187	16	22	68	460340.06
HARBOUR WATCH (IRE)	95	470	34	46	181	396332.53
HARD SPUN (USA)	20	126	9	13	48	137977.87
HARLAN'S HOLIDAY (USA)	4	16	3	4	5	47032.42
HAT TRICK (JPN)	7	35	3	3	10	41380.80
HAVANA GOLD (IRE)	58	223	18	25	75	337174.58
HAWK WING (USA)	4	15	1	1	6	12122.70
HELLVELYN (GB)	45	246	12	19	69	155410.09
HELMET (AUS)	101	442	32	39	151	483634.76
HENRYTHENAVIGATOR (USA)	62	391	29	42	142	309368.92
HERNANDO (FR)	9	50	7	10	21	69811.98
HIGH CHAPARRAL (IRE)	105	422	34	53	153	859691.64
HIGH ROCK (IRE)	1	6	1	3	3	17310.79
HOLY ROMAN EMPEROR (IRE)	135	718	55	82	263	849669.30
HURRICANE CAT (USA)	2	16	1	1	4	11163.05
HURRICANE RUN (IRE)	15	69	4	5	25	50047.00
ICEMAN (GB)	6	29	1	1	9	8236.15
IFFRAAJ (GB)	140	732	49	82	265	2149035.97
IMPERIAL DANCER (GB)	2	12	1	1	1	5872.65
INDESATCHEL (IRE)	7	50	4	4	10	63837.94
INDIAN HAVEN (GB)	10	65	2	4	14	31514.75
INTELLO (GER)	21	42	5	5	15	49619.16

STALLIONS	RNRS	STARTS	WNRS	WINS	PLACES	TOTAL (£)
INTENSE FOCUS (USA)	88	517	27	41	169	472427.82
INTIDAB (USA)	1	12	1	1	1	3130.40
INTIKHAB (USA)	52	278	18	27	99	245512.54
INVINCIBLE SPIRIT (IRE)	187	1032	80	111	405	1830987.23
IRISH WELLS (FR)	2	6	1	2	2	42632.47
ISHIGURU (USA)	9	80	6	12	21	70539.38
IT'S GINO (GER)	1	3	1	1	2	4114.00
JEREMY (USA)	49	265	15	19	82	427439.92
JIMMY CREED (USA)	2	5	1	1	1	4197.00
JOE BEAR (IRE)	2	5	1	1	2	7431.00
JOHANNESBURG (USA)	1	20	1	1	8	8425.30
JUKEBOX JURY (IRE)	5	28	4	10	9	86976.32
KALANISI (IRE)	10	35	3	3	16	25761.44
KAPGARDE (FR)	1	11	1	2	2	5177.65
KAYF TARA (GB)	2	8	1	1	1	3398.60
KENDARGENT (FR)	30	112	10	13	50	163966.15
KEY OF LUCK (USA)	2	25	2	3	7	12845.20
KHELEYF (USA)	121	805	44	65	240	585834.42
KIER PARK (IRE)	3	23	3	3	10	15254.23
KINGSALSA (USA)	3	18	2	5	5	29038.39
KING'S BEST (USA)	13	71	4	4	26	54691.01
KITTEN'S JOY (USA)	31	120	12	17	44	400401.08
KODIAC (GB)	267	1539	126	192	568	2539178.49
KONIGSTIGER (GER)	2	3	1	1	0	2264.15
KYLLACHY (GB)	157	1045	72	126	359	1176250.11
LANDO (GER)	4	20	1	1	8	16008.80
LAWMAN (FR)	154	858	49	77	302	1153924.78
LAYMAN (USA)	1	10	1	1	1	3488.25
LEADERSHIP (GB)	1	13	1	2	1	5621.75
LE CADRE NOIR (IRE)	8	32	1	3	5	19506.41
LE HAVRE (FR)	18	78	7	12	24	254828.06
LEMON DROP KID (USA)	12	52	5	7	28	151262.58
LEPORELLO (IRE)	1	8	1	2	1	5752.40
LEROIDESANIMAUX (BRZ)	15	62	4	4	25	45336.29
LETHAL FORCE (IRE)	55	228	21	24	89	230227.05
LE VIE DEI COLORI (GB)	3	25	1	1	14	13599.05
LIBRANNO (GB)	2	8	1	1	5	5233.60
LIBRETTIST (USA)	4	27	3	6	9	48293.40
LILBOURNE LAD (IRE)	76	403	19	29	132	233880.32
LITERATO (FR)	2	7	1	1	2	3303.52
LOMITAS (GB)	1	7	1	1	3	58717.30
LONHRO (AUS)	41	151	11	20	53	320686.36
LOPE DE VEGA (IRE)	100	496	53	79	206	1046217.67
LORD SHANAKILL (USA)	38	189	9	14	61	129093.16
LUCARNO (USA)	1	3	1	1	0	3557.95
LUCKY STORY (USA)	9	53	4	5	15	27214.71
MAJESTIC MISSILE (IRE)	25	175	9	11	55	112199.44
MAJESTIC WARRIOR (USA)	2	9	1	2	1	19681.20
MAJOR CADEAUX (GB)	32	176	11	21	53	150571.50
MAKFI (GB)	81	364	24	37	132	567564.90
MANDURO (GER)	43	202	13	17	69	281022.34
MARJU (IRE)	9	42	3	3	15	28395.27
MARTALINE (GB)	3	19	2	3	6	25952.73
MASTERCRAFTSMAN (IRE)	170	791	60	82	282	1034108.11
MASTEROFTHEHORSE (IRE)	4	13	1	1	5	14381.59
MAWATHEEQ (USA)	23	101	3	5	33	54516.49
MAXIOS (GB)	9	26	1	2	8	18669.00
MAYSON (GB)	78	409	31	43	189	630592.04
MAZAMEER (IRE)	9	48	2	5	11	33460.67
MEDAGLIA D'ORO (USA)	11	54	5	5	21	35575.77
MEDICEAN (GB)	103	571	38	56	173	429916.42
MILAN (GB)	3	6	1	1	3	8880.77
MILK IT MICK (GB)	10	66	2	2	16	13457.07

STALLIONS	RNRS	STARTS	WNRS	WINS	PLACES	TOTAL (£)
MILLENARY (GB)	3	21	1	1	10	32164.94
MILLKOM (GB)	2	5	1	1	2	31822.45
MINE (IRE)	1	7	1	1	2	5083.90
MISU BOND (IRE)	17	124	4	10	38	54217.84
MIZZEN MAST (USA)	14	46	3	4	13	73626.37
MONSIEUR BOND (IRE)	86	562	30	46	180	401429.91
MONSUN (GER)	11	32	4	5	11	112844.65
MONTJEU (IRE)	26	95	6	10	32	108400.23
MORE THAN READY (USA)	29	113	9	12	41	96209.59
MOROZOV (USA)	1	2	1	1	0	5528.21
MOSS VALE (IRE)	20	140	6	12	41	76296.72
MOST IMPROVED (IRE)	25	90	7	8	21	58319.90
MOTIVATOR (GB)	32	127	9	16	56	274904.88
MOUNT NELSON (GB)	76	366	23	29	160	1098456.44
MUHTATHIR (GB)	6	34	2	2	12	10529.20
MUJADIL (USA)	5	48	2	2	16	14026.74
MUJAHID (USA)	2	22	1	3	7	13495.60
MULLIONMILEANHOUR (IRE)	18	106	8	13	34	71745.40
MULL OF KINTYRE (USA)	2	24	1	2	11	18841.87
MULTIPLEX (GB)	42	293	21	30	109	210719.83
MYBOYCHARLIE (IRE)	26	155	8	9	47	117548.55
NAAQOOS (GB)	7	34	2	2	9	10641.50
NATHANIEL (IRE)	93	344	33	51	144	1930969.37
NATIVE RULER (GB)	5	31	1	1	9	8409.90
NAYEF (USA)	34	171	10	12	47	133937.42
NEEDWOOD BLADE (GB)	7	69	2	3	19	20308.98
NEVER ON SUNDAY (FR)	2	5	1	1	2	3675.25
NEW APPROACH (IRE)	134	524	49	76	195	1170680.09
NIGHT SHIFT (USA)	2	16	1	3	6	14109.54
NORTHERN AFLEET (USA)	1	3	1	1	1	3279.48
NORTH LIGHT (IRE)	2	6	1	1	1	3632.92
NOTNOWCATO (GB)	19	102	5	6	38	106523.53
OASIS DREAM (GB)	136	744	59	102	287	1058335.73
OBSERVATORY (USA)	8	29	1	1	8	6305.80
OLDEN TIMES (GB)	6	35	2	3	18	49133.90
OLD VIC	1	5	1	2	3	28070.08
ONE COOL CAT (USA)	8	67	2	2	18	20265.43
ORATORIO (IRE)	24	188	12	15	70	141154.07
ORIENTOR (GB)	11	88	5	7	32	140995.30
ORPEN (USA)	5	19	1	1	7	10831.62
OSCAR (IRE)	5	15	1	3	4	17188.64
PACO BOY (IRE)	95	444	20	32	145	442032.71
PALAVICINI (USA)	3	29	2	3	10	27478.21
PANIS (USA)	2	5	1	2	0	130832.00
PAPAL BULL (GB)	17	62	4	5	14	50533.64
PARIS HOUSE (GB)	1	17	1	1	4	8711.95
PASSING GLANCE (GB)	18	80	7	8	17	52322.65
PASTORAL PURSUITS (GB)	95	655	38	73	227	607714.12
PEINTRE CELEBRE (USA)	13	48	1	1	13	14754.40
PENNY'S PICNIC (IRE)	2	9	1	1	4	9954.40
PHOENIX REACH (IRE)	13	94	3	9	22	41203.97
PICCOLO (GB)	66	471	20	34	164	296056.80
PIVOTAL (GB)	112	664	58	95	255	1642108.07
PLANTEUR (IRE)	3	13	1	1	3	4078.70
POET'S VOICE (GB)	135	722	53	73	241	1153547.04
POINT OF ENTRY (USA)	2	4	1	1	0	4528.30
POLIGLOTE (GB)	2	5	2	5	0	22278.17
POUNCED (USA)	1	2	1	2	0	7115.90
POUR MOI (IRE)	41	163	16	20	61	1330356.48
POWER (GB)	59	271	16	23	107	215817.51
PRESENTING (GB)	2	6	1	1	1	41453.00
PRIME DEFENDER (GB)	1	9	1	1	3	4525.90
PROCLAMATION (IRE)	13	74	4	8	20	40951.40

STALLIONS	RNRS	STARTS	WNRS	WINS	PLACES	TOTAL (£)
PROUD CITIZEN (USA)	2	10	1	1	1	9097.68
PYRUS (USA)	6	24	1	2	6	6792.17
QUALITY ROAD (USA)	9	44	2	2	15	13736.98
QUWS (GB)	2	4	1	1	1	7251.28
RAHY (USA)	1	16	1	3	5	11777.37
RAIL LINK (GB)	32	209	17	28	79	291321.55
RAJJ (IRE)	4	15	2	3	8	53444.01
RAJSAMAN (FR)	7	36	1	2	12	33074.05
RAKTI (GB)	5	13	1	1	2	13780.06
RAMONTI (FR)	2	16	1	1	7	7947.94
RAVEN'S PASS (USA)	84	406	37	60	155	677786.10
RECKLESS ABANDON (GB)	9	34	3	4	14	58228.52
REDBACK (GB)	5	22	1	1	10	21458.98
RED CLUBS (IRE)	19	156	8	20	51	128014.84
RED JAZZ (USA)	45	193	15	22	60	270831.13
REDOUTE'S CHOICE (AUS)	26	89	10	12	35	98195.28
RED ROCKS (IRE)	2	4	1	1	1	3811.70
REFUSE TO BEND (IRE)	17	107	6	13	39	117624.12
REQUINTO (IRE)	45	218	15	21	73	268879.56
RESPLENDENT GLORY (IRE)	2	9	1	1	0	2264.15
REVOQUE (IRE)	3	9	1	1	3	39076.93
RIO DE LA PLATA (USA)	6	33	4	8	4	51591.01
RIP VAN WINKLE (IRE)	106	524	33	49	206	647125.06
ROCK OF GIBRALTAR (IRE)	98	643	37	57	235	832380.56
RODERIC O'CONNOR (IRE)	60	283	20	40	92	320629.70
ROYAL ANTHEM (USA)	2	12	1	1	5	25798.42
ROYAL APPLAUSE (GB)	112	774	45	75	244	532599.88
SABIANGO (GER)	1	10	1	1	5	9657.65
SAKHEE (USA)	20	101	6	7	29	69425.84
SAKHEE'S SECRET (GB)	69	454	21	34	138	259653.36
SAMUM (GER)	3	5	1	1	0	13666.67
SAYIF (IRE)	29	140	8	15	42	117459.50
SCAT DADDY (USA)	28	101	17	28	32	1435946.50
SEA THE STARS (IRE)	85	336	40	61	157	2004922.15
SEPOY (AUS)	99	396	31	39	133	369426.55
SHACKLEFORD (USA)	1	3	1	1	1	3873.55
SHAKESPEAREAN (IRE)	2	13	2	3	5	13913.50
SHAMARDAL (USA)	133	588	54	84	231	1325936.28
SHANTOU (USA)	5	13	2	3	2	35492.78
SHIROCCO (GER)	34	163	11	16	48	224687.44
SHOLOKHOV (IRE)	6	25	2	2	9	13496.34
SHOWCASING (GB)	105	597	48	65	201	943795.18
SIDNEY'S CANDY (USA)	1	12	1	1	5	7840.57
SILVER DEPUTY (CAN)	1	12	1	1	1	3691.45
SINGSPIEL (IRE)	9	70	4	10	21	190293.83
SIR PERCY (GB)	107	570	40	66	199	641915.72
SIR PRANCEALOT (IRE)	82	459	34	58	165	455034.89
SIXTIES ICON (GB)	83	405	24	32	135	454354.01
SIYOUNI (FR)	34	141	15	24	64	663149.80
SLEEPING INDIAN (GB)	47	302	19	26	99	177610.66
SLICKLY (FR)	2	5	1	1	3	7543.60
SMART STRIKE (CAN)	10	53	5	10	22	71376.62
SOCIETY ROCK (IRE)	70	293	25	36	116	472376.94
SOLDIER HOLLOW (GB)	7	17	1	1	6	6880.23
SOLDIER OF FORTUNE (IRE)	9	51	2	4	18	148558.12
SOVIET STAR (USA)	6	57	3	5	25	32040.09
SO YOU THINK (NZ)	32	144	8	9	60	102077.06
SPEIGHTSTOWN (USA)	22	82	7	9	35	119752.18
SPRING AT LAST (USA)	3	15	2	3	7	55147.90
STARSPANGLEDBANNER (AUS)	13	78	6	11	27	225846.81
STAY THIRSTY (USA)	2	16	1	2	8	18828.17
STIMULATION (IRE)	35	231	11	18	67	141007.57
STRATEGIC PRINCE (GB)	30	249	14	19	88	201054.98

STALLIONS	RNRS	STARTS	WNRS	WINS	PLACES	TOTAL (£)
STREET BOSS (USA)	3	23	2	3	9	22218.99
STREET CRY (IRE)	69	355	30	42	142	503324.73
STRIKING AMBITION (GB)	8	47	2	5	16	24252.55
SUCCESSFUL APPEAL (USA)	2	14	1	2	4	50876.05
SULAMANI (IRE)	11	41	3	5	10	21279.20
SWISS SPIRIT (GB)	38	153	13	18	51	127629.14
TAGULA (IRE)	52	333	18	29	106	480560.22
TAMAYUZ (GB)	55	316	19	35	123	761075.03
TAPIT (USA)	2	4	2	2	1	9679.95
TEOFILO (IRE)	136	656	60	95	248	1700001.46
THEWAYYOUARE (USA)	45	186	5	5	46	52753.44
THOUSAND WORDS (GB)	10	70	2	5	23	57295.73
THREE VALLEYS (USA)	8	58	5	7	21	59687.07
TIGER HILL (IRE)	12	70	2	2	23	26894.91
TIN HORSE (IRE)	2	7	1	1	2	6278.04
TITUS LIVIUS (FR)	3	19	1	1	7	6145.00
TIZNOW (USA)	2	16	1	1	2	3140.75
TOBOUGG (IRE)	12	66	3	4	21	31738.37
TOMBA (GB)	2	30	2	2	12	13894.20
TOUGH AS NAILS (IRE)	5	27	1	1	18	27425.22
TRADE FAIR (GB)	7	34	1	2	10	17174.74
TRANS ISLAND (GB)	10	65	4	9	21	54740.76
UNBRIDLED'S SONG (USA)	1	8	1	1	3	3386.15
UNCLE MO (USA)	2	3	1	1	1	6159.30
URGENT REQUEST (IRE)	1	9	1	1	7	14264.30
U S RANGER (USA)	1	14	1	3	4	7899.95
VALE OF YORK (IRE)	33	215	9	14	69	135359.80
VERGLAS (IRE)	28	147	11	16	49	155744.29
VINNIE ROE (IRE)	1	4	1	1	1	7264.95
VIOLENCE (USA)	2	6	1	2	2	10195.40
VIRTUAL (GB)	9	52	3	4	23	30244.82
VISION D'ETAT (FR)	4	14	1	1	3	15399.05
VITAL EQUINE (IRE)	1	16	1	2	6	13158.51
VOCALISED (USA)	44	212	12	18	59	448877.39
VOIX DU NORD (FR)	3	20	1	2	12	14185.43
WAR FRONT (USA)	59	234	30	43	101	1638395.86
WAY OF LIGHT (USA)	1	6	1	1	3	8382.90
WESTERNER (GB)	12	31	1	1	12	17228.86
WESTLAKE (GB)	2	10	1	1	3	4355.98
WHERE OR WHEN (IRE)	3	12	1	1	2	7197.44
WHIPPER (USA)	12	60	4	4	22	285712.42
WINDSOR KNOT (IRE)	10	57	5	8	24	143283.94
WINKER WATSON (GB)	6	46	1	4	17	20639.84
WOOTTON BASSETT (GB)	7	34	2	3	14	66255.24
YEATS (IRE)	21	70	6	11	23	305712.05
YORGUNNABELUCKY (USA)	5	17	1	1	2	6137.20
YOUMZAIN (IRE)	5	20	3	3	11	17613.28
ZAFEEN (FR)	3	28	2	3	10	42621.87
ZAMINDAR (USA)	26	161	12	17	53	159889.64
ZEBEDEE (GB)	141	864	54	84	287	809879.28
ZOFFANY (IRE)	125	647	52	74	219	1017423.67

BY KIND PERMISSION OF WEATHERBYS

NH STALLIONS' EARNINGS FOR 2016/17

(includes every stallion who sired a winner over jumps in Great Britain and Ireland in 2016/17)

STALLIONS	RNRS	STARTS	WNRS	WINS	PLACES	TOTAL (£)
ACAMBARO (GER)	12	38	2	2	16	28591.02
ACCLAMATION (GB)	5	17	2	2	4	17944.58
ACCORDION	12	37	1	1	10	23810.01
ACT ONE (GB)	20	102	6	11	36	76095.92
AGENT BLEU (FR)	2	6	1	1	3	42388.90
AIR CHIEF MARSHAL (IRE)	3	10	2	2	5	13619.89
ALBERTO GIACOMETTI (IRE)	8	30	3	4	14	39314.01
ALDERBROOK (GB)	28	119	9	12	50	105471.30
ALFLORA (IRE)	62	252	26	37	92	385360.02
ALFRED NOBEL (IRE)	7	26	1	1	7	8073.56
ALHAARTH (IRE)	22	84	6	9	25	85532.58
ALKAADHEM (GB)	17	70	4	6	28	62839.54
ALMUTAWAKEL (GB)	1	3	1	1	0	4069.85
AL NAMIX (FR)	29	134	9	16	50	317222.03
AMERICAN POST (GB)	3	20	2	3	8	24058.37
AMILYNX (FR)	5	20	1	2	8	20598.25
ANABAA BLUE (GB)	3	7	1	1	1	14187.00
AND BEYOND (IRE)	14	73	5	7	23	43591.55
ANSHAN	19	79	5	7	31	80513.13
ANTARCTIQUE (IRE)	8	39	2	2	13	33827.00
ANTONIUS PIUS (USA)	17	93	6	8	37	175536.59
ANZILLERO (GER)	3	11	3	5	3	80264.45
APPLE TREE (FR)	17	58	5	3	20	60986.73
APTITUDE (USA)	1	5	1	2	1	7452.00
AQLAAM (GB)	10	30	5	6	10	33349.09
ARAAFA (IRE)	5	21	3	3	6	18915.83
ARAKAN (USA)	28	94	7	13	27	102346.13
ARCADIO (GER)	52	199	12	18	87	277366.75
ARCANO (IRE)	13	38	2	2	9	9802.59
ARCH (USA)	4	9	1	1	3	6390.90
AREION (GER)	4	11	1	1	9	8290.35
ARISTOTLE (IRE)	3	12	1	2	0	9722.42
ARTAN (IRE)	6	36	2	4	12	55210.18
ASHKALANI (IRE)	4	15	2	3	5	17425.07
ASIAN HEIGHTS (GB)	5	12	2	2	4	9512.64
ASK (GB)	27	107	7	12	43	75583.96
ASSESSOR (IRE)	12	65	3	5	31	120040.77
ASTARABAD (USA)	19	76	5	10	34	219094.50
AUCTION HOUSE (USA)	3	15	1	2	7	19384.15
AUSSIE RULES (USA)	21	78	6	8	29	125244.13
AUTHORIZED (IRE)	63	286	28	49	118	817874.04
AVONBRIDGE (GB)	8	37	3	4	13	21149.52
AXXOS (GER)	1	7	1	2	4	37564.50
AZAMOUR (IRE)	40	164	18	26	49	230825.49
BACH (IRE)	47	207	9	13	69	151866.37
BAHRI (USA)	13	39	1	1	10	9183.15
BALAKHERI (IRE)	5	24	1	2	16	58538.22
BALKO (FR)	24	94	11	17	42	212734.32
BALLINGARRY (IRE)	26	94	7	11	26	110374.97
BALTIC KING (GB)	5	24	1	2	2	6920.22
BANDARI (IRE)	3	15	2	3	1	14906.25
BANDMASTER (USA)	3	13	1	2	6	10975.44
BARASTRAIGHT (GB)	1	4	1	1	2	32695.22
BARATHEA (IRE)	5	34	2	3	10	14732.61
BEAT ALL (USA)	23	91	4	6	28	75528.54
BEAT HOLLOW (GB)	32	108	8	9	40	210123.41
BEAU VENTURE (USA)	1	6	1	1	3	6450.37
BENEFICIAL (GB)	329	1509	97	143	572	1500785.24

STALLIONS	RNRS	STARTS	WNRS	WINS	PLACES	TOTAL (£)
BERING	4	18	2	2	7	13771.80
BERNARDINI (USA)	4	14	1	2	2	30214.12
BERTOLINI (USA)	11	51	2	2	20	18901.52
BEST OF THE BESTS (IRE)	2	14	1	1	4	7208.67
BIENAMADO (USA)	12	57	3	3	17	26611.20
BIG BAD BOB (IRE)	24	94	4	7	29	78520.10
BIG SHUFFLE (USA)	4	27	2	3	12	18096.44
BIRDSTONE (USA)	1	6	1	1	1	7240.50
BISHOP OF CASHEL (GB)	4	24	1	1	12	15079.35
BLACK SAM BELLAMY (IRE)	91	263	25	38	90	213124.57
BLUE BRESIL (FR)	13	44	5	8	18	109621.69
BLUEPRINT (IRE)	35	166	11	15	75	271642.55
BLUSHING FLAME (USA)	1	15	1	2	8	19546.20
BOB BACK (USA)	13	61	3	3	29	43079.97
BOLLIN ERIC (GB)	24	83	5	7	25	56089.07
BOLLIN WILLIAM (GB)	2	5	1	1	2	4327.02
BONBON ROSE (FR)	5	11	2	3	2	17971.15
BORN KING (JPN)	2	3	1	1	0	4993.59
BRIAN BORU (GB)	100	493	38	54	204	633862.30
BRIER CREEK (USA)	4	21	2	5	9	33612.46
BROADWAY FLYER (USA)	11	45	2	2	14	17508.07
BUCK'S BOUM (FR)	5	16	3	5	9	47847.49
BUSHRANGER (IRE)	20	65	2	5	11	23229.25
BUSY FLIGHT (GB)	5	23	3	6	9	38409.64
BYRON (GB)	6	27	2	5	5	43381.60
CABALLO RAPTOR (CAN)	3	8	2	3	4	13852.26
CACHET NOIR (USA)	2	7	2	2	4	12690.60
CACIQUE (IRE)	6	28	3	6	5	30113.88
CADOUDAL (FR)	1	6	1	1	3	19214.00
CALIFET (FR)	22	94	10	17	32	257131.17
CANFORD CLIFFS (IRE)	11	32	2	7	13	69598.00
CAPE BLANCO (IRE)	3	9	2	2	3	10547.37
CAPE CROSS (IRE)	33	114	11	16	42	146221.23
CAPTAIN RIO (GB)	24	62	4	8	16	58962.82
THE CARBON UNIT (USA)	3	11	1	1	6	19309.82
CARLO BANK (IRE)	7	30	2	4	8	18745.14
CARLOTAMIX (FR)	2	13	1	2	6	18242.50
CATCHER IN THE RYE (IRE)	21	106	7	11	35	100735.21
CENTRAL PARK (IRE)	21	100	8	16	40	154048.78
CHAMPS ELYSEES (GB)	26	73	3	3	32	37355.80
CHARMING GROOM (FR)	1	3	1	1	1	9236.86
CHEVALIER (IRE)	9	32	1	1	8	16771.15
CHINEUR (FR)	3	11	1	2	3	9531.10
CHOISIR (AUS)	8	31	2	2	16	24435.95
CLASSIC CLICHE (IRE)	19	78	5	5	25	52555.26
CLODOVIL (IRE)	10	34	2	5	10	41302.31
CLOSE CONFLICT (USA)	4	11	1	1	2	9124.99
CLOUDINGS (IRE)	53	247	17	29	91	468629.96
COASTAL PATH (GB)	5	19	3	6	5	115592.45
COCKNEY REBEL (IRE)	14	34	3	3	10	14086.53
COMPTON PLACE (GB)	7	20	2	2	5	9040.84
CORONER (IRE)	11	38	1	2	7	13277.49
COUNTRY REEL (USA)	4	29	3	5	9	44559.24
COURT CAVE (IRE)	86	406	25	39	161	445533.72
COURTEOUS (GB)	1	4	1	1	0	2924.10
CRAIGSTEEL (GB)	93	408	26	41	142	357595.64
CRILLON (FR)	6	18	5	9	5	401426.96
CROCO ROUGE (IRE)	17	64	5	9	21	121198.45
CURTAIN TIME (IRE)	6	29	2	3	10	32191.25
DADARISSIME (FR)	2	10	1	2	3	25759.40
DALAKHANI (IRE)	23	97	8	9	44	69399.21
DALIAPOUR (IRE)	2	5	2	2	1	6709.76
DANEHILL DANCER (IRE)	34	149	10	14	51	117464.95

STALLIONS	RNRS	STARTS	WNRS	WINS	PLACES	TOTAL (£)
DANROAD (AUS)	6	23	2	3	7	23246.70
DANSANT (GB)	4	9	2	2	5	11575.93
DANSILI (GB)	18	80	6	10	30	70984.32
DARAMSAR (FR)	2	4	1	1	1	3662.40
DARK ANGEL (IRE)	21	99	6	7	41	59239.81
DARNAY (GB)	2	5	1	1	0	1949.40
DARSI (FR)	42	172	10	12	61	120748.52
DAVIDOFF (GER)	4	22	2	3	9	65279.07
DAY FLIGHT (GB)	5	30	3	8	14	136198.71
DAYLAMI (IRE)	37	146	13	19	42	122036.99
DEFINITE ARTICLE (GB)	106	454	31	45	131	521457.18
DELLA FRANCESCA (USA)	10	50	4	6	23	94540.47
DENHAM RED (FR)	4	18	2	5	10	400033.85
DENOUNCE (GB)	6	31	2	3	13	18628.50
DESERT KING (IRE)	25	110	7	11	40	131701.08
DESERT PRINCE (IRE)	5	21	1	3	11	236348.89
DESIDERATUM (GB)	10	38	2	3	14	27667.50
DIABLENEYEV (USA)	2	4	1	1	2	2693.52
DIAMOND GREEN (FR)	15	57	2	2	20	44919.76
DIESIS	1	1	1	1	0	1871.70
DIKTAT (GB)	6	26	1	1	7	7380.62
DISCOVER D'AUTEUIL (FR)	7	36	4	7	14	65053.83
DOCTOR DINO (FR)	3	17	2	6	8	105568.36
DOM ALCO (FR)	30	135	9	15	56	450578.44
DOUBLE ECLIPSE (IRE)	12	41	3	3	12	63963.57
DOUBLETOUR (USA)	1	4	1	1	0	2662.80
DOUBLE TRIGGER (IRE)	17	54	3	4	19	47762.60
DOYEN (IRE)	25	92	11	18	32	150972.04
DRAGON DANCER (GB)	1	9	1	1	4	16785.60
DREAM WELL (FR)	8	39	5	8	18	95440.88
DR FONG (USA)	10	41	1	3	6	31087.09
DR MASSINI (IRE)	79	282	23	35	78	345026.55
DUBAI DESTINATION (USA)	63	204	16	21	66	153092.95
DUBAWI (IRE)	15	41	3	4	12	47867.03
DUKE OF MARMALADE (IRE)	40	155	6	11	41	132299.92
DUSHYANTOR (USA)	22	109	5	11	31	81552.60
DUTCH ART (GB)	12	34	2	2	7	7512.64
DYLAN THOMAS (IRE)	38	151	9	13	48	93337.46
DYNAFORMER (USA)	6	24	2	3	7	284425.07
EARLY MARCH (GB)	12	48	4	5	23	177932.13
ECHO OF LIGHT (GB)	27	98	6	7	33	101602.25
ELMAAMUL (USA)	1	11	1	2	2	6516.00
ELUSIVE CITY (USA)	8	35	1	1	6	22641.89
ELUSIVE PIMPERNEL (USA)	9	30	1	1	15	34690.62
EMPEROR FOUNTAIN	3	7	1	1	3	3675.70
ENDOLI (USA)	2	13	1	2	4	21874.68
ENRIQUE (GB)	14	71	6	9	22	62166.80
EPALO (GER)	12	50	1	3	20	23491.84
EQUERRY (USA)	4	13	3	5	4	24339.00
EREWHON (USA)	7	26	2	2	7	16575.36
ERHAAB (USA)	17	55	4	5	16	43075.17
EXCEED AND EXCEL (AUS)	10	24	1	3	4	26753.69
EXCELLENT ART (GB)	24	72	5	6	16	78014.20
EXECUTIVE PERK	2	8	1	1	2	5732.10
EXIT TO NOWHERE (USA)	37	148	8	14	58	131897.83
FAIR MIX (IRE)	56	219	11	15	79	130823.37
FANTASTIC QUEST (IRE)	3	14	1	1	2	4685.85
FASLIYEV (USA)	3	14	1	1	4	6971.40
FAST COMPANY (IRE)	10	27	4	6	10	39758.51
FASTNET ROCK (AUS)	10	35	1	1	6	17893.83
FATH (USA)	2	13	1	3	2	13053.23
FINE GRAIN (JPN)	1	6	1	2	3	16960.10
FIREBREAK (GB)	5	25	1	2	8	13644.90

STALLIONS	RNRS	STARTS	WNRS	WINS	PLACES	TOTAL (£)
FLEETWOOD (IRE)	9	29	2	3	7	20960.40
FLEMENSFIRTH (USA)	298	1147	103	137	444	1703635.04
FLYING LEGEND (USA)	9	47	1	1	12	8486.68
FOOTSTEPSINTHESAND (GB)	16	43	3	3	15	50013.79
FORESTIER (FR)	8	37	3	6	12	85931.59
FRAAM (GB)	6	15	1	1	5	8863.06
FRAGRANT MIX (IRE)	12	33	3	5	14	50598.75
FROZEN POWER (IRE)	8	28	1	1	9	9841.27
FRUITS OF LOVE (USA)	55	213	12	20	71	281809.13
FUISSE (FR)	7	21	3	4	10	23142.36
GALILEO (IRE)	67	248	19	29	93	399387.28
GAMUT (IRE)	64	259	15	25	101	342302.39
GARUDA (IRE)	3	18	1	2	6	25958.05
GENERAL GAMBUL (GB)	1	6	1	2	1	8036.10
GENEROSITY (GB)	1	10	1	1	1	3487.50
GENEROUS (IRE)	67	285	21	33	101	317975.08
GENTLEMAN'S DEAL (IRE)	3	9	1	2	2	9436.38
GENTLEWAVE (IRE)	7	21	2	5	8	45817.78
GERMANY (USA)	19	93	7	10	35	97388.04
GETAWAY (GER)	55	165	6	9	54	83840.94
GHOSTZAPPER (USA)	1	3	1	1	1	8029.42
GIANT'S CAUSEWAY (USA)	2	10	1	1	7	7449.58
GOLAN (IRE)	75	301	14	20	118	265724.55
GOLD AWAY (IRE)	4	12	1	2	4	13824.22
GOLDEN LARIAT (USA)	5	18	2	3	9	22979.50
GOLDEN TORNADO (IRE)	12	51	4	4	17	33966.64
GOLDMARK (USA)	4	19	1	3	6	52551.12
GOLDNEYEV (USA)	3	14	3	3	9	153329.50
GOLD WELL (GB)	100	425	31	49	187	727165.90
GRAPE TREE ROAD (GB)	26	96	9	14	23	86391.74
GREAT EXHIBITION (USA)	9	47	3	5	14	36881.47
GREAT JOURNEY (JPN)	4	19	2	3	6	14918.30
GREAT PALM (USA)	15	82	4	6	31	60612.76
GREAT PRETENDER (IRE)	20	81	12	18	33	225615.94
GREEN CARD (USA)	1	6	1	1	2	4057.56
GRIS DE GRIS (IRE)	6	14	1	2	4	7171.83
GULLAND (GB)	2	20	1	1	5	6829.30
HAAFHD (GB)	21	69	5	6	20	41884.33
HALLING (USA)	43	161	9	11	66	156007.89
HARD SPUN (USA)	3	13	1	1	5	115750.70
HAWKEYE (IRE)	3	5	1	1	3	4538.30
HAWK WING (USA)	15	58	4	5	13	57475.09
HELIOSTATIC (IRE)	5	19	2	4	7	26734.90
HELISSIO (FR)	30	118	6	10	40	128986.68
HENRYTHENAVIGATOR (USA)	3	15	1	1	7	6908.43
HERNANDO (FR)	17	67	4	6	30	111984.99
HERON ISLAND (IRE)	77	269	20	32	99	393979.77
HIGH CHAPARRAL (IRE)	70	322	18	32	114	559733.33
HIGH-RISE (IRE)	6	30	2	2	11	23748.70
HIGH ROLLER (IRE)	2	12	1	1	3	6806.25
HOLD THAT TIGER (USA)	1	7	1	1	1	3171.60
HOLY ROMAN EMPEROR (IRE)	11	41	4	4	9	23996.21
HONOLULU (IRE)	2	6	1	1	2	7102.08
HUMBEL (USA)	2	5	2	3	1	14380.64
HURRICANE RUN (IRE)	29	98	8	10	36	101037.27
ICEMAN (GB)	7	33	2	2	14	14973.34
IFFRAAJ (GB)	14	51	4	5	19	55733.07
IKTIBAS (GB)	3	12	1	1	2	7909.14
IMPERIAL BALLET (IRE)	3	16	1	1	5	10825.24
INDIAN DANEHILL (IRE)	53	197	12	20	63	137859.61
INDIAN HAVEN (GB)	13	48	2	2	16	28957.87
INDIAN RIVER (FR)	47	244	19	31	105	539706.36
INTIKHAB (USA)	12	45	3	3	14	38486.33

STALLIONS	RNRS	STARTS	WNRS	WINS	PLACES	TOTAL (£)
INVASOR (ARG)	3	19	1	2	5	12925.15
INVINCIBLE SPIRIT (IRE)	17	72	1	4	24	45845.64
IRISH WELLS (FR)	8	33	2	3	16	61243.02
ISLAND HOUSE (IRE)	1	5	1	1	1	16522.45
IT'S GINO (GER)	2	10	2	4	4	43933.30
IVAN DENISOVICH (IRE)	5	13	3	3	4	16465.95
JAMMAAL (GB)	2	4	1	1	1	4662.00
JEREMY (USA)	51	223	15	26	75	255558.83
JIMBLE (FR)	8	49	2	2	26	43886.69
JOHANNESBURG (USA)	2	12	1	1	5	9243.36
KADEED (IRE)	4	11	2	2	5	15206.64
KAHYASI	9	40	3	3	20	41658.11
KAIETEUR (USA)	4	14	1	2	2	11412.60
KALANISI (IRE)	158	559	33	58	170	682232.80
KALLISTO (GER)	1	6	1	1	3	7213.23
KANDAHAR RUN (GB)	2	7	1	1	2	4346.55
KAPGARDE (FR)	41	191	19	34	84	507363.26
KAP ROCK (FR)	3	6	1	1	3	6910.20
KARINGA BAY	24	74	4	5	22	130930.43
KAYF TARA (GB)	280	1179	108	171	493	2420305.02
KELTOS (FR)	1	7	1	2	4	27567.35
KENTUCKY DYNAMITE (USA)	2	13	2	2	3	12668.15
KHALKEVI (IRE)	11	47	8	10	12	76517.68
KHELEYF (USA)	18	61	3	3	18	25008.32
KINGSALSA (USA)	8	34	1	1	4	10741.20
KING'S BEST (USA)	17	91	2	3	27	34310.84
KING'S THEATRE (IRE)	274	1255	104	164	533	2697019.95
KIRKWALL (GB)	9	37	2	2	15	20995.90
KODIAC (GB)	21	76	4	5	16	33984.41
KONIGSTIGER (GER)	1	4	1	1	2	3366.72
KONIG TURF (GER)	4	7	2	2	0	6822.90
KOTKY BLEU (FR)	3	15	1	1	5	9783.00
KRIS KIN (USA)	12	49	1	1	19	18381.45
KUTUB (IRE)	34	149	8	11	46	90742.04
KYLLACHY (GB)	11	32	2	2	16	37744.05
LAHIB (USA)	17	59	4	4	11	34163.75
LAKESHORE ROAD (USA)	2	11	1	1	7	7821.34
LANDO (GER)	9	30	3	7	12	434292.73
LAURO (GER)	3	8	1	1	1	1499.40
LAVEROCK (IRE)	7	33	2	4	12	37385.00
LAVERON (GB)	16	59	5	5	24	47924.73
LAVIRCO (GER)	8	31	1	1	9	9189.30
LAYMAN (USA)	2	16	1	6	5	152430.30
LE BALAFRE (FR)	3	7	1	1	2	6724.80
LE FOU (IRE)	10	47	2	3	21	35558.67
LE TRITON (USA)	1	14	1	2	3	11115.45
LET THE LION ROAR (GB)	9	44	2	6	10	40920.13
LIBRETTIST (USA)	6	14	1	1	2	5763.78
LIMNOS (JPN)	3	16	2	5	7	42348.70
LINAMIX (FR)	1	12	1	3	8	15613.19
LINDA'S LAD (GB)	4	17	1	1	5	8450.84
LINNGARI (IRE)	4	25	4	7	11	73933.35
LOMITAS (GB)	3	19	2	4	6	31358.20
LONE BID (FR)	1	8	1	2	2	7830.60
LOPE DE VEGA (IRE)	5	12	1	1	2	6958.63
LORD AMERICO	8	24	1	1	6	7982.50
LORD DU SUD (FR)	5	10	1	1	1	5441.16
LORD OF ENGLAND (GER)	6	16	2	2	5	18460.45
LORD SHANAKILL (USA)	7	22	2	3	6	12811.67
LOST WORLD (IRE)	10	49	3	4	16	37201.41
LOUP SOLITAIRE (USA)	4	23	2	4	10	20448.24
LUCARNO (USA)	34	139	10	17	37	116227.76
LUCKY STORY (USA)	14	58	5	7	16	44962.79

STALLIONS	RNRS	STARTS	WNRS	WINS	PLACES	TOTAL (£)
LUSO (GB)	31	120	4	5	53	92691.00
MAHLER (GB)	100	405	27	43	122	383218.14
MAJESTIC MISSILE (IRE)	4	18	1	1	7	11729.10
MAKFI (GB)	14	54	4	5	17	34167.21
MALIBU MOON (USA)	1	8	1	1	5	7237.80
MALINAS (GER)	15	40	5	7	14	69277.97
MAMOOL (IRE)	6	21	2	5	12	29511.71
MANDURO (GER)	28	112	12	14	44	128373.25
MARESCA SORRENTO (FR)	7	39	3	3	13	39991.28
MARIENBARD (IRE)	33	128	6	7	43	56205.34
MARJU (GB)	9	39	3	4	12	32592.54
MARK OF ESTEEM (IRE)	2	16	1	2	6	10748.95
MARTALINE (GB)	69	268	24	36	122	570372.66
MASTER BLADE (GB)	1	4	1	1	1	4686.90
MASTERCRAFTSMAN (IRE)	47	165	16	25	59	191914.48
MAWATHEEQ (USA)	2	2	1	1	0	4548.60
MEDAALY (GB)	13	47	3	4	6	32141.54
MEDAGLIA D'ORO (USA)	1	13	1	1	7	10538.27
MEDICEAN (GB)	32	147	10	11	56	137089.13
MERLINO MAGO (GB)	1	6	1	1	3	6287.55
MICHEL GEORGES (GB)	2	16	1	1	7	13185.50
MIDNIGHT LEGEND (GB)	178	802	71	125	334	1627970.75
MILAN (GB)	336	1369	92	130	512	2085132.38
MILLENARY (GB)	40	133	9	10	46	98559.09
MILLENNIUM BIO (JPN)	1	4	1	1	0	2859.12
MILLKOM (GB)	6	32	3	3	17	25390.24
MISTERNANDO (GB)	6	14	1	1	2	3327.28
MISTER SACHA (FR)	2	11	1	2	4	27267.50
MIZZEN MAST (USA)	1	7	1	3	4	16048.80
MONSIEUR BOND (IRE)	8	35	1	2	12	28454.63
MONSUN (GER)	10	44	5	7	14	47510.09
MONTJEU (IRE)	33	156	11	19	64	243384.32
MONTMARTRE (FR)	14	50	7	11	21	191203.21
MOROZOV (USA)	36	166	13	19	55	138451.97
MOSCOW SOCIETY (USA)	21	97	6	7	34	56170.59
MOSS VALE (IRE)	6	20	2	3	4	13391.28
MOTIVATOR (GB)	17	91	6	11	31	129487.92
MOUNTAIN HIGH (IRE)	63	249	15	20	67	189242.67
MOUNT NELSON (GB)	25	87	6	14	31	198686.55
MR COMBUSTIBLE (IRE)	15	35	1	2	2	4885.23
MR DINOS (IRE)	6	27	3	5	13	40728.22
MUHAYMIN (USA)	5	18	2	3	7	10516.60
MUHTARRAM (USA)	4	17	2	4	6	44222.02
MUHTATHIR (GB)	15	51	3	6	15	74137.21
MUJADIL (USA)	2	20	2	3	7	16615.98
MULTIPLEX (GB)	47	190	7	11	72	104037.82
MUSTAMEET (USA)	13	49	1	1	21	30021.33
MYBOYCHARLIE (IRE)	5	23	1	1	8	9273.69
MY RISK (FR)	5	12	1	3	5	101004.62
NAAQOOS (GB)	4	18	1	1	5	19475.59
NAYEF (USA)	29	124	8	9	43	85917.34
NEEDLE GUN (IRE)	15	62	2	2	19	34273.43
NEEDWOOD BLADE (GB)	3	22	1	1	6	7092.96
NETWORK (GER)	52	220	17	34	93	553089.47
NEW APPROACH (IRE)	22	78	7	11	31	82780.97
NEW FRONTIER (IRE)	3	10	1	1	4	5376.46
NICARON (GER)	1	12	1	1	5	6741.90
NICKNAME (FR)	12	55	4	14	25	250298.25
NIGHT TANGO (GER)	2	14	1	3	6	77806.66
NOMADIC WAY (USA)	10	36	2	2	9	15525.15
NONONITO (FR)	1	2	1	1	0	6330.88
NOROIT (GER)	4	9	1	1	6	15036.09
NORSE DANCER (IRE)	24	103	7	13	31	307138.22

STALLIONS	RNRS	STARTS	WNRS	WINS	PLACES	TOTAL (£)
NORWICH	10	41	1	1	15	32767.05
NOTNOWCATO (GB)	18	61	4	6	20	74999.13
OASIS DREAM (GB)	15	52	6	8	18	42666.90
OBSERVATORY (USA)	7	40	2	3	19	32119.10
OLDEN TIMES (GB)	8	20	1	4	5	22997.50
OLD VIC	68	290	25	38	100	439232.65
ONE COOL CAT (USA)	4	23	1	1	9	17774.27
ORPEN (USA)	2	7	1	1	1	68344.51
OSCAR (IRE)	301	1141	98	144	468	2070979.46
OSCAR SCHINDLER (IRE)	7	30	3	5	10	37367.20
OSORIO (GER)	3	20	2	4	5	16895.82
OVERBURY (IRE)	76	316	26	41	107	499433.92
PACO BOY (IRE)	8	26	2	2	8	9860.31
PADDY O'PRADO (USA)	3	15	3	3	6	18423.84
PANIS (USA)	2	13	1	1	4	6924.34
PANORAMIC	6	27	2	3	16	83655.95
PAPAL BULL (GB)	30	118	7	9	32	73400.86
PASSING GLANCE (GB)	32	136	10	18	46	162209.27
PASSING SALE (FR)	4	20	1	2	7	9589.65
PASTERNAK (GB)	13	63	6	11	20	74826.97
PEINTRE CELEBRE (USA)	11	30	5	7	13	102170.52
PELDER (IRE)	6	24	1	1	8	11336.82
PERUGINO (USA)	6	23	1	4	9	45482.07
PHOENIX REACH (IRE)	12	52	2	2	17	15987.78
PIERRE (GB)	13	42	2	4	10	24722.88
PILSUDSKI (IRE)	8	38	2	3	12	20148.41
PIVOTAL (GB)	26	85	4	6	25	135310.49
PLEASANTLY PERFECT (USA)	1	10	1	2	4	14973.79
POET'S VOICE (GB)	8	25	3	5	14	49396.44
POLICY MAKER (IRE)	7	28	2	3	7	51961.08
POLIGLOTE (GB)	28	122	12	25	54	468810.60
PORTRAIT GALLERY (IRE)	23	112	10	19	44	177428.85
POSIDONAS (GB)	2	8	2	2	0	7082.20
POUR MOI (IRE)	7	27	2	3	14	25901.12
PRESENTING (GB)	368	1566	119	179	625	2370855.07
PRIMARY (USA)	10	34	2	3	15	53405.18
PRIMO VALENTINO (IRE)	7	26	3	5	5	20635.80
PROCLAMATION (IRE)	22	67	2	3	19	25944.41
PROTEKTOR (GER)	5	17	3	4	9	60354.04
PUBLISHER (USA)	7	17	1	1	2	3492.45
PUIT D'OR (IRE)	2	7	1	2	1	14868.00
PULPIT (USA)	1	5	1	1	2	4966.20
PURSUIT OF LOVE (GB)	2	19	2	5	7	19801.80
PUSHKIN (IRE)	8	29	2	2	8	18088.24
PUTRA PEKAN (GB)	4	25	1	1	13	13314.69
PUTRA SANDHURST (IRE)	1	9	1	1	6	10062.92
PYRUS (USA)	5	20	1	2	11	24586.73
QUWS (GB)	7	27	2	2	9	23822.25
RACINGER (FR)	2	9	1	4	1	18254.70
RAHY (USA)	1	10	1	1	1	4471.20
RAIL LINK (GB)	17	46	4	7	15	30661.23
RAINWATCH (GB)	6	27	1	1	10	9881.98
RAISE A GRAND (IRE)	3	15	1	2	3	18958.30
RAKAPOSHI KING	3	9	1	2	3	14658.60
RAKTI (GB)	12	44	4	5	12	48448.31
RASHAR (USA)	4	19	1	1	7	9093.50
RAVEN'S PASS (USA)	13	52	3	5	24	98005.23
RECHARGE (IRE)	6	22	1	1	8	8351.28
REDBACK (GB)	3	14	1	1	9	22551.63
RED CLUBS (IRE)	7	39	2	3	15	20441.07
REFUSE TO BEND (IRE)	15	69	4	5	32	51654.42
RELIEF PITCHER	2	8	1	1	1	4203.00
RELIGIOUSLY (USA)	1	6	1	1	2	15895.60

STALLIONS	RNRS	STARTS	WNRS	WINS	PLACES	TOTAL (£)
REVOQUE (IRE)	28	96	5	8	30	95427.37
RIDGEWOOD BEN (GB)	2	20	1	3	9	18154.12
RIP VAN WINKLE (IRE)	26	70	5	6	17	32750.43
ROBERT EMMET (IRE)	2	4	1	1	1	5077.00
ROBIN DES CHAMPS (FR)	114	401	41	59	155	646974.12
ROBIN DES PRES (FR)	86	402	28	44	147	323439.47
ROB ROY (USA)	3	14	1	1	6	6165.15
ROCK OF GIBRALTAR (IRE)	30	138	3	4	49	55755.39
RODERIC O'CONNOR (IRE)	5	21	2	3	10	22309.41
ROMAN SADDLE (IRE)	1	9	1	1	5	37239.60
ROYAL ANTHEM (USA)	44	184	12	22	57	149477.68
ROYAL APPLAUSE (GB)	19	77	2	2	27	19720.42
ROYAL DRAGON (USA)	2	6	1	1	5	5699.70
RUDIMENTARY (USA)	16	81	6	7	26	51295.13
RUNYON (IRE)	5	31	2	4	14	38792.72
SABIANGO (GER)	1	3	1	2	1	134494.50
SABREHILL (USA)	2	6	1	2	3	32259.30
SADDEX (GB)	3	16	2	2	6	12658.17
SADDLER MAKER (IRE)	15	57	8	16	33	486331.22
SADDLERS' HALL (IRE)	20	70	2	4	22	53461.29
SADLER'S WELLS (USA)	8	22	1	1	7	32424.46
SAFFRON WALDEN (FR)	12	58	5	6	19	61302.31
SAGACITY (FR)	1	5	1	2	1	19807.09
SAGAMIX (FR)	13	54	5	10	18	66684.39
SAGEBURG (IRE)	10	23	1	1	11	98945.10
SAINT DES SAINTS (FR)	38	127	10	13	58	305145.58
SAKHEE (USA)	19	66	5	7	31	91455.36
SALFORD EXPRESS (IRE)	2	16	1	3	10	18179.82
SAMUM (GER)	6	14	1	1	4	12496.96
SANDMASON (GB)	14	49	3	3	12	15687.88
SANTIAGO (GER)	1	6	1	1	4	9847.60
SAYARSHAN (FR)	4	24	1	2	17	22422.42
SCHIAPARELLI (GER)	17	42	3	3	15	22203.52
SCORPION (IRE)	165	596	44	66	188	674022.06
SEA THE STARS (IRE)	16	66	5	6	30	65513.28
SECRET SINGER (FR)	6	19	1	1	7	14633.99
SELKIRK (USA)	11	55	2	6	12	31909.79
SEPTEMBER STORM (GER)	24	81	4	6	25	40171.86
SHAANMER (IRE)	10	49	4	4	20	158596.64
SHAMARDAL (USA)	13	37	1	2	15	16254.00
SHANTOU (USA)	115	535	50	88	197	999319.01
SHERNAZAR	4	13	2	3	5	18242.80
SHIROCCO (GER)	58	176	7	12	69	270571.48
SHOLOKHOV (IRE)	19	71	9	9	29	118061.89
SILVER CROSS (FR)	2	9	1	2	3	36223.20
SILVER FROST (FR)	4	19	2	4	7	23505.76
SILVER PATRIARCH (IRE)	17	59	3	3	28	35308.89
SINGSPIEL (IRE)	8	26	3	3	9	83516.93
SIN KIANG (FR)	1	4	1	1	1	4113.45
SINNDAR (IRE)	16	53	5	8	19	109623.81
SIR HARRY LEWIS (USA)	29	121	11	16	45	454438.16
SIR PERCY (GB)	36	127	12	21	51	206297.07
SIXTIES ICON (GB)	13	66	4	5	25	40938.96
SKINS GAME (GB)	1	4	1	2	2	8343.40
SLEEPING CAR (FR)	6	23	3	3	6	40879.55
SLICKLY (FR)	8	28	2	2	6	42601.20
SMADOUN (FR)	16	76	7	14	32	215290.32
SMART STRIKE (CAN)	2	14	1	1	6	7524.00
SNURGE	12	41	1	1	15	19234.90
SOAPY DANGER (GB)	3	14	1	3	4	18054.90
SOLDIER HOLLOW (GB)	8	22	4	5	9	122259.88
SOLDIER OF FORTUNE (IRE)	20	97	12	22	47	387336.21
SOVIET STAR (USA)	6	31	1	2	11	15772.51

STALLIONS	RNRS	STARTS	WNRS	WINS	PLACES	TOTAL (£)
SPADOUN (FR)	24	123	15	24	52	178752.75
SPANISH MOON (USA)	4	7	3	3	3	32649.72
SPARTACUS (IRE)	4	29	1	2	11	16102.67
SPECIAL KALDOUN (IRE)	3	12	2	4	4	62021.83
SPIRIT ONE (FR)	4	20	3	5	10	56144.48
STATE CITY (USA)	1	6	1	1	2	6137.87
STATUE OF LIBERTY (USA)	2	9	1	1	3	10450.37
STERNKOENIG (IRE)	2	5	1	1	0	1247.80
STIMULATION (IRE)	3	17	1	1	8	11800.08
ST JOVITE (USA)	13	59	4	5	24	44592.43
STORMING HOME (GB)	4	33	2	5	13	36171.76
STOWAWAY (GB)	160	646	53	90	246	1014861.12
STRATEGIC CHOICE (USA)	2	9	1	1	3	20620.50
STRATEGIC PRINCE (GB)	11	40	2	2	20	33143.37
STREET CRY (IRE)	16	70	7	10	26	121585.36
SUBTLE POWER (IRE)	16	53	1	2	10	15208.95
SULAMANI (IRE)	36	149	8	9	66	68236.89
SULEIMAN (IRE)	1	3	1	1	2	5618.00
SUPERIOR PREMIUM (GB)	1	7	1	2	4	11278.60
SUPREME SOUND (GB)	7	31	2	4	12	27074.57
SWIFT GULLIVER (IRE)	1	10	1	1	4	7266.42
TAGULA (IRE)	10	53	4	7	18	44182.09
TAJRAASI (USA)	6	34	2	4	10	23145.85
TAMAYAZ (CAN)	7	25	1	2	4	6956.19
TAMAYUZ (GB)	14	59	6	8	24	80574.53
TAMURE (IRE)	12	53	5	7	21	83077.29
TEOFILO (IRE)	34	121	7	12	51	164185.01
THEATRICAL	1	6	1	1	4	11645.70
THEWAYYOUARE (USA)	14	48	2	3	22	24327.94
THOUSAND WORDS (GB)	4	11	1	2	3	9487.80
THREE VALLEYS (USA)	4	15	2	2	7	12483.73
TIGER GROOM (GB)	3	7	1	1	4	17759.13
TIGER HILL (IRE)	21	61	3	4	28	38165.68
TIKKANEN (USA)	57	272	13	16	90	159552.40
TILLERMAN (GB)	4	11	1	1	4	4579.50
TOBOUGG (IRE)	58	246	11	15	88	125514.57
TOUCH OF LAND (FR)	18	90	4	8	39	68288.56
TRADE FAIR (GB)	11	56	3	4	22	45369.01
TRANS ISLAND (GB)	58	264	14	20	72	167432.66
TREMPOLINO (USA)	8	38	4	6	11	40663.73
TRUTH OR DARE (GB)	1	1	1	1	0	15640.00
TURGEON (USA)	26	92	9	12	42	154250.60
TURTLE BOWL (IRE)	7	19	2	4	9	160433.56
TURTLE ISLAND (IRE)	48	211	10	17	81	251580.57
ULTIMATELY LUCKY (IRE)	2	7	1	2	1	7642.80
UNBRIDLED'S SONG (USA)	1	4	1	1	1	4557.60
UNGARO (GER)	1	5	1	1	2	6115.20
URBAN OCEAN (FR)	11	59	5	7	26	97040.35
URBAN POET (USA)	3	9	1	1	3	5724.25
VALANOUR (IRE)	3	9	1	1	3	5989.32
VENDANGEUR (IRE)	8	35	3	3	18	56235.41
VERGLAS (IRE)	19	62	4	6	22	60566.29
VERTICAL SPEED (FR)	23	74	6	9	26	70962.80
VICTORY NOTE (USA)	3	10	1	4	2	37088.54
VIKING RULER (AUS)	2	11	1	1	3	7020.00
VINNIE ROE (IRE)	78	347	28	45	125	570621.96
VIRTUAL (GB)	7	21	1	1	3	8748.63
VISION D'ETAT (FR)	5	11	1	1	6	6284.90
VOIX DU NORD (FR)	27	127	13	24	50	658057.11
VOL DE NUIT (GB)	1	6	1	1	5	10578.20
VOLOCHINE (IRE)	3	25	3	6	10	53053.41
WALK IN THE PARK (IRE)	18	45	6	11	6	229668.67
WAR CHANT (USA)	3	19	1	2	3	15754.32

STALLIONS	RNRS	STARTS	WNRS	WINS	PLACES	TOTAL (£)
WAREED (IRE)	10	46	5	7	14	42730.79
WELD	2	14	1	1	2	4313.97
WELL CHOSEN (GB)	19	83	8	9	38	128974.56
WELSH LION (IRE)	3	9	1	2	2	23198.39
WESTERNER (GB)	239	934	80	117	366	1319148.05
WHERE OR WHEN (IRE)	6	25	1	1	6	36279.83
WHIPPER (USA)	9	38	2	2	17	34713.03
WHITMORE'S CONN (USA)	32	143	7	10	58	148674.72
WINDSOR CASTLE (GB)	4	19	1	2	11	17656.03
WINDSOR KNOT (IRE)	13	55	2	2	20	42104.26
WINGED LOVE (IRE)	66	282	21	31	118	527988.77
WINKER WATSON (GB)	3	16	1	3	6	17224.50
WITHOUT CONNEXION (IRE)	1	12	1	1	2	4537.98
WITH THE FLOW (USA)	11	42	1	1	7	9982.12
WITNESS BOX (USA)	29	131	4	6	46	79058.49
WIZARD KING (GB)	3	12	1	2	2	10183.82
WOLFE TONE (IRE)	1	8	1	2	4	17520.21
WOODS OF WINDSOR (USA)	2	15	1	2	7	21912.99
YEATS (IRE)	109	430	45	65	169	520769.41
YOUMZAIN (IRE)	6	11	2	3	4	8415.02
ZAFEEN (FR)	4	17	2	2	3	10784.80
ZAGREB (USA)	31	134	11	16	42	117875.59
ZAHA (CAN)	2	6	1	1	1	5260.46
ZAMBEZI SUN (GB)	6	26	2	2	15	20582.30
ZAMINDAR (USA)	10	36	3	3	12	24642.92
ZEBEDEE (GB)	7	19	1	1	4	23157.46
ZERPOUR (IRE)	7	35	2	3	12	22742.64
ZOFFANY (IRE)	6	28	2	3	12	39745.24

BY KIND PERMISSION OF WEATHERBYS

HIGH-PRICED YEARLINGS OF 2017 AT TATTERSALLS SALES
The following yearling realised 105,000 Guineas and over at Tattersalls Sales in 2017.

Name and Breeding	Purchaser	Guineas
GLOAM (IRE) B F GALILEO (IRE) - DANK (GB)	GODOLPHIN	4000000
CH C DUBAWI (IRE) - IZZI TOP (GB)	ROGER VARIAN	2600000
KING POWER (GB) CH F FRANKEL (GB) - PROWESS (IRE)	SACKVILLEDONALD	2500000
B C DUBAWI (IRE) - SKY LANTERN (IRE)	MV MAGNIER	2000000
ALL OUR TOMORROWS (IRE) B F KINGMAN (GB) - JUSTLOOKDONTOUCH (IRE)	MOYGLARE STUD	1700000
CH F GALILEO (IRE) - PENCHANT (GB)	MV MAGNIER	1600000
B F INVINCIBLE SPIRIT (IRE) - CASSANDRA GO (IRE)	MV MAGNIER	1600000
B F GALILEO (IRE) - VADAWINA (IRE)	JUSTIN CASSE	1550000
FAYLAQ (GB) B C DUBAWI (IRE) - DANEDREAM (GER)	SHADWELL ESTATE COMPANY	1500000
B F FRANKEL (GB) - STEEL PRINCESS (IRE)	DMM.COM	1400000
MAYDANNY (IRE) B C DUBAWI (IRE) - ATTRACTION (GB)	SHADWELL ESTATE COMPANY	1350000
B C DUBAWI (IRE) - VANITY RULES (GB)	GODOLPHIN	1300000
B C GALILEO (IRE) - SHASTYE (IRE)	MV MAGNIER	1300000
CH F DUBAWI (IRE) - SILK SARI (GB)	GODOLPHIN	1300000
TUK POWER (GB) B F DUBAWI (IRE) - SOON (IRE)	SACKVILLEDONALD	1300000
B F DUBAWI (IRE) - SEAL OF APPROVAL (GB)	GODOLPHIN	1100000
B C SEA THE STARS (IRE) - ELEGANT SHADOW (GER)	KERRI RADCLIFFE BS	1000000
B F KODIAC (GB) - QUEENOFTHEFAIRIES (GB)	MV MAGNIER	925000
ALFAATIK (GB) B C SEA THE STARS (IRE) - BIZ BAR (GB)	SHADWELL ESTATE COMPANY	850000
B C NO NAY NEVER (USA) - MURAVKA (IRE)	JS COMPANY	850000
ROONG ROONG (IRE) GR F DARK ANGEL (IRE) - CUT NO ICE (IRE)	SACKVILLEDONALD	825000
B F GALILEO (IRE) - CASSYDORA (GB)	NARVICK INTERNATIONAL	800000
CH F GALILEO (IRE) - MAUREEN (IRE)	GODOLPHIN	800000
B F GALILEO (IRE) - DIALAFARA (FR)	AMANDA SKIFFINGTON	800000
KHAADEM (IRE) BR C DARK ANGEL (IRE) - WHITE DAFFODIL (IRE)	SHADWELL ESTATE COMPANY	750000
TIPPY TIPPY (FR) B F SEA THE STARS (IRE) - PEINTURE ROSE (USA)	SACKVILLEDONALD	725000
FOX PREMIER (IRE) B C FRANKEL (GB) - FANN (USA)	SACKVILLEDONALD	700000
B F SHAMARDAL (USA) - CLOUD CASTLE (GB)	DAVID REDVERS	680000
CH C DUBAWI (IRE) - FINSCEAL BEO (IRE)	ROGER VARIAN	650000
NOOR DUBAI (GB) B F INVINCIBLE SPIRIT (IRE) - BEACH FROLIC (GB)	SHADWELL ESTATE COMPANY	650000
B C DARK ANGEL (IRE) - FUAIGH MOR (IRE)	GODOLPHIN	625000
HAPPY POWER (IRE) GR C DARK ANGEL (IRE) - TAMARISK (GER)	SACKVILLEDONALD	625000
B C LOPE DE VEGA (IRE) - DOLLED UP (IRE)	KERRI RADCLIFFE BS	600000
B F GALILEO (IRE) - LADY SPRINGBANK (IRE)	GODOLPHIN	575000
TOP FOX (GB) B C FRANKEL (GB) - LADY LINDA (USA)	SACKVILLEDONALD	550000
TAHMEED (IRE) B F WAR FRONT (USA) - AULD ALLIANCE (IRE)	SHADWELL ESTATE COMPANY	550000
B F SEA THE STARS (IRE) - ISLINGTON (IRE)	RABBAH BS	550000
RUX POWER (GB) B F KINGMAN (GB) - CUT SHORT (USA)	SACKVILLEDONALD	550000
CH C AUSTRALIA (GB) - SITARA (GB)	MV MAGNIER	525000
TICKLE THE MOON (GER) B C SEA THE MOON (GER) - TICKLE ME PINK (GB)	ROGER VARIAN	525000
PREJUDICE (GB) CH C DUBAWI (IRE) - EVER RIGG (GB)	VENDOR	525000
BR F IFFRAAJ (GB) - CONSTANT DREAM (GB)	GODOLPHIN	525000
B F SHAMARDAL (USA) - WHAZZIS (GB)	ROGER VARIAN	525000
B C LOPE DE VEGA (IRE) - BOSTON ROCKER (IRE)	ROGER VARIAN	500000
CHIL CHIL (GB) B F EXCEED AND EXCEL (AUS) - TIANA (GB)	SACKVILLEDONALD	500000
B C ACCLAMATION (GB) - MISSISIPI STAR (IRE)	C GORDON-WATSON BS	500000
B F FRANKEL (GB) - DEBONNAIRE (GB)	NARVICK INTERNATIONAL	500000
QUEEN POWER (IRE) CH F SHAMARDAL (USA) - PRINCESS SERENA (USA)	SACKVILLEDONALD	500000
B C SHAMARDAL (USA) - NIGHT FROLIC (GB)	ROGER VARIAN	500000
B C AUSTRALIA (GB) - SENT FROM HEAVEN (IRE)	C GORDON-WATSON BS	500000
BANGKOK (IRE) B C AUSTRALIA (GB) - TANAGHUM (GB)	SACKVILLEDONALD	500000
VIVIONN (GB) CH F DUBAWI (IRE) - GIANTS PLAY (USA)	VENDOR	500000
BR/GR C DARK ANGEL (IRE) - SILVER SHOON (GB)	SACKVILLEDONALD	480000
FOX TAL (GB) B C SEA THE STARS (IRE) - MASKUNAH (IRE)	SACKVILLEDONALD	475000
AMAHITEE (FR) B F GALILEO (IRE) - ALTANA (GB)	VENDOR	475000
B C WAR FRONT (USA) - A STAR IS BORN (IRE)	JS COMPANY	475000
B C CAPE CROSS (IRE) - MATAURI PEARL (IRE)	GODOLPHIN	475000
B C FRANKEL (GB) - GUARANDA (GB)	JEREMY BRUMMITT	475000
B C KODIAC (GB) - INYORDREAMS (GB)	HONG KONG JOCKEY CLUB	450000
B C IFFRAAJ (GB) - FOREST CROWN (GB)	GODOLPHIN	450000
FOX POWER (IRE) GR C DARK ANGEL (IRE) - ZENELLA (GB)	SACKVILLEDONALD	450000
FOX CHAIRMAN (IRE) B C KINGMAN (GB) - STARFISH (IRE)	SACKVILLEDONALD	450000
B C SEA THE STARS (IRE) - COOLREE MARJ (IRE)	MV MAGNIER	425000
DEMARCHELIER (GB) B C DUBAWI (IRE) - LOVEISALLYOUNEED (IRE)	WHITE BIRCH FARM	425000
GHADBBAAN (GB) CH C INTELLO (GER) - ROCK CHOIR (GB)	SHADWELL ESTATE COMPANY	425000
MONYA (IRE) GR F DARK ANGEL (IRE) - BRIDAL DANCE (IRE)	SHADWELL ESTATE COMPANY	425000
DEVIZES (IRE) B C DUBAWI (IRE) - DALASYLA (IRE)	GODOLPHIN	425000
ACAPELLA BLU (IRE) B F DUBAWI (IRE) - GALVAUN (IRE)	MOYGLARE STUD	420000

Name and Breeding	Purchaser	Guineas
CH F DUBAWI (IRE) - KELLY NICOLE (IRE)	GODOLPHIN	420000
B F NO NAY NEVER (USA) - HUREYA (USA)	AL SHAQAB RACING	420000
ANGEL STAR (GB) GR F DARK ANGEL (IRE) - DARK PROMISE (GB)	WHITE BIRCH FARM	400000
B F INVINCIBLE SPIRIT (IRE) - DRESS REHEARSAL (IRE)	C GORDON-WATSON BS	400000
B C DUBAWI (IRE) - GEMSTONE (IRE)	ROGER VARIAN	400000
CH C GALILEO (IRE) - JACQUELINE QUEST (IRE)	GODOLPHIN	400000
B F KINGMAN (GB) - MAKING EYES (IRE)	SHAWN DUGAN	400000
TAMOCK (IRE) B F AUSTRALIA (GB) - ANKLET (IRE)	A C ELLIOTT, AGENT	400000
B F INVINCIBLE SPIRIT (IRE) - EVITA (GB)	BBA IRELAND	400000
B F KINGMAN (GB) - OUR LITTLE SECRET (GB)	JJ GORDON BS	400000
B F DARK ANGEL (IRE) - WARSHAH (IRE)	BLANDFORD BS	400000
U S S SARATOGA (USA) B C WAR FRONT (USA) - STORYBOOK (UAE)	SHADWELL ESTATE COMPANY	400000
CH F LOPE DE VEGA (IRE) - TEBEE (GB)	SHAWN DUGAN, AGENT	400000
B F DARK ANGEL (IRE) - SOXY DOXY (IRE)	JJ GORDON BS	400000
CH C SEA THE STARS (IRE) - WALDLERCHE (GB)	CRISPIN DE MOUBRAY SARL	400000
B C DANSILI (GB) - DASH TO THE FRONT (GB)	KLARAVICH STABLES	400000
B F KODIAC (GB) - ALINA (IRE)	DAVID REDVERS BS	400000
B F GALILEO (IRE) - TEMIDA (IRE)	RABBAH BS	390000
B C AUSTRALIA (GB) - THAI HAKU (IRE)	JOHN & JAKE WARREN	380000
CH F SHOWCASING (GB) - COPLOW (GB)	JOHN GOSDEN	380000
CH C MASTERCRAFTSMAN (IRE) - ANNABELLE JA (FR)	GODOLPHIN	380000
PATTAYA (GB) B F POET'S VOICE (GB) - TALAMPAYA (USA)	SACKVILLEDONALD	375000
TWO BIDS (GB) B C DALAKHANI (IRE) - ECHELON (GB)	SHADWELL ESTATE COMPANY	375000
CH F FARRH (GB) - ZEE ZEE GEE (GB)	GODOLPHIN	375000
B F LOPE DE VEGA (IRE) - KALANDARA (IRE)	GODOLPHIN	370000
B F AUSTRALIA (GB) - NO EXPLAINING (IRE)	RABBAH BS	370000
LYRA'S LIGHT (IRE) B F LOPE DE VEGA (IRE) - DIAMOND SKY (IRE)	CHEVELEY PARK STUD	360000
BR C SHAMARDAL (USA) - LANDMARK (USA)	C GORDON-WATSON BS	360000
CH F LOPE DE VEGA (IRE) - SOLAR EVENT (GB)	ROGER VARIAN	350000
B C SCAT DADDY (USA) - SIMILU (GB)	STEPHEN HILLEN BS	350000
B F GALILEO (IRE) - CATCH THE MOON (IRE)	BBA IRELAND	350000
B F ACCLAMATION (GB) - MALASPINA (IRE)	C GORDON-WATSON BS	350000
CH C DUBAWI (IRE) - SHUMOOS (USA)	RABBAH BS	350000
B C NATHANIEL (IRE) - LANGS LASH (IRE)	CHINA HORSE CLUB	350000
B F IFFRAAJ (GB) - KIYRA WELLS (IRE)	GODOLPHIN	350000
B C AUSTRALIA (GB) - DOROTHY B (IRE)	BLANDFORD BS	350000
MAKE MY DAY (IRE) B C GALILEO (IRE) - POSSET (GB)	VENDOR	350000
B F OASIS DREAM (GB) - NOYELLES (IRE)	MERIDIAN INTERNATIONAL	340000
B F GALILEO (IRE) - LIKE A DAME (GB)	E5 RACING	340000
B C DANSILI (GB) - I AM BEAUTIFUL (IRE)	GODOLPHIN	340000
CH C SEA THE STARS (IRE) - MAMBO LIGHT (USA)	MERIDIAN INTERNATIONAL	340000
B F SEA THE STARS (IRE) - CRYSTAL MAZE (GB)	MERIDIAN INTERNATIONAL	340000
B C ZEBEDEE (GB) - VARENKA (GB)	GODOLPHIN	330000
SPOTTON (IRE) B C TAMAYUZ (IRE) - FARBENSPIEL (IRE)	SHADWELL ESTATE COMPANY	330000
BR F SHOWCASING (GB) - DANCE PEARL (GB)	JOHN & JAKE WARREN	330000
DAARIK (IRE) B C TAMAYUZ (GB) - WHIP AND WIN (FR)	SHADWELL ESTATE COMPANY	325000
ADONIJAH (GB) B C SEA THE STARS (IRE) - MEEZNAH (USA)	H CANDY	325000
B C TORONADO (IRE) - RASKUTANI (GB)	GODOLPHIN	325000
TOP POWER (FR) CH C LE HAVRE (IRE) - ALTAMIRA (GB)	SACKVILLEDONALD	325000
B C INVINCIBLE SPIRIT (IRE) - WILLOW VIEW (USA)	KLARAVICH STABLES	325000
CLUBORA (USA) B F MEDAGLIA D'ORO (USA) - MIDDLE CLUB (GB)	VENDOR	320000
B F KODIAC (GB) - CARVED EMERALD (GB)	C GORDON-WATSON BS	320000
FOX WIN WIN (IRE) CH C LOPE DE VEGA (IRE) - WHAT A PICTURE (FR)	SACKVILLEDONALD	320000
CH C DUBAWI (IRE) - REHN'S NEST (IRE)	GODOLPHIN	320000
B F NEW APPROACH (IRE) - EXCEL'S BEAUTY (GB)	RABBAH BS	320000
B C SEA THE STARS (IRE) - CHIOSINA (IRE)	A SKIFFINGTON, AGENT	310000
RED ROBE (GB) CH F NATHANIEL (IRE) - VICTOIRE CELEBRE (USA)	WHITE BIRCH FARM	310000
FABRIANO (GER) B/BR C SINNDAR (IRE) - FOUR ROSES (IRE)	ROGER VARIAN	300000
B C DUBAWI (IRE) - AMBIVALENT (IRE)	GODOLPHIN	300000
ASAATIER (USA) B F WAR FRONT (USA) - SPRING IN THE AIR (CAN)	NARVICK INTERNATIONAL	300000
B C SEA THE STARS (IRE) - PENNY POST (IRE)	HONG KONG JOCKEY CLUB	300000
B F KODIAC (GB) - DANCE BID (GB)	JJ GORDON BS	300000
B C KODIAC (GB) - ROMIE'S KASTETT (GER)	GODOLPHIN	300000
B C CAMELOT (GB) - SEATONE (USA)	MV MAGNIER	300000
B F INVINCIBLE SPIRIT (IRE) - PLEASANTRY (GB)	WHITE BIRCH FARM	300000
CH C SEA THE MOON (GER) - SOVIET TERMS (GB)	GODOLPHIN	300000
AZETS (GB) B C DUBAWI (IRE) - NASHMIAH (IRE)	PETER & ROSS DOYLE BS	300000
B F SEA THE STARS (IRE) - RAINBOW SPRINGS (GB)	RABBAH BS	290000
B C TEOFILO (IRE) - AMBER SILK (IRE)	SHADWELL ESTATE COMPANY	280000
LOPE ATHENA (GB) B F LOPE DE VEGA (IRE) - ELAS DIAMOND (GB)	GREEN STAR BS	280000
B C KODIAC (GB) - LOCH MA NAIRE (IRE)	ROGER VARIAN	280000

Name and Breeding	Purchaser	Guineas
GR F GALILEO (IRE) - FORK LIGHTNING (USA)	RABBAH BS	280000
BR F NEW APPROACH (IRE) - HOITY TOITY (GB)	VENDOR	280000
CH F LOPE DE VEGA (IRE) - LAUREN LOUISE (GB)	SHAWN DUGAN	280000
GR F DARK ANGEL (IRE) - ELLASHA (GB)	JJ GORDON BS	280000
VANDELLA (IRE) B F INVINCIBLE SPIRIT (IRE) - LADY LIVIUS (IRE)	BLANDFORD BS	280000
MANNGUY (GB) B C OASIS DREAM (GB) - GALAXY HIGHFLYER (GB)	SHADWELL ESTATE COMPANY	280000
MRS WORTHINGTON (IRE) B F DARK ANGEL (IRE) - MIRROR EFFECT (IRE)	HOWSON & HOULDSWORTH BS	270000
BOERHAN (GB) B C SEA THE STARS (IRE) - GREENISLAND (IRE)	SHADWELL ESTATE COMPANY	270000
B G DARK ANGEL (IRE) - HANDANA (IRE)	HONG KONG JOCKEY CLUB	270000
M ANTOINETTE (GB) B F SEA THE STARS (IRE) - WHAZZAT (GB)	VENDOR	260000
GLOBAL DESTINATION (IRE) B C SLADE POWER (IRE) - SILK TRAIL (GB)	C GORDON-WATSON BS	260000
B F INVINCIBLE SPIRIT (IRE) - NIGHT FEVER (IRE)	E5 RACING	260000
CH C AUSTRALIA (GB) - WHAT A TREASURE (IRE)	MV MAGNIER	260000
SERVE THE KING (GB) B C KINGMAN (GB) - FALLEN IN LOVE (GB)	WHITE BIRCH STABLE	260000
USTATH (GB) CH C EXCEED AND EXCEL (AUS) - ADORN (GB)	SHADWELL ESTATE COMPANY	260000
TOP TOP (IRE) B C FRANKEL (GB) - JIRA (GB)	SACKVILLEDONALD	260000
GR C DARK ANGEL (IRE) - SUR CHOIX (GB)	GODOLPHIN	260000
B C ACCLAMATION (GB) - INSAAF (IRE)	HONG KONG JOCKEY CLUB	260000
B F SLADE POWER (IRE) - SLEEPING BEAUTY (IRE)	GODOLPHIN	260000
SABAI SABAI (IRE) B F SHAMARDAL (USA) - SEMAYYEL (IRE)	SACKVILLEDONALD	260000
B C SEA THE STARS (IRE) - LAMAZONIA (IRE)	GODOLPHIN	260000
WELL DONE FOX (GB) B C ACCLAMATION (GB) - EXCELETTE (IRE)	SACKVILLEDONALD	255000
TEODORA DE VEGA (IRE) B F LOPE DE VEGA (IRE) - APPLAUDED (IRE)	GREEN STAR BS	250000
B F EXCHANGE RATE (USA) - NEW GIRLFRIEND (IRE)	GODOLPHIN	250000
B F IFFRAAJ (GB) - HONKY TONK SALLY (GB)	RABBAH BS	250000
CH F NEW APPROACH (IRE) - BOARD MEETING (IRE)	GODOLPHIN	250000
ALKAAMEL (GB) B C HAVANA GOLD (IRE) - GRACE AND GLORY (IRE)	SHADWELL ESTATE COMPANY	250000
BR F KINGMAN (GB) - PALITANA (USA)	SHAWN DUGAN	250000
B C DUBAWI (IRE) - VOW (GB)	RABBAH BS	240000
MOTFAEL (IRE) B C INVINCIBLE SPIRIT (IRE) - FIDELITE (IRE)	SHADWELL ESTATE COMPANY	240000
B/BR F SPEIGHTSTOWN (USA) - DANSETTE (IRE)	JJ GORDON BS	240000
B F KODIAC (GB) - LADY GLINKA (IRE)	SHAWN DUGAN, AGENT	240000
B C NEW APPROACH (IRE) - ARSAADI (IRE)	GODOLPHIN	240000
B C FRANKEL (GB) - LONELY AHEAD (USA)	NARVICK INTERNATIONAL	240000
INTRICATE (GB) B F SHOWCASING (GB) - LAST SLIPPER (GB)	JOHN & JAKE WARREN	240000
B C GALILEO (IRE) - HVEGER (AUS)	MV MAGNIER	240000
SAILING (GER) B F LOPE DE VEGA (IRE) - SAIL (IRE)	JUDDMONTE FARMS	230000
B F IFFRAAJ (GB) - ARAQELLA (IRE)	GODOLPHIN	230000
CH C EXCEED AND EXCEL (AUS) - GREAT HOPE (IRE)	AMANDA SKIFFINGTON	230000
FOX KASPER (IRE) CH C SOCIETY ROCK (IRE) - EASY TIMES (GB)	SACKVILLEDONALD	220000
CH C EXCEED AND EXCEL (AUS) - REGAL REALM (GB)	HONG KONG JOCKEY CLUB	220000
BR C DARK ANGEL (IRE) - COQUETTE ROUGE (IRE)	VENDOR	220000
B C KITTEN'S JOY (USA) - CAT ON A TIN ROOF (USA)	ROGER VARIAN	220000
PHOENIX OF SPAIN (IRE) GR C LOPE DE VEGA (IRE) - LUCKY CLIO (IRE)	HOWSON & HOULDSWORTH BS	220000
B C KODIAC (GB) - OASIS SUNSET (IRE)	A SKIFFINGTON BS	220000
VEGATINA (GB) B F LOPE DE VEGA (IRE) - VALTINA (IRE)	BLANDFORD BS	220000
B C UNION RAGS (USA) - MISS EMILIA (USA)	KENJI RYOTOKUJI	210000
B C MAGICIAN (IRE) - PERFECT STEP (IRE)	M V MAGNIER	210000
BIBLIC (IRE) B F NEW APPROACH (IRE) - SAVANNAH BELLE (GB)	JILL LAMB BS	210000
B C CHARM SPIRIT (IRE) - THANKFUL (GB)	MV MAGNIER	210000
B F SHOWCASING (GB) - SACRE COEUR (GB)	JOE FOLEY	210000
B C HOLY ROMAN EMPEROR (IRE) - MIDNIGHT PARTNER (IRE)	CHINA HORSE CLUB	210000
FOX VARDY (USA) B C FRANKEL (GB) - DANCE WITH ANOTHER (IRE)	SACKVILLEDONALD	210000
B C DARK ANGEL (IRE) - NORWAY CROSS (IRE)	SHAWN DUGAN	210000
B F KITTEN'S JOY (USA) - DYNING OUT (USA)	VENDOR	210000
FOX SHINJI (GB) B C IFFRAAJ (GB) - KEENE DANCER (GB)	SACKVILLEDONALD	210000
SWANSDOWN (GB) CH F DUBAWI (IRE) - PONGEE (GB)	VENDOR	210000
B C NO NAY NEVER (USA) - GILDED VANITY (GB)	BLANDFORD BS	210000
B C OASIS DREAM (GB) - I'M A DREAMER (IRE)	CHINA HORSE CLUB	210000
ZUBA (GB) B C DUBAWI (IRE) - PURR ALONG (GB)	PETER & ROSS DOYLE (P.S.)	210000
B C OASIS DREAM (GB) - INCHINA (GB)	KENJI RYOTOKUJI	200000
B/BR F GALILEO (IRE) - INCA PRINCESS (IRE)	FORM BS	200000
B F OASIS DREAM (GB) - HASTEN (IRE)	VENDOR	200000
B F LOPE DE VEGA (IRE) - SUNDAY TIMES (GB)	KLARAVICH STABLES	200000
INCHARGE (GB) B F KINGMAN (GB) - WHIRLY BIRD (GB)	STROUD COLEMAN BS	200000
B C TEOFILO (IRE) - LORETO (IRE)	GODOLPHIN	200000
SEEING RED (IRE) B F SEA THE STARS (IRE) - RED FANTASY (IRE)	PETER & ROSS DOYLE BS	200000
B C DUBAWI (IRE) - LONGING TO DANCE (GB)	HONG KONG JOCKEY CLUB	200000
GR C DARK ANGEL (IRE) - SAFIYNA (FR)	VENDOR	200000
B C SLADE POWER (IRE) - SUMMER IN FEBRUARY (GB)	MV MAGNIER/P&R DOYLE	200000
B C CAMELOT (GB) - MARE NOSTRUM (GB)	BBA IRELAND	200000

Name and Breeding	Purchaser	Guineas
B C DARK ANGEL (IRE) - NATTY BUMPPO (IRE)	RICHARD KNIGHT BS AGENT	200000
B C ACCLAMATION (GB) - ELLEN (IRE)	C GORDON-WATSON BS	200000
CH F EXCEED AND EXCEL (AUS) - MAGIC NYMPH (IRE)	RABBAH BS	200000
B C NO NAY NEVER (USA) - SEEKING SOLACE (GB)	C GORDON-WATSON BS	200000
ELISHEBA (IRE) B F AUSTRALIA (GB) - LAUGH OUT LOUD (GB)	BLANDFORD BS	200000
MUWARRAD (IRE) B C KODIAC (GB) - MYSTERY BET (IRE)	SHADWELL ESTATE COMPANY	200000
B F EXCEED AND EXCEL (AUS) - CATCH THE SEA (IRE)	BRIAN GRASSICK BS	200000
B F ACCLAMATION (GB) - LOVELY THOUGHT (IRE)	JAMES TOLLER	200000
GLOBAL LIGHT (IRE) B F EXCELEBRATION (IRE) - LUCINA (GB)	C GORDON-WATSON BS	200000
B F FRANKEL (GB) - DUPE (IRE)	NARVICK INTERNATIONAL	200000
B F INVINCIBLE SPIRIT (IRE) - KISSABLE (IRE)	DERMOT FARRINGTON (P.S.)	200000
MAWAKIB (GB) B C HAVANA GOLD (IRE) - KELADORA (USA)	SHADWELL ESTATE COMPANY	190000
B C AUSTRALIA (GB) - HAPPY HOLLY (IRE)	JEREMY BRUMMITT	190000
JASH (IRE) B C KODIAC (GB) - MS AZEZA (GB)	SHADWELL ESTATE COMPANY	185000
B C CAMELOT (GB) - LA VINCHINA (GER)	BBA IRELAND	185000
CH F OLYMPIC GLORY (IRE) - ALPEN GLEN (GB)	AL SHAQAB RACING	180000
GOOD LUCK FOX (IRE) B C SOCIETY ROCK (IRE) - VIOLET BALLERINA (IRE)	SACKVILLEDONALD	180000
AMAZING FOX (IRE) B C ALHEBAYEB (IRE) - GOLD AGAIN (USA)	SACKVILLEDONALD	180000
CH C DAWN APPROACH (IRE) - AL BAIDAA (GB)	RABBAH BS	180000
BR C SLADE POWER (IRE) - KEEPERS HILL (IRE)	HONG KONG JOCKEY CLUB	180000
GR C DARK ANGEL (IRE) - LIGHTWOOD LADY (IRE)	GAELIC BS	180000
GR F MASTERCRAFTSMAN (IRE) - FRONT HOUSE (IRE)	BLANDFORD BS	180000
B C FOOTSTEPSINTHESAND (GB) - MASSEERA (IRE)	C GORDON-WATSON BS	180000
B F KINGMAN (GB) - HIPPY HIPPY SHAKE (GB)	VENDOR	180000
VASILIEV (GB) CH C DUTCH ART (GB) - BARYNYA (GB)	VENDOR	180000
MISS CELESTIAL (IRE) B F EXCEED AND EXCEL (AUS) - LIBER NAUTICUS (IRE)	NORRIS/HUNTINGDON	180000
B C NEW APPROACH (IRE) - SHIROCCO STAR (GB)	VENDOR	180000
B C DARK ANGEL (IRE) - INTERIM PAYMENT (USA)	VENDOR	175000
MORDRED (IRE) B C CAMELOT (GB) - ENDURE (IRE)	PETER & ROSS DOYLE BS	175000
ROXY ART (IRE) CH F DUTCH ART (GB) - CHICAGO GIRL (IRE)	MICHAEL ROY	175000
GLOBAL EXPRESS (GB) CH C NEW APPROACH (IRE) - ALL FOR LAURA (GB)	C GORDON-WATSON BS	175000
B C TORONADO (IRE) - ALAMANNI (USA)	SHADWELL ESTATE COMPANY	170000
B C CAMELOT (GB) - SHAKEYOURBODY (USA)	VENDOR	170000
RHYDWYN (IRE) B C KODIAC (GB) - PILATES (IRE)	JILL LAMB BS	170000
B C DECLARATION OF WAR (USA) - JEMIMA'S PEARL (USA)	WHITE BIRCH FARM	170000
B C WOOTTON BASSETT (GB) - CROSSED FINGERS (IRE)	SHADWELL ESTATE COMPANY	170000
B C OASIS DREAM (GB) - ALSACE LORRAINE (IRE)	KENJI RYOTOKUJI	170000
CH C SHOWCASING (GB) - CAFETIERE (GB)	SHADWELL ESTATE COMPANY	170000
SCENESETTER (IRE) GR F SHAMARDAL (USA) - FREEZY (IRE)	BRIAN GRASSICK BS	170000
CH C PIVOTAL (GB) - GHOSTFLOWER (IRE)	SHADWELL ESTATE COMPANY	170000
CH C TEOFILO (IRE) - WURFSPIEL (GER)	VENDOR	170000
B F SIYOUNI (FR) - RUBY ROCKET (IRE)	JOE FOLEY	165000
GR C KODIAC (GB) - SPINAMIX (GB)	AL SHAQAB RACING	160000
ALAMEERY (GB) B C KINGMAN (GB) - ZACHETA (GB)	SHADWELL ESTATE COMPANY	160000
AIM POWER (IRE) GR F ZEBEDEE (GB) - MONTEFINO (IRE)	SACKVILLEDONALD	160000
FOX FEARLESS (GB) B C CAMELOT (GB) - SILENT MUSIC (IRE)	SACKVILLEDONALD	160000
STARLIGHT (GB) B F IFFRAAJ (GB) - IGHRAA (GB)	A C ELLIOTT, AGENT (P.S.)	160000
B F INVINCIBLE SPIRIT (IRE) - DYNAFORCE (USA)	KLARAVICH STABLES	160000
BOSTON BRUIN (IRE) B C KODIAC (GB) - SOVANA (IRE)	BBA IRELAND	160000
SINATRA (GER) B C DUBAWI (IRE) - SORTILEGE (IRE)	VENDOR	160000
MUTAWAFFER (IRE) B C KODIAC (GB) - GOLDEN FLOWER (GB)	SHADWELL ESTATE COMPANY	160000
BR F SEA THE STARS (IRE) - GREEN MINSTREL (IRE)	FERGUSON BS	160000
CH F LOPE DE VEGA (IRE) - BALLYMORE CELEBRE (IRE)	SACKVILLEDONALD	155000
B C SEA THE STARS (IRE) - WIZZ KID (IRE)	FEDERICO BARBERINI	155000
LYSANDER BELLE (IRE) B F EXCEED AND EXCEL (AUS) - SWITCHER (IRE)	TIM GREDLEY	155000
GLOBAL WARNING (GB) B C POET'S VOICE (GB) - PERSARIO (GB)	C GORDON-WATSON BS	155000
B F NO NAY NEVER (USA) - DANEHILL'S DREAM (IRE)	BLANDFORD BS	155000
BARDO (IRE) B C GALILEO (IRE) - GILT EDGE GIRL (GB)	TIM GREDLEY	150000
CH C DAWN APPROACH (IRE) - NIGHT VISIT (GB)	DMM.COM	150000
GR C DARK ANGEL (IRE) - DAGHASHAH (GB)	MUBARAK AL NAEMI	150000
CH C LOPE DE VEGA (IRE) - KERRY GAL (IRE)	NORRIS/HUNTINGDON	150000
B F IFFRAAJ (GB) - MORNING FROST (GB)	JEREMY BRUMMITT	150000
B C KINGMAN (GB) - PONTENUOVO (FR)	SHADWELL ESTATE COMPANY	150000
CH F LOPE DE VEGA (IRE) - UP IN TIME (GB)	RONALD RAUSCHER BS	150000
B F INVINCIBLE SPIRIT (IRE) - JANE EYRE (GB)	VENDOR	150000
CH C GALILEO (IRE) - DAIVIKA (USA)	FLAXMAN STABLES IRELAND	150000
FOX HAPPY (IRE) B C SHOWCASING (GB) - ROO (GB)	SACKVILLEDONALD	150000
GR C DARK ANGEL (IRE) - BACK IN THE FRAME (GB)	SHADWELL ESTATE COMPANY	150000
BRUSHWORK (GB) B C KYLLACHY (GB) - MISS ELEGANCE (GB)	JUDDMONTE FARMS	150000
B C INVINCIBLE SPIRIT (IRE) - SHARAPOVA (IRE)	RICHARD KNIGHT BS (P.S.)	150000
B C NEW APPROACH (IRE) - MAZUNA (IRE)	RABBAH BS	150000

Name and Breeding	Purchaser	Guineas
B F SIYOUNI (FR) - PHOTO FLASH (IRE)	JOHN & JAKE WARREN	150000
CH F SHOWCASING (GB) - SELINKA (GB)	KEN MCPEEK AGENT	150000
TILMEETH (IRE) B C KODIAC (GB) - TIZ ALL OVER (USA)	SHADWELL ESTATE COMPANY	150000
B C NO NAY NEVER (USA) - SHELLEY BEACH (IRE)	MV MAGNIER	150000
B C NATHANIEL (IRE) - CARAVAN OF DREAMS (IRE)	RABBAH BS	150000
CH C MASTERCRAFTSMAN (IRE) - COCHABAMBA (IRE)	C GORDON-WATSON BS	150000
B C SEA THE STARS (IRE) - LADY HEIDI (GB)	ROGER VARIAN	150000
B F KINGMAN (GB) - QUADUNA (GB)	RONALD RAUSCHER	150000
B C KODIAC (GB) - LA CHICANA (IRE)	RABBAH BS	150000
B C AUSTRALIA (GB) - SWEEPSTAKE (IRE)	MV MAGNIER	150000
POCOTALIGO (GB) B C HELMET (AUS) - PIZZARRA (GB)	BBA IRELAND	145000
GLOBAL STORM (IRE) B C SHAMARDAL (USA) - AMATHIA (IRE)	C GORDON-WATSON BS	145000
YOUARESTAR (GB) B C SEA THE STARS (IRE) - ALUMNIA (USA)	C GORDON-WATSON BS	145000
SURFMAN (GB) B C KINGMAN (GB) - SHIMMERING SURF (IRE)	VENDOR	140000
KHIBRAH (GB) B F DARK ANGEL (IRE) - MI ANNA (GER)	SHADWELL ESTATE COMPANY	140000
CH C HAVANA GOLD (IRE) - BLANC DE CHINE (IRE)	KARL BURKE	140000
B C IFFRAAJ (GB) - LUNAR SPIRIT (GB)	GODOLPHIN	140000
B C SLADE POWER (IRE) - THREE DECADES (IRE)	GALLAGHER BS/HILLEN	140000
B C SHAMARDAL (USA) - VISALIA (IRE)	WILLIE BROWNE	140000
B C GARSWOOD (GB) - HIGHTIME HEROINE (IRE)	BBA IRELAND	140000
B F SHAMARDAL (USA) - ANGELS STORY (IRE)	DAVID REDVERS BS	140000
B C DARK ANGEL (IRE) - RHYTHM AND RHYME (IRE)	SHADWELL ESTATE COMPANY	140000
B C AUSTRALIA (GB) - WATERWAY RUN (IRE)	GODOLPHIN	140000
B F WAR COMMAND (USA) - AREEDA (IRE)	STEPHEN HILLEN BS	140000
CONOR HOGAN (IRE) B C CAMELOT (GB) - LA SYLVIA (IRE)	VENDOR	140000
B C AUSTRALIA (GB) - ROCK KRISTAL (IRE)	JOHN & JAKE WARREN	135000
CH F SHOWCASING (GB) - LOOKS ALL RIGHT (IRE)	AMANDA SKIFFINGTON	135000
B C KODIAC (GB) - NATEEJA (IRE)	C GORDON-WATSON BS	135000
B C CHARM SPIRIT (IRE) - MARIKA (GB)	DAVID REDVERS BS	135000
KHANMURJAN (USA) B C SCAT DADDY (USA) - LATE DAY SUN (IRE)	C GORDON-WATSON BS	130000
AVENIR ROYAL (FR) B C LE HAVRE (FR) - MISHHAR (IRE)	PETER & ROSS DOYLE BS	130000
B F INTELLO (GER) - VENTURA HIGHWAY (GB)	C GORDON-WATSON BS	130000
PUNJAB MAIL (GB) B C CHARM SPIRIT (IRE) - HARRYANA (GB)	JUDDMONTE FARMS INC	130000
B F SEA THE STARS (IRE) - NECTAR DE ROSE (FR)	SHADWELL ESTATE COMPANY	130000
B F CAMELOT (GB) - HURRICANE EMMA (USA)	DAVID REDVERS BS	130000
B F SHAMARDAL (USA) - HONORLINA (FR)	VENDOR	130000
B F LOPE DE VEGA (IRE) - ROYAL BLUE STAR (IRE)	AL SHAQAB RACING	130000
CH C ZOFFANY (IRE) - HOW'S SHE CUTTIN' (IRE)	GAELIC BS	130000
TAPISSERIE (GB) CH F LE HAVRE (IRE) - MISS WORK OF ART (GB)	JOHN & JAKE WARREN	130000
B C CAMELOT (GB) - FIRST OF MANY (IRE)	SAM SANGSTER BS	130000
GREYBYCHOICE (IRE) B C DARK ANGEL (IRE) - KHALICE (GB)	NP LITTMODEN	130000
B C DARK ANGEL (IRE) - GORBAND (USA)	WILLOW SPRING STABLE	130000
CH F DISTORTED HUMOR (USA) - SALONSUN (GER)	VENDOR	130000
B C ZOFFANY (IRE) - MILLESTAN (IRE)	RABBAH BS	130000
B F NEW APPROACH (IRE) - MIZZAVA (IRE)	SONESSA BS	130000
B C DARK ANGEL (IRE) - SECRETS AWAY (IRE)	CLIVE COX RACING	130000
B C NO NAY NEVER (USA) - CORKING (IRE)	C GORDON-WATSON BS	130000
B C AUSTRALIA (GB) - AZEEMA (IRE)	DMM.COM	130000
B F KINGMAN (GB) - CLENOR (IRE)	STEPHEN HILLEN BS	125000
B F OASIS DREAM (GB) - MADAM PRESIDENT (GB)	VENDOR	125000
B C SHOWCASING (GB) - MAY DAY QUEEN (IRE)	SHADWELL ESTATE COMPANY	125000
B F TORONADO (IRE) - ROSE BLOSSOM (GB)	AL SHAQAB RACING	125000
THE LAST UNICORN (GB) B C BATED BREATH (GB) - ROHLINDI (GB)	STROUD COLEMAN BS	125000
B C COACH HOUSE (IRE) - FUNNY ENOUGH (GB)	ROGER VARIAN	125000
LADY AIRA (GB) B F KODIAC (GB) - DOT HILL (GB)	A C ELLIOTT, AGENT	125000
GRENADIER GUARD (IRE) CH C AUSTRALIA (GB) - ANOTHER STORM (USA)	MARK JOHNSTON RACING	125000
NANTUCKET (IRE) B F SEA THE STARS (IRE) - LUCY CAVENDISH (USA)	JOHN & JAKE WARREN	125000
B C LOPE DE VEGA (IRE) - MICKLEBERRY (GB)	WESTWOOD BS	125000
B C KODIAC (GB) - DOLLY COLMAN (IRE)	VENDOR	125000
B C LEROIDESANIMAUX (BRZ) - ALMA MATER (GB)	GODOLPHIN	125000
B C TORONADO (IRE) - GREEN TERN (ITY)	AL SHAQAB RACING	120000
CH C MASTERCRAFTSMAN (IRE) - TARA MOON (GB)	JEREMY BRUMMITT	120000
BR F KODIAC (GB) - VENTURA MIST (GB)	RABBAH BS	120000
B C KINGMAN (GB) - PLEASE SING (IRE)	KLARAVICH STABLES	120000
CAPPTOO (IRE) B C DARK ANGEL (IRE) - CHARLOTTE RUA (IRE)	SHADWELL ESTATE COMPANY	120000
B C INVINCIBLE SPIRIT (IRE) - PARLE MOI (IRE)	VENDOR	120000
B C SLADE POWER (IRE) - MIRANDA FROST (IRE)	SHADWELL ESTATE COMPANY	120000
LEOUBE (IRE) B F KODIAC (GB) - SOJITZEN (FR)	PETER & ROSS DOYLE BS	120000
CH F IFFRAAJ (GB) - DUBAI BOUNTY (GB)	HUGO LASCELLES AGENT	120000
B C MAYSON (GB) - MARYSIENKA (GB)	MARK CROSSMAN	120000
B C ALHEBAYEB (IRE) - CROWN LIGHT (GB)	ANDREW BALDING	120000

Name and Breeding	Purchaser	Guineas
B C BATED BREATH (GB) - ON HER WAY (GB)	CHINA HORSE CLUB	120000
JACK'S POINT (GB) B C SLADE POWER (IRE) - ELECTRA STAR (GB)	WILLIAM R MUIR	120000
B F SIYOUNI (FR) - DAWN TO DANCE (IRE)	SACKVILLEDONALD	120000
B C TORONADO (IRE) - POMPEY GIRL (GB)	POWERSTOWN STUD	120000
B C LOPE DE VEGA (IRE) - HIGH HEEL SNEAKERS (GB)	GODOLPHIN	120000
B F SHAMARDAL (USA) - LADY LIBERTY (IRE)	VENDOR	120000
B F CHARM SPIRIT (IRE) - MAID FOR WINNING (USA)	ROGER VARIAN	120000
LAHESSAR (GB) B C EXCEED AND EXCEL (AUS) - BURLESQUE STAR (IRE)	AL-RABBAN RACING (P.S.)	120000
B C SEA THE STARS (IRE) - SASSENACH (IRE)	MARK JOHNSTON RACING	120000
NO TROUBLE (IRE) B C NO NAY NEVER (USA) - LADY BABOOSHKA (GB)	NORRIS/HUNTINGDON	120000
B C NO NAY NEVER (USA) - AQUARELLE RARE (GB)	GODOLPHIN	120000
B C RAVEN'S PASS (USA) - PETIT CALVA (FR)	VENDOR	120000
CITY WANDERER (IRE) B C KODIAC (GB) - VILETTA (GER)	GILL RICHARDSON BS	120000
B F IFFRAAJ (GB) - PACIFICA HIGHWAY (USA)	GODOLPHIN	120000
CH C PIVOTAL (GB) - MOON SISTER (IRE)	POWERSTOWN STUD	115000
B C CHARM SPIRIT (IRE) - KITE MARK (GB)	STEPHEN HILLEN BS	115000
B F AUSTRALIA (GB) - PRAIA (GB)	VENDOR	115000
GLOBAL ARMY (GB) GR C LETHAL FORCE (IRE) - PATH OF PEACE (GB)	SACKVILLEDONALD	115000
GLOBAL FALCON (GB) CH C SIYOUNI (FR) - MAGGI FONG (GB)	SACKVILLEDONALD	115000
OCEAN PARADISE (GB) B/GR F NEW APPROACH (IRE) - TROPICAL PARADISE (IRE)	JAMIE LLOYD	115000
B F FARHH (GB) - PURPLE TIGER (IRE)	JOE FOLEY	110000
SECRET POTION (GER) B C DABIRSIM (FR) - SOLA GRATIA (IRE)	VENDOR	110000
GR C DUTCH ART (GB) - BITE OF THE CHERRY (GB)	GODOLPHIN	110000
ENTRUSTING (GB) B C NATHANIEL (IRE) - ROYAL EMPRESS (IRE)	SUZANNE ROBERTS	110000
B C KODIAC (GB) - AQLETTE (GB)	KENJI RYOTOKUJI	110000
B/BR F NOBLE MISSION (GB) - SHARED DREAMS (GB)	KLARAVICH STABLES	110000
B C EXCEED AND EXCEL (AUS) - CRYING SHAME (USA)	GAELIC BS	110000
B F KODIAC (GB) - SWEET STREAM (ITY)	VENDOR	110000
B C SHOWCASING (GB) - ROODEYE (GB)	SHADWELL ESTATE COMPANY	110000
KALOOR (GB) B C NATHANIEL (IRE) - BLINKING (GB)	SAM SANGSTER BS	110000
CH C HAVANA GOLD (IRE) - RAGGIANTE (IRE)	SHADWELL ESTATE COMPANY	110000
B G CAMACHO (GB) - VIVA DIVA (GB)	HONG KONG JOCKEY CLUB	110000
B C DARK ANGEL (IRE) - JO BO BO (IRE)	SHADWELL ESTATE COMPANY	110000
SINJAARI (IRE) B C CAMELOT (GB) - HEAVENLY SONG (IRE)	C GORDON-WATSON BS	110000
B C ACCLAMATION (GB) - ELIZABELLE (IRE)	GILL RICHARDSON BS	110000
BR F KODIAC (GB) - ENJOYABLE (IRE)	VENDOR	110000
CH C NO NAY NEVER (USA) - ENHARMONIC (USA)	BLANDFORD BS	110000
B C DANDY MAN (IRE) - CELTIC LYNN (IRE)	BLANDFORD BS	110000
B C EXCEED AND EXCEL (AUS) - SAABIQ (USA)	SHAWN DUGAN, AGENT	110000
B C KINGMAN (GB) - DON'T FORGET FAITH (USA)	VENDOR	110000
CH/GR C MASTERCRAFTSMAN (IRE) - BUNOOD (IRE)	BLANDFORD BS	110000
SOUTHERN SONG (IRE) CH F SLADE POWER (IRE) - KATCHY LADY (GB)	GILL RICHARDSON BS	110000
AQL (IRE) B C EXCEED AND EXCEL (AUS) - PEARL SEA (IRE)	SHADWELL ESTATE COMPANY	110000
B F LE HAVRE (IRE) - DALIANA (GB)	JOHN FERGUSON BS	110000
B C CAMACHO (GB) - SONNING ROSE (IRE)	SHADWELL ESTATE COMPANY	110000
CANTON QUEEN (IRE) B F SHAMARDAL (USA) - HANA LINA (GB)	SACKVILLEDONALD	110000
B C INVINCIBLE SPIRIT (IRE) - PRICELESS JEWEL (GB)	VENDOR	105000
COVADONGA (GB) CH F MEDICEAN (GB) - PLAY BOUZOUKI (GB)	WALLHOUSE SLU	105000
GR C DARK ANGEL (IRE) - DUST FLICKER (GB)	PETER & ROSS DOYLE BS	105000
MOSHARAKKA (IRE) B C ALHEBAYEB (IRE) - AZIA (IRE)	SHADWELL ESTATE COMPANY	105000
B C TAMAYUZ (GB) - SO SWEET (IRE)	SHADWELL ESTATE COMPANY	105000
B C SIYOUNI (FR) - DYVEKE (GER)	POWERSTOWN STUD	105000
CH F SHAMARDAL (USA) - VIOLA DA BRACCIO (IRE)	STROUD COLEMAN BS	105000
B C KODIAC (GB) - PEARL CITY (IRE)	A HARTE BS	105000
B F IFFRAAJ (GB) - DANCEALOT (GB)	GODOLPHIN	105000

HIGH-PRICED YEARLINGS OF 2017 AT GOFFS

The following yearlings realised 64,000 euros and over at Goffs Sales in 2017:-

Name and Breeding	Purchaser	Euros
B C FRANKEL (GB) - BELESTA (GB)	JUSTIN CASSE	1600000
B F GALILEO (IRE) - L'AMOUR DE MA VIE (USA)	GODOLPHIN	1200000
B C KINGMAN (GB) - GO LOVELY ROSE (IRE)	ROGER VARIAN	650000
B F GALILEO (IRE) - HAWALA (IRE)	MAGNIER/MAYFAIR/DOYLE	625000
INVALUABLE (GB) B F INVINCIBLE SPIRIT (IRE) - PRIMA LUCE (IRE)	CHEVELEY PARK STUD	580000
GOOD BIRTHDAY (IRE) B C DABIRSIM (FR) - CHICA LOCA (FR)	SACKVILLEDONALD	500000
B C KODIAC (GB) - WONDERFUL TOWN (USA)	SHADWELL ESTATE COMPANY	500000
B C SHOWCASING (GB) - ROSERAIE (IRE)	GODOLPHIN	460000
MARBELLA (IRE) B F INVINCIBLE SPIRIT (IRE) - GIFT FROM HEAVEN (IRE)	JUDDMONTE FARMS	450000
FLORA DANICA (IRE) B F GALILEO (IRE) - DANELETA (IRE)	FLAXMAN STABLES IRELAND	420000
B F DUBAWI (IRE) - TYRANNY (GB)	CHEYENNE STABLES (PS)	400000
ANGEL'S HIDEAWAY (IRE) GR F DARK ANGEL (IRE) - THE HERMITAGE (IRE)	CHEVELEY PARK STUD	390000
FLEUR DE LUI (IRE) B F GALILEO (IRE) - REPRISE (GB)	BBA (IRELAND)	380000
B C SEA THE STARS (IRE) - SCARLET AND GOLD (IRE)	S DUGAN	380000
BR F CAMELOT (GB) - QUESTION TIMES (GB)	MAGNIER/MAYFAIR/DOYLE	380000
GR F DARK ANGEL (IRE) - SEAGULL (IRE)	GODOLPHIN	375000
CH F LOPE DE VEGA (IRE) - MULTICOLOUR WAVE (IRE)	JOHN MCCORMACK BS	350000
GR C DARK ANGEL (IRE) - CAPULET MONTEQUE (IRE)	FORM BLOODSTOCK	350000
B C INVINCIBLE SPIRIT (IRE) - KITTY LOVE (USA)	SHADWELL ESTATE CO	350000
B C NO NAY NEVER (USA) - THEANN (GB)	MAGNIER/MAYFAIR	350000
SAWASDEE (IRE) BR C SHAMARDAL (USA) - BENEVENTA (GB)	SACKVILLEDONALD	325000
HERO HERO (IRE) B C NO NAY NEVER (USA) - FANCY (IRE)	SACKVILLEDONALD	325000
MARFA LIGHTS (IRE) B F GALILEO (IRE) - MOMENT IN TIME (IRE)	BBA (IRELAND)	320000
AMERICAN GRAFFITI (FR) CH C PIVOTAL (GB) - ADVENTURE SEEKER (FR)	GODOLPHIN	320000
FOX LEICESTER (IRE) GR C DARK ANGEL (IRE) - POP ART (IRE)	SACKVILLEDONALD	310000
BURNING LAKE (IRE) B C LE HAVRE (IRE) - BABY HOUSEMAN (GB)	SACKVILLEDONALD	310000
CONFECTOR (IRE) CH C MASTERCRAFTSMAN (IRE) - ULIANA (IRE)	ORBIS BLOODSTOCK UK	310000
B C FRANKEL (GB) - SEVEN MAGICIANS (USA)	SUN BS	300000
B F WAR COMMAND (USA) - STRAWBERRY FLEDGE (USA)	D FARRINGTON	300000
B C INVINCIBLE SPIRIT (IRE) - BRATISLAVA (GB)	BBA (IRELAND)	300000
CH C NO NAY NEVER (USA) - LAW OF THE JUNGLE (IRE)	MAGNIER/MAYFAIR/DOYLE	300000
GR F KODIAC (GB) - CHIARA WELLS (IRE)	SHAWN DUGAN, AGENT	280000
BR C NO NAY NEVER (USA) - MIXED BLESSING (GB)	S HILLEN	280000
B C DARK ANGEL (IRE) - LOVE IN THE DESERT (GB)	GEORGE MOORE BS	280000
CH C AUSTRALIA (GB) - WINESONG (IRE)	HUGO MERRY BLOODSTOCK	270000
B C KODIAC (GB) - LILLY JUNIOR (GB)	S DUGAN	270000
B C KODIAC (GB) - SECURITY INTEREST (GB)	HKJC	260000
B C DANDY MAN (IRE) - TRIGGERS BROOM (IRE)	SACKVILLEDONALD	240000
B F ZOFFANY (IRE) - NIGHTIME (IRE)	SONESSA	240000
B C NO NAY NEVER (USA) - AL IHSAS (IRE)	STEPHEN HILLEN	240000
B C KINGMAN (GB) - LIBERALLY (IRE)	HUGO MERRY BS	240000
CH C DUBAWI (IRE) - RAINBOW DANCING (GB)	R VARIAN	230000
B C MASTERCRAFTSMAN (IRE) - NEBRAAS (GB)	CHINA HORSE CLUB	230000
MR SECRETARY (IRE) B C SEA THE STARS (IRE) - OUI SAY OUI (IRE)	BBA (IRELAND)	225000
B F EXCEED AND EXCEL (AUS) - HARMONIC NOTE (GB)	BBA (IRELAND)	220000
B F AUSTRALIA (GB) - WEEKEND FLING (USA)	MAYFAIR SPECULATORS	220000
GEOLAI (IRE) CH F NEW APPROACH (IRE) - MARIA LEE (IRE)	BBA (IRELAND)	200000
GR C DARK ANGEL (IRE) - SECRET KEY (IRE)	S HILLEN	200000
ZIGELLO (IRE) B F INTELLO (GER) - ZIGARRA (GB)	ORBIS BLOODSTOCK UK	200000
B C AUSTRALIA (GB) - DUNDALK DUST (USA)	M.V. MAGNIER	200000
B F DABIRSIM (FR) - GLORIOUS ADVENTURE (IRE)	BLANDFORD BLOODSTOCK	190000
B C KODIAC (GB) - PALE ORCHID (IRE)	SACKVILLEDONALD	180000
B F MOTIVATOR (GB) - JOMANA (IRE)	EBONOS	180000
B C ACCLAMATION (GB) - PRECIPITOUS (IRE)	S HILLEN	180000
B F KODIAC (GB) - ARTY CRAFTY (USA)	BBA (IRELAND)	180000
B C SIYOUNI (FR) - ORIENTAL MAGIC (GER)	SHADWELL ESTATE CO	180000
B F ZOFFANY (IRE) - BELLE ISLE (GB)	DE BURGH EQUINE	180000
CH F LOPE DE VEGA (IRE) - SCARLET BELLE (GB)	BIG RED FARM	180000
BR C KYLLACHY (GB) - TRIPLE STAR (GB)	MAYFAIR SPECULATORS	165000
NAN YEHI (IRE) B F CAMELOT (GB) - REBELLINE (IRE)	BBA (IRELAND)	160000
FEMME ARGENT (IRE) B F DARK ANGEL (IRE) - HAVIN' A GOOD TIME (IRE)	BBA (IRELAND)	160000
B F DARK ANGEL (IRE) - MIDNIGHT HUSH (FR)	BLANDFORD BS	160000
ESPOIR ET BONHEUR (IRE) B F DANSILI (GB) - ADESTE FIDELES (USA)	BBA (IRELAND)	160000
B F ZOFFANY (IRE) - SHY BRIDE (IRE)	EMPIRE BS	155000
B C INVINCIBLE SPIRIT (IRE) - ROSE DE FRANCE (IRE)	BBA (IRELAND)	155000
COUP DE GOLD (IRE) BR C MAXIOS (GB) - ASTROGLIA (USA)	JOHN CLARKE	155000
B/BR F DUBAWI (IRE) - MY RENEE (IRE)	BBA (IRELAND)	150000
B F KODIAC (GB) - TOQUETTE (IRE)	MERIDIAN INTERNATIONAL	150000

Name and Breeding	Purchaser	Euros
CH F AUSTRALIA (GB) - WURFKLINGE (GER)	PAUL HARLEY BLOODSTOCK	150000
DANCING VEGA (IRE) CH F LOPE DE VEGA (IRE) - WE CAN SAY IT NOW (AUS)	RALPH BECKETT	150000
RECONDITE (IRE) B C ACCLAMATION (GB) - AQUARIUS STAR (IRE)	JUDDMONTE FARMS	150000
B F TAMAYUZ (GB) - ZIRIA (IRE)	VENDOR	140000
SNAHFEE (GB) CH C DUTCH ART (GB) - POINT OF CONTROL (GB)	C GORDON-WATSON	140000
BLAST OFF (GB) B C SEA THE MOON (GER) - HAVING A BLAST (USA)	ORBIS BLOODSTOCK UK	140000
B C KINGMAN (GB) - STARLET (IRE)	BLANDFORD BS	140000
GR F NATHANIEL (IRE) - ALL HALLOWS (IRE)	RIC WYLIE BLOODSTOCK	140000
CH F DUTCH ART (GB) - SEMBLANCE (GB)	J FOLEY	135000
B F SHOWCASING (GB) - POPPET'S LOVEIN (GB)	CLIVE COX RACING	130000
ANTONIA DE VEGA (IRE) B F LOPE DE VEGA (IRE) - WITCHES BREW (IRE)	RALPH BECKETT	130000
B/BR C SEA THE STARS (IRE) - EVENSONG (GER)	MERRY-HILLEN	130000
CH F EXCEED AND EXCEL (AUS) - CALL LATER (USA)	MAYFAIR SPECULATORS	130000
B C SHOWCASING (GB) - MISS LACEY (IRE)	RICHARD KNIGHT BS	130000
B F SIR PERCY (GB) - SWEET CANDO (IRE)	ELLIOTT & SCOTT	130000
SNOW OCEAN (IRE) B C EXCEED AND EXCEL (AUS) - CALLISTAN (IRE)	SACKVILLEDONALD (PS)	130000
B C LOPE DE VEGA (IRE) - PUSSYCAT LIPS (IRE)	CHURCH FARM	130000
B C ZOFFANY (IRE) - PEIG (IRE)	BLANDFORD BS	130000
CH F SEA THE STARS (IRE) - TABLE BAY (IRE)	RABBAH BS	125000
DANCINGWITHWOLVES (IRE) B C FOOTSTEPSINTHESAND (GB) - CLODOVINA (IRE)	CHARLES GORDON-WATSON	125000
ORCHIDIA (IRE) CH F BATED BREATH (GB) - NEW ORCHID (USA)	BADGERS BS	120000
BR C KODIAC (GB) - FONDA (USA)	BBA (IRELAND)	120000
B C INVINCIBLE SPIRIT (IRE) - ALUMNI (GB)	CHINA HORSE CLUB	120000
B C INVINCIBLE SPIRIT (IRE) - SPIRIT OF TARA (IRE)	J CASSE	120000
B C AUSTRALIA (GB) - SWEEPSTAKE (IRE)	VENDOR	120000
BARBARA HEPWORTH (IRE) B F DARK ANGEL (IRE) - MUZDAAN (IRE)	RICHARD FRISBY BS	115000
CLOCKERS CORNER (IRE) CH C NO NAY NEVER (USA) - STARLIGHT NIGHT (USA)	SACKVILLEDONALD	115000
B F ACCLAMATION (GB) - IRISH FLOWER (IRE)	BBA (IRELAND)	115000
CH C SLADE POWER (IRE) - PIVOTAL'S PRINCESS (IRE)	SACKVILLEDONALD	110000
B C BATED BREATH (GB) - BURN THE BREEZE (IRE)	GODOLPHIN	110000
B C BIG BAD BOB (IRE) - KITOKO (IRE)	HKJC	110000
SEA OF FAITH (IRE) B F SEA THE STARS (IRE) - JUMOOH (IRE)	VENDOR	110000
B F ACCLAMATION (GB) - DELIRA (IRE)	MICHAEL HALFORD	105000
B C DANSILI (GB) - ANTICIPATION (FR)	SACKVILLEDONALD	105000
B F DARK ANGEL (IRE) - ILLUMINATING DREAM (IRE)	BBA (IRELAND)	100000
IMPERIUM (IRE) CH C FRANKEL (GB) - RAMRUMA (USA)	BADGERS BS (P.S.)	100000
IMPETUS (IRE) BR F TAMAYUZ (GB) - DANCING JEST (IRE)	BRIAN GRASSICK BLOODSTOCK	100000
B C IFFRAAJ (GB) - NO SUCH ZONE (GB)	SHADWELL ESTATE CO	100000
ULLION BOSS (IRE) B C WAR COMMAND (USA) - GOLD BUBBLES (USA)	HKJC	100000
GR C DARK ANGEL (IRE) - SULARINA (IRE)	BBA (IRELAND)	100000
B F SEA THE STARS (IRE) - FRENCH FRIEND (IRE)	SUNDERLAND HOLDING	100000
SONGKRAN (IRE) B C SLADE POWER (IRE) - CHOOSE ME (IRE)	SACKVILLEDONALD	100000
CH F AUSTRALIA (GB) - MONA LISA (GB)	RABBAH BS	100000
B F LAWMAN (FR) - BRIGHT SAPPHIRE (IRE)	A SKIFFINGTON/H PALMER	100000
B C EXCEED AND EXCEL (AUS) - SEQUINED (USA)	BBA (IRELAND)	100000
B C ACCLAMATION (GB) - SO DANDY (IRE)	GAELIC BS	100000
LANGHOLM (IRE) B C DARK ANGEL (IRE) - PINDROP (GB)	D CARROLL	100000
CH F SEA THE STARS (IRE) - NINAS TERZ (GER)	GROVE STUD	100000
FERRUM (GB) B C SEA THE MOON (GER) - CLAIOMH SOLAIS (IRE)	BBA (IRELAND)	100000
MANUELA DE VEGA (IRE) B F LOPE DE VEGA (IRE) - ROSCOFF (IRE)	R BECKETT	100000
B F MASTERCRAFTSMAN (IRE) - APPAREL (IRE)	BBA (IRELAND)	100000
B/GR F DARK ANGEL (IRE) - SIODUIL (IRE)	J CARTHY	100000
B F DARK ANGEL (IRE) - BAYJA (IRE)	AMANDA SKIFFINGTON, AGENT	100000
BR C SHAMARDAL (USA) - DANELISSIMA (IRE)	BBA (IRELAND)	100000
SUPERMOND (GER) CH C SEA THE MOON (GER) - SOPRAN GALLOW (IRE)	MAYFAIR SPECULATORS	100000
EXCELLED (IRE) B F EXCEED AND EXCEL (AUS) - ELLE WOODS (IRE)	STROUD COLEMAN	100000
B C CAPE CROSS (IRE) - MOONLIGHT WISH (IRE)	JAMIE B BS	95000
B C DARK ANGEL (IRE) - BRONZE QUEEN (GER)	OAK TREE FARM	95000
B F LE HAVRE (IRE) - NICOLOSIA (GER)	RIFA MUSTANG EUROPE	95000
B F BATED BREATH (GB) - AFRICAN MOONLIGHT (UAE)	WATKINS BLOODSTOCK	90000
B C SEA THE MOON (GER) - MOURIYANA (IRE)	EMERALD BS	90000
B F DARK ANGEL (IRE) - OREGON TRAIL (USA)	GLEN PARK STUD	90000
B F DANDY MAN (IRE) - ESUVIA (IRE)	WATKINS BLOODSTOCK	90000
GUANDI (USA) CH C DECLARATION OF WAR (USA) - HOH BUZZARD (IRE)	SACKVILLEDONALD	90000
B F KODIAC (GB) - PIONEER ALEXANDER (IRE)	GAELIC BS	90000
B C SEA THE STARS (IRE) - STARLIT SANDS (GB)	SACKVILLEDONALD	90000
WINGREEN (IRE) CH F LOPE DE VEGA (IRE) - RELATION ALEXANDER (IRE)	J & J WARREN	88000
B C FOXWEDGE (AUS) - FREQUENT (GB)	HILLEN/RYAN	87000
ELGAR (IRE) B C DANDY MAN (IRE) - SHARKI (GB)	PETER & ROSS DOYLE BS	86000
BR C INVINCIBLE SPIRIT (IRE) - DANUTA (USA)	JIM RYAN	85000
B C BATTLE OF MARENGO (IRE) - MISREPRESENT (USA)	B O'RYAN	85000

Name and Breeding	Purchaser	Euros
B F LOPE DE VEGA (IRE) - DAZZLE DANCER (IRE)	RABBAH BLOODSTOCK	85000
B C CAMELOT (GB) - LESSON IN LIFE (GB)	L WILLIAMS	85000
B F DREAM AHEAD (USA) - TANZANIA (IRE)	BBA (IRELAND)	85000
GLORIOUS DANE (GB) B C OLYMPIC GLORY (IRE) - KAMINARI (IRE)	PETER & ROSS DOYLE BS	85000
VOICEOFTHEEMIRATES (GB) B C SHOWCASING (GB) - MAKAASEB (USA)	R VARIAN	85000
AMOROUSLY (IRE) B F AUSTRALIA (GB) - KNOW ME LOVE ME (IRE)	PETER & ROSS DOYLE BS	85000
B F CAPE CROSS (IRE) - SOLAR MOON (GB)	RABBAH BS	85000
FELICIANA DE VEGA (GB) B F LOPE DE VEGA (IRE) - ALONG CAME CASEY (IRE)	STUART WILLIAMS (PS)	85000
B F OLYMPIC GLORY (IRE) - HIDEAWAY HEROINE (IRE)	SYLVESTER KIRK	85000
B C LAWMAN (FR) - ROYSTONEA (GB)	BBA (IRELAND)	85000
B F KODIAC (GB) - BIG BONED (USA)	MAYFAIR SPECULATORS	85000
B C KODIAC (GB) - TRULY MAGNIFICENT (USA)	RITA MASTERS	82000
B C MORPHEUS (GB) - GLEN GINNIE (IRE)	JOHN MCCONNELL	80000
B F MUKHADRAM (GB) - EURO EMPIRE (USA)	WAVERTREE STABLES	80000
B C CAMELOT (GB) - ZELLOOF (IRE)	STROUD COLEMAN BS	80000
B C DARK ANGEL (IRE) - ASHTOWN GIRL (IRE)	DE BURGH EQUINE	80000
B C SHOWCASING (GB) - GOLDEN LEGACY (IRE)	BBA (IRELAND)	80000
MUCHO TALENTO (GB) B C INTELLO (GER) - MOIAVA (FR)	A BALDING	80000
CH C SPEIGHTSTOWN (USA) - VALAIS GIRL (GB)	THE OLD MEW STABLE	80000
CH C SIYOUNI (FR) - HILL OF GRACE (GB)	SACKVILLEDONALD	80000
B F NO NAY NEVER (USA) - DOWAGER (GB)	CORMAC MCCORMACK BS	80000
B F SEA THE STARS (IRE) - REZYANA (USA)	W MIEDZIANOWSKI	80000
CH F MORE THAN READY (USA) - TABREED (GB)	RICHARD KNIGHT BS	80000
B F DARK ANGEL (IRE) - EVENING FROST (IRE)	VENDOR	80000
GEORGE GERSHWIN (GB) B C BATED BREATH (GB) - SHARP RELIEF (IRE)	ELLIOTT & SCOTT	80000
B F CHARM SPIRIT (IRE) - MILL GUINEAS (USA)	D REDVERS	80000
BR G HOLY ROMAN EMPEROR (IRE) - SNOW SCENE (IRE)	SAM SANGSTER BS	78000
B C CAMELOT (GB) - CONDITION (GB)	LLOYD WILLIAMS	77000
CH F MASTERCRAFTSMAN (IRE) - RENOWNED (IRE)	M O'TOOLE	76000
CH F NO NAY NEVER (USA) - ALAMOUNA (IRE)	PETER & ROSS DOYLE B/S	76000
B C ALHEBAYEB (IRE) - ROSA CLARA (IRE)	GILL RICHARDSON BS (P.S.)	75000
BYRD (IRE) B C KODIAC (GB) - PRECIOUS GEM (IRE)	ELLIOTT & SCOTT	75000
B F KODIAC (GB) - SALMON ROSE (IRE)	VENDOR	75000
B F PIVOTAL (GB) - EBTISAMA (USA)	EQUINE ASSOCIATES	75000
B F HARD SPUN (USA) - GENUINE QUALITY (USA)	RICHARD GUEST	75000
GR C FAST COMPANY (IRE) - EVENING TIME (IRE)	BBA (IRELAND)	75000
CH C NO NAY NEVER (USA) - BRIGIDS CROSS (IRE)	FEDERICO BARBERINI, AGENT	75000
B C OASIS DREAM (GB) - GOTHIC DANCE (IRE)	CLIVE COX RACING	75000
CH C DAWN APPROACH (IRE) - BUILLE CLISTE (IRE)	GILL RICHARDSON BLOODSTOCK	75000
B F LE HAVRE (IRE) - KITHONIA (FR)	PIER HOUSE STUD	75000
B F NO NAY NEVER (USA) - APACHE DREAM (IRE)	MAYFIELD STABLES	72000
TILMEETH (IRE) B C KODIAC (GB) - TIZ ALL OVER (USA)	TALLY HO STUD	72000
LYNDON B (IRE) B C CHARM SPIRIT (IRE) - KELSEY ROSE (IRE)	ELLIOTT & SCOTT (P.S.)	70000
B F CAMELOT (GB) - FLAMINGO SEA (USA)	BBA (IRELAND)	70000
B C XTENSION (IRE) - SUBTLE AFFAIR (IRE)	GEORGE MOORE BS	70000
GR C ALHEBAYEB (IRE) - SUMMER GLOW (IRE)	PETER & ROSS DOYLE BS	70000
B F INVINCIBLE SPIRIT (IRE) - MYTHIE (FR)	VENDOR	70000
B C DARK ANGEL (IRE) - TENDER IS THENIGHT (IRE)	M JOHNSTON	70000
CH C IFFRAAJ (GB) - NINJA LADY (GB)	D REDVERS	70000
DINAH WASHINGTON (IRE) CH F AUSTRALIA (GB) - GAINFUL (USA)	VENDOR	70000
B F CAMELOT (GB) - CLOSE REGARDS (IRE)	MCKEEVER	70000
HUA HIN (IRE) CH C DANDY MAN (IRE) - MIDNIGHT OASIS (GB)	SACKVILLEDONALD	70000
AMON RA (GB) B C EXCEED AND EXCEL (AUS) - ROSES FOR THE LADY (IRE)	JARLSBO JLC AB	68000
B C HOLY ROMAN EMPEROR (IRE) - HOT TICKET (IRE)	CHURCH FARM	68000
B C HOLY ROMAN EMPEROR (IRE) - SET FIRE (IRE)	OAK TREE FARM	68000
CH F COACH HOUSE (IRE) - BIRD KEY (GB)	CHURCH FARM	68000
GALILEO JADE (IRE) B F AUSTRALIA (GB) - DUSTY IN MEMPHIS (USA)	PETER & ROSS DOYLE B/S	67000
B F CAMACHO (GB) - KIMOLA (IRE)	STROUD COLEMAN BS	67000
CH C LOPE DE VEGA (IRE) - SPESIALTA (GB)	GROVE STUD	66000
B/BR C MAGICIAN (IRE) - LOOKS LIKE RAIN (GB)	SACKVILLEDONALD (P.S.)	65000
B C AUSTRALIA (GB) - LADY GLORIA (GB)	L WILLIAMS	65000
BR C NO NAY NEVER (USA) - OPERA FAN (FR)	J O'BRIEN (P.S.)	65000
GR C DARK ANGEL (IRE) - SILCA BOO (GB)	KELLEWAY/MCAULEY	65000
CH F NO NAY NEVER (USA) - APPLE SPIRIT (USA)	GAELIC BLOODSTOCK	65000
BURIRAM (IRE) B C RELIABLE MAN (GB) - WILD STEP (GER)	SACKVILLEDONALD	65000
B C DRAGON PULSE (IRE) - EMSIYAH (USA)	JIM RYAN	64000

HIGH-PRICED YEARLINGS OF 2017 AT GOFFS UK (DONCASTER)

The following yearlings realised £52,000 and over at Goffs UK Sales in 2017:-

Name and Breeding	Purchaser	Pounds
B C BATED BREATH (GB) - NIGHT SPHERE (IRE)	J FOLEY	270000
B C KODIAC (GB) - FOLEGANDROS ISLAND (FR)	HKJC	260000
B C DARK ANGEL (IRE) - LAST BID (GB)	SACKVILLEDONALD	250000
B C DARK ANGEL (IRE) - SNOWFIELDS (IRE)	HKJC	250000
FANAAR (IRE) B C DARK ANGEL (IRE) - INCA TRAIL (USA)	SHADWELL ESTATE CO	240000
B C KODIAC (GB) - SPRING SURPRISE (GB)	G LYONS	210000
RAJWAA (GB) GR F DARK ANGEL (IRE) - THE THRILL IS GONE (GB)	SHADWELL ESTATE CO	200000
CH C TEOFILO (IRE) - MIDGET (GB)	GODOLPHIN	200000
GR C DARK ANGEL (IRE) - ABBAKOVA (IRE)	J FOLEY	200000
B F MUKHADRAM (GB) - WHIRLY DANCER (GB)	BBA (IRELAND)	200000
B C IFFRAAJ (GB) - FIG ROLL (GB)	CHINA HORSE CLUB	190000
LUXOR (GB) B C OASIS DREAM (GB) - EMINENTLY (GB)	J & J WARREN	190000
KODYANNA (IRE) B F KODIAC (GB) - JADANNA (IRE)	STROUD COLEMAN BS	180000
CH F FRANKEL (GB) - LADIES ARE FOREVER (GB)	D FARRINGTON (P.S.)	180000
CASTING (IRE) B C SOCIETY ROCK (IRE) - SUFFER HER (IRE)	PETER & ROSS DOYLE BS	160000
QUTOB (IRE) B C ACCLAMATION (GB) - WHEN NOT IFF (IRE)	SHADWELL ESTATE CO	160000
MOLAAHETH (GB) B C HEERAAT (IRE) - ALL FUR COAT (GB)	SHADWELL ESTATE CO	150000
B C OLYMPIC GLORY (IRE) - RIVER TEST (GB)	SHADWELL ESTATE CO	140000
B C LOPE DE VEGA (IRE) - NATIVE PICTURE (IRE)	SHADWELL ESTATE CO	140000
BRIAN EPSTEIN (IRE) B C DARK ANGEL (IRE) - JEWEL IN THE SAND (IRE)	PETER & ROSS DOYLE BS	140000
B F EXCEED AND EXCEL (AUS) - CORAL MIST (GB)	SACKVILLEDONALD	140000
CLOUDY DANCER (GB) GR F INVINCIBLE SPIRIT (IRE) - RONALDSAY (GB)	R GUEST	125000
B C HOLY ROMAN EMPEROR (IRE) - MUSICAL RAIN (IRE)	HKJC	125000
B C KODIAC (GB) - MELODIQUE (FR)	GODOLPHIN	125000
B C EQUIANO (FR) - FATAL ATTRACTION (GB)	HKJC	120000
B F DARK ANGEL (IRE) - PATIENCE ALEXANDER (IRE)	GAELIC BS	120000
GLOBAL ACCLAMATION (GB) B C ACCLAMATION (GB) - HIGH LUMINOSITY (USA)	E DUNLOP	120000
B C SWISS SPIRIT (GB) - HOT SECRET (GB)	SHADWELL ESTATE CO	120000
LOUIS TREIZE (IRE) CH C SLADE POWER (IRE) - BLACK RODDED (GB)	B O'RYAN	120000
METATRON (IRE) GR C DARK ANGEL (IRE) - ORIKAWA (FR)	R O'RYAN	120000
JACKSTAR (IRE) GR C DARK ANGEL (IRE) - STARBRIGHT (GB)	SACKVILLEDONALD	120000
B C XTENSION (IRE) - PARK GLEN (GB)	SACKVILLEDONALD	115000
BR C TAMAYUZ (GB) - RAHLAH (GB)	SHADWELL ESTATE CO	110000
B F DARK ANGEL (IRE) - PROVIDENCIA (IRE)	J FOLEY	110000
MERGE (IRE) B C DANDY MAN (IRE) - INTERLACING (GB)	ORBIS BS	110000
B F CHARM SPIRIT (IRE) - BIJOU A MOI (GB)	J FOLEY	105000
B C DARK ANGEL (IRE) - LA REINE DE PEARLS (IRE)	SHADWELL ESTATE CO	100000
STALLONE (IRE) B C DANDY MAN (IRE) - TITIAN QUEEN (GB)	B O'RYAN	100000
GREYBYCHOICE (IRE) B C DARK ANGEL (IRE) - KHALICE (GB)	VENDOR	100000
B C HEERAAT (IRE) - PIRANHA (IRE)	A DUARTE	100000
CH C FOOTSTEPSINTHESAND (GB) - MIMISEL (GB)	HKJC	100000
B C DANDY MAN (IRE) - JUST LIKE IVY (CAN)	R O'RYAN	100000
B C DANDY MAN (IRE) - STAR BONITA (GB)	GAELIC BS	100000
B C DARK ANGEL (IRE) - LAPIS BLUE (IRE)	GAELIC BS	95000
BR C ZEBEDEE (GB) - SILK FAN (IRE)	CLIVE COX RACING	95000
B C EXCELEBRATION (IRE) - IT'S TRUE (IRE)	STROUD COLEMAN BS	95000
WALKMAN (IRE) B C WAR COMMAND (USA) - MOOCHING ALONG (IRE)	O COLE	95000
REGENT (IRE) B F WAR COMMAND (USA) - REGENCY GIRL (IRE)	PETER & ROSS DOYLE BS	95000
B C CAMACHO (GB) - VENETIAN RHAPSODY (GB)	EMERALD BS	95000
B F WAR COMMAND (USA) - FOREPLAY (IRE)	BLANDFORD BS	92000
B C OLYMPIC GLORY (IRE) - BLACK MASCARA (IRE)	SAM SANGSTER BS	92000
B F DARK ANGEL (IRE) - LITTLE AUDIO (IRE)	J FOLEY	90000
B C NO NAY NEVER (USA) - DHAMMA (USA)	SACKVILLEDONALD	90000
CH F EXCEED AND EXCEL (AUS) - PRINCESS IRIS (IRE)	MC BS	88000
B C ALHEBAYEB (IRE) - SERENE DREAM (GB)	SHADWELL ESTATE CO	85000
B C KYLLACHY (GB) - RESORT (GB)	J FOLEY	85000
ALFIE SOLOMONS (IRE) B C ACCLAMATION (GB) - VASTITAS (IRE)	B O'RYAN	85000
B C PIVOTAL (GB) - SLATEY HEN (IRE)	GAELIC BS	85000
JABALALY (IRE) B C MOOHAAJIM (GB) - BAHATI (IRE)	SHADWELL ESTATE CO	85000
B C KODIAC (GB) - MINWAH (IRE)	SACKVILLEDONALD	85000
MODAKHAR (IRE) B C BATTLE OF MARENGO (IRE) - LOST HIGHWAY (IRE)	SHADWELL ESTATE CO	85000
B C SIYOUNI (FR) - HAYDN'S LASS (GB)	RABBAH BS	85000
B/BR C ELZAAM (AUS) - SO BLISSFUL (IRE)	SHADWELL ESTATE CO	82000
HERMOCRATES (FR) B C FARHH (GB) - LITTLE SHAMBLES (GB)	PETER & ROSS DOYLE BS	82000
B F DARK ANGEL (IRE) - PADMA (GB)	R O'RYAN	80000
B C BATED BREATH (GB) - RANDOM SUCCESS (IRE)	CRAMPSCASTLE BS	80000
B C DARK ANGEL (IRE) - CLEAR IMPRESSION (IRE)	SACKVILLEDONALD	80000

Name and Breeding	Purchaser	Pounds
B F SIYOUNI (FR) - DEMEANOUR (USA)	GAELIC BS	80000
THRILLA IN MANILA (GB) B C IFFRAAJ (GB) - TESARY (GB)	B O'RYAN	80000
B C HAVANA GOLD (IRE) - SAND DANCER (IRE)	SHADWELL ESTATE CO	80000
B F ZOFFANY (IRE) - IDLE CURIOSITY (IRE)	PETER & ROSS DOYLE BS	75000
B C ELZAAM (AUS) - SERAPHINA (GB)	HIGHFLYER BS	75000
GLOBAL COMMAND (IRE) B C WAR COMMAND (USA) - PARSLEY (IRE)	BLANDFORD BS	75000
B F DARK ANGEL (IRE) - EXTRICATE (IRE)	VENDOR	75000
B C SLADE POWER (IRE) - FRENCH FERN (IRE)	SACKVILLEDONALD	75000
B F SHOWCASING (GB) - LAVENDER AND LACE (GB)	POWERSTOWN STUD	75000
LORCAN (GB) GR C DARK ANGEL (IRE) - VALLADO (IRE)	A ELLIOTT (PS.)	72000
B C LETHAL FORCE (IRE) - HOLBERG SUITE (GB)	GILL RICHARDSON BS	72000
B C SWISS SPIRIT (GB) - GILT LINKED (GB)	M O'TOOLE	72000
GR F DARK ANGEL (IRE) - TIGER MIST (IRE)	BROWN ISLAND	72000
LEROY LEROY (GB) B C COMPTON PLACE (GB) - SMALL FORTUNE (GB)	PETER & ROSS DOYLE BS	72000
PRETTY EYES (IRE) B F KODIAC (GB) - MAOIN DOR (IRE)	HILLEN/HUGHES	70000
B C ZEBEDEE (GB) - WORTHINGTON (GB)	STROUD COLEMAN BS	70000
MY EXCELSA (IRE) B F EXCEED AND EXCEL (AUS) - EMIRATES JOY (USA)	ELLIOTT & SCOTT	70000
FLAUNT IT (IRE) B F MUKHADRAM (GB) - LABISA (IRE)	A SKIFFINGTON	70000
RUMBLE INTHEJUNGLE (IRE) CH C BUNGLE INTHEJUNGLE (GB) - GUANA (IRE)	B O'RYAN	70000
B C DREAM AHEAD (USA) - PERNICA (GB)	HIGHFLYER BS	70000
CH C TAGULA (IRE) - GROTTA DEL FAUNO (IRE)	PETER & ROSS DOYLE BS	70000
BADER (GB) B C ELUSIVE CITY (USA) - GOLBAHAR (IRE)	PETER & ROSS DOYLE BS	70000
BR C KODIAC (GB) - LISIEUX ORCHID (GB)	VENDOR	70000
B C DELEGATOR (GB) - IRRATIONAL (GB)	STROUD COLEMAN BS	70000
GR C DARK ANGEL (IRE) - BROWN EYED HONEY (GB)	BROWN ISLAND	68000
B C ZEBEDEE (GB) - JEBEL MUSA (IRE)	SAM SANGSTER BS	68000
YESTAAHEL (GB) B C FOOTSTEPSINTHESAND (GB) - AZENZAR (GB)	PETER & ROSS DOYLE BS	68000
CH C KODIAC (GB) - VIKING FAIR (GB)	J FOLEY	68000
B C DARK ANGEL (IRE) - RUM RAISIN (GB)	PETER & ROSS DOYLE BS	67000
B C KAYF TARA (GB) - HARRINGAY (GB)	A MURPHY	66000
B C GARSWOOD (GB) - SHIBARA (IRE)	A SKIFFINGTON	65000
BRANDON (FR) B C SHOWCASING (GB) - BE RELEASED (IRE)	MCKEEVER / FERGUSON BS	65000
BELLUM (GB) B C BATTLE OF MARENGO (IRE) - QUAIL LANDING (USA)	ORBIS BS	65000
AWAKE IN ASIA (GB) CH C DRAGON PULSE (IRE) - GLADIATRIX (GB)	HIGHFLYER BS	65000
OLYMPIC SPIRIT (GB) CH C OLYMPIC GLORY (IRE) - MAGIC FLORENCE (IRE)	H D ATKINSON	65000
GR C KENDARGENT (FR) - COULD YOU BE LOVED (IRE)	GAELIC BS	65000
ALICE'S LEGACY (IRE) B F SOCIETY ROCK (IRE) - POETRY ALOUD (IRE)	BLANDFORD BS	65000
ORANGE BLOSSOM (GB) CH F SHOWCASING (GB) - SATSUMA (GB)	STROUD COLEMAN BS	65000
B F SWISS SPIRIT (GB) - LULLA (GB)	J FOLEY	62000
BR C NO NAY NEVER (USA) - HANNAHS TURN (GB)	M V MAGNIER	62000
BRUNO (IRE) B C ES QUE LOVE (IRE) - AJIG DANCER (GB)	CLIVE COX RACING	62000
B C KAYF TARA (GB) - LAGO D'ORO (GB)	D FRISBY	62000
HOOFLEPUFF (IRE) B C GALE FORCE TEN (GB) - HFLAH (IRE)	THE COOL SILK PARTNERSHIP	60000
BR C SOCIETY ROCK (IRE) - WARM WELCOME (GB)	ELLIOTT & SCOTT	60000
EMILANDRA (IRE) B F SLADE POWER (IRE) - SOUL MOUNTAIN (GB)	G DOUGLAS	60000
B C RED JAZZ (USA) - SIGNORA LINA (IRE)	PETER & ROSS DOYLE BS	60000
B C SHOWCASING (GB) - FURBELOW (GB)	D FARRINGTON	60000
B F SOCIETY ROCK (IRE) - BRONZE BABY (USA)	GILL RICHARDSON BS	58000
B F DARK ANGEL (IRE) - LITTLEPROMISEDLAND (IRE)	SACKVILLEDONALD	56000
CH C BUNGLE INTHEJUNGLE (GB) - FANDITHA (IRE)	PETER & ROSS DOYLE BS	56000
ARTAIR (IRE) B C KODIAC (GB) - BONNIE LESLEY (IRE)	A C ELLIOTT	55000
B C MORPHEUS (GB) - SHEPPARD'S WATCH (GB)	A O'RYAN	55000
B C ALHEBAYEB (IRE) - MISTRESS OF ROME (GB)	CRISFORD RACING	55000
B F ACCLAMATION (GB) - THOUSANDFOLD (USA)	M MCDOWALL	55000
B C MOOHAAJIM (IRE) - ALHENA (IRE)	HIGHFLYER BS	55000
GR C DARK ANGEL (IRE) - SHE'S A WORLDIE (IRE)	TOWN MOOR RACING	55000
B C ALHEBAYEB (IRE) - JAWAANEB (GB)	STROUD COLEMAN BS	55000
CH C SHOWCASING (GB) - COPY-CAT (GB)	KT BS	55000
CH C HAVANA GOLD (GB) - BOUNTY BOX (GB)	SHADWELL ESTATE CO	55000
CH F SHOWCASING (GB) - SOLFILIA (GB)	CHURCH FARM BS	55000
ASTRONAUT (GB) CH C OLYMPIC GLORY (IRE) - GIMME SOME LOVIN (IRE)	VENDOR	55000
MATERIAL GIRL (GB) B F PIVOTAL (GB) - APACE (IRE)	RABBAH BS	52000
B C DANDY MAN (GB) - HARVEST JOY (IRE)	B O'RYAN	52000
DISRUPTOR (FR) CH C SIYOUNI (FR) - ULTRADARGENT (FR)	HIGHFLYER BS	52000
CH F ZOFFANY (IRE) - PERINO (IRE)	SACKVILLEDONALD	52000
BR F SOCIETY ROCK (IRE) - QUIZA (GB)	GILL RICHARDSON BS	52000
B C KAYF TARA (GB) - FERNELLO (GB)	A MURPHY	52000

HIGH-PRICED YEARLINGS OF 2017 AT TATTERSALLS IRELAND SALES
The following yearlings realised 36,000 euros and over at Tattersalls Ireland Sales in 2017:-

Name and Breeding	Purchaser	Euros
B C SHOWCASING (GB) - STARFLY (IRE)	GROVENDALE ADVISORY	230000
B C KODIAC (GB) - QUEEN WASP (IRE)	GODOLPHIN	200000
B F SOCIETY ROCK (IRE) - COOLMINX (IRE)	JOE FOLEY	160000
B C KODIAC (GB) - GREEK EASTER (IRE)	GAELIC BS	110000
GR C ACCLAMATION (GB) - NEW DEAL (GB)	MRS MAURA GITTINS	110000
B C GARSWOOD (GB) - ABANDON (USA)	GILL RICHARDSON BS	100000
B C FOOTSTEPSINTHESAND (GB) - VAN DE CAPPELLE (IRE)	JOE FOLEY	100000
B C EXCEED AND EXCEL (AUS) - SO SECRET (IRE)	CON MARNANE	90000
B C REQUINTO (IRE) - MARAGLEN (IRE)	HONG KONG JOCKEY CLUB	85000
B F DARK ANGEL (IRE) - WAVEBAND (GB)	PETER & ROSS DOYLE BS	80000
CH F SLADE POWER (IRE) - BLUE ANGEL (IRE)	RABBAH BS LTD	80000
GR C DARK ANGEL (IRE) - MOONVOY (GB)	SACKVILLEDONALD	80000
B F KODIAC (GB) - GRAPHIC GUEST (GB)	CHURCH FARM	80000
B C ACCLAMATION (GB) - WITH COLOUR (GB)	D FARRINGTON	78000
BL/BR C BATED BREATH (GB) - ADELFIA (IRE)	BBA IRELAND	75000
BR C MARTALINE (GB) - FANTASTIC CUIX (FR)	H KNIGHT	75000
BR C BATED BREATH (GB) - WELCOME SPRING (IRE)	BOBBY O'RYAN/MARCO BOTTI	70000
B F INVINCIBLE SPIRIT (IRE) - MAWAARED (GB)	VENDOR	70000
CH C CHAMPS ELYSEES (GB) - ZA ZA ZOOM (IRE)	JOE FOLEY	68000
ANYONECANBEASTAR (IRE) CH F SHOWCASING (GB) - GENEROUS HEART (GB)	GARETH FREYNE	67000
B C DARK ANGEL (GB) - C'EST MA SOUER (IRE)	JOSEPH O'BRIEN	65000
CH C MASTERCRAFTSMAN (GB) - PENMAYNE (GB)	TONY MARTIN	65000
B C GALE FORCE TEN (GB) - PARIS GLORY (USA)	ARMANDO DUARTE	65000
GR G MARTALINE (GB) - RAITERA (FR)	VENDOR	65000
B C ACCLAMATION (GB) - CAMPFIRE GLOW (IRE)	KILRONAN STUD	62000
FOOTSTEPSINTHEMIST (IRE) BR C FOOTSTEPSINTHESAND (GB) - HIGHLAND MISS (USA)	SACKVILLEDONALD	60000
BR C SWISS SPIRIT (GB) - SUMMER SPICE (IRE)	RICHARD KNIGHT BS AGENT	60000
B C ROCK OF GIBRALTAR (IRE) - VAMPRESS (IRE)	E P HORSE	60000
B F SLADE POWER (IRE) - SLOPE (IRE)	CREIGHTON SCHWARTZ BS	60000
GETCHAGETCHAGETCHA (GB) B C CHAMPS ELYSEES (GB) - PAELLA (IRE)	KEVIN ROSS BS	60000
BR C DANDY MAN (IRE) - AIR MAZE (IRE)	PETER & ROSS DOYLE BS	60000
NEW HORIZON (IRE) CH C FOOTSTEPSINTHESAND (GB) - THE SILVER KEBAYA (FR)	KEVIN PRENDERGAST	60000
B C BATED BREATH (GB) - WELSH ANTHEM (GB)	GROVENDALE ADVISORY	60000
B C ACCLAMATION (GB) - ELUSIVE LAURENCE (IRE)	VENDOR	58000
B C BATED BREATH (GB) - MARACUJA (GB)	CRAMPSCASTLE BS	58000
B C XTENSION (IRE) - LYCA BALLERINA (GB)	JAMIE B BS	58000
B C SOCIETY ROCK (IRE) - SCOTTISH EXILE (IRE)	PETER & ROSS DOYLE BS	57000
B F TAMAYUZ (GB) - MAGS ROCK (IRE)	VENDOR	57000
B C KODIAC (GB) - KNAPTON HILL (GB)	STROUD COLEMAN BS	55000
BR C EQUIANO (FR) - CHRISSYCROSS (IRE)	CRAMPSCASTLE BS	55000
B F SOCIETY ROCK (IRE) - KYANIGHT (IRE)	GAELIC BS	55000
B F TAMAYUZ (GB) - SAFIYA SONG (IRE)	DAVID MYERSCOUGH	52000
CH C RAVEN'S PASS (USA) - PERMSIRI (IRE)	SARAH LYNAM	52000
DARK HAVANA (IRE) B C HAVANA GOLD (IRE) - TOP OF THE ART (IRE)	KARL BURKE	52000
CH F AUSTRALIA (GB) - SUGAR HOUSE (USA)	ALDUINO BOTTI	50000
B C ALHEBAYEB (IRE) - HEAT (GB)	AMANDA SKIFFINGTON (P.S.)	50000
GR C DARK ANGEL (GB) - DJINNI (IRE)	CLIVE COX RACING	50000
B F TORONADO (IRE) - SUSI WONG (IRE)	MAURA GITTINS	50000
CH F DANDY MAN (IRE) - BREAK BREAD (IRE)	T KODAMA	50000
B F WAR COMMAND (USA) - ATTRACTED TO YOU (IRE)	TOM MALONE	50000
B C BATTLE OF MARENGO (IRE) - KAWAHA (IRE)	TOM MALONE	50000
GR C DALAKHANI (IRE) - ST ROCH (IRE)	BLANDFORD BS	50000
B C FOOTSTEPSINTHESAND (GB) - FASTNET LADY (IRE)	MICHAEL O'CALLAGHAN	49000
B C KODIAC (GB) - HEMARIS (GB)	VENDOR	48000
B C EPAULETTE (AUS) - WHERE I BE (GB)	STROUD COLEMAN BS	48000
BR C SLADE POWER (IRE) - SYLVAN MIST (IRE)	CON MARNANE	47000
B C HENRYTHENAVIGATOR (USA) - BULRUSHES (GB)	EOGHAN T O'NEILL	47000
B C IFFRAAJ (GB) - ENTRE NOUS (IRE)	D FARRINGTON	47000
CH C DANDY MAN (IRE) - WHY NOW (GB)	DONNACHA O'BRIEN	46000
B C TAMAYUZ (GB) - SHE'S A CHARACTER (GB)	JASON KELLY	46000
B C SHANTOU (USA) - LAREN (GER)	ORMOND BS	46000
B C ZOFFANY (IRE) - GREEN CASTLE (IRE)	RICHARD KNIGHT	46000
THE CROW (FR) B C MARTALINE (GB) - MY DARLING ROSE (FR)	R FRISBY	46000
B C CAMACHO (GB) - PEANUT BUTTER (GB)	KEVIN PRENDERGAST	45000
B F MOTIVATOR (GB) - ADESTE (GB)	BLANDFORD BS	45000
CHARACTERISTIC (IRE) CH C CASAMENTO (IRE) - STUNNED SILENCE (USA)	AMANDA SKIFFINGTON AGENT	45000
B C KODIAC (GB) - BENELOGE (GB)	GILL RICHARDSON BS	45000
RUDY LEWIS (IRE) B C EXCELEBRATION (IRE) - BLESS YOU (GB)	C GORDON-WATSON BS	45000

Name and Breeding	Purchaser	Euros
B F CAMACHO (GB) - ROYAL MAJESTIC (GB)	RICHARD KNIGHT BS AGENT	44000
EDDIE COCHRAN (IRE) BL C SOCIETY ROCK (IRE) - CROSSREADH (USA)	PETER & ROSS DOYLE BS	44000
BLADE RUNNER (FR) B G GREAT PRETENDER (IRE) - CUTTING EDGE (FR)	R FRISBY	44000
TORNGAT (FR) CH C KAPGARDE (FR) - LOIN DE MOI (FR)	I FERGUSON	44000
B C KODIAC (GB) - FACE REALITY (USA)	KUBLER RACING LTD	43000
BR C SOCIETY ROCK (IRE) - EXISTENTIALIST (GB)	COOPER/O'FLYNN	43000
B C HELMET (AUS) - CHINESE DEMOCRACY (USA)	AIDAN O'RYAN	43000
RO F DARK ANGEL (IRE) - ANADOLU (IRE)	MAURA GITTINS	42000
B C LETHAL FORCE (IRE) - EMPERORS PEARL (IRE)	GAELIC BS	42000
B C TORONADO (IRE) - SPARKLING EYES (GB)	D FARRINGTON	42000
B C ZOFFANY (IRE) - OPEN BOOK (GB)	PAT FLYNN RACING	42000
B C ZOFFANY (IRE) - AHD (USA)	SACKVILLEDONALD	42000
B C SOCIETY ROCK (IRE) - ZELIE MARTIN (IRE)	JOE FOLEY	42000
B F CAMACHO (GB) - SHAMARDYH (IRE)	PETER & ROSS DOYLE BS	42000
ISAAN QUEEN (IRE) B F WAR COMMAND (USA) - DUNDEL'S SPIRIT (IRE)	BLANDFORD BS	42000
B C ZOFFANY (IRE) - SANADAAT (GB)	BLANDFORD BS	42000
B F HELMET (AUS) - BAWAAKEER (USA)	SACKVILLEDONALD	41000
B C DANDY MAN (IRE) - DEIRA (USA)	VENDOR	40000
BR F DAWN APPROACH (IRE) - HALL HEE (IRE)	BBA IRELAND	40000
B C HAVANA GOLD (IRE) - CULTURED PRIDE (IRE)	OAK TREE FARM	40000
BR F BATED BREATH (GB) - PINK TEQUILA (GB)	VENDOR	40000
B F BORN TO SEA (IRE) - GOLDTHROAT (IRE)	URBAN BS	40000
GR C MONTMARTRE (FR) - CAVIAR IZANDRE (FR)	MICHAEL MOORE	40000
B F KODIAC (GB) - TILTHE END OF TIME (IRE)	CHARLIE GORDON WATSON BS	40000
WOLSTONBURY (IRE) B C KODIAC (GB) - LAST HOORAY (GB)	ORCHARDSTOWN FARMS	40000
B C ELZAAM (AUS) - KOLKATA (GB)	GAELIC BS	40000
B F DARK ANGEL (IRE) - ENCORE VIEW (GB)	RICHARD KNIGHT/SEAN QUINN	40000
B C CAMACHO (GB) - MEANWHILE (GB)	MICHAEL O'CALLAGHAN	40000
B F DREAM AHEAD (USA) - TETARD (IRE)	CREIGHTON SCHWARTZ BS	40000
B C ELZAAM (AUS) - PLAYAMONGTHESTARS (AUS)	BBA IRELAND	40000
BR C LETHAL FORCE (IRE) - RUSSIAN DANCE (USA)	KEVIN PRENDERGAST	40000
B C SIR PRANCEALOT (IRE) - VICTORIA LODGE (IRE)	SACKVILLEDONALD	40000
CH C FOOTSTEPSINTHESAND (GB) - RIVER RAPIDS (IRE)	AZOURE BS	40000
B C SIYOUNI (FR) - FINE THREADS (GB)	ARDGLAS STABLES	40000
GEORGE HASTINGS (GB) GR C GREGORIAN (IRE) - PACHANGA (GB)	KARL BURKE/MIDDLEHAM PARK	40000
GRAVE LA KLASS (FR) RO G SADDLER MAKER (IRE) - MARBELA (FR)	I FERGUSON	40000
B F ACCLAMATION (GB) - ACADEMICIENNE (CAN)	EDWARD LYNAM	40000
B C SLADE POWER (IRE) - CLASSIC FALCON (IRE)	CHURCH FARM	40000
BR C PRESENTING (GB) - MADAM BOVARY (IRE)	VENDOR	40000
B C DARK ANGEL (IRE) - BASANDERE (FR)	HOWSON & HOULDSWORTH BS	39000
B C NOBLE MISSION (GB) - KNYSNA (USA)	SACKVILLEDONALD	38000
B F LAWMAN (FR) - MUSICAL NOTE (GB)	BLANDFORD BS	38000
B C DANDY MAN (IRE) - HEAVEN'S VAULT (IRE)	GAELIC BS	38000
B C HAVANA GOLD (IRE) - BEST STEPS (IRE)	EOGHAN T O'NEILL	37000
B/BR C SOCIETY ROCK (IRE) - MY EURYDICE (GB)	BLANDFORD BS	37000
BR C PRESENTING (GB) - BALLYCLOVEN OSCAR (IRE)	KEVIN ROSS BS	37000
B C BORN TO SEA (IRE) - KERRYS REQUIEM (IRE)	EDWARD LYNAM	36000
BR C POWER (GB) - MONEY PENNY (ITY)	BBA IRELAND	36000
GEORGE FORMBY (GB) CH C MAYSON (GB) - SUPA SAL (GB)	AMANDA SKIFFINGTON AGENT	36000
CH F TEOFILO (IRE) - KATDOGAWN (GB)	PETER & ROSS DOYLE BS	36000
B F HOLY ROMAN EMPEROR (IRE) - MANGO GROOVE (IRE)	DAVID WACHMAN	36000
B F DARK ANGEL (IRE) - HUGS 'N KISSES (GB)	VENDOR	36000
FLOW OF WORDS (IRE) B C VOCALISED (USA) - DANEMARQUE (AUS)	BOBBY O'RYAN	36000
CH C FAST COMPANY (IRE) - PORTICO (GB)	KERN/LILLINGSTON ASSOCIATION	36000
CH C IFFRAAJ (GB) - ALABELLE (GB)	D FARRINGTON	36000
SAM COOKE (IRE) B C POUR MOI (IRE) - SATURDAY GIRL (GB)	RALPH BECKETT	36000
SECRET ACE (GB) CH F COMPTON PLACE (GB) - SECRET ROMANCE (GB)	BLANDFORD BS	36000
CH C DOYEN (IRE) - OLD CARTON LASS (IRE)	I FERGUSON	36000

2000 GUINEAS STAKES (3y) Newmarket-1 mile

Year	Owner	Winner and Price	Jockey	Trainer	Second	Third	Ran	Time
1978	J Hayter's	ROLAND GARDENS (28/1)	F Durr	D Sasse	Remainder Man	Welsh Nan	19	47.33
1979	A Shead's	TAP ON WOOD (20/1)	S Cauthen	B Hills	Kris	Young Generation	20	43.60
1980	K Abdullah's	KNOWN FACT (14/1)	W Carson	J Tree	Posse	Night Alert	14	40.46
	(Nureyev finished first but was disqualified)							
1981	Mrs A Muinos's	TO-AGORI-MOU (5/2)	G Starkey	G Harwood	Mattaboy	Bel Bolide	19	41.43
1982	G Oldham's	ZINO (8/1)	F Head	F Boutin	Wind and Wuthering	Tender King	26	37.13
1983	R Sangster's	LOMOND (9/1)	Pat Eddery	V O'Brien	Tolomeo	Muscatite	16	43.87
1984	R Sangster's	EL GRAN SENOR (15/8)	Pat Eddery	V O'Brien	Chief Singer	Lear Fan	14	37.41
1985	Maktoum Al Maktoum's	SHADEED (4/5)	L Piggott	M Stoute	Supreme Leader	Bairn	15	37.41
1986	K Abdullah's	DANCING BRAVE (15/8)	G Starkey	G Harwood	Green Desert	Huntingdale	14	40.00
1987	J Horgan's	DON'T FORGET ME (9/1)	W Carson	R Hannon	Bellotto	Midyan	14	36.74
1988	H H Aga Khan's	DOYOUN (4/5)	W R Swinburn	M Stoute	Charmer	Bellefella	14	41.73
1989	Hamdan Al-Maktoum's	NASHWAN (3/1)	W Carson	R Hannon	Exbourne	Danehill	16	36.44
1990	John Horgan's	TIROL (9/1)	M Kinane	R Hannon	Machiavellian	Anshan	14	35.84
1991	Lady Beaverbrook's	MYSTIKO (13/2)	M Roberts	C Brittain	Lycius	Ganges	16	37.83
1992	R Sangster's	RODRIGO DE TRIANO (6/1)	L Piggott	P Chapple-Hyam	Lucky Lindy	Pursuit of Love	23	38.37
1993	K Abdullah's	ZAFONIC (5/6)	Pat Eddery	A Fabre	Barathea	Bin Ajwaad	11	35.32
1994	G R Bailey Ltd's	MISTER BAILEYS (16/1)	J Weaver	M Johnston	Grand Lodge	Colonel Collins	13	35.08
1995	Sheikh Mohammed's	PENNEKAMP (9/2)	T Jarnet	A Fabre	Celtic Swing	Bahri	16	35.16
1996	Godolphin's	MARK OF ESTEEM (8/1)	L Dettori	S bin Suroor	Even Top	Bijou D'Inde	18	37.59
1997	M Tabor & Mrs J Magnier's	ENTREPRENEUR (11/2)	M Kinane	A O'Brien	Revoque	Border Arrow	18	35.64
1998	M Tabor & Mrs J Magnier's	KING OF KINGS (7/2)	M Kinane	A O'Brien	Lend A Hand	Mujahid	18	39.25
1999	Godolphin's	ISLAND SANDS (10/1)	L Dettori	S Bin Suroor	Enrique		14	37.14
	(Run on July Course)							
2000	Saeed Suhail's	KING'S BEST (13/2)	K Fallon	Sir M Stoute	Giant's Causeway	Barathea Guest	27	37.77
2001	K Weinstock's	GOLAN (11/1)	K Fallon	Sir M Stoute	Tamburlaine	Frenchmans Bay	18	37.48
2002	Sir A Ferguson & Mrs J Magnier's	ROCK OF GIBRALTAR (9/1)	J Murtagh	A O'Brien	Hawk Wing	Redback	22	36.50
2003	Moyglare Stud Farm's	REFUSE TO BEND (9/2)	P J Smullen	D Weld	Zafeen	Norse Dancer	20	37.98
2004	Hamdan Al Maktoum's	HAAFHD (11/2)	R Hills	B Hills	Snow Ridge	Azamour	14	36.60
2005	Mr M Tabor & Mrs John Magnier's	FOOTSTEPSINTHESAND (13/2)	K Fallon	A O'Brien	Rebel Rebel	Kandidate	19	36.10
2006	Mr M Tabor, Mrs John Magnier's, Mr M M Smith & Mr D Smith's	GEORGE WASHINGTON (6/4)	K Fallon	A O'Brien	Sir Percy	Olympian Odyssey	14	36.80
2007	P Cunningham's	COCKNEY REBEL (25/1)	O Peslier	G Huffer	Vital Equine	Dutch Art	24	35.28
2008	Mrs J. Magnier's	HENRYTHENAVIGATOR (11/1)	J Murtagh	A O'Brien	New Approach	Stubbs Art	15	39.14
2009	C Tsui's	SEA THE STARS (8/1)	M Kinane	J Oxx	Delegator	Gan Amhras	15	35.88
2010	M Offenstadt's	MAKFI (33/1)	C Lemaire	M Delzangles	Dick Turpin	Canford Cliffs	19	36.35
2011	K Abdullah's	FRANKEL (1/2)	T Queally	H Cecil	Dubawi Gold	Native Khan	13	37.30
2012	D Smith, Mrs J Magnier & M Tabor's	CAMELOT (15/8)	J O'Brien	A O'Brien	French Fifteen	Hermival	18	42.46
2013	Godolphin's	DAWN APPROACH (11/8)	K Manning	J Bolger	Glory Awaits	Van Der Neer	13	35.84
2014	Saeed Manana's	NIGHT OF THUNDER (40/1)	K Fallon	R Hannon jnr	Kingman	Australia	14	36.61
2015	M Tabor, D Smith & Mrs J Magnier's	GLENEAGLES (4/1)	R Moore	A O'Brien	Territories	Ivawood	18	37.55
2016	Al Shaqab Racing's	GALILEO GOLD (14/1)	L Dettori	H Palmer	Massaat	Ribchester	13	35.91
2017	M Tabor, D Smith & Mrs J Magnier's	CHURCHILL (6/4)	R Moore	A O'Brien	Barney Roy	Al Wukair	10	36.61

Year	Owner	Winner and Price	Jockey	Trainer	Second	Third	Ran	Time
1978	R Bonnycastle's	ENSTONE SPARK (35/1)	E Johnson	B Hills	Fair Salinia	Seraphima	16	1 41.56
1979	Helena Springfield Ltd's	ONE IN A MILLION (evens)	J Mercer	H Cecil	Abbeydale	Yanuka	17	1 43.06
1980	O Phipp's	QUICK AS LIGHTNING (12/1)	B Rouse	J Dunlop	Our Home	Mrs Penny	23	1 41.89
1981	Sir P Oppenheimer's	FAIRY FOOTSTEPS (6/4)	L Piggott	H Cecil	Tolmi	Go Leasing	14	1 40.43
1982	H Joel's	ON THE HOUSE (33/1)	J Reid	H Wragg	Time Charter	Dione	15	1 40.45
1983	Sir P Oppenheimer's	MA BICHE (5/2)	F Head	Mme C Head	Favoridge	Habibti	15	1 41.71
1984	M Lemos's	PEBBLES (8/1)	P Robinson	C Brittain	Meis El-Reem	Desirable	18	1 38.18
1985	Sheikh Mohammed's	OH SO SHARP (2/1)	S Cauthen	H Cecil	Al Bahathri	Bella Colora	15	1 36.85
1986	H Ranier's	MIDWAY LADY (10/1)	R Cochrane	B Hanbury	Maysoon	Sonic Lady	17	1 41.54
1987	S Niarchos's	MIESQUE (15/8)	F Head	F Boutin	Milligram	Interval	14	1 38.48
1988	E Aland's	RAVINELLA (4/5)	G W Moore	Mme C Head	Datawaeyaa	Diminuendo	12	1 40.88
1989	Sheikh Mohammed's	MUSICAL BLISS (7/2)	W R Swinburn	M Stoute	Kerrera	Aldbourne	7	1 42.69
1990	Hamdan Al-Maktoum's	SALSABIL (6/4)	W Carson	J Dunlop	Heart of Joy	Negligent	10	1 38.06
1991	Hamdan Al-Maktoum's	SHADAYID (4/6)	W Carson	J Dunlop	Kooyonga	Crystal Gazing	14	1 38.18
1992	Maktoum Al-Maktoum's	HATOOF (5/1)	W R Swinburn	Mme C Head	Marling	Kenbu	14	1 39.45
1993	Mohamed Obaida's	SAYYEDATI (4/1)	W R Swinburn	C Brittain	Niche	Ajfan	14	1 37.34
1994	R Sangster's	LAS MENINAS (12/1)	J Reid	T Stack	Balanchine	Coup de Genie	15	1 36.71
1995	Hamdan Al-Maktoum's	HARAYIR (5/1)	R Hills	Major W R Hern	Aqaarid	Moonshell	14	1 36.72
1996	Wafic Said's	BOSRA SHAM (10/11)	Pat Eddery	H Cecil	Matiya	Bint Shadayid	13	1 37.75
1997	Greenbay Stables Ltd's	SLEEPYTIME (5/1)	K Fallon	H Cecil	Oh Nellie	Dazzle	15	1 37.66
1998	Godolphin's	CAPE VERDI (100/30)	L Dettori	S Bin Suroor	Shahtoush	Exclusive	16	1 37.86
1999	K Abdullah's	WINCE (4/1)	K Fallon	H Cecil	Wannabe Grand	Valentine Waltz	22	1 37.91

(Run on July Course)

Year	Owner	Winner and Price	Jockey	Trainer	Second	Third	Ran	Time
2000	Hamdan Al-Maktoum's	LAHAN (14/1)	R Hills	J Gosden	Princess Ellen	Petrushka	15	1 36.38
2001	Sheikh Ahmed Al Maktoum's	AMEERAT (11/1)	P Robinson	J Jarvis	Muwakleh	Toroca	18	1 36.36
2002	Godolphin's	KAZZIA (14/1)	L Dettori	S Bin Suroor	Snowfire	Alasha	15	1 37.85
2003	Cheveley Park Stud's	RUSSIAN RHYTHM (12/1)	K Fallon	Sir M Stoute	Six Perfections	Intercontinental	19	1 38.43
2004	Duke of Roxburghe's	ATTRACTION (11/2)	K Darley	M Johnston	Sundrop	Hathrah	16	1 36.70
2005	Mrs John Davies & Mr M Tabor's	VIRGINIA WATERS (12/1)	K Fallon	A O'Brien	Maids Causeway	Vista Bella	20	1 36.50
2006	M Sly, Dr Davies & Mrs P Sly's	SPECIOSA (10/1)	M Fenton	Mrs P Sly	Confidential Lady	Nasheej	21	1 40.50
2007	R Ryan's	FINSCEAL BEO (5/4)	K Manning	Mrs P Sly	Arch Swing	Simply Perfect	21	1 34.94
2008	S Friborg's	NATAGORA (11/4)	C Lemaire	P Bary	Spacious	Sonrise Abu	15	1 34.99
2009	Hamdan Al-Maktoum's	GHANAATI (20/1)	R Hills	B Hills	Cuis Ghaire	Super Sleuth	14	1 34.22
2010	K Abdullah's	SPECIAL DUTY (9/2)	S Pasquier	Mme C Head-Maarek	Jacqueline Quest	Gile Na Greine	17	1 39.66

(The first two placings were reversed by the Stewards)

Year	Owner	Winner and Price	Jockey	Trainer	Second	Third	Ran	Time
2011	Godolphin's	BLUE BUNTING (16/1)	L Dettori	M Al Zarooni	Together	Maqaasid	18	1 39.27
2012	Mrs John Magnier, M Tabor & D Smith's	HOMECOMING QUEEN (25/1)	R Moore	A O'Brien	Starscope	Maybe	17	1 40.45
2013	B Keswick's	SKY LANTERN (9/1)	R Hughes	R Hannon	Just The Judge	Moth	15	1 36.38
2014	Ballymore Thoroughbred Ltd's	MISS FRANCE (7/1)	M Guyon	A Fabre	Lightning Thunder	Ihtimal	17	1 37.40
2015	M Tabor, D Smith & Mrs J Magnier's	LEGATISSIMO (13/2)	R Moore	D Wachman	Lucida	Tiggy Wiggy	13	1 34.60
2016	D Smith, Mrs J Magnier & M Tabor's	MINDING (11/10)	R Moore	A O'Brien	Ballydoyle	Alice Springs	16	1 36.53
2017	Mrs John Magnier, M Tabor & D Smith's	WINTER (9/1)	W Lordan	A O'Brien	Rhododendron	Daban	14	1 35.66

OAKS STAKES (3y fillies) Epsom-1 mile 4 furlongs 6 yards

Year	Owner	Winner and Price	Jockey	Trainer	Second	Third	Ran	Time
1978	S Hanson's	FAIR SALINIA (8/1)	G Starkey	M Stoute	Dancing Maid	Suni	15	2 36.82
1979	J Morrison's	SCINTILLATE (20/1)	Pat Eddery	J Tree	Bonnie Isle	Britannia's Rule	14	2 43.74
1980	R Hollingsworth's	BIREME (9/2)	W Carson	R Hern	Vielle	The Dancer	11	2 34.33
1981	Mrs B Firestone's	BLUE WIND (3/1)	L Piggott	D Weld	Madam Gay	Leap Lively	12	2 40.93
1982	R Barnett's	TIME CHARTER (12/1)	W Newnes	H Candy	Slightly Dangerous	Last Feather	13	2 34.21
1983	Sir M Sobell's	SUN PRINCESS (6/1)	W Carson	H Hern	Acclimatise	New Coins	15	2 40.98
1984	Sir R McAlpine's	CIRCUS PLUME (4/1)	L Piggott	J Dunlop	Media Luna	Poule Queen	15	2 38.97
1985	Sheikh Mohammed's	OH SO SHARP (6/4)	S Cauthen	H Cecil	Triptych	Dubian	15	2 41.37
1986	H Ranier's	MIDWAY LADY (15/8)	R Cochrane	B Hanbury	Untold	Maysoon	12	2 35.60
1987	Sheikh Mohammed's	UNITE (11/1)	W R Swinburn	M Stoute	Bourbon Girl	Three Tails	11	2 38.17
1988	Sheikh Mohammed's	DIMINUENDO (7/4)	S Cauthen	H Cecil	Sudden Love	Animatrice	11	2 35.02
1989	Saeed Maktoum Al Maktoum's	SNOW BRIDE (13/2)	S Cauthen	H Cecil	Roseate Tern	Mamaluna	9	2 34.22
	(Aliysa finished first but was subsequently disqualified)							
1990	Hamdan Al-Maktoum's	SALSABIL (2/1)	W Carson	J Dunlop	Game Plan	Knight's Baroness	8	2 38.70
1991	Maktoum Al-Maktoum's	JET SKI LADY (50/1)	C Roche	J Bolger	Shamshir	Shadayid	9	2 37.30
1992	W J Gredley's	USER FRIENDLY (5/1)	G Duffield	M Brittain	All At Sea	Pearl Angel	14	2 39.77
1993	Sheikh Mohammed's	INTREPIDITY (5/1)	M Roberts	A Fabre	Royal Ballerina	Oakmead	14	2 34.19
1994	Godolphin's	BALANCHINE (6/1)	L Dettori	H Ibrahim	Wind In Her Hair	Hawajiss	10	2 40.37
1995	Maktoum Al Maktoum/ Godolphin's	MOONSHELL (3/1)	L Dettori	H Bin Suroor	Dance A Dream	Pure Grain	10	2 35.44
1996	Wafic Said's	LADY CARLA (100/30)	Pat Eddery	H Cecil	Pricket	Mezzogiorno	11	2 35.55
1997	K Abdullah's	REAMS OF VERSE (5/6)	K Fallon	H Cecil	Gazelle Royale	Crown of Light	11	2 35.59
1998	Mrs D Nagle & Mrs J Magnier's	SHAHTOUSH (12/1)	K Kinane	A O'Brien	Bahr	Midnight Line	8	2 38.23
1999	F Salman's	RAMRUMA (3/1)	K Fallon	H Cecil	Noushkey	Zahrat Dubai	10	2 38.72
2000	Lordship Stud's	LOVE DIVINE (9/4)	T Quinn	H Cecil	Kalypso Katie	Melikah	16	2 43.11
2001	Mrs D Nagle & Mrs J Magnier's	IMAGINE (3/1)	M Kinane	A O'Brien	Flight Of Fancy	Relish The Thought	14	2 36.70
2002	Godolphin's	KAZZIA (100/30)	L Dettori	S Bin Suroor	Quarter Moon	Shadow Dancing	14	2 44.52
2003	W S Farish III's	CASUAL LOOK (10/1)	M Dwyer	A Balding	Yesterday	Summitville	15	2 38.07
2004	Lord Derby's	OUIJA BOARD (7/2)	K Fallon	E Dunlop	All Too Beautiful	Punctilious	7	2 35.40
2005	Hamdan Al Maktoum's	ESWARAH (11/4)	K Fallon	M Jarvis	Something Exciting	Pictavia	12	2 39.00
2006	Mrs J Magnier, Mr M Tabor & Mr D Smith's	ALEXANDROVA (9/4)	K Fallon	A O'Brien	Rising Cross	Short Skirt	10	2 37.70
2007	Niarchos Family's	LIGHT SHIFT (13/2)	T Duncan	H Cecil	Peeping Fawn	All My Loving	14	2 40.38
2008	J H Richmond-Watson's	LOOK HERE (33/1)	S Sanders	R Beckett	Moonstone	Katiyra	16	2 36.89
2009	Lady Bamford's	SARISKA (9/4)	J Spencer	M Bell	Midday	High Heeled	15	2 35.78
2010	Aranmore Ltd's	SNOW FAIRY (9/1)	R Moore	E Dunlop	Remember When	Rumoush	15	2 35.77
	(Meznah finished second but was subsequently disqualified)							
2011	M J & L A Taylor's	DANCING RAIN (20/1)	J Murtagh	W Haggas	Wonder of Wonders	Izzi Top	13	2 41.73
2012	D Smith, Mrs J Magnier & M Tabor's	WAS (20/1)	S Heffernan	A O'Brien	Shirocco Star	The Fugue	12	2 38.68
2013	J L Rowsell & M H Dixon's	TALENT (20/1)	R Hughes	R Beckett	Secret Gesture	The Lark	11	2 42.00
2014	Hamdan Al Maktoum's	TAGHROODA (5/1)	P Hanagan	J Gosden	Tarfasha	Volume	17	2 34.89
2015	Mrs C C Regalado-Gonzalez's	QUALIFY (50/1)	C O'Donoghue	A O'Brien	Legatissimo	Lady of Dubai	17	2 37.41
2016	D Smith, Mrs J Magnier & M Tabor's	MINDING (10/11)	R Moore	A O'Brien	Architecture	Harlequeen	9	2 42.66
				A O'Brien	Rhododendron	Alluringly	9	2 34.13

DERBY STAKES (3y) Epsom-1 mile 4 furlongs 6 yards

Year	Owner	Winner and Price	Jockey	Trainer	Second	Third	Ran	Time
1981	H H Aga Khan's	SHERGAR (10/11)	W Swinburn	M Stoute	Glint of Gold	Scintillating Air	18	2 44.21
1982	R Sangster's	GOLDEN FLEECE (3/1)	Pat Eddery	V O'Brien	Touching Wood	Silver Hawk	18	2 34.27
1983	E Moller's	TEENOSO (9/2)	L Piggott	G Wragg	Carlingford Castle	Shearwalk	21	2 49.07
1984	L Miglitti's	SECRETO (14/1)	C Roche	D O'Brien	El Gran Senor	Mighty Flutter	17	2 39.12
1985	Lord H. de Walden's	SLIP ANCHOR (9/4)	S Cauthen	H Cecil	Law Society	Damister	14	2 36.23
1986	H H Aga Khan's	SHAHRASTANI (11/2)	W Swinburn	M Stoute	Dancing Brave	Mashkour	17	2 37.13
1987	L Freedman's	REFERENCE POINT (6/4)	S Cauthen	H Cecil	Most Welcome	Bellotto	19	2 33.90
1988	H H Aga Khan's	KAHYASI (11/1)	R Cochrane	L Cumani	Glacial Storm	Doyoun	14	2 33.84
1989	Hamdan Al-Maktoum's	NASHWAN (5/4)	W Carson	R Charlton	Terimon	Cacoethes	12	2 34.90
1990	K Abdulla's	QUEST FOR FAME (7/1)	Pat Eddery	R Charlton	Blue Stag	Elmaamul	18	2 37.26
1991	F Salman's	GENEROUS (9/1)	A Munro	P Cole	Marju	Star of Gdansk	13	2 34.00
1992	Sidney H Craig's	DR DEVIOUS (8/1)	J Reid	P Chapple-Hyam	St Jovite	Silver Wisp	18	2 36.19
1993	K Abdulla's	COMMANDER IN CHIEF (15/2)	M Kinane	H Cecil	Blue Judge	Blues Traveller	16	2 34.51
1994	Hamdan Al-Maktoum's	ERHAAB (7/2)	W Carson	J Dunlop	King's Theatre	Colonel Collins	25	2 34.16
1995	Saeed Maktoum Al Maktoum's	LAMMTARRA (14/1)	W Swinburn	S Bin Suroor	Tamure	Presenting	15	2 32.31
1996	K Dasmal's	SHAAMIT (12/1)	M Hills	W Haggas	Dushyantor	Shantou	20	2 35.05
1997	K Knight's	BENNY THE DIP (11/1)	W Ryan	J Gosden	Silver Patriarch	Romanov	13	2 35.77
1998	Sheikh Mohammed Obaid Al Maktoum's	HIGH-RISE (20/1)	O Peslier	L Cumani	City Honours	Border Arrow	15	2 33.88
1999	The Thoroughbred Corporation's	OATH (13/2)	K Fallon	H Cecil	Daliapour	Beat All	16	2 37.43
2000	H H Aga Khan's	SINNDAR (7/1)	J Murtagh	J Oxx	Sakhee	Beat Hollow	15	2 36.75
2001	M Tabor & Mrs J Magnier's	GALILEO (11/4)	M Kinane	A O'Brien	Golan	Tobougg	12	2 33.27
2002	M Tabor & Mrs J Magnier's	HIGH CHAPARRAL (7/2)	J Murtagh	A O'Brien	Hawk Wing	Moon Ballad	12	2 39.45
2003	Saeed Suhail's	KRIS KIN (6/1)	K Fallon	Sir M Stoute	The Great Gatsby	Alamshar	20	2 33.35
2004	Ballymacoll Stud's	NORTH LIGHT (7/2)	K Fallon	Sir M Stoute	Rule Of Law	Let The Lion Roar	14	2 33.70
2005	The Royal Ascot Racing Club's	MOTIVATOR (3/1)	J Murtagh	M Bell	Walk In The Park	Dubawi	13	2 33.60
2006	A E Pakenham's	SIR PERCY (6/1)	M Dwyer	M Tregoning	Dragon Dancer	Dylan Thomas	18	2 35.20
2007	Saleh Al Homaizi & Imad Al Sagar's	AUTHORIZED (5/4)	L Dettori	P Chapple-Hyam	Eagle Mountain	Aqaleem	17	2 34.77
2008	HRH Princess Haya of Jordan's	NEW APPROACH (5/1)	K Manning	J Bolger	Tartan Bearer	Casual Conquest	16	2 36.50
2009	C Tsui's	SEA THE STARS (11/4)	M Kinane	J Oxx	Fame And Glory	Masterofthehorse	12	2 36.74
2010	K Abdulla's	WORKFORCE (6/1)	R Moore	Sir M Stoute	At First Sight	Rewilding	12	2 31.33
2011	Mrs John Magnier, M Tabor & D Smith's	POUR MOI (4/1)	M Barzalona	A Fabre	Treasure Beach	Carlton House	13	2 34.54
2012	D Smith, Mrs J Magnier & M Tabor's	CAMELOT (8/13)	J O'Brien	A O'Brien	Main Sequence	Astrology	9	2 33.90
2013	Mrs John Magnier, Michael Tabor & Derrick Smith's	RULER OF THE WORLD (7/1)	R Moore	A O'Brien	Libertarian	Galileo Rock	12	2 39.06
2014	D Smith, Mrs J Magnier, M Tabor & T Ah King's	AUSTRALIA (11/8)	J O'Brien	A O'Brien	Kingston Hill	Romsdal	16	2 33.63
2015	A E Oppenheimer's	GOLDEN HORN (13/8)	L Dettori	J Gosden	Jack Hobbs	Storm The Stars	12	2 32.32
2016	H H Aga Khan's	HARZAND (13/2)	P Smullen	D Weld	US Army Ranger	Idaho	16	2 40.09
2017	M Tabor's	WINGS OF EAGLES (40/1)	P Beggy	A O'Brien	Cliffs of Moher	Cracksman	18	2 33.02

ST LEGER STAKES (3y) Doncaster-1 mile 6 furlongs 115 yards

Year	Owner	Winner and Price	Jockey	Trainer	Second	Third	Ran	Time
1977	The Queen's	DUNFERMLINE (10/1)	W Carson	W Hern	Alleged	Classic Example	13	3 5.17
1978	M Lemos's	JULIO MARINER (28/1)	E Hide	C Brittain	Le Moss	M-Lolshan	14	3 4.94
1979	A Rolland's	SON OF LOVE (20/1)	A Lequeux	R Collet	Soleil Noir	Niniski	17	3 9.02
1980	H Joel's	LIGHT CAVALRY (3/1)	J Mercer	H Cecil	Water Mill	World Leader	7	3 11.48
1981	Sir J Astor's	CUT ABOVE (28/1)	J Mercer	R Hern	Glint of Gold	Bustomi	7	3 11.60
1982	Maktoum Al Maktoum's	TOUCHING WOOD (7/1)	P Cook	H T Jones	Zilos	Diamond Shoal	15	3 3.53
1983	Sir M Sobell's	SUN PRINCESS (11/8)	W Carson	W Hern	Esprit du Nord	Carlingford Castle	10	3 16.65
1984	I Allan's	COMMANCHE RUN (7/4)	L Piggott	L Cumani	Baynoun	Alphabatim	11	3 9.93
1985	Sheikh Mohammed's	OH SO SHARP (8/11)	S Cauthen	H Cecil	Phardante	Lanfranco	6	3 7.13
1986	Duchess of Norfolk's	MOON MADNESS (9/2)	Pat Eddery	J Dunlop	Celestial Storm	Untold	8	3 5.03
1987	L Freedman's	REFERENCE POINT (4/11)	S Cauthen	H Cecil	Mountain Kingdom	Dry Dock	7	3 5.91
1988	Lady Beaverbrook's	MINSTER SON (15/2)	W Carson	N A Graham	Diminuendo	Sheriff's Star	6	3 6.80
1989	C St George's	MICHELOZZO (6/4)	S Cauthen	H Cecil	Sapience	Roseate Tern	8	3 20.72
	(Run at Ayr)							
1990	M Arbib's	SNURGE (7/2)	T Quinn	P Cole	Hellenic	River God	8	3 8.78
1991	K Abdullah's	TOULON (5/2)	Pat Eddery	A Fabre	Saddlers' Hall	Micheletti	7	3 3.12
1992	W J Gredley's	USER FRIENDLY (7/4)	G Duffield	C Brittain	Sonus	Bonny Scot	10	3 5.48
1993	Ms G A E Smith's	BOB'S RETURN (3/1)	Pat Eddery	M Tompkins	Armiger	Edbaysaan	8	3 7.85
1994	Sheikh Mohammed's	MOONAX (40/1)	Pat Eddery	B Hills	Broadway Flyer	Double Trigger	8	3 4.19
1995	Godolphin's	CLASSIC CLICHE (100/30)	L Dettori	S Bin Suroor	Minds Music	Istidaad	10	3 9.74
1996	Sheikh Mohammed's	SHANTOU (8/1)	L Dettori	J Gosden	Dushyantor	Samraan	11	3 5.10
1997	P Winfield's	SILVER PATRIARCH (5/4)	Pat Eddery	J Dunlop	Vertical Speed	The Fly	9	3 6.92
1998	Godolphin's	NEDAWI (5/2)	L Dettori	S Bin Suroor	High and Low	Sunshine Street	9	3 5.61
1999	Godolphin's	MUTAFAWEQ (11/2)	R Hills	S Bin Suroor	Ramruma	Adair	9	3 2.75
2000	N Jones'	MILLENARY (11/4)	T Quinn	J Dunlop	Air Marshall	Chimes At Midnight	11	3 2.58
2001	M Tabor & Mrs J Magnier's	MILAN (13/8)	M Kinane	A O'Brien	Demophilos	Mr Combustible	10	3 5.16
2002	Sir Neil Westbrook's	BOLLIN ERIC (7/1)	K Darley	T Easterby	Highest	Bandari	8	3 2.92
2003	Mrs J Magnier's	BRIAN BORU (5/4)	J P Spencer	A O'Brien	High Accolade	Phoenix Reach	12	3 4.64
2004	Godolphin's	RULE OF LAW (3/1)	K McEvoy	S Bin Suroor	Quiff	Tycoon	6	3 6.20
2005	M J Magnier & M Tabor's	SCORPION (10/11)	L Dettori	A O'Brien	The Geezer	Tawqeet	6	3 19.00
2006	Mrs S Roy's	SIXTIES ICON (11/8)	L Dettori	J Noseda	The Last Drop	Red Rocks	11	2 57.20
2007	G Strawbridge's	LUCARNO (7/2)	J Fortune	J Gosden	Mahler	Honolulu	10	3 1.90
2008	Ballymacoll Stud's	CONDUIT (14/1)	L Dettori	Sir M Stoute	Unsung Heroine	Look Here	14	3 7.92
2009	Godolphin's	MASTERY (14/1)	T Durcan	Sir M Suroor	Kite Wood	Monitor Closely	10	3 4.81
2010	Ms R Hood & R Geffen's	ARCTIC COSMOS (12/1)	W Buick	J Gosden	Midas Touch	Corsica	10	3 3.12
2011	B Nielsen's	MASKED MARVEL (15/2)	W Buick	J Gosden	Brown Panther	Sea Moon	10	3 0.44
2012	Godolphin's	ENCKE (25/1)	M Barzalona	M Al Zarooni	Camelot	Michelangelo	9	3 3.81
2013	Derrick Smith & Mrs John Magnier & Michael Tabor's	LEADING LIGHT (7/2)	J O'Brien	A O'Brien	Talent	Galileo Rock	11	3 9.20
2014	Paul Smith's	KINGSTON HILL (9/4)	A Atzeni	R Varian	Romsdal	Snow Sky	12	3 5.42
2015	QRL Sheikh Suhaim Al Thani & M Al Kubaisi's	SIMPLE VERSE (8/1)	A Atzeni	R Beckett	Bondi Beach	Fields of Athenry	.7	3 7.12
2016	Mrs Jackie Cornwell's	HARBOUR LAW (22/1)	G Baker	Mrs L Mongan	Ventura Storm	Housesofparliament	9	3 5.48
2017	Derrick Smith & Mrs John Magnier & Capri	CAPRI (3/1)	R Moore	A O'Brien	Crystal Ocean	Stradivarius	11	3 4.04

KING GEORGE VI AND QUEEN ELIZABETH STAKES Ascot-1 mile 3 furlongs 211 yards

Year	Owner	Winner and Price	Trainer	Jockey	Second	Third	Ran	Time
1979	Sir M Sobell's	TROY 3-8-8 (2/5)	W Hern	W Carson	Gay Mecene	Ela-Mara-Mou	10	2 33.75
1980	S Weinstock's	ELA-MARA-MOU 4-9-7 (11/4)	W Hern	W Carson	Mrs Penny	Gregorian	7	2 35.39
1981	H H Aga Khan's	SHERGAR 3-8-8 (2/5)	M Stoute	W Swinburn	Madam Gay	Fingals Cave	7	2 35.40
1982	A Ward's	KALAGLOW 4-9-7 (13-2)	G Harwood	G Starkey	Assert	Glint of Gold	9	2 31.58
1983	R Barnett's	TIME CHARTER 4-9-4 (5/1)	H Candy	J Mercer	Diamond Shoal	Sun Princess	8	2 30.78
1984	E Moller's	TEENOSO 4-9-7 (13/2)	G Wragg	L Piggott	Sadler's Wells	Tolomeo	9	2 27.95
1985	Lady Beaverbrook's	PETOSKI 3-8-8 (12/1)	W Hern	W Carson	Oh So Sharp	Rainbow Quest	12	2 27.61
1986	R Abdullah's	DANCING BRAVE 3-8-8 (6/4)	G Harwood	Pat Eddery	Shardari	Triptych	9	2 29.49
1987	L Freedman's	REFERENCE POINT 3-8-8 (11/10)	H Cecil	S Cauthen	Celestial Storm	Triptych	9	2 34.63
1988	Hamdan Al-Maktoum's	MTOTO 5-9-7 (4/1)	A C Stewart	M Roberts	Untouwan	Tony Bin	10	2 37.33
1989	Sheikh Mohammed's	NASHWAN 3-8-8 (2/9)	R Hern	W Carson	Cacoethes	Top Class	7	2 32.27
1990	Sheikh Mohammed's	BELMEZ 3-8-8 (15/2)	H Cecil	M Kinane	Old Vic	Assatis	11	2 30.76
1991	F Salman's	GENEROUS 3-8-9 (4/6)	P Cole	A Munro	Sanglamore	Rock Hopper	9	2 28.99
1992	Mrs V K Payson's	ST JOVITE 3-8-9 (4/5)	J Bolger	S Craine	Saddlers' Hall	Opera House	8	2 30.85
1993	Sheikh Mohammed's	OPERA HOUSE 5-9-7 (8/1)	M Stoute	M Roberts	White Muzzle	Commander in Chief	10	2 33.94
1994	Sheikh Mohammed's	KING'S THEATRE 3-8-9 (12/1)	H Cecil	M Kinane	White Muzzle	Wagon Master	7	2 28.92
1995	Saeed Mohammed's	LAMMTARRA 3-8-9 (9/4)	S Bin Suroor	L Dettori	Pentire	Strategic Choice	12	2 31.01
	Al Maktoum's							
1996	Mollers Racing's	PENTIRE 4-9-7 (100/30)	G Wragg	M Hills	Classic Cliche	Shaamit	8	2 28.11
1997	Godolphin's	SWAIN 5-9-7 (16/1)	S Bin Suroor	J Reid	Pilsudski	Helissio	8	2 36.45
1998	Godolphin's	SWAIN 6-9-7 (11/2)	S Bin Suroor	L Dettori	High-Rise	Royal Anthem	8	2 29.06
1999	Godolphin's	DAYLAMI 5-9-7 (3/1)	S Bin Suroor	L Dettori	Nedawi	Fruits Of Love	8	2 29.35
2000	M Tabor's	MONTJEU 4-9-7 (1/3)	J Hammond	M Kinane	Fantastic Light	Daliapour	8	2 29.98
2001	Mrs J Magnier & M Tabor's	GALILEO 3-8-9 (1/2)	A O'Brien	M Kinane	Fantastic Light	Hightori	7	2 27.71
2002	Exors of the late Lord Weinstock's	GOLAN 4-9-7 (11/2)	Sir M Stoute	K Fallon	Nayef	Zindabad	9	2 29.70
2003	H H Aga Khan	ALAMSHAR 3-8-9 (13/2)	J Oxx	J Murtagh	Sulamani	Kris Kin	10	2 33.26
2004	Godolphin's	DOYEN 4-9-7 (11/10)	S Bin Suroor	L Dettori	Hard Buck	Sulamani	11	2 33.10
2005	H H Aga Khan's	AZAMOUR 4-9-7 (5/2)	J Oxx	M Kinane	Norse Dancer	Bago	12	2 28.20
	(Run at Newbury)							
2006	M Tabor's	HURRICANE RUN 4-9-7 (5/6)	A Fabre	C Soumillon	Electrocutionist	Heart's Cry	6	2 30.20
2007	Mrs J Magnier & M Tabor's	DYLAN THOMAS 4-9-7 (5/4)	A O'Brien	J Murtagh	Youmzain	Maraahel	7	2 31.10
2008	Mrs J Magnier & M Tabor's	DUKE OF MARMALADE 4-9-7 (4/6)	A O'Brien	J Murtagh	Papal Bull	Youmzain	8	2 27.91
2009	Ballymacoll Stud's	CONDUIT 4-9-7 (13/8)	Sir M Stoute	R Moore	Tartan Bearer	Ask	9	2 28.73
2010	Highclere Thoroughbred Racing (Adm. Rous)'s	HARBINGER 4-9-7 (4/1)	Sir M Stoute	O Peslier	Cape Blanco	Youmzain	6	2 26.78
2011	Lady Rothschild's	NATHANIEL 3-8-9 (11/2)	J Gosden	W Buick	Workforce	St Nicholas Abbey	5	2 35.07
2012	Gestut Burg Eberstein & Teruya Yoshida's	DANEDREAM 4-9-4 (9/1)	P Schiergen	A Starke	Nathaniel	St Nicholas Abbey	10	2 31.62
2013	Dr Christophe Berglar's	NOVELLIST 4-9-7 (13/2)	A Wohler	J Murtagh	Trading Leather	Hillstar	8	2 24.60
2014	Hamdan Al Maktoum's	TAGHROODA 3-8-6 (7/2)	J Gosden	P Hanagan	Telescope	Mukhadram	8	2 28.13
2015	Sheikh Mohammed Obaid Al Maktoum's	POSTPONED 4-9-7 (6/1)	L Currani	A Atzeni	Eagle Top	Romsdal	7	2 31.25
2016	D Smith, Mrs J Magnier & M Tabor's	HIGHLAND REEL 4-9-7 (13/8)	A O'Brien	R Moore	Wings of Desire	Dartmouth	7	2 28.97
2017	K Abdullah's	ENABLE 3-8-7 (5/4)	J Gosden	L Dettori	Ulysses	Idaho	10	2 36.22

PRIX DE L'ARC DE TRIOMPHE Longchamp-1 mile 4 furlongs

Year	Owner	Winner and Price	Jockey	Trainer	Second	Third	Ran	Time
1979	Mme G Head's	THREE TROIKAS 3-8-8 (88/10)	F Head	Mme C Head	Le Marmot	Troy	22	2 28.90
1980	R Sangster's	DETROIT 3-8-8 (67/10)	Pat Eddery	O Douieb	Argument	Ela-Mana-Mou	20	2 28.00
1981	J Wertheimer's	GOLD RIVER 4-9-1 (53/1)	G W Moore	A Head	Bikala	April Run	24	2 35.20
1982	H H Aga Khan's	AKIYDA 3-8-8 (43/4)	Y Saint Martin	F Mathet	Ardross	Awaasif	17	2 37.00
1983	D Wildenstein's	ALL ALONG 4-9-1 (173/10)	W Swinburn	P Biancone	Sun Princess	Luth Enchantee	26	2 28.10
1984	D Wildenstein's	SAGACE 4-9-4 (29/10)	Y Saint Martin	P Biancone	Northern Trick	All Along	22	2 39.10
1985	K Abdullah's	RAINBOW QUEST 4-9-4 (71/10)	Pat Eddery	J Tree	Sagace	Kozana	15	2 29.50
	(The first two placings were reversed by the Stewards)							
1986	K Abdullah's	DANCING BRAVE 3-8-11 (11/10)	Pat Eddery	G Harwood	Bering	Triptych	15	2 27.70
1987	P de Moussac's	TREMPOLINO 3-8-11 (20/1)	Pat Eddery	A Fabre	Tony Bin	Triptych	11	2 26.30
1988	Mrs V Gaucci del Bono's	TONY BIN 5-9-4 (14/1)	J Reid	L Camici	Mtoto	Boyatino	24	2 27.30
1989	A Balzarini's	CARROLL HOUSE 4-9-4 (19/1)	M Kinane	N Clement	Behera	Saint Andrews	19	2 30.80
1990	B McHall's	SAUMAREZ 3-8-11 (15/1)	G Mosse	N Clement	Epervier Bleu	Snurge	21	2 29.80
1991	H Chalhoub's	SUAVE DANCER 3-8-11 (37/10)	C Asmussen	J Hammond	Magic Night	Pistolet Bleu	14	2 31.40
1992	O Lecerf's	SUBOTICA 4-9-4 (88/10)	T Jarnet	A Fabre	User Friendly	Vert Amande	18	2 39.00
1993	D Tsui's	URBAN SEA 4-9-1 (37/1)	E Saint Martin	J Lesbordes	White Muzzle	Opera House	23	2 37.90
1994	Sheikh Mohammed's	CARNEGIE 3-8-11 (3/1)	T Jarnet	A Fabre	Hernando	Apple Tree	20	2 31.10
1995	Saeed Maktoum Al Maktoum's	LAMMTARRA 3-8-11 (2/1)	L Dettori	S Bin Suroor	Freedom Cry	Swain	16	2 31.80
1996	E Sarasola's	HELISSIO 3-8-11 (18/10)	O Peslier	E Lellouche	Pilsudski	Oscar Schindler	16	2 29.90
1997	D Wildenstein's	PEINTRE CELEBRE 3-8-11 (22/10)	O Peslier	A Fabre	Pilsudski	Borgia	18	2 24.60
1998	J-L Lagardere's	SAGAMIX 3-8-11 (5/2)	O Peslier	A Fabre	Leggera	Tiger Hill	14	2 34.50
1999	M Tabor's	MONTJEU 3-8-11 (6/4)	M Kinane	J Hammond	El Condor Pasa	Croco Rouge	14	2 38.50
2000	Godolphin's	SINNDAR 3-8-11 (6/4)	J Murtagh	Jox	Egyptband	Volvoreta	10	2 25.80
2001	Godolphin's	SAKHEE 4-9-5 (22/10)	L Dettori	S Bin Suroor	Aquarelliste	Sagacity	17	2 36.10
2002	Godolphin's	MARIENBARD 5-9-5 (158/10)	L Dettori	S Bin Suroor	Sulamani	High Chaparral	16	2 26.70
2003	H H Aga Khan's	DALAKHANI 3-8-11 (9/4)	C Soumillon	A De Royer-Dupre	Mubtaker	High Chaparral	13	2 32.30
2004	Niarchos Family's	BAGO 3-8-11 (10/1)	T Gillet	J E Pease	Cherry Mix	Ouija Board	13	2 25.00
2005	M Tabor's	HURRICANE RUN 3-8-11 (11/4)	K Fallon	A Fabre	Westerner	Bago	15	2 27.40
2006	K Abdullah's	RAIL LINK 3-8-11 (8/1)	S Pasquier	A Fabre	Pride	Hurricane Run	8	2 26.30
	(Deep Impact disqualified from third place)							
2007	Mrs J Magnier & M Tabor's	DYLAN THOMAS 4-9-5 (11/2)	K Fallon	A O'Brien	Youmzain	Sagara	12	2 28.50
2008	H H Aga Khan's	ZARKAVA 3-8-8 (13/8)	C Soumillon	A De Royer-Dupre	Youmzain	Soldier of Fortune/It's Gino	16	2 28.80
2009	C Tsui's	SEA THE STARS 3-8-11 (4/6)	M Kinane	J Oxx	Youmzain	Cavalryman	19	2 26.30
2010	K Abdullah's	WORKFORCE 3-8-11 (6/1)	R Moore	Sir M Stoute	Nakayama Festa	Sarafina	19	2 35.30
2011	Gestut Burg Eberstein & Y Yoshida's	DANEDREAM 3-8-8 (20/1)	A Starke	P Schiergen	Shareta	Snow Fairy	16	2 24.49
2012	Wertheimer & Frere's	SOLEMIA 4-9-2 (33/1)	O Peslier	C Laffon-Parias	Orfevre	Masterstroke	18	2 37.68
2013	H E Sheikh Joaan Bin Hamad Al Thani's	TREVE 3-8-8 (9/2)	T Jarnet	Mme C Head-Maarek	Orfevre	Intello	17	2 32.04
2014	Al Shaqab Racing's	TREVE 4-9-2 (11/1)	T Jarnet	Mme C Head-Maarek	Flintshire	Taghrooda	20	2 26.05
2015	A E Oppenheimer's	GOLDEN HORN 3-8-11 (9/2)	L Dettori	J Gosden	Flintshire	New Bay	17	2 27.23
2016	M Tabor, D Smith & Mrs J Magnier's	FOUND 4-9-2 (6/1)	R Moore	A O'Brien	Highland Reel	Order of St George	16	2 23.61
	(Run at Chantilly)							
2017	K Abdullah's	ENABLE 3-8-9 (10/11)	L Dettori	J Gosden	Cloth of Stars	Ulysses	18	2 28.69
	(Run at Chantilly)							

GRAND NATIONAL STEEPLECHASE Aintree 4m 2f 74y (4m 4f before 2013)

Year	Winner and Price	Age & Weight	Jockey	Second	Third	Ran	Time
1972	WELL TO DO (14/1)	9 10 1	G Thorner	Gay Trip	Black Secret/General Symons		10 08.40
1973	RED RUM (9/1)	8 10 5	B Fletcher	Crisp	L'Escargot	38	9 01.90
1974	RED RUM (11/1)	9 12 0	B Fletcher	L'Escargot	Charles Dickens	42	9 20.30
1975	L'ESCARGOT (13/2)	12 11 3	T Carberry	Red Rum	Spanish Steps	31	9 31.10
1976	RAG TRADE (14/1)	10 10 12	J Burke	Red Rum	Eyecatcher	32	9 20.90
1977	RED RUM (9/1)	12 11 8	T Stack	Churchtown Boy	Eyecatcher	42	9 30.30
1978	LUCIUS (14/1)	9 10 9	B R Davies	Sebastian V	Drumroan	37	9 33.90
1979	RUBSTIC (25/1)	10 10 0	M Barnes	Zongalero	Rough and Tumble	34	9 52.90
1980	BEN NEVIS (40/1)	12 10 12	Mr C Fenwick	Rough and Tumble	The Pilgarlic	30	10 17.40
1981	ALDANITI (10/1)	11 10 13	R Champion	Spartan Missile	Royal Mail.	39	9 47.20
1982	GRITTAR (7/1)	9 11 5	Mr C Saunders	Hard Outlook	Loving Words.	39	9 12.60
1983	CORBIERE (13/1)	8 11 4	B de Haan	Greasepaint	Yer Man.	41	9 47.04
1984	HALLO DANDY (13/1)	10 10 2	N Doughty	Greasepaint	Corbiere.	40	9 21.04
1985	LAST SUSPECT (50/1)	11 10 5	H Davies	Mr Snugfit	Corbiere.	40	9 42.70
1986	WEST TIP (15/2)	9 10 11	R Dunwoody	Young Driver	Classified.	40	9 33.00
1987	MAORI VENTURE (28/1)	11 10 13	S Knight	The Tsarevich	Lean Ar Aghaidh	40	9 19.30
1988	RHYME 'N' REASON (10/1)	9 11 0	B Powell	Durham Edition.	Monanore.	40	9 53.50
1989	LITTLE POLVEIR (28/1)	12 10 3	J Frost	West Tip	The Thinker	40	10 06.80
1990	MR FRISK (16/1)	11 10 6	Mr M Armytage	Durham Edition.	Rinus.	38	8 47.80
1991	SEAGRAM (12/1)	11 10 6	N Hawke	Garrison Savannah.	Auntie Dot.	40	9 29.90
1992	PARTY POLITICS (14/1)	8 10 7	C Llewellyn	Romany King	Laura's Beau.	40	9 06.30
1993	Race Void – false start						
1994	MINNEHOMA (16/1)	11 10 8	R Dunwoody	Just So.	Moorcroft Boy	36	10 18.80
1995	ROYAL ATHLETE (40/1)	12 10 6	J Titley	Party Politics	Over The Deel.	35	9 04.00
1996	ROUGH QUEST (7/1)	10 10 7	M Fitzgerald	Encore Un Peu.	Superior Finish.	27	9 00.80
1997	LORD GYLLENE (14/1)	9 10 0	A Dobbin	Suny Bay	Camelot Knight.	36	9 05.80
1998	EARTH SUMMIT (7/1)	10 10 5	C Llewellyn	Suny Bay	Samlee.	37	10 51.40
1999	BOBBYJO (10/1)	9 10 0	P Carberry	Blue Charm.	Call It A Day.	32	9 14.00
2000	PAPILLON (10/1)	9 10 12	R Walsh	Mely Moss	Niki Dee	40	9 09.70
2001	RED MARAUDER (33/1)	11 10 11	R Guest	Smarty	Blowing Wind.	40	11 00.10
2002	BINDAREE (20/1)	8 10 4	J Culloty	What's Up Boys	Blowing Wind.	40	9 01.50
2003	MONTY'S PASS (16/1)	10 10 7	B J Geraghty	Supreme Glory.	Amberleigh House.	40	9 21.70
2004	AMBERLEIGH HOUSE (16/1)	12 10 10	G Lee	Clan Royal	Lord Atterbury.	39	9 20.30
2005	HEDGEHUNTER (7/1)	9 11 1	R Walsh	Royal Auclair	Simply Gifted.	40	9 20.80
2006	NUMBERSIXVALVERDE (11/1)	10 10 8	N Madden	Hedgehunter.	Clan Royal.	40	9 41.00
2007	SILVER BIRCH (33/1)	10 10 6	R M Power	McKelvey	Slim Pickings	40	9 13.60
2008	COMPLY OR DIE (7/1)	9 10 9	T Murphy	King Johns Castle	Snowy Morning.	40	9 16.60
2009	MON MOME (100/1)	9 11 0	L Treadwell	Comply Or Die.	My Will.	40	9 32.90
2010	DON'T PUSH IT (10/1)	10 11 5	A P McCoy	Black Apalachi	State Of Play.	40	9 04.60
2011	BALLABRIGGS (14/1)	10 11 0	J Maguire	Oscar Time.	Don't Push It.	40	9 01.20
2012	NEPTUNE COLLONGES (33/1)	11 11 6	D Jacob	Sunnyhillboy	Seabass.	40	9 05.10
2013	AURORAS ENCORE (66/1)	11 10 3	R Mania	Cappa Bleu	Teaforthree.	40	9 12.00
2014	PINEAU DE RE (25/1)	11 10 6	L Aspell	Balthazar King	Double Seven	40	9 09.90
2015	MANY CLOUDS (25/1)	8 11 9	L Aspell	Saint Are	Monbeg Dude.	39	8 56.80
2016	RULE THE WORLD (33/1)	9 10 7	D Mullins	The Last Samuri.	Vics Canvas.	39	9 29.00
2017	ONE FOR ARTHUR (14/1)	8 10 11	D Fox	Cause of Causes	Saint Are.	40	9 03.50

WINNERS OF GREAT RACES

LINCOLN HANDICAP
Doncaster-1m

2008	**SMOKEY OAKEY** 4-8-9	21
2009	**EXPRESSO STAR** 4-8-12	20
2010	**PENITENT** 4-9-2	21
2011	**SWEET LIGHTNING** 6-9-4	21
2012	**BRAE HILL** 6-9-1	22
2013	**LEVITATE** 5-8-4	22
2014	**OCEAN TEMPEST** 5-9-3	17
2015	**GABRIAL** 6-9-0	22
2016	**SECRET BRIEF** 4-9-4	22
2017	**BRAVERY** 4-9-1	22

GREENHAM STAKES (3y)
Newbury-7f

2008	**PACO BOY** 9-0	8
2009	**VOCALISED** 9-0	8
2010	**DICK TURPIN** 9-0	5
2011	**FRANKEL** 9-0	6
2012	**CASPAR NETSCHER** 9-0	5
2013	**OLYMPIC GLORY** 9-0	5
2014	**KINGMAN** 9-0	10
2015	**MUHAARAR** 9-0	10
*2016	**TASLEET** 9-0	3
2017	**BARNEY ROY** 9-0	10

*Run at Chelmsford City on Polytrack

EUROPEAN FREE HANDICAP (3y)
Newmarket-7f

2008	**STIMULATION** 9-3	11
2009	**OUQBA** 8-9	10
2010	**RED JAZZ** 9-6	7
2011	**PAUSANIAS** 8-12	6
2012	**TELWAAR** 8-11	7
2013	**GARSWOOD** 9-0	10
2014	**SHIFTING POWER** 9-1	5
2015	**HOME OF THE BRAVE** 8-13	6
2016	**IBN MALIK** 9-6	6
2017	**WHITECLIFFSOFDOVER** 9-7	7

CRAVEN STAKES (3y)
Newmarket-1m

2008	**TWICE OVER** 8-12	10
2009	**DELEGATOR** 8-12	7
2010	**ELUSIVE PIMPERNEL** 8-12	9
2011	**NATIVE KHAN** 8-12	6
2012	**TRUMPET MAJOR** 9-1	12
2013	**TORONADO** 9-0	4
2014	**TOORMORE** 9-3	6
2015	**KOOL KOMPANY** 9-0	7
2016	**STORMY ANTARCTIC** 9-0	6
2017	**EMINENT** 9-0	7

JOCKEY CLUB STAKES
Newmarket-1m 4f

2008	**GETAWAY** 5-9-1	10
2009	**BRONZE CANNON** 4-8-12	3
2010	**JUKEBOX JURY** 4-9-3	5
2011	**DANDINO** 4-8-11	6
2012	**AL KAZEEM** 4-8-12	8
2013	**UNIVERSAL** 4-8-12	8
2014	**GOSPEL CHOIR** 5-9-0	8

SANDOWN MILE
Sandown-1m

2008	**MAJOR CADEAUX** 4-9-0	8
2009	**PACO BOY** 4-9-6	7
2010	**PACO BOY** 5-9-0	9
2011	**DICK TURPIN** 4-9-0	5
2012	**PENITENT** 6-9-0	6
2013	**TRUMPET MAJOR** 4-9-0	7
2014	**TULLIUS** 6-9-1	6
2015	**CUSTOM CUT** 6-9-5	6
2016	**TOORMORE** 5-9-4	7
2017	**SOVEREIGN DEBT** 8-9-1	9

CHESTER VASE (3y)
Chester-1m 4f 63yds

2008	**DOCTOR FREMANTLE** 8-12	8
2009	**GOLDEN SWORD** 8-12	8
2010	**TED SPREAD** 8-12	7
2011	**TREASURE BEACH** 8-12	6
2012	**MICKDAAM** 8-12	5
2013	**RULER OF THE WORLD** 8-12	4
2014	**ORCHESTRA** 9-0	8
2015	**HANS HOLBEIN** 9-0	6
2016	**US ARMY RANGER** 9-0	6
2017	**VENICE BEACH** 9-0	8

CHESTER CUP
Chester-2m 2f 140yds

2008	**BULWARK** 6-9-4	17
2009	**DARAAHEM** 4-9-0	17
2010	**MAMLOOK** 6-8-12	17
2011	**OVERTURN** 7-8-13	17
2012	**ILE DE RE** 6-8-11	17
2013	**ADDRESS UNKNOWN** 6-9-0	17
2014	**SUEGIOO** 5-9-4	17
2015	**TRIP TO PARIS** 4-8-9	17
2016	**NO HERETIC** 8-8-13	17
2017	**MONTALY** 6-9-6	17

OAKS TRIAL (3y fillies)
Lingfield-1m 3f 133yds

2008	**MIRACLE SEEKER** 8-12	6
2009	**MIDDAY** 8-12	9
2010	**DYNA WALTZ** 8-12	5
2011	**ZAIN AL BOLDAN** 8-12	9
*2012	**VOW** 8-12	8
2013	**SECRET GESTURE** 8-12	8
2014	**HONOR BOUND** 9-0	10
2015	**TOUJOURS L'AMOUR** 9-0	10
2016	**SEVENTH HEAVEN** 9-0	6
2017	**HERTFORD DANCER** 9-0	6

*Run over 1m4f on Polytrack

DERBY TRIAL (3y)
Lingfield-1m 3f 133yds

2008	**ALESSANDRO VOLTA** 8-12	5
2009	**AGE OF AQUARIUS** 8-12	
2010	**BULLET TRAIN** 8-12	7

SANDOWN MILE
(continued at right)

2015	**SECOND STEP** 4-9-0	4
2016	**EXOSPHERE** 4-9-0	6
2017	**SEVENTH HEAVEN** 4-9-1	5

2011 **DORDOGNE** 8-12 6
*2012 **MAIN SEQUENCE** 8-12 8
2013 **NEVIS** 8-12 6
2014 **SNOW SKY** 9-0 9
2015 **KILIMANJARO** 9-0 5
2016 **HUMPHREY BOGART** 9-0 5
2017 **BEST SOLUTION** 9-5 8
*Run over 1m4f on Polytrack

MUSIDORA STAKES (3y fillies)
York-1m 2f 56yds
2008 **LUSH LASHES** 8-12 8
2009 **SARISKA** 8-12 6
2010 **AVIATE** 8-12 8
2011 **JOVIALITY** 8-12 5
2012 **THE FUGUE** 8-12 6
2013 **LIBER NAUTICUS** 8-12 6
2014 **MADAME CHIANG** 9-0 9
2015 **STAR OF SEVILLE** 9-0 5
2016 **SO MI DAR** 9-0 7
2017 **SHUTTER SPEED** 9-0 5

DANTE STAKES (3y)
York-1m 2f 56yds
2008 **TARTAN BEARER** 9-0 6
2009 **BLACK BEAR ISLAND** 9-0 10
2010 **CAPE BLANCO** 9-0 5
2011 **CARLTON HOUSE** 9-0 6
2012 **BONFIRE** 9-0 6
2013 **LIBERTARIAN** 9-0 8
2014 **THE GREY GATSBY** 9-0 6
2015 **GOLDEN HORN** 9-0 7
2016 **WINGS OF DESIRE** 9-0 9
2017 **PERMIAN** 9-0 10

MIDDLETON STAKES
(fillies and mares)
York-1m 2f 56yds
2008 **PROMISING LEAD** 4-8-12 5
2009 **CRYSTAL CAPELLA** 4-9-2 5
2010 **SARISKA** 4-8-12 4
2011 **MIDDAY** 5-9-3 8
2012 **IZZI TOP** 4-8-12 9
2013 **DALKALA** 4-9-0 8
2014 **AMBIVALENT** 5-9-0 8
2015 **SECRET GESTURE** 5-9-0 8
2016 **BEAUTIFUL ROMANCE** 4-9-0 7
2017 **BLOND ME** 5-9-0 4

YORKSHIRE CUP
York-1m 5f 188yds
2008 **GEORDIELAND** 7-8-12 5
2009 **ASK** 6-8-13 8
2010 **MANIFEST** 4-8-12 5
2011 **DUNCAN** 6-9-2 8
2012 **RED CADEAUX** 6-9-0 8
2013 **GLEN'S DIAMOND** 5-9-0 8
2014 **GOSPEL CHOIR** 5-9-0 12
2015 **SNOW SKY** 4-9-0 6
2016 **CLEVER COOKIE** 8-9-1 5
2017 **DARTMOUTH** 5-9-1 8

DUKE OF YORK STAKES
York-6f
2008 **ASSERTIVE** 5-9-7 17
2009 **UTMOST RESPECT** 5-9-7 16
2010 **PRIME DEFENDER** 6-9-7 12
2011 **DELEGATOR** 5-9-7 14
2012 **TIDDLIWINKS** 6-9-7 13
2013 **SOCIETY ROCK** 6-9-13 17
2014 **MAAREK** 7-9-13 13
2015 **GLASS OFFICE** 5-9-8 15
2016 **MAGICAL MEMORY** 4-9-8 12
2017 **TASLEET** 4-9-8 12

LOCKINGE STAKES
Newbury-1m
2008 **CREACHADOIR** 4-9-0 11
2009 **VIRTUAL** 4-9-0 11
2010 **PACO BOY** 5-9-0 9
2011 **CANFORD CLIFFS** 4-9-0 7
2012 **FRANKEL** 4-9-0 6
2013 **FARHH** 5-9-0 12
2014 **OLYMPIC GLORY** 4-9-0 8
2015 **NIGHT OF THUNDER** 4-9-0 16
2016 **BELARDO** 4-9-0 12
2017 **RIBCHESTER** 4-9-0 8

HENRY II STAKES
Sandown-2m 50yds
2008 **FINALMENTE** 6-9-2 8
2009 **GEORDIELAND** 8-9-2 7
2010 **AKMAL** 4-9-0 9
2011 **BLUE BAJAN** 9-9-2 8
2012 **OPINION POLL** 4-9-0 10
2013 **GLOOMY SUNDAY** 4-8-11 10
2014 **BROWN PANTHER** 6-9-4 11
2015 **VENT DE FORCE** 4-9-0 7
2016 **PALLASATOR** 7-9-6 4
2017 **BIG ORANGE** 6-9-2 7

TEMPLE STAKES
Haydock-5f
2008 **FLEETING SPIRIT** 3-8-11 12
2009 **LOOK BUSY** 4-9-1 9
2010 **KINGSGATE NATIVE** 5-9-4 9
2011 **SOLE POWER** 4-9-4 12
2012 **BATED BREATH** 5-9-4 12
2013 **KINGSGATE NATIVE** 8-9-4 10
2014 **HOT STREAK** 3-8-10 9
2015 **PEARL SECRET** 6-9-4 11
2016 **PROFITABLE** 4-9-4 11
2017 **PRICELESS** 4-9-1 12

BRIGADIER GERARD STAKES
Sandown-1m 2f 219yds
2008 **SMOKEY OAKEY** 4-9-0 14
2009 **CIMA DE TRIOMPHE** 4-9-0 12
2010 **STOTSFOLD** 7-9-0 8
2011 **WORKFORCE** 4-9-7 8
2012 **CARLTON HOUSE** 4-9-0 6
2013 **MUKHADRAM** 4-9-0 5
2014 **SHARESTAN** 6-9-0 3
2015 **WESTERN HYMN** 4-9-3 5
2016 **TIME TEST** 4-9-5 7
2017 **AUTOCRATIC** 4-9-0 7

CORONATION CUP
Epsom-1m 4f 6yds
2008	SOLDIER OF FORTUNE 4-9-0	11
2009	ASK 6-9-0	8
2010	FAME AND GLORY 4-9-0	9
2011	ST NICHOLAS ABBEY 4-9-0	5
2012	ST NICHOLAS ABBEY 5-9-0	6
2013	ST NICHOLAS ABBEY 6-9-0	5
2014	CIRRUS DES AIGLES 8-9-0	7
2015	PETHER'S MOON 5-9-0	4
2016	POSTPONED 5-9-0	8
2017	HIGHLAND REEL 5-9-0	10

CHARITY SPRINT HANDICAP (3y)
York-6f
2008	BRAVE PROSPECTOR 9-0	19
2009	SWISS DIVA 9-1	20
2010	VICTOIRE DE LYPHAR 8-7	20
2011	LEXI'S HERO 8-11	20
2012	SHOLAAN 8-9	17
2013	BODY AND SOUL 8-11	19
2014	SEE THE SUN 8-7	20
2015	TWILIGHT SON 8-10	16
2016	MR LUPTON 9-7	17
2017	GOLDEN APOLLO 8-3	18

QUEEN ANNE STAKES
Ascot-1m (st)
2008	HARADASUN 5-9-0	11
2009	PACO BOY 4-9-0	9
2010	GOLDIKOVA 5-8-11	10
2011	CANFORD CLIFFS 4-9-0	7
2012	FRANKEL 4-9-0	11
2013	DECLARATION OF WAR 4-9-0	13
2014	TORONADO 4-9-0	10
2015	SOLOW 5-9-0	8
2016	TEPIN 5-8-11	13
2017	RIBCHESTER 4-9-0	16

PRINCE OF WALES'S STAKES
Ascot-1m 2f
2008	DUKE OF MARMALADE 4-9-0	12
2009	VISION D'ETAT 4-9-0	8
2010	BYWORD 4-9-0	12
2011	REWILDING 4-9-0	7
2012	SO YOU THINK 6-9-0	11
2013	AL KAZEEM 5-9-0	11
2014	THE FUGUE 5-8-11	8
2015	FREE EAGLE 4-9-0	9
2016	MY DREAM BOAT 4-9-0	6
2017	HIGHLAND REEL 5-9-0	8

ST JAMES'S PALACE STAKES (3y)
Ascot-7f 213yds (rnd)
2008	HENRYTHENAVIGATOR 9-0	8
2009	MASTERCRAFTSMAN 9-0	10
2010	CANFORD CLIFFS 9-0	9
2011	FRANKEL 9-0	9
2012	MOST IMPROVED 9-0	16
2013	DAWN APPROACH 9-0	9
2014	KINGMAN 9-0	7
2015	GLENEAGLES 9-0	5
2016	GALILEO GOLD 9-0	7
2017	BARNEY ROY 9-0	8

COVENTRY STAKES (2y)
Ascot-6f
2008	ART CONNOISSEUR 9-1	18
2009	CANFORD CLIFFS 9-1	13
2010	STRONG SUIT 9-1	13
2011	POWER 9-1	23
2012	DAWN APPROACH 9-1	22
2013	WAR COMMAND 9-1	15
2014	THE WOW SIGNAL 9-1	15
2015	BURATINO 9-1	17
2016	CARAVAGGIO 9-1	18
2017	RAJASINGHE 9-1	18

KING EDWARD VII STAKES (3y)
Ascot-1m 4f
2008	CAMPANOLOGIST 8-12	9
2009	FATHER TIME 8-12	12
2010	MONTEROSSO 8-12	8
2011	NATHANIEL 8-12	10
2012	THOMAS CHIPPENDALE 8-12	5
2013	HILLSTAR 8-12	8
2014	EAGLE TOP 9-0	9
2015	BALIOS 9-0	7
2016	ACROSS THE STARS 9-0	9
2017	PERMIAN 9-0	12

JERSEY STAKES (3y)
Ascot-7f
2008	AQLAAM 9-1	16
2009	OUQBA 9-1	16
2010	RAINFALL 8-12	13
2011	STRONG SUIT 9-6	9
2012	ISHVANA 8-12	22
2013	GALE FORCE TEN 9-1	21
2014	MUSTAJEEB 9-4	23
2015	DUTCH CONNECTION 9-4	16
2016	RIBCHESTER 9-6	19
2017	LE BRIVIDO 9-1	20

DUKE OF CAMBRIDGE STAKES
(fillies & mares)
Ascot-1m (st)
(Windsor Forest Stakes before 2013)
2008	SABANA PERDIDA 5-8-12	13
2009	SPACIOUS 4-8-12	9
2010	STRAWBERRYDAIQUIRI 4-8-12	10
2011	LOLLY FOR DOLLY 4-8-12	13
2012	JOVIALITY 4-8-12	13
2013	DUNTLE 4-8-12	9
2014	INTEGRAL 4-9-0	14
2015	AMAZING MARIA 4-9-0	6
2016	USHERETTE 4-9-3	14
2017	QEMAH 4-9-0	14

QUEEN MARY STAKES (2y fillies)
Ascot-5f
2008	LANGS LASH 8-12	17
2009	JEALOUS AGAIN 8-12	13
2010	MAQAASID 8-12	18
2011	BEST TERMS 8-12	14
2012	CEILING KITTY 8-12	27
2013	RIZEENA 8-12	23
2014	ANTHEM ALEXANDER 9-0	21
2015	ACAPULCO 9-0	20
2016	LADY AURELIA 9-0	17
2017	HEARTACHE 9-0	23

CORONATION STAKES (3y fillies)
Ascot-7f 213yds (rnd)
2008	LUSH LASHES 9-0	11
2009	GHANAATI 9-0	10
2010	LILLIE LANGTRY 9-0	13
2011	IMMORTAL VERSE 9-0	12
2012	FALLEN FOR YOU 9-0	10
2013	SKY LANTERN 9-0	17
2014	RIZEENA 9-0	12
2015	ERVEDYA 9-0	9
2016	QEMAH 9-0	13
2017	WINTER 9-0	7

COMMONWEALTH CUP (3y)
Ascot-6f
2015	MUHAARAR 9-3	18
2016	QUIET REFLECTION 9-0	10
2017	CARAVAGGIO 9-3	12

ROYAL HUNT CUP
Ascot-1m (st)
2008	MR AVIATOR 4-9-5	29
2009	FORGOTTEN VOICE 4-9-1	25
2010	INVISIBLE MAN 4-8-9	29
2011	JULIENAS 4-8-8	28
2012	PRINCE OF JOHANNE 6-9-3	30
2013	BELGIAN BILL 5-8-11	28
2014	FIELD OF DREAM 7-9-1	28
2015	GM HOPKINS 4-9-3	30
2016	PORTAGE 4-9-5	28
2017	ZHUI FENG 4-9-0	29

QUEEN'S VASE (3y)
Ascot-1m 5f 211yds (2m before 2017)
2008	PATKAI 9-1	12
2009	HOLBERG 9-1	14
2010	MIKHAIL GLINKA 9-1	12
2011	NAMIBIAN 9-1	14
2012	ESTIMATE 8-12	10
2013	LEADING LIGHT 9-4	15
2014	HARTNELL 9-3	10
2015	ALOFT 9-3	13
2016	SWORD FIGHTER 9-3	18
2017	STRADIVARIUS 9-0	13

DIAMOND JUBILEE STAKES
Ascot-6f
(Golden Jubilee Stakes before 2012)
2008	KINGSGATE NATIVE 3-8-11	17
2009	ART CONNOISSEUR 3-8-11	14
2010	STARSPANGLEDBANNER 4-9-4	24
2011	SOCIETY ROCK 4-9-4	16
2012	BLACK CAVIAR 6-9-1	14
2013	LETHAL FORCE 4-9-4	18
2014	SLADE POWER 5-9-4	14
2015	UNDRAFTED 5-9-3	15
2016	TWILIGHT SON 4-9-3	9
2017	THE TIN MAN 5-9-3	19

NORFOLK STAKES (2y)
Ascot-5f
2008	SOUTH CENTRAL 9-1	11
2009	RADIOHEAD 9-1	11
2010	APPROVE 9-1	9
2011	BAPAK CHINTA 9-1	15
2012	RECKLESS ABANDON 9-1	11

2013	NO NAY NEVER 9-1	14
2014	BAITHA ALGA 9-1	9
2015	WATERLOO BRIDGE 9-1	10
2016	PRINCE OF LIR 9-1	11
2017	SIOUX NATION 9-1	17

GOLD CUP
Ascot-2m 4f
2008	YEATS 7-9-2	10
2009	YEATS 8-9-2	9
2010	RITE OF PASSAGE 6-9-2	12
2011	FAME AND GLORY 5-9-2	15
2012	COLOUR VISION 4-9-0	9
2013	ESTIMATE 4-8-11	14
2014	LEADING LIGHT 4-9-0	12
2015	TRIP TO PARIS 4-9-0	12
2016	ORDER OF ST GEORGE 4-9-0	17
2017	BIG ORANGE 6-9-2	14

RIBBLESDALE STAKES (3y fillies)
Ascot-1m 4f
2008	MICHITA 8-12	9
2009	FLYING CLOUD 8-12	10
2010	HIBAAYEB 8-12	11
2011	BANIMPIRE 8-12	12
2012	PRINCESS HIGHWAY 8-12	14
2013	RIPOSTE 8-12	9
2014	BRACELET 9-0	12
2015	CURVY 9-0	10
2016	EVEN SONG 9-0	14
2017	CORONET 9-0	12

HARDWICKE STAKES
Ascot-1m 4f
2008	MACARTHUR 4-9-0	9
2009	BRONZE CANNON 4-9-3	9
2010	HARBINGER 4-9-0	11
2011	AWAIT THE DAWN 4-9-0	9
2012	SEA MOON 4-9-0	12
2013	THOMAS CHIPPENDALE 4-9-0	8
2014	TELESCOPE 4-9-1	10
2015	SNOW SKY 4-9-1	7
2016	DARTMOUTH 4-9-1	9
2017	IDAHO 4-9-1	12

WOKINGHAM STAKES
Ascot-6f
2008	BIG TIMER 4-9-2	27
2009	HIGH STANDING 4-8-12	26
2010	LADDIES POKER TWO 5-8-11	27
2011	DEACON BLUES 4-8-13	25
2012	DANDY BOY 6-9-8	28
2013	YORK GLORY 5-9-2	26
2014	BACCARAT 5-9-2	28
2015	INTERCEPTION 5-9-3	25
2016	OUTBACK TRAVELLER 5-9-1	28
2017	OUT DO 8-8-13	27

KING'S STAND STAKES
Ascot-5f
2008	EQUIANO 3-8-12	13
2009	SCENIC BLAST 5-9-4	19
2010	EQUIANO 5-9-4	12
2011	PROHIBIT 6-9-4	19
2012	LITTLE BRIDGE 6-9-4	22
2013	SOLE POWER 6-9-4	19
2014	SOLE POWER 7-9-4	16

2015 **GOLDREAM** 6-9-4.................................18
2016 **PROFITABLE** 4-9-4................................17
2017 **LADY AURELIA** 3-8-9...........................17

NORTHUMBERLAND PLATE
Newcastle-2m 56y Tapeta (2m 19y turf before 2016)
2008 **ARC BLEU** 7-8-2.................................17
2009 **SOM TALA** 6-8-8.................................18
2010 **OVERTURN** 6-8-7................................19
2011 **TOMINATOR** 4-8-5..............................19
2012 **ILE DE RE** 6-9-3................................16
2013 **TOMINATOR** 6-9-10............................18
2014 **ANGEL GABRIAL** 5-8-12.....................19
2015 **QUEST FOR MORE** 5-9-4.....................19
2016 **ANTIQUARIUM** 4-9-5..........................20
2017 **HIGHER POWER** 5-9-9.........................20

ECLIPSE STAKES
Sandown-1m 2f 219yds
2008 **MOUNT NELSON** 4-9-7...........................8
2009 **SEA THE STARS** 3-8-10..........................5
2010 **TWICE OVER** 5-9-7...............................5
2011 **SO YOU THINK** 5-9-7.............................5
2012 **NATHANIEL** 4-9-7.................................9
2013 **AL KAZEEM** 5-9-7.................................7
2014 **MUKHADRAM** 5-9-7...............................9
2015 **GOLDEN HORN** 3-8-10............................5
2016 **HAWKBILL** 3-8-10..................................7
2017 **ULYSSES** 4-9-7....................................9

LANCASHIRE OAKS (fillies and mares)
Haydock-1m 3f 175yds
2008 **ANNA PAVLOVA** 5-9-8............................9
2009 **BARSHIBA** 5-9-5...................................8
2010 **BARSHIBA** 6-9-5.................................10
2011 **GERTRUDE BELL** 4-9-5...........................7
2012 **GREAT HEAVENS** 3-8-6..........................9
2013 **EMIRATES QUEEN** 4-9-5.........................8
2014 **POMOLOGY** 4-9-5.................................9
2015 **LADY TIANA** 4-9-5...............................10
2016 **ENDLESS TIME** 4-9-5.............................6
2017 **THE BLACK PRINCESS** 4-9-5.....................7

DUCHESS OF CAMBRIDGE STAKES (2y fillies)
Newmarket-6f
(Cherry Hinton Stakes before 2013)
2008 **PLEASE SING** 8-12.................................8
2009 **MISHEER** 8-12...................................10
2010 **MEMORY** 8-12......................................7
2011 **GAMILATI** 8-12..................................11
2012 **SENDMYLOVETOROSE** 8-12...................10
2013 **LUCKY KRISTALE** 8-12..........................8
2014 **ARABIAN QUEEN** 9-0.............................5
2015 **ILLUMINATE** 9-0..................................9
2016 **ROLY POLY** 9-0..................................10
2017 **CLEMMIE** 9-0......................................8

BUNBURY CUP
(Run as 32Red Trophy in 2010)
Newmarket-7f
2008 **LITTLE WHITE LIE** 4-9-0.......................18
2009 **PLUM PUDDING** 6-9-10.........................19
2010 **ST MORITZ** 4-9-1................................19
2011 **BRAE HILL** 5-9-1.................................20
2012 **BONNIE BRAE** 5-9-9............................15

2013 **FIELD OF DREAM** 6-9-7.........................19
2014 **HEAVEN'S GUEST** 4-9-3.........................13
2015 **RENE MATHIS** 5-9-1............................17
2016 **GOLDEN STEPS** 5-9-9...........................16
2017 **ABOVE THE REST** 6-8-10.......................18

PRINCESS OF WALES'S STAKES
Newmarket-1m 4f
2008 **LUCARNO** 4-9-7....................................6
2009 **DOCTOR FREMANTLE** 4-9-2.....................9
2010 **SANS FRONTIERES** 4-9-2.......................8
2011 **CRYSTAL CAPELLA** 6-8-13......................7
2012 **FIORENTE** 4-9-2....................................7
2013 **AL KAZEEM** 4-9-5.................................6
2014 **CAVALRYMAN** 8-9-2..............................6
2015 **BIG ORANGE** 4-9-2...............................8
2016 **BIG ORANGE** 5-9-2...............................7
2017 **HAWKBILL** 4-9-2..................................6

JULY STAKES (2y)
Newmarket-6f
2008 **CLASSIC BLADE** 8-12............................7
2009 **ARCANO** 8-12....................................11
2010 **LIBRANNO** 8-12...................................7
2011 **FREDERICK ENGELS** 8-12.......................7
2012 **ALHEBAYEB** 8-12.................................7
2013 **ANJAAL** 8-12.....................................11
2014 **IVAWOOD** 9-0.....................................12
2015 **SHALAA** 9-0...9
2016 **MEHMAS** 9-0..9
2017 **CARDSHARP** 9-0..................................12

FALMOUTH STAKES (fillies & mares)
Newmarket-1m
2008 **NAHOODH** 3-8-10................................11
2009 **GOLDIKOVA** 4-9-5................................8
2010 **MUSIC SHOW** 3-8-10.............................8
2011 **TIMEPIECE** 4-9-5................................11
2012 **GIOFRA** 4-9-5.....................................10
2013 **ELUSIVE KATE** 4-9-5.............................4
2014 **INTEGRAL** 4-9-7...................................7
2015 **AMAZING MARIA** 4-9-7...........................7
2016 **ALICE SPRINGS** 3-8-12..........................7
2017 **ROLY POLY** 3-8-12...............................12

SUPERLATIVE STAKES (2y)
Newmarket-7f
2008 **FIRTH OF FIFTH** 9-0...............................9
2009 **SILVER GRECIAN** 9-0.............................8
2010 **KING TORUS** 9-0...................................6
2011 **RED DUKE** 9-0....................................11
2012 **OLYMPIC GLORY** 9-0..............................9
2013 **GOOD OLD BOY LUKEY** 9-0......................8
2014 **ESTIDHKAAR** 9-1..................................8
2015 **BIRCHWOOD** 9-1...................................8
2016 **BOYNTON** 9-1......................................9
2017 **GUSTAV KLIMT** 9-1..............................10

JULY CUP
Newmarket-6f
2008 **MARCHAND D'OR** 5-9-5.........................13
2009 **FLEETING SPIRIT** 4-9-2.........................13
2010 **STARSPANGLEDBANNER** 4-9-5................14
2011 **DREAM AHEAD** 3-8-13...........................16
2012 **MAYSON** 4-9-5....................................13
2013 **LETHAL FORCE** 4-9-5............................11
2014 **SLADE POWER** 5-9-6.............................13

2015 **MUHAARAR** 3-9-0 14
2016 **LIMATO** 4-9-6 18
2017 **HARRY ANGEL** 3-9-0 10

WEATHERBYS SUPER SPRINT (2y)
Newbury-5f 34 yds
2008 **JARGELLE** 8-6 23
2009 **MONSIEUR CHEVALIER** 8-12 20
2010 **TEMPLE MEADS** 8-6 24
2011 **CHARLES THE GREAT** 8-11 25
2012 **BODY AND SOUL** 7-12 22
2013 **PENIAPHOBIA** 8-8 24
2014 **TIGGY WIGGY** 9-1 24
2015 **LATHOM** 9-0 22
2016 **MRS DANVERS** 8-0 23
2017 **BENGALI BOYS** 8-7 23

SUMMER MILE
Ascot-7f 213yds (rnd)
2008 **ARCHIPENKO** 4-9-6 7
2009 **AQLAAM** 4-9-1 7
2010 **PREMIO LOCO** 6-9-1 8
2011 **DICK TURPIN** 4-9-4 5
2012 **FANUNALTER** 6-9-1 8
2013 **ALJAMAAHEER** 4-9-1 11
2014 **GUEST OF HONOUR** 5-9-1 9
2015 **AROD** 4-9-1 6
2016 **MUTAKAYYEF** 5-9-1 10
2017 **MUTAKAYYEF** 6-9-1 7

PRINCESS MARGARET STAKES
(2y fillies)
Ascot-6f
2008 **AFRICAN SKIES** 8-12 16
2009 **LADY OF THE DESERT** 8-12 9
2010 **SORAAYA** 8-12 11
2011 **ANGELS WILL FALL** 8-12 7
2012 **MAUREEN** 8-12 6
2013 **PRINCESS NOOR** 8-12 10
2014 **OSAILA** 9-0 8
2015 **BESHARAH** 9-0 6
2016 **FAIR EVA** 9-0 12
2017 **NYALETI** 9-0 7

LENNOX STAKES
Goodwood-7f
2008 **PACO BOY** 3-8-9 9
2009 **FINJAAN** 3-8-9 8
2010 **LORD SHANAKILL** 4-9-2 12
2011 **STRONG SUIT** 3-8-9 9
2012 **CHACHAMAIDEE** 5-8-13 7
2013 **GARSWOOD** 3-8-9 10
2014 **ES QUE LOVE** 5-9-3 7
2015 **TOORMORE** 4-9-3 7
2016 **DUTCH CONNECTION** 4-9-3 8
2017 **BRETON ROCK** 7-9-3 13

STEWARDS' CUP
Goodwood-6f
2008 **CONQUEST** 4-8-9 27
2009 **GENKI** 5-9-1 26
2010 **EVENS AND ODDS** 6-8-10 28
2011 **HOOF IT** 4-10-0 27
2012 **HAWKEYETHENOO** 6-9-9 27
2013 **REX IMPERATOR** 4-9-4 27
2014 **INTRINSIC** 4-8-11 24

2015 **MAGICAL MEMORY** 3-8-12 27
2016 **DANCING STAR** 3-8-12 27
2017 **LANCELOT DU LAC** 7-9-5 26
*Run as 32Red Cup in 2014

GORDON STAKES (3y)
Goodwood-1m 4f
2008 **CONDUIT** 9-0 6
2009 **HARBINGER** 9-0 9
2010 **REBEL SOLDIER** 9-0 10
2011 **NAMIBIAN** 9-3 10
2012 **NOBLE MISSION** 9-0 7
2013 **CAP O'RUSHES** 9-0 7
2014 **SNOW SKY** 9-1 7
2015 **HIGHLAND REEL** 9-1 9
2016 **ULYSSES** 9-1 9
2017 **CRYSTAL OCEAN** 9-1 5

VINTAGE STAKES (2y)
Goodwood-7f
2008 **ORIZABA** 9-0 9
2009 **XTENSION** 9-0 10
2010 **KING TORUS** 9-3 7
2011 **CHANDLERY** 9-0 7
2012 **OLYMPIC GLORY** 9-3 10
2013 **TOORMORE** 9-0 12
2014 **HIGHLAND REEL** 9-1 8
2015 **GALILEO GOLD** 9-1 8
2016 **WAR DECREE** 9-1 9
2017 **EXPERT EYE** 9-1 10

SUSSEX STAKES
Goodwood-1m
2008 **HENRYTHENAVIGATOR** 3-8-13 6
2009 **RIP VAN WINKLE** 3-8-13 8
2010 **CANFORD CLIFFS** 3-8-13 7
2011 **FRANKEL** 3-8-13 4
2012 **FRANKEL** 4-9-7 4
2013 **TORONADO** 3-8-13 7
2014 **KINGMAN** 3-9-0 4
2015 **SOLOW** 5-9-8 8
2016 **THE GURKHA** 3-9-0 10
2017 **HERE COMES WHEN** 7-9-8 7

RICHMOND STAKES (2y)
Goodwood-6f
2008 **PROLIFIC** 9-0 12
2009 **DICK TURPIN** 9-0 9
2010 **LIBRANNO** 9-3 6
2011 **HARBOUR WATCH** 9-0 10
2012 **HEAVY METAL** 9-0 8
2013 **SAAYERR** 9-0 10
2014 **IVAWOOD** 9-3 8
2015 **SHALAA** 9-3 8
2016 **MEHMAS** 9-3 4
2017 **BARRAQUERO** 9-0 7

KING GEORGE STAKES
Goodwood-5f
2008 **ENTICING** 4-8-11 12
2009 **KINGSGATE NATIVE** 4-9-0 17
2010 **BORDERLESCOTT** 8-9-0 15
2011 **MASAHN** 5-9-0 11
2012 **ORTENSIA** 7-9-0 17
2013 **MOVIESTA** 3-8-12 17
2014 **TAKE COVER** 7-9-1 15
2015 **MUTHMIR** 5-9-6 15

2016 **TAKE COVER** 9-9-2.................................17
2017 **BATTAASH** 3-8-13.................................11

GOODWOOD CUP
Goodwood-2m
2008 **YEATS** 7-9-12.....................................8
2009 **SCHIAPARELLI** 6-9-7..........................10
2010 **ILLUSTRIOUS BLUE** 7-9-7...................10
2011 **OPINION POLL** 5-9-7..........................15
2012 **SADDLER'S ROCK** 4-9-7......................10
2013 **BROWN PANTHER** 5-9-7.......................14
2014 **CAVALRYMAN** 8-9-8.............................8
2015 **BIG ORANGE** 4-9-8.............................11
2016 **BIG ORANGE** 5-9-8.............................14
2017 **STRADIVARIUS** 3-8-8..........................14

MOLECOMB STAKES (2y)
Goodwood-5f
2008 **FINJAAN** 9-0.....................................11
2009 **MONSIEUR CHEVALIER** 9-0...................11
2010 **ZEBEDEE** 9-0....................................12
2011 **REQUINTO** 9-0...................................13
2012 **BUNGLE INTHEJUNGLE** 9-0..................10
2013 **BROWN SUGAR** 9-0..............................8
2014 **COTAI GLORY** 9-1................................8
2015 **KACHY** 9-1......................................10
2016 **YALTA** 9-1.......................................8
2017 **HAVANA GREY** 9-1..............................10

NASSAU STAKES (fillies and mares)
Goodwood-1m 1f 197yds
2008 **HALFWAY TO HEAVEN** 3-8-10 9
2009 **MIDDAY** 3-8-10.................................10
2010 **MIDDAY** 4-9-6....................................7
2011 **MIDDAY** 5-9-6....................................6
2012 **THE FUGUE** 3-8-11..............................8
2013 **WINSILI** 3-8-11................................14
2014 **SULTANINA** 4-9-7................................6
2015 **LEGATISSIMO** 3-8-12...........................9
2016 **MINDING** 3-8-11.................................5
2017 **WINTER** 3-8-13..................................6

HUNGERFORD STAKES
Newbury-7f
2008 **PACO BOY** 3-9-0..................................9
2009 **BALTHAZAAR'S GIFT** 6-9-3....................9
2010 **SHAKESPEAREAN** 3-8-11.......................7
2011 **EXCELEBRATION** 3-8-13........................9
2012 **LETHAL FORCE** 3-8-12..........................9
2013 **GREGORIAN** 4-9-3................................5
2014 **BRETON ROCK** 4-9-5............................6
2015 **ADAAY** 3-9-2...................................11
2016 **RICHARD PANKHURST** 4-9-6....................6
2017 **MASSAAT** 4-9-6..................................8

GEOFFREY FREER STAKES
Newbury-1m 5f 61yds
2008 **SIXTIES ICON** 5-9-5...........................10
2009 **KITE WOOD** 3-8-8................................8
2010 **SANS FRONTIERES** 4-9-8.......................8
2011 **CENSUS** 3-8-6..................................10
2012 **MOUNT ATHOS** 5-9-4............................6
2013 **ROYAL EMPIRE** 4-9-4..........................10
2014 **SEISMOS** 6-9-4.................................11
2015 **AGENT MURPHY** 4-9-5...........................6
2016 **KINGS FETE** 5-9-7..............................5
2017 **DEFOE** 3-8-10...................................8

INTERNATIONAL STAKES
York-1m 2f 56yds
*2008 **DUKE OF MARMALADE** 4-9-5..................9
2009 **SEA THE STARS** 3-8-11.........................4
2010 **RIP VAN WINKLE** 4-9-5.........................9
2011 **TWICE OVER** 6-9-5..............................5
2012 **FRANKEL** 4-9-5..................................9
2013 **DECLARATION OF WAR** 4-9-5...................6
2014 **AUSTRALIA** 3-8-11..............................6
2015 **ARABIAN QUEEN** 3-8-9..........................7
2016 **POSTPONED** 5-9-6..............................12
2017 **ULYSSES** 4-9-6..................................7
*Run at Newmarket (July) over 1m 2f

GREAT VOLTIGEUR STAKES (3y)
York-1m 3f 188yds
*2008 **CENTENNIAL** 8-12..............................5
2009 **MONITOR CLOSELY** 8-12........................7
2010 **REWILDING** 8-12...............................10
2011 **SEA MOON** 8-12.................................8
2012 **THOUGHT WORTHY** 8-12.........................6
2013 **TELESCOPE** 8-12................................7
2014 **POSTPONED** 9-0.................................9
2015 **STORM THE STARS** 9-0..........................7
2016 **IDAHO** 9-0......................................6
2017 **CRACKSMAN** 9-0.................................6
*Run at Goodwood

LOWTHER STAKES (2y fillies)
York-6f
*2008 **INFAMOUS ANGEL** 8-12.........................7
2009 **LADY OF THE DESERT** 8-12....................12
2010 **HOORAY** 8-12....................................8
2011 **BEST TERMS** 9-1...............................11
2012 **ROSDHU QUEEN** 8-12...........................10
2013 **LUCKY KRISTALE** 9-1...........................9
2014 **TIGGY WIGGY** 9-0...............................9
2015 **BESHARAH** 9-0..................................9
2016 **QUEEN KINDLY** 9-0.............................9
2017 **THREADING** 9-0.................................9
*Run at Newmarket (July)

YORKSHIRE OAKS (fillies and mares)
York-1m 3f 188yds
*2008 **LUSH LASHES** 3-8-11..........................6
2009 **DAR RE MI** 4-9-7...............................6
2010 **MIDDAY** 4-9-7...................................8
2011 **BLUE BUNTING** 3-8-11..........................8
2012 **SHARETA** 4-9-7..................................6
2013 **THE FUGUE** 4-9-7...............................7
2014 **TAPESTRY** 3-8-11...............................7
2015 **PLEASCACH** 3-8-11.............................11
2016 **SEVENTH HEAVEN** 3-8-11.......................12
2017 **ENABLE** 3-8-12..................................6
*Run at Newmarket (July)

EBOR HANDICAP
York-1m 5f 188yds
*2008 **ALL THE GOOD** 5-9-0..........................20
2009 **SESENTA** 5-8-8.................................20
2010 **DIRAR** 5-9-1...................................20
2011 **MOYENNE CORNICHE** 6-8-10....................19
2012 **WILLING FOE** 5-9-2............................19
2013 **TIGER CLIFF** 4-9-0............................14
2014 **MUTUAL REGARD** 5-9-4.........................19
2015 **LITIGANT** 7-9-1................................19

2016 **HEARTBREAK CITY** 6-9-1 20
2017 **NAKEETA** 6-9-0 19
*Run as Newburgh Handicap at Newbury over 1m 5f 61yds

GIMCRACK STAKES (2y)
York-6f
*2008 **SHAWEEL** 8-12 12
2009 **SHOWCASING** 8-12 6
2010 **APPROVE** 9-1 11
2011 **CASPAR NETSCHER** 8-12 9
2012 **BLAINE** 8-1 8
2013 **ASTAIRE** 8-12 7
2014 **MUHAARAR** 9-0 9
2015 **AJAYA** 9-0 8
2016 **BLUE POINT** 9-0 10
2017 **SANDS OF MALI** 9-0 10
*Run at Newbury

NUNTHORPE STAKES
York-5f
*2008 **BORDERLESCOTT** 6-9-11 14
2009 **BORDERLESCOTT** 7-9-11 16
2010 **SOLE POWER** 3-9-9 12
2011 **MARGOT DID** 3-9-6 15
2012 **ORTENSIA** 7-9-8 19
2013 **JWALA** 4-9-8 17
2014 **SOLE POWER** 7-9-11 13
2015 **MECCA'S ANGEL** 4-9-10 19
2016 **MECCA'S ANGEL** 5-9-8 19
2017 **MARSHA** 4-9-8 11
*Run at Newmarket (July)

LONSDALE CUP
York-2m 56yds
2008 ABANDONED
2009 **ASKAR TAU** 4 9-1 5
2010 **OPINION POLL** 4 9-1 8
2011 **OPINION POLL** 5 9-4 10
2012 **TIMES UP** 6 9-1 11
2013 **AHZEEMAH** 4 9-3 7
2014 **PALE MIMOSA** 5-9-0 7
2015 **MAX DYNAMITE** 5-9-3 8
2016 **QUEST FOR MORE** 6-9-3 7
2017 **MONTALY** 6-9-3 9

PRESTIGE STAKES (2y fillies)
Goodwood-7f
2008 **FANTASIA** 9-0 10
2009 **SENT FROM HEAVEN** 9-0 8
2010 **THEYSKENS' THEORY** 9-0 7
2011 **REGAL REALM** 9-0 6
2012 **OLLIE OLGA** 9-0 8
2013 **AMAZING MARIA** 9-0 7
2014 **MALABAR** 9-0 8
2015 **HAWKSMOOR** 9-0 9
2016 **KILMAH** 9-0 7
2017 **BILLESDON BROOK** 9-0 10

CELEBRATION MILE
Goodwood-1m
2008 **RAVEN'S PASS** 3-8-9 5
2009 **DELEGATOR** 3-8-9 7
2010 **POET'S VOICE** 3-8-9 4
2011 **DUBAWI GOLD** 3-8-9 7
2012 **PREMIO LOCO** 8-9-1 5
2013 **AFSARE** 6-9-1 8
2014 **BOW CREEK** 3-8-12 8

2015 **KODI BEAR** 3-8-12 6
2016 **LIGHTNING SPEAR** 5-9-4 5
2017 **LIGHTNING SPEAR** 6-9-4 6

SOLARIO STAKES (2y)
Sandown-7f 16yds
2008 **SRI PUTRA** 9-0 11
2009 **SHAKESPEAREAN** 9-0 8
2010 **NATIVE KHAN** 9-0 6
2011 **TALWAR** 9-0 4
2012 **FANTASTIC MOON** 9-0 7
2013 **KINGMAN** 9-0 4
2014 **AKTABANTAY** 9-1 5
2015 **FIRST SELECTION** 9-1 10
2016 **SOUTH SEAS** 9-1 10
2017 **MASAR** 9-1 7

SPRINT CUP
Haydock-6f
*2008 **AFRICAN ROSE** 3-8-12 15
2009 **REGAL PARADE** 5-9-3 14
2010 **MARKAB** 7-9-3 13
2011 **DREAM AHEAD** 3-9-1 16
2012 **SOCIETY ROCK** 5-9-3 13
2013 **GORDON LORD BYRON** 5-9-3 13
2014 **G FORCE** 3-9-1 17
2015 **TWILIGHT SON** 3-9-1 15
2016 **QUIET REFLECTION** 3-8-12 14
2017 **HARRY ANGEL** 3-9-1 11
*Run at Doncaster

SEPTEMBER STAKES
Kempton-1m 3f 219yds Polytrack
2008 **HATTAN** 6-9-7 12
2009 **KIRKLEES** 5-9-9 10
2010 **LAAHEB** 4-9-4 9
2011 **MODUN** 4-9-4 7
2012 **DANDINO** 5-9-4 9
2013 **PRINCE BISHOP** 6-9-4 10
2014 **PRINCE BISHOP** 7-9-12 7
2015 **JACK HOBBS** 3-9-3 7
2016 **ARAB SPRING** 6-9-5 6
2017 **CHEMICAL CHARGE** 5-9-5 6

MAY HILL STAKES (2y fillies)
Doncaster-1m
2008 **RAINBOW VIEW** 9-1 7
2009 **POLLENATOR** 8-12 7
2010 **WHITE MOONSTONE** 8-12 7
2011 **LYRIC OF LIGHT** 8-12 8
2012 **CERTIFY** 8-12 7
2013 **ITHIMAL** 8-12 7
2014 **AGNES STEWART** 9-0 8
2015 **TURRET ROCKS** 9-0 8
2016 **RICH LEGACY** 9-0 9
2017 **LAURENS** 9-0 8

PORTLAND HANDICAP
Doncaster-5f 143yds
2008 **HOGMANEIGH** 5-9-6 21
2009 **SANTO PADRE** 5-9-1 22
2010 **POET'S PLACE** 5-9-4 22
2011 **NOCTURNAL AFFAIR** 5-9-5 21
2012 **DOC HAY** 5-8-11 20
2013 **ANGELS WILL FALL** 4-9-2 21
2014 **MUTHMIR** 4-9-7 20
2015 **STEPS** 7-9-7 20

| 2016 | **CAPTAIN COLBY** 4-9-0 | 20 |
| 2017 | **SPRING LOADED** 5-8-9 | 22 |

PARK HILL STAKES (fillies and mares)
Doncaster-1m 6f 115yds

2008	**ALLEGRETTO** 5-9-4	8
2009	**THE MINIVER ROSE** 3-8-6	9
2010	**EASTERN ARIA** 4-9-4	12
2011	**MEEZNAH** 4-9-4	7
2012	**WILD COCO** 4-9-4	9
2013	**THE LARK** 3-8-6	9
2014	**SILK SARI** 4-9-5	13
2015	**GRETCHEN** 3-8-7	11
2016	**SIMPLE VERSE** 4-9-5	12
2017	**ALYSSA** 4-9-5	10

DONCASTER CUP
Doncaster-2m 1f 197yds

2008	**HONOLULU** 4-9-1	9
2009	**ASKAR TAU** 4-9-4	5
2010	**SAMUEL** 6-9-1	10
2011	**SADDLER'S ROCK** 3-8-1	9
2012	**TIMES UP** 6-9-1	10
2013	**TIMES UP** 7-9-3	7
2014	**ESTIMATE** 5-9-0	12
2015	**PALLASATOR** 6-9-3	11
2016	**SHEIKHZAYEDROAD** 7-9-3	8
2017	**DESERT SKYLINE** 3-8-5	9

CHAMPAGNE STAKES (2y)
Doncaster-7f 6yds

2008	**WESTPHALIA** 8-12	7
2009	**POET'S VOICE** 8-12	7
2010	**SAAMIDD** 8-12	6
2011	**TRUMPET MAJOR** 8-12	5
2012	**TORONADO** 8-12	5
2013	**OUTSTRIP** 8-12	4
2014	**ESTIDHKAAR** 9-3	6
2015	**EMOTIONLESS** 9-0	6
2016	**RIVET** 9-0	6
2017	**SEAHENGE** 9-0	7

PARK STAKES
Doncaster-7f 6yds

2008	**ARABIAN GLEAM** 4-9-4	9
2009	**DUFF** 6-9-4	6
2010	**BALTHAZAR'S GIFT** 7-9-4	12
2011	**PREMIO LOCO** 7-9-4	5
2012	**LIBRANNO** 4-9-4	8
2013	**VIZTORIA** 3-8-11	9
2014	**ANSGAR** 6-9-4	7
2015	**LIMATO** 3-9-0	15
2016	**BRETON ROCK** 6-9-4	8
2017	**ACLAIM** 4-9-4	8

FLYING CHILDERS STAKES (2y)
Doncaster-5f

2008	**MADAME TROP VITE** 8-11	12
2009	**SAND VIXEN** 8-11	10
2010	**ZEBEDEE** 9-0	12
2011	**REQUINTO** 9-0	10
2012	**SIR PRANCEALOT** 9-0	9
2013	**GREEN DOOR** 9-0	7
2014	**BEACON** 9-1	14
2015	**GUTAIFAN** 9-1	9

| 2016 | **ARDAD** 9-1 | 11 |
| 2017 | **HEARTACHE** 8-12 | 9 |

AYR GOLD CUP
Ayr-6f

2008	**REGAL PARADE** 4-8-10	27
2009	**JIMMY STYLES** 5-9-2	26
2010	**REDFORD** 5-9-2	26
2011	**OUR JONATHAN** 4-9-6	26
2012	**CAPTAIN RAMIUS** 6-9-0	26
2013	**HIGHLAND COLORI** 5-8-13	26
2014	**LOUIS THE PIOUS** 6-9-4	27
2015	**DON'T TOUCH** 3-9-1	25
2016	**BRANDO** 4-9-10	23
*2017	**DONJUAN TRIUMPHANT** 4-9-10	17

*Run at Haydock Park as 32Red Gold Cup

MILL REEF STAKES (2y)
Newbury-6f 8yds

2008	**LORD SHANAKILL** 9-1	9
2009	**AWZAAN** 9-1	7
2010	**TEMPLE MEADS** 9-1	7
2011	**CASPAR NETSCHER** 9-4	9
2012	**MOOHAAJIM** 9-1	8
2013	**SUPPLICANT** 9-1	7
2014	**TOOCOOLFORSCHOOL** 9-1	6
2015	**RIBCHESTER** 9-1	6
2016	**HARRY ANGEL** 9-1	7
2017	**JAMES GARFIELD** 9-1	9

ROYAL LODGE STAKES (2y)
Newmarket-1m (run at Ascot before 2011)

2008	**JUKEBOX JURY** 8-12	8
2009	**JOSHUA TREE** 8-12	10
2010	**FRANKEL** 8-12	5
2011	**DADDY LONG LEGS** 8-12	6
2012	**STEELER** 8-12	8
2013	**BERKSHIRE** 8-12	5
2014	**ELM PARK** 9-0	6
2015	**FOUNDATION** 9-0	6
2016	**BEST OF DAYS** 9-0	9
2017	**ROARING LION** 9-0	5

CHEVELEY PARK STAKES (2y fillies)
Newmarket-6f

2008	**SERIOUS ATTITUDE** 8-12	16
2009	**SPECIAL DUTY** 8-12	8
2010	**HOORAY** 8-12	11
2011	**LIGHTENING PEARL** 8-12	9
2012	**ROSDHU QUEEN** 8-12	11
2013	**VORDA** 8-12	7
2014	**TIGGY WIGGY** 9-0	9
2015	**LUMIERE** 9-0	6
2016	**BRAVE ANNA** 9-0	6
2017	**CLEMMIE** 9-0	11

SUN CHARIOT STAKES (fillies and mares)
Newmarket-1m

2008	**HALFWAY TO HEAVEN** 3-8-13	10
2009	**SAHPRESA** 4-9-2	8
2010	**SAHPRESA** 5-9-2	11
2011	**SAHPRESA** 6-9-3	9
2012	**SIYOUMA** 4-9-3	8
2013	**SKY LANTERN** 3-8-13	9
2014	**INTEGRAL** 4-9-3	7

2015 **ESOTERIQUE** 5-9-3.................................9
2016 **ALICE SPRINGS** 3-9-0..........................8
2017 **ROLY POLY** 3-9-0................................13

CAMBRIDGESHIRE
Newmarket-1m 1f
2008 **TAZEEZ** 4-9-2....................................28
2009 **SUPASEUS** 6-9-1................................32
2010 **CREDIT SWAP** 5-8-7.............................35
2011 **PRINCE OF JOHANNE** 5-8-9....................32
2012 **BRONZE ANGEL** 3-8-8...........................33
2013 **EDUCATE** 4-9-9...................................31
2014 **BRONZE ANGEL** 5-8-8...........................31
2015 **THIRD TIME LUCKY** 3-8-4......................34
2016 **SPARK PLUG** 5-9-4..............................31
2017 **DOLPHIN VISTA** 4-8-7..........................34

CUMBERLAND LODGE STAKES
Ascot-1m 4f
2008 **SIXTIES ICON** 5-9-3..............................5
2009 **MAWATHEEQ** 4-9-0.............................12
2010 **LAAHEB** 4-9-3.....................................6
2011 **QUEST FOR PEACE** 3-8-7.......................7
2012 **HAWAAFEZ** 4-8-11...............................6
2013 **SECRET NUMBER** 3-8-7.........................7
2014 **PETHER'S MOON** 4-9-6..........................5
2015 **STAR STORM** 3-8-8...............................8
2016 **MOVE UP** 3-8-13..................................9
2017 **DANEHILL KODIAC** 4-9-2........................9

FILLIES' MILE (2y fillies)
Newmarket-1m (run at Ascot before 2011)
2008 **RAINBOW VIEW** 8-12.............................8
2009 **HIBAAYEB** 8-12...................................9
2010 **WHITE MOONSTONE** 8-12.......................5
2011 **LYRIC OF LIGHT** 8-12............................8
2012 **CERTIFY** 8-12......................................6
2013 **CHRISELLIAM** 8-12...............................8
2014 **TOGETHER FOREVER** 9-0........................7
2015 **MINDING** 9-0.....................................10
2016 **RHODODENDRON** 9-0............................8
2017 **LAURENS** 9-0....................................11

MIDDLE PARK STAKES (2y)
Newmarket-6f
2008 **BUSHRANGER** 8-12...............................9
2009 **AWZAAN** 8-12.....................................5
2010 **DREAM AHEAD** 8-12..............................8
2011 **CRUSADE** 8-12...................................16
2012 **RECKLESS ABANDON** 8-12....................10
2013 **ASTAIRE** 9-0.....................................10
2014 **CHARMING THOUGHT** 9-0.......................6
2015 **SHALAA** 9-0..7
2016 **THE LAST LION** 9-0.............................10
2017 **U S NAVY FLAG** 9-0............................12

CHALLENGE STAKES
Newmarket-7f
2008 **STIMULATION** 3-9-1..............................15
2009 **ARABIAN GLEAM** 5-9-3...........................9
2010 **RED JAZZ** 3-9-1..................................14
2011 **STRONG SUIT** 3-9-5...............................8
2012 **FULBRIGHT** 3-9-1.................................11
2013 **FIESOLANA** 4-9-0.................................9
2014 **HERE COMES WHEN** 4-9-7.....................13
2015 **CABLE BAY** 4-9-3................................10

2016 **ACLAIM** 3-9-1.....................................12
2017 **LIMATO** 5-9-3.....................................11

DEWHURST STAKES (2y)
Newmarket-7f
2008 **INTENSE FOCUS** 9-1.............................13
2009 **BEETHOVEN** 9-1..................................15
2010 **FRANKEL** 9-1......................................6
2011 **PARISH HALL** 9-1.................................9
2012 **DAWN APPROACH** 9-1...........................6
2013 **WAR COMMAND** 9-1..............................6
2014 **BELARDO** 9-1......................................6
2015 **AIR FORCE BLUE** 9-1............................7
2016 **CHURCHILL** 9-1...................................7
2017 **U S NAVY FLAG** 9-1..............................9

CESAREWITCH
Newmarket-2m 2f
2008 **CARACCIOLA** 11-9-6.............................32
2009 **DARLEY SUN** 3-8-6..............................32
2010 **AIIM TO PROSPER** 6-7-13.......................32
2011 **NEVER CAN TELL** 4-8-11........................33
2012 **AAIM TO PROSPER** 8-9-10.......................34
2013 **SCATTER DICE** 4-8-8.............................33
2014 **BIG EASY** 7-8-7...................................33
2015 **GRUMETI** 7-8-2...................................34
2016 **SWEET SELECTION** 4-8-8........................33
2017 **WITHHOLD** 4-8-8..................................34

ROCKFEL STAKES (2y fillies)
Newmarket-7f
2008 **LAHALEEB** 8-12..................................12
2009 **MUSIC SHOW** 8-12...............................11
2010 **CAPE DOLLAR** 8-12..............................10
2011 **WADING** 8-12.......................................9
2012 **JUST THE JUDGE** 8-12..........................11
2013 **AL THAKHIRA** 8-12................................8
2014 **LUCIDA** 9-0...9
2015 **PROMISING RUN** 9-0.............................7
2016 **SPAIN BURG** 9-0..................................8
2017 **JULIET CAPULET** 9-0............................10

QIPCO BRITISH CHAMPIONS SPRINT STAKES
Ascot-6f
(run as Diadem Stakes before 2011)
2011 **DEACON BLUES** 4-9-0............................16
2012 **MAAREK** 5-9-0.....................................15
2013 **SLADE POWER** 4-9-0.............................14
2014 **GORDON LORD BYRON** 6-9-2...................15
2015 **MUHAARAR** 3-9-1.................................20
2016 **THE TIN MAN** 4-9-2..............................12
2017 **LIBRISA BREEZE** 5-9-2..........................12

QUEEN ELIZABETH II STAKES (BRITISH CHAMPIONS MILE)
Ascot-1m (st - rnd before 2011)
2008 **RAVEN'S PASS** 3-8-13.............................7
2009 **RIP VAN WINKLE** 3-8-13..........................4
2010 **POET'S VOICE** 3-8-13.............................8
2011 **FRANKEL** 3-9-0.....................................8
2012 **EXCELEBRATION** 4-9-3...........................8
2013 **OLYMPIC GLORY** 3-9-0..........................12
2014 **CHARM SPIRIT** 3-9-1.............................11
2015 **SOLOW** 5-9-4.......................................9
2016 **MINDING** 3-8-12..................................13
2017 **PERSUASIVE** 4-9-1...............................15

QIPCO BRITISH CHAMPIONS LONG DISTANCE CUP
(formerly Jockey Club Cup, run at Newmarket before 2011)
Ascot-2m
2011	FAME AND GLORY 5 9-10	10
2012	RITE OF PASSAGE 8-9-7	9
2013	ROYAL DIAMOND 7-9-7	12
2014	FORGOTTEN RULES 4-9-7	9
2015	FLYING OFFICER 5-9-7	9
2016	SHEIKHZAYEDROAD 7-9-7	10
2017	ORDER OF ST GEORGE 5-9-7	13

QIPCO BRITISH CHAMPIONS FILLIES' AND MARES' STAKES
(formerly Pride Stakes, run at Newmarket before 2011)
Ascot-1m 4f
2011	DANCING RAIN 3-8-10	10
2012	SAPPHIRE 4-9-3	10
2013	SEAL OF APPROVAL 4-9-3	8
2014	MADAME CHIANG 3-8-12	10
2015	SIMPLE VERSE 3-8-12	12
2016	JOURNEY 4-9-5	13
2017	HYDRANGEA 3-8-13	10

QIPCO CHAMPION STAKES (BRITISH CHAMPIONS MIDDLE DISTANCE)
Ascot-1m 2f
(run at Newmarket before 2011)
2008	NEW APPROACH 3-8-12	11
2009	TWICE OVER 4-9-3	14
2010	TWICE OVER 5-9-3	10
2011	CIRRUS DES AIGLES 5-9-3	12
2012	FRANKEL 4-9-3	6
2013	FARHH 5-9-3	10
2014	NOBLE MISSION 5-9-5	9
2015	FASCINATING ROCK 4-9-5	13
2016	ALMANZOR 3-9-0	10
2017	CRACKSMAN 3-9-1	10

CORNWALLIS STAKES (2y)
Newmarket-5f (run at Ascot before 2014)
2008	AMOUR PROPRE 9-0	19
2009	OUR JONATHAN 9-0	17
2010	ELECTRIC WAVES 8-11	14
2011	PONTY ACCLAIM 8-11	16
2012	BUNGLE INTHEJUNGLE 9-3	6
2013	HOT STREAK 9-0	12
2014	ROYAL RAZALMA 8-12	12
2015	QUIET REFLECTION 8-12	11
2016	MRS DANVERS 8-12	9
2017	ABEL HANDY 9-1	12

TWO-YEAR-OLD TROPHY (2y)
Redcar-6f
2008	TOTAL GALLERY 8-9	22
2009	LUCKY LIKE 8-6	22
2010	LADIES ARE FOREVER 7-12	22
2011	BOGART 8-12	22
2012	BODY AND SOUL 8-1	21
2013	VENTURA MIST 8-7	23
2014	LIMATO 8-11	23
2015	LOG OUT ISLAND 9-2	20
2016	WICK POWELL 8-3	20
2017	DARKANNA 8-11	23

HORRIS HILL STAKES (2y)
Newbury-7f
2008	EVASIVE 8-12	13
2009	CARNABY STREET 8-12	14
2010	KLAMMER 8-12	10
2011	TELL DAD 8-12	14
2012	TAWHID 8-12	8
2013	PIPING ROCK 8-12	11
2014	SMAIH 9-0	6
2015	CRAZY HORSE 9-0	9
2016	PLEASELETMEWIN 9-0	13
2017	NEBO 9-0	6

RACING POST TROPHY (2y)
Doncaster-1m (St)
2008	CROWDED HOUSE 9-0	15
2009	ST NICHOLAS ABBEY 9-0	11
2010	CASAMENTO 9-0	10
2011	CAMELOT 9-0	5
2012	KINGSBARNS 9-0	10
2013	KINGSTON HILL 9-0	11
2014	ELM PARK 9-1	8
2015	MARCEL 9-1	7
2016	RIVET 9-1	10
2017	SAXON WARRIOR 9-1	12

NOVEMBER HANDICAP
Doncaster-1m 3f 197yds
2008	TROPICAL STRAIT 5-8-13	21
2009	CHARM SCHOOL 4-8-12	23
2010	TIMES UP 4-8-13	22
2011	ZUIDER ZEE 4-8-13	23
2012	ART SCHOLAR 5-8-7	23
2013	CONDUCT 6-9-2	23
2014	OPEN EAGLE 5-8-12	23
2015	LITIGANT 7-9-10	22
2016	PRIZE MONEY 3-8-10	15
2017	SAUNTER 4-8-13	23

WINNERS OF PRINCIPAL RACES IN IRELAND

IRISH 2000 GUINEAS (3y)
The Curragh-1m

2008 HENRYTHENAVIGATOR 9-0..................5
2009 MASTERCRAFTSMAN 9-0....................9
2010 CANFORD CLIFFS 9-0.......................13
2011 RODERIC O'CONNOR 9-0.....................8
2012 POWER 9-0...................................10
2013 MAGICIAN 9-0................................10
2014 KINGMAN 9-0.................................11
2015 GLENEAGLES 9-0............................11
2016 AWTAAD 9-0...................................8
2017 CHURCHILL 9-0................................6

TATTERSALLS GOLD CUP
The Curragh-1m 2f 110yds

2008 DUKE OF MARMALADE 4-9-0..............6
2009 CASUAL CONQUEST 4-9-0...................5
2010 FAME AND GLORY 4-9-0......................6
2011 SO YOU THINK 5-9-1..........................5
2012 SO YOU THINK 6-9-1..........................5
2013 AL KAZEEM 5-9-3..............................4
2014 NOBLE MISSION 5-9-3........................5
2015 AL KAZEEM 7-9-3..............................6
2016 FASCINATING ROCK 5-9-3...................6
2017 DECORATED KNIGHT 5-9-3..................8

IRISH 1000 GUINEAS (3y fillies)
The Curragh-1m

2008 HALFWAY TO HEAVEN 9-0..................13
2009 AGAIN 9-0.....................................16
2010 BETHRAH 9-0.................................19
2011 MISTY FOR ME 9-0...........................15
2012 SAMITAR 9-0....................................8
2013 JUST THE JUDGE 9-0........................15
2014 MARVELLOUS 9-0.............................11
2015 PLEASCACH 9-0..............................18
2016 JET SETTING 9-0.............................10
2017 WINTER 9-0......................................8

IRISH DERBY (3y)
The Curragh-1m 4f

2008 FROZEN FIRE 9-0.............................11
2009 FAME AND GLORY 9-0........................11
2010 CAPE BLANCO 9-0............................10
2011 TREASURE BEACH 9-0........................8
2012 CAMELOT 9-0...................................5
2013 TRADING LEATHER 9-0........................9
2014 AUSTRALIA 9-0.................................5
2015 JACK HOBBS 9-0..............................8
2016 HARZAND 9-0...................................9
2017 CAPRI 9-0.......................................9

PRETTY POLLY STAKES (fillies and mares)
Curragh-1m 2f

2008 PROMISING LEAD 4-9-9......................9
2009 DAR RE MI 4-9-9...............................7
2010 CHINESE WHITE 5-9-9........................9

2011 MISTY FOR ME 3-8-12........................7
2012 IZZI TOP 4-9-9.................................4
2013 AMBIVALENT 4-9-10...........................9
2014 THISTLE BIRD 6-9-10.........................8
2015 DIAMONDSANDRUBIES 3-8-12............9
2016 MINDING 3-8-12................................5
2017 NEZWAAH 4-9-8...............................11

IRISH OAKS (3y fillies)
The Curragh-1m 4f

2008 MOONSTONE 9-0.............................14
2009 SARISKA 9-0..................................10
2010 SNOW FAIRY 9-0.............................15
2011 BLUE BUNTING 9-0............................9
2012 GREAT HEAVENS 9-0.........................7
2013 CHICQUITA 9-0.................................7
2014 BRACELET 9-0................................10
2015 COVERT LOVE 9-0.............................9
2016 SEVENTH HEAVEN 9-0.....................11
2017 ENABLE 9-0.....................................9

PHOENIX STAKES (2y)
The Curragh-6f

2008 MASTERCRAFTSMAN 9-1.....................5
2009 ALFRED NOBEL 9-1.............................8
2010 ZOFFANY 9-1....................................7
2011 LA COLLINA 8-12..............................9
2012 PEDRO THE GREAT 9-3......................6
2013 SUDIRMAN 9-3.................................5
2014 DICK WHITTINGTON 9-3......................6
2015 AIR FORCE BLUE 9-3..........................7
2016 CARAVAGGIO 9-3..............................5
2017 SIOUX NATION 9-3.............................8

MATRON STAKES (fillies and mares)
Leopardstown-1m

2008 LUSH LASHES 3-8-12........................10
2009 RAINBOW VIEW 3-8-12........................7
2010 LILLIE LANGTRY 3-8-12.......................6
2011 EMULOUS 4-9-5................................8
*2012 CHACHAMAIDEE 5-9-5......................11
2013 LA COLLINA 3-9-0.............................12
2014 FIESOLANA 5-9-5.............................10
2015 LEGATISSIMO 3-9-0............................9
2016 ALICE SPRINGS 3-9-0.........................8
2017 HYDRANGEA 3-9-0............................10
*Duntle disqualified from first place

IRISH CHAMPION STAKES
Leopardstown-1m 2f

2008 NEW APPROACH 3-9-0........................8
2009 SEA THE STARS 3-9-0.........................9
2010 CAPE BLANCO 3-9-0...........................6
2011 SO YOU THINK 5-9-7...........................6
2012 SNOW FAIRY 5-9-4.............................6
2013 THE FUGUE 4-9-4..............................6
2014 THE GREY GATSBY 3-9-0.....................7
2015 GOLDEN HORN 3-9-0..........................7
2016 ALMANZOR 3-9-0.............................12
2017 DECORATED KNIGHT 5-9-7.................10

IRISH CAMBRIDGESHIRE
The Curragh-1m
2008	**TIS MIGHTY** 5-8-1	21
2009	**POET** 4-9-9	27
2010	**HUJAYLEA** 7-8-3	25
2011	**CASTLE BAR SLING** 6-8-11	21
2012	**PUNCH YOUR WEIGHT** 3-8-6	18
2013	**MORAN GRA** 6-8-13	20
2014	**SRETAW** 5-8-8	21
2015	**HINT OF A TINT** 5-9-3	22
2016	**SEA WOLF** 4-9-5	24
2017	**ELUSIVE TIME** 9-8-9	27

MOYGLARE STUD STAKES (2y fillies)
The Curragh-7f
2008	**AGAIN** 8-12	12
2009	**TERMAGANT** 8-12	7
2010	**MISTY FOR ME** 8-12	12
2011	**MAYBE** 9-1	8
2012	**SKY LANTERN** 9-0	13
2013	**RIZEENA** 9-0	7
2014	**CURSORY GLANCE** 9-0	10
2015	**MINDING** 9-0	9
2016	**INTRICATELY** 9-0	7
2017	**HAPPILY** 9-0	8

VINCENT O'BRIEN (NATIONAL) STAKES (2y)
The Curragh-7f
2008	**MASTERCRAFTSMAN** 9-1	7
2009	**KINGSFORT** 9-1	6
2010	**PATHFORK** 9-1	9
2011	**POWER** 9-1	9
2012	**DAWN APPROACH** 9-3	7
2013	**TOORMORE** 9-3	5
2014	**GLENEAGLES** 9-3	5
2015	**AIR FORCE BLUE** 9-3	5
2016	**CHURCHILL** 9-3	7
2017	**VERBAL DEXTERITY** 9-3	7

IRISH ST LEGER
The Curragh-1m 6f
2008	**SEPTIMUS** 5-9-11	9
2009	**ALANDI** 4-9-11	8
2010	**SANS FRONTIERES** 4-9-11	8
2011	**DUNCAN** 6-9-11 dead heated with	6
	JUKEBOX JURY 5-9-11	6
2012	**ROYAL DIAMOND** 6-9-11	9
2013	**VOLEUSE DE COEURS** 4-9-8	10
2014	**BROWN PANTHER** 6-9-11	11
2015	**ORDER OF ST GEORGE** 3-9-0	11
2016	**WICKLOW BRAVE** 7-9-11	4
2017	**ORDER OF ST GEORGE** 5-9-10	10

IRISH CESAREWITCH
The Curragh-2m
2008	**SUAILCE** 3-8-1	28
2009	**DANI CALIFORNIA** 5-8-0	29
2010	**BRIGHT HORIZON** 3-8-7	23
2011	**MINSK** 3-8-9	19
2012	**VOLEUSE DE COEURS** 3-9-1	27
2013	**MONTEFELTRO** 5-9-4	30
2014	**EL SALVADOR** 5-9-5	21
2015	**DIGENATA** 8-9-10	20
2016	**LAWS OF SPIN** 3-8-6	20
*2017	**LORD ERSKINE** 4-8-5	24

*Run at Navan

CORAL HURDLE
Leopardstown-2m
(Pierse Hurdle 2006-9, MCR Hurdle in 2010-11, Boylesports Hurdle 2012-15)
2009	**PENNY'S BILL** 7-9-9	29
2010	**PUYOL** 8-10-10	30
2011	**FINAL APPROACH** 5-10-9	26
2012	**CITIZENSHIP** 6-10-3	30
2013	**ABBEY LANE** 8-10-8	28
2014	**GILGAMBOA** 6-10-9	24
2015	**KATIE T** 6-10-9	24
2016	**HENRY HIGGINS** 6-10-10	23
2017	**ICE COLD SOUL** 7-10-2	20
2018	**OFF YOU GO** 5-10-9	28

IRISH CHAMPION HURDLE
Leopardstown-2m
2009	**BRAVE INCA** 11-11-10	9
2010	**SOLWHIT** 6-11-10	7
2011	**HURRICANE FLY** 7-11-10	5
2012	**HURRICANE FLY** 8-11-10	5
2013	**HURRICANE FLY** 9-11-10	5
2014	**HURRICANE FLY** 10-11-10	4
2015	**HURRICANE FLY** 11-11-10	4
2016	**FAUGHEEN** 8-11-10	5
2017	**PETIT MOUCHOIR** 6 11-10	4
2018	**SUPASUNDAE** 8-11-10	8

IRISH GOLD CUP
Leopardstown-3m
(Hennessy Gold Cup before 2016)
2009	**NEPTUNE COLLONGES** 8-11-10	6
2010	**JONCOL** 7-11-10	7
2011	**KEMPES** 8-11-10	9
2012	**QUEL ESPRIT** 8-11-10	7
2013	**SIR DES CHAMPS** 7-11-10	4
2014	**LAST INSTALMENT** 9-11-10	7
2015	**CARLINGFORD LOUGH** 9-11-10	8
2016	**CARLINGFORD LOUGH** 10-11-10	10
2017	**SIZING JOHN** 7-11-10	10
2018	**EDWULF** 9-11-10	10

IRISH GRAND NATIONAL
Fairyhouse-3m 5f
2008	**HEAR THE ECHO** 7-10-0	23
2009	**NICHE MARKET** 8-10-5	30
2010	**BLUESEA CRACKER** 8-10-4	26
2011	**ORGANISEDCONFUSION** 6-9-13	25
2012	**LION NA BEARNAI** 10-10-5	29
2013	**LIBERTY COUNSEL** 10-9-5	28
2014	**SHUTTHEFRONTDOOR** 7-10-13	26
2015	**THUNDER AND ROSES** 7-10-6	27
2016	**ROGUE ANGEL** 8-10-6	27
2017	**OUR DUKE** 7-11-4	28

WINNERS OF PRINCIPAL RACES IN FRANCE

PRIX GANAY
Longchamp-1m 2f 110yds
2008	**DUKE OF MARMALADE** 4-9-2		6
2009	**VISION D'ETAT** 4-9-2		8
2010	**CUTLASS BAY** 4-9-2		9
2011	**PLANTEUR** 4-9-2		7
2012	**CIRRUS DES AIGLES** 6-9-2		6
2013	**PASTORIUS** 4-9-2		9
2014	**CIRRUS DES AIGLES** 8-9-2		8
2015	**CIRRUS DES AIGLES** 9-9-2		7
*2016	**DARIYAN** 4-9-2		10
*2017	**CLOTH OF STARS** 4-9-2		7

*Run at Saint-Cloud

POULE D'ESSAI DES POULAINS (3y)
Longchamp-1m
2008	**FALCO** 9-2		19
2009	**SILVER FROST** 9-2		6
2010	**LOPE DE VEGA** 9-2		15
2011	**TIN HORSE** 9-2		14
2012	**LUCAYAN** 9-2		12
2013	**STYLE VENDOME** 9-2		18
2014	**KARAKONTIE** 9-2		12
2015	**MAKE BELIEVE** 9-2		18
*2016	**THE GURKHA** 9-2		13
*2017	**BRAMETOT** 9-2		13

*Run at Deauville

POULE D'ESSAI DES POULICHES (3y fillies)
Longchamp-1m
2008	**ZARKAVA** 9-0		14
2009	**ELUSIVE WAVE** 9-0		11
*2010	**SPECIAL DUTY** 9-0		10
2011	**GOLDEN LILAC** 9-0		16
2012	**BEAUTY PARLOUR** 9-0		13
2013	**FLOTILLA** 9-0		20
2014	**AVENIR CERTAIN** 9-0		16
2015	**ERVEDYA** 9-0		14
*2016	**LA CRESSONNIERE** 9-0		14
*2017	**PRECIEUSE** 9-0		18

*Liliside disqualified from first place
*Run at Deauville

PRIX SAINT-ALARY (3y fillies)
Longchamp-1m 2f
2008	**BELLE ET CELEBRE** 9-0		7
2009	**STACELITA** 9-0		7
2010	**SARAFINA** 9-0		9
2011	**WAVERING** 9-0		12
2012	**SAGAWARA** 9-0		8
2013	**SILASOL** 9-0		8
*2014	**VAZIRA** 9-0		8
2015	**QUEEN'S JEWEL** 9-0		9
*2016	**JEMAYEL** 9-0		9
*2017	**SOBETSU** 9-0		11

*We Are disqualified from first place
*Run at Deauville

PRIX D'ISPAHAN
Longchamp-1m 1f 55yds
2008	**SAGEBURG** 4-9-2		6
2009	**NEVER ON SUNDAY** 4-9-2		9
2010	**GOLDIKOVA** 5-8-13		8
2011	**GOLDIKOVA** 6-8-13		9
2012	**GOLDEN LILAC** 4-8-13		8
2013	**MAXIOS** 5-9-2		7
2014	**CIRRUS DES AIGLES** 8-9-2		6
2015	**SOLOW** 5-9-2		4
*2016	**A SHIN HIKARI** 5-9-2		9
*2017	**MEKHTAAL** 4-9-2		5

*Run at Chantilly

PRIX DU JOCKEY CLUB (3y)
Chantilly-1m 2f 110yds
2008	**VISION D'ETAT** 9-2		20
2009	**LE HAVRE** 9-2		17
2010	**LOPE DE VEGA** 9-2		22
2011	**RELIABLE MAN** 9-2		16
2012	**SAONOIS** 9-2		20
2013	**INTELLO** 9-2		19
2014	**THE GREY GATSBY** 9-2		16
2015	**NEW BAY** 9-2		14
2016	**ALMANZOR** 9-2		16
2017	**BRAMETOT** 9-2		12

PRIX DE DIANE (3y fillies)
Chantilly-1m 2f 110yds
2008	**ZARKAVA** 9-0		13
2009	**STACELITA** 9-0		12
2010	**SARAFINA** 9-0		9
2011	**GOLDEN LILAC** 9-0		9
2012	**VALYRA** 9-0		12
2013	**TREVE** 9-0		11
2014	**AVENIR CERTAIN** 9-0		12
2015	**STAR OF SEVILLE** 9-0		17
2016	**LA CRESSONNIERE** 9-0		16
2017	**SENGA** 9-1		16

GRAND PRIX DE SAINT-CLOUD
Saint-Cloud-1m 4f
2008	**YOUMZAIN** 5-9-2		9
2009	**SPANISH MOON** 5-9-2		10
2010	**PLUMANIA** 4-8-13		7
2011	**SARAFINA** 4-8-13		5
2012	**MEANDRE** 4-9-2		4
2013	**NOVELLIST** 4-9-2		11
*2014	**NOBLE MISSION** 5-9-2		7
2015	**TREVE** 5-8-13		9
2016	**SILVERWAVE** 4-9-2		11
2017	**ZARAK** 4-9-2		10

*Spiritjim disqualified from first place

PRIX JEAN PRAT (3y)
Chantilly-1m
2008	**TAMAYUZ** 9-2		16
2009	**LORD SHANAKILL** 9-2		9
2010	**DICK TURPIN** 9-2		8

2011	**MUTUAL TRUST** 9-2	7
2012	**AESOP'S FABLES** 9-2	8
2013	**HAVANA GOLD** 9-2	12
2014	**CHARM SPIRIT** 9-2	7
2015	**TERRITORIES** 9-2	8
2016	**ZELZAL** 9-2	9
2017	**THUNDER SNOW** 9-3	5

GRAND PRIX DE PARIS (3y)
Longchamp-1m 4f

2008	**MONTMARTRE** 9-2	13
2009	**CAVALRYMAN** 9-2	8
2010	**BEHKABAD** 9-2	9
2011	**MEANDRE** 9-2	7
2012	**IMPERIAL MONARCH** 9-2	9
2013	**FLINTSHIRE** 9-2	8
2014	**GALLANTE** 9-2	11
2015	**ERUPT** 9-2	9
*2016	**MONT ORMEL** 9-2	8
*2017	**SHAKEEL** 9-2	9

*Run at Saint-Cloud

PRIX ROTHSCHILD
(fillies and mares)
Deauville-1m
(run as Prix d'Astarte before 2008)

2008	**GOLDIKOVA** 3-8-8	9
2009	**GOLDIKOVA** 4-9-0	12
2010	**GOLDIKOVA** 5-9-0	7
2011	**GOLDIKOVA** 6-9-2	8
2012	**ELUSIVE KATE** 3-8-9	5
2013	**ELUSIVE KATE** 4-9-2	12
2014	**ESOTERIQUE** 4-9-2	4
2015	**AMAZING MARIA** 4-9-2	8
2016	**QEMAH** 3-8-9	9
2017	**ROLY POLY** 3-8-9	10

PRIX MAURICE DE GHEEST
Deauville-6f 110yds

2008	**MARCHAND D'OR** 5-9-2	16
2009	**KING'S APOSTLE** 5-9-2	12
2010	**REGAL PARADE** 6-9-2	15
2011	**MOONLIGHT CLOUD** 3-8-8	13
2012	**MOONLIGHT CLOUD** 4-8-13	9
2013	**MOONLIGHT CLOUD** 5-8-13	14
2014	**GARSWOOD** 4-9-2	14
2015	**MUHAARAR** 3-8-11	12
2016	**SIGNS OF BLESSING** 5-9-2	15
2017	**BRANDO** 5-9-3	13

PRIX JACQUES LE MAROIS
Deauville-1m

2008	**TAMAYUZ** 3-8-11	8
2009	**GOLDIKOVA** 4-9-0	8
2010	**MAKFI** 3-8-11	9
2011	**IMMORTAL VERSE** 3-8-8	8
2012	**EXCELEBRATION** 4-9-4	11
2013	**MOONLIGHT CLOUD** 5-9-1	13
2014	**KINGMAN** 3-8-13	5
2015	**ESOTERIQUE** 5-9-1	9
2016	**RIBCHESTER** 3-8-13	11
2017	**AL WUKAIR** 3-8-13	6

PRIX MORNY (2y)
Deauville-6f

2008	**BUSHRANGER** 9-0	14
2009	**ARCANO** 9-0	5
2010	**DREAM AHEAD** 9-0	11
2011	**DABIRSIM** 9-0	7
2012	**RECKLESS ABANDON** 9-0	11
2013	**NO NAY NEVER** 9-0	10
2014	**THE WOW SIGNAL** 9-0	9
2015	**SHALAA** 9-0	5
2016	**LADY AURELIA** 8-10	5
2017	**UNFORTUNATELY** 9-0	8

PRIX JEAN ROMANET
(fillies and mares)
Deauville-1m 2f

2008	**FOLK OPERA** 4-8-12	9
2009	**ALPINE ROSE** 4-9-0	6
2010	**STACELITA** 4-9-0	8
2011	**ANNOUNCE** 4-9-0	5
*2012	**IZZI TOP** 4-9-0	8
2013	**ROMANTICA** 4-9-0	6
2014	**RIBBONS** 4-9-0	11
2015	**ODELIZ** 5-9-0	11
2016	**SPEEDY BOARDING** 4-9-0	10
2017	**AJMAN PRINCESS** 4-9-0	10

*Snow Fairy disqualified from first place

PRIX DU MOULIN DE LONGCHAMP
Longchamp-1m

2008	**GOLDIKOVA** 3-8-8	11
2009	**AQLAAM** 4-9-2	9
2010	**FUISSE** 4-9-2	6
2011	**EXCELEBRATION** 3-8-11	8
2012	**MOONLIGHT CLOUD** 4-8-13	4
2013	**MAXIOS** 5-9-2	7
2014	**CHARM SPIRIT** 3-8-11	10
2015	**ERVEDYA** 3-8-9	6
*2016	**VADAMOS** 5-9-3	6
*2017	**RIBCHESTER** 4-9-3	7

*Run at Chantilly

PRIX VERMEILLE (fillies and mares)
Longchamp-1m 4f

2008	**ZARKAVA** 3-8-8	12
*2009	**STACELITA** 3-8-8	12
2010	**MIDDAY** 4-9-3	12
2011	**GALIKOVA** 3-8-8	6
2012	**SHARETA** 4-9-2	13
2013	**TREVE** 3-8-8	10
2014	**BALTIC BARONESS** 4-9-3	9
2015	**TREVE** 5-9-3	9
**2016	**LEFT HAND** 3-8-8	6
**2017	**BATEEL** 5-9-3	11

*Dar Re Mi disqualified from first place
**Run at Chantilly

PRIX DE LA FORET
Longchamp-7f

2008	**PACO BOY** 3-9-0	8
2009	**VARENAR** 3-9-0	14
2010	**GOLDIKOVA** 5-8-13	9
2011	**DREAM AHEAD** 3-9-0	8
2012	**GORDON LORD BYRON** 4-9-2	11
2013	**MOONLIGHT CLOUD** 5-8-13	11
2014	**OLYMPIC GLORY** 4-9-2	14

```
2015  MAKE BELIEVE 3-9-0.................................13
*2016  LIMATO 4-9-2........................................11
*2017  ACLAIM 4-9-2........................................10
*Run at Chantilly
```

PRIX DU CADRAN
Longchamp-2m 4f
```
2008  BANNABY 5-9-2........................................11
2009  ALANDI 4-9-2..........................................12
2010  GENTOO 6-9-2...........................................8
2011  KASBAH BLISS 9-9-2..................................10
2012  MOLLY MALONE 4-8-13...............................10
2013  ALTANO 7-9-2..........................................10
2014  HIGH JINX 6-9-2........................................8
2015  MILLE ET MILLE 5-9-2................................10
*2016  QUEST FOR MORE 6-9-2.............................12
*2017  VAZIRABAD 5-9-2........................................6
*Run at Chantilly
```

PRIX DE L'ABBAYE DE LONGCHAMP
Longchamp-5f
```
*2008  MARCHAND D'OR 5-9-11.............................17
2009  TOTAL GALLERY 3-9-11..............................16
2010  GILT EDGE GIRL 4-9-7...............................21
2011  TANGERINE TREES 6-9-11..........................15
2012  WIZZ KID 4-9-7.........................................18
2013  MAAREK 6-9-11........................................20
2014  MOVE IN TIME 6-9-11................................18
2015  GOLDREAM 6-9-11....................................18
**2016  MARSHA 3-9-7..........................................17
**2017  BATTAASH 3-9-11.....................................13
* re-run; Overdose won void first running
**Run at Chantilly
```

PRIX JEAN-LUC LAGARDERE (2y)
Longchamp-1m (7f before 2015)
```
2008  NAAQOOS 9-0.............................................7
2009  SIYOUNI 9-0...............................................7
2010  WOOTTON BASSETT 9-0................................9
2011  DABIRSIM 9-0.............................................7
2012  OLYMPIC GLORY 9-0.....................................8
2013  KARAKONTIE 9-0..........................................8
*2014  FULL MAST 9-0.............................................9
2015  ULTRA 9-0................................................11
**2016  NATIONAL DEFENSE 9-0................................7
**2017  HAPPILY 8-10...............................................6
*Gleneagles disqualified from first place
**Run at Chantilly
```

PRIX MARCEL BOUSSAC (2y fillies)
Longchamp-1m
```
2008  PROPORTIONAL 8-11....................................16
2009  ROSANARA 8-11..........................................11
2010  MISTY FOR ME 8-11.......................................8
2011  ELUSIVE KATE 8-11........................................5
2012  SILASOL 8-11..............................................9
2013  INDONESIENNE 8-11....................................12
```

```
2014  FOUND 8-11...............................................12
2015  BALLYDOYLE 8-11..........................................8
*2016  WUHEIDA 8-11............................................11
*2017  WILD ILLUSION 8-11.......................................7
*Run at Chantilly
```

PRIX DE L'OPERA (fillies and mares)
Longchamp-1m 2f
```
2007  SATWA QUEEN 5-9-2....................................11
2008  LADY MARIAN 3-8-11...................................14
2009  SHALANAYA 3-8-11........................................9
2010  LILY OF THE VALLEY 3-8-11..........................11
2011  NAHRAIN 3-8-11.........................................10
2012  RIDASIYNA 3-8-11.......................................13
2013  DALKALA 4-9-2.............................................9
2014  WE ARE 3-8-11...........................................11
2015  COVERT LOVE 3-8-11...................................13
*2016  SPEEDY BOARDING 4-9-2...............................7
*2017  RHODODENDRON 3-8-11...............................13
*Run at Chantilly
```

PRIX ROYAL-OAK
Longchamp-1m 7f 110yds
```
2008  YEATS 7-9-4..............................................11
2009  ASK 6-9-4...................................................9
2010  GENTOO 6-9-4............................................10
2011  BE FABULOUS 4-9-1.....................................14
2012  LES BEAUFS 3-8-9.........................................9
2013  TAC DE BOISTRON 6-9-4.............................15
2014  TAC DE BOISTRON 7-9-4.............................13
2015  VAZIRABAD 3-8-10......................................13
*2016  VAZIRABAD 4-9-4........................................15
**2017  ICE BREEZE 3-8-10........................................9
*Run at Chantilly
**Run at Saint-Cloud
```

CRITERIUM INTERNATIONAL (2y)
Saint-Cloud-7f (1m before 2015)
```
2008  ZAFISIO 9-0...............................................11
2009  JAN VERMEER 9-0..........................................7
2010  RODERIC O'CONNOR 9-0..............................10
2011  FRENCH FIFTEEN 9-0....................................11
2012  LOCH GARMAN 9-0.........................................6
2013  ECTOT 9-0...................................................4
2014  VERT DE GRECE 9-0........................................9
2015  JOHANNES VERMEER 9-0................................8
2016  THUNDER SNOW 9-0.......................................9
2017  ABANDONED
```

CRITERIUM DE SAINT-CLOUD (2y)
Saint-Cloud-1m 2f
```
2008  FAME AND GLORY 9-0....................................11
2009  PASSION FOR GOLD 9-0...................................9
2010  RECITAL 9-0...............................................10
2011  MANDAEAN 9-0.............................................8
2012  MORANDI 9-0................................................8
2013  PRINCE GIBRALTAR 9-0.................................12
2014  EPICURIS 9-0................................................6
2015  ROBIN OF NAVAN 9-0....................................10
2016  WALDGEIST 9-0...........................................13
2017  ABANDONED
```

WINNERS OF OTHER OVERSEAS RACES

DUBAI WORLD CUP
Meydan-1m 2f Tapeta
(Run at Nad Al Sheba on dirt before 2010)

2008	**CURLIN** 4-9-0	12
2009	**WELL ARMED** 6-9-0	14
2010	**GLORIA DE CAMPEAO** 7-9-0	14
2011	**VICTOIRE PISA** 4-9-0	14
2012	**MONTEROSSO** 5-9-0	13
2013	**ANIMAL KINGDOM** 5-9-0	13
2014	**AFRICAN STORY** 7-9-0	16
2015	**PRINCE BISHOP** 8-9-0	12
2016	**CALIFORNIA CHROME** 5-9-0	12
2017	**ARROGATE** 4-9-0	14

KENTUCKY DERBY
Churchill Downs-1m 2f dirt

2008	**BIG BROWN** 9-0	20
2009	**MINE THAT BIRD** 9-0	19
2010	**SUPER SAVER** 9-0	20
2011	**ANIMAL KINGDOM** 9-0	19
2012	**I'LL HAVE ANOTHER** 9-0	20
2013	**ORB** 9-0	19
2014	**CALIFORNIA CHROME** 9-0	19
2015	**AMERICAN PHAROAH** 9-0	18
2016	**NYQUIST** 9-0	20
2017	**ALWAYS DREAMING** 9-0	20

BREEDERS' CUP TURF
Various courses-1m 4f

2008	**CONDUIT** 3-8-9	11
2009	**CONDUIT** 4-9-0	7
2010	**DANGEROUS MIDGE** 4-9-0	7
2011	**ST NICHOLAS ABBEY** 4-9-0	9
2012	**LITTLE MIKE** 5-9-0	12
2013	**MAGICIAN** 3-8-10	12
2014	**MAIN SEQUENCE** 5-9-0	12
2015	**FOUND** 3-8-7	12
2016	**HIGHLAND REEL** 4-9-0	12
2017	**TALISMANIC** 4-9-0	13

BREEDERS' CUP CLASSIC
Various courses-1m 2f dirt/pro-ride

2008	**RAVEN'S PASS** 3-8-9	12
2009	**ZENYATTA** 5-8-11	12
2010	**BLAME** 4-9-0	12
2011	**DROSSELMEYER** 4-9-0	12
2012	**FORT LARNED** 4-9-0	12
2013	**MUCHO MACHO MAN** 5-9-0	11
2014	**BAYERN** 3-8-10	14
2015	**AMERICAN PHAROAH** 3-8-10	8
2016	**ARROGATE** 3-8-10	12
2017	**GUN RUNNER** 4-9-0	11

MELBOURNE CUP
Flemington-2m

2008	**VIEWED** 5-8-5	24
2009	**SHOCKING** 4-8-0	23
2010	**AMERICAIN** 5-8-8	23
2011	**DUNADEN** 5-8-8	23
2012	**GREEN MOON** 5-8-6	24
2013	**FIORENTE** 5-8-9	24
2014	**PROTECTIONIST** 4-8-13	22
2015	**PRINCE OF PENZANCE** 6-8-5	24
2016	**ALMANDIN** 6-8-3	24
2017	**REKINDLING** 3-8-2	23

JAPAN CUP
Tokyo-1m 4f

2008	**SCREEN HERO** 4-9-0	17
2009	**VODKA** 5-8-10	18
*2010	**ROSE KINGDOM** 3-8-9	18
2011	**BUENA VISTA** 5-8-9	16
2012	**GENTILDONNA** 3-8-5	17
2013	**GENTILDONNA** 4-8-9	17
2014	**EPIPHANEIA** 4-9-0	18
2015	**SHONAN PANDORA** 4-8-9	18
2016	**KITASAN BLACK** 4-9-0	17
2017	**CHEVAL GRAND** 5-9-0	17

*Buena Vista disqualified from first place

WINNERS OF PRINCIPAL NATIONAL HUNT RACES

BETVICTOR GOLD CUP (HANDICAP CHASE)
Cheltenham-2m 4f 78yds

2008	**IMPERIAL COMMANDER** 7-10-7	19
2009	**TRANQUIL SEA** 7-10-13	16
2010	**LITTLE JOSH** 8-10-5	18
2011	**GREAT ENDEAVOUR** 7-10-3	20
2012	**AL FEROF** 7-11-8	18
2013	**JOHNS SPIRIT** 6-10-2	20
2014	**CAID DU BERLAIS** 5-10-13	18
2015	**ANNACOTTY** 7-11-0	20
2016	**TAQUIN DU SEUIL** 9-11-11	17
2017	**SPLASH OF GINGE** 9-10-6	17

BETFAIR CHASE
Haydock-3m 1f 125yds (3m 24yds before 2017)

2008	**SNOOPY LOOPY** 10-11-7	6
2009	**KAUTO STAR** 9-11-7	7
2010	**IMPERIAL COMMANDER** 9-11-7	7
2011	**KAUTO STAR** 11-11-7	6
2012	**SILVINIACO CONTI** 6-11-7	5
2013	**CUE CARD** 7-11-7	8
2014	**SILVINIACO CONTI** 8-11-7	9

2015 **CUE CARD** 9-11-7 5
2016 **CUE CARD** 10-11-7 6
2017 **BRISTOL DE MAI** 6-11-7 6

LADBROKES TROPHY HANDICAP CHASE

Newbury-3m 1f 214yds
Run as Hennessy Gold Cup before 2017
2008 **MADISON DU BERLAIS** 7-11-4 15
2009 **DENMAN** 9-11-12 19
2010 **DIAMOND HARRY** 7-10-0 20
2011 **CARRUTHERS** 8-10-4 18
2012 **BOBS WORTH** 7-11-6 19
2013 **TRIOLO D'ALENE** 6-11-1 21
2014 **MANY CLOUDS** 7-11-6 19
2015 **SMAD PLACE** 8-11-4 15
2016 **NATIVE RIVER** 6-11-1 19
2017 **TOTAL RECALL** 8-10-8 20

TINGLE CREEK CHASE

Sandown-2m
2008 **MASTER MINDED** 5-11-7 7
2009 **TWIST MAGIC** 7-11-7 5
2010 **MASTER MINDED** 7-11-7 9
2011 **SIZING EUROPE** 9-11-7 7
2012 **SPRINTER SACRE** 6-11-7 7
2013 **SIRE DE GRUGY** 7-11-7 9
2014 **DODGING BULLETS** 6-11-7 10
2015 **SIRE DE GRUGY** 9-11-7 7
2016 **UN DE SCEAUX** 8-11-7 6
2017 **POLITOLOGUE** 6-11-7 6
Run at Cheltenham over 2m 110yds

CHRISTMAS HURDLE

Kempton-2m
2008 **HARCHIBALD** 9-11-7 7
2009 **GO NATIVE** 6-11-7 7
2010 **BINOCULAR** 7-11-7 6
2011 **BINOCULAR** 7-11-7 5
2012 **DARLAN** 5-11-7 7
2013 **MY TENT OR YOURS** 6-11-7 6
2014 **FAUGHEEN** 6-11-7 6
2015 **FAUGHEEN** 7-11-7 5
2016 **YANWORTH** 6-11-7 5
2017 **BUVEUR D'AIR** 6-11-7 4
Run in January 2011

KING GEORGE VI CHASE

Kempton-3m
2008 **KAUTO STAR** 8-11-10 10
2009 **KAUTO STAR** 9-11-10 13
2010 **LONG RUN** 6-11-10 9
2011 **KAUTO STAR** 11-11-10 7
2012 **LONG RUN** 7-11-10 9
2013 **SILVINIACO CONTI** 7-11-10 9
2014 **SILVINIACO CONTI** 8-11-10 10
2015 **CUE CARD** 9-11-10 9
2016 **THISTLECRACK** 8-11-10 5
2017 **MIGHT BITE** 8-11-10 8
Run in January 2011

WELSH GRAND NATIONAL (HANDICAP CHASE)

Chepstow-3m 5f 110yds
2008 **NOTRE PERE** 7-11-0 20
2009 **DREAM ALLIANCE** 8-10-8 18
*2010 **SYNCHRONISED** 8-11-6 18
2011 **LE BEAU BAI** 8-10-1 20
2012 **MONBEG DUDE 8-10-1 17
2013 **MOUNTAINOUS** 8-10-0 20
2014 **EMPEROR'S CHOICE** 7-10-8 19
***2015 **MOUNTAINOUS** 11-10-6 20
2016 **NATIVE RIVER** 6-11-12 20
****2017 **RAZ DE MAREE** 13-10-10 20
*Run in January 2011
**Run in January 2013
***Run in January 2016
****Run in January 2018

CLARENCE HOUSE CHASE

(Victor Chandler Chase before 2014)
Ascot-2m 167yds
2009 **MASTER MINDED** 6-11-7 5
2010 **TWIST MAGIC** 8-11-7 7
2011 **MASTER MINDED** 8-11-7 9
2012 **SOMERSBY** 8-11-7 8
*2013 **SPRINTER SACRE** 7-11-7 7
2014 **SIRE DE GRUGY** 7-11-7 7
2015 **DODGING BULLETS** 7-11-7 5
2016 **UN DE SCEAUX** 8-11-7 5
*2017 **UN DE SCEAUX** 9-11-7 7
2018 **UN DE SCEAUX** 10-11-7 5
*Run at Cheltenham

BETFAIR HANDICAP HURDLE

Newbury-2m 69yds
(Totesport Trophy before 2012)
2009 ABANDONED ....
2010 **GET ME OUT OF HERE** 6-10-6 23
2011 **RECESSION PROOF** 5-10-8 15
2012 **ZARKANDAR** 5-11-1 20
2013 **MY TENT OR YOURS** 6-11-2 21
2014 **SPLASH OF GINGE** 6-10-3 20
2015 **VIOLET DANCER** 5-10-9 23
2016 **AGRAPART** 5-10-5 22
2017 **BALLYANDY** 6-11-1 16
2018 **KALASHNIKOV** 5-11-5 24

SUPREME NOVICES' HURDLE

Cheltenham-2m 87yds
2008 **CAPTAIN CEE BEE** 7-11-7 22
2009 **GO NATIVE** 6-11-7 20
2010 **MENORAH** 5-11-7 18
2011 **AL FEROF** 6-11-7 15
2012 **CINDERS AND ASHES** 5-11-7 19
2013 **CHAMPAGNE FEVER** 6-11-7 12
2014 **VAUTOUR** 5-11-7 18
2015 **DOUVAN** 5-11-7 12
2016 **ALTIOR** 6-11-7 14
2017 **LABAIK** 6-11-7 14

ARKLE CHALLENGE TROPHY (NOVICES' CHASE)

Cheltenham-1m 7f 199yds
2008 **TIDAL BAY** 7-11-7 14
2009 **FORPADYDEPLASTERER** 7-11-7 17
2010 **SIZING EUROPE** 8-11-7 12

2011 CAPTAIN CHRIS 7-11-7................................10
2012 SPRINTER SACRE 6-11-7................................6
2013 SIMONSIG 7-11-7................................
2014 WESTERN WARHORSE 6-11-4................................9
2015 UN DE SCEAUX 7-11-4................................11
2016 DOUVAN 6-11-4................................7
2017 ALTIOR 7-11-4................................9

CHAMPION HURDLE
Cheltenham-2m 87yds
2008 KATCHIT 5-11-10................................15
2009 PUNJABI 6-11-10................................23
2010 BINOCULAR 6-11-10................................12
2011 HURRICANE FLY 7-11-10................................11
2012 ROCK ON RUBY 7-11-10................................10
2013 HURRICANE FLY 9-11-10................................9
2014 JEZKI 6-11-10................................9
2015 FAUGHEEN 7-11-10................................8
2016 ANNIE POWER 8-11-3................................12
2017 BUVEUR D'AIR 6-11-10................................11

QUEEN MOTHER CHAMPION CHASE
Cheltenham-1m 7f 199yds
2008 MASTER MINDED 5-11-10................................8
2009 MASTER MINDED 6-11-10................................12
2010 BIG ZEB 9-11-10................................9
2011 SIZING EUROPE 9-11-10................................11
2012 FINIAN'S RAINBOW 9-11-10................................8
2013 SPRINTER SACRE 7-11-10................................7
2014 SIRE DE GRUGY 8-11-10................................11
2015 DODGING BULLETS 7-11-10................................11
2016 SPRINTER SACRE 10-11-10................................10
2017 SPECIAL TIARA 10-11-10................................10

NEPTUNE INVESTMENT
MANAGEMENT NOVICES' HURDLE
(Ballymore Hurdle 2008-9)
Cheltenham-2m 5f 26yds
2008 FIVEFORTHREE 6-11-7................................15
2009 MIKAEL D'HAGUENET 5-11-7................................14
2010 PEDDLERS CROSS 5-11-7................................17
2011 FIRST LIEUTENANT 6-11-7................................12
2012 SIMONSIG 6-11-7................................17
2013 THE NEW ONE 5-11-7................................8
2014 FAUGHEEN 6-11-7................................15
2015 WINDSOR PARK 6-11-7................................10
2016 YORKHILL 6-11-7................................11
2017 WILLOUGHBY COURT 6-11-7................................15

RSA CHASE
(Royal & SunAlliance Chase before 2009)
Cheltenham-3m 80yds
2008 ALBERTAS RUN 7-11-4................................11
2009 COOLDINE 7-11-4................................15
2010 WEAPON'S AMNESTY 7-11-4................................9
2011 BOSTONS ANGEL 7-11-4................................12
2012 BOBS WORTH 7-11-4................................9
2013 LORD WINDERMERE 7-11-4................................11
2014 O'FAOLAINS BOY 7-11-4................................15
2015 DON POLI 6-11-4................................8
2016 BLAKLION 7-11-4................................8
2017 MIGHT BITE 8-11-4................................12

STAYERS HURDLE
(World Hurdle before 2017)
Cheltenham-2m 7f 213 yds
2008 INGLIS DREVER 9-11-10................................17
2009 BIG BUCK'S 6-11-10................................14
2010 BIG BUCK'S 7-11-10................................14
2011 BIG BUCK'S 8-11-10................................13
2012 BIG BUCK'S 9-11-10................................11
2013 SOLWHIT 9-11-10................................13
2014 MORE OF THAT 6-11-10................................10
2015 COLE HARDEN 6-11-10................................16
2016 THISTLECRACK 8-11-10................................12
2017 NICHOLS CANYON 7-11-10................................12

TRIUMPH HURDLE (4y)
Cheltenham-2m 179yds
2008 CELESTIAL HALO 11-0................................14
2009 ZAYNAR 11-0................................18
2010 SOLDATINO 11-0................................17
2011 ZARKANDAR 11-0................................23
2012 COUNTRYWIDE FLAME 11-0................................20
2013 OUR CONOR 11-0................................14
2014 TIGER ROLL 11-0................................15
2015 PEACE AND CO 11-0................................16
2016 IVANOVICH GORBATOV 11-0................................15
2017 DEFI DU SEUIL 11-0................................15

CHELTENHAM GOLD CUP
Cheltenham-3m 2f 110yds
2008 DENMAN 8-11-10................................12
2009 KAUTO STAR 9-11-10................................16
2010 IMPERIAL COMMANDER 9-11-10................................11
2011 LONG RUN 6-11-0................................13
2012 SYNCHRONISED 9-11-10................................14
2013 BOBS WORTH 8-11-10................................9
2014 LORD WINDERMERE 8-11-10................................13
2015 CONEYGREE 8-11-10................................16
2016 DON COSSACK 9-11-10................................9
2017 SIZING JOHN 7-11-10................................13

RYANAIR CHASE
(FESTIVAL TROPHY)
Cheltenham-2m 4f 166yds
2008 OUR VIC 10-11-10................................9
2009 IMPERIAL COMMANDER 8-11-10................................10
2010 ALBERTAS RUN 9-11-10................................11
2011 ALBERTAS RUN 10-11-10................................11
2012 RIVERSIDE THEATRE 8-11-10................................12
2013 CUE CARD 7-11-10................................8
2014 DYNASTE 8-11-10................................11
2015 UXIZANDRE 7-11-10................................14
2016 VAUTOUR 7-11-10................................15
2017 UN DE SCEAUX 9-11-10................................8

BOWL CHASE
Aintree-3m 210yds
2008 OUR VIC 10-11-10................................5
2009 MADISON DU BERLAIS 8-11-10................................10
2010 WHAT A FRIEND 7-11-7................................5
2011 NACARAT 10-11-7................................6
2012 FOLLOW THE PLAN 9-11-7................................11
2013 FIRST LIEUTENANT 8-11-7................................8
2014 SILVINIACO CONTI 8-11-7................................6
2015 SILVINIACO CONTI 9-11-7................................7
2016 CUE CARD 10-11-7................................7
2017 TEA FOR TWO 8-11-7................................7

MELLING CHASE
Aintree-2m 3f 200yds

2008	**VOY POR USTEDES** 7-11-10	6
2009	**VOY POR USTEDES** 8-11-10	10
2010	**ALBERTAS RUN** 9-11-10	11
2011	**MASTER MINDED** 8-11-10	10
2012	**FINIAN'S RAINBOW** 9-11-10	8
2013	**SPRINTER SACRE** 7-11-10	6
2014	**BOSTON BOB** 9-11-10	10
2015	**DON COSSACK** 8-11-10	10
2016	**GOD'S OWN** 8-11-10	6
2017	**FOX NORTON** 7-11-7	9

AINTREE HURDLE
Aintree-2m 4f

2008	**AL EILE** 8-11-7	9
2009	**SOLWHIT** 5-11-7	16
2010	**KHYBER KIM** 8-11-7	7
2011	**OSCAR WHISKY** 6-11-7	8
2012	**OSCAR WHISKY** 7-11-7	5
2013	**ZARKANDAR** 6-11-7	9
2014	**THE NEW ONE** 6-11-7	7
2015	**JEZKI** 7-11-7	6
2016	**ANNIE POWER** 8-11-0	6
2017	**BUVEUR D'AIR** 6-11-7	6

SCOTTISH GRAND NATIONAL (H'CAP CHASE)
Ayr-3m 7f 176 yds

2008	**IRIS DE BALME** 8-9-7	24
2009	**HELLO BUD** 11-10-9	17

2010	**MERIGO** 9-10-0	30
2011	**BESHABAR** 9-10-4	28
2012	**MERIGO** 11-10-2	24
2013	**GODSMEJUDGE** 7-11-3	24
2014	**AL CO** 9-10-0	29
2015	**WAYWARD PRINCE** 11-10-1	29
2016	**VICENTE** 7-11-3	28
2017	**VICENTE** 8-11-10	30

BET365 GOLD CUP (H'CAP CHASE)
Sandown-3m 4f 166yds

2008	**MONKERHOSTIN** 11-10-13	19
2009	**HENNESSY** 8-10-7	14
2010	**CHURCH ISLAND** 11-10-5	19
2011	**POKER DE SIVOLA** 8-10-12	18
2012	**TIDAL BAY** 11-11-12	19
2013	**QUENTIN COLLONGES** 9-10-12	19
2014	**HADRIAN'S APPROACH** 7-11-0	19
2015	**JUST A PAR** 8-10-0	20
2016	**THE YOUNG MASTER** 7-10-12	20
2017	**HENLLAN HARRI** 9-10-0	13

DISTANCE CONVERSION

5f	1,000m	10f	2,000m	15f	3,000m	20f	4,000m
6f	1,200m	11f	2,200m	16f	3,200m	21f	4,200m
7f	1,400m	12f	2,400m	17f	3,400m	22f	4,400m
8f	1,600m	13f	2,600m	18f	3,600m		
9f	1,800m	14f	2,800m	19f	3,800m		

RACE REPLAYS*

*Remember no matter how many times you watch the race the result won't change.

Take your form study to the next level. Subscribe to Members' Club Ultimate and you can watch unlimited video replays of every race from all 86 courses in Britain and Ireland.

Visit **racingpost.com/replays**

LEADING TRAINERS ON THE FLAT: 1901-2017

1901 J Huggins	1940 F Darling	1979 H Cecil
1902 R S Sievier	1941 F Darling	1980 W Hern
1903 G Blackwell	1942 F Darling	1981 M Stoute
1904 P P Gilpin	1943 W Nightingall	1982 H Cecil
1905 W T Robinson	1944 Frank Butters	1983 W Hern
1906 Hon G Lambton	1945 W Earl	1984 H Cecil
1907 A Taylor	1946 Frank Butters	1985 H Cecil
1908 C Morton	1947 F Darling	1986 M Stoute
1909 A Taylor	1948 C F N Murless	1987 H Cecil
1910 A Taylor	1949 Frank Butters	1988 H Cecil
1911 Hon G Lambton	1950 C H Semblat	1989 M Stoute
1912 Hon G Lambton	1951 J L Jarvis	1990 H Cecil
1913 R Wootton	1952 M Marsh	1991 P Cole
1914 A Taylor	1953 J L Jarvis	1992 R Hannon Snr
1915 P P Gilpin	1954 C Boyd-Rochfort	1993 H Cecil
1916 R C Dawson	1955 C Boyd-Rochfort	1994 M Stoute
1917 A Taylor	1956 C F Elsey	1995 J Dunlop
1918 A Taylor	1957 C F N Murless	1996 Saeed bin Suroor
1919 A Taylor	1958 C Boyd-Rochfort	1997 M Stoute
1920 A Taylor	1959 C F N Murless	1998 Saeed bin Suroor
1921 A Taylor	1960 C F N Murless	1999 Saeed bin Suroor
1922 A Taylor	1961 C F N Murless	2000 Sir M Stoute
1923 A Taylor	1962 W Hern	2001 A O'Brien
1924 R C Dawson	1963 P Prendergast	2002 A O'Brien
1925 A Taylor	1964 P Prendergast	2003 Sir M Stoute
1926 F Darling	1965 P Prendergast	2004 Saeed bin Suroor
1927 Frank Butters	1966 M V O'Brien	2005 Sir M Stoute
1928 Frank Butters	1967 C F N Murless	2006 Sir M Stoute
1929 R C Dawson	1968 C F N Murless	2007 A O'Brien
1930 H S Persse	1969 A M Budgett	2008 A O'Brien
1931 J Lawson	1970 C F N Murless	2009 Sir M Stoute
1932 Frank Butters	1971 I Balding	2010 R Hannon Snr
1933 F Darling	1972 W Hern	2011 R Hannon Snr
1934 Frank Butters	1973 C F N Murless	2012 J Gosden
1935 Frank Butters	1974 P Walwyn	2013 R Hannon Snr
1936 J Lawson	1975 P Walwyn	2014 R Hannon Jnr
1937 C Boyd-Rochfort	1976 H Cecil	2015 J Gosden
1938 C Boyd-Rochfort	1977 M V O'Brien	2016 A O'Brien
1939 J L Jarvis	1978 H Cecil	2017 A O'Brien

CHAMPION JOCKEYS ON THE FLAT: 1900-2017

1900 L Reiff 143	1920 S Donoghue 143	1939 G Richards 155
1901 O Madden 130	1921 S Donoghue 141	1940 G Richards 68
1902 W Lane 170	1922 S Donoghue 102	1941 H Wragg 71
1903 O Madden 154	1923 S Donoghue 89	1942 G Richards 67
1904 O Madden 161	C Elliott 89	1943 G Richards 65
1905 E Wheatley 124	1924 C Elliott 106	1944 G Richards 88
1906 W Higgs 149	1925 G Richards 118	1945 G Richards 104
1907 W Higgs 146	1926 T Weston 95	1946 G Richards 212
1908 D Maher 139	1927 G Richards 164	1947 G Richards 269
1909 F Wootton 165	1928 G Richards 148	1948 G Richards 224
1910 F Wootton 137	1929 G Richards 135	1949 G Richards 261
1911 F Wootton 187	1930 F Fox 129	1950 G Richards 201
1912 F Wootton 118	1931 G Richards 145	1951 G Richards 227
1913 D Maher 115	1932 G Richards 190	1952 G Richards 231
1914 S Donoghue 129	1933 G Richards 259	1953 Sir G Richards 191
1915 S Donoghue 62	1934 G Richards 212	1954 D Smith 129
1916 S Donoghue 43	1935 G Richards 217	1955 D Smith 168
1917 S Donoghue 42	1936 G Richards 174	1956 D Smith 155
1918 S Donoghue 66	1937 G Richards 216	1957 A Breasley 173
1919 S Donoghue 129	1938 G Richards 206	1958 D Smith 165

1959 D Smith	157	1979 J Mercer	164	1999 K Fallon	200
1960 L Piggott	170	1980 W Carson	166	2000 K Darley	152
1961 A Breasley	171	1981 L Piggott	179	2001 K Fallon	166
1962 A Breasley	179	1982 L Piggott	188	2002 K Fallon	144
1963 A Breasley	176	1983 W Carson	159	2003 K Fallon	208
1964 L Piggott	140	1984 S Cauthen	130	2004 L Dettori	192
1965 L Piggott	160	1985 S Cauthen	195	2005 J Spencer	163
1966 L Piggott	191	1986 Pat Eddery	176	2006 R Moore	180
1967 L Piggott	117	1987 S Cauthen	197	2007 S Sanders	190
1968 L Piggott	139	1988 Pat Eddery	183	J Spencer	190
1969 L Piggott	163	1989 Pat Eddery	171	2008 R Moore	186
1970 L Piggott	162	1990 Pat Eddery	209	2009 R Moore	174
1971 L Piggott	162	1991 Pat Eddery	165	2010 P Hanagan	191
1972 W Carson	132	1992 M Roberts	206	2011 P Hanagan	165
1973 W Carson	164	1993 Pat Eddery	169	2012 R Hughes	172
1974 Pat Eddery	148	1994 L Dettori	233	2013 R Hughes	203
1975 Pat Eddery	164	1995 L Dettori	211	2014 R Hughes	161
1976 Pat Eddery	162	1996 Pat Eddery	186	2015 S De Sousa	132
1977 Pat Eddery	176	1997 K Fallon	196	2016 J Crowley	148
1978 W Carson	182	1998 K Fallon	185	2017 S De Sousa	206

CHAMPION APPRENTICES ON THE FLAT 1982-2017

1982 W Newnes	57	1994 S Davies	45	2006 S Donohoe	44
1983 M Hills	39	1995 S Sanders	61	2007 G Fairley	65
1984 T Quinn	62	1996 D O'Neill	79	2008 W Buick	50
1985 G Carter	37	1997 R Ffrench	77	D Probert	50
W Ryan	37	1998 C Lowther	72	2009 F Tylicki	60
1986 G Carter	34	1999 R Winston	49	2010 M Lane	41
1987 G Bardwell	27	2000 L Newman	87	2011 M Harley	57
1988 G Bardwell	39	2001 C Catlin	71	2012 A Ryan	40
1989 L Dettori	71	2002 P Hanagan	81	2013 J Hart	51
1990 J Fortune	46	2003 R Moore	52	2014 O Murphy	74
1991 D Holland	79	2004 T Queally	59	2015 T Marquand	54
1992 D Harrison	56	2005 S Golam	44	2016 J Gordon	50
1993 J Weaver	60	H Turner	44	2017 D Egan	61

LEADING OWNERS ON THE FLAT: 1897-2017

1897 Mr J Gubbins	1921 Mr S B Joel	1945 Ld Derby
1898 Ld de Rothschild	1922 Ld Woolavington	1946 H.H. Aga Khan
1899 Duke of Westminster	1923 Ld Derby	1947 H.H. Aga Khan
1900 H.R.H. The Prince of Wales	1924 H.H. Aga Khan	1948 H.H. Aga Khan
1901 Sir G Blundell Maple	1925 Ld Astor	1949 H.H. Aga Khan
1902 Mr R S Sievier	1926 Ld Woolavington	1950 M M Boussac
1903 Sir James Miller	1927 Ld Derby	1951 M M Boussac
1904 Sir James Miller	1928 Ld Derby	1952 H.H. Aga Khan
1905 Col W Hall Walker	1929 H.H. Aga Khan	1953 Sir Victor Sassoon
1906 Ld Derby (late)	1930 H.H. Aga Khan	1954 Her Majesty
1907 Col W Hall Walker	1931 Mr J A Dewar	1955 Lady Zia Wernner
1908 Mr J B Joel	1932 H.H. Aga Khan	1956 Maj L B Holliday
1909 Mr "Fairie"	1933 Ld Derby	1957 Her Majesty
1910 Mr "Fairie"	1934 H.H. Aga Khan	1958 Mr J McShain
1911 Ld Derby	1935 H.H. Aga Khan	1959 Prince Aly Khan
1912 Mr T Pilkington	1936 Ld Astor	1960 Sir Victor Sassoon
1913 Mr J B Joel	1937 H.H. Aga Khan	1961 Maj L B Holliday
1914 Mr J B Joel	1938 Ld Derby	1962 Maj L B Holliday
1915 Mr L Neumann	1939 Ld Rosebery	1963 Mr J R Mullion
1916 Mr E Hulton	1940 Lord Rothermere	1964 Mrs H E Jackson
1917 Mr "Fairie"	1941 Ld Glanely	1965 M J Ternynck
1918 Lady James Douglas	1942 His Majesty	1966 Lady Zia Wernher
1919 Ld Glanely	1943 Miss D Paget	1967 Mr H J Joel
1920 Sir Robert Jardine	1944 H.H. Aga Khan	1968 Mr Raymond R Guest

1969 Mr D Robinson	1986 Sheikh Mohammed	2003 K Abdullah
1970 Mr C Engelhard	1987 Sheikh Mohammed	2004 Godolphin
1971 Mr P Mellon	1988 Sheikh Mohammed	2005 Mr Hamdan Al-Maktoum
1972 Mrs J Hislop	1989 Sheikh Mohammed	2006 Godolphin
1973 Mr N B Hunt	1990 Mr Hamdan Al-Maktoum	2007 Godolphin
1974 Mr N B Hunt	1991 Sheikh Mohammed	2008 HRH Princess Haya of Jordan
1975 Dr C Vittadini	1992 Sheikh Mohammed	2009 Mr Hamdan Al-Maktoum
1976 Mr D Wildenstein	1993 Sheikh Mohammed	2010 K Abdullah
1977 Mr R Sangster	1994 Mr Hamdan Al-Maktoum	2011 K Abdullah
1978 Mr R Sangster	1995 Mr Hamdan Al-Maktoum	2012 Godolphin
1979 Sir M Sobell	1996 Godolphin	2013 Godolphin
1980 S Weinstock	1997 Sheikh Mohammed	2014 Mr Hamdan Al-Maktoum
1981 H.H. Aga Khan	1998 Godolphin	2015 Godolphin
1982 Mr R Sangster	1999 Godolphin	2016 Godolphin
1983 Mr R Sangster	2000 H.H. Aga Khan	2017 Godolphin
1984 Mr R Sangster	2001 Godolphin	
1985 Sheikh Mohammed	2002 Mr Hamdan Al-Maktoum	

LEADING SIRES ON THE FLAT: 1897-2017

1897 Kendal	1938 Blandford	1979 Petingo
1898 Galopin	1939 Fairway	1980 Pitcairn
1899 Orme	1940 Hyperion	1981 Great Nephew
1900 St Simon	1941 Hyperion	1982 Be My Guest (USA)
1901 St Simon	1942 Hyperion	1983 Northern Dancer
1902 Persimmon	1943 Fairway	1984 Northern Dancer
1903 St Frusquin	1944 Fairway	1985 Kris
1904 Gallinule	1945 Hyperion	1986 Nijinsky (CAN)
1905 Gallinule	1946 Hyperion	1987 Mill Reef (USA)
1906 Persimmon	1947 Nearco	1988 Caerleon (USA)
1907 St Frusquin	1948 Big Game	1989 Blushing Groom (FR)
1908 Persimmon	1949 Nearco	1990 Sadler's Wells (USA)
1909 Cyllene	1950 Fair Trial	1991 Caerleon (USA)
1910 Cyllene	1951 Nasrullah	1992 Sadler's Wells (USA)
1911 Sundridge	1952 Tehran	1993 Sadler's Wells (USA)
1912 Persimmon	1953 Chanteur II	1994 Sadler's Wells (USA)
1913 Desmond	1954 Hyperion	1995 Sadler's Wells (USA)
1914 Polymelus	1955 Alycidon	1996 Sadler's Wells (USA)
1915 Polymelus	1956 Court Martial	1997 Sadler's Wells (USA)
1916 Polymelus	1957 Court Martial	1998 Sadler's Wells (USA)
1917 Bayardo	1958 Mossborough	1999 Sadler's Wells (USA)
1918 Bayardo	1959 Petition	2000 Sadler's Wells (USA)
1919 The Tetrarch	1960 Aureole	2001 Sadler's Wells (USA)
1920 Polymelus	1961 Aureole	2002 Sadler's Wells (USA)
1921 Polymelus	1962 Never Say Die	2003 Sadler's Wells (USA)
1922 Lemberg	1963 Ribot	2004 Sadler's Wells (USA)
1923 Swynford	1964 Chamossaire	2005 Danehill (USA)
1924 Son-in-Law	1965 Court Harwell	2006 Danehill (USA)
1925 Phalaris	1966 Charlottesville	2007 Danehill (USA)
1926 Hurry On	1967 Ribot	2008 Galileo (IRE)
1927 Buchan	1968 Ribot	2009 Danehill Dancer (IRE)
1928 Phalaris	1969 Crepello	2010 Galileo (IRE)
1929 Tetratema	1970 Northern Dancer	2011 Galileo (IRE)
1930 Son-in-Law	1971 Never Bend	2012 Galileo (IRE)
1931 Pharos	1972 Queen's Hussar	2013 Galileo (IRE)
1932 Gainsborough	1973 Vaguely Noble	2014 Galileo (IRE)
1933 Gainsborough	1974 Vaguely Noble	2015 Galileo (IRE)
1934 Blandford	1975 Great Nephew	2016 Galileo (IRE)
1935 Blandford	1976 Wolver Hollow	2017 Galileo (IRE)
1936 Fairway	1977 Northern Dancer	
1937 Solario	1978 Mill Reef (USA)	

LEADING BREEDERS ON THE FLAT: 1913-2017

1913 Mr J B Joel
1914 Mr J B Joel
1915 Mr L Neumann
1916 Mr E Hulton
1917 Mr "Fairie"
1918 Lady James Douglas
1919 Ld Derby
1920 Ld Derby
1921 Mr S B Joel
1922 Ld Derby
1923 Ld Derby
1924 Lady Sykes
1925 Ld Astor
1926 Ld Woolavington
1927 Ld Derby
1928 Ld Derby
1929 Ld Derby
1930 Ld Derby
1931 Ld Dewar
1932 H.H. Aga Khan
1933 Sir Alec Black
1934 H.H. Aga Khan
1935 H.H. Aga Khan
1936 Ld Astor
1937 H.H. Aga Khan
1938 Ld Derby
1939 Ld Rosebery
1940 Mr H E Morriss
1941 Ld Glanely
1942 National Stud
1943 Miss D Paget
1944 Ld Rosebery
1945 Ld Derby
1946 Lt- Col H Boyd-Rochfort
1947 H.H. Aga Khan
1948 H.H. Aga Khan

1949 H.H. Aga Khan
1950 M M Boussac
1951 M M Boussac
1952 H. H. Aga Khan
1953 Mr F Darling
1954 Maj L B Holliday
1955 Someries Stud
1956 Maj L B Holliday
1957 Eve Stud
1958 Mr R Ball
1959 Prince Aly Khan and the late
          H.H. Aga Khan
1960 Eve Stud Ltd
1961 Eve Stud Ltd
1962 Maj L B Holliday
1963 Mr H F Guggenheim
1964 Bull Run Stud
1965 Mr J Ternynck
1966 Someries Stud
1967 Mr H J Joel
1968 Mill Ridge Farm
1969 Lord Rosebery
1970 Mr E P Taylor
1971 Mr P Mellon
1972 Mr J Hislop
1973 Claiborne Farm
1974 Mr N B Hunt
1975 Overbury Stud
1976 Dayton Ltd
1977 Mr E P Taylor
1978 Cragwood Estates Inc
1979 Ballymacoll Stud
1980 P Clarke
1981 H.H. Aga Khan
1982 Someries Stud
1983 White Lodge Stud

1984 Mr E P Taylor
1985 Dalham Stud Farms
1986 H.H. Aga Khan
1987 Cliveden Stud
1988 H. H. Aga Khan
1989 Mr Hamdan Al-Maktoum
1990 Capt. Macdonald- Buchanan
1991 Barronstown Stud
1992 Swettenham Stud
1993 Juddmonte Farms
1994 Shadwell Farm & Estate Ltd
1995 Shadwell Farm & Estate Ltd
1996 Sheikh Mohammed
1997 Sheikh Mohammed
1998 Sheikh Mohammed
1999 H. H. The Aga Khan's Studs
2000 H. H. The Aga Khan's Studs
2001 Shadwell Farm & Estate Ltd
2002 Gainsborough Stud
2003 Juddmonte
2004 Juddmonte
2005 Shadwell Farm & Estate Ltd
2006 Darley
2007 Darley
2008 Darley
2009 Darley
2010 Juddmonte
2011 Juddmonte
2012 Juddmonte
2013 Darley
2014 Darley
2015 Darley
2016 Darley
2017 Darley

LEADING TRAINERS OVER JUMPS: 1948-2017

1948-49 F T T Walwyn
1949-50 P V F Cazalet
1950-51 T F Rimell
1951-52 N Crump
1952-53 M V O'Brien
1953-54 M V O'Brien
1954-55 H R Price
1955-56 W Hall
1956-57 N Crump
1957-58 F T T Walwyn
1958-59 H R Price
1959-60 P V F Cazalet
1960-61 T F Rimell
1961-62 H R Price
1962-63 K Piggott
1963-64 F T T Walwyn
1964-65 P V F Cazalet
1965-66 H R Price
1966-67 H R Price
1967-68 Denys Smith
1968-69 T F Rimell
1969-70 T F Rimell
1970-71 F T Winter
1971-72 F T Winter

1972-73 F T Winter
1973-74 F T Winter
1974-75 F T Winter
1975-76 T F Rimell
1976-77 F T Winter
1977-78 F T Winter
1978-79 M H Easterby
1979-80 M H Easterby
1980-81 M H Easterby
1981-82 M W Dickinson
1982-83 M W Dickinson
1983-84 M W Dickinson
1984-85 F T Winter
1985-86 N J Henderson
1986-87 N J Henderson
1987-88 D R C Elsworth
1988-89 M C Pipe
1989-90 M C Pipe
1990-91 M C Pipe
1991-92 M C Pipe
1992-93 M C Pipe
1993-94 D Nicholson
1994-95 D Nicholson
1995-96 M C Pipe

1996-97 M C Pipe
1997-98 M C Pipe
1998-99 M C Pipe
1999-00 M C Pipe
2000-01 M C Pipe
2001-02 M C Pipe
2002-03 M C Pipe
2003-04 M C Pipe
2004-05 M C Pipe
2005-06 P F Nicholls
2006-07 P F Nicholls
2007-08 P F Nicholls
2008-09 P F Nicholls
2009-10 P F Nicholls
2010-11 P F Nicholls
2010-11 P F Nicholls
2011-12 P F Nicholls
2012-13 N J Henderson
2013-14 P F Nicholls
2014-15 P F Nicholls
2015-16 P F Nicholls
2016-17 N J Henderson

CHAMPION JOCKEYS OVER JUMPS: 1903-2017

Prior to the 1925-26 season the figure relates to racing between January and December

1903	P Woodland	54
1904	F Mason	59
1905	F Mason	73
1906	F Mason	58
1907	F Mason	59
1908	P Cowley	65
1909	R Gordon	45
1910	E Piggott	67
1911	W Payne	76
1912	I Anthony	78
1913	E Piggott	60
1914	Mr J R Anthony	60
1915	E Piggott	44
1916	C Hawkins	17
1917	W Smith	15
1918	G Duller	17
1919	Mr H Brown	48
1920	F B Rees	64
1921	F B Rees	65
1922	J Anthony	78
1923	F B Rees	64
1924	F B Rees	108
1925	E Foster	76
1925-26	T Leader	61
1926-27	F B Rees	59
1927-28	W Stott	88
1928-29	W Stott	65
1929-30	W Stott	77
1930-31	W Stott	81
1931-32	W Stott	77
1932-33	G Wilson	61
1933-34	G Wilson	56
1934-35	G Wilson	73
1935-36	G Wilson	57
1936-37	G Wilson	45
1937-38	G Wilson	59
1938-39	T F Rimell	61
1939-40	T F Rimell	24
1940-41	G Wilson	22
1941-42	R Smyth	12

1942-43	No racing	
1943-44	No racing	
1944-45	N Nicholson	15
	T F Rimell	15
1945-46	T F Rimell	54
1946-47	J Dowdeswell	58
1947-48	B Marshall	66
1948-49	T Moloney	60
1949-50	T Moloney	95
1950-51	T Moloney	83
1951-52	T Moloney	99
1952-53	F Winter	121
1953-54	R Francis	76
1954-55	T Moloney	67
1955-56	F Winter	74
1956-57	F Winter	80
1957-58	F Winter	82
1958-59	T Brookshaw	83
1959-60	S Mellor	68
1960-61	S Mellor	118
1961-62	S Mellor	80
1962-63	J Gifford	70
1963-64	J Gifford	94
1964-65	T Biddlecombe	114
1965-66	T Biddlecombe	102
1966-67	J Gifford	122
1967-68	J Gifford	82
1968-69	B R Davies	77
	T Biddlecombe	77
1969-70	B R Davies	91
1970-71	G Thorner	74
1971-72	B R Davies	89
1972-73	B Barry	125
1973-74	R Barry	94
1974-75	T Stack	82
1975-76	J Francome	96
1976-77	T Stack	97
1977-78	J J O'Neill	149
1978-79	J Francome	95
1979-80	J J O'Neill	117

1980-81	J Francome	105
1981-82	J Francome	120
	P Scudamore	120
1982-83	J Francome	106
1983-84	J Francome	131
1984-85	J Francome	101
1985-86	P Scudamore	91
1986-87	P Scudamore	123
1987-88	P Scudamore	132
1988-89	P Scudamore	221
1989-90	P Scudamore	170
1990-91	P Scudamore	141
1991-92	P Scudamore	175
1992-93	R Dunwoody	173
1993-94	R Dunwoody	197
1994-95	R Dunwoody	160
1995-96	A P McCoy	175
1996-97	A P McCoy	190
1997-98	A P McCoy	253
1998-99	A P McCoy	186
1999-00	A P McCoy	245
2000-01	A P McCoy	191
2001-02	A P McCoy	289
2002-03	A P McCoy	256
2003-04	A P McCoy	209
2004-05	A P McCoy	200
2005-06	A P McCoy	178
2006-07	A P McCoy	184
2007-08	A P McCoy	140
2008-09	A P McCoy	186
2009-10	A P McCoy	195
2010-11	A P McCoy	218
2011-12	A P McCoy	199
2012-13	A P McCoy	185
2013-14	A P McCoy	218
2014-15	A P McCoy	231
2015-16	R Johnson	235
2016-17	R Johnson	189

LEADING OWNERS OVER JUMPS: 1948-2017

(Please note that prior to the 1994-95 season the leading owner was determined by win prizemoney only)

1948-49	Mr W F Williamson
1949-50	Mrs L Brotherton
1950-51	Mr J Royle
1951-52	Miss D Paget
1952-53	Mr J H Griffin
1953-54	Mr J H Griffin
1954-55	Mrs W H E Welman
1955-56	Mrs L Carver
1956-57	Mrs Geoffrey Kohn
1957-58	Mr D J Coughlan
1958-59	Mr J E Bigg
1959-60	Miss W H Wallace
1960-61	Mr C Vaughan
1961-62	Mr N Cohen
1962-63	Mr P B Raymond
1963-64	Mr J K Goodman
1964-65	Mrs M Stephenson
1965-66	Duchess of Westminster

1966-67	Mr C P T Watkins
1967-68	Mr H S Alper
1968-69	Mr B P Jenks
1969-70	Mr E R Courage
1970-71	Mr F Pontin
1971-72	Capt T A Forster
1972-73	Mr N H Le Mare
1973-74	Mr N H Le Mare
1974-75	Mr R Guest
1975-76	Mr P B Raymond
1976-77	Mr N H Le Mare
1977-78	Mrs O Jackson
1978-79	Snailwell Stud Co Ltd
1979-80	Mr H J Joel
1980-81	Mr R J Wilson
1981-82	Sheikh Ali Abu Khamsin
1982-83	Sheikh Ali Abu Khamsin
1983-84	Sheikh Ali Abu Khamsin

1984-85	T Kilroe and Son Ltd
1985-86	Sheikh Ali Abu Khamsin
1986-87	Mr H J Joel
1987-88	Miss Juliet E Reed
1988-89	Mr R Burridge
1989-90	Mrs Harry J Duffey
1990-91	Mr P Piller
1991-92	Whitcombe Manor Racing Stables Ltd
1992-93	Mrs J Mould
1993-94	Pell-Mell Partners
1994-95	Roach Foods Limited
1995-96	Mr A T A Wates
1996-97	Mr R Ogden
1997-98	Mr D A Johnson
1998-99	Mr J P McManus
1999-00	Mr R Ogden
2000-01	Sir R Ogden

2001-02 Mr D A Johnson
2002-03 Mr D A Johnson
2003-04 Mr D A Johnson
2004-05 Mr D A Johnson
2005-06 Mr J P McManus
2006-07 Mr J P McManus

2007-08 Mr D A Johnson
2008-09 Mr J P McManus
2009-10 Mr J P McManus
2010-11 Mr T Hemmings
2011-12 Mr J P McManus
2012-13 Mr J P McManus

2013-14 Mr J P McManus
2014-15 Mr J P McManus
2015-16 Gigginstown House Stud
2016-17 Mr J P McManus

LEADING AMATEUR RIDERS OVER JUMPS: 1950-2017

1950-51 Mr P Chisman.............. 13
1951-52 Mr C Straker 19
1952-53 Mr A H Moralee........ 22
1953-54 Mr A H Moralee........ 22
1954-55 Mr A H Moralee........ 16
1955-56 Mr R McCreery 13
        Mr A H Moralee........ 13
1956-57 Mr R McCreery 23
1957-58 Mr J Lawrence 18
1958-59 Mr J Sutcliffe............ 18
1959-60 Mr G Kindersley 22
1960-61 Sir W Pigott-Brown 28
1961-62 Mr A Biddlecombe...... 30
1962-63 Sir W Pigott-Brown ... 20
1963-64 Mr S Davenport........ 32
1964-65 Mr M Gifford 15
1965-66 Mr C Collins 24
1966-67 Mr C Collins 33
1967-68 Mr R Tate 30
1968-69 Mr R Tate 17
1969-70 Mr M Dickinson 23
1970-71 Mr J Lawrence 17
1971-72 Mr W Foulkes 26

1972-73 Mr R Smith................ 56
1973-74 Mr A Webber............. 21
1974-75 Mr R Lamb 22
1975-76 Mr P Greenall 25
        Mr G Jones 25
1976-77 Mr P Greenall 27
1977-78 Mr G Sloan............... 23
1978-79 Mr T G Dun 26
1979-80 Mr O Sherwood 29
1980-81 Mr P Webber............. 32
1981-82 Mr D Browne 28
1982-83 Mr D Browne 33
1983-84 Mr S Sherwood 28
1984-85 Mr S Sherwood 30
1985-86 Mr T Thomson Jones... 25
1986-87 Mr T Thomson Jones.. 19
1987-88 Mr T Thomson Jones.. 15
1988-89 Mr P Fenton 18
1989-90 Mr P McMahon 15
1990-91 Mr K Johnson............ 24
1991-92 Mr M P Hourigan 24
1992-93 Mr A Thornton 26
1993-94 Mr J Greenall.............. 21

1994-95 Mr D Parker................ 16
1995-96 Mr J Culloty.............. 40
1996-97 Mr R Thornton............ 30
1997-98 Mr S Durack.............. 41
1998-99 Mr A Dempsey 47
1999-00 Mr P Flynn................ 41
2000-01 Mr T Scudamore 24
2001-02 Mr D Crosse.............. 19
2002-03 Mr C Williams............ 23
2003-04 Mr O Nelmes 14
2004-05 Mr T Greenall 31
2005-06 Mr T O'Brien............ 32
2006-07 Mr T Greenall 31
2007-08 Mr T Greenall 23
2008-09 Mr O Greenall............ 23
2009-10 Mr O Greenall.......... 41
2010-11 Mr R Mahon............. 19
2011-12 Miss E Sayer............. 11
2012-13 Mr N de Boinville........ 16
2013-14 Mr H Bannister............ 11
2014-15 Mr H Bannister........... 15
2015-16 Mr D Noonan 19
2016-17 Mr J King.................... 15

LEADING SIRES OVER JUMPS: 1988-2017

1988   Deep Run
1989   Deep Run
1989-90 Deep Run
1990-91 Deep Run
1991-92 Deep Run
1992-93 Deep Run
1993-94 Strong Gale
1994-95 Strong Gale
1995-96 Strong Gale
1996-97 Strong Gale

1997-98 Strong Gale
1998-99 Strong Gale
1999-00 Strong Gale
2000-01 Be My Native (USA)
2001-02 Be My Native (USA)
2002-03 Be My Native (USA)
2003-04 Be My Native (USA)
2004-05 Supreme Leader
2005-06 Supreme Leader
2006-07 Presenting

2007-08 Old Vic
2008-09 Presenting
2009-10 Presenting
2010-11 Presenting
2011-12 King's Theatre
2012-13 Beneficial
2013-14 King's Theatre
2014-15 King's Theatre
2015-16 King's Theatre
2016-17 King's Theatre

JOCKEYS' AGENTS

Jockeys' Agents and their Contact Details

Agent	Telephone	Mobile/Email	Fax
NICKY ADAMS	01488 72004/72964	07796 547659 nickadams2594@hotmail.com	
NEIL ALLAN	01243 543870	07985 311141 email: aneilaallan@aol.com	
NIGEL BAXTER	01942 575148	07973 561521 email: sales@clubfactfile.com.	
ALF BISSETT	0131 3325552	07801 634379 alfbissett@blueyonder.co.uk	
CHRIS BROAD	01452 760482/447	07836 622858 chrisd.broad@yahoo.co.uk	
GLORIA CHARNOCK	01653 695004	07951 576912 gloriacharnock@hotmail.com	
PAUL CLARKE	01638 660804	07885 914306 paul.clarke79@btinternet.com	
RAY COCHRANE	01223 812008	07798 651247 ray@raysagency.co.uk	
STEVEN CROFT		07809 205556 steven.croft6@googlemail.com	
SIMON DODDS		07974 924735 simon.dodds@btinternet.com	
SHELLEY DWYER	01638 578651	07949 612256 getadwyer@aol.com	

Agent	Telephone	Mobile/Email	Fax
SHIPPY ELLIS	01638 668484	07860 864864 shippysjockeys@btconnect.com	
MARK FURNASS	01347 824633	07474 242332 jockeysagent@gmail.com	
MICHAEL HAGGAS	01638 660811	07740 624550 mhaggas@ntlworld.com	
RICHARD HALE	01768 88699	07909 520542 richardhale77@hotmail.co.uk	
NIALL HANNITY	01677 423363	07710 141084 niallhannity@yahoo.co.uk	
ALAN HARRISON	01969 625006	07846 187991 ahjockagent60@yahoo.co.uk	
TONY HIND	01638 724997	07807 908599 anthonyhind77@icloud.com	
GAVIN HORNE	01392 433610	07914 897170 gavin.horne@hotmail.co.uk	
RUSS JAMES	01653 699466	07947 414001 russjames2006@btinternet.com	
BRUCE JEFFREY	01750 21521	07747 854684 brucejeffrey@live.co.uk	
GUY JEWELL	01672 861231	07765 248859 guyjewell@btconnect.com	
ANDY LEWIS	01908 386983	07838 506594 andrew.lewis11@sky.com	
SARA-LOUISE METCALFE	01635 269647	07918 525354 troopersjockeys@hotmail.co.uk	

Agent	Telephone	Mobile/Email	Fax
SIMON MITCHELL		07922 459042 smitchell.bramble@virgin.net	
LEE NEWTON	01302 376370	07710 422437 newton808@btinternet.com	
GARETH OWEN	01603 569390	07958 335206 garethowenracing@gmail.com	
SHASHI RIGHTON	01353 688594	07825 381350 srighton.sr@googlemail.com	
DAVE ROBERTS	01737 221368	07860 234342 daveroberts.racing@gmail.com	
PHILIP SHEA	01638 667456	07585 120297 pucklad2@hotmail.com	
ANNA WALLACE	01903 774884	07867 923642 awallace51@yahoo.com	
IAN WARDLE	01793 688858	07831 865974 ian.wardlex@googlemail.com	
LAURA WAY	01704 834488	07775 777494 laura.way@btconnect.com	
IAN WOOD		07733 156380 ianwood@chase3c.com	

FLAT JOCKEYS

Riding weights and contact details

An index of agents appears on page 703

DAVID ALLAN	8 - 9	Mrs G. S. Charnock	
PADDY ASPELL	8 - 4	07841 091125	
ANDREA ATZENI	8 - 5	07970 185675	
GEORGE BAKER	9 - 0	07833 221221	
LUCY K. BARRY	8 - 10	Mr L. R. James	
CONNOR BEASLEY	8 - 6	Mr N. Hannity	
HARRY BENTLEY	8 - 5	Mr Paul Clarke	
FRAN BERRY	8 - 9	Mr Tony Hind	
ADAM BESCHIZZA	8 - 5	M. Furnass	
CHARLES BISHOP	8 - 10	Mr S. T. Dodds	
DANNY BROCK	8 - 0	M. Furnass	
THOMAS BROWN	8 - 9	07446 898795	
WILLIAM BUICK	8 - 6	Mr M. R. Haggas	
WILLIAM CARSON	8 - 2	Mr Neil Allan	
PAT COSGRAVE	8 - 8	P. C. Shea	
MATT COSHAM	8 - 0	07875 601737	
DOUGIE COSTELLO	8 - 10	Mr N. Hannity	
JIM CROWLEY	8 - 7	Mr Tony Hind	
BEN CURTIS	8 - 7	Mr S. T. Dodds	
RAUL DA SILVA	8 - 0	07453 240659	
LEMOS DE SOUZA	8 - 6	07526 692654	
SILVESTRE DE SOUSA	8 - 0	Mrs Shelley Dwyer	
FRANKIE DETTORI	8 - 9	Mr R. Cochrane	
PAT DOBBS	8 - 7	Mr G. J. Horne	
STEVIE DONOHOE	8 - 8	Mr L. R. James	
GEORGE DOWNING	8 - 9	Mr N. M. Adams	
BRETT DOYLE	8 - 6	07393 938744	
HOLLIE DOYLE	8 - 0	Mr G. D. Jewell	
JAMES DOYLE	8 - 10	Mr M. R. Haggas	
TED DURCAN	8 - 6	Mr Tony Hind	
MARTIN DWYER	8 - 3	Mr S. T. Dodds	
TOM EAVES	8 - 7	Mr R. A. Hale	
JOHN EGAN	8 - 3	Mr S. Croft	
ANDREW ELLIOTT	8 - 4	07709 222004	
JOHN FAHY	8 - 5	Mr N. M. Adams	
JOE FANNING	8 - 2	Mr N. Hannity	
DURAN FENTIMAN	8 - 2	Mr Alan Harrison	
MANUEL FERNANDES	8 - 0	07760 673640	
ROYSTON FFRENCH	8 - 4	M. Furnass	
KIEREN FOX	8 - 5	Mr G. D. Jewell	
ANTONIO FRESU	8 - 5	Mr Tony Hind	
NOEL GARBUTT	8 - 0	M. Furnass	
JACK GARRITTY	8 - 10	Mr R. A. Hale	
SALEEM GOLAM	8 - 8	07930 211115	
IRINEU GONCALVES	8 - 7	07599 638686	
JOSEPHINE GORDON	8 - 2	P. C. Shea	
SHANE GRAY	8 - 3	Mr R. A. Hale	
TONY HAMILTON	8 - 7	Mr N. Hannity	
PAUL HANAGAN	8 - 3	Mr R. A. Hale	
CAM HARDIE	8 - 0	Mr R. A. Hale	
MARTIN HARLEY	8 - 9	Mr Neil Allan	
JASON HART	8 - 7	Mr Alan Harrison	
ROBERT HAVLIN	8 - 6	Mr I. P. Wardle	
JOEY HAYNES	8 - 2	Mr S. T. Dodds	
SAM HITCHCOTT	8 - 5	Mr N. M. Adams	
ROB HORNBY	8 - 6	Mr N. M. Adams	
SAM JAMES	8 - 6	Mrs L. H. Way	
ROSIE JESSOP	8 - 0	Mr N. A. Baxter	
LIAM JONES	8 - 4	Mr G. D. Jewell	
SHANE KELLY	8 - 7	Mr Tony Hind	
LIAM KENIRY	8 - 7	Mr N. M. Adams	
RICHARD KINGSCOTE	8 - 8	Mr G. D. Jewell	
ADAM KIRBY	9 - 0	Mr N. M. Adams	
RACHEAL KNELLER	8 - 9	Miss A. Wallace	
MARTIN LANE	8 - 4	Mr S. T. Dodds	
GRAHAM LEE	8 - 9	Mr R. A. Hale	
SEAN LEVEY	8 - 10	Mr S. M. Righton	
NICKY MACKAY	8 - 0	Mr N. A. Baxter	
PHILLIP MAKIN	8 - 11	Mrs L. H. Way	
GINA MANGAN	7 - 12	07871 013673	
TOM MARQUAND	8 - 7	Mr S. M. Righton	
PATRICK MATHERS	8 - 2	M. Furnass	
P. J. MCDONALD	8 - 4	Mr G. R. Owen	
BARRY MCHUGH	8 - 6	Mrs L. H. Way	
ALICE MILLS	8 - 2	07792 504534	
JACK MITCHELL	8 - 9	Mr Paul Clarke	
RYAN MOORE	8 - 9	Mr Tony Hind	
LUKE MORRIS	8 - 0	Mr Neil Allan	
ANDREW MULLEN	8 - 0	Mr R. A. Hale	
PAUL MULRENNAN	8 - 7	Mr R. A. Hale	
OISIN MURPHY	8 - 6	Mr G. J. Horne	
TIMMY MURPHY	9 - 0	Mr S. T. Dodds	
DANIEL MUSCUTT	8 - 8	Mr Paul Clarke	
DAVID NOLAN	9 - 0	Mr R. A. Hale	
FRANNY NORTON	8 - 0	Mr I. P. Wardle	
DANE O'NEILL	8 - 7	Mr N. M. Adams	
KIERAN O'NEILL	8 - 0	Mr N. M. Adams	
SIMON PEARCE	8 - 4	07818 038770	
OSCAR PEREIRA	8 - 7	07766 658392	
RYAN POWELL	8 - 0	Mr Neil Allan	
DAVID PROBERT	8 - 6	Mr R. A. Hale	
TOM QUEALLY	8 - 8	Mr S. M. Righton	
AMIR QUINN	9 - 3	07913 416683	
JIMMY QUINN	8 - 0	Mr G. J. Horne	
PAUL QUINN	8 - 2	07802 486494	
ALISTAIR RAWLINSON	8 - 11	Mr S. Croft	
RACHEL RICHARDSON	8 - 3	Mr Alan Harrison	
KIERAN SHOEMARK	8 - 10	Mr Tony Hind	
PAOLO SIRIGU	8 - 0	07585 308267	
RENATO SOUZA	8 - 0	Mr Ian Wood	
JAMIE SPENCER	8 - 7	Mr N. Hannity	
LOUIS STEWARD	8 - 11	P. C. Shea	
KEVIN STOTT	8 - 10	Mr R. A. Hale	
JAMES SULLIVAN	8 - 0	Mr R. A. Hale	
FERGUS SWEENEY	8 - 7	Mr Neil Allan	
RYAN TATE	8 - 4	Mr G. D. Jewell	
DANIEL TUDHOPE	8 - 11	Mrs L. H. Way	
HAYLEY TURNER	8 - 2	Mr G. D. Jewell	
R. P. WALSH	7 - 5	Andy Lewis	
TREVOR WHELAN	8 - 12	Mr Dave Roberts\ P. C. Shea	
GARRY WHILLANS	8 - 9	Mr L. R. James	
ROBERT WINSTON	8 - 7	Mr N. M. Adams	

APPRENTICES

Riding weights and contact details

An index of agents appears on page 703

SHARNA ARMSTRONG (Mark Johnston)	8 - 2	c/o 01969 622237
GAVIN ASHTON (Sir Mark Prescott Bt)	8 - 6	c/o 01638 662117
KEELAN BAKER (Michael Appleby)	8 - 2	Andy Lewis
GEORGE BASS (David Simcock)	8 - 0	c/o 07808 954109
ALED BEECH (Tony Carroll)	8 - 2	Mr L. R. James
CHARLIE BENNETT (Hughie Morrison)	8 - 2	P. C. Shea
SHELLEY BIRKETT (David O'Meara)	8 - 0	Mr R. A. Hale\M. Furnass
PADDY BRADLEY (Pat Phelan)	8 - 11	Mr L. R. James
ANDREW BRESLIN (Mark Johnston)	7 - 9	c/o 01969 622237
JOSHUA BRYAN (Andrew Balding)	8 - 4	Mr G. D. Jewell
WILLIAM CARVER (Andrew Balding)	8 - 3	Mr S. T. Dodds
LUKE CATTON (Ian Williams)	8 - 3	M. Furnass
TIM CLARK (John Butler)	8 - 6	Mr L. R. James
LAURA COUGHLAN (David Loughnane)	8 - 2	c/o 07960 495845 Sarah Hoyland
GEORGIA COX (William Haggas)	8 - 2	Mr S. Croft
WILLIAM COX (Andrew Balding)	7 - 12	Mr N. M. Adams
HECTOR CROUCH (Gary Moore)	8 - 4	Mr G. D. Jewell
STEPHEN CUMMINS (Richard Hughes)	8 - 7	Andy Lewis
NICOLA CURRIE (Richard Hughes)	8 - 0	P. C. Shea
OLIVER DAYKIN (Paul D'Arcy)	7 - 12	c/o 01638 662000 office
PHIL DENNIS (Declan Carroll)	8 - 2	Mr Alan Harrison
JACK DINSMORE (Jamie Osborne)	8 - 3	c/o 01488 73139
ROBERT DODSWORTH (Tim Easterby)	7 - 12	Mrs G. S. Charnock
JOSH DOYLE (David O'Meara)	8 - 9	Mrs L. H. Way
JACK DUERN (Dean Ivory)	8 - 3	Mr L. Newton
LEWIS EDMUNDS (Nigel Tinkler)	8 - 7	Mr R. A. Hale
MEGAN ELLINGWORTH (John Holt)	8 - 0	M. Furnass
JANE ELLIOTT (George Margarson)	8 - 0	Mr S. Croft
SARA DEL FABBRO (Michael Bell)	8 - 1	c/o 07802 264514
LEANNE FERGUSON (Linda Perratt)	8 - 1	c/o 07931 306147
JONATHAN FISHER (Robert Cowell)	8 - 4	M. Furnass
MARCO GHIANI (Luca Cumani)	8 - 5	c/o 01638 665432
AMELIA GLASS (Clive Cox)	8 - 2	c/o 01488 73072
KATHERINE GLENISTER (David Evans)	8 - 2	Miss A. Wallace
MITCH GODWIN (Sylvester Kirk)	8 - 0	Miss S. L. Metcalfe
JAMIE GORMLEY (Iain Jardine)	8 - 0	Mr R. A. Hale
EDWARD GREATREX (Archie Watson)	8 - 3	Mr G. J. Horne
NATALIE HAMBLING (Noel Wilson)	8 - 3	c/o 07939 905477
RUSSELL HARRIS (K. R. Burke)	8 - 4	Mr G. R. Owen
LENKA HELMECKA (Mick Channon)	8 - 3	c/o 01635 281 166
RYAN HOLMES (Daniel Loughnane)	8 - 4	c/o 07805 531021
RHIAIN INGRAM (Roger Ingram)	7 - 8	Mr L. R. James
PIERRE-LOUIS JAMIN (Archie Watson)	8 - 3	c/o 07717 133844
PAUL ST. JOHN-DENNIS (Mick Channon)	8 - 3	c/o 01635 281166
AARON JONES (Stuart Williams)	8 - 0	M. Furnass
DARRAGH KEENAN (Robert Eddery)	7 - 7	Mr S. Croft
THEODORE LADD (Hughie Morrison)	8 - 1	Mr S. T. Dodds
KATE LEAHY (John O'Shea)	8 - 4	c/o 01452 760835
CLIFFORD LEE (K. R. Burke)	8 - 10	Mr N. Hannity
KEVIN LUNDIE (Michael Appleby)	8 - 5	M. Furnass
GARY MAHON (Richard Hannon)	8 - 6	Mr S. T. Dodds
GABRIELE MALUNE (Marco Botti)	7 - 10	Mr S. T. Dodds
FINLEY MARSH (Richard Hughes)	8 - 5	Mr Tony Hind
CHARLOTTE MCFARLAND (Derek Shaw)	7 - 10	c/o 07721 039645
FAYE MCMANOMAN (Nigel Tinkler)	7 - 13	Mr L. R. James
ADAM MCNAMARA (Roger Charlton)	8 - 11	Mr G. D. Jewell
SHARIQ MOHD (Sylvester Kirk)	7 - 10	c/o 07768 855261
MARC MONAGHAN (Marco Botti)	8 - 7	Mr Neil Allan

PAULA MUIR (Patrick Holmes) .... 7 - 12   Mr Alan Harrison
CONNOR MURTAGH (Richard Fahey) .... 7 - 12   Mr R. A. Hale
MILLY NASEB (Stuart Williams) .... 7 - 8   P. C. Shea
MEGAN NICHOLLS (Paul Nicholls) .... 8 - 3   c/o 01749 860 656 Sarah or Georgina
CAMERON NOBLE (Michael Bell) .... 8 - 5   Mr Paul Clarke
PATRICK O'HANLON (K. R. Burke) .... 8 - 4   Mr G. R. Owen
GER O'NEILL (Declan Carroll) .... 8 - 8   c/o 01653 698517
JACK OSBORN (John Ryan) .... 8 - 0   P. C. Shea
JAMIE PARKES (Martyn Meade) .... 8 - 7   c/o 01638 666100
PADDY PILLEY (Tom Dascombe) .... 8 - 7   Mr G. D. Jewell
RHONA PINDAR (Alistair Whillans) .... 8 - 2   Mr J. B. Jeffrey
SOPHIE RALSTON (Pat Phelan) .... 7 - 12   Mr L. R. James
KERRIE RAYBOULD (Milton Bradley) .... 8 - 8   c/o 07860 570003
BEN ROBINSON (Brian Ellison) .... 8 - 0   Mr S. T. Dodds
CALLUM RODRIGUEZ (Michael Dods) .... 8 - 4   Mr R. A. Hale
HARRY RUSSELL (Bryan Smart) .... 8 - 7   c/o 07748 634797
ROSSA RYAN (Richard Hannon) .... 8 - 7   Mr G. D. Jewell
BEN SANDERSON (Roger Fell) .... 8 - 3   Mr L. R. James
TYLER SAUNDERS (Marcus Tregoning) .... 8 - 6   Mr G. D. Jewell
ROWAN SCOTT (Keith Dalgleish) .... 8 - 4   Mr G. R. Owen\Mr N. Hannity
HARRISON SHAW (Michael Easterby) .... 8 - 3   Mr R. A. Hale
CALLUM SHEPHERD (Charles Hills) .... 8 - 7   Mr N. M. Adams
OLIVER STAMMERS (Mark Johnston) .... 7 - 7   c/o 01969 622237
LAUREN STEADE (Micky Hammond) .... 7 - 4   c/o 07808 572777
KAYLEIGH STEPHENS (Andrew Balding) .... 8 - 2   Andy Lewis
EMMA TAFF (Jamie Osborne) .... 8 - 4   c/o 01488 73139
ERI TOLA (Roger Charlton) .... 8 - 5   c/o 01672 539533
GEMMA TUTTY (Karen Tutty) .... 8 - 2   c/o 01609 883067
JORDAN UYS (Brian Meehan) .... 8 - 4   Andy Lewis
PATRICK VAUGHAN (David O'Meara) .... 8 - 7   Mr N. Hannity
EOIN WALSH (Robert Cowell) .... 8 - 6   Mr N. M. Adams
JASON WATSON (Andrew Balding) .... 8 - 4   Miss S. L. Metcalfe
ZAK WHEATLEY (David O'Meara) .... 8 - 0   c/o 01759 372427
ELISHA WHITTINGTON (Tom Dascombe) .... 7 - 13   c/o 01948 820485 Alex
ABBIE WIBREW (Jane Chapple-Hyam) .... 8 - 2   c/o 07917 166740 Andrea
EMMA WILKINSON (Ralph Beckett) .... 8 - 0   c/o 01264 772278
LEVI WILLIAMS (Simon Dow) .... 7 - 10   c/o 07860 800109
GEORGE WOOD (James Fanshawe) .... 8 - 0   Mr S. M. Righton
SEBASTIAN WOODS (Richard Fahey) .... 8 - 7   Mr R. A. Hale
HANNAH WORRALL (Tim Easterby) .... 7 - 7   c/o 01653 668566
FLETCHER YARHAM (George Scott) .... 8 - 5   c/o 07833 461294

JUMP JOCKEYS

Riding weights and contact details

An index of agents appears on page 703

LUCY ALEXANDER	9 - 10	Mr R. A. Hale	
LEIGHTON ASPELL	10 - 3	Mr Dave Roberts	
HARRY BANNISTER	9 - 7	Mr C. D. Broad	
LUCY K. BARRY	9 - 0	Mr L. R. James	
DAVID BASS	10 - 5	Mr C. D. Broad	
MATTIE BATCHELOR	10 - 0	Mr Dave Roberts	
TOM BELLAMY	10 - 5	Mr Dave Roberts	
JAMES BEST	10 - 0	Mr Dave Roberts	
JONATHON BEWLEY	10 - 0	01450 860651	
SEAN BOWEN	9 - 7	Mr Dave Roberts	
PADDY BRENNAN	9 - 12	Mr Dave Roberts	
HENRY BROOKE	10 - 0	Mr R. A. Hale	
JONATHAN BURKE	10 - 0	Mr C. D. Broad	
TOM CANNON	10 - 5	Mr Dave Roberts	
ALAIN CAWLEY	9 - 10	Mr Dave Roberts	
HARRY COBDEN	9 - 8	Mr Dave Roberts	
AIDAN COLEMAN	9 - 10	Mr Dave Roberts	
JOE COLLIVER	9 - 12	Mr R. A. Hale	
DANNY COOK	10 - 7	Mr J. B. Jeffrey	
DAVE CROSSE	10 - 0	Mr C. D. Broad	
JAMES DAVIES	10 - 0	Mr L. R. James	
NICO DE BOINVILLE	10 - 0	Mr Dave Roberts	
TOMMY DOWLING	9 - 10	Mr L. R. James	
ROBERT DUNNE	10 - 7	Mr Dave Roberts	
MARTIN DWYER	8 - 3	Mr S. T. Dodds	
LEE EDWARDS	10 - 0	Mr C. D. Broad	
DAVID ENGLAND	10 - 0	Mr Dave Roberts	
JONATHAN ENGLAND	9 - 10	Mr S. Croft	
JAN FALTEJSEK	10 - 0	Mr J. B. Jeffrey	
NOEL FEHILY	10 - 7	Mr C. D. Broad	
RHYS FLINT	10 - 12	07711 057969	
DEREK FOX	10 - 0	Mr R. A. Hale	
LUCY GARDNER	10 - 0	07814 979699	
THOMAS GARNER	10 - 0	Mr Dave Roberts	
ANDREW GLASSONBURY	10 - 7	Mr L. R. James	
MARC GOLDSTEIN	10 - 0	Mr Dave Roberts	
MARK GRANT	10 - 4	Mr C. D. Broad	
MATT GRIFFITHS	10 - 6	Mr Dave Roberts	
LIAM HEARD	10 - 5	Mr L. R. James	
A. P. HESKIN	10 - 0	Mr C. D. Broad	
DANIEL HISKETT	9 - 10	Mr Dave Roberts	
BRIAN HUGHES	9 - 7	Mr R. A. Hale	
WAYNE HUTCHINSON	10 - 3	Mr C. D. Broad	
DARYL JACOB	10 - 3	Mr Dave Roberts	
ALAN JOHNS	10 - 0	Mr Dave Roberts	
RICHARD JOHNSON	10 - 0	Mr Dave Roberts	
KEVIN JONES	10 - 4	Mr Dave Roberts	
TONY KELLY	10 - 0	Mr R. A. Hale	
WILL KENNEDY	10 - 0	Mr R. A. Hale	
CONNOR KING	10 - 0	Mr R. A. Hale	
JOHN KINGTON	10 - 0	Mr R. A. Hale	
ADRIAN LANE	10 - 7	Mr R. A. Hale	
GRAHAM LEE	8 - 9	Mr R. A. Hale	
NIALL P. MADDEN	9 - 8	Mr Dave Roberts	
COLM MCCORMACK	10 - 0	01287 650456	
RACHAEL MCDONALD	9 - 5	07494 422275	
JEREMIAH MCGRATH	10 - 0	Mr Dave Roberts	
RICHIE MCLERNON	9 - 10	Mr Dave Roberts	
ALICE MILLS	8 - 2	07792 504534	
JAMIE MOORE	10 - 0	Mr Dave Roberts	
JOSHUA MOORE	10 - 4	Mr Dave Roberts	
KILLIAN MOORE	10 - 4	Mr Dave Roberts	
NATHAN MOSCROP	10 - 5	Mr R. A. Hale	
CRAIG NICHOL	10 - 0	Mr R. A. Hale	
ADAM NICOL	9 - 11	Mr R. A. Hale	
MICHEAL NOLAN	10 - 4	Mr Dave Roberts	
DAVID NOONAN	9 - 10	Mr Dave Roberts	
PAUL O'BRIEN	10 - 5	Mr C. D. Broad	
TOM O'BRIEN	10 - 2	Mr Dave Roberts	
CONOR O'FARRELL	10 - 3	Mr R. A. Hale	
FINIAN O'TOOLE	10 - 0	Mr R. A. Hale	
TOMMY PHELAN	10 - 0	Mr L. R. James	
ADAM POGSON	10 - 10	07977 016155	
IAN POPHAM	10 - 0	Mr C. D. Broad	
BEN POSTE	9 - 7	Mr Dave Roberts	
CHARLIE POSTE	10 - 3	Mr Dave Roberts	
BRENDAN POWELL	9 - 11	Mr Dave Roberts	
JACK QUINLAN	9 - 10	Mr Dave Roberts	
SEAN QUINLAN	10 - 0	Mr R. A. Hale	
NICK SCHOLFIELD	10 - 4	Mr Dave Roberts	
TOM SCUDAMORE	10 - 0	Mr Dave Roberts	
GAVIN SHEEHAN	10 - 0	Mr C. D. Broad	
JACK SHERWOOD	9 - 11	Mr Dave Roberts	
CONOR SHOEMARK	10 - 0	Mr Dave Roberts	
HARRY SKELTON	10 - 0	Mr Dave Roberts	
CONOR SMITH	10 - 0	Mr Dave Roberts	
ANDREW THORNTON	10 - 7	Mr Dave Roberts	
ANDREW TINKLER	10 - 3	Mr Dave Roberts	
MAXIME TISSIER	9 - 4	07724 398734	
SAM TWISTON-DAVIES	10 - 0	Mr C. D. Broad	
JOSH WALL	9 - 10	07951 291484	
CHRIS WARD	9 - 12	Mr L. R. James	
ADAM WEDGE	9 - 11	Mr Dave Roberts	
TREVOR WHELAN	9 - 10	Mr Dave Roberts\ P. C. Shea	
CALLUM WHILLANS	9 - 11	07894 573557	
RYAN WINKS	9 - 9	01226 340011	
KIELAN WOODS	10 - 0	Mr C. D. Broad	

CONDITIONALS

Their employer and contact details

An index of agents appears on page 703

BRIDGET ANDREWS (Dan Skelton)	9 - 3	c/o 01789 336339
EDWARD AUSTIN (Ian Williams)	9 - 5	Mr L. R. James
JAMIE BARGARY (Nigel Twiston-Davies)	9 - 9	Mr C. D. Broad
MITCHELL BASTYAN (Evan Williams)	9 - 10	Mr Dave Roberts
HARRISON BESWICK (Oliver Sherwood)	10 - 0	Mr Dave Roberts
CALLUM BEWLEY (Keith Dalgleish)	9 - 10	Mr R. A. Hale
AIDEN BLAKEMORE (Ruth Jefferson)	9 - 0	Mr R. A. Hale
JAMES BOWEN (Nicky Henderson)	9 - 7	Mr Dave Roberts
TOM BROUGHTON (Nick Kent)	9 - 7	Mr J. B. Jeffrey
HUGO THOMPSON BROWN (Micky Hammond)	10 - 4	c/o 07808 572777
BLAIR CAMPBELL (Lucinda Russell)	9 - 0	Mr R. A. Hale
GRAHAM CARSON (Sarah Humphrey)	9 - 10	Mr L. R. James
ROSS CHAPMAN (Iain Jardine)	9 - 8	Mr R. A. Hale
THOMAS CHEESMAN (Philip Hobbs)	9 - 7	Mr Dave Roberts
ANGUS CHELEDA (Charlie Mann)	9 - 1	Mr C. D. Broad
WILLIAM CLARKE (Gary Moore)	10 - 0	Mr Dave Roberts
GRANT COCKBURN (N. W. Alexander)	10 - 4	Mr R. A. Hale
SAM COLTHERD (Sue Smith)	9 - 11	Mr J. B. Jeffrey
JAMES CORBETT (Susan Corbett)	9 - 7	Mr L. R. James
PATRICK COWLEY (Emma Lavelle)	10 - 0	Mr Dave Roberts
NED CURTIS (Nicky Henderson)	9 - 9	Mr Dave Roberts
CHARLIE DAVIES (Charlie Longsdon)	10 - 0	c/o 07779 93263
RYAN DAY (Nicky Richards)	9 - 10	Mr R. A. Hale
CHARLIE DEUTSCH (Venetia Williams)	10 - 0	Mr Dave Roberts
PHILIP DONOVAN (Neil Mulholland)	9 - 7	Mr Dave Roberts
KEVIN DOWLING (Alan King)	10 - 0	Mr C. D. Broad
THOMAS DOWSON (Philip Kirby)	9 - 9	Mr J. B. Jeffrey
ALAN DOYLE (Nicky Henderson)	10 - 0	Mr Dave Roberts
KIERON EDGAR (Harry Fry)	10 - 0	Mr L. R. James
STEVEN FOX (James Ewart)	10 - 11	Mr J. B. Jeffrey
BRYONY FROST (Paul Nicholls)	9 - 7	Mr Dave Roberts
CIARAN GETHINGS (Tom George)	10 - 2	Mr Dave Roberts
THOMAS GREATREX (Warren Greatrex)	9 - 4	Mr Dave Roberts
FERGUS GREGORY (Olly Murphy)	10 - 0	Mr Dave Roberts
MIKEY HAMILL (Kim Bailey)	10 - 2	Mr C. D. Broad
JAMIE HAMILTON (Mark Walford)	9 - 11	Mr R. A. Hale
CHARLIE HAMMOND (Dr Richard Newland)	9 - 7	Mr Dave Roberts
ROBERT HAWKER (Jeremy Scott)	10 - 5	Mr Dave Roberts
MICHAEL HEARD (David Pipe)	9 - 7	Mr Dave Roberts
BEN HICKS (Warren Greatrex)	9 - 12	Mr C. D. Broad
ROBERT HOGG (Kenneth Slack)	10 - 2	Mr J. B. Jeffrey
SEAN HOULIHAN (Philip Hobbs)	9 - 7	Mr Dave Roberts
TOM HUMPHRIES (Nigel Twiston-Davies)	9 - 12	Mr C. D. Broad
DALE IRVING (Maurice Barnes)	10 - 0	Mr J. B. Jeffrey
CHARLOTTE JONES (James Moffatt)	8 - 11	c/o 01539 533808
LIZZIE KELLY (Nick Williams)	10 - 6	c/o 07855 450379
MAX KENDRICK (Ben Case)	9 - 12	Mr Dave Roberts
GARRY LAVERY (Johnny Farrelly)	9 - 7	Mr L. R. James
AARON MCGLINCHEY (Donald McCain)	10 - 0	c/o 01829 720352
CALLUM MCKINNES (David Bridgwater)	9 - 8	c/o 07831 635817
HENRY MORSHEAD (Paul Nicholls)	10 - 0	c/o 01749 860656 Sarah or Georgina
STEPHEN MULQUEEN (Lucinda Russell)	10 - 0	Mr J. B. Jeffrey
LORCAN MURTAGH (Donald McCain)	9 - 7	Mr R. A. Hale
MEGAN NICHOLLS (Paul Nicholls)	8 - 3	c/o 01749 860656 Sarah or Georgina
JAMES NIXON (Robin Dickin)	10 - 0	Mr Dave Roberts
JONJO O'NEILL (Jonjo O'Neill)	10 - 0	Mr Dave Roberts
RICHARD PATRICK (Kerry Lee)	9 - 7	Mr Dave Roberts
HARRY REED (Neil Mulholland)	9 - 7	Mr Dave Roberts

CONOR RING (Evan Williams)	10 - 5	Mr C. D. Broad
DANIEL SANSOM (Seamus Mullins)	10 - 0	Mr Dave Roberts
JACK SAVAGE (Nigel Twiston-Davies)	10 - 0	Mr L. R. James
STAN SHEPPARD (Paul Nicholls)	10 - 0	Mr C. D. Broad
HARRY STOCK (Martin Keighley)	9 - 12	c/o 01451 830209
HARRY TEAL (Neil King)	10 - 0	Mr Dave Roberts
ALEXANDER THORNE (Paul Nicholls)	9 - 6	Mr C. D. Broad
ROSS TURNER (Oliver Greenall)	9 - 0	Mr R. A. Hale
ROBERT WILLIAMS (Bernard Llewellyn)	9 - 12	c/o 07971 233473
THOMAS WILLMOTT (Lucinda Russell)	9 - 7	Mr J. B. Jeffrey
KAINE WOOD (Brian Ellison)	10 - 0	Mr J. B. Jeffrey

AMATEUR RIDERS

Riding weights and contact details

An index of agents appears on page 703

GREENOCK, G. 11 - 7 .... 07919 554517
GREENWAY, C. A. 9 - 10 .... 07526 923647
GREGOIRE, M. 9 - 12 .... 07376 200134
GREGORY, H. J. 8 - 10 .... 07772 008845
GREGORY, K. A. 10 - 6 .... 07789 394488
HAIGH, M. 9 - 3 .... 07902 864464
HAMMOND, L. K. 9 - 10 .... 01299 896057
HAMPSON, B. 9 - 0. .... 07468 418883
HAMPTON, M. L. 10 - 7 .... 07515 269391
HARDING, J. 9 - 6. .... Miss A. Wallace
HARDWICK, C. V. 9 - 10. .... 07808 511705
HARK, A. 10 - 0. .... 07929 435118
HAWKER, C. R. 10 - 0 .... 07825 210749
HAWKINS, S. 9 - 4. .... 07733 265836
HAYNES, A. 9 - 3 .... 07585 558717
HEAL, H. 9 - 0. .... Mr Ian Wood
HENDERSON, E. 10 - 7 .... 07730 680553
HENDERSON, G. 11 - 0. .... 07901 716716
HESKETH, A. 8 - 11 .... 07791 437969
HICKMAN, W. H. W. 11 - 0 .... 07841 488935
HILL, J. P. 11 - 7 .... 07584 373313
HILL, R. L. 9 - 0. .... 07557 53940
HISCOCK, G. 10 - 7. .... 07815 475518
HOLMES, D. T. R. 12 - 0 .... 01912 847093
HOWIE, N. A. 9 - 5. .... 07899 459443
HUGHES, JODIE 9 - 7 .... 07884 432672
HUGHES, JAMES 11 - 0. .... Mrs Joanna Hughes
HUMPHREY, L. A. 10 - 2 .... 07557 772679
HUNT, H. 8 - 9. .... 07913 726003
HURST, D. B. 9 - 3. .... Mr L. R. James
JAMES, B. 9 - 10 .... 07544 726587
JEAVONS, J. 9 - 5. .... 07972 871876
JENKINS, L. L. 9 - 0 .... 07557 041595
JENKINS, M. R. 9 - 4. .... 07917 005540
JOHNSON, B. 9 - 7. .... 07866 012885
JOHNSON, L. 9 - 10 .... 01952 730722
JOHNSON, M. S. 9 - 3 .... 07816 609314
JONES, B. R. 10 - 2 .... 07767 408806
JONES, C. A. 9 - 0 .... Miss A. Wallace
JONES, J. C. 9 - 7 .... 07794 912090
JONES, JACK H. 10 - 5. .... 07870 610067
JUKES, S. M. 10 - 7 .... 07860 130833
KELLARD, W. A. 10 - 7 .... 07968 242663
KENDRICK, J. 8 - 13 .... 07734 193815
KERR, D. 9 - 5. .... Andy Lewis
KING, A. 10 - 2. .... 07943 947001
KING, J. 9 - 9. .... Mr Dave Roberts
KLUG, S. 10 - 0. .... 01507 534367
KNOX, J. S. 10 - 7. .... 07792 196146
LAWTON, N. 10 - 7. .... 07525 179482
LEE, S. 9 - 2. .... 07745 327430
LEES, H. T. 9 - 0. .... 07818 782662
LEGG, M. D. 9 - 7. .... Mr Dave Roberts
LENIHAN, K. G. C. 9 - 4 .... 07486 309239
LEVINSON, G. 9 - 7. .... 07956 223456
LEWIS, H. M. 9 - 2 .... 07899 649644
LYNN, B. 9 - 3. .... 07809 449617
LYONS, K. 9 - 10. .... 07760 124147
LYTTLE, J. 10 - 8 .... 07774 060675
MACKENZIE, E. 9 - 0 .... Miss A. Wallace
MAHON, L. 10 - 7 .... 07961 101795
MANSELL, D. 11 - 0. .... 07912 974653
MARGARSON, K. L. 9 - 0 .... 07711 898265
MARSHALL, C. 10 - 10 .... 07516 296716
MARSHALL, I. 8 - 7. .... 07581 371480
MARSHALL, W. 9 - 0. .... 07758 815201
MARTENSSON, J. 8 - 5 .... 07709 195442
MARTIN, J. I. 10 - 3 .... 07815 698359

MASON, J. L. 8 - 10 .... Mr N. Hannity
MASON, P. W. 11 - 4. .... 07921 707292
MAXWELL, D. 11 - 0. .... 02077 993429
MCBRIDE, C. 9 - 7. .... 07496 887118
MCCAIN, A. 9 - 7. .... Mr R. A. Hale
MCCAIN, E. 8 - 7. .... Mr R. A. Hale
MCCLOREY, T. A. 10 - 7 .... 07545 073468
MCINTYRE, M. J. 9 - 10. .... 07557 360664
MCMENAMIN, D. 9 - 7 .... 07860 819145
MCSHARRY, F. 9 - 5. .... 07554 060705
MEEK, N. 9 - 2 .... 07494 489520
MIDGLEY, T. E. 9 - 10. .... 07494 654503
MILBURN, W. J. 10 - 7. .... 07769 618732
MILLER, C. 10 - 5. .... 07498 201434
MILLMAN, P. B. 9 - 7. .... Mr Ian Wood
MOORE, H. J. 9 - 8. .... 07736 149 669
MORGAN, L. 10 - 1. .... 07850 505476
MORGAN, S. A. 9 - 2. .... 07397 565965
MORLEY, J. R. 9 - 2. .... 07415 463347
MULLINEAUX, M. 8 - 7. .... 01829 261444
MURRAY, T. H. 11 - 0. .... 07595 396806
MYDDELTON, H. 9 - 7. .... 07713 837857
NAILOR, J. 9 - 7. .... Mr C. D. Broad
NEILD, J. D. 9 - 0. .... 07557 605914
NEWMAN, J. 9 - 7 .... 07920 464705
NUGENT, H. F. 9 - 7. .... Mr C. D. Broad
O'BRIEN, J. 9 - 7 .... 07764 304906
O'BRIEN, T. M. 10 - 0. .... Mr Dave Roberts
O'CONNOR, A. B. 9 - 2 .... 07407 723309
O'CONNOR, J. 10 - 0 00353838195617
O'SHEA, A. 9 - 7. .... 07968 242663
O'SHEA, C. 10 - 10 .... 07779 788748
OLLIVER, J. M. 8 - 9. .... 07885 412708
ORPWOOD, N. 10 - 12 .... 07831 836626
PAINTING, S. W. 10 - 7 .... 07919 454844
PARIS-CROFTS, B. 10 - 4. .... 07748 311684
PARKER, N. L. 9 - 5. .... 07877 151521
PEACOCK, S. 8 - 10 .... 07775 791153
PENFORD, F. 9 - 4. .... 07480 256811
PERRETT, J. E. 9 - 9 .... 07539 526900
PETERS, D. M. 10 - 13 .... 07789 997367
PETTIS, W. 9 - 2. .... 07908 572141
PHILLIPS, N. J. 11 - 0. .... 07976 240874
PINCHIN, L. M. 9 - 9. .... 07823 887656
POOLES, R. L. 10 - 7. .... 07766 244716
POTTER, W. E. 10 - 7 .... 07872 933534
POWNALL, C. L. 9 - 1 .... 07825 064776
PRICE, C. 8 - 12. .... 07470 174596
PRICE, C. BICKERS 10 - 4. .... 07598 925913
PRICHARD, D. G. 10 - 0. .... 07983 162251
PROCTER, F. 10 - 7. .... 07772 241195
PUGH, S. 9 - 0. .... 07486 460585
QUINLAN, C. 9 - 5. .... 07398 537694
QUINLAN, SHANE M. 9 - 8. .... 07739 909723
RAHMAN, N. 9 - 7 .... 07772 968541
RAMSAY, W. B. 11 - 12 .... 07764 960054
RAWDON-MOGG, C. J. D. 11 - 3 .... 07759 451287
REYNOLDS, N. 9 - 7 .... 07768 639278
RID, A. D. 10 - 1 .... 07539 889684
RIDLEY, J. M. 10 - 7. .... 07557 879646
RIPPON, S. 9 - 7. .... 07812 165566
ROBERTS, ANNABEL 9 - 0 .... 07709 430667
ROBERTS, B. 9 - 4. .... 07871 504897
ROBERTSON, C. J. 9 - 3. .... 07708 455292
ROBINSON, C. E. 8 - 2 .... 07876 123580
ROBINSON, M. 10 - 8. .... 07715 563038
ROBINSON, STUART C. 12 - 0. .... 01424 204190
ROBINSON, SARAH E. 10 - 10 .... 07518 785291

ROCHE, S. T. 10 - 0 .... 07521 419157
RUDDY, L. M. 10 - 0 .... 07900 687701
RUNDELL, K. C. 8 - 8 .... 07557 104051
SAINSBURY, S. N. 10 - 2 .... 07887 792943
SANDERS, L. 9 - 4 .... 01969 624351
SAYER, E. C. 9 - 0 .... Mr R. A. Hale
SAYERS, S. 9 - 10 .... 07397 886125
SCOTT, C. R. 8 - 3 .... 07495 198673
SCOTT, D. C. 9 - 2 .... 01372 426200
SCOTT, L. 10 - 0 .... 07443 597049
SHARPE, R. E. L. 8 - 5 .... 07446 907489
SHEPHERD, P. 9 - 6 .... 07794 467583
SLACK, A. M. 8 - 10 .... 07946 022056
SMITH, D. 9 - 8 .... 07585 118344
SMITH, E. J. 9 - 7 .... 07824 158142
SMITH, G. R. 10 - 4 .... 07748 064384
SMITH, BECKY 9 - 2 .... Mrs G. S. Charnock
SMITH, RYAN 10 - 0 .... 07377 368168
SMITH, SOPHIE 7 - 10 .... 07736 111550
SMITH, SAM 9 - 10 .... 07874 651951
SMITH-MAXWELL, J. 11 - 1 .... 07535 459701
SOLE, J. D. 10 - 1 .... 07968 947091
SOLLITT, V. A. 10 - 6 .... 07540 229941
SPENCER, M. E. 9 - 0 .... 07568 513984
STEARN, R. R. P. 11 - 0 .... 07879 412414
STEVENS, S. 9 - 2 .... 07972 365372
STIRLING, A. E. 10 - 0 .... 07557 952057
STONES, L. 9 - 3 .... 07834 596801
STRATTON, M. 8 - 10 .... 07470 004253
SUMMERS, P. F. 10 - 0 .... 07552 219962
SWARBRICK, J. C. 9 - 13 .... 07802 477557
TAYLOR, A. R. 9 - 4 .... 07484 723211
TAYLOR, R. M. 8 - 12 .... 07973 774660
TETT, F. 9 - 0 .... 07786 314587
THIRLBY, W. 11 - 0 .... 07773 885256
THOMAS, J. 11 - 3 .... 07516 657526
TICKLE, L. 9 - 12 .... 07769 183447
TIMMIS, F. 10 - 3 .... 07984 880435
TODD, C. J. 9 - 3 .... 07564 274975
TODD, E. L. 9 - 3 .... Mr J. B. Jeffrey
TREACY, G. 10 - 7 .... 07909 175567

TREGONING, G. 10 - 0 .... 07818 441714
TRENEER, B. 10 - 9 .... 07842 820495
TROTT, L. 10 - 5 .... 07814 537290
TROTTER, S. A. 8 - 7 .... 07472 279627
TUCKER, H. C. 9 - 5 .... 07703 848955
TURNER, L. M. 10 - 0 .... 07984 531836
VOIKHANSKY, M. 9 - 7 .... 01213 772133
WADE, V. L. 9 - 8 .... 07772 925721
WADGE, C. 10 - 10 .... 07825 959425
WALEY-COHEN, S. B. 10 - 0 .... 07887 848425
WALKER, SIMON. 9 - 7 .... 07778 061662
WALKER, SOPHIE 9 - 5 .... 07794 715220
WALLACE, H. A. R. 11 - 0 .... 07974 360462
WALTERS, G. 9 - 2 .... 01572 756447
WALTON, C. M. 9 - 4 .... Mr J. B. Jeffrey
WAUGH, A. 8 - 5 .... Mr J. B. Jeffrey
WEBB, J. 9 - 2 .... 07775 332583
WELCH, H. J. 9 - 10 .... 07501 060620
WHIFFEN, G. 9 - 8 .... 07495 898893
WHITE, C. R. 9 - 7 .... 07808 844242
WILLIAMS, C. 10 - 5 .... 07849 833672
WILLIAMS, I. K. 9 - 0 .... 07714 170062
WILLIAMS, J. P. 9 - 7 .... Mr Dave Roberts
WILLIAMS, L. 10 - 0 .... Mr Dave Roberts
WILLIAMS, S. R. 10 - 12 .... 07590 208675
WILLIAMSON, C. L. 9 - 10 .... 07572 463468
WILLIAMSON, J. C. 9 - 8 .... 07472 330646
WILSON, GEORGE 11 - 0 .... 07720 849919
WILSON, L. J. 8 - 10 .... 07411 902747
WILSON, R. 10 - 7 .... 07510 888442
WONNACOTT, M. 9 - 4 .... 07710 461900
WOODWARD, M. J. 10 - 7 .... 07724 627766
WORSLEY, T. 9 - 0 .... 07825 067820
WRIGHT, J. 10 - 0 .... 07787 365500
YARDLEY, E. H. 9 - 7 .... 07495 649967
YEOMAN, K. 8 - 10 .... Mr J. B. Jeffrey
YORK, P. 10 - 7 .... 07774 962168

Are your contact details missing or incorrect?
If so please update us by email:
richard.lowther@racingpost.com

NOTES

NOTES

NOTES

NOTES

NOTES

NOTES

SUPER SOUND ®

The fastest selling race plate on the market!

The Super Sound® race plate meets all your demands, offering unique features where other race plates fall short. Years of listening to farriers all over the world have created this ultimate multi-faced race plate.

The Super Sound® really has it all! A combination of unique patented Kerckhaert features guarantees:

- more comfort, more support & more pitch
- far more protection
- natural, unimpeded hoof expansion
- drastic reduction of bruising & soreness
- Also available with Cu Shield Technology™

Super Pitch Plus in first 3 nail holes

stronger nailing & tighter clenches

Heel elevation

better hoof balance reduces stress to the limb

Steel insert

Moorcroft
Racehorse Welfare Centre

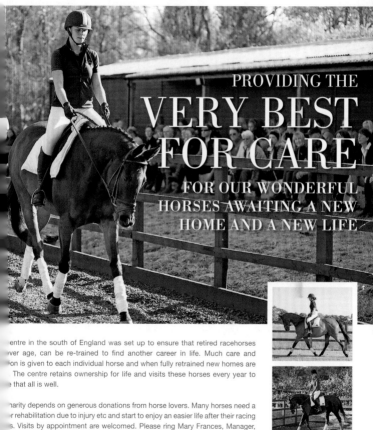

PROVIDING THE
VERY BEST
FOR CARE
FOR OUR WONDERFUL
HORSES AWAITING A NEW
HOME AND A NEW LIFE

...entre in the south of England was set up to ensure that retired racehorses ...ver age, can be re-trained to find another career in life. Much care and ...on is given to each individual horse and when fully retrained new homes are ... The centre retains ownership for life and visits these horses every year to ...e that all is well.

...harity depends on generous donations from horse lovers. Many horses need a ...r rehabilitation due to injury etc and start to enjoy an easier life after their racing ...s. Visits by appointment are welcomed. Please ring Mary Frances, Manager, ...929 666408 for more information or to arrange a visit.

Huntingrove Stud, Slinfold, West Sussex. RH13 0RB
7929 666408 | Email: moorcroftracehorse@gmail.com | www.moorcroftracehorse.org.uk